CENTRAL

CAUTION

To reduce the chance of personal injury and/or property damage, the following instructions must be carefully observed:

Proper service and repair are important to the safety of the service technician and the safe, reliable operation of all motor vehicles. If part replacement is necessary, the part must be replaced with one of the same part number or with an equivalent part. Do not use a replacement part of lesser quality.

The service procedures recommended and described in this service manual are effective methods of performing service and repair. Some of these procedures require the use of tools specifically designed for the purpose.

Accordingly, anyone who intends to use a replacement part, service procedure or tool, which is not recommended by the vehicle manufacturer, must first determine that neither his safety nor the safe operation of the vehicle will be jeopardized by the replacement part, service procedure or tool selected.

It is important to note that this manual contains various 'Cautions' and 'Notices' that must be carefully observed in order to reduce the risk of personal injury during service or repair, or the possibility that improper service or repair may damage the vehicle or render it unsafe. It is also important to understand that these 'Cautions' and 'Notices' are not exhaustive, because it is impossible to warn of all the possible hazardous consequences that might result from failure to follow these instructions.

This vehicle is equipped with Supplemental Inflatable Restraint (SIR). Refer to CAUTIONS in Section 9J under "ON-VEHICLE SERVICE" and the SIR Component and Wiring Location view in Section 9J before performing service on or around SIR components or wiring. Failure to follow CAUTIONS could result in possible air bag deployment, personal injury, or otherwise unneeded SIR system repairs.

To help avoid accidental air bag deployment and personal injury, when servicing a vehicle that requires repair of the SIR system and another vehicle system, it is recommended that the SIR system be repaired first using service manual procedures.

CONTRA COSTA COUNTY LIBRARY

D1096451

3 1901 00683 2671

CAUTION: General Motors service manuals are intended for use by professional, qualified technicians. Attempting repairs or service without the appropriate training, tools, and equipment could cause injury to you or others and damage to your vehicle that may cause it not to operate properly.

1994 BUICK REGAL SERVICE MANUAL BOOK 2

FOREWORD

This manual provides information on diagnosis, service procedures, adjustments and specifications for the 1994 Buick Regal.

All understanding of the material contained herein and in Dealer Technical, Service Manual Update, and Management Bulletins, issued when necessary, will assist service personnel in properly maintaining the quality to which Buick cars are built.

All information, illustrations and specifications contained in this manual are based on the latest product information available at the time of publication approval. The right is reserved to make changes at any time without notice.

TABLE OF CONTENTS

BUICK MOTOR DIVISION
General Motors Corporation
Flint, Michigan

©1993 GENERAL MOTORS CORPORATION ALL RIGHTS RESERVED June 1993 • LITHO IN U.S.A.

No part of this publication may be reproduced, stored in any retrieval system or transmitted, in any form or by any means, including but not limited to electronic, mechanical, photocopying, recording or otherwise, without the prior written permission of General Motors Corp. This includes all text, illustrations, tables and charts.

BUICK REGAL
CONTENTS – BOOK 1

CONTENTS – BOOK 2

GENERAL MOTORS SERVICE MANUAL COMMENTS

Technicians and Vehicle Owners and Operators:
If you find an error, omission, or have a suggestion on any General Motors Service Manual, we want to hear from you.

Starting September 1, 1993, please call:

United States:
1-800-828-6860
8:00 AM to 5:00 PM Eastern Time Zone

Canada (General Motors Dealers Employees Only):
Quebec 1-800-263-7960, Select Option 5
Nationally 1-800-263-7740, Select Option 5
Oshawa, Ontario "Local" Area, 644-7060, Select Option 5
8:30 AM to 5:00 PM Eastern Time Zone

These phone numbers can be called Monday through Friday. Be prepared to give the following information:

- Your name
- Your dealership's name (technicians only)
- Your phone number
- Model year and vehicle line
- Publication book number (if present)
- Vehicle Identification Number of vehicle being worked on
- Section and page numbers
- Description of problem

This phone number cannot provide Technical Assistance. Contact your Technical Assistance source.

The personnel who answer this phone number will provide the author of the information with your comments and will follow up until an answer is given.

If you wish to send examples or marked-up pages, the person who takes your call will tell you how to do that.

Canadian Vehicle Owner or Operator:
If you are the owner or operator of the vehicle, please give your comments to the Customer Assistance Centre. The phone number and address are in your Owner's Manual.

SECTION 6E

DRIVEABILITY AND EMISSIONS GENERAL INFORMATION

CAUTION: On vehicles equipped with Supplemental Inflatable Restraint (SIR), refer to CAUTIONS in Section 9J under "ON-VEHICLE SERVICE" and the SIR Component and Wiring Location view in Section 9J before performing service on or around SIR components or wiring. Failure to follow CAUTIONS could result in possible air bag deployment, personal injury, or otherwise unneeded SIR system repairs.

CONTENTS

SECTION CONTENT

The driveability and emissions section describes the function and operation of the engine control module system that controls the driveability and emissions of the vehicle. Emphasis is placed on the diagnosis and repair of problems related to the system.

It is divided into three major sub-sections dealing with diagnosis and repair. They can be summarized as follows:

SECTION A: ENGINE COMPONENTS/WIRING DIAGRAMS/DIAGNOSTIC CHARTS

- Component Locations.
- Wiring Diagrams.
- ECM/PCM/VCM Terminal End View and Terminal Definitions.
- On-Board Diagnostic System Check. This must be the first step of any diagnostic procedure.
- Diagnostic Trouble Code Charts with facing pages containing circuit diagrams, circuit operation information, and helpful diagnostic information.

SECTION B: SYMPTOMS

- This sub-section assists in diagnosis of intermittent problems or problems which don't result in the storing of diagnostic trouble codes. It is arranged by symptoms of poor driveability and emissions and lists possible causes of the problems.

SECTION C: COMPONENT SYSTEMS

- Component and Circuit Descriptions.
- On-Vehicle Service for each Sub-System.
- Functional Checks/Diagnostic Charts.

HOW TO USE ELECTRICAL SYSTEMS DIAGNOSTIC INFORMATION

STRATEGY BASED DIAGNOSTICS

The strategy based diagnostic is a uniform approach to repair all electrical/electronics systems. The diagnostic flow can always be used to resolve an E/E system problem and is the place to start when repairs are necessary. The steps found in Figure 1, that the technician should follow, are outlined below:

1. **Verify the Customer Complaint**
   To verify the customer complaint the technician will need to know the correct t or normal operation of the system and verify the customer complaint is a deviation from normal operation.

2. **Preliminary Checks**
   This step is a visual confirmation of systems or components that are malfunctioning. With the additional information gained the technician may now conduct a thorough visual inspection, consult the service history, listen for unusual sounds or odors, and gather diagnostic code information to further effect a good repair.

3. **Check Bulletins and Other Service Information**
   From the steps above the technician should have enough information updates. This includes videos, newsletters, or Pulsat programs.

4. **Service information (Manual) System Check(s)**
   Most service manual sections contain "System Checks" that verify proper operation of the system and lead the technician on a very organized approach to diagnostics that closely follows the original development process and failure mode testing.

5. **Service Diagnostics (Paper/Electronic)**

5a. DTC Stored - Follow the designated DTC chart exactly to make an effective repair.

5b. No DTC - Select the symptom from the symptom tables and follow the diagnostic paths or suggestions to complete the repair.

5c. No Matching Symptom - Analyze the complaint and develop a plan for diagnostics utilizing the wiring diagrams, theory of operation, call technical assistance for like instances where repair history may be available, and technician knowledge combined with efficient use of the service available information.

5d. Intermittents - Conditions that are not always present are intermittent. These may be resolved by observing history DTC's, evaluating the symptoms and conditions described by the customer and using a check sheet or other method to pinpoint the circuit or electrical system component. Most important is to follow the suggestions for intermittent diagnosis found in the service documentation. The Tech 1 and Fluke 87 both have excellent data capture capabilities that can assist in detection of intermittents.

5e. Vehicle operates as designed/No trouble Found - This condition exists when the vehicle is found to operate normally. It is most important to verify that the condition described by the owner is normal compared to other vehicles. The condition may be intermittent so verify the complaint under the conditions described by the customer before the vehicle is released.

6. **Re-Examine the Complaint**
   When the complaint cannot be successfully found or isolated a re-evaluation is necessary. The complaint should be re-verified and could be found to be intermittent or normal as per 5c or 5e above.

7. **Repair and Verification Tests**
   After a cause has been isolated the repairs should be made and validated for proper operation and verification that the symptom has been corrected. This may involve road testing or other methods to verify the complaint has been resolved under the conditions noted by the customer.

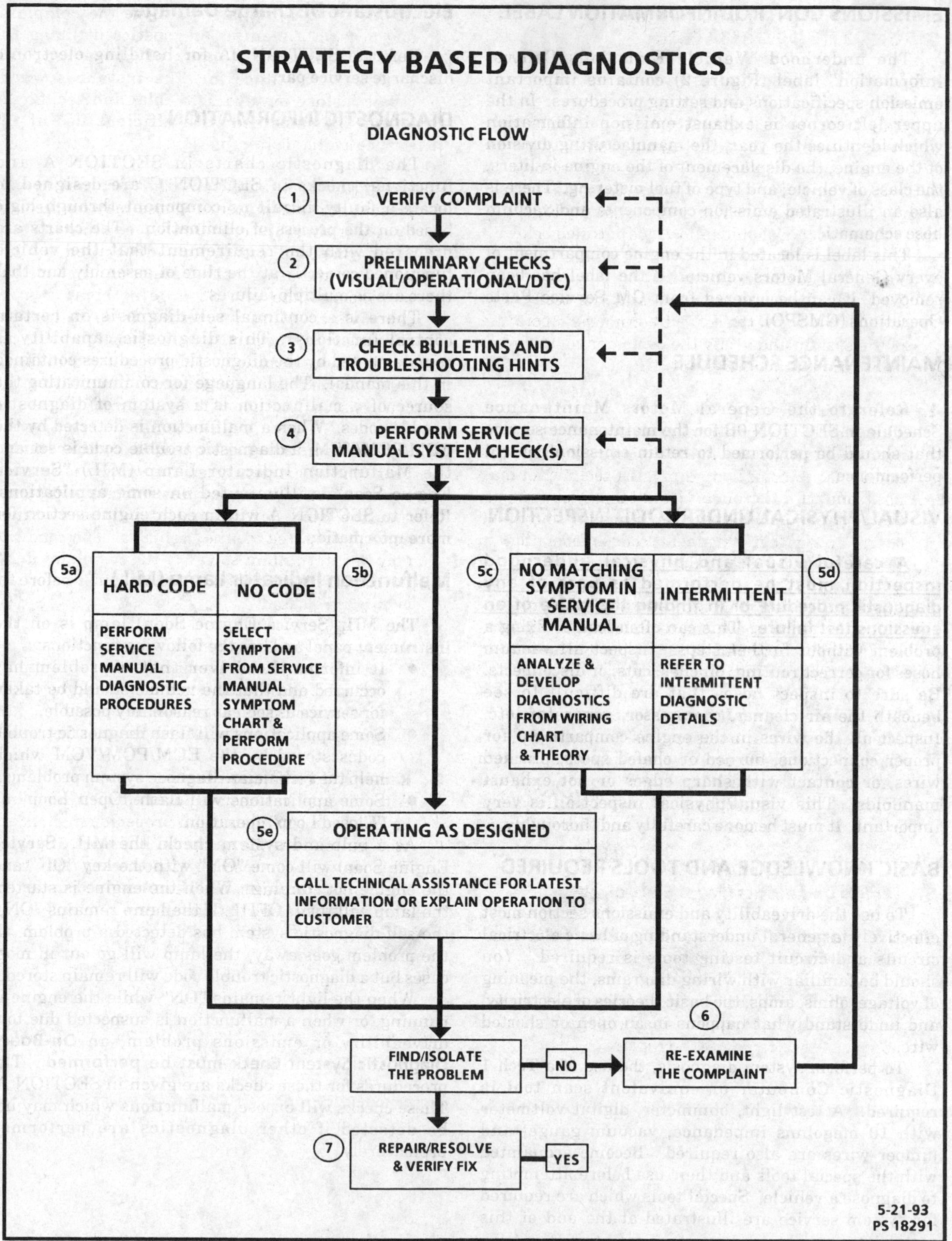
STRATEGY BASED DIAGNOSTICS
DIAGNOSTIC FLOW
1 VERIFY COMPLAINT
2 PRELIMINARY CHECKS (VISUAL/OPERATIONAL/DTC)
3 CHECK BULLETINS AND TROUBLESHOOTING HINTS
4 PERFORM SERVICE MANUAL SYSTEM CHECK(s)
5a HARD CODE
PERFORM SERVICE MANUAL DIAGNOSTIC PROCEDURES
5b NO CODE
SELECT SYMPTOM FROM SERVICE MANUAL SYMPTOM CHART & PERFORM PROCEDURE
5c NO MATCHING SYMPTOM IN SERVICE MANUAL
ANALYZE & DEVELOP DIAGNOSTICS FROM WIRING CHART & THEORY
5d INTERMITTENT
REFER TO INTERMITTENT DIAGNOSTIC DETAILS
5e OPERATING AS DESIGNED
CALL TECHNICAL ASSISTANCE FOR LATEST INFORMATION OR EXPLAIN OPERATION TO CUSTOMER
FIND/ISOLATE THE PROBLEM
NO
6 RE-EXAMINE THE COMPLAINT
7 REPAIR/RESOLVE & VERIFY FIX
YES
5-21-93
PS 18291

Figure 1 - Strategy Based Diagnostics

EMISSIONS CONTROL INFORMATION LABEL

The underhood "Vehicle Emissions Control Information" label (Figure 2) contains important emission specifications and setting procedures. In the upper left corner is exhaust emission information which identifies the year, the manufacturing division of the engine, the displacement of the engine in liters, the class of vehicle, and type of fuel metering. There is also an illustrated emission components and vacuum hose schematic.

This label is located in the engine compartment of every General Motors vehicle. If the label has been removed, it can be ordered from GM Service Parts Operations (GMSPO).

MAINTENANCE SCHEDULE

Refer to the General Motors Maintenance Schedule in SECTION 0B for the maintenance service that should be performed to retain emission control performance.

VISUAL/PHYSICAL UNDERHOOD INSPECTION

A careful visual and physical underhood inspection must be performed as part of any diagnostic procedure or in finding the cause of an emissions test failure. This can often lead to fixing a problem without further steps. Inspect all vacuum hoses for correct routing, pinches, cuts, or disconnects. Be sure to inspect hoses that are difficult to see beneath the air cleaner, compressor, generator, etc. Inspect all the wires in the engine compartment for proper connections, burned or chafed spots, pinched wires, or contact with sharp edges or hot exhaust manifolds. This visual/physical inspection is very important. It must be done carefully and thoroughly.

BASIC KNOWLEDGE AND TOOLS REQUIRED

To use the driveability and emissions section most effectively, a general understanding of basic electrical circuits and circuit testing tools is required. You should be familiar with wiring diagrams, the meaning of voltage, ohms, amps, the basic theories of electricity, and understand what happens in an open or shorted wire.

To perform system diagnosis, the use of a Tech 1 Diagnostic Computer or equivalent scan tool is required. A test light, ohmmeter, digital voltmeter with 10 megohms impedance, vacuum gauge, and jumper wires are also required. Become acquainted with the special tools and their use before attempting to diagnose a vehicle. Special tools which are required for system service are illustrated at the end of this section.

Electrostatic Discharge Damage

Refer to SECTION 0A for handling electronic discharge service parts.

DIAGNOSTIC INFORMATION

The diagnostic charts in SECTION A and functional checks in SECTION C are designed to locate a faulty circuit or component through logic based on the process of elimination. The charts are prepared with the requirement that the vehicle functioned correctly at the time of assembly and that there are no multiple failures.

There is a continual self-diagnosis on certain control functions. This diagnostic capability is complemented by the diagnostic procedures contained in this manual. The language for communicating the source of a malfunction is a system of diagnostic trouble codes. When a malfunction is detected by the ECM/PCM/VCM, a diagnostic trouble code is set and the Malfunction Indicator Lamp (MIL) "Service Engine Soon" is illuminated on some applications. Refer to SECTION A within each engine section for more information.

Malfunction Indicator Lamp (MIL)

The MIL (Service Engine Soon) lamp is on the instrument panel and has the following functions:

- It informs the driver that a problem has occurred and that the vehicle should be taken for service as soon as reasonably possible.
- Some applications will flash diagnostic trouble codes stored by the ECM/PCM/VCM which help the technician diagnose system problems.
- Some applications will flash "Open Loop" or "Closed Loop" operation.

As a bulb and system check, the MIL (Service Engine Soon) will come "ON" with the key "ON" and the engine not running. When the engine is started, the lamp will turn "OFF." If the lamp remains "ON," the self-diagnostic system has detected a problem. If the problem goes away, the lamp will go out in most cases but a diagnostic trouble code will remain stored.

When the light remains "ON" while the engine is running, or when a malfunction is suspected due to a driveability or emissions problem, an **On-Board Diagnostic System Check must be performed**. The procedures for these checks are given in SECTION A. These checks will expose malfunctions which may not be detected if other diagnostics are performed prematurely.

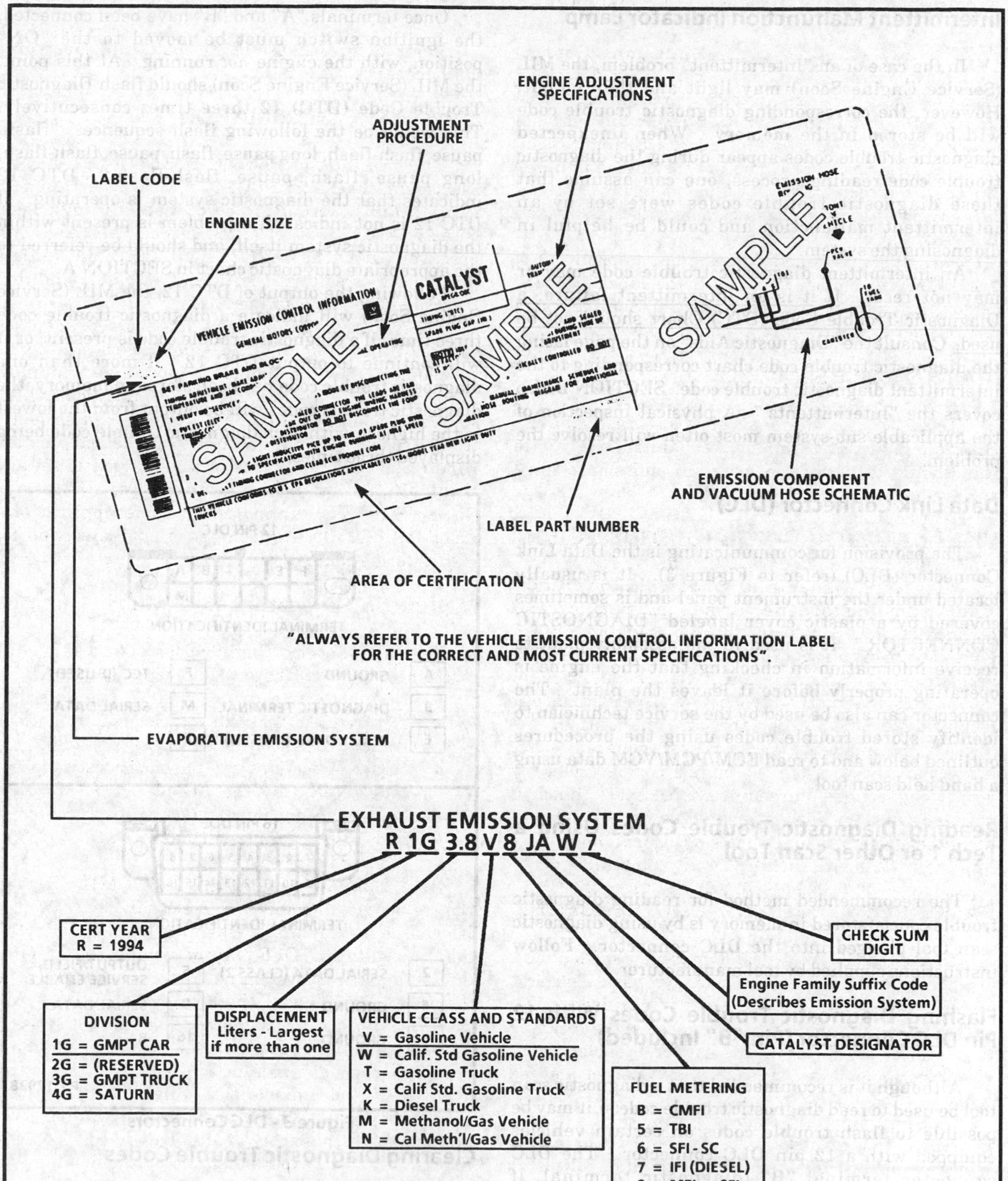
ENGINE ADJUSTMENT SPECIFICATIONS
ADJUSTMENT PROCEDURE
LABEL CODE
ENGINE SIZE
VEHICLE EMISSION CONTROL INFORMATION
GENERAL MOTORS CORP
CATALYST
SAMPLE
SAMPLE
SAMPLE
EMISSION COMPONENT AND VACUUM HOSE SCHEMATIC
LABEL PART NUMBER
AREA OF CERTIFICATION
"ALWAYS REFER TO THE VEHICLE EMISSION CONTROL INFORMATION LABEL FOR THE CORRECT AND MOST CURRENT SPECIFICATIONS".
EVAPORATIVE EMISSION SYSTEM
EXHAUST EMISSION SYSTEM
R 1G 3.8 V 8 JA W 7
CERT YEAR
R = 1994
CHECK SUM DIGIT
Engine Family Suffix Code (Describes Emission System)
DIVISION
1G = GMPT CAR
2G = (RESERVED)
3G = GMPT TRUCK
4G = SATURN
DISPLACEMENT
Liters - Largest if more than one
VEHICLE CLASS AND STANDARDS
V = Gasoline Vehicle
W = Calif. Std Gasoline Vehicle
T = Gasoline Truck
X = Calif Std. Gasoline Truck
K = Diesel Truck
M = Methanol/Gas Vehicle
N = Cal Meth'l/Gas Vehicle
CATALYST DESIGNATOR
FUEL METERING
B = CMFI
5 = TBI
6 = SFI - SC
7 = IFI (DIESEL)
8 = MFI or SFI or MFI/SFI
4-8-92
MS 11461-6E

Figure 2 - Vehicle Emission Control Information Label

Intermittent Malfunction Indicator Lamp

In the case of an "Intermittent" problem, the MIL (Service Engine Soon) may light and then go out. However, the corresponding diagnostic trouble code will be stored in the memory. When unexpected diagnostic trouble codes appear during the diagnostic trouble code reading process, one can assume that these diagnostic trouble codes were set by an intermittent malfunction and could be helpful in diagnosing the system.

An intermittent diagnostic trouble code may or may not reset. If it is an intermittent failure, a Diagnostic Trouble Code (DTC) Chart should not be used. Consult the "Diagnostic Aids" on the page facing the diagnostic trouble code chart corresponding to the intermittent diagnostic trouble code. SECTION B also covers the "Intermittents." A physical inspection of the applicable sub-system most often will resolve the problem.

Data Link Connector (DLC)

The provision for communicating is the Data Link Connector (DLC) (refer to Figure 3). It is usually located under the instrument panel and is sometimes covered by a plastic cover labeled "DIAGNOSTIC CONNECTOR." It is used in the assembly plant to receive information in checking that the engine is operating properly before it leaves the plant. The connector can also be used by the service technician to identify stored trouble codes using the procedures outlined below and to read ECM/PCM/VCM data using a hand held scan tool.

Reading Diagnostic Trouble Codes Using a Tech 1 or Other Scan Tool

The recommended method for reading diagnostic trouble code(s) stored in memory is by using diagnostic scan tool plugged into the DLC connector. Follow instructions supplied by tool manufacturer.

Flashing Diagnostic Trouble Codes With 12 Pin DLC Connector (Pin "B" Included)

Although it is recommended that a diagnostic scan tool be used to read diagnostic trouble code(s), it may be possible to flash trouble codes on certain vehicles equipped with a 12 pin DLC connector. The DLC connector terminal "B" (diagnostic terminal, if equipped) is the second terminal from the right of the DLC connector's top row. The terminal is grounded by connecting it to terminal "A" (internal ECM/PCM/VCM ground), the terminal to the right of terminal "B" on the top row of the DLC connector.

Once terminals "A" and "B" have been connected, the ignition switch must be moved to the "ON" position, with the engine *not* running. At this point, the MIL (Service Engine Soon) should flash Diagnostic Trouble Code (DTC) 12 three times consecutively. This would be the following flash sequence: "flash, pause, flash-flash, long pause, flash, pause, flash-flash, long pause, flash, pause, flash-flash." DTC 12 indicates that the diagnostic system is operating. If DTC 12 is not indicated, a problem is present within the diagnostic system itself, and should be referred to the appropriate diagnostic chart in SECTION A.

Following the output of DTC 12, the MIL (Service Engine Soon) will indicate a diagnostic trouble code three times if a diagnostic trouble code is present, or it will continue to output DTC 12. If more than one diagnostic trouble code has been stored in memory, the diagnostic trouble codes will be output from the lowest to the highest, with each diagnostic trouble code being displayed three times.

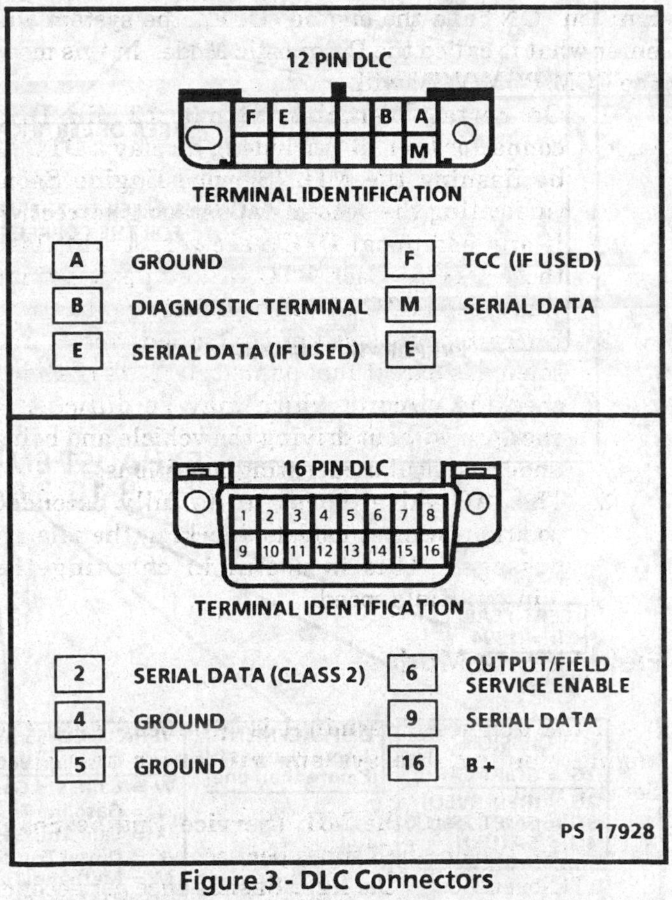

12 PIN DLC
F E B A
M
TERMINAL IDENTIFICATION
A GROUND
B DIAGNOSTIC TERMINAL
E SERIAL DATA (IF USED)
F TCC (IF USED)
M SERIAL DATA
E
16 PIN DLC
1 2 3 4 5 6 7 8
9 10 11 12 13 14 15 16
TERMINAL IDENTIFICATION
2 SERIAL DATA (CLASS 2)
4 GROUND
5 GROUND
6 OUTPUT/FIELD SERVICE ENABLE
9 SERIAL DATA
16 B+
PS 17928

Figure 3 - DLC Connectors

Clearing Diagnostic Trouble Codes

To clear any Diagnostic Trouble Code (DTC) from the memory, either to determine if the malfunction will occur again or because repair has been completed, power feed must be disconnected for at least thirty (30) seconds.

Depending on application, the following methods may be used to clear DTC's:

- Disconnect power source to ECM/PCM/VCM ie., fuse, pigtail at battery etc.
- Disconnect negative battery cable. (The negative battery cable may be disconnected, but other on-board memory data, such as preset radio tuning, will also be lost.)

NOTICE: To prevent system damage, the key must be "OFF" when disconnecting or reconnecting power.

It is also possible to clear a Diagnostic Trouble Code (DTC) using a diagnostic scan tool. Follow instructions supplied by tool manufacturer.

Diagnostic Mode

When the diagnostic terminal is grounded with the ignition "ON" and the engine "OFF," the system will enter what is called the Diagnostic Mode. In this mode the ECM/PCM/VCM will:

1. On certain vehicles with a 12 pin DLC connector (pin "B" included), display a DTC 12 by flashing the MIL (Service Engine Soon) (indicating the system is operating correctly). If any additional DTC's are set, it will flash those DTC's. Each DTC will be flashed three times, then DTC 12 will be flashed again.
2. Energize most system controlled relays and solenoids except fuel pump relay. This allows checking circuits which may be difficult to energize without driving the vehicle and being under particular operating conditions.
3. The IAC valve moves to its fully extended position on most models, blocking the idle air passage. This is useful in checking the minimum idle speed.

Field Service Mode

If the diagnostic terminal is grounded with the engine running, the system will enter the Field Service mode.

In "Open Loop" the MIL (Service Engine Soon) flashes two and one-half times per second.

In "Closed Loop," the light flashes once per second. Also, in "Closed Loop," the light will stay "OFF" most of the time if the system is running lean. It will stay "ON" most of the time if the system is running rich.

While the system is in Field Service Mode, new codes cannot be stored and the "Closed Loop" timer is bypassed.

Learning Ability

The system has a "learning" ability which allows it to make corrections for minor variations in the fuel system to improve driveability. If the battery is disconnected, to clear diagnostic trouble codes or for other repair, the "learning" process resets and begins again. A change may be noted in the vehicle's performance. To "teach" the vehicle, ensure that the engine is at operating temperature. The vehicle should be driven at part throttle, with moderate acceleration and idle conditions until normal performance returns.

ON-BOARD DIAGNOSTIC SYSTEM CHECK

Refer to "On-Board Diagnostic System Check" in SECTION A.

DLC SCAN TOOLS

The system can communicate a variety of information through DLC connector terminals "E" or "M" (depending on the engine). This data is transmitted at a high frequency which requires a Tech 1 Diagnostic Computer (scan) tool for interpretation. There are several scan tools available for reading this information.

With an understanding of the data which the tool displays, and knowledge of the circuits involved, the tool can be very useful in obtaining information which would be more difficult or impossible to obtain with other equipment.

Tech 1 and scan tools do not make the use of diagnostic trouble code charts unnecessary, nor can they indicate exactly where a problem is in a particular circuit. Tree charts incorporate diagnosis procedures using a Tech 1 tool where possible and most charts require the use of a Tech 1 when it is applicable.

A TECH 1 TOOL THAT DISPLAYS FAULTY DATA SHOULD NOT BE USED AND THE PROBLEM SHOULD BE REPORTED TO THE MANUFACTURER. THE USE OF A FAULTY SCAN TOOL CAN RESULT IN MISDIAGNOSIS AND UNNECESSARY PARTS REPLACEMENT.

TECH 1 TOOL USE WITH INTERMITTENTS

In some scan tool applications, the data update rate makes the tool less effective than a voltmeter, such as when trying to detect an intermittent problem which lasts for a very short time. However, the Tech 1 allows manipulation of wiring harnesses or components under the hood with the engine not running, while observing the Tech 1 readout.

The Tech 1 tool can be plugged in and observed while driving the vehicle under the condition when the MIL (Service Engine Soon) turns "ON" momentarily or when the engine driveability is momentarily poor. If the problem seems to be related to certain parameters that can be checked on the Tech 1, they should be checked while driving the vehicle. If there does not seem to be any correlation between the problem and any specific circuit, the Tech 1 can be checked on each position, watching for a period of time to see if there is any change in the readings that indicates intermittent operation.

The Tech 1 is also an easy way to compare the operating parameters of a poorly operating engine with those of a known good one. For example, a sensor may shift in value but not set a diagnostic trouble code. Comparing the sensor's readings with those of a known good vehicle may uncover the problem.

The Tech 1 has the ability to save time in diagnosis and prevent the replacement of good parts. The key to using the Tech 1 successfully for diagnosis lies in the technician's ability to understand the system he is trying to diagnose as well as an understanding of the Tech 1 operation and limitations. The technician should read the tool manufacturer's operating manual to become familiar with the tool's operation.

WIRING HARNESS SERVICE

Refer to SECTION 8A for wiring harness service.
Special tools needed to service:

J 38125-A	Terminal Repair Kit.
J 34636	Circuit Tester.
J 35689-A	Metri-Pack Terminal Remover.
J 28742-A	Weather-Pack Terminal Remover.
J 33095	Micro-Pack Terminal Remover.

TOOLS NEEDED TO SERVICE THE SYSTEM

Refer to "Special Tools" at the end of this section for driveability and emissions tools needed to service system.

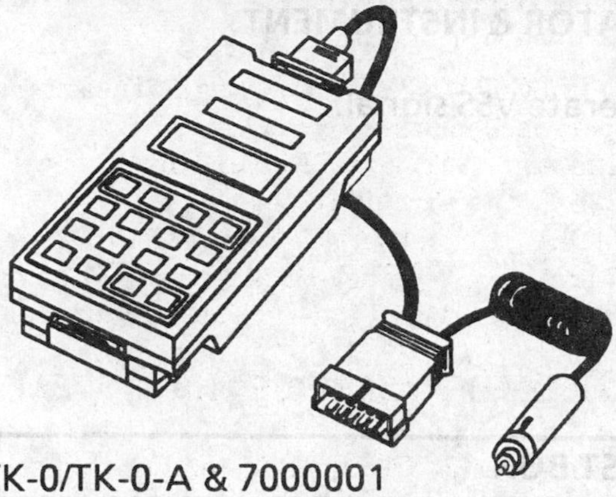

TK-0/TK-0-A & 7000001

TECH 1 DIAGNOSTIC SCAN TOOL
A hand-held scan tool used to analyze and diagnose control module systems. To be used with interchangeable program cartridge kits, or mass storage cartridge.

MASS STORAGE CARTRIDGE KIT
Use with GM Powertrain, Chassis Body System Service Programming Software.

12 to 16 PIN DLC HARNESS ADAPTER - 3000055
Necessary for some applications.

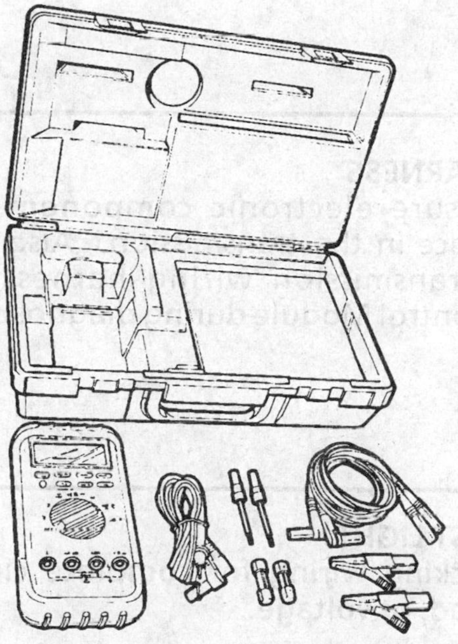

FLUKE 87 WITH Hz METER
HIGH IMPEDANCE MULTIMETER
(DIGITAL VOLTMETER-DVM)

J 39200

REFER TO USERS MANUAL FOR COMPLETE INSTRUCTIONS.

VOLTMETER - Voltage position measures magnitude of voltage when connected in parallel to an existing circuit. A digital voltmeter with a 10 megohm input impedance is used because this type of meter will not load down the circuit and result in faulty readings. Some circuits require accurate low voltage readings because they have a very high resistance .

AMMETER - When used as an ammeter, this meter accurately measures extremely low current flow. Refer to meter instructions for more information.

- Selector must be set properly for both function and range. DC is used for most automotive measurements.

OHMMETER - Measures resistance of circuit directly in ohms.

- OL display in all ranges indicates open circuit.
- Zero display in all ranges indicates a short circuit.
- An intermittent connection in a circuit may be indicated by a digital reading that will not stabilize on the circuit.
- Range Switch - Automatic and Manual.
  400Ω – Reads ohms directly
  4K,40K,400KΩ – Reads ohms in thousands
  4M,40MΩ,400MΩ - Reads ohms in millions

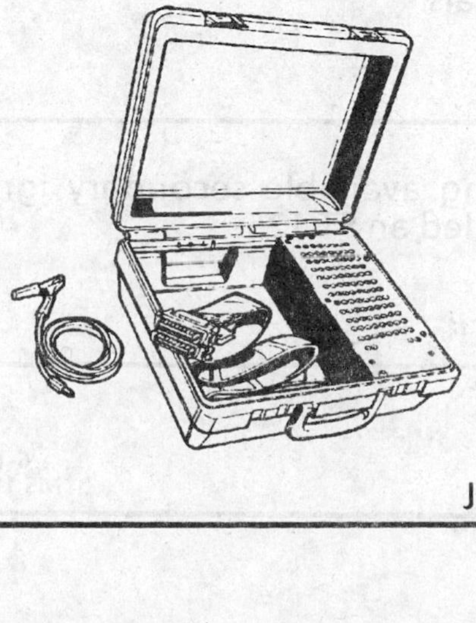

J 39700

UNIVERSAL BREAKOUT BOX
Used to test individual circuits in the system by monitoring voltage or resistance using a high impedance multimeter. Can also be used for pinout circuit checks by disconnecting the option adapters at the vehicle system control module. Refer to ECM/PCM/VCM Connector End View tables in appropriate engine section for specific engine adapter harness J 39700-XXX.

6-11-93
7S 3382-6E

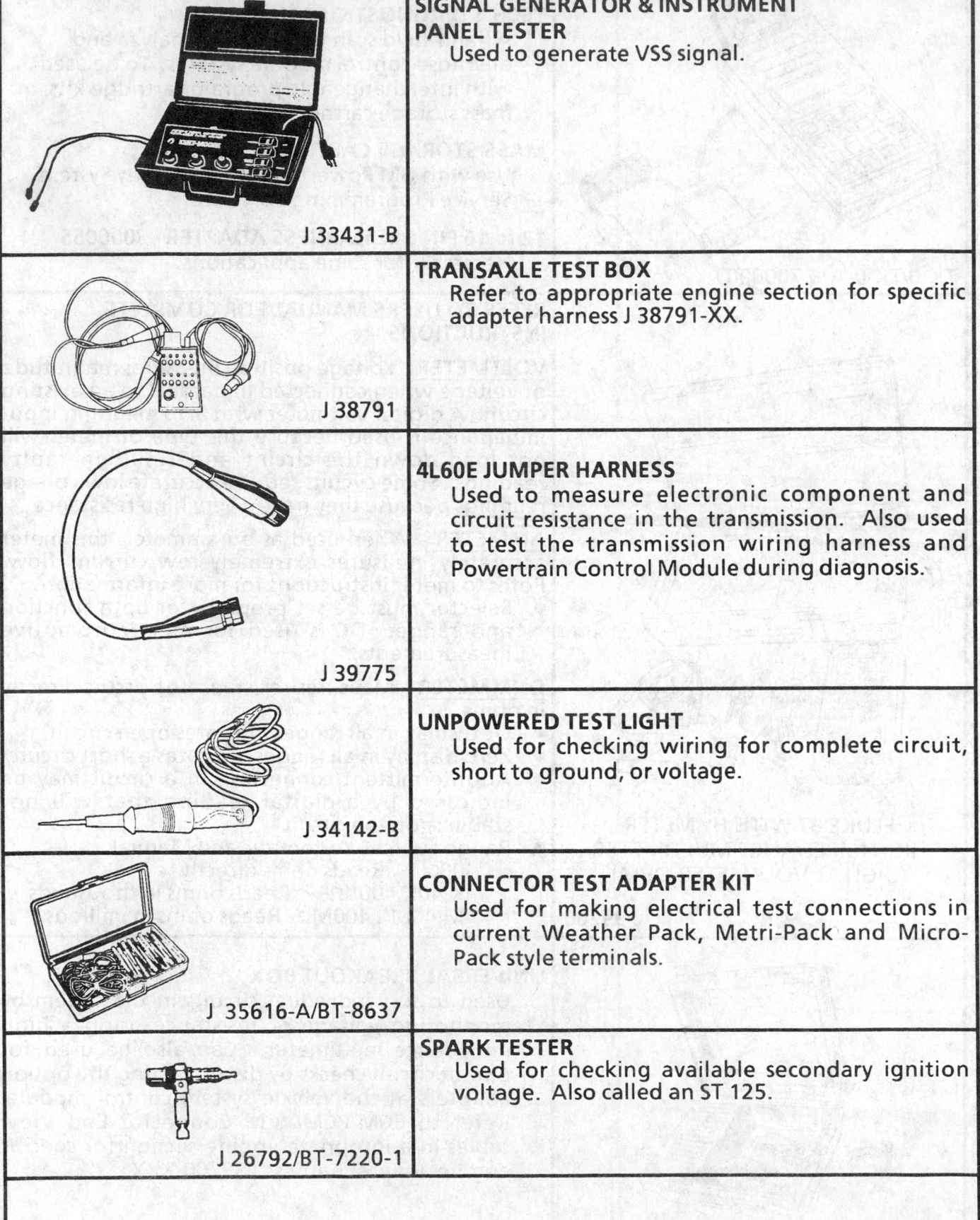

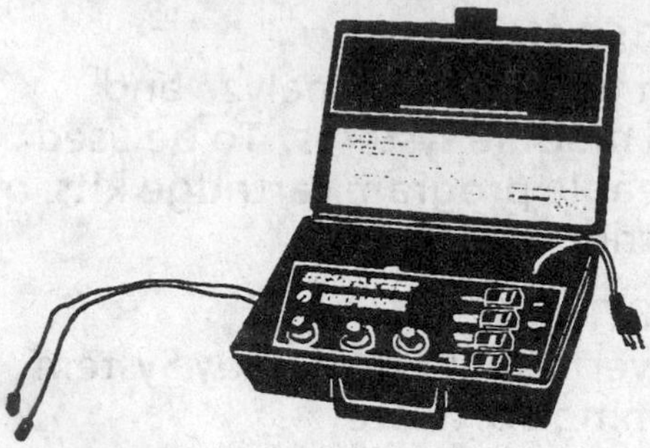 J 33431-B	**SIGNAL GENERATOR & INSTRUMENT PANEL TESTER** Used to generate VSS signal.
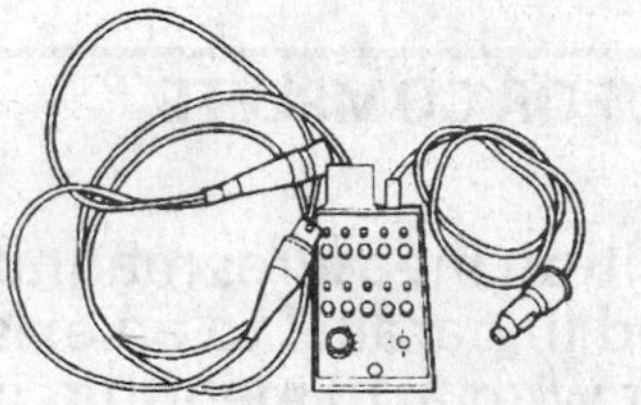 J 38791	**TRANSAXLE TEST BOX** Refer to appropriate engine section for specific adapter harness J 38791-XX.
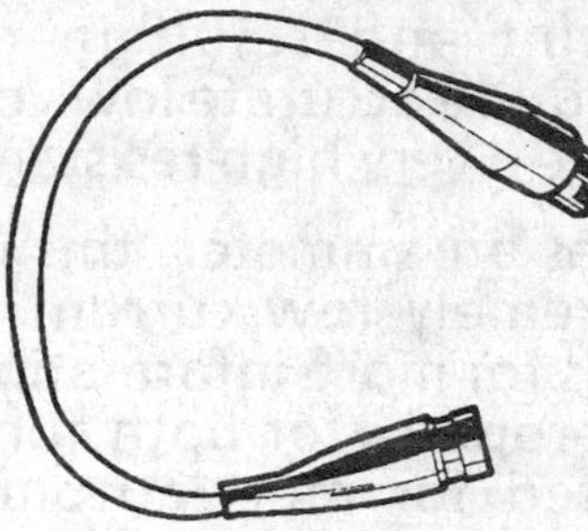 J 39775	**4L60E JUMPER HARNESS** Used to measure electronic component and circuit resistance in the transmission. Also used to test the transmission wiring harness and Powertrain Control Module during diagnosis.
 J 34142-B	**UNPOWERED TEST LIGHT** Used for checking wiring for complete circuit, short to ground, or voltage.
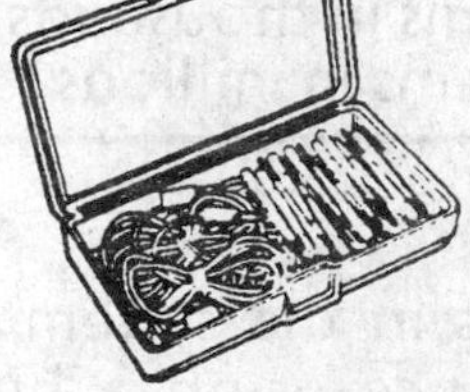 J 35616-A/BT-8637	**CONNECTOR TEST ADAPTER KIT** Used for making electrical test connections in current Weather Pack, Metri-Pack and Micro-Pack style terminals.
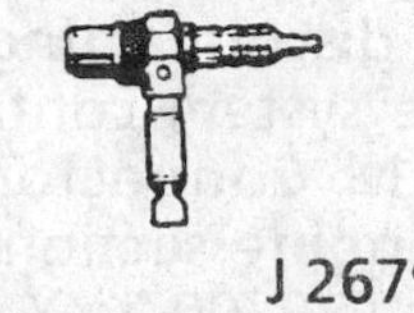 J 26792/BT-7220-1	**SPARK TESTER** Used for checking available secondary ignition voltage. Also called an ST 125.

6-11-93
MS 11188-6E

Special Tools (2 of 6)

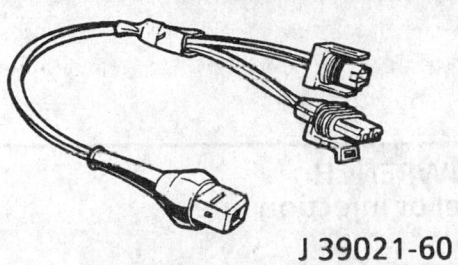

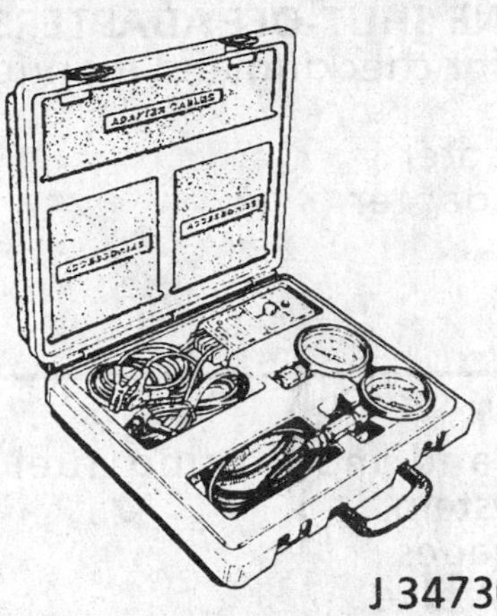 J 34730-E	**PORT FUEL INJECTION DIAGNOSTIC KIT** Used to diagnose port fuel injection systems. The kit includes: • Fuel Pressure Gage - (J 34730-1A) • Injector Test Light - (J 34730-2C) • Test Harness Adapter - (J 34730-225) - used to connect J 39021 to CPI engine harness • Injector Poppet Tester - (J 34730-230) - used to check CPI fuel flow. • Fuel Injector Tester - (J 39021) - used to check injector coils and to perform injector balance (fuel flow) check
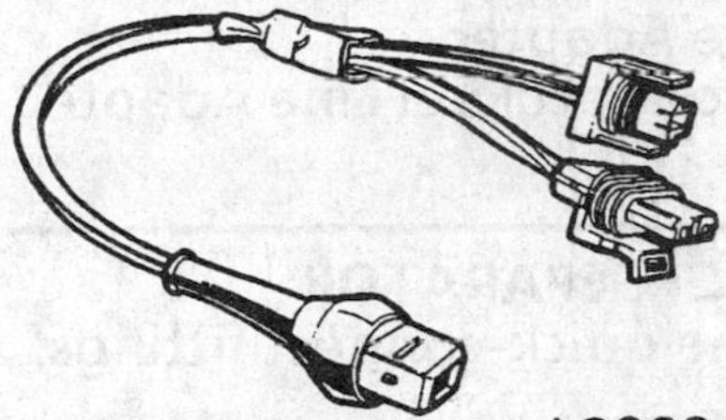 J 39021-70	**TEST HARNESS ADAPTER** Used to connect J 39021 to 2.2L Passenger.
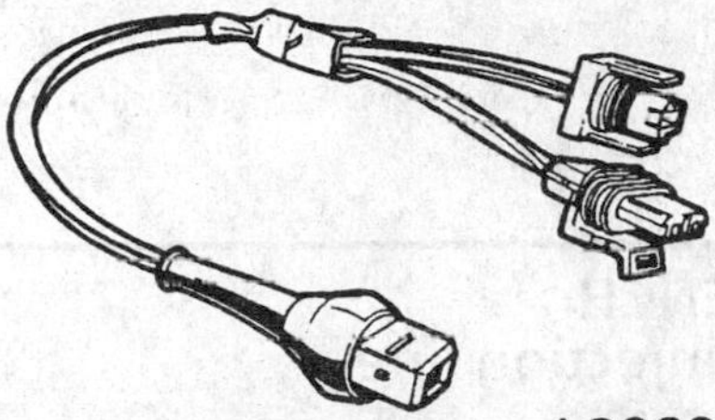 J 39021-60	**TEST HARNESS ADAPTER** Used to connect J 39021 to 2.2L Truck.
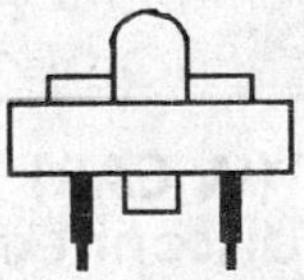 J 34730-350/BT-8320	**INJECTOR HARNESS TESTER** Used for checking the electrical circuit to a TBI fuel injector.
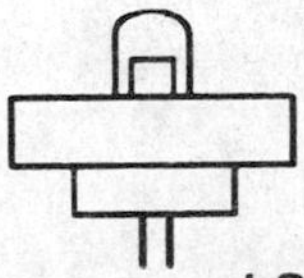 J 34730-2A/BT-8329A	**INJECTOR HARNESS TESTER** Used for checking the electrical circuit to a TBI fuel injector.
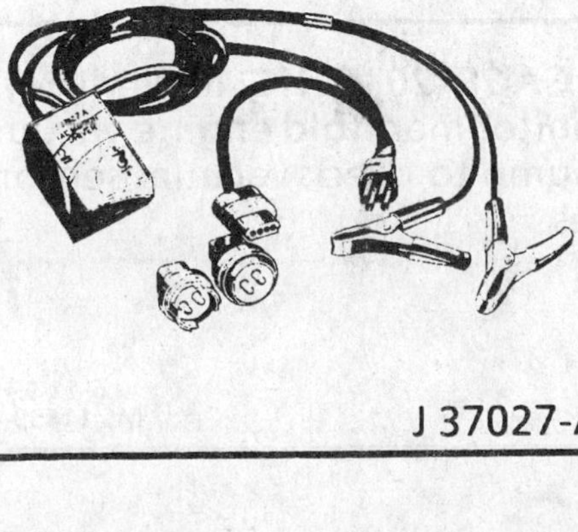 J 37027-A	**IAC MOTOR ANALYZER** Used to test IAC motors for correct functioning and proper response to commands. J 37027-3 IAC System Check Lights ALSO 222-L IAC Driver and Node Light Kit 6-8-93 MS 11457-6E

Special Tools (3 of 6)

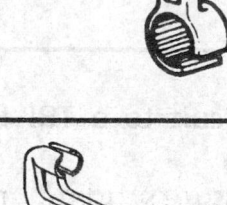

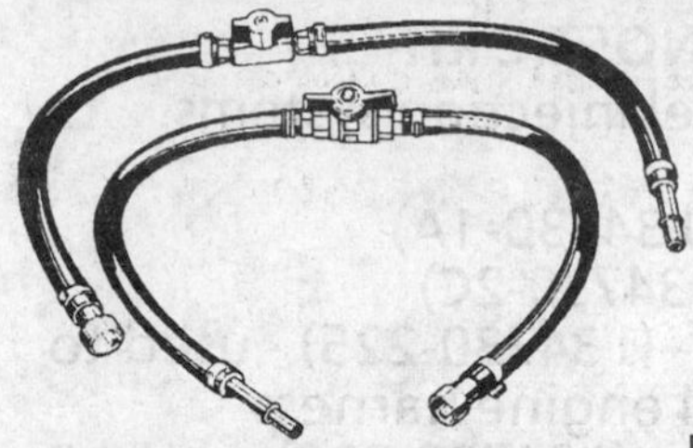 J 37287	**INLET & RETURN FUEL LINE SHUT-OFF ADAPTERS** Used with J 34730-1 for checking and monitoring fuel line pressure. • J37287-1 Inlet Adapter • J37287-2 Return Adapter
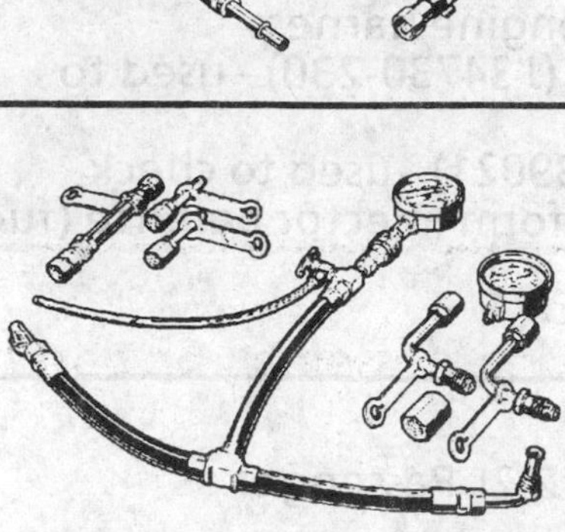 J 29658-D	**FUEL PRESSURE GAGE KIT** Used for checking and monitoring fuel line pressure of TBI fuel system. • 15 PSI and 60 PSI gages • J 29658-150 Relief Valve • J 29658-82 Fuel Line Adapter • J 29658-85 Fuel Line Adapter • J 29658-89 Quick-Connect Fuel Line Adapter
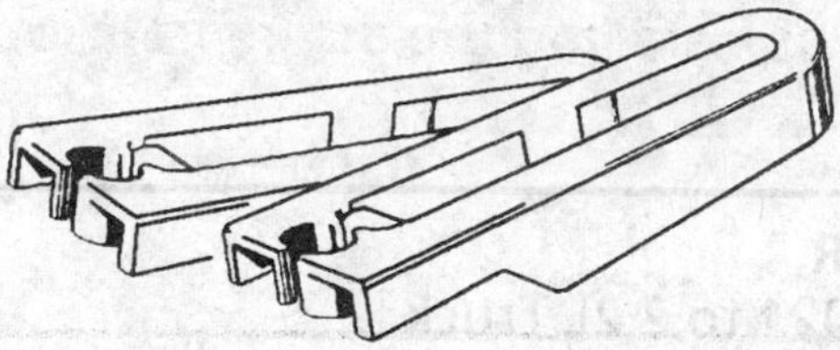 J 37088-A/BT-9171	**FUEL LINE QUICK-CONNECT SEPARATOR** Used to release fuel line quick-connect fittings.
 J 29698-A/BT-8251	**FUEL/INJECTION LINE WRENCH** Used to service fuel or injection line.
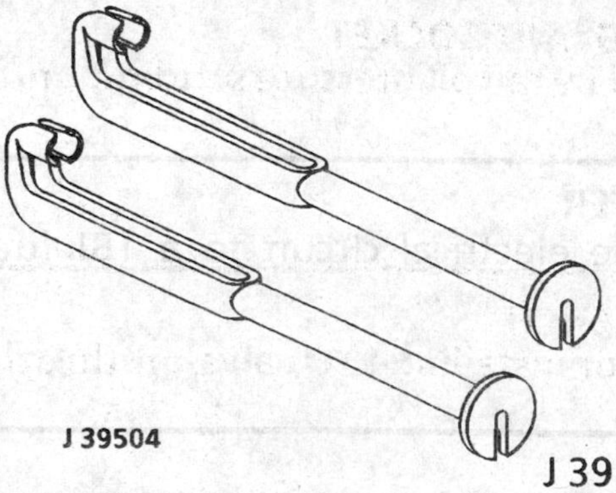J 39504 J 39504	**FUEL LINE DISCONNECT TOOL SET (W CAR)** Used to disconnect fuel line disconnect locking tabs under ABS modulator.
 J 23738-A	**VACUUM PUMP WITH GAGE (20 IN. HG. MINIMUM)** Use the gage to monitor manifold engine vacuum and use the hand pump to check vacuum sensors, solenoids and valves. 6-11-93 MS 11459-6E

Special Tools (4 of 6)

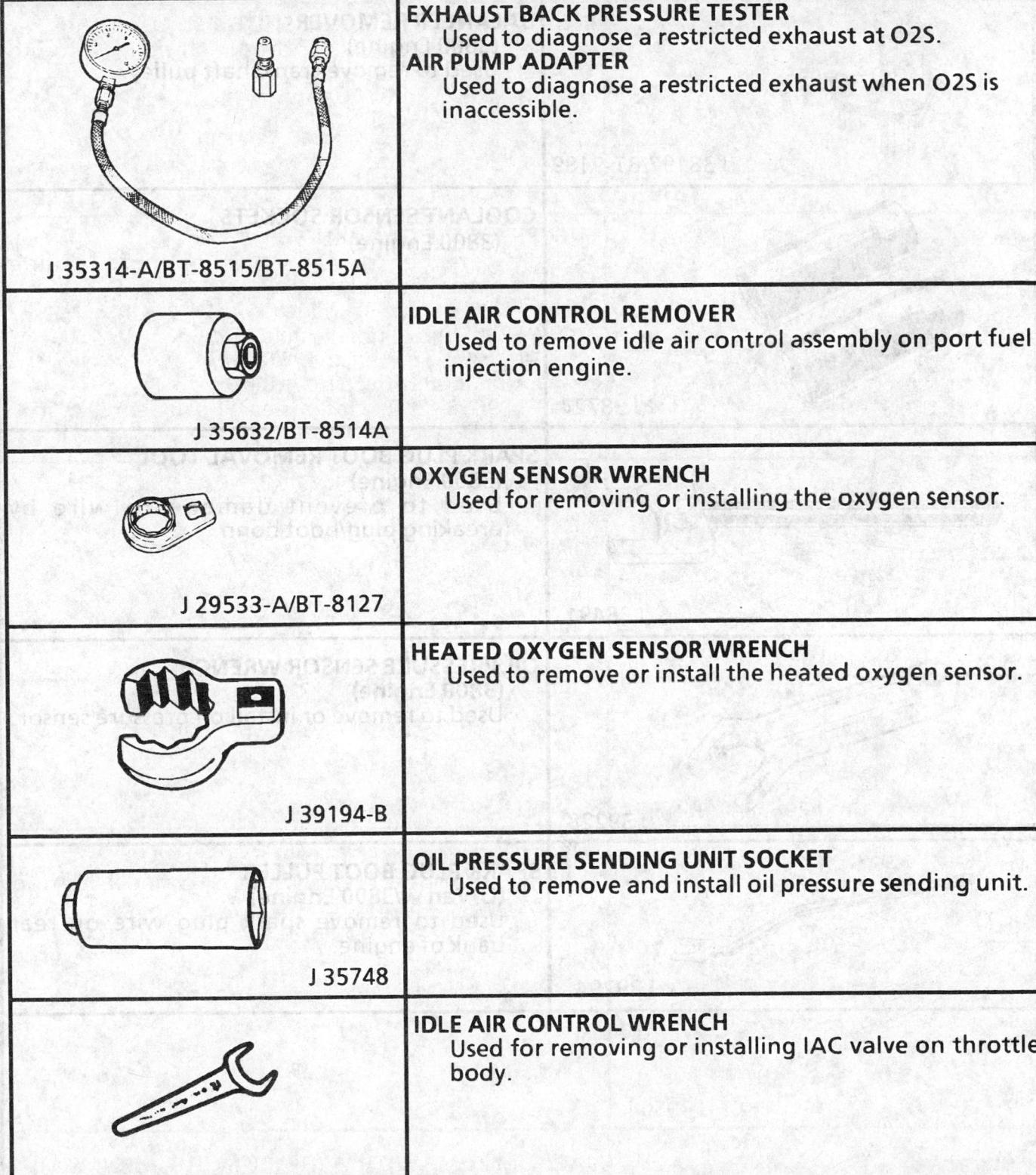

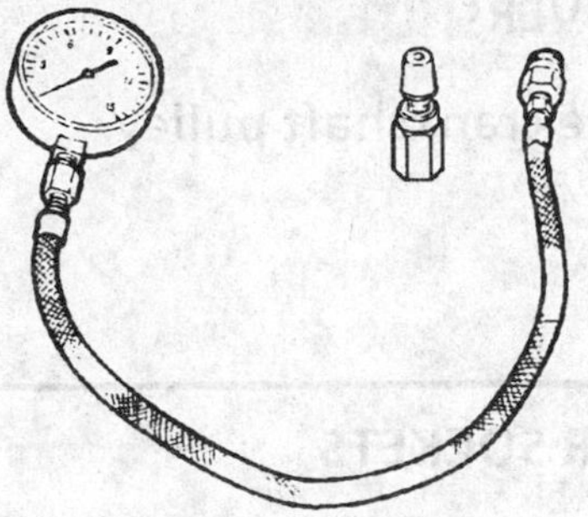 J 35314-A/BT-8515/BT-8515A	**EXHAUST BACK PRESSURE TESTER** Used to diagnose a restricted exhaust at O2S. **AIR PUMP ADAPTER** Used to diagnose a restricted exhaust when O2S is inaccessible.
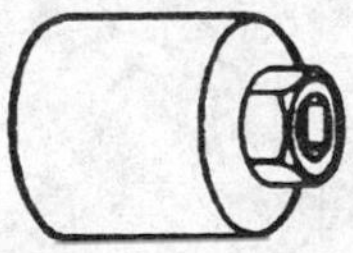 J 35632/BT-8514A	**IDLE AIR CONTROL REMOVER** Used to remove idle air control assembly on port fuel injection engine.
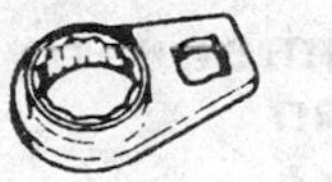 J 29533-A/BT-8127	**OXYGEN SENSOR WRENCH** Used for removing or installing the oxygen sensor.
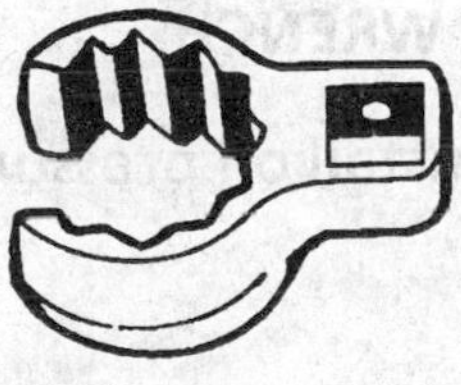 J 39194-B	**HEATED OXYGEN SENSOR WRENCH** Used to remove or install the heated oxygen sensor.
 J 35748	**OIL PRESSURE SENDING UNIT SOCKET** Used to remove and install oil pressure sending unit.
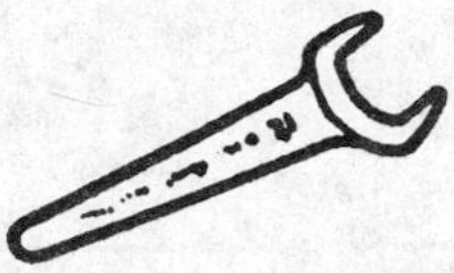 J 33031/BT-8130	**IDLE AIR CONTROL WRENCH** Used for removing or installing IAC valve on throttle body.

6-11-93
MS 11460-6E

Special Tools (5 of 6)

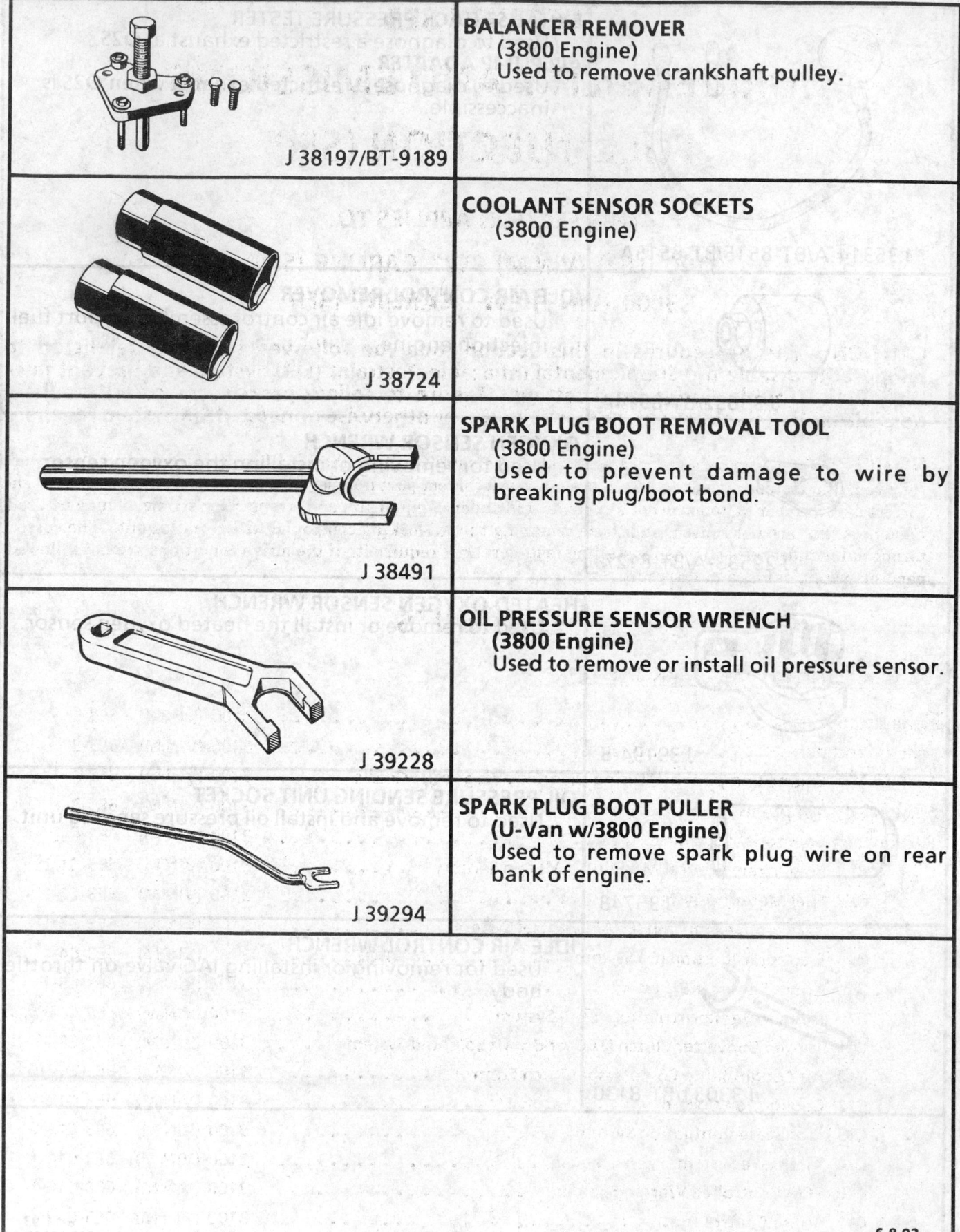

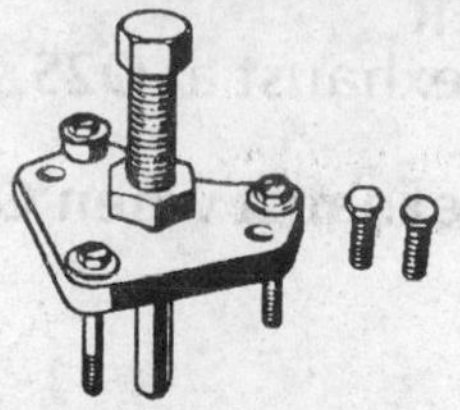 J 38197/BT-9189	**BALANCER REMOVER** (3800 Engine) Used to remove crankshaft pulley.
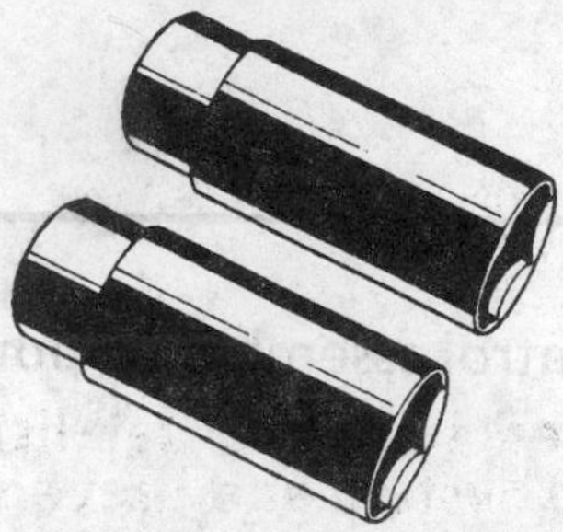 J 38724	**COOLANT SENSOR SOCKETS** (3800 Engine)
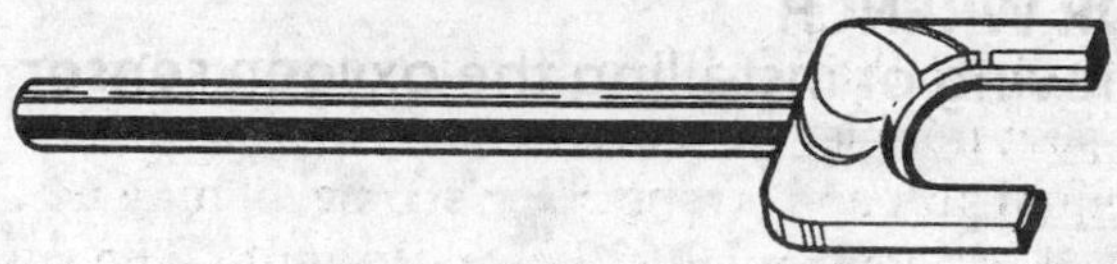 J 38491	**SPARK PLUG BOOT REMOVAL TOOL** (3800 Engine) Used to prevent damage to wire by breaking plug/boot bond.
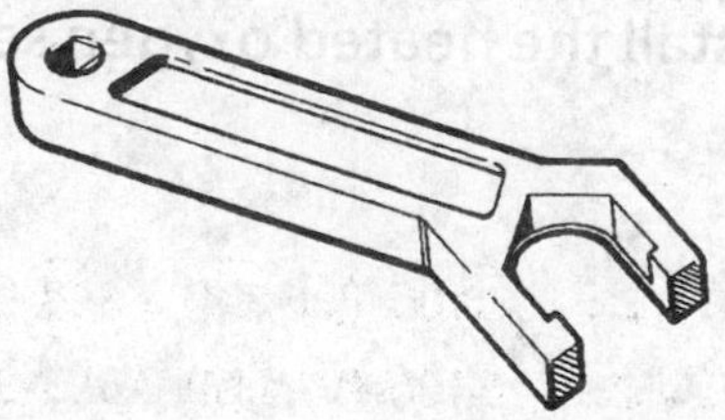 J 39228	**OIL PRESSURE SENSOR WRENCH** (3800 Engine) Used to remove or install oil pressure sensor.
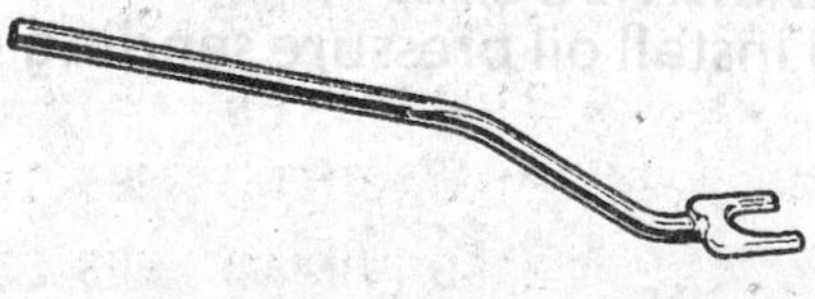 J 39294	**SPARK PLUG BOOT PULLER** (U-Van w/3800 Engine) Used to remove spark plug wire on rear bank of engine.

6-8-93
MS 11466-6E

SECTION 6E3

DRIVEABILITY AND EMISSIONS FUEL INJECTION (SFI)

THIS SECTION APPLIES TO:

3100 (L82) (VIN M) "W" CARLINE (SFI)
3800 (VIN L) "W" CARLINE (SFI)

CAUTION: The procedures in this section must be followed in the order listed to temporarily disable the Supplemental Inflatable Restraint (SIR) System and prevent false Diagnostic Trouble Codes from setting. Failure to follow procedures could result in possible air bag deployment, personal injury, or otherwise unneeded SIR system repairs.

NOTICE: When fasteners are removed, always reinstall them at the same location from which they were removed. If a fastener needs to be replaced, use the correct part number fastener for that application. If the correct part number fastener is not available, a fastener of equal size and strength (or stronger) may be used. Fasteners that are not reused, and those requiring thread-locking compound will be called out. The correct torque value must be used when installing fasteners that require it. If the above conditions are not followed, parts or system damage could result.

CONTENTS

3100 (L82) (VIN M) "W" CARLINE

3800 (VIN L) "W" CARLINE

ALL NEW GENERAL MOTORS VEHICLES ARE CERTIFIED BY THE UNITED STATES ENVIRONMENTAL PROTECTION AGENCY AS CONFORMING TO THE REQUIREMENTS OF THE REGULATIONS FOR THE CONTROL OF AIR POLLUTION FROM NEW MOTOR VEHICLES. THIS CERTIFICATION IS CONTINGENT ON CERTAIN ADJUSTMENTS BEING SET TO FACTORY STANDARDS. IN MOST CASES, THESE ADJUSTMENT POINTS EITHER HAVE BEEN PERMANENTLY SEALED AND/OR MADE INACCESSIBLE, TO PREVENT INDISCRIMINATE OR ROUTINE ADJUSTMENT IN THE FIELD. FOR THIS REASON, THE FACTORY PROCEDURE FOR TEMPORARILY REMOVING PLUGS, CAPS, ETC., FOR PURPOSES OF SERVICING THE PRODUCT, MUST BE STRICTLY FOLLOWED AND, WHEREVER PRACTICABLE, RETURNED TO THE ORIGINAL INTENT OF THE DESIGN.

INTRODUCTION

GENERAL DESCRIPTION

This section applies to engines with Sequential Fuel Injection (SFI) fuel delivery systems. These engines have a fuel injector in the intake manifold near the intake valve for each cylinder.

These engines have controls that reduce exhaust emissions, and maintain good driveability and fuel economy.

The Powertrain Control Module (PCM) is the heart of this control system. A network of sensors provides the PCM with information about engine operation and the various systems it controls. Details of basic operation, diagnosis, functional checks, and on-vehicle service are covered in "Component Systems," Section "6E3-C".

The PCM has the ability to do some diagnosis of itself, as well as other parts of the system. When the PCM finds a problem, it will light a Malfunction Indicator Lamp (MIL) "Service Engine Soon" on the instrument panel and a Diagnostic Trouble Code (DTC) will be stored in the PCM's memory. The Malfunction Indicator Lamp (MIL) "Service Engine Soon" does not indicate that the engine should be stopped right away, but that the vehicle should be checked as soon as reasonably possible.

DIAGNOSIS PROCEDURE

The following sections are written for specific engine applications and are clearly identified. Be sure to use only the section which applies to the engine family being diagnosed.

Before using this section of the manual, you should be familiar with the information and the proper diagnosing procedures that are described in SECTION 6E. If the proper diagnosis procedures are not followed, as described in SECTION 6E, it may result in unnecessary replacement of good parts.

Diagnostic charts incorporate diagnosis procedures using a Tech 1 diagnostic computer whenever possible. The scan tool has the ability to save time in diagnosis and prevent the replacement of good parts.

The key to using a scan tool successfully for diagnosis lies in the technician's ability to understand the system being diagnosed, as well as having an understanding of the scan tool's limitations. Refer to SECTION 6E for more information.

BLANK

SECTION A

ENGINE COMPONENTS/WIRING DIAGRAMS/ DIAGNOSTIC CHARTS

BASIC PROCEDURE

If you have not reviewed the basic information on how to use the diagnostic procedures, go to the "Introduction" of this section. The facing page of each chart in this section will provide a general circuit description and in some instances, alternate diagnostic steps or other diagnostic aids specific to that chart or circuit.

ON-BOARD DIAGNOSTIC (OBD) SYSTEM CHECK

The OBD system check verifies the system is functioning correctly and is the starting point for diagnosing. Some special considerations to keep in mind when diagnosing are:

Blocking Drive Wheels

The vehicle drive wheels should always be blocked and the emergency brake set while checking the system.

CONTENTS

"W" CARLINE | RPO: L82 | 3100 V6 MFI

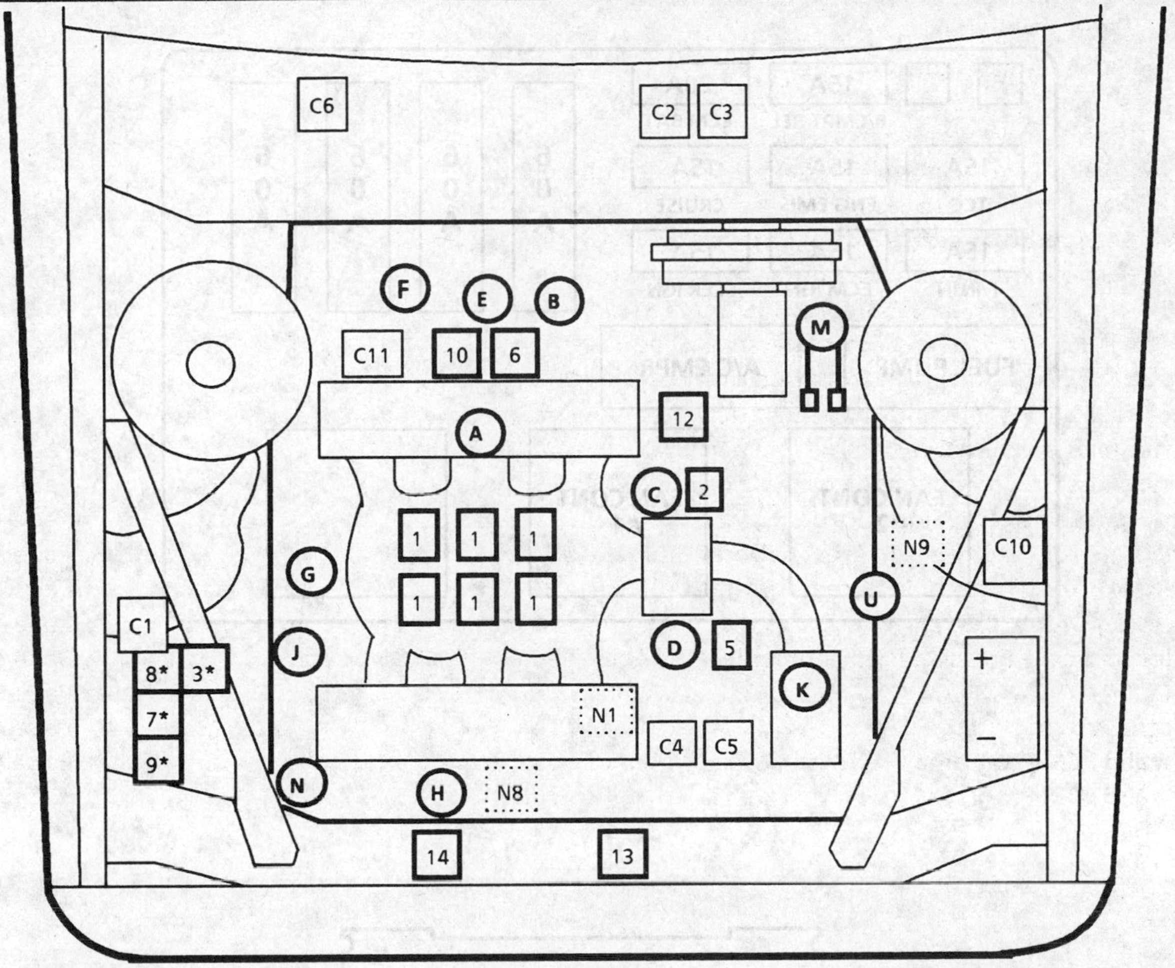
C6
C2
C3
F
E
B
C11
10
6
M
12
A
C
2
1
N9
C10
G
U
C1
8*
3*
J
D
5
K
+
–
7*
N1
C4
C5
9*
N
H
N8
14
13

COMPUTER HARNESS

- C1 Powertrain Control Module (PCM).
- C2 Data link connector.
- C3 MIL (Service Engine Soon).
- C4 Power ground.
- C5 Power ground.
- C6 I/P Fuse panel.
- C10 Underhood (U/H) electrical center (#2).
- C11 10 Pin and 1 pin injector harness connector (black).

NOT PCM CONNECTED

- N1 Crankcase ventilation valve.
- N8 Oil pressure switch (fuel pump).
- N9 Fuel pump prime connector.

CONTROLLED DEVICES

1. SFI fuel injectors.
2. Idle air control motor.
3. Fuel pump relay.*
5. Torque converter clutch connector.
6. Electronic ignition system module.
7. Primary cooling fan (#1) control relay.*
8. Secondary cooling fan (#2) control relay.*
9. A/C compressor clutch relay.*
10. EVAP purge solenoid.
12. Digital EGR.
13. Primary cooling fan (#1).
14. Secondary cooling fan (#2).

INFORMATION SENSORS

- A Manifold Absolute Pressure (MAP).
- B Heated Oxygen Sensor (HO2S).
- C Throttle Position (TP) sensor.
- D Engine Coolant Temperature (ECT) sensor.
- E 3X crankshaft position sensor.
- F Vehicle Speed Sensor (VSS).
- G Camshaft position sensor.
- H Knock Sensor (KS).
- J 24X crankshaft position sensor.
- K Intake Air Temperature (IAT) sensor.
- M Transaxle range switch with 4-way and 7-way pigtail connectors.
- N A/C clutch. (on comp.)
- U A/C refrigerant pressure sensor.

* THESE COMPONENTS ARE LOCATED WITHIN THE UNDERHOOD (U/H) ELECTRICAL CENTER (#1). (REFER TO FIGURE A-2 FOR COMPLETE ILLUSTRATION.)

5-19-93
PS 16826

Figure A-1 - Engine Component Locations 3100 (VIN M) "W" Carline

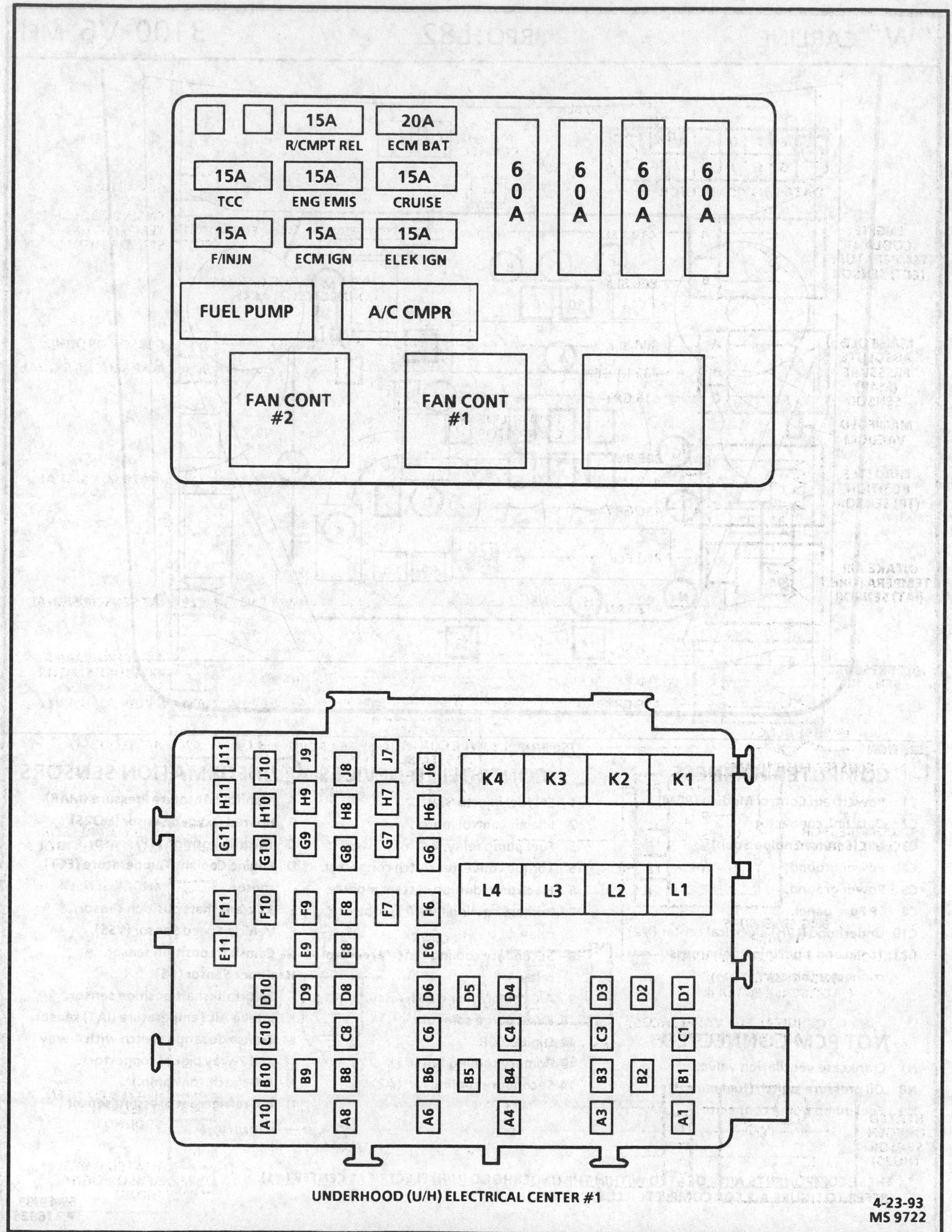
15A
R/CMPT REL
20A
ECM BAT
15A
TCC
15A
ENG EMIS
15A
CRUISE
15A
F/INJN
15A
ECM IGN
15A
ELEK IGN
60A
60A
60A
60A
FUEL PUMP
A/C CMPR
FAN CONT #2
FAN CONT #1
J11 J10 J9 J8 J7 J6
H11 H10 H9 H8 H7 H6
G11 G10 G9 G8 G7 G6
K4 K3 K2 K1
L4 L3 L2 L1
F11 F10 F9 F8 F7 F6
E11 E9 E8 E6
D10 D9 D8 D6 D5 D4 D3 D2 D1
C10 C8 C6 C4 C3 C1
B10 B9 B8 B6 B5 B4 B3 B2 B1
A10 A8 A6 A4 A3 A1
UNDERHOOD (U/H) ELECTRICAL CENTER #1
4-23-93
MS 9722

Figure A-2 - Underhood (U/H) Electrical Center #1 3100 (VIN M) "W" Carline

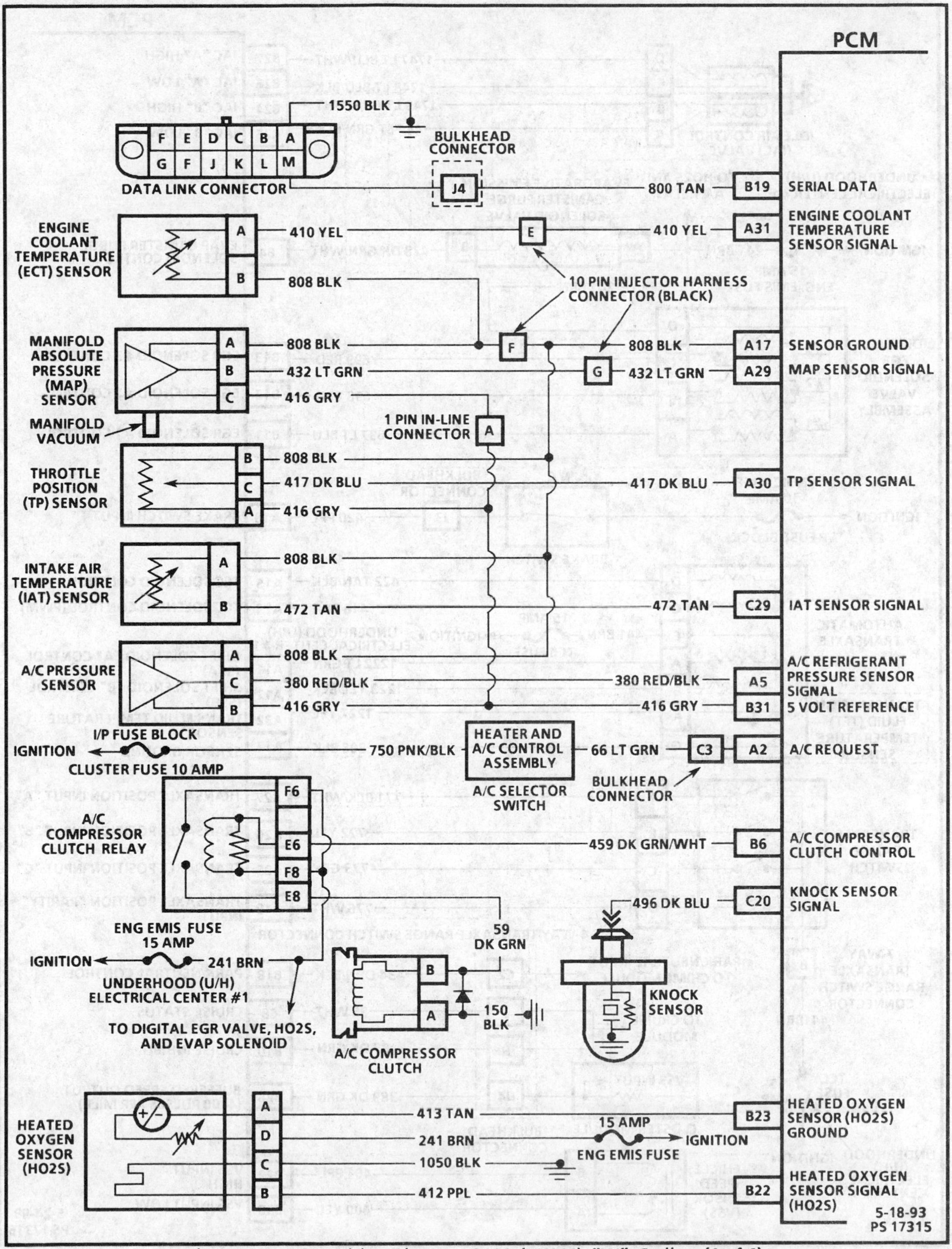
PCM
1550 BLK
BULKHEAD CONNECTOR
F E D C B A
G F J K L M
DATA LINK CONNECTOR
J4
800 TAN
B19
SERIAL DATA
ENGINE COOLANT TEMPERATURE (ECT) SENSOR
410 YEL
E
410 YEL
A31
ENGINE COOLANT TEMPERATURE SENSOR SIGNAL
808 BLK
10 PIN INJECTOR HARNESS CONNECTOR (BLACK)
MANIFOLD ABSOLUTE PRESSURE (MAP) SENSOR
808 BLK
F
808 BLK
A17
SENSOR GROUND
432 LT GRN
G
432 LT GRN
A29
MAP SENSOR SIGNAL
416 GRY
MANIFOLD VACUUM
1 PIN IN-LINE CONNECTOR
THROTTLE POSITION (TP) SENSOR
808 BLK
417 DK BLU
417 DK BLU
A30
TP SENSOR SIGNAL
416 GRY
INTAKE AIR TEMPERATURE (IAT) SENSOR
808 BLK
472 TAN
472 TAN
C29
IAT SENSOR SIGNAL
A/C PRESSURE SENSOR
808 BLK
380 RED/BLK
380 RED/BLK
A5
A/C REFRIGERANT PRESSURE SENSOR SIGNAL
416 GRY
416 GRY
B31
5 VOLT REFERENCE
I/P FUSE BLOCK
IGNITION
CLUSTER FUSE 10 AMP
750 PNK/BLK
HEATER AND A/C CONTROL ASSEMBLY
A/C SELECTOR SWITCH
66 LT GRN
C3
A2
A/C REQUEST
BULKHEAD CONNECTOR
A/C COMPRESSOR CLUTCH RELAY
F6
E6
F8
E8
459 DK GRN/WHT
B6
A/C COMPRESSOR CLUTCH CONTROL
496 DK BLU
C20
KNOCK SENSOR SIGNAL
ENG EMIS FUSE 15 AMP
IGNITION
241 BRN
UNDERHOOD (U/H) ELECTRICAL CENTER #1
TO DIGITAL EGR VALVE, HO2S, AND EVAP SOLENOID
59 DK GRN
150 BLK
A/C COMPRESSOR CLUTCH
KNOCK SENSOR
HEATED OXYGEN SENSOR (HO2S)
413 TAN
B23
HEATED OXYGEN SENSOR (HO2S) GROUND
241 BRN
15 AMP
IGNITION
ENG EMIS FUSE
1050 BLK
412 PPL
B22
HEATED OXYGEN SENSOR SIGNAL (HO2S)
5-18-93
PS 17315

Figure A-3 - PCM Wiring Diagram 3100 (VIN M) "W" Carline (1 of 4)

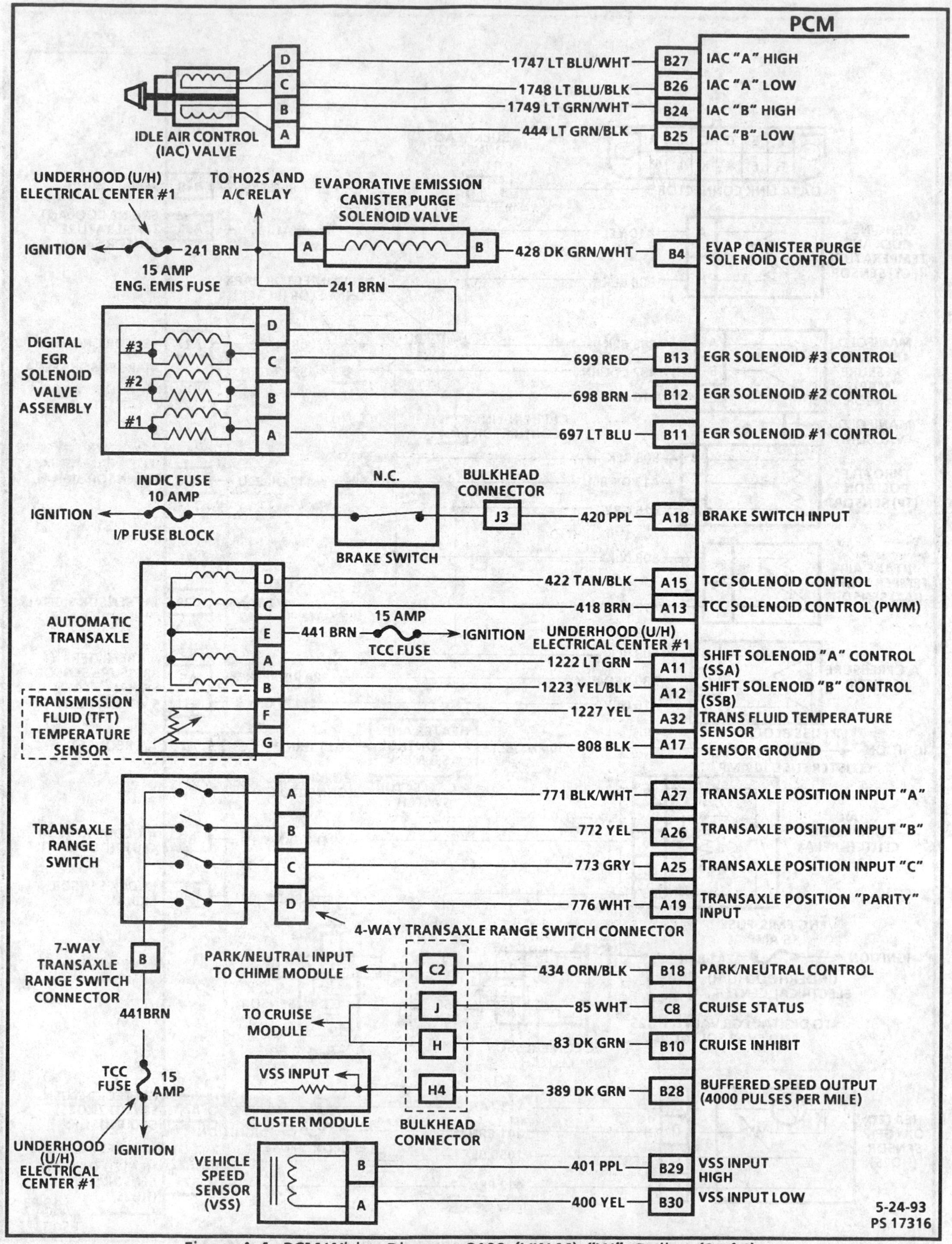
PCM
IDLE AIR CONTROL (IAC) VALVE
D
C
B
A
1747 LT BLU/WHT
1748 LT BLU/BLK
1749 LT GRN/WHT
444 LT GRN/BLK
B27 IAC "A" HIGH
B26 IAC "A" LOW
B24 IAC "B" HIGH
B25 IAC "B" LOW
UNDERHOOD (U/H) ELECTRICAL CENTER #1
TO HO2S AND A/C RELAY
EVAPORATIVE EMISSION CANISTER PURGE SOLENOID VALVE
IGNITION
241 BRN
15 AMP ENG. EMIS FUSE
428 DK GRN/WHT
B4 EVAP CANISTER PURGE SOLENOID CONTROL
DIGITAL EGR SOLENOID VALVE ASSEMBLY
#3
#2
#1
699 RED
698 BRN
697 LT BLU
B13 EGR SOLENOID #3 CONTROL
B12 EGR SOLENOID #2 CONTROL
B11 EGR SOLENOID #1 CONTROL
INDIC FUSE 10 AMP
I/P FUSE BLOCK
N.C.
BRAKE SWITCH
BULKHEAD CONNECTOR
J3
420 PPL
A18 BRAKE SWITCH INPUT
AUTOMATIC TRANSAXLE
TRANSMISSION FLUID (TFT) TEMPERATURE SENSOR
422 TAN/BLK
418 BRN
441 BRN
15 AMP
TCC FUSE
UNDERHOOD (U/H) ELECTRICAL CENTER #1
1222 LT GRN
1223 YEL/BLK
1227 YEL
808 BLK
A15 TCC SOLENOID CONTROL
A13 TCC SOLENOID CONTROL (PWM)
A11 SHIFT SOLENOID "A" CONTROL (SSA)
A12 SHIFT SOLENOID "B" CONTROL (SSB)
A32 TRANS FLUID TEMPERATURE SENSOR
A17 SENSOR GROUND
TRANSAXLE RANGE SWITCH
771 BLK/WHT
772 YEL
773 GRY
776 WHT
A27 TRANSAXLE POSITION INPUT "A"
A26 TRANSAXLE POSITION INPUT "B"
A25 TRANSAXLE POSITION INPUT "C"
A19 TRANSAXLE POSITION "PARITY" INPUT
4-WAY TRANSAXLE RANGE SWITCH CONNECTOR
7-WAY TRANSAXLE RANGE SWITCH CONNECTOR
441BRN
TCC FUSE 15 AMP
UNDERHOOD (U/H) ELECTRICAL CENTER #1
PARK/NEUTRAL INPUT TO CHIME MODULE
C2
434 ORN/BLK
B18 PARK/NEUTRAL CONTROL
TO CRUISE MODULE
J
85 WHT
C8 CRUISE STATUS
H
83 DK GRN
B10 CRUISE INHIBIT
VSS INPUT
CLUSTER MODULE
H4
389 DK GRN
B28 BUFFERED SPEED OUTPUT (4000 PULSES PER MILE)
BULKHEAD CONNECTOR
VEHICLE SPEED SENSOR (VSS)
401 PPL
400 YEL
B29 VSS INPUT HIGH
B30 VSS INPUT LOW
5-24-93
PS 17316

Figure A-4 - PCM Wiring Diagram 3100 (VIN M) "W" Carline (2 of 4)

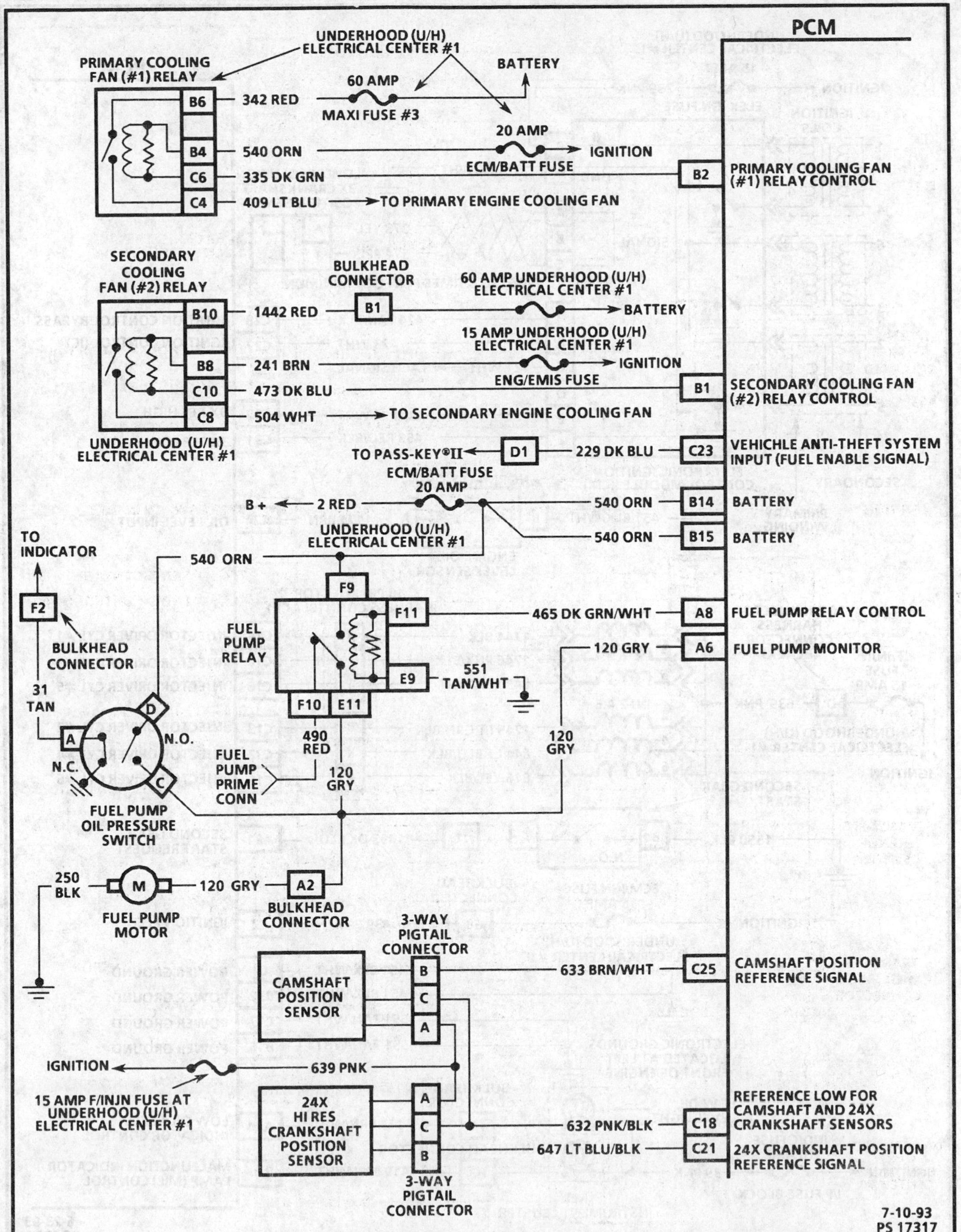
PCM
UNDERHOOD (U/H) ELECTRICAL CENTER #1
PRIMARY COOLING FAN (#1) RELAY
BATTERY
60 AMP
B6
342 RED
MAXI FUSE #3
20 AMP
B4
540 ORN
IGNITION
C6
335 DK GRN
ECM/BATT FUSE
B2
PRIMARY COOLING FAN (#1) RELAY CONTROL
C4
409 LT BLU
TO PRIMARY ENGINE COOLING FAN
SECONDARY COOLING FAN (#2) RELAY
BULKHEAD CONNECTOR
60 AMP UNDERHOOD (U/H) ELECTRICAL CENTER #1
B10
1442 RED
B1
BATTERY
15 AMP UNDERHOOD (U/H) ELECTRICAL CENTER #1
B8
241 BRN
IGNITION
ENG/EMIS FUSE
C10
473 DK BLU
B1
SECONDARY COOLING FAN (#2) RELAY CONTROL
C8
504 WHT
TO SECONDARY ENGINE COOLING FAN
UNDERHOOD (U/H) ELECTRICAL CENTER #1
TO PASS-KEY®II
D1
229 DK BLU
C23
VEHICHLE ANTI-THEFT SYSTEM INPUT (FUEL ENABLE SIGNAL)
ECM/BATT FUSE
20 AMP
B +
2 RED
540 ORN
B14
BATTERY
UNDERHOOD (U/H) ELECTRICAL CENTER #1
540 ORN
B15
BATTERY
TO INDICATOR
540 ORN
F9
F2
FUEL PUMP RELAY
F11
465 DK GRN/WHT
A8
FUEL PUMP RELAY CONTROL
120 GRY
A6
FUEL PUMP MONITOR
BULKHEAD CONNECTOR
E9
551 TAN/WHT
31 TAN
F10
E11
D
A
N.O.
490 RED
120 GRY
N.C.
FUEL PUMP PRIME CONN
120 GRY
C
FUEL PUMP OIL PRESSURE SWITCH
250 BLK
M
120 GRY
A2
FUEL PUMP MOTOR
BULKHEAD CONNECTOR
3-WAY PIGTAIL CONNECTOR
CAMSHAFT POSITION SENSOR
B
633 BRN/WHT
C25
CAMSHAFT POSITION REFERENCE SIGNAL
C
A
IGNITION
639 PNK
15 AMP F/INJN FUSE AT UNDERHOOD (U/H) ELECTRICAL CENTER #1
24X HI RES CRANKSHAFT POSITION SENSOR
A
C
632 PNK/BLK
C18
REFERENCE LOW FOR CAMSHAFT AND 24X CRANKSHAFT SENSORS
B
647 LT BLU/BLK
C21
24X CRANKSHAFT POSITION REFERENCE SIGNAL
3-WAY PIGTAIL CONNECTOR
7-10-93
PS 17317

Figure A-5 - PCM Wiring Diagram 3100 (VIN M) "W" Carline (3 of 4)

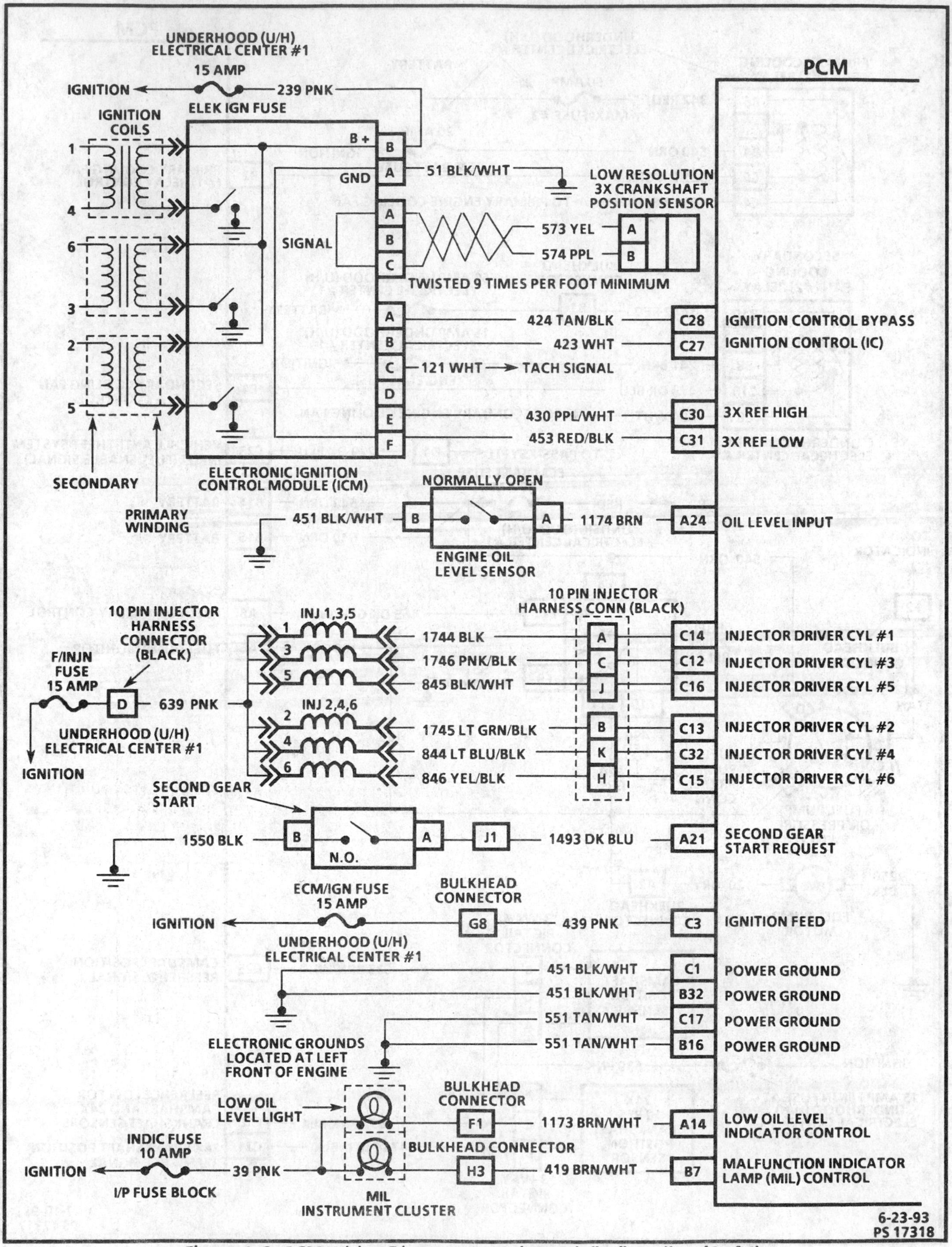
UNDERHOOD (U/H)
ELECTRICAL CENTER #1
15 AMP
IGNITION
239 PNK
ELEK IGN FUSE
IGNITION
COILS
B+
B
GND
A
51 BLK/WHT
LOW RESOLUTION
3X CRANKSHAFT
POSITION SENSOR
SIGNAL
573 YEL
574 PPL
TWISTED 9 TIMES PER FOOT MINIMUM
PCM
424 TAN/BLK
C28
IGNITION CONTROL BYPASS
423 WHT
C27
IGNITION CONTROL (IC)
121 WHT
TACH SIGNAL
430 PPL/WHT
C30
3X REF HIGH
453 RED/BLK
C31
3X REF LOW
SECONDARY
ELECTRONIC IGNITION
CONTROL MODULE (ICM)
PRIMARY
WINDING
NORMALLY OPEN
451 BLK/WHT
1174 BRN
A24
OIL LEVEL INPUT
ENGINE OIL
LEVEL SENSOR
10 PIN INJECTOR
HARNESS CONN (BLACK)
10 PIN INJECTOR
HARNESS
CONNECTOR
(BLACK)
INJ 1,3,5
1744 BLK
C14
INJECTOR DRIVER CYL #1
1746 PNK/BLK
C12
INJECTOR DRIVER CYL #3
845 BLK/WHT
C16
INJECTOR DRIVER CYL #5
F/INJN
FUSE
15 AMP
639 PNK
INJ 2,4,6
1745 LT GRN/BLK
C13
INJECTOR DRIVER CYL #2
844 LT BLU/BLK
C32
INJECTOR DRIVER CYL #4
846 YEL/BLK
C15
INJECTOR DRIVER CYL #6
UNDERHOOD (U/H)
ELECTRICAL CENTER #1
IGNITION
SECOND GEAR
START
1550 BLK
N.O.
J1
1493 DK BLU
A21
SECOND GEAR
START REQUEST
ECM/IGN FUSE
15 AMP
BULKHEAD
CONNECTOR
IGNITION
G8
439 PNK
C3
IGNITION FEED
UNDERHOOD (U/H)
ELECTRICAL CENTER #1
451 BLK/WHT
C1
POWER GROUND
451 BLK/WHT
B32
POWER GROUND
551 TAN/WHT
C17
POWER GROUND
551 TAN/WHT
B16
POWER GROUND
ELECTRONIC GROUNDS
LOCATED AT LEFT
FRONT OF ENGINE
LOW OIL
LEVEL LIGHT
BULKHEAD
CONNECTOR
F1
1173 BRN/WHT
A14
LOW OIL LEVEL
INDICATOR CONTROL
INDIC FUSE
10 AMP
BULKHEAD CONNECTOR
IGNITION
39 PNK
H3
419 BRN/WHT
B7
MALFUNCTION INDICATOR
LAMP (MIL) CONTROL
I/P FUSE BLOCK
MIL
INSTRUMENT CLUSTER
6-23-93
PS 17318

Figure A-6 - PCM Wiring Diagram 3100 (VIN M) "W" Carline (4 of 4)

PCM TERMINAL CONNECTOR END VIEWS

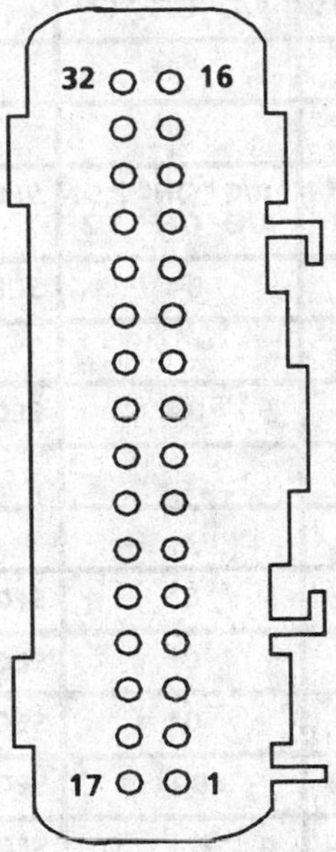
32
16
17
1

FRONT VIEW
32 PIN
PCM CONNECTOR "A"
(CLEAR)

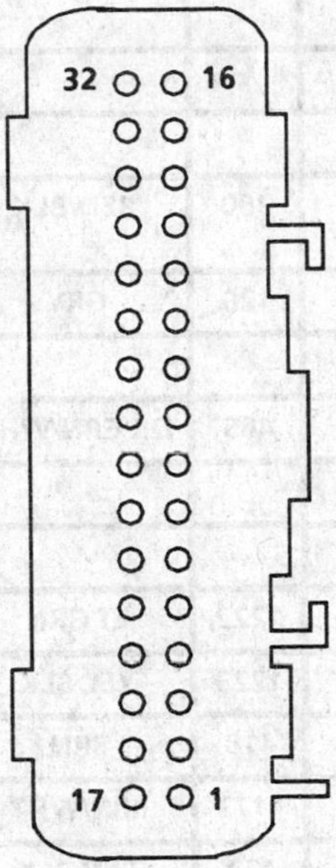
32
16
17
1

FRONT VIEW
32 PIN
PCM CONNECTOR "B"
(BLACK)

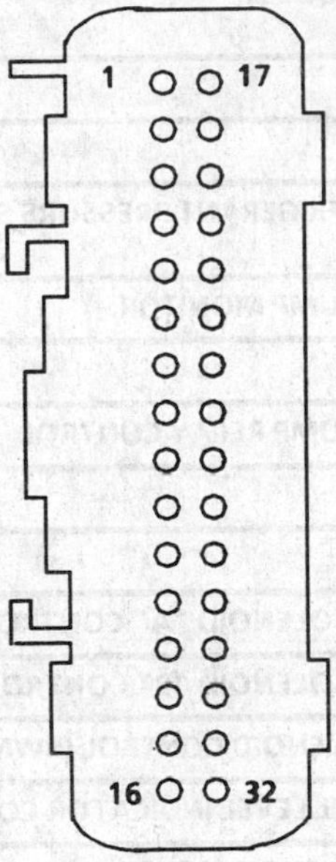
1
17
16
32

FRONT VIEW
32 PIN
PCM CONNECTOR "C"
(BLUE)

NOTICE: DO NOT BACKPROBE PCM CONNECTORS!
Install the BOB between the PCM harness connectors and the PCM, then probe the pin listed under "BOB PIN #." Voltage may vary due to low battery charge or other reasons, but should be close. All voltages shown in the ENG "RUN" column are typical with engine at idle, closed throttle, normal operating temperature, park or neutral, system in "Closed Loop," all accessories "OFF," and scan tool <u>not</u> installed.

DVM NEGATIVE LEAD MUST BE CONNECTED TO A KNOWN GOOD GROUND.

(1) INCREASES WITH VEHICLE SPEED (MEASURE ON AC SCALE).
(2) NORMAL OPERATING TEMPERATURE.
(3) VARIES
(4) 12 VOLTS FIRST TWO SECONDS.
(5) VARIES WITH TEMPERATURE.
* LESS THAN 1 VOLT.

5-25-93
PS 17933

USE KENT MOORE UNIVERSAL BREAKOUT BOX J 39700 WITH J 39700-110 ADAPTER AND J 39700-112 OVERLAY **3100** (VIN M)

PCM CONNECTOR "A" (CLEAR)

RPO: L82

PCM PIN/FUNCTION	CKT #	WIRE COLOR	BOB # PIN	VOLTAGE KEY "ON"	VOLTAGE ENG "RUN"	REFERENCE
A1			201			
A2 A/C REQUEST	66	LT GRN	202	A/C "ON" 8.3 A/C "OFF" 0*	A/C "ON" 9.4 A/C "OFF" 0*	SECTION C10
A3			203			
A4			204			
A5 A/C REFRIGERANT PRESSURE SENSOR SIGNAL	380	RED/BLK	205	A/C "OFF" 1.09	A/C "ON" 2.3 A/C "OFF" 1.2	SECTION C10
A6 FUEL PUMP MONITOR	120	GRY	206	0*	B+	SCECTION C2
A7			207			
A8 FUEL PUMP RELAY CONTROL	465	DK GRN/WHT	208	(4) 0*	B+	SECTION C2
A9			209			
A10			210			
A11 SHIFT SOLENOID "A" CONTROL	1222	LT GRN	211	B+	0*	SECTION C8
A12 SHIFT SOLENOID "B" CONTROL	1223	YEL/BLK	212	B+	0*	SECTION C8
A13 TCC SOLENOID CONTROL (PWM)	418	BRN	213	0*	0*	SECTION C8
A14 LOW OIL LEVEL INDICATOR CONTROL	1173	BRN/WHT	214	B+	B+	SECTION C16
A15 TCC SOLENOID CONTROL	422	TAN/BLK	215	B+	B+	SECTION C8
A16			216			
A17 SENSOR GROUND	808	BLK	217	0*	0*	SECTION C1
A18 BRAKE SWITCH INPUT	420	PPL	218	B+	B+	CHT DTC 37
A19 TRANSAXLE POSITION SWITCH PARITY INPUT	776	WHT	219	B+	B+	CHT DTC 28
A20			220			
A21 SECOND GEAR START SWITCH	1493	DK BLU	221	B+	B+	SECTION C8
A22			222			
A23			223			
A24 OIL LEVEL INPUT	1174	BRN	224	0*	0*	SECTION C16
A25 TRANSAXLE POSITION SWITCH INPUT "C"	773	GRY	225	0*	0*	CHT DTC 28
A26 TRANSAXLE POSITION SWITCH INPUT "B"	772	YEL	226	0*	0*	CHT DTC 28
A27 TRANSAXLE POSITION SWITCH INPUT "A"	771	BLK/WHT	227	B+	B+	CHT DTC 28
A28			228			
A29 MAP SENSOR SIGNAL	432	LT GRN	229	5V	(3)	SECTION C1
A30 TP SENSOR SIGNAL	417	DK BLU	230	0*	(3)	SECTION C1
A31 ENGINE COOLANT TEMPERATURE SENSOR SIGNAL	410	YEL	231	(5)	(5)	SECTION C1
A32 TRANS FLUID TEMPERATURE SENSOR SIGNAL	1227	YEL/BLK	232	(5)	(5)	SECTION C1

* LESS THAN 1 VOLT.
(4) 12 VOLTS FIRST TWO SECONDS.
(5) VARIES WITH TEMPERTURE.

7-11-93
PS 16675

Figure A-7 - PCM Connector End View 3100 (VIN M) "W" Carline (1 of 3)

USE KENT MOORE UNIVERSAL BREAKOUT BOX J 39700 WITH J 39700-110 ADAPTER AND J 39700-112 OVERLAY 3100 (VIN M)

PCM CONNECTOR "B" (BLACK)

RPO: L82

PCM PIN/FUNCTION	CKT #	WIRE COLOR	BOB # PIN	VOLTAGE KEY "ON"	VOLTAGE ENG "RUN"	REFERENCE
B1 ENGINE SECONDARY COOLANT FAN #2 RELAY CONTROL	473	DK BLU	101	FAN "OFF" B +	FAN "OFF" B +	SECTION C12
B2 ENGINE PRIMARY COOLANT FAN #1 RELAY CONTROL	335	DK GRN	102	FAN "OFF" B +	FAN "OFF" B +	SECTION C12
B3			103			
B4 EVAP CANISTER PURGE SOLENOID CONTROL	428	DK GRN/WHT	104	B +	B +	SECTION C3
B5			105			
B6 A/C COMPRESSOR CLUTCH CONTROL	459	DK GRN/WHT	106	B +	A/C "OFF" B + A/C "ON" 0*	SECTION C10
B7 MALFUNCTION INDICATOR LAMP (MIL) "SERVICE ENGINE SOON" CONTROL	419	BRN/WHT	107	0*	B +	CHT A-1
B8			108			
B9			109			
B10 CRUISE INHIBIT	83	DK GRN	110	9.6	B +	SECTION C17
B11 EGR SOLENOID #1 CONTROL	697	LT BLU	111	B +	B +	SECTION C7
B12 EGR SOLENOID #2 CONTROL	698	BRN	112	B +	B +	SECTION C7
B13 EGR SOLENOID #3 CONTROL	699	RED	113	B +	B +	SECTION C7
B14 BATTERY	540	ORN	114	B +	B +	SECTION 8A
B15 BATTERY	540	ORN	115	B +	B +	SECTION 8A
B16 POWER GROUND	551	TAN/WHT	116	0*	0*	SECTION 8A
B17			117			
B18 PARK/NEUTRAL CONTROL	434	ORN/BLK	118	0*	0*	SECTION 8A
B19 SERIAL DATA	461	ORN	119	4-8 (3)	4-8 (3)	CHT A-1
B20			120			
B21			121			
B22 HEATED OXYGEN SENSOR (H02S) SIGNAL	412	PPL	122	0*	(3)	SECTION C1
B23 HEATED OXYGEN SENSOR (H02S) GROUND	413	TAN	123	0*	0*	SECTION C1
B24 IAC "B" HIGH	1749	LT GRN/WHT	124	NOT USABLE		CHT C-2B
B25 IAC "B" LOW	444	LT GRN/BLK	125	NOT USABLE		CHT C-2B
B26 IAC "A" LOW	1748	LT BLU/BLK	126	NOT USABLE		CHT C-2B
B27 IAC "A" HIGH	1747	LT BLU/WHT	127	NOT USABLE		CHT C-2B
B28 BUFFERED SPEED OUTPUT (4000 PULSES PER MILE)	389	DK GRN	128	B +	B +	SECTION 8A
B29 VSS INPUT LOW	401	PPL	129	0*	(1)	SECTION 8A
B30 VSS INPUT HIGH	400	YEL	130	0*	(1)	SECTION 8A
B31 5 VOLT REFERENCE	416	GRY	131	5	5	SECTION C1
B32 POWER GROUND	450	BLK/WHT	132	0*	0*	SECTION 8A

* LESS THAN 1 VOLT.
(1) INCREASES WITH VEHICLE SPEED (MEASURE ON A/C SCALE)
(3) VARIES

7-11-93
PS 16676

Figure A-8 - PCM Connector End View 3100 (VIN M) "W" Carline (2 of 3)

USE KENTMOORE BREAKOUT BOX J 39700 WITH J 39700-110 ADAPTER AND J 39700-112 OVERLAY

3100 (VIN M)

PCM CONNECTOR "C" (BLUE)

RPO: L82

PCM PIN/FUNCTION	CKT #	WIRE COLOR	BOB # PIN	VOLTAGE KEY "ON"	VOLTAGE ENG "RUN"	REFERENCE
C1 POWER GROUND	451	BLK/WHT	301	0*	0*	SECTION 8A
C2			302			
C3 IGNITION FEED	439	PNK	303	B +	B +	SECTION 8A
C4			304			
C5			305			
C6			306			
C7			307			
C8 CRUISE STATUS	85	WHT	308	B +	B +	SECTION C17
C9			309			
C10			310			
C11			311			
C12 INJECTOR DRIVER CYL #3	1746	PNK/BLK	312	B +	B +	SECTION C2
C13 INJECTOR DRIVER CYL #2	1745	LT GRN/BLK	313	B +	B +	SECTION C2
C14 INJECTOR DRIVER CYL #1	1744	BLK	314	B +	B +	SECTION C2
C15 INJECTOR DRIVER CYL #6	846	YEL/BLK	315	B +	B +	SECTION C2
C16 INJECTOR DRIVER CYL #5	845	BLK/WHT	316	B +	B +	SECTION C2
C17 POWER GROUND	551	TAN/WHT	317	0*	0*	SECTION 8A
C18 REFERENCE LOW FOR CAMSHAFT POSITION & 24X CRANKSHAFT POSITION SENSORS	632	PNK/BLK	318	0*	0*	SECTION C4
C19			319			
C20 KNOCK SENSOR SIGNAL	496	DK BLU	320	2.5	2.5	SECTION C5
C21 24X CRANKSHAFT POSITION REFERENCE SIGNAL	647	LT BLU/BLK	321	B +	5	SECTION C4
C22			322			
C23 VEHICLE ANTI-THEFT SYSTEM INPUT	229	DK BLU	323	2.5	2.5	SECTION 9D
C24			324			
C25 CAMSHAFT POSITION REFERENCE SIGNAL	633	BRN/WHT	325	B +	0*	SECTION C4
C26			326			
C27 IGNITION CONTROL	423	WHT	327	0*	1.3 (3)	SECTION C4
C28 IGNITION CONTROL BYPASS	424	TAN/BLK	328	0*	5	SECTION C4
C29 IAT SENSOR SIGNAL	472	TAN	329	(5)	(5)	SECTION C1
C30 3X REFERENCE HIGH	430	PPL/WHT	330	0*	2.5 (3)	SECTION C4
C31 3X REFERENCE LOW	453	RED/BLK	331	0*	0*	SECTION C4
C32 INJECTOR DRIVER CYL #4	844	LT BLU/BLK	332	B +	B +	SECTION C2

* LESS THAN 1 VOLT.
(3) VARIES.
(5) VARIES WITH TEMPERATURE.

7-9-93
PS 16677

Figure A-9 - PCM Connector End View 3100 (VIN M) "W" Carline (3 of 3)

BLANK

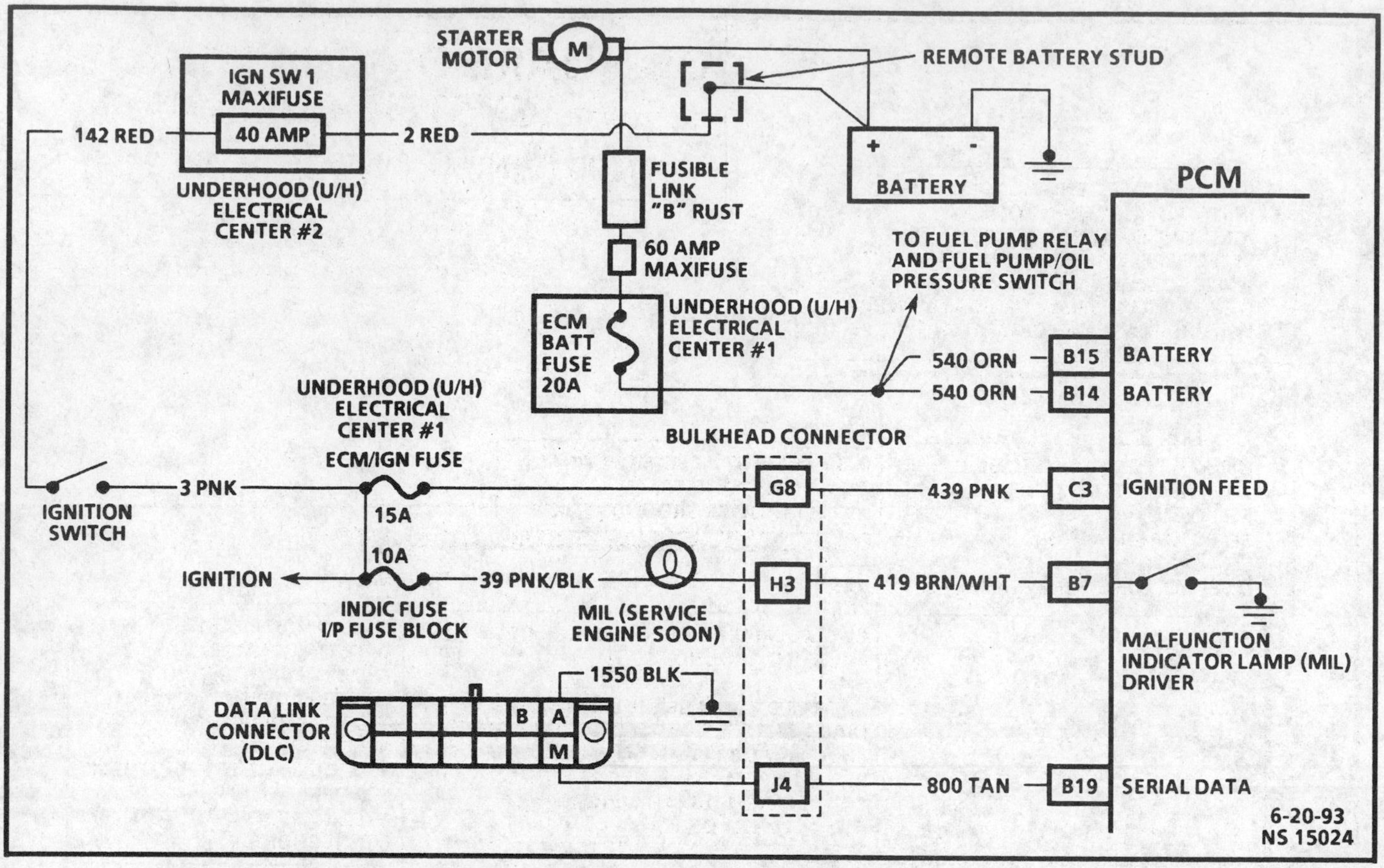
STARTER MOTOR
M
REMOTE BATTERY STUD
IGN SW 1 MAXIFUSE
40 AMP
142 RED
2 RED
UNDERHOOD (U/H) ELECTRICAL CENTER #2
FUSIBLE LINK "B" RUST
60 AMP MAXIFUSE
BATTERY
PCM
TO FUEL PUMP RELAY AND FUEL PUMP/OIL PRESSURE SWITCH
ECM BATT FUSE 20A
UNDERHOOD (U/H) ELECTRICAL CENTER #1
540 ORN
B15
BATTERY
540 ORN
B14
BATTERY
UNDERHOOD (U/H) ELECTRICAL CENTER #1
ECM/IGN FUSE
BULKHEAD CONNECTOR
3 PNK
G8
439 PNK
C3
IGNITION FEED
IGNITION SWITCH
15A
10A
IGNITION
39 PNK/BLK
H3
419 BRN/WHT
B7
INDIC FUSE I/P FUSE BLOCK
MIL (SERVICE ENGINE SOON)
MALFUNCTION INDICATOR LAMP (MIL) DRIVER
1550 BLK
DATA LINK CONNECTOR (DLC)
B
A
M
J4
800 TAN
B19
SERIAL DATA
6-20-93
NS 15024

ON-BOARD DIAGNOSTIC (OBD) SYSTEM CHECK

3100 (VIN M) "W" CARLINE (SFI)

Circuit Description:

The on-board diagnostic system check is an organized approach to identifying a problem created by an electronic powertrain control system malfunction. It must be the starting point for any driveability complaint diagnosis, because it directs the service technician to the next logical step in diagnosing the complaint. Understanding the chart and using it correctly will reduce diagnostic time and prevent the unnecessary replacement of good parts.

Chart Test Description: Number(s) below refer to circled number(s) on the diagnostic chart.

1. This step is to determine if the Tech 1 can establish communication with the PCM. If it cannot, "No DLC Data" will be displayed on the Tech 1. It is necessary to have both B+ and ground available at the PCM for serial data to be established.
2. This test is to determine if the PCM can control the MIL using the MIL system check.

Important

- This vehicle is equipped with a Powertrain Control Module (PCM) utilizing an Electrically Erasable Programmable Read Only Memory (EEPROM). When diagnostics call for replacement of the PCM, the new PCM must be programmed. Refer to "PCM Replacement and Programming Procedures" in Section "6E3-C1".

ON-BOARD DIAGNOSTIC (OBD) SYSTEM CHECK
3100 (VIN M) "W" CARLINE (SFI)

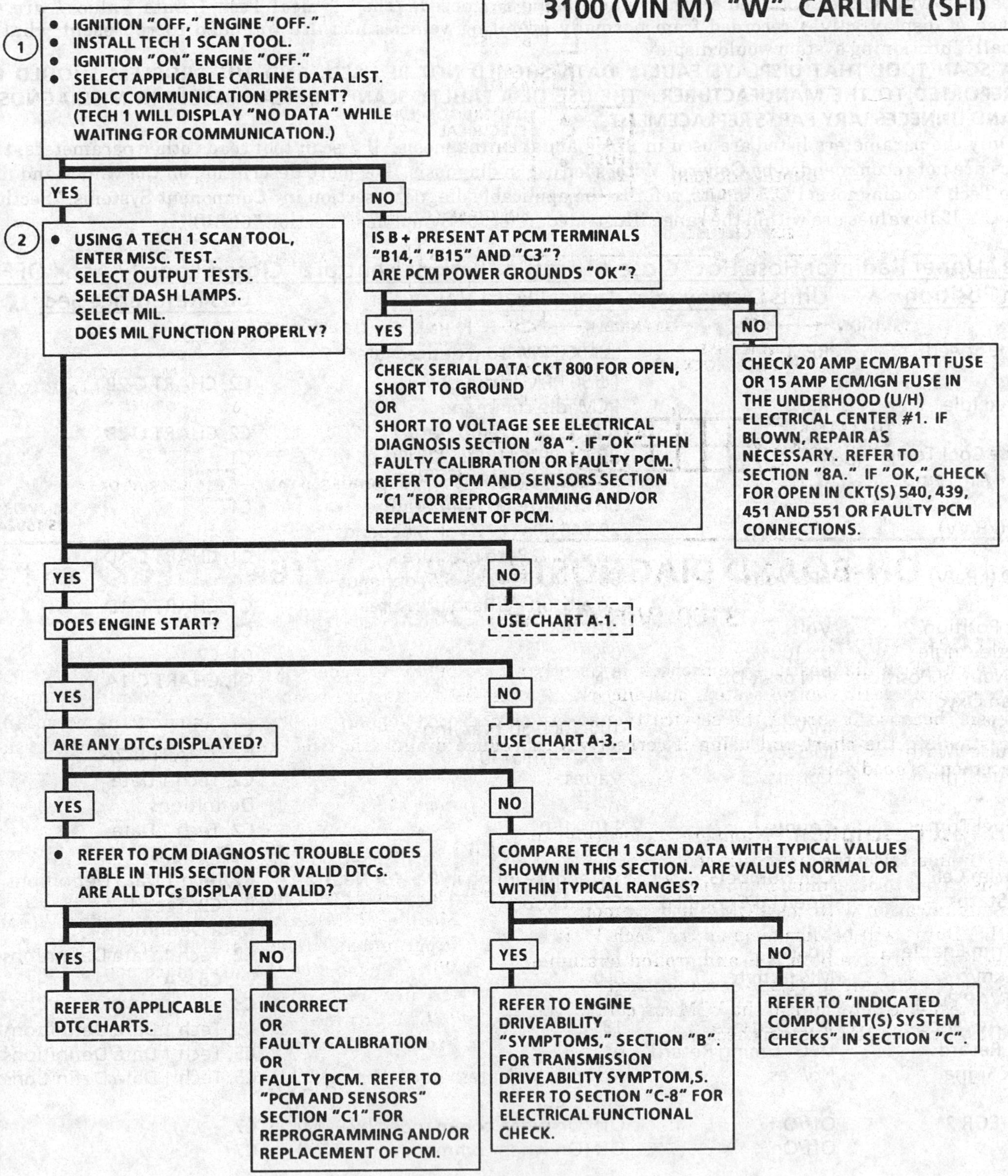
1
• IGNITION "OFF," ENGINE "OFF."
• INSTALL TECH 1 SCAN TOOL.
• IGNITION "ON" ENGINE "OFF."
• SELECT APPLICABLE CARLINE DATA LIST.
IS DLC COMMUNICATION PRESENT? (TECH 1 WILL DISPLAY "NO DATA" WHILE WAITING FOR COMMUNICATION.)
YES
NO
2
• USING A TECH 1 SCAN TOOL, ENTER MISC. TEST. SELECT OUTPUT TESTS. SELECT DASH LAMPS. SELECT MIL. DOES MIL FUNCTION PROPERLY?
IS B + PRESENT AT PCM TERMINALS "B14," "B15" AND "C3"? ARE PCM POWER GROUNDS "OK"?
YES
NO
CHECK SERIAL DATA CKT 800 FOR OPEN, SHORT TO GROUND OR SHORT TO VOLTAGE SEE ELECTRICAL DIAGNOSIS SECTION "8A". IF "OK" THEN FAULTY CALIBRATION OR FAULTY PCM. REFER TO PCM AND SENSORS SECTION "C1 "FOR REPROGRAMMING AND/OR REPLACEMENT OF PCM.
CHECK 20 AMP ECM/BATT FUSE OR 15 AMP ECM/IGN FUSE IN THE UNDERHOOD (U/H) ELECTRICAL CENTER #1. IF BLOWN, REPAIR AS NECESSARY. REFER TO SECTION "8A." IF "OK," CHECK FOR OPEN IN CKT(S) 540, 439, 451 AND 551 OR FAULTY PCM CONNECTIONS.
YES
NO
DOES ENGINE START?
USE CHART A-1.
YES
NO
ARE ANY DTCs DISPLAYED?
USE CHART A-3.
YES
NO
• REFER TO PCM DIAGNOSTIC TROUBLE CODES TABLE IN THIS SECTION FOR VALID DTCs. ARE ALL DTCs DISPLAYED VALID?
COMPARE TECH 1 SCAN DATA WITH TYPICAL VALUES SHOWN IN THIS SECTION. ARE VALUES NORMAL OR WITHIN TYPICAL RANGES?
YES
NO
YES
NO
REFER TO APPLICABLE DTC CHARTS.
INCORRECT OR FAULTY CALIBRATION OR FAULTY PCM. REFER TO "PCM AND SENSORS" SECTION "C1" FOR REPROGRAMMING AND/OR REPLACEMENT OF PCM.
REFER TO ENGINE DRIVEABILITY "SYMPTOMS," SECTION "B". FOR TRANSMISSION DRIVEABILITY SYMPTOM,S. REFER TO SECTION "C-8" FOR ELECTRICAL FUNCTIONAL CHECK.
REFER TO "INDICATED COMPONENT(S) SYSTEM CHECKS" IN SECTION "C".

5-25-93
PS 17829

TYPICAL TECH 1 SCAN DATA

If after completing the "On-Board Diagnostic (OBD) System Check" and finding the Tech 1 diagnostics functioning properly and no diagnostic trouble codes displayed, the "Typical Tech 1 Data Values" may be used for comparison with values obtained on the vehicle being diagnosed. The "Typical Tech 1 Data Values," are an average of display values recorded from normally operating vehicles and are intended to represent what a normally functioning system would display.

A SCAN TOOL THAT DISPLAYS FAULTY DATA SHOULD NOT BE USED, AND THE PROBLEM SHOULD BE REPORTED TO THE MANUFACTURER. THE USE OF A FAULTY SCAN TOOL CAN RESULT IN MISDIAGNOSIS AND UNNECESSARY PARTS REPLACEMENT.

Only the parameters listed are used in this manual for diagnosis. If a scan tool reads other parameters, the values are not recommended by General Motors for use in diagnosis. For more description on the values and use of the Tech 1 to diagnosis PCM inputs, refer to the applicable diagnosis section in "Component Systems," Section "6E3-C". If all values are within the range illustrated, refer to "Symptoms," Section "6E3-B".

Idle / Upper Radiator Hose Hot / Closed Throttle / Park or Neutral / "Closed Loop" / Acc. "OFF"

Scan Position	Units Displayed	Typical Data Value	6E3 Reference Sec.
Engine Speed	RPM	± 100 RPM from desired Idle (± 50 RPM in drive)	C2, CHART C-2B
Desired Idle	RPM	PCM idle command (varies with temperature)	C2, CHART C-2B
Engine Cool Temp	C°/F°	85°C-109°C (185°F-223°F)	C1
Intake Air Temp	C°/F°	10°C-80°C (50°F-176°F) depends on underhood temperature.	C1
MAP (kPa/V)	kPa/Volts	29 - 48 kPa (1 - 2 volts) depends on Vac. & Baro pressure.	C1, CHART C-1D
BARO (kPa/V)	kPa/Volts	58 - 114 kPa (2.5 - 5.5) depends on altitude & Baro pressure.	C1, CHART C-1D
Throt Position	Volts	.29 - .98	C1, C2
Throttle Angle	0 - 100%	0%	C1, C2
Park/Neutral Position	P/N or -R-DL	P/N	C1, CHART C-1A
Heated Oxygen (HO2S)	M/Volts	100-1000 and varying	C1, C2
INJ. Pulse Width	M/Sec	3-6 and varying	C2, CHART C-2A
S. T. Fuel Trim	Counts	Varies	C2, Tech 1 Data Definitions
L. T. Fuel Trim	Counts	110 - 150	C2, Tech 1 Data Definitions
Fuel Trim Cell	Cell Numbers	16 (engine idling in Park or Neutral)	C2,Tech 1 Data Definitions
Loop Status	Open Lp/Closed Lp	Closed Loop	C1, C2, Tech 1 Data Definitions
Fuel Trim Enable	No/Yes	Yes	C2, Tech 1 Data Definitions
MPH km/h	MPH km/h	0 0	C1, C8, 8A
Fuel EVAP Purge	0-100%	0%	C3
Spark Advance	# of Degrees	18°-24°	C5, Tech 1 Data Definitions
Spark Retard	DEG. Timing Retard	0*	C5, Tech 1 Data Definitions
Knock Signal	No/Yes	No (Yes, indicates knock is being detected)	C5, Tech 1 Data Definitions
EGR 1/EGR 2	Off/On	Off (On when commanded by PCM)	C7
EGR 3	Off/On	Off (On when commanded by PCM)	C7

* **NOTICE:** If maximum retard is indicated, go to CHART C-5

Scan Position	Units Displayed	Typical Data Value	6E3 Reference Sec.
Idle Air Control	Counts (steps)	5-50	C2, CHART C-2B
Ign Cntrl 24X Sig	RPM	± 100 RPM from desired idle ± 50 RPM in drive)	C1, C4 Tech 1 Data Definitions
Ign Cntrl CAM Sig	0/1	Varies Off-On-Off-On...	C1, C4 Tech 1 Data Definitions
TCC Apply Sol.	Off/On	Off	C8
System Voltage	Volts	13.5 - 14.5 Volts	Tech 1 Data Definitions
Fuel Pump Volts	Volts	13.5 - 14.5 Volts	C2
A/C Request	No/Yes	No (Yes, with A/C requested)	C10
A/C Clutch	On/Off	Off (On, with A/C commanded On)	C10
A/C Ref. Pressure	psi/Volt	Varies (Depends on temperature)	C10, C12
Fan #1, Fan #2*	Off/On Off/On	On/108°C, (228°F) with A/C Off/106°C, (223°F) with A/C On (Fan #2 "ON"@ 113°C)	C10, C12
Injector Fault	OK/Fault	OK	Tech 1 Data Definitions C4, Symptoms Section B
SSA SSB	Off/On Off/On	Off (On when command by PCM)	C8, 8A, Tech 1 Data Definitions
P A (PRNDL)	Lo/Hi Lo/Hi	Park (Lo Lo)	C8, Tech 1 Data Definitions
B C (PRNDL)	Lo/Hi Lo/Hi	Park (Hi Hi)	C8, Tech 1 Data Definitions
Trans Range Switch	Gear Selected	Park or Neutral	C8, Tech 1 Data Definitions
TCC PWM Sol.	0-100%	0%	C8, Tech 1 Data Definitions
Trans Fluid Temp.	-40°C-151°C	75°C-100°C	C8, Tech 1 Data Definitions
TCC Brake Switch	Released/Applied	Released (applied when brake pedal is depressed)	C8, 8A, Tech 1 Data Definitions
TCC Slip Speed	RPM	0-4000 RPM	C8, Tech 1 Data Definitions
DTC Ign Counter	Varies	0 (Counts Key Cycles)	Tech 1 Data Definitions
#DTC Stored	Varies	0 (Counts DTC(s) Stored)	Tech 1 Data Definitions
Time From Start	Hrs/Min	Varies	Tech 1 Data Definitions
SMCC Engaged*	Yes/No	No (Yes when commanded by PCM)	C17, Tech 1 Data Definitions
SMCC Inhibited*	No/Yes	No (Yes when commanded by PCM)	C17, Tech 1 Data Definitions
Low Oil Light*	Off/On	Off (On when commanded by PCM)	C16, Tech 1 Data Definitions
2nd GR. Start SW.*	On/Off	On (Off in 2nd gear)	Tech 1 Data Definitions
TCC	Off/On	Off (On when commanded by PCM)	C-8, Tech 1 Data Definitions
2nd 3rd	Yes/No No/Yes	No (Yes, with transmission 2nd gear enabled)	C-8, Tech 1 Data Definitions
		No (Yes, with transmission 3rd gear enabled	C-8, Tech 1 Data Definitions

* If Applicable

PCM DATA DESCRIPTION

A list of explanations for each data message displayed on the Tech 1 scan tool begins below. This information will assist in tracking down emission or driveability problems, since the displays can be viewed while the vehicle is being driven. Refer to the "Typical Tech 1 Data Values" for additional information.

ENGINE SPEED - Engine speed is computed by the PCM from the low resolution 3X crankshaft position sensor. It should remain close to desired idle under various engine loads with engine idling.

DESIRED IDLE - The calculated idle speed that is commanded by the PCM. The PCM will compensate for various engine loads to keep the engine at the desired idle speed.

ENGINE COOLANT TEMP - The Engine Coolant Temperature (ECT) sensor is mounted in the intake manifold and sends engine temperature information to the PCM. The sensor is a thermistor which changes internal resistance as temperature changes. When the sensor is cold (internal resistance high), the PCM monitors a high signal voltage which it interprets as a cold engine. As the sensor warms (internal resistance decreases), the voltage signal will decrease and the PCM will interpret the lower voltage as a warm engine.

INT AIR TEMP - The PCM converts the resistance of the intake air temperature sensor to degrees. Intake Air Temp (IAT) is used by the PCM to adjust fuel delivery and spark timing according to incoming air temperature.

MAP - The Manifold Absolute Pressure (MAP) sensor measures the changes in the intake manifold pressure which results from engine load and RPM changes and converts these into a voltage output. The voltage is also converted to kilopascals (kPa) units.

BARO - The MAP sensor is also used to measure barometric pressure during the ignition key "ON" cycle and during Wide Open Throttle (WOT), allowing the PCM to make fuel adjustments for altitudes. The PCM uses the MAP sensor to control fuel delivery and ignition timing.

THROT POSITION - Used by the PCM to determine the amount of throttle demanded by the driver. Should read .29 - .98 volt at idle to above 4 volts at Wide Open Throttle (WOT).

THROTTLE ANGLE - Computed by the PCM from TP sensor voltage (Throt position); should read 0% at idle, 100% at Wide Open Throttle (WOT).

PARK/NEUTRAL POSITION - "P/N" displayed indicates that the gear select lever is in "Park" or "Neutral."

HEATED OXYGEN SENSOR - Represents the amount of O2 in the exhaust. Should fluctuate constantly within a range between 100 mV (lean exhaust or high O2 content) and 1000 mV (rich exhaust or low O2 content) when operating in "Closed Loop."

INJ PULSE WIDTH - This represents the duration that the injectors are turned on each time they are enabled. Time units are scaled in thousandths of seconds or milliseconds.

SHORT TERM FUEL TRIM - This represents a short-term correction to fuel delivery by the PCM in response to the amount of time the heated oxygen sensor voltage spends above or below the 450 mV threshold. If the heated oxygen sensor voltage has mainly been below 450 mV, indicating a lean air/fuel mixture, short term fuel trim will increase to tell the PCM to add fuel. If the heated oxygen sensor voltage stays mainly above the threshold, the PCM will reduce fuel delivery to compensate for the indicated rich condition. **Under certain conditions such as high ambient temperatures, evap canister purge may cause short term fuel trim to read less than 100 counts.**

LONG TERM FUEL TRIM - Long term fuel trim is derived from the short term fuel trim value and is used for long-term correction of fuel delivery. A value of 128 counts indicates that fuel delivery requires no compensation to maintain a 14.7:1 air/fuel ratio. A value below 128 counts means that the fuel system is too rich and fuel delivery is being reduced (decreased injector pulse width). A value above 128 counts indicates that a lean HO2S signal condition exists and the PCM is compensating by adding fuel (increased injector pulse width). **Long term fuel trim tends to follow short term fuel trim; normal values of 110-150 counts at idle should not be considered unusual.**

TECH 1 DATA DEFINITIONS

FUEL TRIM CELL - The 60° V6 engine uses sixteen fuel trim cells. Cell sixteen is the idle mode cell. Throttle position and MAP determine which cell the engine will be in.

LOOP STATUS - "Closed Loop" displayed indicates that the PCM is controlling fuel delivery according to heated oxygen sensor voltage. In "Open Loop," the PCM ignores the heated oxygen sensor voltage and bases the amount of fuel to be delivered on TP sensor, engine coolant, and MAP sensor inputs only. "Closed Loop" operation should begin when the HO2S becomes active and engine coolant temperature exceeds 65°C (149°F) for more than 30 seconds.

FUEL TRIM ENABLE - If the fuel trim enable system is learning (indicated with "YES") the L. T. fuel trim is responding to the S. T. fuel trim. If the fuel trim enable reads "NO" then L. T. fuel trim will not respond to changes in S. T. fuel trim.

MPH km/h - The Vehicle Speed Sensor (VSS) signal is converted into km/h and mph for display.

FUEL EVAP PURGE - A proportional signal used to control canister purge function. 0% indicates the valve is commanded fully closed while 100% indicates that the valve is fully open.

SPARK ADVANCE - This is a display of the spark advance (IC) calculation which the PCM is delivering to the ignition control module. It computes the desired spark advance using data such as engine coolant temperature, RPM, load, vehicle speed, and operating mode.

SPARK RETARD - Indicates the amount of spark advance the PCM is removing from Ignition Control (IC) timing in response to the Knock Sensor (KS) signal. Should read 0° at idle.

KNOCK SIGNAL - Indicates whether or not a knock signal is being detected by the PCM. Should read "NO" at idle. "YES" may be indicated under hard acceleration.

EGR 1/EGR 2/EGR 3 - Any combination of the three EGR solenoids may be opened during engine operation. The Tech 1 can indicate which solenoids are open or when all three are closed, such as at idle. The Tech 1 can also cycle each solenoid open and closed to evaluate their operation.

IDLE AIR CONTROL - Displays the commanded position of the Idle Air Control (IAC) pintle in counts. The Idle Air Control (IAC) valve should respond fairly quickly to changes in engine load to maintain desired idle RPM.

IGNITION CONTROL 24X SIGNAL - This signal is represented in RPM and indicates the 24X crankshaft position sensor is operating and the PCM is receiving it's signal.

IGNITION CONTROL CAM SIGNAL - The ignition control CAM signal provides the PCM with the information to determine when the intake valve on number one cylinder will open. "0" CLOSED, "1" OPENED - The PCM sequences the injectors in cylinder firing order based on the input from the camshaft sensor.

TCC APPLY SOLENOID - Tech 1 displays TCC "OFF" or "ON" as commanded by the PCM.

SYSTEM VOLTAGE - This represents the system voltage measured by the PCM.

FUEL PUMP VOLTS - This parameter indicates how much voltage is applied to the fuel pump motor. This voltage is sensed from a splice located between the fuel pump relay and the pump motor. This voltage should indicate 12 volts when the ignition key is cycled "ON" for 2 seconds, or whenever the 3X crankshaft position sensor is supplying reference pulses.

A/C REQUEST - Represents the state of the A/C request input from the control head.

A/C CLUTCH - Represents the commanded state of the A/C clutch control relay. Clutch should be engaged when "ON" is displayed.

A/C REFRIGERANT PRESSURE - Tech 1 displays high side refrigerant pressure represented by psi and voltage.

FAN 1 - When the PCM is commanding Fan 1 "ON," the Tech 1 display will switch from "OFF" to "ON."

FAN 2 (IF APPLICABLE) - When the PCM is commanding Fan 2 "ON," the Tech 1 display will switch from "OFF" to "ON."

TECH 1 DATA DEFINITIONS

INJECTOR FAULT - The PCM can determine if any of the six injectors are misfiring. "FAULT" will be displayed if this is occurring.

SMCC ENGAGED (IF APPLICABLE) - The PCM monitors the "Cruise Status" circuit and determines whether the Stepper Motor Cruise Control (SMCC) module is actually energized, "YES" or not engaged "NO."

SMCC INHIBITED (IF APPLICABLE) - The PCM retains the ability to disallow Stepper Motor Cruise Control (SMCC) operation if vehicle speed and other specific criteria are not met. If cruise control is being inhibited, the Tech 1 should display "YES." If the PCM senses all criteria has been met for cruise control operation Tech 1 will display "NO" (not inhibited).

LOW OIL LIGHT (IF APPLICABLE) - The PCM monitors the signal from the oil level sensor and turns this telltale "ON" if oil level is below the desirable level. The lamp is energized for about one second after "Key On" (bulb check) the lamp turns "OFF" as long as the PCM is satisfied that the oil level is sufficient.

HOT ENGINE LIGHT (IF APPLICABLE) - Some vehicles are equipped with a "Temp" symbol telltale. This warns the driver of an engine overheating condition. Other vehicles are equipped with a "Check Gauges" lamp which can warn the driver of several other detected conditions including low fuel level, generator output, engine overheating etc. The Tech 1 can energize the "Check Gauges" or "Temp" telltale depending on the particular application, as long as it is a PCM controlled lamp.

SHIFT SOLENOID "A" (SSA) - The PCM monitors the TP sensor and VSS vs. RPM to determine the correct shift points. 1st gear "ON," 2nd gear "OFF," 3rd gear "OFF," and 4th gear "ON."

SHIFT SOLENOID "B" (SSB) - The PCM monitors the TP sensor and VSS vs. RPM to determine the correct shift points. 1st gear "ON," 2nd gear "ON," 3rd gear "OFF," and 4th gear "OFF."

PRNDL - The Tech 1 can determine through 4 inputs from the transaxle range switch what position the gearshift lever is in. These inputs are A, B, C and a parity input.

TRANS RANGE SWITCH - The tech 1 displays the decoded position of the Trans Range Switch PRNDL inputs. If an error combination is seen by the PCM, "INVALID" or an incorrect gear range will be displayed.

2ND GEAR START SWITCH - Some 4T60E transaxles are equipped with a 2nd gear start switch. When this switch displays "ON," shift solenoid "A" is "OFF" while shift solenoid "B" is "ON." This gives the vehicle the ability to start out in second gear.

TCC PWM SOLENOID - This is the relative position of the pulse width modulated (PWM) solenoid that controls TCC apply pressure. This allows TCC to apply evenly and reduce any harsh engagement.

TRANS FLUID TEMP. - This signal is received from a 2 wire sensor located in the transaxle fluid stream. The PCM uses this input to determine shift points and TCC engagement points.

TCC BRAKE SWITCH - Tech 1 displays from "Released" to "Applied" when the brake pedal is applied. The switch sends a signal to the PCM to disengage the TCC.

TCC SLIP SPEED - The RPM difference between engine crankshaft speed and torque converter output speed. When TCC mode is "ON," there should be a small amount of slip.

DTC IGNITION COUNTER - Tech 1 displays the number of key cycles after a DTC was stored in PCM memory. The count increases by 1 with each key cycle.

DTC STORED - Tech 1 displays the number of history DTCs stored in PCM memory.

CALIBRATION ID - The calibration identification describes the particular program being used in the PCM. The Tech 1 display number is not the service part number.

TIME FROM START - A measure of how long the engine has been running. When the engine stops, it is reset zero.

PCM DIAGNOSTIC TROUBLE CODES

DTC	DESCRIPTION	ILLUMINATE MIL
13	Heated Oxygen Sensor (HO2S) - open circuit	YES
14	Engine Coolant Temperature (ECT) Sensor Circuit (high temperature indicated)	YES
15	Engine Coolant Temperature (ECT) Sensor Circuit (low temperature indicated)	YES
16	System Low Voltage (low battery voltage)	YES
17	Camshaft Position Sensor Circuit Error	NO
21	Throttle Position (TP) Sensor Circuit (signal voltage high)	YES
22	Throttle Position (TP) Sensor Circuit (signal voltage low)	YES
23	Intake Air Temperature (IAT) Sensor Circuit (low temperature indicated)	YES
24	Vehicle Speed Sensor (VSS) Circuit (no signal voltage)	YES
25	Intake Air Temperature (IAT) Sensor Circuit (high temperature indicated)	YES
28	Transmission Range Switch Error	NO
33	Manifold Absolute Pressure (MAP) Sensor Circuit (signal voltage high - high MAP)	YES
34	Manifold Absolute Pressure (MAP) Sensor Circuit (signal voltage low - low MAP)	YES
35	Idle Speed Error	YES
36	Ignition Control 24X Signal Circuit Error	NO
37	TCC Brake Switch Error	NO
41	Ignition Control (EST) Error	NO
42	Ignition Control (EST) Bypass Error	YES
43	Knock Sensor (KS) Circuit Error	YES
44	Heated Oxygen Sensor (HO2S) Circuit (lean exhaust indicated)	YES
45	Heated Oxygen Sensor (HO2S) Circuit (rich exhaust indicated)	YES
46*	PASS KeyII® Circuit (out of frequency range)	NO
51	PROM Error (faulty or incorrect calibration)	YES
53	System Voltage High	YES
54	Fuel Pump Circuit (low voltage)	YES
58	Trans Fluid Temperature (TFT) Sensor Circuit Low (high temperature)	NO
59	Trans Fluid Temperature (TFT) Sensor Circuit High (low temperature)	NO

* If Applicable

PCM DIAGNOSTIC TROUBLE CODES

DTC	DESCRIPTION	ILLUMINATE MIL
66	A/C Refrigerant Pressure Sensor Circuit (low pressure)	NO
70	A/C Refrigerant Pressure Sensor Circuit (high pressure)	NO
72	Vehicle Speed Sensor (VSS) Circuit Signal Error	NO
75	Digital EGR #1 Solenoid (error)	YES
76	Digital EGR #2 Solenoid (error)	YES
77	Digital EGR #3 Solenoid (error)	YES
79	Transmission Fluid Overtemp	NO
80	Transmission Component Error	NO
82	Ignition Control 3X Signal Error	NO
85	PROM Error (faulty or incorrect calibration)	YES
86	Analog/Digital PCM Error	YES
87	Electrically Erasable Programmable Read Only Memory (EEPROM) Error	NO
90	TCC Error	NO
96	Trans System Voltage Low	NO
98	Invalid PCM Program	NO
99	Invalid PCM Program	NO

7-13-93
PS 16969

BLANK

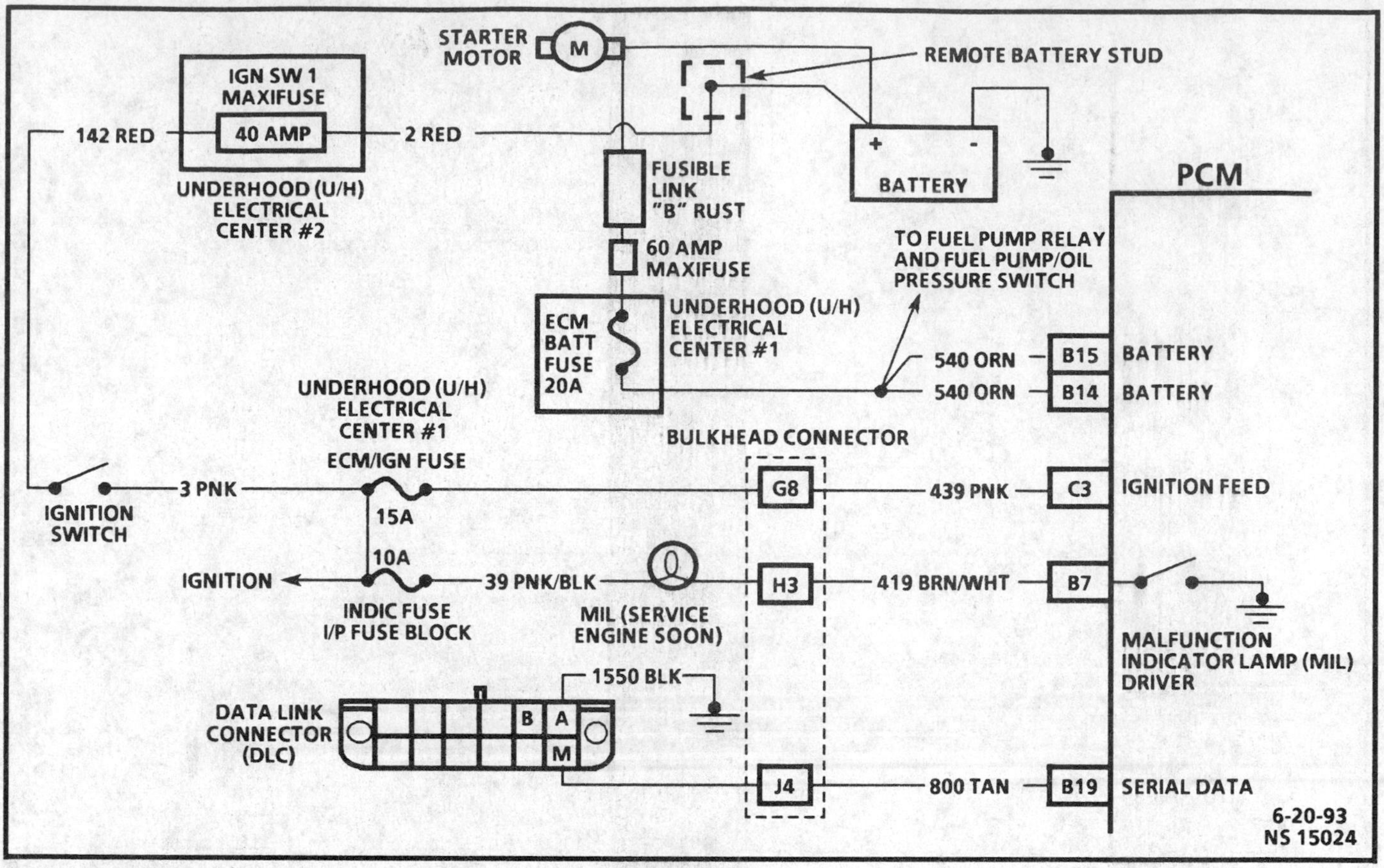
STARTER MOTOR
M
REMOTE BATTERY STUD
IGN SW 1 MAXIFUSE
40 AMP
142 RED
2 RED
UNDERHOOD (U/H) ELECTRICAL CENTER #2
FUSIBLE LINK "B" RUST
BATTERY
PCM
60 AMP MAXIFUSE
TO FUEL PUMP RELAY AND FUEL PUMP/OIL PRESSURE SWITCH
ECM BATT FUSE 20A
UNDERHOOD (U/H) ELECTRICAL CENTER #1
540 ORN
B15
BATTERY
540 ORN
B14
BATTERY
UNDERHOOD (U/H) ELECTRICAL CENTER #1
ECM/IGN FUSE
BULKHEAD CONNECTOR
3 PNK
G8
439 PNK
C3
IGNITION FEED
IGNITION SWITCH
15A
10A
IGNITION
39 PNK/BLK
H3
419 BRN/WHT
B7
INDIC FUSE I/P FUSE BLOCK
MIL (SERVICE ENGINE SOON)
MALFUNCTION INDICATOR LAMP (MIL) DRIVER
1550 BLK
DATA LINK CONNECTOR (DLC)
B
A
M
J4
800 TAN
B19
SERIAL DATA
6-20-93
NS 15024

CHART A-1

NO MALFUNCTION INDICATOR LAMP (MIL) "SERVICE ENGINE SOON" 3100 (VIN M) "W" CARLINE (SFI)

Circuit Description:

When the ignition switch is turned "ON" (engine "OFF,") except for a brief flash, the MIL should remain "ON."

Battery voltage is applied directly to the lamp via the INDIC fuse (I/P fuse block), and 40 amp maxifuse (Underhood (U/H) electrical center #2). The Powertrain Control Module (PCM) provides the ground for the MIL when the ignition is "ON," and engine "OFF."

Chart Test Description: Number(s) below refer to circled number(s) on the diagnostic chart.

1. If the PCM fuse is blown, refer to SECTION 8A.
2. Using a test light connected to B+, probe each of the system ground circuits to be sure a good ground is present. Refer to "PCM Connector End View" in the front of this section for PCM pin locations of ground circuits.

Diagnostic Aids: Engine runs OK, check:

- Faulty light bulb.
- CKT 419 open.
- INDIC fuse blown. This will result in no stop lamps, oil or generator lights, seat belt reminder, etc.

Engine cranks but will not run.

- Continuous battery - fuse or fusible link open.
- Fuse open.
- Battery CKT 540 to PCM open.
- Ignition feed CKT 439 to PCM open.
- Poor connection(s) to PCM.

CHART A-1

NO MALFUNCTION INDICATOR LAMP (MIL) "SERVICE ENGINE SOON" 3100 (VIN M) "W" CARLINE (SFI)

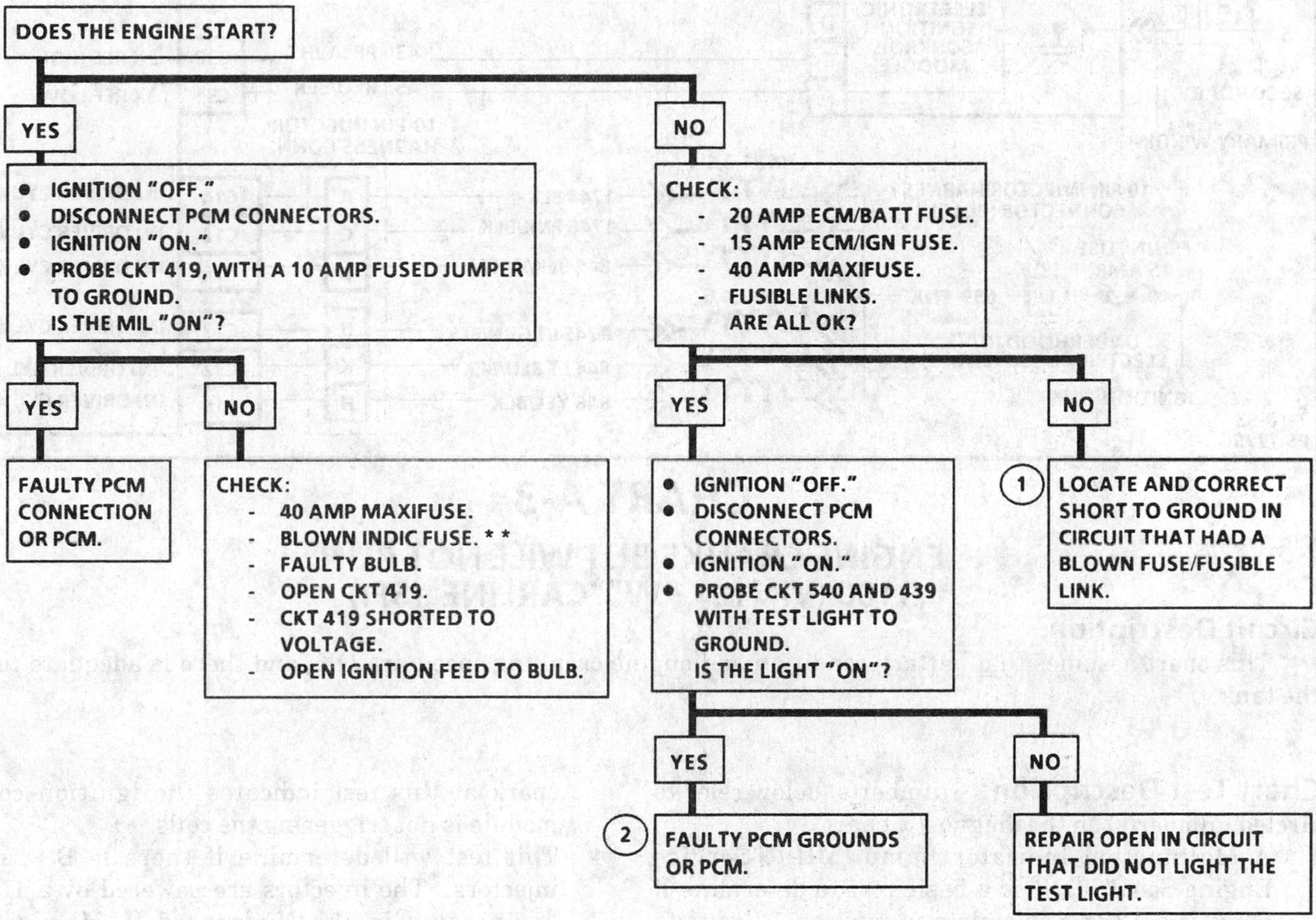
DOES THE ENGINE START?
YES
NO
• IGNITION "OFF."
• DISCONNECT PCM CONNECTORS.
• IGNITION "ON."
• PROBE CKT 419, WITH A 10 AMP FUSED JUMPER TO GROUND.
IS THE MIL "ON"?
YES
NO
FAULTY PCM CONNECTION OR PCM.
CHECK:
- 40 AMP MAXIFUSE.
- BLOWN INDIC FUSE. * *
- FAULTY BULB.
- OPEN CKT 419.
- CKT 419 SHORTED TO VOLTAGE.
- OPEN IGNITION FEED TO BULB.
CHECK:
- 20 AMP ECM/BATT FUSE.
- 15 AMP ECM/IGN FUSE.
- 40 AMP MAXIFUSE.
- FUSIBLE LINKS.
ARE ALL OK?
YES
NO
• IGNITION "OFF."
• DISCONNECT PCM CONNECTORS.
• IGNITION "ON."
• PROBE CKT 540 AND 439 WITH TEST LIGHT TO GROUND.
IS THE LIGHT "ON"?
1
LOCATE AND CORRECT SHORT TO GROUND IN CIRCUIT THAT HAD A BLOWN FUSE/FUSIBLE LINK.
YES
NO
2
FAULTY PCM GROUNDS OR PCM.
REPAIR OPEN IN CIRCUIT THAT DID NOT LIGHT THE TEST LIGHT.

* * SEVERAL BRANCH CIRCUITS ARE PROTECTED BY THIS FUSE. REFER TO SECTION 8A-11 FOR OTHER BRANCH CIRCUITS THAT COULD CAUSE A BLOWN FUSE.

5-13-93
PS 17144

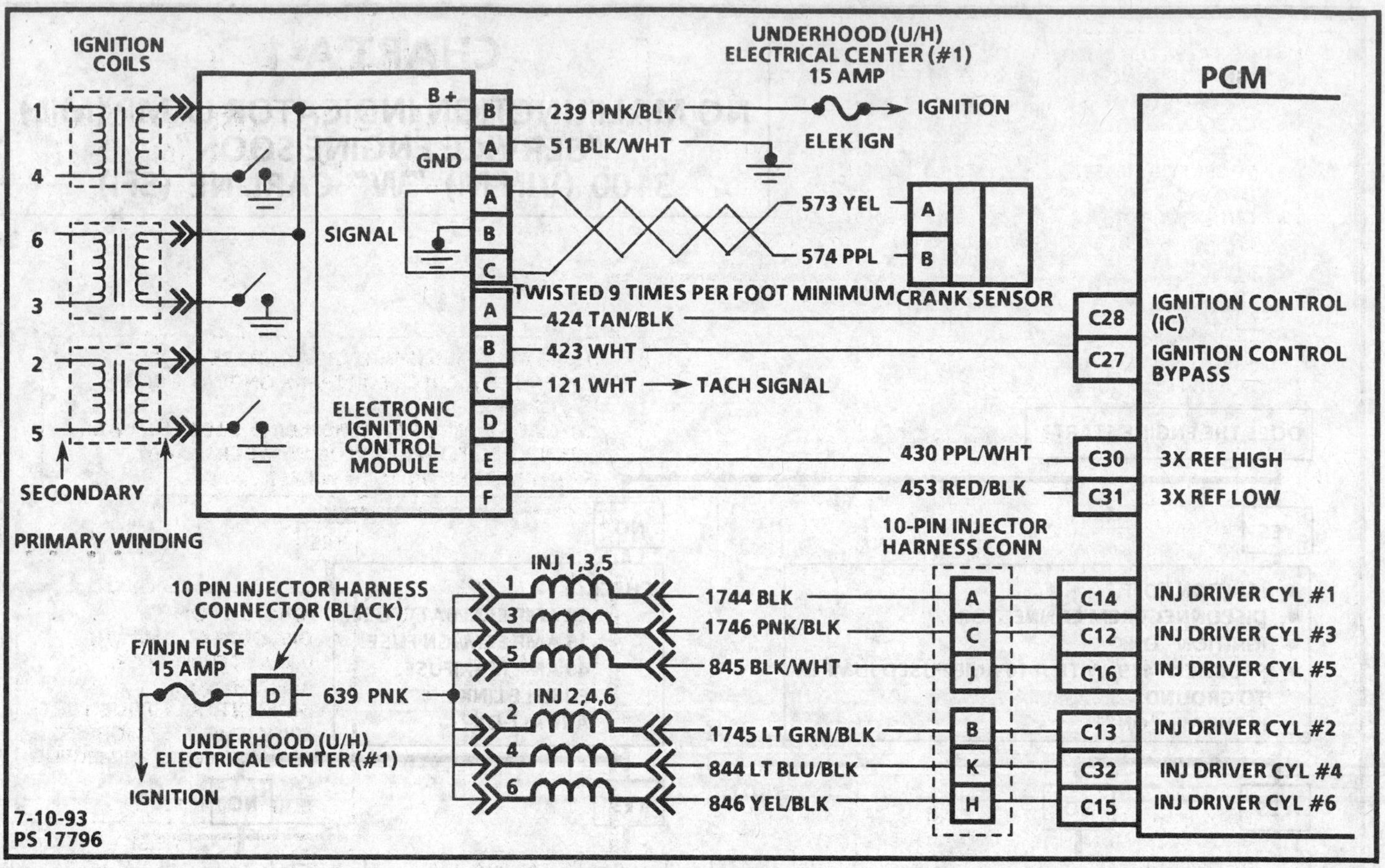
IGNITION COILS
1
4
6
3
2
5
SECONDARY
PRIMARY WINDING
B+
GND
SIGNAL
ELECTRONIC IGNITION CONTROL MODULE
B
A
A
B
C
A
B
C
D
E
F
UNDERHOOD (U/H) ELECTRICAL CENTER (#1) 15 AMP
239 PNK/BLK
IGNITION
51 BLK/WHT
ELEK IGN
573 YEL
574 PPL
A
B
TWISTED 9 TIMES PER FOOT MINIMUM
CRANK SENSOR
424 TAN/BLK
423 WHT
121 WHT
TACH SIGNAL
430 PPL/WHT
453 RED/BLK
PCM
C28
IGNITION CONTROL (IC)
C27
IGNITION CONTROL BYPASS
C30
3X REF HIGH
C31
3X REF LOW
10-PIN INJECTOR HARNESS CONN
INJ 1,3,5
INJ 2,4,6
10 PIN INJECTOR HARNESS CONNECTOR (BLACK)
F/INJN FUSE 15 AMP
D
639 PNK
UNDERHOOD (U/H) ELECTRICAL CENTER (#1)
IGNITION
1744 BLK
1746 PNK/BLK
845 BLK/WHT
1745 LT GRN/BLK
844 LT BLU/BLK
846 YEL/BLK
A
C
J
B
K
H
C14
INJ DRIVER CYL #1
C12
INJ DRIVER CYL #3
C16
INJ DRIVER CYL #5
C13
INJ DRIVER CYL #2
C32
INJ DRIVER CYL #4
C15
INJ DRIVER CYL #6
7-10-93
PS 17796

CHART A-3

ENGINE CRANKS BUT WILL NOT RUN
3100 (VIN M) "W" CARLINE (SFI)

Circuit Description:

This chart assumes that battery condition and engine cranking speed are OK, and there is adequate fuel in the tank.

Chart Test Description:

Number(s) below refer to circled number(s) on the diagnostic chart.

1. A Malfunction Indicator Lamp (MIL) "Service Engine Soon" "ON" is a basic test to determine if there is a 12 volts supply and ignition 12 volts to PCM. No DLC may be due to a PCM problem. If TP sensor is over 2.5 volts, the engine may be in the clear flood mode which will cause starting problems. The engine will not start without reference pulses and therefore the Tech 1 scan tool should read RPM (reference) during crank.
2. For the first two seconds with ignition "ON," or whenever reference pulses are being received, Tech 1 should indicate fuel pump circuit voltage (8 to 12 volts).
3. Because the electronic ignition system uses two plugs and wires to complete the circuit of each coil, the companion plug should be left connected. If RPM was indicated during crank, the ignition control module is receiving a crank signal, but no spark at this test indicates the ignition control module is not triggering the coils.
4. This test will determine if there is B+ at the injectors. The injectors are powered by a 15 amp fuse located in the Underhood (U/H) electrical center (#1).
5. This test will determine if the ignition control module is not triggering the suspect coil, or if the tested coil is at fault. This test could also be performed by using another known good coil.
6. This test will determine if the ignition control module is not generating the reference pulse, or if the wiring or PCM are at fault. By touching and removing a test light to B+ on CKT 430, a reference pulse should be generated. If RPM is indicated, the PCM and wiring are OK.

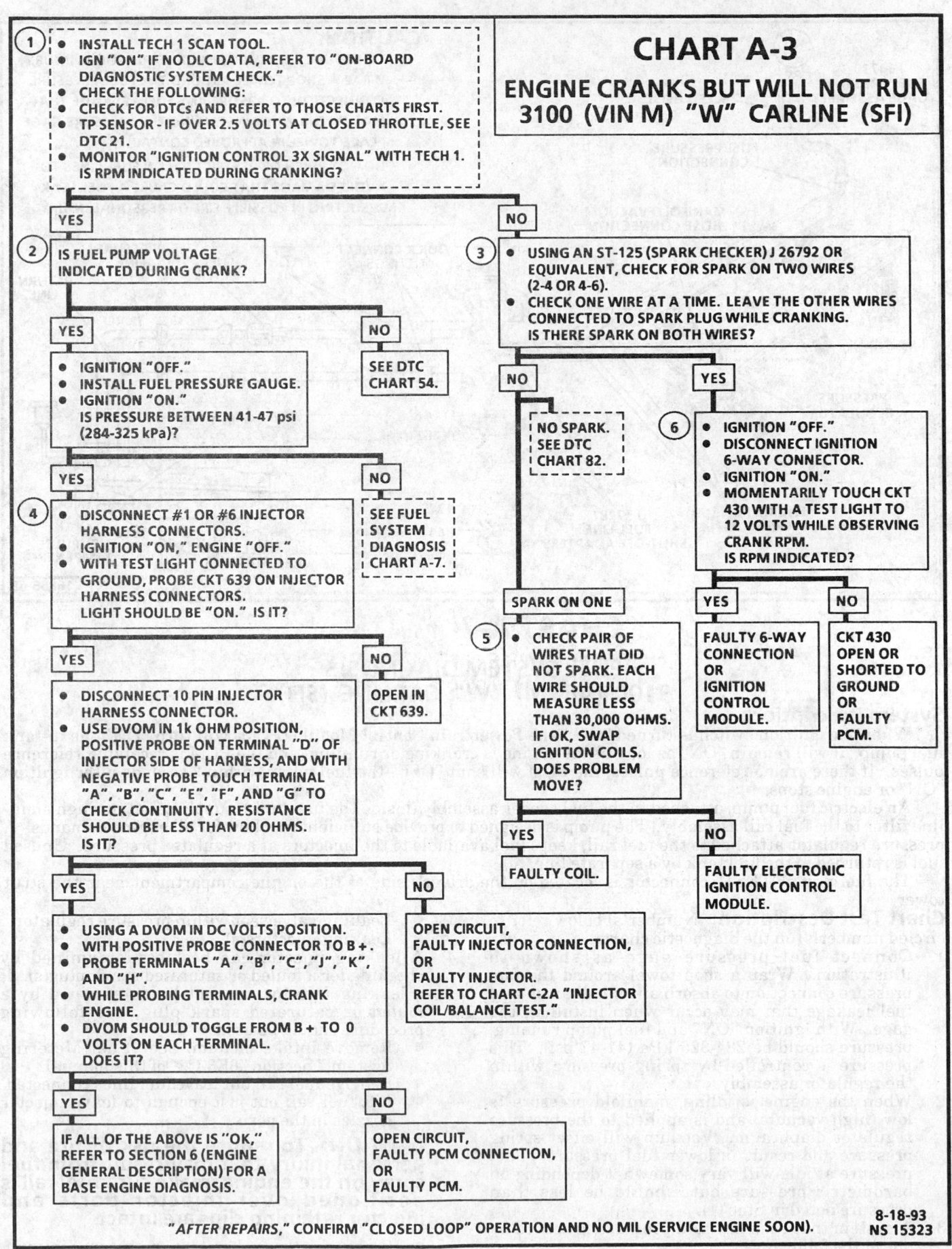

CHART A-3

ENGINE CRANKS BUT WILL NOT RUN 3100 (VIN M) "W" CARLINE (SFI)

1
- INSTALL TECH 1 SCAN TOOL.
- IGN "ON" IF NO DLC DATA, REFER TO "ON-BOARD DIAGNOSTIC SYSTEM CHECK."
- CHECK THE FOLLOWING:
- CHECK FOR DTCs AND REFER TO THOSE CHARTS FIRST.
- TP SENSOR - IF OVER 2.5 VOLTS AT CLOSED THROTTLE, SEE DTC 21.
- MONITOR "IGNITION CONTROL 3X SIGNAL" WITH TECH 1.

IS RPM INDICATED DURING CRANKING?

YES

2 IS FUEL PUMP VOLTAGE INDICATED DURING CRANK?

YES
- IGNITION "OFF."
- INSTALL FUEL PRESSURE GAUGE.
- IGNITION "ON."

IS PRESSURE BETWEEN 41-47 psi (284-325 kPa)?

YES

4
- DISCONNECT #1 OR #6 INJECTOR HARNESS CONNECTORS.
- IGNITION "ON," ENGINE "OFF."
- WITH TEST LIGHT CONNECTED TO GROUND, PROBE CKT 639 ON INJECTOR HARNESS CONNECTORS.

LIGHT SHOULD BE "ON." IS IT?

YES
- DISCONNECT 10 PIN INJECTOR HARNESS CONNECTOR.
- USE DVOM IN 1k OHM POSITION, POSITIVE PROBE ON TERMINAL "D" OF INJECTOR SIDE OF HARNESS, AND WITH NEGATIVE PROBE TOUCH TERMINAL "A", "B", "C", "E", "F", AND "G" TO CHECK CONTINUITY. RESISTANCE SHOULD BE LESS THAN 20 OHMS.

IS IT?

YES
- USING A DVOM IN DC VOLTS POSITION.
- WITH POSITIVE PROBE CONNECTOR TO B+.
- PROBE TERMINALS "A", "B", "C", "J", "K", AND "H".
- WHILE PROBING TERMINALS, CRANK ENGINE.
- DVOM SHOULD TOGGLE FROM B+ TO 0 VOLTS ON EACH TERMINAL.

DOES IT?

YES

IF ALL OF THE ABOVE IS "OK," REFER TO SECTION 6 (ENGINE GENERAL DESCRIPTION) FOR A BASE ENGINE DIAGNOSIS.

NO

OPEN CIRCUIT, FAULTY PCM CONNECTION, OR FAULTY PCM.

NO (resistance)

OPEN CIRCUIT, FAULTY INJECTOR CONNECTION, OR FAULTY INJECTOR. REFER TO CHART C-2A "INJECTOR COIL/BALANCE TEST."

NO (test light)

OPEN IN CKT 639.

NO (fuel pressure)

SEE FUEL SYSTEM DIAGNOSIS CHART A-7.

NO (fuel pump voltage)

SEE DTC CHART 54.

NO (RPM during cranking)

3
- USING AN ST-125 (SPARK CHECKER) J 26792 OR EQUIVALENT, CHECK FOR SPARK ON TWO WIRES (2-4 OR 4-6).
- CHECK ONE WIRE AT A TIME. LEAVE THE OTHER WIRES CONNECTED TO SPARK PLUG WHILE CRANKING.

IS THERE SPARK ON BOTH WIRES?

NO

NO SPARK. SEE DTC CHART 82.

SPARK ON ONE

5
- CHECK PAIR OF WIRES THAT DID NOT SPARK. EACH WIRE SHOULD MEASURE LESS THAN 30,000 OHMS. IF OK, SWAP IGNITION COILS.

DOES PROBLEM MOVE?

YES

FAULTY COIL.

NO

FAULTY ELECTRONIC IGNITION CONTROL MODULE.

YES

6
- IGNITION "OFF."
- DISCONNECT IGNITION 6-WAY CONNECTOR.
- IGNITION "ON."
- MOMENTARILY TOUCH CKT 430 WITH A TEST LIGHT TO 12 VOLTS WHILE OBSERVING CRANK RPM.

IS RPM INDICATED?

YES

FAULTY 6-WAY CONNECTION OR IGNITION CONTROL MODULE.

NO

CKT 430 OPEN OR SHORTED TO GROUND OR FAULTY PCM.

"*AFTER REPAIRS,*" CONFIRM "CLOSED LOOP" OPERATION AND NO MIL (SERVICE ENGINE SOON).

8-18-93
NS 15323

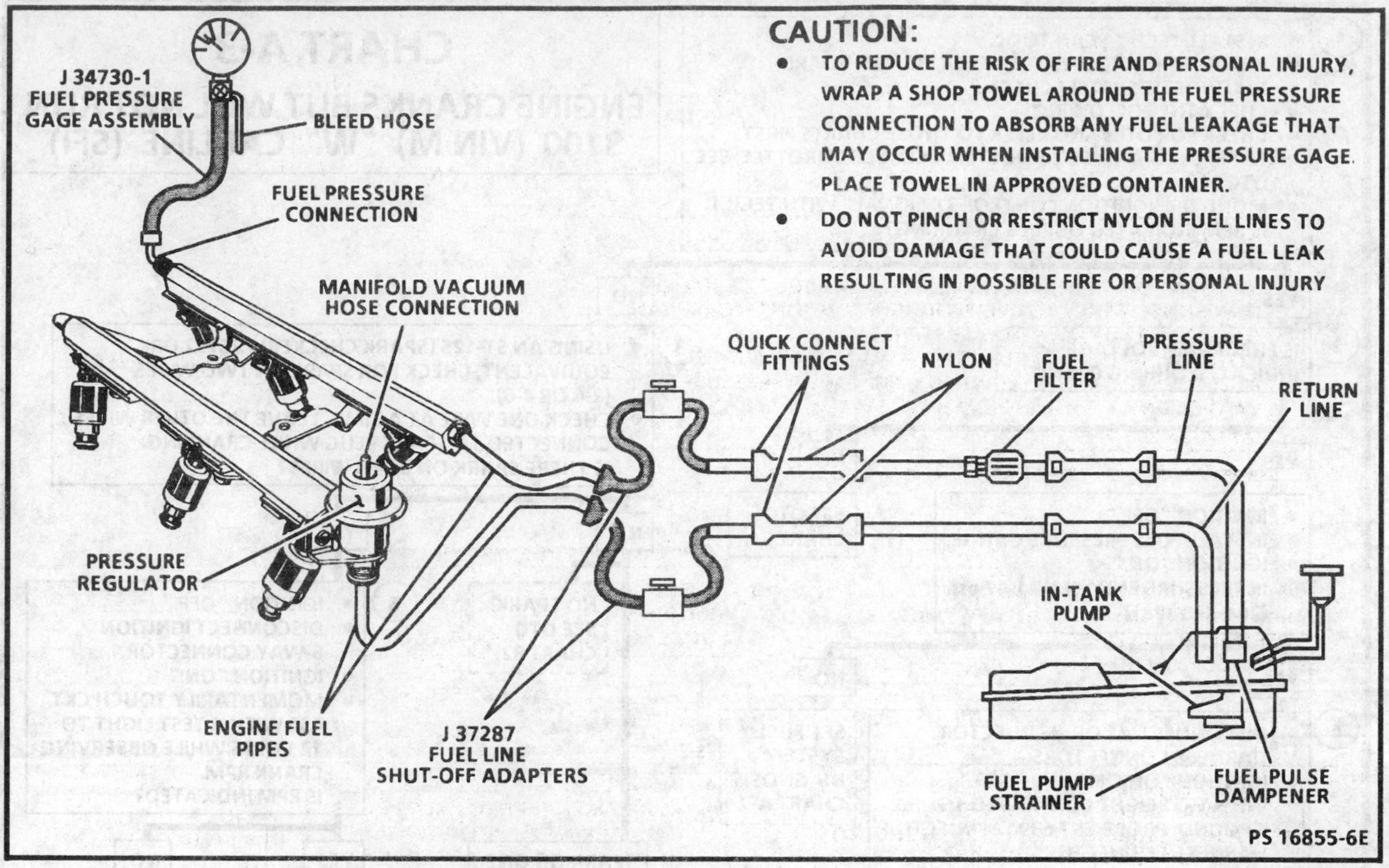
J 34730-1
FUEL PRESSURE
GAGE ASSEMBLY
BLEED HOSE
FUEL PRESSURE
CONNECTION
MANIFOLD VACUUM
HOSE CONNECTION
PRESSURE
REGULATOR
ENGINE FUEL
PIPES
J 37287
FUEL LINE
SHUT-OFF ADAPTERS
QUICK CONNECT
FITTINGS
NYLON
FUEL
FILTER
PRESSURE
LINE
RETURN
LINE
IN-TANK
PUMP
FUEL PUMP
STRAINER
FUEL PULSE
DAMPENER
PS 16855-6E

CAUTION:

- **TO REDUCE THE RISK OF FIRE AND PERSONAL INJURY, WRAP A SHOP TOWEL AROUND THE FUEL PRESSURE CONNECTION TO ABSORB ANY FUEL LEAKAGE THAT MAY OCCUR WHEN INSTALLING THE PRESSURE GAGE. PLACE TOWEL IN APPROVED CONTAINER.**
- **DO NOT PINCH OR RESTRICT NYLON FUEL LINES TO AVOID DAMAGE THAT COULD CAUSE A FUEL LEAK RESULTING IN POSSIBLE FIRE OR PERSONAL INJURY**

CHART A-7 (Page 1 of 3)

FUEL SYSTEM DIAGNOSIS
3100 (VIN M) "W" CARLINE (SFI)

System Description:

When the ignition switch is turned "ON," the Powertrain Control Module (PCM) will turn "ON" the in-tank fuel pump. It will remain "ON" as long as the engine is cranking or running, and the PCM is receiving reference pulses. If there are no reference pulses, the PCM will shut "OFF" the fuel pump within 2 seconds after ignition "ON" or engine stops.

An electric fuel pump, attached to the fuel sender assembly (inside the fuel tank), supplies fuel through an in-line filter to the fuel rail assembly. The pump is designed to provide sufficient fuel flow for all engine demands. A pressure regulator attached to the fuel rail, keeps fuel available to the injectors at a regulated pressure. Unused fuel is returned to the fuel tank by a separate line.

The fuel pump "TEST" connector is located on the driver's side of the engine compartment near the strut tower.

Chart Test Description: Number(s) below refer to circled number(s) on the diagnostic chart.

1. Connect fuel pressure gage as shown in illustration. Wrap a shop towel around the fuel pressure connection to absorb any small amount of fuel leakage that may occur when installing the gage. With ignition "ON" and fuel pump running, pressure should be 284-325 kPa (41-47 psi). This pressure is controlled by spring pressure within the regulator assembly.
2. When the engine is idling, manifold pressure is low (high vacuum) and is applied to the pressure regulator diaphragm. Vacuum will offset spring pressure and result in lower fuel pressure. Fuel pressure at idle will vary somewhat depending on barometric pressure but, should be less than pressure noted in Step (1).
3. A system that does not hold pressure is caused by one of the following:
   - Leaking fuel pump check ball.
   - Leaking fuel pulse dampener.
   - Leaking valve/seat within pressure regulator.
   - Leaking injectors(s).
4. A leaking injector can best be determined by checking for a fouled or saturated spark plug(s). If a leaking injector can not be determined by a fouled or saturated spark plug, the following procedure should be used:
   - Remove intake plenum. See "Fuel Metering System," Section "6E3-C2" of this manual.
   - Remove fuel rail but leave fuel lines connected.
   - Lift fuel rail out just enough to leave injector nozzles in the ports.

CAUTION: To reduce the risk of fire and personal injury that may result from fuel spray on the engine, make sure fuel rail is positioned over injector ports and injector retaining clips are intact.

   - Pressurize the fuel system and observe injector nozzles.

CHART A-7

(Page 1 of 3)
FUEL SYSTEM DIAGNOSIS
3100 (VIN M) "W" CARLINE (SFI)

(1)
- INSTALL FUEL PRESSURE GAGE AS SHOWN ON FACING PAGE.
- IGNITION "OFF" FOR 10 SECONDS. A/C "OFF."
- IGNITION "ON." FUEL PUMP WILL RUN FOR ABOUT 2 SECONDS. IT MAY BE NECESSARY TO CYCLE THE IGNITION "ON" MORE THAN ONCE TO OBTAIN MAXIMUM PRESSURE.
- NOTE FUEL PRESSURE WITH PUMP RUNNING, PRESSURE SHOULD BE 284-325 kPa (41-47 psi). WHEN PUMP STOPS, PRESSURE MAY VARY SLIGHTLY THEN SHOULD HOLD STEADY.

IS PRESSURE CORRECT AND DOES IT HOLD?

YES

IF FUEL PRESSURE IS WITHIN NORMAL RANGE BUT IS SUSPECTED OF DROPPING OFF DURING ACCELERATION, CRUISE OR HARD CORNERING, SEE CHART A-7 (2 OF 3).

(2)
- START ENGINE, ALLOW IT TO IDLE AT NORMAL OPERATING TEMPERATURE.
- FUEL PRESSURE NOTED IN STEP (1) SHOULD DROP APPROXIMATELY 21-69 kPa (3-10 psi).

DOES IT?

YES

NO TROUBLE FOUND, REVIEW "SYMPTOMS," SECTION "B".

NO

- DISCONNECT VACUUM HOSE FROM PRESSURE REGULATOR ASSEMBLY.
- WITH ENGINE IDLING, APPLY 12-14 INCHES OF VACUUM TO PRESSURE REGULATOR. FUEL PRESSURE NOTED IN STEP (1) SHOULD DROP APPROXIMATELY 21-69 kPa (3-10 psi).

DOES IT?

YES

LOCATE AND REPAIR LOSS OF VACUUM TO PRESSURE REGULATOR.

NO

PRESSURE REGULATOR IS FAULTY.

NO (from step 1) — FROM CHART A-3

(3) FUEL PRESSURE WITHIN SPEC., BUT DOES NOT HOLD.

- INSTALL J 37287 FUEL LINE SHUT-OFF ADAPTORS, REFER TO PAGES 3 OF 3 AND FACING PAGE ILLUSTRATION.
- MAKE SURE VALVES ARE OPEN.
- IGNITION "OFF."
- USING A 10 AMP FUSED JUMPER WIRE, CONNECT FUEL PUMP "TEST" CONNECTOR TO B + AND WAIT FOR PRESSURE TO BUILD.
- DISCONNECT JUMPER AND CLOSE VALVE IN FUEL PRESSURE LINE. PRESSURE SHOULD HOLD.

DOES IT?

NO

- OPEN VALVE IN FUEL PRESSURE LINE.
- RECONNECT PUMP "TEST" JUMPER AND WAIT FOR PRESSURE TO BUILD.
- DISCONNECT JUMPER AND CLOSE VALVE IN FUEL RETURN LINE. PRESSURE SHOULD HOLD.

DOES IT?

NO

(4) LOCATE AND CORRECT LEAKING INJECTOR(S).

YES

PRESSURE REGULATOR IS FAULTY.

YES

CHECK FOR:
- LEAKING FUEL PULSE DAMPENER.

IF OK

FUEL PUMP IS FAULTY. (LEAKING CHECK BALL INSIDE PUMP.)

FUEL PRESSURE OUT OF SPEC.

SEE CHART A-7 (2 OF 3)

NO FUEL PRESSURE.

USE DTC 54 CHART TO DIAGNOSE FUEL PUMP ELECTRICAL CIRCUIT.

IF OK

CHECK FOR:
- PLUGGED IN-LINE FILTER.
- RESTRICTED FUEL PRESSURE LINE.
- PLUGGED FUEL PUMP STRAINER.
- LEAKING FUEL PULSE DAMPENER.

IF OK

FUEL PUMP IS FAULTY.

4-30-93
PS 17043-6E

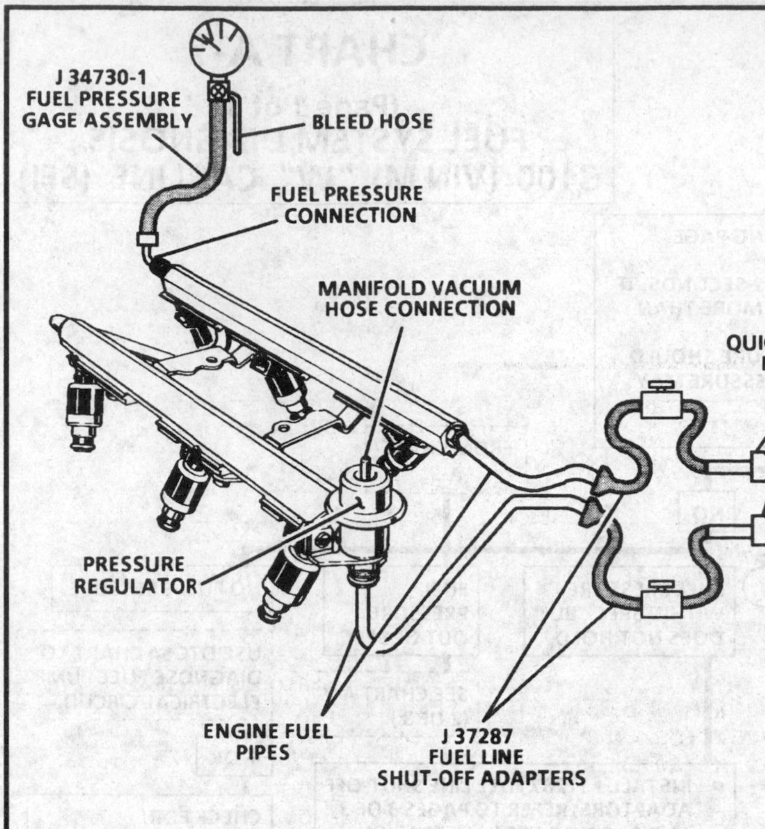
J 34730-1
FUEL PRESSURE
GAGE ASSEMBLY
BLEED HOSE
FUEL PRESSURE
CONNECTION
MANIFOLD VACUUM
HOSE CONNECTION
QUICK CONNECT
FITTINGS
NYLON
FUEL
FILTER
PRESSURE
LINE
RETURN
LINE
PRESSURE
REGULATOR
IN-TANK
PUMP
ENGINE FUEL
PIPES
J 37287
FUEL LINE
SHUT-OFF ADAPTERS
FUEL PUMP
STRAINER
FUEL PULSE
DAMPENER
PS 16855-6E

CAUTION:

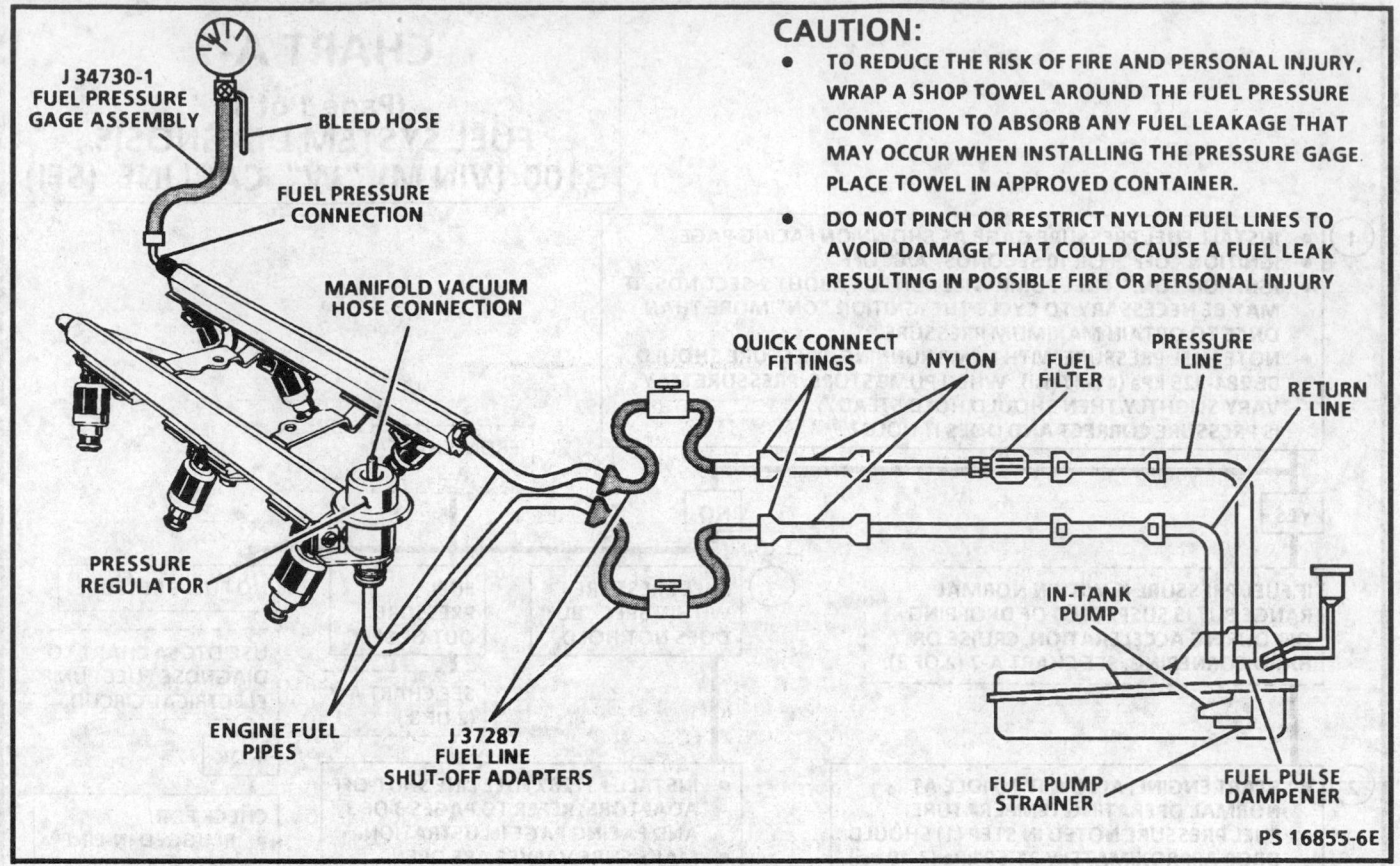

- TO REDUCE THE RISK OF FIRE AND PERSONAL INJURY, WRAP A SHOP TOWEL AROUND THE FUEL PRESSURE CONNECTION TO ABSORB ANY FUEL LEAKAGE THAT MAY OCCUR WHEN INSTALLING THE PRESSURE GAGE. PLACE TOWEL IN APPROVED CONTAINER.
- DO NOT PINCH OR RESTRICT NYLON FUEL LINES TO AVOID DAMAGE THAT COULD CAUSE A FUEL LEAK RESULTING IN POSSIBLE FIRE OR PERSONAL INJURY

CHART A-7
(Page 2 of 3)
FUEL SYSTEM DIAGNOSIS
3100 (VIN M) "W" CARLINE (SFI)

Chart Test Description: Number(s) below refer to circled number(s) on the diagnostic chart.

5. Fuel pressure that drops off during acceleration, cruise or hard cornering may cause a lean condition and result in a loss of power, surging or misfire. This condition can be diagnosed using a Tech 1 scan tool. If the fuel system is very lean, the HO2S will stop toggling and output voltage will drop below 500 mV. Also, injector pulse width will increase.

[!] Important

- Make sure system is not operating at "Fuel-Cutoff" which may cause false readings on the scan tool.

6. Fuel pressure below 284 kPa (41 psi) may cause a lean condition and may set a DTC 44. Driveability conditions can include hard starting cold, hesitation, poor driveability, lack of power, surging or misfire.
7. Restricting fuel flow in the fuel return line as directed causes fuel pressure to build above regulated pressure. With battery voltage applied to the pump "test" connector, pressure should rise above 325 kPa (47 psi) as the valve in the return line is partially closed.

NOTICE: Do not allow pressure to exceed 414 kPa (60 psi) as damage to the regulator may result.

8. Fuel pressure above 325 kPa (47 psi) may cause a rich condition and may set a DTC 45. A driveability condition can include hard starting (followed by black smoke) and a strong sulphur smell in the exhaust.
9. This test determines if the high fuel pressure is due to a restricted fuel return line or a faulty fuel pressure regulator.
10. The pressure regulator filter screen is designed to trap any contaminants introduced during engine assembly. If dirty, it can be removed with a small pick and discarded without potential harm to the regulator.

CHART A-7

(Page 2 of 3)

FUEL SYSTEM DIAGNOSIS
3100 (VIN M) "W" CARLINE (SFI)

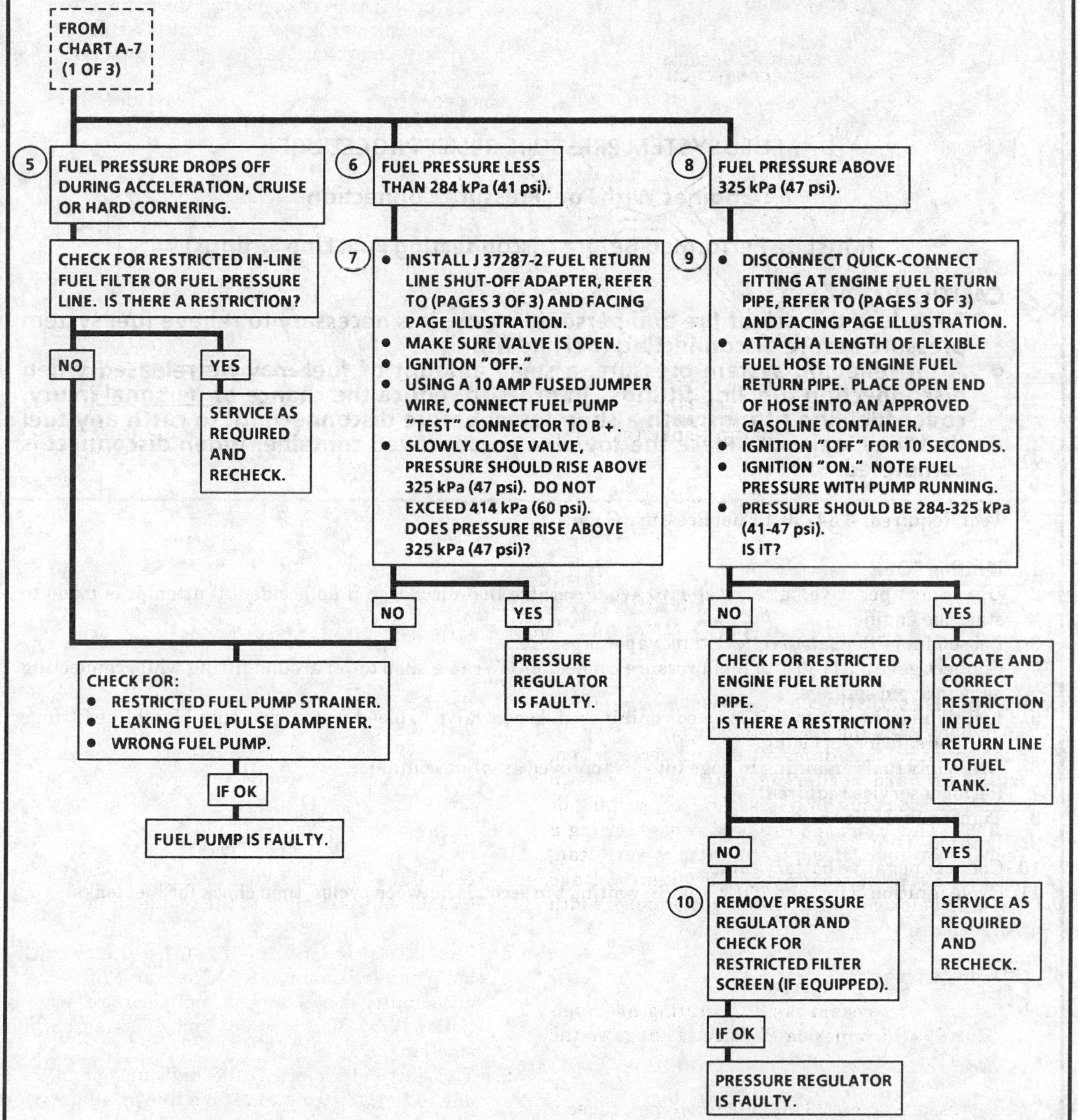
FROM CHART A-7 (1 OF 3)
5
FUEL PRESSURE DROPS OFF DURING ACCELERATION, CRUISE OR HARD CORNERING.
CHECK FOR RESTRICTED IN-LINE FUEL FILTER OR FUEL PRESSURE LINE. IS THERE A RESTRICTION?
NO
YES
SERVICE AS REQUIRED AND RECHECK.
6
FUEL PRESSURE LESS THAN 284 kPa (41 psi).
7
• INSTALL J 37287-2 FUEL RETURN LINE SHUT-OFF ADAPTER, REFER TO (PAGES 3 OF 3) AND FACING PAGE ILLUSTRATION.
• MAKE SURE VALVE IS OPEN.
• IGNITION "OFF."
• USING A 10 AMP FUSED JUMPER WIRE, CONNECT FUEL PUMP "TEST" CONNECTOR TO B +.
• SLOWLY CLOSE VALVE, PRESSURE SHOULD RISE ABOVE 325 kPa (47 psi). DO NOT EXCEED 414 kPa (60 psi). DOES PRESSURE RISE ABOVE 325 kPa (47 psi)?
NO
YES
PRESSURE REGULATOR IS FAULTY.
CHECK FOR:
• RESTRICTED FUEL PUMP STRAINER.
• LEAKING FUEL PULSE DAMPENER.
• WRONG FUEL PUMP.
IF OK
FUEL PUMP IS FAULTY.
8
FUEL PRESSURE ABOVE 325 kPa (47 psi).
9
• DISCONNECT QUICK-CONNECT FITTING AT ENGINE FUEL RETURN PIPE, REFER TO (PAGES 3 OF 3) AND FACING PAGE ILLUSTRATION.
• ATTACH A LENGTH OF FLEXIBLE FUEL HOSE TO ENGINE FUEL RETURN PIPE. PLACE OPEN END OF HOSE INTO AN APPROVED GASOLINE CONTAINER.
• IGNITION "OFF" FOR 10 SECONDS.
• IGNITION "ON." NOTE FUEL PRESSURE WITH PUMP RUNNING.
• PRESSURE SHOULD BE 284-325 kPa (41-47 psi). IS IT?
NO
YES
CHECK FOR RESTRICTED ENGINE FUEL RETURN PIPE. IS THERE A RESTRICTION?
LOCATE AND CORRECT RESTRICTION IN FUEL RETURN LINE TO FUEL TANK.
NO
YES
10
REMOVE PRESSURE REGULATOR AND CHECK FOR RESTRICTED FILTER SCREEN (IF EQUIPPED).
SERVICE AS REQUIRED AND RECHECK.
IF OK
PRESSURE REGULATOR IS FAULTY.

3-1-93
PS 17044-6E

CHART A-7

(Page 3 of 3)

FUEL SYSTEM DIAGNOSIS
3100 (VIN M) "W" CARLINE (SFI)

FUEL SYSTEM PRESSURE RELIEF PROCEDURE

Engines With Fuel Pressure Connection

(Must Be Performed Before Disconnecting Fuel Line Fittings)

CAUTION:

- **To reduce the risk of fire and personal injury, it is necessary to relieve fuel system pressure before disconnecting fuel line fittings.**
- **After relieving system pressure, a small amount of fuel may be released when disconnecting fuel line fittings. In order to reduce the chance of personal injury, cover fuel line fittings with a shop towel before disconnecting, to catch any fuel that may leak out. Place the towel in an approved container when disconnect is completed.**

Tool Required: J 34730-1 Fuel Pressure Gage

1. Ignition "OFF."
2. Disconnect negative battery cable to avoid possible fuel discharge if an accidental attempt is made to start the engine.
3. Loosen fuel filler cap to relieve tank vapor pressure.
4. Connect gage J 34730-1 to fuel pressure connection. Wrap a shop towel around fitting while connecting gage to avoid spillage.
5. Install bleed hose into an approved container and open valve to bleed system pressure. Fuel line fittings are now safe for servicing.
6. Drain any fuel remaining in gage into an approved gasoline container.
7. Perform service required.
8. Tighten fuel filler cap.
9. Ignition "OFF."
10. Connect negative battery cable.
11. Cycle ignition "ON" and "OFF" twice, waiting ten seconds between cycles, then check for fuel leaks.

CHART A-7

(Page 3 of 3)

FUEL SYSTEM DIAGNOSIS 3100 (VIN M) "W" CARLINE (SFI)

SERVICING QUICK-CONNECT FITTINGS

Important

- In order to install fuel system diagnostic equipment on vehicles equipped with plastic quick-connect fittings, fuel line separator tools must be used to disconnect the fittings. Using the separator tools to release the fittings will cause the plastic retainer to remain inside the female connector allowing diagnostic equipment to be connected.

Tools required:

J 37088-A tool set, fuel line quick-connect separator;
J 39504 tool set, fuel line quick-connect separator (restricted access).

Remove or Disconnect

1. Relieve fuel system pressure (see "Fuel System Pressure Relief").
2. If equipped, slide dust cover back to access quick-connect fitting.
3. Grasp both sides of fitting. Twist female connector 1/4 turn in each direction to loosen any dirt within fitting.

CAUTION: Safety glasses must be worn when using compressed air, as flying dirt particles may cause eye injury.

4. Using compressed air, blow dirt out of fitting.
5. Choose correct tool from J 37088-A or J 39504 tool set for size of fitting. Insert tool into female connector, then push/pull inward to release locking tabs.
6. Pull connection apart.

Clean and Inspect

NOTICE: If it is necessary to remove rust or burrs from fuel pipe, use emery cloth in a radial motion with the pipe end to prevent damage to O-ring sealing surface.

- Using a clean shop towel, wipe off male pipe end.
- Inspect both ends of fitting for dirt and burrs. Clean or replace components/assemblies as required.

Install or Connect

CAUTION: To Reduce the Risk of Fire and Personal Injury:

- **Before connecting fitting, always apply a few drops of clean engine oil to the male pipe end of engine fuel pipe, pressure gage adapter or fuel line shut-off adapter. This will ensure proper reconnection and prevent a possible fuel leak. (During normal operation, the O-rings located in the female connector will swell and may prevent proper reconnection if not lubricated.)**

1. Apply a few drops of clean engine oil to the male pipe end of engine fuel pipe, pressure gage adapter or fuel line shut-off adapter.
2. Push both sides of fitting together to cause the retaining tabs/fingers to snap into place.
3. Once installed, pull on both sides of fitting to make sure connection is secure.
4. If equipped, reposition dust cover over quick-connect fitting.

11-21-92
NS 14628

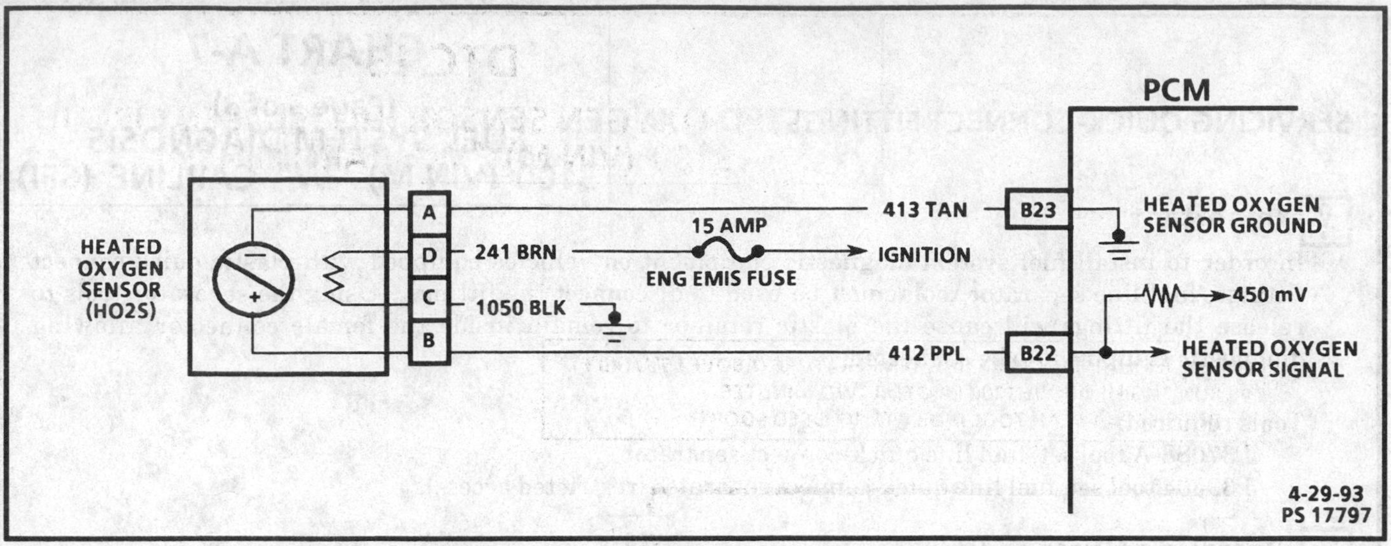
PCM
HEATED OXYGEN SENSOR (HO2S)
A
D
C
B
241 BRN
1050 BLK
15 AMP
ENG EMIS FUSE
IGNITION
413 TAN
412 PPL
B23
B22
HEATED OXYGEN SENSOR GROUND
450 mV
HEATED OXYGEN SENSOR SIGNAL
4-29-93
PS 17797

DTC 13

HEATED OXYGEN SENSOR (HO2S) OPEN CIRCUIT 3100 (VIN M) "W" CARLINE (SFI)

Circuit Description:

The heated oxygen sensor has 450 millivolts applied to it by the PCM on CKT 412. This voltage may vary slightly when measured with a 10 megohm (minimum) impedance DVM. As the HO2S warms and becomes active, it also produces a voltage which will vary from 100 to 1000 millivolts. The PCM then detects whichever voltage is greater at the HO2S signal input. If the HO2S voltage is less than the 450 millivolts reference, the sensor acts as a ground and functionally reduces the voltage level at the input. This effect causes the Tech 1 scan tool to display a 100 to 1000 millivolt operating range.

The heater in the HO2S allows for faster sensor warmup and better temperature stabilization during engine operation.

DTC 13 Will Set When: The engine is in "Closed Loop," ECT is greater than 65°C (149°F), no current DTC 21 or 22, HO2S voltage is between 350 and 550 millivolts, throttle angle is greater than 3% with all conditions met for 30 seconds.

Action Taken (PCM will default to): The PCM will default to "Open Loop" operation and the MIL will become illuminated.

DTC 13 Will Clear When: A current DTC 13 will clear when the HO2S voltage begins to vary outside of the 350 to 550 millivolt window. A History DTC 13 will clear after 50 ignition key cycles without a current DTC 13 being stored.

DTC Chart Test Description: Number(s) below refer to circled number(s) on the diagnostic chart.

1. If the conditions for a DTC 13 exist, the system will not go "Closed Loop."
2. This will determine if the sensor is at fault, or the wiring or PCM is the cause of the DTC 13.
3. In doing this test use only a high impedance digital volt ohmmeter. This test checks the continuity of CKT 412 and CKT 413 because if CKT 413 is open, the PCM voltage on CKT 412 will be greater than .6 volt (600 mV).

Diagnostic Aids: Normal Tech 1 scan voltage varies between 100 mV to 999 mV (.1 and 1.0 volt) while in "Closed Loop." DTC 13 sets if voltage remains between .35 and .55 volt, but the system will go "Open Loop" in about 15 seconds. Refer to "Intermittents," in "Symptoms," Section "6E3-B".

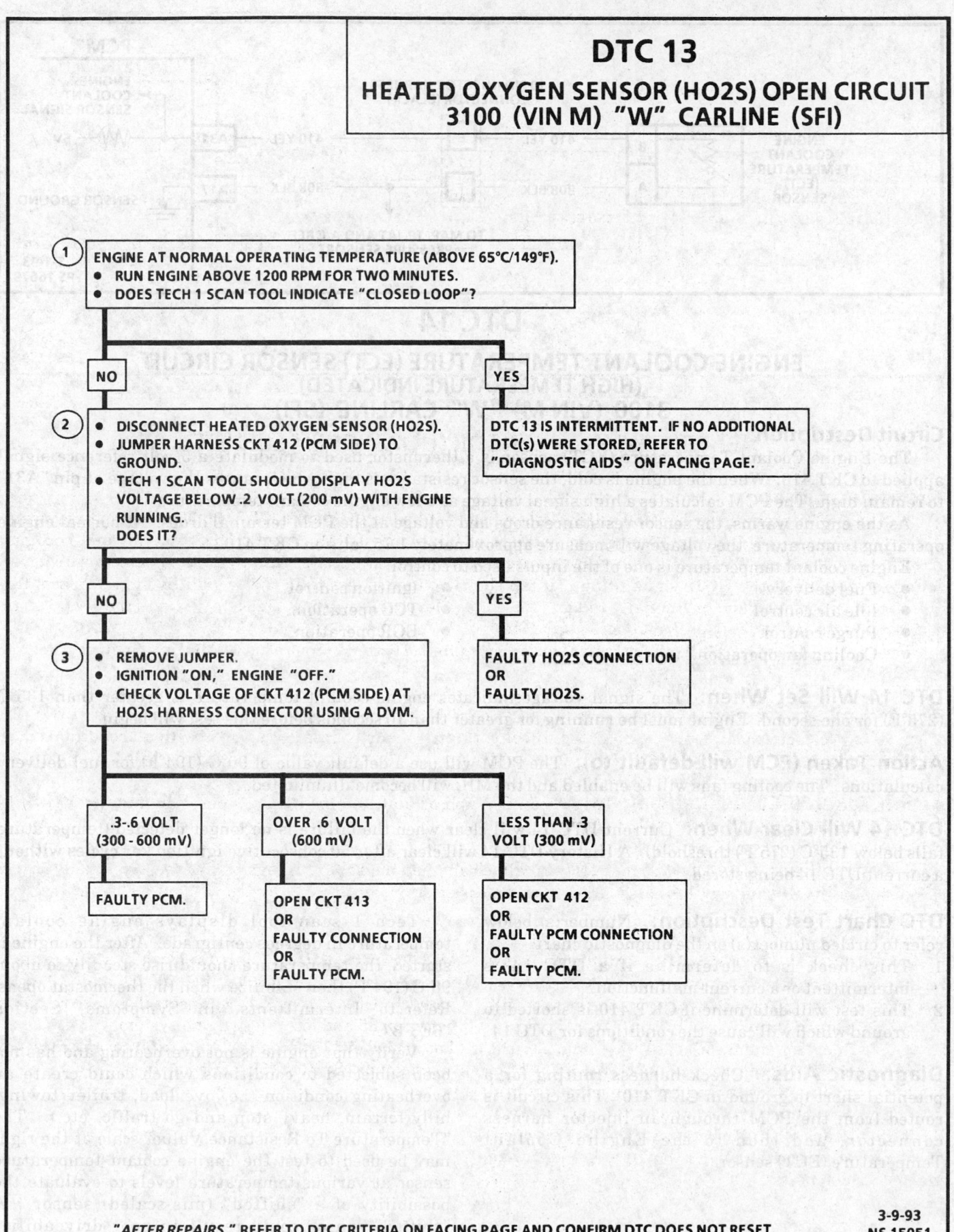

DTC 13
HEATED OXYGEN SENSOR (HO2S) OPEN CIRCUIT
3100 (VIN M) "W" CARLINE (SFI)

1 ENGINE AT NORMAL OPERATING TEMPERATURE (ABOVE 65°C/149°F).
- RUN ENGINE ABOVE 1200 RPM FOR TWO MINUTES.
- DOES TECH 1 SCAN TOOL INDICATE "CLOSED LOOP"?

NO → step 2

YES → DTC 13 IS INTERMITTENT. IF NO ADDITIONAL DTC(s) WERE STORED, REFER TO "DIAGNOSTIC AIDS" ON FACING PAGE.

2
- DISCONNECT HEATED OXYGEN SENSOR (HO2S).
- JUMPER HARNESS CKT 412 (PCM SIDE) TO GROUND.
- TECH 1 SCAN TOOL SHOULD DISPLAY HO2S VOLTAGE BELOW .2 VOLT (200 mV) WITH ENGINE RUNNING. DOES IT?

NO → step 3

YES → FAULTY HO2S CONNECTION OR FAULTY HO2S.

3
- REMOVE JUMPER.
- IGNITION "ON," ENGINE "OFF."
- CHECK VOLTAGE OF CKT 412 (PCM SIDE) AT HO2S HARNESS CONNECTOR USING A DVM.

.3-.6 VOLT (300 - 600 mV) → FAULTY PCM.

OVER .6 VOLT (600 mV) → OPEN CKT 413 OR FAULTY CONNECTION OR FAULTY PCM.

LESS THAN .3 VOLT (300 mV) → OPEN CKT 412 OR FAULTY PCM CONNECTION OR FAULTY PCM.

"AFTER REPAIRS," REFER TO DTC CRITERIA ON FACING PAGE AND CONFIRM DTC DOES NOT RESET.

3-9-93
NS 15051

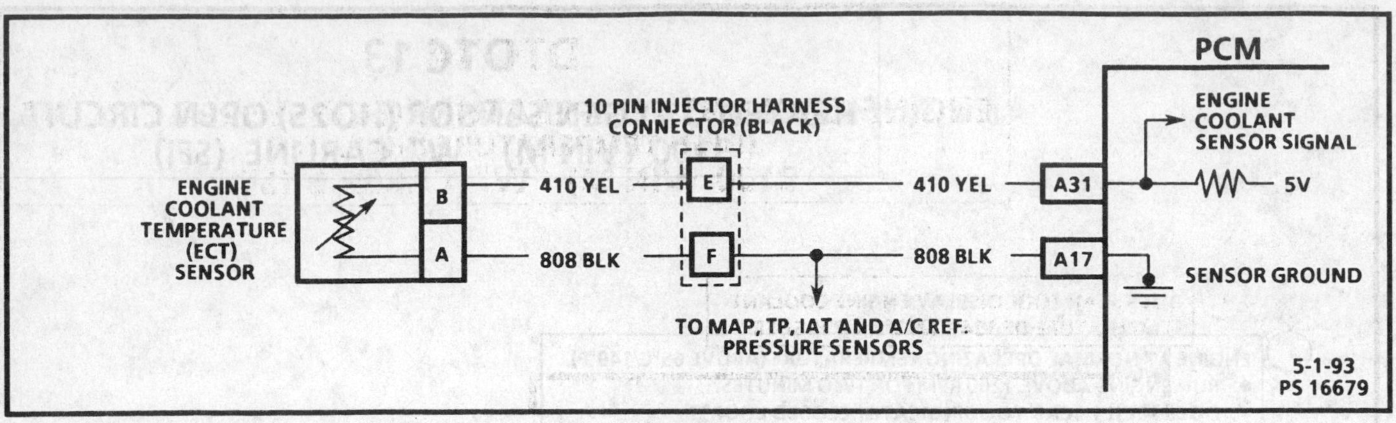
PCM
10 PIN INJECTOR HARNESS CONNECTOR (BLACK)
ENGINE COOLANT SENSOR SIGNAL
ENGINE COOLANT TEMPERATURE (ECT) SENSOR
B
A
410 YEL
E
410 YEL
A31
5V
808 BLK
F
808 BLK
A17
SENSOR GROUND
TO MAP, TP, IAT AND A/C REF. PRESSURE SENSORS
5-1-93
PS 16679

DTC 14

ENGINE COOLANT TEMPERATURE (ECT) SENSOR CIRCUIT (HIGH TEMPERATURE INDICATED) 3100 (VIN M) "W" CARLINE (SFI)

Circuit Description:

The Engine Coolant Temperature (ECT) sensor is a thermistor used to modulate a 5 volt reference signal applied to CKT 410. When the engine is cold, the sensor resistance is high which causes the voltage at pin "A31" to remain high. The PCM calculates a high signal voltage as a low engine coolant temperature.

As the engine warms, the sensor resistance drops and voltage at the PCM terminal drops. At normal engine operating temperature, the voltage will measure approximately 1.75 volts on CKT 410.

Engine coolant temperature is one of the inputs used to control:

- Fuel delivery.
- Idle air control.
- Purge control.
- Cooling fan operation.
- Ignition control.
- TCC operation.
- EGR operation.

DTC 14 Will Set When: The signal voltage indicates engine coolant temperature is greater than 135°C (275°F) for one second. Engine must be running for greater than 10 seconds before this test will begin.

Action Taken (PCM will default to): The PCM will use a default value of 90°C (194°F) for fuel delivery calculations. The cooling fans will be enabled and the MIL will become illuminated.

DTC 14 Will Clear When: Current DTC 14 will clear when the failure is no longer detected (temperature falls below 135°C (275°F) threshold). A History DTC 14 will clear after 50 consecutive ignition key cycles without a current DTC 14 being stored.

DTC Chart Test Description: Number(s) below refer to circled number(s) on the diagnostic chart.

1. This check is to determine if a DTC 14 is intermittent or a current malfunction.
2. This test will determine if CKT 410 is shorted to ground which will cause the conditions for DTC 14.

Diagnostic Aids: Check harness routing for a potential short to ground in CKT 410. This circuit is routed from the PCM through an injector harness connector, and then to the Engine Coolant Temperature (ECT) sensor.

Tech 1 scan tool displays engine coolant temperature in degrees centigrade. After the engine is started, the temperature should rise steadily to about 90°C (194°F) then stabilize when the thermostat opens. Refer to "Intermittents," in "Symptoms," Section "6E3-B".

Verify that engine is not overheating and has not been subjected to conditions which could create an overheating condition (i.e. overload, trailer towing, hilly terrain, heavy stop and go traffic, etc.). The "Temperature To Resistance Value" scale at the right may be used to test the engine coolant temperature sensor at various temperature levels to evaluate the possibility of a "shifted" (mis-scaled) sensor. A "shifted" sensor could result in poor driveability complaints.

DTC 14

ENGINE COOLANT TEMPERATURE (ECT) SENSOR CIRCUIT
(HIGH TEMPERATURE INDICATED)
3100 (VIN M) "W" CARLINE (SFI)

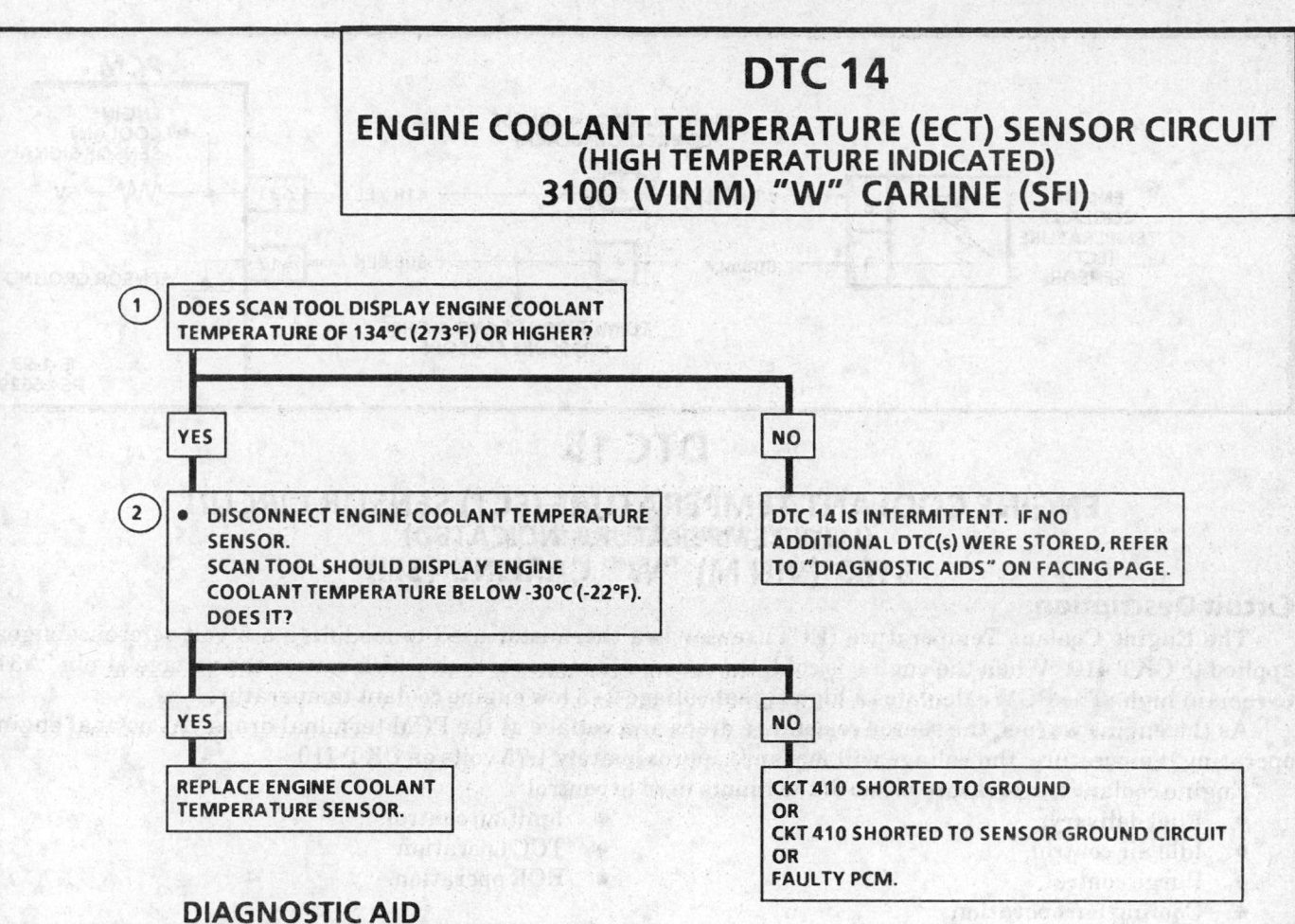

(1) DOES SCAN TOOL DISPLAY ENGINE COOLANT TEMPERATURE OF 134°C (273°F) OR HIGHER?

- YES → (2)
- NO → DTC 14 IS INTERMITTENT. IF NO ADDITIONAL DTC(s) WERE STORED, REFER TO "DIAGNOSTIC AIDS" ON FACING PAGE.

(2)
- DISCONNECT ENGINE COOLANT TEMPERATURE SENSOR.

SCAN TOOL SHOULD DISPLAY ENGINE COOLANT TEMPERATURE BELOW -30°C (-22°F). DOES IT?

- YES → REPLACE ENGINE COOLANT TEMPERATURE SENSOR.
- NO → CKT 410 SHORTED TO GROUND OR CKT 410 SHORTED TO SENSOR GROUND CIRCUIT OR FAULTY PCM.

DIAGNOSTIC AID

ENGINE COOLANT TEMPERATURE SENSOR

TEMPERATURE VS. RESISTANCE VALUES (APPROXIMATE)

°C	°F	OHMS
100	212	177
90	194	241
80	176	332
70	158	467
60	140	667
50	122	973
45	113	1188
40	104	1459
35	95	1802
30	86	2238
25	77	2796
20	68	3520
15	59	4450
10	50	5670
5	41	7280
0	32	9420
-5	23	12300
-10	14	16180
-15	5	21450
-20	-4	28680
-30	-22	52700
-40	-40	100700

4-6-93
NS 15939

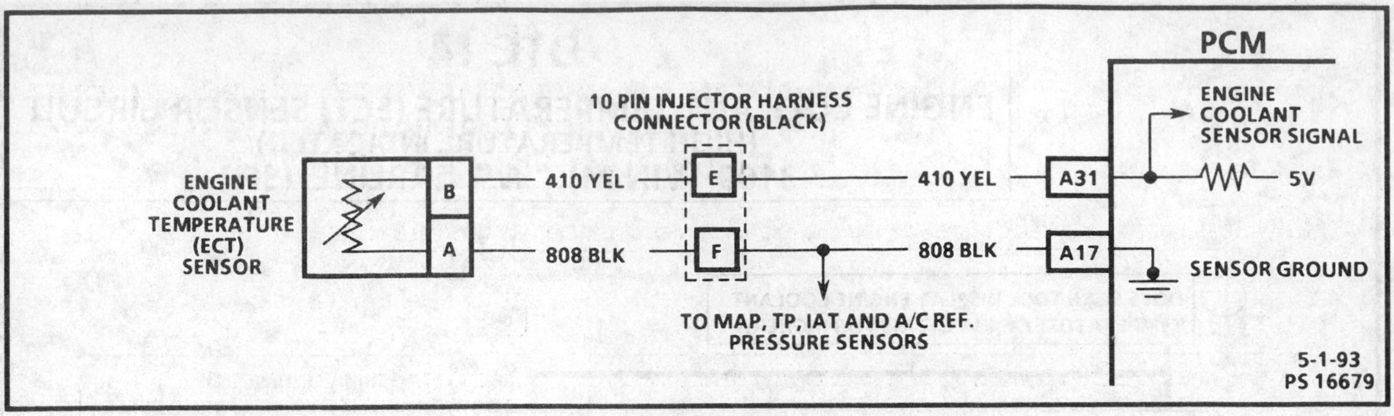
PCM
ENGINE COOLANT SENSOR SIGNAL
10 PIN INJECTOR HARNESS CONNECTOR (BLACK)
ENGINE COOLANT TEMPERATURE (ECT) SENSOR
B
A
410 YEL
808 BLK
E
F
410 YEL
808 BLK
A31
A17
5V
SENSOR GROUND
TO MAP, TP, IAT AND A/C REF. PRESSURE SENSORS
5-1-93
PS 16679

DTC 15

ENGINE COOLANT TEMPERATURE (ECT) SENSOR CIRCUIT
(LOW TEMPERATURE INDICATED)
3100 (VIN M) "W" CARLINE (SFI)

Circuit Description:

The Engine Coolant Temperature (ECT) sensor is a thermistor used to modulate a 5 volt reference signal applied to CKT 410. When the engine is cold, the sensor resistance is high which causes the voltage at pin "A31" to remain high. The PCM calculates a high signal voltage as a low engine coolant temperature.

As the engine warms, the sensor resistance drops and voltage at the PCM terminal drops. At normal engine operating temperature, the voltage will measure approximately 1.75 volts on CKT 410.

Engine coolant temperature is one of the inputs used to control:

- Fuel delivery.
- Idle air control.
- Purge control.
- Cooling fan operation.
- Ignition control.
- TCC operation.
- EGR operation.

DTC 15 Will Set When: A DTC 15 will set when the ECT sensor indicates an engine coolant temperature less than -38°C (-37°F) for more than 2 seconds.

Action Taken (PCM will default to): The PCM will use a default value of 90°C (194°F) for fuel delivery calculations. The cooling fans will be enabled and the MIL will become illuminated.

DTC 15 Will Clear When: A current DTC 15 will clear when the low temperature failure is no longer detected [temperature rises above -38°C (-37°F) threshold]. A History DTC 15 will clear after 50 consecutive ignition key cycles without a current DTC 15 being stored.

DTC Chart Test Description: Number(s) below refer to circled number(s) on the diagnostic chart.

1. This is to verify that the temperature fault is not intermittent.
2. This test simulates a DTC 14. If the PCM recognizes the low signal voltage (high temperature), and the Tech 1 scan tool reads 135°C (275°F), the PCM and wiring are OK.
3. This test will determine if CKT 410 is open. There should be 5 volts present at sensor connector if measured with a DVM.

Diagnostic Aids: A Tech 1 scan tool reads engine temperature in degrees centigrade. After the engine is started, the temperature should rise steadily to about 90°C (194°F) then stabilize when the thermostat opens. CKT 410 is routed from the PCM through an injector harness connector, and then to the Engine Coolant Temperature (ECT) sensor.

A faulty connection, or an open in CKT 410 or 808 will result in a DTC 15.

The "Temperature to Resistance Value" scale at the right may be used to test the engine coolant temperature sensor at various temperature levels to evaluate the possibility of a "shifted" (mis-scaled) sensor. A "shifted" sensor could result in poor driveability complaints.

Refer to "Intermittents," in "Symptoms," Section "6E3-B".

DTC 15

ENGINE COOLANT TEMPERATURE (ECT) SENSOR CIRCUIT
(LOW TEMPERATURE INDICATED)
3100 (VIN M) "W" CARLINE (SFI)

(1) DOES TECH 1 SCAN TOOL DISPLAY ENGINE COOLANT TEMPERATURE OF -38°C (-37°F) OR LESS?

- **YES** → (2)
  - DISCONNECT ENGINE COOLANT TEMPERATURE SENSOR.
  - JUMPER HARNESS TERMINALS TOGETHER.
  - TECH 1 SCAN TOOL SHOULD DISPLAY 130°C (266°F) OR MORE. DOES IT?
    - **NO** → (3)
      - JUMPER CKT 410 TO GROUND.
      - TECH 1 SCAN TOOL SHOULD DISPLAY OVER 130°C (266°F). DOES IT?
        - **YES** → OPEN ENGINE COOLANT TEMPERATURE SENSOR GROUND CIRCUIT, FAULTY CONNECTION OR FAULTY PCM.
        - **NO** → OPEN CKT 410, FAULTY CONNECTION AT PCM, OR FAULTY PCM.
    - **YES** → FAULTY CONNECTION OR ENGINE COOLANT TEMPERATURE SENSOR.
- **NO** → DTC 15 IS INTERMITTENT. IF NO ADDITIONAL DTC(s) WERE STORED, REFER TO "DIAGNOSTIC AIDS" ON FACING PAGE.

DIAGNOSTIC AID

ENGINE COOLANT TEMPERATURE SENSOR
TEMPERATURE VS. RESISTANCE VALUES
(APPROXIMATE)

°C	°F	OHMS
100	212	177
90	194	241
80	176	332
70	158	467
60	140	667
50	122	973
45	113	1188
40	104	1459
35	95	1802
30	86	2238
25	77	2796
20	68	3520
15	59	4450
10	50	5670
5	41	7280
0	32	9420
-5	23	12300
-10	14	16180
-15	5	21450
-20	-4	28680
-30	-22	52700
-40	-40	100700

"AFTER REPAIRS," REFER TO DTC CRITERIA ON FACING PAGE AND CONFIRM DTC DOES NOT RESET.

3-10-93
NS 15052

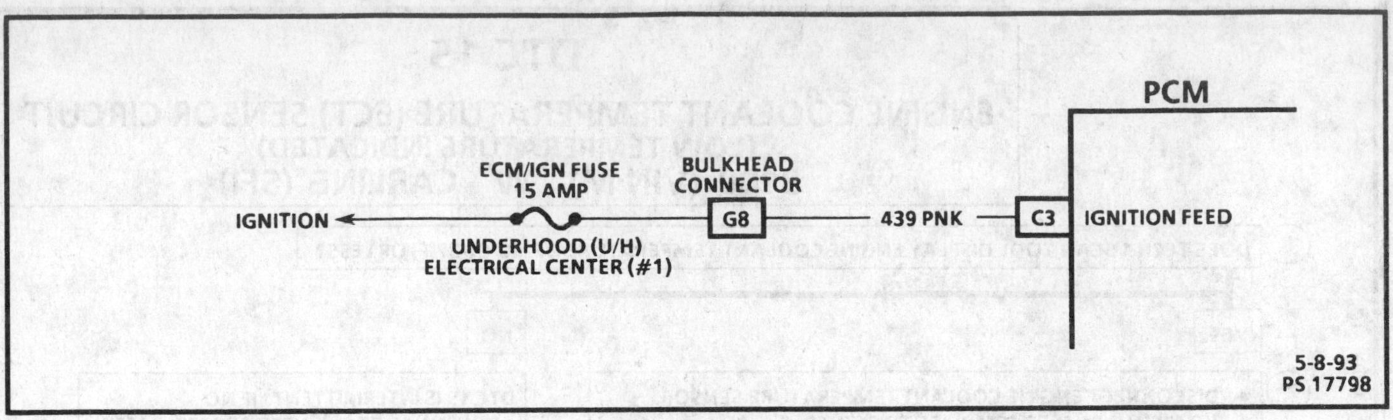
PCM
ECM/IGN FUSE
15 AMP
BULKHEAD
CONNECTOR
IGNITION
G8
439 PNK
C3
IGNITION FEED
UNDERHOOD (U/H)
ELECTRICAL CENTER (#1)
5-8-93
PS 17798

DTC 16

SYSTEM VOLTAGE LOW
3100 (VIN M) "W" CARLINE (SFI)

Circuit Description:

The PCM will perform a test of the ignition voltage applied to pin "C3" of the PCM. A comparison is done between the voltage applied to the input and a calibrated voltage value.

During the time a low voltage failure is present, all PCM outputs will become disabled. This may result in the additional setting of other seemingly unrelated DTCs.

DTC 16 Will Set When: The PCM detects 8 volts or less on the ignition feed CKT 439, engine speed is greater than 1000 RPM with both conditions met for 5 seconds.

Action Taken (PCM will default to): The MIL will become illuminated.

DTC 16 Will Clear When: A current DTC 16 will clear when ignition feed voltage is detected above 8 volts. A History DTC 16 will clear after 50 consecutive ignition key cycles without a current DTC 16 being stored.

DTC Chart Test Description: Number(s) below refer to circled number(s) on the diagnostic chart.

1. Test generator output as outlined in SECTION 6D3 to determine proper operation of the voltage regulator. Run engine at moderate speed and measure voltage across the battery. If less than 8 volts, repair generator as outlined in SECTION 6D3.

Diagnostic Aids: An intermittent may be caused by poor connections, chaffed insulation, a wire broken inside the insulation or poor PCM grounds.

- Intermittent test. Monitor "System Volts" display with a Tech 1 while moving related connectors. If the failure is induced, the display will abruptly change. This may help to isolate the location of the malfunction.

DTC 16

SYSTEM VOLTAGE LOW
3100 (VIN M) "W" CARLINE (SFI)

- INSTALL TECH 1.
- START ENGINE, WITH ENGINE RUNNING ABOVE 1000 RPM.
- SCAN SYSTEM VOLTAGE.

LESS THAN 8 VOLTS

1
- INSTALL DVM ACROSS BATTERY.
- RUN ENGINE ABOVE 1000 RPM.
- DOES DVM SHOW BATTERY VOLTAGE ABOVE 12 VOLTS OR LESS THAN 8 VOLTS?

BETWEEN 9 AND 14 VOLTS

- LOAD ELECTRICAL SYSTEM WITH HEADLAMPS AND HIGH A/C BLOWER.
- RAISE ENGINE RPM TO 2000.
- NOTE SYSTEM VOLTAGE ON TECH 1.

LESS THAN 8 VOLTS

SEE SECTION 6D FOR REPAIR.

BETWEEN 8 AND 14 VOLTS

FAULT IS NOT PRESENT. REFER TO "DIAGNOSTIC AIDS" ON FACING PAGE.

ABOVE 12 VOLTS

- LOAD ELECTRICAL SYSTEM WITH HEADLAMPS AND HIGH A/C BLOWER.
- RAISE ENGINE RPM TO 2000.
- NOTE BATTERY VOLTAGE AT BATTERY.

BELOW 8 VOLTS

- SEE SECTION 6D FOR REPAIR.

ABOVE 12 VOLTS

- COMPARE TECH 1 READING OF SYSTEM VOLTAGE WITH DVM READING.

LESS THAN 8 VOLTS

SEE SECTION 6D FOR REPAIR.

TECH 1 DATA DOES NOT REFLECT DVM VALUES.

FAULTY PCM CONNECTOR OR FAULTY PCM.

BOTH ABOVE 12 VOLTS

FAULT IS NOT PRESENT. REFER TO "DIAGNOSTIC AIDS" ON FACING PAGE.

"*AFTER REPAIRS,*" REFER TO DTC CRITERIA ON FACING PAGE AND CONFIRM DTC DOES NOT RESET.

3-8-93
NS 15043

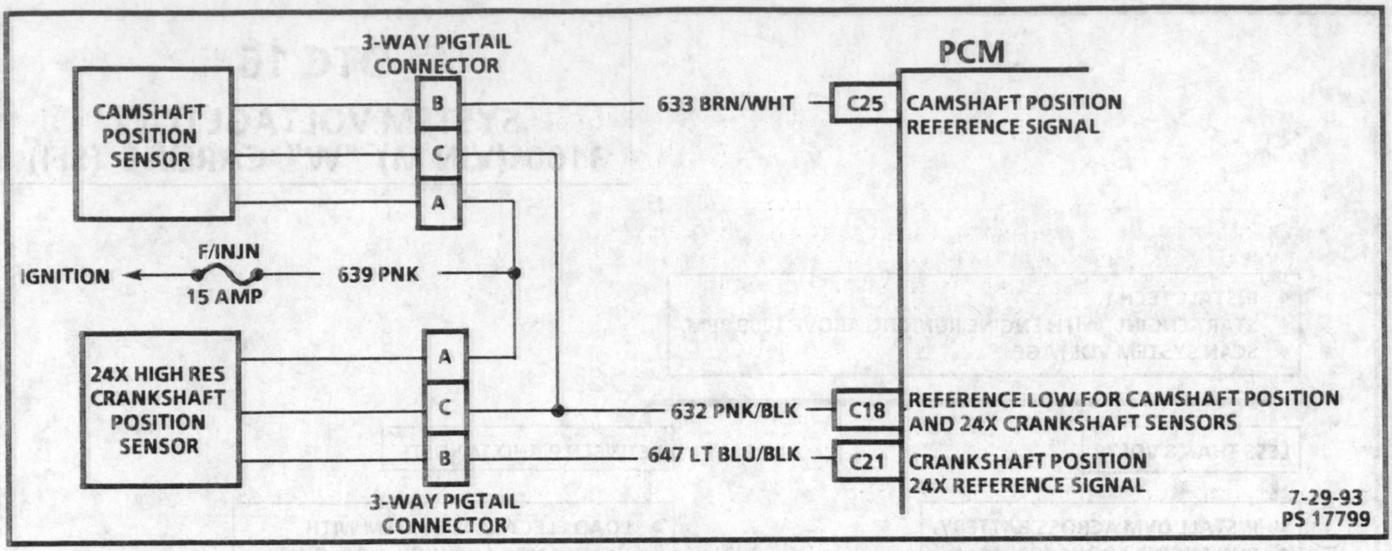
3-WAY PIGTAIL CONNECTOR
PCM
CAMSHAFT POSITION SENSOR
B
C
A
633 BRN/WHT
C25
CAMSHAFT POSITION REFERENCE SIGNAL
F/INJN
IGNITION
15 AMP
639 PNK
24X HIGH RES CRANKSHAFT POSITION SENSOR
A
C
B
632 PNK/BLK
C18
REFERENCE LOW FOR CAMSHAFT POSITION AND 24X CRANKSHAFT SENSORS
647 LT BLU/BLK
C21
CRANKSHAFT POSITION 24X REFERENCE SIGNAL
3-WAY PIGTAIL CONNECTOR
7-29-93
PS 17799

DTC 17

CAMSHAFT POSITION SENSOR CIRCUIT ERROR 3100 (VIN M) "W" CARLINE (SFI)

Circuit Description:

The camshaft position sensor is a "Hall-effect" switch located on the front of the engine. This sensor sends a signal to the PCM indicating when to begin sequencing the injectors starting with cylinder #1. If the cam reference signal is not received by the PCM, the injectors will pulse sequentially, although proper sequencing may not occur resulting in a rough or unstable idle.

DTC 17 Will Set When: Cam reference pulses are not detected by the PCM for 3 seconds while the engine is running.

Action Taken (PCM will default to): The PCM will pulse the injectors sequentially though possibly not in the correct sequence. The malfunction indicator lamp will not be illuminated.

DTC 17 Will Clear When: A current DTC 17 will clear when the cam signal begins to toggle. A History DTC 17 will clear after 50 consecutive ignition key cycles without a current DTC 17 being stored.

DTC Chart Test Description: Number(s) below refer to circled number(s) on the diagnostic chart.

1. The PCM performs a test for DTC 17 when the engine is running or during cranking.
2. By repeatedly "bumping" the starter, the camshaft timing mark and the camshaft position sensor will align with each other. At this point, the voltage from the sensor applied to the PCM should drop to near zero temporarily. This indicates that the camshaft position sensor is capable of sending a signal to the PCM.
3. Before replacing the camshaft position sensor, inspect the sensor for proper installation.

Diagnostic Aids: An intermittent cam reference signal can be caused by poor connections, cracked sensor or internal engine problem.

DTC 17

CAMSHAFT POSITION SENSOR CIRCUIT ERROR 3100 (VIN M) "W" CARLINE (SFI)

(1)
- IF ENGINE CRANKS BUT WON'T RUN, USE CHART A-3.
- INSTALL TECH 1 SCAN TOOL.
- IGNITION "ON" ENGINE IDLING. TECH 1 SCAN TOOL SHOULD DISPLAY CAM SIGNAL PULSES CONSTANTLY CHANGING "0" TO "1". DOES IT?

YES

DTC 17 IS INTERMITTENT. REFER TO "DIAGNOSTIC AIDS" ON FACING PAGE.

NO

- IGNITION "OFF."
- DISCONNECT PCM HARNESS CONNECTOR "C".
- IGNITION "ON."
- PROBE PCM HARNESS PIN "C25" WITH A DVM TO GROUND (SET DVM TO DC VOLTAGE). DOES DVM DISPLAY APPROXIMATE SYSTEM VOLTAGE?

YES

(2)
- WITH KEY IN THE "ON" POSITION, CYCLE IGNITION TO CRANK POSITION MOMENTARILY SEVERAL TIMES WHILE OBSERVING DVM.
- VOLTAGE SHOULD TEMPORARILY DROP TO NEAR ZERO EACH TIME THE CAMSHAFT TIMING MARK ALIGNS WITH THE CAMSHAFT POSITION SENSOR. DOES IT?

NO

- IGNITION "OFF."
- RECONNECT PCM HARNESS CONNECTOR "C".
- DISCONNECT CAM SENSOR 3-WAY HARNESS.
- IGNITION "ON."
- PROBE TERMINAL "C" (PCM HARNESS SIDE) WITH A TEST LIGHT TO BATTERY VOLTAGE. IS TEST LIGHT "ON"?

YES

(3) FAULTY HARNESS CONNECTION OR OPEN CAMSHAFT POSITION SENSOR GROUND WIRE OR FAULTY CAMSHAFT POSITION SENSOR.

NO

OPEN HARNESS GROUND CIRCUIT.

YES

FAULTY PCM CONNECTION OR FAULTY PCM.

NO

- IGNITION "OFF."
- DISCONNECT CAMSHAFT POSITION SENSOR PIGTAIL HARNESS CONNECTOR.
- IGNITION "ON."
- CONNECT DVM BETWEEN TERMINAL "A" (PCM HARNESS SIDE) AND GROUND. DOES DVM DISPLAY APPROXIMATE BATTERY VOLTAGE?

YES

- WITH A FUSED JUMPER, JUMP CAM SENSOR PIGTAIL TERMINAL "A" TO BATTERY VOLTAGE.
- PROBE TERMINAL "B" WITH DVM TO GROUND. DOES DVM DISPLAY APPROXIMATE BATTERY VOLTAGE?

NO

OPEN OR SHORTED CAMSHAFT POSITION SENSOR IGNITION FEED WIRE TO SENSOR OR OPEN OR SHORTED CAMSHAFT POSITION SENSOR PIGTAIL SIGNAL WIRE FROM SENSOR OR FAULTY CAMSHAFT POSITION SENSOR.

YES

FAULTY CAMSHAFT PIGTAIL CONNECTION OR FAULTY PCM CONNECTION OR OPEN CAMSHAFT POSITION SENSOR SIGNAL WIRE TO PCM.

NO

FAULTY HARNESS IGNITION FEED CIRCUIT.

"AFTER REPAIRS," REFER TO DTC CRITERIA ON FACING PAGE AND CONFIRM DTC DOES NOT RESET.

3-9-93
NS 15255

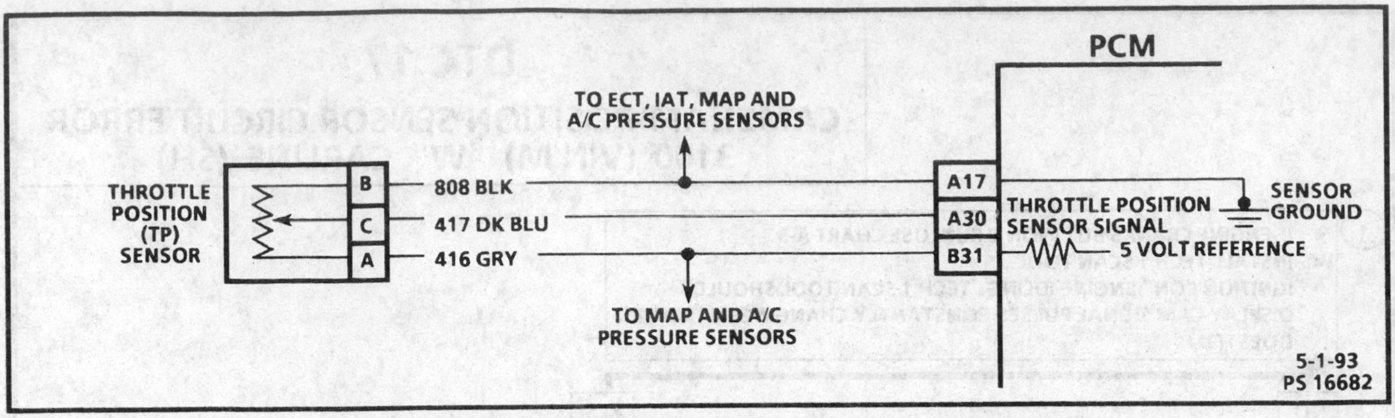
PCM
TO ECT, IAT, MAP AND
A/C PRESSURE SENSORS
THROTTLE
POSITION
(TP)
SENSOR
B
C
A
808 BLK
417 DK BLU
416 GRY
A17
A30
B31
THROTTLE POSITION
SENSOR SIGNAL
SENSOR
GROUND
5 VOLT REFERENCE
TO MAP AND A/C
PRESSURE SENSORS
5-1-93
PS 16682

DTC 21

THROTTLE POSITION (TP) SENSOR CIRCUIT
(SIGNAL VOLTAGE HIGH)
3100 (VIN M) "W" CARLINE (SFI)

Circuit Description:

The Throttle Position (TP) sensor provides a voltage signal to the PCM that increases as the throttle blade angle increases. This signal voltage will vary from approximately .5 volt at idle to 4.8 volts at Wide Open Throttle (WOT). The TP sensor is one of the most important inputs to the PCM for governing fuel control of the engine.

DTC 21 Will Set When: TP sensor voltage is greater than 3.8 volts, engine speed is above 600 RPM, both conditions met for 5 seconds under steady throttle, road load conditions. A gross failure of 4.9 volts applied to the signal circuit will set DTC 21 immediately upon key "ON."

Action Taken (PCM will default to): The PCM will determine fuel and air calculations using calibrated values from a default table. The MIL will become illuminated.

DTC 21 Will Clear When: A current DTC 21 will clear when a high signal voltage above the calibrated threshold is no longer detected. A History DTC 21 will clear after 50 consecutive ignition key cycles without a current DTC 21 being stored.

DTC Chart Test Description: Number(s) below refer to circled number(s) on the diagnostic chart.

1. With throttle closed, the TP sensor should read less than .98 volt. If it doesn't, make sure cruise control and throttle cables are not being held open.
2. With the TP sensor disconnected, the TP sensor voltage should go low, if the PCM and wiring are OK.
3. Probing CKT 808 with a test light checks the 5 volt return circuit. A faulty sensor ground circuit will cause a DTC 21.

Diagnostic Aids: A Tech 1 scan tool reads throttle position in volts. Voltage should increase at a steady rate as throttle is moved toward WOT.

Also some scan tools will read: throttle angle 0% = closed throttle, 100% = WOT.

An open in CKT 808 will result in a DTC 21.

Scan TP sensor while depressing accelerator pedal with engine stopped and ignition "ON." Display should vary from about .5 volt when throttle was closed, to about 4.8 volts when throttle is held at Wide Open Throttle (WOT) position.

Refer to "Intermittents," in "Symptoms," Section "6E3-B".

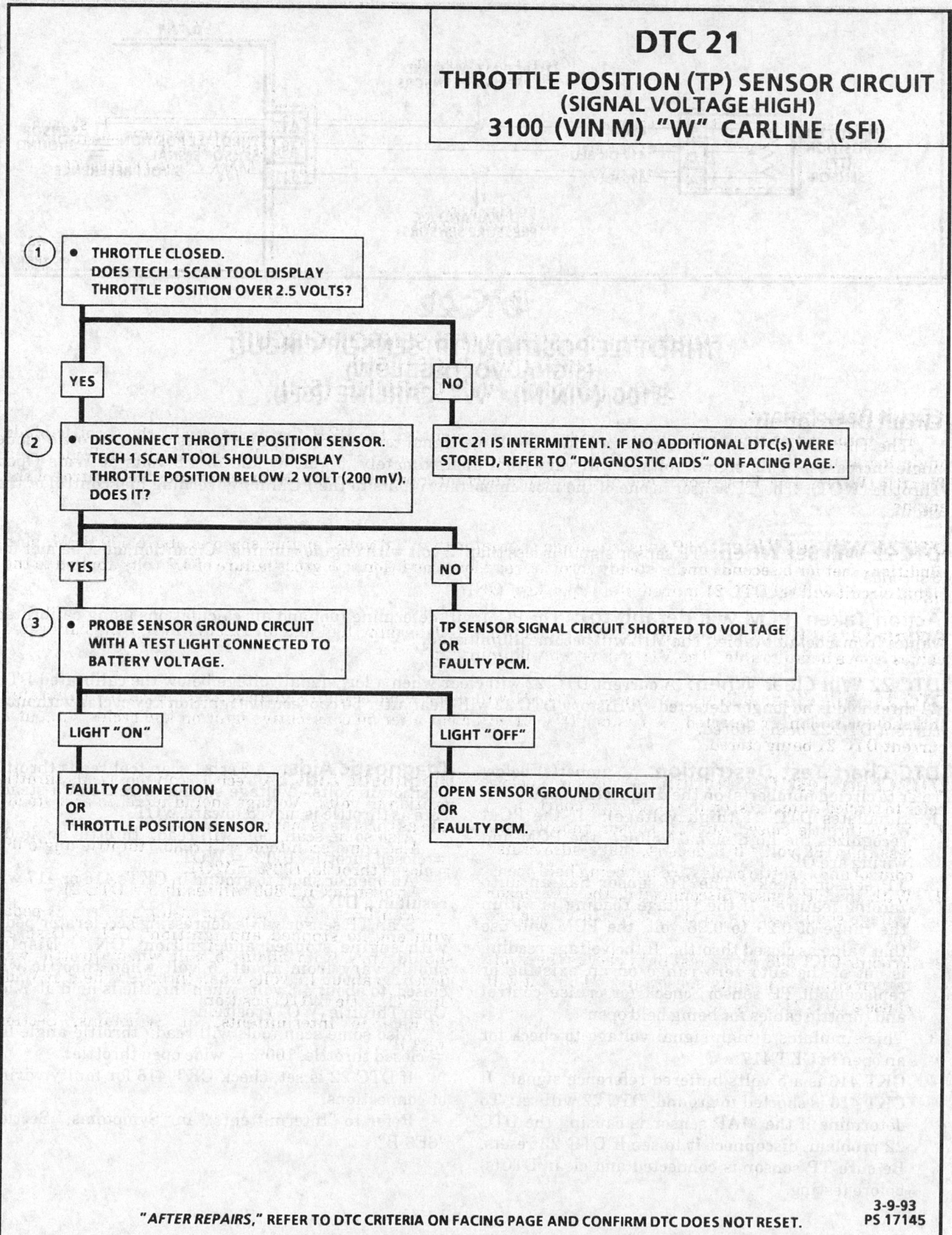

DTC 21

THROTTLE POSITION (TP) SENSOR CIRCUIT
(SIGNAL VOLTAGE HIGH)
3100 (VIN M) "W" CARLINE (SFI)

1. • THROTTLE CLOSED.
   DOES TECH 1 SCAN TOOL DISPLAY THROTTLE POSITION OVER 2.5 VOLTS?

   - YES → go to step 2.
   - NO → DTC 21 IS INTERMITTENT. IF NO ADDITIONAL DTC(s) WERE STORED, REFER TO "DIAGNOSTIC AIDS" ON FACING PAGE.

2. • DISCONNECT THROTTLE POSITION SENSOR.
   TECH 1 SCAN TOOL SHOULD DISPLAY THROTTLE POSITION BELOW .2 VOLT (200 mV).
   DOES IT?

   - YES → go to step 3.
   - NO → TP SENSOR SIGNAL CIRCUIT SHORTED TO VOLTAGE OR FAULTY PCM.

3. • PROBE SENSOR GROUND CIRCUIT WITH A TEST LIGHT CONNECTED TO BATTERY VOLTAGE.

   - LIGHT "ON" → FAULTY CONNECTION OR THROTTLE POSITION SENSOR.
   - LIGHT "OFF" → OPEN SENSOR GROUND CIRCUIT OR FAULTY PCM.

"AFTER REPAIRS," REFER TO DTC CRITERIA ON FACING PAGE AND CONFIRM DTC DOES NOT RESET.

3-9-93
PS 17145

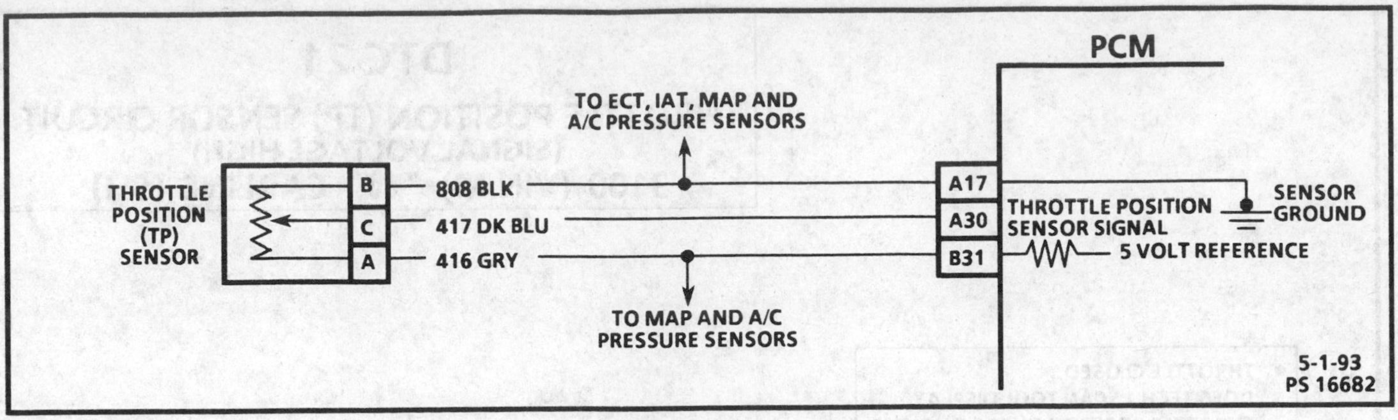
PCM
TO ECT, IAT, MAP AND
A/C PRESSURE SENSORS
THROTTLE
POSITION
(TP)
SENSOR
B
C
A
808 BLK
417 DK BLU
416 GRY
A17
A30
B31
THROTTLE POSITION
SENSOR SIGNAL
SENSOR
GROUND
5 VOLT REFERENCE
TO MAP AND A/C
PRESSURE SENSORS
5-1-93
PS 16682

DTC 22

THROTTLE POSITION (TP) SENSOR CIRCUIT
(SIGNAL VOLTAGE LOW)
3100 (VIN M) "W" CARLINE (SFI)

Circuit Description:

The Throttle Position (TP) sensor provides a voltage signal to the PCM that increases as the throttle blade angle increases. This signal voltage will vary from approximately .5 volt at idle to 4.8 volts at Wide Open Throttle (WOT). The TP sensor is one of the most important inputs to the PCM for governing fuel control of the engine.

DTC 22 Will Set When: TP sensor signal is less than .2 volt with engine running. Condition must be met for 3 seconds.

Action Taken (PCM will default to): The PCM will determine fuel and air calculations using calibrated values from a default table. The MIL will become illuminated.

DTC 22 Will Clear When: A current DTC 22 will clear when a low signal voltage below the calibrated DTC 22 threshold is no longer detected. A History DTC 22 will clear after 50 consecutive ignition key cycles without a current DTC 22 being stored.

DTC Chart Test Description: Number(s) below refer to circled number(s) on the diagnostic chart.

1. Simulates DTC 21 (high voltage): If the PCM recognizes the high signal voltage, the PCM and wiring are OK.
2. TP sensor check: The TP sensor has an auto zeroing feature. If the voltage reading is within the range of 0.29 to 0.98 volt, the PCM will use that value as closed throttle. If the voltage reading is out of the auto zero range on an existing or replacement TP sensor, check for cruise control and throttle cables for being held open.
3. This simulates a high signal voltage to check for an open in CKT 417.
4. CKT 416 is a 5 volts buffered reference signal. If CKT 416 is shorted to ground, DTC 22 will set. To determine if the MAP sensor is causing the DTC 22 problem, disconnect it to see if DTC 22 resets. Be sure TP sensor is connected and clear DTC(s) before testing.

Diagnostic Aids: A Tech 1 scan tool reads throttle position in volts. Voltage should increase at a steady rate as throttle is moved toward WOT.

Also some scan tools will read: throttle angle 0% = closed throttle, 100% = WOT.

An open or short to ground in CKTs 416 or 417 will result in a DTC 22.

Scan TP sensor while depressing accelerator pedal with engine stopped and ignition "ON." Display should vary from about .5 volt when throttle was closed, to about 4.8 volts when throttle is held at Wide Open Throttle (WOT) position.

Also some scan tools will read: throttle angle 0% = closed throttle, 100% = wide open throttle.

If DTC 22 is set, check CKT 416 for faulty wiring or connections.

Refer to "Intermittents," in "Symptoms," Section "6E3-B".

DTC 22
THROTTLE POSITION (TP) SENSOR CIRCUIT
(SIGNAL VOLTAGE LOW)
3100 (VIN M) "W" CARLINE (SFI)

- THROTTLE CLOSED.

DOES TECH 1 SCAN TOOL DISPLAY TP SENSOR .2V (200 mV) OR BELOW?

NO → DTC 22 IS INTERMITTENT. IF NO ADDITIONAL DTCs WERE STORED, REFER TO "DIAGNOSTIC AIDS" ON FACING PAGE.

YES →

(1)
- DISCONNECT TP SENSOR.
- JUMPER HARNESS CKTs 416 AND 417 TOGETHER.

TECH 1 SCAN TOOL SHOULD DISPLAY TP SENSOR OVER 4.0V.
DOES IT?

YES → (2) REFER TO FACING PAGE FOR SPECIFIC INSTRUCTIONS.

NO →

(3)
- PROBE CKT 417 WITH A TEST LIGHT CONNECTED TO 12 VOLTS.

TECH 1 SCAN TOOL SHOULD DISPLAY TP SENSOR OVER 4.0V.
DOES IT?

YES → (4) CKT 416 OPEN, SHORTED TO GROUND. IF OK, IT IS A FAULTY CONNECTION OR FAULTY PCM.

NO → CKT 417 OPEN, SHORTED TO GROUND, FAULTY CONNECTION OR FAULTY PCM.

"AFTER REPAIRS," REFER TO DTC CRITERIA ON FACING PAGE AND CONFIRM DTC DOES NOT RESET.

3-9-93
NS 15387

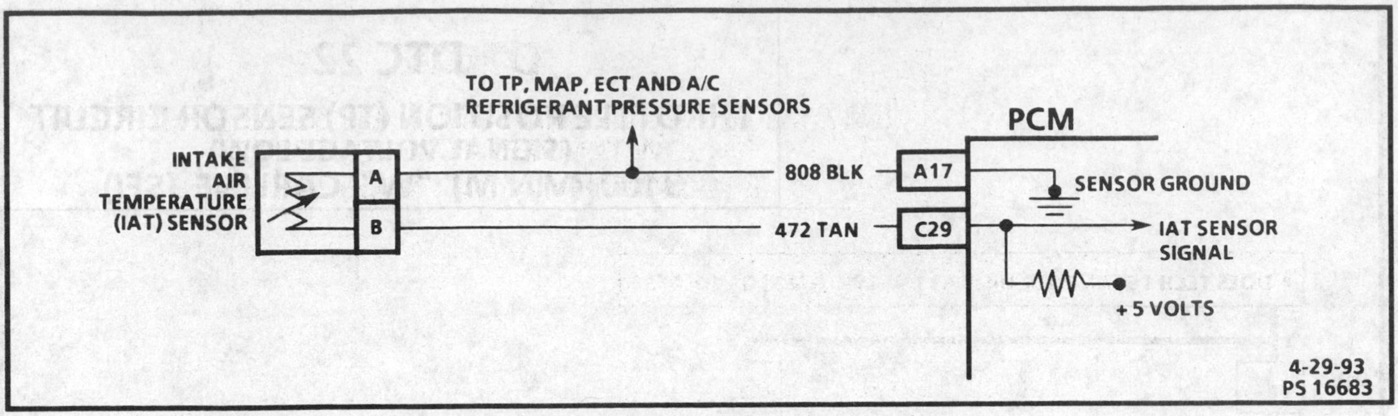
TO TP, MAP, ECT AND A/C
REFRIGERANT PRESSURE SENSORS
PCM
INTAKE
AIR
TEMPERATURE
(IAT) SENSOR
A
B
808 BLK
A17
SENSOR GROUND
472 TAN
C29
IAT SENSOR
SIGNAL
+5 VOLTS
4-29-93
PS 16683

DTC 23

INTAKE AIR TEMPERATURE (IAT) SENSOR CIRCUIT
(LOW TEMPERATURE INDICATED)
3100 (VIN M) "W" CARLINE (SFI)

Circuit Description:

The Intake Air Temperature (IAT) sensor is a thermistor that controls a signal voltage to the PCM. The PCM applies approximately 5 volts to the sensor on CKT 472. When the intake air is cold, the sensor resistance is high, therefore the voltage sensed at the input "C29" is high. If the air is warm, the sensor resistance will be low, and the voltage input to the PCM will be low.

DTC 23 Will Set When: IAT signal indicates a temperature of -35°C (-31°F) or less for greater than 4 minutes.

Action Taken (PCM will default to): The PCM will use an IAT default value of 37°C (108°F) and the MIL will become illuminated.

DTC 23 Will Clear When: A current DTC 23 will clear when the intake air temperature is indicated above the DTC 23 threshold. A History DTC 23 will clear after 50 consecutive ignition key cycles without a current DTC 23 being stored.

DTC Chart Test Description: Number(s) below refer to circled number(s) on the diagnostic chart.

1. A DTC 23 will set due to an open sensor, wire, or connection. This test will determine if the wiring and PCM are OK.
2. This will determine if the signal CKT 472 or the 5 volts return CKT 808 is open.

Diagnostic Aids: A Tech 1 scan tool reads the temperature of the air entering the engine, and should read close to ambient air temperature when the engine is cold. IAT values will rise as underhood temperature increases.

A faulty connection, or an open in CKT 472 or CKT 808 will result in a DTC 23.

DTCs 23 and 34 stored at the same time could be the result of an open CKT 808. A faulty connection could result in intermittent failures. The "Temperature to Resistance Values" scale at the right may be used to test the IAT sensor at various temperature levels to evaluate the possibility of a "shifted" (mis-scaled) sensor. A "slewed" sensor could result in poor driveability complaints.

Refer to "Intermittents," in "Symptoms," Section "6E3-B".

DTC 23

INTAKE AIR TEMPERATURE (IAT) SENSOR CIRCUIT
(LOW TEMPERATURE INDICATED)
3100 (VIN M) "W" CARLINE (SFI)

- DOES TECH 1 SCAN TOOL DISPLAY IAT -37°C (-32°F) OR COLDER?

YES

(1)
- DISCONNECT SENSOR.
- JUMPER HARNESS TERMINALS TOGETHER.
- TECH 1 SCAN TOOL SHOULD DISPLAY TEMPERATURE OVER 140°C (284°F). DOES IT?

  YES

  FAULTY CONNECTION OR SENSOR.

  NO

  (2)
  - JUMPER CKT 472 TO GROUND.
  - TECH 1 SCAN TOOL SHOULD DISPLAY TEMPERATURE OVER 140°C (284°F). DOES IT?

    YES

    OPEN SENSOR GROUND CIRCUIT, FAULTY CONNECTION OR FAULTY PCM.

    NO

    OPEN CKT 472, FAULTY CONNECTION OR FAULTY PCM.

NO

DTC 23 IS INTERMITTENT. IF NO ADDITIONAL DTC(s) WERE STORED, REFER TO "DIAGNOSTIC AIDS" ON FACING PAGE.

DIAGNOSTIC AID

INTAKE AIR TEMPERATURE SENSOR

TEMPERATURE VS. RESISTANCE VALUES (APPROXIMATE)

°C	°F	OHMS
100	212	177
90	194	241
80	176	332
70	158	467
60	140	667
50	122	973
45	113	1188
40	104	1459
35	95	1802
30	86	2238
25	77	2796
20	68	3520
15	59	4450
10	50	5670
5	41	7280
0	32	9420
-5	23	12300
-10	14	16180
-15	5	21450
-20	-4	28680
-30	-22	52700
-40	-40	100700

"*AFTER REPAIRS,*" REFER TO DTC CRITERIA ON FACING PAGE AND CONFIRM DTC DOES NOT RESET.

3-9-93
PS 17146

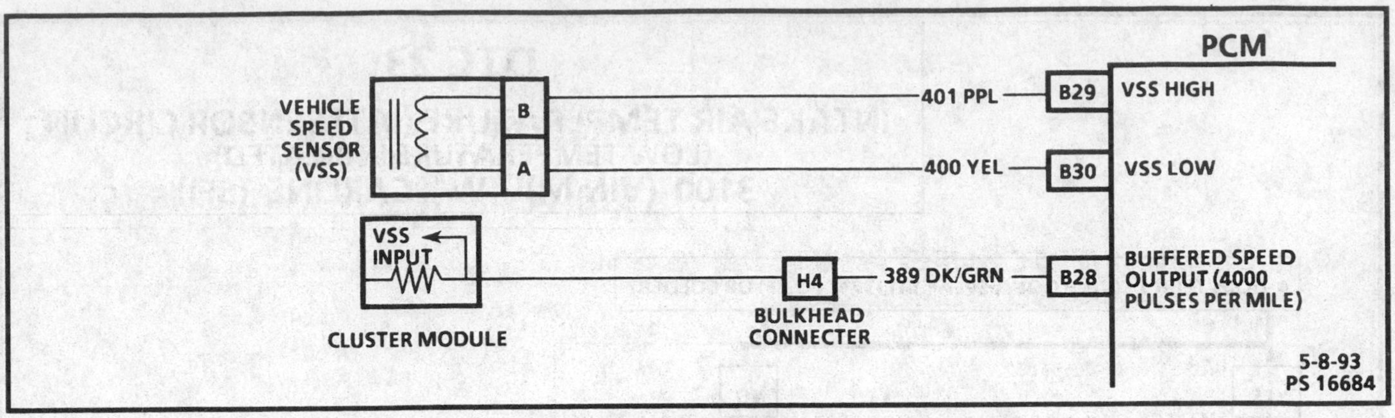
PCM
VEHICLE SPEED SENSOR (VSS)
B
A
401 PPL
B29
VSS HIGH
400 YEL
B30
VSS LOW
VSS INPUT
H4
389 DK/GRN
B28
BUFFERED SPEED OUTPUT (4000 PULSES PER MILE)
BULKHEAD CONNECTER
CLUSTER MODULE
5-8-93
PS 16684

DTC 24

VEHICLE SPEED SENSOR (VSS) CIRCUIT
(NO SIGNAL VOLTAGE)
3100 (VIN M) "W" CARLINE (SFI)

Circuit Description:

A vehicle speed signal is provided to the PCM by the Vehicle Speed Sensor (VSS). This sensor produces a pulsing waveform voltage whenever vehicle speed is greater than 2 mph. The voltage level or amplitude and the frequency of pulses increases with vehicle speed. The PCM conditions this signal and calculates the vehicle speed. The PCM will then supply the signal to the instrument panel (4000 pulses per mile).

DTC 24 Will Set When: DTC 28 is not present, brake is released, engine RPM is greater than 3000, vehicle speed is less than 5 mph with all conditions met for 4 seconds.

Action Taken (PCM will default to): The vehicle will default to 3rd gear and the MIL will become illuminated.

DTC 24 Will Clear When: A current DTC 24 will clear after each ignition key cycle. A History DTC 24 will clear after 50 consecutive ignition key cycles without a current DTC 24 being stored.

DTC Chart Test Description: Number(s) below refer to circled number(s) on the diagnostic chart.

1. Disregard DTC 24 that sets when drive wheels are not turning.
   The sensor only produces a signal if drive wheels are turning faster than 3 mph.
2. If CKTs 400, 401 and 389 are OK, and if the speedometer works properly, DTC 24 is being caused by a faulty PCM, or an incorrect program.

Diagnostic Aids: Tech 1 scan tool should indicate a vehicle speed whenever the drive wheels are turning greater than 3 mph.

A problem in CKT 389 will not affect the VSS input or the readings on a Tech 1 scan tool.

Check CKT 400 and CKT 401 for proper connections to be sure they are clean and tight, and that the harness is routed correctly. Refer to "Intermittents" in "Symptoms," Section "6E3-B".

DTC 24

VEHICLE SPEED SENSOR (VSS) CIRCUIT
(NO SIGNAL VOLTAGE)
3100 (VIN M) "W" CARLINE (SFI)

DISREGARD DTC 24 IF SET WHILE DRIVE WHEELS ARE NOT TURNING.

(1)
- RAISE DRIVE WHEELS.
- **NOTICE:** DO NOT PERFORM THIS TEST WITHOUT SUPPORTING THE LOWER CONTROL ARMS SO THAT THE DRIVE AXLES ARE IN A NORMAL HORIZONTAL POSITION. RUNNING THE VEHICLE IN GEAR WITH THE WHEELS HANGING DOWN AT FULL TRAVEL MAY DAMAGE THE DRIVE AXLES.
- WITH ENGINE IDLING IN GEAR, TECH 1 SCAN TOOL SHOULD DISPLAY VEHICLE SPEED ABOVE 0.
  DOES IT?

NO → DOES SPEEDOMETER DISPLAY SPEED CORRECTLY?

YES → DTC 24 IS INTERMITTENT. IF NO ADDITIONAL DTC(s) WERE STORED, REFER TO "DIAGNOSTIC AIDS" ON FACING PAGE.

DOES SPEEDOMETER DISPLAY SPEED CORRECTLY?

NO →
- IGNITION "OFF."
- DISCONNECT VSS HARNESS CONNECTOR AT TRANSAXLE.
- CONNECT SIGNAL GENERATOR TESTER J 33431-B OR EQUIVALENT TO VSS HARNESS CONNECTOR.
- IGNITION "ON," SIGNAL GENERATOR TESTER "ON" AND SET TO GENERATE A VSS SIGNAL.
- TECH 1 SCAN TOOL SHOULD DISPLAY VEHICLE SPEED ABOVE 0.
  DOES IT?

YES → **(2)** REPROGRAM THE PCM. IF DTC 24 IS STILL PRESENT, REPLACE PCM.

TECH 1 SCAN TOOL SHOULD DISPLAY VEHICLE SPEED ABOVE 0. DOES IT?

NO → CKT 400 OR 401 OPEN, SHORTED TO GROUND, SHORTED TOGETHER, FAULTY CONNECTIONS, OR FAULTY PCM.

YES → REPLACE VEHICLE SPEED SENSOR.

8-18-93
PS 17147

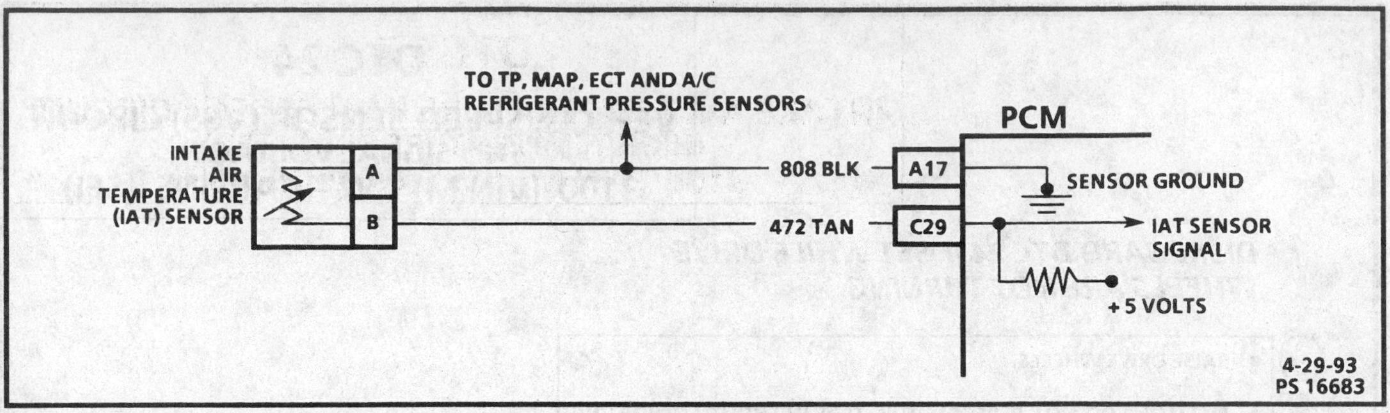
TO TP, MAP, ECT AND A/C
REFRIGERANT PRESSURE SENSORS
PCM
INTAKE
AIR
TEMPERATURE
(IAT) SENSOR
A
B
808 BLK
A17
SENSOR GROUND
472 TAN
C29
IAT SENSOR
SIGNAL
+5 VOLTS
4-29-93
PS 16683

DTC 25

INTAKE AIR TEMPERATURE (IAT) SENSOR CIRCUIT
(HIGH TEMPERATURE INDICATED)
3100 (VIN M) "W" CARLINE (SFI)

Circuit Description:

The Intake Air Temperature (IAT) sensor is a thermistor that controls a signal voltage to the PCM. The PCM applies approximately 5 volts to the sensor on CKT 472. When the intake air is cold, the sensor resistance is high, therefore the voltage sensed at the input "C29" is high. If the air is warm, the sensor resistance will be low, and the voltage input to the PCM will be low.

DTC 25 Will Set When: Vehicle speed is greater than 1 mph and intake air temperature indicates 145°C (297°F) for 5 seconds.

Action Taken (PCM will default to): The PCM will use an IAT default value of 37°C (108°F) and the MIL will become illuminated.

DTC 25 Will Clear When: A current DTC 25 will clear when the intake air temperature is indicated below the high temperature threshold. A History DTC 25 will clear after 50 consecutive ignition key cycles without a current DTC 25 being stored.

DTC Chart Test Description: Number(s) below refer to circled number(s) on the diagnostic chart.

1. This test is a verification that the DTC is not intermittent.
2. This test helps determine between a circuit fault and a faulty sensor.

Diagnostic Aids: A Tech 1 scan tool reads the temperature of the air entering the engine and should read close to ambient air temperature when engine is cold. IAT values will rises as underhood temperature increases.

A short to ground in CKT 472 will result in a DTC 25.

The "Temperature to Resistance Values" scale at the right may be used to test the IAT sensor at various temperature levels to evaluate the possibility of a "shifted" (mis-scaled) sensor. A "slewed" sensor could result in poor driveability complaints.

Refer to "Intermittents," in "Symptoms," Section "6E3-B".

DTC 25

INTAKE AIR TEMPERATURE (IAT) SENSOR CIRCUIT

(HIGH TEMPERATURE INDICATED)

3100 (VIN M) "W" CARLINE (SFI)

1. DOES TECH 1 SCAN TOOL DISPLAY IAT OF 145°C (293°F) OR HOTTER?

   - YES → go to step 2.
   - NO → DTC 25 IS INTERMITTENT. IF NO ADDITIONAL DTC(s) WERE STORED, REFER TO "DIAGNOSTIC AIDS" ON FACING PAGE.

2. • DISCONNECT SENSOR.
   TECH 1 SCAN TOOL SHOULD DISPLAY TEMPERATURE BELOW -30°C (-22°F).
   DOES IT?

   - YES → REPLACE SENSOR.
   - NO → CKT 472 SHORTED TO GROUND OR TO SENSOR GROUND OR PCM IS FAULTY.

DIAGNOSTIC AID

INTAKE AIR TEMPERATURE SENSOR

TEMPERATURE VS. RESISTANCE VALUES (APPROXIMATE)

°C	°F	OHMS
100	212	177
90	194	241
80	176	332
70	158	467
60	140	667
50	122	973
45	113	1188
40	104	1459
35	95	1802
30	86	2238
25	77	2796
20	68	3520
15	59	4450
10	50	5670
5	41	7280
0	32	9420
-5	23	12300
-10	14	16180
-15	5	21450
-20	-4	28680
-30	-22	52700
-40	-40	100700

"*AFTER REPAIRS,*" REFER TO DTC CRITERIA ON FACING PAGE AND CONFIRM DTC DOES NOT RESET.

3-8-93
PS 17148

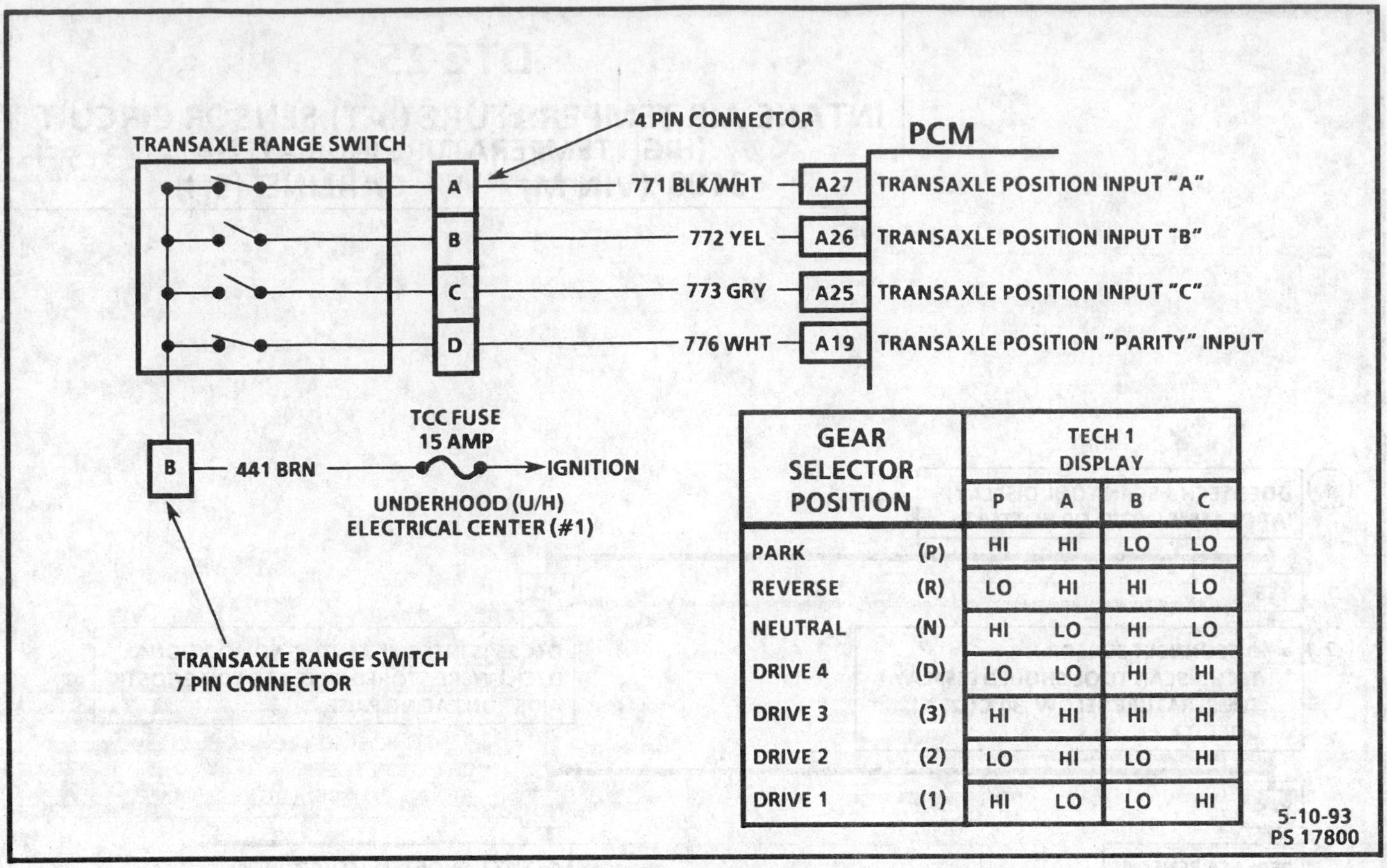
TRANSAXLE RANGE SWITCH
4 PIN CONNECTOR
PCM
A
B
C
D
771 BLK/WHT
772 YEL
773 GRY
776 WHT
A27
A26
A25
A19
TRANSAXLE POSITION INPUT "A"
TRANSAXLE POSITION INPUT "B"
TRANSAXLE POSITION INPUT "C"
TRANSAXLE POSITION "PARITY" INPUT
TCC FUSE
15 AMP
B
441 BRN
IGNITION
UNDERHOOD (U/H)
ELECTRICAL CENTER (#1)
TRANSAXLE RANGE SWITCH
7 PIN CONNECTOR
5-10-93
PS 17800

GEAR SELECTOR POSITION		TECH 1 DISPLAY			
		P	A	B	C
PARK	(P)	HI	HI	LO	LO
REVERSE	(R)	LO	HI	HI	LO
NEUTRAL	(N)	HI	LO	HI	LO
DRIVE 4	(D)	LO	LO	HI	HI
DRIVE 3	(3)	HI	HI	HI	HI
DRIVE 2	(2)	LO	HI	LO	HI
DRIVE 1	(1)	HI	LO	LO	HI

DTC 28

TRANS RANGE SWITCH ERROR
3100 (VIN M) "W" CARLINE (SFI)

Circuit Description:

The transaxle range switch is a multiple signal switch that sends gear selector position information to the PCM. The PCM can decode what gear has been selected from a table. This is important to maintain idle quality when shifting for "Park" to "Drive," as well as for maintaining correct TCC engagement points.

DTC 28 Will Set When: The PCM indicates an incorrect combination of lows and highs from the transaxle range switch input for more than 10 seconds.

Action Taken (PCM will default to): When a DTC 28 is present, the PCM will default the transaxle to 3rd gear, until a correct combination is indicated by the PCM. Therefore, some gear select positions may not be possible until the fault is repaired.

DTC 28 Will Clear When: A current DTC 28 will clear after each ignition key cycle. A History DTC 28 will clear after 50 consecutive ignition key cycles without a current DTC 28 being stored.

DTC Chart Test Description: Number(s) below refer to circled number(s) on the diagnostic chart.

1. & 2. These steps check for proper operation of the transmission range switch.
3. This test checks for an open or grounded or shorted to B+ circuit.

Diagnostic Aids: An intermittent may be caused by a poor connection, chaffed wire insulation or a wire broken inside the insulation.

Check for:

- Poor connection or damaged harness. Inspect PCM harness connectors for backed out terminals, improper mating, broken locks, improperly formed or damaged terminals, poor terminal to wire connection and damaged harness.
- Intermittent test. Monitor a Tech 1 while moving related connectors and wiring harness. If the failure is induced, the scan data will change from low to high or high to low. This may help to isolate the location of the malfunction.

DTC 28

TRANS RANGE SWITCH ERROR
3100 (VIN M) "W" CARLINE (SFI)

1
- INSTALL TECH 1.
- KEY "ON," ENGINE "OFF." TRANS. IN "PARK."
- OBSERVE "PRNDL" DISPLAY.
- DISPLAY SHOULD BE:

P	A
HIGH	HIGH
B	C
LOW	LOW

IS IT?

NO → ARE ALL "LOW"?

- **YES** → OPEN CKT 441 OR PRNDL INPUT HARNESS DISCONNECTED OR FAULTY TRANSMISSION RANGE SWITCH OR FAULTY PCM.
- **NO** → ARE ALL "HIGH"?
  - **YES** → DISCONNECT PCM CONNECTOR A. ARE ALL "HIGH"?
    - **YES** → FAULTY PCM.
    - **NO** → PRNDL INPUT WIRES SHORTED TO B + OR FAULTY TRANSMISSION RANGE SWITCH.
  - **NO** → **3** SHIFT TRANS. FROM PARK TO (D) AND REPAIR CIRCUIT FOR DISPLAY WHICH DOES NOT CHANGE.
    - P - CKT 776
    - A - CKT 771
    - B - CKT 772
    - C - CKT 773

    AN OPEN/GROUNDED CIRCUIT = LOW ALL THE TIME.
    A CIRCUIT SHORTED TO B + = HIGH ALL THE TIME.

YES → **2** COMPARE TECH 1 DISPLAY IN EACH GEAR SELECT POSITION TO THE CORRESPONDING CHART ON THE FACING PAGE. ARE ALL COMBINATIONS CORRECT?

- **NO** → COMPARE THE WIRES IN THE 4 WIRE CONNECTOR ON THE TRANSAXLE TO THE FIGURE ON THE FACING PAGE TO CHECK FOR CROSSED WIRES. IF OK, CHECK FOR AN OPEN CIRCUIT OR A SHORT TO GROUND IN THE CIRCUIT WHICH CAUSES THE INCORRECT COMBINATION.
- **YES** → NO TROUBLE FOUND. REFER TO "DIAGNOSTIC AIDS" ON THE FACING PAGE.

"AFTER REPAIRS," REFER TO DTC CRITERIA ON FACING PAGE AND CONFIRM DTC DOES NOT RESET.

5-1-93
PS 17149

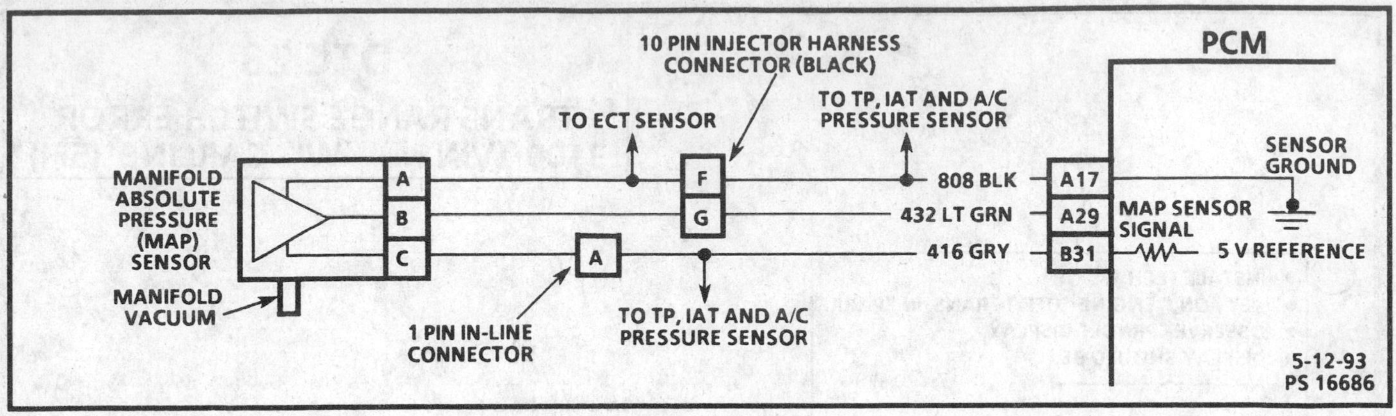
10 PIN INJECTOR HARNESS CONNECTOR (BLACK)
PCM
TO ECT SENSOR
TO TP, IAT AND A/C PRESSURE SENSOR
SENSOR GROUND
MANIFOLD ABSOLUTE PRESSURE (MAP) SENSOR
A
B
C
F
G
A
808 BLK
432 LT GRN
416 GRY
A17
A29
B31
MAP SENSOR SIGNAL
5 V REFERENCE
MANIFOLD VACUUM
1 PIN IN-LINE CONNECTOR
TO TP, IAT AND A/C PRESSURE SENSOR
5-12-93
PS 16686

DTC 33

MANIFOLD ABSOLUTE PRESSURE (MAP) SENSOR CIRCUIT
(SIGNAL VOLTAGE HIGH - HIGH MAP)
3100 (VIN M) "W" CARLINE (SFI)

Circuit Description:

The Manifold Absolute Pressure (MAP) sensor responds to changes in the intake manifold pressure. MAP is the inverse of vacuum, so as MAP increases such as during WOT, vacuum decreases.

The MAP sensor should indicate approximately 1-2 volts at idle, and between 4 and 5 volts at Wide Open Throttle (WOT). MAP is one of the most important inputs for calculating fuel delivery.

DTC 33 Will Set When: No current DTC 21 or 22 is present, MAP is greater than 84 kPa (A/C "OFF") 87 kPa (A/C "ON"), throttle angle is between 3% and 30% and held steady. All conditions met for 4 seconds.

Action Taken (PCM will default to): A default table of MAP values will be used by the PCM to calculate air flow. The MIL will become illuminated and MAP values on the Tech 1 will become maximum (5 volts).

DTC 33 Will Clear When: A current DTC 33 will clear when the MAP value falls below the calibrated high MAP threshold. A History DTC 33 will clear after 50 consecutive key cycles without a current DTC 33 being stored.

DTC Chart Test Description: Number(s) below refer to circled number(s) on the diagnostic chart.

1. Engine misfire or a low unstable idle may set DTC 33.
2. With the MAP sensor disconnected, the PCM should see a low voltage if the PCM and wiring are OK.

Diagnostic Aids: If idle is rough or unstable, refer to "Symptoms," Section "6E3-B" for items which can cause an unstable idle.

An open in CKT 808 or the connection will result in a DTC 33.

With the ignition "ON" and engine stopped, the manifold pressure is equal to atmospheric pressure and the signal voltage will be high. This information is used by the PCM as an indication of vehicle altitude. Comparison of this reading with a known good vehicle with the same sensor is a good way to check accuracy of a "suspect" sensor. Readings should be the same ± .4 volt.

- Check all connections.

Important

- Make sure electrical connector remains securely fastened.

- Disconnect sensor from bracket and twist sensor (by hand only) to check for intermittent connections. Output changes greater than .1 volt indicates a bad connector or connections. If OK, replace sensor.
- Refer to CHART C-1D, "MAP Sensor Voltage Output Check" for further diagnosis.

Refer to "Intermittents," in "Symptoms," Section "6E3-B".

DTC 33

MANIFOLD ABSOLUTE PRESSURE (MAP) SENSOR CIRCUIT
(SIGNAL VOLTAGE HIGH - HIGH MAP)
3100 (VIN M) "W" CARLINE (SFI)

(1)
- IF ENGINE IDLE IS ROUGH, UNSTABLE OR INCORRECT, CORRECT BEFORE USING CHART. REFER TO "SYMPTOMS," SECTION "B".
- ENGINE IDLING.

DOES TECH 1 SCAN TOOL DISPLAY A MAP OF 3.75 VOLTS OR OVER?

- **NO:** DTC 33 IS INTERMITTENT. IF NO ADDITIONAL DTC(s) WERE STORED, REFER TO "DIAGNOSTIC AIDS" ON FACING PAGE.
- **YES:**

(2)
- IGNITION "OFF."
- DISCONNECT MAP SENSOR ELECTRICAL CONNECTOR.
- IGNITION "ON."
- TECH 1 SCAN TOOL SHOULD READ A VOLTAGE OF 1 VOLT OR LESS.

DOES IT?

- **NO:** CKT 432 SHORTED TO VOLTAGE, SHORTED TO CKT 416 OR FAULTY PCM.
- **YES:**

- PROBE CKT 808 WITH A TEST LIGHT TO 12 VOLTS.
- TEST LIGHT SHOULD LIGHT.

DOES IT?

- **YES:** PLUGGED OR LEAKING SENSOR VACUUM HOSE OR FAULTY MAP SENSOR.
- **NO:** OPEN CKT 808.

"AFTER REPAIRS," REFER TO DTC CRITERIA ON FACING PAGE AND CONFIRM DTC DOES NOT RESET.

3-8-93
NS 15355

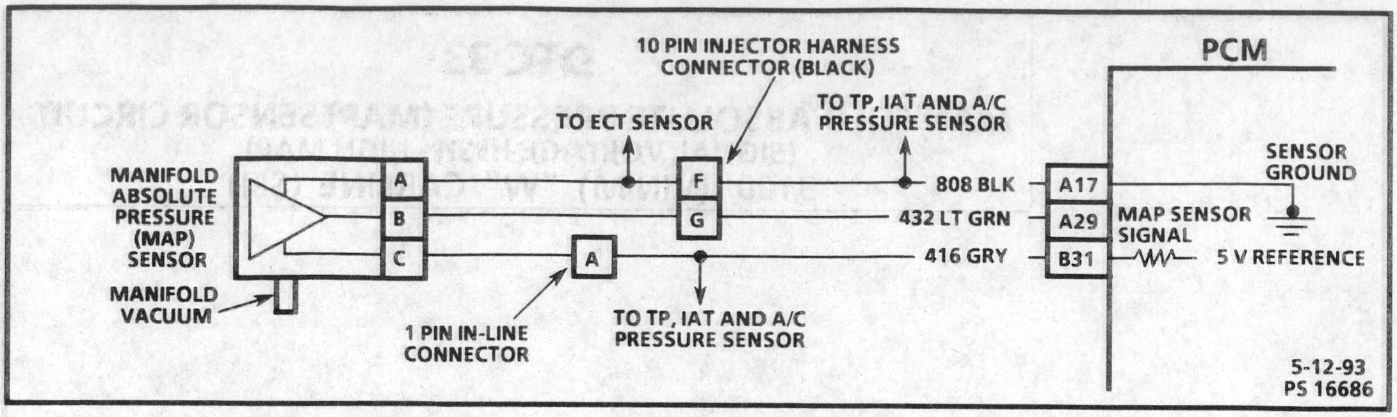
10 PIN INJECTOR HARNESS CONNECTOR (BLACK)
PCM
TO ECT SENSOR
TO TP, IAT AND A/C PRESSURE SENSOR
SENSOR GROUND
MANIFOLD ABSOLUTE PRESSURE (MAP) SENSOR
A
B
C
F
G
808 BLK
432 LT GRN
416 GRY
A17
A29
B31
MAP SENSOR SIGNAL
5 V REFERENCE
MANIFOLD VACUUM
A
1 PIN IN-LINE CONNECTOR
TO TP, IAT AND A/C PRESSURE SENSOR
5-12-93
PS 16686

DTC 34

MANIFOLD ABSOLUTE PRESSURE (MAP) SENSOR CIRCUIT
(SIGNAL VOLTAGE LOW - LOW MAP)
3100 (VIN M) "W" CARLINE (SFI)

Circuit Description:

The Manifold Absolute Pressure (MAP) sensor responds to changes in intake manifold pressure. MAP is the inverse of vacuum, so as MAP increases such as during WOT, vacuum decreases.

The MAP sensor should indicate approximately 1-2 volts at idle, and between 4 and 5 volts at Wide Open Throttle (WOT). MAP is one of the most important inputs for calculating fuel delivery.

DTC 34 Will Set When: Engine speed is greater than 500 RPM, throttle angle is greater than 3% and MAP is less than 11 kPa. All conditions must be met for 3 seconds.

Action Taken (PCM will default to): A default table of MAP values will be used by the PCM to calculate air flow. The MIL will become illuminated and MAP values on the Tech 1 will become minimum (11 kPa).

DTC 34 Will Clear When: A current DTC 34 will clear when the MAP value exceeds the minimum low MAP threshold value. A History DTC 34 will clear after 50 consecutive ignition key cycles without a current DTC 34 being stored.

DTC Chart Test Description: Number(s) below refer to circled number(s) on the diagnostic chart.

1. This test is to see if the sensor is at fault for the low voltage or if there is a PCM or wiring problem.
2. This simulates a high signal voltage to check for an open in CKT 432. If the test light is bright during this test, CKT 432 is probably shorted to ground. If Tech 1 scan tool reads over 4 volts at this test, CKT 416 can be checked by measuring the voltage at terminal "C" (should be 5 volts).

Diagnostic Aids: An intermittent open in CKT 432 or CKT 416 will result in a DTC 34.

With the ignition "ON" and engine stopped, the manifold pressure is equal to atmospheric pressure and the signal voltage will be high. This information is used by the PCM as an indication of vehicle altitude. Comparison of this reading with a known good vehicle with the same sensor is a good way to check accuracy of a "suspect" sensor. Readings should be the same ± .4 volt.

- Check all connections.

Important

- Make sure electrical connector remains securely fastened.

- Disconnect sensor from bracket and twist sensor (by hand only) to check for intermittent connections. Output changes greater than .1 volt indicates a bad connector or connections. If OK, replace sensor.
- Refer to CHART C-1D, "MAP Sensor Voltage Output Check" for further diagnosis.

Refer to "Intermittents," in "Symptoms," Section "6E3-B".

DTC 34

MANIFOLD ABSOLUTE PRESSURE (MAP) SENSOR CIRCUIT
(SIGNAL VOLTAGE LOW - LOW MAP)
3100 (VIN M) "W" CARLINE (SFI)

(1)
- IGNITION "OFF" FOR 10 SECONDS.
- START ENGINE AND IMMEDIATELY NOTE MAP VALUE ON TECH 1 SCAN TOOL.

DOES SCAN DISPLAY MAP BELOW .25 VOLT?

NO: DTC 34 IS INTERMITTENT. IF NO ADDITIONAL DTC(s) WERE STORED, REFER TO "DIAGNOSTIC AIDS" ON FACING PAGE.

YES:
- IGNITION "OFF."
- DISCONNECT SENSOR ELECTRICAL CONNECTOR.
- JUMPER HARNESS TERMINALS "B" TO "C".
- IGNITION "ON."

DOES MAP VOLTAGE READ OVER 4 VOLTS?

YES: FAULTY CONNECTION OR SENSOR.

NO:

(2)
- IGNITION "OFF."
- REMOVE JUMPER WIRE.
- PROBE TERMINAL "B" (CKT 432) WITH A LIGHT TO 12 VOLTS.
- IGNITION "ON."

DOES TECH 1 SCAN TOOL READ OVER 4 VOLTS?

YES: CKT 416 OPEN OR SHORTED TO GROUND OR FAULTY PCM.

NO: CKT 432 OPEN OR SHORTED TO GROUND OR FAULTY PCM.

"AFTER REPAIRS," REFER TO DTC CRITERIA ON FACING PAGE AND CONFIRM DTC DOES NOT RESET.

3-25-93
NS 15386

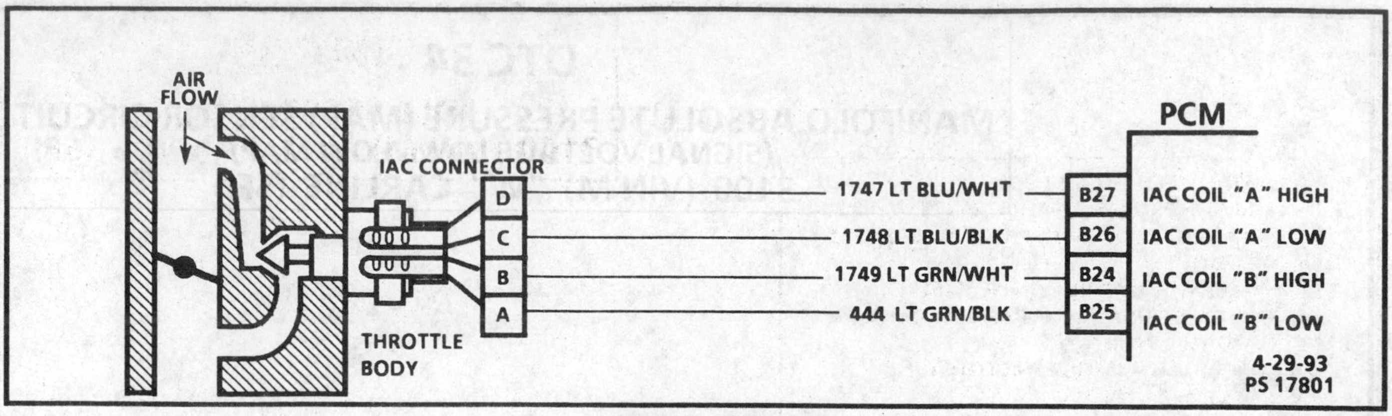
AIR FLOW
IAC CONNECTOR
D
C
B
A
THROTTLE BODY
1747 LT BLU/WHT
1748 LT BLU/BLK
1749 LT GRN/WHT
444 LT GRN/BLK
PCM
B27
B26
B24
B25
IAC COIL "A" HIGH
IAC COIL "A" LOW
IAC COIL "B" HIGH
IAC COIL "B" LOW
4-29-93
PS 17801

DTC 35
IDLE SPEED ERROR
3100 (VIN M) "W" CARLINE (SFI)

Circuit Description:

The IAC motor will constantly adjust its valve position to maintain the desired idle speed. If idle speed is below the desired idle, the valve will open to allow more air flow and increase RPM. If the idle is too high, the IAC will slowly close to limit air flow and therefore engine RPM will decrease. If engine RPM becomes out of control for a long enough period, then a DTC 35 will be set. Review the "General Description" of the IAC operation in "Fuel Metering System," Section "6E3-C2".

DTC 35 Will Set When: DTC 24 is not present. Power steering is not cramped. Closed throttle engine speed is 350 RPM above or below desired idle for 50 seconds.

Action Taken (PCM will default to): The PCM will turn the MIL "ON" and set a DTC 35. The RPM will remain controlling erratically until the problem is corrected.

DTC 35 Will Clear When: A current DTC 35 will clear when the engine speed controls within a 350 RPM range of desired idle. A History DTC 35 will clear after 50 consecutive ignition key cycles without a current DTC 35 being stored.

DTC Chart Test Description: Number(s) below refer to circled number(s) on the diagnostic chart.

1. The Tech 1 RPM control mode is used to extend and retract the IAC valve. The valve should move smoothly within the specified range. If the idle speed is commanded (IAC extended) too low (below 700 RPM), the engine may stall. This may be normal and would not indicate a problem. Retracting the IAC beyond its controlled range (above 1500 RPM) will cause a delay before the RPMs start dropping. This too is normal.
2. This test uses the Tech 1 scan tool to command the IAC controlled idle speed. The PCM issues commands to obtain commanded idle speed. The node lights each should flash red and green to indicate a good circuit as the PCM issues commands. While the sequence of color is not important if either light is "OFF" or does not flash red and green, check the circuits for faults beginning with poor terminal contacts.

Diagnostic Aids: A slow, unstable, or fast idle may be caused by a non-IAC system problem that cannot be overcome by the IAC valve. Out of range IAC counts will be above 60 if idle is too low and zero counts if idle is too high. If idle speed is above 600-700 RPM in drive with an A/T, locate and correct vacuum leak. If RPM is below spec., check for foreign material around throttle plates. Refer to "Fuel Metering System," Section "6E3-C2". The following checks should be made to repair a non-IAC system problem.

- Vacuum leak (high idle). If idle is too high, stop the engine. Fully extend IAC with tester. Start engine. If idle speed is above 800 RPM, locate and correct vacuum leak including crankcase ventilation system. Also check for binding of throttle blade or linkage.
- System too lean (high air/fuel ratio). The idle speed may be too high or too low. Engine speed may vary up and down and disconnecting the IAC valve does not help. DTC 44 may set. Tech 1 HO2S voltage will be less than 300 mV (.3 volt). Check for low regulated fuel pressure, water in the fuel or a restricted injector.
- System too rich (low air/fuel ratio). The idle speed will be too low. Tech 1 IAC counts will usually be above 80. System is obviously rich and may exhibit black smoke in exhaust. DTC 45 may set. Tech 1 scan tool HO2S voltage will be fixed above 800 mV (.8 volt).
  Check for high fuel pressure, leaking or sticking injector. Silicone contaminated HO2S will cause sluggish voltage variations on Tech 1 scan tool.
- Throttle body. Remove IAC valve and inspect bore for foreign material.
- IAC valve electrical connections. IAC valve connections should be carefully checked for proper contact.
- Crankcase ventilation valve. An incorrect or faulty valve may result in an incorrect idle speed.
- Refer to "Rough, Unstable, Incorrect Idle, or Stalling," in "Symptoms," Section "6E3-B".
- If intermittent poor driveability or idle symptoms are resolved by disconnecting the IAC, carefully recheck connections, valve terminal resistance, or replace IAC.
- A/C compressor or relay failure. Refer to CHART C-10 if the A/C control relay drive circuit is shorted to ground or if the relay is faulty, an idle problem may exist.
- If above are OK, see "Rough, Unstable, Incorrect Idle, or Stalling," in "Symptoms," Section "6E3-B".

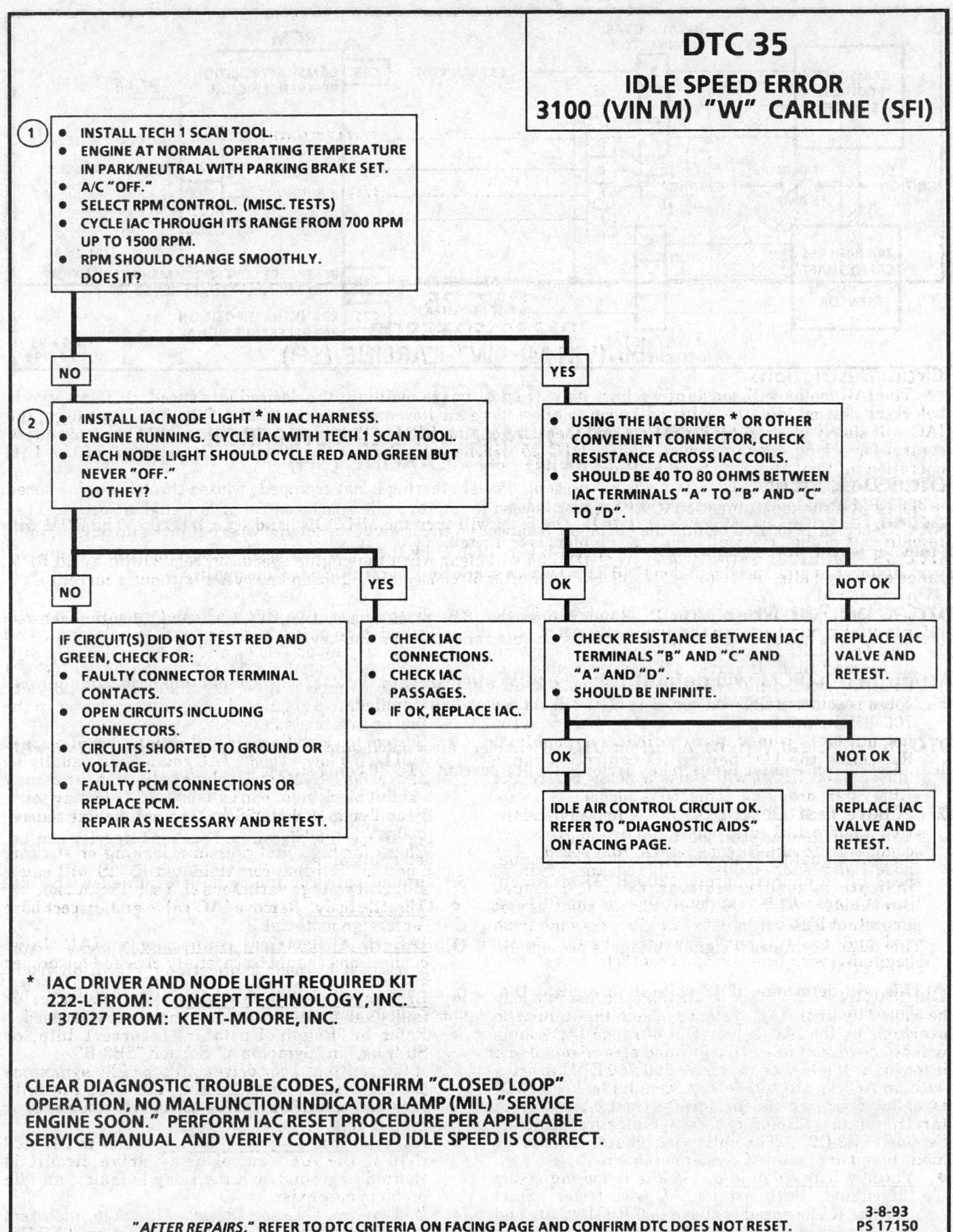

DTC 35
IDLE SPEED ERROR
3100 (VIN M) "W" CARLINE (SFI)

(1)
- INSTALL TECH 1 SCAN TOOL.
- ENGINE AT NORMAL OPERATING TEMPERATURE IN PARK/NEUTRAL WITH PARKING BRAKE SET.
- A/C "OFF."
- SELECT RPM CONTROL. (MISC. TESTS)
- CYCLE IAC THROUGH ITS RANGE FROM 700 RPM UP TO 1500 RPM.
- RPM SHOULD CHANGE SMOOTHLY.

DOES IT?

NO

(2)
- INSTALL IAC NODE LIGHT * IN IAC HARNESS.
- ENGINE RUNNING. CYCLE IAC WITH TECH 1 SCAN TOOL.
- EACH NODE LIGHT SHOULD CYCLE RED AND GREEN BUT NEVER "OFF."

DO THEY?

NO

IF CIRCUIT(S) DID NOT TEST RED AND GREEN, CHECK FOR:
- FAULTY CONNECTOR TERMINAL CONTACTS.
- OPEN CIRCUITS INCLUDING CONNECTORS.
- CIRCUITS SHORTED TO GROUND OR VOLTAGE.
- FAULTY PCM CONNECTIONS OR REPLACE PCM.

REPAIR AS NECESSARY AND RETEST.

YES

- CHECK IAC CONNECTIONS.
- CHECK IAC PASSAGES.
- IF OK, REPLACE IAC.

YES (from 1)

- USING THE IAC DRIVER * OR OTHER CONVENIENT CONNECTOR, CHECK RESISTANCE ACROSS IAC COILS.
- SHOULD BE 40 TO 80 OHMS BETWEEN IAC TERMINALS "A" TO "B" AND "C" TO "D".

OK

- CHECK RESISTANCE BETWEEN IAC TERMINALS "B" AND "C" AND "A" AND "D".
- SHOULD BE INFINITE.

OK

IDLE AIR CONTROL CIRCUIT OK. REFER TO "DIAGNOSTIC AIDS" ON FACING PAGE.

NOT OK

REPLACE IAC VALVE AND RETEST.

NOT OK

REPLACE IAC VALVE AND RETEST.

* IAC DRIVER AND NODE LIGHT REQUIRED KIT
222-L FROM: CONCEPT TECHNOLOGY, INC.
J 37027 FROM: KENT-MOORE, INC.

CLEAR DIAGNOSTIC TROUBLE CODES, CONFIRM "CLOSED LOOP" OPERATION, NO MALFUNCTION INDICATOR LAMP (MIL) "SERVICE ENGINE SOON." PERFORM IAC RESET PROCEDURE PER APPLICABLE SERVICE MANUAL AND VERIFY CONTROLLED IDLE SPEED IS CORRECT.

"AFTER REPAIRS," REFER TO DTC CRITERIA ON FACING PAGE AND CONFIRM DTC DOES NOT RESET.

3-8-93
PS 17150

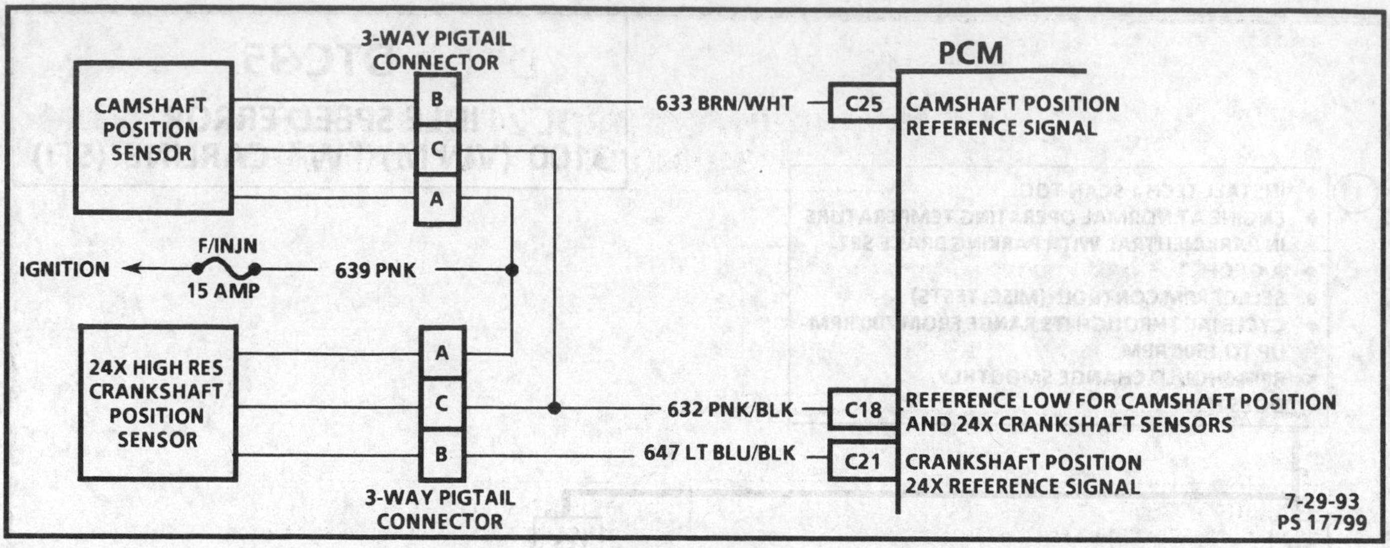
3-WAY PIGTAIL
CONNECTOR
PCM
CAMSHAFT
POSITION
SENSOR
B
C
A
633 BRN/WHT
C25
CAMSHAFT POSITION
REFERENCE SIGNAL
F/INJN
IGNITION
15 AMP
639 PNK
24X HIGH RES
CRANKSHAFT
POSITION
SENSOR
A
C
B
632 PNK/BLK
C18
REFERENCE LOW FOR CAMSHAFT POSITION
AND 24X CRANKSHAFT SENSORS
647 LT BLU/BLK
C21
CRANKSHAFT POSITION
24X REFERENCE SIGNAL
3-WAY PIGTAIL
CONNECTOR
7-29-93
PS 17799

DTC 36

IGNITION CONTROL 24X SIGNAL CIRCUIT ERROR
3100 (VIN M) "W" CARLINE (SFI)

Circuit Description:

The 24X Crankshaft Position (CKP) sensor is used to improve idle spark control at low engine speeds. The 24X CKP sensor is located behind the harmonic balancer on the front of the engine where it picks up pulses from a reluctor wheel on the crankshaft. Its signal is conditioned by the PCM and used to more accurately control spark at lower engine speeds (under 1200 RPM) where spark control is critical for idle quality.

DTC 36 Will Set When: The PCM determines that 6 or more consecutive 24X crankshaft position sensor reference pulses have not occurred. This test is executed once per ignition key cycle immediately after startup.

Action Taken (PCM will default to): The PCM will disregard the 24X sensor input and base timing from the 3X low resolution CKP sensor. The MIL will not become illuminated.

DTC 36 Will Clear When: A current DTC 36 will clear after each ignition key cycle. A History DTC 36 will clear after 50 consecutive ignition key cycles without a current DTC 36 being stored.

DTC Chart Test Description: Number(s) below refer to circled number(s) on the diagnostic chart.

1. The 24X signal RPM should be the same as engine speed up to approximately 1200 RPM at which time it stops. This test determines if the PCM is putting out a 24X signal.
2. This test determines if signal voltage is present up to the PCM.
3. This will determine if 12 volts is present at the sensor input.
4. By applying 12 volts to the 24X crankshaft sensor pigtail circuit, pigtail and sensor integrity can be determined.
5. Ground path continuity is determined with this test.

Diagnostic Aids: An intermittent 24X signal error can be caused by poor connections. Ignition feed, reference low and the signal circuits should all be checked for poor connections.

DTC 36

IGNITION CONTROL 24X SIGNAL CIRCUIT ERROR 3100 (VIN M) "W" CARLINE (SFI)

1
- IF ENGINE CRANKS BUT WON'T RUN, USE CHART A-3.
- INSTALL TECH 1 SCAN TOOL.
- IGNITION "ON" ENGINE IDLING. MONITOR "IGNITION CONTROL 24X SIGNAL."

IS RPM INDICATED?

YES: DTC 36 IS INTERMITTENT. REFER TO "DIAGNOSTIC AIDS" ON FACING PAGE.

NO:

2
- IGNITION "OFF."
- DISCONNECT PCM HARNESS CONNECTOR "C".
- IGNITION "ON."
- PROBE PCM HARNESS PIN "C21" WITH A DVM TO GROUND (SET DVM TO DC VOLTAGE).

DOES DVM DISPLAY APPROXIMATE SYSTEM VOLTAGE?

YES:

5
- IGNITION "OFF."
- RECONNECT PCM HARNESS CONNECTOR "C".
- DISCONNECT 24X SENSOR 3-WAY PIGTAIL HARNESS.
- IGNITION "ON."
- PROBE TERMINAL "C" (PCM HARNESS SIDE) WITH A TEST LIGHT TO BATTERY VOLTAGE.

IS TEST LIGHT "ON"?

YES: FAULTY HARNESS CONNECTION OR OPEN CRANKSHAFT POSITION SENSOR PIGTAIL GROUND WIRE OR FAULTY 24X CRANKSHAFT POSITION SENSOR.

NO: OPEN PCM HARNESS GROUND CIRCUIT OR FAULTY TERMINAL CONNECTION OR FAULTY PCM.

NO:

3
- IGNITION "OFF."
- DISCONNECT 24X CRANKSHAFT POSITION SENSOR PIGTAIL HARNESS CONNECTOR.
- IGNITION "ON."
- CONNECT DVM BETWEEN TERMINAL "A" (PCM HARNESS SIDE) AND GROUND.

DOES DVM DISPLAY APPROXIMATE BATTERY VOLTAGE?

NO: FAULTY HARNESS IGNITION FEED CIRCUIT.

YES:

4
- WITH A FUSED JUMPER, JUMP 24X SENSOR PIGTAIL TERMINAL "A" TO BATTERY VOLTAGE.
- PROBE TERMINAL "B" WITH DVM TO GROUND.

DOES DVM DISPLAY APPROXIMATE BATTERY VOLTAGE?

NO: OPEN OR SHORTED 24X CRANKSHAFT POSITION SENSOR IGNITION FEED PIGTAIL WIRE TO SENSOR OR OPEN OR SHORTED CRANKSHAFT POSITION SENSOR PIGTAIL SIGNAL WIRE FROM SENSOR OR FAULTY CRANKSHAFT POSITION SENSOR.

YES: FAULTY CRANKSHAFT SENSOR PIGTAIL CONNECTION OR FAULTY PCM CONNECTION OR OPEN CRANKSHAFT POSITION SENSOR SIGNAL WIRE TO PCM.

"AFTER REPAIRS," REFER TO DTC CRITERIA ON FACING PAGE AND CONFIRM DTC DOES NOT RESET.

3-9-93
NS 15938

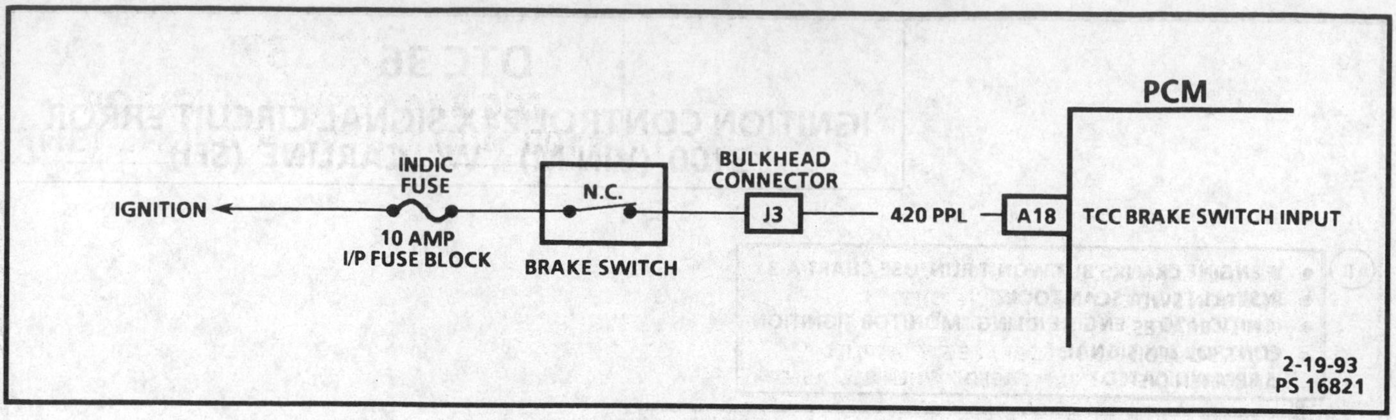
PCM
INDIC
FUSE
BULKHEAD
CONNECTOR
N.C.
IGNITION
J3
420 PPL
A18
TCC BRAKE SWITCH INPUT
10 AMP
I/P FUSE BLOCK
BRAKE SWITCH
2-19-93
PS 16821

DTC 37

TCC BRAKE SWITCH ERROR
3100 (VIN M) "W" CARLINE (SFI)

Circuit Description:

The PCM monitors brake switch activity through PCM terminal "A18". The brake switch is a normally closed switch that opens to interrupt system voltage to the PCM input when the brake pedal is applied.

DTC 37 Will Set When: Vehicle speed is maintained above 35 mph for 10 seconds and back to 0 mph for 4 consecutive times without the PCM sensing a voltage change on CKT 420 (displayed "RELEASED" to "APPLIED" on Tech 1).

Action Taken (PCM will default to): The PCM will not illuminate the MIL. If the switch has failed in an open state, the TCC will not engage.

DTC 37 Will Clear When: A current DTC 37 will clear when the PCM begins detecting "APPLIED" to "RELEASED" transitions. A History DTC 37 will clear after 50 consecutive ignition key cycles without a current DTC 37 being stored.

DTC Chart Test Description: Number(s) below refer to circled number(s) on the diagnostic chart.

1. This test checks for voltage at brake switch.
2. This test simulates brake switch closed or brakes "OFF."
3. This test checks CKT 420 from brake switch to PCM.
4. This test opens CKT 420 and simulates brakes being applied.

Diagnostic Aids: A DTC 37 can be caused by a misadjusted brake switch or a poor connection.

Check customer driving habits and/or unusual traffic conditions (i.e. stop and go expressway traffic).

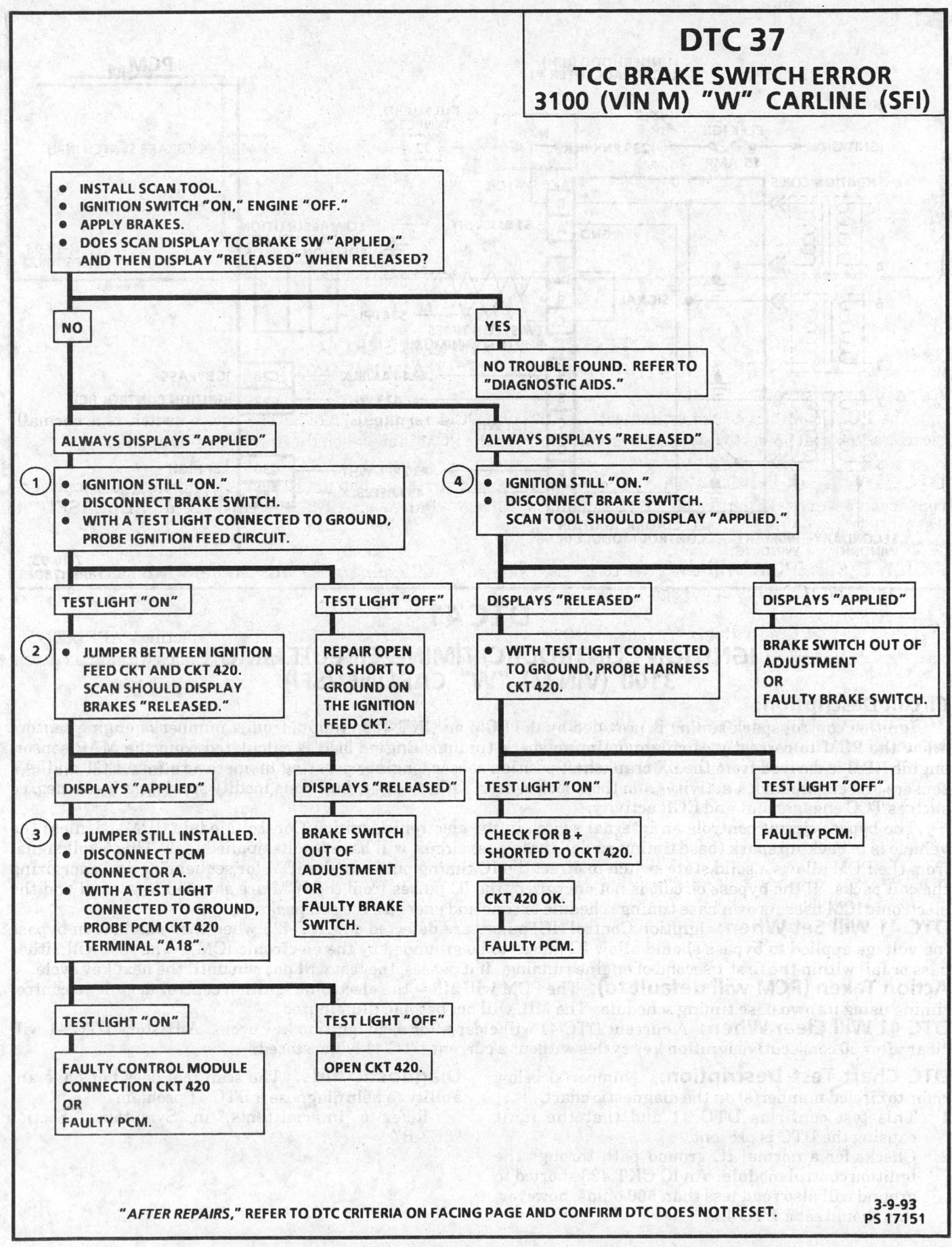

DTC 37

TCC BRAKE SWITCH ERROR
3100 (VIN M) "W" CARLINE (SFI)

- INSTALL SCAN TOOL.
- IGNITION SWITCH "ON," ENGINE "OFF."
- APPLY BRAKES.
- DOES SCAN DISPLAY TCC BRAKE SW "APPLIED," AND THEN DISPLAY "RELEASED" WHEN RELEASED?

NO

ALWAYS DISPLAYS "APPLIED"

(1)
- IGNITION STILL "ON."
- DISCONNECT BRAKE SWITCH.
- WITH A TEST LIGHT CONNECTED TO GROUND, PROBE IGNITION FEED CIRCUIT.

TEST LIGHT "ON"

(2)
- JUMPER BETWEEN IGNITION FEED CKT AND CKT 420. SCAN SHOULD DISPLAY BRAKES "RELEASED."

DISPLAYS "APPLIED"

(3)
- JUMPER STILL INSTALLED.
- DISCONNECT PCM CONNECTOR A.
- WITH A TEST LIGHT CONNECTED TO GROUND, PROBE PCM CKT 420 TERMINAL "A18".

TEST LIGHT "ON"

FAULTY CONTROL MODULE CONNECTION CKT 420 OR FAULTY PCM.

TEST LIGHT "OFF"

OPEN CKT 420.

DISPLAYS "RELEASED"

BRAKE SWITCH OUT OF ADJUSTMENT OR FAULTY BRAKE SWITCH.

TEST LIGHT "OFF"

REPAIR OPEN OR SHORT TO GROUND ON THE IGNITION FEED CKT.

YES

NO TROUBLE FOUND. REFER TO "DIAGNOSTIC AIDS."

ALWAYS DISPLAYS "RELEASED"

(4)
- IGNITION STILL "ON."
- DISCONNECT BRAKE SWITCH. SCAN TOOL SHOULD DISPLAY "APPLIED."

DISPLAYS "RELEASED"

- WITH TEST LIGHT CONNECTED TO GROUND, PROBE HARNESS CKT 420.

TEST LIGHT "ON"

CHECK FOR B + SHORTED TO CKT 420.

CKT 420 OK.

FAULTY PCM.

TEST LIGHT "OFF"

FAULTY PCM.

DISPLAYS "APPLIED"

BRAKE SWITCH OUT OF ADJUSTMENT OR FAULTY BRAKE SWITCH.

"AFTER REPAIRS," REFER TO DTC CRITERIA ON FACING PAGE AND CONFIRM DTC DOES NOT RESET.

3-9-93
PS 17151

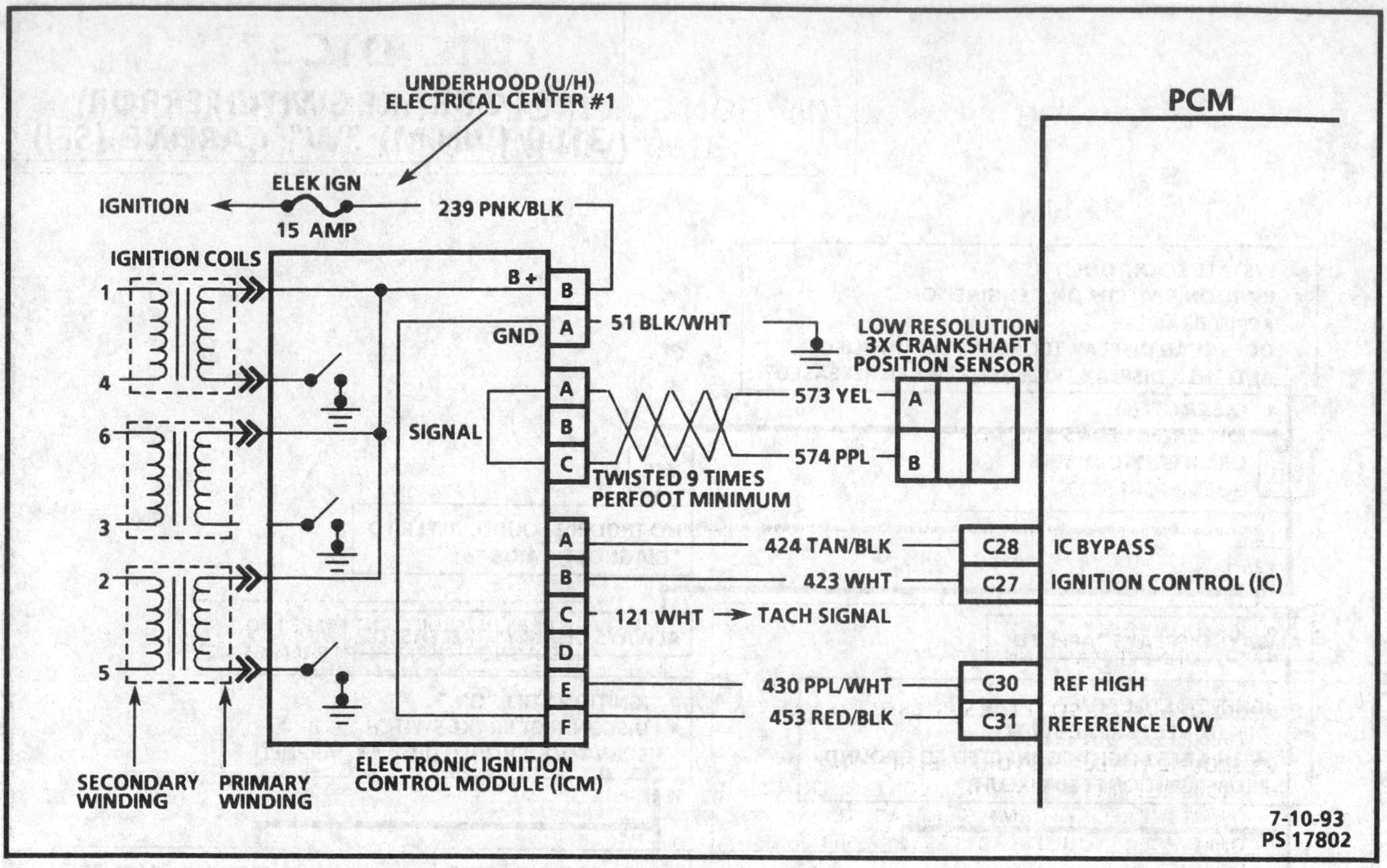
UNDERHOOD (U/H)
ELECTRICAL CENTER #1
ELEK IGN
IGNITION
15 AMP
239 PNK/BLK
PCM
IGNITION COILS
B+
GND
51 BLK/WHT
LOW RESOLUTION
3X CRANKSHAFT
POSITION SENSOR
SIGNAL
573 YEL
574 PPL
TWISTED 9 TIMES
PERFOOT MINIMUM
424 TAN/BLK
C28
IC BYPASS
423 WHT
C27
IGNITION CONTROL (IC)
121 WHT
TACH SIGNAL
430 PPL/WHT
C30
REF HIGH
453 RED/BLK
C31
REFERENCE LOW
ELECTRONIC IGNITION
CONTROL MODULE (ICM)
SECONDARY
WINDING
PRIMARY
WINDING
7-10-93
PS 17802

DTC 41

IGNITION CONTROL (IC) TIMING CIRCUIT ERROR
3100 (VIN M) "W" CARLINE (SFI)

Circuit Description:

Ignition control spark timing is provided by the PCM on CKT 423. Inputs from a number of engine sensors allow the PCM to correctly calculate optimum spark timing. Engine load is calculated from the MAP sensor, engine RPM is derived from the 3X crankshaft position sensor, engine operating temperature from ECT and IAT sensors and engine knock activity from the knock sensor. Other engine functions modify spark to a lesser degree such as TCC engagement and EGR activity.

The bypass circuit controls an internal switch in the electronic Ignition Control Module (ICM). Unless the vehicle is in back-up spark (base timing mode), the bypass circuit will have 5 volts applied to it. This 5 volt signal from the PCM allows a solid state switch to direct the IC timing pulses to the ICM for sequencing and energizing the coil packs. If the bypass circuit is not energized, the IC pulses from the ICM are shunted to ground and the electronic ICM uses its own base timing schedule to time and energize the coil packs.

DTC 41 Will Set When: Ignition Control (IC) pulses are detected on CKT 423 when the vehicle is in bypass (no voltage applied to bypass should allow IC pulses to be grounded by the electronic ICM). The test will either pass or fail within the first 1 second of engine running. If it passes, the test will not run until the next key cycle.

Action Taken (PCM will default to): The PCM will allow the electronic ignition control module to control timing using its own base timing schedule. The MIL will not become illuminated.

DTC 41 Will Clear When: A current DTC 41 will clear after each ignition key cycle. A History DTC 41 will clear after 50 consecutive ignition key cycles without a current DTC 41 being stored.

DTC Chart Test Description: Number(s) below refer to circled number(s) on the diagnostic chart.

1. This test confirms DTC 41 and that the fault causing the DTC is present.
2. Checks for a normal IC ground path through the ignition control module. An IC CKT 423 shorted to ground will also read less than 500 ohms; however, this should set a DTC 42.

Diagnostic Aids: The scan tool does not have any ability to help diagnose a DTC 41 problem.

Refer to "Intermittents," in "Symptoms," Section "6E3-B".

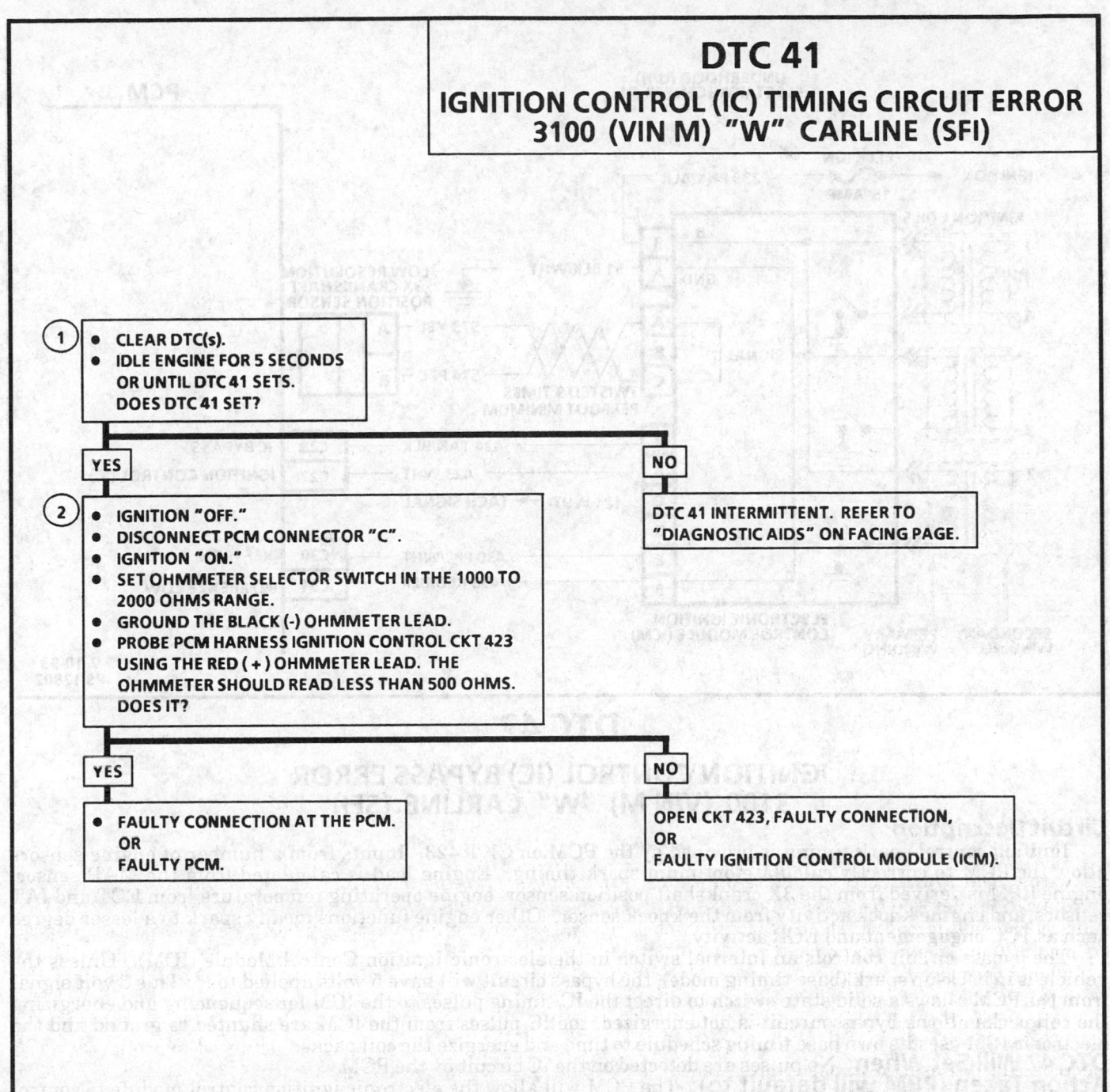

DTC 41

IGNITION CONTROL (IC) TIMING CIRCUIT ERROR 3100 (VIN M) "W" CARLINE (SFI)

(1)
- CLEAR DTC(s).
- IDLE ENGINE FOR 5 SECONDS OR UNTIL DTC 41 SETS.

DOES DTC 41 SET?

NO: DTC 41 INTERMITTENT. REFER TO "DIAGNOSTIC AIDS" ON FACING PAGE.

YES:

(2)
- IGNITION "OFF."
- DISCONNECT PCM CONNECTOR "C".
- IGNITION "ON."
- SET OHMMETER SELECTOR SWITCH IN THE 1000 TO 2000 OHMS RANGE.
- GROUND THE BLACK (-) OHMMETER LEAD.
- PROBE PCM HARNESS IGNITION CONTROL CKT 423 USING THE RED (+) OHMMETER LEAD. THE OHMMETER SHOULD READ LESS THAN 500 OHMS.

DOES IT?

YES:
- FAULTY CONNECTION AT THE PCM.
  OR
  FAULTY PCM.

NO: OPEN CKT 423, FAULTY CONNECTION, OR FAULTY IGNITION CONTROL MODULE (ICM).

* IF PCM IS FAULTY AND MUST BE REPLACED, THE NEW PCM MUST BE PROGRAMMED. REFER TO PCM REPLACEMENT AND PROGRAMMING PROCEDURES IN SECTION "6E3-C1".

"*AFTER REPAIRS*," REFER TO DTC CRITERIA ON FACING PAGE AND CONFIRM DTC DOES NOT RESET.

3-9-93
PS 17152

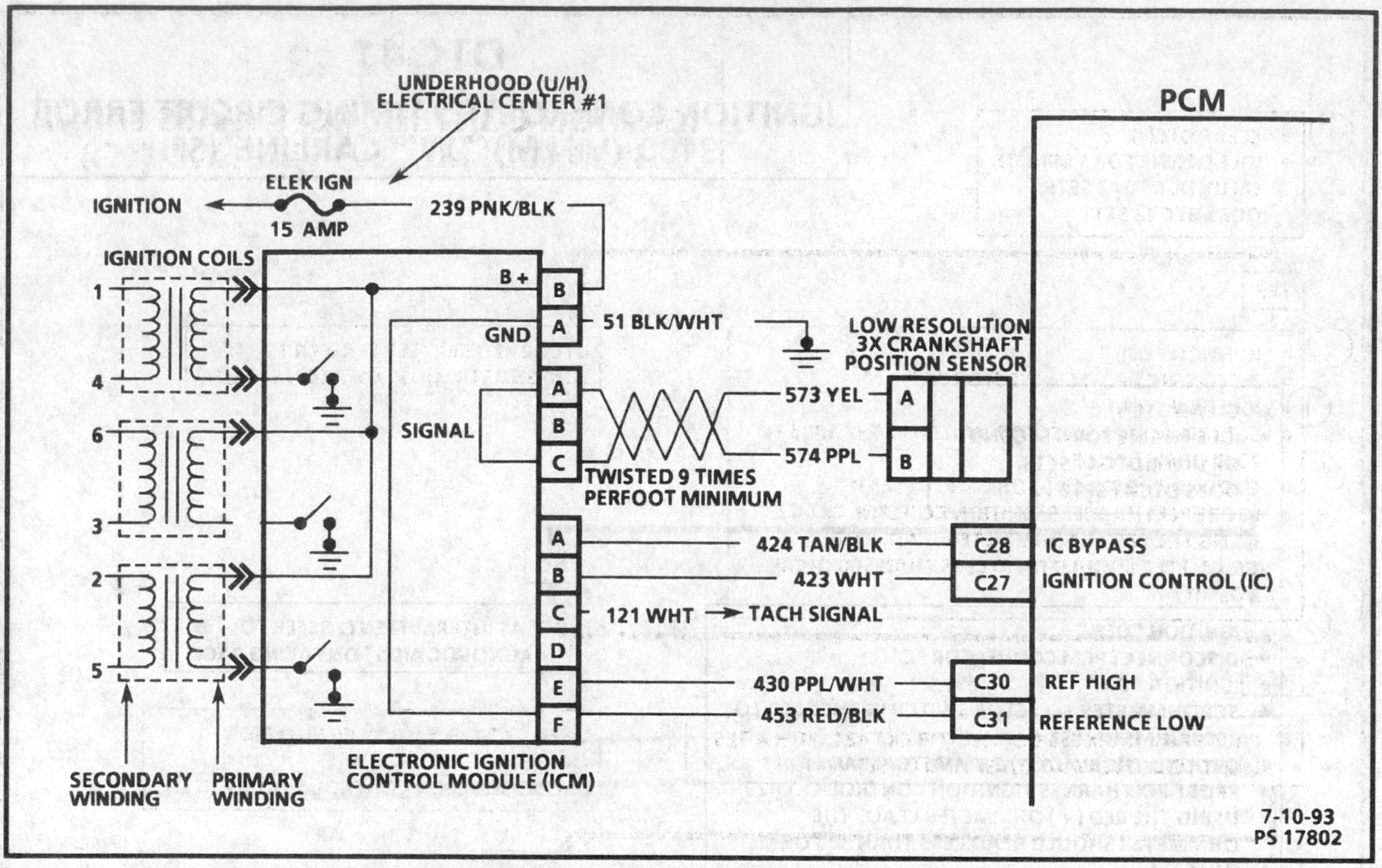
UNDERHOOD (U/H) ELECTRICAL CENTER #1
PCM
ELEK IGN
IGNITION
15 AMP
239 PNK/BLK
IGNITION COILS
B+
B
A
GND
51 BLK/WHT
LOW RESOLUTION 3X CRANKSHAFT POSITION SENSOR
SIGNAL
573 YEL
574 PPL
TWISTED 9 TIMES PERFOOT MINIMUM
424 TAN/BLK
C28
IC BYPASS
423 WHT
C27
IGNITION CONTROL (IC)
121 WHT
TACH SIGNAL
430 PPL/WHT
C30
REF HIGH
453 RED/BLK
C31
REFERENCE LOW
ELECTRONIC IGNITION CONTROL MODULE (ICM)
SECONDARY WINDING
PRIMARY WINDING
7-10-93
PS 17802

DTC 42

IGNITION CONTROL (IC) BYPASS ERROR 3100 (VIN M) "W" CARLINE (SFI)

Circuit Description:

Ignition control spark timing is provided by the PCM on CKT 423. Inputs from a number of engine sensors allow the PCM to correctly calculate optimum spark timing. Engine load is calculated from the MAP sensor, engine RPM is derived from the 3X crankshaft position sensor, engine operating temperature from ECT and IAT sensors, and engine knock activity from the knock sensor. Other engine functions modify spark to a lesser degree such as TCC engagement and EGR activity.

The bypass circuit controls an internal switch in the electronic Ignition Control Module (ICM). Unless the vehicle is in back-up spark (base timing mode), the bypass circuit will have 5 volts applied to it. This 5 volt signal from the PCM allows a solid state switch to direct the IC timing pulses to the ICM for sequencing and energizing the coil packs. If the bypass circuit is not energized, the IC pulses from the ICM are shunted to ground and the electronic ICM uses its own base timing schedule to time and energize the coil packs.

DTC 42 Will Set When: No pulses are detected on the IC circuit by the PCM.

Action Taken (PCM will default to): The PCM will allow the electronic ignition control module to control timing using its own base timing schedule. The MIL will become illuminated.

DTC 42 Will Clear When: A current DTC 42 will clear after each ignition key cycle. A History DTC 42 will clear after 50 consecutive ignition key cycles without a current DTC 42 being stored.

DTC Chart Test Description: Number(s) below refer to circled number(s) on the diagnostic chart.

1. DTC 42 indicates the PCM has detected an open or short to ground in the bypass circuit, or a grounded I/C circuit. This test confirms DTC 42 and that the fault causing the DTC is present.
2. Checks for a normal IC ground path through the ignition control module. An IC CKT 423 shorted to ground will also read less than 500 ohms; however, this will be checked later.
3. As the test light voltage touches CKT 424, the module should switch causing the ohmmeter to "overrange" if the meter is in the 1000-2000 ohms position. Selecting the 10-20,000 ohms position will indicate above 5000 ohms. The important thing is that the module "switched."
4. The module did not switch and this step checks for:
   - IC CKT 423 shorted to ground.
   - Bypass CKT 424 open.
   - Faulty electronic ignition control module connection or module.
5. Confirms that DTC 42 is a faulty PCM and not an intermittent in CKT 423 or 424.

Diagnostic Aids: The Tech 1 scan tool does not have any ability to help diagnose a DTC 42 problem.

Refer to "Intermittents," in "Symptoms," Section "6E3-B".

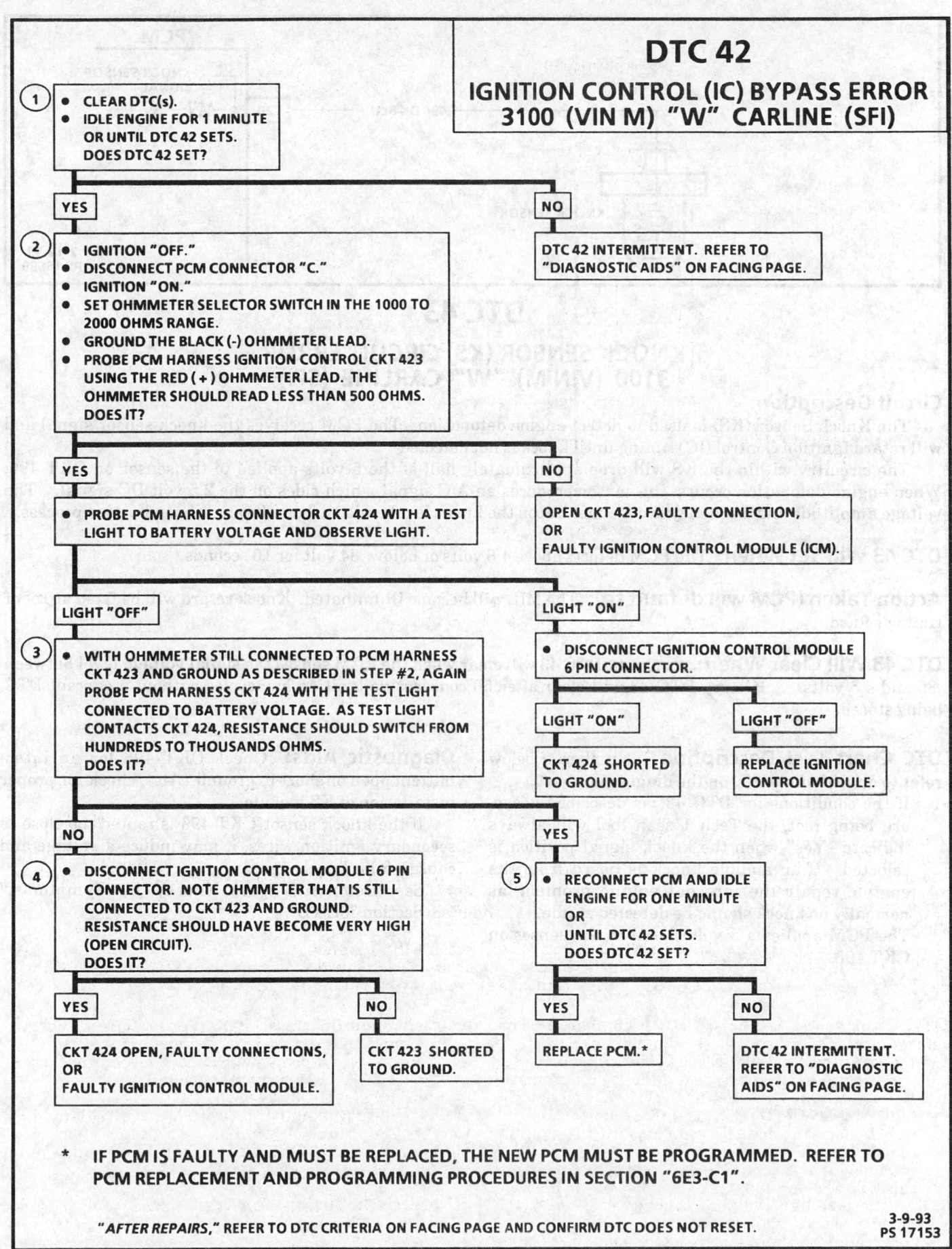

DTC 42

IGNITION CONTROL (IC) BYPASS ERROR 3100 (VIN M) "W" CARLINE (SFI)

1
- CLEAR DTC(s).
- IDLE ENGINE FOR 1 MINUTE OR UNTIL DTC 42 SETS. DOES DTC 42 SET?

YES →

2
- IGNITION "OFF."
- DISCONNECT PCM CONNECTOR "C."
- IGNITION "ON."
- SET OHMMETER SELECTOR SWITCH IN THE 1000 TO 2000 OHMS RANGE.
- GROUND THE BLACK (-) OHMMETER LEAD.
- PROBE PCM HARNESS IGNITION CONTROL CKT 423 USING THE RED (+) OHMMETER LEAD. THE OHMMETER SHOULD READ LESS THAN 500 OHMS. DOES IT?

NO → DTC 42 INTERMITTENT. REFER TO "DIAGNOSTIC AIDS" ON FACING PAGE.

2 — YES →
- PROBE PCM HARNESS CONNECTOR CKT 424 WITH A TEST LIGHT TO BATTERY VOLTAGE AND OBSERVE LIGHT.

2 — NO → OPEN CKT 423, FAULTY CONNECTION, OR FAULTY IGNITION CONTROL MODULE (ICM).

LIGHT "OFF" →

3
- WITH OHMMETER STILL CONNECTED TO PCM HARNESS CKT 423 AND GROUND AS DESCRIBED IN STEP #2, AGAIN PROBE PCM HARNESS CKT 424 WITH THE TEST LIGHT CONNECTED TO BATTERY VOLTAGE. AS TEST LIGHT CONTACTS CKT 424, RESISTANCE SHOULD SWITCH FROM HUNDREDS TO THOUSANDS OHMS. DOES IT?

LIGHT "ON" →
- DISCONNECT IGNITION CONTROL MODULE 6 PIN CONNECTOR.

  - **LIGHT "ON"** → CKT 424 SHORTED TO GROUND.
  - **LIGHT "OFF"** → REPLACE IGNITION CONTROL MODULE.

3 — NO →

4
- DISCONNECT IGNITION CONTROL MODULE 6 PIN CONNECTOR. NOTE OHMMETER THAT IS STILL CONNECTED TO CKT 423 AND GROUND. RESISTANCE SHOULD HAVE BECOME VERY HIGH (OPEN CIRCUIT). DOES IT?

  - **YES** → CKT 424 OPEN, FAULTY CONNECTIONS, OR FAULTY IGNITION CONTROL MODULE.
  - **NO** → CKT 423 SHORTED TO GROUND.

3 — YES →

5
- RECONNECT PCM AND IDLE ENGINE FOR ONE MINUTE OR UNTIL DTC 42 SETS. DOES DTC 42 SET?

  - **YES** → REPLACE PCM.*
  - **NO** → DTC 42 INTERMITTENT. REFER TO "DIAGNOSTIC AIDS" ON FACING PAGE.

* IF PCM IS FAULTY AND MUST BE REPLACED, THE NEW PCM MUST BE PROGRAMMED. REFER TO PCM REPLACEMENT AND PROGRAMMING PROCEDURES IN SECTION "6E3-C1".

"AFTER REPAIRS," REFER TO DTC CRITERIA ON FACING PAGE AND CONFIRM DTC DOES NOT RESET.

3-9-93
PS 17153

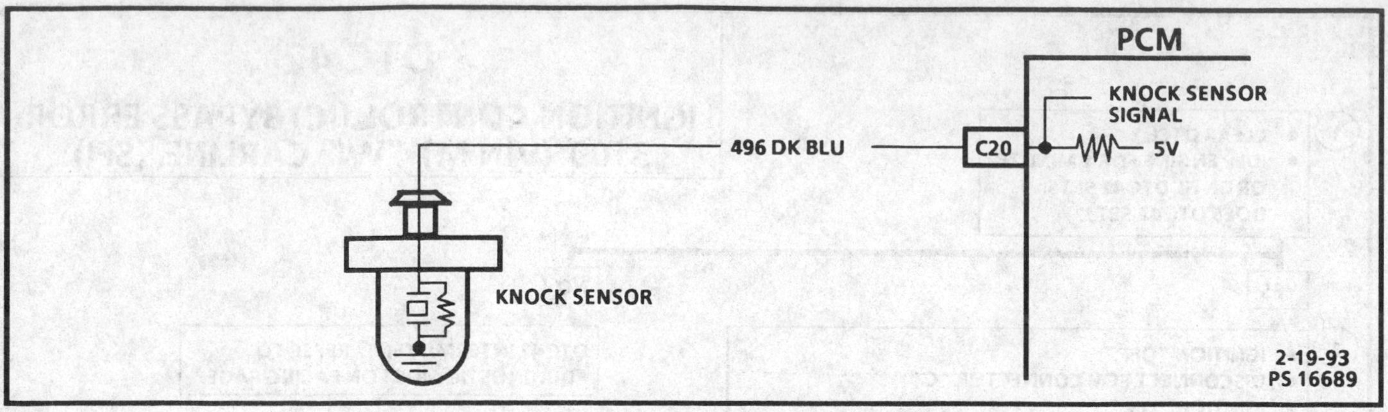
PCM
KNOCK SENSOR SIGNAL
496 DK BLU
C20
5V
KNOCK SENSOR
2-19-93
PS 16689

DTC 43

KNOCK SENSOR (KS) CIRCUIT ERROR 3100 (VIN M) "W" CARLINE (SFI)

Circuit Description:

The Knock Sensor (KS) is used to detect engine detonation. The PCM receives the knock sensor signal and will retard Ignition Control (IC) timing until knock is not detected.

The circuitry within the KS will drop approximately half of the 5 volts applied to the sensor on CKT 496. When engine detonation occurs, the sensor produces an A/C signal which rides on the 2.5 volt DC signal. The voltage amplitude and frequency is dependent upon the knock level emitted from the engine combustion process.

DTC 43 Will Set When: The PCM detects above 4.6 volts or below .84 volt for 10 seconds.

Action Taken (PCM will default to): The MIL will become illuminated. Knock retard will be fixed at 15° of timing retard.

DTC 43 Will Clear When: A current DTC 43 will clear when the PCM senses the signal voltage level between .85 and 4.5 volts. A History DTC 43 will clear after 50 consecutive ignition key cycles without a current DTC being stored.

DTC Chart Test Description: Number(s) below refer to circled number(s) on the diagnostic chart.

1. If the conditions for DTC 43, as described above, are being met, the Tech 1 scan tool will always indicate "Yes" when the knock signal position is selected. If an audible knock is heard from the engine, repair the internal engine problem, as normally no knock should be detected at idle.
2. The PCM applies a 5 volt signal to the sensor on CKT 496.

Diagnostic Aids: Check CKT 496 for an intermittent open or short to ground. Also, check for proper installation of KS module.

If the knock sensor CKT 496 is routed too close to secondary ignition wires, it may induce a voltage and cause a false knock signal.

- See "Detonation/Spark Knock," in "Symptoms," Section "6E3-B".

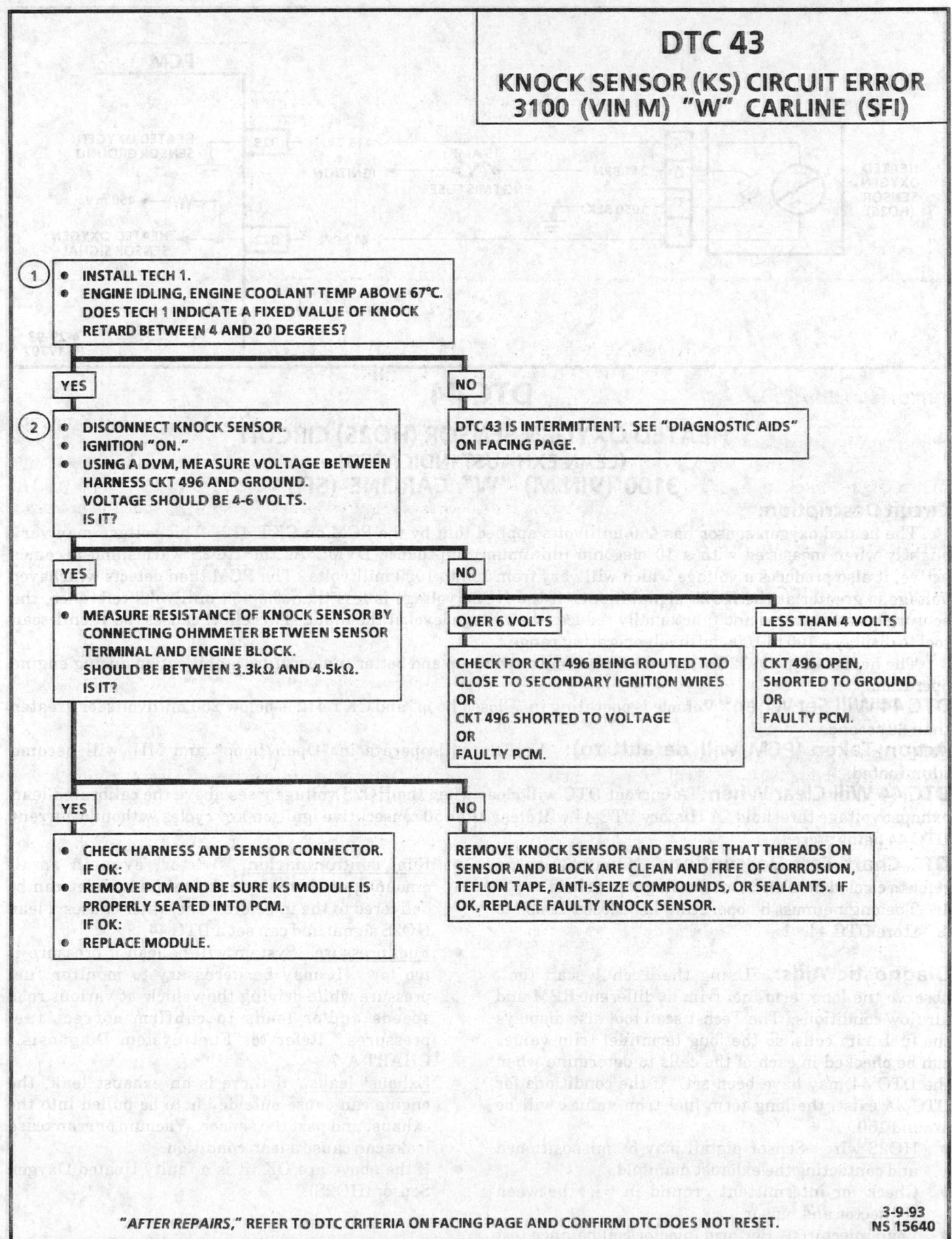

DTC 43

KNOCK SENSOR (KS) CIRCUIT ERROR
3100 (VIN M) "W" CARLINE (SFI)

1
- INSTALL TECH 1.
- ENGINE IDLING, ENGINE COOLANT TEMP ABOVE 67°C.
  DOES TECH 1 INDICATE A FIXED VALUE OF KNOCK RETARD BETWEEN 4 AND 20 DEGREES?

YES → go to 2

NO → DTC 43 IS INTERMITTENT. SEE "DIAGNOSTIC AIDS" ON FACING PAGE.

2
- DISCONNECT KNOCK SENSOR.
- IGNITION "ON."
- USING A DVM, MEASURE VOLTAGE BETWEEN HARNESS CKT 496 AND GROUND.
  VOLTAGE SHOULD BE 4-6 VOLTS.
  IS IT?

YES
- MEASURE RESISTANCE OF KNOCK SENSOR BY CONNECTING OHMMETER BETWEEN SENSOR TERMINAL AND ENGINE BLOCK.
  SHOULD BE BETWEEN 3.3kΩ AND 4.5kΩ.
  IS IT?

  YES
  - CHECK HARNESS AND SENSOR CONNECTOR.
    IF OK:
  - REMOVE PCM AND BE SURE KS MODULE IS PROPERLY SEATED INTO PCM.
    IF OK:
  - REPLACE MODULE.

  NO → REMOVE KNOCK SENSOR AND ENSURE THAT THREADS ON SENSOR AND BLOCK ARE CLEAN AND FREE OF CORROSION, TEFLON TAPE, ANTI-SEIZE COMPOUNDS, OR SEALANTS. IF OK, REPLACE FAULTY KNOCK SENSOR.

NO

- **OVER 6 VOLTS** → CHECK FOR CKT 496 BEING ROUTED TOO CLOSE TO SECONDARY IGNITION WIRES OR CKT 496 SHORTED TO VOLTAGE OR FAULTY PCM.
- **LESS THAN 4 VOLTS** → CKT 496 OPEN, SHORTED TO GROUND OR FAULTY PCM.

"AFTER REPAIRS," REFER TO DTC CRITERIA ON FACING PAGE AND CONFIRM DTC DOES NOT RESET.

3-9-93
NS 15640

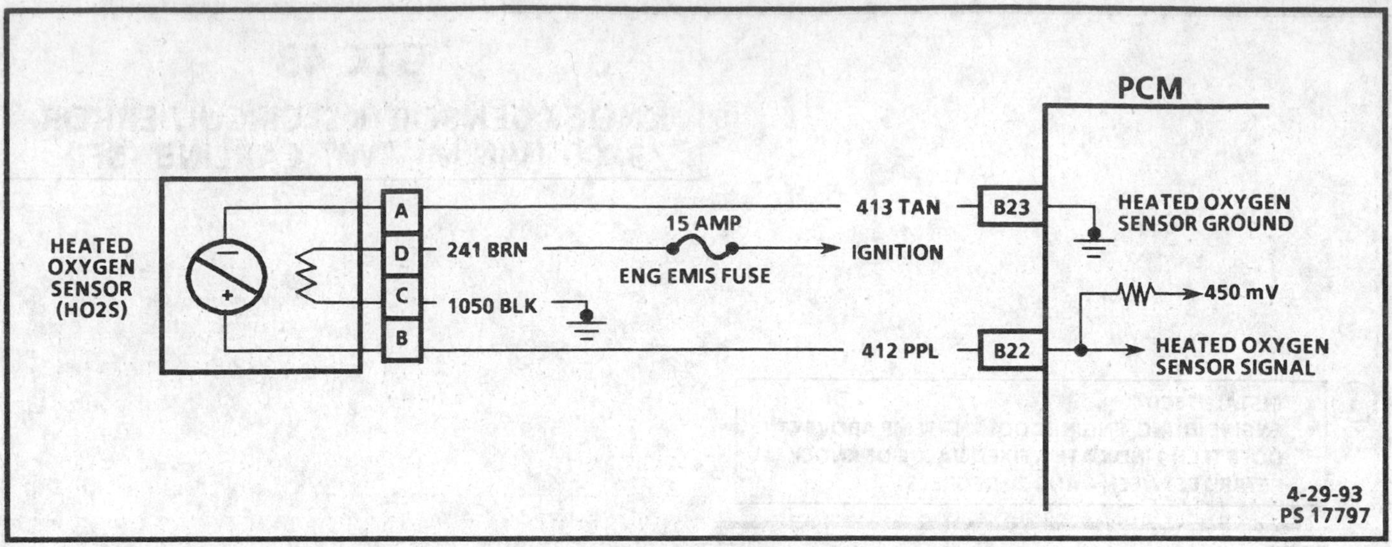
PCM
HEATED OXYGEN SENSOR (HO2S)
A
D
C
B
413 TAN
B23
HEATED OXYGEN SENSOR GROUND
15 AMP
241 BRN
ENG EMIS FUSE
IGNITION
1050 BLK
450 mV
412 PPL
B22
HEATED OXYGEN SENSOR SIGNAL
4-29-93
PS 17797

DTC 44

HEATED OXYGEN SENSOR (HO2S) CIRCUIT
(LEAN EXHAUST INDICATED)
3100 (VIN M) "W" CARLINE (SFI)

Circuit Description:

The heated oxygen sensor has 450 millivolts applied to it by the PCM on CKT 412. This voltage may vary slightly when measured with a 10 megohm (minimum) impedance DVM. As the HO2S warms and becomes active, it also produces a voltage which will vary from 100 to 1000 millivolts. The PCM then detects whichever voltage is greater at the HO2S signal input. If the HO2S voltage is less than the 450 millivolts reference, the sensor acts as a ground and functionally reduces the voltage level at the input. This effect causes the Tech 1 scan tool to display a 100 to 1000 millivolt operating range.

The heater in the HO2S allows for faster sensor warmup and better temperature stabilization during engine operation.

DTC 44 Will Set When: Vehicle is operating in "Closed Loop" and CKT 412 is below 250 millivolts for greater than 60 seconds.

Action Taken (PCM will default to): Vehicle will operate in "Open Loop" and MIL will become illuminated.

DTC 44 Will Clear When: A current DTC will clear when the HO2S voltage rises above the calibrated lean exhaust voltage threshold. A History DTC 44 will clear after 50 consecutive ignition key cycles without a current DTC 44 being stored.

DTC Chart Test Description: Number(s) below refer to circled number(s) on the diagnostic chart.

1. The engine must be operating in "Closed Loop" to store DTC 44.

Diagnostic Aids: Using the Tech 1 scan tool, observe the long term fuel trim at different RPM and air flow conditions. The Tech 1 scan tool also displays the fuel trim cells, so the long term fuel trim values can be checked in each of the cells to determine when the DTC 44 may have been set. If the conditions for DTC 44 exist, the long term fuel trim values will be around 150.

- HO2S wire. Sensor pigtail may be mispositioned and contacting the exhaust manifold.
- Check for intermittent ground in wire between connector and sensor.
- Lean injector(s). Perform injector/coil balance test CHART C-2A.
- Fuel contamination. Water, even in small amounts, near the in-tank fuel pump inlet can be delivered to the injectors. The water causes a lean HO2S signal and can set a DTC 44.
- Fuel pressure. System will be lean if pressure is too low. It may be necessary to monitor fuel pressure while driving the vehicle at various road speeds and/or loads to confirm correct fuel pressures. Refer to "Fuel System Diagnosis," CHART A-7.
- Exhaust leaks. If there is an exhaust leak, the engine can cause outside air to be pulled into the exhaust and past the sensor. Vacuum or crankcase leaks can cause a lean condition.
- If the above are OK, it is a faulty Heated Oxygen Sensor (HO2S).

DTC 44

HEATED OXYGEN SENSOR (HO2S) CIRCUIT
(LEAN EXHAUST INDICATED)
3100 (VIN M) "W" CARLINE (SFI)

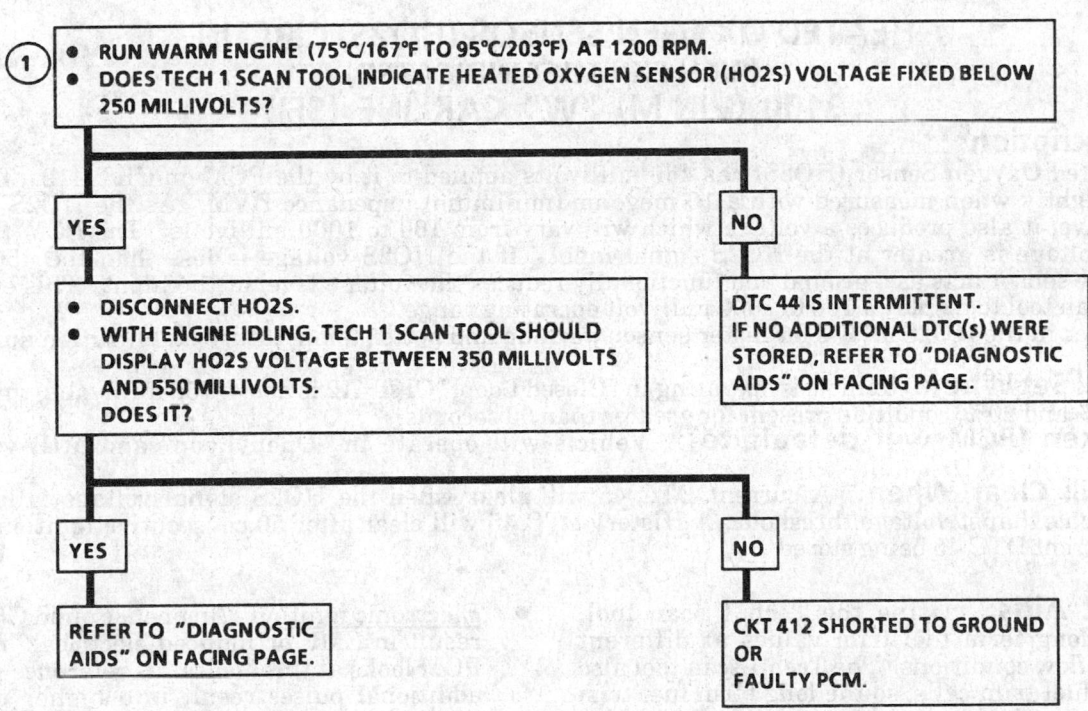

(1)
- RUN WARM ENGINE (75°C/167°F TO 95°C/203°F) AT 1200 RPM.
- DOES TECH 1 SCAN TOOL INDICATE HEATED OXYGEN SENSOR (HO2S) VOLTAGE FIXED BELOW 250 MILLIVOLTS?

YES
- DISCONNECT HO2S.
- WITH ENGINE IDLING, TECH 1 SCAN TOOL SHOULD DISPLAY HO2S VOLTAGE BETWEEN 350 MILLIVOLTS AND 550 MILLIVOLTS.

DOES IT?

- **YES** → REFER TO "DIAGNOSTIC AIDS" ON FACING PAGE.
- **NO** → CKT 412 SHORTED TO GROUND OR FAULTY PCM.

NO
DTC 44 IS INTERMITTENT.
IF NO ADDITIONAL DTC(s) WERE STORED, REFER TO "DIAGNOSTIC AIDS" ON FACING PAGE.

"AFTER REPAIRS," REFER TO DTC CRITERIA ON FACING PAGE AND CONFIRM DTC DOES NOT RESET.

3-9-93
NS 15053

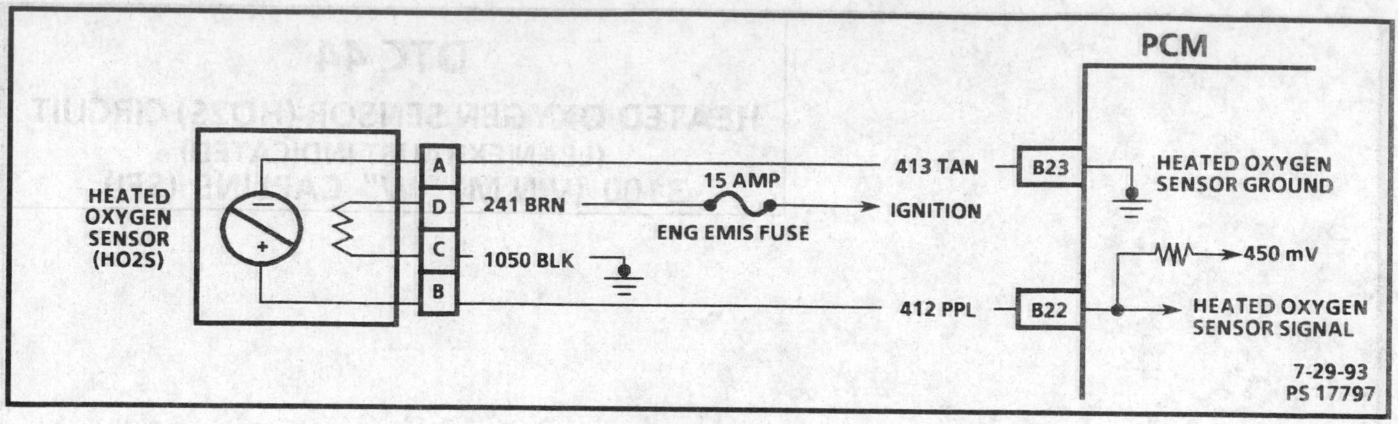
PCM
HEATED OXYGEN SENSOR (HO2S)
A
D
C
B
15 AMP
241 BRN
ENG EMIS FUSE
1050 BLK
413 TAN
B23
IGNITION
412 PPL
B22
HEATED OXYGEN SENSOR GROUND
450 mV
HEATED OXYGEN SENSOR SIGNAL
7-29-93
PS 17797

DTC 45

HEATED OXYGEN SENSOR (HO2S) CIRCUIT
(RICH EXHAUST INDICATED)
3100 (VIN M) "W" CARLINE (SFI)

Circuit Description:

The Heated Oxygen Sensor (HO2S) has 450 millivolts applied to it by the PCM on CKT 412. This voltage may vary slightly when measured with a 10 megohm (minimum) impedance DVM. As the HO2S warms and becomes active, it also produces a voltage which will vary from 100 to 1000 millivolts. The PCM then detects whichever voltage is greater at the HO2S signal input. If the HO2S voltage is less than the 450 millivolts reference, the sensor acts as a ground and functionally reduces the voltage level at the input. This effect causes the Tech 1 scan tool to display a 100 to 1000 millivolt operating range.

The heater in the HO2S allows for faster sensor warmup and better temperature stabilization during engine operation.

DTC 45 Will Set When: Vehicle is operating in "Closed Loop," CKT 412 is above 750 millivolts, throttle angle is between 6% and 20%, condition present for greater than 60 seconds.

Action Taken (PCM will default to): Vehicle will operate in "Open Loop" and MIL will become illuminated.

DTC 45 Will Clear When: A current DTC 45 will clear when the HO2S signal voltage falls below the calibrated rich exhaust voltage threshold. A History DTC 45 will clear after 50 consecutive ignition key cycles without a current DTC 45 being stored.

Diagnostic Aids: Using the Tech 1 scan tool, observe the long term fuel trim values at different RPM and air flow conditions. The Tech 1 scan tool also displays the fuel trim cells, so the long term fuel trim values can be checked in each of the cells to determine when the DTC 45 may have been set. If the conditions for DTC 45 exist, the long term fuel trim values will be around 115.

- Fuel pressure. System will go rich if pressure is too high. The PCM can compensate for some increase. However, if it gets too high, a DTC 45 may be set. Refer to "Fuel System Diagnosis," CHART A-7.
- Rich injector. Perform "Injector Coil/Balance Test," CHART C-2A.
- Leaking injector. Refer to CHART A-7.
- Crankcase oil. Check for fuel contaminated oil.
- HO2S contamination. Inspect Heated Oxygen Sensor (HO2S) for silicone contamination from fuel, or use of improper RTV sealant. The sensor may have a white, powdery coating and result in a high but false signal voltage (rich HO2S signal indication). The PCM will then reduce the amount of fuel delivered to the engine, causing a severe surge driveability problem.
- Electronic ignition. An open ground CKT 453 may result in EMI, or induced electrical "noise." The PCM looks at this "noise" as reference pulses. The additional pulses result in a higher than actual engine speed signal. The PCM then delivers too much fuel, causing system to go rich. Engine tachometer will also show higher than actual engine speed, which can help in diagnosing this problem.
- EVAP canister purge. Check for fuel saturation. If full of fuel, check canister control and hoses. Refer to "Evaporative Emission (EVAP) Control System," Section "6E3-C3".
- Check for leaking fuel pressure regulator diaphragm by checking vacuum line to regulator for fuel.
- Throttle Position (TP) sensor. An intermittent Throttle Position (TP) sensor output will cause the system to go rich, due to a false indication of the engine accelerating.
- EGR. An EGR staying open (especially at idle) will cause the Heated Oxygen Sensor (HO2S) to indicate a rich HO2S signal and this could result in a DTC 45.
- CKT 412. Shorted to voltage will set a DTC 45, because it simulates a rich condition.

DTC 45

HEATED OXYGEN SENSOR (HO2S) CIRCUIT

(RICH EXHAUST INDICATED)

3100 (VIN M) "W" CARLINE (SFI)

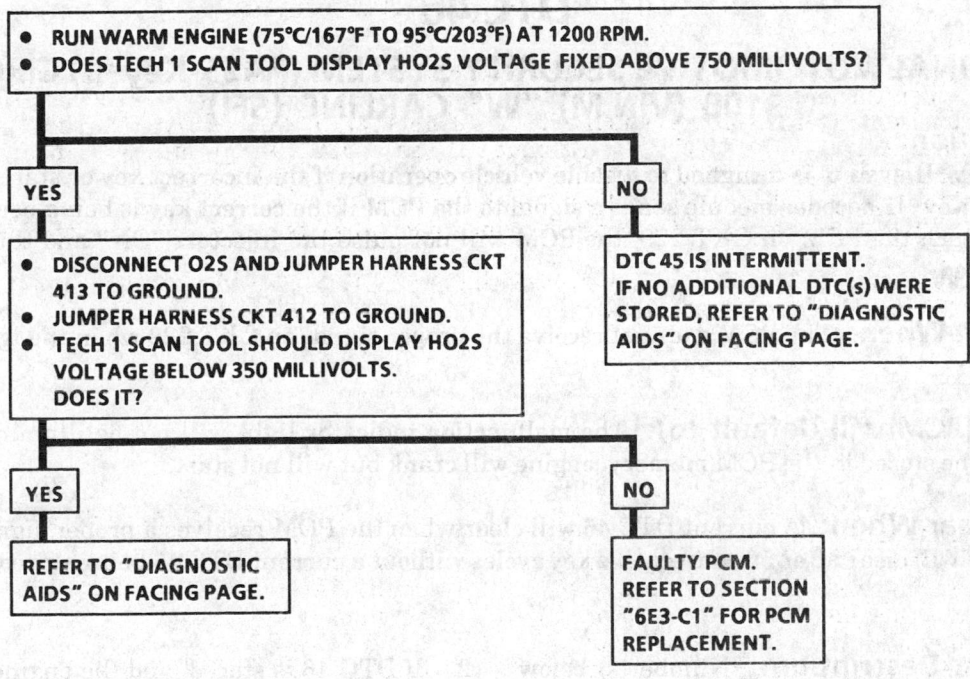

- RUN WARM ENGINE (75°C/167°F TO 95°C/203°F) AT 1200 RPM.
- DOES TECH 1 SCAN TOOL DISPLAY HO2S VOLTAGE FIXED ABOVE 750 MILLIVOLTS?

YES

- DISCONNECT O2S AND JUMPER HARNESS CKT 413 TO GROUND.
- JUMPER HARNESS CKT 412 TO GROUND.
- TECH 1 SCAN TOOL SHOULD DISPLAY HO2S VOLTAGE BELOW 350 MILLIVOLTS.
  DOES IT?

  YES

  REFER TO "DIAGNOSTIC AIDS" ON FACING PAGE.

  NO

  FAULTY PCM.
  REFER TO SECTION "6E3-C1" FOR PCM REPLACEMENT.

NO

DTC 45 IS INTERMITTENT.
IF NO ADDITIONAL DTC(s) WERE STORED, REFER TO "DIAGNOSTIC AIDS" ON FACING PAGE.

"AFTER REPAIRS," REFER TO DTC CRITERIA ON FACING PAGE AND CONFIRM DTC DOES NOT RESET.

7-26-93
PS 18453

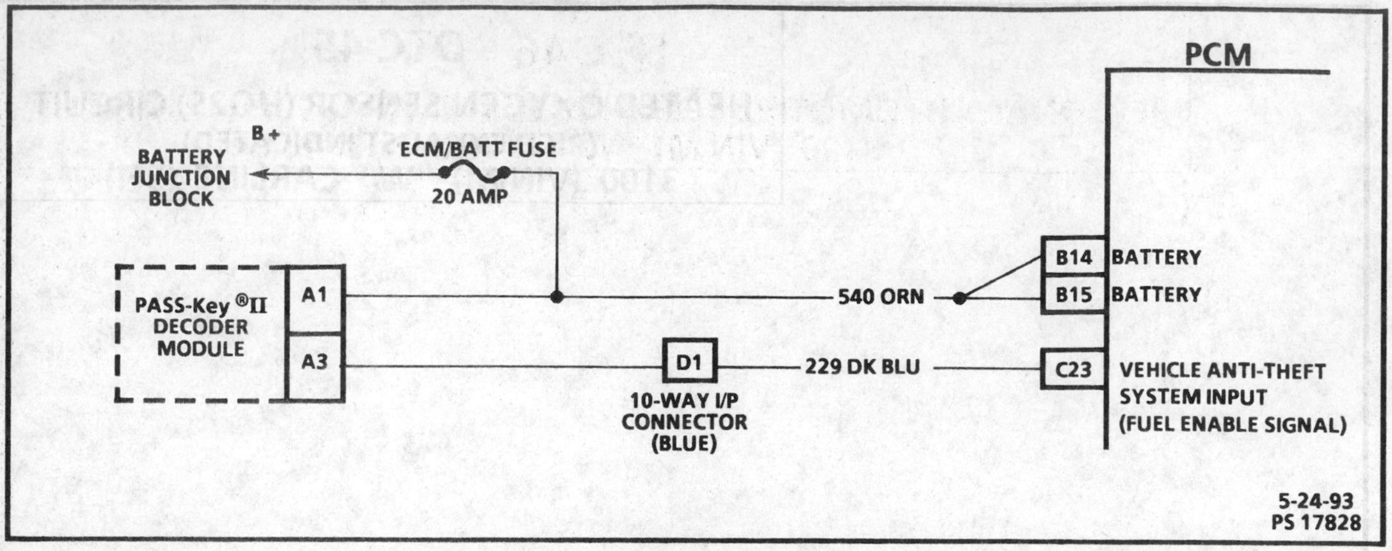
PCM
B+
BATTERY
JUNCTION
BLOCK
ECM/BATT FUSE
20 AMP
PASS-Key ®II
DECODER
MODULE
A1
A3
540 ORN
B14 BATTERY
B15 BATTERY
D1
229 DK BLU
C23 VEHICLE ANTI-THEFT
SYSTEM INPUT
(FUEL ENABLE SIGNAL)
10-WAY I/P
CONNECTOR
(BLUE)
5-24-93
PS 17828

DTC 46

PERSONAL AUTOMOTIVE SECURITY SYSTEM (PASS-Key®II) CIRCUIT 3100 (VIN M) "W" CARLINE (SFI)

Circuit Description:

The PASS-Key®II system is designed to disable vehicle operation if the incorrect key or starting procedure is used. The PASS-Key®II decoder module sends a signal to the PCM if the correct key is being used. If the proper signal does not reach the PCM on CKT 229, the PCM will not pulse the injectors "ON" and thus not allow the vehicle to be started.

DTC 46 Will Set When: The PCM does not receive the proper signal on CKT 229 when the ignition is turned "ON."

Action Taken (PCM will default to): The malfunction indicator light will not be illuminated. A PASS-Key®II fault will be stored in the PCM memory, engine will crank but will not start.

DTC 46 Will Clear When: A current DTC 46 will clear when the PCM receives a proper signal on CKT 229. A History DTC 46 will clear after 50 consecutive key cycles without a current DTC 46 being stored.

DTC Chart Test Description: Number(s) below refer to circled number(s) on the diagnostic chart.

1. If the engine cranks, but doesn't start. It indicates that the portion of the module which generates the signal to the PCM is not operating or CKT 229 is open or shorted to ground. If the decoder module is found to be OK, as determined from SECTION 8A, the PCM may be at fault, but this is not a likely condition.
2. If DTC 46 is stored, and the engine will not crank, it indicates that there is a PASS-Key®II problem or an incorrect key or starting procedure is being used.

DTC 46

PERSONAL AUTOMOTIVE SECURITY SYSTEM (PASS-Key®II) CIRCUIT 3100 (VIN M) "W" CARLINE (SFI)

- IGNITION "ON."

DOES SCAN TOOL INDICATE PASS-Key®II STATUS AS "OK"?

- **YES** → PROBLEM IS INTERMITTENT. IF NO OTHER DTC(s) IS STORED, REFER TO "INTERMITTENTS" IN SECTION "B".
- **NO** → DOES ENGINE CRANK?
  - **YES** → (1) CHECK FOR OPEN OR SHORT TO GROUND IN CKT 229 OR FAULTY PCM.
  - **NO** → (2) PASS-Key®II SYSTEM PROBLEM. REFER TO PASS-Key®II DIAGNOSIS" IN SECTION "8A" AND "9D".

"*AFTER REPAIRS,*" REFER TO DTC CRITERIA ON FACING PAGE AND CONFIRM DTC DOES NOT RESET.

5-13-93
PS 17827

DTC 51

PROM ERROR
(FAULTY OR INCORRECT CALIBRATION)
3100 (VIN M) "W" CARLINE (SFI)

DTC 51 WILL BE STORED WHEN AN INVALID PROGRAM IS DETECTED BY THE PCM. CHECK THAT ALL CONNECTIONS ARE FULLY INSERTED IN THE SOCKET. IF OK, REPROGRAM THE PCM. REFER TO SECTION "6E3-C1" (PCM AND SENSORS). IF PCM WILL NOT REPROGRAM, REPLACE PCM.

NOTICE: REPLACEMENT PCMs MUST BE REPROGRAMMED, IT IS ALSO NECESSARY TO TRANSFER THE KNOCK SENSOR (KS) MODULE WHEN REPLACING THE PCM. TO PREVENT POSSIBLE ELECTROSTATIC DISCHARGE DAMAGE TO THE PCM, DO NOT TOUCH THE COMPONENT LEADS.

"AFTER REPAIRS," REFER TO DTC CRITERIA ON FACING PAGE AND CONFIRM DTC DOES NOT RESET.

7-27-93
PS 18720

BLANK

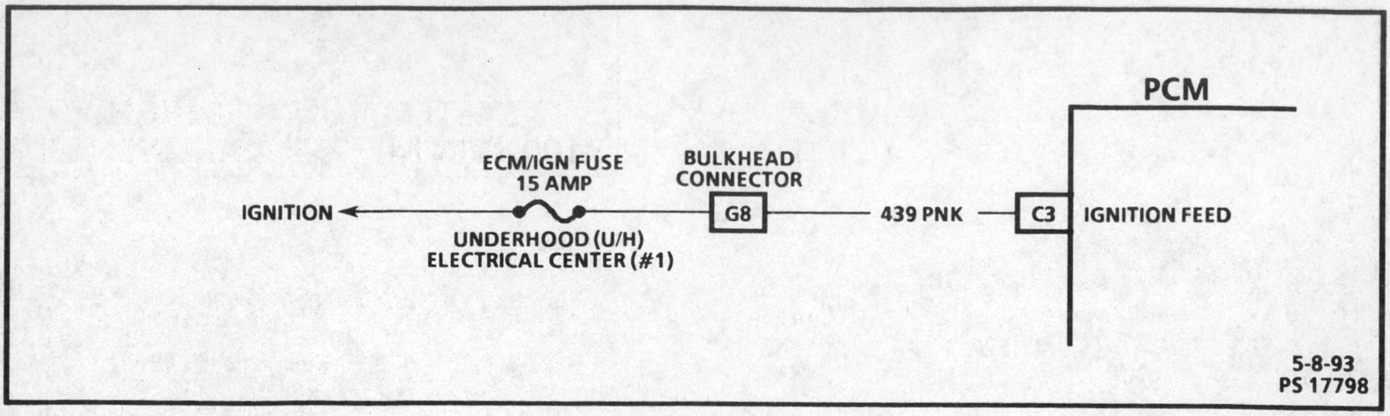
PCM
ECM/IGN FUSE
15 AMP
BULKHEAD
CONNECTOR
IGNITION
G8
439 PNK
C3
IGNITION FEED
UNDERHOOD (U/H)
ELECTRICAL CENTER (#1)
5-8-93
PS 17798

DTC 53

SYSTEM VOLTAGE HIGH
3100 (VIN M) "W" CARLINE (SFI)

Circuit Description:

The PCM has the ability to determine if the ignition feed circuit has more than 16.5 volts applied to it. This feature is to protect the PCM circuitry as well as components that have voltage applied to them by the PCM. The circuit that is monitored for an over voltage condition is CKT 439 (ignition feed).

DTC 53 Will Set When: The engine speed is greater than 800 RPM and the PCM is sensing greater than 16.5 volts at PCM terminal "C3".

Action Taken (PCM will default to): The MIL will become illuminated and all PCM outputs will be disengaged.

DTC 53 Will Clear When: A current DTC 53 will clear when battery voltage is sensed below 16.5 volts. A History DTC 53 will clear after 50 consecutive ignition key cycles without a current DTC 53 being stored.

DTC Chart Test Description: Number(s) below refer to circled number(s) on the diagnostic chart.

1. Normal battery output is between 8 - 16.5 volts.
2. Checks to see if the high voltage reading is due to the generator or PCM. With engine running, check voltage at the battery with a DVM. If the voltage is above 12.1 volts, the PCM is OK.
3. Checks to see if generator is faulty under load condition. If the voltage is above 16.5 volts, refer to SECTION 6D.

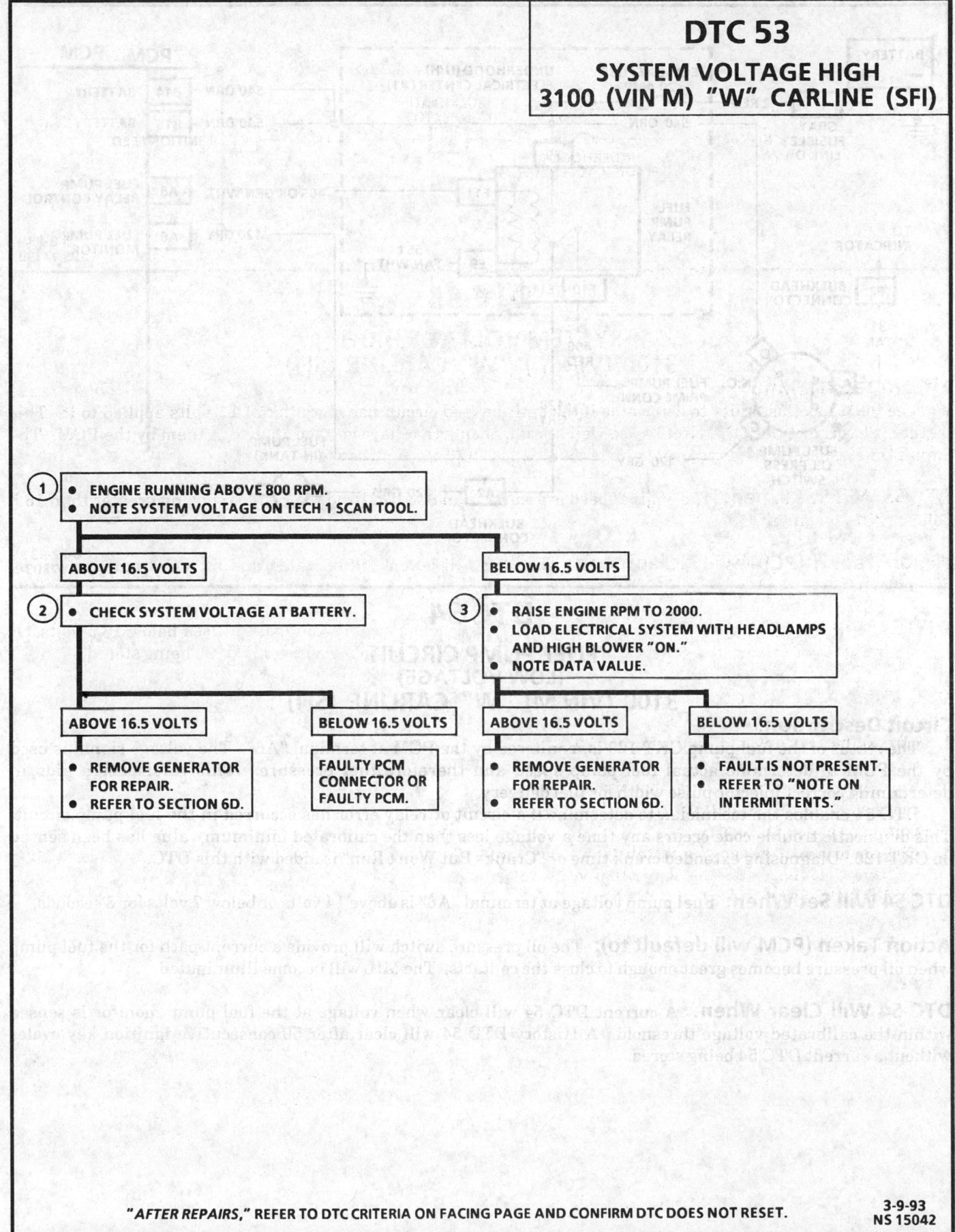

DTC 53
SYSTEM VOLTAGE HIGH
3100 (VIN M) "W" CARLINE (SFI)

1
- ENGINE RUNNING ABOVE 800 RPM.
- NOTE SYSTEM VOLTAGE ON TECH 1 SCAN TOOL.

ABOVE 16.5 VOLTS

2
- CHECK SYSTEM VOLTAGE AT BATTERY.

ABOVE 16.5 VOLTS
- REMOVE GENERATOR FOR REPAIR.
- REFER TO SECTION 6D.

BELOW 16.5 VOLTS

FAULTY PCM CONNECTOR OR FAULTY PCM.

BELOW 16.5 VOLTS

3
- RAISE ENGINE RPM TO 2000.
- LOAD ELECTRICAL SYSTEM WITH HEADLAMPS AND HIGH BLOWER "ON."
- NOTE DATA VALUE.

ABOVE 16.5 VOLTS
- REMOVE GENERATOR FOR REPAIR.
- REFER TO SECTION 6D.

BELOW 16.5 VOLTS
- FAULT IS NOT PRESENT.
- REFER TO "NOTE ON INTERMITTENTS."

"*AFTER REPAIRS*," REFER TO DTC CRITERIA ON FACING PAGE AND CONFIRM DTC DOES NOT RESET.

3-9-93
NS 15042

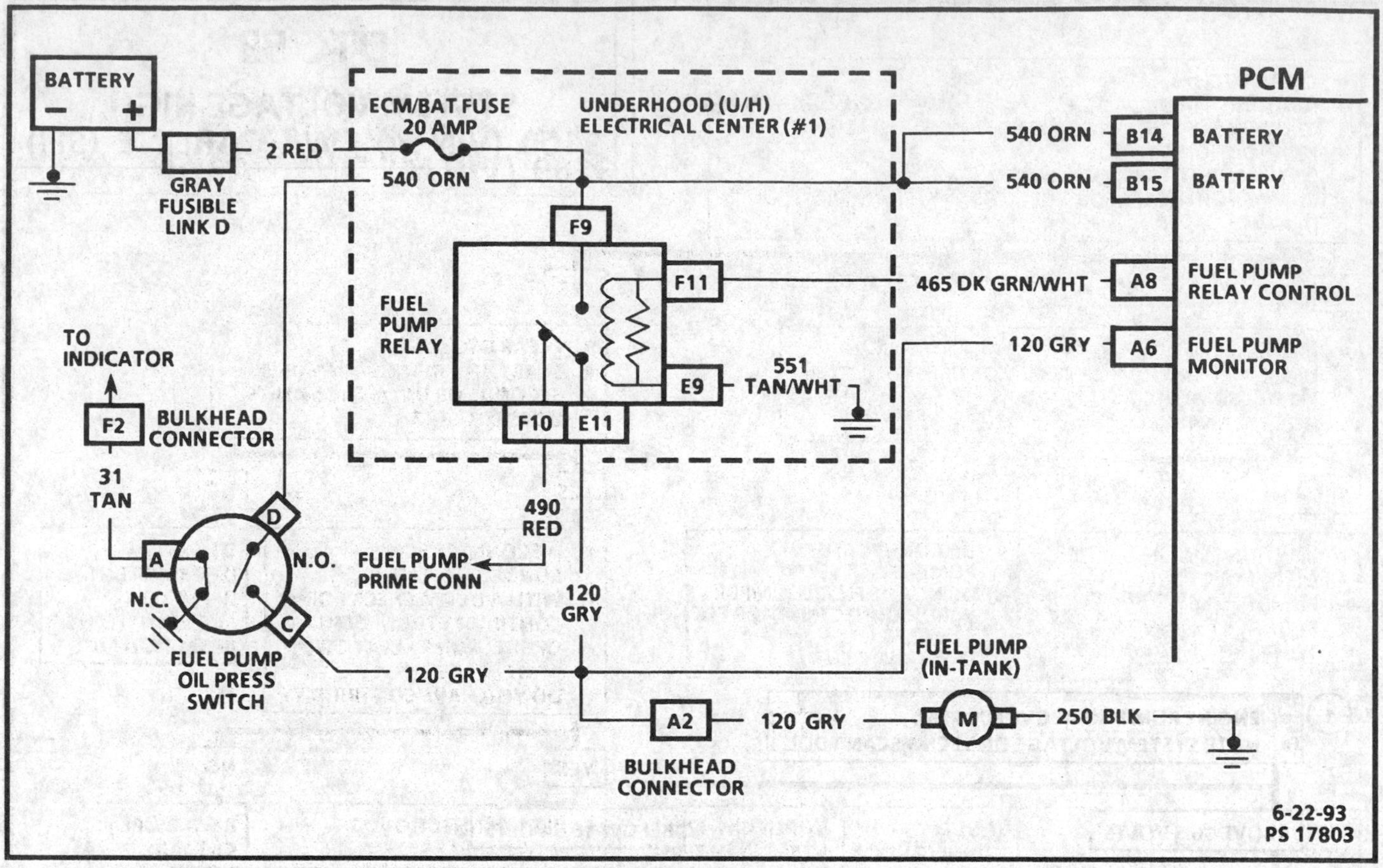
BATTERY
– +
GRAY FUSIBLE LINK D
2 RED
ECM/BAT FUSE 20 AMP
UNDERHOOD (U/H) ELECTRICAL CENTER (#1)
540 ORN
PCM
540 ORN
B14
BATTERY
540 ORN
B15
BATTERY
F9
F11
465 DK GRN/WHT
A8
FUEL PUMP RELAY CONTROL
FUEL PUMP RELAY
120 GRY
A6
FUEL PUMP MONITOR
TO INDICATOR
551 TAN/WHT
E9
F2
BULKHEAD CONNECTOR
F10
E11
31 TAN
D
490 RED
A
N.O.
FUEL PUMP PRIME CONN
N.C.
120 GRY
C
FUEL PUMP OIL PRESS SWITCH
120 GRY
FUEL PUMP (IN-TANK)
A2
120 GRY
M
250 BLK
BULKHEAD CONNECTOR
6-22-93
PS 17803

DTC 54

FUEL PUMP CIRCUIT
(LOW VOLTAGE)
3100 (VIN M) "W" CARLINE (SFI)

Circuit Description:

The status of the fuel pump CKT 120 is monitored by the PCM at terminal "A6". The voltage signal is used by the PCM to determine actual fuel pump speed and therefore fuel pressure. This information aids in determining correct injector pulse width for fuel delivery.

DTC 54 enables the technician to determine if a circuit or relay error has occurred in the fuel pump circuit. This diagnostic trouble code occurs any time a voltage less than the calibrated minimum value has been sensed on CKT 120. Diagnosing extended crank time or "Cranks But Won't Run" is aided with this DTC.

DTC 54 Will Set When: Fuel pump voltage at terminal "A6" is above 14 volts or below 7 volts for 3 seconds.

Action Taken (PCM will default to): The oil pressure switch will provide a current path for the fuel pump when oil pressure becomes great enough to close the contacts. The MIL will become illuminated.

DTC 54 Will Clear When: A current DTC 54 will clear when voltage at the fuel pump monitor is sensed within the calibrated voltage threshold. A History DTC 54 will clear after 50 consecutive ignition key cycles without a current DTC 54 being stored.

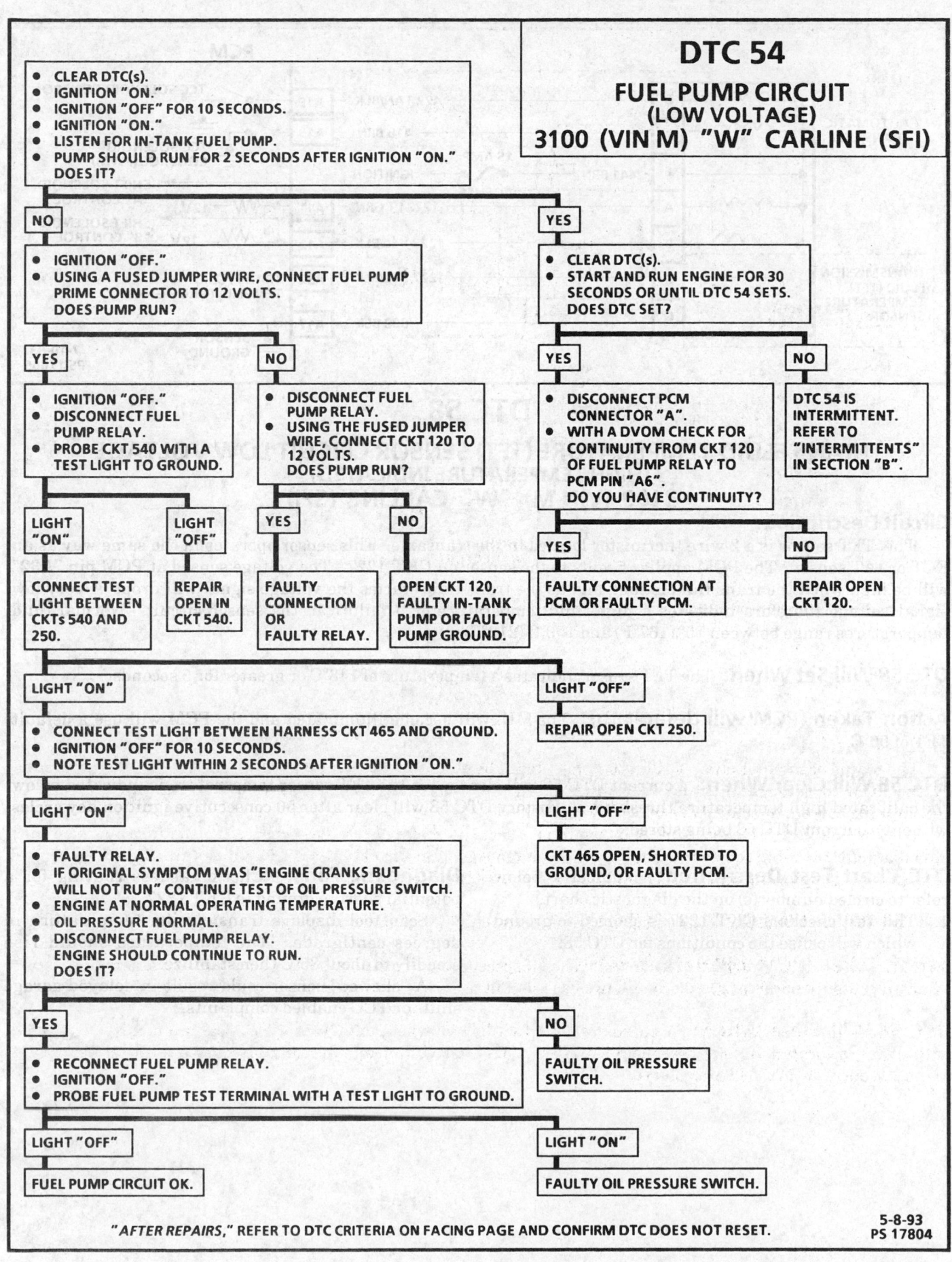

DTC 54
FUEL PUMP CIRCUIT
(LOW VOLTAGE)
3100 (VIN M) "W" CARLINE (SFI)

- CLEAR DTC(s).
- IGNITION "ON."
- IGNITION "OFF" FOR 10 SECONDS.
- IGNITION "ON."
- LISTEN FOR IN-TANK FUEL PUMP.
- PUMP SHOULD RUN FOR 2 SECONDS AFTER IGNITION "ON."
  DOES IT?

NO

- IGNITION "OFF."
- USING A FUSED JUMPER WIRE, CONNECT FUEL PUMP PRIME CONNECTOR TO 12 VOLTS.
  DOES PUMP RUN?

  - **YES**
    - IGNITION "OFF."
    - DISCONNECT FUEL PUMP RELAY.
    - PROBE CKT 540 WITH A TEST LIGHT TO GROUND.
      - **LIGHT "ON"**: CONNECT TEST LIGHT BETWEEN CKTs 540 AND 250.
        - **LIGHT "ON"**
          - CONNECT TEST LIGHT BETWEEN HARNESS CKT 465 AND GROUND.
          - IGNITION "OFF" FOR 10 SECONDS.
          - NOTE TEST LIGHT WITHIN 2 SECONDS AFTER IGNITION "ON."
            - **LIGHT "ON"**
              - FAULTY RELAY.
              - IF ORIGINAL SYMPTOM WAS "ENGINE CRANKS BUT WILL NOT RUN" CONTINUE TEST OF OIL PRESSURE SWITCH.
              - ENGINE AT NORMAL OPERATING TEMPERATURE.
              - OIL PRESSURE NORMAL.
              - DISCONNECT FUEL PUMP RELAY.
                ENGINE SHOULD CONTINUE TO RUN.
                DOES IT?
                - **YES**
                  - RECONNECT FUEL PUMP RELAY.
                  - IGNITION "OFF."
                  - PROBE FUEL PUMP TEST TERMINAL WITH A TEST LIGHT TO GROUND.
                    - **LIGHT "OFF"**: FUEL PUMP CIRCUIT OK.
                    - **LIGHT "ON"**: FAULTY OIL PRESSURE SWITCH.
                - **NO**: FAULTY OIL PRESSURE SWITCH.
            - **LIGHT "OFF"**: CKT 465 OPEN, SHORTED TO GROUND, OR FAULTY PCM.
        - **LIGHT "OFF"**: REPAIR OPEN CKT 250.
      - **LIGHT "OFF"**: REPAIR OPEN IN CKT 540.
  - **NO**
    - DISCONNECT FUEL PUMP RELAY.
    - USING THE FUSED JUMPER WIRE, CONNECT CKT 120 TO 12 VOLTS.
      DOES PUMP RUN?
      - **YES**: FAULTY CONNECTION OR FAULTY RELAY.
      - **NO**: OPEN CKT 120, FAULTY IN-TANK PUMP OR FAULTY PUMP GROUND.

YES

- CLEAR DTC(s).
- START AND RUN ENGINE FOR 30 SECONDS OR UNTIL DTC 54 SETS.
  DOES DTC SET?

  - **YES**
    - DISCONNECT PCM CONNECTOR "A".
    - WITH A DVOM CHECK FOR CONTINUITY FROM CKT 120 OF FUEL PUMP RELAY TO PCM PIN "A6".
      DO YOU HAVE CONTINUITY?
      - **YES**: FAULTY CONNECTION AT PCM OR FAULTY PCM.
      - **NO**: REPAIR OPEN CKT 120.
  - **NO**: DTC 54 IS INTERMITTENT. REFER TO "INTERMITTENTS" IN SECTION "B".

"*AFTER REPAIRS*," REFER TO DTC CRITERIA ON FACING PAGE AND CONFIRM DTC DOES NOT RESET.

5-8-93
PS 17804

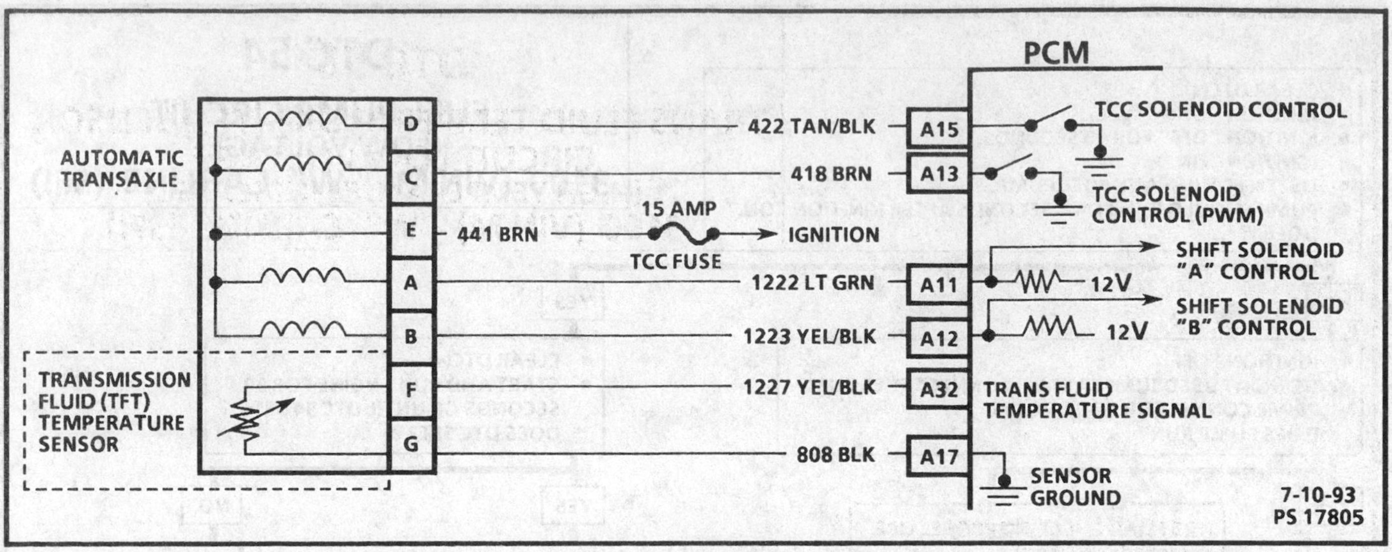
PCM
AUTOMATIC TRANSAXLE
D
C
E
A
B
F
G
422 TAN/BLK
418 BRN
441 BRN
15 AMP
TCC FUSE
IGNITION
1222 LT GRN
1223 YEL/BLK
1227 YEL/BLK
808 BLK
A15
A13
A11
A12
A32
A17
TCC SOLENOID CONTROL
TCC SOLENOID CONTROL (PWM)
SHIFT SOLENOID "A" CONTROL
SHIFT SOLENOID "B" CONTROL
12V
12V
TRANS FLUID TEMPERATURE SIGNAL
SENSOR GROUND
TRANSMISSION FLUID (TFT) TEMPERATURE SENSOR
7-10-93
PS 17805

DTC 58
TRANS FLUID TEMPERATURE (TFT) SENSOR CIRCUIT LOW VOLTAGE
(HIGH TEMPERATURE INDICATED)
3100 (VIN M) "W" CARLINE (SFI)

Circuit Description:

The TFT sensor is a 2 wire thermistor located in the transaxle. This sensor operates in the same way as an ECT or IAT sensor. The PCM applies 5 volts to the sensor on CKT 1227. The voltage sensed at PCM pin "A32" will be high when the trans fluid is cold, and as the trans fluid warms the voltage signal will drop. A very low signal voltage therefore indicates a high fluid temperature or a failure in the sensor circuit. Normal fluid temperatures range between 75° (167°F) and 100°C (212°F).

DTC 58 Will Set When: The TFT sensor indicates a temperature of 148°C or greater for 5 seconds.

Action Taken (PCM will default to): The MIL will become illuminated and the PCM will use a default TFT of 90°C.

DTC 58 Will Clear When: a current DTC 58 will clear when the TFT sensor temperature is indicated below the calibrated high temperature threshold. A History DTC 58 will clear after 50 consecutive ignition key cycles without a current DTC 58 being stored.

DTC Chart Test Description: Number(s) below refer to circled number(s) on the diagnostic chart.

1. This test checks if CKT 1227 is shorted to ground which will cause the conditions for DTC 58.

Diagnostic Aids: Check harness routing for a potential short to ground in CKT 1227.

Scan tool displays transmission temperature in degrees centigrade. The temperature should rise steadily to about 85°C then stabilize.

A "skewed" sensor could result in delayed garage shifts or TCC enabled complaints.

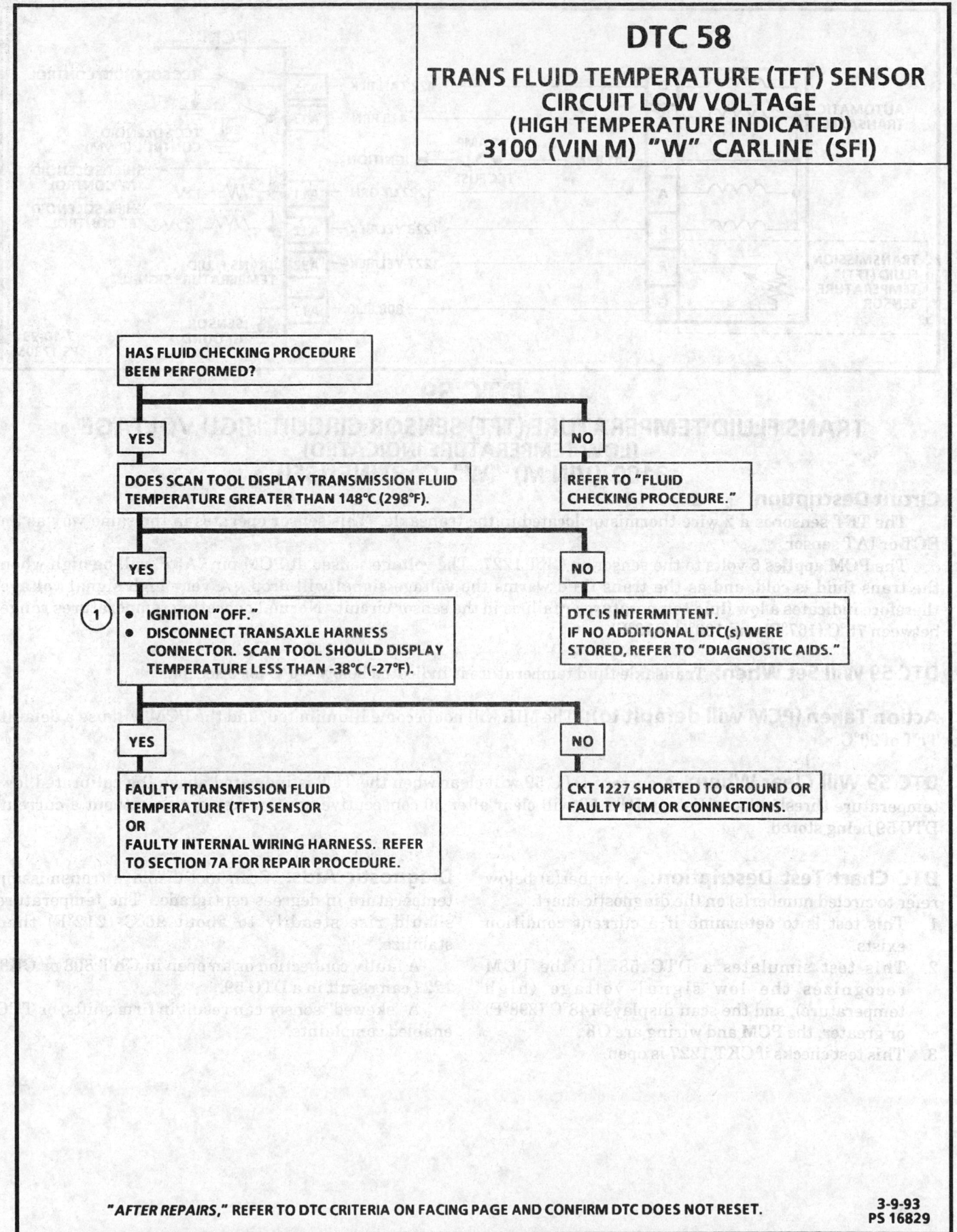

DTC 58

TRANS FLUID TEMPERATURE (TFT) SENSOR CIRCUIT LOW VOLTAGE (HIGH TEMPERATURE INDICATED) 3100 (VIN M) "W" CARLINE (SFI)

HAS FLUID CHECKING PROCEDURE BEEN PERFORMED?

- **YES** → **DOES SCAN TOOL DISPLAY TRANSMISSION FLUID TEMPERATURE GREATER THAN 148°C (298°F).**
  - **YES** → (1)
    - **IGNITION "OFF."**
    - **DISCONNECT TRANSAXLE HARNESS CONNECTOR. SCAN TOOL SHOULD DISPLAY TEMPERATURE LESS THAN -38°C (-27°F).**
      - **YES** → **FAULTY TRANSMISSION FLUID TEMPERATURE (TFT) SENSOR OR FAULTY INTERNAL WIRING HARNESS. REFER TO SECTION 7A FOR REPAIR PROCEDURE.**
      - **NO** → **CKT 1227 SHORTED TO GROUND OR FAULTY PCM OR CONNECTIONS.**
  - **NO** → **DTC IS INTERMITTENT. IF NO ADDITIONAL DTC(s) WERE STORED, REFER TO "DIAGNOSTIC AIDS."**
- **NO** → **REFER TO "FLUID CHECKING PROCEDURE."**

"AFTER REPAIRS," **REFER TO DTC CRITERIA ON FACING PAGE AND CONFIRM DTC DOES NOT RESET.**

3-9-93
PS 16829

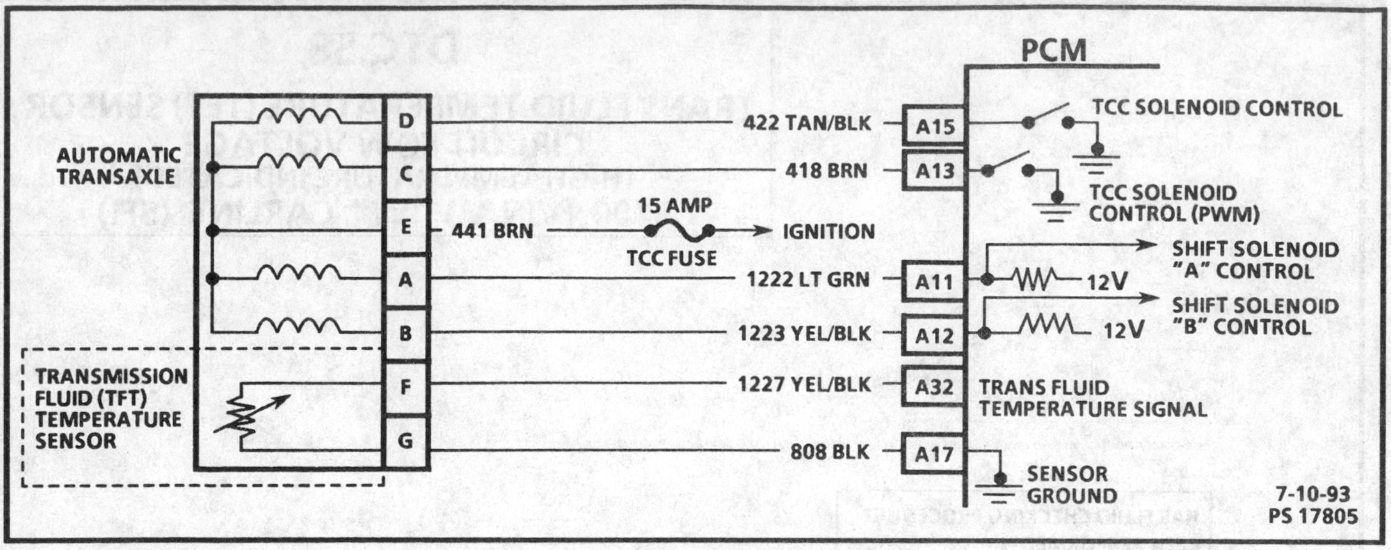
PCM
TCC SOLENOID CONTROL
AUTOMATIC TRANSAXLE
D
422 TAN/BLK
A15
C
418 BRN
A13
TCC SOLENOID CONTROL (PWM)
15 AMP
E
441 BRN
IGNITION
TCC FUSE
SHIFT SOLENOID "A" CONTROL
A
1222 LT GRN
A11
12V
SHIFT SOLENOID "B" CONTROL
B
1223 YEL/BLK
A12
12V
TRANSMISSION FLUID (TFT) TEMPERATURE SENSOR
F
1227 YEL/BLK
A32
TRANS FLUID TEMPERATURE SIGNAL
G
808 BLK
A17
SENSOR GROUND
7-10-93
PS 17805

DTC 59
TRANS FLUID TEMPERATURE (TFT) SENSOR CIRCUIT HIGH VOLTAGE
(LOW TEMPERATURE INDICATED)
3100 (VIN M) "W" CARLINE (SFI)

Circuit Description:

The TFT sensor is a 2 wire thermistor located in the transaxle. This sensor operates in the same way as an ECT or IAT sensor.

The PCM applies 5 volts to the sensor on CKT 1227. The voltage sensed at PCM pin "A32" will be high when the trans fluid is cold, and as the trans fluid warms the voltage signal will drop. A very high signal voltage therefore indicates a low fluid temperature or failure in the sensor circuit. Normal operating temperatures range between 75°C (167°F) and 100°C (212°F).

DTC 59 Will Set When: Transaxle fluid temperature is indicated below -40°C for 5 seconds.

Action Taken (PCM will default to): The MIL will not become illuminated, and the PCM will use a default TFT of 90°C.

DTC 59 Will Clear When: A current DTC 59 will clear when the TFT is indicated above the calibrated low temperature threshold. A History DTC 59 will clear after 50 consecutive ignition key cycles without a current DTC 59 being stored.

DTC Chart Test Description: Number(s) below refer to circled number(s) on the diagnostic chart.

1. This test is to determine if a current condition exists.
2. This test simulates a DTC 58. If the PCM recognizes the low signal voltage (high temperature), and the scan displays 148°C (298°F) or greater, the PCM and wiring are OK.
3. This test checks if CKT 1227 is open.

Diagnostic Aids: Scan tool displays transmission temperature in degrees centigrade. The temperature should rise steadily to about 90°C (212°F) then stabilize.

A faulty connection or an open in CKT 808 or CKT 1227 can result in a DTC 59.

A "skewed" sensor can result in firm shifts, or TCC enabled complaints.

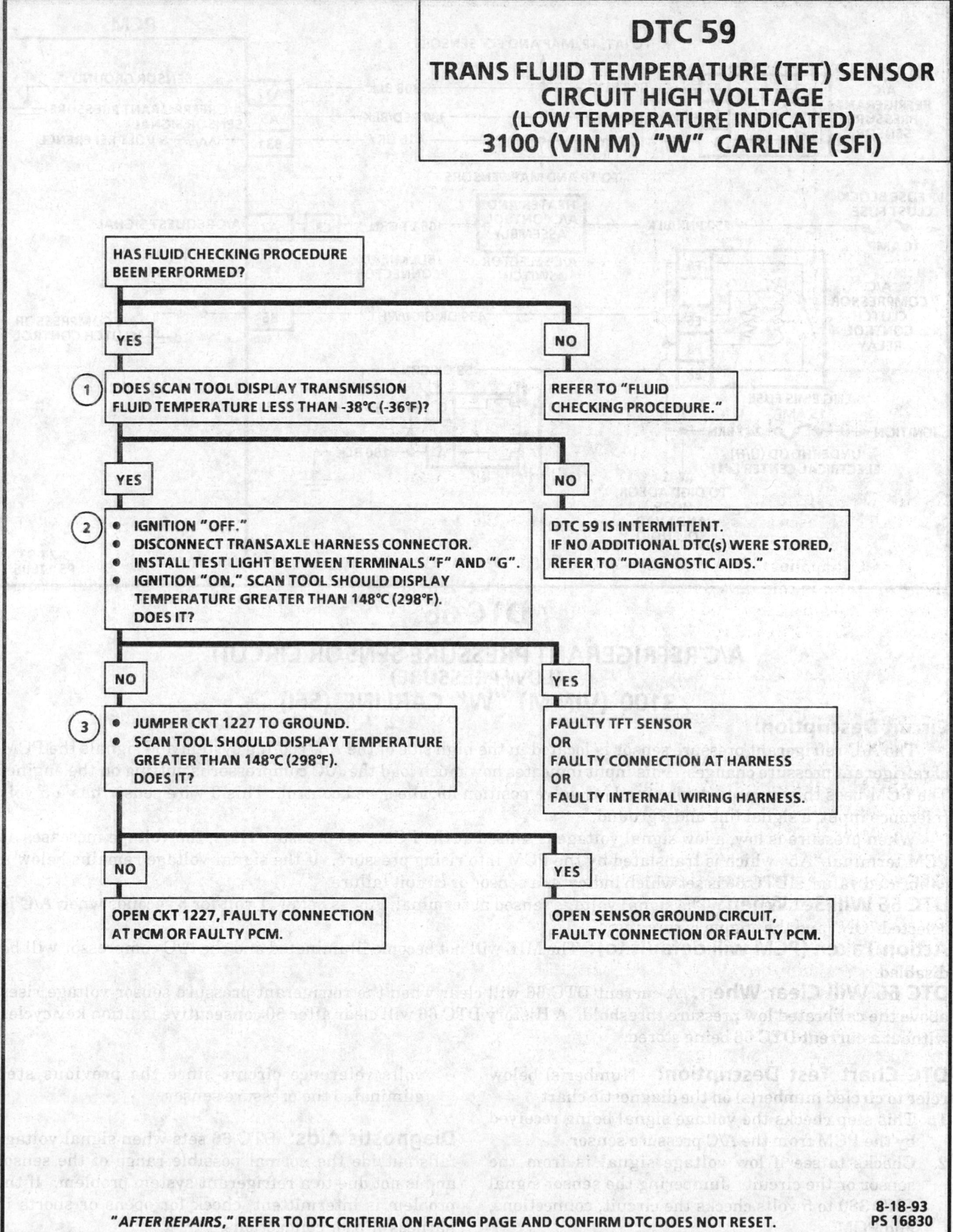

DTC 59
TRANS FLUID TEMPERATURE (TFT) SENSOR CIRCUIT HIGH VOLTAGE
(LOW TEMPERATURE INDICATED)
3100 (VIN M) "W" CARLINE (SFI)

HAS FLUID CHECKING PROCEDURE BEEN PERFORMED?

- YES → go to step 1.
- NO → REFER TO "FLUID CHECKING PROCEDURE."

1. DOES SCAN TOOL DISPLAY TRANSMISSION FLUID TEMPERATURE LESS THAN -38°C (-36°F)?
   - YES → go to step 2.
   - NO → DTC 59 IS INTERMITTENT. IF NO ADDITIONAL DTC(s) WERE STORED, REFER TO "DIAGNOSTIC AIDS."

2.
   - IGNITION "OFF."
   - DISCONNECT TRANSAXLE HARNESS CONNECTOR.
   - INSTALL TEST LIGHT BETWEEN TERMINALS "F" AND "G".
   - IGNITION "ON," SCAN TOOL SHOULD DISPLAY TEMPERATURE GREATER THAN 148°C (298°F). DOES IT?

   - NO → go to step 3.
   - YES → FAULTY TFT SENSOR OR FAULTY CONNECTION AT HARNESS OR FAULTY INTERNAL WIRING HARNESS.

3.
   - JUMPER CKT 1227 TO GROUND.
   - SCAN TOOL SHOULD DISPLAY TEMPERATURE GREATER THAN 148°C (298°F). DOES IT?

   - NO → OPEN CKT 1227, FAULTY CONNECTION AT PCM OR FAULTY PCM.
   - YES → OPEN SENSOR GROUND CIRCUIT, FAULTY CONNECTION OR FAULTY PCM.

"*AFTER REPAIRS,*" REFER TO DTC CRITERIA ON FACING PAGE AND CONFIRM DTC DOES NOT RESET.

8-18-93
PS 16830

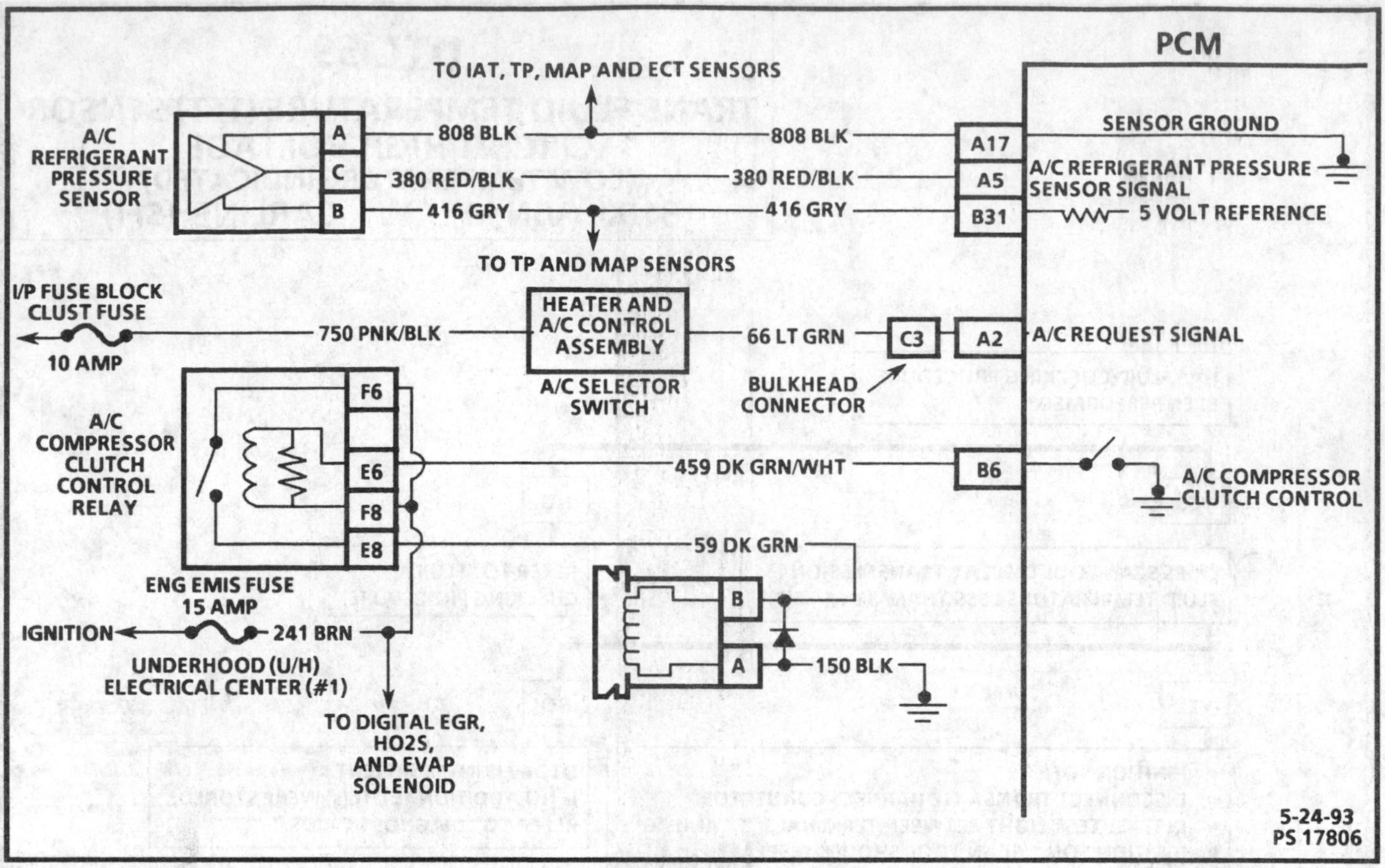

PCM
TO IAT, TP, MAP AND ECT SENSORS
A/C REFRIGERANT PRESSURE SENSOR
A
C
B
808 BLK
808 BLK
380 RED/BLK
380 RED/BLK
416 GRY
416 GRY
A17
A5
B31
SENSOR GROUND
A/C REFRIGERANT PRESSURE SENSOR SIGNAL
5 VOLT REFERENCE
TO TP AND MAP SENSORS
I/P FUSE BLOCK CLUST FUSE
10 AMP
750 PNK/BLK
HEATER AND A/C CONTROL ASSEMBLY
A/C SELECTOR SWITCH
66 LT GRN
C3
A2
A/C REQUEST SIGNAL
BULKHEAD CONNECTOR
A/C COMPRESSOR CLUTCH CONTROL RELAY
F6
E6
F8
E8
459 DK GRN/WHT
B6
A/C COMPRESSOR CLUTCH CONTROL
59 DK GRN
B
A
150 BLK
ENG EMIS FUSE 15 AMP
IGNITION
241 BRN
UNDERHOOD (U/H) ELECTRICAL CENTER (#1)
TO DIGITAL EGR, HO2S, AND EVAP SOLENOID
5-24-93
PS 17806

DTC 66

A/C REFRIGERANT PRESSURE SENSOR CIRCUIT
(LOW PRESSURE)
3100 (VIN M) "W" CARLINE (SFI)

Circuit Description:

The A/C refrigerant pressure sensor is located in the high side of the A/C cooling system and signals the PCM of refrigerant pressure changes. This input indicates how much load the A/C compressor is putting on the engine. The PCM uses this input to determine IAC valve position for idle speed control. This 3 wire sensor has a 5 volt reference input, a signal line and a ground.

When pressure is low, a low signal voltage is sensed at the PCM. As pressure rises, the voltage increases at PCM terminal "A5" which is translated by the PCM into rising pressure. If the signal voltage remains below a calibrated value, a DTC 66 is set which indicates a sensor or circuit failure.

DTC 66 Will Set When: The signal voltage sensed at terminal "A5" is below .1 volt for 5 seconds when A/C is selected "ON" and the engine is running.

Action Taken (PCM will default to): The MIL will not become illuminated and the A/C compressor will be disabled.

DTC 66 Will Clear When: A current DTC 66 will clear when the refrigerant pressure sensor voltage rises above the calibrated low pressure threshold. A History DTC 66 will clear after 50 consecutive ignition key cycles without a current DTC 66 being stored.

DTC Chart Test Description: Number(s) below refer to circled number(s) on the diagnostic chart.

1. This step checks the voltage signal being received by the PCM from the A/C pressure sensor.
2. Checks to see if low voltage signal is from the sensor or the circuit. Jumpering the sensor signal CKT 380 to 5 volts checks the circuit, connections, and PCM.
3. This step checks to see if the low signal voltage was due to an open in the sensor circuit or the 5 volts reference circuit since the previous step eliminated the pressure sensor.

Diagnostic Aids: DTC 66 sets when signal voltage falls outside the normal possible range of the sensor and is not due to a refrigerant system problem. If the problem is intermittent, check for opens or shorts in harness or poor connections.

DTC 66

A/C REFRIGERANT PRESSURE SENSOR CIRCUIT
(LOW PRESSURE)
3100 (VIN M) "W" CARLINE (SFI)

1
- IGNITION "ON," ENGINE "OFF."
- INSTALL TECH 1 SCAN TOOL
- IGNITION "ON" ENGINE NOT RUNNING
- SCAN A/C PRESSURE SENSOR VOLTAGE

IS VOLTAGE BELOW .1V?

YES → go to 2

NO → DTC 66 INTERMITTENT REFER TO "DIAGNOSTIC AIDS" ON FACING PAGE.

2
- DISCONNECT A/C PRESSURE SENSOR CONNECTOR.
- JUMPER TERMINALS "B" AND "C".

DOES TECH 1 SCAN DISPLAY ABOVE 4.6 VOLTS?

NO → go to 3

YES → FAULTY A/C PRESSURE SENSOR CONNECTION OR FAULTY PRESSURE SENSOR.

3
- REMOVE JUMPER.
- CONNECT VOLTMETER FROM TERMINAL "A" TO "B".

IS VOLTAGE ABOUT 5 VOLTS?

NO → WITH TEST LIGHT TO B +, PROBE REFRIGERANT PRESSURE SENSOR CONNECTOR TERMINAL "A". IS LIGHT "ON"?

- **NO** → OPEN A/C PRESSURE GROUND CKT 808.
- **YES** → OPEN CKT 416.

YES → FAULTY CKT 380 PCM CONNECTION OR OPEN CKT 380 OR FAULTY PCM CONNECTION OR FAULTY PCM.

"AFTER REPAIRS," REFER TO DTC CRITERIA ON FACING PAGE AND CONFIRM DTC DOES NOT RESET.

3-9-93
NS 15098

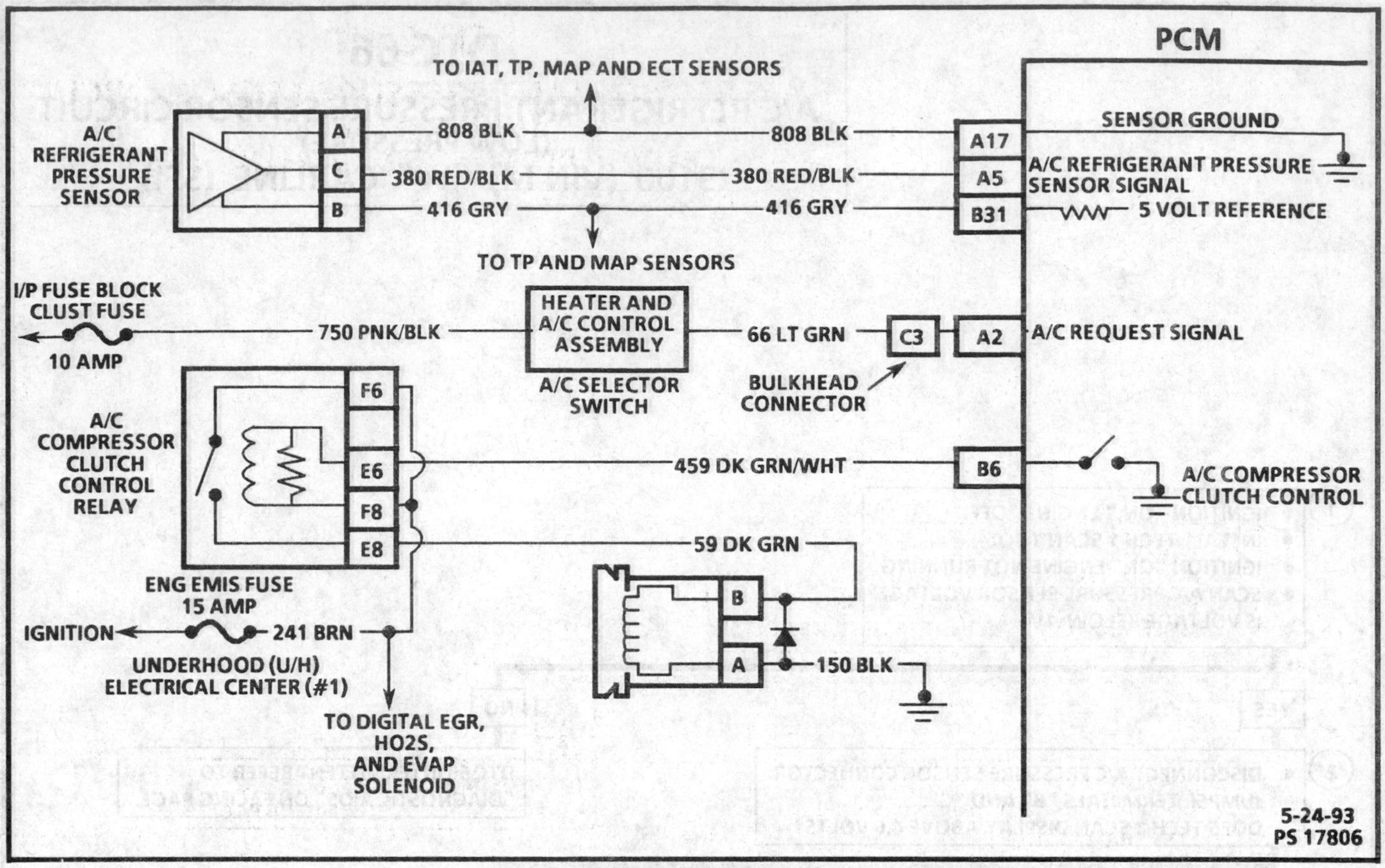
PCM
TO IAT, TP, MAP AND ECT SENSORS
A/C REFRIGERANT PRESSURE SENSOR
A
C
B
808 BLK
808 BLK
380 RED/BLK
380 RED/BLK
416 GRY
416 GRY
A17
A5
B31
SENSOR GROUND
A/C REFRIGERANT PRESSURE SENSOR SIGNAL
5 VOLT REFERENCE
TO TP AND MAP SENSORS
I/P FUSE BLOCK CLUST FUSE
10 AMP
750 PNK/BLK
HEATER AND A/C CONTROL ASSEMBLY
A/C SELECTOR SWITCH
66 LT GRN
C3
A2
A/C REQUEST SIGNAL
BULKHEAD CONNECTOR
A/C COMPRESSOR CLUTCH CONTROL RELAY
F6
E6
F8
E8
459 DK GRN/WHT
B6
A/C COMPRESSOR CLUTCH CONTROL
59 DK GRN
ENG EMIS FUSE 15 AMP
IGNITION
241 BRN
UNDERHOOD (U/H) ELECTRICAL CENTER (#1)
B
A
150 BLK
TO DIGITAL EGR, HO2S, AND EVAP SOLENOID
5-24-93
PS 17806

DTC 70

A/C REFRIGERANT PRESSURE SENSOR CIRCUIT (HIGH PRESSURE) 3100 (VIN M) "W" CARLINE (SFI)

Circuit Description:

The A/C refrigerant pressure sensor is located in the high side of the A/C cooling system and signals the PCM of refrigerant pressure changes. This input indicates how much load the A/C compressor is putting on the engine. The PCM uses this input to determine IAC valve position for idle speed control. This 3 wire sensor has a 5 volt reference input, a signal line and a ground.

When pressure is low, a low signal voltage is sensed at the PCM. As pressure rises, the voltage increases at PCM terminal "A5" which is translated by the PCM into rising pressure. If the signal voltage remains above a calibrated value, a DTC 70 is set which indicates a sensor or circuit failure.

DTC 70 Will Set When: The signal voltage sensed at terminal "A5" is above 4.9 volts for 5 seconds when A/C is selected and the engine is running.

Action Taken (PCM will default to): The MIL will not become illuminated, the A/C compressor will be disabled and the engine cooling fans will be enabled.

DTC 70 Will Clear When: A current DTC 70 will clear when the refrigerant pressure sensor signal falls below the calibrated high pressure threshold. A History DTC 70 will clear after 50 consecutive ignition key cycles without a current DTC 70 being stored.

DTC Chart Test Description: Number(s) below refer to circled number(s) on the diagnostic chart.

1. This step checks the voltage signal being received by the PCM from the A/C pressure sensor.
2. Checks to see if the high voltage signal is from a shorted sensor or a short to voltage in the circuit. Normally, disconnecting the sensor would make a normal circuit go to near zero volts.

Diagnostic Aids: DTC 70 sets when signal voltage falls outside the normal possible range of the sensor and is not due to a refrigerant system problem. If problem is intermittent, check for opens or shorts in harness or poor connections.

DTC 70
A/C REFRIGERANT PRESSURE SENSOR CIRCUIT
(HIGH PRESSURE)
3100 (VIN M) "W" CARLINE (SFI)

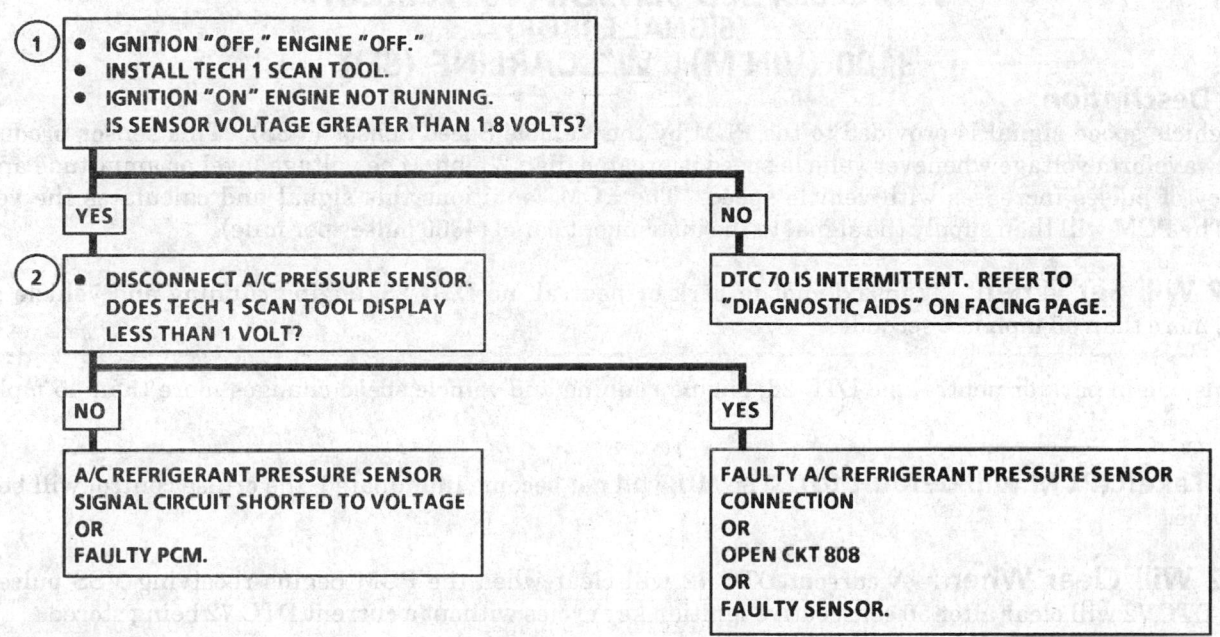

1
- IGNITION "OFF," ENGINE "OFF."
- INSTALL TECH 1 SCAN TOOL.
- IGNITION "ON" ENGINE NOT RUNNING.

IS SENSOR VOLTAGE GREATER THAN 1.8 VOLTS?

YES → go to step 2

NO → DTC 70 IS INTERMITTENT. REFER TO "DIAGNOSTIC AIDS" ON FACING PAGE.

2
- DISCONNECT A/C PRESSURE SENSOR.

DOES TECH 1 SCAN TOOL DISPLAY LESS THAN 1 VOLT?

NO → A/C REFRIGERANT PRESSURE SENSOR SIGNAL CIRCUIT SHORTED TO VOLTAGE OR FAULTY PCM.

YES → FAULTY A/C REFRIGERANT PRESSURE SENSOR CONNECTION OR OPEN CKT 808 OR FAULTY SENSOR.

"*AFTER REPAIRS,*" REFER TO DTC CRITERIA ON FACING PAGE AND CONFIRM DTC DOES NOT RESET.

3-10-93
NS 15097

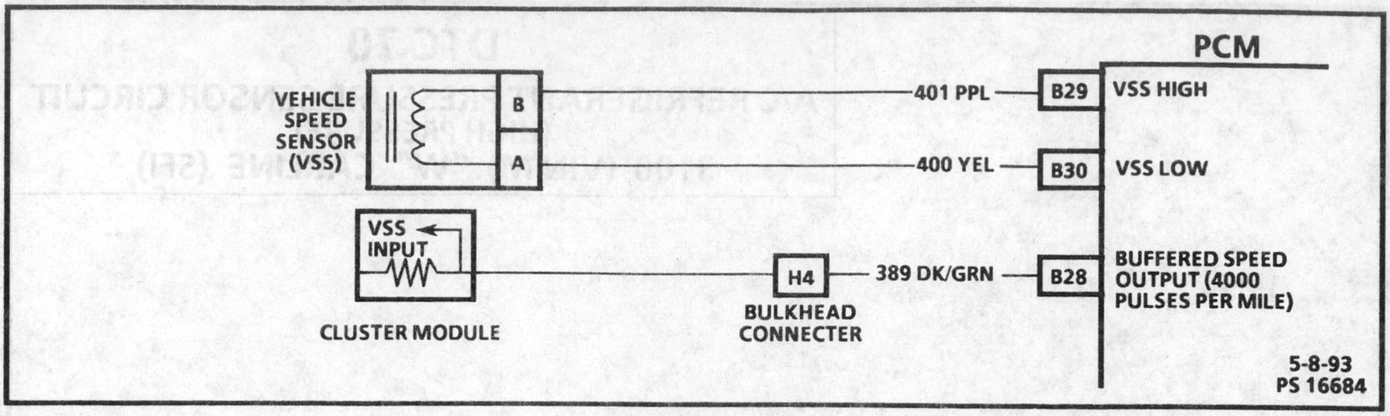
PCM
VEHICLE SPEED SENSOR (VSS)
B
A
401 PPL
B29
VSS HIGH
400 YEL
B30
VSS LOW
VSS INPUT
CLUSTER MODULE
H4
BULKHEAD CONNECTER
389 DK/GRN
B28
BUFFERED SPEED OUTPUT (4000 PULSES PER MILE)
5-8-93
PS 16684

DTC 72

VEHICLE SPEED SENSOR (VSS) CIRCUIT
(SIGNAL ERROR)
3100 (VIN M) "W" CARLINE (SFI)

Circuit Description:

A vehicle speed signal is provided to the PCM by the Vehicle Speed Sensor (VSS). This sensor produces a pulsing waveform voltage whenever vehicle speed is greater than 2 mph. The voltage level or amplitude and the frequency of pulses increases with vehicle speed. The PCM conditions this signal and calculates the vehicle speed. The PCM will then supply the signal to the instrument panel (4000 pulses per mile).

DTC 72 Will Set When: Transaxle not in park or neutral, no DTC 28, engine running and vehicle speed changes more than 33 mph in 2 seconds.

OR

Transaxle in park or neutral, no DTC 28, engine running and vehicle speed changes more than 45 mph in 2 seconds.

Action Taken (PCM will default to): The MIL will not become illuminated, the cruise control will become inoperative.

DTC 72 Will Clear When: A current DTC 72 will clear when the PCM begins receiving VSS pulses. A History DTC 72 will clear after 50 consecutive ignition key cycles without a current DTC 72 being stored.

DTC Chart Test Description: Number(s) below refer to circled number(s) on the diagnostic chart.

1. The sensor will produce a signal and vehicle speed only if the wheels are turning faster than 3 mph.
2. If CKTs 400, 401 and 389 are OK, and if the speedometer works correctly, DTC 24 is being caused by a faulty PCM or an incorrect program.

Diagnostic Aids: Tech 1 scan tool should indicate a vehicle speed whenever the drive wheels are turning at greater than 3 mph.

A problem in CKT 389 will not affect the VSS input or the readings on a Tech 1 scan tool.

Check CKT 400 and CKT 401 for proper connections to be sure they are clean and tight, and the harness is routed correctly. Refer to "Intermittents," in "Symptoms," Section "6E3-B".

DTC 72 is set when the PCM detects a loss of the VSS signal as the vehicle is moving at road speeds. This would typically indicate a hardware or circuit failure rather than a software or calibration error.

DTC 72

VEHICLE SPEED SENSOR (VSS) CIRCUIT (SIGNAL ERROR)

3100 (VIN M) "W" CARLINE (SFI)

DISREGARD DTC 24 IF SET WHILE DRIVE WHEELS ARE NOT TURNING.

(1)
- RAISE DRIVE WHEELS.
- **NOTICE:** DO NOT PERFORM THIS TEST WITHOUT SUPPORTING THE LOWER CONTROL ARMS SO THAT THE DRIVE AXLES ARE IN A NORMAL HORIZONTAL POSITION. RUNNING THE VEHICLE IN GEAR WITH THE WHEELS HANGING DOWN AT FULL TRAVEL MAY DAMAGE THE DRIVE AXLES.
- WITH ENGINE IDLING IN GEAR, TECH 1 SCAN TOOL SHOULD DISPLAY VEHICLE SPEED ABOVE 0.

DOES IT?

YES: DTC 24 IS INTERMITTENT. IF NO ADDITIONAL DTC(s) WERE STORED, REFER TO "DIAGNOSTIC AIDS" ON FACING PAGE.

NO: DOES SPEEDOMETER DISPLAY SPEED CORRECTLY?

- **YES:** (2) REPROGRAM THE PCM. IF DTC 24 IS STILL PRESENT, REPLACE PCM.
- **NO:**
  - IGNITION "OFF."
  - DISCONNECT VSS HARNESS CONNECTOR AT TRANSAXLE.
  - CONNECT SIGNAL GENERATOR TESTER J 33431-B OR EQUIVALENT TO VSS HARNESS CONNECTOR.
  - IGNITION "ON," SIGNAL GENERATOR TESTER "ON" AND SET TO GENERATE A VSS SIGNAL.
  - TECH 1 SCAN TOOL SHOULD DISPLAY VEHICLE SPEED ABOVE 0.

  DOES IT?

  - **NO:** CKT 400 OR 401 OPEN, SHORTED TO GROUND, SHORTED TOGETHER, FAULTY CONNECTIONS, OR FAULTY PCM.
  - **YES:** REPLACE VEHICLE SPEED SENSOR.

8-18-93
PS 17147

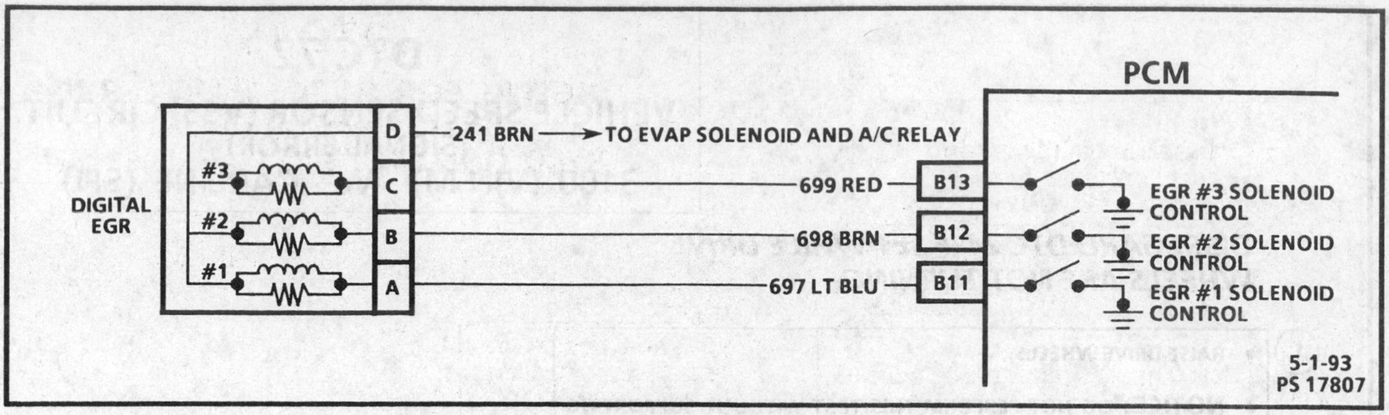
PCM
DIGITAL EGR
#3
#2
#1
D
C
B
A
241 BRN
TO EVAP SOLENOID AND A/C RELAY
699 RED
698 BRN
697 LT BLU
B13
B12
B11
EGR #3 SOLENOID CONTROL
EGR #2 SOLENOID CONTROL
EGR #1 SOLENOID CONTROL
5-1-93
PS 17807

DTC 75

DIGITAL EGR #1 SOLENOID ERROR
(ELECTRICAL DIAGNOSIS)
3100 (VIN M) "W" CARLINE (SFI)

Circuit Description:

Exhaust Gas Recirculation (EGR) is administered through a digitally controlled 3 solenoid valve unit. Each of the 3 valves is controlled individually and can be open or closed in any combination. During a long closed throttle deceleration, the PCM will cycle each valve open and measure a change in MAP. This test indicates if the valve is nonoperational electrically, or if an EGR passage is obstructed. If the PCM does not detect a change in MAP associated with solenoid #1 being commanded "ON," a DTC 75 will be set.

DTC 75 Will Set When: The engine speed is between 1400 and 2000 RPM, MAP is between 20 and 30 kPa, TP sensor angle is at 0%, all values must be held fairly constant for the test to run. The test must fail 3 consecutive times for a DTC 75 to be set.

Action Taken (PCM will default to): The MIL will become illuminated.

DTC 75 Will Clear When: The current DTC 75 will clear after each ignition key cycle, and will only reset when the test is run and fails again. A History DTC 75 will clear after 50 consecutive ignition key cycles without a current DTC 75 being stored.

DTC Chart Test Description: Number(s) below refer to circled number(s) on the diagnostic chart.

1. This test determines if there is power to the EGR valve.
2. This test will determine if there is an open circuit in the EGR wiring or if the EGR valve is at fault.
3. This test will determine if there is a short to ground in CKT 697 going to the EGR valve or if the PCM is at fault.

Diagnostic Aids: An intermittent may be caused by a poor connection, chaffed wire insulation, or a wire broken inside the insulation.

Intake plenum should be checked for possible plugged passages.

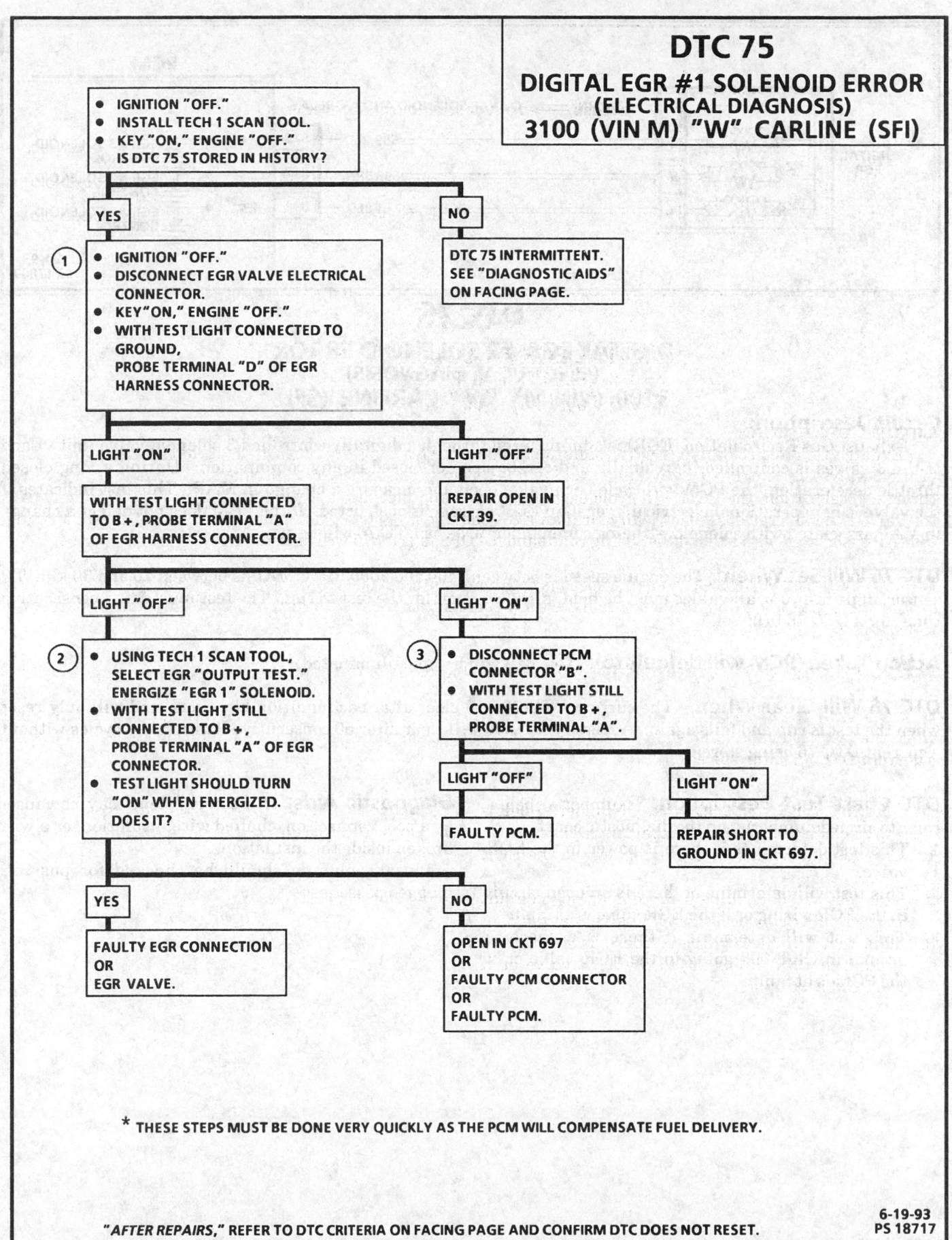

DTC 75
DIGITAL EGR #1 SOLENOID ERROR
(ELECTRICAL DIAGNOSIS)
3100 (VIN M) "W" CARLINE (SFI)

- IGNITION "OFF."
- INSTALL TECH 1 SCAN TOOL.
- KEY "ON," ENGINE "OFF." IS DTC 75 STORED IN HISTORY?

NO

DTC 75 INTERMITTENT. SEE "DIAGNOSTIC AIDS" ON FACING PAGE.

YES

(1)
- IGNITION "OFF."
- DISCONNECT EGR VALVE ELECTRICAL CONNECTOR.
- KEY "ON," ENGINE "OFF."
- WITH TEST LIGHT CONNECTED TO GROUND, PROBE TERMINAL "D" OF EGR HARNESS CONNECTOR.

LIGHT "OFF"

REPAIR OPEN IN CKT 39.

LIGHT "ON"

WITH TEST LIGHT CONNECTED TO B+, PROBE TERMINAL "A" OF EGR HARNESS CONNECTOR.

LIGHT "ON"

(3)
- DISCONNECT PCM CONNECTOR "B".
- WITH TEST LIGHT STILL CONNECTED TO B+, PROBE TERMINAL "A".

LIGHT "OFF"

FAULTY PCM.

LIGHT "ON"

REPAIR SHORT TO GROUND IN CKT 697.

LIGHT "OFF"

(2)
- USING TECH 1 SCAN TOOL, SELECT EGR "OUTPUT TEST." ENERGIZE "EGR 1" SOLENOID.
- WITH TEST LIGHT STILL CONNECTED TO B+, PROBE TERMINAL "A" OF EGR CONNECTOR.
- TEST LIGHT SHOULD TURN "ON" WHEN ENERGIZED. DOES IT?

YES

FAULTY EGR CONNECTION OR EGR VALVE.

NO

OPEN IN CKT 697 OR FAULTY PCM CONNECTOR OR FAULTY PCM.

* THESE STEPS MUST BE DONE VERY QUICKLY AS THE PCM WILL COMPENSATE FUEL DELIVERY.

"*AFTER REPAIRS*," REFER TO DTC CRITERIA ON FACING PAGE AND CONFIRM DTC DOES NOT RESET.

6-19-93
PS 18717

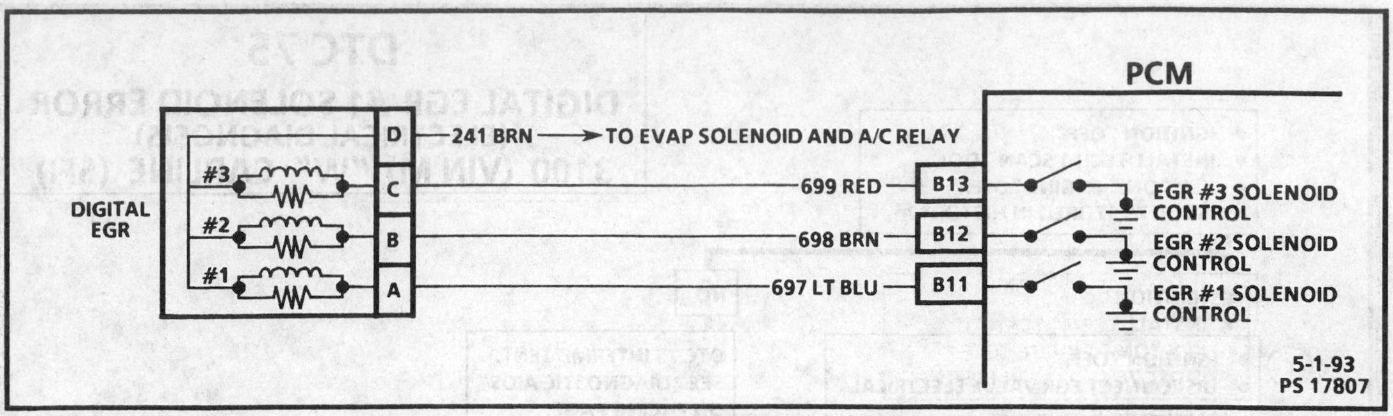
PCM
DIGITAL EGR
#3
#2
#1
D
C
B
A
241 BRN
TO EVAP SOLENOID AND A/C RELAY
699 RED
698 BRN
697 LT BLU
B13
B12
B11
EGR #3 SOLENOID CONTROL
EGR #2 SOLENOID CONTROL
EGR #1 SOLENOID CONTROL
5-1-93
PS 17807

DTC 76

DIGITAL EGR #2 SOLENOID ERROR
(ELECTRICAL DIAGNOSIS)
3100 (VIN M) "W" CARLINE (SFI)

Circuit Description:

Exhaust Gas Recirculation (EGR) is administered through a digitally controlled 3 solenoid valve unit. Each of the 3 valves is controlled individually and can be open or closed in any combination. During a long closed throttle deceleration, the PCM will cycle each valve open and measure a change in MAP. This test indicates if the valve is nonoperational electrically, or if an EGR passage is obstructed. If the PCM does not detect a change in MAP associated with solenoid #2 being commanded "ON," a DTC 76 will be set.

DTC 76 Will Set When: The engine speed is between 1400 and 2000 RPM, MAP is between 20 and 30 kPa, TP sensor angle is at 0%, all values must be held fairly constant for the test to run. The test must fail 3 consecutive times for a DTC 76 to be set.

Action Taken (PCM will default to): The MIL will become illuminated.

DTC 76 Will Clear When: The current DTC 76 will clear after each ignition key cycle, and will only reset when the test is run and fails again. A History DTC 76 will clear after 50 consecutive ignition key cycles without a current DTC 76 being stored.

DTC Chart Test Description: Number(s) below refer to circled number(s) on the diagnostic chart.

1. This test determines if there is power to the EGR valve.
2. This test will determine of there is an open circuit in the EGR wiring or if the EGR valve is at fault.
3. This test will determine if there is a short to ground in CKT 698 going to the EGR valve or if the PCM is at fault.

Diagnostic Aids: An intermittent may be caused by a poor connection, chaffed wire insulation, or a wire broken inside the insulation.

Intake plenum should be checked for possible plugged passages.

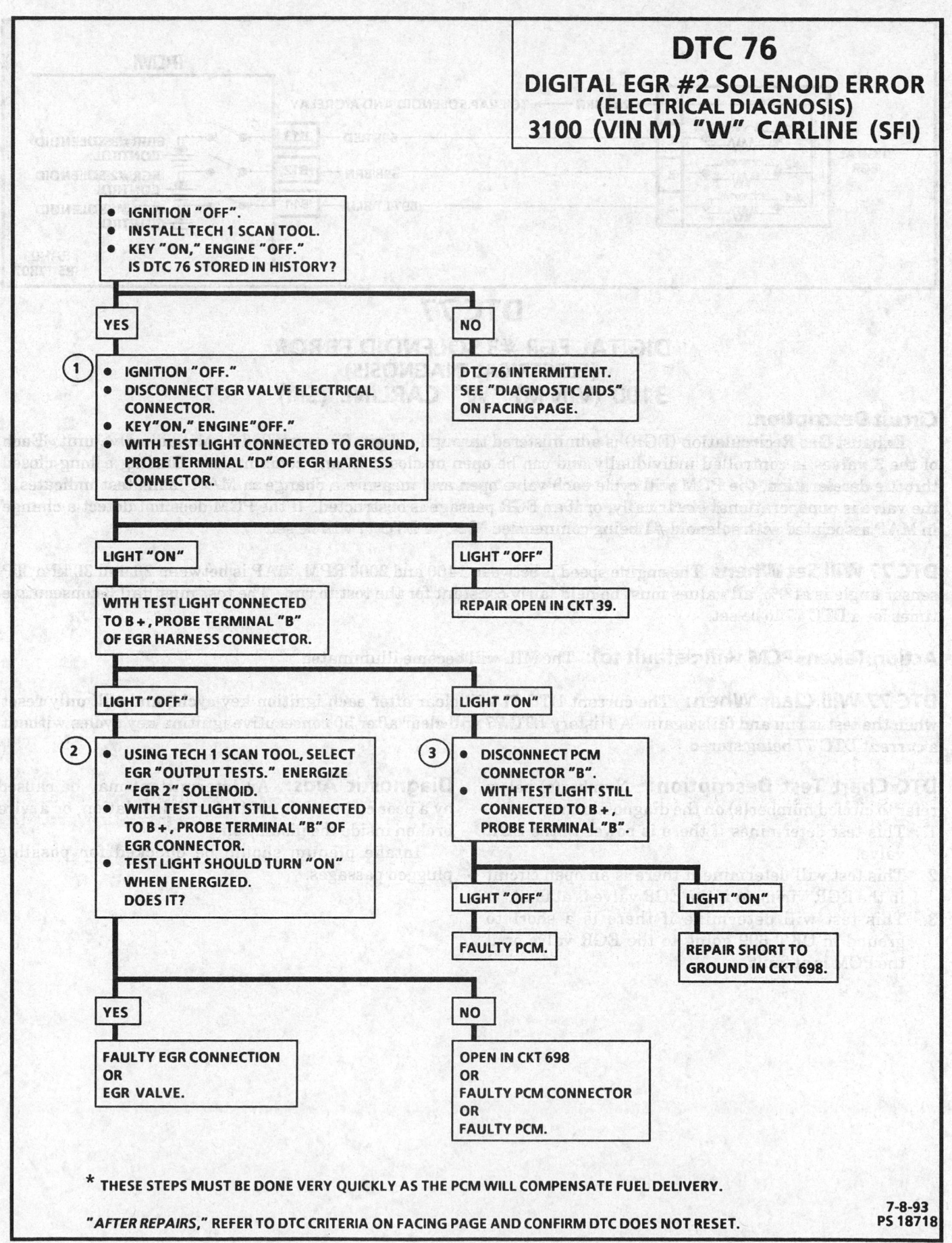

DTC 76

DIGITAL EGR #2 SOLENOID ERROR
(ELECTRICAL DIAGNOSIS)
3100 (VIN M) "W" CARLINE (SFI)

- IGNITION "OFF".
- INSTALL TECH 1 SCAN TOOL.
- KEY "ON," ENGINE "OFF."

IS DTC 76 STORED IN HISTORY?

YES

1
- IGNITION "OFF."
- DISCONNECT EGR VALVE ELECTRICAL CONNECTOR.
- KEY"ON," ENGINE"OFF."
- WITH TEST LIGHT CONNECTED TO GROUND, PROBE TERMINAL "D" OF EGR HARNESS CONNECTOR.

LIGHT "ON"

WITH TEST LIGHT CONNECTED TO B+, PROBE TERMINAL "B" OF EGR HARNESS CONNECTOR.

LIGHT "OFF"

2
- USING TECH 1 SCAN TOOL, SELECT EGR "OUTPUT TESTS." ENERGIZE "EGR 2" SOLENOID.
- WITH TEST LIGHT STILL CONNECTED TO B+, PROBE TERMINAL "B" OF EGR CONNECTOR.
- TEST LIGHT SHOULD TURN "ON" WHEN ENERGIZED.

DOES IT?

YES

FAULTY EGR CONNECTION OR EGR VALVE.

NO

OPEN IN CKT 698 OR FAULTY PCM CONNECTOR OR FAULTY PCM.

LIGHT "ON"

3
- DISCONNECT PCM CONNECTOR "B".
- WITH TEST LIGHT STILL CONNECTED TO B+, PROBE TERMINAL "B".

LIGHT "OFF"

FAULTY PCM.

LIGHT "ON"

REPAIR SHORT TO GROUND IN CKT 698.

LIGHT "OFF"

REPAIR OPEN IN CKT 39.

NO

DTC 76 INTERMITTENT. SEE "DIAGNOSTIC AIDS" ON FACING PAGE.

* THESE STEPS MUST BE DONE VERY QUICKLY AS THE PCM WILL COMPENSATE FUEL DELIVERY.

"*AFTER REPAIRS*," REFER TO DTC CRITERIA ON FACING PAGE AND CONFIRM DTC DOES NOT RESET.

7-8-93
PS 18718

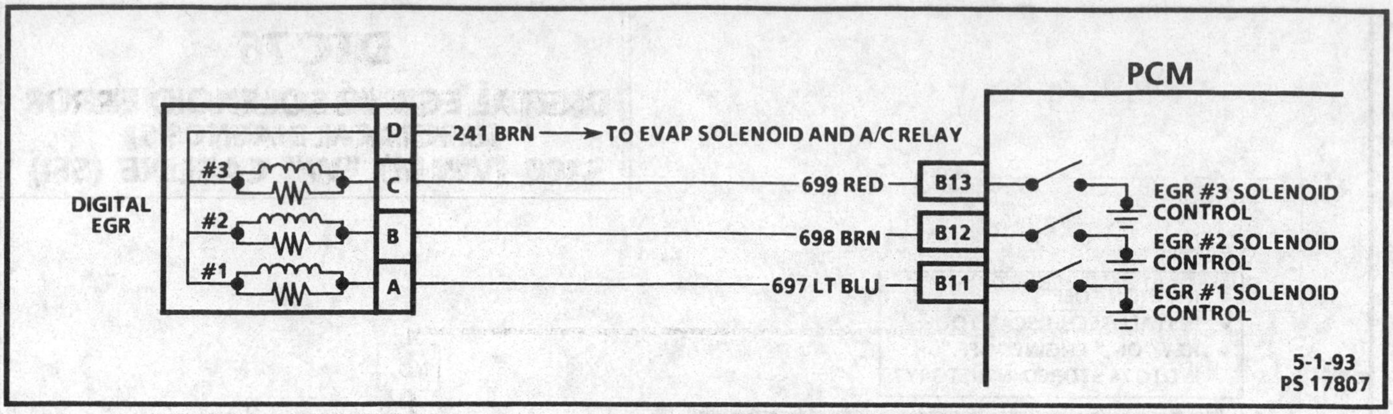
PCM
D
241 BRN
TO EVAP SOLENOID AND A/C RELAY
DIGITAL EGR
#3
#2
#1
C
B
A
699 RED
698 BRN
697 LT BLU
B13
B12
B11
EGR #3 SOLENOID CONTROL
EGR #2 SOLENOID CONTROL
EGR #1 SOLENOID CONTROL
5-1-93
PS 17807

DTC 77

DIGITAL EGR #3 SOLENOID ERROR
(ELECTRICAL DIAGNOSIS)
3100 (VIN M) "W" CARLINE (SFI)

Circuit Description:

Exhaust Gas Recirculation (EGR) is administered through a digitally controlled 3 solenoid valve unit. Each of the 3 valves is controlled individually and can be open or closed in any combination. During a long closed throttle deceleration, the PCM will cycle each valve open and measure a change in MAP. This test indicates if the valve is nonoperational electrically, or if an EGR passage is obstructed. If the PCM does not detect a change in MAP associated with solenoid #1 being commanded "ON," a DTC 77 will be set.

DTC 77 Will Set When: The engine speed is between 1400 and 2000 RPM, MAP is between 20 and 30 kPa, TP sensor angle is at 0%, all values must be held fairly constant for the test to run. The test must fail 3 consecutive times for a DTC 77 to be set.

Action Taken (PCM will default to): The MIL will become illuminated.

DTC 77 Will Clear When: The current DTC 77 will clear after each ignition key cycle, and will only reset when the test is run and fails again. A History DTC 77 will clear after 50 consecutive ignition key cycles without a current DTC 77 being stored.

DTC Chart Test Description: Number(s) below refer to circled number(s) on the diagnostic chart.

1. This test determines if there is power to the EGR valve.
2. This test will determine if there is an open circuit in the EGR wiring or if the EGR valve is at fault.
3. This test will determine if there is a short to ground in CKT 699 going to the EGR valve or if the PCM is at fault.

Diagnostic Aids: An intermittent may be caused by a poor connection, chaffed wire insulation, or a wire broken inside the insulation.

Intake plenum should be checked for possible plugged passages.

DTC 77
DIGITAL EGR #3 SOLENOID ERROR
(ELECTRICAL DIAGNOSIS)
3100 (VIN M) "W" CARLINE (SFI)

- IGNITION "OFF."
- INSTALL TECH 1 SCAN TOOL.
- KEY "ON," ENGINE "OFF."
  IS DTC 77 STORED IN HISTORY?

NO

DTC 77 INTERMITTENT.
SEE "DIAGNOSTIC AIDS" ON FACING PAGE.

YES

(1)
- IGNITION "OFF."
- DISCONNECT EGR VALVE ELECTRICAL CONNECTOR.
- KEY "ON," ENGINE "OFF."
- WITH TEST LIGHT CONNECTED TO GROUND, PROBE TERMINAL "D" OF EGR HARNESS CONNECTOR.

LIGHT "OFF"

REPAIR OPEN IN CKT 39.

LIGHT "ON"

WITH TEST LIGHT CONNECTED TO B +, PROBE TERMINAL "C" OF EGR HARNESS CONNECTOR.

LIGHT "ON"

(3)
- DISCONNECT PCM CONNECTOR "B."
- WITH TEST LIGHT STILL CONNECTED TO B +, PROBE TERMINAL "C".

LIGHT "OFF"

FAULTY PCM

LIGHT "ON"

REPAIR SHORT TO GROUND IN CKT 699.

LIGHT "OFF"

(2)
- USING TECH 1 SCAN TOOL, SELECT EGR "OUTPUT TEST." ENERGIZE "EGR 3" SOLENOID.
- WITH TEST LIGHT STILL CONNECTED TO B +, PROBE TERMINAL "C" OF EGR CONNECTOR.
- TEST LIGHT SHOULD TURN "ON" WHEN ENERGIZED.
  DOES IT?

YES

FAULTY EGR CONNECTION
OR
EGR VALVE.

NO

OPEN IN CKT 699
OR
FAULTY PCM CONNECTION
OR
FAULTY PCM.

* THESE STEPS MUST BE DONE VERY QUICKLY AS THE PCM WILL COMPENSATE FUEL DELIVERY.

"AFTER REPAIRS," REFER TO DTC CRITERIA ON FACING PAGE AND CONFIRM DTC DOES NOT RESET.

6-19-93
PS 18719

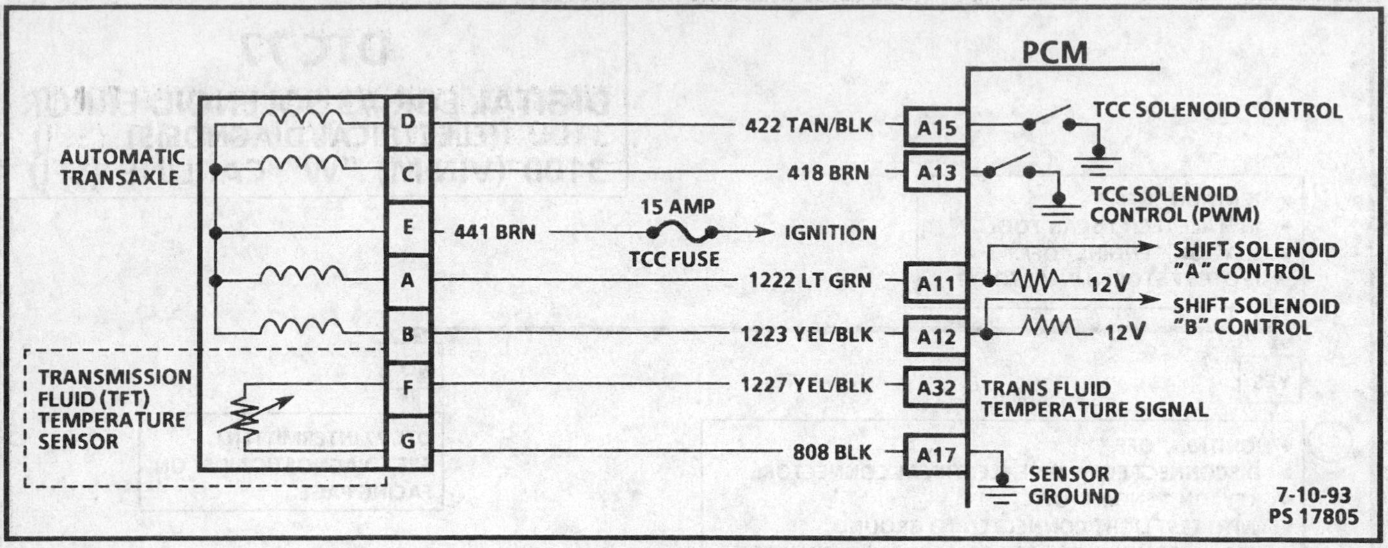
PCM
TCC SOLENOID CONTROL
AUTOMATIC TRANSAXLE
D
C
E
A
B
F
G
422 TAN/BLK
A15
418 BRN
A13
TCC SOLENOID CONTROL (PWM)
15 AMP
441 BRN
TCC FUSE
IGNITION
SHIFT SOLENOID "A" CONTROL
1222 LT GRN
A11
12V
SHIFT SOLENOID "B" CONTROL
1223 YEL/BLK
A12
12V
TRANSMISSION FLUID (TFT) TEMPERATURE SENSOR
1227 YEL/BLK
A32
TRANS FLUID TEMPERATURE SIGNAL
808 BLK
A17
SENSOR GROUND
7-10-93
PS 17805

DTC 79

TRANSMISSION FLUID OVERTEMP
3100 (VIN M) "W" CARLINE (SFI)

Circuit Description:

The TFT sensor is a 2 wire thermistor located in the transaxle. This sensor operates in the same way as an ECT or IAT sensor. 5 volts is applied to the sensor on CKT 1227 by the PCM. The voltage sensed at PCM pin "A32" will be high when the trans fluid is cold, and as the transaxle fluid warms the signal voltage will drop. A very low signal voltage therefore indicates a high fluid temperature. If the transaxle is driven under harsh conditions for an extended period, a DTC 79 will set to alert the driver of a transaxle over temperature condition. A trans fluid check should be made any time this DTC is stored.

Refer to SECTION 7A for the correct procedure.

DTC 79 Will Set When: No current DTC 58 or 59 is set and trans fluid temp is between 120°C and 130°C for 5 seconds.

Action Taken (PCM will default to): TCC will become engaged, in 2nd, 3rd or 4th gears to help cool the trans fluid. Shift patterns will change to best enable cooler transaxle operation. The MIL will not become illuminated.

DTC 79 Will Clear When: A current DTC 79 will clear when the TFT senses fluid temperature has fallen below 120°C. A History DTC 79 will clear after 50 consecutive ignition key cycles without a current DTC 79 being stored.

DTC 79
TRANSMISSION FLUID OVERTEMP 3100 (VIN M) "W" CARLINE (SFI)

DTC 79 INDICATES A TRANSMISSION FLUID OVER TEMPERATURE CONDITION HAS OCCURRED. THE PCM DETERMINES IF THE TFT TEMPERATURE IS ACCURATE BY CHECKING FOR GROSS FAILURES OF THE TFT SENSOR FIRST (DTC 58, 59). WHEN VALID DATA IS ESTABLISHED, A DTC 79 WILL BE SET IF THE TFT SENSOR INDICATES ABOVE 130°C AND WILL CLEAR FROM CURRENT DTC WHEN THE TEMPERATURE FALLS BELOW 120°C. SECTION 7A SHOULD BE CONSULTED FOR POSSIBLE CONDITIONS THAT WOULD CAUSE A TRANSMISSION OVER TEMPERATURE CONDITION. DRIVING CONDITIONS i.e. TRAILER TOWING, STEEP GRADES ect., SHOULD NOT BE DISCOUNTED. REFER TO SECTION 7A FOR TRANSMISSION FLUID CHECKING PROCEDURES.

***"AFTER REPAIRS,"* REFER TO DTC CRITERIA ON FACING PAGE AND CONFIRM DTC DOES NOT RESET.**

3-9-93
PS 16827

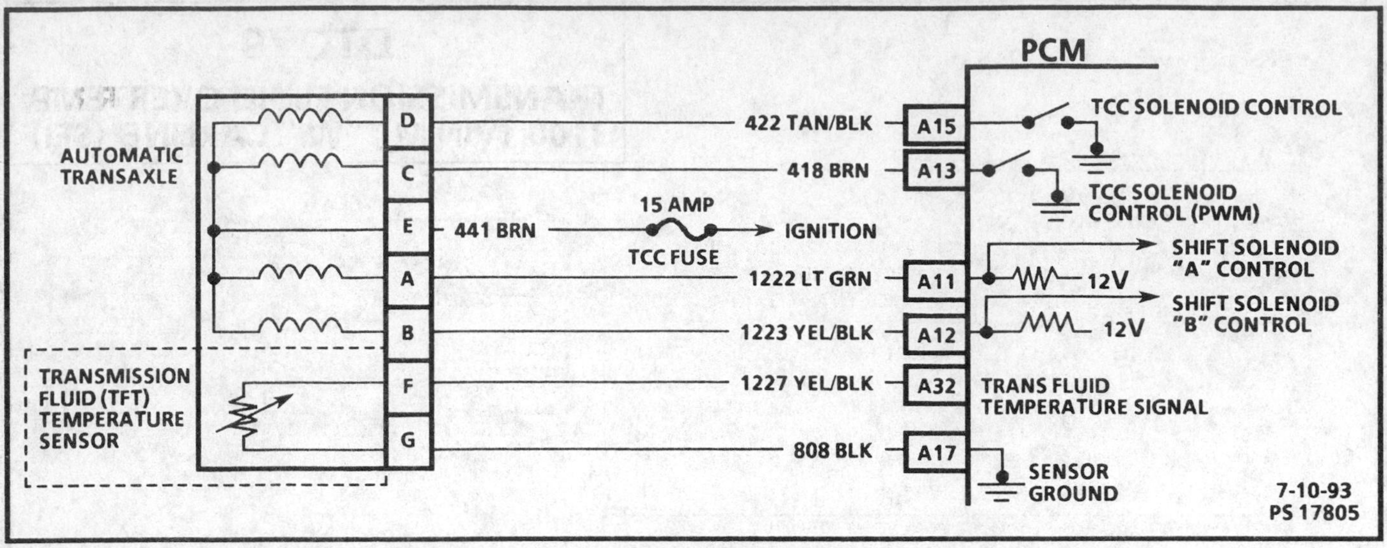
PCM
AUTOMATIC TRANSAXLE
D
C
E
A
B
F
G
TRANSMISSION FLUID (TFT) TEMPERATURE SENSOR
422 TAN/BLK
418 BRN
441 BRN
15 AMP
TCC FUSE
IGNITION
1222 LT GRN
1223 YEL/BLK
1227 YEL/BLK
808 BLK
A15
A13
A11
A12
A32
A17
TCC SOLENOID CONTROL
TCC SOLENOID CONTROL (PWM)
SHIFT SOLENOID "A" CONTROL
12V
SHIFT SOLENOID "B" CONTROL
12V
TRANS FLUID TEMPERATURE SIGNAL
SENSOR GROUND
7-10-93
PS 17805

DTC 80
TRANSMISSION COMPONENT ERROR
3100 (VIN M) "W" CARLINE (SFI)

Circuit Description:

The Torque Converter Clutch (TCC) is monitored for slip by calculating the difference between engine speed and transaxle output shaft speed (VSS). When the TCC is engaged, a nominal amount of slippage will be acceptable and is caused by small calculation errors. A slippage of 10 to 25 RPM is not uncommonly seen using a scan tool when TCC is engaged.

DTC 80 Will Set When: Gear selector in 3rd or 4th gear, engine running, TCC is commanded "ON," throttle angle is between 1% and 74%, TFT is between 40° and 80° and more than 150 RPM slippage is detected for 8 seconds.

Action Taken (PCM will default to): TCC and 4th gear will become disengaged. "D1", "D2" and "D3" will continue to be selected. The MIL will not become illuminated.

DTC 80 Will Clear When: A current DTC 80 will clear after each ignition cycle. A History DTC 80 will clear after 50 consecutive ignition key cycles without a current DTC 80 being stored.

DTC Chart Test Description: Number(s) below refer to circled number(s) on the diagnostic chart.

1. This test checks for circuit continuity of the TCC apply solenoid.
2. This checks for an open in the power feed CKT 441.
3. This test checks the PWM return circuitry to the PCM.

Diagnostic Aids: The Tech 1 only indicates when the PCM has commanded the TCC driver "ON"; this does not confirm that the TCC is actually engaged. To determine if TCC is functioning properly, road test the vehicle. Engine RPM should decrease when the Tech 1 indicates the TCC has been turned "ON." If diagnosis indicates that all electrical circuits and components are OK, refer to "Automatic Transaxle Diagnosis," SECTION 4T60-E for hydraulic and mechanical diagnosis.

DTC 80

TRANSMISSION COMPONENT ERROR 3100 (VIN M) "W" CARLINE (SFI)

- INSTALL TECH 1.
- IGNITION "ON," ENGINE "OFF."
- SCAN TCC BRAKE SW. WITH TECH 1 WHILE APPLYING AND RELEASING BRAKE PEDAL. TECH 1 SHOULD INDICATE PROPER STATE OF BRAKE SWITCH. IF NOT, REFER TO DTC 37 CHART FOR DIAGNOSIS. IF OK, CONTINUE.
- UNDER MISCELLANEOUS TEST, SELECT TRANSMISSION OUTPUT, TCC SOLENOID CONTROL.
- USING A STETHOSCOPE ON THE TRANSAXLE, YOU SHOULD BE ABLE TO HEAR THE TCC APPLY SOLENOID CLICK "ON" WHEN THE "↑" IS PRESSED AND CLICK "OFF" WHEN "↓" IS PRESSED.

DOES THE SOLENOID CLICK?

NO → (1)

- IGNITION "ON," ENGINE "OFF."
- DISCONNECT TRANSAXLE HARNESS CONNECTOR.
- CONNECT A TEST LIGHT BETWEEN TERMINALS "E" AND "D" OF TRANSAXLE HARNESS CONNECTOR.
- CYCLE TCC SOLENOID "ON" AND "OFF" USING TECH 1.
- TEST LIGHT SHOULD TURN "ON" AND "OFF."

DOES IT?

- **NO**
  - IGNITION "ON," ENGINE "OFF."
  - USING TEST LIGHT CONNECTED TO GROUND, PROBE TERMINAL "E" OF TCC HARNESS CONNECTOR.
  - LIGHT SHOULD BE "ON."

  IS IT?
  - **YES** → CKT 422 OPEN OR SHORTED TO GROUND OR POOR CONNECTION AT PCM TERMINAL "A15" OR FAULTY PCM.
  - **NO** → CHECK TCC FUSE AND REPAIR SHORT TO GROUND IN CKT 441 BRN IF BLOWN IF FUSE IS OK, REPAIR OPEN IN CKT 441 TO TRANSAXLE.
- **YES** → FAULTY INTERNAL TRANSAXLE WIRING OR FAULTY TCC APPLY SOLENOID.

YES → (2)

- DISCONNECT TRANSAXLE HARNESS CONNECTOR.
- CONNECT A TEST LIGHT BETWEEN TERMINALS "E" AND GROUND.
- TEST LIGHT SHOULD BE "ON."

IS IT?

- **NO** → OPEN CIRCUIT 441 OR FAULTY CONNECTION AT TRANSAXLE HARNESS CONNECTOR.
- **YES**
  - IGNITION "OFF."
  - WITH DVM, CHECK RESISTANCE OF TCC PWM SOLENOID BETWEEN TRANSAXLE CONNECTOR TERMINALS "E" AND "C" AT TRANSAXLE.
  - REFER TO TABLE FOR TCC PWM RESISTANCE SPECIFICATION.

  IS RESISTANCE OK?
  - **NO** → FAULTY INTERNAL TRANSAXLE WIRING OR FAULTY TCC PWM SOLENOID.
  - **YES** → (3)
    - IGNITION ON.
    - WITH TEST LIGHT CONNECTED TO B +, PROBE TERMINAL "C" OF TCC HARNESS.
    - LIGHT SHOULD BE "ON."

    IS IT?
    - **YES** → TCC CIRCUITS OK. SEE "DIAGNOSTIC AIDS" ON FACING PAGE.
    - **NO**
      - IGNITION "OFF."
      - RECONNECT TCC HARNESS CONNECTOR.
      - DISCONNECT PCM CONNECTOR A.
      - IGNITION "ON."
      - WITH TEST LIGHT CONNECTED TO GROUND, PROBE TERMINAL "A13".
      - LIGHT SHOULD BE "ON."

      IS IT?
      - **YES** → FAULTY PCM CONNECTION OR FAULTY PCM.
      - **NO** → OPEN CKT 418 OR FAULTY TERMINAL CONNECTIONS.

SOLENOID RESISTANCE VS. TRANSAXLE TEMPERATURE TABLE

SOLENOID	RESISTANCE AT 68°F (20°C)	RESISTANCE AT 190°F (88°C)
SHIFT A & B	20-30Ω	23-50Ω
TCC APPLY	20-30Ω	23-50Ω
TCC PWM	10-15Ω	11-27Ω

* RESISTANCE VALUES INCREASE AT HIGHER TEMPERATURES AND DECREASE AT LOWER TEMPERATURES.

"AFTER REPAIRS," REFER TO DTC CRITERIA ON FACING PAGE AND CONFIRM DTC DOES NOT RESET.

5-1-93
PS 17826

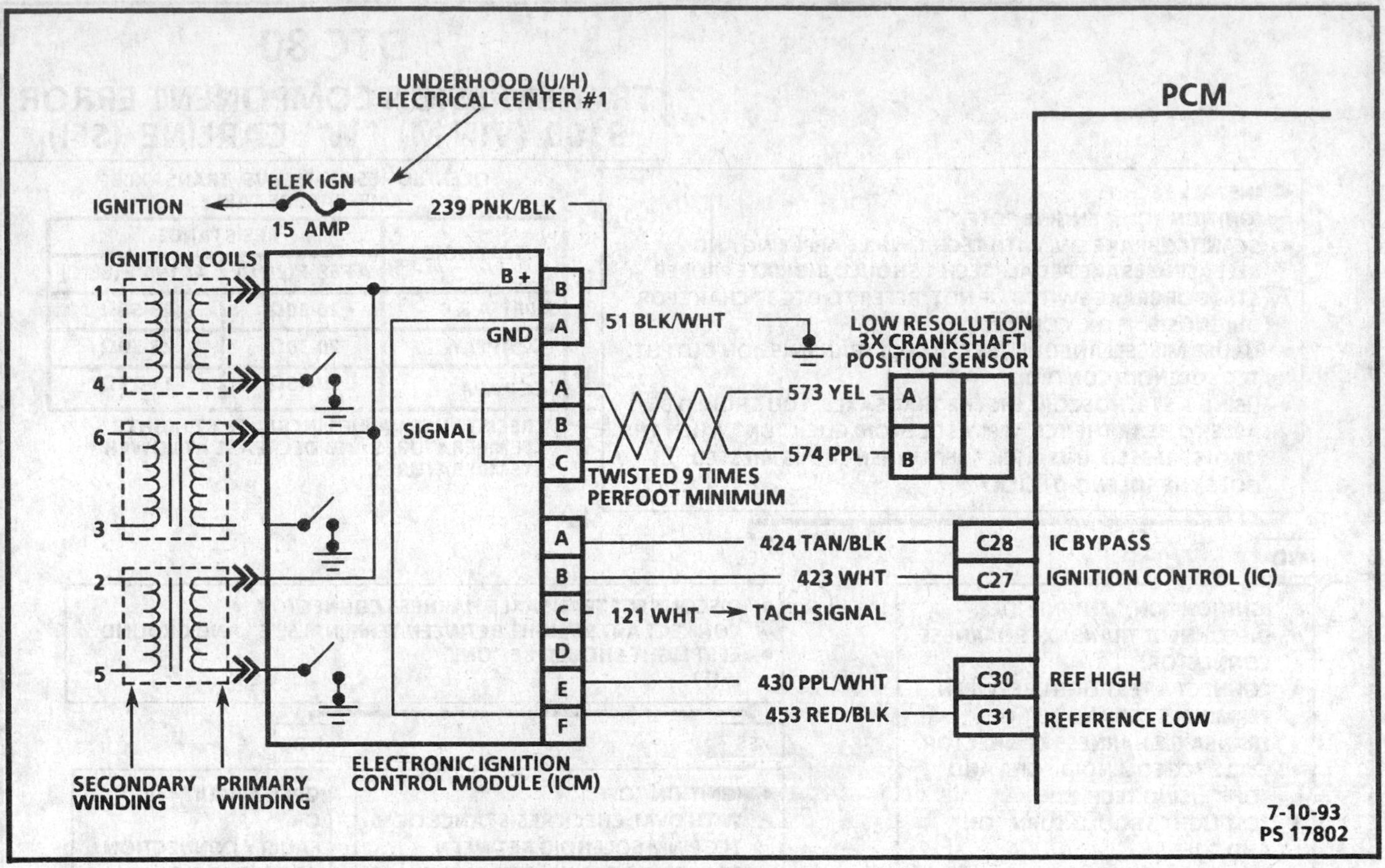
UNDERHOOD (U/H) ELECTRICAL CENTER #1
PCM
ELEK IGN
IGNITION
239 PNK/BLK
15 AMP
IGNITION COILS
B+
B
A
51 BLK/WHT
GND
LOW RESOLUTION 3X CRANKSHAFT POSITION SENSOR
573 YEL
574 PPL
SIGNAL
TWISTED 9 TIMES PERFOOT MINIMUM
424 TAN/BLK
C28
IC BYPASS
423 WHT
C27
IGNITION CONTROL (IC)
121 WHT
TACH SIGNAL
430 PPL/WHT
C30
REF HIGH
453 RED/BLK
C31
REFERENCE LOW
ELECTRONIC IGNITION CONTROL MODULE (ICM)
SECONDARY WINDING
PRIMARY WINDING
7-10-93
PS 17802

DTC 82

IGNITION CONTROL 3X SIGNAL ERROR
3100 (VIN M) "W" CARLINE (SFI)

Circuit Description:

A 3X low resolution crankshaft position sensor is mounted in the block near a seven slot reluctor wheel fixed to the crankshaft. A voltage pulse is transmitted to the electronic ICM each time a slot in the wheel is aligned to the sensor. Six slots account for each cylinder with a seventh slot indicating a synchronizing pulse which allows the PCM to determine correct crank position. These pulses directly control spark timing and enable the fuel injectors.

DTC 82 Will Set When: If no 3X reference pulses are detected by the PCM during cranking, a DTC 82 will be set.

Action Taken (PCM will default to): The engine will not start, a DTC 82 will be stored and the MIL will remain illuminated.

DTC 82 Will Clear When: A current DTC 82 is cleared immediately after key "OFF," or when the engine is running. A History DTC 82 will clear after 50 consecutive ignition key cycles without a current DTC 82 being stored.

DTC Chart Test Description: Number(s) below refer to circled number(s) on the diagnostic chart.

1. This test will determine if the 12 volts supply and a good ground is available at the electronic ignition control module.
2. Checks for continuity of the crankshaft position sensor and connections.
3. Voltage will vary in this test depending on cranking speed of engine.

Diagnostic Aids: An open or shorted 3X signal will cause a "Cranks But Won't Run" condition. An intermittent connection however may set a DTC 82 and then disappear when a connection is made. A History DTC 82 may indicate poor terminal connections, a marginally faulty sensor or a marginal ICM.

DTC 82
IGNITION CONTROL 3X SIGNAL ERROR 3100 (VIN M) "W" CARLINE (SFI)

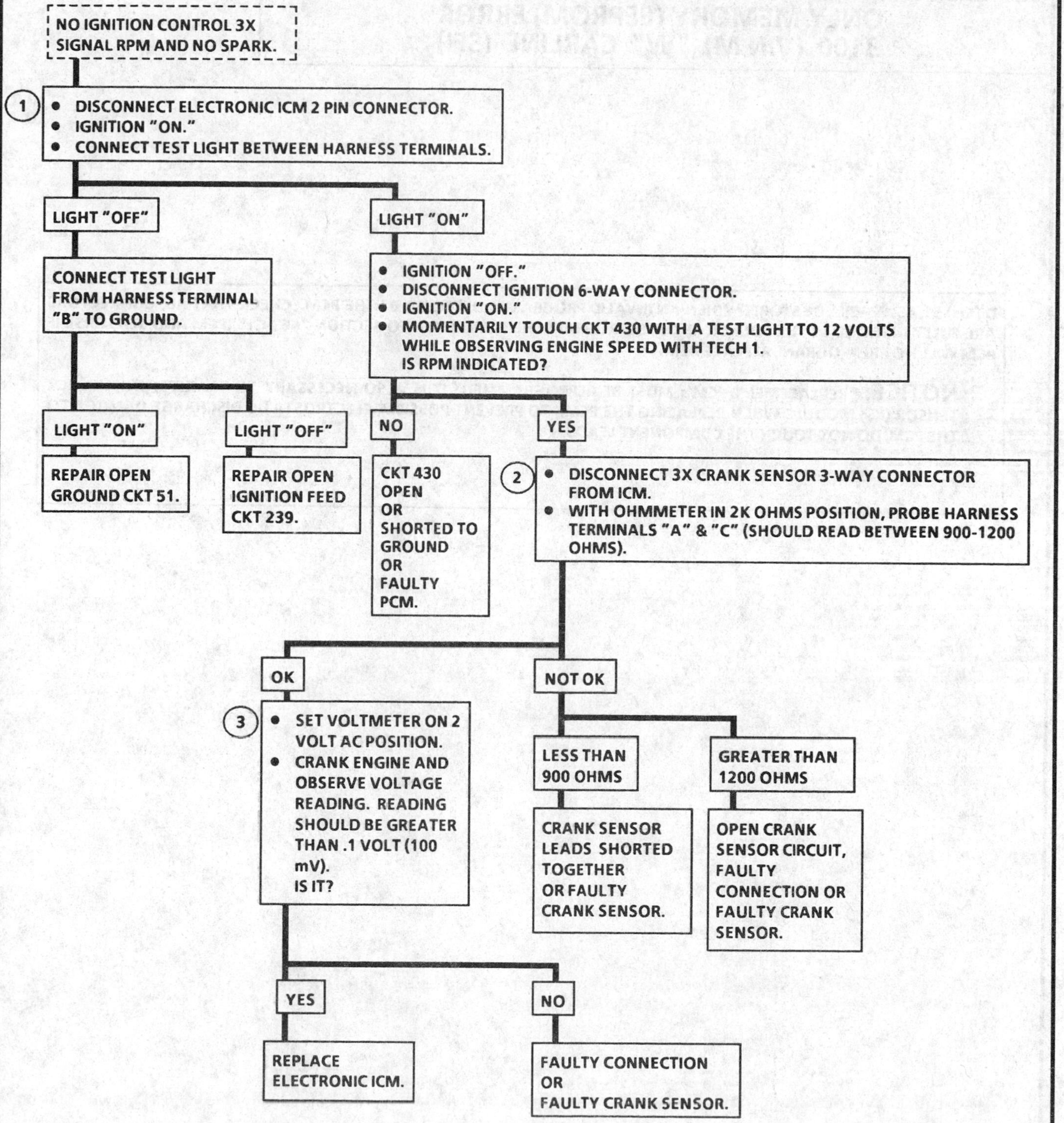
NO IGNITION CONTROL 3X SIGNAL RPM AND NO SPARK.
1
• DISCONNECT ELECTRONIC ICM 2 PIN CONNECTOR.
• IGNITION "ON."
• CONNECT TEST LIGHT BETWEEN HARNESS TERMINALS.
LIGHT "OFF"
LIGHT "ON"
CONNECT TEST LIGHT FROM HARNESS TERMINAL "B" TO GROUND.
• IGNITION "OFF."
• DISCONNECT IGNITION 6-WAY CONNECTOR.
• IGNITION "ON."
• MOMENTARILY TOUCH CKT 430 WITH A TEST LIGHT TO 12 VOLTS WHILE OBSERVING ENGINE SPEED WITH TECH 1. IS RPM INDICATED?
LIGHT "ON"
LIGHT "OFF"
NO
YES
REPAIR OPEN GROUND CKT 51.
REPAIR OPEN IGNITION FEED CKT 239.
CKT 430 OPEN OR SHORTED TO GROUND OR FAULTY PCM.
2
• DISCONNECT 3X CRANK SENSOR 3-WAY CONNECTOR FROM ICM.
• WITH OHMMETER IN 2K OHMS POSITION, PROBE HARNESS TERMINALS "A" & "C" (SHOULD READ BETWEEN 900-1200 OHMS).
OK
NOT OK
3
• SET VOLTMETER ON 2 VOLT AC POSITION.
• CRANK ENGINE AND OBSERVE VOLTAGE READING. READING SHOULD BE GREATER THAN .1 VOLT (100 mV). IS IT?
LESS THAN 900 OHMS
GREATER THAN 1200 OHMS
CRANK SENSOR LEADS SHORTED TOGETHER OR FAULTY CRANK SENSOR.
OPEN CRANK SENSOR CIRCUIT, FAULTY CONNECTION OR FAULTY CRANK SENSOR.
YES
NO
REPLACE ELECTRONIC ICM.
FAULTY CONNECTION OR FAULTY CRANK SENSOR.

5-1-93
PS 17825

DTC 51, 85, 87

51 PROM ERROR (FAULTY OR INCORRECT CALIBRATION)
85 PROM ERROR (FAULTY OR INCORRECT CALIBRATION)
87 ELECTRONICALLY ERASABLE PROGRAMMABLE READ ONLY MEMORY (EEPROM) ERROR
3100 (VIN M) "W" CARLINE (SFI)

DTC(s) 51, 85, 87 WILL BE STORED WHEN AN INVALID PROGRAM IS DETECTED BY THE PCM. CHECK THAT ALL CONNECTORS ARE FULLY INSERTED IN THE SOCKET. IF OK, REPROGRAM THE PCM. REFER TO SECTION "6E3-C1" (PCM AND SENSORS). IF PCM WILL NOT REPROGRAM, REPLACE PCM.

NOTICE: REPLACEMENT PCM's MUST BE REPROGRAMMED,. IT IS ALSO NECESSARY TO TRANSFER THE KNOCK SENSOR (KS) MODULE WHEN REPLACING THE PCM. TO PREVENT POSSIBLE ELECTROSTATIC DISCHARGE DAMAGE TO THE PCM, DO NOT TOUCH THE COMPONENT LEADS.

"AFTER REPAIRS," REFER TO DTC CRITERIA ON FACING PAGE AND CONFIRM DTC DOES NOT RESET.

BLANK

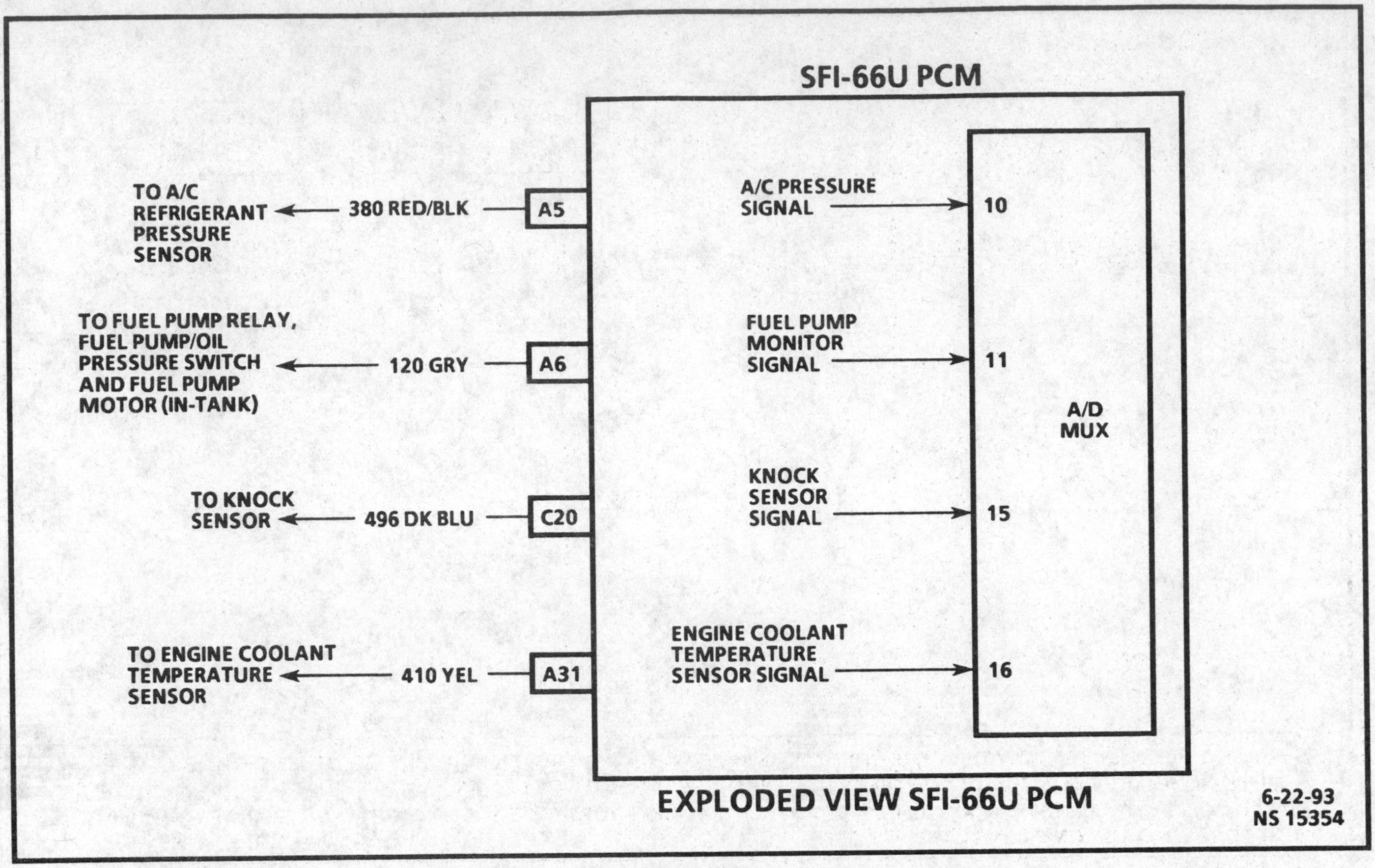
SFI-66U PCM
TO A/C REFRIGERANT PRESSURE SENSOR
380 RED/BLK
A5
A/C PRESSURE SIGNAL
10
TO FUEL PUMP RELAY, FUEL PUMP/OIL PRESSURE SWITCH AND FUEL PUMP MOTOR (IN-TANK)
120 GRY
A6
FUEL PUMP MONITOR SIGNAL
11
A/D MUX
TO KNOCK SENSOR
496 DK BLU
C20
KNOCK SENSOR SIGNAL
15
TO ENGINE COOLANT TEMPERATURE SENSOR
410 YEL
A31
ENGINE COOLANT TEMPERATURE SENSOR SIGNAL
16
EXPLODED VIEW SFI-66U PCM
6-22-93
NS 15354

DTC 86

ANALOG/DIGITAL (A/D) ERROR
3100 (VIN M) "W" CARLINE (SFI)

Circuit Description:

The A/D multiplexer chip is an internal part of the PCM. The above exploded view SFI-U PCM shows sensor inputs to the A/D multiplexer that can affect driveability and diagnostics.

DTC 86 Will Set When: Any of the above circuits is shorted to system voltage for 15 seconds.

Action Taken (PCM will default to): The MIL will become illuminated.

DTC 86 Will Clear When: A current DTC 86 will clear when B+ is no longer sensed on the above circuits. A History DTC 86 will clear after 50 consecutive ignition key cycles without a current DTC 86 being stored.

Diagnostic Aids: If DTC 86 is not present, all circuits leading to the PCM that are connected to the A/D multiplexer should be checked for an intermittent short to B+. Move the harnesses of each component and watch the scan data on the Tech 1. The circuit that is shorted to B+ will show erratic changes in data on the Tech 1.

DTC 86

ANALOG/DIGITAL (A/D) ERROR
3100 (VIN M) "W" CARLINE (SFI)

FOR DTC 86, CHECK FOR ANY DTCs THAT ARE STORED AND REFER TO THOSE CHARTS. IF NO OTHER DTCs ARE STORED, CHECK ALL PCM CONNECTORS AND TERMINALS FOR PROPER LOCATION. DTC 86 WILL SET ONLY WHEN THE CIRCUITS LEADING TO THE A/D MULTIPLEXER, INTERNAL TO THE PCM GETS SHORTED TO B+. IF DTC 86 IS INTERMITTENT, REFER TO "DIAGNOSTIC AIDS" ON FACING PAGE.

"AFTER REPAIRS," **REFER TO DTC CRITERIA ON FACING PAGE AND CONFIRM DTC DOES NOT RESET.**

3-9-93
NS 15377

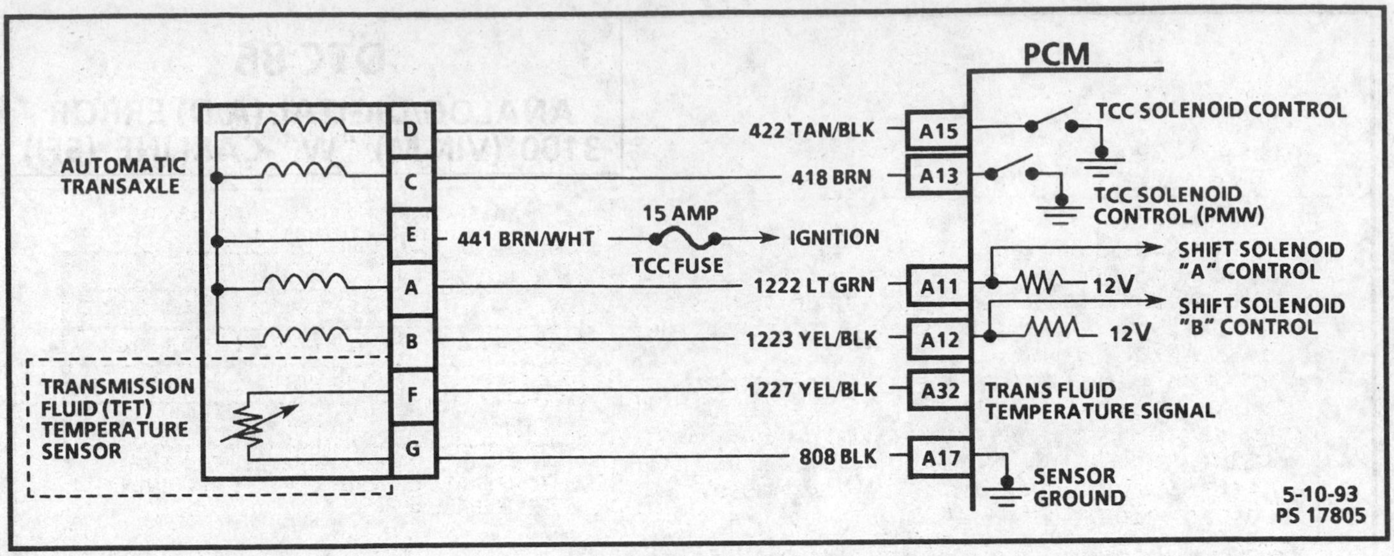
PCM
AUTOMATIC TRANSAXLE
D
C
E
A
B
F
G
422 TAN/BLK
418 BRN
441 BRN/WHT
15 AMP
TCC FUSE
IGNITION
1222 LT GRN
1223 YEL/BLK
1227 YEL/BLK
808 BLK
A15
A13
A11
A12
A32
A17
TCC SOLENOID CONTROL
TCC SOLENOID CONTROL (PMW)
SHIFT SOLENOID "A" CONTROL
SHIFT SOLENOID "B" CONTROL
12V
12V
TRANS FLUID TEMPERATURE SIGNAL
SENSOR GROUND
TRANSMISSION FLUID (TFT) TEMPERATURE SENSOR
5-10-93
PS 17805

DTC 90

TCC ERROR
3100 (VIN M) "W" CARLINE (SFI)

Circuit Description:

The purpose of the Torque Converter Clutch (TCC) feature is to eliminate the power loss of the torque converter when the vehicle is in a steady cruise condition. The heart of the system is two PCM controlled solenoids located inside the transaxle.

The PCM can determine if the TCC has become engaged when the TCC has not been commanded "ON," or stuck "ON" when it should be "OFF."

DTC 90 Will Set When: No DTC 21, 22, 24, 72 or 82 is set. Throttle angle is greater than 30%, trans temp is between 40°C and 100°C, trans range switch indicates "D4" or "D3", transaxle is not in 1st gear, TCC is commanded "OFF," and TCC slip speed is between -10 and 40 RPM for 10 seconds.

Action Taken (PCM will default to): 4th gear will become disabled. The MIL will not become illuminated.

DTC 90 Will Clear When: A current DTC 90 will clear after each ignition key cycle. A History DTC 90 will clear after 50 consecutive ignition key cycles without a current DTC 90 being stored.

DTC Chart Test Description: Number(s) below refer to circled number(s) on the diagnostic chart.

1. This test checks for circuit continuity of the TCC apply solenoid.
2. This checks for an open in the power feed CKT 441.
3. This test checks the PWM return circuitry to the PCM.

Diagnostic Aids: The Tech 1 indicates when the PCM has commanded the TCC apply solenoid or PWM solenoid driver "ON" or "OFF." This does not however confirm that the TCC apply or PWM is "ON" or "OFF." To determine if TCC is functioning properly, road test the vehicle. Engine RPM should decrease when the Tech 1 indicates that all electrical circuits and components are OK, refer to "Automatic Transaxle Diagnosis" in SECTION 7A for hydraulic and mechanical diagnosis.

DTC 90

TCC ERROR
3100 (VIN M) "W" CARLINE (SFI)

SOLENOID RESISTANCE VS. TRANSAXLE TEMPERATURE TABLE

SOLENOID	RESISTANCE AT 68°F (20°C)	RESISTANCE AT 190°F (88°C)
SHIFT A & B	20-30Ω	23-50Ω
TCC APPLY	20-30Ω	23-50Ω
TCC PWM	10-15Ω	11-27Ω

* RESISTANCE VALUES INCREASE AT HIGHER TEMPERATURES AND DECREASE AT LOWER TEMPERATURES.

- INSTALL TECH 1.
- IGNITION "ON," ENGINE "OFF."
- SCAN TCC BRAKE SW. WITH TECH 1 WHILE APPLYING AND RELEASING BRAKE PEDAL. TECH 1 SHOULD INDICATE PROPER STATE OF BRAKE SWITCH. IF NOT, REFER TO DTC 37 CHART FOR DIAGNOSIS. IF OK, CONTINUE.
- UNDER MISCELLANEOUS TEST, SELECT TRANSMISSION OUTPUT, TCC SOLENOID CONTROL.
- USING A STETHOSCOPE ON THE TRANSAXLE, YOU SHOULD BE ABLE TO HEAR THE TCC APPLY SOLENOID CLICK "ON" WHEN THE "↑" IS PRESSED AND CLICK "OFF" WHEN "↓" IS PRESSED.

DOES THE SOLENOID CLICK?

NO

(1)
- IGNITION "ON," ENGINE "OFF."
- DISCONNECT TRANSAXLE HARNESS CONNECTOR.
- CONNECT A TEST LIGHT BETWEEN TERMINALS "E" AND "D" OF TRANSAXLE HARNESS CONNECTOR.
- CYCLE TCC SOLENOID "ON" AND "OFF" USING TECH 1.
- TEST LIGHT SHOULD TURN "ON" AND "OFF."

DOES IT?

NO

- IGNITION "ON," ENGINE "OFF."
- USING TEST LIGHT CONNECTED TO GROUND, PROBE TERMINAL "E" OF TCC HARNESS CONNECTOR.
- LIGHT SHOULD BE "ON."

IS IT?

YES

CKT 422 OPEN OR SHORTED TO GROUND OR POOR CONNECTION AT PCM TERMINAL "A15" OR FAULTY PCM.

NO

CHECK TCC FUSE AND REPAIR SHORT TO GROUND IN CKT 441 BRN IF BLOWN - IF FUSE IS OK, REPAIR OPEN IN CKT 441 TO TRANSAXLE.

YES

FAULTY INTERNAL TRANSAXLE WIRING OR FAULTY TCC APPLY SOLENOID.

YES

(2)
- DISCONNECT TRANSAXLE HARNESS CONNECTOR.
- CONNECT A TEST LIGHT BETWEEN TERMINALS "E" AND GROUND.
- TEST LIGHT SHOULD BE "ON."

IS IT?

YES

- IGNITION "OFF."
- WITH DVM, CHECK RESISTANCE OF TCC PWM SOLENOID BETWEEN TRANSAXLE CONNECTOR TERMINALS "E" AND "C" AT TRANSAXLE.
- REFER TO TABLE FOR TCC PWM RESISTANCE SPECIFICATION.

IS RESISTANCE OK?

YES

(3)
- IGNITION ON.
- WITH TEST LIGHT CONNECTED TO B +, PROBE TERMINAL "C" OF TCC HARNESS.
- LIGHT SHOULD BE "ON."

IS IT?

YES

TCC CIRCUITS OK. SEE "DIAGNOSTIC AIDS" ON FACING PAGE.

NO

- IGNITION "OFF."
- RECONNECT TCC HARNESS CONNECTOR.
- DISCONNECT PCM CONNECTOR A.
- IGNITION "ON."
- WITH TEST LIGHT CONNECTED TO GROUND, PROBE TERMINAL "A13".
- LIGHT SHOULD BE "ON."

IS IT?

YES

FAULTY PCM CONNECTION OR FAULTY PCM.

NO

OPEN CKT 418 OR FAULTY TERMINAL CONNECTIONS.

NO

FAULTY INTERNAL TRANSAXLE WIRING OR FAULTY TCC PWM SOLENOID.

NO

OPEN CIRCUIT 441 OR FAULTY CONNECTION AT TRANSAXLE HARNESS CONNECTOR.

5-1-93
PS 17826

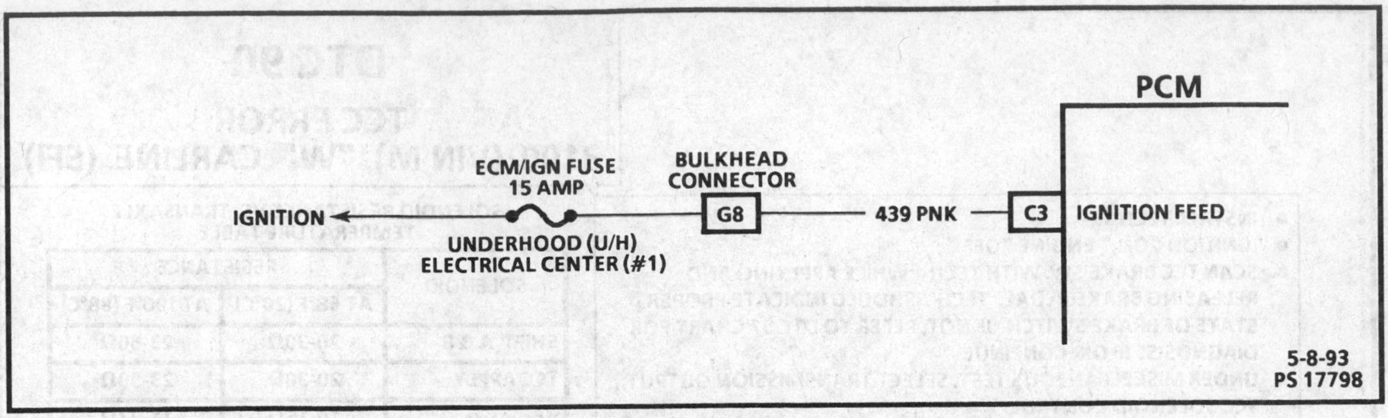
PCM
ECM/IGN FUSE
15 AMP
BULKHEAD
CONNECTOR
IGNITION
G8
439 PNK
C3
IGNITION FEED
UNDERHOOD (U/H)
ELECTRICAL CENTER (#1)
5-8-93
PS 17798

DTC 96

TRANS SYSTEM VOLTAGE LOW
3100 (VIN M) "W" CARLINE (SFI)

Circuit Description:

The internal electronic components of the transaxle have specific optimum temperature operating ranges in which they best perform. As trans fluid temperature rises, components such as shift solenoids heat up and their internal resistance rises. This effect will demand higher voltages to allow correct operation of these devices. Similarly low temperatures require less voltage for correct operation.

DTC 96 Will Set When: Minimum voltage sensed at the ignition feed is as follows:

- -40°C (-32°F) = 7.3 volts
- 90°C (194°F) = 10.3 volts
- 150°C (304°F) = 11.4 volts

Engine speed must be above 1000 RPM for 2 seconds to set DTC 96.

Action Taken (PCM will default to): All devices will become disabled causing transaxle to default to 3rd gear. The MIL will not illuminate.

DTC 96 Will Clear When: A current DTC 96 will clear when the voltage that caused DTC 96 rises 1 volt.

A History DTC 96 will clear after 50 consecutive ignition key cycles without a current DTC 96 being stored.

DTC Chart Test Description: Number(s) below refer to circled number(s) on the diagnostic chart.

Minimum voltage allowed for DTC 96 to set is on a graduated scale and will change with temperature.

Minimum voltage at:

- -40°C (-40°F) = 7.3 volts
- 90°C (194°F) = 10.3 volts
- 150°C (304°F) = 11.7 volts

1. This test checks for normal battery voltage between 9-15 volts.
2. This test checks if the low voltage display is due to the generator, CKT 439 or PCM. If the voltage is less than 8.6 volts, the PCM is OK.

Diagnostic Aids: CKT 439 supplies ignition voltage to the PCM.

If DTC 96 sets when an accessory is operated, check for poor connections or excessive current draw. Refer to SECTION 8A for circuit details.

DTC 96

TRANS SYSTEM VOLTAGE LOW 3100 (VIN M) "W" CARLINE (SFI)

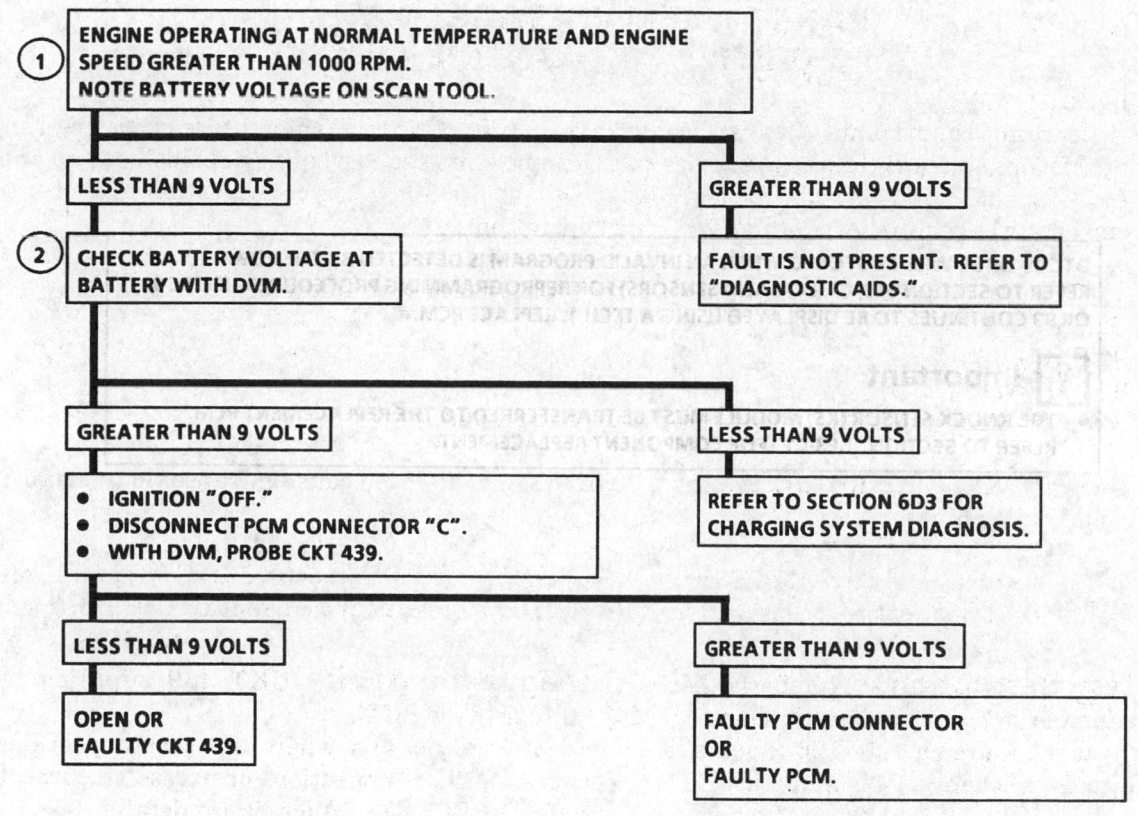

1. ENGINE OPERATING AT NORMAL TEMPERATURE AND ENGINE SPEED GREATER THAN 1000 RPM. NOTE BATTERY VOLTAGE ON SCAN TOOL.

- LESS THAN 9 VOLTS
  2. CHECK BATTERY VOLTAGE AT BATTERY WITH DVM.
     - GREATER THAN 9 VOLTS
       - IGNITION "OFF."
       - DISCONNECT PCM CONNECTOR "C".
       - WITH DVM, PROBE CKT 439.
         - LESS THAN 9 VOLTS: OPEN OR FAULTY CKT 439.
         - GREATER THAN 9 VOLTS: FAULTY PCM CONNECTOR OR FAULTY PCM.
     - LESS THAN 9 VOLTS: REFER TO SECTION 6D3 FOR CHARGING SYSTEM DIAGNOSIS.
- GREATER THAN 9 VOLTS: FAULT IS NOT PRESENT. REFER TO "DIAGNOSTIC AIDS."

"AFTER REPAIRS," REFER TO DTC CRITERIA ON FACING PAGE AND CONFIRM DTC DOES NOT RESET.

3-9-93
PS 17175

DTCs 98, 99

INVALID PCM PROGRAM
3100 (VIN M) "W" CARLINE (SFI)

DTC 98 OR 99 WILL BE STORED WHEN AN INVALID PROGRAM IS DETECTED BY THE PCM. REFER TO SECTION 6E3-C1 (PCM AND SENSORS) FOR REPROGRAMMING PROCEDURES. IF DTC 98 OR 99 CONTINUES TO BE DISPLAYED USING A TECH 1, REPLACE PCM.

Important

- THE KNOCK SENSOR (KS) MODULE MUST BE TRANSFERRED TO THE REPLACEMENT PCM. REFER TO SECTION "6E3-C1" FOR COMPONENT REPLACEMENT.

6-17-93
PS 17174

SECTION B

SYMPTOMS

CONTENTS

IMPORTANT PRELIMINARY CHECKS

BEFORE USING THIS SECTION

Before using this section you should have performed the "On-Board Diagnostic (OBD) System Check" and determined that:

1. The PCM and Malfunction Indicator Lamp (MIL) "Service Engine Soon" are operating correctly.
2. There are no diagnostic trouble codes stored, or there is a diagnostic trouble code but no Malfunction Indicator Lamp (MIL) "Service Engine Soon."

SYMPTOM

Verify the customer complaint and locate the correct symptom in the table of contents. Check the items indicated under that symptom.

VISUAL/PHYSICAL CHECK

Several of the symptom procedures call for a careful visual/physical check. The importance of this step cannot be stressed too strongly - it can lead to correcting a problem without further checks and can save valuable time. This check should include:

- PCM grounds and sensors for being clean, tight and in their proper location.
- Vacuum hoses for splits, kinks, and proper connections, as shown on "Vehicle Emission Control Information" label. Check thoroughly for any type of leak or restriction.
- Air leaks at throttle body mounting area and intake manifold sealing surfaces.
- Ignition wires for cracking, hardness, proper routing and carbon tracking.
- Wiring for proper connections, pinches and cuts.

INTERMITTENTS

(Page 1 of 2)

Definition: Problem may or may not turn "ON" the Malfunction Indicator Lamp (MIL) "Service Engine Soon" or store a Diagnostic Trouble Code (DTC).

DO NOT use the Diagnostic Trouble Code (DTC) charts in "Engine Components/Wiring Diagrams/Diagnostic Charts," Section "6E3-A" for intermittent problems. The fault must be present to locate the problem. If a fault is intermittent, use of Diagnostic Trouble Code (DTC) charts may result in replacement of good parts.

- Most intermittent problems are caused by faulty electrical connections or wiring. Perform careful visual/physical check as described at start of "Symptoms," Section "6E3-B". Check for:
  - Poor mating of the connector halves or terminal not fully seated in the connector body (backed out).
  - Improperly formed or damaged terminal. All connector terminals in the problem circuit should be carefully reformed or replaced to insure proper contact tension.
  - Poor terminal to wire connection. This requires removing the terminal from the connector body to check. Refer to SECTION 8A-5, "Repair Procedures."

- If a visual/physical check does not find the cause of the problem, the vehicle can be driven with a voltmeter connected to a suspected circuit. A Tech 1 scan tool can also be used to help detect intermittent conditions. An abnormal voltage or Tech 1 scan tool reading, when the problem occurs, indicates the problem may be in that circuit.

- Loss of diagnostic trouble code memory. To check, disconnect Throttle Position (TP) sensor and idle engine until Malfunction Indicator Lamp (MIL) "Service Engine Soon" comes "ON." DTC 22 should be stored and kept in memory when ignition is turned "OFF." If not, the PCM connections or the PCM is faulty.

- An intermittent Malfunction Indicator Lamp (MIL) "Service Engine Soon" with no stored diagnostic trouble code may be caused by:
  - Ignition coil shorted to ground and arcing at spark plug wires or plugs.
  - Malfunction Indicator Lamp (MIL) "Service Engine Soon" wire to PCM shorted to ground (CKT 419).
  - PCM grounds, refer to PCM wiring diagrams.

INTERMITTENTS

(Page 2 of 2)

Definition: Problem may or may not turn "ON" the Malfunction Indicator Lamp (MIL) "Service Engine Soon" or store a Diagnostic Trouble Code (DTC).

- Check for an electrical system interference caused by a defective relay, PCM driven solenoid, electrical motors or switch. They can cause a sharp electrical surge. Normally, the problem will occur when the faulty component is operated.

- Check for improper installation of electrical options such as lights, 2-way radios, etc.

- Ignition Control (IC) wires should be routed away from spark plug wires, ignition system components, and generator. Wires from PCM to electronic Ignition Control Module (ICM) should have a good connection.

- Check for open diode across A/C compressor clutch, and for other open diodes (SECTION 8A).

- If problem has not been found, refer to "PCM Connector Symptoms" charts at the end of "Symptoms," Section "6E3-B".

- Check for improperly formed or damaged terminal on CKT 423. Refer to Section "6E3-A", DTC 41.

HARD START

Definition: Engine cranks OK, but does not start for a long time. Does eventually run, or may start but immediately dies.

PRELIMINARY CHECKS

- Perform the careful visual/physical checks as described at start of "Symptoms," Section "6E3-B".
- Make sure the driver is using the correct starting procedure.

ADDITIONAL CHECKS

- **CHECK:** IAC valve operation - use CHART C-2B.
- **CHECK:** Basic engine problem. Refer to SECTION 6A.
- **CHECK:** Service Bulletins for updates.

SENSORS

- **CHECK:** Engine Coolant Temperature (ECT) sensor using a Tech 1 scan tool, compare engine coolant temperature with ambient temperature on cold engine.
  - If engine coolant temperature readings are 5 degrees greater than or less than ambient air temperature on a cold engine, check resistance in engine coolant temperature sensor circuit or sensor itself. Compare ECT sensor resistance value to the "Diagnostic Aids" chart on Diagnostic Trouble Code (DTC) 15 chart.
- **CHECK:** MAP sensor. Check for flooding.
- **CHECK:** Throttle Position (TP) sensor for binding or a high Throttle Position (TP) sensor voltage with the throttle closed (should read between .29 volt and .98 volt).

IGNITION SYSTEM

- **CHECK:** For proper ignition voltage output with spark tester J 26792 or equivalent (ST-125).
- **CHECK:** Spark plugs. Remove spark plugs, check for wet plugs, cracks, wear, improper gap, burned electrodes, or heavy deposits. Repair or replace as necessary.
- **CHECK:** Bare or shorted ignition wires.
- **CHECK:** Crankshaft position sensor, resistance and connections.

FUEL SYSTEM

- **CHECK:** Fuel pump relay operation. Pump should turn "ON" for 2 seconds when ignition is turned "ON." Use Diagnostic Trouble Code (DTC) 54.
- **CHECK:** Fuel pressure, use CHART A-7.
- **CHECK:** Contaminated fuel.
- **CHECK:** Fuel injector fuse.

NOTICE: A faulty in-tank fuel pump check valve will allow the fuel in the lines to drain back to the tank after engine is stopped. To check for this condition, perform fuel system diagnosis CHART A-7.

SURGES AND/OR CHUGGLES

Definition: Engine power variation under steady throttle or cruise feels like the vehicle speeds up and slows down with no change in the accelerator pedal.

PRELIMINARY CHECKS

- Perform the careful visual checks as described at start of "Symptoms," Section "6E3-B".
- Be sure driver understands transmission torque converter clutch and A/C compressor operation as explained in the owner's manual.

ADDITIONAL CHECKS

- **CHECK:** PCM grounds for being clean, tight and in their proper location.
- **CHECK:** Vacuum lines for kinks or leaks.
- **CHECK:** Generator output voltage. Repair if less than 9 volts or more than 16 volts.
- **CHECK:** Speedometer display with the reading on a Tech 1 scan tool are equal.
- **CHECK:** Service Bulletins for updates.

SENSORS

- **CHECK:** Heated Oxygen Sensor (HO2S). The Heated Oxygen Sensor (HO2S) should respond quickly to different throttle position. If it does not, check the Heated Oxygen Sensor (HO2S) for silicon or other contaminations from fuel or improper use of RTV sealant. The sensor may have a white, powdery coating and result in a high but false signal voltage (rich exhaust indication). The PCM will then reduce the amount of fuel delivered to the engine, causing a severe driveability problem. Also, watch for green (glycol) contamination or cracking.

IGNITION SYSTEM

- **CHECK:** For proper ignition voltage output using spark tester (ST-125) J 26792 or equivalent.
- **CHECK:** Spark plugs. Remove spark plugs, check for wet plugs, cracks, wear, improper gap, burned electrodes, or heavy deposits. Repair or replace as necessary. Also, check spark plug wires.

FUEL SYSTEM

NOTICE: To determine if the condition is caused by a rich or lean system, the vehicle should be driven at the speed of the complaint. Monitoring long term and short term fuel trim will help identify a problem.

Lean - Long term fuel trim above 150. Refer to "Diagnostic Aids" on facing page of Diagnostic Trouble Code (DTC) 44.

Rich - Long term fuel trim below 110. Refer to "Diagnostic Aids" on facing page of Diagnostic Trouble Code (DTC) 45.

- **CHECK:** Fuel pressure while condition exists. Use CHART A-7.
- **CHECK:** In-line fuel filter. Replace if dirty or plugged.

LACK OF POWER, SLUGGISH OR SPONGY

Definition: Engine delivers less than expected power. Little or no increase in speed when accelerator pedal is pushed down part way.

PRELIMINARY CHECKS

- Perform the careful visual/physical checks as described at start of "Symptoms," Section "6E3-B".
- Compare customer's vehicle to similar unit. Make sure the customer has an actual problem.
- Remove air filter and check air filter for dirt, or for being plugged. Replace as necessary.

ADDITIONAL CHECKS

- **CHECK:** PCM grounds for being clean, tight and in their proper locations. Refer to PCM wiring diagrams.
- **CHECK:** EGR operation EGR valve may be open or partly open all the time. Refer to CHART C-7.
- **CHECK:** Generator output voltage. Repair if less than 9 volts or more than 16 volts.
- **CHECK:** Exhaust system for possible restriction. Use CHART B-1.
  - Inspect exhaust system for damaged or collapsed pipes.
  - Inspect muffler for heat distress or possible internal failure.
- **CHECK:** Torque Converter Clutch (TCC) for proper operation. Refer to SECTION 7A.

ENGINE MECHANICAL

- **CHECK:** Engine valve timing and compression.
- **CHECK:** Engine for correct or worn camshaft. Refer to SECTION 6A.

IGNITION SYSTEM

- **CHECK:** Knock Sensor (KS) system for excessive spark retard activity. Refer to CHART C-5. Use Tech 1 scan tool.
- **CHECK:** Secondary voltage using a shop oscilloscope or a spark tester J 26792 (ST-125), or equivalent.

FUEL SYSTEM

- **CHECK:** Restricted fuel filter.
- **CHECK:** Fuel pressure, use CHART A-7.
- **CHECK:** Contaminated fuel.

DETONATION/SPARK KNOCK

Definition: A mild to severe ping, usually worse under acceleration. The engine makes sharp metallic knocks that change with throttle opening.

PRELIMINARY CHECKS

- Perform the careful visual/physical checks as described at start of "Symptoms," Section "6E3-B".
- Transaxle range switch. Be sure Tech 1 scan indicates correct range.

NOTICE: If Tech 1 scan tool readings are normal [refer to facing page of "On-Board Diagnostic (OBD) System Check"] and there are no engine mechanical faults, fill fuel tank with a premium gasoline that has a minimum octane reading of 92 and revaluate vehicle performance.

- **CHECK:** EGR system for not opening. Use CHART C-7.
- **CHECK:** TCC operation, TCC applying too soon. Use CHART C-8.

ADDITIONAL CHECKS

- **CHECK:** Service Bulletins for updates.

IGNITION SYSTEM

- **CHECK:** Spark plugs for proper heat range. Refer to SECTION 0B.
- **CHECK:** Knock Sensor (KS) system for no retard, use CHART C-5.

ENGINE MECHANICAL

- **CHECK:** For excessive oil in the combustion chamber.
  - Valve oil seals for leaking.
- **CHECK:** Combustion chambers for excessive carbon build-up. Remove carbon with top engine cleaner and follow instructions on can.
- **CHECK:** Combustion chamber pressure by performing a compression test. Refer to SECTION 6A.
- **CHECK:** For incorrect basic engine parts such as cam, heads, pistons, etc.

COOLING SYSTEM

- Check for obvious overheating problems:
  - Low engine coolant.
  - Loose water pump belt.
  - Restricted air flow to radiator, or restricted water flow through radiator.
  - Inoperative electric cooling fan circuit, use CHART C-12.
  - Correct coolant solution should be a 50/50 mix of GM #1052753 anti-freeze coolant (or equivalent) and water.

FUEL SYSTEM

NOTICE: To determine if the condition is caused by a rich or lean system, the vehicle should be driven at the speed of the complaint. Monitoring long term fuel trim will help identify problem.
Lean - Long term fuel trim above 150. Refer to "Diagnostic Aids" on facing page of Diagnostic Trouble Code (DTC) 44.
Rich - Long term fuel trim below 110. Refer to "Diagnostic Aids" on facing page of Diagnostic Trouble Code (DTC) 45.

- **CHECK:** Fuel pressure, use CHART A-7.

HESITATION, SAG, STUMBLE

Definition: Momentary lack of response as the accelerator is pushed down. Can occur at all vehicle speeds. Usually most severe when first trying to make the vehicle move, as from a stop sign. May cause engine to stall if severe enough.

PRELIMINARY CHECKS

- Perform the careful visual/physical checks as described at start of "Symptoms," Section "6E3-B".

SENSORS

- **CHECK:** Throttle Position (TP) sensor - Check TP sensor for binding or sticking. Voltage should increase at a steady rate as throttle is moved toward Wide Open Throttle (WOT).
- **CHECK:** MAP sensor - use CHART C-1D.

IGNITION SYSTEM

- **CHECK:** Spark plugs for being fouled or for faulty spark plug wire routing.
- **CHECK:** Electronic ignition system ground, CKT 51.

FUEL SYSTEM

- **CHECK:** Fuel pressure, use CHART A-7.
- **CHECK:** Contaminated fuel.
- **CHECK:** EVAP canister purge system for proper operation. Use CHART C-3.
- **CHECK:** Fuel injectors. Perform fuel injector coil/balance test, use CHART C-2A.

ADDITIONAL CHECKS

- **CHECK:** Service Bulletins for updates.
- **CHECK:** EGR operation, use CHART C-7.
- **CHECK:** Engine thermostat functioning correctly and proper heat range.
- **CHECK:** Generator output voltage. Repair if less than 9 volts or more than 16 volts.

CUTS OUT, MISSES

(Page 1 of 2)

Definition: Steady pulsation or jerking that follows engine speed, usually more pronounced as engine load increases, not normally felt above 1500 RPM or 48 km/h (30 mph). The exhaust has a steady spitting sound at idle or low speed.

PRELIMINARY CHECKS

- Perform the careful visual/physical checks as described at start of "Symptoms," Section "6E3-B".

ADDITIONAL CHECKS

- **CHECK:** For EMI interference. A missing condition can be caused by Electromagnetic Interference (EMI) on the reference circuit. EMI can usually be detected by monitoring engine RPM with a Tech 1 scan tool. A sudden increase in RPM with little change in actual engine RPM change indicates EMI is present. If the problem exists, check routing of spark plug wires and electronic Ignition Control (IC) ground circuit.
- **CHECK:** Intake and exhaust manifold passage for casting flash.

IGNITION SYSTEM

- Check for cylinder miss:
  1. Start engine allowing engine to stabilize then disconnect IAC valve. Remove one spark plug wire at a time using insulated pliers.

     CAUTION: Do Not perform this test for more than 2 minutes, as this test may cause damage to the catalytic converter.

  2. If there is an RPM drop on all cylinders (equal to within 50 RPM), go to "Rough, Unstable, or Incorrect Idle, Stalling" symptom. Reconnect IAC valve.
  3. If there is no RPM drop on one or more cylinders or excessive variation in RPM drop, check for spark on the suspected cylinder(s) using a shop oscilloscope or with J 26792 (ST-125) spark tester or equivalent. If no spark, refer to SECTION 6D for intermittent operation or miss. If there is a spark, remove spark plug(s) in these cylinders and check for:
     - Insulator cracks.
     - Wear.
     - Improper gap.
     - Burned electrodes.
     - Heavy deposits.
- **CHECK:** Spark plug wires by connecting ohmmeter to ends of each wire in question. If meter reads over 30,000 ohms, replace wire(s).

CUTS OUT, MISSES

(Page 2 of 2)

Definition: Steady pulsation or jerking that follows engine speed, usually more pronounced as engine load increases, not normally felt above 1500 RPM or 48 km/h (30 mph). The exhaust has a steady spitting sound at idle or low speed.

ENGINE MECHANICAL

- **CHECK:** Compression. Perform compression check on questionable cylinder(s) found above. If compression is low, repair as necessary. Refer to SECTION 6A.
- **CHECK:** Base engine. Remove rocker covers. Check for bent pushrods, worn rocker arms, broken valve springs, worn camshaft lobes and valve timing. Repair as necessary. Refer to SECTION 6A.

FUEL SYSTEM

- **CHECK:** Scan tool for injector fault which could indicate one or more faulty injectors or wiring.
- **CHECK:** Fuel system - Plugged fuel filter, low pressure. Use CHART A-7.
- **CHECK:** Contaminated fuel.
- **CHECK:** Injector drivers. Disconnect all injector harness connectors. Connect J 34730-2 injector test light or equivalent 6 volts test light between the harness terminals of each injector connector and note light while cranking. If test light fails to blink at any connector, it is a faulty injector drive circuit harness, connector or terminal or PCM.
- **CHECK:** Perform the fuel injector coil/balance test. Refer to CHART C-2A.

ROUGH, UNSTABLE, OR INCORRECT IDLE, STALLING

(Page 1 of 2)

Definition: Engine runs unevenly at idle. If severe, the engine or vehicle may shake. Engine idle speed may vary in RPM. Either condition may be severe enough to stall engine.

PRELIMINARY CHECKS

- Perform the careful visual/physical checks as described at start of "Symptoms," Section "6E3-B".
- **CHECK:** For vacuum leaks.
- **CHECK:** PCM grounds for being clean, tight and proper routing. Refer to PCM wiring diagrams.

ADDITIONAL CHECKS

- Inspect front air intake duct for proper installation. If this component sucks shut during WOT maneuvers the vehicle may hesitate or stall. Refer to "Air Intake System" Section "6E3-C14".
- **CHECK:** MAP sensor. Refer to CHART C-10.
- **CHECK:** Throttle linkage for sticking or binding.
- **CHECK:** Transaxle range switch circuit. Use Tech 1 scan tool and be sure tool indicates gear range selected.
- **CHECK:** IAC valve operation, use CHART C-2C.
- **CHECK:** EGR valve. There should be no EGR at idle. Refer to CHART C-7.
- **CHECK:** A/C request signal to PCM, Tech 1 scan tool should indicate A/C is being requested whenever A/C is selected. If problem exists with A/C "ON," check A/C system operation CHART C-10.
- **CHECK:** Crankcase ventilation valve for proper operation by placing finger over inlet hole in valve end several times. Valve should snap back. If not, replace valve. Refer to "Crankcase Ventilation System," Section "6E3-C13".
- **CHECK:** Service Bulletins for updates.
- **CHECK:** For broken motor mounts.
- **CHECK:** Generator output voltage. Repair if less than 9 volts or more than 16 volts.

IGNITION SYSTEM

- **CHECK:** Ignition system; wires, plugs, etc.
- **CHECK:** For open ignition control CKT 423. Refer to Section "6E3-A", DTC 41.

ENGINE MECHANICAL

- **CHECK:** Perform a cylinder compression check. Refer to SECTION 6.
- **CHECK:** For correct camshaft or weak valve springs.

ROUGH, UNSTABLE, OR INCORRECT IDLE, STALLING

(Page 2 of 2)

Definition: Engine runs unevenly at idle. If severe, the engine or vehicle may shake. Engine idle speed may vary in RPM. Either condition may be severe enough to stall engine.

FUEL SYSTEM

NOTICE: Monitoring long term fuel trim will help identify the cause of the problem. If the system is running lean (long term fuel trim greater than 150), refer to "Diagnostic Aids" on facing page of Diagnostic Trouble Code (DTC) 44. If the system is running rich (long term fuel trim less than 110), refer to "Diagnostic Aids" on facing page of Diagnostic Trouble Code (DTC) 45.

- **CHECK:** Fuel injector coil/balance. Refer to CHART C-2A.
- **CHECK:** For fuel in pressure regulator hose. If fuel is present, replace regulator assembly.
- **CHECK:** Evaporative Emission (EVAP) control system, use CHART C-3.
- **CHECK:** The Heated Oxygen Sensor (HO2S) should respond quickly to different throttle positions. If it does not, check the Heated Oxygen Sensor (HO2S) for silicon contamination from fuel or improper use of RTV sealant. The sensor will have a white, powdery coating and will result in a high but false signal voltage (rich exhaust indication). The PCM will then reduce the amount of fuel delivered to the engine, causing a severe driveability problem.
- **CHECK:** Scan tool for injector fault which could indicate one or more faulty injectors or wiring.

POOR FUEL ECONOMY

Definition: Fuel economy, as measured by an actual road test, is noticeably lower than expected. Also, economy is noticeably lower than it was on this vehicle at one time, as previously shown by an actual road test.

PRELIMINARY CHECKS

- Perform the careful visual checks as described at start of "Symptoms," Section "6E3-B".
- Visually (physically) check: Vacuum hoses for splits, kinks, and proper connections as shown on "Vehicle Emission Control Information" label.
- Check owner's driving habits.
  - Is A/C "ON" full time (Defroster mode "ON")?
  - Are tires at correct pressure?
  - Are excessively heavy loads being carried?
  - Is acceleration too much, too often?
- Check for a dirty or plugged air cleaner.
  - Fuel leaks.

ADDITIONAL CHECKS

- **CHECK:** TCC operation. Use CHART C-8. A Tech 1 scan tool should indicate an RPM drop, when the TCC is commanded "ON."
- **CHECK:** For exhaust system restriction. Use CHART B-1.
- **CHECK:** For proper calibration of speedometer.
- **CHECK:** Induction system and crankcase for air leaks.

IGNITION SYSTEM

- **CHECK:** Spark plugs. Remove spark plugs, check for wet plugs, cracks, wear, improper gap, burned electrodes, or heavy deposits. Repair or replace as necessary.
- **CHECK:** For open ignition control CKT 423. Refer to Section "6E3-A", DTC 41.

COOLING SYSTEM

- **CHECK:** Engine coolant level.
- **CHECK:** Engine thermostat for faulty part (always open) or for wrong heat range. Refer to SECTION 6B.

ENGINE MECHANICAL

- **CHECK:** Compression. Refer to SECTION 6A.

EXCESSIVE EXHAUST EMISSIONS OR ODORS

Definition: Vehicle fails an emission test. Vehicle has excessive "rotten egg" smell. Excessive odors do not necessarily indicate excessive emissions.

PRELIMINARY CHECKS

- Perform "On-Board Diagnostic (OBD) System Check."

NOTICE: IF EMISSION TEST shows excessive CO and HC check items which cause vehicle to run RICH (long term fuel trim less than 110), refer to "Diagnostic Aids" on facing page of Diagnostic Trouble Code (DTC) 45.

NOTICE: If EMISSION TEST shows excessive NOx, check items which cause vehicle to run lean or too hot.

ADDITIONAL CHECKS

- **CHECK:** For vacuum leaks.
- **CHECK:** EGR valve for not opening. Use CHART C-7.
- **CHECK:** For lead contamination for catalytic converter (look for the removal of fuel filler neck restrictor).
- **CHECK:** Carbon build-up. Remove carbon with top engine cleaner. Follow instructions on can.
- **CHECK:** Crankcase ventilation valve for being plugged or stuck or fuel in the crankcase.
- **CHECK:** Service Bulletins for updates.

IGNITION SYSTEM

- **CHECK:** Spark plugs, plug wires, and ignition components. Refer to SECTION 6D.

COOLING SYSTEM

NOTICE: If the Tech 1 scan tool indicates a very high engine coolant temperature and the system is running lean:

- **CHECK:** Engine coolant level.
- **CHECK:** Engine thermostat for faulty part (always open) or for wrong heat range. Refer to SECTION 6B.
- **CHECK:** Cooling fan operation, use CHART C-12.

FUEL SYSTEM

NOTICE: If the system is running RICH (long term fuel trim near 110), refer to "Diagnostic Aids" on facing page of Diagnostic Trouble Code (DTC) 45.
If the system is running LEAN (long term fuel trim near 150) refer to "Diagnostic Aids" on facing page of Diagnostic Trouble Code (DTC) 44.

- **CHECK:** For properly installed fuel cap.
- **CHECK:** Fuel pressure. Use CHART A-7.
- **CHECK:** Fuel injector coil/balance test. Use CHART C-2A.
- **CHECK:** Canister for fuel loading. Use CHART C-3.

DIESELING, RUN-ON

Definition: Engine continues to run after key is turned "OFF," but runs very roughly. If engine runs smoothly, check ignition switch and adjustment.

PRELIMINARY CHECKS

- Perform the careful visual/physical checks as described at start of "Symptoms," Section "6E3-B".

FUEL SYSTEM

- **CHECK:** Injectors for leaking. Refer to "Fuel System Diagnosis" CHART A-7.

BACKFIRE

Definition: Fuel ignites inside intake manifold or in exhaust system, making loud popping noise.

PRELIMINARY CHECKS

- Perform the careful visual/physical checks as described at start of "Symptoms," Section "6E3-B".

ADDITIONAL CHECKS

- **CHECK:** EGR gasket for faulty or loose fit.
- **CHECK:** EGR operation for being open all the time. Refer to "Exhaust Gas Recirculation (EGR)" CHART C-7.
- **CHECK:** Intake and exhaust manifold for casting flash.

IGNITION SYSTEM

- **CHECK:** Proper ignition coil output voltage with spark tester J 26792 or equivalent (ST-125).
- **CHECK:** Spark plugs. Remove spark plugs, check for wet plugs, cracks, wear, improper gap, burned electrodes, or heavy deposits. Repair or replace as necessary.
- **CHECK:** Spark plug wires for crossfire, also inspect Ignition Control (IC) system assembly, spark plug wires, and proper routing of plug wires.

NOTICE: If an intermittent condition exists in the ignition system, refer to "Ignition Control (IC) System," Section "6E3-C4" or SECTION 6D.

ENGINE MECHANICAL

- **CHECK:** Compression - Look for sticking or leaking valves.
- **CHECK:** Valve timing, refer to SECTION 6A.
- **CHECK:** Intake and exhaust manifold passages for casting flash.

FUEL SYSTEM

- **CHECK:** Perform fuel system diagnosis check, see CHART A-7.
- **CHECK:** Fuel injectors. Perform fuel injector coil/balance test, refer to CHART C-2A.

PCM CONNECTOR "A" SYMPTOMS CHART
CLEAR 32 PIN CONNECTOR

PCM PIN/FUNCTION	CKT #	WIRE COLOR	COMPONENT CONNECTOR CAVITY	DTC(s) AFFECTED	POSSIBLE SYMPTOMS FROM FAULTY CIRCUIT
A1					
A2 A/C REQUEST	66	LT GRN	HEATER AND A/C CONTROL ASSEMBLY	NONE	A/C INOPERATIVE. REFER TO SECTION C10.
A3					
A4					
A5 A/C REFRIGERANT PRESSURE SENSOR SIGNAL	380	RED/BLK	A/C REFRIGERANT PRESSURE SENSOR HARN CONNECTOR "C"	66 (2) 70 (4)	NO A/C, REFER TO SECTION C10 HIGH AND UNSTABLE IDLE, BOTH FANS RUN.
A6 FUEL PUMP MONITOR	120	GRY	UNDERHOOD ELECTRICAL CENTER #1 FUEL PUMP RELAY TERMINAL "E11" AND FUEL PUMP/OIL PRESSURE SWITCH CONNECTOR "C" AND FUEL PUMP	54 (2)	NO SYMPTOMS. REFER TO DTC 54.
A7					
A8 FUEL PUMP RELAY CONTROL	465	DK GRN/WHT	UNDERHOOD ELECTRICAL CENTER #1 FUEL PUMP RELAY TERMINAL "F11"	NONE	HARD TO START, LONG CRANK TIME. REFER TO CHART A7.
A9					
A10					
A11 SHIFT SOLENOID "A" CONTROL	1222	LT GRN	TCC HARNESS CONNECTOR "A"	NONE	(3) NO TCC, POOR FUEL ECONOMY, CHUGGLE OR TRANS BUMP, DEFAULTS TO 3RD GEAR, LATE UPSHIFT. REFER TO SECTION C8.
A12 SHIFT SOLENOID " B" CONTROL	1223	YEL/BLK	TCC HARNESS CONNECTOR "B"	NONE	(3) NO TCC, POOR FUEL ECONOMY, CHUGGLE OR TRANS BUMP, TRANS SLIP, LATE UPSHIFT. REFER TO SECTION C8.
A13 TCC SOLENOID CONTROL (PWM)	418	BRN	TCC HARNESS CONNECTOR "C"	80 (2)	(1) TRANS BUMP.
A14 LOW OIL LEVEL INDICATOR CONTROL	1173	BRN/WHT	BULKHEAD CONNECTOR "F1" TO INSTRUMENT CLUSTER TERMINAL "C8"	NONE	(2) LOW OIL LEVEL INDICATOR "ON" (1) NO BULB CHECK, WILL NOT ILLUMINATE
A15 TCC SOLENOID CONTROL	422	TAN/BLK	TCC HARNESS CONNECTOR "D"	80 (1)	NO TCC, POOR FUEL ECONOMY, CHUGGLE OR TRANS BUMP. REFER TO SECTION C8.
A16					
A17 SENSOR GROUND	808	BLK	TP SENSOR "B" ECT SENSOR "A" A/C REFRIGERANT PRESSURE SENSOR "A" AND IAT SENSOR "A"	22 (4) 15, 21 (1) 35 (2)	ENGINE STARTS AND STALLS, NO POWER, ENGINE WILL NOT RUN, HIGH IDLE.
A18 BRAKE SWITCH INPUT	420	PPL	BULKHEAD CONN "J3" AND BRAKE SWITCH	37 (2)	REFER TO SECTION C8. *
A19 TRANSAXLE POSITION SWITCH PARITY INPUT	776	WHT	AUTOMATIC TRANSAXLE RANGE SWITCH "D"	28 (3) (4)	DISPLAY LOW ALL THE TIME. DISPLAY HIGH ALL THE TIME.

(1) OPEN CIRCUIT
(2) GROUNDED CIRCUIT
(3) OPEN/GROUNDED CIRCUIT
(4) SHORTED TO VOLTAGE
* REFER TO ELECTRICAL DIAGNOSIS (SECTION 8A)

8-6-93
PS 16725

PCM Connector Symptoms "A" Chart (1 of 2)

PCM CONNECTOR "A" SYMPTOMS CHART
CLEAR 32 PIN CONNECTOR

PCM PIN/FUNCTION	CKT #	WIRE COLOR	COMPONENT CONNECTOR CAVITY	DTC(s) AFFECTED	POSSIBLE SYMPTOMS FROM FAULTY CIRCUIT
A20					
A21 SECOND GEAR START SWITCH	1493	DK BLU	BULKHEAD CONNECTOR "J1" TO 2ND GEAR START SWITCH "E"	NONE	(1) 2ND GEAR START WILL NOT ENABLE (2) 2ND GEAR ENABLED
A21 3RD GEAR SIGNAL (3T40 ONLY)	108	DK GRN	CONNECTOR "B"	NONE	REFER TO SECTION "C8"
A22					
A23 2ND GEAR SIGNAL (3T40 ONLY)	232	WHT	CONNECTER "C"	NONE	REFER TO SECTION "C8"
A24 OIL LEVEL INPUT	1174	BRN	OIL LEVEL SENSOR "A"	NONE	(1) LOW OIL LIGHT "ON"
A25 TRANSAXLE POSITION SWITCH "C"	773	GRY	AUTOMATIC TRANSAXLE RANGE SWITCH "C"	28 (3) (4)	DISPLAY LOW ALL THE TIME. DISPLAY HIGH ALL THE TIME.
A26 TRANSAXLE POSITION SWITCH "B"	772	YEL	AUTOMATIC TRANSAXLE RANGE SWITCH "B"	28 (3) (4)	DISPLAY LOW ALL THE TIME. DISPLAY HIGH ALL THE TIME.
A27 TRANSAXLE POSITION SWITCH "A"	771	BLK/WHT	AUTOMATIC TRANSAXLE RANGE SWITCH "A"	28 (3) (4)	DISPLAY LOW ALL THE TIME. DISPLAY HIGH ALL THE TIME.
A28					
A29 MAP SENSOR SIGNAL	432	LT GRN	MAP SENSOR "B"	33 (4) 34 (3) 44 (3)	UNSTABLE IDLE, ROUGH, HESITATION, HIGH IDLE, HUNTING IDLE, LEAN EXHAUST, POOR PERFORMANCE, STALLS, MISFIRE, SURGE.
A30 TP SENSOR SIGNAL	417	DK BLU	TP SENSOR "C"	21 (4) 22 (3)	HIGH IDLE, SURGE, LACK OF PERFORMANCE, HESITATION, LATE UPSHIFT
A31 ECT SENSOR SIGNAL	410	YEL	ECT SENSOR "B"	14 (2) 15 (1,4)	HARD TO START, LACK OF PERFORMANCE, POOR FUEL ECONOMY, HIGH IDLE.
A32 TRANS FLUID TEMPERATURE SENSOR SIGNAL	1227	YEL/BLK	TRANSMISSION FLUID TEMPERATURE SENSOR "F"	58 (3) 59 (3)	TRANS BUMP FROM A STOP.

(1) OPEN CIRCUIT
(2) GROUNDED CIRCUIT
(3) OPEN/GROUNDED CIRCUIT
(4) SHORTED TO VOLTAGE
* REFER TO SECTION 8A

8-6-93
PS 16726

PCM Connector "A" Symptoms Chart (2 of 2)

PCM CONNECTOR "B" SYMPTOMS CHART
BLACK 32 PIN CONNECTOR

PCM PIN/FUNCTION	CKT #	WIRE COLOR	COMPONENT CONNECTOR CAVITY	DTC(s) AFFECTED	POSSIBLE SYMPTOMS FROM FAULTY CIRCUIT
B1 SECONDARY COOLING FAN RELAY CONTROL	473	DK BLU	UNDERHOOD ELECTRICAL CENTER #1 SECONDARY COOLING FAN #2 RELAY TERMINAL "C10"	NONE	(1) INOPERATIVE FAN. (2) FAN RUNS ALL THE TIME. REFER TO SECTION C12
B2 PRIMARY COOLING FAN RELAY CONTROL	335	DK GRN	UNDERHOOD ELECTRICAL CENTER #1 PRIMARY COOLING FAN #1 RELAY TERMINAL "C6"	NONE	(1) INOPERATIVE FAN. (2) FAN RUNS ALL THE TIME. REFER TO SECTION C12
B3					
B4 EVAP CANISTER PURGE SOLENOID CONTROL	428	DK GRN/WHT	EVAP CANISTER PURGE SOLENOID VALVE "B"	NONE	FUEL LOSS OR FUEL VAPOR ODOR. POOR IDLE, STALLING, POOR DRIVEABILITY. REFER TO SECTION C3
B5					
B6 A/C COMPRESSOR CLUTCH CONTROL	459	DK GRN/WHT	UNDERHOOD ELECTRICAL CENTER #1 A/C COMPRESSOR CLUTCH CONTROL RELAY TERMINAL "E6"	NONE	(1) NO A/C CLUTCH ENGAGEMENT (2) A/C ON ALL THE TIME (2). REFER TO SECTION C10
B7 MALFUNCTION INDICATOR LAMP (MIL) "SERVICE ENGINE SOON" CONTROL	419	BRN/WHT	BULKHEAD CONN "H3" AND INSTRUMENT CLUSTER	NONE	(1) NO MIL (2) MIL ON ALL THE TIME. REFER TO "ON-BOARD DIAGNOSTIC SYSTEM CHECK."*
B8					
B9					
B10 CRUISE INHIBIT	83	DK GRN	CRUISE CNTL MODULE "H"	NONE	(2) CRUISE WILL NOT ENABLE
B11 EGR SOLENOID #1 CONTROL	697	LT BLU	DIGITAL EGR HARNESS CONNECTOR "A"	75 (3)	ROUGH IDLE, SPARK KNOCK, STALLS AFTER COLD START, SURGE DURING CRUISE. REFER TO SECTION C6
B12 EGR SOLENOID #2 CONTROL	698	BRN	DIGITAL EGR HARNESS CONNECTOR "B"	76 (3)	ROUGH IDLE, SPARK KNOCK, STALLS AFTER COLD START, SURGE DURING CRUISE. REFER TO SECTION C6
B13 EGR SOLENOID #3 CONTROL	699	RED	DIGITAL EGR HARN CONN "C"	77 (3)	ROUGH IDLE, SPARK KNOCK, STALLS AFTER COLD START, SURGE DURING CRUISE. REFER TO SECTION C6
B14 BATTERY	540	ORN	UNDERHOOD ELECTRICAL CENTER #1 FUEL PUMP RELAY CAVITY "F9" 20 AMP ECM/BATT FUSE BATTERY (B+)	NONE	CRANKS, BUT WILL NOT START IF BOTH BATTERY FEEDS ARE OPEN. REFER TO "ON-BOARD DIAGNOSTIC SYSTEM CHECK."*
B15 BATTERY	540	ORN	UNDERHOOD ELECTRICAL CENTER #1 FUEL PUMP RELAY CAVITY "F9" 20 AMP ECM/BATT FUSE BATTERY (B+)	NONE	CRANKS, BUT WILL NOT START IF BOTH BATTERY FEEDS ARE OPEN. REFER TO "ON-BOARD DIAGNOSTIC SYSTEM CHECK." *
B16 POWER GROUND	551	TAN/WHT	ENGINE GROUND LOCATED AT LFT FRT OF ENGINE	NONE	CRANKS, BUT WILL NOT START IF ALL POWER GROUNDS ARE OPEN. CHECK GROUNDS AT ENGINE BLOCK, ELECTRONIC IGNITION CONTROL MODULE AND AUTOMATIC TRANSAXLE RANGE SWITCH. REFER TO "ON-BOARD DIAGNOSTIC SYSTEM CHECK." *
B17					
B18 PARK/NEUTRAL CONTROL	434	ORN/BLK	BULKHEAD CONN "G1" CHIME MODULE	NONE	UNSTABLE, INCORRECT IDLE UNDER HIGH ACCESSORY LOADS OR HIGH POWER STEERING LOADS.
B19 SERIAL DATA	800	TAN	BULKHEAD CONN "J4" DATA LINK CONNECTOR "M"	NONE	NO DLC DATA. REFER TO "ON-BOARD DIAGNOSTIC SYSTEM CHECK."*

(1) OPEN CIRCUIT.
(2) GROUNDED CIRCUIT.
(3) OPEN/GROUNDED CIRCUIT.
* REFER TO SECTION 8A.

7-10-93
PS 16727

PCM Connector "B" Symptoms Chart (1 of 2)

PCM CONNECTOR "B" SYMPTOMS CHART
BLACK 32 PIN CONNECTOR

PCM PIN/FUNCTION	CKT #	WIRE COLOR	COMPONENT CONNECTOR CAVITY	DTC(s) AFFECTED	POSSIBLE SYMPTOMS FROM FAULTY CIRCUIT
B20					
B21					
B22 HEATED OXYGEN SENSOR (HO2S) SIGNAL	412	PPL	HEATED OXYGEN SENSOR HARNESS CONNECTOR "B"	13 (1) 44 (3) 45 (4)	ROUGH OR INCORRECT IDLE, LEAN OR RICH EXHAUST, HESITATION, SURGE, POOR PERFORMANCE, POOR FUEL ECONOMY.
B23 HEATED OXYGEN SENSOR (HO2S) GROUND	413	TAN	HEATED OXYGEN SENSOR HARNESS CONNECTOR "A"	13 (1) 44 (3) 45 (4)	ROUGH OR INCORRECT IDLE, LEAN OR RICH EXHAUST, HESITATION, SURGE, POOR PERFORMANCE, POOR FUEL ECONOMY.
B24 IAC "B" HIGH	1749	LT GRN/WHT	IAC VALVE HARNESS CONNECTOR "B"	35 (3)	HIGH OR LOW IDLE, STALLS. REFER TO CHART C-2B.
B25 IAC "B" LOW	444	LT GRN/BLK	IAC VALVE HARNESS CONNECTOR "A"	35 (3)	HIGH OR LOW IDLE, STALLS. REFER TO CHART C-2B.
B26 IAC "A" LOW	1748	LT BLU/BLK	IAC VALVE HARNESS CONNECTOR "C"	35 (3)	HIGH OR LOW IDLE, STALLS. REFER TO CHART C-2B.
B27 IAC "A" HIGH	1747	LT BLU/WHT	IAC VALVE HARNESS CONNECTOR "D"	35 (3)	HIGH OR LOW IDLE, STALLS. REFER TO CHART C-2B.
B28 BUFFERED SPEED OUTPUT (4000 PULSES PER MILE)	389	DK GRN	BULKHEAD CONNECTOR "H4" CLUSTER MODULE	NONE	INOPERATIVE SPEEDOMETER, INOPERATIVE CRUISE CONTROL.*
B29 VSS INPUT LOW	401	PPL	VSS HARNESS CONNECTOR "B"	72 (3) 24 (3)	INOPERATIVE SPEEDOMETER, INOPERATIVE CRUISE CONTROL, TRANS SHIFT FROM DRIVE TO NEUTRAL.*
B30 VSS INPUT HIGH	400	YEL	VSS HARNESS CONNECTOR "A"	72 (3) 24 (3)	INOPERATIVE SPEEDOMETER, INOPERATIVE CRUISE CONTROL, TRANS SHIFT FROM DRIVE TO NEUTRAL.*
B31 5 VOLT REFERENCE	416	GRY	TP SENSOR "A", A/C REF. PRESSURE SENSOR "B", INJECTOR HARNESS CONNECTOR "A" AND MAP SENSOR "C"	22 (3) 34 (3)	ENGINE STARTS AND STALLS, NO POWER, ENGINE WILL NOT RUN.
B32 POWER GROUND	450	BLK/WHT	ENGINE GROUND LOCATED AT LOWER LH OF ENGINE ELECTRONIC (ICM) 2 PIN CONNECTOR	NONE	CRANKS BUT WILL NOT START IF BOTH POWER GROUNDS ARE OPEN. CHECK GROUNDS AT ENGINE BLOCK, ELECTRONIC IGNITION CONTROL MODULE, AUTOMATIC TRANSAXLE RANGE SWITCH. REFER TO "ON-BOARD DIAGNOSTIC SYSTEM CHECK."*

(1) OPEN CIRCUIT.
(2) GROUNDED CIRCUIT.
(3) OPEN/GROUNDED CIRCUIT.
* REFER TO SECTION 8A.

6-22-93
PS 16728

PCM Connector "B" Symptoms Chart (2 of 2)

PCM CONNECTOR "C" SYMPTOMS CHART
BLUE 32 PIN CONNECTOR

PCM PIN/FUNCTION	CKT #	WIRE COLOR	COMPONENT CONNECTOR CAVITY	DTC(s) AFFECTED	POSSIBLE SYMPTOMS FROM FAULTY CIRCUIT
C1 POWER GROUND	451	BLK/WHT	ENGINE GROUND LOCATED AT LOWER LH FRONT OF ENGINE	NONE	CRANKS BUT WILL NOT START IF ALL POWER GROUNDS OPEN. CHECK GROUNDS AT ENGINE BLOCK, ELECTRONIC IGNITION CONTROL MODULE AND AUTOMATIC TRANSAXLE RANGE SWITCH OR PNP SWITCH. REFER TO "ON-BOARD DIAGNOSTIC SYSTEM CHECK." *
C2					
C3 IGNITION FEED	439	PNK	BULKHEAD CONNECTOR "C2" AND 15 AMP ECM FUSE AND TO IGNITION SWITCH	NONE	NO START. REFER TO "ON-BOARD DIAGNOSTIC SYSTEM CHECK." *
C4					
C5					
C6					
C7					
C8 CRUISE STATUS	85	WHT	BULKHEAD CONNECTOR "H5"	NONE	NO CRUISE CONTROL SYMPTOMS.
C9					
C10					
C11 PARK NEUTRAL POSITION (3T40 ONLY)	434	ORN/BLK	PNP SWITCH CONNECTOR "A"	NONE	REFER TO SECTION C1
C12 INJECTOR DRIVER CYL #3	1746	PNK/BLK	10-PIN IN-LINE INJECTOR HARNESS CONNECTOR "C"	NONE	MISFIRE, RUNS ROUGH, POOR PERFORMANCE, POOR FUEL ECONOMY. REFER TO CHART C 2A. *
C13 INJECTOR DRIVER CYL #2	1745	LT GRN/BLK	10-PIN IN-LINE INJECTOR HARNESS CONNECTOR "B"	NONE	MISFIRE, RUNS ROUGH, POOR PERFORMANCE, POOR FUEL ECONOMY. REFER TO CHART C 2A. *
C14 INJECTOR DRIVER CYL #1	1744	BLK	10-PIN IN-LINE INJECTOR HARNESS CONNECTOR "A"	NONE	MISFIRE, RUNS ROUGH, POOR PERFORMANCE, POOR FUEL ECONOMY. REFER TO CHART C 2A. *
C15 INJECTOR DRIVER CYL #6	846	YEL/BLK	10-PIN IN-LINE INJECTOR HARNESS CONNECTOR "H"	NONE	MISFIRE, RUNS ROUGH, POOR PERFORMANCE, POOR FUEL ECONOMY. REFER TO CHART C 2A. *
C16 INJECTOR DRIVER CYL #5	845	BLK/WHT	10-PIN IN-LINE INJECTOR HARNESS CONNECTOR "J"	NONE	MISFIRE, RUNS ROUGH, POOR PERFORMANCE, POOR FUEL ECONOMY. REFER TO CHART C 2A. *
C17 POWER GROUND	551	TAN/WHT	ENGINE GROUND LOCATED AT LOWER LH FRONT OF ENGINE	NONE	CRANKS BUT WILL NOT START IF ALL POWER GROUNDS ARE OPEN. CHECK GROUNDS AT ENGINE BLOCK, ELECTRONIC IGNITION CONTROL MODULE AND AUTOMATIC TRANSAXLE RANGE SWITCH OR PNP SWITCH. REFER TO "ON-BOARD DIAGNOSTIC SYSTEM CHECK." *
C18 REFERENCE LOW FOR CAMSHAFT POSITION & 24X CRANKSHAFT POSITION SENSORS	632	PNK/BLK	CAM HARNESS CONNECTOR "C" CRANKSHAFT HARNESS CONNECTOR "C"	36 (3) 17 (3)	SLIGHT ENGINE MISFIRE, POOR PERFORMANCE, POOR FUEL ECONOMY.
C19					

(1) OPEN CIRCUIT.
(2) GROUNDED CIRCUIT.
(3) OPEN/GROUNDED CIRCUIT.
(4) SHORTED TO VOLTAGE.
* REFER TO ELECTRICAL DIAGNOSIS (SECTION 8A).

8-6-93
PS 16729

PCM Connector "C" Symptoms Chart (1 of 2)

PCM CONNECTOR "C" SYMPTOMS CHART
BLUE 32-PIN CONNECTOR

PCM PIN/FUNCTION	CKT #	WIRE COLOR	COMPONENT CONNECTOR CAVITY	DTC(s) AFFECTED	POSSIBLE SYMPTOMS FROM FAULTY CIRCUIT
C20 KNOCK SENSOR SIGNAL	496	DK/BLU	KNOCK SENSOR	43 (3)	LACK OF PERFORMANCE, SPARK KNOCK. REFER TO SECTION C5.
C21 24X CRANKSHAFT POSITION REFERENCE SIGNAL	647	DK BLU/WHT	24X CRANKSHAFT POSITION SENSOR "B"	36 (3)	INCORRECT IDLE
C22					
C23 PASS-Key (V.A.T.S.)	229	DK BLU	BULKHEAD CONNECTOR "D1" TO TERMINAL "A3" OF THEFT DETERRENT MODULE	NONE	(3) (4) CRANKS, NO START
C24					
C25 CAMSHAFT POSITION REFERENCE SIGNAL	633	BRN/WHT	CAMSHAFT POSITION SENSOR "B"	17 (3)	SLIGHT ENGINE MISFIRE, POOR PERFORMANCE, POOR FUEL ECONOMY.
C26					
C27 IGNITION CONTROL (IC)	423	WHT	ELECTRONIC IGNITION CONTROL MODULE 6-PIN CONNECTOR "B"	41 (1) 42 (2)	SURGE, HESITATION, RUNS ROUGH, STALLS, LACK OF PERFORMANCE.
C28 IGNITION CONTROL BYPASS	424	TAN/BLK	ELECTRONIC IGNITION CONTROL MODULE 6-PIN CONNECTOR "A"	42 (3)	SURGE, HESITATION, RUNS ROUGH, STALLS, LACK OF PERFORMANCE.
C29 IAT SENSOR SIGNAL	472	TAN	IAT SENSOR HARNESS CONNECTOR "B"	23 (1) 25 (2)	HARD TO START, POOR PERFORMANCE.
C30 3X REFERENCE HIGH	430	PPL/WHT	ELECTRONIC IGNITION CONTROL MODULE 6-PIN CONNECTOR "E"	82 (3)	CRANKS BUT WILL NOT START. REFER TO "ON-BOARD DIAGNOSTIC SYSTEM CHECK." *
C31 3X REFERENCE LOW	453	RED/BLK	ELECTRONIC IGNITION CONTROL MODULE 6-PIN CONNECTOR "F"	NONE	NO SYMPTOMS, REFER TO SECTION C4.
C32 INJECTOR DRIVER CYL #4	844	LT BLU/BLK	10-PIN IN-LINE INJECTOR HARNESS CONNECTOR "K"	NONE	MISFIRE, RUNS ROUGH, POOR PERFORMANCE, POOR FUEL ECONOMY. REFER TO CHART C-2A.

(1) OPEN CIRCUIT.
(2) GROUNDED CIRCUIT.
(3) OPEN/GROUNDED CIRCUIT.
(4) SHORTED TO VOLTAGE.
* REFER TO ELECTRICAL DIAGNOSIS (SECTION 8A).

6-22-93
PS 16730

PCM Connector "C" Symptoms Chart (2 of 2)

CHART B-1

RESTRICTED EXHAUST SYSTEM CHECK

CHECK AT HEATED OR UNHEATED OXYGEN SENSORS:

1. Carefully remove oxygen sensor.
2. Install exhaust backpressure tester (BT-8515 or BT-8603) or equivalent in place of oxygen sensor (see illustration).
3. After completing test described below, be sure to coat threads of oxygen sensor with anti-seize compound P/N 5613695 or equivalent prior to re-installation.

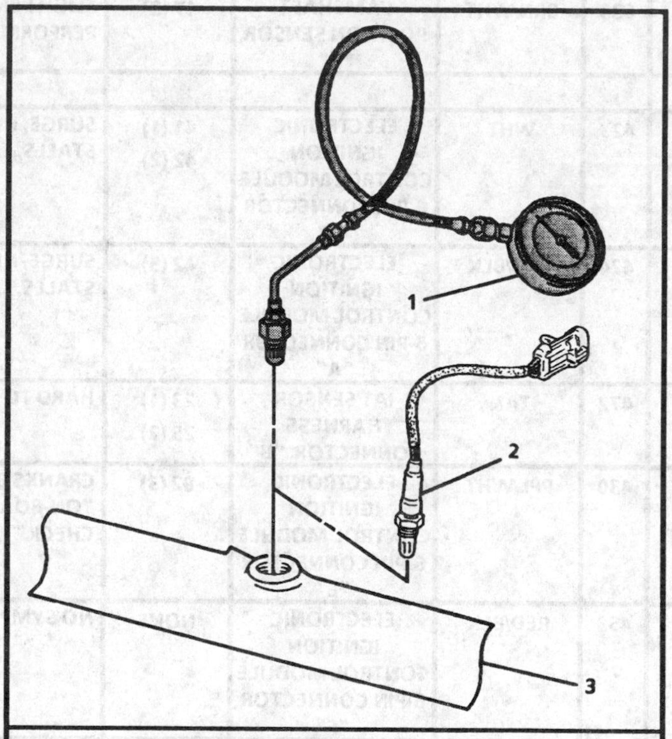
1
2
3

1 BACK PRESSURE GAGE
2 HEATED OR UNHEATED OXYGEN SENSOR
3 EXHAUST MANIFOLD (TYPICAL)

NS 15056

DIAGNOSIS:

1. With the engine idling at normal operating temperature, observe the exhaust system backpressure reading on the gage. Reading should not exceed 8.6 kPa (1.25 psi).
2. Increase engine speed to 2000 RPM and observe gage. Reading should not exceed 20.7 kPa (3 psi).
3. If the backpressure at either speed exceeds specification, a restricted exhaust system is indicated.
4. Inspect the entire exhaust system for a collapsed pipe, heat distress, or possible internal muffler failure.
5. If there are no obvious reasons for the excessive backpressure, the catalytic converter is suspected to be restricted and should be replaced using current recommended procedures.

7-7-93
PS 18058

BLANK

SECTION C

COMPONENT SYSTEMS

NOTICE: When fasteners are removed, always reinstall them at the same location from which they were removed. If a fastener needs to be replaced, use the correct part number fastener for that application. If the correct part number fastener is not available, a fastener of equal size and strength (or stronger) may be used. Fasteners that are not reused, and those requiring thread-locking compound will be called out. The correct torque value must be used when installing fasteners that require it. If the above conditions are not followed, parts or system damage could result.

Section "C" provides information on the following:

- General description of components and systems.
- On-vehicle service.
- Part names.
- Diagnostic charts. These include a functional check of the system as well as diagnosis of any problem found in the functional check.

For locations of components, wiring diagrams, and PCM terminal end view, refer to the front on the "A" Section of the engine being diagnosed.

Following are the sub-section identification and the system covered:

DIAGNOSTIC CHARTS

The diagnostic charts for each system are found after the on-vehicle service and parts information at the back of each section. Following are the charts found in this section.

SECTION C1

POWERTRAIN CONTROL MODULE (PCM) AND SENSORS

CONTENTS

GENERAL DESCRIPTION

POWERTRAIN CONTROL MODULE (PCM)

NOTICE: To prevent possible Electrostatic Discharge damage to the PCM, **Do Not** touch the connector pins or soldered components on the circuit board.

The Powertrain Control Module (PCM) (Figure C1-1), is located underhood in front of the right shock tower near the engine coolant reservoir. It is the control center of the fuel injection system and constantly looks at the information from various sensors and controls the systems that affect vehicle performance. The PCM also performs the diagnostic function of the system. It can recognize operational problems, alert the driver through the Malfunction Indicator Lamp (MIL) "Service Engine Soon," and store a DTC which identifies the problem areas to aid the technician in making repairs. Refer to "Introduction," SECTION 6E for more information on using the diagnostic function of the PCM.

The PCM used on the 3100 engine is referred to as SFI-66. For service, this PCM consists of two parts: a dual processor controller and an electronic Knock Sensor (KS) module.

PCM FUNCTION

The PCM contains a power supply which regulates the 12 volts vehicle supply input to 5 and 12 volts, and these voltages are used for various internal and external functions.

The PCM supplies a buffered 5 or 12 volts to power various sensors or switches. This is done through resistances in the PCM which are so high in value that a test light will not light when connected to the circuit. In some cases, even an ordinary shop voltmeter will not give an accurate reading because its resistance is too low.

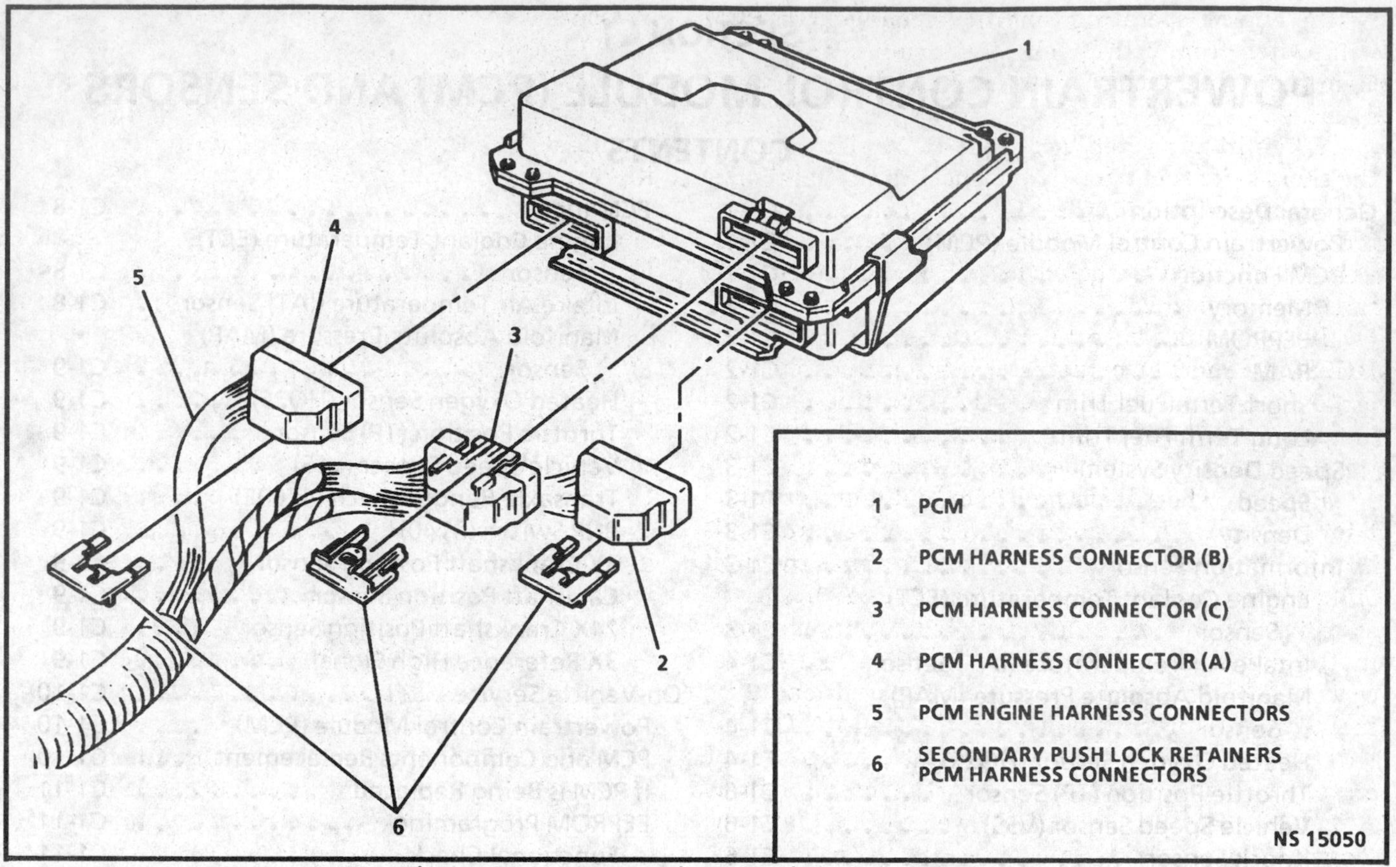
1 PCM
2 PCM HARNESS CONNECTOR (B)
3 PCM HARNESS CONNECTOR (C)
4 PCM HARNESS CONNECTOR (A)
5 PCM ENGINE HARNESS CONNECTORS
6 SECONDARY PUSH LOCK RETAINERS PCM HARNESS CONNECTORS
NS 15050

Figure C1-1 - Powertrain Control Module (PCM)

Therefore, the use of a 10 megohm input impedance digital voltmeter or a Tech 1 scan tool is necessary to assure accurate voltage readings.

The Input/Output (I/O) devices in the PCM include analog to digital converters, signal buffers, counters and special drivers. The PCM controls output circuits such as the fuel injectors, IAC valve, cooling fan relays, etc. by controlling the ground circuit through transistors or a device called a "quad-driver" in the PCM.

Memory

There are two types of memory storage within the PCM: EEPROM and RAM.

EEPROM

Electrically Erasable Programmable Read Only Memory (EEPROM) is a permanent memory that is physically soldered to the circuit boards within the PCM. The EEPROM contains the overall control algorithms. The EEPROM can be reprogrammed by using the Tech 1 scan tool or other Techline "T" series terminals/equipment.

RAM

Random Access Memory (RAM) is the microprocessor "scratch pad." The processor can write into or read from this memory as needed. This memory is volatile and needs a constant supply of voltage to be retained. If the voltage is lost, the memory is lost and the PCM logs a DTC 16 indicating this loss.

Short Term Fuel Trim

Short term fuel trim is a PCM volatile memory register that will contain a number between 0 and 255. The neutral value for the short term fuel trim is 128; any deviation from this value indicates the short term fuel trim is changing the injector pulse width. The amount of pulse width change depends on how far the short term fuel trim value is from 128. The short term fuel trim changes the pulse width by varying the "Closed Loop" factor of the base pulse width equation. As the PCM monitors the Heated Oxygen Sensor (HO2S) input, it is constantly varying the short term fuel trim value. The value is updated very quickly, therefore, the short term fuel trim only corrects for short term fuel trim trends. The correction of long term fuel trim trends is the function of the long term fuel trim.

Long Term Fuel Trim

The long term fuel trim is a matrix of cells arranged by RPM and MAP. Each cell of the long term fuel trim is a register like the short term fuel trim.

As the engine operating conditions change, the PCM will switch from cell to cell to determine what "long term fuel trim" factor to use in the base pulse width equation.

While in any given block, the PCM also monitors the short term fuel trim. If the short term fuel trim is far enough from 128, the PCM will change the long term fuel trim value. Once the long term fuel trim value is changed it should force the short term fuel trim back toward 128.

If the mixture is still not correct (as judged by the HO2S), the short term fuel trim will continue to have a large deviation from the ideal 128. In this case, the long term fuel trim value will continue to change until the short term fuel trim becomes balanced.

Both the short term fuel trim and long term fuel trim are limited by calibrated values. If the air/fuel is off enough so that long term fuel trim reaches the limit of its control and still cannot correct the condition, the short term fuel trim would also go to its limit of control in the same direction. If the mixture is still not corrected by both short term fuel trim and long term fuel trim at their extreme values, a DTC 44 or DTC 45 will likely result. Under the conditions of power enrichment, the PCM sets the short term fuel trim to 128 and freezes it there until power enrichment is no longer in effect. This is done so the "Closed Loop" factor and the long term fuel trim will not try to correct for the commanded richness of power enrichment.

SPEED DENSITY SYSTEM

The Sequential Fuel Injection (SFI) system is a speed and air density system. The system is based on "speed density" fuel management, so let's define their basis of operation.

Three specific data sensors provide the PCM with the basic information for the fuel management portion of its operation. That is, three specific signals to the PCM establish the engine speed and air density factors.

Speed

The engine speed signal comes from the 3X crankshaft position sensor is conditioned by the electronic Ignition Control Module (ICM). This signal is input to the PCM on the crank reference high, CKT 430. The PCM uses this information to determine the "speed" or RPM factor for fuel and ignition management.

Density

Three sensors contribute to the density factor, the Intake Air Temperature (IAT), the Manifold Absolute Pressure (MAP) and the Engine Coolant Temperature (ECT) sensor.

The IAT sensor is a 2-wire sensor that measures the temperature of the air entering the intake manifold. The IAT sensor is a thermistor that changes its resistance as an inverse function of temperature. When the temperature is low, the resistance is high, and when the temperature is high, the resistance is low.

The engine coolant temperature sensor is also a 2-wire sensor that measures temperature. It is mounted in the engine coolant stream and operates the same way as the IAT sensor.

The IAT and ECT sensor work together to assure that proper temperature information gets to the PCM.

The Manifold Absolute Pressure (MAP) sensor is a 3-wire sensor that monitors the changes in intake manifold pressure which results from changes in engine loading. These pressure changes are supplied to the PCM in the form of analog electrical signals.

As intake manifold pressure increases, the air density in the intake manifold also increases and additional fuel is required. The MAP sensor sends this pressure information to the PCM and the PCM increases the amount of fuel injected by increasing the injector pulse width. Conversely, as manifold pressure decreases, the amount of fuel is decreased.

These four inputs MAP, IAT, ECT sensor, and RPM are the major determinants of the air/fuel mixture delivered by the fuel injection system.

The remaining sensors and switches provide electrical inputs to the PCM which are used for modification of the air/fuel mixture, as well as for other PCM control functions, such as Idle Air Control (IAC).

INFORMATION SENSORS

Engine Coolant Temperature (ECT) Sensor *Figure C1-2*

The engine coolant temperature sensor is a thermistor (a resistor which changes value based on temperature) mounted in the engine coolant stream. Low coolant temperature produces a high resistance (100,000 ohms at -40°C/-40°F) while high temperature causes low resistance (70 ohms at 130°C/266°F).

The PCM supplies a 5 volt signal to the engine coolant temperature sensor through a resistor in the PCM and measures the voltage. The voltage will be high when the engine is cold, and low when the engine is hot. By measuring the voltage, the PCM calculates the engine coolant temperature. Engine coolant temperature affects most systems the PCM controls.

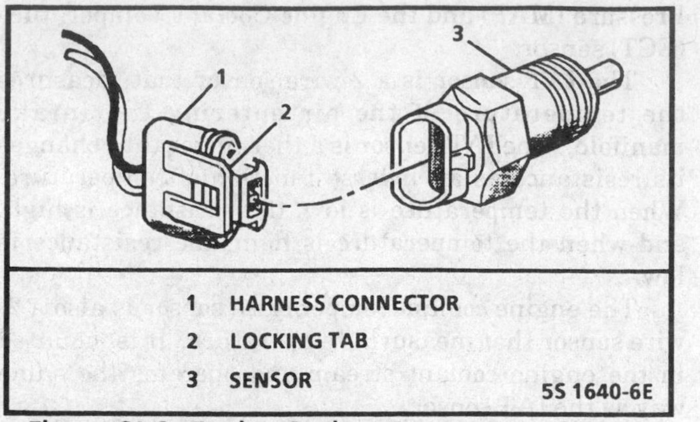
1
2
3
1 HARNESS CONNECTOR
2 LOCKING TAB
3 SENSOR
5S 1640-6E

Figure C1-2 - Engine Coolant Temperature Sensor

A failure in the ECT sensor circuit should set either a DTC 14 or DTC 15. Remember, these DTC(s) indicate a failure in the engine coolant temperature circuit so proper use of the chart will lead to either repairing a wiring problem or replacing the sensor to properly repair a problem.

Intake Air Temperature (IAT) Sensor

The Intake Air Temperature (IAT) sensor is a thermistor (a resistor which changes value based on the temperature of air entering the engine and is mounted in the air cleaner). Low temperature produces a high resistance (approximately 100,000 ohms at -40°C/-40°F) while high temperature causes low resistance (approximately 70 ohms at 130°C/266°F). The PCM supplies a 5 volts signal to the sensor through a resistor in the PCM and measures the voltage. The voltage will be high when the intake air is cold and low when the air is hot. By measuring the voltage the PCM calculates the intake air temperature.

The IAT sensor is used to control spark timing and delays EGR when the intake air is cold.

A failure in the IAT sensor circuit should set either a DTC 23 or DTC 25. Once a diagnostic trouble code is set, the PCM will use an artificial default value for IAT and some vehicle performance will return.

Manifold Absolute Pressure (MAP) Sensor *Figure C1-3*

The Manifold Absolute Pressure (MAP) sensor measures the changes in the intake manifold pressure which result from engine load and speed changes, and converts this to a voltage output.

A closed throttle on engine coastdown would produce a relatively low MAP output, while a wide-open throttle would produce a high output. Manifold Absolute Pressure (MAP) is the OPPOSITE of what you would measure on a vacuum gage. When manifold pressure is high, vacuum is low. The MAP sensor is also used to measure barometric pressure under certain conditions, which allows the PCM to automatically adjust for different altitudes. The PCM sends a 5 volt reference signal to the MAP sensor. As the manifold pressure changes, the electrical resistance of the sensor also changes. By monitoring the sensor output voltage, the PCM calculates the manifold pressure. A higher pressure, low vacuum (high voltage) requires more fuel, while a lower pressure, higher vacuum (low voltage) requires less fuel.

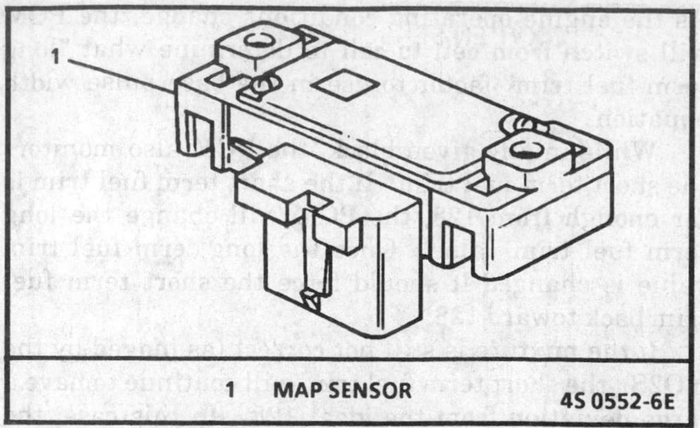
1
1 MAP SENSOR
4S 0552-6E

Figure C1-3 - MAP Sensor

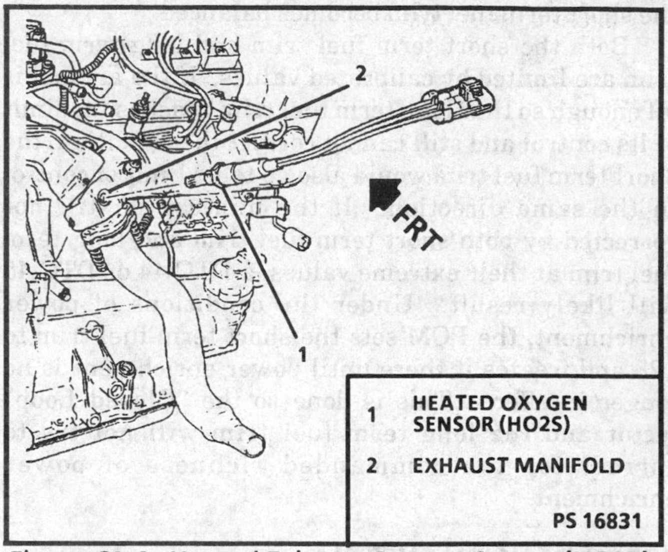
2
FRT
1
1 HEATED OXYGEN SENSOR (HO2S)
2 EXHAUST MANIFOLD
PS 16831

Figure C1-4 - Heated Exhaust Oxygen Sensor (HO2S)

A failure in the MAP sensor circuit should set a DTC 33 or DTC 34. CHART C-1D can also be used to check this MAP sensor.

Heated Oxygen Sensor (HO2S)

The Heated Oxygen Sensor (HO2S) is essentially a small variable battery; it has the ability to produce a low voltage signal that feeds information on engine exhaust oxygen content to the PCM (Figure C1-5).

The HO2S is constructed from a zirconia/platinum electrolytic element. Zirconia is an electrolyte that conducts electricity under certain chemical conditions. The element is made of a ceramic material. The element is an insulator when cold. At operating temperature 315°C (600°F), the element becomes a semiconductor.

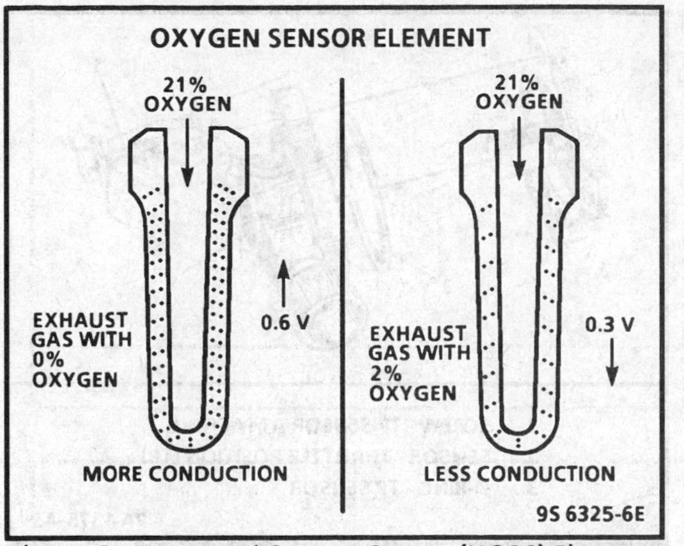
OXYGEN SENSOR ELEMENT
21% OXYGEN
21% OXYGEN
0.6 V
EXHAUST GAS WITH 0% OXYGEN
EXHAUST GAS WITH 2% OXYGEN
0.3 V
MORE CONDUCTION
LESS CONDUCTION
9S 6325-6E

Figure C1-5 - Heated Oxygen Sensor (HO2S) Element

A platinum coating on the outer surface of the element stimulates further combustion of the exhaust gases right at the surface and this helps maintain a high operating temperature at the element. The electric heater in the HO2S decreases warmup time and helps maintain operating temperature at idle. The heated oxygen sensor has an inner cavity which is filled with atmospheric (reference) air. The atmosphere has approximately 21% oxygen in it. In the electrical circuit this inner cavity is the positive (+) terminal. The outer surface of the element is exposed to the exhaust gas stream. It is the negative (-) or ground terminal. Due to the electrolytic properties of the element the oxygen concentration differences between the reference air and exhaust gases produce small voltages.

A rich exhaust (excessive fuel) has almost no oxygen. When there is a large difference in the amount of oxygen touching the inside and outside surfaces, there is more conduction, and the sensor puts out a voltage signal above 0.6 volt.

When lean exhaust (excessive oxygen) there is about two percent oxygen in the exhaust. This is a smaller difference in oxygen from the outside surfaces which results in less conduction and a voltage signal below 0.3 volt. The voltages are monitored and used by the PCM to "fine tune" the air fuel ratio to achieve the ideal mixture desired.

The PCM puts out a reference signal of 0.45 volt (refer to Figure C1-6). The reference signal serves two purposes. The first is to run the engine when it is in "Open Loop" mode of operation. When the air/fuel ratio is correct the PCM "senses" 0.45 volt. When the engine is operating with a rich air/fuel ratio there is a reduction of free oxygen in the exhaust stream and the HO2S voltage rises above the reference voltage. When the engine is run lean, the voltage drops below the reference voltage due to excess oxygen in the exhaust stream.

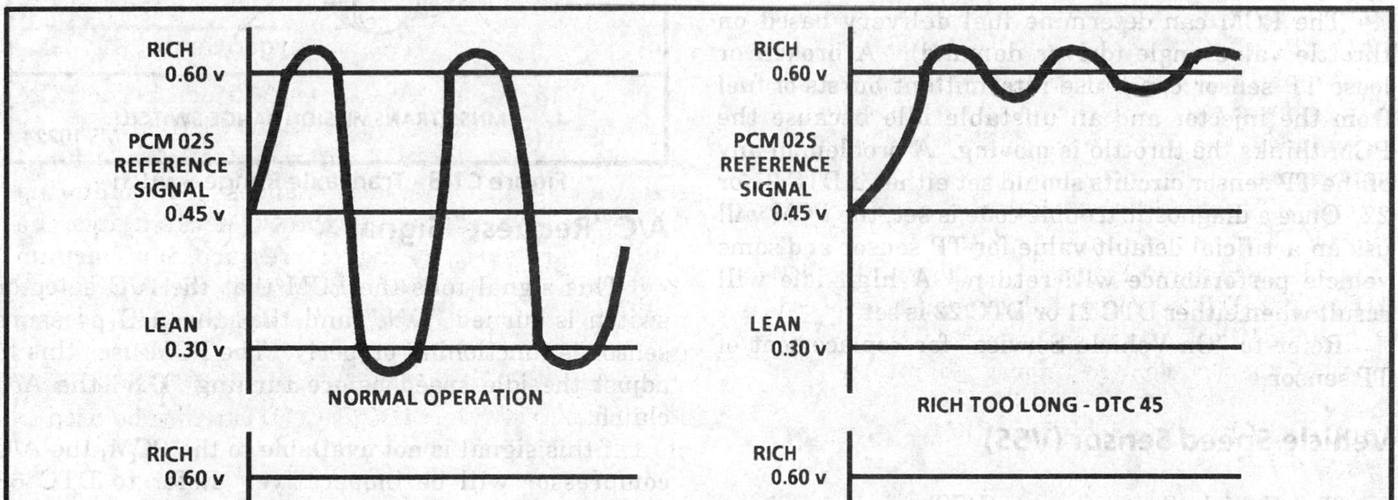
RICH 0.60 v
PCM 02S REFERENCE SIGNAL 0.45 v
LEAN 0.30 v
NORMAL OPERATION
RICH 0.60 v
PCM 02S REFERENCE SIGNAL 0.45 v
LEAN 0.30 v
RICH TOO LONG - DTC 45
RICH 0.60 v
PCM 02S REFERENCE SIGNAL 0.45 v
LEAN 0.30 v
LEAN TOO LONG - DTC 44
RICH 0.60 v
PCM 02S REFERENCE SIGNAL 0.45 v
LEAN 0.30 v
BETWEEN 0.3-0.6v TOO LONG - DTC 13
6-2-93
PS 18270

Figure C1-6 - Normal Voltage and Abnormal Trends

The Heated Oxygen Sensor (HO2S) provides the feedback information for the "Closed Loop" operating mode of the fuel delivery system. The heated oxygen sensor indicates to the PCM what is happening in the exhaust. It does not cause things to happen. It is a type of gage: Low voltage output = lean mixture = high oxygen content in the exhaust; high voltage output = rich mixture = low oxygen content in the exhaust.

An open Heated Oxygen Sensor (HO2S) circuit should set a DTC 13. A constant low voltage in the Heated Oxygen Sensor (HO2S) circuit should set a DTC 44.

Throttle Position (TP) Sensor
Figure C1-7

The Throttle Position (TP) sensor is a potentiometer connected to the throttle shaft on the throttle body. The TP sensor electrical circuit consists of a 5 volts supply line and a ground line, both provided by the PCM. By monitoring the voltage on this signal line the PCM calculates throttle position. As the throttle valve angle is changed (accelerator pedal moved), the output of the TP sensor also changes. At a closed throttle position, the output of the TP sensor is low (approximately .29 to .98 volt). As the throttle valve opens, the output increases so that, at wide open throttle, the output voltage should be approximately 5 volts.

The PCM can determine fuel delivery based on throttle valve angle (driver demand). A broken or loose TP sensor can cause intermittent bursts of fuel from the injector and an unstable idle because the PCM thinks the throttle is moving. A problem in any of the TP sensor circuits should set either a DTC 21 or 22. Once a diagnostic trouble code is set, the PCM will use an artificial default value for TP sensor and some vehicle performance will return. A high idle will result when either DTC 21 or DTC 22 is set.

Refer to "On-Vehicle Service" for replacement of TP sensor.

Vehicle Speed Sensor (VSS)

The Vehicle Speed Sensor (VSS) sends a pulsing voltage signal to the PCM which the PCM converts to mph/km/h. This sensor mainly controls the operation of the TCC system. Refer to "Torque Converter Clutch (TCC) and Shift Solenoid System," Section "6E3-C8", DTC 24 or SECTION 8A for more information.

Knock Sensor

Refer to "Knock Sensor (KS) System," Section "6E3-C5" for description of KS system.

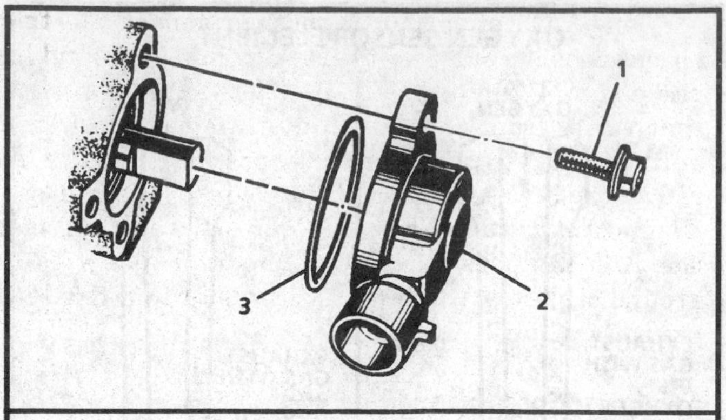
1
2
3

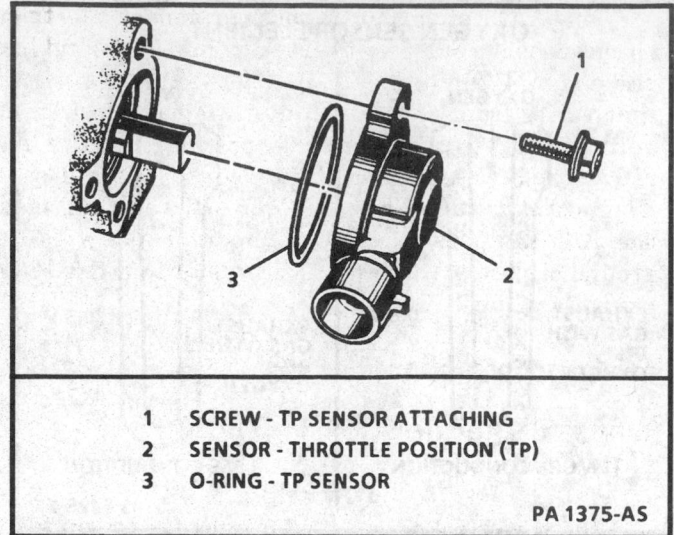

1 SCREW - TP SENSOR ATTACHING
2 SENSOR - THROTTLE POSITION (TP)
3 O-RING - TP SENSOR

PA 1375-AS

Figure C1-7 - Throttle Position (TP) Sensor

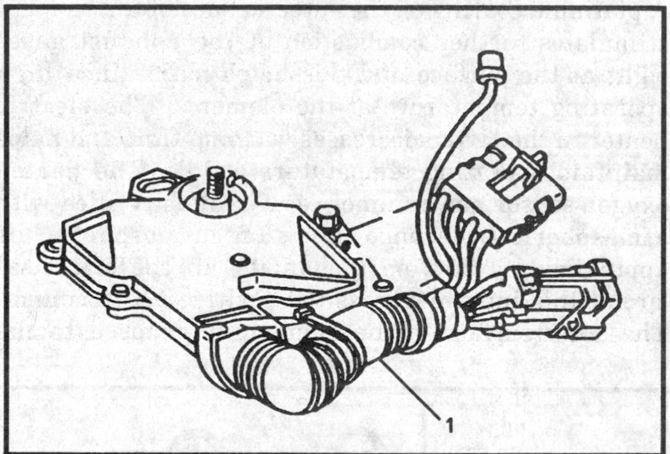
1

1 TMNSS/TRANSMISSION RANGE SWITCH

MS 10224

Figure C1-8 - Transaxle Range Switch

A/C "Request" Signal

This signal tells the PCM that the A/C selector switch is turned "ON," and that the A/C pressure sensor is functioning properly. The PCM uses this to adjust the idle speed before turning "ON" the A/C clutch.

If this signal is not available to the PCM, the A/C compressor will be inoperative. Refer to DTC 66 diagnostics and "A/C Compressor Clutch Control," Section "6E3-C10".

A/C Refrigerant Pressure Sensor

The Air Conditioning (A/C) refrigerant pressure sensor provides a signal to the Powertrain Control Module (PCM) which indicates varying high side refrigerant pressure between approximately 0 psi and 450 psi.

The PCM uses this input to determine A/C compressor load on the engine to help control idle speed with the IAC valve.

The A/C refrigerant pressure sensor electrical circuit consists of a 5 volt reference line, a ground line, and a signal line to the PCM. The signal is a voltage that varies from approximately .1 volt at 0 psi, to 4.9 volts at 450 psi or more. A problem in the A/C refrigerant pressure circuits or sensor should set a Diagnostic Trouble Code (DTC) 66 or 70 and will make the A/C compressor clutch inoperative. A faulty ground circuit at the sensor will result in a fixed high pressure value.

Refer to DTC 66 or 70 for diagnosis of the A/C refrigerant pressure sensor.

Transaxle Range Switch (4T60E)
Figure C1-8

The transaxle range switch indicates to the PCM what gear the transaxle is in. This information is used for the TCC, EGR, and the IAC valve operation.

Park/Neutral Position (PNP) Switch (3T40)

The Park/Neutral Position (PNP) switch indicates to the PCM when the transmission is in park or neutral or drive. This information is used for the TCC, EGR, and the IAC valve operation.

Refer to "On-Vehicle Service," in SECTION 7A for more information on the PNP switch, which is part of the neutral/start and backup light switch assembly, mounted on the transaxle. Refer to CHART C-1A for PNP switch check.

Important

- Vehicle should not be driven with transaxle range switch (4T60E) or park/neutral position switch (3T40) disconnected, as idle quality and transaxle performance will be affected.

2nd Gear Start Switch

Tech 1 displays "ON" when shift solenoid "A" is "OFF" while shift solenoid "B" is "ON." This gives the vehicle the ability to start out in second gear.

3X CRANKSHAFT POSITION SENSOR

The 3X crankshaft position sensor provides a signal through the electronic ignition control module which the PCM uses as reference to calculate RPM and crankshaft position. Refer to "Electronic Ignition (EI) System," Section "6E3-C4" for further information.

CAMSHAFT POSITION SENSOR

The camshaft position sensor is a "Hall-effect" switch, located on the front top of the engine is supplied ignition voltage and has its own ground. The sensor sends a signal to the PCM prior to when the #1

FRT
1
2

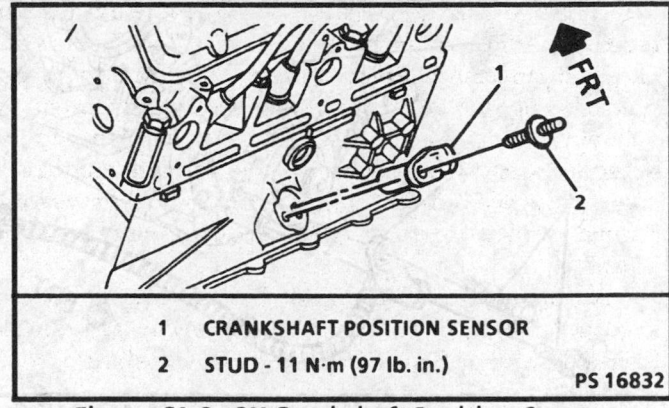

1 CRANKSHAFT POSITION SENSOR
2 STUD - 11 N·m (97 lb. in.)
PS 16832

Figure C1-9 - 3X Crankshaft Position Sensor

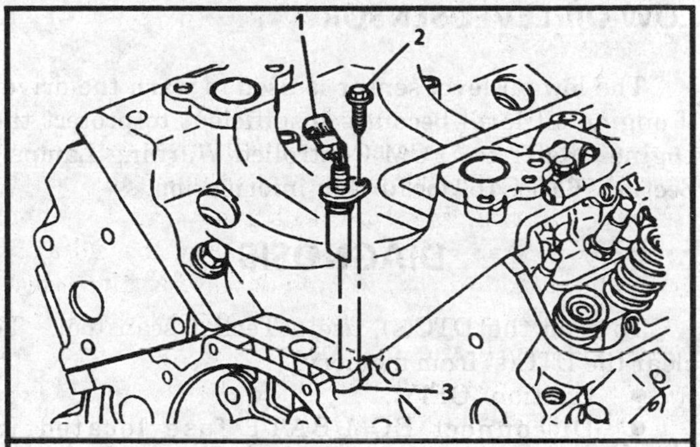
1
2
3

1 CAMSHAFT POSITION SENSOR ASSEMBLY
2 BOLT (1) TORQUE 10 N·m (8 lb. ft.)
3 ENGINE BLOCK ASSEMBLY
NS 15091

Figure C1-10 - Camshaft Position Sensor

cylinder is on the intake stroke. This signal is used by the PCM to synchronize Sequential Fuel Injection (SFI) mode of operation with each intake valve opening. If the cam signal is not received by the PCM, the PCM will still operate in SFI mode based on the reference signal, however, SFI mode timing may not be as accurate because the PCM does not know the exact time the intake valves are opening. A loss of this signal or extra cam signals, above 500 RPM, to the PCM will set a DTC 17. A slightly rough idle and reduced fuel economy may result.

24X CRANKSHAFT POSITION SENSOR
Figure C1-11

The 24X crankshaft position sensor is used to improve idle spark control at engine speeds up to approximately 1250 RPM. Refer to "Electronic Ignition (EI) System," Section "6E3-C4" for further information.

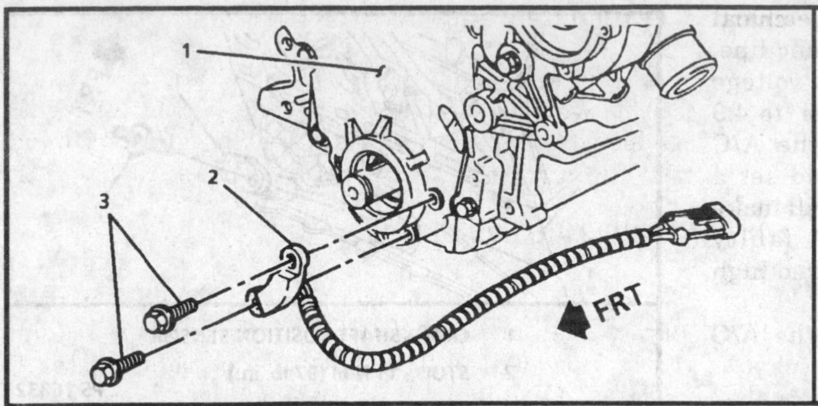
1
2
3
FRT
1 FRONT ENGINE COVER
2 24x CRANKSHAFT POSITION SENSOR ASSEMBLY
3 BOLT (2) TORQUE 10 N·m (8 lb. ft.)
NS 15092

Figure C1-11 - 24X Crankshaft Position Sensor

LOW OIL LEVEL SENSOR

The low oil level sensor is used to warn the driver if engine oil level becomes insufficient to protect the engine. Refer to "PCM Controlled Warning Lamps," Section "6E3-C16" for further information.

DIAGNOSIS

To read the DTC(s), use a Tech 1 scan tool. To clear the DTC(s) from memory:

- Ignition "OFF."
- Disconnect ECM/BATT fuse located in underhood electrical center #1 for 30 seconds or use the Tech 1 scan tool clear DTC(s) function.

Since the PCM can have a failure which may affect only one circuit, following the diagnostic procedures in this section will determine which circuit has a problem and where it is.

If a diagnostic chart indicates that the PCM connections or PCM is the cause of a problem and the PCM is replaced, the Knock Sensor (KS) module must be transferred to the new PCM and the new PCM must then be programmed. If this does not correct the problem, one of the following may be the reason:

- There is a problem with the PCM terminal connections. The diagnostic chart will say PCM connections or PCM. The terminals may have to be removed from the connector in order to check them properly.
- The problem is intermittent. This means that the problem is not present at the time the system is being checked. In this case, refer to the "Symptoms," Section "6E3-B" portion of the manual and make a careful physical inspection of all portions of the system involved.
- Shorted solenoid, relay coil, or harness. Solenoids and relays are turned "ON" and "OFF" by the PCM using internal electronic switches called "drivers." Each driver is part of a group of four called "quad-drivers." Failure of one driver can damage any other driver in the set.

  A shorted solenoid, relay coil, or harness computer will not damage the PCM but will cause the component to be inoperative.

  J 34636 or BT-8405 testers or equivalent provide a fast, accurate means of checking for a shorted coil or a short to battery voltage.

PCM INPUTS

All of the sensors and input switches can be diagnosed by the use of a Tech 1 scan tool. The following is a short description of how the sensors and switches can be diagnosed by the use of a Tech 1. The Tech 1 can also be used to compare the values for a normal running engine with the engine you're diagnosing.

Engine Coolant Temperature (ECT) Sensor

A Tech 1 scan tool displays engine temperature in degrees centigrade. After the engine is started, the temperature should rise steadily to about 90°C (194°F) then stabilize when the thermostat opens. If the engine has not been run for several hours (overnight) the engine coolant temperature and intake air temperature should read close to each other. A fault in the ECT sensor circuit should set a DTC 14 or DTC 15. The diagnostic trouble code charts also contain a "Diagnostic Aid" chart to check for sensor resistance values relative to temperature.

Intake Air Temperature (IAT) Sensor

A Tech 1 scan tool displays temperature of the air entering the engine and should read close to ambient air temperature when engine is cold, and rise as underhood temperature increases. If the engine has not been run for several hours (overnight) the intake air temperature and engine coolant temperature should read close to each other. A failure in the IAT sensor circuit should set a DTC 23 or 25.

The DTC charts also contain a "Diagnostic Aid" chart to check for sensor resistance values relative to temperature.

Manifold Absolute Pressure (MAP) Sensor

A Tech 1 scan tool displays manifold pressure in volts. Low pressure (high vacuum) displays a low voltage while a high pressure (low vacuum) displays a high voltage. A failure in the MAP sensor circuit should set a DTC 33 or 34 and using the chart will find the cause of the problem. A DTC 33 may be set if a rough or unstable idle exists. CHART C-1D can also be used to check MAP sensor output.

Heated Oxygen Sensor (HO2S)

The Tech 1 scan tool has several positions that will indicate the state of the exhaust gases, Heated Oxygen Sensor (HO2S) voltage, short term fuel trim and long term fuel trim. Refer to Tech 1 scan tool position information in "Introduction," in SECTION 6E.

A problem in the Heated Oxygen Sensor (HO2S) circuit, or fuel system, should set a DTC 13 (open circuit), DTC 44 (lean indication), DTC 45 (rich indication). Refer to applicable chart if any of these DTC(s) were stored in memory.

Throttle Position (TP) Sensor

A Tech 1 scan tool displays throttle position in volts. Voltage should increase at a steady rate as throttle is moved toward WOT.

The PCM has the ability to auto-zero the TP sensor voltage if it is between .29 volt (290 mV) and .98 volt (980 mV). This means that any voltage between .29 and .98 volt will be determined by the PCM to be 0% throttle. Tech 1 scan tools have the ability to read the throttle angle and should display 0% when the throttle is closed.

If the throttle angle at idle displayed on the Tech 1 at a value greater than 1%, check for cable binding or a stuck throttle valve. If there is no mechanical fault, remove power from the PCM for 20 seconds. This will clear throttle angle from memory. Restore PCM power and then monitor throttle angle with the Tech 1 at idle. If the value indicated is still greater than 1% at idle, the TP sensor or PCM may be at fault.

A failure in the TP sensor or circuit should set a DTC 21 or 22.

Vehicle Speed Sensor (VSS)

The Tech 1 scan tool reading should closely match with speedometer display with drive wheels turning. A failure in the VSS circuit should set a DTC 24.

Transaxle Range Switch (4T60E)

The input from the range switch indicates to the PCM which gear the transaxle selector lever has selected. This information is used for ignition timing, EVAP canister purge and IAC valve operation.

PNP Switch (3T40)

A Tech 1 scan tool should read PNP when in park, or neutral, and R-D, L, when in drive. This reading may vary with different makes of tools. Refer to CHART C-1A for PNP switch diagnosis.

Important

- Vehicle should not be driven with the transaxle range switch (4T60E) or park/neutral position switch (3T40) disconnected, as idle quality will be affected.

Refer to SECTION 7A for more information on transaxle range switch.

3X Crankshaft Position Sensor

The Tech 1 scan tool displays crankshaft position sensor data as engine speed (RPM). An error in the crankshaft position sensor circuit should set a DTC 82.

Camshaft Position Sensor

The Tech 1 scan tool will display camshaft position sensor data as a 0 and 1. As the sensor pulses, the scan data will switch from 0 to 1. All camshaft position sensor data should be checked at idle. An error in the camshaft position sensor circuit should set a DTC 17.

24X Crankshaft Position Sensor

The Tech 1 scan tool will display 24X crankshaft sensor data in RPM. An error in the 24X sensor circuit should set a DTC 36.

3X Reference High Signal

The ignition control module receives signals from the 3X crankshaft position sensor located in the engine block. This signal is then conditioned and sent to the PCM as a 5 volt digital signal. The PCM uses this input as part of it's final calculation for Ignition Control (IC) timing. Refer to "Electronic Ignition (EI) System," Section "6E3-C4", for more information on the Electronic Ignition (EI) system.

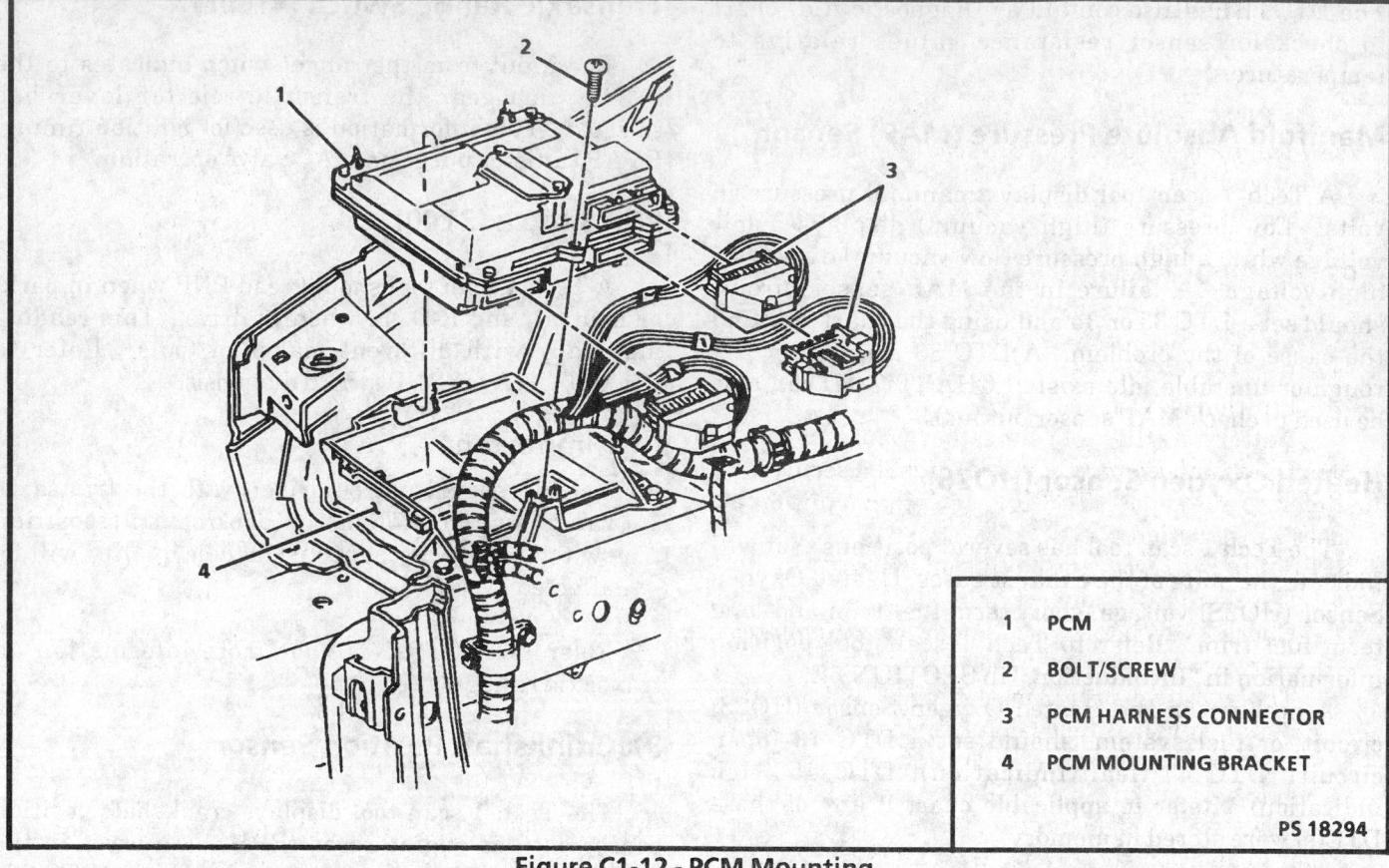

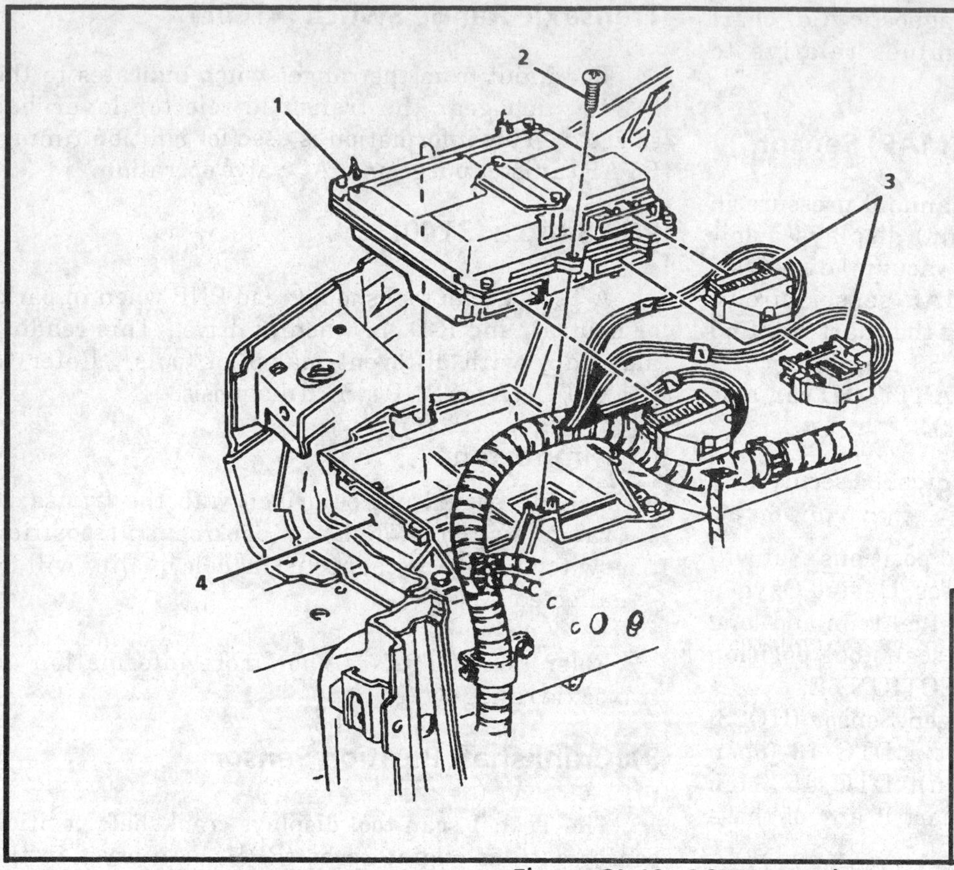
1
2
3
4
1 PCM
2 BOLT/SCREW
3 PCM HARNESS CONNECTOR
4 PCM MOUNTING BRACKET
PS 18294

Figure C1-12 - PCM Mounting

ON-VEHICLE SERVICE

POWERTRAIN CONTROL MODULE (PCM)

NOTICE: To prevent possible Electrostatic Discharge damage to the PCM, Do Not touch the connector pins or soldered components on the circuit board.

Service of the PCM should normally consist of either replacement of the PCM or reprogramming of the EEPROM.

Important

- When replacing the production PCM with a service PCM (controller), it is important to transfer the broadcast code and production PCM number to the service PCM label. Please do not record on PCM cover. This will allow positive identification of PCM parts throughout the service life of the vehicle.

Important

- To prevent internal PCM damage, the ignition must be "OFF" when disconnecting or reconnecting power to PCM (for example, battery cable, PCM connectors, power feed fuse(s), jumper cables, etc.).

PCM AND COMPONENTS REPLACEMENT

NOTICE: To prevent possible Electrostatic Discharge damage to the PCM, Do Not touch the connector pins or soldered components on the circuit board.

↔ Remove or Disconnect

1. Negative battery cable.
2. Engine coolant reservoir. Refer to SECTION 6B.
3. PCM mounting hardware.
4. Connectors from PCM.
5. PCM from engine compartment.
6. PCM access cover.
7. Knock Sensor (KS) module. Refer to Section "6E3-C5".

Important

- The Knock Sensor (KS) module must be transferred to the replacement PCM.
- The replacement PCM is supplied without a EEPROM program, the replacement PCM must be programmed before the vehicle will run.

IF PCM IS BEING REPLACED

↔ Remove or Disconnect

1. New PCM from its packaging and check the service number to make sure it is the same as the defective PCM.
2. Access cover.

EEPROM PROGRAMMING

1. Set-up:
   - Battery is charged.
   - Ignition is "ON."
   - Battery/cig. lighter connection secure.
   - Data Link Connector (DLC) must be secure.
2. Refer to up-to-date Techline terminal/equipment user's instructions.
3. If PCM fails to program, do the following:
   - Check all PCM connections.
   - Check Techline terminal/equipment for latest software version.
   - Try again to program the PCM. If it fails again, replace the PCM. Replacement PCM must be programmed.
4. If vehicle is equipped with an aftermarket anti-theft system, it may require a reset procedure. Refer to appropriate service manual/section.

Functional Check

- Use Techline terminal/equipment to verify proper operation of the Malfunction Indicator Lamp (MIL) "Service Engine Soon."

→← Install or Connect

1. Knock Sensor (KS) module.
2. Access cover on PCM.
3. Connectors to PCM.
4. PCM located underhood.
5. Engine coolant reservoir.
6. Negative battery cable.

ENGINE COOLANT TEMPERATURE (ECT) SENSOR
Figure C1-13

NOTICE: Care must be taken when handling sensor. Damage to sensor will affect proper operation of the fuel injection system.

↔ Remove or Disconnect

1. Relieve coolant pressure.
2. Remove air intake duct.
3. Negative battery cable.

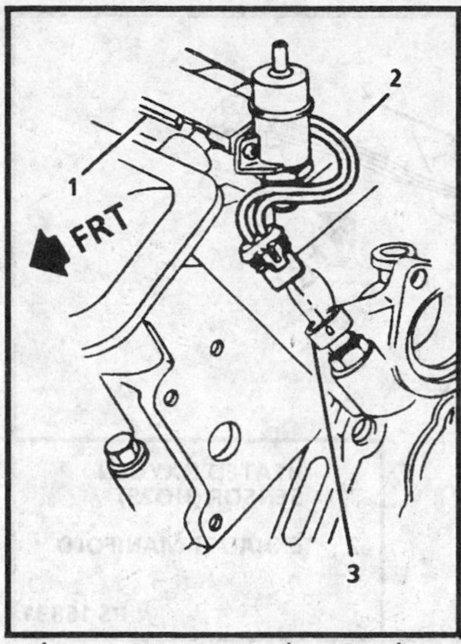

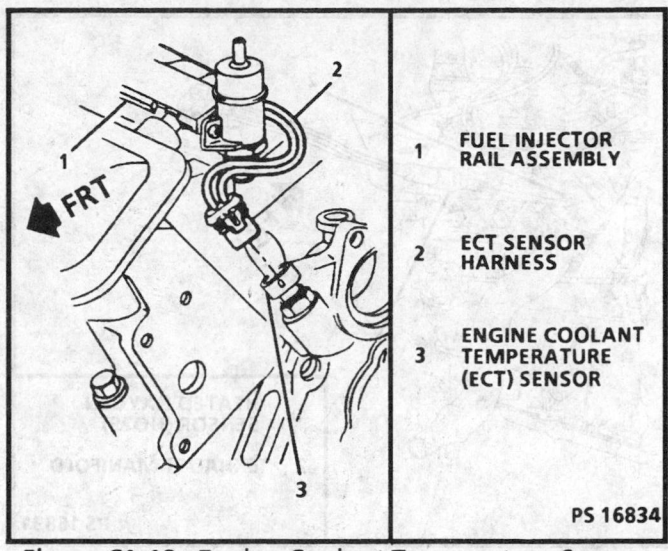

1
2
3
FRT
1 FUEL INJECTOR RAIL ASSEMBLY
2 ECT SENSOR HARNESS
3 ENGINE COOLANT TEMPERATURE (ECT) SENSOR
PS 16834

Figure C1-13 - Engine Coolant Temperature Sensor

4. Electrical connector.
5. Carefully back out engine coolant temperature sensor.

→← Install or Connect

1. Coat threads (only) with sealer P/N 9985253 or equivalent and torque to 14 N·m (10 lb. ft.).
2. Sensor in engine. Locking tab on sensor assembly must be located within area shown in Figure C1-13.
3. Electrical connector.
4. Re-install air duct.
5. Negative battery cable.
6. Refill lost coolant.

IAT SENSOR

The IAT sensor is located in the air cleaner.

↔ Remove or Disconnect

1. Electrical connector.
2. Grasp IAT sensor, twist and pull out from rear air intake duct.

→← Install or Connect

- Reverse removel procedure.

HEATED OXYGEN SENSOR (HO2S)
Figure C1-14

NOTICE: The Heated Oxygen Sensor (HO2S) uses a permanently attached pigtail and connector. This pigtail should not be removed from the heated oxygen sensor. Damage or removal of the pigtail or connector could affect proper operation of the oxygen sensor.

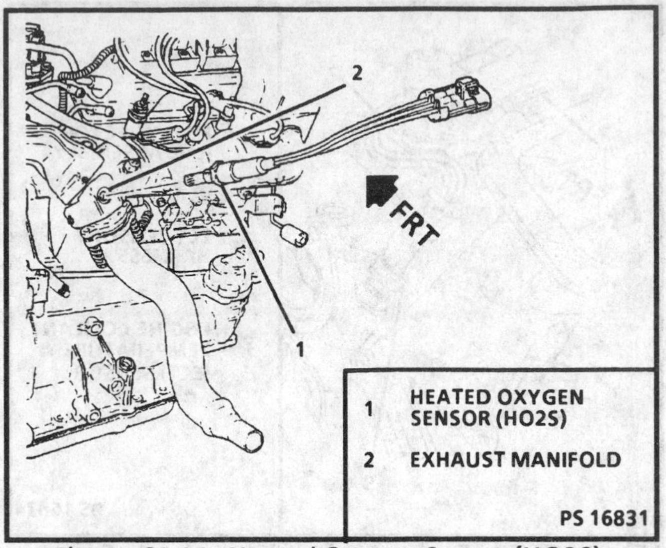
2
FRT
1
1 HEATED OXYGEN SENSOR (HO2S)
2 EXHAUST MANIFOLD
PS 16831

Figure C1-14 - Heated Oxygen Sensor (HO2S)

Important

- Take care when handling the Heated Oxygen Sensor (HO2S). The in-line electrical connector and louvered end must be kept free of grease, dirt or other contaminants. Also, avoid using cleaning solvents of any type. Do not drop or roughly handle the Heated Oxygen Sensor (HO2S).

Remove or Disconnect

- The heated oxygen sensor may be difficult to remove when engine coolant temperature is less than 48°C (120°F).

Excessive force may damage threads in exhaust manifold or exhaust pipe.

1. Negative battery cable.
2. Electrical connector.
3. Carefully back out Heated Oxygen Sensor (HO2S) using tool J 29533A/BT-8127.

Install or Connect

Important

- A special anti-seize compound is used on the Heated Oxygen Sensor (HO2S) threads. The compound consists of a liquid graphite and glass beads. The graphite will burn away, but the glass beads will remain making the sensor easier to remove.

New or service sensors will already have the compound applied to the threads. If a sensor is removed from an engine and if for any reason it is to be reinstalled, the threads must have anti-seize compound applied before reinstallation.

1. Coat threads of Heated Oxygen Sensor (HO2S) with anti-seize compound P/N 5613695, or equivalent if necessary.
2. Sensor, and torque to 41 N·m (30 lb. ft.).
3. Electrical connector.
4. Engine torque strut and bolt.
5. Negative battery cable.

MAP SENSOR

Figure C1-15

Remove or Disconnect

1. Negative battery cable.
2. MAP sensor retaining clip from engine bracket.
3. Electrical connector.
4. Inlet vacuum hose.
5. MAP sensor retainer and MAP sensor.
6. Retainer from MAP sensor. Refer to Figure C1-15.

Install or Connect

1. MAP sensor to retainer. Refer to Figure C1-15.
2. Electrical connector.
3. Inlet vacuum hose.
4. MAP sensor and retainer to engine bracket.
5. Negative battery cable.
6. Retaining clip.

THROTTLE POSITION (TP) SENSOR

Figure C1-16

Remove or Disconnect

1. Air inlet duct.
2. TP sensor electrical connector.
3. TP sensor attaching screws and retainers.
4. Sensor and O-ring.

Install or Connect

1. With throttle valve in the normal closed idle position, install throttle position sensor on throttle body assembly (refer to Figure C1-16).
2. Two TP sensor screws. Tighten to 2.0 N·m (18.0 lb. in.).
3. TP sensor electrical connector.
4. Air inlet duct.

VSS

Refer to SECTION 7 for transaxle mounted VSS.

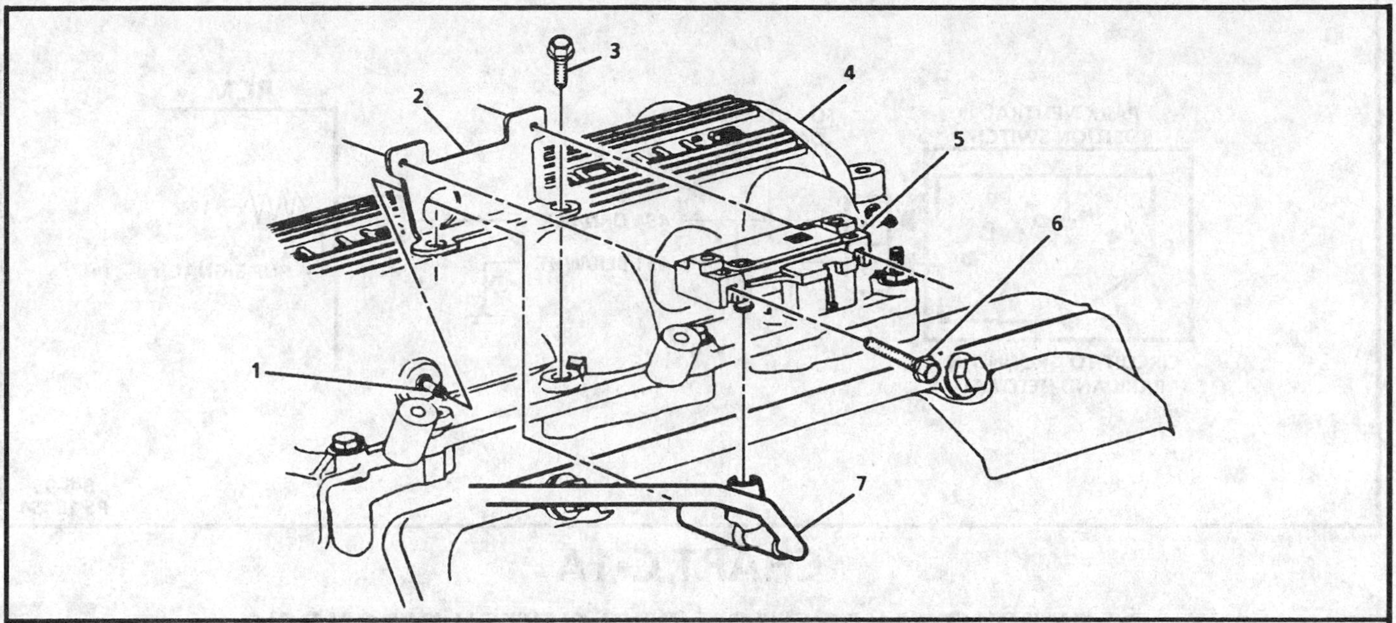
1
2
3
4
5
6
7

1	UPPER INTAKE MANIFOLD VACUUM TUBE	5	MAP SENSOR
2	MAP SENSOR BRACKET	6	BOLT/SCREW
3	BOLT/SCREW	7	VACUUM HARNESS ASSEMBLY
4	UPPER INTAKE MANIFOLD		

PS 16833

Figure C1-15 - MAP Sensor Service

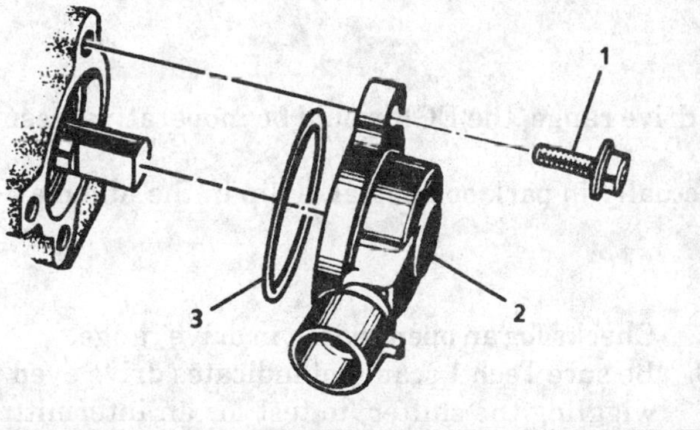
1
2
3

1 SCREW - TP SENSOR ATTACHING
2 SENSOR - THROTTLE POSITION (TP)
3 O-RING - TP SENSOR

PA 1375-AS

Figure C1-16 - Throttle Position (TP) Sensor Service

TRANSAXLE RANGE SWITCH (4T60E)

Refer to "On-Vehicle Service," in SECTION 7A for transaxle range switch. "On-Vehicle Service" and "Adjustment Procedures" are also listed there.

PARK/NEUTRAL POSITION (PNP) SWITCH (3T40)

Refer to "On-Vehicle Service," in SECTION 7A for Park/Neutral Position (PNP) switch. "On-Vehicle Service" and "Adjustment Procedures" are also listed there.

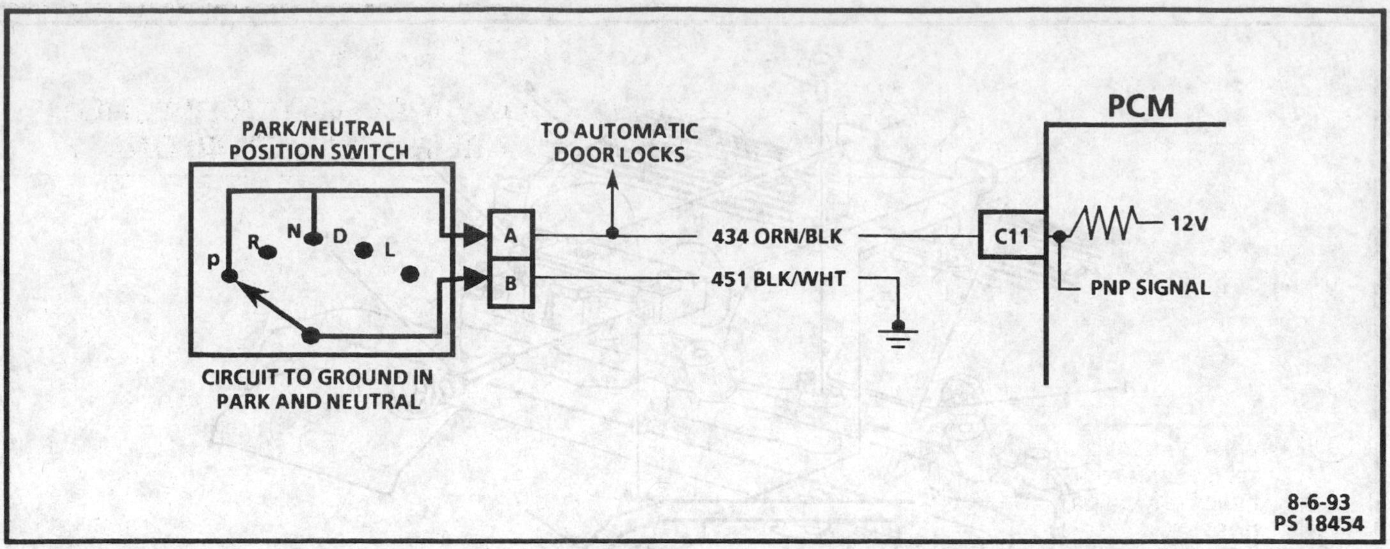
PARK/NEUTRAL POSITION SWITCH
TO AUTOMATIC DOOR LOCKS
PCM
P
R
N
D
L
A
B
434 ORN/BLK
451 BLK/WHT
C11
12V
PNP SIGNAL
CIRCUIT TO GROUND IN PARK AND NEUTRAL
8-6-93
PS 18454

CHART C-1A

PARK/NEUTRAL POSITION (PNP) SWITCH DIAGNOSIS
3100 (VIN M) "W" CARLINE (SFI) (3T40 ONLY)

Circuit Description:

The Park/Neutral Position (PNP) switch contacts are a part of the neutral start switch and are closed ground in park or neutral, and open in drive ranges.

The PCM supplies ignition voltage through a current limiting resistor to CKT 434 and senses a closed switch when the voltage on CKT 434 drops to less than 1 volt.

The PCM uses the PNP signal as one of the inputs to control:

- Idle Air Control (IAC).
- Vehicle Speed Sensor (VSS) diagnostics.
- EGR.
- Torque Converter Clutch (TCC).

If CKT 434 indicates PNP switch is grounded while in a drive range, the EGR would be inoperative, resulting in possible detonation.

If CKT 434 indicates drive (open), when the vehicle is actually in park or neutral, a dip in the idle may exist when the gear selector is moved into a drive range.

Chart Test Description: Number(s) below refer to circled number(s) on the diagnostic chart.

1. Checks for a closed switch to ground in park position. Different makes of scan tools will read PNP differently. Refer to tool operator's manual for type of display used for a specific tool.
2. Checks for an open switch in drive range.
3. Be sure Tech 1 scan tool indicates drive even when wiggling the shifter, to test for an intermittent or misadjusted switch in drive or overdrive range.

CHART C-1A

PARK/NEUTRAL POSITION (PNP) SWITCH DIAGNOSIS 3100 (VIN M) "W" CARLINE (SFI) (3T40 ONLY)

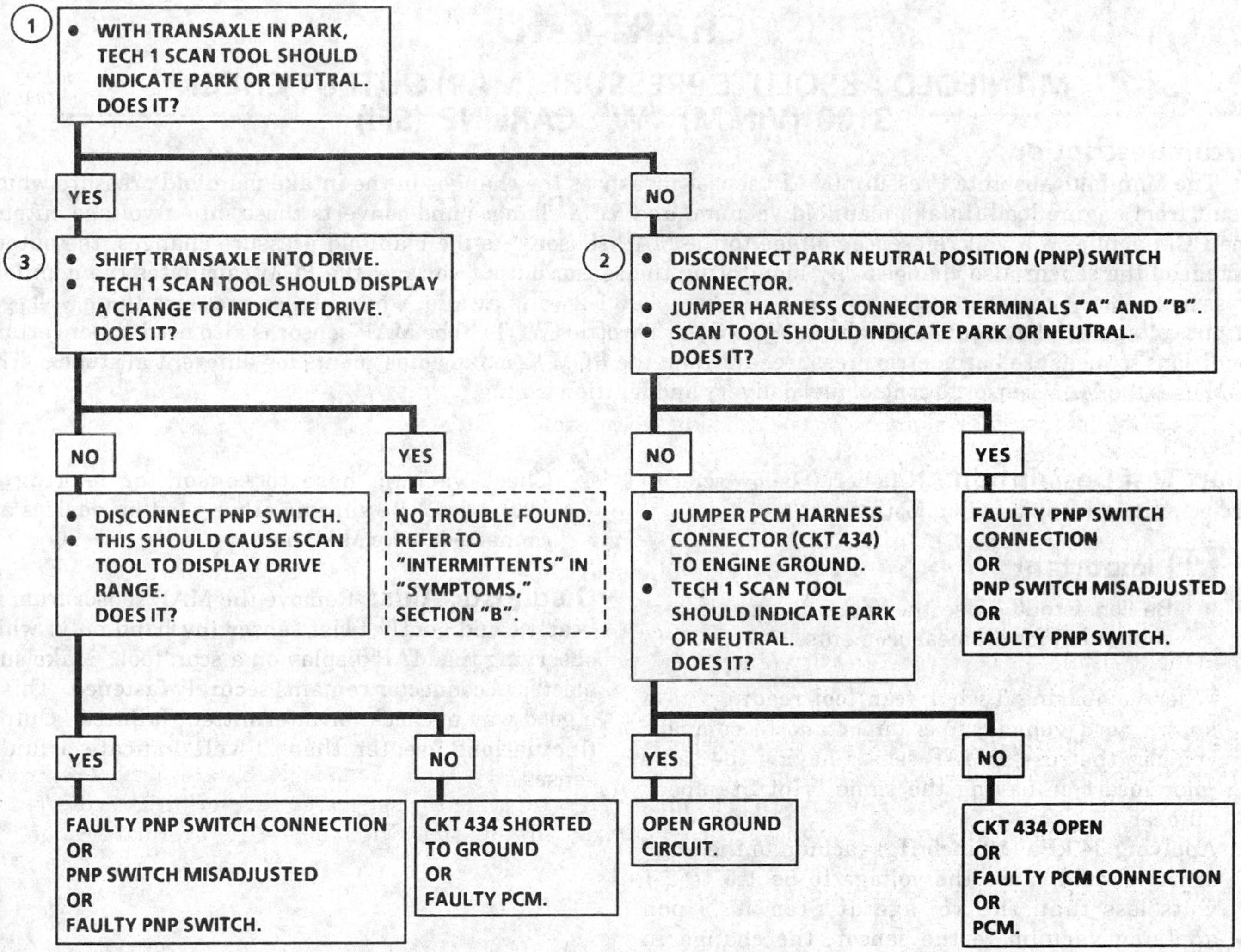
1
• WITH TRANSAXLE IN PARK, TECH 1 SCAN TOOL SHOULD INDICATE PARK OR NEUTRAL. DOES IT?
YES
NO
3
• SHIFT TRANSAXLE INTO DRIVE.
• TECH 1 SCAN TOOL SHOULD DISPLAY A CHANGE TO INDICATE DRIVE. DOES IT?
2
• DISCONNECT PARK NEUTRAL POSITION (PNP) SWITCH CONNECTOR.
• JUMPER HARNESS CONNECTOR TERMINALS "A" AND "B".
• SCAN TOOL SHOULD INDICATE PARK OR NEUTRAL. DOES IT?
NO
YES
NO
YES
• DISCONNECT PNP SWITCH.
• THIS SHOULD CAUSE SCAN TOOL TO DISPLAY DRIVE RANGE. DOES IT?
NO TROUBLE FOUND. REFER TO "INTERMITTENTS" IN "SYMPTOMS," SECTION "B".
• JUMPER PCM HARNESS CONNECTOR (CKT 434) TO ENGINE GROUND.
• TECH 1 SCAN TOOL SHOULD INDICATE PARK OR NEUTRAL. DOES IT?
FAULTY PNP SWITCH CONNECTION OR PNP SWITCH MISADJUSTED OR FAULTY PNP SWITCH.
YES
NO
YES
NO
FAULTY PNP SWITCH CONNECTION OR PNP SWITCH MISADJUSTED OR FAULTY PNP SWITCH.
CKT 434 SHORTED TO GROUND OR FAULTY PCM.
OPEN GROUND CIRCUIT.
CKT 434 OPEN OR FAULTY PCM CONNECTION OR PCM.

8-6-93
PS 18455

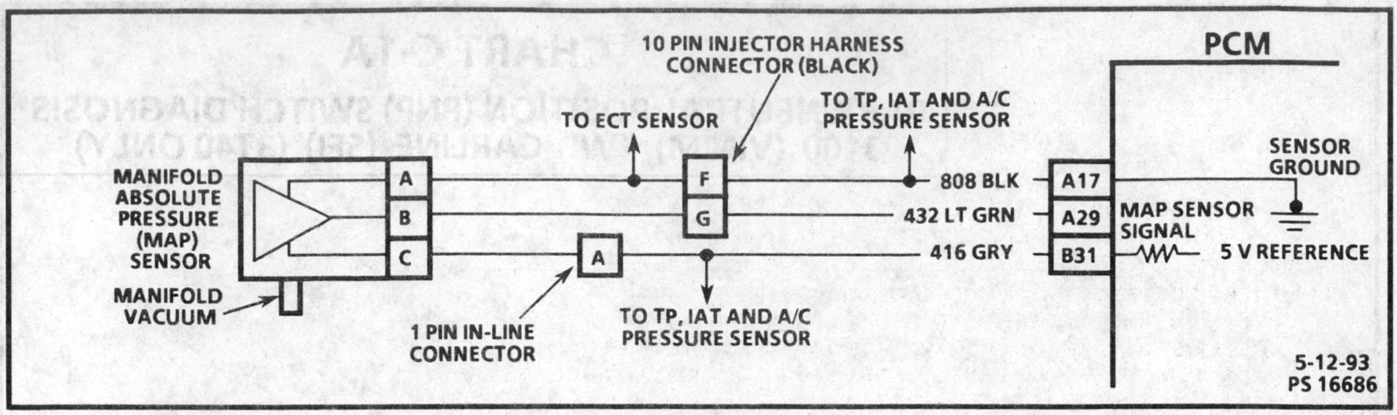
10 PIN INJECTOR HARNESS CONNECTOR (BLACK)
PCM
TO ECT SENSOR
TO TP, IAT AND A/C PRESSURE SENSOR
SENSOR GROUND
MANIFOLD ABSOLUTE PRESSURE (MAP) SENSOR
A
B
C
F
G
808 BLK
A17
432 LT GRN
A29
MAP SENSOR SIGNAL
A
416 GRY
B31
5 V REFERENCE
MANIFOLD VACUUM
1 PIN IN-LINE CONNECTOR
TO TP, IAT AND A/C PRESSURE SENSOR
5-12-93
PS 16686

CHART C-1D

MANIFOLD ABSOLUTE PRESSURE (MAP) OUTPUT CHECK
3100 (VIN M) "W" CARLINE (SFI)

Circuit Description:

The Manifold Absolute Pressure (MAP) sensor measures the changes in the intake manifold pressure which result from engine load (intake manifold vacuum) and RPM changes and converts these into a voltage output. The PCM applies a 5 volt reference voltage to the MAP sensor. As the manifold pressure changes, the output voltage of the sensor also changes. By monitoring the sensor output voltage, the PCM calculates the manifold pressure. A lower pressure (low voltage) will be about 1-2 volts at idle, while higher pressure (high voltage) output voltage will be about 4-4.8 volts at Wide Open Throttle (WOT). The MAP sensor is also used under certain conditions to measure barometric pressure, allowing the PCM to make adjustments for different altitudes. The PCM uses the MAP sensor to control fuel delivery and ignition timing.

Chart Test Description: Number(s) below refer to circled number(s) on the diagnostic chart.

Important

- Be consistent. Use the same diagnostic test equipment for all measurements.

1. When comparing Tech 1 scan tool readings to a known good vehicle, it is important to compare vehicles that use a MAP sensor having the same color insert or having the same "Hot Stamped" number.
2. Applying 34 kPa (10 inch Hg) vacuum to the MAP sensor should cause the voltage to be 1.5 to 2.1 volts less than the voltage at Step 1. Upon applying vacuum to the sensor, the change in voltage should be instantaneous. A slow or erratic voltage change indicates a faulty sensor.
3. Check vacuum hose to sensor for leaking or restriction. Be sure no other vacuum devices are connected to the MAP hose.

Diagnostic Aids: Remove the MAP sensor from its bracket and gently twist sensor (by hand only) while observing the MAP display on a scan tool. Make sure electrical connector remains securely fastened. This is a good way to check for intermittent failures. Output fluctuations greater than .1 volt indicate a faulty sensor.

CHART C-1D

MANIFOLD ABSOLUTE PRESSURE (MAP) OUTPUT CHECK 3100 (VIN M) "W" CARLINE (SFI)

NOTICE: THIS CHART ONLY APPLIES TO MAP SENSORS HAVING GREEN OR BLACK COLOR KEY INSERT (SEE BELOW).

(1)
- IF DTC 33 OR 34 IS SET, USE THOSE CHARTS FIRST.
- IGNITION "ON," ENGINE "OFF."
- INSTALL SCAN TOOL AND MONITOR MAP SENSOR VOLTAGE.
- COMPARE THIS READING WITH THE READING OF A KNOWN GOOD VEHICLE. SEE FACING PAGE TEST DESCRIPTION, STEP 1. VOLTAGE READING SHOULD BE WITHIN ± .4 VOLT. IS IT?

NO: REPLACE MAP SENSOR.

YES:

(2)
- DISCONNECT AND PLUG VACUUM SOURCE TO MAP SENSOR.
- CONNECT A HAND VACUUM PUMP TO MAP SENSOR.
- START ENGINE.
- NOTE MAP SENSOR VOLTAGE.
- APPLY 34 kPa (10" Hg) OF VACUUM WHILE RAISING RPM (TO KEEP ENGINE RUNNING) AND NOTE VOLTAGE CHANGE. SUBTRACT SECOND READING FROM THE FIRST. VOLTAGE VALUE SHOULD BE GREATER THAN 1.4 VOLTS. IS IT?

YES:

(3) NO TROUBLE FOUND. CHECK MAP SENSOR VACUUM SOURCE FOR LEAKAGE OR RESTRICTION.

NO: CHECK MAP SENSOR CONNECTION. IF OK, REFER TO "DIAGNOSTIC AIDS" ON FACING PAGE. IF CONNECTION IS OK, REPLACE MAP SENSOR.

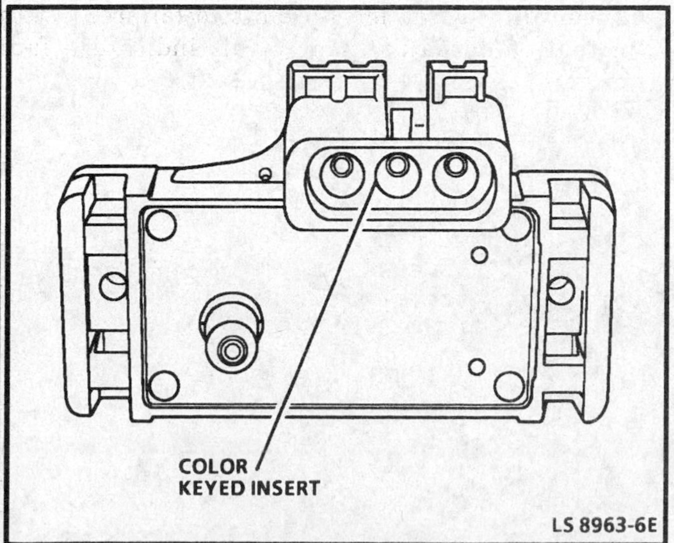
COLOR
KEYED INSERT
LS 8963-6E

Figure 1 - Color Key Insert

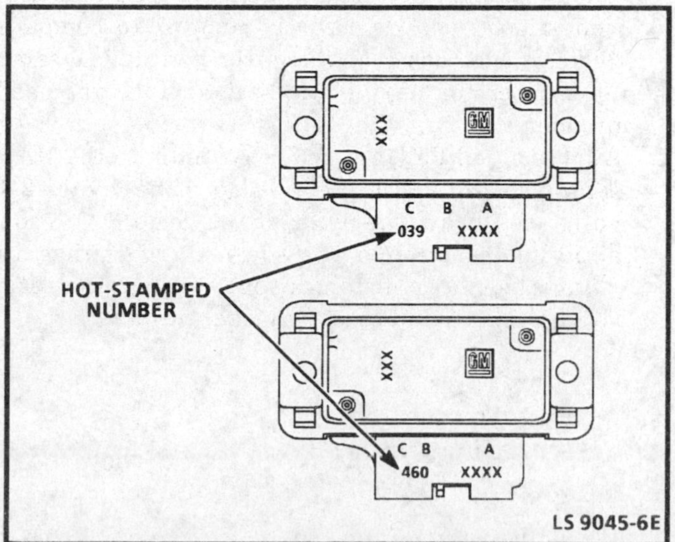
XXX
C B A
039 XXXX
HOT-STAMPED
NUMBER
XXX
C B A
460 XXXX
LS 9045-6E

Figure 2 - Hot Stamped Number

"*AFTER REPAIRS*," CONFIRM "CLOSED LOOP" OPERATION AND NO MIL (SERVICE ENGINE SOON).

2-22-93
PS 16838

BLANK

SECTION C2

FUEL METERING SYSTEM

CONTENTS

GENERAL DESCRIPTION

PURPOSE

The function of the fuel metering system is to deliver the correct amount of fuel to the engine under all operating conditions.

Fuel is delivered to the engine by individual fuel injectors mounted in the intake manifold near each cylinder.

The main control sensor is the Heated Oxygen Sensor (HO2S) located in the exhaust manifold. This sensor tells the Powertrain Control Module (PCM) how much oxygen is in the exhaust gas, and the PCM changes the air/fuel ratio to the engine by controlling the fuel injectors. The best mixture to minimize exhaust emissions is 14.7:1 which allows the catalytic converter to operate most efficiently. Because of the constant measuring and adjusting of the air/fuel ratio, the fuel injection system is called a "Closed Loop" system.

MODES OF OPERATION

The PCM monitors information from several sensors to determine how much fuel to give the engine. Fuel is delivered under one of several conditions called modes. All modes are controlled by the PCM as described below.

Starting Mode

When the ignition is first turned "ON," before engaging starter, the PCM energizes the fuel pump relay for two seconds, allowing the fuel pump to build up pressure. The PCM then checks the Engine Coolant Temperature (ECT), Manifold Absolute Pressure (MAP), and Throttle Position (TP) sensors to determine the proper air/fuel ratio for starting. This ranges from 1.5:1 at -36°C (-33°F) to 14.7:1 at 94°C (201°F) operating temperature. The PCM controls the amount of fuel delivered in the starting mode by changing how long the injectors are energized. This is done by pulsing the injectors for very short times.

Clear Flood Mode

If the engine floods, it can be cleared by pushing the accelerator pedal down all the way. The PCM then completely turns "OFF" the fuel. No fuel is delivered from the injectors as long as the throttle stays wide open, and the engine speed is below 600 RPM. If the throttle position becomes less than 80%, the PCM returns to the starting mode.

Run Mode

The run mode consists of both "Open Loop" and "Closed Loop" operation.

When the engine is first started and engine speed is above 400 RPM, the system goes into "Open Loop" operation. In "Open Loop," the PCM ignores the signal from the HO2S and calculates the air/fuel ratio based on inputs from the ECT and Intake Air Temperature (IAT) sensors.

The system stays in "Open Loop" until the following conditions are met:

1. The HO2S has varying voltage output, showing that it is hot enough to operate properly. (This depends on temperature.)
2. The ECT sensor is above a specified temperature.
3. A specific amount of time has elapsed after starting the engine.

The specific values for the above conditions vary with different engines, and are stored in the Programmable Read Only Memory (PROM) portion of the PCM. When these conditions are met, the system goes into "Closed Loop" operation. In "Closed Loop," the PCM calculates the air/fuel ratio (injector on-time) based on the signal from the HO2S. This allows the air/fuel ratio to stay very close to 14.7:1.

Acceleration Mode

When the driver pushes on the accelerator pedal, air flow into the cylinders increases rapidly, while fuel flow tends to lag behind. To prevent possible hesitation, the PCM increases the pulse width to the injectors to provide extra fuel during acceleration. The amount of fuel required is based on throttle position, manifold air pressure, and engine speed.

Fuel Cutoff Mode

To prevent possible engine damage from over-speed, the PCM "cuts off" fuel from the injectors when engine speed is above approximately 6200 RPM with the vehicle in any forward gear or reverse, and approximately 4000 RPM in park or neutral. To prevent tire damage, the PCM also has a fuel cutoff in excess of 100 mph (161 km/h) based on the speed rating of the tires.

Deceleration Mode

When the driver releases the accelerator pedal, air flow into the engine is reduced. The corresponding changes in throttle position and manifold air pressure are relayed to the PCM, which reduces the injector pulse width to reduce fuel flow. If the deceleration is very rapid, or for long periods (such as long closed throttle coast-down), the PCM shuts "OFF" fuel completely to protect the catalytic converter.

Converter Protection Mode

The PCM constantly monitors engine operation, and estimates conditions that could result in high converter temperatures. If the PCM determines the converter may overheat, it causes the system to return to "Open Loop" operation and enriches the fuel mixture.

Battery Voltage Correction Mode

When battery voltage is low, the PCM can compensate for the weak spark by:

- Increasing the amount of fuel delivered.
- Increasing the idle RPM.
- Increasing ignition dwell time.

FUEL METERING SYSTEM COMPONENTS

The fuel metering system consists of the following parts:

- Fuel supply components (fuel tank, pump, lines).
- Fuel rail assembly, including:
  - Fuel pump electrical circuit.
  - SFI fuel injector assemblies.
  - Fuel pressure regulator assembly.
- Throttle body assembly, including:
  - Idle Air Control (IAC) valve assembly.
  - Throttle Position (TP) sensor.

FUEL SUPPLY COMPONENTS

The fuel supply is stored in the fuel tank. An electric fuel pump, located in the fuel tank with the gage sending unit, pumps fuel through an in-line fuel filter to the fuel rail assembly. The pump provides fuel at a pressure greater than is needed by the injectors. A fuel pressure regulator, part of the fuel rail assembly, keeps fuel available to the injectors at a controlled pressure. Unused fuel is returned to the fuel tank by a separate line. (For further information, refer to SECTION 6C for replacement procedures covering the fuel tank, fuel pump, in-line filter, and fuel lines.)

FUEL PUMP ELECTRICAL CIRCUIT

When the ignition switch is turned to the "ON" position, without the engine running, the PCM energizes the fuel pump relay for two seconds, causing the fuel pump to pressurize the fuel system.

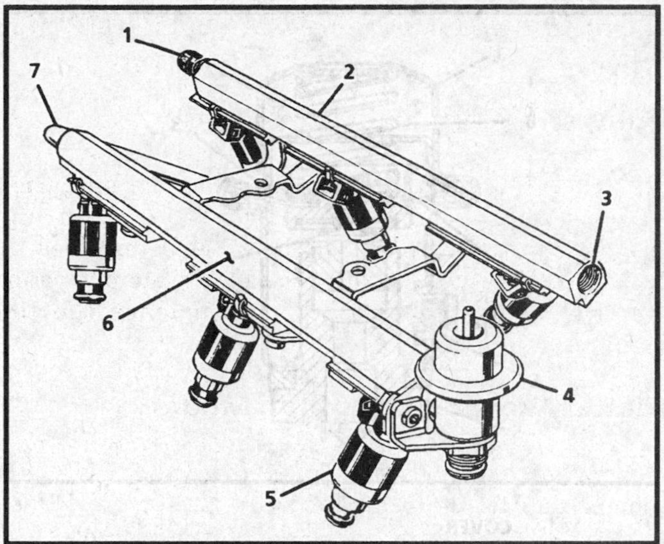
1
2
3
4
5
6
7

1	CONNECTION ASSEMBLY - FUEL PRESSURE
2	RAIL ASSEMBLY - R/H FUEL
3	INLET - FUEL
4	REGULATOR ASSEMBLY - FUEL PRESSURE
5	INJECTOR ASSEMBLY - FUEL
6	RAIL ASSEMBLY - L/H FUEL
7	TUBE ASSEMBLY - CROSSOVER

NA 1365-AS

Figure C2-1 - Fuel Rail Assembly

If the PCM does not receive ignition reference pulses (engine cranking or running) within two seconds, it shuts "OFF" the fuel pump relay, causing the fuel pump to stop.

As a backup system to the fuel pump relay, the fuel pump also can be energized by the fuel pump and engine oil pressure indicator switch. The switch has two internal circuits. One operates the oil pressure indicator or gage in the instrument cluster, and the other is a normally open switch which closes when oil pressure reaches about 28 kPa (4 psi). If the fuel pump relay fails, a DTC 54 will be set in the PCM, and the fuel pump and engine oil pressure indicator switch runs the fuel pump. An inoperative fuel pump relay can result in long cranking times, particularly if the engine is cold. The fuel pump and engine oil pressure indicator switch energizes the fuel pump as soon as oil pressure reaches about 28 kPa (4 psi).

FUEL RAIL ASSEMBLY
Figure C2-1

The fuel rail assembly is made up of the left hand rail, which delivers fuel to the even cylinders (2, 4, 6); the right hand rail, which delivers fuel to the odd cylinders (1, 3, 5); the fuel injectors; and the fuel pressure regulator assembly. The rail assembly is mounted to the lower section of the intake manifold and distributes fuel to the cylinders through the individual injectors.

Fuel is delivered from the pump through the fuel feed line to the inlet fitting on the fuel rail. From there it is directed, via the crossover tube, to the other fuel rail. Fuel in each rail flows through the main supply conduit supplying fuel at the same pressure to each of the injectors. Fuel in excess of injector needs flows back through the pressure regulator assembly which maintains correct system pressure. Fuel then flows from the regulator through the fuel return line back to the tank.

Fuel Injector Assembly
Figure C2-2

The fuel injector assembly is a solenoid-operated device, controlled by the PCM, that meters pressurized fuel to a single engine cylinder. The PCM energizes the injector solenoid, which opens a ball valve, allowing fuel to flow past the ball valve and through a recessed flow director plate. The director plate has machined holes that control the fuel flow, generating a conical spray pattern of finely atomized fuel at the injector tip. Fuel is directed at the intake valve, causing it to become further atomized and vaporized before entering the combustion chamber.

An injector that is stuck partly open would cause loss of pressure after engine shut down, so long cranking times would be noticed on some engines. Dieseling could also occur because some fuel could be delivered to the engine after the ignition is turned "OFF."

Fuel Pressure Regulator Assembly
Figure C2-3

The fuel pressure regulator is a diaphragm-operated relief valve with fuel pump pressure on one side, and regulator spring pressure and intake manifold vacuum on the other. The function of the regulator is to maintain a constant pressure differential across the injectors at all times. The pressure regulator compensates for engine load by increasing fuel pressure as engine vacuum drops.

With the ignition "ON" and engine "OFF" (zero vacuum), fuel pressure at the pressure connection should be 284-325 kPa (41-47 psi). If the pressure is too low, poor performance could result. If the pressure is too high, excessive odor and DTC 45 may result. CHART A-7 has information on diagnosing fuel pressure conditions.

THROTTLE BODY ASSEMBLY
Figure C2-4

The throttle body assembly is mounted on the intake manifold plenum, and is used to control air flow into the engine, thereby controlling engine output.

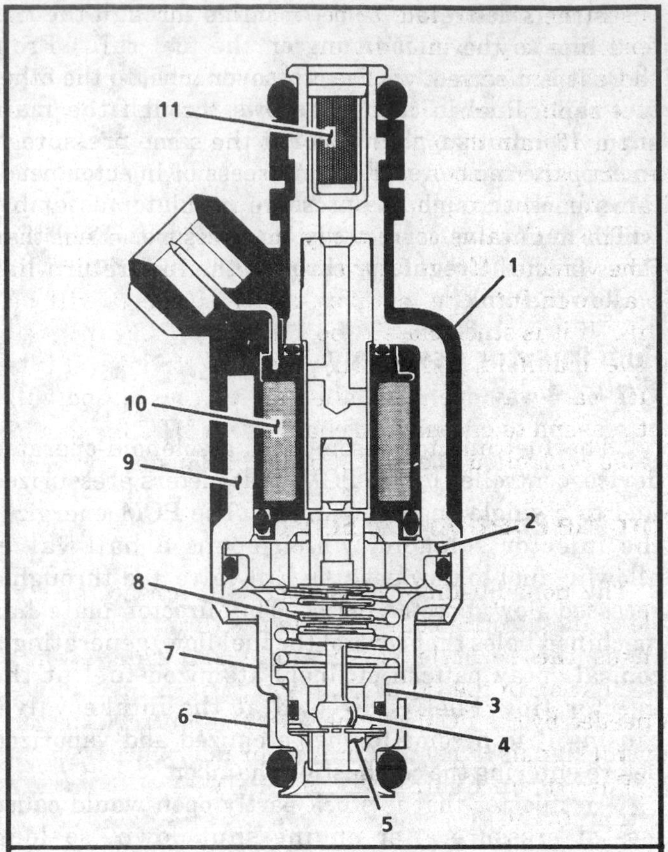

1 SOLENOID ASSEMBLY
2 SPACER & GUIDE ASM
3 CORE SEAT
4 VALVE - BALL
5 PLATE - DIRECTOR
6 BACKUP - O-RING
7 HOUSING - SPRAY
8 SPRING - CORE
9 HOUSING - SOLENOID
10 SOLENOID
11 FILTER - FUEL INLET

PA 0496-SY

Figure C2-2 - Fuel Injector Assembly

The throttle valve within the throttle body is opened by the driver through the accelerator controls. During engine idle, the throttle valve is almost closed, and air flow control is handled by the Idle Air Control (IAC) valve described later.

The throttle body also provides the location for mounting the Throttle Position (TP) sensor and for sensing changes in engine vacuum due to throttle valve position. Vacuum ports are located at, above, or below the throttle valve to generate vacuum signals needed by various components.

Idle Air Control (IAC) Valve Assembly *Figure C2-5*

The purpose of the IAC valve assembly is to control engine idle speed, while preventing stalls due to changes in engine load.

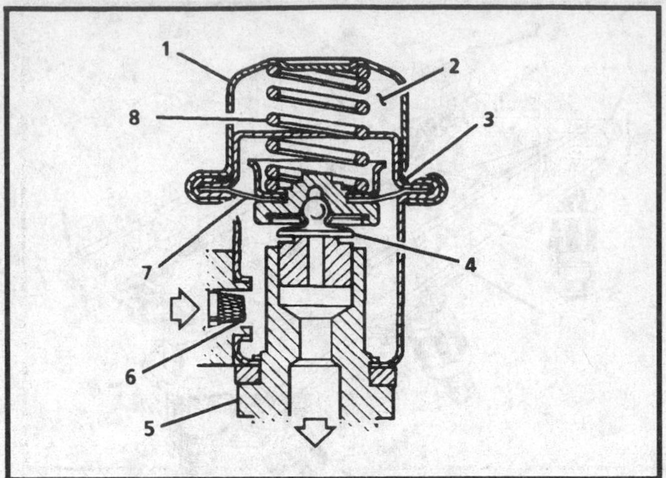

1 COVER
2 VACUUM CHAMBER (VACUUM SOURCE TUBE NOT SHOWN)
3 SEAL - O-RING
4 VALVE - FUEL PRESSURE REGULATOR
5 BASE ASSEMBLY
6 FILTER - SCREEN (IF EQUIPPED)
7 DIAPHRAGM
8 SPRING

NA 0493-SY

Figure C2-3 - Fuel Pressure Regulator Assembly

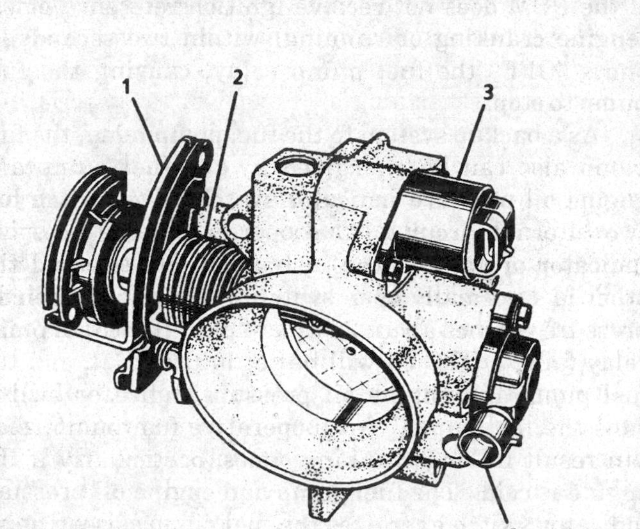

1 LEVER ASSSEMBLY - THROTTLE SHAFT AND CAM
2 SPRING - THROTTLE RETURN
3 VALVE ASSEMBLY - IDLE AIR CONTROL (IAC)
4 SENSOR ASSEMBLY - THROTTLE POSITION (TP)

NA 1367-AS

Figure C2-4 - Throttle Body

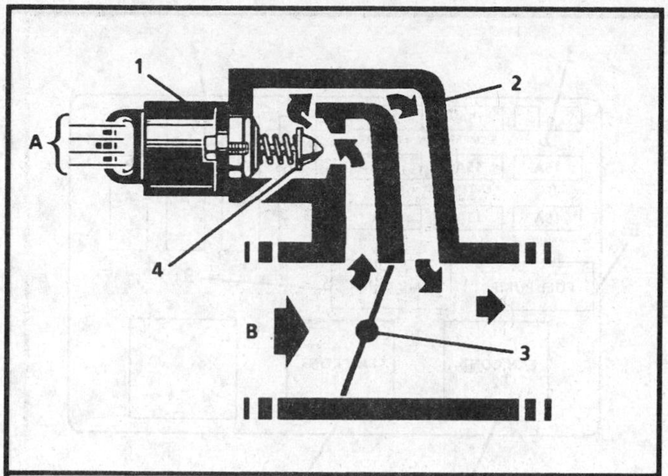
1
2
A
4
B
3

1 VALVE ASSEMBLY - IDLE AIR CONTROL (IAC)

2 BODY ASSEMBLY - THROTTLE

3 VALVE - THROTTLE

4 PINTLE - IAC VALVE

A ELECTRICAL INPUT SIGNAL

B AIR INLET

NA 0494-SY

Figure C2-5 - IAC Valve Air Flow Diagram

The IAC valve, mounted in the throttle body, controls bypass air around the throttle valve. By moving a conical valve known as a pintle, IN toward the seat (to decrease air flow), or OUT away from the seat (to increase air flow), a controlled amount of air moves around the throttle plate. If engine speed is too low, more air is bypassed around the throttle valve to increase RPM. If engine speed is too high, less air is bypassed around the throttle valve to decrease RPM. The PCM moves the IAC valve in small steps called counts which can be measured using a scan tool connected to the Data Link Connector (DLC).

During idle, the proper position of the IAC valve is calculated by the PCM based on battery voltage, coolant temperature, engine load, and engine RPM. If the RPM drops below specification and the throttle valve is closed, the PCM senses a near stall condition and calculates a new valve position to prevent stalling.

If the IAC valve is disconnected and reconnected while the engine is running, the resulting idle RPM may be wrong and resetting of the IAC valve will be required.

After running the engine, the IAC valve will reset when the ignition is turned "OFF." When servicing the IAC valve, it should only be disconnected or connected with the ignition "OFF."

If the PCM is without battery power for any reason, the programmed position of the IAC valve pintle is lost, and replaced with a default value. This causes the engine idle to be unstable for a period of approximately seven minutes.

Different shaped pintles are used for different IAC valve applications. The throttle body has an IAC valve with a 12 mm dual taper pintle. Be sure to use the correct part number, with the correct pintle shape and diameter, when replacement is required.

The IAC valve affects only the idle characteristics of the vehicle. If it is fully retracted, too much air will be allowed into the manifold and idle speed will be high. If it is stuck closed, too little air will be allowed in the manifold, and idle speed will be too low. If it is stuck part way open, the idle may be rough, and will not respond to engine load changes. A DTC 35 should set if a controlled idle cannot be maintained.

Throttle Position (TP) Sensor

The nonadjustable TP sensor is mounted on the side of the throttle body opposite the throttle lever. It senses the throttle valve angle and relays that information to the PCM. Knowledge of throttle angle is needed by the PCM to generate the required injector control signals (pulses). For further information, refer to "Powertrain Control Module (PCM) and Sensors," Section "6E3-C1".

DIAGNOSIS

FUEL PUMP RELAY

The fuel pump relay is mounted in the engine compartment. Refer to illustration in "On-Vehicle Service." For diagnosis of the fuel pump relay circuit, refer to the DTC 54 chart.

FUEL PUMP AND ENGINE OIL PRESSURE INDICATOR SWITCH

The fuel pump and engine oil pressure indicator switch is mounted on the side of the engine at the oil filter boss. Refer to illustration in "On-Vehicle Service." For diagnosis of the fuel pump relay circuit, refer to the DTC 54 chart.

FUEL METERING SYSTEM

Some failures of this system will result in an engine cranks but won't run symptom. If this condition exists, see CHART A-3. This chart will determine if the problem is caused by the ignition system, PCM, or fuel pump circuit. If its determined to be a fuel problem, CHART A-7 will be used. This includes the fuel injectors, fuel pressure regulator, fuel pump, and fuel pump relay. The fuel system wiring schematic diagram is covered on the facing page of DTC 54.

If a problem occurs in the fuel metering system, it usually results in either a rich or lean exhaust condition. This condition is sensed by the HO2S and causes the PCM to change the fuel calculation (injector pulse width). The change made to the fuel calculation will be indicated by a change in the short and long term fuel trim values which can be monitored with a scan tool. A momentary change to the fuel calculation is indicated by the short term fuel trim value, while a prolonged change is indicated by the long term fuel trim value. Average fuel trim values will be around 128, but vary slightly from engine to engine.

Important

- When using a scan tool to observe fuel trim values, remember that if the system is in control, no action is required unless a driveability symptom is present.

Listed below are examples of lean and rich HO2S signals with the system in control and out of control.

- A momentary *lean* HO2S signal (system is *in* control) will appear on the scan tool as:
  - Short term fuel trim value above 128 (adding fuel).
  - Long term fuel trim value around 128.
- A prolonged *lean* HO2S signal (system is *in* control) will appear on the scan tool as:
  - Short term fuel trim value around 128.
  - Long term fuel trim value above 128 (added fuel).
- A prolonged *lean* HO2S signal (system is *out of control)* will appear on the scan tool as:
  - Short term fuel trim value well above 128 (adding fuel).
  - Long term fuel trim value well above 128 (added fuel).

If both fuel trim values are fixed well above 128, refer to DTC 44 for items which can cause a lean system.

- A momentary *rich* HO2S signal (system is *in* control) will appear on the scan tool as:
  - Short term fuel trim value less than 128 (reducing fuel).
  - Long term fuel trim value around 128.
- A prolonged *rich* HO2S signal (system is *in* control) will appear on the scan tool as:
  - Short term fuel trim value around 128.
  - Long term fuel trim value less than 128 (reduced fuel).
- A prolonged *rich* HO2S signal (system is *out of control)* will appear on the scan tool as:
  - Short term fuel trim value much less than 128 (reducing fuel).
  - Long term fuel trim value much less than 128 (reduced fuel).

If both fuel trim values are fixed well below 128, refer to DTC 45 for items which can cause the system to run rich. If a driveability symptom exists, refer to the particular symptom in the "Symptoms," Section "6E3-B" for additional items to check.

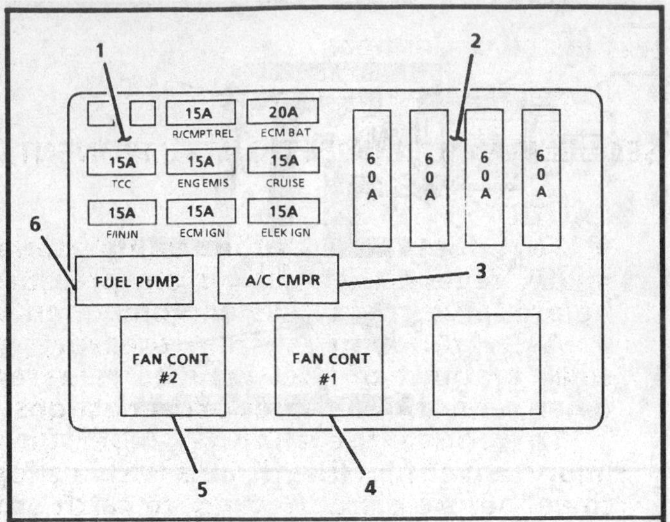

1
2
15A
R/CMPT REL
20A
ECM BAT
15A
TCC
15A
ENG EMIS
15A
CRUISE
60A
60A
60A
60A
15A
FAN IN
15A
ECM IGN
15A
ELEK IGN
6
FUEL PUMP
A/C CMPR
3
FAN CONT #2
FAN CONT #1
5
4

1 FUSE CENTER
2 FUSIBLE ELEMENT CENTER
3 A/C COMPRESSOR CLUTCH CONTROL RELAY
4 PRIMARY COOLING FAN #1 CONTROL RELAY
5 SECONDARY COOLING FAN #2 CONTROL RELAY
6 FUEL PUMP RELAY

MS 12609

Figure C2-6 - Fuel Pump Relay

ON-VEHICLE SERVICE

FUEL PUMP RELAY
Figure C2-6

Remove or Disconnect

1. Fuel pump relay cover.
2. Fuel pump relay.

Install or Connect

- Reverse removal procedure.

FUEL PUMP AND ENGINE OIL PRESSURE INDICATOR SWITCH

The fuel pump and engine oil pressure indicator switch is mounted on the side of the engine at the oil filter boss.

Remove or Disconnect

1. Electrical connector.
2. Fuel pump and engine oil pressure indicator switch.

Install or Connect

- Reverse removal procedure.

SEQUENTIAL FUEL INJECTION COMPONENTS

CAUTION:
• To reduce the risk of fire and personal injury, relieve the fuel system pressure before servicing fuel system components.
• After relieving system pressure, a small amount of fuel may be released when servicing fuel lines or connections.
To reduce the chance of personal injury, cover fuel line fittings with a shop towel before disconnecting, to catch any fuel that may leak out. Place the towel in an approved container when disconnect is completed.

FUEL PRESSURE RELIEF PROCEDURE

Tool Required:
J 34730-1, Fuel Pressure Gage

1. Disconnect negative battery cable to avoid possible fuel discharge if an accidental attempt is made to start the engine.
2. Loosen fuel filler cap to relieve tank vapor pressure.
3. Connect gage J 34730-1 to fuel pressure connection. Wrap a shop towel around fitting while connecting gage to avoid spillage.
4. Install bleed hose into an approved container and open valve to bleed system pressure. Fuel connections are now safe for servicing.
5. Drain any fuel remaining in gage into an approved container.

THROTTLE BODY ASSEMBLY
Figures C2-7 through C2-9

The throttle body assembly repair procedures cover component replacement with the unit on the vehicle. However, throttle body replacement requires that the complete unit be removed from the engine.

An eight digit part identification number is stamped on the bottom of the throttle body casting. Refer to this number if servicing, or part replacement is required.

For identification of parts during repair, refer to Figure C2-9.

Clean

- Throttle bore and valve deposits may be cleaned on-vehicle using carburetor cleaner and a parts cleaning brush. Follow instructions on container.

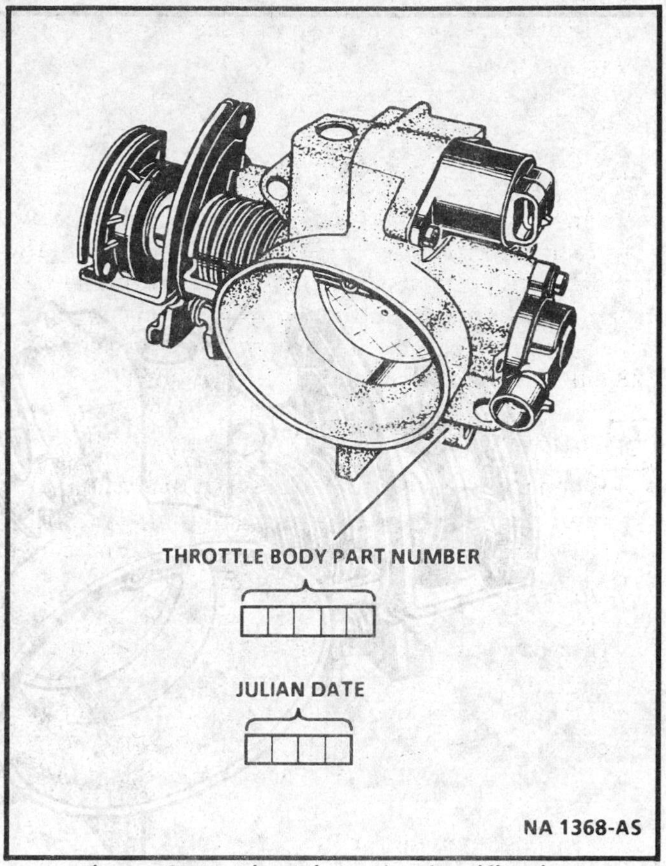
THROTTLE BODY PART NUMBER
JULIAN DATE
NA 1368-AS

Figure C2-7 - Throttle Body Identification

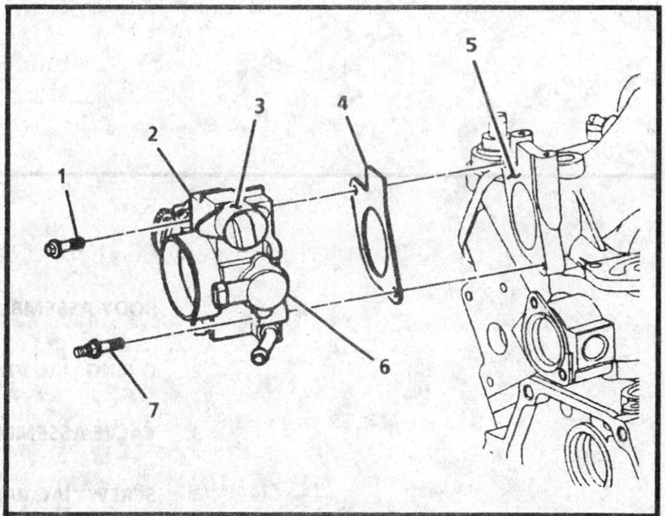
1
2
3
4
5
6
7

1	BOLT
2	THROTTLE BODY
3	IDLE AIR CONTROL (IAC) VALVE
4	GASKET
5	INTAKE PLENUM
6	THROTTLE POSITION (TP) SENSOR
7	STUD

PS 17261

Figure C2-8 - Throttle Body Removal

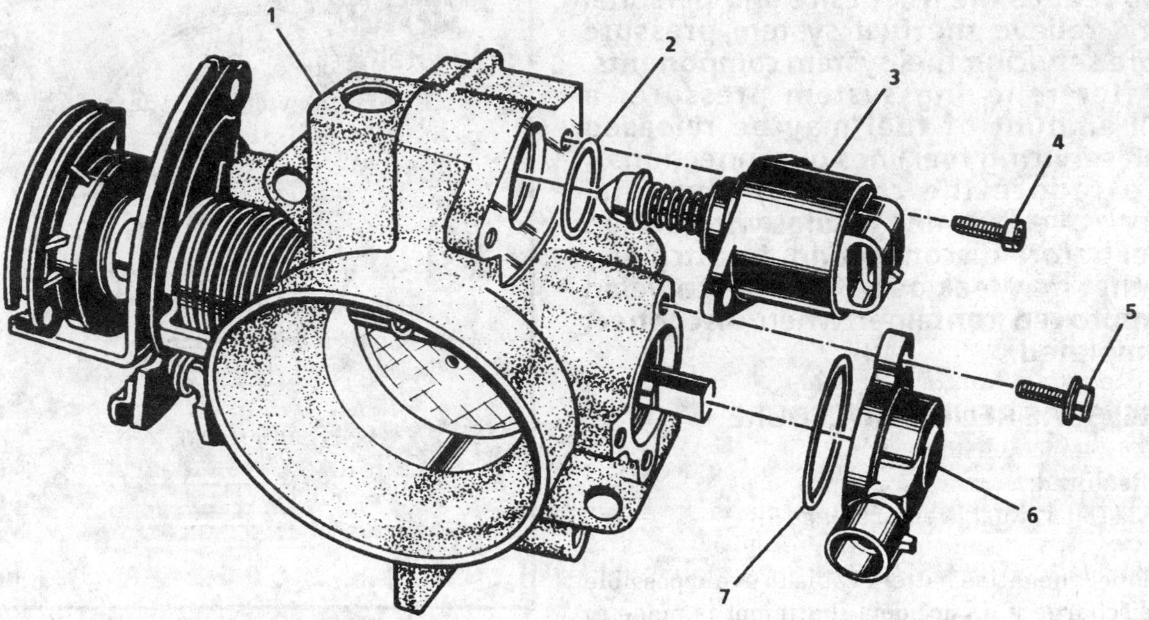
1
2
3
4
5
6
7

1 BODY ASSEMBLY - THROTTLE

2 O-RING - IAC VALVE

3 VALVE ASSEMBLY - IDLE AIR CONTROL (IAC)

4 SCREW - IAC VALVE ATTACHING

5 SCREW - TP SENSOR ATTACHING

6 SENSOR - THROTTLE POSITION (TP)

7 O-RING - TP SENSOR

3-8-93
PA 0202-XV

Figure C2-9 - Throttle Body Assembly

Do Not use a cleaner that contains methyl ethyl ketone, an extremely strong solvent, and not necessary for this type of deposit.

- The throttle body metal parts may be cleaned following disassembly in a cold immersion-type cleaner such as GM X-55 or equivalent.

NOTICE: Since the TP sensor and IAC valve are electronic devices, Do Not immerse them in any type of cleaner.

Remove or Disconnect

1. Negative battery cable.
2. Air inlet duct.
3. IAC valve and TP sensor electrical connectors.
4. Throttle, and cruise control cables.
5. Accelerator cable bracket bolts and bracket.
6. Engine coolant pipe nut to gain access to throttle body attaching stud.
7. Throttle body retaining bolt/stud.
8. Throttle body assembly.
9. Flange gasket and discard.

NOTICE: Use care in cleaning old gasket material from machined aluminum surfaces as sharp tools may damage sealing surfaces.

Clean

- Gasket surface on intake manifold.

Install or Connect

1. New flange gasket.
2. Throttle body assembly.
3. Throttle body retaining bolt/stud.

Tighten

- Throttle body attaching bolt/stud to 25 N·m (18 lb. ft.).

4. Throttle and cruise control cables.

Important

- Make sure throttle and cruise control linkage does not hold throttle open. Refer to SECTION 6C, for additional information on accelerator controls.

5. IAC valve and TP sensor electrical connectors.
6. Air inlet duct.
7. Negative battery cable.

Inspect

- With the engine "OFF," check to see that the accelerator pedal is free:
  - Depress pedal to the floor and release.

THROTTLE POSITION (TP) SENSOR
Figure C2-9

Remove or Disconnect

1. Air inlet duct.
2. TP sensor electrical connector.
3. Remove TP sensor attaching screws and retainers.
4. Sensor and O-ring.

Install or Connect

1. With throttle valve in the normal closed idle position, install TP sensor and O-ring on throttle body assembly.
2. Two TP sensor screws.

Tighten

- Screws to 2.0 N·m (18 lb. in.).

3. TP sensor electrical connector.
4. Air inlet duct.

IDLE AIR CONTROL (IAC) VALVE
Figure C2-9 and C2-10

Remove or Disconnect

1. Electrical connector from IAC valve.
2. IAC valve attaching screws.
3. IAC valve assembly.

NOTICE: If IAC valve has been in service: Do Not push or pull on the IAC valve pintle. The force required to move the pintle may damage the threads on the worm drive. Also, **Do Not** soak IAC valve in any liquid cleaner or solvent as damage may result.

Clean and Inspect

- Clean IAC valve O-ring sealing surface, pintle valve seat, and air passage.
  - Use carburetor cleaner and a parts cleaning brush to remove carbon deposits. Follow instructions on container. Do Not use a cleaner that contains methyl ethyl ketone, an extremely strong solvent, and not necessary for this type of deposit.
  - Shiny spots on the pintle or seat are normal and do not indicate misalignment or a bent pintle shaft.
  - If air passage has heavy deposits, remove throttle body for complete cleaning.
- Inspect IAC valve O-ring for cuts, cracks, or distortion. Replace if damaged.

Important

- If installing a new IAC valve, be sure to replace with an identical part. IAC valve pintle shape and diameter are designed for the specific application.

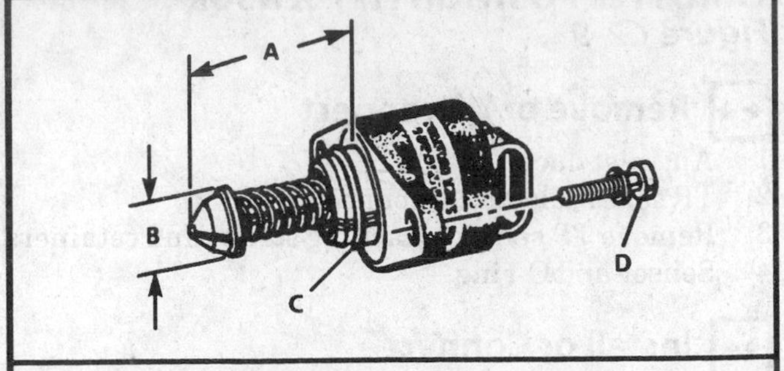
A
B
C
D

A DISTANCE OF PINTLE EXTENSION
B DIAMETER OF PINTLE
C IACV O-RING
D IACV ATTACHING SCREW ASSEMBLY

7S 3422-6E

Figure C2-10 - Idle Air Control (IAC) Valve

Measure

- Distance between tip of IAC valve pintle and mounting flange.
  - If greater than 28 mm, use finger pressure to slowly retract the pintle. The force required to retract the pintle of a *new* valve will not cause damage to the valve.

Install or Connect

1. Lubricate IAC valve O-ring with clean engine oil.
2. IAC valve assembly.
3. Attaching screws.

Tighten

- IAC valve attaching screws to 3.0 N·m (27 lb. in.).

4. Electrical connector.
5. Reset IAC valve pintle position:
   A. Turn ignition "ON" for five seconds.
   B. Turn ignition "OFF" for ten seconds.
   C. Start engine, check for proper idle operation.

INTAKE MANIFOLD PLENUM
Figure C2-11

Removing the fuel rail assembly from the engine requires removing the top portion of the tuned intake manifold called the plenum.

Remove or Disconnect

1. Negative battery cable.
2. Vacuum lines, noting positions of hoses.
3. EGR to plenum nuts.
4. Throttle body.
   - Refer to "Throttle Body Assembly."
5. Ignition coil assembly front bolts.
6. Braces to alternator.
7. MAP sensor and bracket.
8. Plenum bolts.
9. Plenum and gaskets. Discard gaskets.

NOTICE: Use care in cleaning old gasket material from machined aluminum surfaces as sharp tools may damage sealing surfaces.

Clean

- Gasket sealing surfaces.

Install or Connect

1. New plenum gaskets.

Important

- Be sure to route MAP sensor electrical connector to the outside of plenum gasket.

2. Plenum.
3. Plenum bolts.

Tighten

- Plenum bolts to 25 N·m (18 lb. ft.).

4. MAP sensor.
5. Braces to alternator.
6. Ignition coil assembly front bolts.
7. EGR to plenum bolts.
8. Vacuum lines as noted during disassembly.
9. Throttle body.
   - Refer to "Throttle Body Assembly."
10. Negative battery cable.

Inspect

- With the engine "OFF," check to see that the accelerator cable is free:
  - Depress pedal to the floor and release.

FUEL RAIL ASSEMBLY
Figures C2-11 through C2-13

An eight digit identification number is stamped on the left hand fuel rail (fueling even cylinders 2, 4, 6), as shown. Refer to this number if servicing or part replacement is required.

Part names appear in the numbered list on Figure C2-13.

NOTICE:

- Use care in removing the fuel rail assembly to prevent damage to the injector electrical connector terminals and the injector spray tips.
- Prevent dirt and other contaminants from entering open lines and passages. Fittings should be capped, and holes plugged, during servicing.

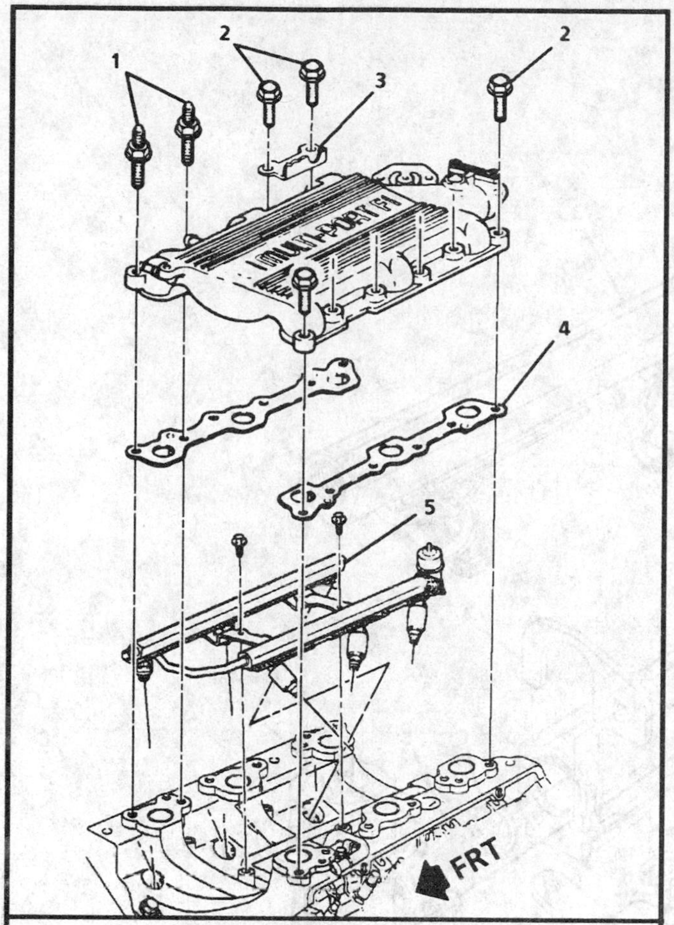
1
2
2
3
4
5
FRT

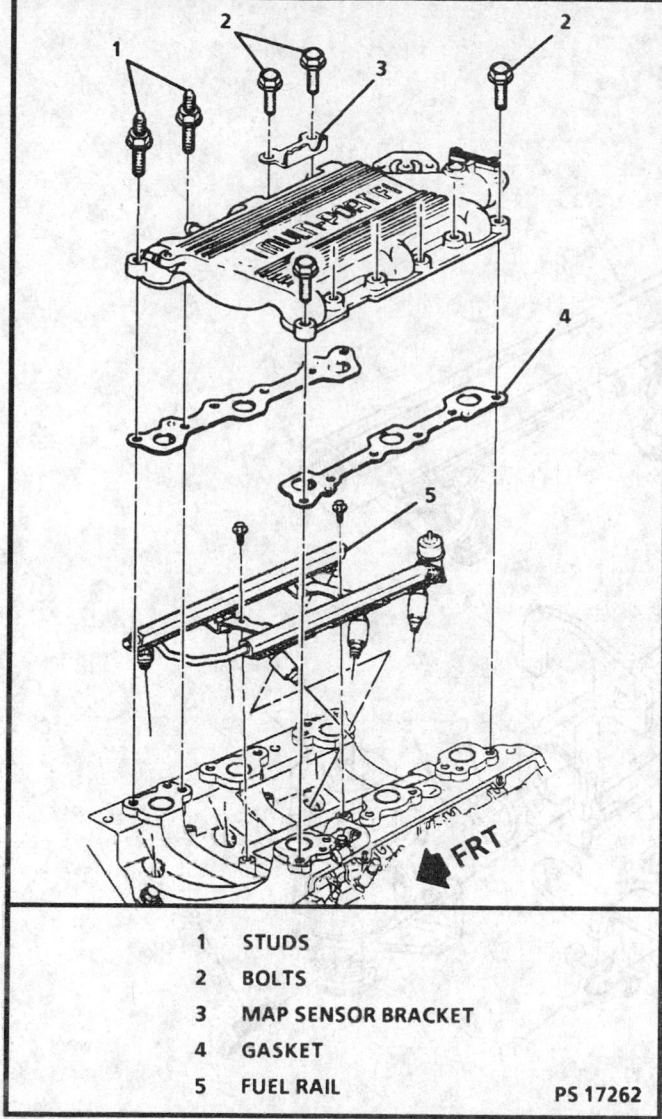

1 STUDS
2 BOLTS
3 MAP SENSOR BRACKET
4 GASKET
5 FUEL RAIL

PS 17262

Figure C2-11 - Removing Plenum and Fuel Rail

Clean

- Before removal, the fuel rail assembly may be cleaned with a spray type engine cleaner, GM X-30A or equivalent, following package instructions. Do not soak fuel rails in liquid cleaning solvent.

Remove or Disconnect

1. Negative battery cable.
2. Relieve fuel system pressure.
   - Refer to the "Fuel Pressure Relief Procedure."
3. Intake manifold plenum.
   - Refer to "Intake Manifold Plenum."
4. Engine fuel pipe bracket bolt.
5. Engine fuel pipes at rail.
6. Fuel inlet and return line O-rings and discard.
7. Injector electrical connectors.
8. Rail retaining bolts.
9. Fuel rail assembly.

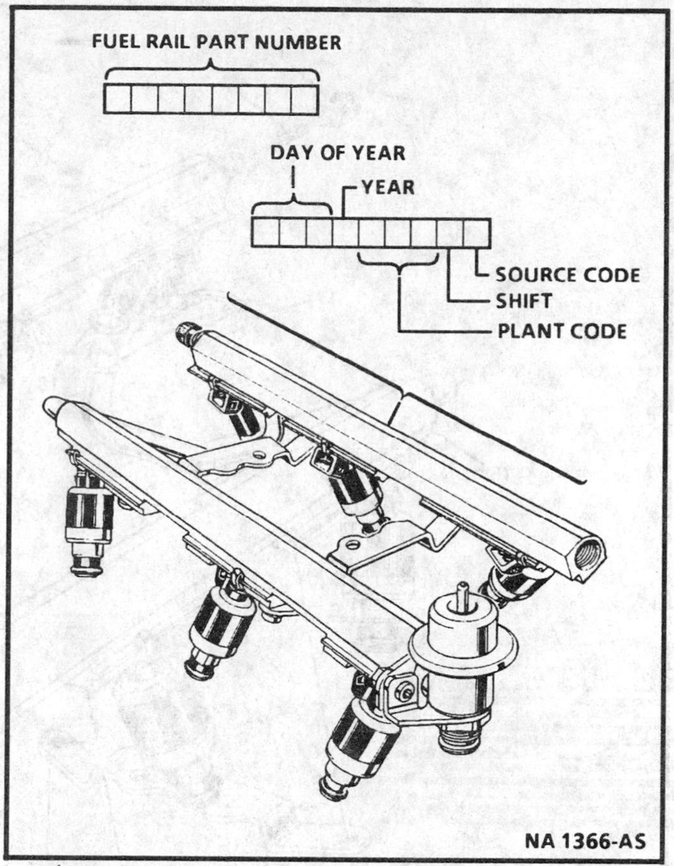
FUEL RAIL PART NUMBER
DAY OF YEAR
YEAR
SOURCE CODE
SHIFT
PLANT CODE
NA 1366-AS

Figure C2-12 - Fuel Rail Assembly Identification

Disassemble

- Injector O-ring seal from spray tip end of each injector. Discard seals. With the O-ring removed, the O-ring backup may slip off of the injector. Be sure to retain O-ring backup for reuse.

Assemble

- Ensure that O-ring backups are on injectors before installing new O-rings. Lubricate new injector O-ring seals with clean engine oil and install on spray tip end of each injector.

Install or Connect

1. Fuel rail assembly in intake manifold. Tilt rail assembly to install injectors.
2. Fuel rail attaching bolts.

Tighten

- Fuel rail attaching bolts to 10 N·m (89 lb. in.).

3. Injector electrical connectors.
4. New O-rings on fuel lines.
5. Fuel feed and return lines.

Tighten

- Engine fuel pipe nuts to 17 N·m (13 lb. ft.).

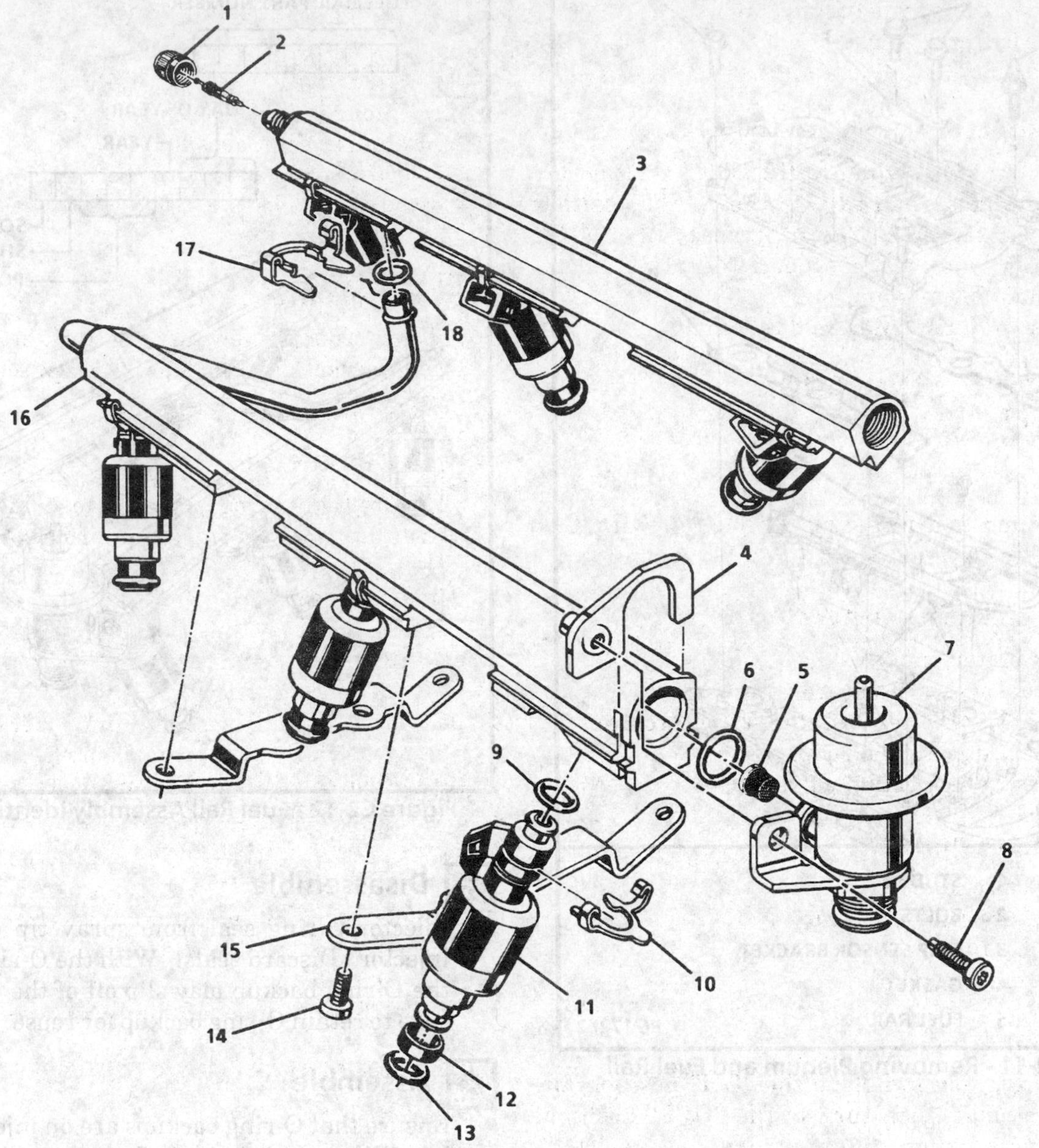
1
2
3
17
18
16
4
6
5
7
9
8
15
10
11
14
12
13

1	CAP - FUEL PRESSURE CONNECTION	11	INJECTOR ASSEMBLY - FUEL
2	VALVE ASSEMBLY - FUEL PRESSURE CONNECTION	12	BACKUP - O-RING
3	RAIL ASSEMBLY - RH FUEL	13	O-RING - LOWER INJECTOR (BROWN)
4	BRACKET - RETAINER AND SPACER	14	SCREW - RAIL MOUNTING BRACKET ATTACHING
5	SCREEN - FILTER	15	BRACKET - RAIL MOUNTING (2 EA.)
6	O-RING - PRESSURE REGULATOR INLET	16	RAIL ASSEMBLY - LH FUEL (WITH CROSSOVER TUBE)
7	REGULATOR ASSEMBLY - FUEL PRESSURE	17	CLIP - CROSSOVER TUBE RETAINER
8	SCREW - PRESSURE REGULATOR ATTACHING	18	O-RING - CROSSOVER TUBE
9	O-RING - UPPER INJECTOR (BLACK)		
10	CLIP - INJECTOR RETAINER		

4-16-93
NA 0203-XV

Figure C2-13 - Fuel Rail Assembly

- Use a back-up wrench on the fittings to prevent them from turning.

6. Negative battery cable.
7. Fuel filler cap.

Inspect

- Turn ignition switch to the "ON" position for two seconds, then turn to the "OFF" position for ten seconds. Again turn to the "ON" position, and check for fuel leaks.

8. Intake manifold plenum.
   - Refer to "Intake Manifold Plenum."

FUEL PRESSURE CONNECTION
Figure C2-13

Clean

- Area around fuel pressure connection with GM X-30A or equivalent.

Remove or Disconnect

1. Negative battery cable.
2. Relieve fuel system pressure.
   - Refer to the "Fuel Pressure Relief Procedure."
3. Fuel pressure connection cap.
4. Fuel pressure connection valve.

Install or Connect

1. Fuel pressure connection valve.
2. Fuel pressure connection cap.
3. Tighten fuel filler cap.
4. Negative battery cable.

Inspect

- Turn ignition switch to the "ON" position for two seconds, then turn to the "OFF" position for ten seconds. Again turn to the "ON" position, and check for fuel leaks.

SFI FUEL INJECTOR ASSEMBLIES
Figures C2-13 through C2-15

NOTICE: Use care in removing injectors to prevent damage to the electrical connector pins on the injector and the nozzle. The fuel injector is serviced as a complete assembly only. Since it is an electrical component, it should not be immersed in any type of cleaner.

Remove or Disconnect

1. Negative battery cable.
2. Relieve fuel system pressure.
   - Refer to the "Fuel Pressure Relief Procedure."
3. Intake manifold plenum.
   - Refer to "Intake Manifold Plenum."
4. Fuel rail assembly.
   - Refer to "Fuel Rail Assembly."

Disassemble

1. Injector retainer clip and discard.
2. SFI fuel injector assembly.
3. Injector O-ring seals from both ends of injector and discard. Save the O-ring backups for use on reassembly.

Important

- When ordering new fuel injectors, be sure to order the correct injector for the application being serviced.

Assemble

1. Ensure that O-ring backups are on injectors before installing new O-rings. Lubricate new injector O-ring seals with clean engine oil and install on injector assembly.
2. New injector retainer clips on injector assembly.
   - Position open end of clip facing injector electrical connector.
3. SFI fuel injector assembly into fuel rail injector socket with electrical connectors facing outward.
   - Push in far enough to engage retainer clip with machined slots on rail socket.

Install or Connect

1. Fuel rail assembly.
   - Refer to "Fuel Rail Assembly."
2. Intake manifold plenum.
   - Refer to "Intake Manifold Plenum."

FUEL PRESSURE REGULATOR ASSEMBLY
Figure C2-13

Remove or Disconnect

1. Negative battery cable.
2. Relieve fuel system pressure.
   - Refer to the "Fuel Pressure Relief Procedure."
3. Intake manifold plenum.
   - Refer to "Intake Manifold Plenum Removal."
4. Vacuum line to regulator.
5. Fuel pressure regulator attaching screw.
6. Place towel under regulator to catch any fuel, then remove pressure regulator from fuel rail.
   - Twist back and forth while pulling from rail.
7. Retainer and spacer bracket from rail and discard.
8. Fuel pressure regulator from engine fuel return pipe.
9. Pressure regulator inlet O-ring and discard.

Inspect

- Filter screen for contamination. If contami-nated, remove and discard filter screen.

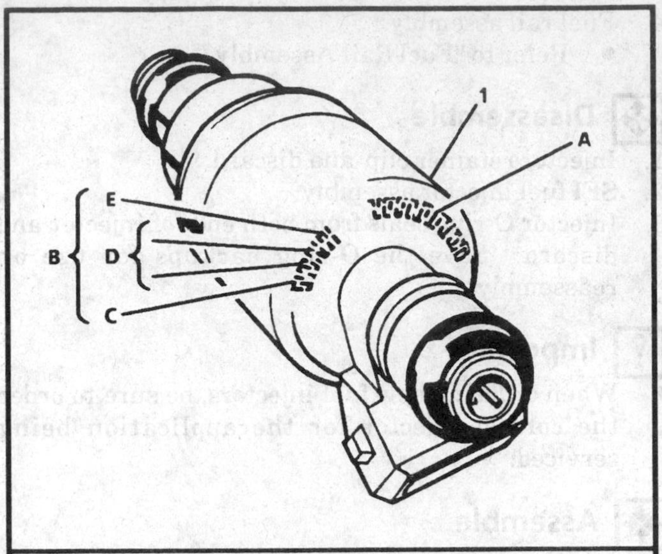
1
A
E
B
D
C

1 INJECTOR ASSEMBLY - FUEL
A PART NUMBER IDENTIFICATION
B BUILD DATE CODE
C MONTH 1-9 (JAN-SEPT) O, N, D (OCT, NOV, DEC)
D DAY
E YEAR

MP 1222-AS

Figure C2-14 - Injector Part Number Location

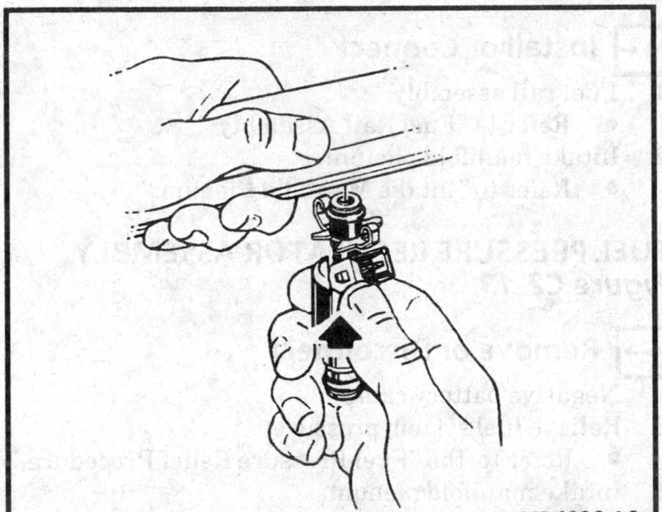
MP 1296-AS

Figure C2-15 - Installing Injector

Install or Connect

1. Lubricate new pressure regulator inlet O-ring with clean engine oil and install on regulator inlet.

CAUTION: The fuel return line must be connected before tightening the regulator attaching screw to prevent the regulator from rotating. Rotation of regulator could damage retainer and spacer bracket and lead to fuel leak at regulator inlet.

2. Fuel return pipe to regulator.
3. New retainer and spacer bracket into slot on fuel rail.
4. Pressure regulator to fuel rail.

Tighten

- Engine fuel return pipe nut to 17 N·m (13 lb. ft.).

5. Pressure regulator attaching screw.
6. Vacuum line to regulator.

Tighten

- Pressure regulator attaching screw to 8.5 N·m (6 lb.ft.).

Inspect

- Verify that retainer and spacer bracket is engaged in slots in fuel rail. Grasp and pull on regulator to ensure that it is properly seated.
- Turn ignition to "ON" for two seconds and then turn "OFF" for 10 seconds. Once again turn the ignition to "ON" and check for fuel leaks.

7. Intake manifold plenum.
   - Refer to "Intake Manifold Plenum Removal."

TORQUE SPECIFICATIONS

Intake Plenum Bolts	25 N·m (18 lb. ft.)
Throttle Body Attach. Bolts .	25 N·m (18 lb. ft.)
Fuel Rail Attaching Bolts ..	10 N·m (89 lb. in.)
Engine Fuel Pipe Nuts	17 N·m (13 lb. ft.)
Pressure Regulator Attach. Screw	8.5 N·m (6 lb. ft.)
Throttle Position Sensor ...	2.0 N·m (18 lb. in.)
Idle Air Control Valve	3.0 N·m (27 lb. in.)

BLANK

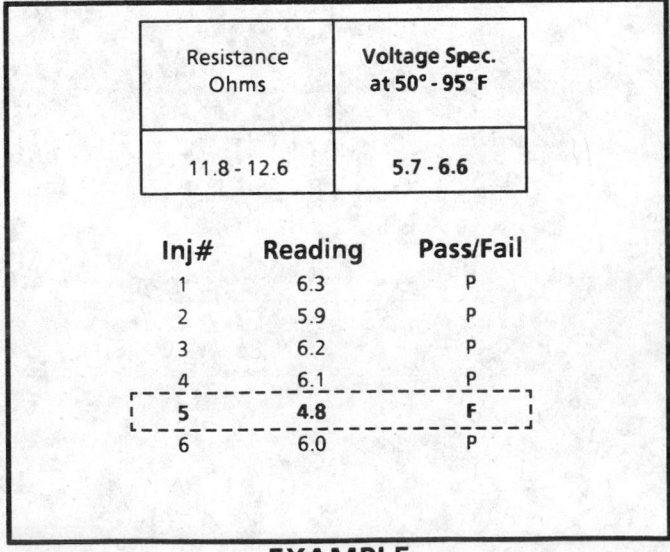

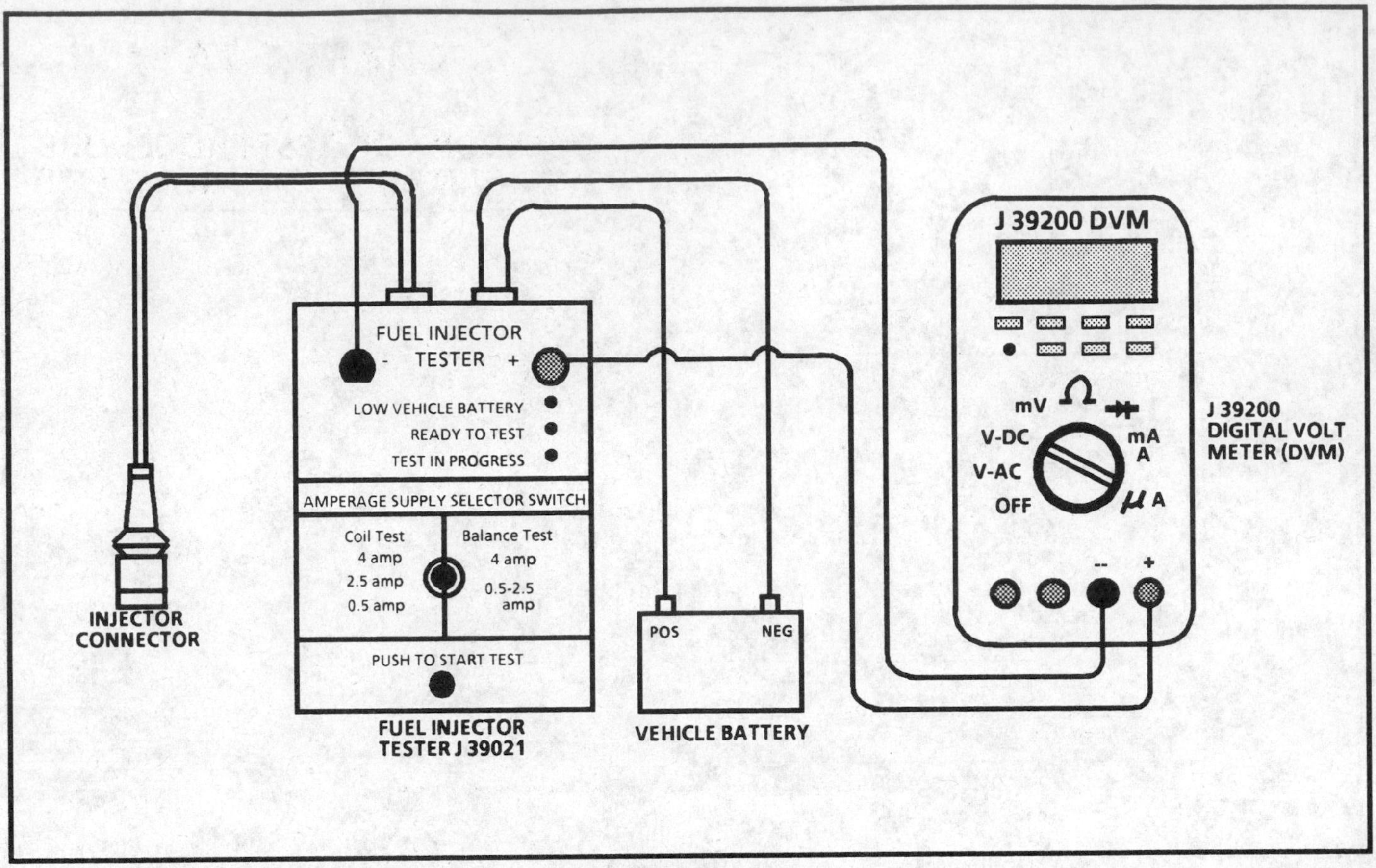
J 39200 DVM
mV
V-DC
mA
A
V-AC
OFF
μA
J 39200
DIGITAL VOLT
METER (DVM)
FUEL INJECTOR
- TESTER +
LOW VEHICLE BATTERY
READY TO TEST
TEST IN PROGRESS
AMPERAGE SUPPLY SELECTOR SWITCH
Coil Test
4 amp
2.5 amp
0.5 amp
Balance Test
4 amp
0.5-2.5
amp
PUSH TO START TEST
INJECTOR
CONNECTOR
FUEL INJECTOR
TESTER J 39021
POS
NEG
VEHICLE BATTERY

CHART C-2A

(Page 1 of 3)
INJECTOR COIL TEST PROCEDURE
3100 (VIN M) "W" CARLINE (SFI)

Chart Test Description: Number(s) below refer to circled number(s) on the diagnostic chart.

1. This is the set-up step for performing the injector coil test. Also read instructions included with tools used for test.
2. Engine coolant temperature affects the tool's ability to detect a faulty injector. If engine coolant temperature is _NOT_ between 50°F and 95°F the comparison chart (Page 2 of 3) must be used.
3. The first second of the voltage reading may be inaccurate due to initial current surge, therefore, record the lowest voltage displayed after the first second of test. The voltage reading should be within range (see example). The voltage reading may increase throughout the test as the injector windings warm and the resistance changes. An erratic voltage reading (one that jumps up and down) indicates an intermittent connection within the fuel injector.
4. To check the mechanical (fuel delivery) portion of the fuel injector, perform an injector balance test.

Resistance Ohms	Voltage Spec. at 50° - 95° F
11.8 - 12.6	5.7 - 6.6

Inj#	Reading	Pass/Fail
1	6.3	P
2	5.9	P
3	6.2	P
4	6.1	P
5	4.8	F
6	6.0	P

EXAMPLE

5-20-93
PS 17395

CHART C-2A

(Page 1 of 3)
INJECTOR COIL TEST PROCEDURE
3100 (VIN M) "W" CARLINE (SFI)

1
- ENGINE "OFF."
- RELIEVE FUEL PRESSURE. (REFER TO "FUEL PRESSURE RELIEF" IN THIS SECTION.)
- ACCESS INJECTORS AS REQUIRED (REFER TO "ON-VEHICLE SERVICE" IN THIS SECTION.)
- CONNECT FUEL INJECTOR TESTER J 39021 TO VEHICLE BATTERY.
- SET AMPERAGE SUPPLY SELECTOR SWITCH TO THE "COIL TEST" 0.5 AMP POSITION.
- CONNECT LEADS FROM THE J 39200 DIGITAL VOLT METER (DVM) TO THE FUEL INJECTOR TESTER.
- SET DVM TO THE TENTHS SCALE (0.0).

2
- CHECK ENGINE COOLANT TEMPERATURE. IS IT BETWEEN 50° AND 95° F?

YES → 3

NO
- PROCEED TO "CHART C-2A (PAGE 2 OF 3)".

3
- CONNECT TESTER TO AN INJECTOR.
- PRESS THE "PUSH TO START TEST" BUTTON AND OBSERVE DVM. VOLTAGE MAY CLIMB DURING TEST. WATCH FOR ERRATIC READING (VOLTAGE JUMPS UP AND DOWN).
- RECORD LOWEST VOLTAGE DISPLAYED AFTER FIRST SECOND OF READING.
- REPEAT FOR EACH INJECTOR.
- DOES ANY INJECTOR VOLTAGE READING FALL OUTSIDE 5.7-6.6 VOLTS, OR DO ANY HAVE ERRATIC VOLTAGE READINGS?

YES
- REPLACE FAULTY INJECTORS. → 4

NO → 4

4
- PERFORM "INJECTOR BALANCE TEST (PAGE 3 OF 3)".

3-24-93
PS 17396

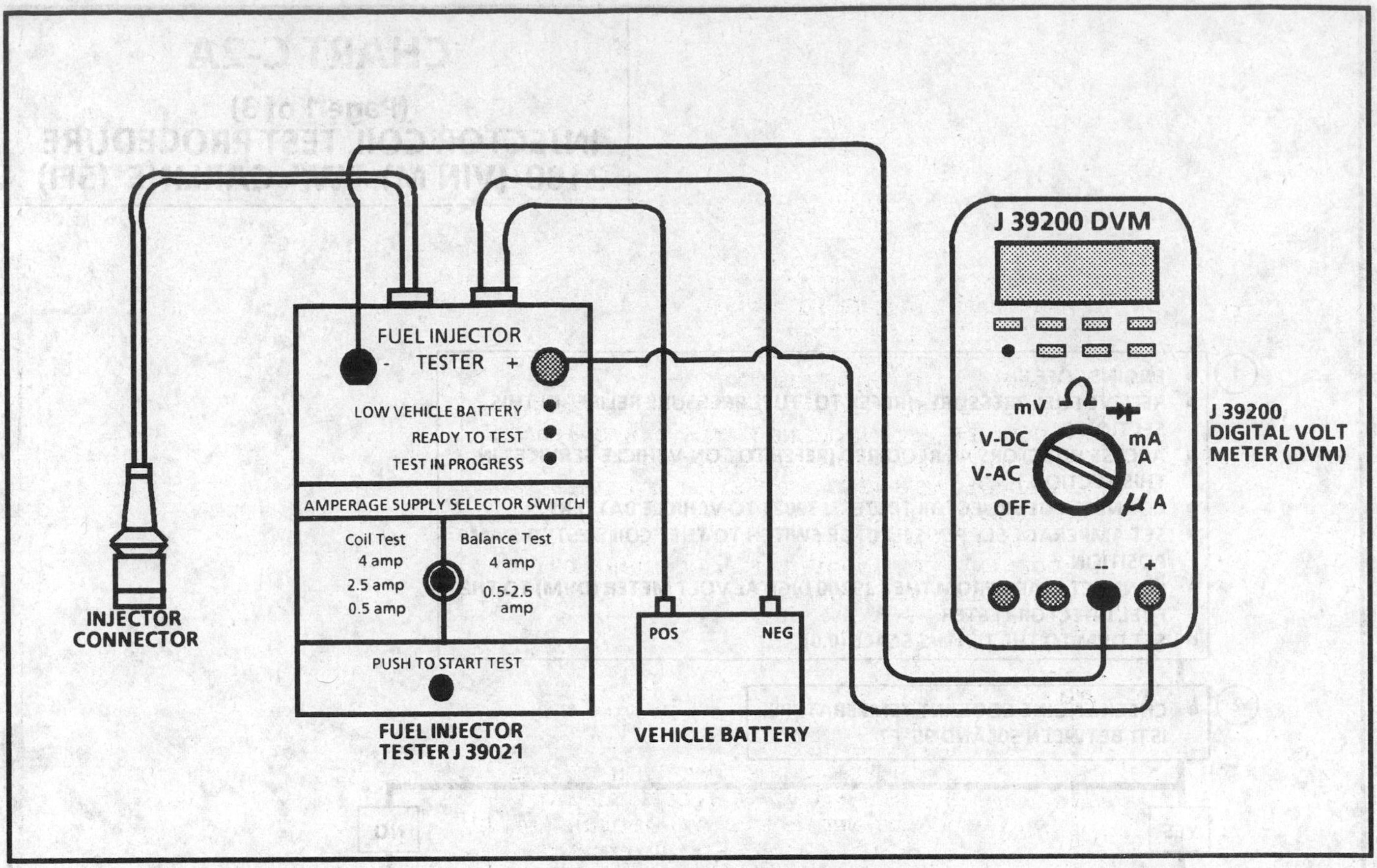
J 39200 DVM
FUEL INJECTOR
- TESTER +
LOW VEHICLE BATTERY
READY TO TEST
TEST IN PROGRESS
AMPERAGE SUPPLY SELECTOR SWITCH
Coil Test
4 amp
2.5 amp
0.5 amp
Balance Test
4 amp
0.5-2.5 amp
PUSH TO START TEST
FUEL INJECTOR TESTER J 39021
POS
NEG
VEHICLE BATTERY
INJECTOR CONNECTOR
mV
V-DC
V-AC
OFF
mA A
μA
J 39200 DIGITAL VOLT METER (DVM)

CHART C-2A

(Page 2 of 3)

INJECTOR COIL TEST PROCEDURE
3100 (VIN M) "W" CARLINE (SFI)

Chart Test Description: Number(s) below refer to circled number(s) on the diagnostic chart.

1. The first second of the voltage reading may be inaccurate due to initial current surge, therefore, record the lowest voltage displayed after the first second of test. The voltage reading may increase throughout the test as the injector windings warm and the resistance changes. An erratic voltage reading (one that jumps up and down) indicates an intermittent connection within the fuel injector.
2. From recorded voltages (see example), identify the highest voltage reading recorded (other than those above 9.5 volts). Subtract all other voltages from the highest voltage recorded. The subtracted value for any injector must not exceed 0.6 volt.
3. To check the mechanical (fuel delivery) portion of the fuel injector, perform an injector balance test.

Highest Voltage Reading	7.1 Volts
Acceptable Subtracted Value Above/Below 50°-95°F.	0.6 Volt

Inj. No.	Voltage Reading	Subtracted Value	Pass/Fail
1	9.8	---	F
2	6.6	0.5	P
3	6.9	0.2	P
4	5.8	1.3	F
5	7.0	0.1	P
6	7.1	0.0	P

EXAMPLE

CHART C-2A

(Page 2 of 3)

INJECTOR COIL TEST PROCEDURE
3100 (VIN M) "W" CARLINE (SFI)

FROM "CHART C-2A (PAGE 1 OF 3)"

1
- CONNECT TESTER TO AN INJECTOR.
- PRESS "PUSH TO START TEST" BUTTON AND OBSERVE DVM. VOLTAGE MAY CLIMB DURING TEST. WATCH FOR ERRATIC READING (VOLTAGE JUMPS UP AND DOWN).
- RECORD LOWEST VOLTAGE DISPLAYED AFTER THE FIRST SECOND OF READING.
- REPEAT FOR EACH INJECTOR.
- DOES ANY INJECTOR HAVE AN ERRATIC READING OR A READING ABOVE 9.5 VOLTS?

NO → go to step 2.

YES
- DISREGARD INJECTOR(S) WITH VOLTAGE READING ABOVE 9.5 VOLTS OR ERRATIC READINGS (JUMPS UP AND DOWN) FROM CALCULATIONS. THESE INJECTORS ARE FAULTY AND MUST BE REPLACED.

→ go to step 2.

2
- FROM RECORDED VOLTAGES, IDENTIFY THE HIGHEST VOLTAGE READING RECORDED (OTHER THAN THOSE ABOVE 9.5 VOLTS).
- SUBTRACT ALL OTHER VOLTAGES FROM THE HIGHEST VOLTAGE RECORDED.
- DOES ANY SUBTRACTED VALUE EXCEED 0.6 VOLTS?

YES

REPLACE ANY INJECTOR:
- WHOSE SUBTRACTED VALUE HAS EXCEEDED 0.6 VOLTS.
- WHOSE INITIAL READING WAS ABOVE 9.5 VOLTS.
- THAT HAD AN ERRATIC READING.

→ go to step 3.

NO → go to step 3.

3 PERFORM "INJECTOR BALANCE TEST (PAGE 3 OF 3)".

3-24-93
PS 17398

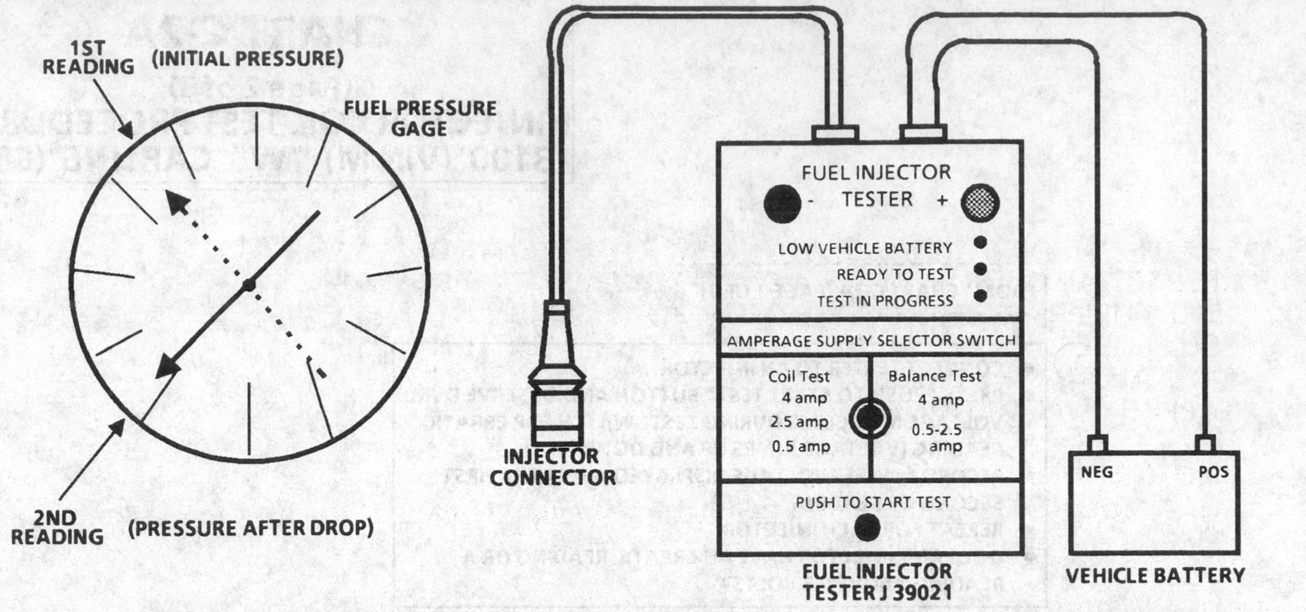
1ST READING (INITIAL PRESSURE)
FUEL PRESSURE GAGE
2ND READING (PRESSURE AFTER DROP)
INJECTOR CONNECTOR
FUEL INJECTOR TESTER
-
+
LOW VEHICLE BATTERY
READY TO TEST
TEST IN PROGRESS
AMPERAGE SUPPLY SELECTOR SWITCH
Coil Test
4 amp
2.5 amp
0.5 amp
Balance Test
4 amp
0.5-2.5 amp
PUSH TO START TEST
FUEL INJECTOR TESTER J 39021
NEG
POS
VEHICLE BATTERY

EXAMPLE

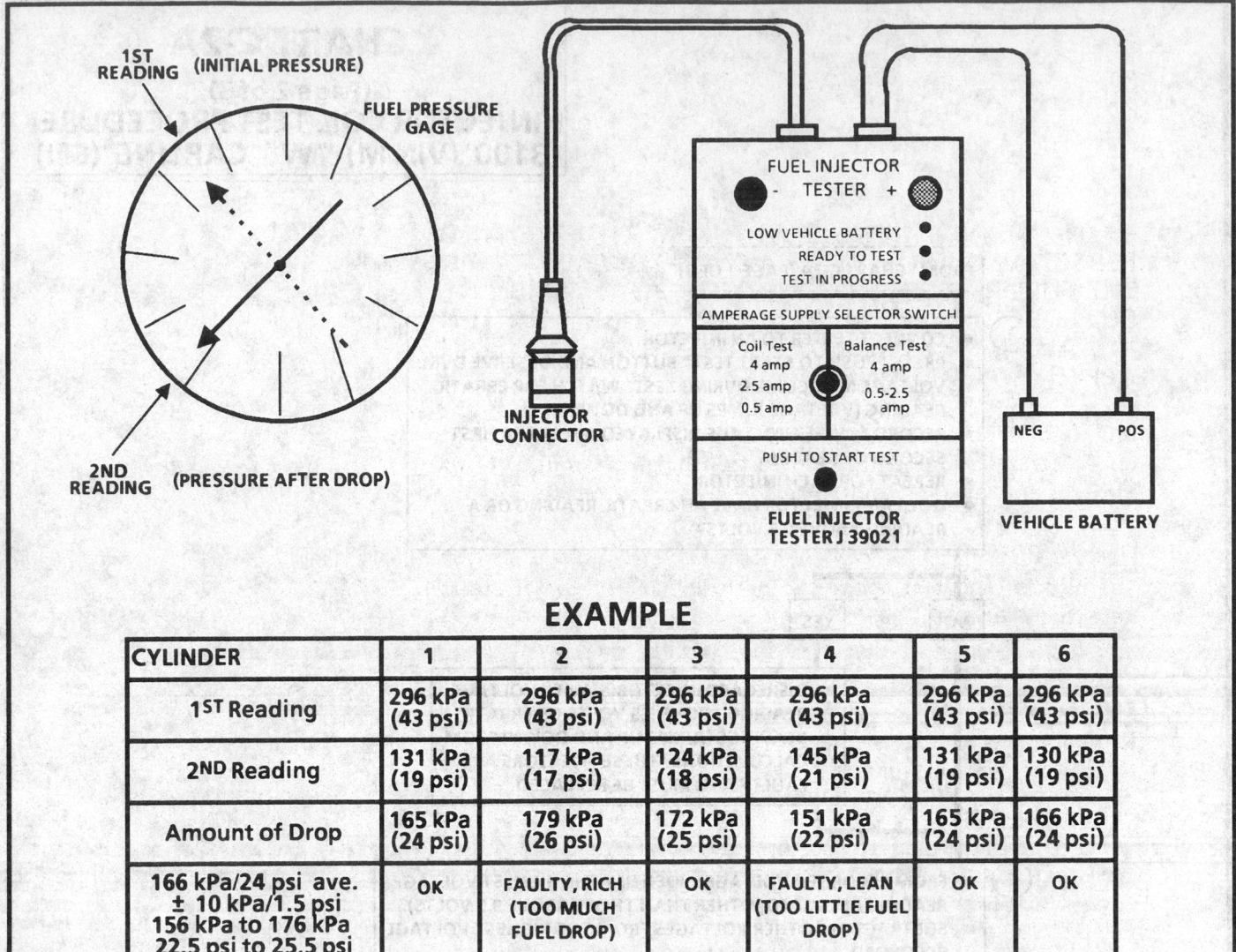

CYLINDER	1	2	3	4	5	6
1ST Reading	296 kPa (43 psi)	296 kPa (43 psi)	296 kPa (43 psi)	296 kPa (43 psi)	296 kPa (43 psi)	296 kPa (43 psi)
2ND Reading	131 kPa (19 psi)	117 kPa (17 psi)	124 kPa (18 psi)	145 kPa (21 psi)	131 kPa (19 psi)	130 kPa (19 psi)
Amount of Drop	165 kPa (24 psi)	179 kPa (26 psi)	172 kPa (25 psi)	151 kPa (22 psi)	165 kPa (24 psi)	166 kPa (24 psi)
166 kPa/24 psi ave. ± 10 kPa/1.5 psi 156 kPa to 176 kPa 22.5 psi to 25.5 psi	OK	FAULTY, RICH (TOO MUCH FUEL DROP)	OK	FAULTY, LEAN (TOO LITTLE FUEL DROP)	OK	OK

CHART C-2A

(Page 3 of 3)
INJECTOR BALANCE TEST PROCEDURE
3100 (VIN M) "W" CARLINE (SFI)

Chart Test Description: Number(s) below refer to circled number(s) on the diagnostic chart.

1. Engine cool down period (10 minutes) is necessary to avoid irregular fuel pressure readings due to "Hot Soak" fuel boiling.
2. Energize tester one time and record pressure drop at the lowest point (Disregard any slight pressure variations).
3. If the pressure drop of all injectors is within 10 kPa (1.5 psi) of the average fuel pressure drop, the injectors are flowing properly. The actual amount of pressure drop is calculated by subtracting the second pressure reading from the first pressure reading.

ENGINE	FUEL PRESSURE RANGE
All engines EXCEPT 5.7L (VIN J) Corvette 3.1L (VIN W) Lumina VFV	284-325 kPa (41-47 psi)
5.7L (VIN J) Corvette 3.1L(VIN W) Lumina VFV	333-376 kPa (48-55 psi)

5-25-93
PS 17399

CHART C-2A

(Page 3 of 3)

INJECTOR BALANCE TEST PROCEDURE
3100 (VIN M) "W" CARLINE (SFI)

CAUTION: TO REDUCE THE RISK OF FIRE AND PERSONAL INJURY, WRAP A SHOP TOWEL AROUND THE FUEL PRESSURE CONNECTION TO ABSORB ANY FUEL LEAKAGE THAT MAY OCCUR WHEN INSTALLING THE PRESSURE GAGE. PLACE TOWEL IN APPROVED CONTAINER.

NOTICE: The entire test should NOT be repeated more than once without running the engine to prevent flooding. (This includes any retest on faulty injectors.)

[!] Important

The injector coil test should be performed prior to this test. Refer to Page 1 of 3.

(1)
- IF ENGINE IS AT OPERATING TEMPERATURE, ALLOW A 10 MINUTE "COOL DOWN" PERIOD.
- IGNITION "OFF."
- CONNECT FUEL PRESSURE GAGE.
- ENERGIZE FUEL PUMP USING AVAILABLE METHOD FOR VEHICLE (FUEL PUMP TEST CONNECTOR OR TECH 1 SCAN TOOL ENABLE).
- PLACE OPEN END OF BLEED HOSE INTO AN APPROVED GASOLINE CONTAINER AND BLEED AIR FROM FUEL GAGE.
- WITH FUEL PUMP RUNNING NOTE FUEL PRESSURE, PRESSURE SHOULD BE WITHIN SPECIFIED RANGE SHOWN ON FACING PAGE. IF NOT, REFER TO CHART A-7.
- TURN FUEL PUMP "OFF." WHEN PUMP STOPS, PRESSURE MAY VARY SLIGHTLY THEN SHOULD HOLD STEADY. IF NOT, REFER TO CHART A-7

(2)
- CONNECT FUEL INJECTOR TESTER TO AN INJECTOR.
  - SET AMPERAGE SUPPLY SELECTOR SWITCH TO THE "BALANCE TEST" 0.5 - 2.5 AMP POSITION.
- CYCLE FUEL PUMP "ON"/"OFF" TO PRESSURIZE FUEL SYSTEM.
- RECORD STABILIZED FUEL PRESSURE (1ST PRESSURE READING - SEE EXAMPLE ON FACING PAGE)
- ENERGIZE FUEL INJECTOR BY DEPRESSING "PUSH TO START TEST" BUTTON.
- NOTE FUEL PRESSURE THE INSTANT THE FUEL PRESSURE GAGE NEEDLE STOPS. RECORD FUEL PRESSURE READING (2ND PRESSURE READING - SEE EXAMPLE ON FACING PAGE).

(3)
- REPEAT STEP 2 ON ALL INJECTORS.
- SUBTRACT 2ND PRESSURE READING FROM 1ST PRESSURE READING TO OBTAIN PRESSURE DROP VALUES.
- ADD ALL PRESSURE DROP VALUES AND DIVIDE BY THE NUMBER OF FUEL INJECTORS TO GET THE AVERAGE PRESSURE DROP.
- ANY INJECTOR THAT HAS A 10 KPA (1.5 PSI) DIFFERENCE, EITHER MORE OR LESS FROM THE AVERAGE, IS CONSIDERED FAULTY.
- RETEST ANY INJECTOR THAT APPEARS FAULTY.
- ANY INJECTOR THAT FAILS THE RETEST IS FAULTY AND NEEDS TO BE REPLACED.
- IF NO PROBLEM IS FOUND, REVIEW "SYMPTOMS" SECTION "B".

3-24-93
PS 17400

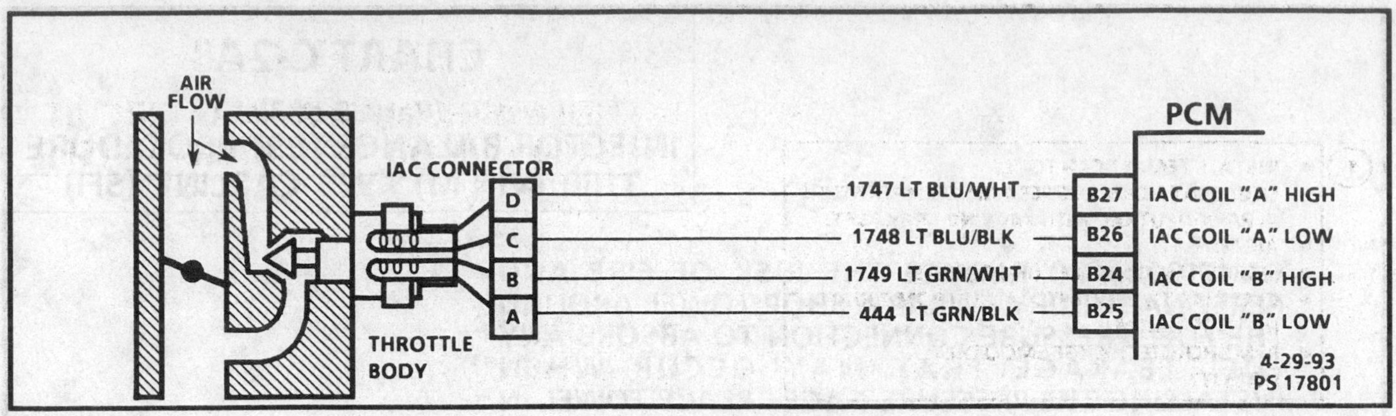
AIR FLOW
IAC CONNECTOR
D
C
B
A
THROTTLE BODY
PCM
1747 LT BLU/WHT
1748 LT BLU/BLK
1749 LT GRN/WHT
444 LT GRN/BLK
B27
B26
B24
B25
IAC COIL "A" HIGH
IAC COIL "A" LOW
IAC COIL "B" HIGH
IAC COIL "B" LOW
4-29-93
PS 17801

CHART C-2B

IDLE AIR CONTROL (IAC) CIRCUIT
3100 (VIN M) "W" CARLINE (SFI)

Circuit Description:

The PCM controls engine idle speed with the IAC valve. To increase idle speed, the PCM retracts the IAC valve pintle away from its seat, allowing more air to bypass the throttle bore. To decrease idle speed, it extends the IAC valve pintle towards its seat, reducing bypass air flow. A Tech 1 scan tool will read the PCM commands to the IAC valve in counts. Higher counts indicate more air bypass (higher idle). The lower the counts indicates less air is allowed to bypass (lower idle).

Chart Test Description: Number(s) below refer to circled number(s) on the diagnostic chart.

1. The Tech 1 RPM control mode is used to extend and retract the IAC valve. The valve should move smoothly within the specified range. If the idle speed is commanded (IAC extended) too low (below 700 RPM), the engine may stall. This may be normal and would not indicate a problem. Retracting the IAC beyond its controlled range (above 1500 RPM) will cause a delay before the RPMs start dropping. This too is normal.
2. This test uses the Tech 1 to command the IAC controlled idle speed. The PCM issues commands to obtain commanded idle speed. The node lights each should flash red and green to indicate a good circuit as the PCM issues commands. While the sequence of color is not important if either light is "OFF" or does not flash red and green, check the circuits for faults, beginning with poor terminal contacts.

Diagnostic Aids: A slow, unstable, or fast idle may be caused by a non-IAC system problem that cannot be overcome by the IAC valve. Out of control range IAC Tech 1 scan tool counts will be greater than 60 if idle is too low, and zero counts if idle is too high. The following checks should be made to repair a non-IAC system problem:

- Vacuum leak (high idle). If idle is too high, stop the engine. Fully extend (low) IAC with tester. Start engine. If idle speed is above 800 RPM, locate and correct vacuum leak including crankcase ventilation system. Also check for binding of throttle blade or linkage.
- System too lean (high air/fuel ratio). The idle speed may be too high or too low. Engine speed may vary up and down and disconnecting the IAC valve does not help. DTC 44 may be set. Tech 1 scan tool HO2S voltage will be less than 300 mV (.3 volt). Check for low regulated fuel pressure, water in the fuel or a restricted injector.
- System too rich (low air/fuel ratio). The idle speed will be too low. Tech 1 scan tool IAC counts will usually be greater than 80. System is obviously rich and may exhibit black smoke in exhaust.
  Tech 1 scan tool HO2S voltage will be fixed above 800 mV (.8 volt).
  Check for high fuel pressure, leaking or sticking injector. Silicone contaminated HO2S sensors Tech 1 scan tool voltage will be slow to respond.
- Throttle body. Remove IAC valve and inspect bore for foreign material.
- IAC valve electrical connections. IAC valve connections should be carefully checked for proper contact.
- Crankcase ventilation valve. An incorrect or faulty valve may result in an incorrect idle speed.
- Refer to "Rough, Unstable, Incorrect Idle or Stalling" in "Symptoms," Section "6E3-B".
- If intermittent poor driveability or idle symptoms are resolved by disconnecting the IAC, carefully recheck connections, valve terminal resistance, or replace IAC.

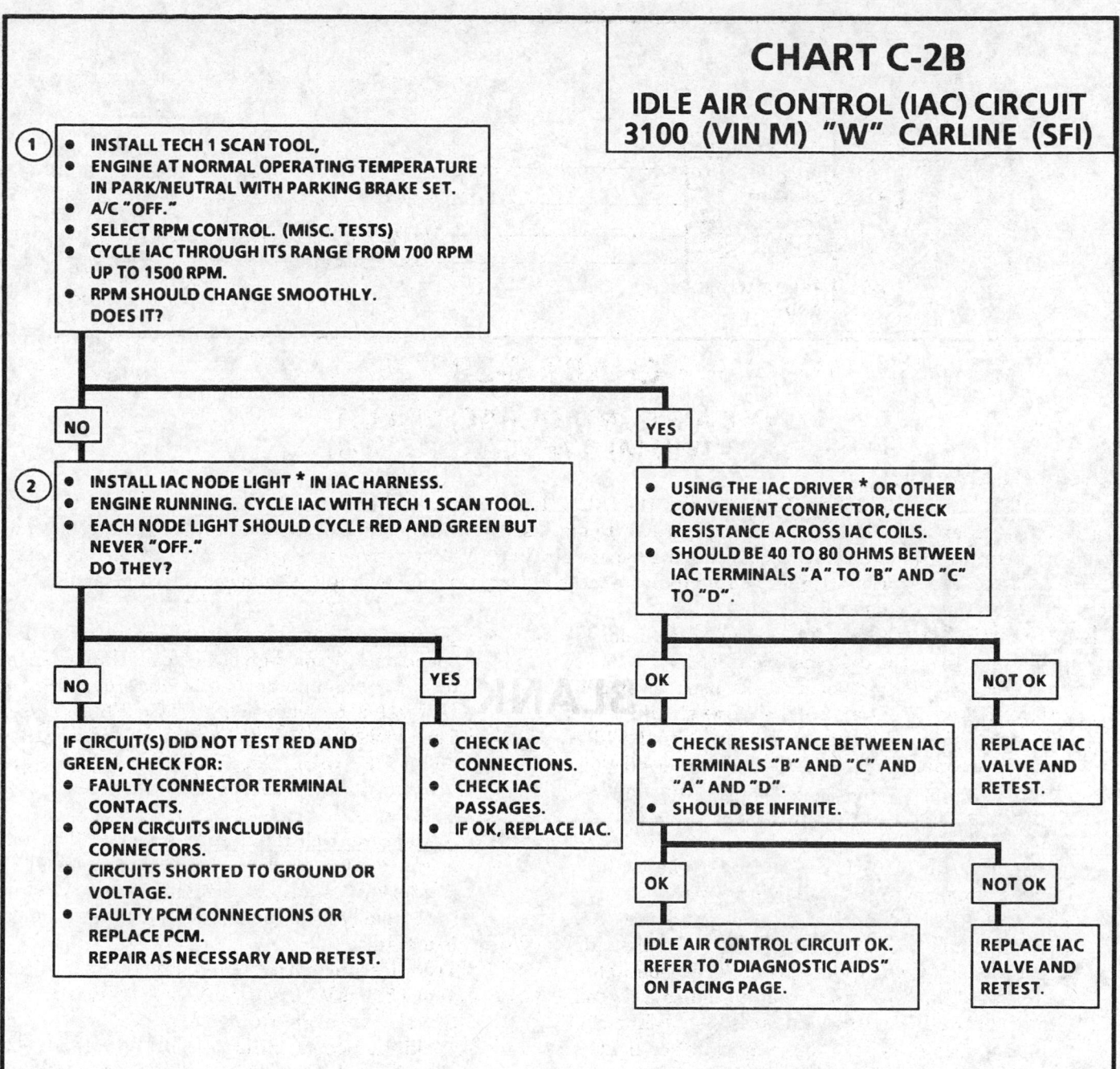

CHART C-2B

IDLE AIR CONTROL (IAC) CIRCUIT
3100 (VIN M) "W" CARLINE (SFI)

(1)
- INSTALL TECH 1 SCAN TOOL,
- ENGINE AT NORMAL OPERATING TEMPERATURE IN PARK/NEUTRAL WITH PARKING BRAKE SET.
- A/C "OFF."
- SELECT RPM CONTROL. (MISC. TESTS)
- CYCLE IAC THROUGH ITS RANGE FROM 700 RPM UP TO 1500 RPM.
- RPM SHOULD CHANGE SMOOTHLY.
  DOES IT?

NO

(2)
- INSTALL IAC NODE LIGHT * IN IAC HARNESS.
- ENGINE RUNNING. CYCLE IAC WITH TECH 1 SCAN TOOL.
- EACH NODE LIGHT SHOULD CYCLE RED AND GREEN BUT NEVER "OFF."
  DO THEY?

NO

IF CIRCUIT(S) DID NOT TEST RED AND GREEN, CHECK FOR:
- FAULTY CONNECTOR TERMINAL CONTACTS.
- OPEN CIRCUITS INCLUDING CONNECTORS.
- CIRCUITS SHORTED TO GROUND OR VOLTAGE.
- FAULTY PCM CONNECTIONS OR REPLACE PCM.
  REPAIR AS NECESSARY AND RETEST.

YES

- CHECK IAC CONNECTIONS.
- CHECK IAC PASSAGES.
- IF OK, REPLACE IAC.

YES

- USING THE IAC DRIVER * OR OTHER CONVENIENT CONNECTOR, CHECK RESISTANCE ACROSS IAC COILS.
- SHOULD BE 40 TO 80 OHMS BETWEEN IAC TERMINALS "A" TO "B" AND "C" TO "D".

OK

- CHECK RESISTANCE BETWEEN IAC TERMINALS "B" AND "C" AND "A" AND "D".
- SHOULD BE INFINITE.

OK

IDLE AIR CONTROL CIRCUIT OK. REFER TO "DIAGNOSTIC AIDS" ON FACING PAGE.

NOT OK

REPLACE IAC VALVE AND RETEST.

NOT OK

REPLACE IAC VALVE AND RETEST.

* IAC DRIVER AND NODE LIGHT REQUIRED KIT 222-L FROM: CONCEPT TECHNOLOGY, INC.
J 37027 FROM: KENT-MOORE, INC.

CLEAR DIAGNOSTIC TROUBLE CODES, CONFIRM "CLOSED LOOP" OPERATION, NO MALFUNCTION INDICATOR LAMP (MIL) "SERVICE ENGINE SOON." PERFORM IAC RESET PROCEDURE PER APPLICABLE SERVICE MANUAL AND VERIFY CONTROLLED IDLE SPEED IS CORRECT.

"*AFTER REPAIRS,*" REFER TO DTC CRITERIA ON FACING PAGE AND CONFIRM DTC DOES NOT RESET.

4-15-93
PS 17649

BLANK

SECTION C3

EVAPORATIVE EMISSION (EVAP) CONTROL SYSTEM

CONTENTS

GENERAL DESCRIPTION

PURPOSE

The basic Evaporative Emission (EVAP) control system used on all vehicles is the charcoal canister storage method. This method transfers fuel vapor from the fuel tank to an activated carbon (charcoal) storage device (canister) to hold the vapors when the vehicle is not operating. When the engine is running the fuel vapor is purged from the carbon element by intake air flow and consumed in the normal combustion process.

EVAPORATIVE EMISSION CONTROL SYSTEM

This system uses a basic two tube evaporative emission canister. The venting of vapors to the canister is controlled by a remotely mounted normally closed pulse width modulated solenoid valve. The fuel vapors vent from the fuel tank through the tank tube to the canister. This canister is located in the left rear wheel well of the car behind an access cover.

The PCM operates this normally closed pulse width modulated solenoid valve which controls vacuum to the purge valve in the charcoal canister. Under cold engine or idle conditions, the solenoid is turned "OFF" by the PCM, which closes the solenoid and blocks vacuum to the EVAP canister purge solenoid valve.

The PCM turns "ON" the solenoid valve and allows purge when:

- Engine is warm.
- After the engine has been running a specified time.
- Above a specified road speed.
- Above a specified throttle opening.

RESULTS OF INCORRECT OPERATION

Poor idle, stalling and poor driveability can be caused by:

- An improperly connected or faulty EVAP canister purge solenoid valve. This would usually be accompanied by a start that is not as fast as normal (once started, the engine does not build up speed as fast as it normally would) and a puff of black smoke at the tailpipe.
- Damaged canister.
- Hoses split, cracked and/or not connected to the proper tubes.

Evidence of fuel loss or fuel vapor odor can be caused by:

- Liquid fuel leaking from front fuel lines.
- Cracked or damaged canister.
- Disconnected, misrouted, kinked, deteriorated or damaged hoses.
- Air cleaner or air cleaner gasket improperly seated.

DIAGNOSIS

The evaporative emission canister purge solenoid valve operation is covered in CHART C-3 at the end of this section.

VISUAL CHECK OF EVAP CANISTER

If cracked, leaking raw fuel, or damaged, replace canister.

ON-VEHICLE SERVICE

EVAPORATIVE EMISSION CANISTER
Figure C3-1

←→ Remove or Disconnect

1. Remove access cover at left rear wheel well.
2. Hoses from canister. Mark hoses to install on new canister.
3. Canister.

→← Install or Connect

1. Canister.
2. Hoses. Make sure connections are correct.
3. Re-install access cover.

EVAPORATIVE EMISSION (EVAP) CANISTER PURGE SOLENOID VALVE
Figure C3-4

←→ Remove or Disconnect

1. Negative battery cable.
2. Electrical connector, hose and line from EVAP solenoid valve.
3. Release lock tab on solenoid bracket. Remove EVAP purge solenoid valve from bracket. Refer to Figure C3-4.

→← Install or Connect

1. EVAP purge solenoid valve to the engine bracket. Snap the EVAP purge solenoid valve down over the lock tabs of bracket.
2. Inlet hose and electrical connector on solenoid.
3. Negative battery cable.

EVAPORATIVE EMISSION HOSES

Refer to "Vehicle Emission Control Information" label for routing of evaporative emission hoses.

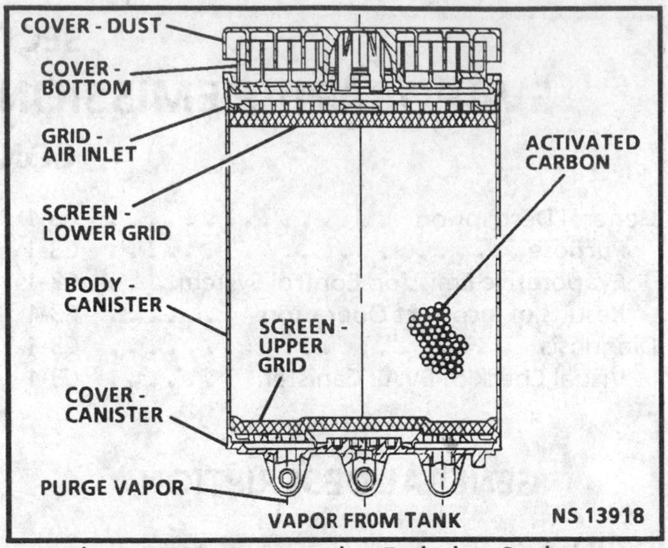
COVER - DUST
COVER - BOTTOM
GRID - AIR INLET
ACTIVATED CARBON
SCREEN - LOWER GRID
BODY - CANISTER
SCREEN - UPPER GRID
COVER - CANISTER
PURGE VAPOR
VAPOR FROM TANK
NS 13918

Figure C3-1 - Evaporative Emission Canister

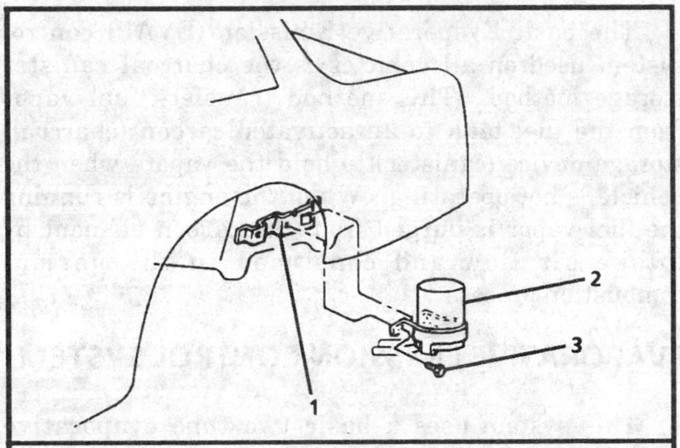
1
2
3

1 CANISTER MOUNTING BRACKET
2 CANISTER
3 BOLT/SCREW

NS 13917

Figure C3-2 - Evaporative Emission Canister Location

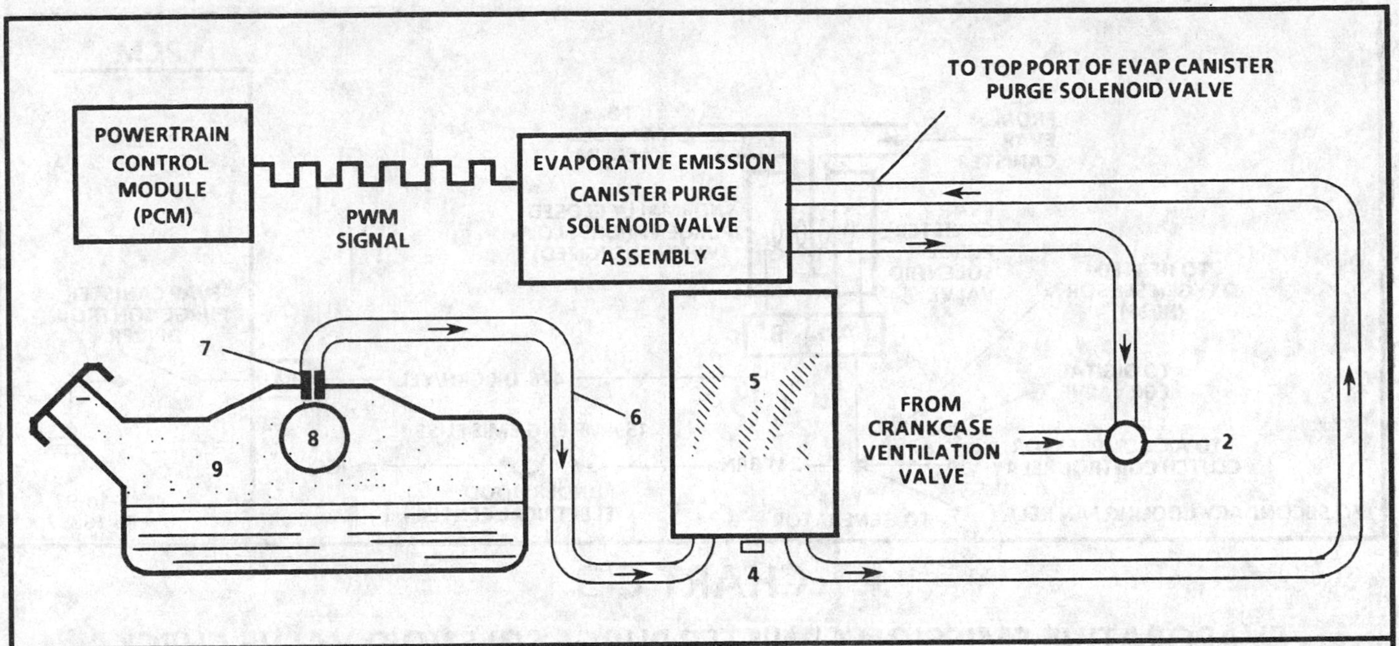
TO TOP PORT OF EVAP CANISTER
PURGE SOLENOID VALVE
POWERTRAIN
CONTROL
MODULE
(PCM)
PWM
SIGNAL
EVAPORATIVE EMISSION
CANISTER PURGE
SOLENOID VALVE
ASSEMBLY
FROM
CRANKCASE
VENTILATION
VALVE
1
2
3
4
5
6
7
8
9

1	PURGE LINE	4	AIR INLET	7	IN-TANK VAPOR RESTRICTION
2	MANIFOLD VACUUM SOURCE	5	EVAPORATIVE EMISSION CANISTER	8	ROLL-OVER VALVE
3	PURGE LINE	6	TANK LINE	9	FUEL TANK

4-29-93
PS 16836

Figure C3-3 - Evaporative Emission (EVAP) Control System Schematic

FRT
1
2

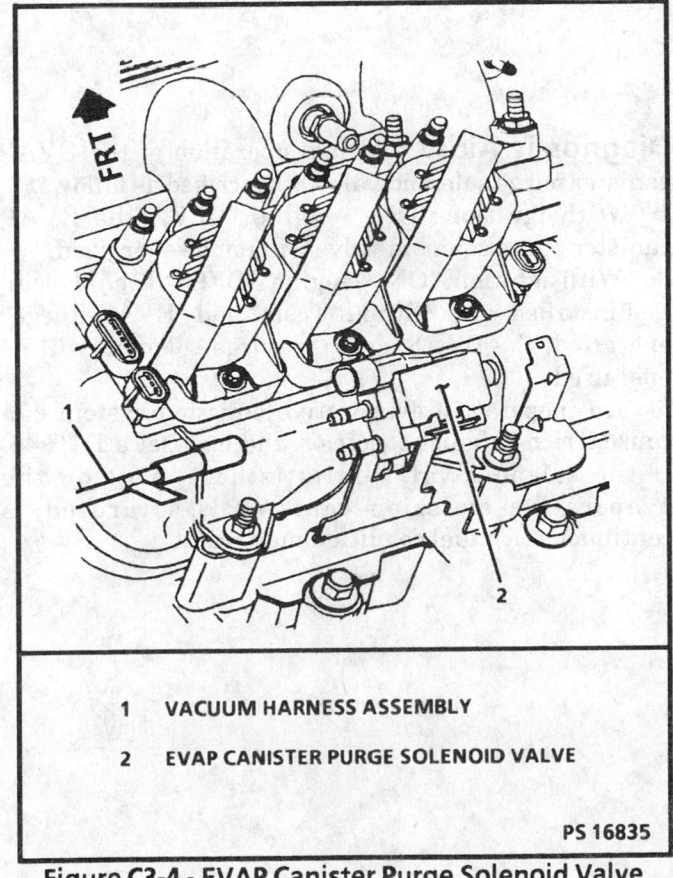

1 VACUUM HARNESS ASSEMBLY

2 EVAP CANISTER PURGE SOLENOID VALVE

PS 16835

Figure C3-4 - EVAP Canister Purge Solenoid Valve Assembly

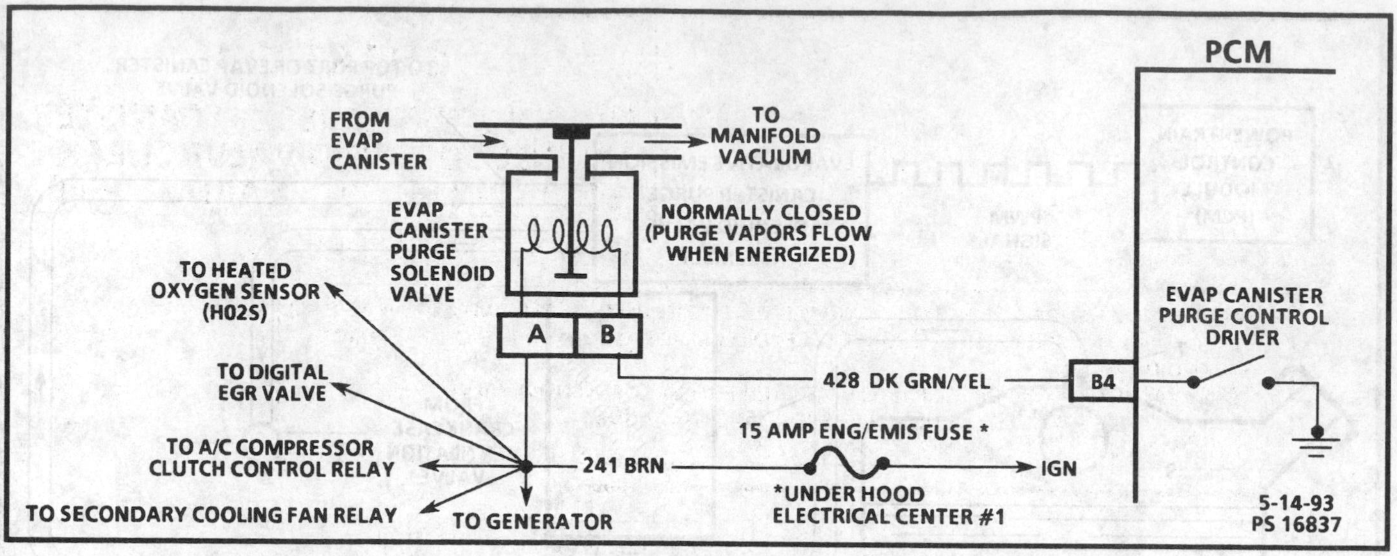

PCM
FROM EVAP CANISTER
TO MANIFOLD VACUUM
EVAP CANISTER PURGE SOLENOID VALVE
NORMALLY CLOSED (PURGE VAPORS FLOW WHEN ENERGIZED)
TO HEATED OXYGEN SENSOR (HO2S)
A
B
EVAP CANISTER PURGE CONTROL DRIVER
TO DIGITAL EGR VALVE
428 DK GRN/YEL
B4
15 AMP ENG/EMIS FUSE *
TO A/C COMPRESSOR CLUTCH CONTROL RELAY
241 BRN
IGN
*UNDER HOOD ELECTRICAL CENTER #1
TO SECONDARY COOLING FAN RELAY
TO GENERATOR
5-14-93
PS 16837

CHART C-3

EVAPORATIVE EMISSION CANISTER PURGE SOLENOID VALVE CHECK
3100 (VIN M) "W" CARLINE (SFI)

Circuit Description:

EVAP canister purge is controlled by a solenoid that allows manifold vacuum to purge the canister when energized. The PCM supplies a ground to energize the solenoid (purge "ON"). The purge solenoid controlled by the PCM is pulse width modulated (turned "ON" and "OFF" several times a second). The duty cycle (pulse width) is determined by the amount of air flow and engine vacuum as indicated by the MAP sensor input. The duty cycle is calculated by the PCM and the output commanded when the following conditions have been met:

- Engine run time after start more than 3 minutes.
- Engine coolant temperature above 80°C (176°F).
- Vehicle speed above 13 mph.
- Throttle at idle (greater than 3%).

Chart Test Description: Number(s) below refer to circled number(s) on the diagnostic chart.

1. Checks to see if the solenoid is opened or closed. The solenoid is normally de-energized in this step; so it should be closed.
2. Determines whether solenoid was open due to an electrical circuit problem or solenoid valve itself is faulty.
3. Completes functional check by enabling "Evap Purge" output test. This should normally energize the solenoid opening the valve which should allow the vacuum to drop (purge "ON").
4. Vacuum hose to manifold vacuum is either open or obstructed.

Diagnostic Aids: Normal operation of the EVAP canister purge solenoid valve is described as follows:

With ignition "ON," engine "OFF," the EVAP canister purge solenoid valve will not be energized.

With ignition "ON," engine "OFF," Tech 1 scan tool installed with "Output Tests" and "EVAP Purge" energized, the EVAP canister purge solenoid will be energized.

An inoperative evaporative emission system can cause a rich exhaust condition and may set a DTC 45. If the solenoid valve fails (stuck open) or the evaporative emission canister is saturated, a continuous rich fuel condition may result.

CHART C-3

EVAPORATIVE EMISSION CANISTER PURGE SOLENOID VALVE CHECK 3100 (VIN M) "W" CARLINE (SFI)

1
- IGNITION "ON," ENGINE STOPPED. (DO NOT CRANK ENGINE BEFORE FOLLOWING STEPS BELOW.)
- DISCONNECT THROTTLE BODY TO PURGE SOLENOID VALVE VACUUM HOSE FROM THE PURGE SOLENOID VALVE.
- APPLY VACUUM (10" Hg OR 34 kPa) TO EVAP CANISTER PURGE SOLENOID VALVE. EVAP CANISTER PURGE SOLENOID VALVE SHOULD HOLD VACUUM. DOES IT?

YES → **3**
- USING TECH 1 SCAN TOOL, SELECT EVAP PURGE "OUTPUT TEST."
- ENERGIZE SOLENOID.
- VACUUM SHOULD DROP. DOES IT?

  NO
  - DISCONNECT PURGE SOLENOID VALVE ELECTRICAL CONNECTOR.
  - CONNECT TEST LIGHT BETWEEN HARNESS TERMINALS. TEST LIGHT SHOULD LIGHT. DOES IT?

    YES → FAULTY EVAP CANISTER PURGE SOLENOID VALVE.

    NO → PROBE HARNESS TERMINAL "A" (CKT 241) WITH TEST LIGHT TO GROUND.

      LIGHT "ON"
      - CKT 428 OPEN OR SHORTED TO VOLTAGE.
      - FAULTY CONNECTION OR FAULTY PCM.

      LIGHT "OFF"
      - CKT 241 OPEN OR SHORTED TO GROUND OR OPEN ENG/EMIS FUSE.

  YES
  - CONNECT VACUUM GAUGE TO HOSE PREVIOUSLY DISCONNECTED.
  - START ENGINE AND IDLE.
  - MANIFOLD VACUUM SHOULD BE DISPLAYED ON THE VACUUM GAGE. IS IT?

    YES → NO PROBLEM FOUND.

    NO → **4** FAULTY VACUUM SOURCE.

NO → **2**
- DISCONNECT SOLENOID ELECTRICAL CONNECTOR.
- APPLY VACUUM TO PURGE SOLENOID VALVE AS IN STEP 1. PURGE SOLENOID VALVE SHOULD HOLD VACUUM. DOES IT?

  YES → CHECK FOR SHORT TO GROUND IN CKT 428. IF CIRCUIT IS OK, PCM IS FAULTY.

  NO → FAULTY EVAP CANISTER PURGE SOLENOID VALVE.

"AFTER REPAIRS," CONFIRM "CLOSED LOOP" OPERATION AND NO MIL (SERVICE ENGINE SOON).

6-23-93
PS 18744

BLANK

SECTION C4

ELECTRONIC IGNITION (EI) SYSTEM

CONTENTS

GENERAL DESCRIPTION

The Electronic Ignition (EI) system controls fuel combustion by providing a spark to ignite the compressed air/fuel mixture at the correct time. To provide optimum engine performance, fuel economy, and control of exhaust emissions, the PCM controls spark advance of the ignition system. Electronic ignition has several advantages over a mechanical system:

- No moving parts.
- Less maintenance.
- Remote mounting capability.
- No mechanical load on the engine.
- More coil cool down time between firing events.
- Elimination of mechanical timing adjustments.
- Increased available ignition coil saturation time.

OPERATION

The electronic ignition system does not use the conventional distributor and coil. This ignition system consists of three ignition coils, an ignition control module, a camshaft position sensor, two Hall-effect crankshaft position sensors, related connecting wires, and the ignition control and fuel metering portion of the PCM.

Conventional ignition coils have one end of the secondary winding connected to the engine ground. In this ignition system, neither end of the secondary winding is grounded. Instead, both ends of each coil secondary winding is attached to a spark plug. Each cylinder is paired with the cylinder that is opposite it (1-4, 2-5, 3-6).

These two plugs are on "companion" cylinders, i.e., on top dead center at the same time. When the coil discharges, both plugs fire at the same time to complete the series circuit. The cylinder on compression is said to be the "event" cylinder and the one on exhaust is the "waste" cylinder.

The cylinder on the exhaust stroke requires very little of the available energy to fire the spark plug. The remaining energy will be used as required by the cylinder on the compression stroke. The same process is repeated when the cylinders reverse roles. This method of ignition is called a "waste spark" ignition system.

Since the polarity of the ignition coil primary and secondary windings is fixed, one spark plug always fires with a forward current flow and its "companion" plug fires with a reverse current flow. This is different from a conventional ignition system that fires all the plugs with the same direction of current flow. Since it requires approximately 30% more voltage to fire a spark plug backwards, the ignition coil design is improved, with saturation time and primary current flow increased. This allows higher secondary voltage to be available from the ignition coils - greater than 40 kilovolts (*40,000 volts*) at any engine RPM. The voltage required by each spark plug is determined by the polarity and the cylinder pressure. The cylinder on compression requires more voltage to fire the spark plug than the one on exhaust.

It is possible for one spark plug to fire even though a plug wire from the same coil may be disconnected from its "companion" plug. The disconnected plug wire acts as one plate of a capacitor, with the engine being the other plate. These two "capacitor plates" are charged as a spark jumps across the gap of the connected spark plug. The "plates" are then discharged as the secondary energy is dissipated in an oscillating current across the gap of the still-connected spark plug.

Secondary voltage requirements are very high with an "open" spark plug or wire. The ignition coil has enough reserve energy to fire the still-connected plug at idle, but possibly not under high engine load. A more noticeable misfire may be evident under load; both spark plugs may then be misfiring.

SYSTEM COMPONENTS

24X and 3X Crankshaft Position Sensors

The 24X crankshaft position sensor, secured in an aluminum mounting bracket and bolted to the front side of the engine timing chain cover, is partially behind the crankshaft balancer ("On-Vehicle Service," Figure C4-3).

The 3X crankshaft position sensor uses a two wire connector at the crankshaft position sensor and a three wire connector at the ignition control module. Refer to Figure C4-1.

The 24X crankshaft position sensor contains a Hall-effect switch. The magnet and Hall-effect switch are separated by an air gap. A Hall-effect switch reacts like a solid-state switch, grounding a low-current signal voltage when a magnetic field is present. When the magnetic field is shielded from the switch by a piece of steel placed in the air gap between the magnet and the switch, the signal voltage is not grounded. If the piece of steel (called an interrupter) is repeatedly moved in and out of the air gap, the signal voltage will appear to go "ON-OFF-ON-OFF-ON-OFF." Compared to a conventional mechanical distributor, this "ON-OFF" signal is similar to the signal that a set of breaker points in the distributor would generate as the distributor shaft turned and the points opened and closed.

In the case of the electronic ignition system, a concentric interrupter ring mounted to the rear of the crankshaft balancer has blades and windows that, with crankshaft rotation, either block the magnetic field or allow it to reach the Hall-effect switch. The Hall-effect switch is called a 24X crankshaft position sensor, because the interrupter ring has 24 evenly-spaced same-width blades and windows. The 24X crankshaft sensor produces 24 "ON-OFF" pulses per crankshaft revolution. The Hall-effect switch closest to the crankshaft, the 3X crankshaft position sensor, is so called because the interrupter ring has a special wheel cast on the crankshaft that has seven machined slots, six of which are equally spaced 60° apart. The seventh slot is spaced 10° from one of the other slots. As the interrupter ring rotates with the crankshaft, the slots change the magnetic field. This will cause the 3X Hall-effect switch to ground the 3X signal voltage supplied from the ignition control module. The ignition control module interprets the 3X "ON-OFF" signals as an indication of crankshaft position, and must have the 3X signal to "fire" the correct ignition coil.

The 24X interrupter ring and Hall-effect switch react similarly. The 24X signal is used for better resolution at a calibrated RPM.

Camshaft Position Sensor

The camshaft position sensor ("On-Vehicle Service," Figure C4-5) is located on the timing cover behind the water pump near the camshaft sprocket.

As the camshaft sprocket turns, a magnet in it activates the Hall-effect switch in the cam sensor. When the Hall-effect switch is activated, it grounds the signal line to the PCM, pulling the cam signal line's applied voltage low. This is interpreted as a cam signal.

The cam signal is created as piston #1 is on the intake stroke.

When the cam signal is not received by the PCM DTC 17 will be set.

Ignition Coils

Three twin-tower ignition coils are individually mounted to the ignition control module (Figure C4-2). Each coil provides spark for two plugs simultaneously (waste spark distribution). Each coil is serviced separately.

Two terminals connect each coil pack to the module. The ignition coils share a fused ignition feed. The other terminal at each coil is individually connected to the module, which will energize one coil at a time by completing and interrupting the primary circuit ground path to each coil at the proper time.

Ignition Control Module

The ignition control module performs several functions:

- It powers the 3X crankshaft sensor circuit.
- It determines the correct ignition coil firing sequence, based on 3X pulse. This coil sequencing occurs at startup. After the engine is running, the module determines the sequence, and continues triggering the ignition coils in proper sequence.
- It sends a "3X crankshaft reference" (fuel control) signal to the PCM. The PCM determines engine RPM from this signal. It is also used by the PCM to determine crankshaft position for ignition control spark advance calculations. The signal sent to the PCM by the ignition control module is an "ON-OFF" pulse occurring 3 times per crankshaft revolution.

Circuits Affecting Ignition Control

To properly control timing, the PCM relies on the following information:

- Engine load (manifold pressure or vacuum).
- Atmospheric (barometric) pressure.
- Engine temperature.
- Intake air temperature.
- Crankshaft position.
- Engine speed (RPM).

The IC system consists of the ignition coil and module assembly (ignition coils, electronic ignition control module), the 3X crankshaft position sensor and the 24X crankshaft position sensor, PCM and connecting wires. The electronic Ignition Control Module (ICM) connector terminals are lettered as shown in Figure C4-1. These circuits perform the following functions:

- 3X reference high - CKT 430. The crankshaft position sensor sends a signal to the electronic ignition control module which generates a reference pulse which is sent to the PCM. The PCM uses this signal to calculate crankshaft position and engine speed (also used to trigger the injector).
- 3X reference low - CKT 453. This wire is grounded through the module and makes sure the ground circuit has no voltage drop between the ignition module and the PCM, which if open, could affect performance.
- Ignition control bypass - CKT 424. During initial cranking, the PCM will look for synchronizing pulses from the camshaft and 3X crankshaft position sensor indicating the position of #1 piston and intake valve. 5 volts is applied to the bypass circuit the instant these signals are received by the PCM. This generally occurs within 1 or 2 revolutions of the crankshaft. An open or grounded bypass circuit will set a DTC 42 and the engine will run at base timing. A small amount of advance is built into the ignition control module to enhance performance.
- IC - CKT 423. The PCM uses this circuit to trigger the electronic ignition control module. The PCM uses the crankshaft reference signal to base its calculation of the amount of spark advance needed under present engine conditions.
- 24X reference signal. Additional to the electronic ignition system is the 24X crankshaft position sensor. Its function is to smooth idle quality and provide improved low speed driveability.

How DTC 42 is Determined

An open in the IC circuit while running will result in the engine continuing to run although in a base timing mode (module timing). The timing values are stored in the ignition control module to allow for basic engine performance.

If the IC circuit is shorted to ground, the MIL will be turned "ON," and a DTC 42 will be set and the engine will operate in module timing. Either condition may cause poor performance and reduced fuel economy.

If the bypass line is open or grounded, the ignition control module will not switch to IC timing mode so the IC voltage will be low and DTC 42 will be set.

If the IC circuit is grounded, the ignition control module will switch to base timing and a DTC 42 will be set and MIL illuminated.

DIAGNOSIS

If the engine cranks but will not run, CHART A-3 will be used to determine if the "EI" system is the cause of the problem or if it is another part of the fuel injection system.

If DTC 42 is set, that DTC chart should be used for diagnosis. If no DTC is set and the ignition system is suspected, use CHART C-4F "Misfire" for diagnosis.

RESULTS OF INCORRECT OPERATION

An open or ground in the ignition control or bypass circuit will set a DTC 42. If a fault occurs in the ignition control output circuit when the engine is running, the engine may falter or quit running but will restart and run in base timing mode once the ignition has been cycled. A fault in either circuit will force the ignition system to operate on base timing (10° BTDC), which will result in reduced performance and fuel economy.

The PCM uses information from the engine coolant temperature sensor in addition to RPM to calculate the main spark advance values as follows:

High RPM	=	more advance
Cold engine	=	more advance
Low RPM	=	less advance
Hot engine	=	less advance

Therefore, detonation could be caused by high resistance in the engine coolant temperature sensor circuit. Poor performance could be caused by low resistance in the engine coolant temperature sensor circuit.

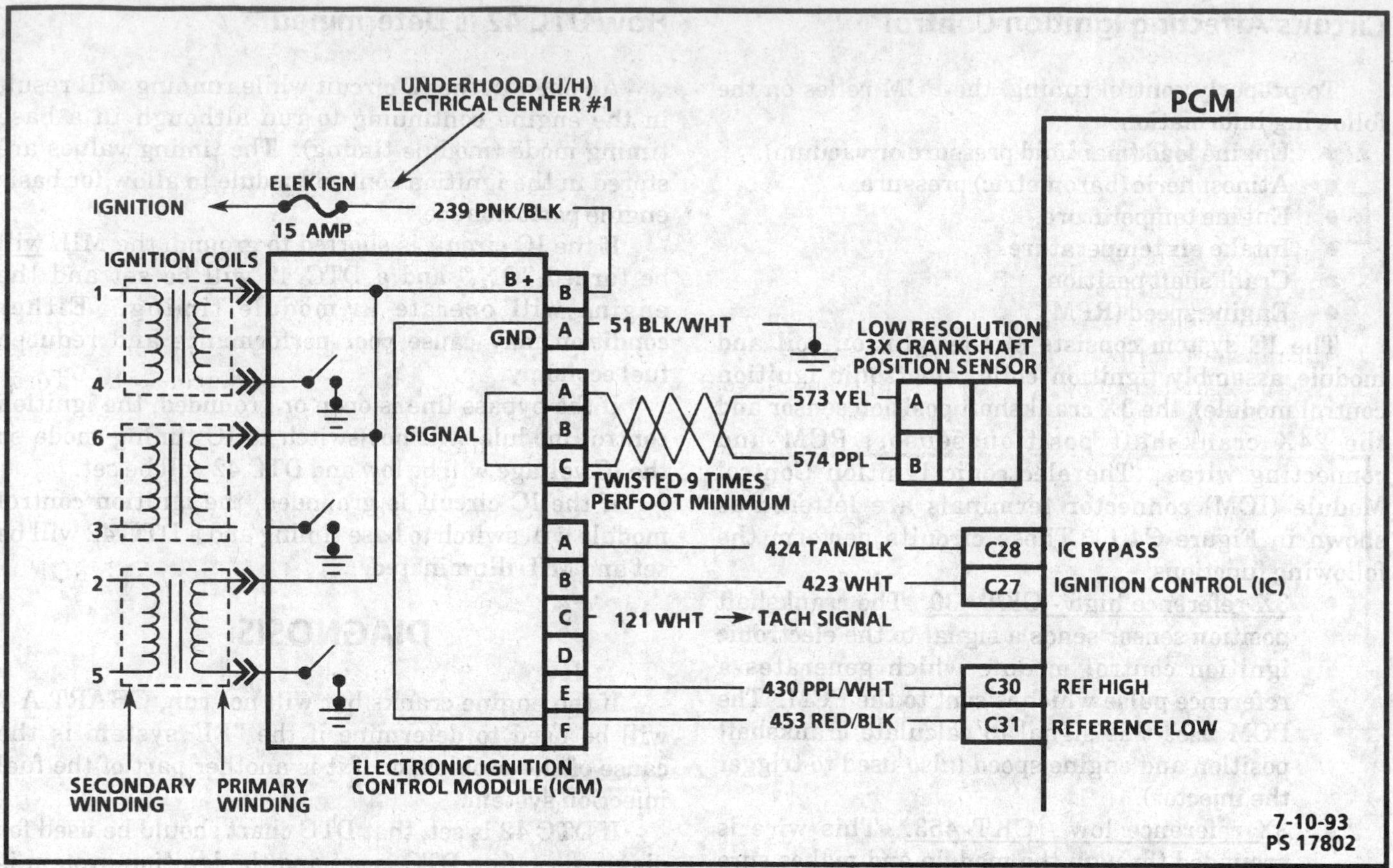
UNDERHOOD (U/H) ELECTRICAL CENTER #1
ELEK IGN
IGNITION
15 AMP
239 PNK/BLK
IGNITION COILS
PCM
B+
GND
51 BLK/WHT
LOW RESOLUTION 3X CRANKSHAFT POSITION SENSOR
573 YEL
574 PPL
SIGNAL
TWISTED 9 TIMES PERFOOT MINIMUM
424 TAN/BLK
C28
IC BYPASS
423 WHT
C27
IGNITION CONTROL (IC)
121 WHT
TACH SIGNAL
430 PPL/WHT
C30
REF HIGH
453 RED/BLK
C31
REFERENCE LOW
SECONDARY WINDING
PRIMARY WINDING
ELECTRONIC IGNITION CONTROL MODULE (ICM)
7-10-93
PS 17802

Figure C4-1 - Electronic Ignition (EI) System with Ignition Control (IC)

DIAGNOSIS

If the Engine Cranks But Will Not Run or immediately stalls, CHART A-3 must be used to determine if the failure is in the ignition system or the fuel system.

If a DTC 17, 36 or 82 is set, the appropriate DTC chart must be used for diagnosis.

If the symptom is "Engine Miss" and the ignition system is suspected, CHART C-4F will provide a systematic diagnostic procedure.

ON-VEHICLE SERVICE

IGNITION COIL

↔ Remove or Disconnect

1. Spark plug wires.
2. 2 screws securing coil to ignition control module.
3. Ignition coil. Refer to Figure C4-2.

→← Install or Connect

1. Ignition coil.
2. 2 screws, torque to 4-5 N·m (40 lb. in.).
3. Spark plug wires.

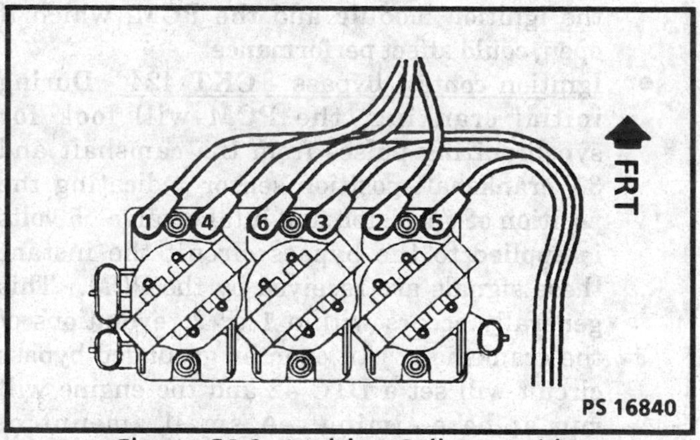
FRT
1
4
6
3
2
5
PS 16840

Figure C4-2 - Ignition Coil Assembly

IGNITION CONTROL MODULE

↔ Remove or Disconnect

1. 6-way connector, 3-way connector and 2-way connector at ignition control module.
2. Spark plug wires from ignition coils. Refer to Figure C4-2.
3. 6 screws securing ignition coils to ignition control module.
4. Disconnect coils from ignition control module.
5. Ignition control module.

→← Install or Connect

1. Ignition coils to ignition control module.
2. 6 screws, torque to 4-5 N·m (40 lb. in.).

3. Plug wires. Refer to Figure C4-2.
4. 6-way connector, 3-way connector and 2-way connector to module.

24X CRANKSHAFT POSITION SENSOR

Remove or Disconnect

1. Negative battery cable.
2. Serpentine belt from crankshaft pulley.
3. Raise vehicle on hoist.
4. Crankshaft harmonic balancer retaining bolt.
5. Crankshaft harmonic balancer using special tool (J 38197).

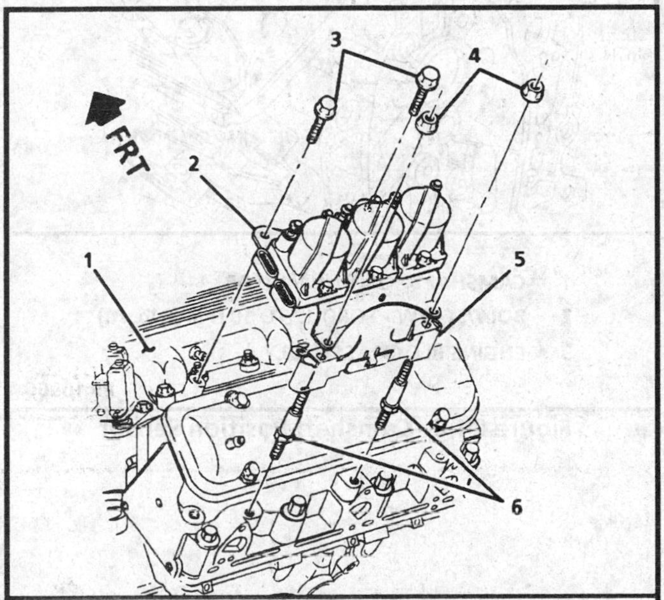
3
4
FRT
2
1
5
6

1	UPPER INTAKE MANIFOLD ASSEMBLY
2	IGNITION COIL ASSEMBLY
3	BOLT/SCREW
4	NUT
5	EVAP PURGE SOLENOID VALVE BRACKET
6	STUD

PS 16839

Figure C4-3 - Ignition Control Module and Coil Assembly

6. Sensor electrical connector.
7. Sensor bolts (2). Refer to Figure C4-3.
8. Sensor.

Install or Connect

1. Crankshaft position sensor with bolt (2). Refer to Figure C4-3.
2. Torque bolts (2) to 10 N·m (8 lb. ft.).
3. Sensor electrical connector.
4. Balancer on crankshaft.
5. Apply thread sealer GM #1052080 or equivalent to threads of crankshaft balancer bolt. Torque bolt to 150 N·m (110 lb. ft.).
6. Lower vehicle.
7. Serpentine belt.
8. Negative battery cable.

3X CRANKSHAFT POSITION (CKP) SENSOR
Figure C4-5

Remove or Disconnect

1. Negative battery cable.
2. Crank steering wheel full left.
3. Raise vehicle.
4. Sensor harness connector at sensor.
5. Sensor to block bolt (1).
6. Sensor from engine.

Inspect

- Sensor O-ring for wear, cracks or leakage. Replace if necessary. Lube new O-ring with clean engine oil before installing.

Install or Connect

1. Sensor into hole in block.
2. Sensor to block bolt (1).

Tighten

- Torque to 8 N·m (71 lb. in.).

3. Sensor harness connector at sensor.
4. Negative battery cable.

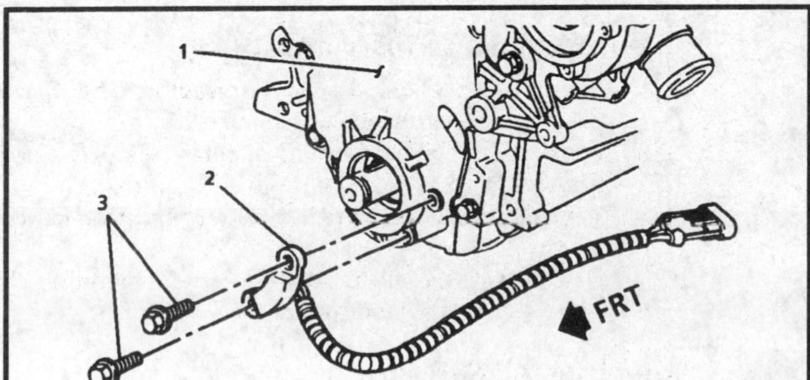
1
2
3
FRT

1	FRONT ENGINE COVER
2	24x CRANKSHAFT POSITION SENSOR ASSEMBLY
3	BOLT (2) TORQUE 10 N·m (8 lb. ft.)

NS 15092

Figure C4-4 - 24X Crankshaft Position Sensor

CAMSHAFT POSITION SENSOR
Figure C4-6

↔ Remove or Disconnect

1. Negative battery cable.
2. Serpentine drive belt.
3. Refer to SECTION 3B1 for removal of power steering pump assembly.
4. Electrical connector.
5. Bolt (1).
6. Camshaft position sensor.

→← Install or Connect

1. Camshaft position sensor.
2. Bolt (1) torque to 10 N·m (8 lb. ft.).
3. Electrical connector.
4. Power steering pump.
5. Serpentine drive belt.
6. Negative battery cable.

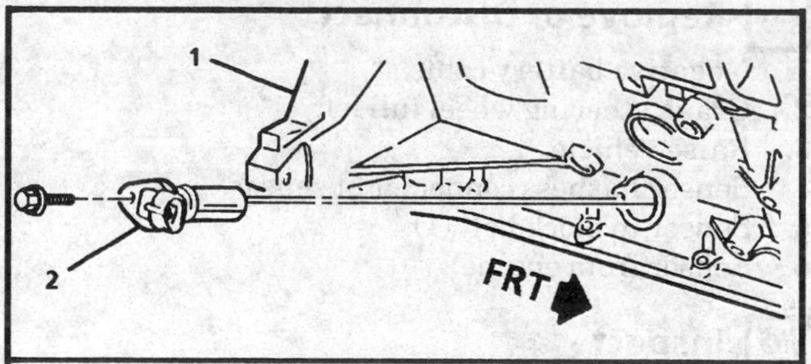
1
2
FRT

1 ENGINE BLOCK ASSEMBLY
2 CRANKSHAFT POSITION (CKP) SENSOR

MS 11914

Figure C4-5 - 3X Crankshaft Position Sensor

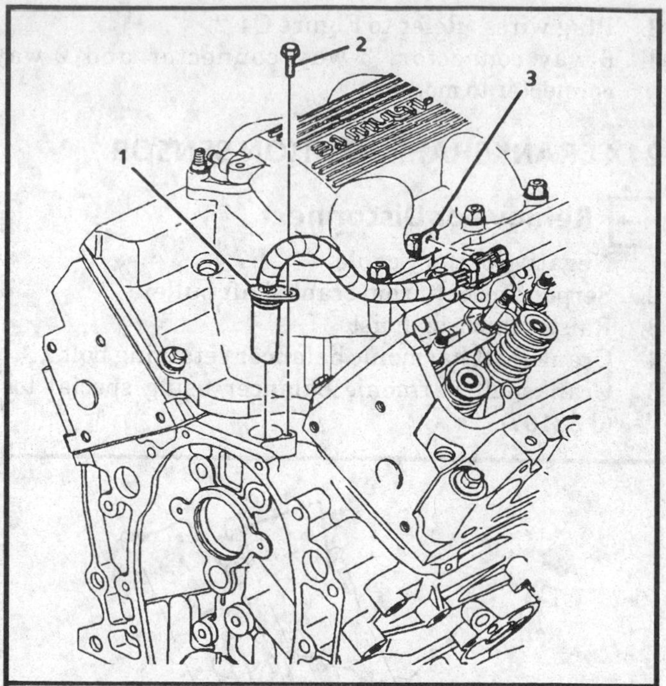
1
2
3

1 CAMSHAFT POSITION SENSOR
2 BOLT/SCREW - TORQUE TO 10 N·m (8 lb. ft.)
3 ENGINE BLOCK ASSEMBLY

PS 16966

Figure C4-6 - Camshaft Position Sensor

BLANK

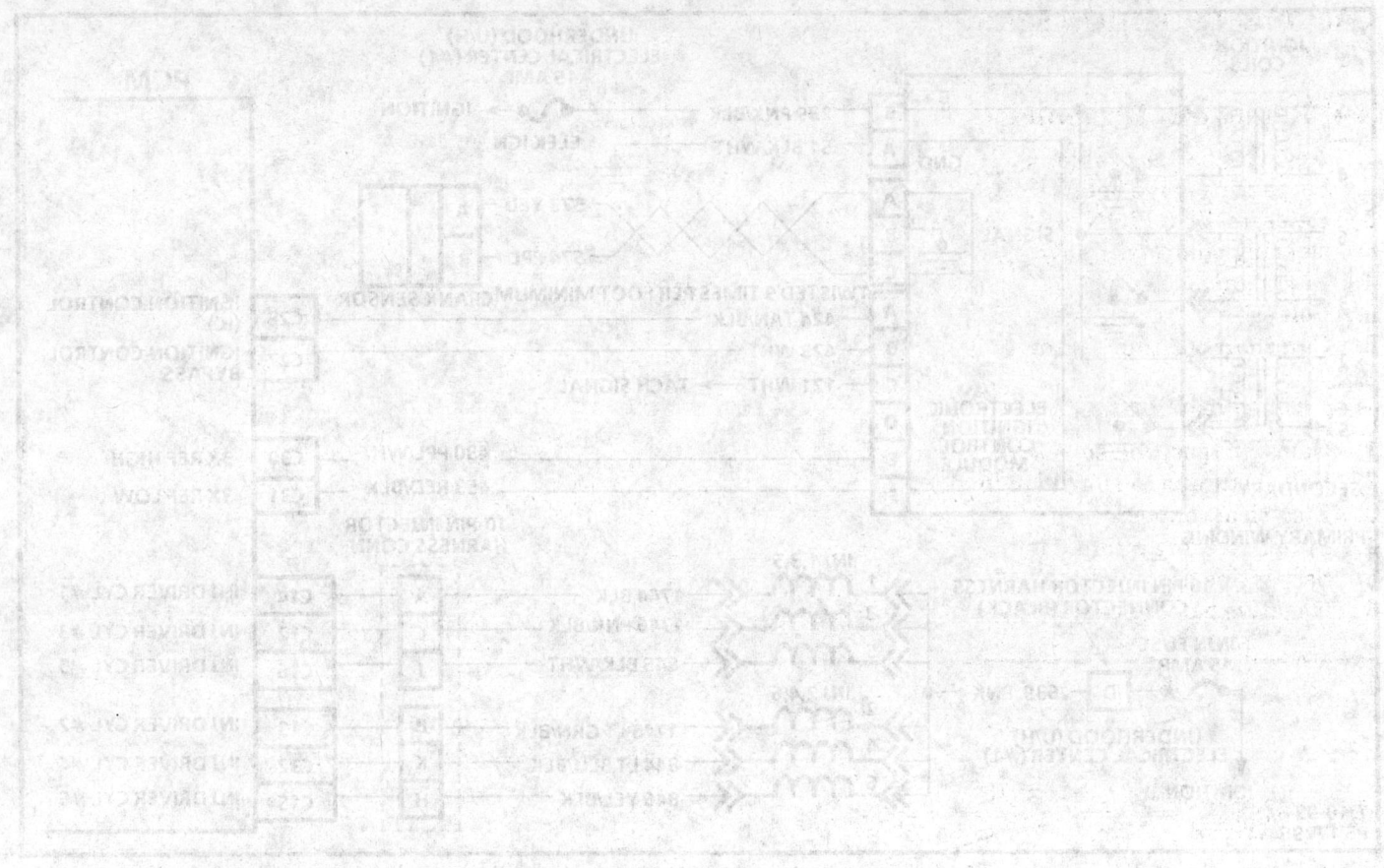

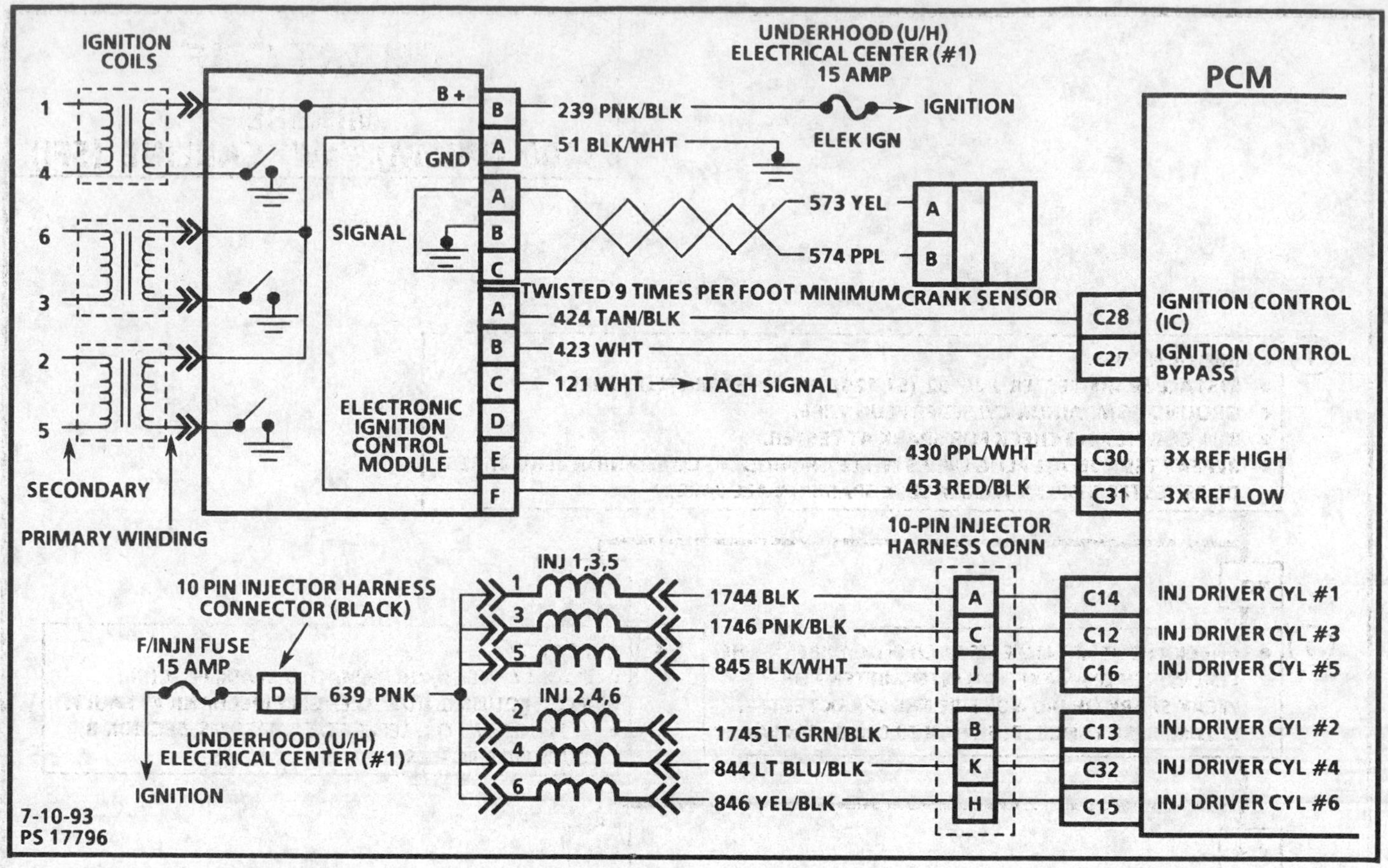
IGNITION COILS
UNDERHOOD (U/H) ELECTRICAL CENTER (#1) 15 AMP
PCM
B+
239 PNK/BLK
IGNITION
51 BLK/WHT
ELEK IGN
GND
SIGNAL
573 YEL
574 PPL
TWISTED 9 TIMES PER FOOT MINIMUM
CRANK SENSOR
424 TAN/BLK
423 WHT
121 WHT → TACH SIGNAL
IGNITION CONTROL (IC)
IGNITION CONTROL BYPASS
ELECTRONIC IGNITION CONTROL MODULE
430 PPL/WHT
453 RED/BLK
3X REF HIGH
3X REF LOW
SECONDARY
PRIMARY WINDING
10-PIN INJECTOR HARNESS CONN
INJ 1,3,5
10 PIN INJECTOR HARNESS CONNECTOR (BLACK)
1744 BLK
1746 PNK/BLK
845 BLK/WHT
INJ DRIVER CYL #1
INJ DRIVER CYL #3
INJ DRIVER CYL #5
F/INJN FUSE 15 AMP
639 PNK
INJ 2,4,6
UNDERHOOD (U/H) ELECTRICAL CENTER (#1)
IGNITION
1745 LT GRN/BLK
844 LT BLU/BLK
846 YEL/BLK
INJ DRIVER CYL #2
INJ DRIVER CYL #4
INJ DRIVER CYL #6
C28
C27
C30
C31
C14
C12
C16
C13
C32
C15
7-10-93
PS 17796

CHART C-4F

MISFIRE
3100 (VIN M) "W" CARLINE (SFI)

Circuit Description:

The Electronic Ignition (EI) system uses a waste spark method of distribution. In this type of system, the electronic ignition control module triggers the #1/4 coil pair resulting in both #1 and #4 spark plugs firing at the same time. #1 cylinder is on the compression stroke at the same time #4 is on the exhaust stroke, resulting in a lower energy requirement to fire #4 spark plug. This leaves the remainder of the high voltage to be used to fire #1 spark plug. On this application, the low resolution 3X crankshaft position sensor is mounted to the engine block and protrudes through the block to within approximately .050" of the crankshaft reluctor. Since the reluctor is a machined portion of the crankshaft and the sensor is mounted in a fixed position on the block, timing adjustments are neither possible or necessary.

Chart Test Description: Number(s) below refer to circled number(s) on the diagnostic chart.

1. Checks for voltage output of ignition system. The companion cylinder spark plug cable in the circuit must be connected to a good ground to create a good spark and avoid over stressing the coil. Test each spark plug cable with the engine idling (the ignition must be cycled "OFF" when moving the ST-125 tester to a different spark plug cable).
   - Keep disconnected spark plug leads away from sensors and other electronic components.
   - Move quickly through this test. Don't leave any spark plug lead disconnected for longer than 15 seconds.
   - Let the engine run normally for 30 seconds between tests to avoid an excessive buildup of fuel.
2. If the spark tester fires on all wires, the ignition system, with the exception of the spark plugs, may be considered in good working order. If the spark plugs show no evidence of wear, damage or fouling, an engine mechanical fault should be suspected. Refer to "Cuts Out, Misses," in "Symptoms," Section "6E3-B".
3. Plug wires should be inspected for cuts or abrasions leading to shorts to ground or other components. This would cause a weak or absent spark yet the resistance valve when measured may be correct.
4. If carbon tracking is evident replace coil and be sure plug wires relating to that coil are clean and tight. Excessive wire resistance or faulty connections could have caused the coil to be damaged.
5. If the no spark condition follows the suspected coil, that coil is faulty. Otherwise, the electronic ignition control module is the cause of no spark. This test could also be performed by substituting a known good coil for the one causing the no spark condition.

CHART C-4F

MISFIRE
3100 (VIN M) "W" CARLINE (SFI)

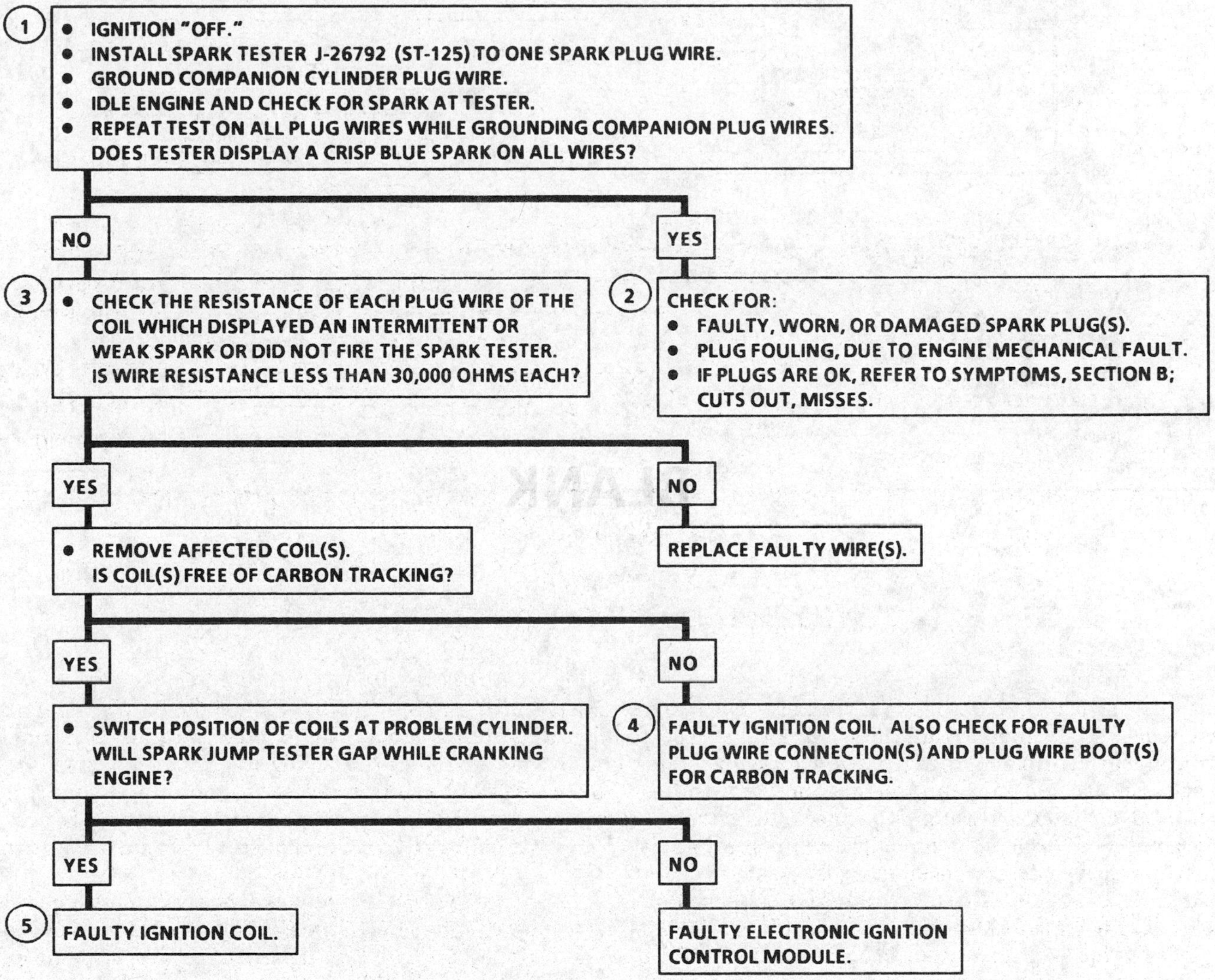
1
• IGNITION "OFF."
• INSTALL SPARK TESTER J-26792 (ST-125) TO ONE SPARK PLUG WIRE.
• GROUND COMPANION CYLINDER PLUG WIRE.
• IDLE ENGINE AND CHECK FOR SPARK AT TESTER.
• REPEAT TEST ON ALL PLUG WIRES WHILE GROUNDING COMPANION PLUG WIRES.
DOES TESTER DISPLAY A CRISP BLUE SPARK ON ALL WIRES?
NO
YES
3
• CHECK THE RESISTANCE OF EACH PLUG WIRE OF THE COIL WHICH DISPLAYED AN INTERMITTENT OR WEAK SPARK OR DID NOT FIRE THE SPARK TESTER.
IS WIRE RESISTANCE LESS THAN 30,000 OHMS EACH?
2
CHECK FOR:
• FAULTY, WORN, OR DAMAGED SPARK PLUG(S).
• PLUG FOULING, DUE TO ENGINE MECHANICAL FAULT.
• IF PLUGS ARE OK, REFER TO SYMPTOMS, SECTION B; CUTS OUT, MISSES.
YES
NO
• REMOVE AFFECTED COIL(S).
IS COIL(S) FREE OF CARBON TRACKING?
REPLACE FAULTY WIRE(S).
YES
NO
• SWITCH POSITION OF COILS AT PROBLEM CYLINDER.
WILL SPARK JUMP TESTER GAP WHILE CRANKING ENGINE?
4
FAULTY IGNITION COIL. ALSO CHECK FOR FAULTY PLUG WIRE CONNECTION(S) AND PLUG WIRE BOOT(S) FOR CARBON TRACKING.
YES
NO
5
FAULTY IGNITION COIL.
FAULTY ELECTRONIC IGNITION CONTROL MODULE.

"AFTER REPAIRS," CONFIRM "CLOSED LOOP" OPERATION AND NO MIL (SERVICE ENGINE SOON).

9-30-92
NS 15849

BLANK

SECTION C5

KNOCK SENSOR (KS) SYSTEM

CONTENTS

GENERAL DESCRIPTION

PURPOSE

Varying octane levels in today's gasoline can cause detonation in high performance engines. Detonation is sometimes called spark knock.

To control spark knock, a Knock Sensor (KS) system is used. This system is designed to retard spark timing up to 10° to reduce spark knock in the engine. This allows the engine to use maximum spark advance to improve driveability and fuel economy.

OPERATION

The KS system has two major components:

- KS module (located in the PCM).
- Knock Sensor (KS).

The Knock Sensor (KS) detects abnormal vibration (spark knocking) in the engine. The sensor is mounted in the engine block near the cylinders. The sensor produces an AC output voltage which increases with the severity of the knock. This signal voltage inputs to the PCM. The PCM in conjunction with the KS module then adjust the Ignition Control (IC) timing to reduce spark knocking.

DIAGNOSIS

The Tech 1 scan tool will have two positions to check for diagnosing this circuit. The knock signal is used to monitor the input signal from the knock sensor. This position should display "Yes" whenever detonation is being detected. Knock retard is the indication of how much the PCM is retarding the spark.

DTC 43 is designed to diagnose the knock sensor and wiring so problems encountered with this circuit should set a DTC. However, if no DTC 43 was set but the KS system is suspected because detonation was the customer's complaint, refer to CHART C-5.

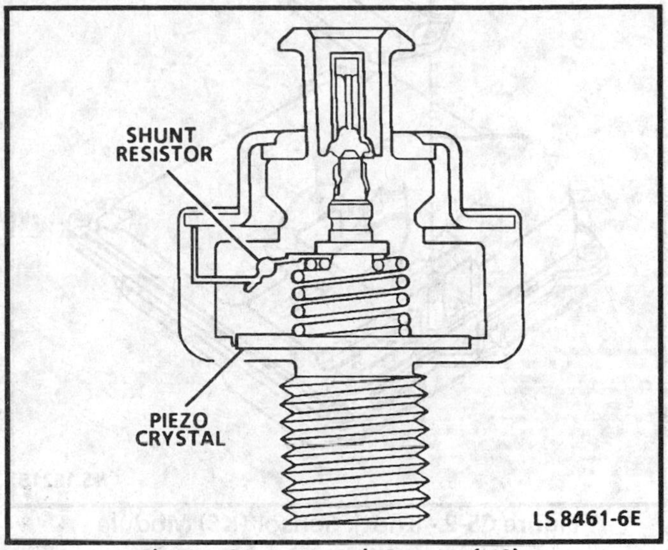
SHUNT RESISTOR
PIEZO CRYSTAL
LS 8461-6E

Figure C5-1 - Knock Sensor (KS)

ON-VEHICLE SERVICE

KNOCK SENSOR

Remove or Disconnect

1. Negative battery cable.
2. Raise vehicle.
3. KS wiring harness connector from knock sensor.
4. Knock sensor from engine block.

Install or Connect

1. Knock sensor into engine block. Be sure threads are clean. Do not over tighten knock sensor. Over torquing could damage the sensor.

Tighten

- Tighten to 19 N·m (14 lb. ft.).

2. KS wiring harness connector to the knock sensor.
3. Lower vehicle.
4. Negative battery cable.

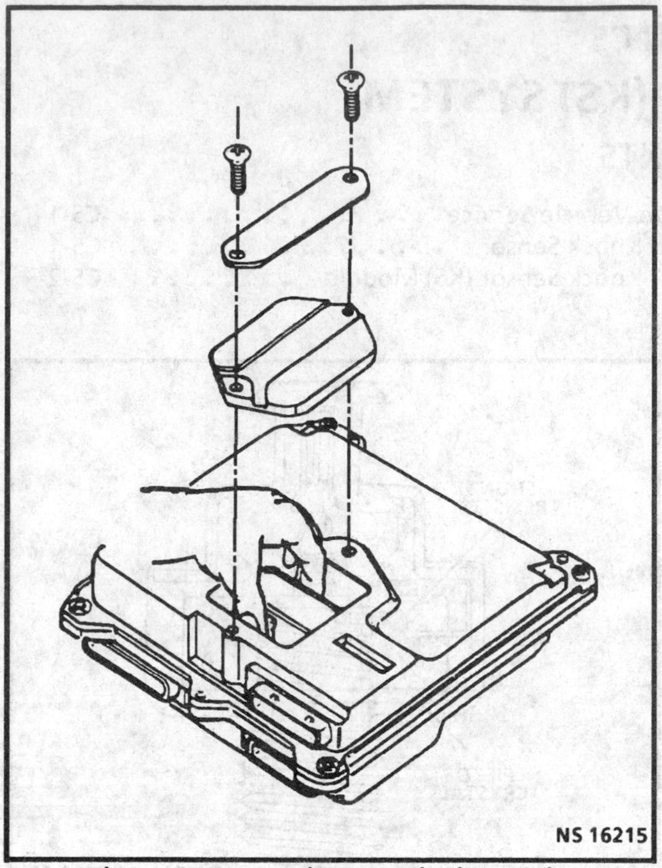
NS 16215
Figure C5-2 - Knock Sensor (KS) Module

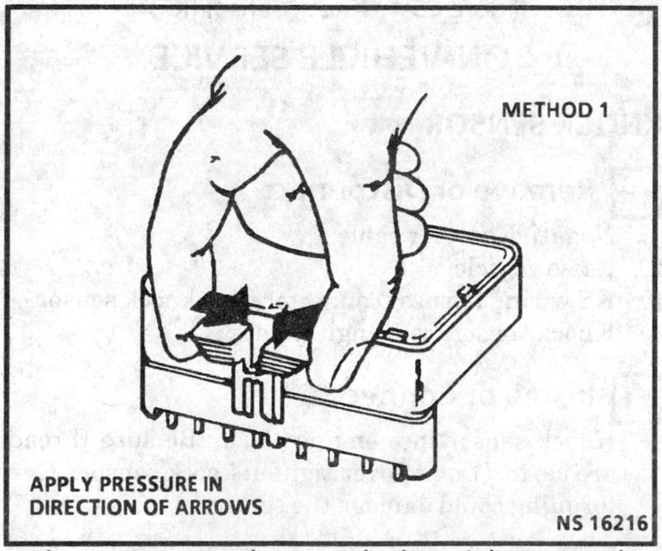
METHOD 1
APPLY PRESSURE IN
DIRECTION OF ARROWS
NS 16216
Figure C5-3 - Knock Sensor (KS) Module Removal

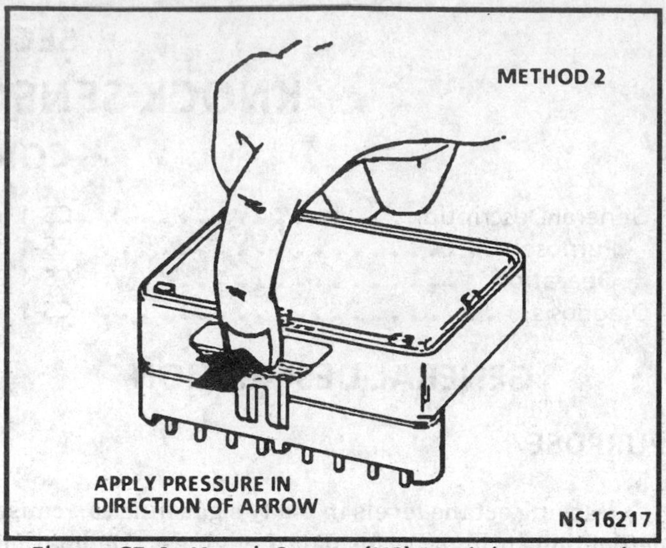
METHOD 2
APPLY PRESSURE IN
DIRECTION OF ARROW
NS 16217
Figure C5-4 - Knock Sensor (KS) Module Removal

KNOCK SENSOR (KS) MODULE

↔ Remove or Disconnect

1. Wiring harness from Powertrain Control Module (PCM).
2. Mounting bracket from PCM.
3. Access cover from PCM.

! Important

- DO NOT remove any other screws.

Remove of the plug-in knock sensor module can be accomplished by two methods as illustrated.

Method 1:

1. Apply two opposing forces on either side of the latch mechanism as shown below and pull unit up from the header. Reinstallation is accomplished by pushing the unit toward the header.

Method 2:

2. Apply force toward the plug-in knock sensor module with the thumb or forefinger with an opposing force on the opposite side of the module as shown below. Reinstallation is done as stated in Method 1.

BLANK

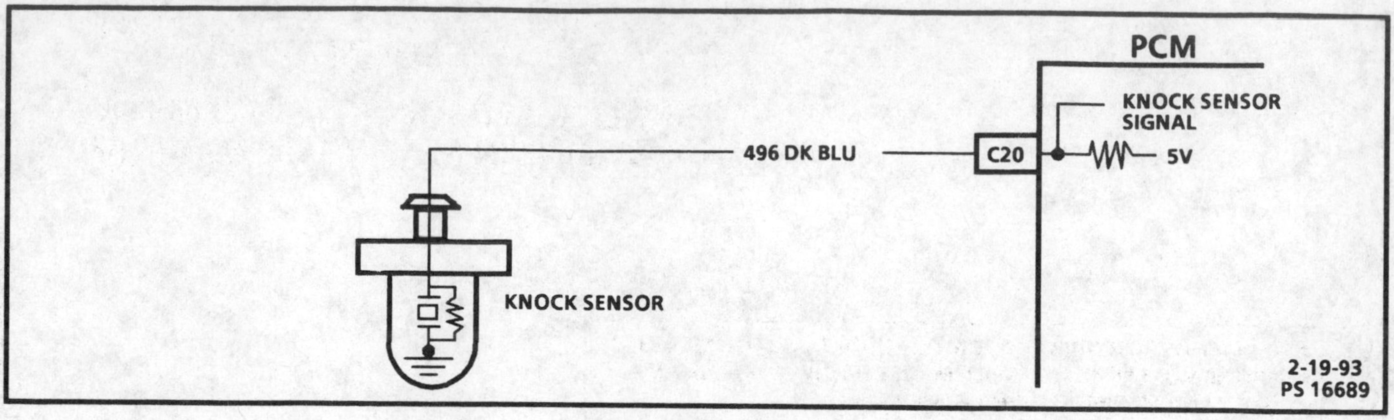
PCM
KNOCK SENSOR
SIGNAL
496 DK BLU
C20
5V
KNOCK SENSOR
2-19-93
PS 16689

CHART C-5

KNOCK SENSOR (KS) SYSTEM CHECK
3100 (VIN M) "W" CARLINE (SFI)

Circuit Description:

The Knock Sensor (KS) is used to detect engine detonation and the PCM will retard the ignition control timing based on the signal being received. The circuitry within the knock sensor causes the PCMs 5 volts to be pulled down so that under a no knock condition CKT 496 would measure about 2.5 volts. The knock sensor produces an AC signal which rides on the 2.5 volts DC voltage. The amplitude and frequency are dependent upon the knock level.

The PCM used with this engine contains a knock sensor module which contains the spark control logic. Spark timing is retarded by this circuit which reduces engine detonation.

The knock sensor module receives the signal on CKT 496, then commands the PCM to retard spark timing.

Chart Test Description: Number(s) below refer to circled number(s) on the diagnostic chart.

1. With engine idling, there should not be a knock signal present at the PCM, because detonation is not likely under a no load condition.
2. Tapping on the engine block should simulate a knock signal to determine if the sensor is capable of detecting detonation. If no knock is detected, try tapping on engine block closer to sensor before replacing sensor.
3. If the engine has an internal problem which is creating a knock, the knock sensor may be responding to the internal failure.
4. This tests the integrity of the Knock Sensor (KS) module.

Diagnostic Aids: While observing knock signal on the Tech 1 scan tool, there should be an indication that knock is present when detonation can be heard. Detonation is most likely to occur under high engine load conditions.

CHART C-5

KNOCK SENSOR (KS) SYSTEM CHECK 3100 (VIN M) "W" CARLINE (SFI)

1
- IF DIAGNOSTIC TROUBLE CODE (DTC) 43 IS SET, USE THE DTC CHART.
- ENGINE MUST BE IDLING AT NORMAL OPERATING TEMPERATURE.
- USE TECH 1 TO OBSERVE KNOCK SIGNAL.

IS KNOCK INDICATED?

NO → 2; YES → 3

2
- TAP ON ENGINE BLOCK WHILE OBSERVING KNOCK SIGNAL.
- TECH 1 SHOULD INDICATE KNOCK WHILE TAPPING ON ENGINE BLOCK.

DOES IT?

YES: SYSTEM IS OPERATING PROPERLY. REFER TO "DIAGNOSTIC AIDS" ON FACING PAGE.

NO → 4

3
IF AN ENGINE KNOCK CAN BE HEARD, REPAIR THE BASIC ENGINE PROBLEM. IF NO AUDIBLE KNOCK IS HEARD, FOLLOW THE STEPS:
- IGNITION "OFF."
- DISCONNECT KNOCK SENSOR.
- CONNECT DVM TO KNOCK SENSOR AND ENGINE GROUND.
- SET DVM ON 2 VOLT A.C. SCALE.
- IGNITION "ON," ENGINE "ON."

IS A SIGNAL INDICATED ON DVM?

NO: CHECK CKT 496 FOR BEING NEAR A SPARK PLUG WIRE OR A FAULTY PCM CONNECTION OR FAULTY PCM.

YES: REPLACE KNOCK SENSOR.

4
- IGNITION "OFF."
- DISCONNECT KNOCK SENSOR ELECTRICAL CONNECTOR.
- CONNECT DVM TO KNOCK SENSOR TERMINAL AND ENGINE GROUND.
- SET DVM ON 2 VOLT A.C. SCALE.
- IGNITION "ON," ENGINE "ON."
- TAP ON ENGINE BLOCK NEAR SENSOR.

IS A SIGNAL INDICATED ON DVM WHILE TAPPING ON ENGINE BLOCK?

YES: POOR CONNECTION AT KNOCK SENSOR HARNESS CONNECTOR OR KNOCK SENSOR MODULE NOT SEATED PROPERLY OR FAULTY KNOCK SENSOR MODULE.

NO: REPLACE KNOCK SENSOR.

"AFTER REPAIRS," CONFIRM "CLOSED LOOP" OPERATION AND NO MIL (SERVICE ENGINE SOON).

4-15-93
NS 16218

BLANK

SECTION C7

EXHAUST GAS RECIRCULATION (EGR) SYSTEM

CONTENTS

GENERAL DESCRIPTION

PURPOSE

The EGR system is used to lower NOx (Oxides of Nitrogen) emission levels caused by high combustion temperature. It does this by decreasing combustion temperature.

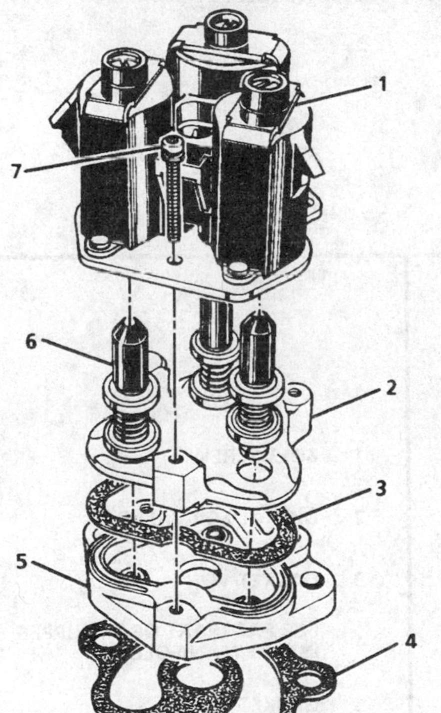

1
2
3
4
5
6
7

1 SOLENOID & MOUNTING PLATE ASSEMBLY
2 EGR BASE PLATE
3 EGR BASE GASKET
4 INSULATOR GASKET
5 EGR BASE
6 ARMATURE ASSEMBLY
7 SCREW ASSEMBLY

9P 0161-XV

Figure C7-1 - Digital EGR Valve (Typical)

The main element of the system is the digital EGR valve.

The digital EGR valve feeds small amounts of exhaust gas back into the intake manifold and then into the combustion chamber.

OPERATION

Digital EGR Valve

The digital (EGR) valve is designed to accurately supply EGR to an engine, independent of intake manifold vacuum. The valve controls EGR flow from the exhaust to the intake manifold through three orifices which increment in size to produce seven combinations. When a solenoid is energized, the armature, with attached shaft and swivel pintle is lifted, opening the orifice.

The flow accuracy is dependent on metering orifice size only, which results in improved control.

The swivel pintle feature insures good sealing of exhaust gas, reducing the need of critical assembly alignment. In addition, the effects of EGR leakage on idle quality are reduced because the shaft and seals are exposed to exhaust pressure instead of manifold vacuum. The shafts are sealed from the exhaust chamber by floating seals held in place by the seal spring. These springs also hold the upper seals that seal the armature cavity in the solenoids.

The solenoid coils are fastened together to maximize reliability and to seal the coils from the environment. The coils use a common power terminal with individual ground terminals.

The digital EGR valve is opened by the PCM QDR, grounding each respective solenoid circuit. This quad-driver activates the solenoid, raises the pintle, and allows exhaust gas flow into the intake manifold. The exhaust gas then moves with the air/fuel mixture into the combustion chamber. If too much exhaust gas enters, combustion will not occur. For this reason, very little exhaust gas is allowed to pass through the valve, with virtually none at idle. The EGR valve is usually open under the following conditions:

- Warm engine operation.
- Above idle speed.

EGR CONTROL

To regulate EGR flow, the PCM controls the EGR solenoids to vary the amount of EGR flow. The PCM uses information from the following sensors to regulate the solenoid:

- Engine Coolant Temperature (ECT) sensor.
- Throttle Position (TP) sensor.
- Manifold Absolute Pressure (MAP).

DIAGNOSIS

An EGR flow check diagnosis of the digital EGR system is covered in CHART C-7.

RESULTS OF INCORRECT EGR SYSTEM OPERATION

With too much EGR flow at idle, cruise, or cold operation, any of the following conditions may occur:

- Engine stalls after cold start.
- Engine stalls at idle after deceleration.
- Car surges during cruise.
- Rough idle.

Too little or no EGR flow allows combustion temperatures to get too high. This could cause:

- Spark knock (detonation).
- Engine overheating.
- Emission test failure.

DIGITAL EGR VALVE

Figure C7-2

↔ Remove or Disconnect

1. Negative battery cable.
2. Electrical connector at solenoid.
3. Two base to pad bolts/screws.
4. Digital EGR valve. Refer to Figure C7-2.

→← Install or Connect

1. EGR valve gasket and visually align holes.
2. Align bolts through EGR valve assembly and cast EGR pad of the upper intake manifold and into pipe assembly and torque to 25 N·m (18 lb. ft.).
3. Electrical connector at solenoid.
4. Negative battery cable.

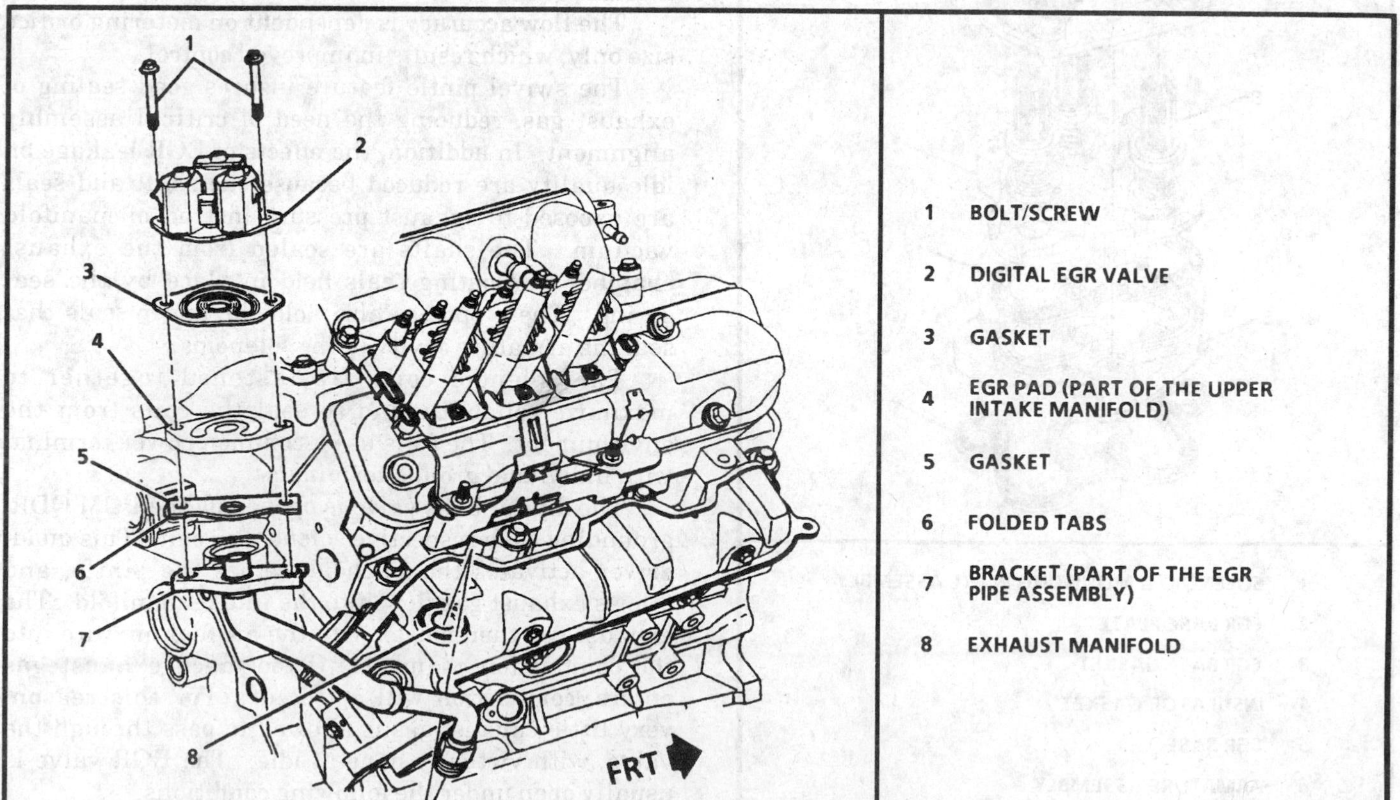
1
2
3
4
5
6
7
8
FRT
1 BOLT/SCREW
2 DIGITAL EGR VALVE
3 GASKET
4 EGR PAD (PART OF THE UPPER INTAKE MANIFOLD)
5 GASKET
6 FOLDED TABS
7 BRACKET (PART OF THE EGR PIPE ASSEMBLY)
8 EXHAUST MANIFOLD
PS 16967

Figure C7-2 - Digital EGR Valve Assembly

BLANK

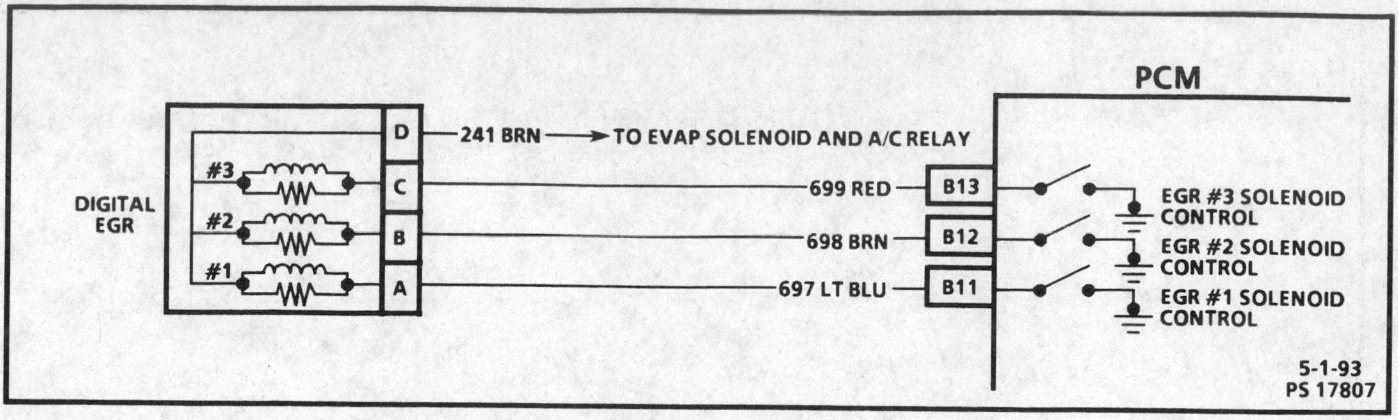
PCM
DIGITAL EGR
#3
#2
#1
D
C
B
A
241 BRN
TO EVAP SOLENOID AND A/C RELAY
699 RED
698 BRN
697 LT BLU
B13
B12
B11
EGR #3 SOLENOID CONTROL
EGR #2 SOLENOID CONTROL
EGR #1 SOLENOID CONTROL
5-1-93
PS 17807

CHART C-7

EXHAUST GAS RECIRCULATION (EGR) FLOW CHECK 3100 (VIN M) "W" CARLINE (SFI)

Circuit Description:

The digital (EGR) valve is designed to accurately supply EGR to an engine independent of intake manifold vacuum. The valve controls EGR flow from the exhaust to the intake manifold through three orifices which increment in size to produce seven combinations. When a solenoid is energized, the armature with attached shaft and swivel pintle is lifted, opening the orifice.

The flow accuracy is dependent on metering orifice size only, which results in improved control.

Important

- If the digital EGR valve shows signs of excessive heat check the exhaust system for blockage (possibly a plugged converter) using the procedure found on CHART B-1. If the exhaust system is restricted, repair the cause. One possibility is an injector which is open due to one of the following reasons:
  1. Stuck valve ball.
  2. Grounded driver circuit.
  3. Defective PCM.

  If any one of these conditions is found, the oil should be checked for fuel contamination.

Chart Test Description: Number(s) below refer to circled number(s) on the diagnostic chart.

1. DTC(s) should be diagnosed using appropriate chart before preparing a functional check.
2. This step activates each solenoid individually. As you energize #1 or #2 solenoid, the engine RPM should drop. #3 solenoid has the large port and may stall the engine when energized.

CHART C-7

EXHAUST GAS RECIRCULATION (EGR) FLOW CHECK 3100 (VIN M) "W" CARLINE (SFI)

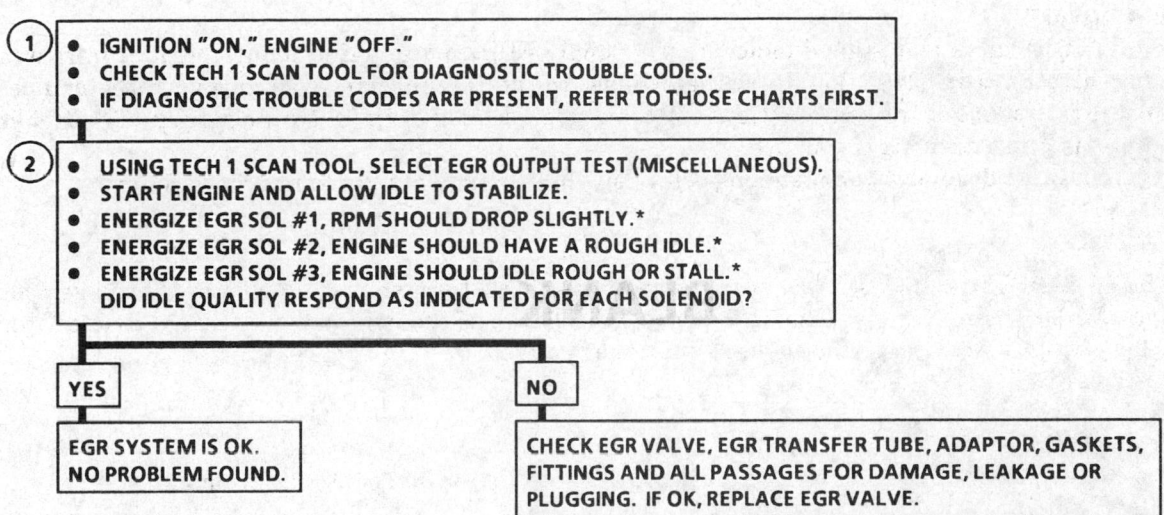

(1)
- IGNITION "ON," ENGINE "OFF."
- CHECK TECH 1 SCAN TOOL FOR DIAGNOSTIC TROUBLE CODES.
- IF DIAGNOSTIC TROUBLE CODES ARE PRESENT, REFER TO THOSE CHARTS FIRST.

(2)
- USING TECH 1 SCAN TOOL, SELECT EGR OUTPUT TEST (MISCELLANEOUS).
- START ENGINE AND ALLOW IDLE TO STABILIZE.
- ENERGIZE EGR SOL #1, RPM SHOULD DROP SLIGHTLY.*
- ENERGIZE EGR SOL #2, ENGINE SHOULD HAVE A ROUGH IDLE.*
- ENERGIZE EGR SOL #3, ENGINE SHOULD IDLE ROUGH OR STALL.*

DID IDLE QUALITY RESPOND AS INDICATED FOR EACH SOLENOID?

YES

EGR SYSTEM IS OK.
NO PROBLEM FOUND.

NO

CHECK EGR VALVE, EGR TRANSFER TUBE, ADAPTOR, GASKETS, FITTINGS AND ALL PASSAGES FOR DAMAGE, LEAKAGE OR PLUGGING. IF OK, REPLACE EGR VALVE.

* THESE STEPS MUST BE DONE VERY QUICKLY, AS THE PCM WILL ADJUST THE IDLE AIR CONTROL VALVE TO CORRECT IDLE SPEED.

"AFTER REPAIRS," CONFIRM "CLOSED LOOP" OPERATION AND NO MIL (SERVICE ENGINE SOON).

4-15-93
NS 16236

BLANK

SECTION C8

TORQUE CONVERTER CLUTCH (TCC) AND SHIFT SOLENOID SYSTEM

CONTENTS

GENERAL DESCRIPTION

PURPOSE

The Torque Converter Clutch (TCC) system uses two PCM controlled solenoids for engagement; a Pulse Width Modulated (PWM) solenoid valve, and an apply solenoid valve in the automatic transaxle to couple the engine flywheel to the output shaft of the transaxle through the torque converter. This reduces the slippage losses in the converter, increasing fuel economy.

TCC OPERATION

For the torque converter clutch to apply two conditions must be met:

- Internal transaxle fluid pressure must be correct. For information on internal transaxle operation, refer to SECTION 7A. (Section 6E3 will cover only the electrical operation of the TCC system.)
- The PCM grounds switches internally to turn "ON" solenoids in the transaxle. This moves check balls, which will allow the torque converter clutch to apply, if the hydraulic pressure is correct as described above.

  The TCC "APPLY" solenoid controls the flow of transmission fluid to the TCC. The TCC Pulse Width Modulated (PWM) solenoid varies the hydraulic pressure at the converter clutch regulator valve to make locking and unlocking of TCC smoother.

The PCM controls the TCC apply and PWM solenoids after looking at several parameters:

- Vehicle Speed Sensor (VSS). Speed must be above a certain value before the clutch can apply.
- Engine Coolant Temperature (ECT) sensor. Engine must be warmed up before clutch can apply.

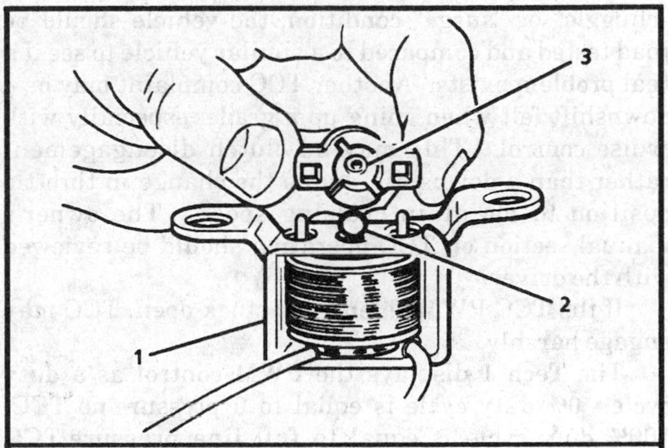

3
2
1

1	TCC SOLENOID	3	CHECK BALL SEAT
2	CHECK BALL		4S 0548-6E

Figure C8-1 - TCC Solenoid

- Throttle Position (TP) sensor. After the converter clutch applies, the PCM uses the information from the TP sensor to release the clutch when the vehicle is accelerating or decelerating at a certain rate.
- The TCC brake switch, which opens a 12 volt signal to the PCM when the brake pedal is depressed.

SHIFT SOLENOIDS OPERATION

The 4T60E transaxle uses two solenoids for shifting. Based on the N/V ratio (engine speed vs. vehicle speed) the PCM determines which gear the transaxle is operating in. The PCM uses this information along with other inputs such as TP sensor, RPM and air flow to determine the correct shift points for the transaxle.

TRANSMISSION FLUID TEMPERATURE (TFT) SENSOR

The transmission fluid temperature (TFT) sensor is a thermistor which changes resistance based on the temperature of the transaxle fluid.

A high transaxle temperature may cause the vehicle to operate in "Hot Mode."

While in "Hot Mode," shift points may be altered, 4th gear disabled, TCC forced "ON" in 2nd, and traction control disabled. A failure in the TFT sensor or associated wiring should cause a DTC 58 or 59 to set.

Results of Incorrect Operation

If the torque converter clutch does not apply, fuel economy may be lower than expected. If the vehicle speed sensor fails, the TCC will not apply.

The Torque Converter Clutch (TCC) system has different operating characteristics than an automatic transaxle without TCC. If the driver complains of a "chuggle" or "surge" condition, the vehicle should be road tested and compared to a similar vehicle to see if a real problem exists. Another TCC complaint may be a downshift felt when going up a grade, especially with cruise control. This may be clutch disengagement rather than a downshift, due to the change in throttle position to maintain cruising speed. The owner's manual section on TCC operation should be reviewed with the driver.

If the TCC PWM solenoid is stuck open, TCC may engage harshly.

The Tech 1 displays the PWM control as a duty cycle. 0% duty cycle is equal to 0 pressure/no TCC. 100% duty cycle is equal to full line pressure/TCC locked.

DIAGNOSIS

The diagnosis of the TCC system is covered in CHART C-8A. If the PCM detects a problem with the VSS signal, DTC 24 or 72 should set. In this case, refer to the appropriate chart.

If the PCM doesn't switch the TCC "ON" when it should while driving, but the TCC solenoid activates using the Tech 1 under "Misc. Test," then sensors such as engine coolant temperature, vehicle speed, and throttle position and TFT should be checked.

Diagnosis of the shift solenoids is covered in CHART C-8B.

If any of the following diagnostic trouble codes are set, TCC may not be allowed to engage and transaxle shifting may be incorrect. Repair any existing diagnostic trouble codes and then recheck TCC or shift control.

DTC	Description
16	System low voltage
21	Throttle Position (TP) sensor circuit high
22	Throttle Position (TP) sensor circuit low
24	Vehicle Speed Sensor (VSS) circuit no signal voltage
34	MAP sensor circuit (signal voltage low)
35	Idle speed error
58	TFT sensor circuit (high temp)
59	TFT sensor circuit (low temp)
72	VSS signal circuit error
79	Transmission fluid overtemp
80	Transmission component error
96	Trans system voltage low

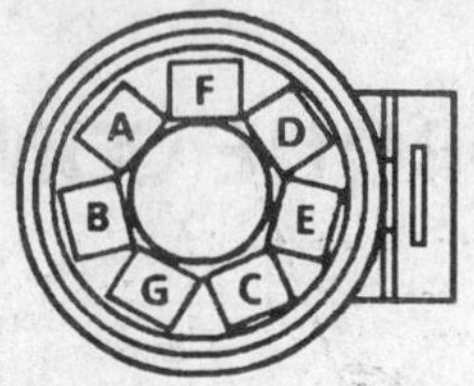
F
A
D
B
E
G
C

A - SHIFT SOLENOID A (CKT 1222)

B - SHIFT SOLENOID B (CKT 1223)

C - TCC PWM SOLENOID (CKT 418)

D - TCC APPLY SOLENOID (CKT 422)

E - B + SUPPLY TO SHIFT SOLENOIDS (CKT 441)

F - TRANSMISSION FLUID TEMPERATURE (TFT) SENSOR SIGNAL (CKT 1227)

G - TFT SENSOR GROUND (CKT 808)

PS 17140

Figure C8-2 - Transaxle Harness Connector

ON-VEHICLE SERVICE

- Refer to SECTION 7A for TCC solenoids, shift solenoids and vehicle speed sensor.

TCC BRAKE SWITCH

Remove or Disconnect

1. Drivers side hush panel.
2. Electrical connector(s).
3. Vacuum hose.
4. Switch assembly.

Inspect

- Switch retainer for cracks.

Install or Connect

1. New switch assembly into retainer.
   A. Hold brake pedal depressed while installing switch or valve. Switch should bottom on retainer. Note that audible clicks can be heard as the threaded portion of the switch is pushed through the retainer.
   B. Slowly pull brake pedal fully rearward against pedal stop moving switch or valve assembly rearward.
   C. Release brake pedal and pull back again to assure proper adjustment of switch or valve.
   D. Visually reinspect retainer for cracks.
2. Electrical connector(s).
3. Driver's side hush panel.

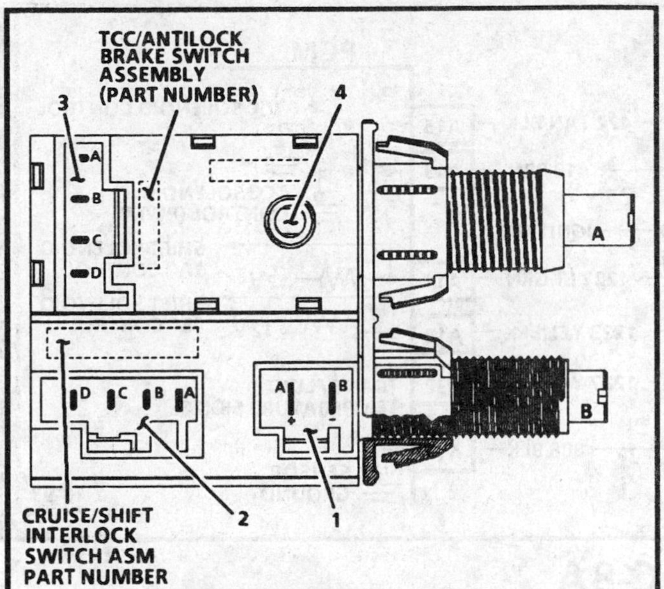
TCC/ANTILOCK
BRAKE SWITCH
ASSEMBLY
(PART NUMBER)
3
4
A
B
C
D
A
D
C
B
A
A
B
B
CRUISE/SHIFT
INTERLOCK
SWITCH ASM
PART NUMBER
2
1

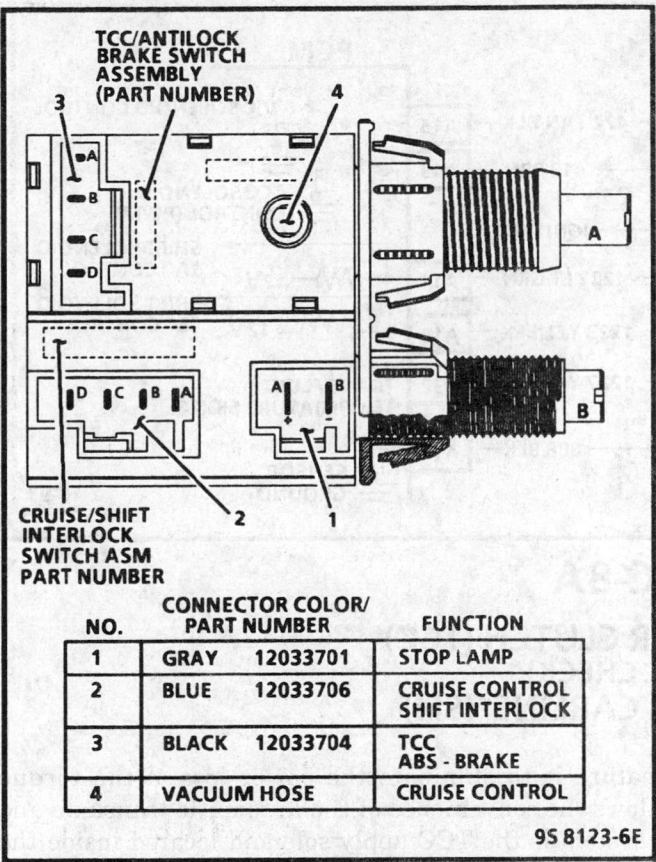

NO.	CONNECTOR COLOR/ PART NUMBER		FUNCTION
1	GRAY	12033701	STOP LAMP
2	BLUE	12033706	CRUISE CONTROL SHIFT INTERLOCK
3	BLACK	12033704	TCC ABS - BRAKE
4	VACUUM HOSE		CRUISE CONTROL

9S 8123-6E

Figure C8-3 - TCC Brake Switch (Part of Electronic Brake Control Pedal Switch Assembly)

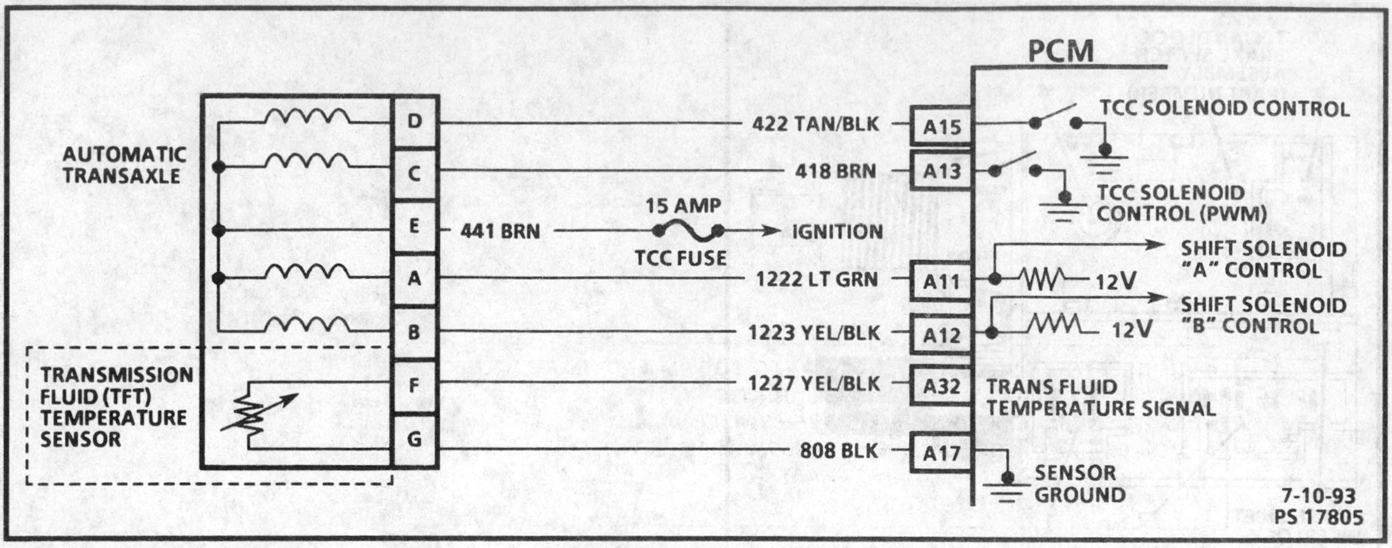
PCM
AUTOMATIC TRANSAXLE
D
C
E
A
B
F
G
422 TAN/BLK
418 BRN
441 BRN
15 AMP
TCC FUSE
IGNITION
1222 LT GRN
1223 YEL/BLK
1227 YEL/BLK
808 BLK
A15
A13
A11
A12
A32
A17
TCC SOLENOID CONTROL
TCC SOLENOID CONTROL (PWM)
SHIFT SOLENOID "A" CONTROL
SHIFT SOLENOID "B" CONTROL
12V
12V
TRANS FLUID TEMPERATURE SIGNAL
SENSOR GROUND
TRANSMISSION FLUID (TFT) TEMPERATURE SENSOR
7-10-93
PS 17805

CHART C-8A

TORQUE CONVERTER CLUTCH (TCC)
(FUNCTIONAL CHECK)
3100 (VIN M) "W" CARLINE (SFI)

Circuit Description:

The purpose of the Torque Converter Clutch (TCC) feature is to eliminate the power loss of the torque converter when the vehicle is in a cruise condition. This allows the convenience of the automatic transaxle and the fuel economy of a manual transaxle. The heart of the system is the TCC apply solenoid located inside the transaxle which is controlled by the PCM.

When the solenoid coil is activated ("ON"), the Torque Converter Clutch (TCC) is applied which results in a straight through mechanical coupling from the engine to the wheels. When the solenoid coil is deactivated ("OFF"), the Torque Converter Clutch (TCC) is released which allows the torque converter to operate in the conventional manner (fluid coupling between engine and transaxle).

The TCC PWM solenoid varies the hydraulic pressure at the converter clutch regulator valve to make locking and unlocking of TCC smoother. TCC will engage if:

- Engine warmed up.
- Vehicle speed above a calibrated value about 42 mph A/C "OFF," 46 mph A/C "ON" transaxle range switch in overdrive.
- Throttle position sensor output not changing, indicating a steady road speed.
- Brake switch closed.

Chart Test Description: Number(s) below refer to circled number(s) on the diagnostic chart.

1. Checks the functional operation of the TCC circuit.
2. Checks integrity of CKT 422.
3. Checks integrity of CKT 422 and the PCM's capability to turn the TCC apply solenoid "ON" and "OFF."

Diagnostic Aids: The Tech 1 only indicates when the PCM has commanded the TCC solenoid driver "ON" and does not confirm that the TCC has engaged. To determine if TCC is functioning properly, road test the vehicle. Engine RPM should decrease when the Tech 1 indicates the TCC driver has turned "ON."

CHART C-8A

TORQUE CONVERTER CLUTCH (TCC)
(FUNCTIONAL CHECK)
3100 (VIN M) "W" CARLINE (SFI)

(1)
- USING A TECH 1 SCAN TOOL, CHECK THE FOLLOWING AND CORRECT IF NECESSARY.
- COOLANT TEMPERATURE SHOULD BE GREATER THAN 65°C.
- TP SENSOR - BE SURE TP SENSOR SIGNAL IS NOT ERRATIC.
- VSS - BE SURE TECH 1 SCAN DISPLAYS VSS WITH DRIVE WHEELS TURNING. IF DTC 24 OR 72 IS PRESENT, SEE APPROPRIATE CHART.
- DTC 37, IF PRESENT, SEE DTC 37.

- MECHANICAL CHECKS, SUCH AS LINKAGE, OIL LEVEL, ETC., SHOULD BE PERFORMED PRIOR TO USING THIS CHART.
- RAISE DRIVE WHEELS.

NOTICE: DO NOT PERFORM THIS TEST WITHOUT SUPPORTING THE LOWER CONTROL ARMS SO THAT THE DRIVE AXLES ARE IN A NORMAL HORIZONTAL POSITION. RUNNING THE VEHICLE IN GEAR WITH THE WHEELS HANGING DOWN AT FULL TRAVEL MAY DAMAGE THE DRIVE AXLES.

- USING TECH 1 SCAN TOOL, ENTER MISC. OUTPUT TEST, TRANSAXLE/TCC SOLENOID.
- RUN VEHICLE IN DRIVE AT 45 TO 50 MPH.
- TURN TCC "ON" AND "OFF," OBSERVE RPM.
- RPM SHOULD DROP WHEN TCC IS TURNED "ON" AND A STEADY THROTTLE IS MAINTAINED. DOES IT DROP?

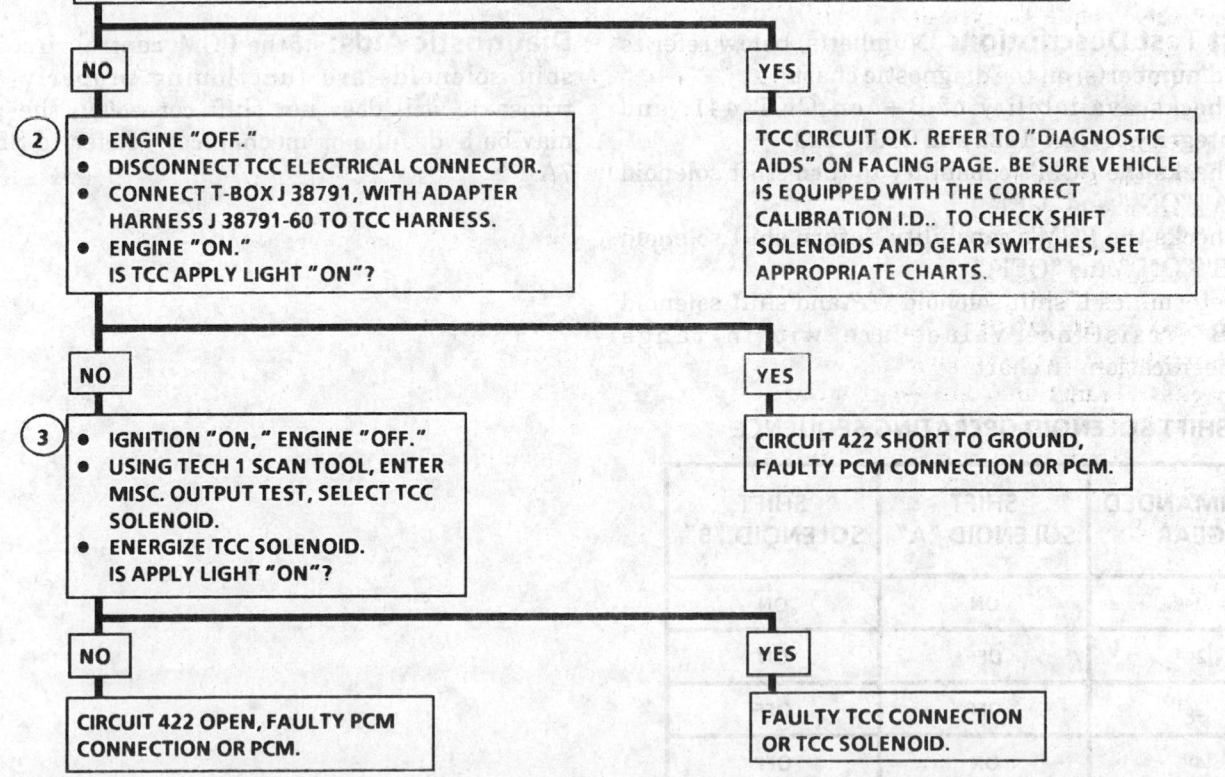

NO →

(2)
- ENGINE "OFF."
- DISCONNECT TCC ELECTRICAL CONNECTOR.
- CONNECT T-BOX J 38791, WITH ADAPTER HARNESS J 38791-60 TO TCC HARNESS.
- ENGINE "ON."

IS TCC APPLY LIGHT "ON"?

- **NO** →

(3)
- IGNITION "ON," ENGINE "OFF."
- USING TECH 1 SCAN TOOL, ENTER MISC. OUTPUT TEST, SELECT TCC SOLENOID.
- ENERGIZE TCC SOLENOID.

IS APPLY LIGHT "ON"?

- **NO** → CIRCUIT 422 OPEN, FAULTY PCM CONNECTION OR PCM.
- **YES** → FAULTY TCC CONNECTION OR TCC SOLENOID.

- **YES** (from 2) → CIRCUIT 422 SHORT TO GROUND, FAULTY PCM CONNECTION OR PCM.

YES (from first check) → TCC CIRCUIT OK. REFER TO "DIAGNOSTIC AIDS" ON FACING PAGE. BE SURE VEHICLE IS EQUIPPED WITH THE CORRECT CALIBRATION I.D.. TO CHECK SHIFT SOLENOIDS AND GEAR SWITCHES, SEE APPROPRIATE CHARTS.

"AFTER REPAIRS," CONFIRM "CLOSED LOOP" OPERATION AND NO MIL (SERVICE ENGINE SOON).

7-10-93
PS 17633

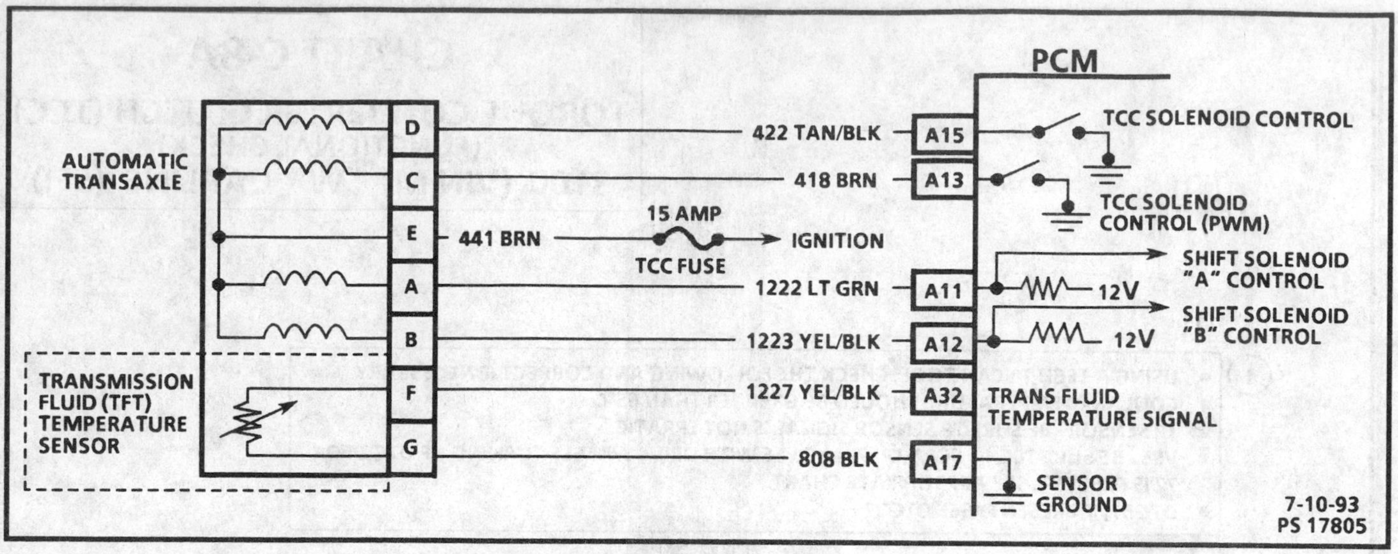

PCM
AUTOMATIC TRANSAXLE
D
C
E
A
B
F
G
422 TAN/BLK
A15
TCC SOLENOID CONTROL
418 BRN
A13
TCC SOLENOID CONTROL (PWM)
441 BRN
15 AMP
TCC FUSE
IGNITION
1222 LT GRN
A11
12V
SHIFT SOLENOID "A" CONTROL
1223 YEL/BLK
A12
12V
SHIFT SOLENOID "B" CONTROL
TRANSMISSION FLUID (TFT) TEMPERATURE SENSOR
1227 YEL/BLK
A32
TRANS FLUID TEMPERATURE SIGNAL
808 BLK
A17
SENSOR GROUND
7-10-93
PS 17805

CHART C-8B

4T60E TRANSAXLE SHIFT SOLENOID FUNCTIONAL CHECK 3100 (VIN M) "W" CARLINE (SFI)

Circuit Description:

The 4T60E transaxle uses shift solenoid "A" and shift solenoid "B" to control shifting. Refer to table below for solenoid operating sequence.

The PCM monitors the TP sensor and vehicle speed vs. engine speed to determine the correct shift points.

If the transaxle range switch indicates manual low position, the PCM will keep both solenoids "A" and "B" energized until 5400 RPM at which point the PCM will force a shift by de-energizing solenoid "A". Manual 2nd and manual 3rd are controlled hydraulically within the transaxle.

Chart Test Description: Number(s) below refer to circled number(s) on the diagnostic chart.

1. Checks availability of B+ on CKT 441, and integrity of CKT 1222 and CKT 1223.
2. Checks the PCM's capability to turn shift solenoid "A" "ON," and "OFF."
3. Checks the PCM's capability to turn shift solenoid "B" "ON," and "OFF."
4. Determines if shift solenoid "A" and shift solenoid "B" resistance values are within range specifications in chart.

SHIFT SOLENOID OPERATING SEQUENCE

COMMANDED GEAR	SHIFT SOLENOID "A"	SHIFT SOLENOID "B"
1st	ON	ON
2nd	OFF	ON
3rd	OFF	OFF
4th	ON	OFF

OFF = DE-ENERGIZED

Diagnostic Aids: If the PCM, control circuitry, and shift solenoids are functioning properly and the transaxle still does not shift correctly, the problem may be hydraulic or mechanical. Refer to SECTION 7A.

CHART C-8B

4T60E TRANSAXLE SHIFT SOLENOID FUNCTIONAL CHECK 3100 (VIN M) "W" CARLINE (SFI)

NOTICE: IF ANY DTC(s) ARE STORED IN THE PCM MEMORY, THEY MUST BE REPAIRED BEFORE DIAGNOSING THE TRANSAXLE CIRCUITRY.

SOLENOID RESISTANCE VS. TRANSAXLE TEMPERATURE TABLE

SOLENOID	RESISTANCE	
	AT 68°F (20°C)	AT 190°F (88°C)
SHIFT A & B	20-30Ω	23-50Ω
TCC APPLY	20-30Ω	23-50Ω
TCC PWM	10-15Ω	11-27Ω

* RESISTANCE VALUES INCREASE AT HIGHER TEMPERATURES AND DECREASE AT LOWER TEMPERATURES. TEST BOX MUST BE DISCONNECTED FROM CIGAR LIGHTER RECEPTACLE PRIOR TO MEASURING SOLENOID RESISTANCES.

- KEY "OFF," ENGINE "OFF."
- DISCONNECT TRANSAXLE HARNESS CONNECTOR.
- INSTALL TRANSAXLE TEST BOX J 38791 AND J 38791-60 ADAPTOR HARNESS AND TECH 1 SCAN TOOL.
- KEY "ON," ENGINE RUNNING.

(1)
- "GEAR SELECTOR" ROTARY SWITCH TO "NORMAL."
- OBSERVE "SHIFT A" AND "SHIFT B" INDICATOR LIGHTS ON TEST BOX.
- BOTH SHOULD BE "ON."

ARE THEY?

NO → IS THE LIGHT "OFF" ON BOTH?
- **YES** → REPAIR OPEN IN IGNITION FEED CKT 441 TO HARNESS TERMINAL "E".
- **NO** → CHECK FOR AN OPEN IN THE CIRCUIT WHICH DID NOT LIGHT, 1222 OR 1223. IF THE CIRCUIT IS OK, REPLACE PCM.

YES →

(2)
- UNDER MISC. TEST, SELECT TRANSMISSION CONTROL OUTPUT TEST AND CYCLE SHIFT A SOLENOID "OFF" WHILE OBSERVING "SHIFT A" INDICATOR ON TEST BOX.
- "SHIFT A" INDICATOR LIGHT SHOULD TURN "OFF" WHEN SHIFT A SOLENOID IS CYCLED "OFF."

DOES IT?

NO → CKT 1222 SHORTED TO GROUND OR FAULTY INTERNAL TRANSAXLE WIRING OR FAULTY PCM.

YES →

(3)
- CYCLE SHIFT B SOLENOID "OFF" WHILE OBSERVING "SHIFT B" INDICATOR ON TEST BOX.
- "SHIFT B" INDICATOR LIGHT SHOULD TURN "OFF" WHEN SHIFT B SOLENOID IS CYCLED "OFF."

DOES IT?

NO → CKT 1223 SHORTED TO GROUND OR FAULTY INTERNAL TRANSAXLE WIRING OR FAULTY PCM.

YES →

(4)
- IGNITION "OFF" FOR AT LEAST 10 SECONDS.
- WITH IGNITION "OFF," MEASURE RESISTANCE BETWEEN TEST POINTS FOR "IGN" AND "SHIFT A" ON TEST BOX.
- REFER TO TABLE FOR RESISTANCE SPECIFICATION.

IS RESISTANCE OK?

NO → FAULTY INTERNAL TRANSAXLE WIRING OR FAULTY SHIFT A SOLENOID.

YES →

- WITH IGNITION "OFF," MEASURE RESISTANCE BETWEEN TEST POINTS FOR "IGN" AND "SHIFT B" ON TEST BOX.
- REFER TO TABLE FOR RESISTANCE SPECIFICATION.

IS RESISTANCE OK?

NO → FAULTY INTERNAL TRANSAXLE WIRING OR FAULTY SHIFT B SOLENOID.

YES → NO TROUBLE FOUND - REFER TO "AUTOMATIC TRANSAXLE DIAGNOSIS" (SECTION 7A) FOR MECHANICAL AND HYDRAULIC DIAGNOSIS.

"AFTER REPAIRS," CONFIRM "CLOSED LOOP" OPERATION AND NO MIL (SERVICE ENGINE SOON).

7-10-93
PS 17634

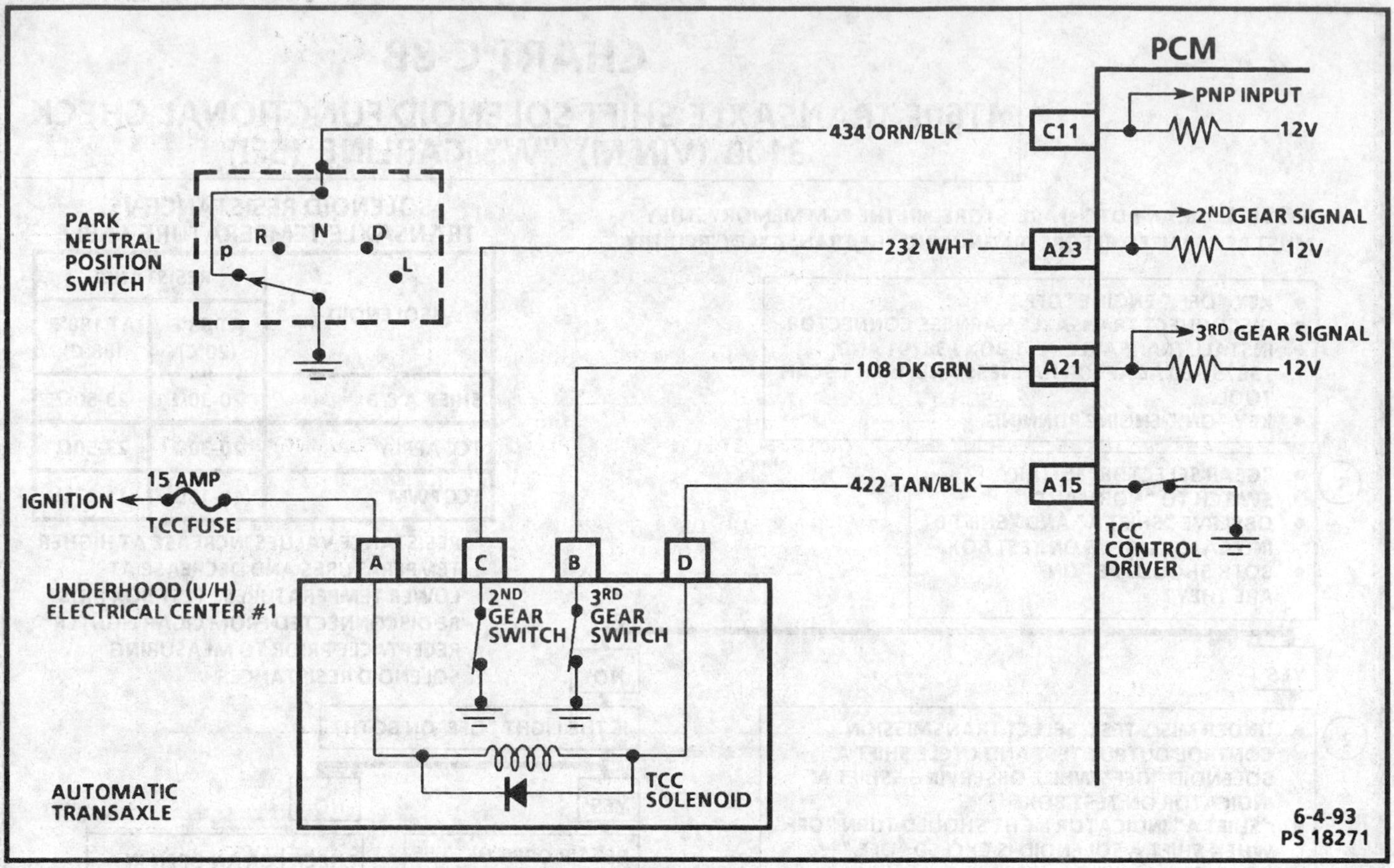
PCM
PNP INPUT
434 ORN/BLK
C11
12V
PARK NEUTRAL POSITION SWITCH
P
R
N
D
L
2ND GEAR SIGNAL
232 WHT
A23
12V
3RD GEAR SIGNAL
108 DK GRN
A21
12V
15 AMP
IGNITION
TCC FUSE
422 TAN/BLK
A15
TCC CONTROL DRIVER
A
C
B
D
UNDERHOOD (U/H) ELECTRICAL CENTER #1
2ND GEAR SWITCH
3RD GEAR SWITCH
AUTOMATIC TRANSAXLE
TCC SOLENOID
6-4-93
PS 18271

CHART C-8C (Page 1 of 2)

3T40 TORQUE CONVERTER CLUTCH (TCC)
(ELECTRICAL DIAGNOSIS)
3100 (VIN M) "W" CARLINE (SFI)

Circuit Description:

The purpose of the automatic transaxle torque converter clutch feature is to eliminate the power loss of the torque converter when the vehicle is in a cruise condition. This allows the convenience of the automatic transaxle and the fuel economy of a manual transaxle. The heart of the system is a solenoid located inside the automatic transaxle which is controlled by the PCM.

When the solenoid coil is activated ("ON"), the Torque Converter Clutch (TCC) is applied which results in straight through mechanical coupling from the engine to transaxle. When the transaxle solenoid is deactivated, the Torque Converter Clutch (TCC) is released, which allows the torque converter to operate in the conventional manner (fluidic coupling between engine and transaxle).

The TCC will engage on a warm engine under given road load in 2nd and 3rd gears.

TCC will engage when:

- Brake switch closed.
- Engine coolant temperature is greater than 65°C (149°F).
- Engine "Closed Loop" condition.
- Vehicle speed above a calibrated value (about 28 mph 45 km/h).
- Throttle position not changing, indicating a steady speed.

Chart Test Description:

Number(s) below refer to circled number(s) on the diagnostic chart.

1. This test checks the functional operation of the TCC circuit.
2. This test checks the TCC control driver in the PCM.
3. This test will confirm that there is battery voltage to terminal "A".
4. This test confirms that the PCM has the ability to turn the TCC "ON."

Diagnostic Aids:

A Tech 1 scan tool only indicates when the PCM has turned "ON" the TCC driver, and this does not confirm that the TCC has engaged. To determine if TCC is functioning properly, engine RPM should decrease when the Tech 1 scan tool indicates the TCC driver has turned "ON" during a road test. A thermostat that is stuck open or opens at too low a temperature may result in an inoperative TCC.

CHART C-8C

(Page 1 of 2)

3T40 TORQUE CONVERTER CLUTCH (TCC)
(ELECTRICAL DIAGNOSIS)
3100 (VIN M) "W" CARLINE (SFI)

- USING A TECH 1 SCAN TOOL, CHECK THE FOLLOWING AND CORRECT IF NECESSARY.
- ENGINE COOLANT TEMPERATURE SHOULD BE ABOVE 65°C.
- TP SENSOR - BE SURE TP SENSOR SIGNAL IS NOT ERRATIC.
- VSS - BE SURE TECH 1 SCAN TOOL DISPLAYS VSS WITH DRIVE WHEELS TURNING. IF DTC 24 IS PRESENT, REFER TO DTC 24 CHART.

(1)
- MECHANICAL CHECKS, SUCH AS LINKAGE, OIL LEVEL, ETC., SHOULD BE PERFORMED PRIOR TO USING THIS CHART.
- RAISE DRIVE WHEELS.

NOTICE: DO NOT PERFORM THIS TEST WITHOUT SUPPORTING THE LOWER CONTROL ARMS SO THAT THE DRIVE AXLES ARE IN A NORMAL HORIZONTAL POSITION. RUNNING THE VEHICLE IN GEAR WITH THE WHEELS HANGING DOWN AT FULL TRAVEL MAY DAMAGE THE DRIVE AXLES.

- INSTALL TECH 1 SCAN TOOL, OBSERVE TCC AND RPM.
- RUN VEHICLE IN DRIVE AT 15 TO 20 MPH.
- WHEN TCC ENGAGES, RPM SHOULD DROP WITH STEADY THROTTLE, ETC.
  DOES IT?

NO

(2)
- DISCONNECT TCC ELECTRICAL CONNECTOR.
- CONNECT TEST LIGHT BETWEEN TERMINALS "A" AND "D".

LIGHT "OFF"

(3)
- CONNECT TEST LIGHT FROM TERMINAL "A" TO GROUND.
- BULB SHOULD "LIGHT."
  DOES IT?

YES

(4)
- IGNITION "ON," ENGINE "OFF."
- WITH TECH 1 SCAN TOOL SELECT "OUTPUT TESTS," AND ENERGIZE "TCC SOLENOID."
- TEST LIGHT CONNECTED BETWEEN TCC ELECTRICAL CONNECTOR TERMINALS "A" AND "D". THE TEST LIGHT SHOULD LIGHT WHEN TCC SOLENOID IS ENERGIZED.
  DOES IT?

YES

FAULTY TCC CONNECTION OR TCC SOLENOID.

NO

OPEN IN CKT 422 OR FAULTY PCM CONNECTION OR FAULTY PCM.

NO (from step 3)

OPEN IN IGNITION FEED CIRCUIT, CKT 441 OR OPEN TCC FUSE.

LIGHT "ON" (from step 2)

CKT 422 SHORTED TO GROUND OR FAULTY PCM.

YES (from step 1)

TCC CIRCUIT OK. REFER TO "DIAGNOSTIC AIDS" ON FACING PAGE. BE SURE VEHICLE IS EQUIPPED WITH THE CORRECT PROM OR CALIBRATION. TO CHECK 2nd AND 3rd GEAR SWITCHES, REFER TO GEAR SWITCH DIAGNOSIS CHARTS.

"*AFTER REPAIRS*," CONFIRM "CLOSED LOOP" OPERATION AND NO MIL (SERVICE ENGINE SOON).

5-29-93
PS 18344

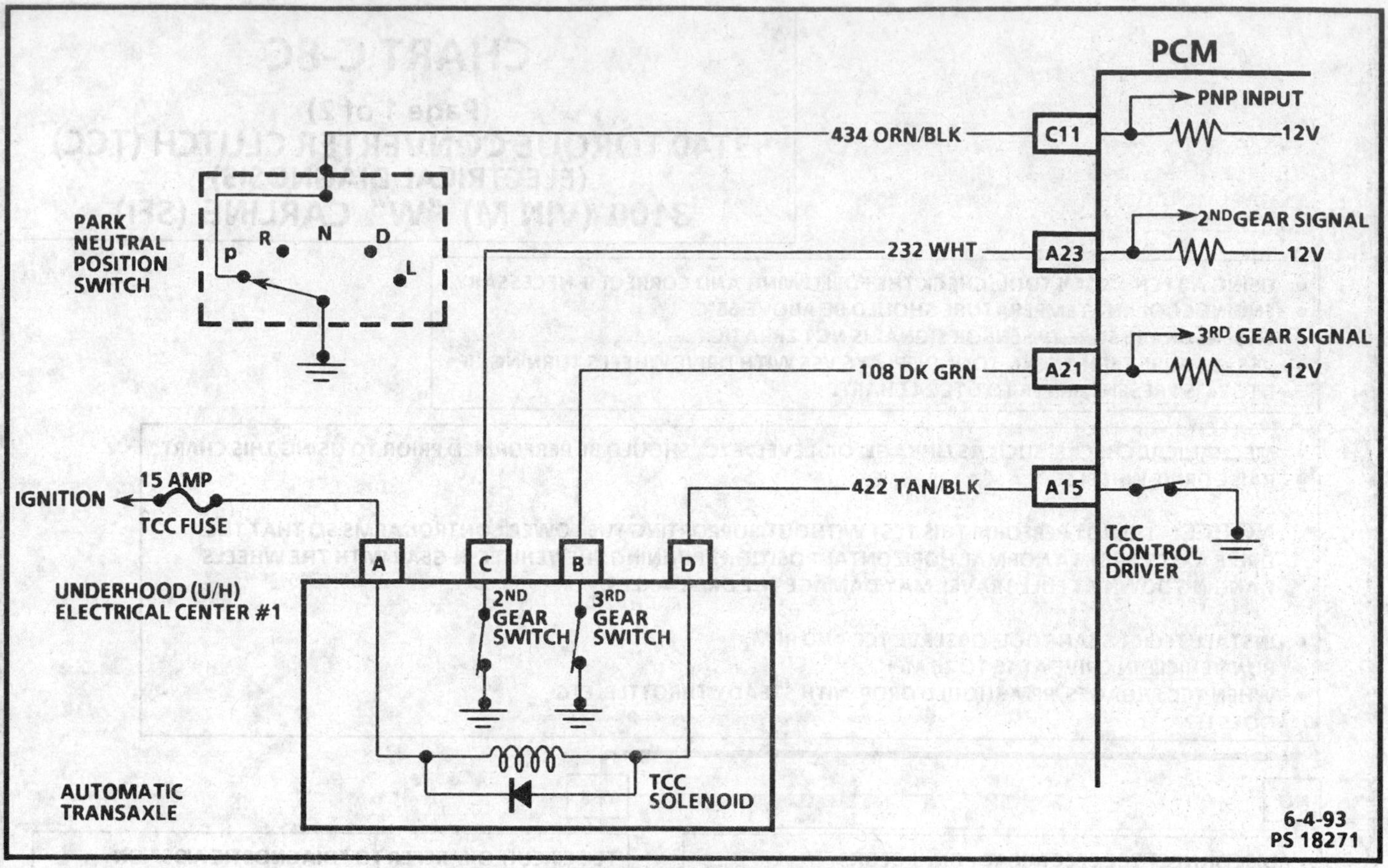
PCM
PNP INPUT
434 ORN/BLK
C11
12V
PARK
NEUTRAL
POSITION
SWITCH
P R N D L
2ND GEAR SIGNAL
232 WHT
A23
12V
3RD GEAR SIGNAL
108 DK GRN
A21
12V
15 AMP
IGNITION
TCC FUSE
422 TAN/BLK
A15
TCC
CONTROL
DRIVER
A C B D
UNDERHOOD (U/H)
ELECTRICAL CENTER #1
2ND
GEAR
SWITCH
3RD
GEAR
SWITCH
AUTOMATIC
TRANSAXLE
TCC
SOLENOID
6-4-93
PS 18271

CHART C-8C

(Page 2 of 2)

3T40 TORQUE CONVERTER CLUTCH (TCC)
(GEAR SWITCH DIAGNOSIS)
3100 (VIN M) "W" CARLINE (SFI)

Circuit Description:

The 2nd gear signal switch in this vehicle should be open in 2nd and 3rd gear. The PCM uses this 2nd gear signal to disengage the TCC when going into a downshift.

The 3rd gear switch should be open in 3rd gear.

Chart Test Description: Number(s) below refer to circled number(s) on the diagnostic chart.

1. Some scan tools display the state of these switches in different ways. Be familiar with the type of tool being used. Since both switches should be in the closed state during this test, the tool should read the same for either the 2nd or 3rd gear switch.
2. Determines whether the switch or signal circuit is open. The circuit can be checked for an open by measuring the voltage (with a voltmeter) at the TCC connector (should be about 12 volts).
3. Because the switch(es) should be grounded in this step, disconnecting the TCC connector should cause the Tech 1 scan tool switch state to change.
4. The switch state should change when the vehicle shifts into 2nd gear.

Diagnostic Aids: If vehicle is road tested because of a TCC related problem, be sure the switch states do not change while in 3rd gear because the TCC will disengage. If switches change state, carefully check wire routing and connections.

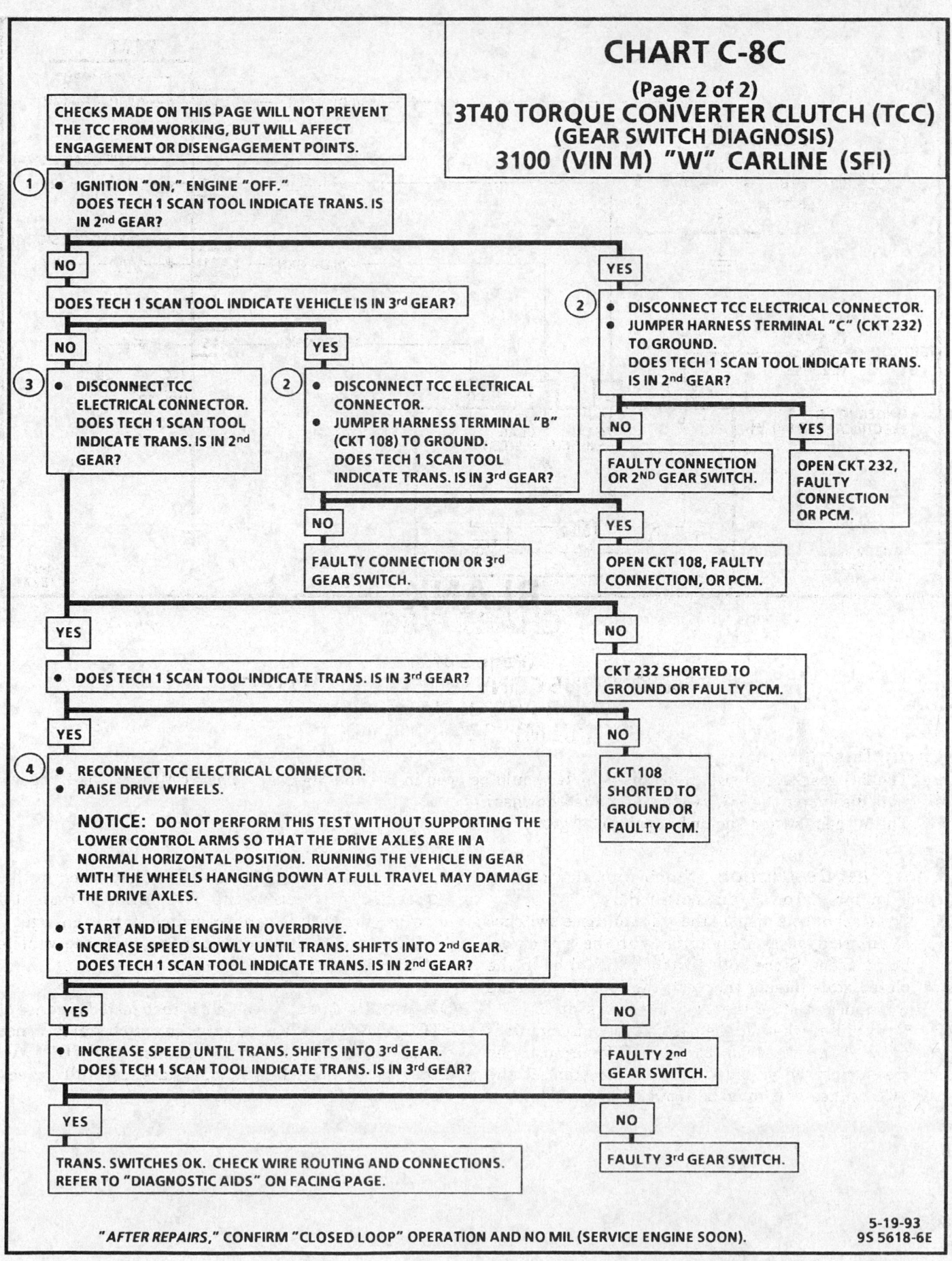

CHART C-8C

(Page 2 of 2)

3T40 TORQUE CONVERTER CLUTCH (TCC)
(GEAR SWITCH DIAGNOSIS)
3100 (VIN M) "W" CARLINE (SFI)

CHECKS MADE ON THIS PAGE WILL NOT PREVENT THE TCC FROM WORKING, BUT WILL AFFECT ENGAGEMENT OR DISENGAGEMENT POINTS.

(1)
- IGNITION "ON," ENGINE "OFF."
  DOES TECH 1 SCAN TOOL INDICATE TRANS. IS IN 2nd GEAR?

NO →

DOES TECH 1 SCAN TOOL INDICATE VEHICLE IS IN 3rd GEAR?

NO →

(3)
- DISCONNECT TCC ELECTRICAL CONNECTOR.
  DOES TECH 1 SCAN TOOL INDICATE TRANS. IS IN 2nd GEAR?

YES →

(2)
- DISCONNECT TCC ELECTRICAL CONNECTOR.
- JUMPER HARNESS TERMINAL "B" (CKT 108) TO GROUND.
  DOES TECH 1 SCAN TOOL INDICATE TRANS. IS IN 3rd GEAR?

NO → FAULTY CONNECTION OR 3rd GEAR SWITCH.

YES → OPEN CKT 108, FAULTY CONNECTION, OR PCM.

YES (from step 1) →

(2)
- DISCONNECT TCC ELECTRICAL CONNECTOR.
- JUMPER HARNESS TERMINAL "C" (CKT 232) TO GROUND.
  DOES TECH 1 SCAN TOOL INDICATE TRANS. IS IN 2nd GEAR?

NO → FAULTY CONNECTION OR 2ND GEAR SWITCH.

YES → OPEN CKT 232, FAULTY CONNECTION OR PCM.

(From step 3:)

YES →

- DOES TECH 1 SCAN TOOL INDICATE TRANS. IS IN 3rd GEAR?

NO (from step 3) → CKT 232 SHORTED TO GROUND OR FAULTY PCM.

YES →

(4)
- RECONNECT TCC ELECTRICAL CONNECTOR.
- RAISE DRIVE WHEELS.

NOTICE: DO NOT PERFORM THIS TEST WITHOUT SUPPORTING THE LOWER CONTROL ARMS SO THAT THE DRIVE AXLES ARE IN A NORMAL HORIZONTAL POSITION. RUNNING THE VEHICLE IN GEAR WITH THE WHEELS HANGING DOWN AT FULL TRAVEL MAY DAMAGE THE DRIVE AXLES.

- START AND IDLE ENGINE IN OVERDRIVE.
- INCREASE SPEED SLOWLY UNTIL TRANS. SHIFTS INTO 2nd GEAR.
  DOES TECH 1 SCAN TOOL INDICATE TRANS. IS IN 2nd GEAR?

NO (3rd gear check) → CKT 108 SHORTED TO GROUND OR FAULTY PCM.

YES →

- INCREASE SPEED UNTIL TRANS. SHIFTS INTO 3rd GEAR.
  DOES TECH 1 SCAN TOOL INDICATE TRANS. IS IN 3rd GEAR?

NO (2nd gear check) → FAULTY 2nd GEAR SWITCH.

YES → TRANS. SWITCHES OK. CHECK WIRE ROUTING AND CONNECTIONS. REFER TO "DIAGNOSTIC AIDS" ON FACING PAGE.

NO → FAULTY 3rd GEAR SWITCH.

"*AFTER REPAIRS*," CONFIRM "CLOSED LOOP" OPERATION AND NO MIL (SERVICE ENGINE SOON).

5-19-93
9S 5618-6E

BLANK

SECTION C10

AIR CONDITIONING COMPRESSOR CLUTCH CONTROL

CONTENTS

GENERAL DESCRIPTION

In order to improve idle quality, wide open throttle performance, and to protect the system, the A/C compressor clutch is controlled by the Powertrain Control Module (PCM).

The system uses a compressor with a variable displacement, referred to as the V-5 type compressor. The V-5 type meets A/C requirements without cycling. For a description of the system and an explanation of the components used, refer to SECTION 1B of the service manual.

OPERATION

This system consists of an A/C select switch, a control relay and the compressor clutch. An A/C refrigerant pressure sensor is also used to indicate high side refrigerant pressure to the PCM for use in controlling the engine cooling fans, A/C compressor clutch and Idle Air Control (IAC) valve. A fault in the A/C refrigerant pressure sensor circuit should set a Diagnostic Trouble Code (DTC) 66 or 70, which will cause the PCM to disable the compressor clutch.

The A/C refrigerant pressure sensor also provides low and high pressure protection for the system. If the A/C refrigerant pressure sensor signal exceeds about 4.7 volts, indicating pressure of about 429 psi, the compressor clutch is disabled. It will remain disabled until A/C refrigerant pressure sensor signal voltage falls below about 2.3 volts, indicating about 199 psi. This protects the system from over-pressure.

If the A/C refrigerant pressure sensor voltage is less than about .6 volt, indicating about 38 psi the compressor clutch is disabled. It will remain disabled until the A/C refrigerant pressure sensor voltage signal rises above about .7 volt, indicating about 47 psi. This protects the system in case of loss of refrigerant and prevents the compressor from operating in cold weather.

The A/C compressor clutch control relay is controlled by the PCM so that the PCM can increase idle speed before turning "ON" the clutch and can disable the clutch during WOT, high RPM, or during hot engine restarts. A/C is also disabled if coolant temperature exceeds 124°C.

Refer to CHART C-10 for specific wiring, circuit and calibration description.

DIAGNOSIS

CHART C-10 should be used for diagnosing the electrical portion of the A/C circuit. SECTION 1B should be used for diagnosing the refrigerant portion of the system.

The Tech 1 scan tool is used to diagnose the system, as it has the ability to display the A/C request input to the PCM, as well as displaying when the PCM has commanded the A/C clutch "ON," and the A/C refrigerant pressure sensor input.

ON-VEHICLE SERVICE

For removal and replacement procedures of A/C components, refer to SECTION 1B of the service manual.

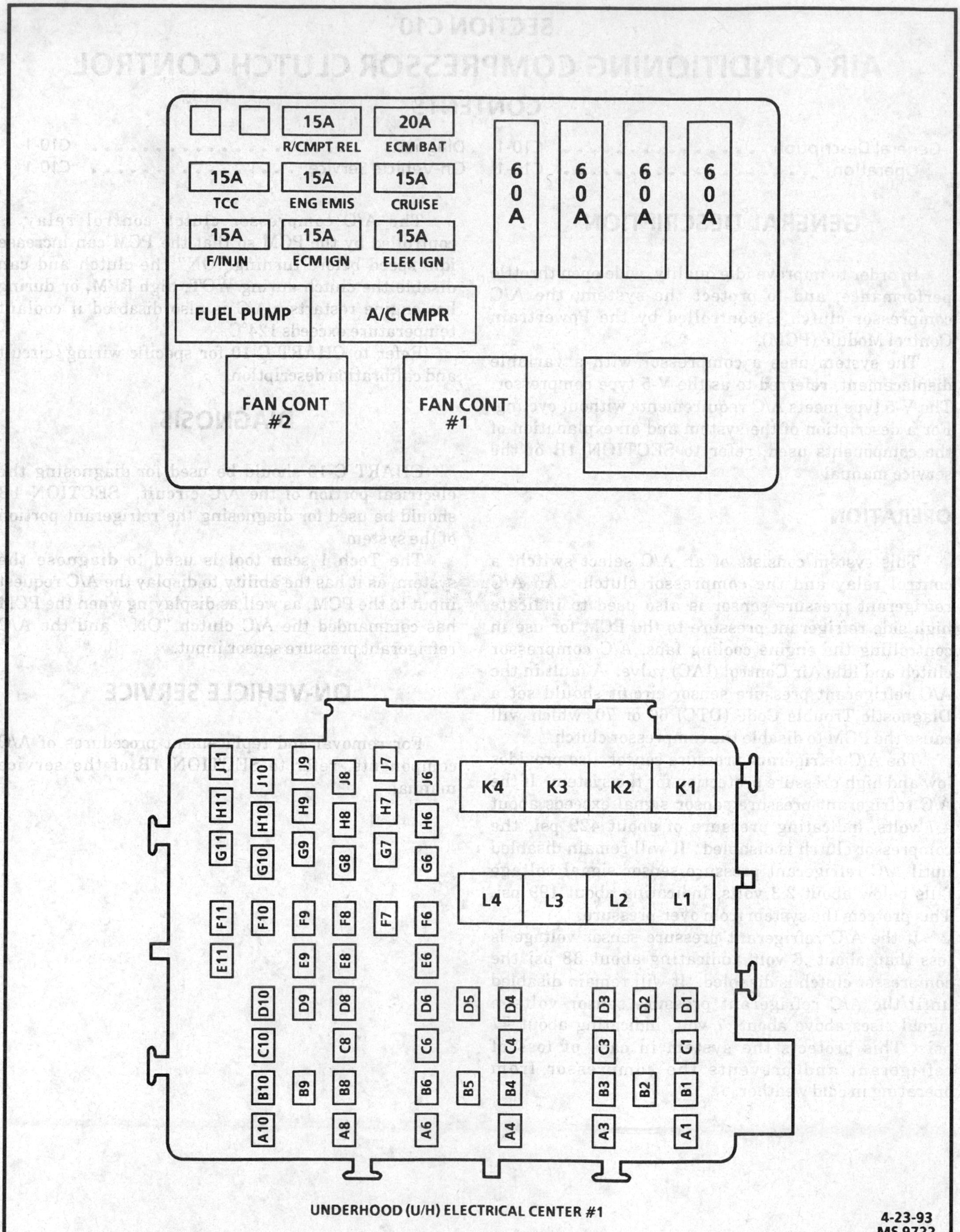
15A
R/CMPT REL
20A
ECM BAT
15A
TCC
15A
ENG EMIS
15A
CRUISE
15A
F/INJN
15A
ECM IGN
15A
ELEK IGN
60A
60A
60A
60A
FUEL PUMP
A/C CMPR
FAN CONT #2
FAN CONT #1
J11 J10 J9 J8 J7 J6
H11 H10 H9 H8 H7 H6
G11 G10 G9 G8 G7 G6
F11 F10 F9 F8 F7 F6
E11 E9 E8 E6
D10 D9 D8 D6 D5 D4 D3 D2 D1
C10 C8 C6 C4 C3 C1
B10 B9 B8 B6 B5 B4 B3 B2 B1
A10 A8 A6 A4 A3 A1
K4 K3 K2 K1
L4 L3 L2 L1
UNDERHOOD (U/H) ELECTRICAL CENTER #1
4-23-93
MS 9722

Figure C10-1 - Relays and Fuses

BLANK

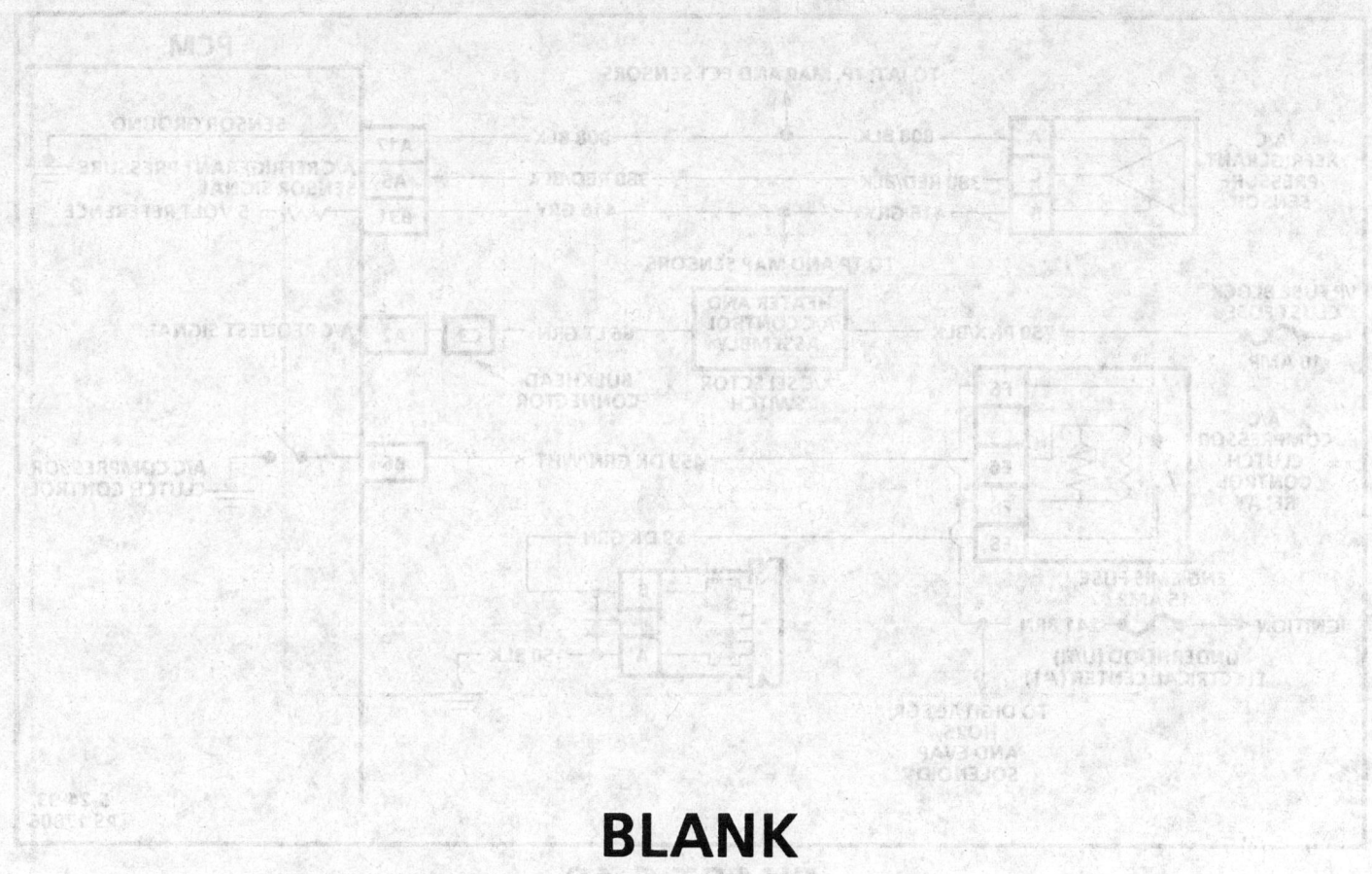

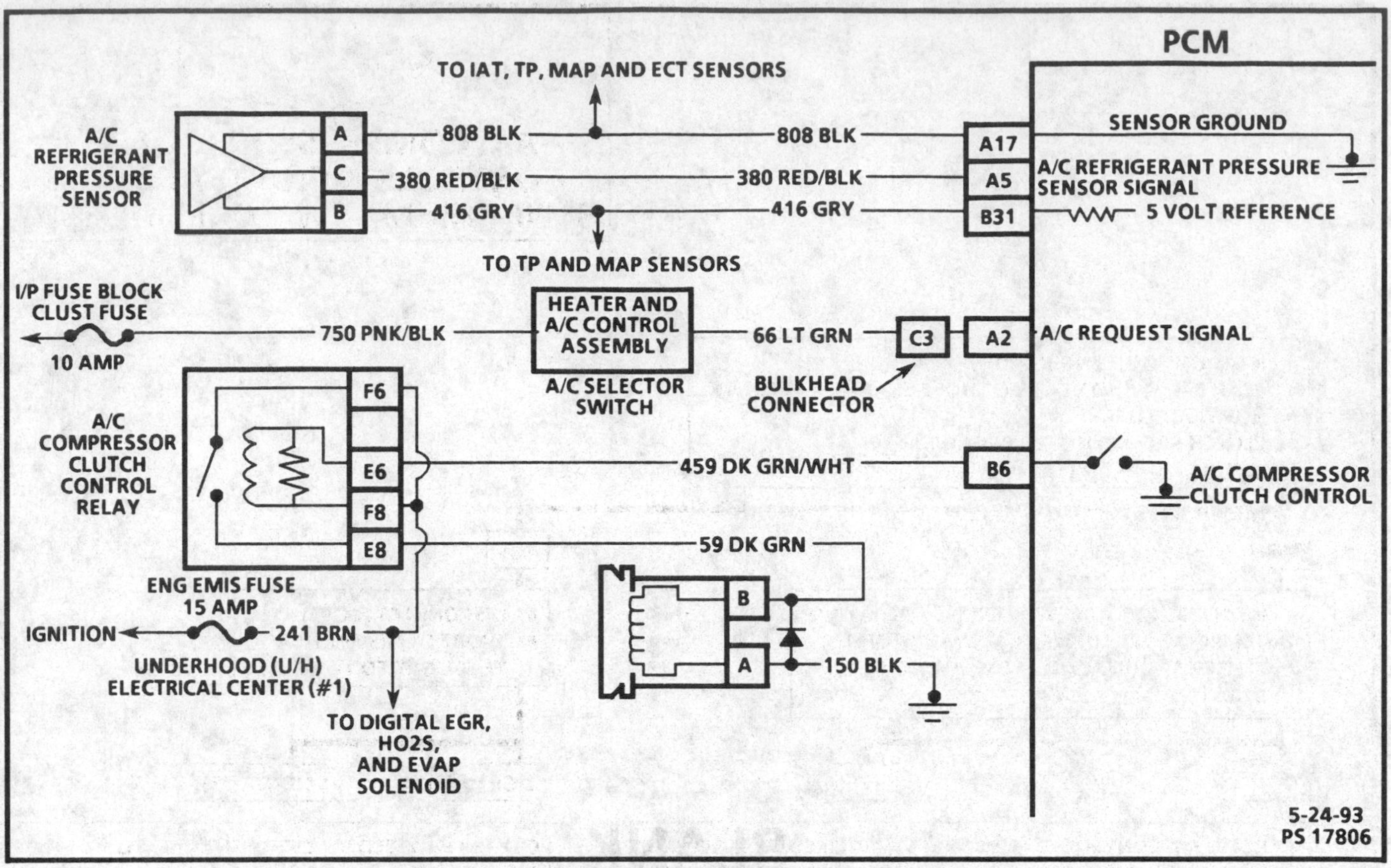

PCM
TO IAT, TP, MAP AND ECT SENSORS
A/C REFRIGERANT PRESSURE SENSOR
A
C
B
808 BLK
808 BLK
380 RED/BLK
380 RED/BLK
416 GRY
416 GRY
A17
A5
B31
SENSOR GROUND
A/C REFRIGERANT PRESSURE SENSOR SIGNAL
5 VOLT REFERENCE
TO TP AND MAP SENSORS
I/P FUSE BLOCK CLUST FUSE
10 AMP
750 PNK/BLK
HEATER AND A/C CONTROL ASSEMBLY
A/C SELECTOR SWITCH
66 LT GRN
C3
A2
A/C REQUEST SIGNAL
BULKHEAD CONNECTOR
A/C COMPRESSOR CLUTCH CONTROL RELAY
F6
E6
F8
E8
459 DK GRN/WHT
B6
A/C COMPRESSOR CLUTCH CONTROL
59 DK GRN
ENG EMIS FUSE 15 AMP
IGNITION
241 BRN
UNDERHOOD (U/H) ELECTRICAL CENTER (#1)
B
A
150 BLK
TO DIGITAL EGR, HO2S, AND EVAP SOLENOID
5-24-93
PS 17806

CHART C-10

(Page 1 of 2)
A/C COMPRESSOR CLUTCH CONTROL CIRCUIT DIAGNOSIS 3100 (VIN M) "W" CARLINE (SFI)

Circuit Description:

The A/C compressor clutch control relay is energized when the A/C is requested the Powertrain Control Module (PCM) provides a ground path through CKT 459. A/C compressor clutch is delayed about .3 second after A/C is requested. This will allow the IAC valve to adjust engine RPM for the additional load.

The PCM will disable the A/C compressor clutch control relay for any of the following reasons:

- Engine not running.
- Diagnostic Trouble Code (DTC) 66 or 70 is set, and fault is current.
- Engine coolant temperature is about 124°C (255 °F) or greater.
- A/C refrigerant pressure is about 429 psi or greater.
- A/C refrigerant pressure is about 38 psi or less.

If the PCM temporarily disabled the A/C compressor clutch, the clutch will be energized as follows:

- Coolant temperature drops below above 119°C (246°F).
- A/C refrigerant pressure drops below about 199 psi.
- A/C refrigerant pressure rises above 47 psi.
- DTC(s) are cleared from current status.

Chart Test Description: Number(s) below refer to circled number(s) on the diagnostic chart.

1. The PCM will only energize the A/C relay when the engine is running. This test will determine if the relay or CKT 459 is faulty.
2. Determines if the signal is reaching the PCM through CKT 66 from the A/C control panel. Signal should only be present when an A/C mode or defrost mode has been selected.

Diagnostic Aids: Be sure to consider branch circuits and splices to other components. If complaint is insufficient cooling, the problem may be caused by an inoperative cooling fan. Refer to CHART C-12 for cooling fan diagnosis. If fan operates correctly, refer to A/C diagnosis in SECTION 1B. A/C pressure outside of a range of 38 to 429 psi will cause the compressor clutch to be disabled by the PCM. Observe Tech 1 A/C refrigerant pressure for 2 minutes with engine idling and A/C "ON." If pressure goes out of range, refer to SECTION 1B to measure and diagnose. Tech 1 pressure should be within 20 psi of actual. If not, check for a circuit problem using Diagnostic Trouble Code (DTC) 66 or 70 chart or replace the A/C refrigerant pressure sensor.

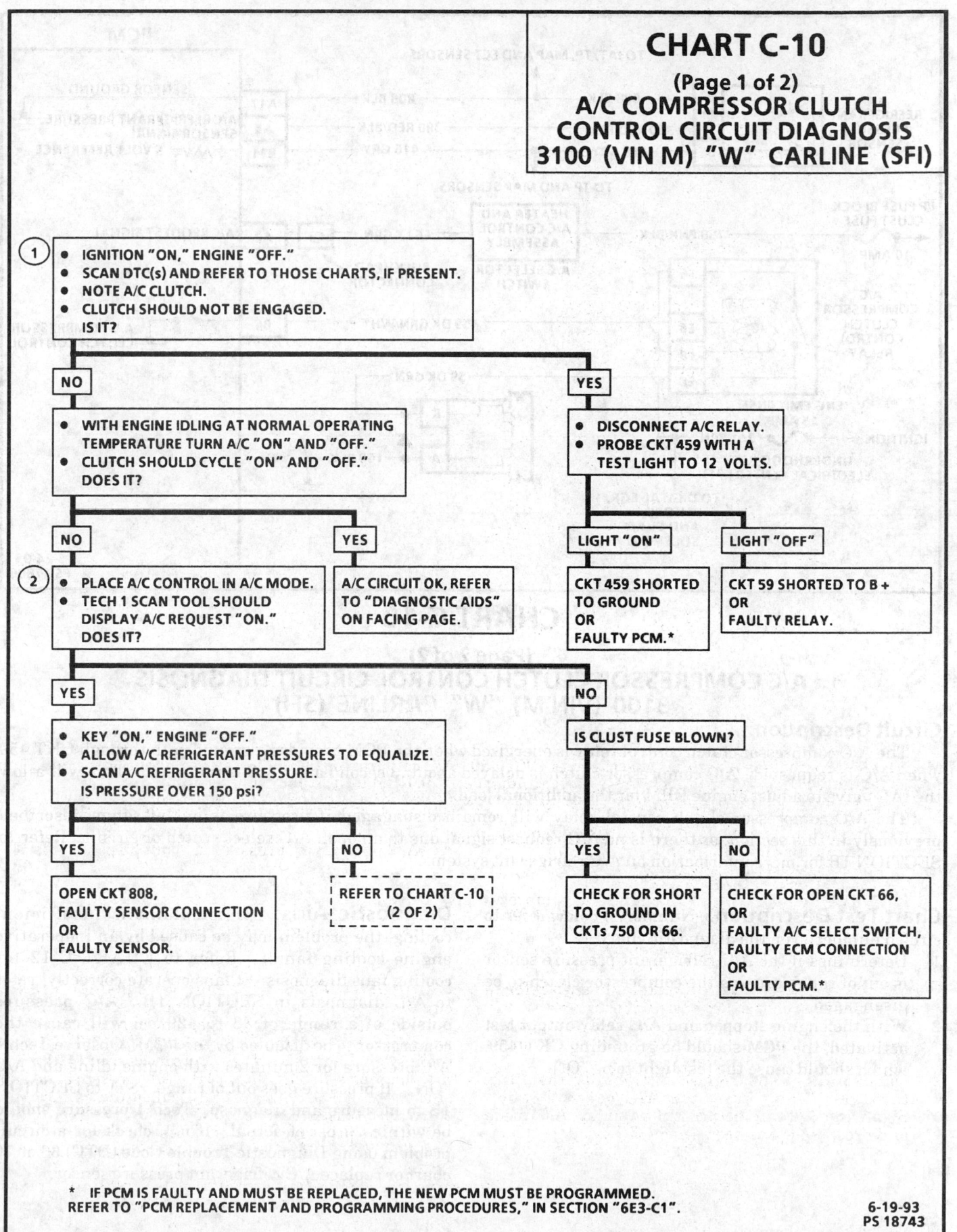

CHART C-10

(Page 1 of 2)
A/C COMPRESSOR CLUTCH CONTROL CIRCUIT DIAGNOSIS
3100 (VIN M) "W" CARLINE (SFI)

(1)
- IGNITION "ON," ENGINE "OFF."
- SCAN DTC(s) AND REFER TO THOSE CHARTS, IF PRESENT.
- NOTE A/C CLUTCH.
- CLUTCH SHOULD NOT BE ENGAGED.

IS IT?

- **NO**
  - WITH ENGINE IDLING AT NORMAL OPERATING TEMPERATURE TURN A/C "ON" AND "OFF."
  - CLUTCH SHOULD CYCLE "ON" AND "OFF."

  DOES IT?
  - **NO**
    - (2)
    - PLACE A/C CONTROL IN A/C MODE.
    - TECH 1 SCAN TOOL SHOULD DISPLAY A/C REQUEST "ON."

    DOES IT?
    - **YES**
      - KEY "ON," ENGINE "OFF."
      - ALLOW A/C REFRIGERANT PRESSURES TO EQUALIZE.
      - SCAN A/C REFRIGERANT PRESSURE.

      IS PRESSURE OVER 150 psi?
      - **YES** — OPEN CKT 808, FAULTY SENSOR CONNECTION OR FAULTY SENSOR.
      - **NO** — REFER TO CHART C-10 (2 OF 2)
    - **NO** — IS CLUST FUSE BLOWN?
      - **YES** — CHECK FOR SHORT TO GROUND IN CKTs 750 OR 66.
      - **NO** — CHECK FOR OPEN CKT 66, OR FAULTY A/C SELECT SWITCH, FAULTY ECM CONNECTION OR FAULTY PCM.*
  - **YES** — A/C CIRCUIT OK, REFER TO "DIAGNOSTIC AIDS" ON FACING PAGE.
- **YES**
  - DISCONNECT A/C RELAY.
  - PROBE CKT 459 WITH A TEST LIGHT TO 12 VOLTS.
  - **LIGHT "ON"** — CKT 459 SHORTED TO GROUND OR FAULTY PCM.*
  - **LIGHT "OFF"** — CKT 59 SHORTED TO B + OR FAULTY RELAY.

* IF PCM IS FAULTY AND MUST BE REPLACED, THE NEW PCM MUST BE PROGRAMMED. REFER TO "PCM REPLACEMENT AND PROGRAMMING PROCEDURES," IN SECTION "6E3-C1".

6-19-93
PS 18743

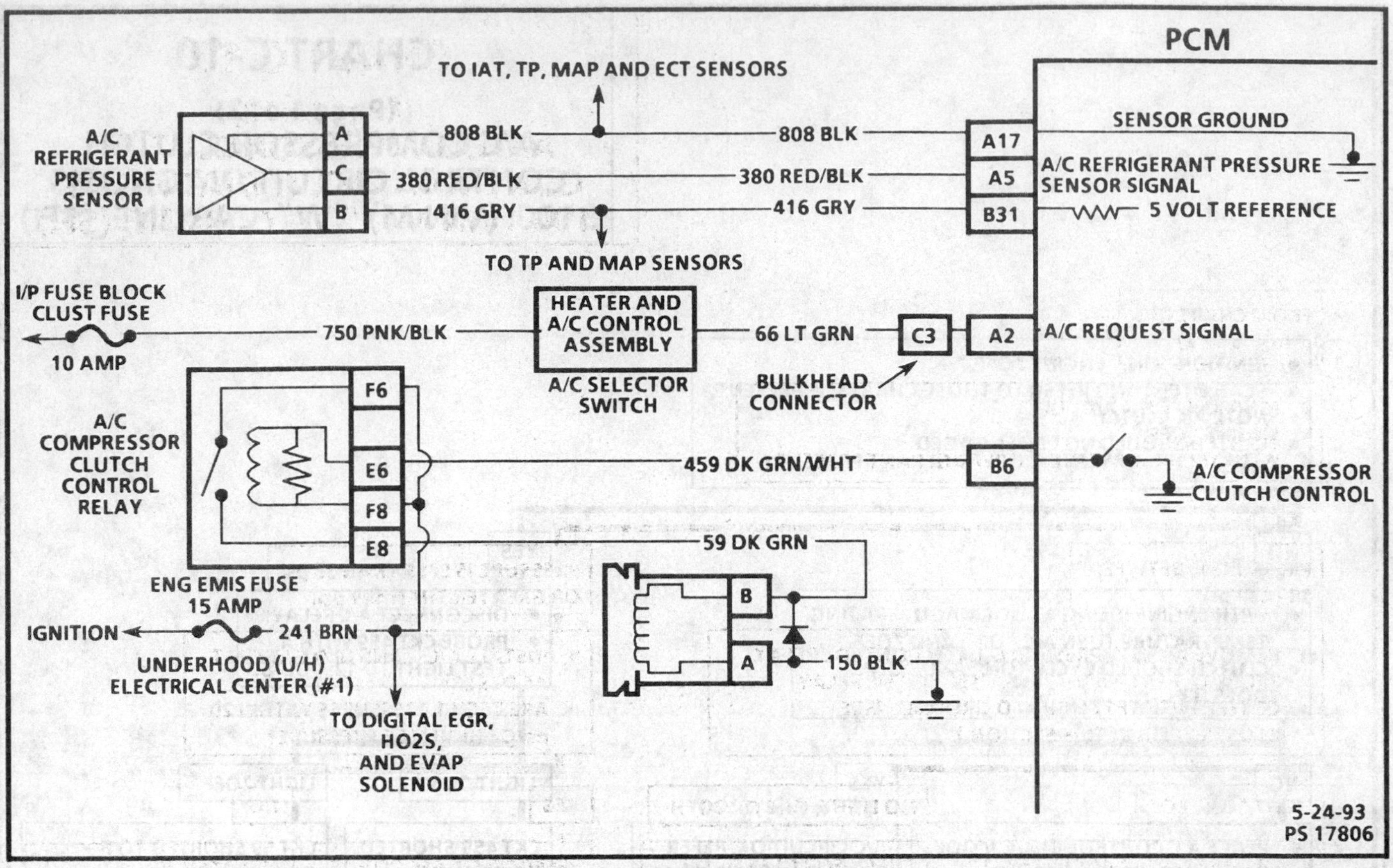
PCM
TO IAT, TP, MAP AND ECT SENSORS
A/C REFRIGERANT PRESSURE SENSOR
A
C
B
808 BLK
808 BLK
380 RED/BLK
380 RED/BLK
416 GRY
416 GRY
A17
A5
B31
SENSOR GROUND
A/C REFRIGERANT PRESSURE SENSOR SIGNAL
5 VOLT REFERENCE
TO TP AND MAP SENSORS
I/P FUSE BLOCK CLUST FUSE
10 AMP
750 PNK/BLK
HEATER AND A/C CONTROL ASSEMBLY
A/C SELECTOR SWITCH
66 LT GRN
C3
A2
A/C REQUEST SIGNAL
BULKHEAD CONNECTOR
A/C COMPRESSOR CLUTCH CONTROL RELAY
F6
E6
F8
E8
459 DK GRN/WHT
B6
A/C COMPRESSOR CLUTCH CONTROL
59 DK GRN
ENG EMIS FUSE 15 AMP
IGNITION
241 BRN
B
A
150 BLK
UNDERHOOD (U/H) ELECTRICAL CENTER (#1)
TO DIGITAL EGR, HO2S, AND EVAP SOLENOID
5-24-93
PS 17806

CHART C-10

(Page 2 of 2)

A/C COMPRESSOR CLUTCH CONTROL CIRCUIT DIAGNOSIS
3100 (VIN M) "W" CARLINE (SFI)

Circuit Description:

The A/C compressor clutch control relay is energized when the PCM provides a ground path through CKT 459 when A/C is requested. A/C compressor clutch is delayed about .3 second after A/C is requested. This will allow the IAC valve to adjust engine RPM for the additional load.

The A/C compressor clutch control relay will remain disengaged if pressure is out of range described previously in this section, or there is no A/C request signal due to an open A/C select switch or circuit. Refer to SECTION 1B for more information on A/C refrigerant systems.

Chart Test Description: Number(s) below refer to circled number(s) on the diagnostic chart.

1. Determines if the A/C refrigerant pressure sensor is out of range causing the compressor clutch to be disengaged.
2. With the engine stopped and A/C relay output test activated, the PCM should be grounding CKT 459, which should cause the test light to be "ON."

Diagnostic Aids: If complaint is insufficient cooling, the problem may be caused by an inoperative engine cooling fan(s). Refer to CHART C-12 for cooling fans diagnosis. If fans operate correctly, refer to A/C diagnosis in SECTION 1B. A/C pressure outside of a range of 38 to 429 psi will cause the compressor to be disabled by the PCM. Observe Tech 1 A/C pressure for 2 minutes with engine idling and A/C "ON." If pressure goes out of range, refer to SECTION 1B to measure and diagnose. Tech 1 pressure should be within 20 psi of actual. If not, check for a circuit problem using Diagnostic Trouble Code (DTC) 66 or 70 chart or replace A/C refrigerant pressure sensor.

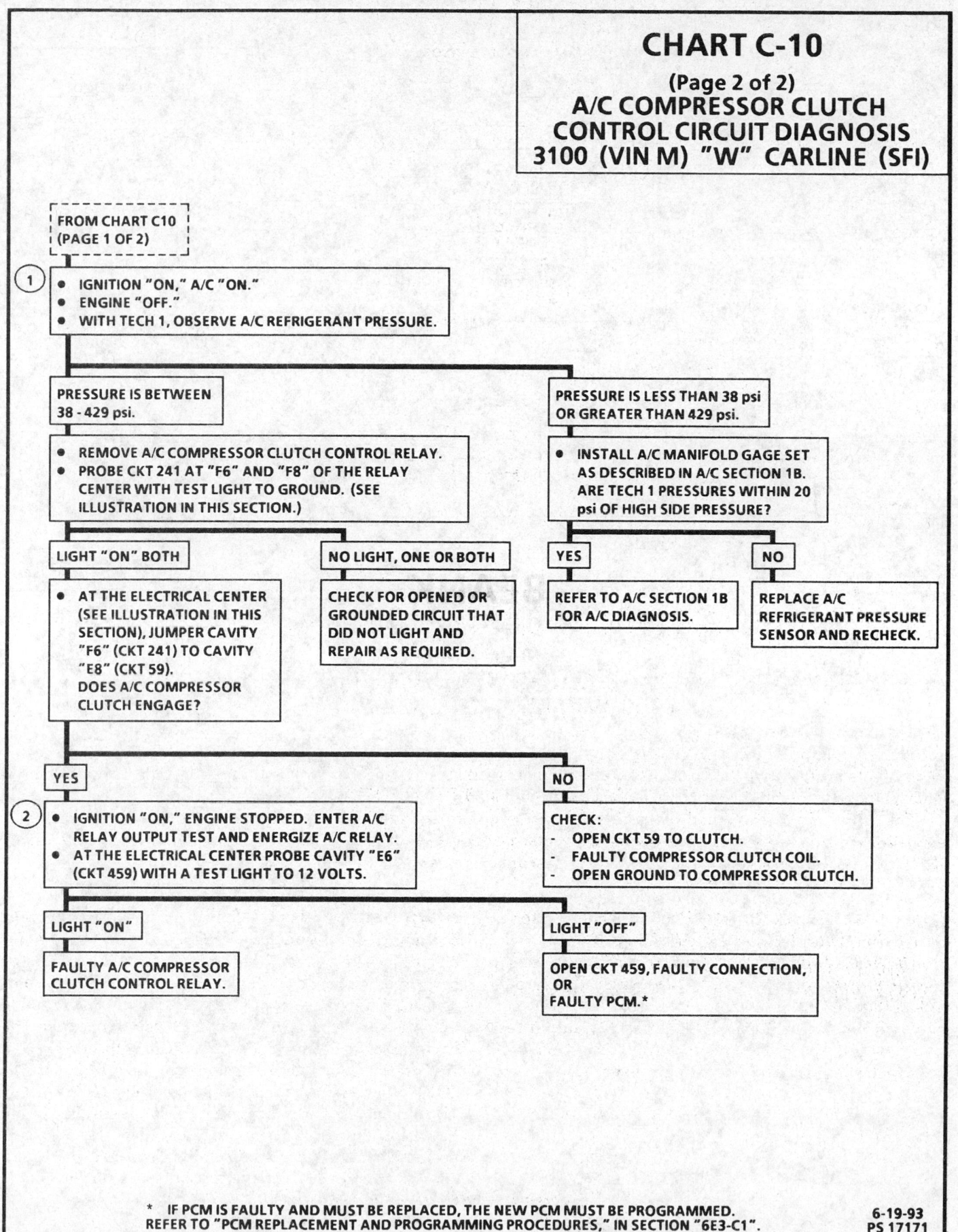

CHART C-10

(Page 2 of 2)
A/C COMPRESSOR CLUTCH CONTROL CIRCUIT DIAGNOSIS 3100 (VIN M) "W" CARLINE (SFI)

FROM CHART C10 (PAGE 1 OF 2)

1
- IGNITION "ON," A/C "ON."
- ENGINE "OFF."
- WITH TECH 1, OBSERVE A/C REFRIGERANT PRESSURE.

PRESSURE IS BETWEEN 38 - 429 psi.

- REMOVE A/C COMPRESSOR CLUTCH CONTROL RELAY.
- PROBE CKT 241 AT "F6" AND "F8" OF THE RELAY CENTER WITH TEST LIGHT TO GROUND. (SEE ILLUSTRATION IN THIS SECTION.)

LIGHT "ON" BOTH

- AT THE ELECTRICAL CENTER (SEE ILLUSTRATION IN THIS SECTION), JUMPER CAVITY "F6" (CKT 241) TO CAVITY "E8" (CKT 59). DOES A/C COMPRESSOR CLUTCH ENGAGE?

YES

2
- IGNITION "ON," ENGINE STOPPED. ENTER A/C RELAY OUTPUT TEST AND ENERGIZE A/C RELAY.
- AT THE ELECTRICAL CENTER PROBE CAVITY "E6" (CKT 459) WITH A TEST LIGHT TO 12 VOLTS.

LIGHT "ON"

FAULTY A/C COMPRESSOR CLUTCH CONTROL RELAY.

LIGHT "OFF"

OPEN CKT 459, FAULTY CONNECTION, OR FAULTY PCM.*

NO

CHECK:
- OPEN CKT 59 TO CLUTCH.
- FAULTY COMPRESSOR CLUTCH COIL.
- OPEN GROUND TO COMPRESSOR CLUTCH.

NO LIGHT, ONE OR BOTH

CHECK FOR OPENED OR GROUNDED CIRCUIT THAT DID NOT LIGHT AND REPAIR AS REQUIRED.

PRESSURE IS LESS THAN 38 psi OR GREATER THAN 429 psi.

- INSTALL A/C MANIFOLD GAGE SET AS DESCRIBED IN A/C SECTION 1B. ARE TECH 1 PRESSURES WITHIN 20 psi OF HIGH SIDE PRESSURE?

YES

REFER TO A/C SECTION 1B FOR A/C DIAGNOSIS.

NO

REPLACE A/C REFRIGERANT PRESSURE SENSOR AND RECHECK.

* IF PCM IS FAULTY AND MUST BE REPLACED, THE NEW PCM MUST BE PROGRAMMED. REFER TO "PCM REPLACEMENT AND PROGRAMMING PROCEDURES," IN SECTION "6E3-C1".

6-19-93
PS 17171

BLANK

SECTION C12

COOLING FAN CONTROL

CONTENTS

GENERAL DESCRIPTION

This vehicle utilizes two electric cooling fans for engine and A/C condenser cooling. The fans operate as outlined below.

OPERATION

The engine is equipped with two PCM controlled electric cooling fan(s). The secondary fan (#2) is used for heavy duty cooling with A/C.

Primary fan (#1) will be "ON" with any of the following criteria:

- Engine Coolant Temperature (ECT) sensor signal indicating a temperature greater than 108°C (226°F) with A/C "OFF," 106°C (223°F) with A/C "ON."
- A/C is requested and vehicle speed less than 50 mph (81 km/h).
- A/C refrigerant pressure sensor is "open" [pressure greater than 1275 kPa (185 psi)].

  OR
- When a DTC 14, 15 or 70 is set.

  OR
- When PCM is in back-up mode.

Secondary fan (#2) will be "ON" with any of the following criteria:

- Engine Coolant Temperature (ECT) sensor signal indicating a temperature greater than 113°C (235°F) with A/C "OFF," or "ON."

  OR
- A/C is requested and vehicle speed less than 40 mph (64 km/h).
- A/C refrigerant pressure sensor is "open" (pressure greater than 136 psi [938 kPa]).

DIAGNOSIS

The following C-12 charts will diagnose the PCM controlled cooling fans.

ON-VEHICLE SERVICE

Cooling system component replacement can be found in SECTION 6B.

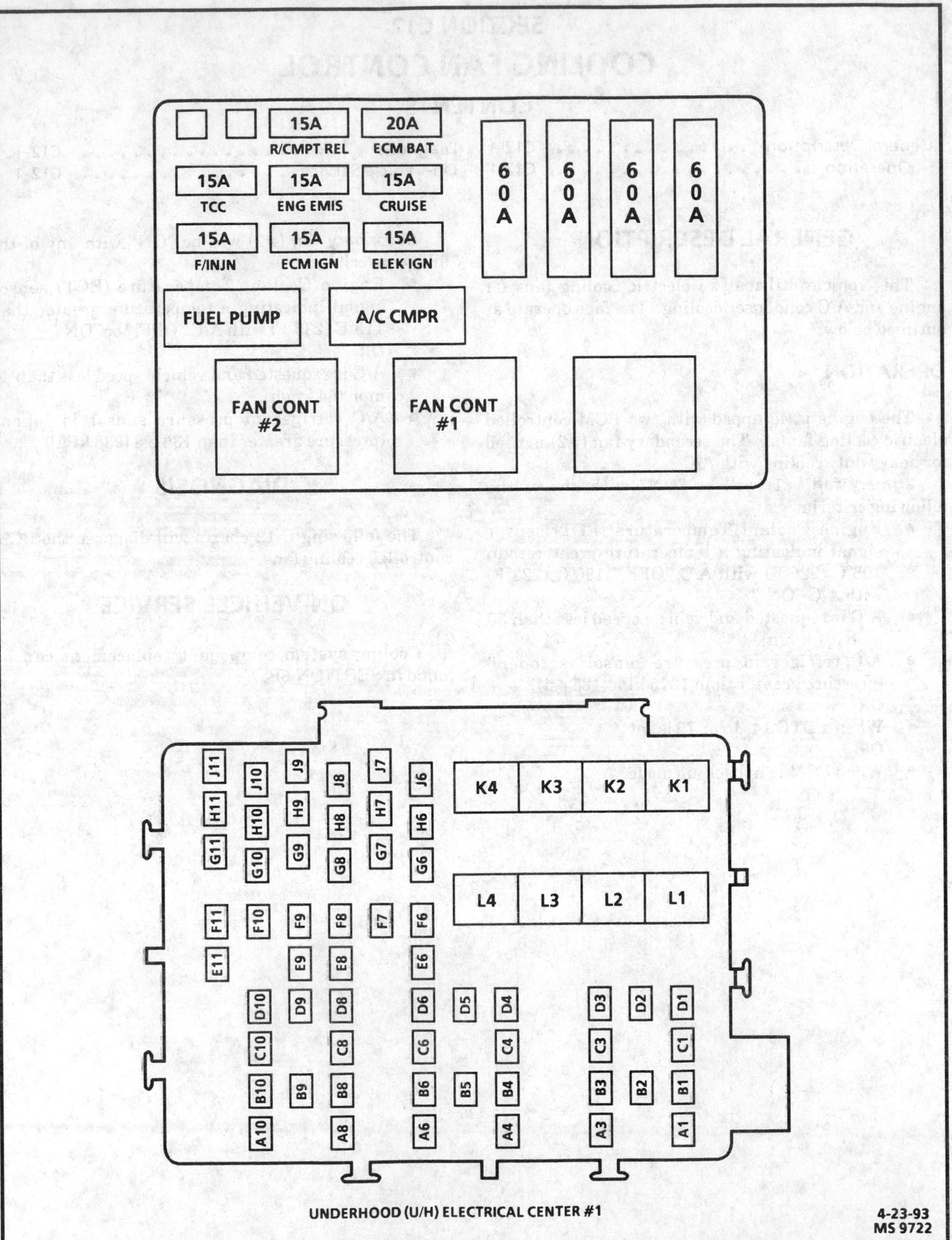

15A
R/CMPT REL
20A
ECM BAT
15A
TCC
15A
ENG EMIS
15A
CRUISE
15A
F/INJN
15A
ECM IGN
15A
ELEK IGN
60A
60A
60A
60A
FUEL PUMP
A/C CMPR
FAN CONT #2
FAN CONT #1
J11
J10
J9
J8
J7
J6
K4
K3
K2
K1
H11
H10
H9
H8
H7
H6
G11
G10
G9
G8
G7
G6
L4
L3
L2
L1
F11
F10
F9
F8
F7
F6
E11
E9
E8
E6
D10
D9
D8
D6
D5
D4
D3
D2
D1
C10
C8
C6
C4
C3
C1
B10
B9
B8
B6
B5
B4
B3
B2
B1
A10
A8
A6
A4
A3
A1
UNDERHOOD (U/H) ELECTRICAL CENTER #1
4-23-93
MS 9722

Figure C12-1 - Relays and Fuses

BLANK

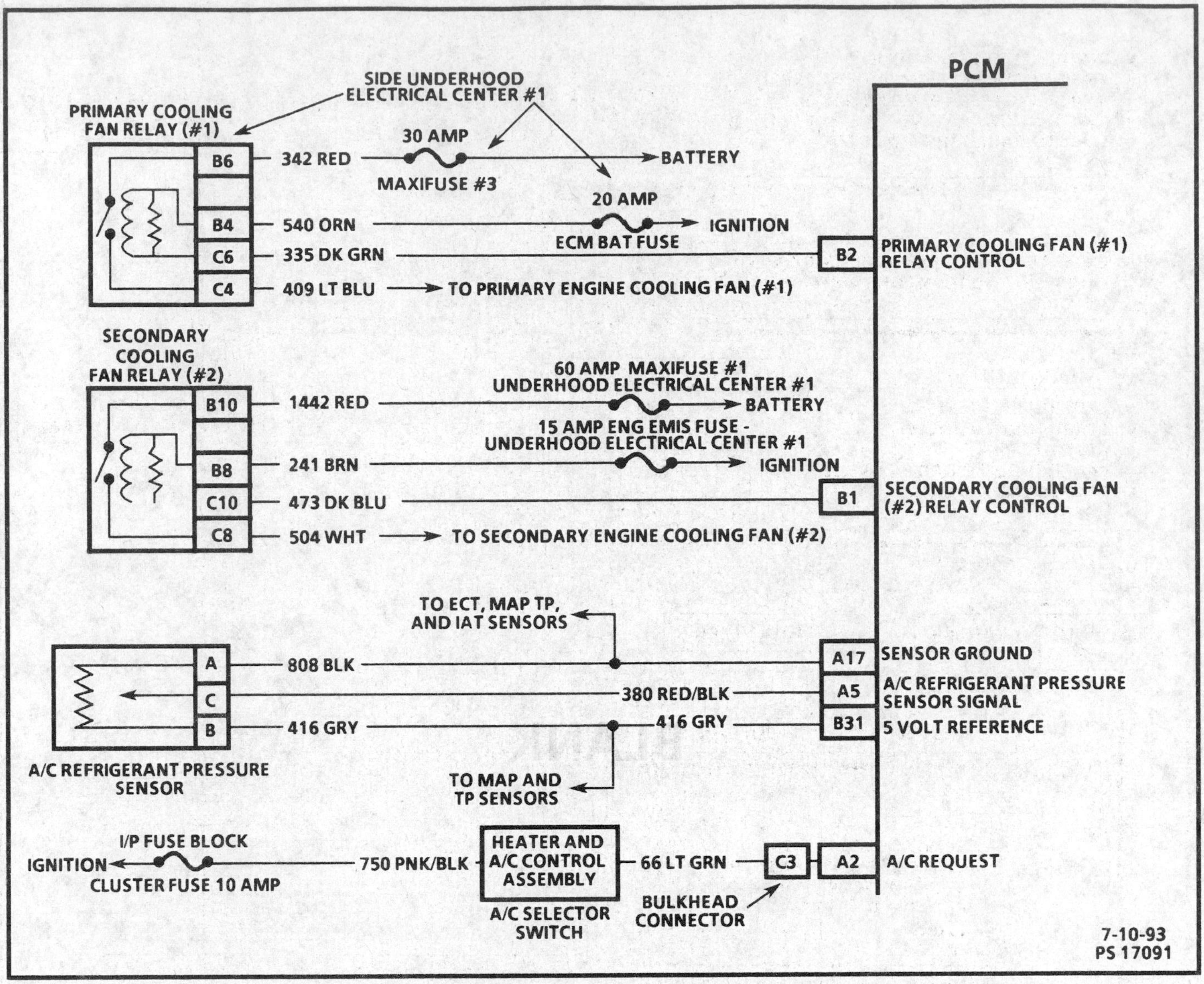
PCM
SIDE UNDERHOOD ELECTRICAL CENTER #1
PRIMARY COOLING FAN RELAY (#1)
B6
342 RED
30 AMP
BATTERY
MAXIFUSE #3
20 AMP
B4
540 ORN
IGNITION
ECM BAT FUSE
C6
335 DK GRN
B2
PRIMARY COOLING FAN (#1) RELAY CONTROL
C4
409 LT BLU
TO PRIMARY ENGINE COOLING FAN (#1)
SECONDARY COOLING FAN RELAY (#2)
60 AMP MAXIFUSE #1
UNDERHOOD ELECTRICAL CENTER #1
B10
1442 RED
BATTERY
15 AMP ENG EMIS FUSE - UNDERHOOD ELECTRICAL CENTER #1
B8
241 BRN
IGNITION
C10
473 DK BLU
B1
SECONDARY COOLING FAN (#2) RELAY CONTROL
C8
504 WHT
TO SECONDARY ENGINE COOLING FAN (#2)
TO ECT, MAP TP, AND IAT SENSORS
A
808 BLK
A17
SENSOR GROUND
C
380 RED/BLK
A5
A/C REFRIGERANT PRESSURE SENSOR SIGNAL
B
416 GRY
416 GRY
B31
5 VOLT REFERENCE
A/C REFRIGERANT PRESSURE SENSOR
TO MAP AND TP SENSORS
I/P FUSE BLOCK
IGNITION
CLUSTER FUSE 10 AMP
750 PNK/BLK
HEATER AND A/C CONTROL ASSEMBLY
66 LT GRN
C3
A2
A/C REQUEST
A/C SELECTOR SWITCH
BULKHEAD CONNECTOR
7-10-93
PS 17091

CHART C-12 (Page 1 of 2)

COOLING FAN CONTROL DIAGNOSIS
3100 (VIN M) "W" CARLINE (SFI)

Circuit Description:

Battery voltage to operate the primary cooling fan is supplied to the primary cooling fan (#1) relay by CKT 342. Ignition voltage to energize the primary cooling fan (#1) relay is supplied by CKT 540. When the PCM grounds CKT 335, the relay is energized and the primary cooling fan (#1) is turned "ON."

When the engine is running, the PCM will turn the primary cooling fan (#1) "ON" for any one of the following reasons:

- Diagnostic Trouble Code (DTC) 14, 15 or 70 is set.
- A/C is requested and vehicle speed is less than 50 mph (81 km/h).
- Engine coolant temperature is 108°C (226°F) or greater, with A/C "OFF." [106°C (223°F) with A/C "ON."]
- A/C refrigerant pressure is greater than 1275 kPa (185 psi).

Once the primary cooling fan (#1) is enabled, the PCM will turn the primary cooling fan (#1) "OFF" when:

- Engine is turned "OFF."
- Engine coolant temperature drops to 104°C (210°F) or less.
- A/C refrigerant pressure drops to 189 psi or less with A/C selected.

Diagnostic Aids: If the owner comments about an overheating problem, it must be determined whether the comment was due to an actual boil over, or the hot light, or temperature gage indicated overheating.

If the gage or light indicates overheating, but no boil over is detected, the gage circuit should be checked. The gage accuracy can also be checked by comparing the engine coolant temperature reading using a scan tool and comparing its display with the gage reading.

If the engine is actually overheating and the gage indicates overheating, but the cooling fan is not coming "ON," the Engine Coolant Temperature (ECT) sensor has probably shifted out of calibration and should be replaced.

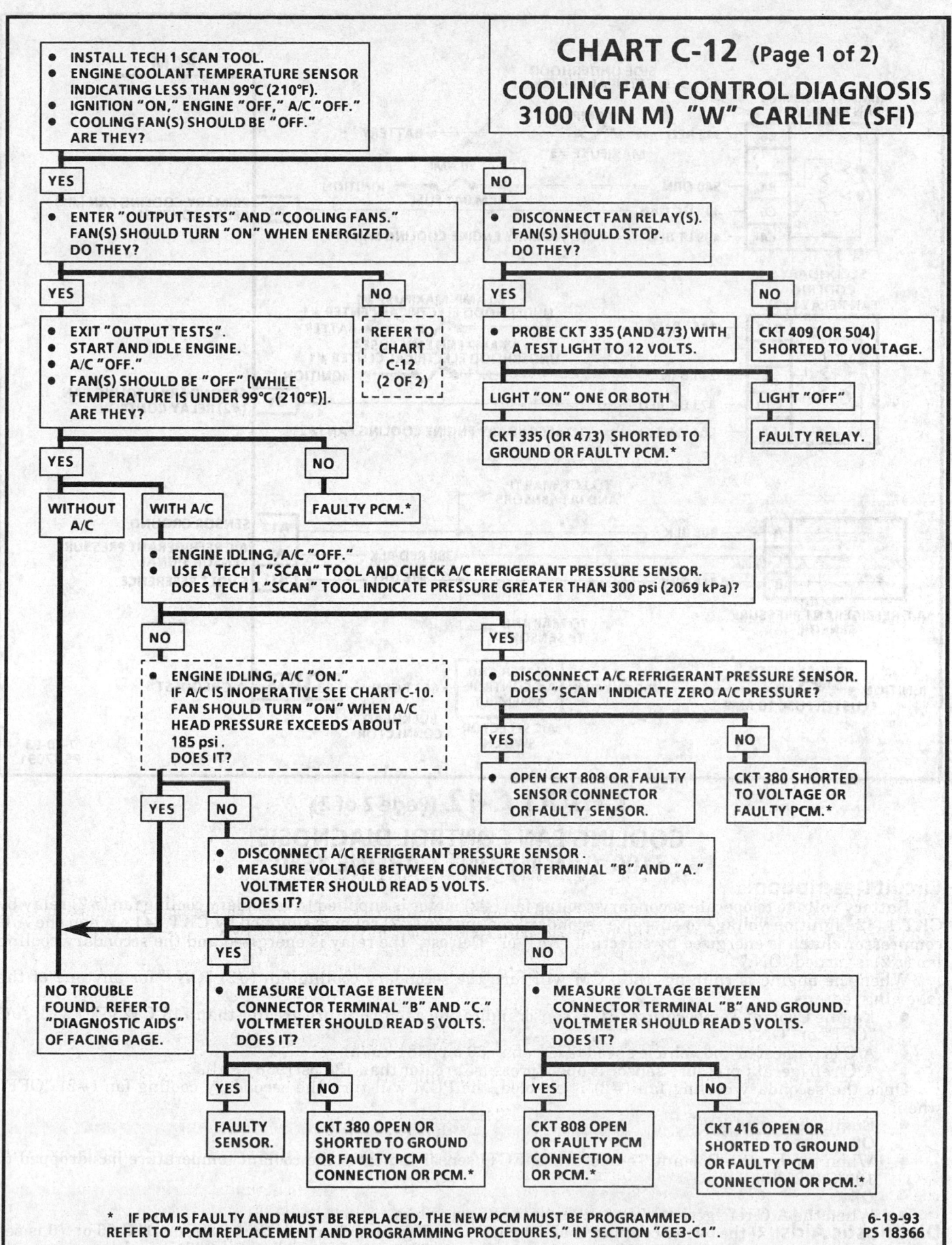

CHART C-12 (Page 1 of 2)

COOLING FAN CONTROL DIAGNOSIS 3100 (VIN M) "W" CARLINE (SFI)

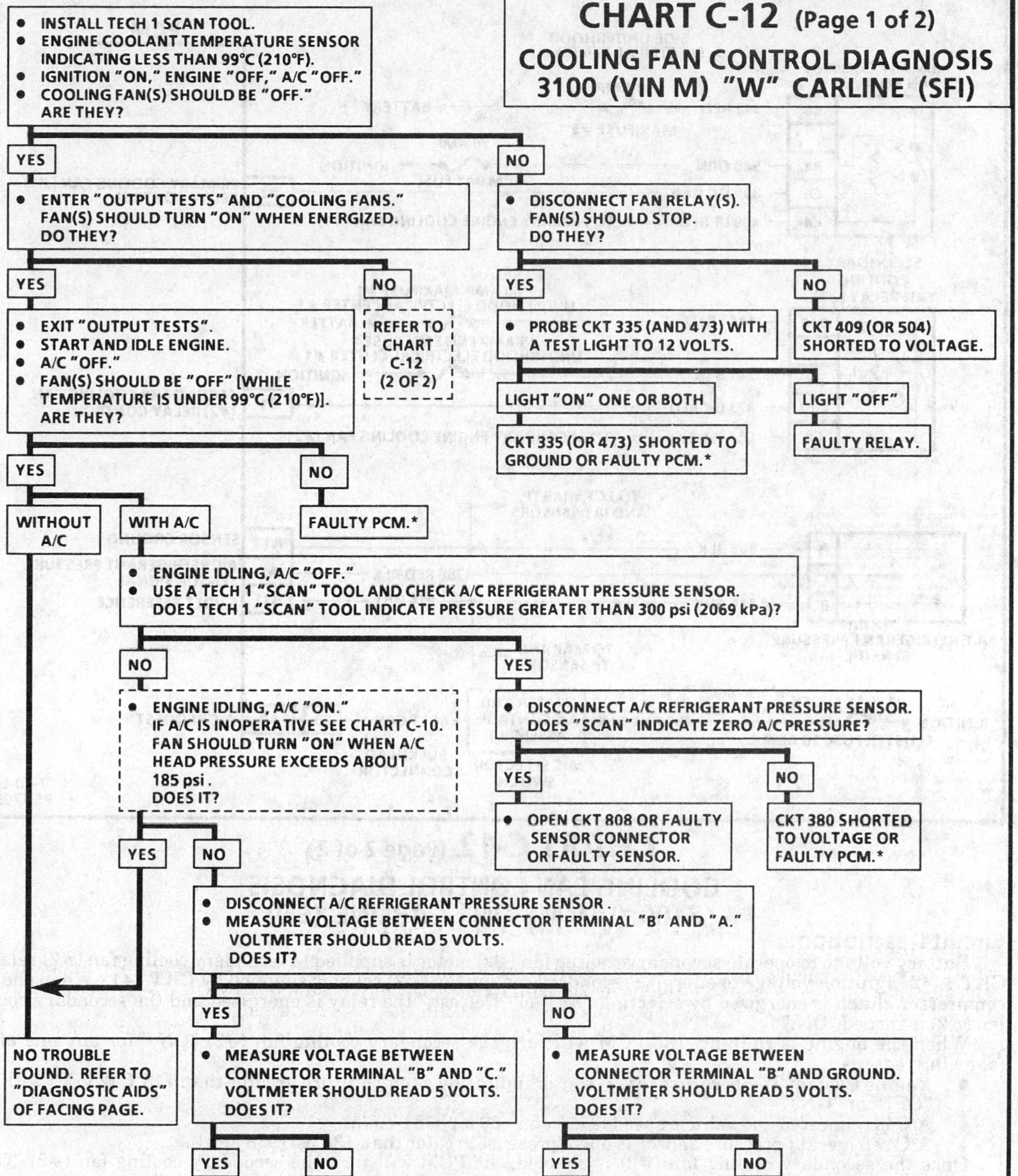
• INSTALL TECH 1 SCAN TOOL.
• ENGINE COOLANT TEMPERATURE SENSOR INDICATING LESS THAN 99°C (210°F).
• IGNITION "ON," ENGINE "OFF," A/C "OFF."
• COOLING FAN(S) SHOULD BE "OFF." ARE THEY?
YES
NO
• ENTER "OUTPUT TESTS" AND "COOLING FANS." FAN(S) SHOULD TURN "ON" WHEN ENERGIZED. DO THEY?
• DISCONNECT FAN RELAY(S). FAN(S) SHOULD STOP. DO THEY?
YES
NO
YES
NO
• EXIT "OUTPUT TESTS".
• START AND IDLE ENGINE.
• A/C "OFF."
• FAN(S) SHOULD BE "OFF" [WHILE TEMPERATURE IS UNDER 99°C (210°F)]. ARE THEY?
REFER TO CHART C-12 (2 OF 2)
• PROBE CKT 335 (AND 473) WITH A TEST LIGHT TO 12 VOLTS.
CKT 409 (OR 504) SHORTED TO VOLTAGE.
LIGHT "ON" ONE OR BOTH
LIGHT "OFF"
CKT 335 (OR 473) SHORTED TO GROUND OR FAULTY PCM.*
FAULTY RELAY.
YES
NO
WITHOUT A/C
WITH A/C
FAULTY PCM.*
• ENGINE IDLING, A/C "OFF."
• USE A TECH 1 "SCAN" TOOL AND CHECK A/C REFRIGERANT PRESSURE SENSOR. DOES TECH 1 "SCAN" TOOL INDICATE PRESSURE GREATER THAN 300 psi (2069 kPa)?
NO
YES
• ENGINE IDLING, A/C "ON." IF A/C IS INOPERATIVE SEE CHART C-10. FAN SHOULD TURN "ON" WHEN A/C HEAD PRESSURE EXCEEDS ABOUT 185 psi. DOES IT?
• DISCONNECT A/C REFRIGERANT PRESSURE SENSOR. DOES "SCAN" INDICATE ZERO A/C PRESSURE?
YES
NO
• OPEN CKT 808 OR FAULTY SENSOR CONNECTOR OR FAULTY SENSOR.
CKT 380 SHORTED TO VOLTAGE OR FAULTY PCM.*
YES
NO
• DISCONNECT A/C REFRIGERANT PRESSURE SENSOR.
• MEASURE VOLTAGE BETWEEN CONNECTOR TERMINAL "B" AND "A." VOLTMETER SHOULD READ 5 VOLTS. DOES IT?
YES
NO
NO TROUBLE FOUND. REFER TO "DIAGNOSTIC AIDS" OF FACING PAGE.
• MEASURE VOLTAGE BETWEEN CONNECTOR TERMINAL "B" AND "C." VOLTMETER SHOULD READ 5 VOLTS. DOES IT?
• MEASURE VOLTAGE BETWEEN CONNECTOR TERMINAL "B" AND GROUND. VOLTMETER SHOULD READ 5 VOLTS. DOES IT?
YES
NO
YES
NO
FAULTY SENSOR.
CKT 380 OPEN OR SHORTED TO GROUND OR FAULTY PCM CONNECTION OR PCM.*
CKT 808 OPEN OR FAULTY PCM CONNECTION OR PCM.*
CKT 416 OPEN OR SHORTED TO GROUND OR FAULTY PCM CONNECTION OR PCM.*

* IF PCM IS FAULTY AND MUST BE REPLACED, THE NEW PCM MUST BE PROGRAMMED. REFER TO "PCM REPLACEMENT AND PROGRAMMING PROCEDURES," IN SECTION "6E3-C1".

6-19-93
PS 18366

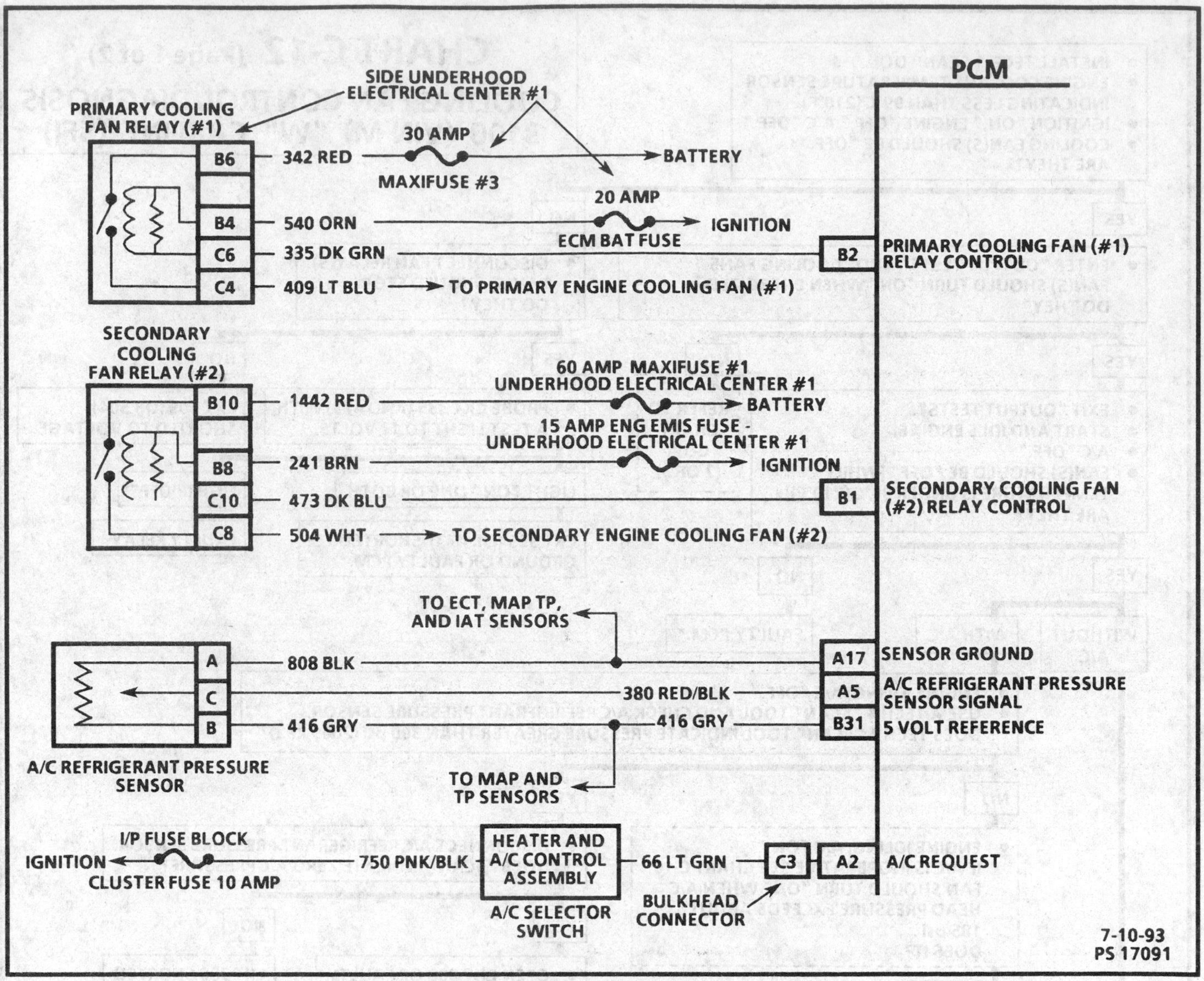
PCM
SIDE UNDERHOOD ELECTRICAL CENTER #1
PRIMARY COOLING FAN RELAY (#1)
30 AMP
B6
342 RED
BATTERY
MAXIFUSE #3
20 AMP
B4
540 ORN
IGNITION
ECM BAT FUSE
C6
335 DK GRN
B2
PRIMARY COOLING FAN (#1) RELAY CONTROL
C4
409 LT BLU
TO PRIMARY ENGINE COOLING FAN (#1)
SECONDARY COOLING FAN RELAY (#2)
60 AMP MAXIFUSE #1
UNDERHOOD ELECTRICAL CENTER #1
B10
1442 RED
BATTERY
15 AMP ENG EMIS FUSE - UNDERHOOD ELECTRICAL CENTER #1
B8
241 BRN
IGNITION
C10
473 DK BLU
B1
SECONDARY COOLING FAN (#2) RELAY CONTROL
C8
504 WHT
TO SECONDARY ENGINE COOLING FAN (#2)
TO ECT, MAP TP, AND IAT SENSORS
A
808 BLK
A17
SENSOR GROUND
C
380 RED/BLK
A5
A/C REFRIGERANT PRESSURE SENSOR SIGNAL
B
416 GRY
416 GRY
B31
5 VOLT REFERENCE
A/C REFRIGERANT PRESSURE SENSOR
TO MAP AND TP SENSORS
I/P FUSE BLOCK
IGNITION
CLUSTER FUSE 10 AMP
750 PNK/BLK
HEATER AND A/C CONTROL ASSEMBLY
A/C SELECTOR SWITCH
66 LT GRN
C3
A2
A/C REQUEST
BULKHEAD CONNECTOR
7-10-93
PS 17091

CHART C-12 (Page 2 of 2)

COOLING FAN CONTROL DIAGNOSIS 3100 (VIN M) "W" CARLINE (SFI)

Circuit Description:

Battery voltage to operate secondary cooling fan (#2) motor is supplied to secondary cooling fan (#2) relay by CKT 1442. Ignition voltage to energize secondary cooling fan (#2) relay is supplied by CKT 241. When the A/C compressor clutch is energized by selecting "A/C" or "Defrost," the relay is energized and the secondary cooling fan (#2) is turned "ON."

When the engine is running, the PCM will turn the secondary cooling fan (#2) "ON," for any one of the following reasons:

- Engine Coolant Temperature (ECT) sensor indicating a temperature greater than 113°C (235°F) with A/C "OFF" or "ON."
- A/C is requested and vehicle speed is less than 50 mph (81 km/h).
- A/C refrigerant pressure sensor is open (pressure greater than 136 psi [938 kPa]).

Once the secondary cooling fan (#2) is enabled, the PCM will turn the secondary cooling fan (#2) "OFF" when:

- Engine is turned "OFF."
  OR
- When the Engine Coolant Temperature (ECT) sensor indicates the coolant temperature has dropped to 109°C (228°F) or less.
  OR
- When the A/C refrigerant pressure drops to 185 psi or less.

Diagnostic Aids: If the owner comments about poor A/C cooling, it must be determined whether a low A/C refrigerant charge is the cause, or DTC 66 or 70 is set, or the secondary cooling fan (#2) is faulty.

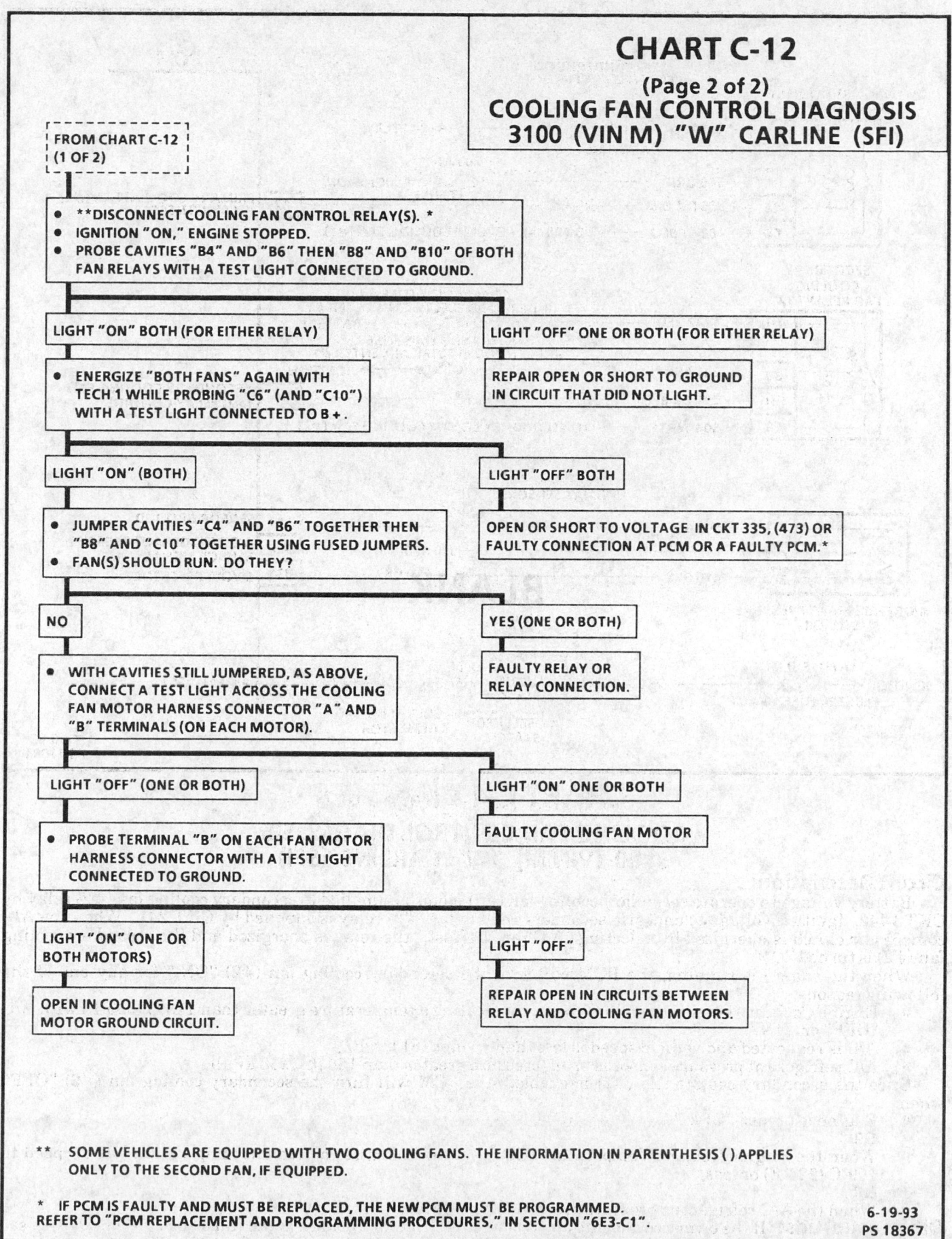

CHART C-12

(Page 2 of 2)
COOLING FAN CONTROL DIAGNOSIS
3100 (VIN M) "W" CARLINE (SFI)

FROM CHART C-12 (1 OF 2)

- **DISCONNECT COOLING FAN CONTROL RELAY(S). *
- IGNITION "ON," ENGINE STOPPED.
- PROBE CAVITIES "B4" AND "B6" THEN "B8" AND "B10" OF BOTH FAN RELAYS WITH A TEST LIGHT CONNECTED TO GROUND.

LIGHT "ON" BOTH (FOR EITHER RELAY)

- ENERGIZE "BOTH FANS" AGAIN WITH TECH 1 WHILE PROBING "C6" (AND "C10") WITH A TEST LIGHT CONNECTED TO B +.

LIGHT "OFF" ONE OR BOTH (FOR EITHER RELAY)

REPAIR OPEN OR SHORT TO GROUND IN CIRCUIT THAT DID NOT LIGHT.

LIGHT "ON" (BOTH)

- JUMPER CAVITIES "C4" AND "B6" TOGETHER THEN "B8" AND "C10" TOGETHER USING FUSED JUMPERS.
- FAN(S) SHOULD RUN. DO THEY?

LIGHT "OFF" BOTH

OPEN OR SHORT TO VOLTAGE IN CKT 335, (473) OR FAULTY CONNECTION AT PCM OR A FAULTY PCM.*

NO

- WITH CAVITIES STILL JUMPERED, AS ABOVE, CONNECT A TEST LIGHT ACROSS THE COOLING FAN MOTOR HARNESS CONNECTOR "A" AND "B" TERMINALS (ON EACH MOTOR).

YES (ONE OR BOTH)

FAULTY RELAY OR RELAY CONNECTION.

LIGHT "OFF" (ONE OR BOTH)

- PROBE TERMINAL "B" ON EACH FAN MOTOR HARNESS CONNECTOR WITH A TEST LIGHT CONNECTED TO GROUND.

LIGHT "ON" ONE OR BOTH

FAULTY COOLING FAN MOTOR

LIGHT "ON" (ONE OR BOTH MOTORS)

OPEN IN COOLING FAN MOTOR GROUND CIRCUIT.

LIGHT "OFF"

REPAIR OPEN IN CIRCUITS BETWEEN RELAY AND COOLING FAN MOTORS.

** SOME VEHICLES ARE EQUIPPED WITH TWO COOLING FANS. THE INFORMATION IN PARENTHESIS ( ) APPLIES ONLY TO THE SECOND FAN, IF EQUIPPED.

* IF PCM IS FAULTY AND MUST BE REPLACED, THE NEW PCM MUST BE PROGRAMMED. REFER TO "PCM REPLACEMENT AND PROGRAMMING PROCEDURES," IN SECTION "6E3-C1".

6-19-93
PS 18367

BLANK

SECTION C13

CRANKCASE VENTILATION SYSTEM

CONTENTS

GENERAL DESCRIPTION

A crankcase ventilation system is used to provide more complete scavenging of crankcase vapors. Fresh air from the air cleaner is supplied to the crankcase, mixed with blow-by gases and then passed through a crankcase ventilation valve into the intake manifold (Figure C13-1).

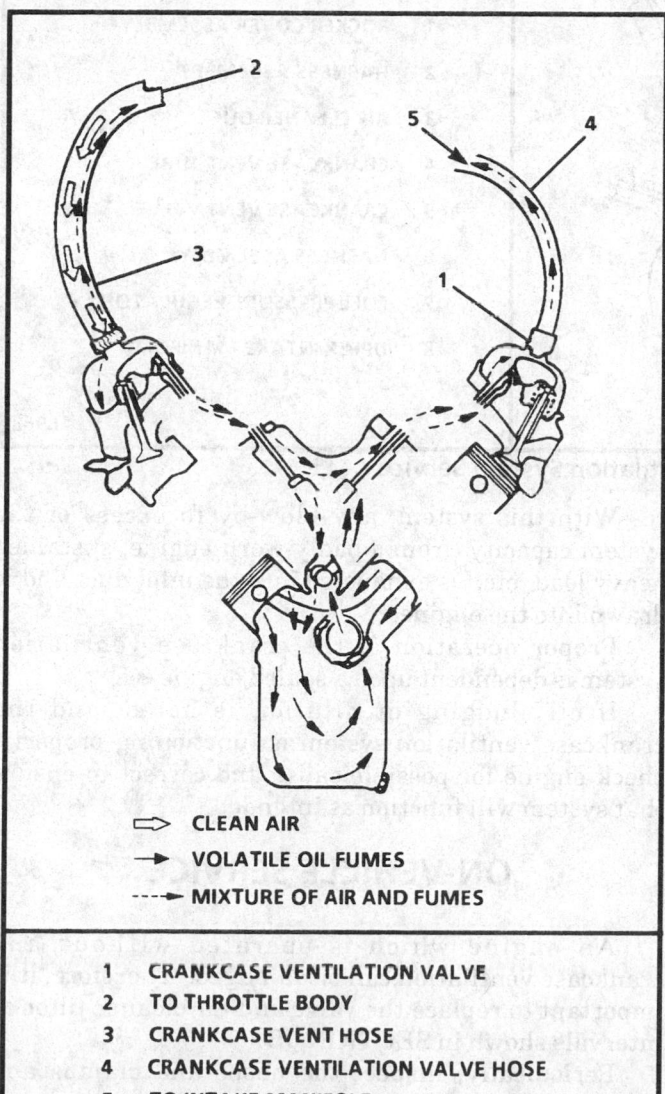

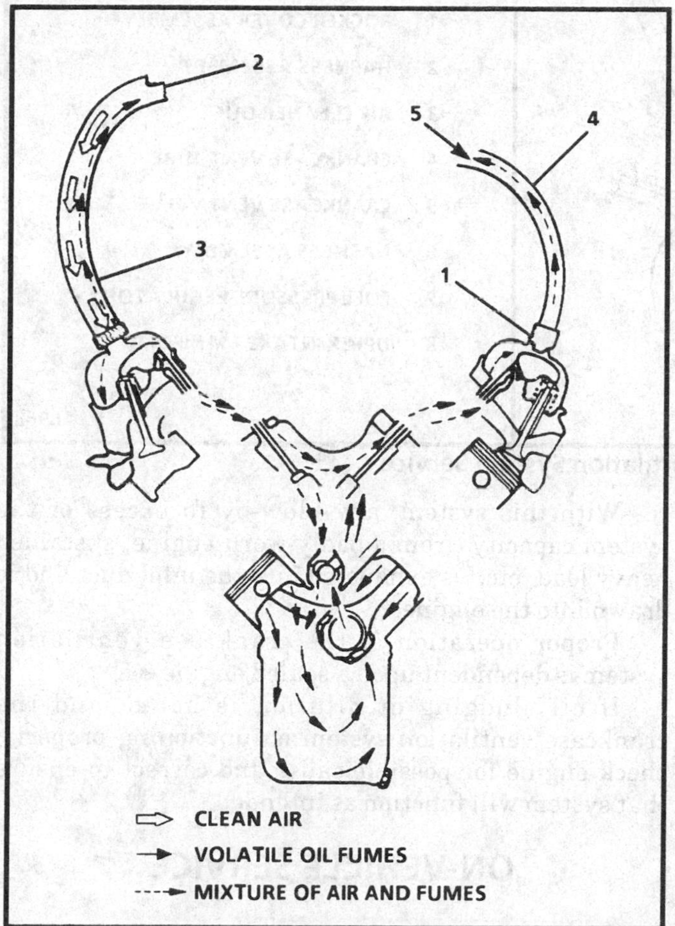
2
5
4
3
1
CLEAN AIR
VOLATILE OIL FUMES
MIXTURE OF AIR AND FUMES
1 CRANKCASE VENTILATION VALVE
2 TO THROTTLE BODY
3 CRANKCASE VENT HOSE
4 CRANKCASE VENTILATION VALVE HOSE
5 TO INTAKE MANIFOLD
5S 1725-6E

Figure C13-1 - Crankcase Ventilation Flow

OPERATION

The primary control is through the crankcase ventilation valve (Figure C13-2) which meters the flow at a rate depending on manifold vacuum.

To maintain idle quality, this valve restricts the flow when intake manifold vacuum is high. If abnormal operating conditions arise, the system is designed to allow excessive amounts of blow-by gases to back flow through the crankcase vent tube into the air inlet duct to be consumed by normal combustion.

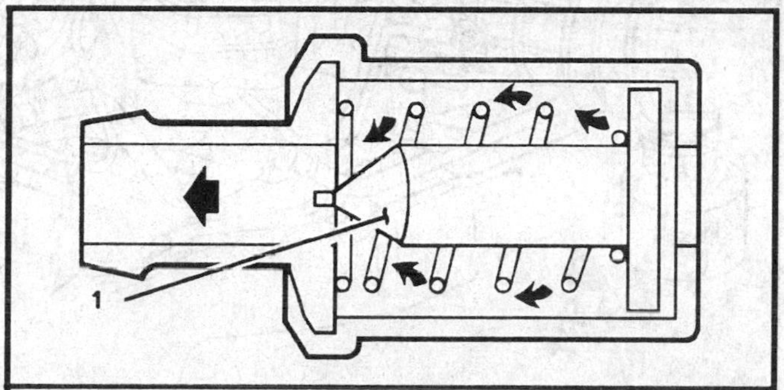
1
1 CHECK VALVE
4S 0068-6E

Figure C13-2 - Crankcase Ventilation Valve Cross Section

RESULTS OF INCORRECT OPERATION

A plugged valve or hose may cause:

- Rough idle.
- Stalling or slow idle speed.
- Oil leaks.
- Oil in throttle body or plenum.
- Sludge in engine.

A leaking valve or hose would cause:

- Rough idle.
- Stalling.
- High idle speed.

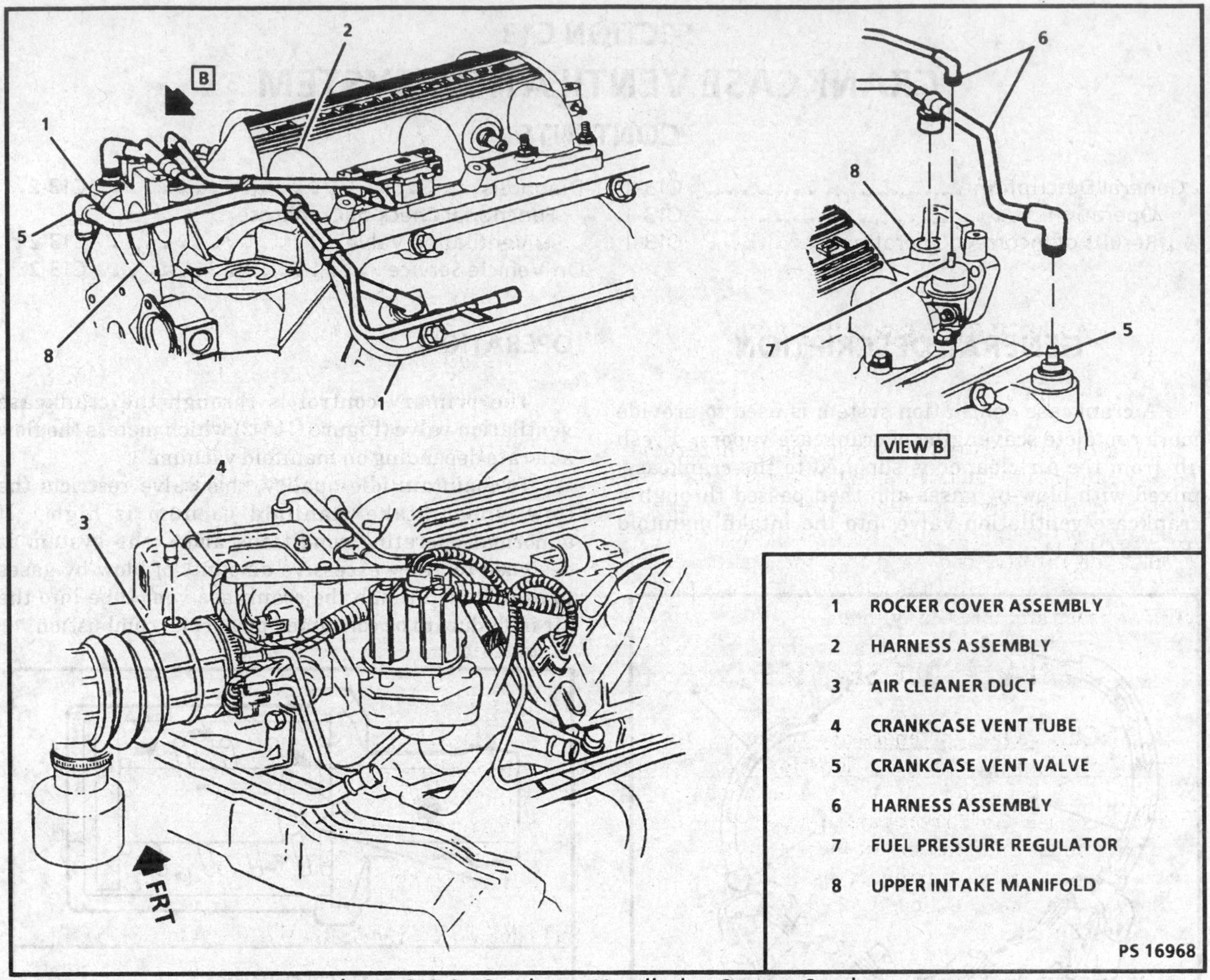
B
VIEW B
FRT
1 ROCKER COVER ASSEMBLY
2 HARNESS ASSEMBLY
3 AIR CLEANER DUCT
4 CRANKCASE VENT TUBE
5 CRANKCASE VENT VALVE
6 HARNESS ASSEMBLY
7 FUEL PRESSURE REGULATOR
8 UPPER INTAKE MANIFOLD
PS 16968

Figure C13-3 - Crankcase Ventilation System Service

DIAGNOSIS

FUNCTIONAL CHECK OF CRANKCASE VENTILATION VALVE

If an engine is idling rough, check for a clogged crankcase ventilation valve or plugged hose. Check valve part number to be sure the correct crankcase ventilation valve is installed. Replace as required. Use the following procedure:

1. Remove valve from rocker arm cover.
2. Run the engine at idle.
3. Place your thumb over end of valve to check for vacuum. If there is no vacuum at valve, check for plugged hoses or manifold port, or valve. Replace plugged or deteriorated hoses.
4. Turn "OFF" the engine and remove valve. Shake valve and listen for the rattle of check needle inside the valve. If valve does not rattle, replace valve.

With this system, any blow-by in excess of the system capacity (from a badly-worn engine, sustained heavy load, etc.) is exhausted into the inlet duct and is drawn into the engine.

Proper operation of the crankcase ventilation system is dependent upon a sealed engine.

If oil sludging or dilution is noted, and the crankcase ventilation system is functioning properly, check engine for possible cause and correct to ensure that system will function as intended.

ON-VEHICLE SERVICE

An engine which is operated without any crankcase ventilation can be damaged. Therefore, it is important to replace the valve and air cleaner filter at intervals shown in SECTION 0B.

Periodically, inspect the hoses and clamps and replace any showing signs of deterioration.

SECTION C14
AIR INTAKE SYSTEM
CONTENTS

GENERAL DESCRIPTION

AIR INTAKE SYSTEM

The air intake system draws outside air in through the front air intake duct. Intake air flows through the air cleaner assembly and filter. The air then enters the engine by flowing through the rear air intake duct, through the throttle body and into the plenum. The air is then directed into the plenum intake runners, cylinder heads and into the cylinder.

ON-VEHICLE SERVICE

NOTICE: When fasteners are removed, always reinstall them at the same location from which they were removed. If a fastener needs to be replaced, use the correct part number fastener for that application. The correct torque value must be used, as specified, during reassembly to ensure proper retention of all parts, or damage to the part may result.

AIR CLEANER FILTER

←→ Remove or Disconnect

1. Bolts/screws from air cleaner cover, lift cover.
2. Inspect air cleaner filter for dust, dirt, water and replace if required. Refer to SECTION 0B.

→← Install or Connect

1. Air cleaner filter and cover.
2. Bolts/screws to air cleaner cover.

AIR CLEANER ASSEMBLY
Figure C14-1

←→ Remove or Disconnect

1. IAT sensor electrical connector.
2. Air cleaner cover.
3. Clamp and rear air intake duct from air cleaner assembly.
4. One bolt/screw from air cleaner bracket and lift entire assembly up and out of its location.

→← Install or Connect

1. Sub-assemble rear intake duct over flange of air cleaner assembly in position shown in Figure C14-1.
2. Position assembled air cleaner and duct assembly over hole in air cleaner support bracket.
3. Seat air cleaner assembly to seal and align to the front air intake duct. Make certain this is aligned properly. Otherwise the front air intake duct could suck shut on WOT maneuvers, causing the engine to stall.

Tighten

- Bolt/screw 10 N·m (7 lb. ft.).

4. IAT sensor - (if replacing rear air intake duct, transfer IAT sensor from old unit). Refer to procedure below.
5. Air cleaner filter, cover and fasten screws securely.
6. Securely fasten clamps.

INTAKE AIR TEMPERATURE (IAT) SENSOR

NOTICE: Care must be taken when handling the Intake Air Temperature (IAT) sensor. Damage to the IAT sensor will affect proper operation of the fuel injection system.

←→ Remove or Disconnect

1. Negative battery cable.
2. IAT sensor electrical connector.
3. Grasp IAT sensor then carefully twist and pull from rear air intake duct.

→← Install or Connect

- Reverse removal procedure.

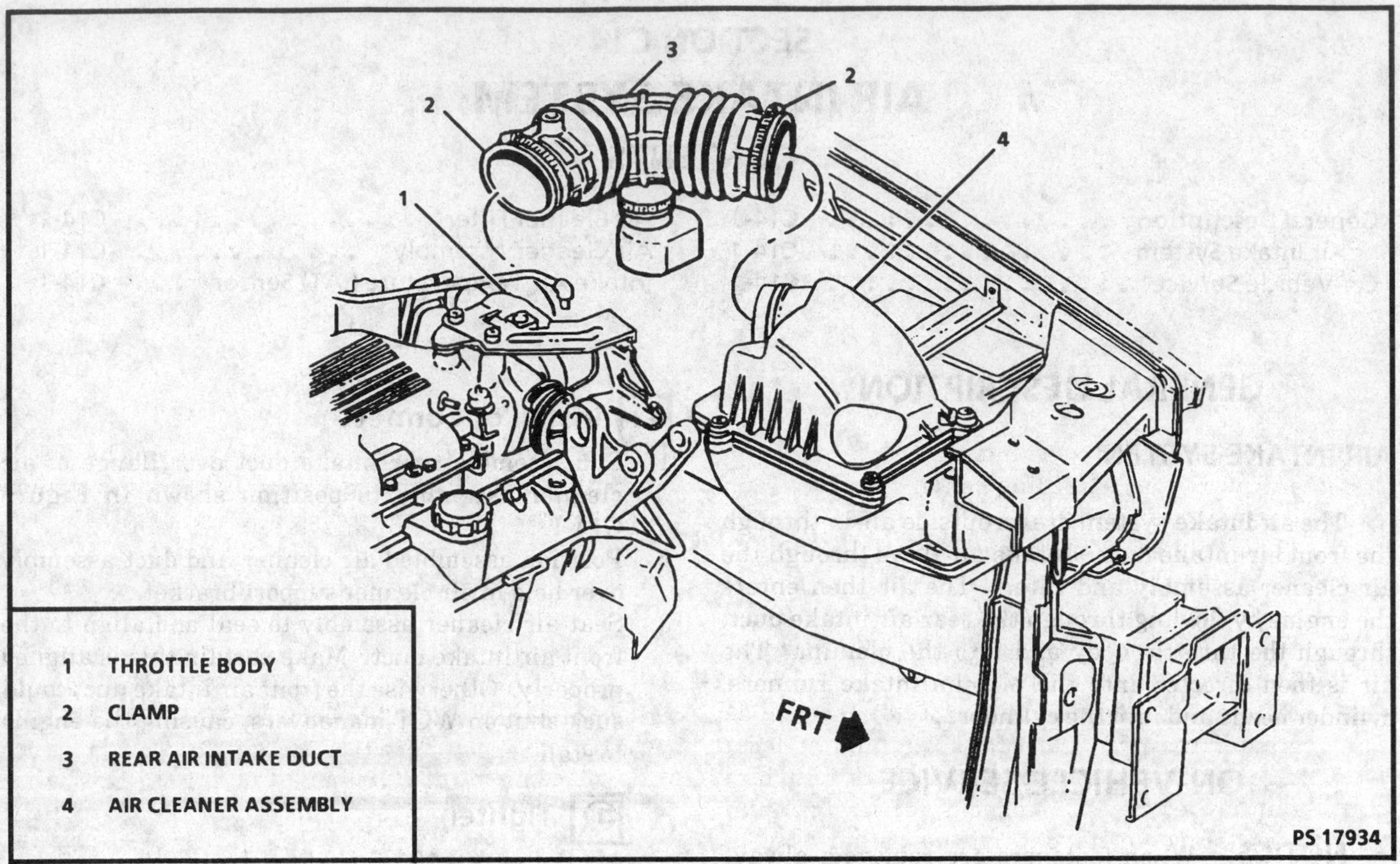
1
2
3
2
4
FRT
1 THROTTLE BODY
2 CLAMP
3 REAR AIR INTAKE DUCT
4 AIR CLEANER ASSEMBLY
PS 17934

Figure C14-1 - Air Intake System Components

SECTION C16

PCM CONTROLLED WARNING LAMPS

CONTENTS

GENERAL DESCRIPTION

The PCM controlled warning lamp is intended to alert the driver to an operating condition which may require immediate attention.

The "Low Oil Level" lamp operates as follows:

- When energized during key "ON," the PCM controlled low oil warning lamp is turned "ON." This indicates the system is functioning properly (one second bulb check).
- As long as engine coolant temperature is greater than 75°C on shutdown, and at least three minutes have elapsed since the last shutdown, the PCM checks oil level signal upon start-up, to determine either of two conditions:
  - Engine oil level is OK (lamp goes "OFF").

    OR
  - Engine oil level is low (lamp stays "ON").

  If engine coolant temperature is less than 75°C on shutdown, the PCM records the coolant temperature at shutdown. Now, when the engine is restarted, the PCM checks for coolant temperature again. If the coolant temperature has dropped by at least 11°C since the last shutdown, the PCM checks the oil level signal and determines whether or not the oil level is within the acceptable range. If DTC 14 or 15 or a combination of DTC 36 and 82, occurred anytime during ignition cycle before shutdown, there will be no bulb check upon start-up. In this case, the PCM will not run the test to check oil level.

DIAGNOSIS

The following chart will diagnose the PCM controlled low oil warning lamp. For specific system components and wiring refer to SECTION 8A.

ON-VEHICLE SERVICE

For specific system components and wiring refer to SECTION 8A or SECTION 8C. For PCM replacement information refer to "Powertrain Control Module (PCM) and Sensors," Section "6E3-C1".

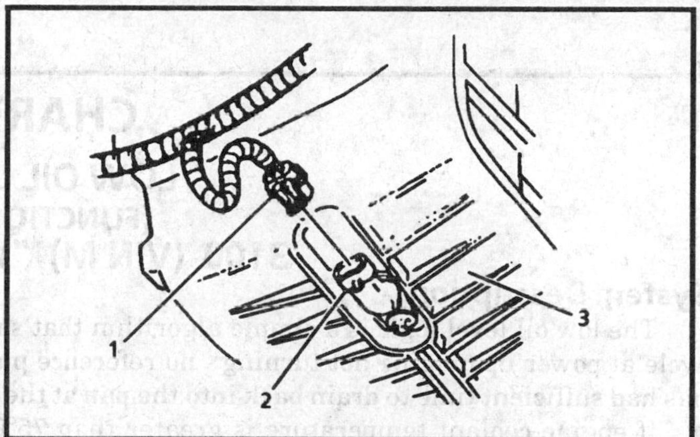
1
2
3

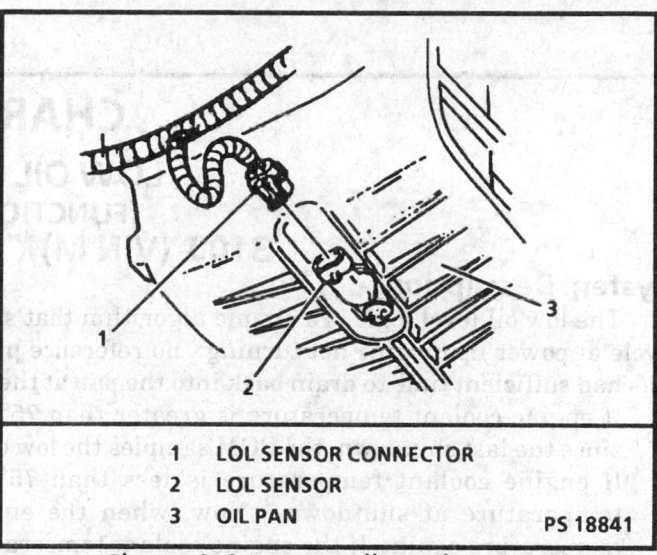

1 LOL SENSOR CONNECTOR
2 LOL SENSOR
3 OIL PAN

PS 18841

Figure C16-1 - Low Oil Level Sensor

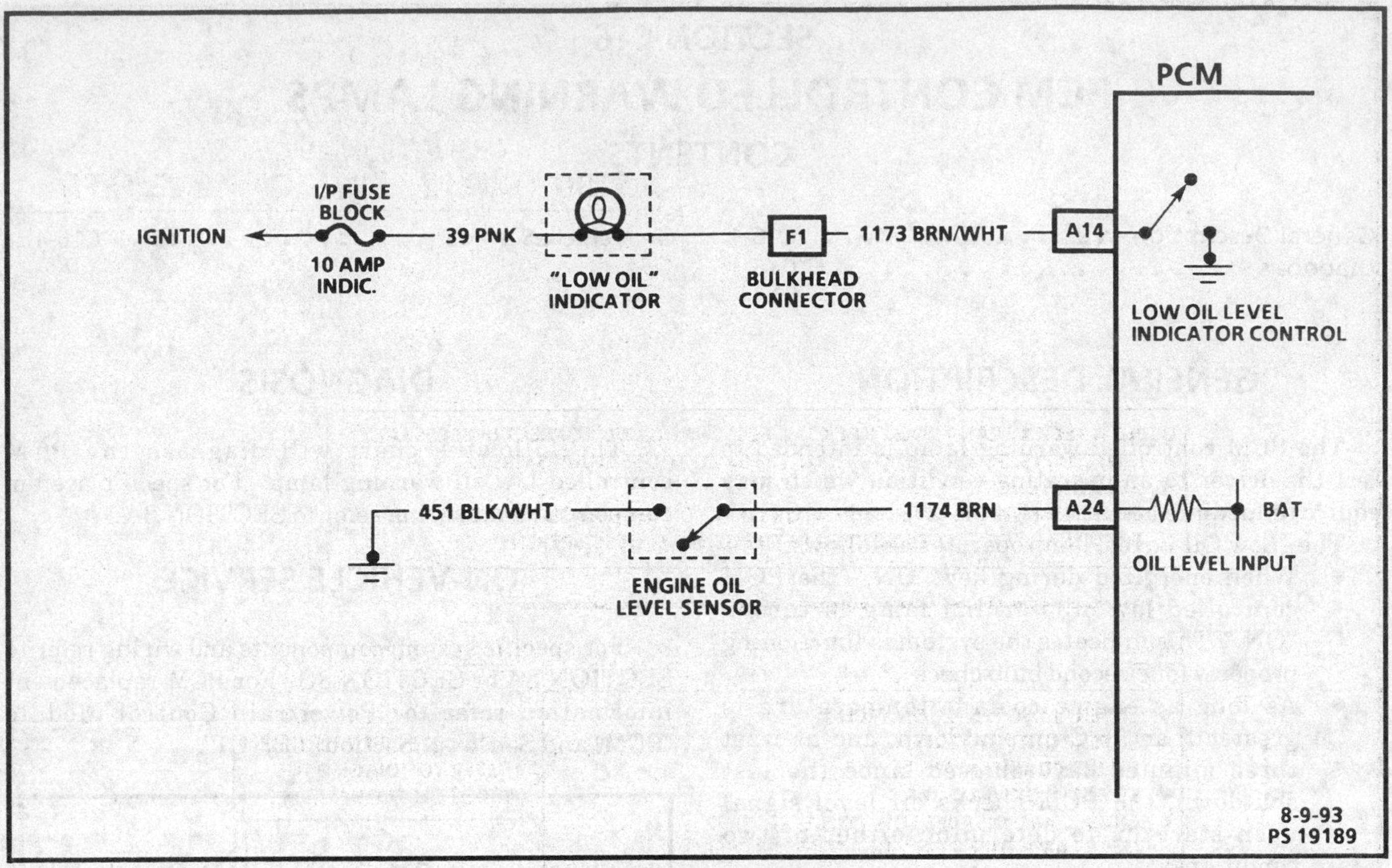
PCM
I/P FUSE
BLOCK
IGNITION
10 AMP
INDIC.
39 PNK
"LOW OIL"
INDICATOR
F1
BULKHEAD
CONNECTOR
1173 BRN/WHT
A14
LOW OIL LEVEL
INDICATOR CONTROL
451 BLK/WHT
ENGINE OIL
LEVEL SENSOR
1174 BRN
A24
BAT
OIL LEVEL INPUT
8-9-93
PS 19189

CHART C-16A

LOW OIL LEVEL LAMP
(FUNCTIONAL CHECK)
3100 (VIN M) "W" CARLINE (SFI)

System Description:

The low oil level logic is a simple algorithm that samples the level of the engine oil once per typical ignition cycle at power up (engine not turning - no reference pulses), only if criteria has been met indicating that the oil has had sufficient time to drain back into the pan at the last power down.

- If engine coolant temperature is greater than 75°C on shutdown, and at least three minutes have elapsed since the last shutdown, the PCM samples the low oil level sensor signal upon start-up.
- If engine coolant temperature is less than 75°C on shutdown, the PCM records the engine coolant temperature at shutdown. Now, when the engine is restarted, the PCM checks for engine coolant temperature again. If the engine coolant temperature has dropped by at least 11°C since the last shutdown, the PCM samples the low oil level sensor signal at start-up.
- If a DTC 14, 15, 36 or 82 is set, the PCM exits all low oil level functions including the one second bulb check upon the next start-up.

Diagnostic Aids: An intermittent may be caused by a poor connection, chaffed wire insulation or a wire broken inside the insulation.

Remember, if a DTC 14 or 15 or a combination of DTC 36 and 82 occurred at anytime during the ignition cycle before shutdown, the low oil level lamp will not illuminate for the one second bulb check. In this case the PCM will not sample the low oil level sensor signal.

CHART C16-A

LOW OIL LEVEL LAMP
(FUNCTIONAL CHECK)
3100 (VIN M) "W" CARLINE (SFI)

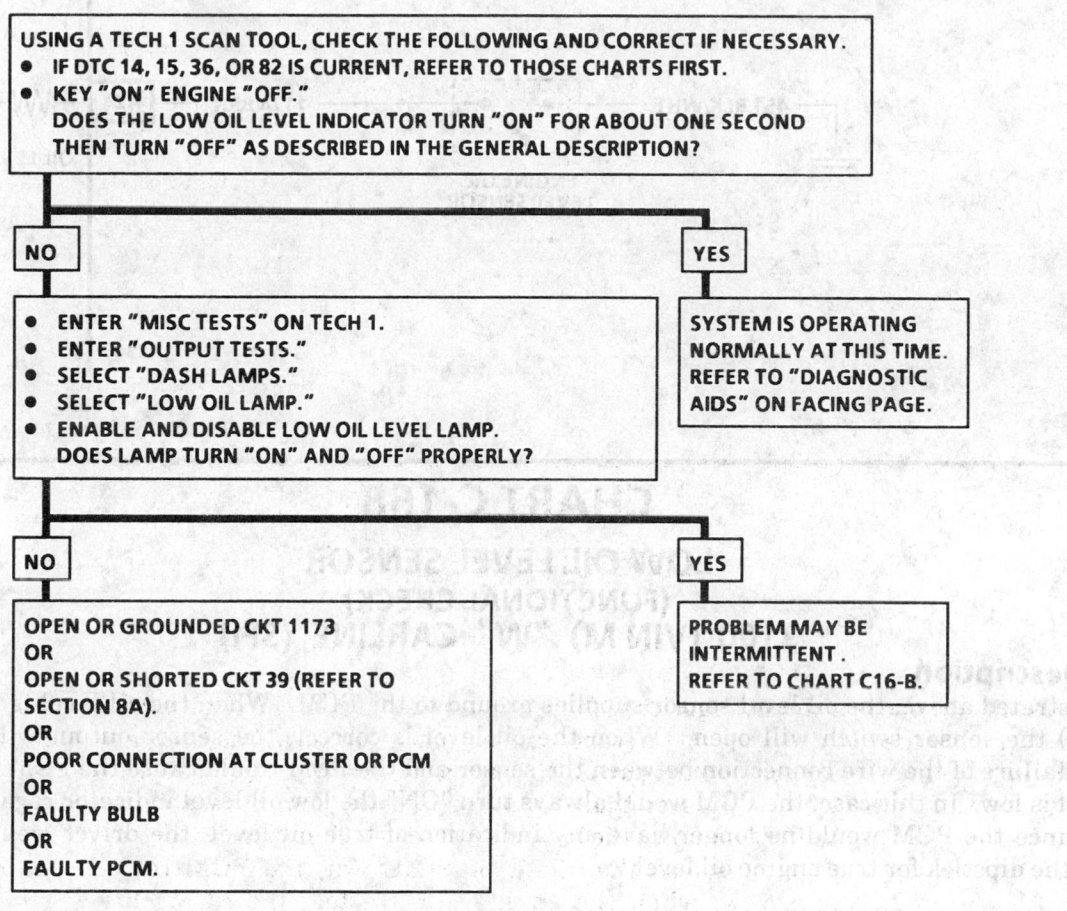

USING A TECH 1 SCAN TOOL, CHECK THE FOLLOWING AND CORRECT IF NECESSARY.

- IF DTC 14, 15, 36, OR 82 IS CURRENT, REFER TO THOSE CHARTS FIRST.
- KEY "ON" ENGINE "OFF."

DOES THE LOW OIL LEVEL INDICATOR TURN "ON" FOR ABOUT ONE SECOND THEN TURN "OFF" AS DESCRIBED IN THE GENERAL DESCRIPTION?

NO

- ENTER "MISC TESTS" ON TECH 1.
- ENTER "OUTPUT TESTS."
- SELECT "DASH LAMPS."
- SELECT "LOW OIL LAMP."
- ENABLE AND DISABLE LOW OIL LEVEL LAMP.

DOES LAMP TURN "ON" AND "OFF" PROPERLY?

NO

OPEN OR GROUNDED CKT 1173
OR
OPEN OR SHORTED CKT 39 (REFER TO SECTION 8A).
OR
POOR CONNECTION AT CLUSTER OR PCM
OR
FAULTY BULB
OR
FAULTY PCM.

YES

PROBLEM MAY BE INTERMITTENT . REFER TO CHART C16-B.

YES

SYSTEM IS OPERATING NORMALLY AT THIS TIME. REFER TO "DIAGNOSTIC AIDS" ON FACING PAGE.

"*AFTER REPAIRS*," CONFIRM "CLOSED LOOP" OPERATION AND NO MIL (SERVICE ENGINE SOON).

7-10-93
PS 18191

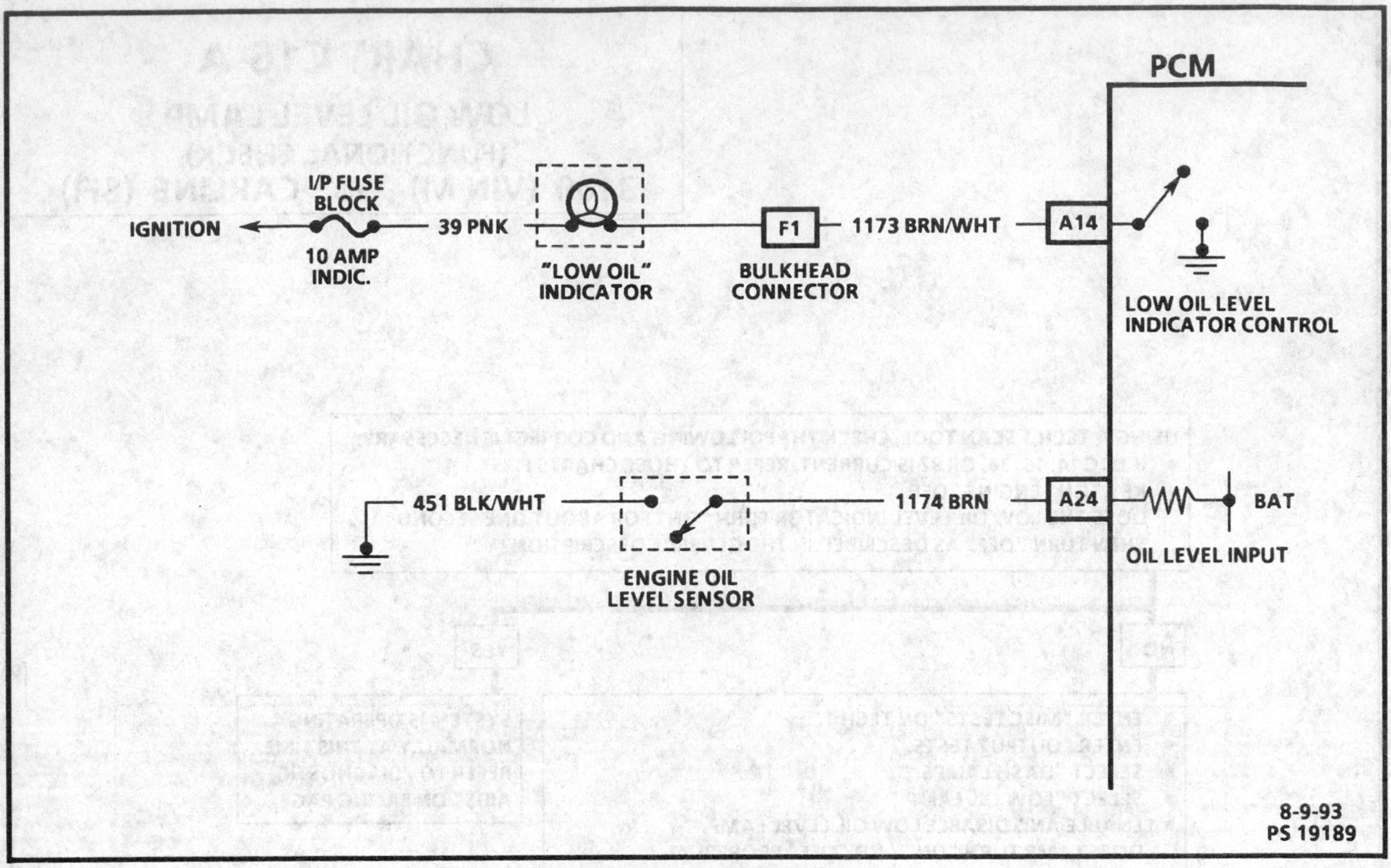
PCM
I/P FUSE
BLOCK
IGNITION
10 AMP
INDIC.
39 PNK
"LOW OIL"
INDICATOR
F1
BULKHEAD
CONNECTOR
1173 BRN/WHT
A14
LOW OIL LEVEL
INDICATOR CONTROL
451 BLK/WHT
ENGINE OIL
LEVEL SENSOR
1174 BRN
A24
BAT
OIL LEVEL INPUT
8-9-93
PS 19189

CHART C-16B

LOW OIL LEVEL SENSOR
(FUNCTIONAL CHECK)
3100 (VIN M) "W" CARLINE (SFI)

System Description:

As illustrated above, the oil level sensor supplies ground to the PCM. When the oil level is low (about 2.25 quarts full) the sensor switch will open. When the oil level is correct, the sensor output will be grounded. Therefore, failure of the wire connection between the sensor and the PCM would cause the PCM to falsely sense the oil level is low. In this case, the PCM would always turn "ON" the low oil level indicator regardless of actual oil level. Since the PCM would no longer have any indication of true oil level, the driver would have to rely strictly on the dipstick for true engine oil level.

Diagnostic Aids: An intermittent may be caused by a poor connection, chaffed wire insulation or a wire broken inside the insulation. Prolonged exposure to contaminated engine oil could eventually cause the sensor to fail (open).

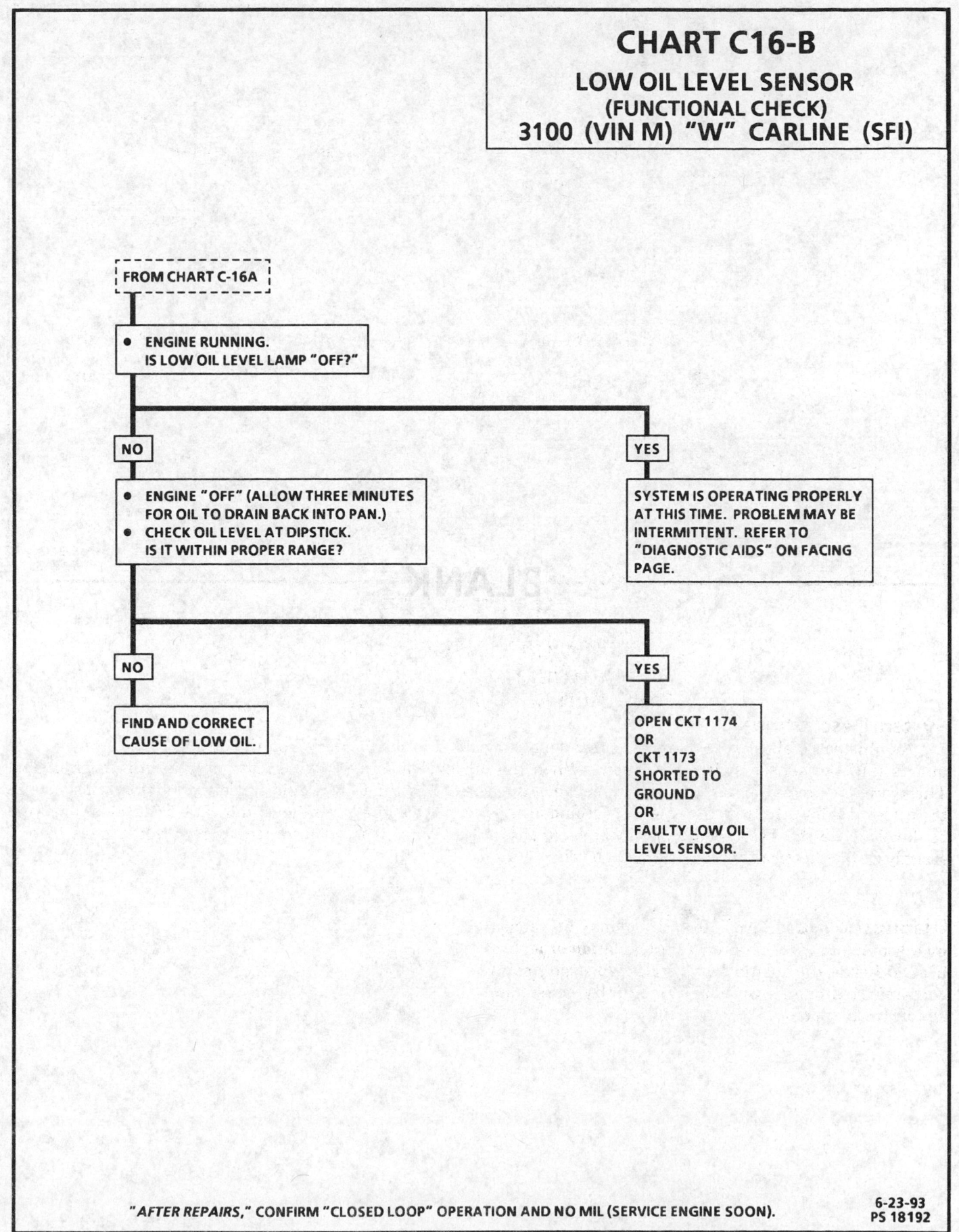

CHART C16-B
LOW OIL LEVEL SENSOR
(FUNCTIONAL CHECK)
3100 (VIN M) "W" CARLINE (SFI)

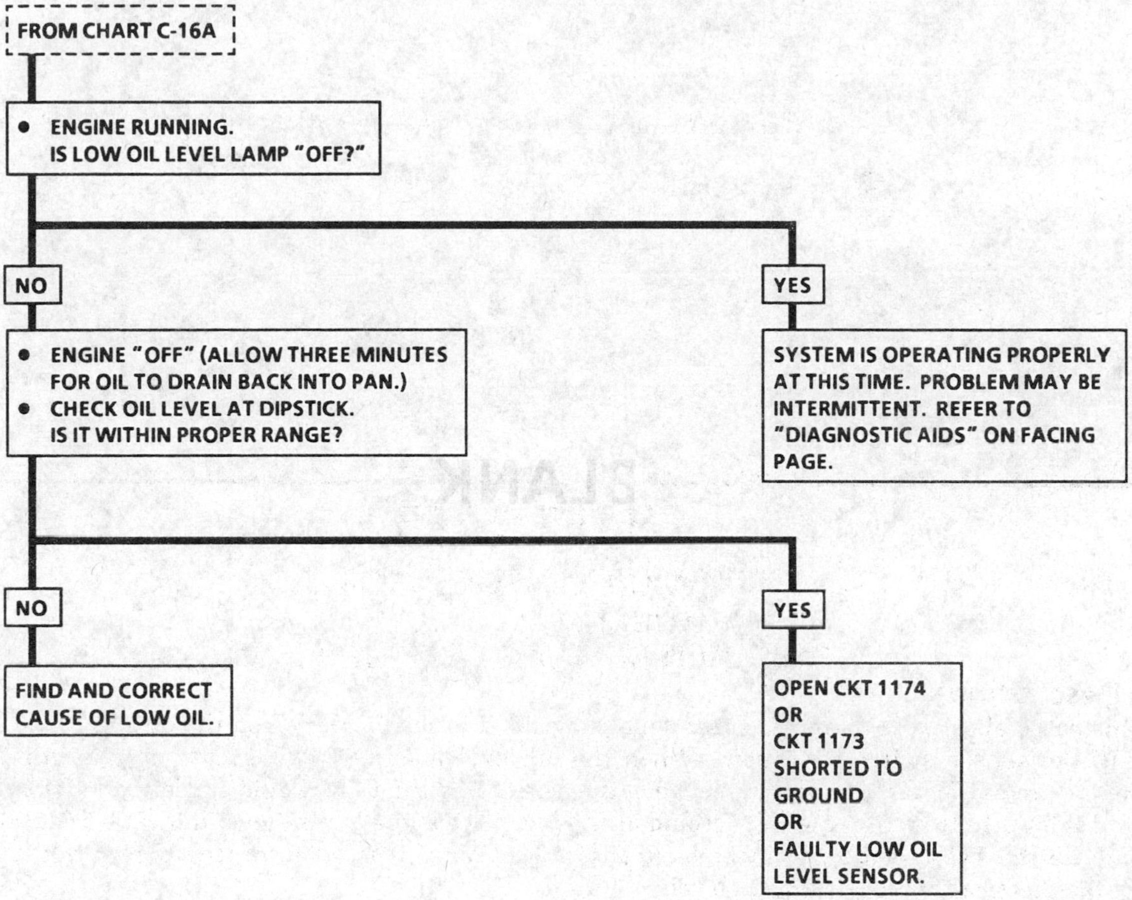
FROM CHART C-16A
• ENGINE RUNNING.
IS LOW OIL LEVEL LAMP "OFF?"
NO
YES
• ENGINE "OFF" (ALLOW THREE MINUTES FOR OIL TO DRAIN BACK INTO PAN.)
• CHECK OIL LEVEL AT DIPSTICK.
IS IT WITHIN PROPER RANGE?
SYSTEM IS OPERATING PROPERLY AT THIS TIME. PROBLEM MAY BE INTERMITTENT. REFER TO "DIAGNOSTIC AIDS" ON FACING PAGE.
NO
YES
FIND AND CORRECT CAUSE OF LOW OIL.
OPEN CKT 1174 OR CKT 1173 SHORTED TO GROUND OR FAULTY LOW OIL LEVEL SENSOR.

"*AFTER REPAIRS*," CONFIRM "CLOSED LOOP" OPERATION AND NO MIL (SERVICE ENGINE SOON).

6-23-93
PS 18192

BLANK

SECTION C17

CRUISE CONTROL

CONTENTS

GENERAL DESCRIPTION

Cruise control is a speed control system that maintains a desired vehicle speed under normal driving conditions. However, steep grades up or down may cause variations in the selected speeds. The electronic cruise control system has the capability to cruise, coast, resume speed, accelerate, and "tap-up" and "tap-down."

The main parts of the cruise control system are the functional control switches, cruise control module assembly, speed sensor and cruise control release switch and stoplamp switch assemblies.

The cruise control system uses a cruise control module assembly to obtain the desired vehicle cruise operation. Two important components in the module assembly help to do this. One is an electronic controller and the second is an electric stepper motor. The controller monitors vehicle speed and operates the electric stepper motor. The motor moves a band and throttle linkage, in response to the controller, to maintain the desired cruise speed. The cruise control module assembly contains a low speed limit which will prevent system engagement below a minimum speed of 40 km/h (25 mph). The operation of the controller is controlled by functional control switches located on the cruise control actuator lever assembly.

Cruise control release switch and stoplamp switch assemblies are provided to disengage the cruise system. The switch assemblies are mounted on the brake pedal bracket assembly. When the brake pedal assembly is depressed, the cruise control system is electrically disengaged an the throttle is returned to the idle position.

CRUISE CONTROL MODULE ASSEMBLY

The cruise control module assembly is mounted on the left wheelhouse panel assembly near the brake master cylinder assembly. The module assembly has an electronic controller and an electric stepper motor to vary the throttle with each different cruise control mode. The module assembly is not serviceable.

DIAGNOSIS

The following chart will diagnose the "Cruise Inhibit" and "Cruise Status" circuits. Diagnosis of the remaining cruise control circuits are covered in SECTION 8A and 9B.

ON-VEHICLE SERVICE

Refer to SECTION 9B for removal and replacement of cruise control components.

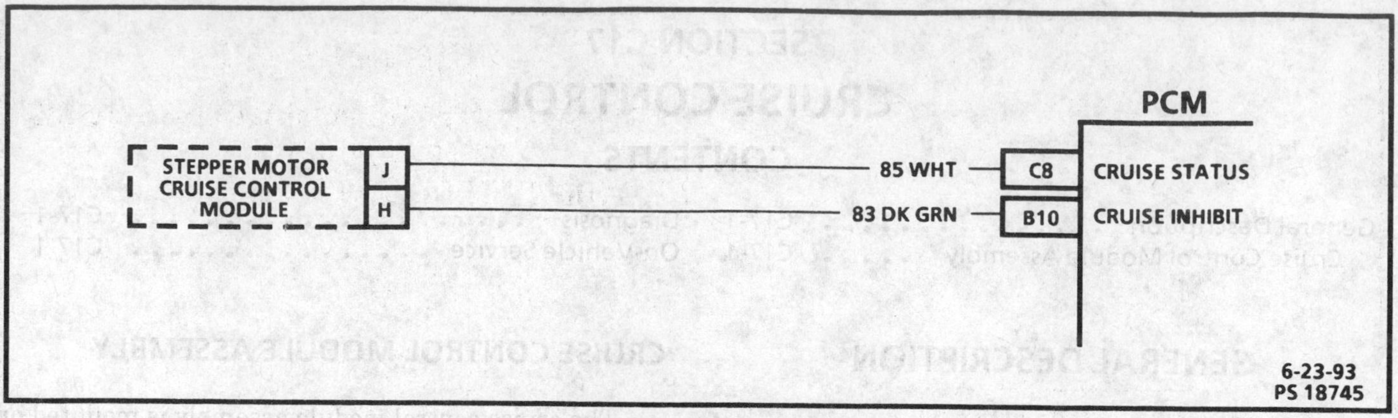
PCM
STEPPER MOTOR CRUISE CONTROL MODULE
J
H
85 WHT
83 DK GRN
C8
B10
CRUISE STATUS
CRUISE INHIBIT
6-23-93
PS 18745

CHART C-17

CRUISE CONTROL INHIBIT DIAGNOSIS
(FUNCTIONAL CHECK)
3100 (VIN M) "W" CARLINE (SFI)

Circuit Description:

The stepper motor cruise system differs from the upintegrated (PCM-controlled) cruise system previously used in that it is a stand-alone system. The PCM still retains the ability to disable cruise if conditions are detected which would make cruise control operation undesirable. Any one of the following conditions may cause cruise control to be inhibited by the PCM:

- DTC 16 or 53 set (current).
- Park, neutral, reverse or 1st gear is indicated by the transaxle range switch.
- Vehicle Speed Sensor (VSS) indicates less than 25 mph.
- Engine not running.
- High engine RPM (fuel cutoff).
- Any transaxle related DTC which causes the use of a default gear.

If the PCM detects any one of the above conditions, it will interrupt the ground at the cruise inhibit signal (CKT 83) to request that cruise control be disengaged.

Diagnostic Aids: An intermittent may be caused by a poor connection, rubbed through wire insulation or a wire broken inside the insulation.

Check for:

- Poor connection or damaged harness - Inspect PCM harness for open or short to ground in CKT 85, improper mating, broken locks, improperly formed or damaged terminals, poor terminal to wire connections, and damaged harness.
- Intermittent test - Observe "SMCC status" on Tech 1 while moving related connectors and wiring harness with engine running. If the failure is induced, the "SMCC status" display will change to "engaged." This may help to isolate the location of the malfunction.

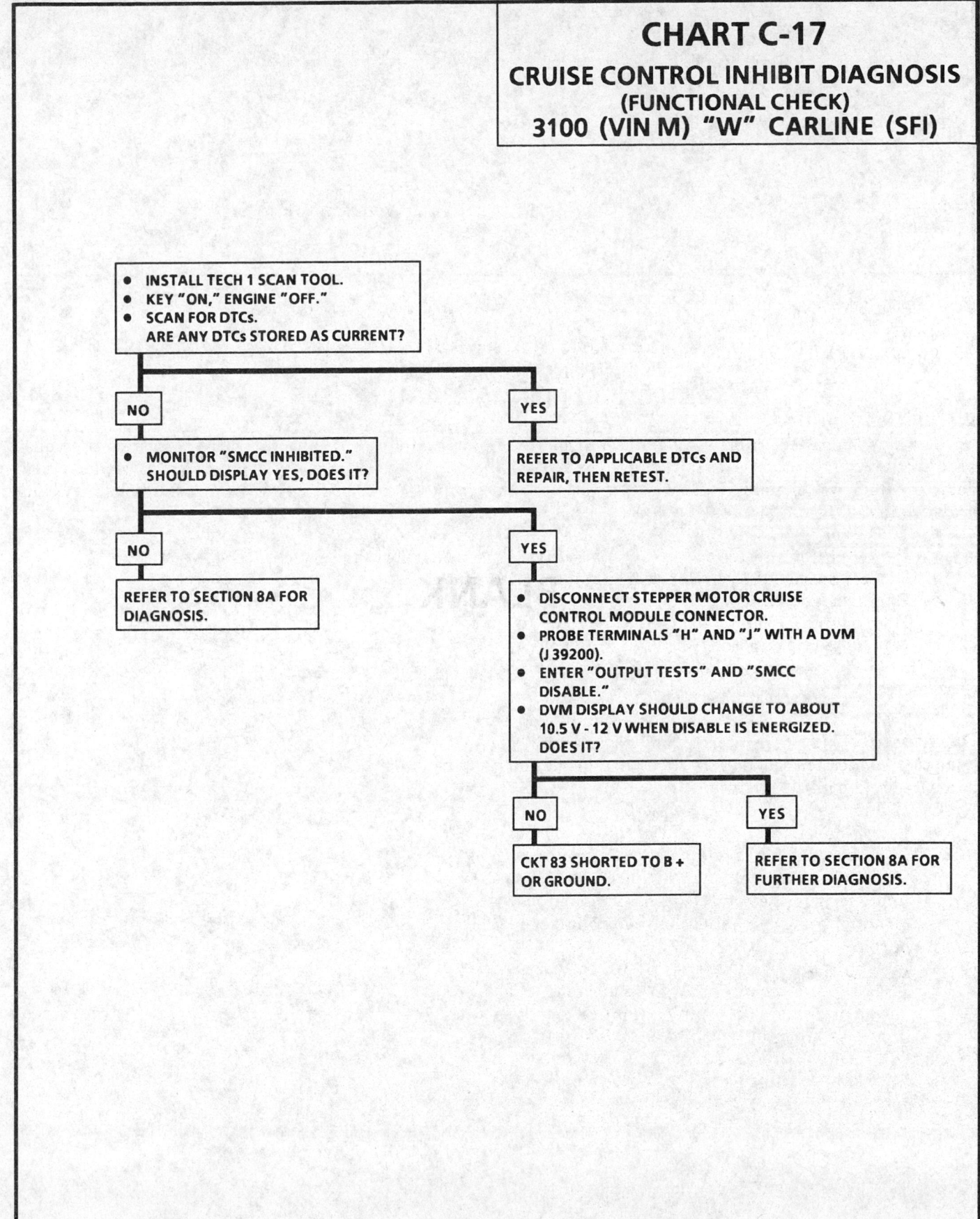

CHART C-17

CRUISE CONTROL INHIBIT DIAGNOSIS
(FUNCTIONAL CHECK)
3100 (VIN M) "W" CARLINE (SFI)

- INSTALL TECH 1 SCAN TOOL.
- KEY "ON," ENGINE "OFF."
- SCAN FOR DTCs.
  ARE ANY DTCs STORED AS CURRENT?

NO

- MONITOR "SMCC INHIBITED."
  SHOULD DISPLAY YES, DOES IT?

  NO

  REFER TO SECTION 8A FOR DIAGNOSIS.

  YES

  - DISCONNECT STEPPER MOTOR CRUISE CONTROL MODULE CONNECTOR.
  - PROBE TERMINALS "H" AND "J" WITH A DVM (J 39200).
  - ENTER "OUTPUT TESTS" AND "SMCC DISABLE."
  - DVM DISPLAY SHOULD CHANGE TO ABOUT 10.5 V - 12 V WHEN DISABLE IS ENERGIZED. DOES IT?

    NO

    CKT 83 SHORTED TO B + OR GROUND.

    YES

    REFER TO SECTION 8A FOR FURTHER DIAGNOSIS.

YES

REFER TO APPLICABLE DTCs AND REPAIR, THEN RETEST.

"*AFTER REPAIRS,*" CONFIRM "CLOSED LOOP" OPERATION AND NO MIL (SERVICE ENGINE SOON).

5-29-93
PS 18368

BLANK

SECTION A

ENGINE COMPONENTS/WIRING DIAGRAMS/DIAGNOSTIC CHARTS

BASIC PROCEDURE

If you have not reviewed the basic information on how to use the diagnostic procedures, go to the introduction of this section.

ON-BOARD DIAGNOSTIC SYSTEM CHECK

The on-board diagnostic system check verifies the system is functioning correctly.

Some special considerations to keep in mind **before** making the on-board diagnostic system check are:

1. PCM and engine grounds for being clean and tight at ignition module bracket.
2. PCM B+ wires for being clean and tight at starter and/or junction block.

Block Drive Wheels

The vehicle drive wheels should always be blocked while checking the system.

CONTENTS

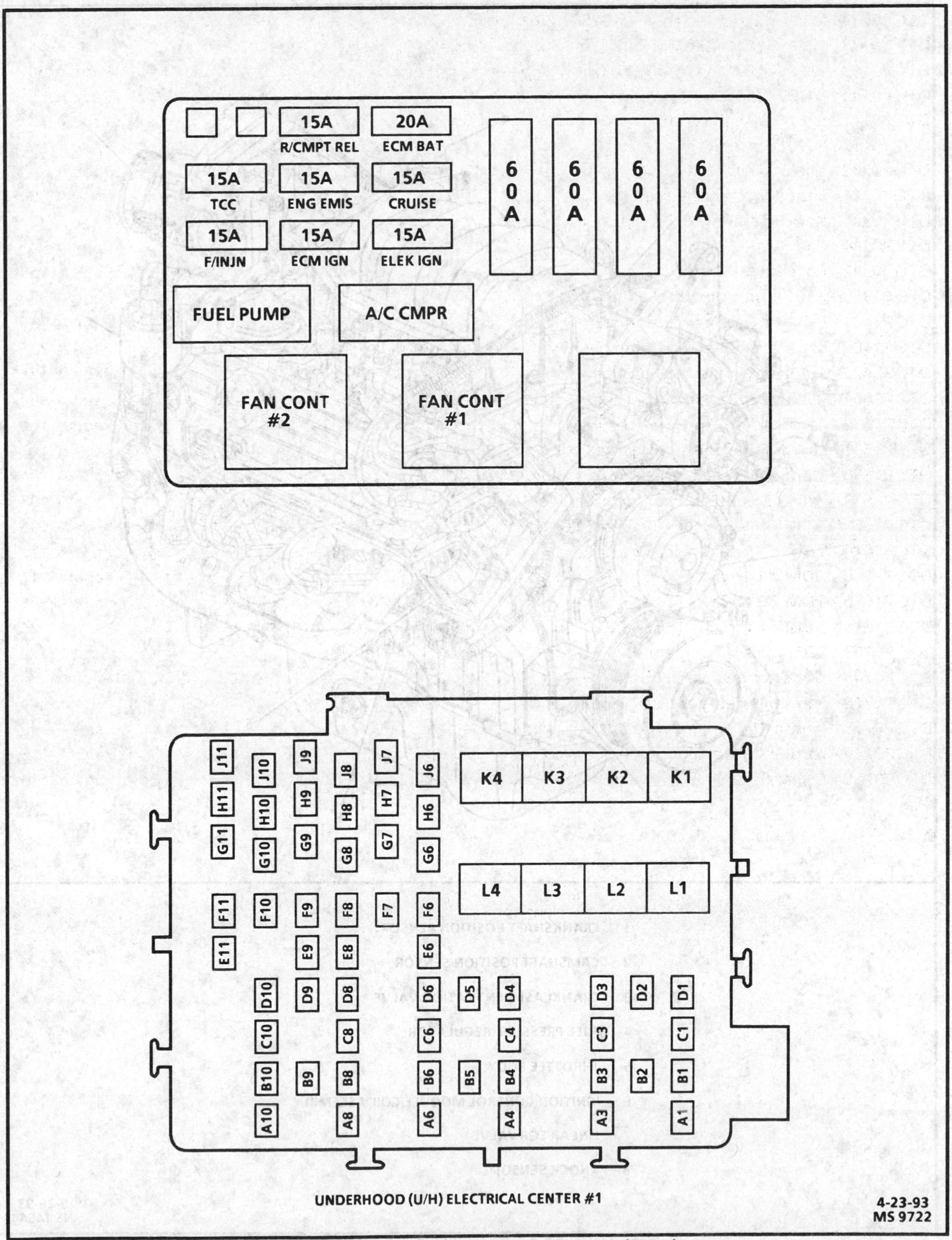
15A
R/CMPT REL
20A
ECM BAT
15A
TCC
15A
ENG EMIS
15A
CRUISE
15A
F/INJN
15A
ECM IGN
15A
ELEK IGN
60A
60A
60A
60A
FUEL PUMP
A/C CMPR
FAN CONT #2
FAN CONT #1
J11 J10 J9 J8 J7 J6
H11 H10 H9 H8 H7 H6
G11 G10 G9 G8 G7 G6
F11 F10 F9 F8 F7 F6
E11 E9 E8 E6
D10 D9 D8 D6 D5 D4 D3 D2 D1
C10 C8 C6 C4 C3 C1
B10 B9 B8 B6 B5 B4 B3 B2 B1
A10 A8 A6 A4 A3 A1
K4 K3 K2 K1
L4 L3 L2 L1
UNDERHOOD (U/H) ELECTRICAL CENTER #1
4-23-93
MS 9722

Figure A-1 - Engine Electrical Center 3800 (VIN L)

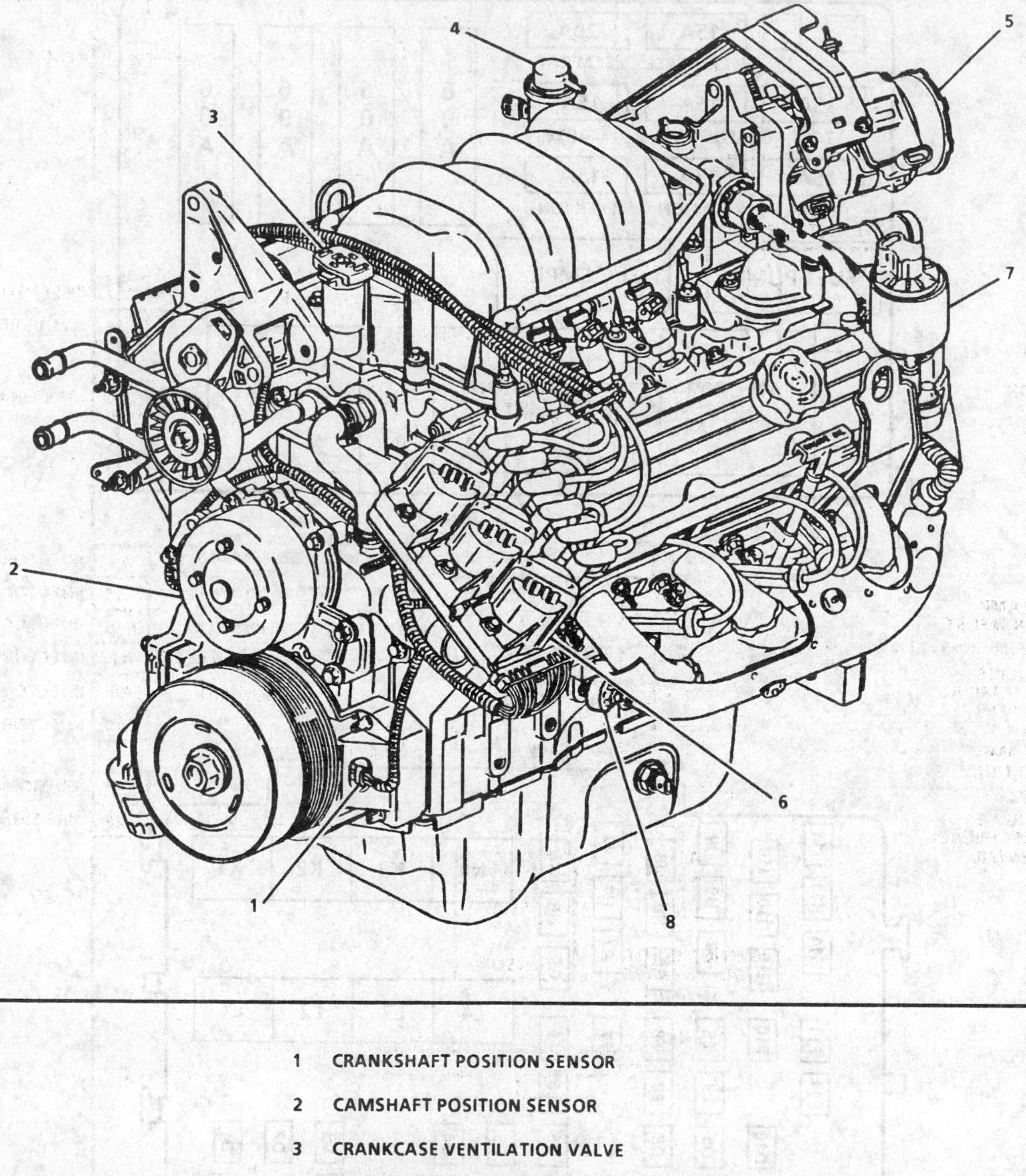
1
2
3
4
5
6
7
8

1 CRANKSHAFT POSITION SENSOR
2 CAMSHAFT POSITION SENSOR
3 CRANKCASE VENTILATION VALVE
4 FUEL PRESSURE REGULATOR
5 THROTTLE BODY
6 IGNITION CONTROL MODULE/COIL ASSEMBLY
7 LINEAR EGR VALVE
8 KNOCK SENSOR

5-28-93
NS 14544

Figure A-2 - Composite View 3800 (VIN L)

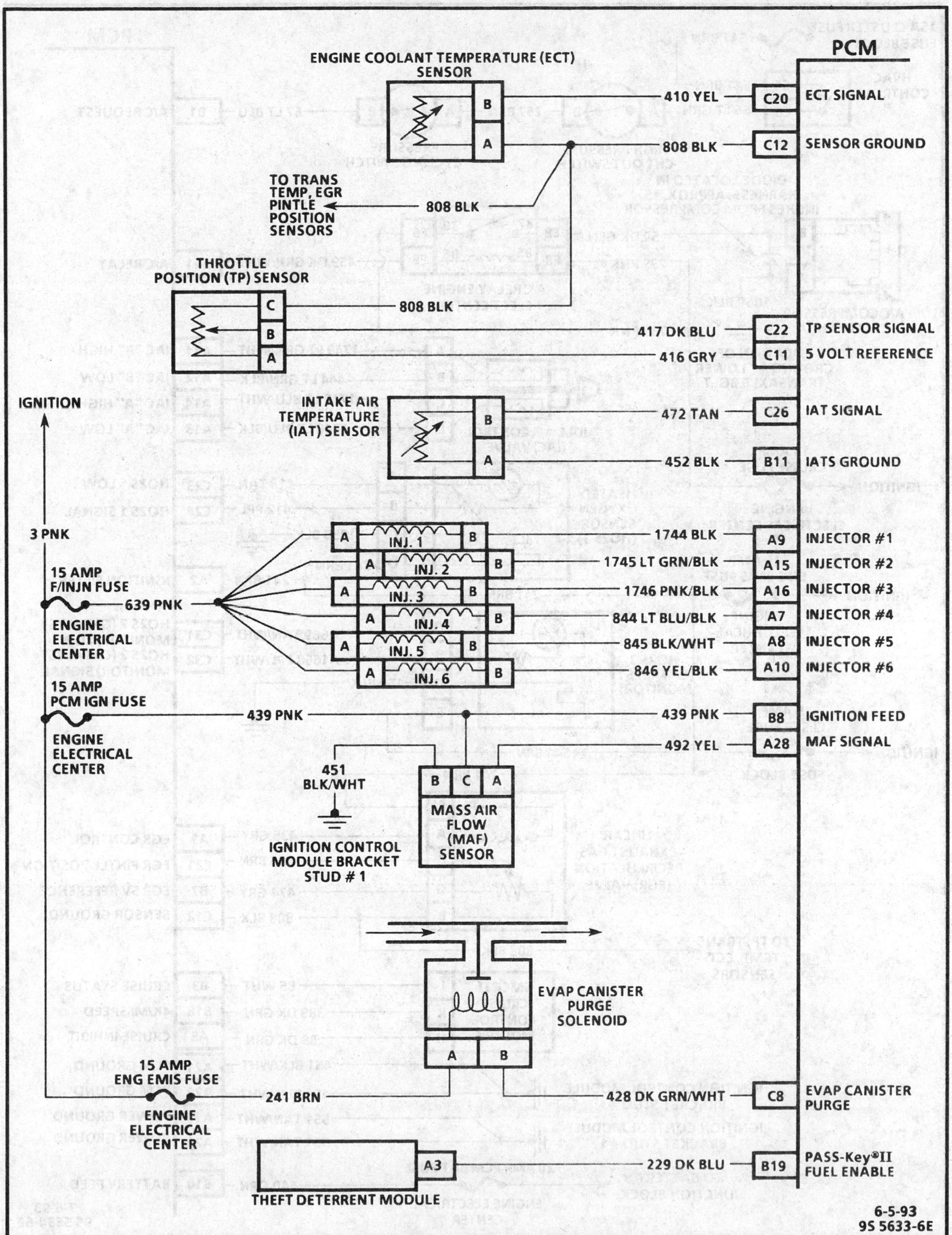
PCM
ENGINE COOLANT TEMPERATURE (ECT) SENSOR
B
A
410 YEL
C20
ECT SIGNAL
808 BLK
C12
SENSOR GROUND
TO TRANS TEMP, EGR PINTLE POSITION SENSORS
808 BLK
THROTTLE POSITION (TP) SENSOR
C
B
A
808 BLK
417 DK BLU
C22
TP SENSOR SIGNAL
416 GRY
C11
5 VOLT REFERENCE
IGNITION
INTAKE AIR TEMPERATURE (IAT) SENSOR
472 TAN
C26
IAT SIGNAL
452 BLK
B11
IATS GROUND
3 PNK
INJ. 1
1744 BLK
A9
INJECTOR #1
INJ. 2
1745 LT GRN/BLK
A15
INJECTOR #2
INJ. 3
1746 PNK/BLK
A16
INJECTOR #3
INJ. 4
844 LT BLU/BLK
A7
INJECTOR #4
INJ. 5
845 BLK/WHT
A8
INJECTOR #5
INJ. 6
846 YEL/BLK
A10
INJECTOR #6
15 AMP F/INJN FUSE
639 PNK
ENGINE ELECTRICAL CENTER
15 AMP PCM IGN FUSE
439 PNK
439 PNK
B8
IGNITION FEED
ENGINE ELECTRICAL CENTER
492 YEL
A28
MAF SIGNAL
451 BLK/WHT
B C A
MASS AIR FLOW (MAF) SENSOR
IGNITION CONTROL MODULE BRACKET STUD # 1
EVAP CANISTER PURGE SOLENOID
A
B
15 AMP ENG EMIS FUSE
241 BRN
428 DK GRN/WHT
C8
EVAP CANISTER PURGE
ENGINE ELECTRICAL CENTER
A3
229 DK BLU
B19
PASS-Key®II FUEL ENABLE
THEFT DETERRENT MODULE
6-5-93
9S 5633-6E

Figure A-3 - PCM Wiring Diagram 3800 (VIN L) (1 of 4)

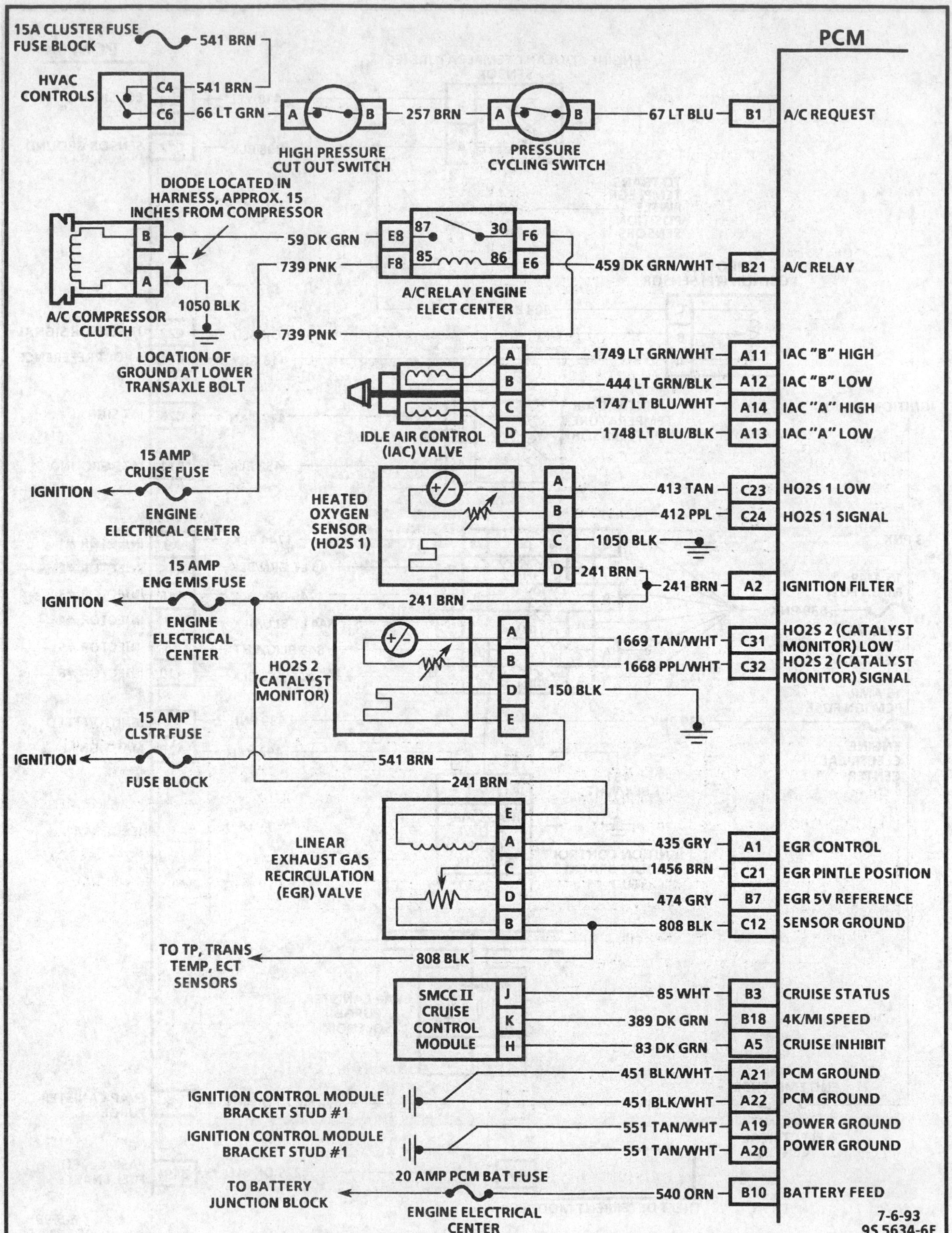
PCM
15A CLUSTER FUSE
FUSE BLOCK
541 BRN
HVAC CONTROLS
C4
C6
541 BRN
66 LT GRN
A
B
257 BRN
HIGH PRESSURE CUT OUT SWITCH
PRESSURE CYCLING SWITCH
67 LT BLU
B1
A/C REQUEST
DIODE LOCATED IN HARNESS, APPROX. 15 INCHES FROM COMPRESSOR
59 DK GRN
E8
87
30
F6
739 PNK
F8
85
86
E6
459 DK GRN/WHT
B21
A/C RELAY
A/C RELAY ENGINE ELECT CENTER
1050 BLK
A/C COMPRESSOR CLUTCH
739 PNK
LOCATION OF GROUND AT LOWER TRANSAXLE BOLT
1749 LT GRN/WHT
A11
IAC "B" HIGH
444 LT GRN/BLK
A12
IAC "B" LOW
1747 LT BLU/WHT
A14
IAC "A" HIGH
1748 LT BLU/BLK
A13
IAC "A" LOW
IDLE AIR CONTROL (IAC) VALVE
15 AMP CRUISE FUSE
IGNITION
ENGINE ELECTRICAL CENTER
HEATED OXYGEN SENSOR (HO2S 1)
413 TAN
C23
HO2S 1 LOW
412 PPL
C24
HO2S 1 SIGNAL
1050 BLK
241 BRN
241 BRN
A2
IGNITION FILTER
15 AMP ENG EMIS FUSE
IGNITION
ENGINE ELECTRICAL CENTER
241 BRN
HO2S 2 (CATALYST MONITOR)
1669 TAN/WHT
C31
HO2S 2 (CATALYST MONITOR) LOW
1668 PPL/WHT
C32
HO2S 2 (CATALYST MONITOR) SIGNAL
150 BLK
15 AMP CLSTR FUSE
IGNITION
FUSE BLOCK
541 BRN
241 BRN
LINEAR EXHAUST GAS RECIRCULATION (EGR) VALVE
435 GRY
A1
EGR CONTROL
1456 BRN
C21
EGR PINTLE POSITION
474 GRY
B7
EGR 5V REFERENCE
808 BLK
C12
SENSOR GROUND
TO TP, TRANS TEMP, ECT SENSORS
808 BLK
SMCC II CRUISE CONTROL MODULE
85 WHT
B3
CRUISE STATUS
389 DK GRN
B18
4K/MI SPEED
83 DK GRN
A5
CRUISE INHIBIT
451 BLK/WHT
A21
PCM GROUND
IGNITION CONTROL MODULE BRACKET STUD #1
451 BLK/WHT
A22
PCM GROUND
551 TAN/WHT
A19
POWER GROUND
IGNITION CONTROL MODULE BRACKET STUD #1
551 TAN/WHT
A20
POWER GROUND
20 AMP PCM BAT FUSE
TO BATTERY JUNCTION BLOCK
540 ORN
B10
BATTERY FEED
ENGINE ELECTRICAL CENTER
7-6-93
9S 5634-6E

Figure A-4 - PCM Wiring Diagram 3800 (VIN L) (2 of 4)

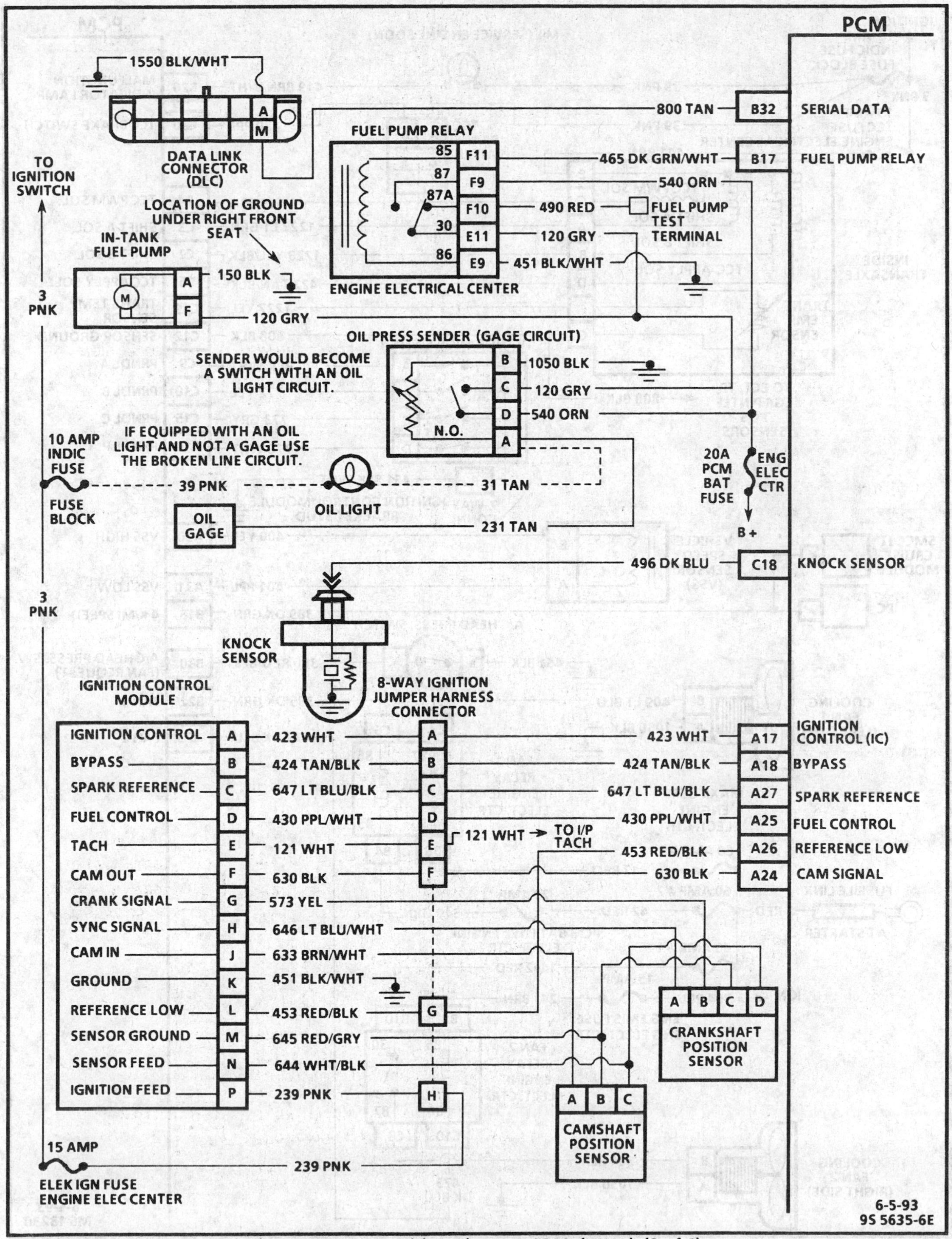
PCM
1550 BLK/WHT
A
M
DATA LINK CONNECTOR (DLC)
800 TAN
B32
SERIAL DATA
FUEL PUMP RELAY
85
F11
87
F9
87A
F10
30
E11
86
E9
465 DK GRN/WHT
B17
FUEL PUMP RELAY
540 ORN
490 RED
FUEL PUMP TEST TERMINAL
120 GRY
451 BLK/WHT
ENGINE ELECTRICAL CENTER
TO IGNITION SWITCH
LOCATION OF GROUND UNDER RIGHT FRONT SEAT
IN-TANK FUEL PUMP
150 BLK
A
F
M
3 PNK
120 GRY
OIL PRESS SENDER (GAGE CIRCUIT)
SENDER WOULD BECOME A SWITCH WITH AN OIL LIGHT CIRCUIT.
B
1050 BLK
C
120 GRY
D
540 ORN
N.O.
A
IF EQUIPPED WITH AN OIL LIGHT AND NOT A GAGE USE THE BROKEN LINE CIRCUIT.
10 AMP INDIC FUSE
39 PNK
31 TAN
FUSE BLOCK
OIL LIGHT
20A PCM BAT FUSE
ENG ELEC CTR
OIL GAGE
231 TAN
B+
496 DK BLU
C18
KNOCK SENSOR
3 PNK
KNOCK SENSOR
IGNITION CONTROL MODULE
8-WAY IGNITION JUMPER HARNESS CONNECTOR
IGNITION CONTROL
A
423 WHT
A
423 WHT
A17
IGNITION CONTROL (IC)
BYPASS
B
424 TAN/BLK
B
424 TAN/BLK
A18
BYPASS
SPARK REFERENCE
C
647 LT BLU/BLK
C
647 LT BLU/BLK
A27
SPARK REFERENCE
FUEL CONTROL
D
430 PPL/WHT
D
430 PPL/WHT
A25
FUEL CONTROL
TACH
E
121 WHT
E
121 WHT → TO I/P TACH
453 RED/BLK
A26
REFERENCE LOW
CAM OUT
F
630 BLK
F
630 BLK
A24
CAM SIGNAL
CRANK SIGNAL
G
573 YEL
SYNC SIGNAL
H
646 LT BLU/WHT
CAM IN
J
633 BRN/WHT
GROUND
K
451 BLK/WHT
REFERENCE LOW
L
453 RED/BLK
G
SENSOR GROUND
M
645 RED/GRY
SENSOR FEED
N
644 WHT/BLK
IGNITION FEED
P
239 PNK
H
A B C D
CRANKSHAFT POSITION SENSOR
A B C
CAMSHAFT POSITION SENSOR
15 AMP
239 PNK
ELEK IGN FUSE ENGINE ELEC CENTER
6-5-93
9S 5635-6E

Figure A-5 - PCM Wiring Diagram 3800 (VIN L) (3 of 4)

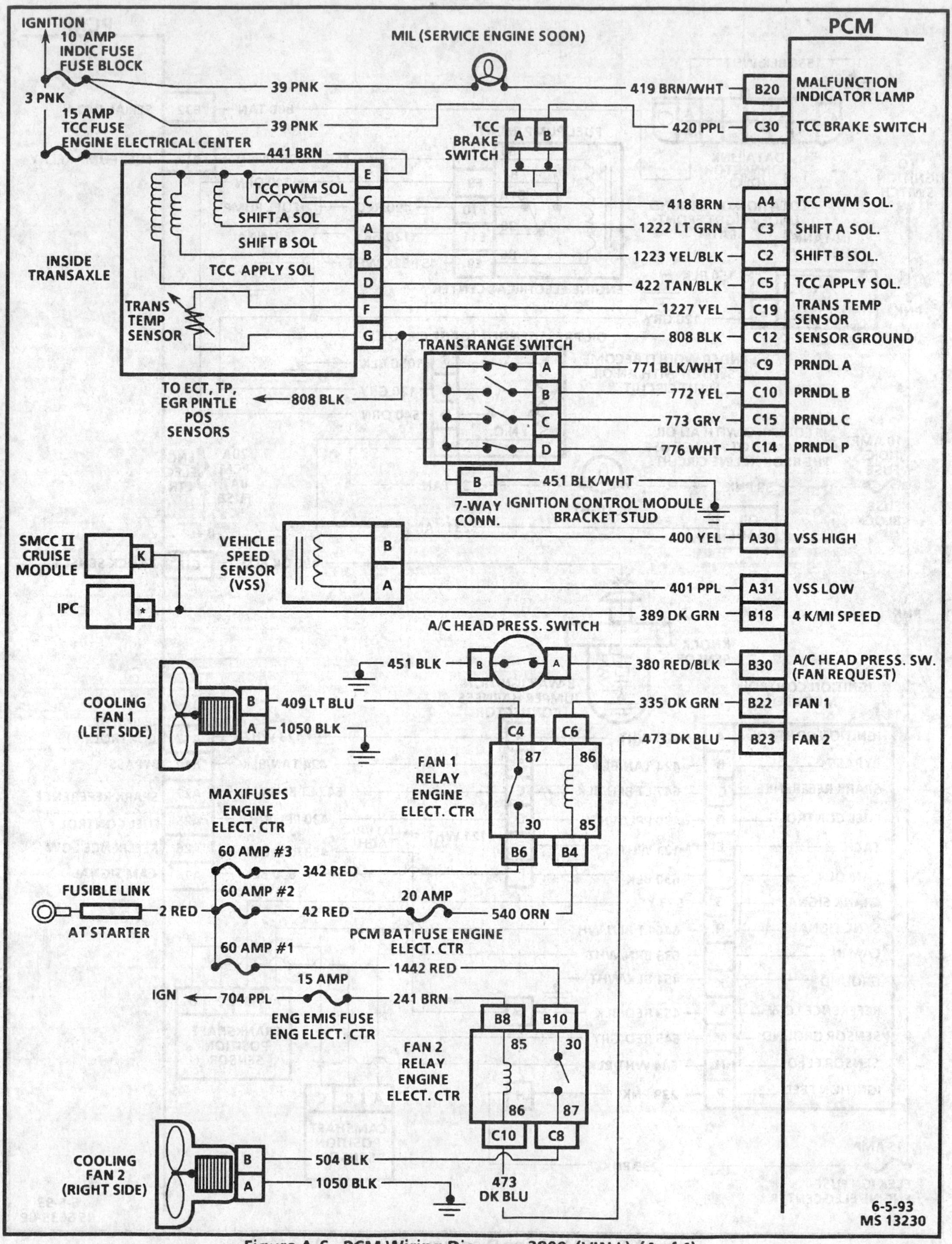
PCM
IGNITION
10 AMP
INDIC FUSE
FUSE BLOCK
3 PNK
15 AMP
TCC FUSE
ENGINE ELECTRICAL CENTER
MIL (SERVICE ENGINE SOON)
39 PNK
39 PNK
441 BRN
419 BRN/WHT
B20
MALFUNCTION INDICATOR LAMP
TCC BRAKE SWITCH
420 PPL
C30
TCC BRAKE SWITCH
TCC PWM SOL
SHIFT A SOL
SHIFT B SOL
TCC APPLY SOL
INSIDE TRANSAXLE
TRANS TEMP SENSOR
418 BRN
A4
TCC PWM SOL.
1222 LT GRN
C3
SHIFT A SOL.
1223 YEL/BLK
C2
SHIFT B SOL.
422 TAN/BLK
C5
TCC APPLY SOL.
1227 YEL
C19
TRANS TEMP SENSOR
808 BLK
C12
SENSOR GROUND
TRANS RANGE SWITCH
771 BLK/WHT
C9
PRNDL A
772 YEL
C10
PRNDL B
773 GRY
C15
PRNDL C
776 WHT
C14
PRNDL P
TO ECT, TP, EGR PINTLE POS SENSORS
808 BLK
451 BLK/WHT
7-WAY CONN.
IGNITION CONTROL MODULE BRACKET STUD
SMCC II CRUISE MODULE
IPC
VEHICLE SPEED SENSOR (VSS)
400 YEL
A30
VSS HIGH
401 PPL
A31
VSS LOW
389 DK GRN
B18
4 K/MI SPEED
A/C HEAD PRESS. SWITCH
451 BLK
380 RED/BLK
B30
A/C HEAD PRESS. SW. (FAN REQUEST)
COOLING FAN 1 (LEFT SIDE)
409 LT BLU
1050 BLK
335 DK GRN
B22
FAN 1
473 DK BLU
B23
FAN 2
FAN 1 RELAY ENGINE ELECT. CTR
MAXIFUSES ENGINE ELECT. CTR
60 AMP #3
342 RED
FUSIBLE LINK
AT STARTER
2 RED
60 AMP #2
42 RED
20 AMP
540 ORN
PCM BAT FUSE ENGINE ELECT. CTR
60 AMP #1
1442 RED
15 AMP
IGN
704 PPL
241 BRN
ENG EMIS FUSE ENG ELECT. CTR
FAN 2 RELAY ENGINE ELECT. CTR
COOLING FAN 2 (RIGHT SIDE)
504 BLK
1050 BLK
473 DK BLU
6-5-93
MS 13230

Figure A-6 - PCM Wiring Diagram 3800 (VIN L) (4 of 4)

1994 "W" CARLINE BLACK PCM CONNECTOR "A" 3800 (VIN L)
RPO: L27

PCM PIN/FUNCTION	CKT #	WIRE COLOR	J 39700-A PIN #	VOLTAGE KEY "ON"	VOLTAGE ENG "RUN"	6E3 REFERENCE
A1 EGR CONTROL	435	GRY	101	B +	B +	SECT. C7
A2 IGNITION FILTER	241	BRN	102	B +	B +	SECT. C1
A3 N/C			103			
A4 TCC PWM SOLENOID	418	BRN	104	B +	B +	SECT. C8
A5 CRUISE ENABLE	83	DK GRN	105	*	*	SECTION 8A
A6 N/C			106			
A7 INJECTOR #4	844	BLK	107	B +	B +	SECT. C2
A8 INJECTOR #5	845	BLK/WHT	108	B +	B +	SECT. C2
A9 INJECTOR #1	1744	BLK	109	B +	B +	SECT. C2
A10 INJECTOR #6	846	BLK/YEL	110	B +	B +	SECT. C2
A11 IAC "B" HIGH	1749	LT GRN/WHT	111	(2)	(2)	SECT. C2
A12 IAC "B" LOW	444	LT GRN/BLK	112	(2)	(2)	SECT. C2
A13 IAC "A" LOW	1748	LT BLU/BLK	113	(2)	(2)	SECT. C2
A14 IAC "A" HIGH	1747	LT BLU/WHT	114	(2)	(2)	SECT. C2
A15 INJECTOR #2	1745	LT GRN/BLK	115	B +	B +	SECT. C2
A16 INJECTOR #3	1746	PNK/BLK	116	B +	B +	SECT. C2
A17 IGNITION CONTROL (IC)	423	WHT	117	*	1.5	SECT. C4
A18 BYPASS	424	TAN/BLK	118	*	5	SECT. C4
A19 PWR GND	551	TAN/WHT	119	*	*	SECT. C1
A20 PWR GND	551	TAN/WHT	120	*	*	SECT. C1
A21 PCM GND	451	BLK/WHT	121	*	*	SECT. C1
A22 PCM GND	451	BLK/WHT	122	*	*	SECT. C1
A23 N/C			123			
A24 CAM SIGNAL	630	BLK	124	5	(2)	SECT. C4
A25 FUEL CONTROL	430	PPL/WHT	125	5	2.5	SECT. C1
A26 REFERENCE LOW (GROUND)	453	RED/BLK	126	*	*	SECT. C4
A27 SPARK REFERENCE	647	LT BLU/BLK	127	5	2.5	SECT. C4
A28 MAF SIGNAL	492	YEL	128	2.5	2.5	SECT. C1
A29 N/C			129			
A30 VSS HIGH	400	YEL	130	*	*	SECT. C1, C8
A31 VSS LOW	401	PPL	131	*	*	SECT. C1, C8
A32 N/C			132			

(1) VARIES WITH TEMPERATURE.
(2) VARIES.
(3) B + FIRST TWO SECONDS.
* LESS THAN .5 V (500 mV).

4-19-93
9S 5636-6E

Figure A-7 - PCM Connector Details 3800 (VIN L) (1 of 3)

1994 "W" CARLINE CLEAR PCM CONNECTOR "B" 3800 (VIN L) RPO: L27

PCM PIN/FUNCTION	CKT #	WIRE COLOR	J 39700-A PIN #	VOLTAGE KEY "ON"	VOLTAGE ENG "RUN"	6E3 REFERENCE
B1 A/C REQUEST	67	LT BLU	201	*	*	SECT. C10
B2 N/C			202			
B3 CRUISE STATUS	85	WHT	203	*	*	DTC P1550
B4 N/C			204			
B5 N/C			205			
B6 N/C			206			
B7 EGR 5V REFERENCE	474	GRY	207	5	5	SECT. C7
B8 IGNITION FEED	439	PNK	208	B +	B +	CHART A-1
B9 N/C			209			
B10 BATTERY FEED	540	ORN	210	B +	B +	CHART A-1
B11 IATS GROUND	452	BLK	211	*	*	SECT. C1
B12 N/C			212			
B13 N/C			213			
B14 N/C			214			
B15 N/C			215			
B16 N/C			216			
B17 FUEL PUMP RELAY	465	DK GRN/WHT	217	*(3)	B +	CHART A-5
B18 4K/MI SPEED	389	DK GRN	218	*	*	SECT. C1
B19 PASS Key® II FUEL ENABLE	229	DK BLU	219	2.5	2.5	DTC P1626/ P1629
B20 MALFUNCTION INDICATION LAMP	419	BRN/WHT	220	*	B +	CHART A-1
B21 A/C RELAY	459	DK GRN/WHT	221	B +	B +	SECT. C10
B22 FAN 1	335	DK GRN	222	B + "OFF" * "ON"	B + "OFF" * "ON"	SECT. C12
B23 FAN 2	473	DK BLU	223	B + "OFF" * "ON"	B + "OFF" * "ON"	SECT. C12
B24 N/C			224			
B25 N/C			225			
B26 N/C			226			
B27 N/C			227			
B28 N/C			228			
B29 N/C			229			
B30 A/C HEAD PRESSURE SWITCH (FAN REQUEST)	380	RED/BLK	230	*	*	SECT. C12
B31 N/C			231			
B32 SERIAL DATA	800	TAN	232	(2)	(2)	SECT. C1

(1) VARIES WITH TEMPERATURE.
(2) VARIES.
(3) B + FIRST TWO SECONDS.
* LESS THAN .5 V (500 mV).

6-5-93
9S 7568-6E

Figure A-8 - PCM Connector Details 3800 (VIN L) (2 of 3)

1994 "W" CARLINE BLUE PCM CONNECTOR "C"

3800 (VIN L)
RPO: L27

PCM PIN/FUNCTION	CKT #	WIRE COLOR	J 39700-A PIN #	VOLTAGE KEY "ON"	VOLTAGE ENG "RUN"	6E3 REFERENCE
C1 N/C			301			
C2 SHIFT B SOLENOID	1223	YEL/BLK	302	0*	0*	SECT. C8
C3 SHIFT A SOLENOID	1222	LT GRN	303	0*	0*	SECT. C8
C4 N/C			304			
C5 TCC APPLY SOLENOID	422	TAN/BLK	305	B +	B +	SECT. C8
C6 N/C			306			
C7 N/C			307			
C8 EVAP CANISTER PURGE	428	DK GRN/YEL	308	B +	(2)	SECT. C3
C9 PRNDL A	771	BLK/WHT	309	*	*	DTC P0705
C10 PRNDL B	772	YEL	310	B +	B +	DTC P0705
C11 5 VOLT REFERENCE	416	GRY	311	5	5	SECT. C1
C12 SENSOR GROUND	808	BLK	312	*	*	SECT. C1
C13 N/C			313			
C14 PRNDL P	776	WHT	314	*	*	DTC P0705
C15 PRNDL C	773	GRY	315	B +	B +	DTC P0705
C16 N/C			316			
C17 N/C			317			
C18 KNOCK SIGNAL	496	DK BLU	318	2.3	2.3	SECT. C5
C19 TRANS TEMP SENSOR	1227	YEL/BLK	319	(1)	(1)	SECT. C1
C20 ECT SIGNAL	410	YEL	320	(1)	2.0	SECT. C1
C21 EGR PINTLE POSITION	1456	BRN	321	.7	.7	SECT. C7
C22 THROTTLE POSITION SENSOR SIGNAL	417	DK BLU	322	.2 - .74	.2 - .74	SECT. C1
C23 H02S 1 LOW REFERENCE	413	TAN	323	*	*	SECT. C1
C24 H02S 1 SIGNAL	412	PPL	324	.1 - .45	.1 - .9	SECT. C1
C25 N/C			325			
C26 IAT SIGNAL	472	TAN	326	(1)	(1)	SECT. C1
C27 N/C			327			
C28 N/C			328			
C29 N/C			329			
C30 TCC BRAKE SWITCH	420	PPL	330	B +	B +	SECT. C8
C31 H02S 2 LOW	1669	TAN/WHT	331	*	*	SECT. C1
C32 H02S 2 SIGNAL	1668	PPL/WHT	332	.1 - .45	.1 - .9	SECT. C1

(1) VARIES WITH TEMPERATURE.
(2) VARIES.

* LESS THAN .5 V (500 mV).

4-19-93
9S 7571-6E

Figure A-9 - PCM Connector Details 3800 (VIN L) (3 of 3)

"W" CARLINE — 3800 V6 SFI

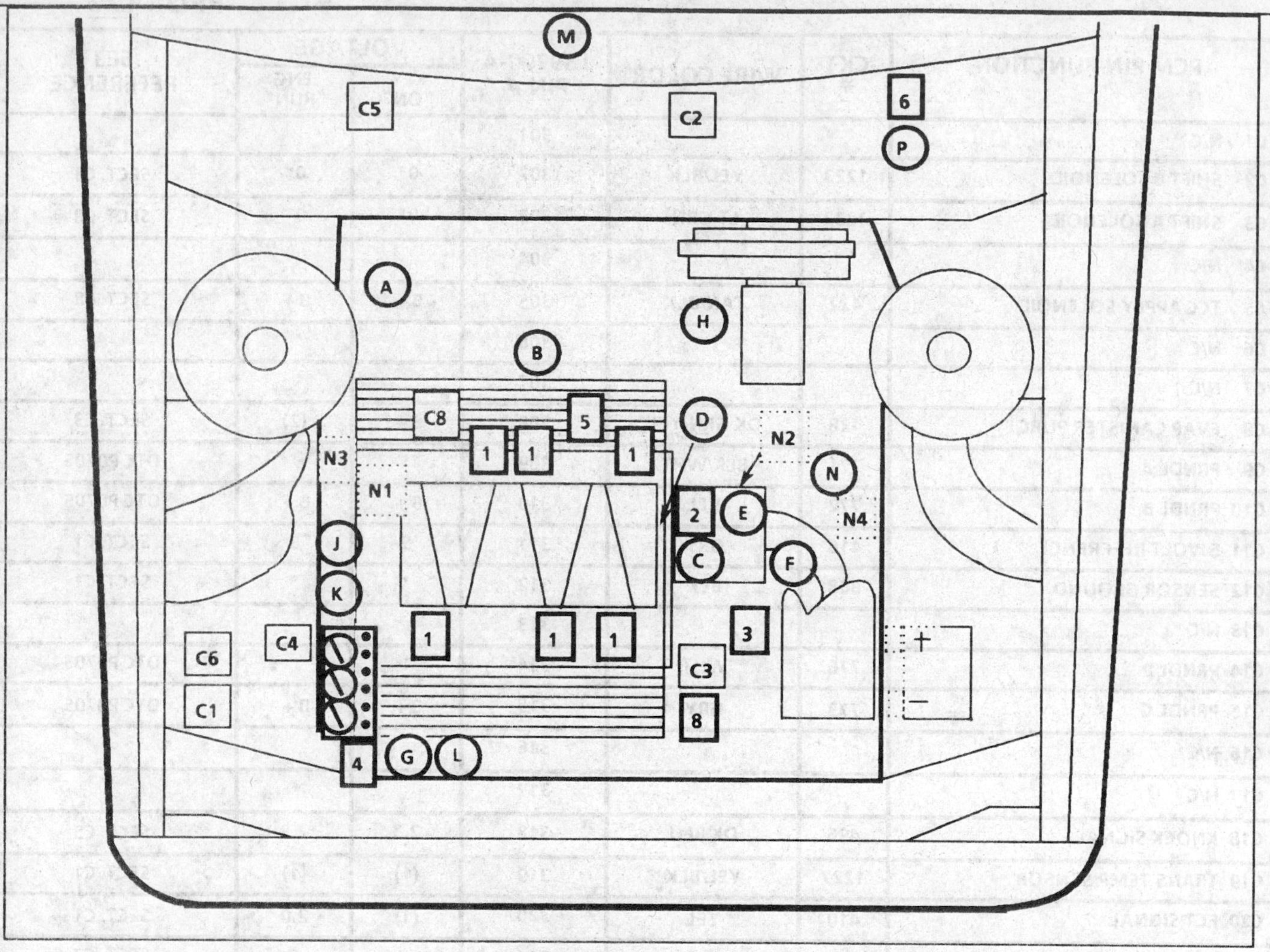
M
C5
C2
6
P
A
H
B
C8
5
1
1
1
D
N2
N3
N1
N
2
E
N4
J
C
F
K
3
1
1
1
C4
C6
C3
C1
8
4
G
L
+
−

COMPUTER HARNESS

- C1 Powertrain Control Module (PCM).
- C2 DLC diagnostic connector.
- C3 Cooling fans and A/C clutch ground.
- C4 PCM harness ground.
- C5 Fuse block.
- C6 Engine electrical center.
  - Cooling fan relays.
  - A/C compressor relay.
  - F/INJN fuse.
  - PCM BAT fuse.
  - ENG EMIS fuse.
  - Fan MAXIFUSES.
  - Fuel pump relay.
  - CRUISE fuse.
  - TCC fuse.
  - ELEK IGN fuse.
  - PCM IGN fuse.
- C8 8-way ignition jumper harness connector.

NOT PCM CONNECTED

- N1 Crankcase vent valve.
- N2 Throttle body.
- N3 Fuel pump/oil pressure switch.
- N4 Fuel pump test connector.

CONTROLLED DEVICES

- 1 Fuel injector.
- 2 Idle Air Control (IAC) motor.
- 3 Transaxle connector.
- 4 Ignition control module and coils.
- 5 EVAP canister purge solenoid.
- 6 Malfunction Indicator Lamp (MIL) "Service Engine Soon."
- 8 Linear Exhaust Gas Recirculation (EGR) valve.

INFORMATION SENSORS

- A Vehicle Speed Sensor (VSS).
- B Heated Oxygen Sensor (HO2S 1).
- D Engine Coolant Temperature (ECT) sensor.
- E Mass Air Flow (MAF) sensor.
- F Intake Air Temperature (IAT) sensor.
- G A/C head pressure switch.
- H TMNSS/PRNDL switch.
- J Camshaft position sensor.
- K Crankshaft position sensor.
- L Knock sensor.
- M Catalyst monitor (HO2S 2) (on exhaust behind converter).
- N SMCC II module.
- P Theft deterrent module.

6-5-93
9S 5631-6E

Figure A-10 - Engine Component Location 3800 (VIN L)

JLG
VEHICLE EMISSION CONTROL INFORMATION
GM
GENERAL MOTORS CORPORATION
CATALYST
EGR / HO2S / TWC
ENGINE DISPL: 3.8 LITER
ENGINE FAMILY: R1G3.8V8GFEA
EVAP FAMILY: R1G1058AYM0J
SPARK PLUG GAP: .060 INCH
38V8GFEU
NO OTHER ADJUSTMENTS NEEDED.
SEE SERVICE MANUAL AND MAINTENANCE SCHEDULE FOR ADDITIONAL INFORMATION.
THIS VEHICLE CONFORMS TO U.S. EPA AND CALIFORNIA REGULATIONS APPLICABLE TO 1994 MODEL-YEAR NEW PASSENGER CARS AND IS CERTIFIED TO THE PHASE-IN STANDARDS IN CALIFORNIA. IF THIS VEHICLE IS BUILT FOR USE OUTSIDE THE U.S., IT MAY NOT COMPLY WITH U.S. EPA FUEL LABELING REGULATIONS. OBD I CERTIFIED.
PRINTED IN U.S.A.
24503101
TO EVAP CNSTR (AT RR OF VEH)
TO ACSRY
TO VAC BRAKE BOOSTER
EVAP CNSTR PURGE VLV
FUEL PRESS REG
MANIF PRESS
TO TRANS
FRONT OF VEH
8S 4314-6E

Figure A-11 - Emission Control Information 3800 (VIN L) (SFI)

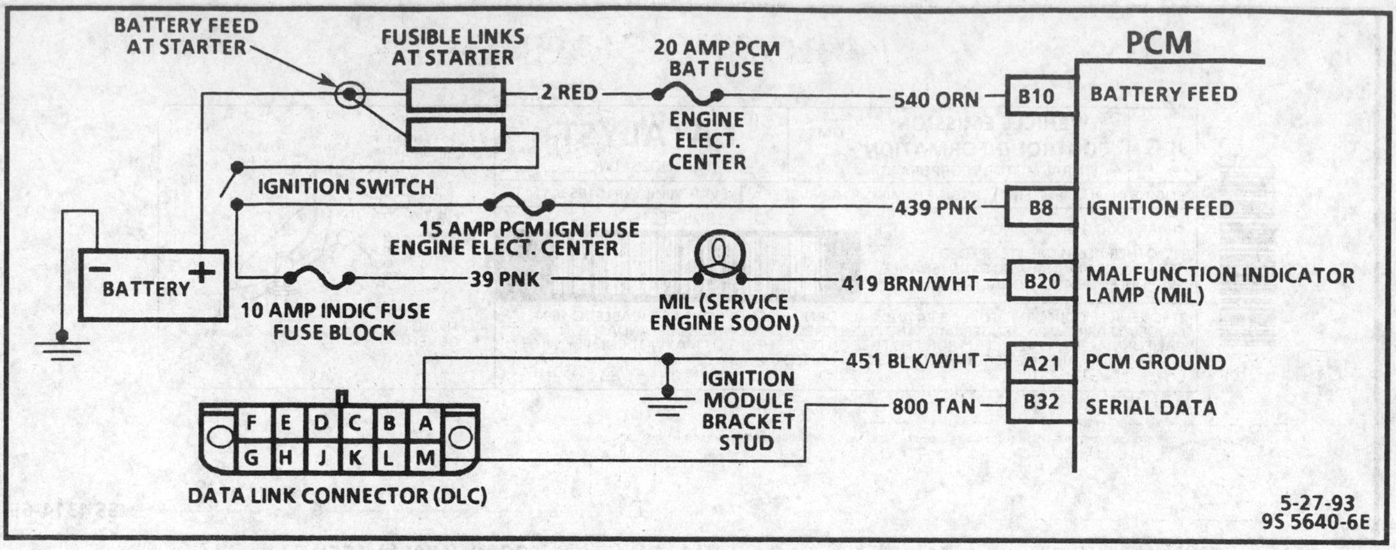
BATTERY FEED AT STARTER
FUSIBLE LINKS AT STARTER
2 RED
20 AMP PCM BAT FUSE
ENGINE ELECT. CENTER
540 ORN
PCM
B10
BATTERY FEED
IGNITION SWITCH
15 AMP PCM IGN FUSE ENGINE ELECT. CENTER
439 PNK
B8
IGNITION FEED
BATTERY
10 AMP INDIC FUSE FUSE BLOCK
39 PNK
MIL (SERVICE ENGINE SOON)
419 BRN/WHT
B20
MALFUNCTION INDICATOR LAMP (MIL)
451 BLK/WHT
A21
PCM GROUND
IGNITION MODULE BRACKET STUD
800 TAN
B32
SERIAL DATA
F E D C B A
G H J K L M
DATA LINK CONNECTOR (DLC)
5-27-93
9S 5640-6E

ON-BOARD DIAGNOSTIC SYSTEM CHECK

(USING A TECH 1 SCAN TOOL)
3800 (VIN L) (SFI)

Circuit Description:

The on-board diagnostic system check must be the starting point for any driveability complaint diagnosis. Before using this you should perform a careful visual/physical check of the PCM and engine grounds for being clean and tight.

The on-board diagnostic system check is an organized approach to identifying a problem created by an electronic engine control system malfunction because it directs the service technician to the next logical step in diagnosing the complaint.

Chart Test Description: Number(s) below refer to circled number(s) on the diagnostic chart.

1. The MIL (Service Engine Soon) should be "ON" steady with the key "ON"/engine "OFF."
2. This test ensures that the PCM is capable of controlling the MIL (Service Engine Soon) and CKT 419 is not shorted to ground.
3. A displayed Tech 1 parameter which is not within the typical range may indicate the area which is causing the problem.

ON-BOARD DIAGNOSTIC SYSTEM CHECK
(USING A TECH 1 SCAN TOOL)
3800 (VIN L) (SFI)

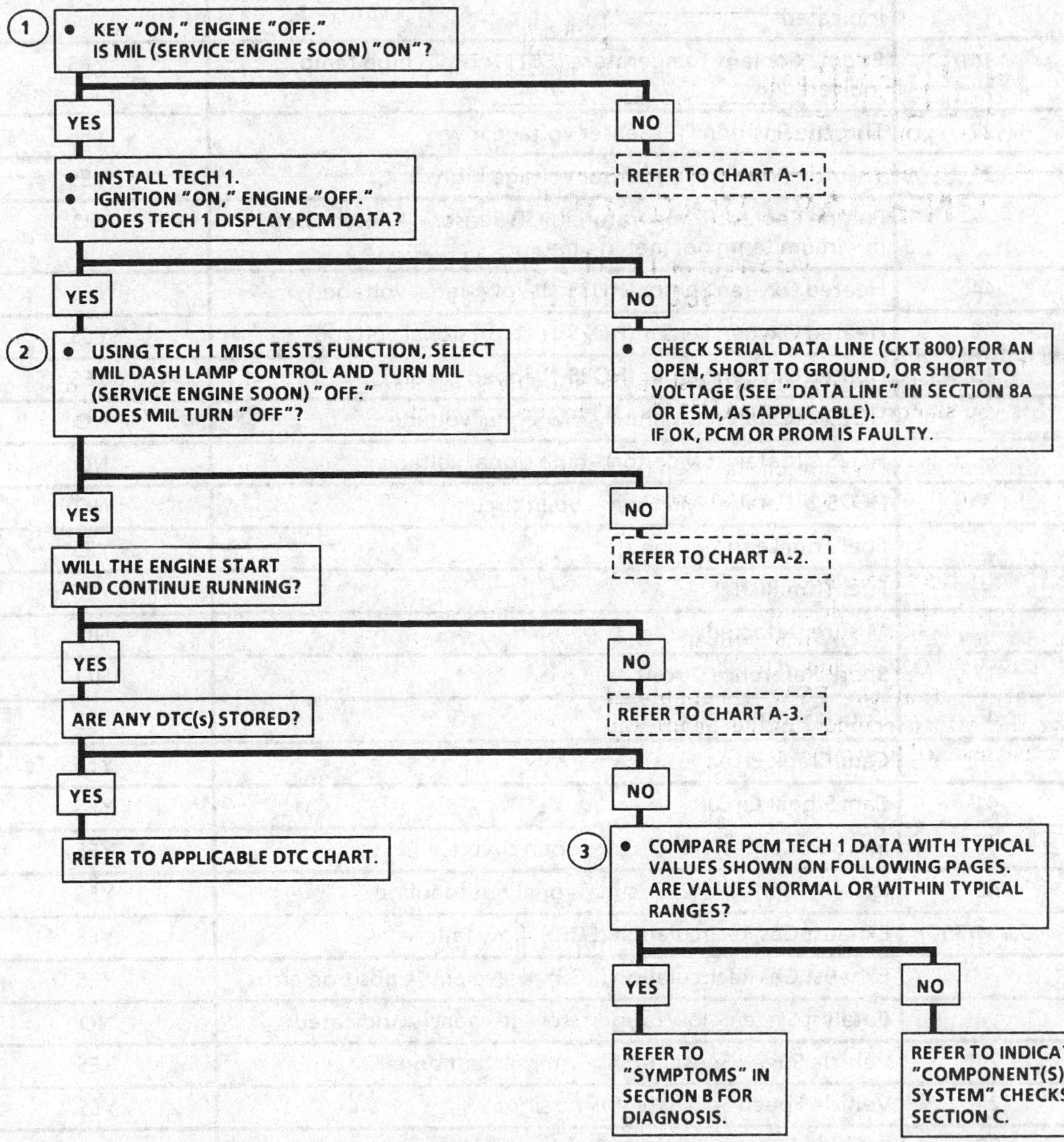
1
• KEY "ON," ENGINE "OFF." IS MIL (SERVICE ENGINE SOON) "ON"?
YES
NO
REFER TO CHART A-1.
• INSTALL TECH 1.
• IGNITION "ON," ENGINE "OFF." DOES TECH 1 DISPLAY PCM DATA?
YES
NO
2
• USING TECH 1 MISC TESTS FUNCTION, SELECT MIL DASH LAMP CONTROL AND TURN MIL (SERVICE ENGINE SOON) "OFF." DOES MIL TURN "OFF"?
• CHECK SERIAL DATA LINE (CKT 800) FOR AN OPEN, SHORT TO GROUND, OR SHORT TO VOLTAGE (SEE "DATA LINE" IN SECTION 8A OR ESM, AS APPLICABLE). IF OK, PCM OR PROM IS FAULTY.
YES
NO
REFER TO CHART A-2.
WILL THE ENGINE START AND CONTINUE RUNNING?
YES
NO
REFER TO CHART A-3.
ARE ANY DTC(s) STORED?
YES
NO
REFER TO APPLICABLE DTC CHART.
3
• COMPARE PCM TECH 1 DATA WITH TYPICAL VALUES SHOWN ON FOLLOWING PAGES. ARE VALUES NORMAL OR WITHIN TYPICAL RANGES?
YES
NO
REFER TO "SYMPTOMS" IN SECTION B FOR DIAGNOSIS.
REFER TO INDICATED "COMPONENT(S) SYSTEM" CHECKS IN SECTION C.

5-6-93
PS 17177

PCM DIAGNOSTIC TROUBLE CODES

DTC	FORMER DTC	DESCRIPTION	ILLUMINATE MIL
P0101	34	Mass Air Flow (MAF) Sensor - low gm/sec indicated	YES
P0112	23	Intake Air Temperature (IAT) Sensor - low temp. indicated	NO
P0113	25	Intake Air Temperature (IAT) Sensor - high temp. indicated	NO
P0117	15	Engine Coolant Temperature (ECT) Sensor - low temp. indicated	YES
P0118	14	Engine Coolant Temperature (ECT) Sensor - high temp. indicated	YES
P0122	22	Throttle Position (TP) Sensor voltage low	YES
P0123	21	Throttle Position (TP) Sensor voltage high	YES
P0125	-	Engine Coolant Temperature (ECT) Sensor - "Closed Loop" minimum temp not met In time	NO
P0131	44	Heated Oxygen Sensor (HO2S 1) - low signal voltage	YES
P0132	45	Heated Oxygen Sensor (HO2S 1) - high signal voltage	YES
P0134	13	Heated Oxygen Sensor (HO2S 1) - open circuit	YES
P0137	-	HO2S 2 (Catalyst Monitor) - low signal voltage	NO
P0138	-	HO2S 2 (Catalyst Monitor) - high signal voltage	NO
P0140	-	HO2S 2 (Catalyst Monitor) - open circuit	NO
P0171	-	Fuel Trim Lean	YES
P0172	-	Fuel Trim Rich	YES
P0300	-	Misfire Detected	NO
P0321	17	Spark Reference Circuit	NO
P0325	43	Knock Sensor (KS) Circuit	YES
P0341	18	Cam/Crank Error	YES
P0342	41	Cam Signal Circuit	YES
P1350	42	Ignition Control (IC) Circuit - open circuit	YES
P1361	42	Ignition Control (IC) Circuit - signal not toggling	YES
P0401	53/54/55	Exhaust Gas Recirculation (EGR) - flow failure	YES
P1406	-	Exhaust Gas Recirculation (EGR) - valve pintle position error	YES
P0420	-	Catalyst System- low oxygen storage capacity indicated	NO
P0501	24	Vehicle Speed Sensor (VSS) - intermittent signal	YES
P0502	24	Vehicle Speed Sensor (VSS) - no signal	YES
P1530	69	A/C Head Pressure Switch Circuit	NO
P1531	66	Excessive A/C Cycling (low refrigerant charge)	NO
P1550	-	Stepper Motor Cruise Control Problem	NO

PCM DIAGNOSTIC TROUBLE CODES

DTC	FORMER DTC	DESCRIPTION	ILLUMINATE MIL
P1623	51	PROM Error	YES
P1626	58	PASS Key ® II Fuel Enable Circuit - invalid frequency seen after start-up	NO
P1629	-	PASS Key ® II Fuel Enable Circuit - invalid frequency seen during crank	NO
P1630	16	System Voltage High or Low	YES
P1640	26/56	QDM 1 Circuit	YES
P1650	26/56	QDM 2 Circuit	NO
P1670	26/56	QDM 4 Circuit	NO
P0703	38	TCC Brake Input Circuit	NO
P0705	31	Trans Range Switch Circuit	NO
P0712	-	Transaxle Temperature Sensor - low temp. indicated	NO
P0713	-	Transaxle Temperature Sensor - high temp. indicated	NO
P0740	39	Torque Convertor Clutch (TCC) Problem	NO
P0755	36	Transaxle Shift B Solenoid Problem	NO

4-22-93
MS 13630

If after completing the on-board diagnostic system check and finding the on-board diagnostics functioning properly and no diagnostic trouble codes displayed "Typical Scan Values" for the appropriate engine may be used for comparison. The "Typical Values" are an average of display values recorded from normally operating vehicles and are intended to represent what a normally functioning system would display.

A SCAN TOOL THAT DISPLAYS FAULTY DATA SHOULD NOT BE USED, AND THE PROBLEM SHOULD BE REPORTED TO THE MANUFACTURER. THE USE OF A FAULTY SCAN TOOL CAN RESULT IN MISDIAGNOSIS AND UNNECESSARY PARTS REPLACEMENT.

Only the parameters listed below are used in this manual for diagnosis. If a scan tool reads other parameters, the values are not recommended by General Motors for use in diagnosis. For more description on the values and use of the scan tool to diagnose PCM inputs, refer to the applicable diagnosis section in "Component Systems," Section "C". If all values are within the range illustrated, refer to "Symptoms," Section "B".

TYPICAL SCAN DATA VALUES
3800 (VIN L) (SFI)

Idle / Upper Radiator Hose Hot / Closed Throttle / Park or Neutral / Closed Loop / Acc. off Brake Not Applied

Tech 1 Parameter	Units Displayed	Typical Data Value	6E3 REFERENCE SECTION
Engine Speed	RPM	650–750	C1, C2
Desired Idle	RPM	675	C1
Eng Cool Temp	°C °F	Varies (85°–105°C) (185°–220°F)	C1
Intake Air Temp	°C °F	Varies with air temp.	C1
Throt Position	Volts	.20–.74	C1
Throttle Angle	Percent	0%	C1
Mass Air Flow	Gm/Sec	4.9 (varies)	C1
Calc Eng Load	Counts	70–80	C1
HO2S 1	mV	Varies (100–1000)	C1, C2
HO2S 2 (Refer to Notice)	mV	Varies (100–1000)	C1
HO2S 1 Cross Cnts	Counts	Varies	C1, C2
Rich/Lean Status	Rich/Lean	Rich/Lean Changing Constantly	C1,C2
Mph / Km/h	Mph, Km/h	0, 0	C1, C2
Spark Advance	Degrees	16° (Varies)	C4
S.T. Fuel Trim	Counts	95–140*	C2
L.T. Fuel Trim	Counts	95–138*	C2
Loop Status	Open Lp/Closed Lp	Closed Loop	C2
Fuel Trim Cell	Cell #	0	C2
Knock Retard	Degrees	0°	C5
Knock Signal	Yes/No	No	C5
Idle Air Control	Counts	16–20	C2
Park/Neutral Pos	P-N/R-DL	P-N	C1
TCC Brake Switch	Applied/Released	Released	C8
TCC Mode	On/Apply/Off/Release	Off	C8
TCC Duty Cycle	Percent	0%	C8
TCC Slip	RPM	+ 254	C8
N/V Ratio	Counts	0	C8
Current Weak Cyl	Cylinder #/None	None	C4
EGR Pintle Pos	Volts	0-1	C7
Cam/Crank Error	Counts	0-2 (Varies)	C4

* A poor PCM ground at the ignition mounting bracket to engine, could cause short term fuel trim and long term fuel trim to read around 150, make a careful physical inspection of this critical connection.

NOTICE: Early production vehicles may not be equipped with an H02S 2; in this case, the Tech 1 will display a constant voltage of approximately 450 mv.

Trans Temp	°C °F	Varies	C1
Fuel Evap Purge	Percent	Varies	C3
System Voltage	Voltage	13.5 (varies)	C2, SECTION 6D
A/C Request	Yes/No	No	C1, C10
A/C Clutch	On/Off	Off	C10
Fan 1 Fan 2	On/Off	Off	C12
A/C Head Press.	OK/High	OK	C12
Actual EGR Pos	Percent	0%	C7
Desired EGR Pos	Percent	0%	C7
SMCC Inhibited	Yes/No	Yes	DTC P1550
SMCC Status	Engage/Disengage	Disengage	DTC P1550
Shift A Sol	On/Off	On	C8
Shift B Sol	On/Off	On	C8
PRNDL P	High/Low	Low	C1
PRNDL A	High/Low	Low	C1
PRNDL B	High/Low	High	C1
PRNDL C	High/Low	High	C1
Trans Range Switch	Low/Drive 2/Drive 3/ Drive 4/ Neutral/Reverse/Park	Park	C1
Commanded Gear	First/Second/Third/Fourth	1st	SECTION 7A
P/N	Yes/No	Yes	C1
2nd Actual	Yes/No	No	SECTION 7A
3rd Actual	Yes/No	No	SECTION 7A
4th Actual	Yes/No	No	SECTION 7A
QDM 1	High/Low	Low	Refer to DTC P1640 Chart in Section 6E3-A
QDM 2	High/Low	Low	Refer to DTC P1650 Chart in Section 6E3-A
QDM 4	High/Low	Low	Refer to DTC P1670 Chart in Section 6E3-A
PASS-KEY®II Fuel	Enabled/Disabled	Enabled	Refer to DTC P1626 /P1629 Charts in Section 6E3-A
Calibration ID	Prom ID #	Internal I.D. only	C1
Time From Start	Minutes	Varies	C1

NOTICE: IF all values are within the range illustrated, refer to "Symtoms," Section "B".

TYPICAL TECH 1 DATA DEFINITIONS

PCM DATA DESCRIPTION

A list of explanations for each data message displayed on the Tech 1 scan tool begins below.
This information will assist in tracking down emission or driveability problems, since the displays can be viewed while the vehicle is being driven. See the "On-Board (OBD) Diagnostic System Check" for additional information.

ENGINE SPEED - Range 0-9999 RPM - Engine speed is computed by the PCM from the fuel control reference input. It should remain close to desired idle under various engine loads with engine idling.

DESIRED IDLE - Range 0-3175 RPM - The idle speed that is commanded by the PCM. The PCM will compensate for various engine loads to keep the engine at the desired idle speed.

ENG. COOLANT TEMP - Range -40° to 199°C, -40° to 389°F - The Engine Coolant Temperature (ECT) sensor is mounted in the intake manifold and sends engine coolant temperature information to the PCM. The PCM supplies 5 volts to the engine coolant temperature sensor circuit. The sensor is a thermistor which changes internal resistance as temperature changes. When the sensor is cold (internal resistance high), the PCM monitors a high signal voltage which it interprets as a cold engine. As the sensor warms (internal resistance decreases), the voltage signal will decrease and the PCM will interpret the lower voltage as a warm engine.

INTAKE AIR TEMP - Range -40° to 199°C, -40° to 389°F - The PCM converts the resistance of the Intake Air Temperature (IAT) sensor to degrees. Intake air temperature is used by the PCM to adjust fuel delivery and spark timing according to incoming air density.

THROT POSITION - Range 0-5.10 Volts - Used by the PCM to determine the amount of throttle demanded by the driver. Should read .20-.74 volt at idle to above 4 volts at wide open throttle.

THROTTLE ANGLE - Range 0-100% - Computed by the PCM from TP sensor voltage (Throt position); should read 0% at idle, 100% at Wide Open Throttle (WOT).

MASS AIR FLOW - Range 0-255.9 GM/SEC - The PCM converts the mass air flow sensor input signal into grams per second, indicating the amount of airflow entering the engine.

CALC ENG LOAD - Range 0-255 - Engine load is calculated by the PCM by engine speed and mass airflow. Should increase with an increase in RPM or airflow.

HO2S 1 - Range 0-1096 mV - Represents the heated oxygen sensor output voltage. Should fluctuate constantly within a range between 100 mV (lean exhaust) and 1000 mV (Rich exhaust) when operating in "Closed Loop."

HO2S 2 - Range 0-1096 mV - Represents the HO2S 2 (catalyst monitor) output voltage. Should fluctuate much more slowly than the HO2S 1 signal when operating in "Closed Loop."

HO2S 1 CROSS COUNTS - Range 0-255 - The number of times the oxygen sensor voltage crosses over the rich/lean threshold during a one second interval.

RICH/LEAN STATUS - Tech 1 Displays RICH or LEAN - Indicates whether exhaust oxygen sensor voltage is above (rich) or below (lean) the 450 mV oxygen sensor threshold voltage. Should change constantly indicating that the PCM is controlling the air/fuel mixture properly.

VEHICLE SPEED - Range 0-255 km/h, 0-159 MPH - The vehicle speed sensor signal is converted into km/h and mph for display.

SPARK ADVANCE - Range -90° to 90° - This is a display of the spark advance calculation which the PCM is programming into the ignition system. It computes the desired spark advance using data such as engine temperature, RPM, load, vehicle speed, and operating mode.

S.T. FUEL TRIM - Range 0-255 - Short term fuel trim represents a short term correction to fuel delivery by the PCM in response to the amount of time the oxygen sensor voltage spends above or below the 450 mV threshold. If the oxygen sensor voltage has mainly been below 450 mV, indicating a lean air/fuel mixture, short term fuel trim will increase to tell the PCM to add fuel. If the oxygen sensor voltage stays mainly above the threshold, the PCM will reduce fuel delivery to compensate for the indicated rich condition. **Under certain conditions such as extended idle and high ambient temperatures, canister purge may cause short term fuel trim to read less than 100 counts.**

TYPICAL TECH 1 DATA DEFINITIONS

L.T. FUEL TRIM - Range 0-255 - Long term fuel trim is derived from the short term fuel trim value and is used for long term correction of fuel delivery. A value of 128 counts indicates that fuel delivery requires no compensation to maintain a 14.7:1 air/fuel ratio. A value below 128 counts means that the fuel system is too rich and fuel delivery is being reduced (decreased injector pulse width). A value above 128 counts indicates that a lean condition exists and the PCM is compensating by adding fuel (increased injector pulse width). **LONG TERM FUEL TRIM tends to follow SHORT TERM FUEL TRIM; a value of less than 100 counts due to canister purge at idle should not be considered unusual.**

LOOP STATUS - Tech 1 Displays "OPEN LOOP" or "CLOSED LOOP" - "Closed Loop" displayed indicates that the PCM is controlling fuel delivery according to oxygen sensor voltage. In "Open Loop," the PCM ignores the oxygen sensor voltage and bases the amount of fuel to be delivered on TP sensor, engine coolant temperature, and MAF sensor inputs only. "Closed Loop" operation should begin when the oxygen sensor becomes active, engine coolant temperature exceeds 50°C (122°F) for more than 30 seconds and the PCM has seen a RPM of 1200 or greater for 10 seconds. At extremely high ambient temperatures or when towing a trailer, it is possible for the system to remain in "Open Loop" operation to control catalytic converter temperatures.

FUEL TRIM CELL - Range 0-15 - Fuel trim cell is dependent upon engine speed and mass air flow readings. A plot of RPM vs. MAF is broken into 16 cells. Fuel trim cell indicates which cell is currently active.

KNOCK RETARD - Range 0°-90° - Indicates the amount of spark advance the PCM is removing from ignition control in response to the knock sensor signal. Should read 0° at idle.

KNOCK SIGNAL - Tech 1 Displays "YES" or "NO" - Indicates whether or not a knock signal is being detected by the PCM. Should read "NO" at idle.

IDLE AIR CONTROL - Range 0-255 - Displays the commanded position of the idle air control pintle in counts. The higher the number of counts, the greater the commanded idle speed. Idle air control should respond fairly quickly to changes in engine load to maintain desired idle RPM.

PARK/NEUTRAL POS - Tech 1 Displays P-N or -R-DL - "P-N" displayed indicates that the gear select lever is in park or neutral as indicated by the transmission range switch PRNDL inputs.

TCC BRAKE SWITCH - Tech 1 Displays "APPLIED" or "RELEASED" - When the brake pedal is applied, the switch sends a signal to the PCM to disengage the TCC and cruise control.

TCC MODE - The modes of operation are "OFF," "RELEASE," "APPLY," and "ON." The "APPLY" mode will be active for approximately 1 to 5 seconds.

TCC DUTY CYCLE - Range 0-100% - This is the relative position of the PWM solenoid that controls TCC apply pressure. 100% is low pressure, 0% is full line pressure.

N/V RATIO - Range 0-255 Counts - Represents the ratio derived by dividing engine RPM by vehicle speed. Should remain steady in 3rd or 4th gear with the TCC applied.

TCC SLIP - Range 0-255 RPM - The RPM difference between engine crankshaft speed and torque converter turbine speed. When TCC mode is "ON" there should only be a small amount of slip.

CURRENT WEAK CYL - Tech 1 Displays Cylinder Number or None - The PCM monitors RPM and crankshaft position, and when an apparent misfire is detected for more than 25 consecutive crankshaft revolutions the weak cylinder number is displayed.

EGR PINTLE POSITION - Range 0-5 Volts - Represents the linear EGR pintle position sensor output voltage. Should be under 1 volt at idle.

CAM/CRANK ERROR - Range 0-255 - The Tech 1 displays the number of times an incorrect ratio of cam sensor pulses to fuel control pulses has been detected. A normally operating system may detect 0-2 errors during start up.

TRANS FLUID TEMP - Range -40° to 151°C, -40° to 304°F - The PCM converts the resistance of the transaxle fluid temperature sensor to degrees. Trans fluid temp is used to determine "Hot Mode" TCC operation.

FUEL EVAP PURGE - Range 0-100% - A proportional signal used to control evap canister purge function. 0% implies the valve is commanded fully closed while 100% implies that the valve is fully open.

TYPICAL TECH 1 DATA DEFINITIONS

SYSTEM VOLTAGE - Range 0-25.5 Volts - This represents the system voltage measured by the PCM at its ignition feed (CKT 439).

A/C REQUEST - Tech 1 Displays "YES" or "NO" - Represents the state of the A/C request input from the control head.

A/C CLUTCH - Tech 1 Displays "ON" or "OFF" - Represents the commanded state of the A/C clutch control relay. Clutch should be engaged when "ON" is displayed.

FAN 1 - When the PCM is commanding the left fan "ON," the Tech 1 display will switch from "OFF" to "ON."

FAN 2 - When the PCM is commanding the right fan "ON," the Tech 1 display will switch from "OFF" to "ON."

A/C HEAD PRESSURE - Tech 1 Displays OK or HIGH Press - Represents the state of the A/C head pressure switch. When the A/C refrigerant pressure rises above 1448 kPa (210 psi) the switch should open, informing the PCM to turn "ON" the fan 2 relay.

ACTUAL EGR POS - Range 0-100% - Represents the linear EGR pintle position signal in percent of travel. 0% displayed indicates a closed EGR Valve (EGR flow not allowed).

DESIRED EGR POS - Range 0-100% - The EGR Pintle position which is being commanded by the PCM; should be very close to "ACTUAL EGR POS."

SMCC INHIBITED - Tech 1 Displays "YES" or "NO" - "YES" displayed indicates that the PCM is requesting that cruise control not be allowed to engage. Should display "YES" at idle.

SMCC STATUS - Tech 1 Displays "ENGAGE" or "DISENGAGE" - Represents the SMCC status input from the SMCC II module. Should display "DISENGAGE" unless operating in a cruise control mode.

SHIFT A SOL/SHIFT B SOL - Tech 1 displays "ON" or "OFF" - Represents the state of the transaxle shift solenoids. Both should display "ON" in park or neutral (1st gear commanded).

PRNDL P,A,B,C - Tech 1 Displays "HIGH" or "LOW" - A transaxle mounted switch is used as an input to let the PCM know what position the gear select lever is in. Tech 1 status will switch from "HIGH" to "LOW" as different combinations are met. In "PARK," PRNDL P and A will be "LOW"; B and C will be "HIGH."

TRANS. RANGE - The Tech 1 displays the decoded position of the transmission range switch PRNDL inputs. If a valid combination is not seen by the PCM, "D4" will be displayed.

COMMANDED GEAR - The gear that the PCM is commanding the 4T60E transaxle to be in. **In "PARK," the Tech 1 will display "First."**

P/N - Tech 1 Displays "YES" or "NO" - "YES" displayed indicates that the gear select lever is in park or neutral.

2nd, 3rd, 4th, ACTUAL - Tech 1 Displays "YES" or "NO" - The PCM looks at "PRNDL SWITCH" position and commanded gear. The actual forward gear that the transaxle is in will be the lower of the two because the manual valve can override the PCM commanded gear.

QDM 1, 2, 4 - Tech 1 Displays "HIGH" or "LOW" - Quad-driver modules are used to switch "ON" various components. The Tech 1 will display "LOW" normally and will switch to "HIGH" if there is a circuit problem.

PASS-Key®II FUEL - Tech 1 Displays "ENABLED" or "DISABLED" - Indicates if the PCM is receiving a correct fuel enable signal from the Theft Deterrent System. If "DISABLED" is displayed, the PCM will not allow fuel delivery and the engine will not start.

CALIBRATION I.D. - Range 0-9999 - The calibration identification describes the particular PROM being used in the PCM. The displayed number is not the service part number.

TIME FROM START - Range 0:00:00-18:12:15 HR/MIN/SEC - A measure of how long the engine has been running. When the engine stops, it is reset to zero.

BLANK

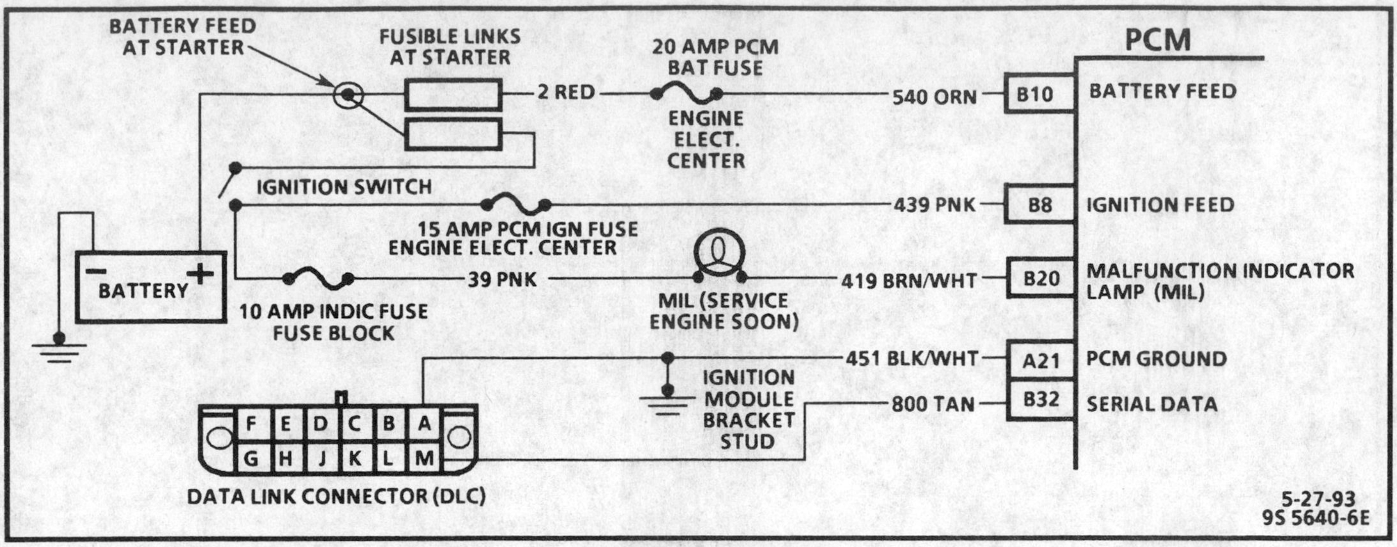
BATTERY FEED AT STARTER
FUSIBLE LINKS AT STARTER
20 AMP PCM BAT FUSE
2 RED
ENGINE ELECT. CENTER
PCM
540 ORN
B10
BATTERY FEED
IGNITION SWITCH
15 AMP PCM IGN FUSE ENGINE ELECT. CENTER
439 PNK
B8
IGNITION FEED
BATTERY
10 AMP INDIC FUSE FUSE BLOCK
39 PNK
MIL (SERVICE ENGINE SOON)
419 BRN/WHT
B20
MALFUNCTION INDICATOR LAMP (MIL)
451 BLK/WHT
A21
PCM GROUND
IGNITION MODULE BRACKET STUD
800 TAN
B32
SERIAL DATA
F E D C B A
G H J K L M
DATA LINK CONNECTOR (DLC)
5-27-93
9S 5640-6E

CHART A-1

NO MALFUNCTION INDICATOR LAMP (MIL) "SERVICE ENGINE SOON" 3800 (VIN L) (SFI)

Circuit Description:

There should always be a steady MIL (Service Engine Soon) when the ignition is "ON" and engine stopped. Ignition is supplied directly to the light bulb. The Powertrain Control Module (PCM) will turn the MIL "ON" by grounding CKT 419 at the PCM.

Chart Test Description: Number(s) below refer to circled number(s) on the diagnostic chart.

1. MIL (Service Engine Soon) should be "ON."
2. Using a test light connected to 12 volts, probe each of the system ground circuits to be sure a good ground is present. Refer to "PCM Terminal End View" in front of this section for PCM pin locations of ground circuits.

Diagnostic Aids: Engine runs OK, check:

- Faulty light bulb.
- CKT 419 open.
- 10 amp indicators fuse open.

Engine cranks, but will not run:

- Continuous battery - 20 amp PCM fuse open.
- Ignition CKT 439 to PCM open.
- 15 amp PCM ignition fuse.
- Poor connection at PCM.

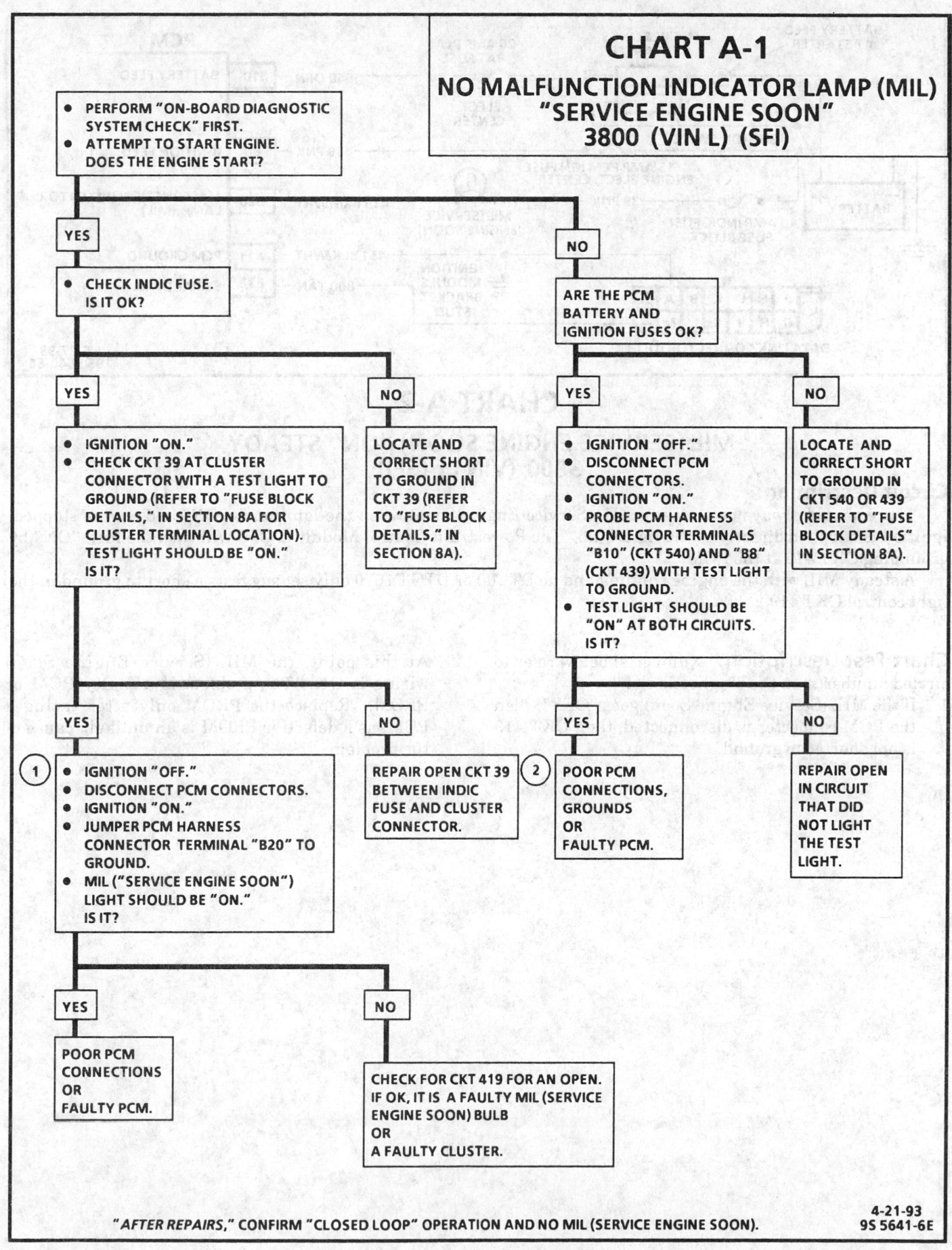

CHART A-1

NO MALFUNCTION INDICATOR LAMP (MIL) "SERVICE ENGINE SOON" 3800 (VIN L) (SFI)

- PERFORM "ON-BOARD DIAGNOSTIC SYSTEM CHECK" FIRST.
- ATTEMPT TO START ENGINE. DOES THE ENGINE START?

YES

- CHECK INDIC FUSE. IS IT OK?

YES

- IGNITION "ON."
- CHECK CKT 39 AT CLUSTER CONNECTOR WITH A TEST LIGHT TO GROUND (REFER TO "FUSE BLOCK DETAILS," IN SECTION 8A FOR CLUSTER TERMINAL LOCATION). TEST LIGHT SHOULD BE "ON." IS IT?

YES

1

- IGNITION "OFF."
- DISCONNECT PCM CONNECTORS.
- IGNITION "ON."
- JUMPER PCM HARNESS CONNECTOR TERMINAL "B20" TO GROUND.
- MIL ("SERVICE ENGINE SOON") LIGHT SHOULD BE "ON." IS IT?

YES

POOR PCM CONNECTIONS OR FAULTY PCM.

NO

CHECK FOR CKT 419 FOR AN OPEN. IF OK, IT IS A FAULTY MIL (SERVICE ENGINE SOON) BULB OR A FAULTY CLUSTER.

NO (test light)

REPAIR OPEN CKT 39 BETWEEN INDIC FUSE AND CLUSTER CONNECTOR.

NO (indic fuse)

LOCATE AND CORRECT SHORT TO GROUND IN CKT 39 (REFER TO "FUSE BLOCK DETAILS," IN SECTION 8A).

NO (engine start)

ARE THE PCM BATTERY AND IGNITION FUSES OK?

YES

- IGNITION "OFF."
- DISCONNECT PCM CONNECTORS.
- IGNITION "ON."
- PROBE PCM HARNESS CONNECTOR TERMINALS "B10" (CKT 540) AND "B8" (CKT 439) WITH TEST LIGHT TO GROUND.
- TEST LIGHT SHOULD BE "ON" AT BOTH CIRCUITS. IS IT?

YES

2

POOR PCM CONNECTIONS, GROUNDS OR FAULTY PCM.

NO

REPAIR OPEN IN CIRCUIT THAT DID NOT LIGHT THE TEST LIGHT.

NO (fuses)

LOCATE AND CORRECT SHORT TO GROUND IN CKT 540 OR 439 (REFER TO "FUSE BLOCK DETAILS" IN SECTION 8A).

"*AFTER REPAIRS,*" CONFIRM "CLOSED LOOP" OPERATION AND NO MIL (SERVICE ENGINE SOON).

4-21-93
9S 5641-6E

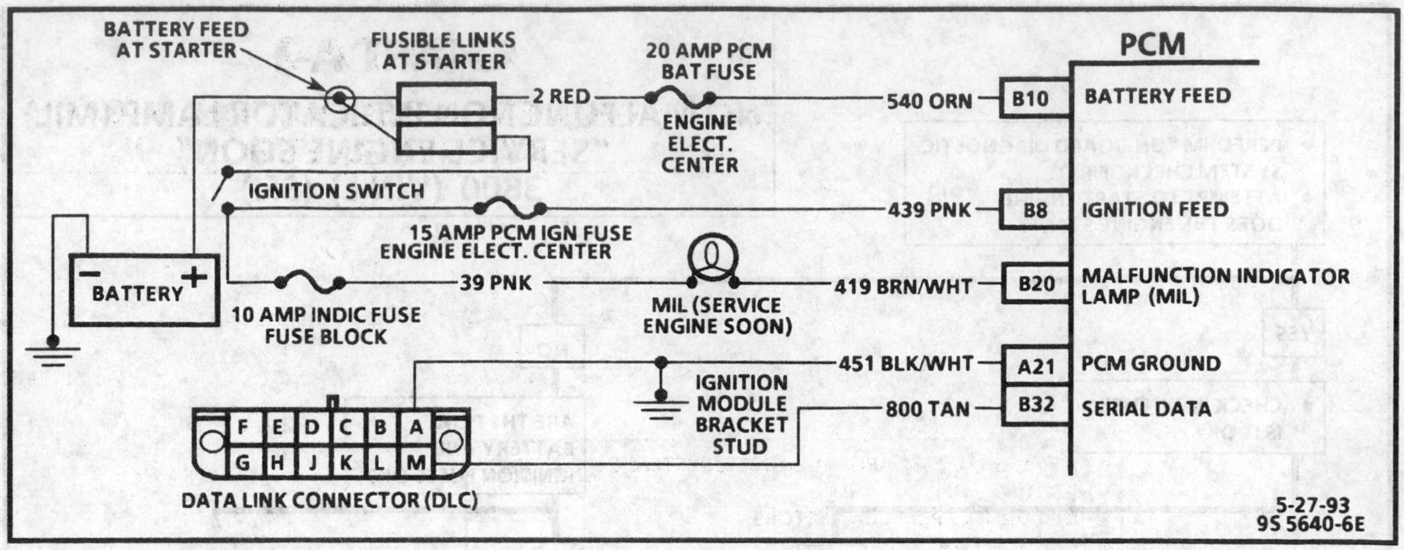
BATTERY FEED AT STARTER
FUSIBLE LINKS AT STARTER
2 RED
20 AMP PCM BAT FUSE
ENGINE ELECT. CENTER
540 ORN
PCM
B10
BATTERY FEED
IGNITION SWITCH
15 AMP PCM IGN FUSE ENGINE ELECT. CENTER
439 PNK
B8
IGNITION FEED
BATTERY
10 AMP INDIC FUSE FUSE BLOCK
39 PNK
MIL (SERVICE ENGINE SOON)
419 BRN/WHT
B20
MALFUNCTION INDICATOR LAMP (MIL)
451 BLK/WHT
A21
PCM GROUND
IGNITION MODULE BRACKET STUD
800 TAN
B32
SERIAL DATA
F E D C B A
G H J K L M
DATA LINK CONNECTOR (DLC)
5-27-93
9S 5640-6E

CHART A-2

MIL (SERVICE ENGINE SOON) "ON" STEADY
3800 (VIN L) (SFI)

Circuit Description:

There should always be a steady MIL (Service Engine Soon) when the ignition is "ON" and engine stopped. Ignition is supplied directly to the light bulb. The Powertrain Control Module (PCM) will turn the MIL "ON" by grounding CKT 419 at the PCM.

A steady MIL with the engine running and no DTC(s) or DTC P1670 only set suggests a short to ground in the light control CKT 419.

Chart Test Description: Number(s) below refer to circled number(s) on the diagnostic chart.

1. If the MIL (Service Engine Soon) goes "OFF" when the PCM connector is disconnected, then CKT 419 is not shorted to ground.
2. At this point, the MIL (Service Engine Soon) wiring is OK. The problem is a faulty PCM or PROM. Replace the PROM only after trying a PCM, as a defective PROM is an unlikely cause of the problem.

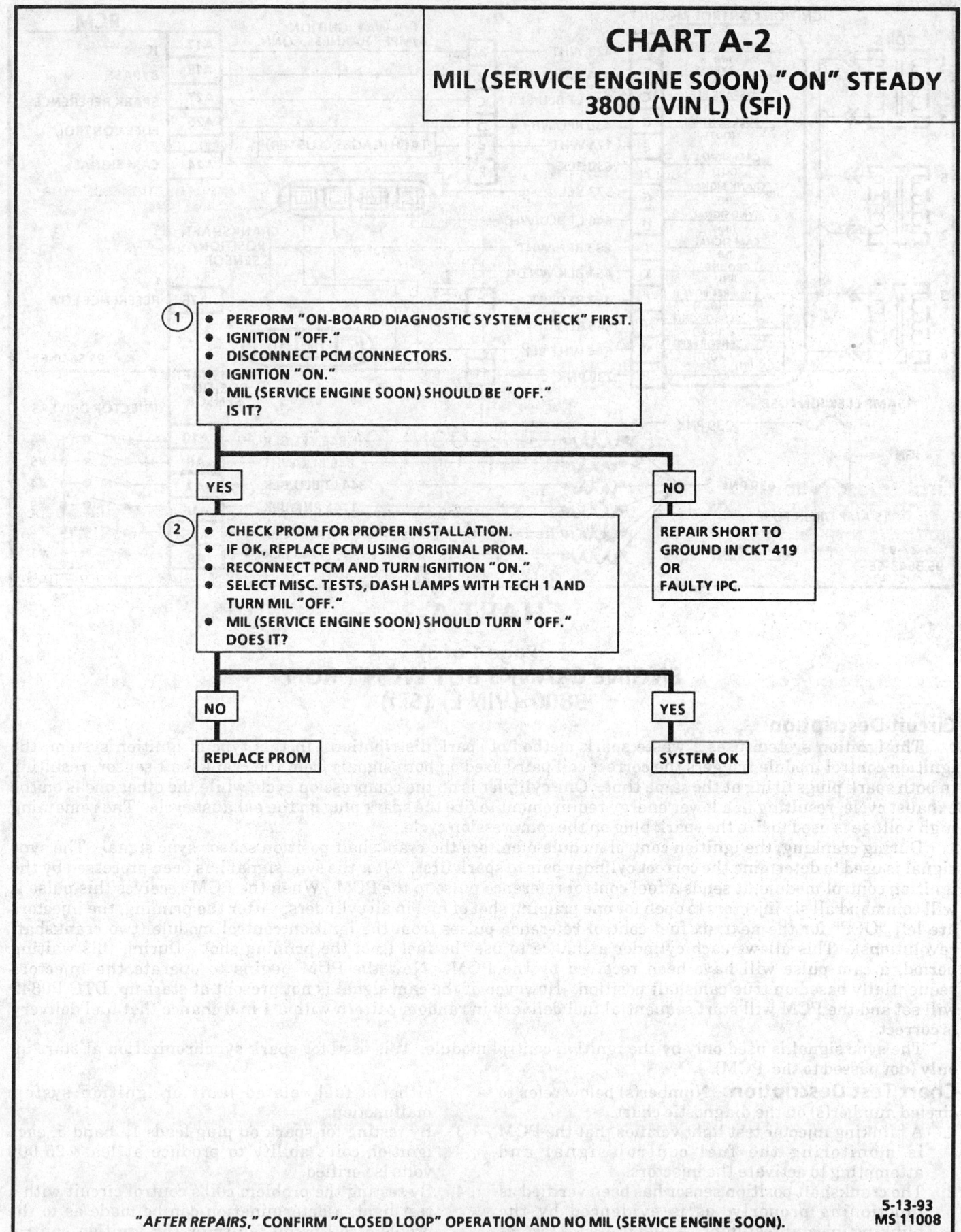

CHART A-2

MIL (SERVICE ENGINE SOON) "ON" STEADY 3800 (VIN L) (SFI)

(1)
- PERFORM "ON-BOARD DIAGNOSTIC SYSTEM CHECK" FIRST.
- IGNITION "OFF."
- DISCONNECT PCM CONNECTORS.
- IGNITION "ON."
- MIL (SERVICE ENGINE SOON) SHOULD BE "OFF." IS IT?

YES

(2)
- CHECK PROM FOR PROPER INSTALLATION.
- IF OK, REPLACE PCM USING ORIGINAL PROM.
- RECONNECT PCM AND TURN IGNITION "ON."
- SELECT MISC. TESTS, DASH LAMPS WITH TECH 1 AND TURN MIL "OFF."
- MIL (SERVICE ENGINE SOON) SHOULD TURN "OFF." DOES IT?

NO

REPLACE PROM

YES

SYSTEM OK

NO (from 1)

REPAIR SHORT TO GROUND IN CKT 419 OR FAULTY IPC.

"*AFTER REPAIRS,*" CONFIRM "CLOSED LOOP" OPERATION AND NO MIL (SERVICE ENGINE SOON).

5-13-93
MS 11008

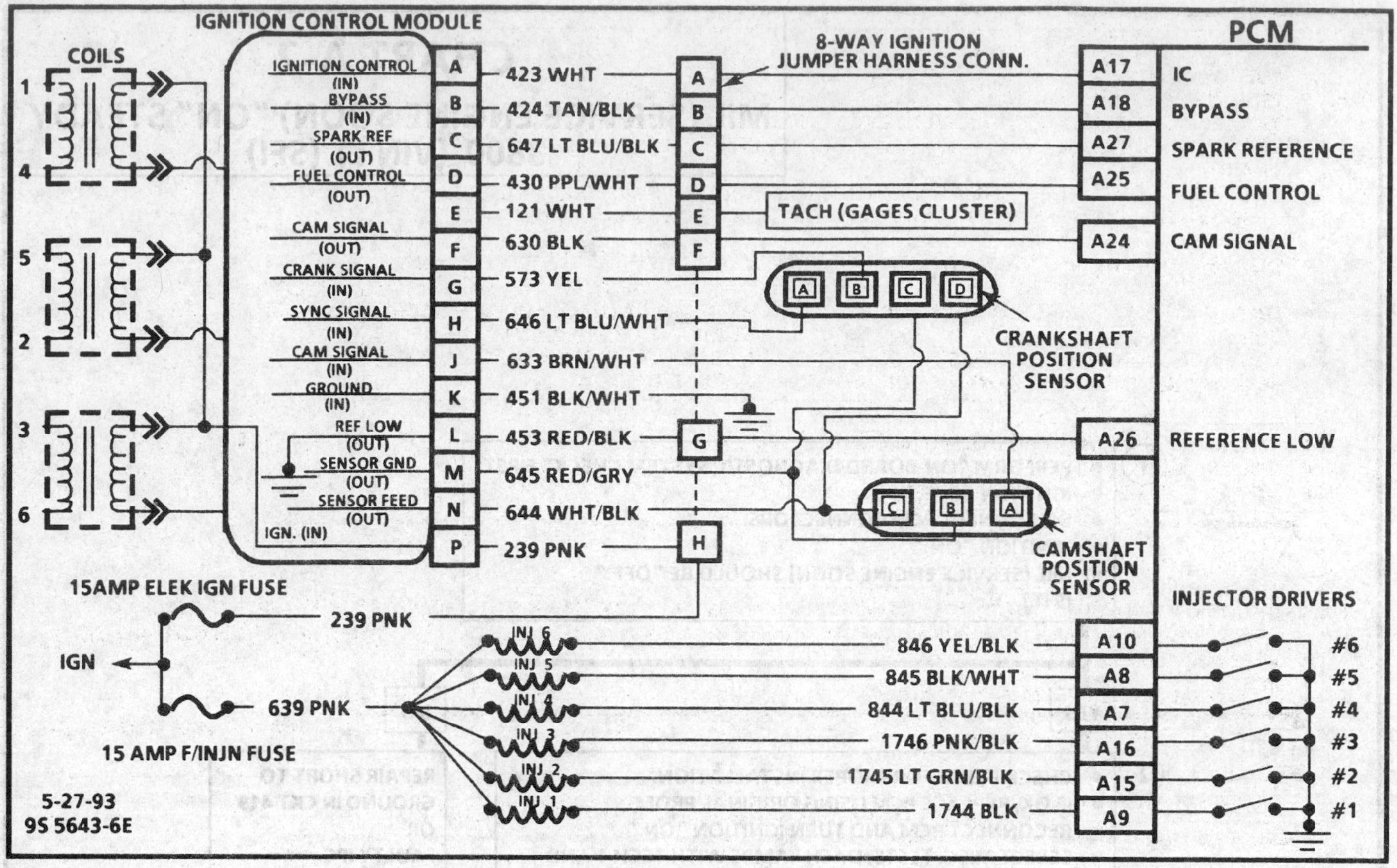
IGNITION CONTROL MODULE
COILS
IGNITION CONTROL (IN)
BYPASS (IN)
SPARK REF (OUT)
FUEL CONTROL (OUT)
CAM SIGNAL (OUT)
CRANK SIGNAL (IN)
SYNC SIGNAL (IN)
CAM SIGNAL (IN)
GROUND (IN)
REF LOW (OUT)
SENSOR GND (OUT)
SENSOR FEED (OUT)
IGN. (IN)
423 WHT
424 TAN/BLK
647 LT BLU/BLK
430 PPL/WHT
121 WHT
630 BLK
573 YEL
646 LT BLU/WHT
633 BRN/WHT
451 BLK/WHT
453 RED/BLK
645 RED/GRY
644 WHT/BLK
239 PNK
8-WAY IGNITION JUMPER HARNESS CONN.
TACH (GAGES CLUSTER)
CRANKSHAFT POSITION SENSOR
CAMSHAFT POSITION SENSOR
PCM
A17 IC
A18 BYPASS
A27 SPARK REFERENCE
A25 FUEL CONTROL
A24 CAM SIGNAL
A26 REFERENCE LOW
INJECTOR DRIVERS
15AMP ELEK IGN FUSE
239 PNK
IGN
639 PNK
15 AMP F/INJN FUSE
INJ 6
INJ 5
INJ 4
INJ 3
INJ 2
INJ 1
846 YEL/BLK
845 BLK/WHT
844 LT BLU/BLK
1746 PNK/BLK
1745 LT GRN/BLK
1744 BLK
A10
A8
A7
A16
A15
A9
#6
#5
#4
#3
#2
#1
5-27-93
9S 5643-6E

CHART A-3

(Page 1 of 3)
ENGINE CRANKS BUT WON'T RUN
3800 (VIN L) (SFI)

Circuit Description:

The ignition system uses a waste spark method of spark distribution. In this type of ignition system, the ignition control module triggers the correct coil pair based on both signals from the crankshaft sensor, resulting in both spark plugs firing at the same time. One cylinder is on the compression cycle while the other one is on the exhaust cycle, resulting in a lower energy requirement to fire the spark plug on the exhaust cycle. The remaining high voltage is used to fire the spark plug on the compression cycle.

During cranking, the ignition control module monitors the crankshaft position sensor sync signal. The sync signal is used to determine the correct cylinder pair to spark first. After the sync signal has been processed by the ignition control module, it sends a fuel control reference pulse to the PCM. When the PCM receives this pulse it will command all six injectors to open for one priming shot of fuel in all cylinders. After the priming, the injectors are left "OFF" for the next six fuel control reference pulses from the ignition control module (two crankshaft revolutions). This allows each cylinder a chance to use the fuel from the priming shot. During this waiting period, a cam pulse will have been received by the PCM. Now the PCM begins to operate the injectors sequentially based on true camshaft position. However, if the cam signal is not present at start-up, DTC P0342 will set and the PCM will start sequential fuel delivery in random pattern with a 1 in 6 chance that fuel delivery is correct.

The sync signal is used only by the ignition control module. It is used for spark synchronization at start-up only (not passed to the PCM).

Chart Test Description: Number(s) below refer to circled number(s) on the diagnostic chart.

1. A blinking injector test light verifies that the PCM is monitoring the fuel control signal and attempting to activate the injectors.
2. The crankshaft position sensor has been verified as functioning properly, as is evidenced by the blinking injector test light. A fuel pressure test, at this point, will separate the diagnostic path into either a fuel related fault or ignition system malfunction.
3. By testing for spark on plug leads 1, 3 and 5, each ignition coil's ability to produce at least 25,000 volts is verified.
4. By testing the problem coil's control circuit with a test light, a determination can be made as to the problem coil being faulty or the ignition control module's internal driver for that coil being the source of the complaint.

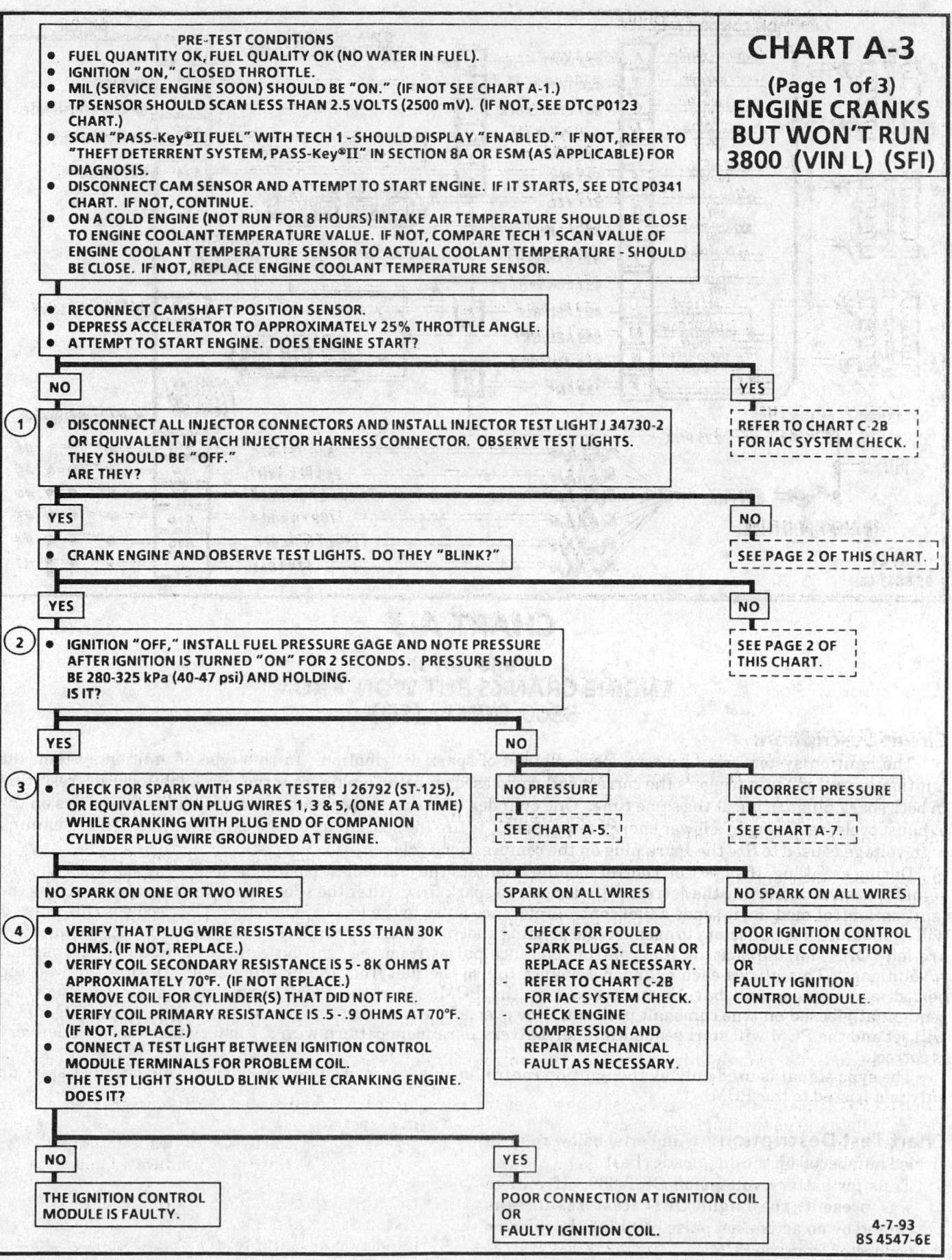

CHART A-3
(Page 1 of 3)
ENGINE CRANKS BUT WON'T RUN 3800 (VIN L) (SFI)

PRE-TEST CONDITIONS

- FUEL QUANTITY OK, FUEL QUALITY OK (NO WATER IN FUEL).
- IGNITION "ON," CLOSED THROTTLE.
- MIL (SERVICE ENGINE SOON) SHOULD BE "ON." (IF NOT SEE CHART A-1.)
- TP SENSOR SHOULD SCAN LESS THAN 2.5 VOLTS (2500 mV). (IF NOT, SEE DTC P0123 CHART.)
- SCAN "PASS-Key®II FUEL" WITH TECH 1 - SHOULD DISPLAY "ENABLED." IF NOT, REFER TO "THEFT DETERRENT SYSTEM, PASS-Key®II" IN SECTION 8A OR ESM (AS APPLICABLE) FOR DIAGNOSIS.
- DISCONNECT CAM SENSOR AND ATTEMPT TO START ENGINE. IF IT STARTS, SEE DTC P0341 CHART. IF NOT, CONTINUE.
- ON A COLD ENGINE (NOT RUN FOR 8 HOURS) INTAKE AIR TEMPERATURE SHOULD BE CLOSE TO ENGINE COOLANT TEMPERATURE VALUE. IF NOT, COMPARE TECH 1 SCAN VALUE OF ENGINE COOLANT TEMPERATURE SENSOR TO ACTUAL COOLANT TEMPERATURE - SHOULD BE CLOSE. IF NOT, REPLACE ENGINE COOLANT TEMPERATURE SENSOR.

- RECONNECT CAMSHAFT POSITION SENSOR.
- DEPRESS ACCELERATOR TO APPROXIMATELY 25% THROTTLE ANGLE.
- ATTEMPT TO START ENGINE. DOES ENGINE START?

YES → REFER TO CHART C-2B FOR IAC SYSTEM CHECK.

NO ↓

(1)
- DISCONNECT ALL INJECTOR CONNECTORS AND INSTALL INJECTOR TEST LIGHT J 34730-2 OR EQUIVALENT IN EACH INJECTOR HARNESS CONNECTOR. OBSERVE TEST LIGHTS. THEY SHOULD BE "OFF." ARE THEY?

NO → SEE PAGE 2 OF THIS CHART.

YES ↓

- CRANK ENGINE AND OBSERVE TEST LIGHTS. DO THEY "BLINK?"

NO → SEE PAGE 2 OF THIS CHART.

YES ↓

(2)
- IGNITION "OFF," INSTALL FUEL PRESSURE GAGE AND NOTE PRESSURE AFTER IGNITION IS TURNED "ON" FOR 2 SECONDS. PRESSURE SHOULD BE 280-325 kPa (40-47 psi) AND HOLDING. IS IT?

NO →
- NO PRESSURE → SEE CHART A-5.
- INCORRECT PRESSURE → SEE CHART A-7.

YES ↓

(3)
- CHECK FOR SPARK WITH SPARK TESTER J 26792 (ST-125), OR EQUIVALENT ON PLUG WIRES 1, 3 & 5, (ONE AT A TIME) WHILE CRANKING WITH PLUG END OF COMPANION CYLINDER PLUG WIRE GROUNDED AT ENGINE.

SPARK ON ALL WIRES →
- CHECK FOR FOULED SPARK PLUGS. CLEAN OR REPLACE AS NECESSARY.
- REFER TO CHART C-2B FOR IAC SYSTEM CHECK.
- CHECK ENGINE COMPRESSION AND REPAIR MECHANICAL FAULT AS NECESSARY.

NO SPARK ON ALL WIRES → POOR IGNITION CONTROL MODULE CONNECTION OR FAULTY IGNITION CONTROL MODULE.

NO SPARK ON ONE OR TWO WIRES ↓

(4)
- VERIFY THAT PLUG WIRE RESISTANCE IS LESS THAN 30K OHMS. (IF NOT, REPLACE.)
- VERIFY COIL SECONDARY RESISTANCE IS 5 - 8K OHMS AT APPROXIMATELY 70°F. (IF NOT REPLACE.)
- REMOVE COIL FOR CYLINDER(S) THAT DID NOT FIRE.
- VERIFY COIL PRIMARY RESISTANCE IS .5 - .9 OHMS AT 70°F. (IF NOT, REPLACE.)
- CONNECT A TEST LIGHT BETWEEN IGNITION CONTROL MODULE TERMINALS FOR PROBLEM COIL.
- THE TEST LIGHT SHOULD BLINK WHILE CRANKING ENGINE. DOES IT?

NO → THE IGNITION CONTROL MODULE IS FAULTY.

YES → POOR CONNECTION AT IGNITION COIL OR FAULTY IGNITION COIL.

4-7-93
8S 4547-6E

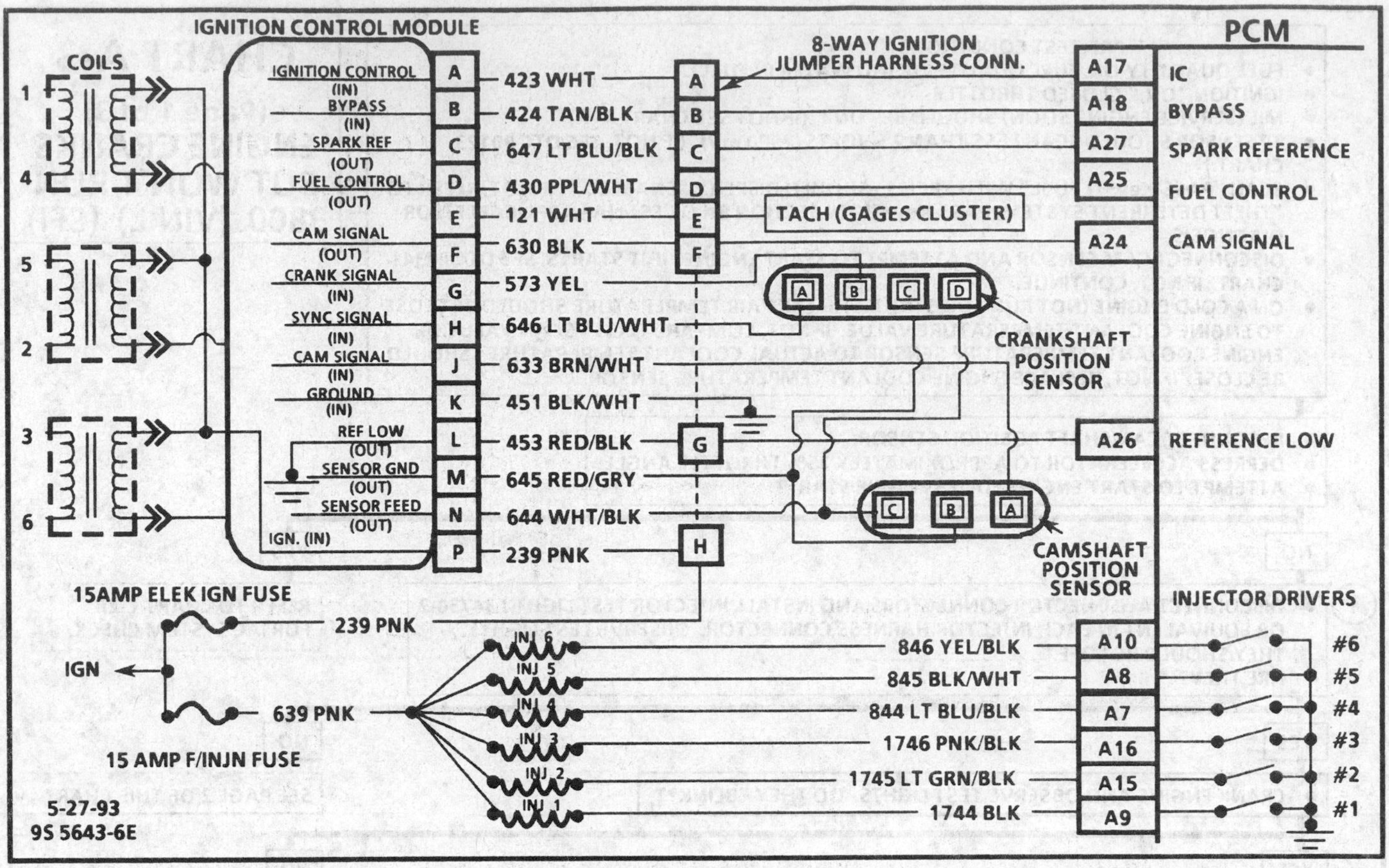

IGNITION CONTROL MODULE
COILS
PCM
8-WAY IGNITION JUMPER HARNESS CONN.
IGNITION CONTROL (IN)
BYPASS (IN)
SPARK REF (OUT)
FUEL CONTROL (OUT)
CAM SIGNAL (OUT)
CRANK SIGNAL (IN)
SYNC SIGNAL (IN)
CAM SIGNAL (IN)
GROUND (IN)
REF LOW (OUT)
SENSOR GND (OUT)
SENSOR FEED (OUT)
IGN. (IN)
423 WHT
424 TAN/BLK
647 LT BLU/BLK
430 PPL/WHT
121 WHT
630 BLK
573 YEL
646 LT BLU/WHT
633 BRN/WHT
451 BLK/WHT
453 RED/BLK
645 RED/GRY
644 WHT/BLK
239 PNK
TACH (GAGES CLUSTER)
A17 IC
A18 BYPASS
A27 SPARK REFERENCE
A25 FUEL CONTROL
A24 CAM SIGNAL
CRANKSHAFT POSITION SENSOR
A26 REFERENCE LOW
CAMSHAFT POSITION SENSOR
INJECTOR DRIVERS
15AMP ELEK IGN FUSE
IGN
639 PNK
15 AMP F/INJN FUSE
INJ 6
INJ 5
INJ 4
INJ 3
INJ 2
INJ 1
846 YEL/BLK
845 BLK/WHT
844 LT BLU/BLK
1746 PNK/BLK
1745 LT GRN/BLK
1744 BLK
A10
A8
A7
A16
A15
A9
#6
#5
#4
#3
#2
#1
5-27-93
9S 5643-6E

CHART A-3

(Page 2 of 3)

ENGINE CRANKS BUT WON'T RUN 3800 (VIN L) (SFI)

Circuit Description:

The ignition system uses a waste spark method of spark distribution. In this type of ignition system, the ignition control module triggers the correct coil pair based on both signals from the crankshaft sensor, resulting in both spark plugs firing at the same time. One cylinder is on the compression cycle while the other one is on the exhaust cycle, resulting in a lower energy requirement to fire the spark plug on the exhaust cycle. The remaining high voltage is used to fire the spark plug on the compression cycle.

During cranking, the ignition control module monitors the crankshaft position sensor sync signal. The sync signal is used to determine the correct cylinder pair to spark first. After the sync signal has been processed by the ignition control module, it sends a fuel control reference pulse to the PCM. When the PCM receives this pulse it will command all six injectors to open for one priming shot of fuel in all cylinders. After the priming, the injectors are left "OFF" for the next six fuel control reference pulses from the ignition control module (two crankshaft revolutions). This allows each cylinder a chance to use the fuel from the priming shot. During this waiting period, a cam pulse will have been received by the PCM. Now the PCM begins to operate the injectors sequentially based on true camshaft position. However, if the cam signal is not present at start-up, DTC P0342 will set and the PCM will start sequential fuel delivery in random pattern with a 1 in 6 chance that fuel delivery is correct.

The sync signal is used only by the ignition control module. It is used for spark synchronization at start-up only (not passed to the PCM).

Chart Test Description: Number(s) below refer to circled number(s) on the diagnostic chart.

5. Tests for battery voltage on CKT 639. If voltage was present, the "light OFF" test result was caused by no activation pulse reaching the injector connector from the PCM.

CHART A-3

(Page 2 of 3)
ENGINE CRANKS BUT WON'T RUN
3800 (VIN L) (SFI)

FROM CHART A-3 (PAGE 1).

LIGHT "OFF"

CHECK FUSE FOR INJECTOR FEED CKT 639. IS IT OK?

- **YES**
  - (5)
    - REMOVE INJECTOR TEST LIGHT.
    - PROBE INJECTOR HARNESS CKT 639 AT EACH INJECTOR TERMINAL "A" WITH A TEST LIGHT TO GROUND.
    - TEST LIGHT SHOULD BE "ON." IS IT?
  - **NO**: INJECTOR FEED CKT 639 IS OPEN.
  - **YES**: SEE (PAGE 3) OF THIS CHART.
- **NO**: REPAIR SHORT TO GROUND IN CKT 639. REFER TO "FUSE BLOCK/ELECTRICAL CENTER DETAILS" IN SECTION 8A .

STEADY LIGHT

- DISCONNECT BLACK PCM CONNECTOR "A".
- ARE ALL LIGHTS OFF?

- **YES**: FAULTY PCM.
- **NO**: REPAIR SHORT TO GROUND IN INJECTOR WIRING.*

* IF AN INJECTOR DRIVER CIRCUIT HAS BEEN CONTINUOUSLY GROUNDED, THE FOLLOWING SHOULD ALSO BE CHECKED.

1. OIL FOR FUEL CONTAMINATION.
2. EXHAUST SYSTEM RESTRICTION USING PROCEDURE FOUND IN "SYMPTOMS," SECTION 6E3-B, CHART B-1.

3-1-93
9S 5645-6E

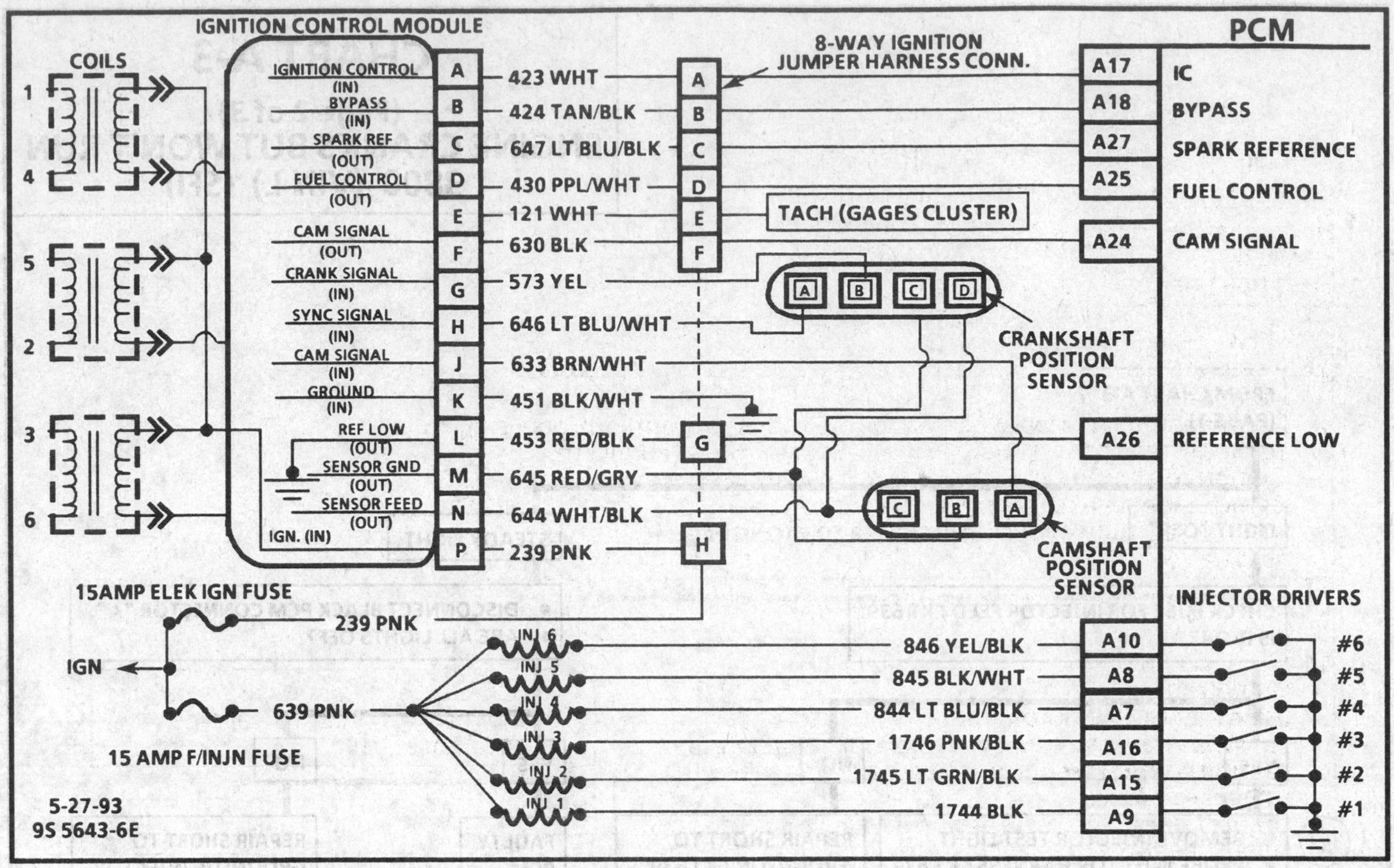
IGNITION CONTROL MODULE
COILS
1
4
5
2
3
6
IGNITION CONTROL (IN)
BYPASS (IN)
SPARK REF (OUT)
FUEL CONTROL (OUT)
CAM SIGNAL (OUT)
CRANK SIGNAL (IN)
SYNC SIGNAL (IN)
CAM SIGNAL (IN)
GROUND (IN)
REF LOW (OUT)
SENSOR GND (OUT)
SENSOR FEED (OUT)
IGN. (IN)
A
B
C
D
E
F
G
H
J
K
L
M
N
P
423 WHT
424 TAN/BLK
647 LT BLU/BLK
430 PPL/WHT
121 WHT
630 BLK
573 YEL
646 LT BLU/WHT
633 BRN/WHT
451 BLK/WHT
453 RED/BLK
645 RED/GRY
644 WHT/BLK
239 PNK
8-WAY IGNITION JUMPER HARNESS CONN.
TACH (GAGES CLUSTER)
CRANKSHAFT POSITION SENSOR
CAMSHAFT POSITION SENSOR
PCM
A17
A18
A27
A25
A24
A26
IC
BYPASS
SPARK REFERENCE
FUEL CONTROL
CAM SIGNAL
REFERENCE LOW
INJECTOR DRIVERS
15AMP ELEK IGN FUSE
239 PNK
IGN
639 PNK
15 AMP F/INJN FUSE
INJ 6
INJ 5
INJ 4
INJ 3
INJ 2
INJ 1
846 YEL/BLK
845 BLK/WHT
844 LT BLU/BLK
1746 PNK/BLK
1745 LT GRN/BLK
1744 BLK
A10
A8
A7
A16
A15
A9
#6
#5
#4
#3
#2
#1
5-27-93
9S 5643-6E

CHART A-3

(Page 3 of 3)
ENGINE CRANKS BUT WON'T RUN
3800 (VIN L) (SFI)

Circuit Description:

The ignition system uses a waste spark method of spark distribution. In this type of ignition system, the ignition control module triggers the correct coil pair based on both signals from the crankshaft sensor, resulting in both spark plugs firing at the same time. One cylinder is on the compression cycle while the other one is on the exhaust cycle, resulting in a lower energy requirement to fire the spark plug on the exhaust cycle. The remaining high voltage is used to fire the spark plug on the compression cycle.

During cranking, the ignition control module monitors the crankshaft position sensor sync signal. The sync signal is used to determine the correct cylinder pair to spark first. After the sync signal has been processed by the ignition control module, it sends a fuel control reference pulse to the PCM. When the PCM receives this pulse it will command all six injectors to open for one priming shot of fuel in all cylinders. After the priming, the injectors are left "OFF" for the next six fuel control reference pulses from the ignition control module (two crankshaft revolutions). This allows each cylinder a chance to use the fuel from the priming shot. During this waiting period, a cam pulse will have been received by the PCM. Now the PCM begins to operate the injectors sequentially based on true camshaft position. However, if the cam signal is not present at start-up, DTC P0342 will set and the PCM will start sequential fuel delivery in random pattern with a 1 in 6 chance that fuel delivery is correct.

The sync signal is used only by the ignition control module. It is used for spark synchronization at start-up only (not passed to the PCM).

Chart Test Description: Number(s) below refer to circled number(s) on the diagnostic chart.

6. The test light to 12 volts simulates a reference signal to the PCM which will result in an injector test light blink with each touch of the test light to terminal "D". It may take up to three touches to get an injector test light flash. CKT 430, the PCM, and the injector driver circuits are all OK. Ensure that all injectors are disconnected prior to this step to avoid possible flooding.
7. Checks CKTs 644, 645, 646 and 3X portion of the crankshaft position sensor. If CKT 646 has been shorted to voltage, make sure crankshaft position sensor has not been damaged.
8. Checks CKT 573 and the 18X portion of the crankshaft position sensor. If CKT 573 has been shorted to voltage, make sure crankshaft position sensor has not been damaged.
9. Verifies ignition feed to the ignition control module.

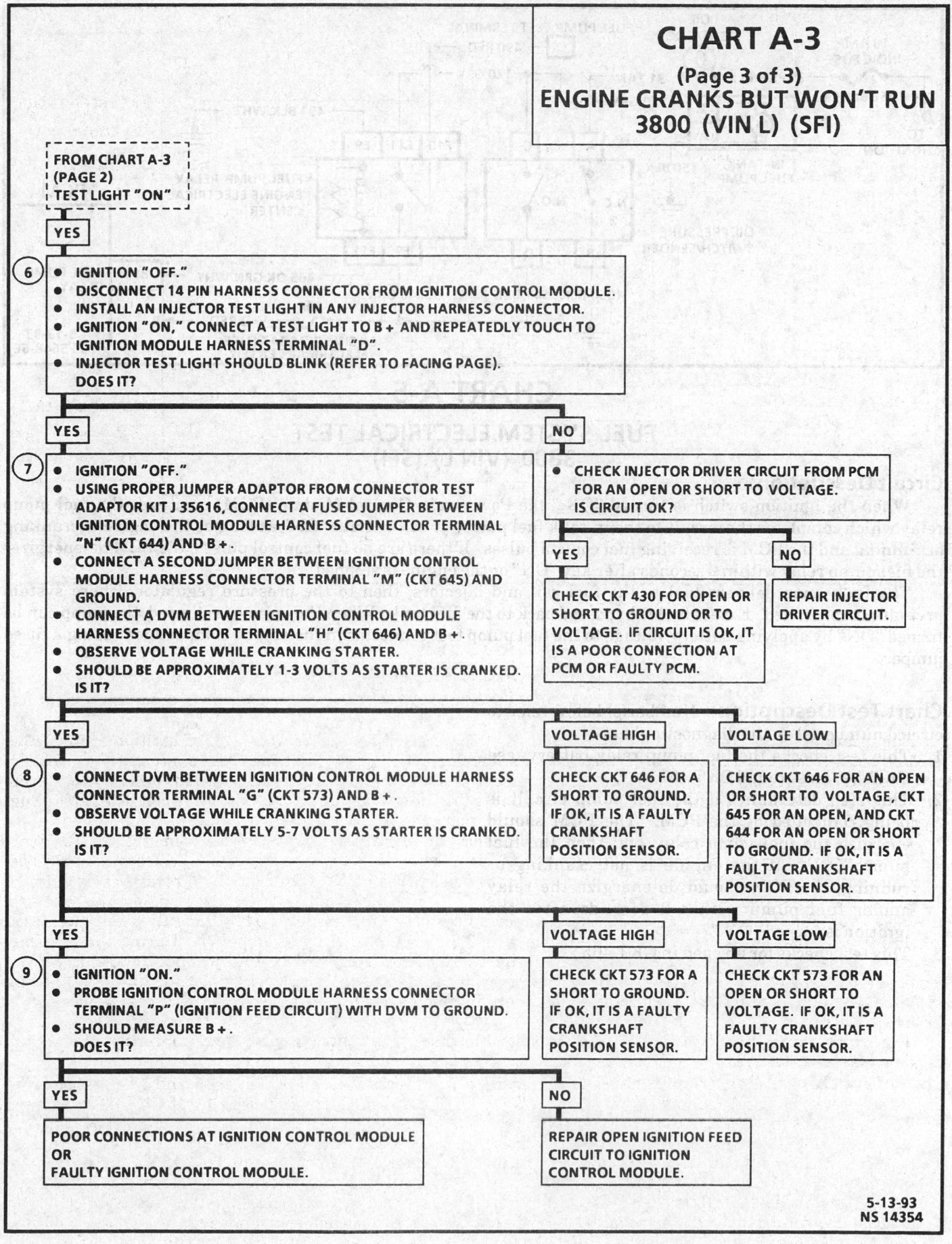

CHART A-3
(Page 3 of 3)
ENGINE CRANKS BUT WON'T RUN
3800 (VIN L) (SFI)

FROM CHART A-3 (PAGE 2) TEST LIGHT "ON"

YES

6
- IGNITION "OFF."
- DISCONNECT 14 PIN HARNESS CONNECTOR FROM IGNITION CONTROL MODULE.
- INSTALL AN INJECTOR TEST LIGHT IN ANY INJECTOR HARNESS CONNECTOR.
- IGNITION "ON," CONNECT A TEST LIGHT TO B + AND REPEATEDLY TOUCH TO IGNITION MODULE HARNESS TERMINAL "D".
- INJECTOR TEST LIGHT SHOULD BLINK (REFER TO FACING PAGE). DOES IT?

NO
- CHECK INJECTOR DRIVER CIRCUIT FROM PCM FOR AN OPEN OR SHORT TO VOLTAGE. IS CIRCUIT OK?

YES: CHECK CKT 430 FOR OPEN OR SHORT TO GROUND OR TO VOLTAGE. IF CIRCUIT IS OK, IT IS A POOR CONNECTION AT PCM OR FAULTY PCM.

NO: REPAIR INJECTOR DRIVER CIRCUIT.

YES

7
- IGNITION "OFF."
- USING PROPER JUMPER ADAPTOR FROM CONNECTOR TEST ADAPTOR KIT J 35616, CONNECT A FUSED JUMPER BETWEEN IGNITION CONTROL MODULE HARNESS CONNECTOR TERMINAL "N" (CKT 644) AND B +.
- CONNECT A SECOND JUMPER BETWEEN IGNITION CONTROL MODULE HARNESS CONNECTOR TERMINAL "M" (CKT 645) AND GROUND.
- CONNECT A DVM BETWEEN IGNITION CONTROL MODULE HARNESS CONNECTOR TERMINAL "H" (CKT 646) AND B +.
- OBSERVE VOLTAGE WHILE CRANKING STARTER.
- SHOULD BE APPROXIMATELY 1-3 VOLTS AS STARTER IS CRANKED. IS IT?

VOLTAGE HIGH: CHECK CKT 646 FOR A SHORT TO GROUND. IF OK, IT IS A FAULTY CRANKSHAFT POSITION SENSOR.

VOLTAGE LOW: CHECK CKT 646 FOR AN OPEN OR SHORT TO VOLTAGE, CKT 645 FOR AN OPEN, AND CKT 644 FOR AN OPEN OR SHORT TO GROUND. IF OK, IT IS A FAULTY CRANKSHAFT POSITION SENSOR.

YES

8
- CONNECT DVM BETWEEN IGNITION CONTROL MODULE HARNESS CONNECTOR TERMINAL "G" (CKT 573) AND B +.
- OBSERVE VOLTAGE WHILE CRANKING STARTER.
- SHOULD BE APPROXIMATELY 5-7 VOLTS AS STARTER IS CRANKED. IS IT?

VOLTAGE HIGH: CHECK CKT 573 FOR A SHORT TO GROUND. IF OK, IT IS A FAULTY CRANKSHAFT POSITION SENSOR.

VOLTAGE LOW: CHECK CKT 573 FOR AN OPEN OR SHORT TO VOLTAGE. IF OK, IT IS A FAULTY CRANKSHAFT POSITION SENSOR.

YES

9
- IGNITION "ON."
- PROBE IGNITION CONTROL MODULE HARNESS CONNECTOR TERMINAL "P" (IGNITION FEED CIRCUIT) WITH DVM TO GROUND.
- SHOULD MEASURE B +. DOES IT?

YES: POOR CONNECTIONS AT IGNITION CONTROL MODULE OR FAULTY IGNITION CONTROL MODULE.

NO: REPAIR OPEN IGNITION FEED CIRCUIT TO IGNITION CONTROL MODULE.

5-13-93
NS 14354

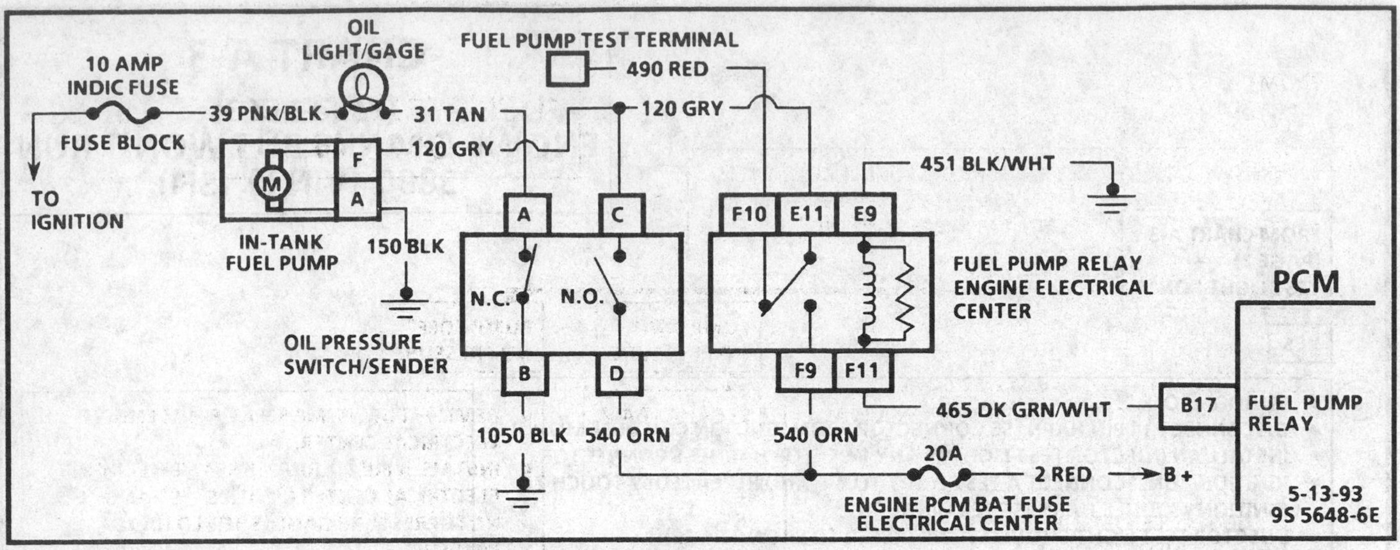
OIL LIGHT/GAGE
FUEL PUMP TEST TERMINAL
490 RED
10 AMP INDIC FUSE
39 PNK/BLK
31 TAN
120 GRY
FUSE BLOCK
120 GRY
F
A
TO IGNITION
451 BLK/WHT
F10 E11 E9
A
C
IN-TANK FUEL PUMP
150 BLK
FUEL PUMP RELAY ENGINE ELECTRICAL CENTER
PCM
N.C.
N.O.
OIL PRESSURE SWITCH/SENDER
B
D
F9 F11
465 DK GRN/WHT
B17
FUEL PUMP RELAY
1050 BLK
540 ORN
540 ORN
20A
2 RED
B+
ENGINE PCM BAT FUSE ELECTRICAL CENTER
5-13-93
9S 5648-6E

CHART A-5

FUEL SYSTEM ELECTRICAL TEST
3800 (VIN L) (SFI)

Circuit Description:

When the ignition switch is turned "ON," the Powertrain Control Module (PCM) energizes the fuel pump relay which completes the circuit to the in-tank fuel pump. It will remain "ON" as long as the engine is cranking or running and the PCM is receiving fuel control pulses. If there are no fuel control pulses, the PCM de-energizes the fuel pump relay within 2 seconds after key "ON" or the engine is stopped.

The fuel pump delivers fuel to the fuel rail and injectors, then to the pressure regulator, where system pressure is controlled. Excess fuel is bypassed back to the fuel tank. When the engine is stopped, the pump can be turned "ON" by applying battery voltage to the fuel pump test connector in the engine compartment using a fused jumper.

Chart Test Description: Number(s) below refer to circled number(s) on the diagnostic chart.

1. This test checks the fuel pump relay battery feed CKT 540 and ground CKT 451.
2. This step determines if the fuel pump circuit is being controlled by the PCM. The PCM should energize the fuel pump relay and turn the fuel pump "ON." If the engine is not cranking or running, the PCM should de-energize the relay and/or fuel pump within 2 seconds after the ignition is turned "ON."
3. This test checks for an open in CKT 465.

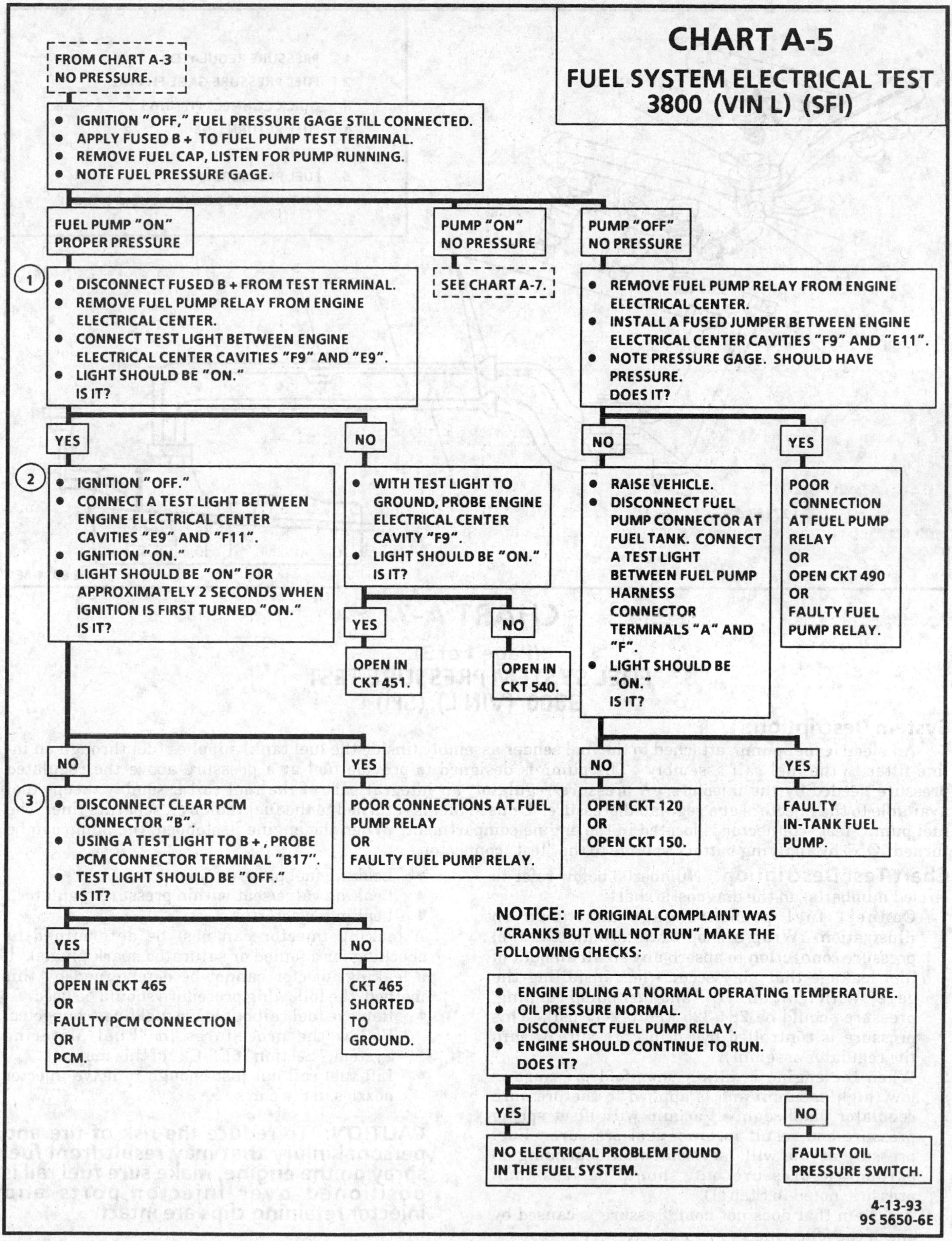
CHART A-5
FUEL SYSTEM ELECTRICAL TEST
3800 (VIN L) (SFI)
FROM CHART A-3
NO PRESSURE.
• IGNITION "OFF," FUEL PRESSURE GAGE STILL CONNECTED.
• APPLY FUSED B + TO FUEL PUMP TEST TERMINAL.
• REMOVE FUEL CAP, LISTEN FOR PUMP RUNNING.
• NOTE FUEL PRESSURE GAGE.
FUEL PUMP "ON"
PROPER PRESSURE
PUMP "ON"
NO PRESSURE
PUMP "OFF"
NO PRESSURE
1
• DISCONNECT FUSED B + FROM TEST TERMINAL.
• REMOVE FUEL PUMP RELAY FROM ENGINE ELECTRICAL CENTER.
• CONNECT TEST LIGHT BETWEEN ENGINE ELECTRICAL CENTER CAVITIES "F9" AND "E9".
• LIGHT SHOULD BE "ON."
IS IT?
SEE CHART A-7.
• REMOVE FUEL PUMP RELAY FROM ENGINE ELECTRICAL CENTER.
• INSTALL A FUSED JUMPER BETWEEN ENGINE ELECTRICAL CENTER CAVITIES "F9" AND "E11".
• NOTE PRESSURE GAGE. SHOULD HAVE PRESSURE.
DOES IT?
YES
NO
NO
YES
2
• IGNITION "OFF."
• CONNECT A TEST LIGHT BETWEEN ENGINE ELECTRICAL CENTER CAVITIES "E9" AND "F11".
• IGNITION "ON."
• LIGHT SHOULD BE "ON" FOR APPROXIMATELY 2 SECONDS WHEN IGNITION IS FIRST TURNED "ON."
IS IT?
• WITH TEST LIGHT TO GROUND, PROBE ENGINE ELECTRICAL CENTER CAVITY "F9".
• LIGHT SHOULD BE "ON."
IS IT?
• RAISE VEHICLE.
• DISCONNECT FUEL PUMP CONNECTOR AT FUEL TANK. CONNECT A TEST LIGHT BETWEEN FUEL PUMP HARNESS CONNECTOR TERMINALS "A" AND "F".
• LIGHT SHOULD BE "ON."
IS IT?
POOR CONNECTION AT FUEL PUMP RELAY OR OPEN CKT 490 OR FAULTY FUEL PUMP RELAY.
YES
NO
OPEN IN CKT 451.
OPEN IN CKT 540.
NO
YES
NO
YES
3
• DISCONNECT CLEAR PCM CONNECTOR "B".
• USING A TEST LIGHT TO B +, PROBE PCM CONNECTOR TERMINAL "B17".
• TEST LIGHT SHOULD BE "OFF."
IS IT?
POOR CONNECTIONS AT FUEL PUMP RELAY OR FAULTY FUEL PUMP RELAY.
OPEN CKT 120 OR OPEN CKT 150.
FAULTY IN-TANK FUEL PUMP.
YES
NO
OPEN IN CKT 465 OR FAULTY PCM CONNECTION OR PCM.
CKT 465 SHORTED TO GROUND.
NOTICE: IF ORIGINAL COMPLAINT WAS "CRANKS BUT WILL NOT RUN" MAKE THE FOLLOWING CHECKS:
• ENGINE IDLING AT NORMAL OPERATING TEMPERATURE.
• OIL PRESSURE NORMAL.
• DISCONNECT FUEL PUMP RELAY.
• ENGINE SHOULD CONTINUE TO RUN.
DOES IT?
YES
NO
NO ELECTRICAL PROBLEM FOUND IN THE FUEL SYSTEM.
FAULTY OIL PRESSURE SWITCH.
4-13-93
9S 5650-6E

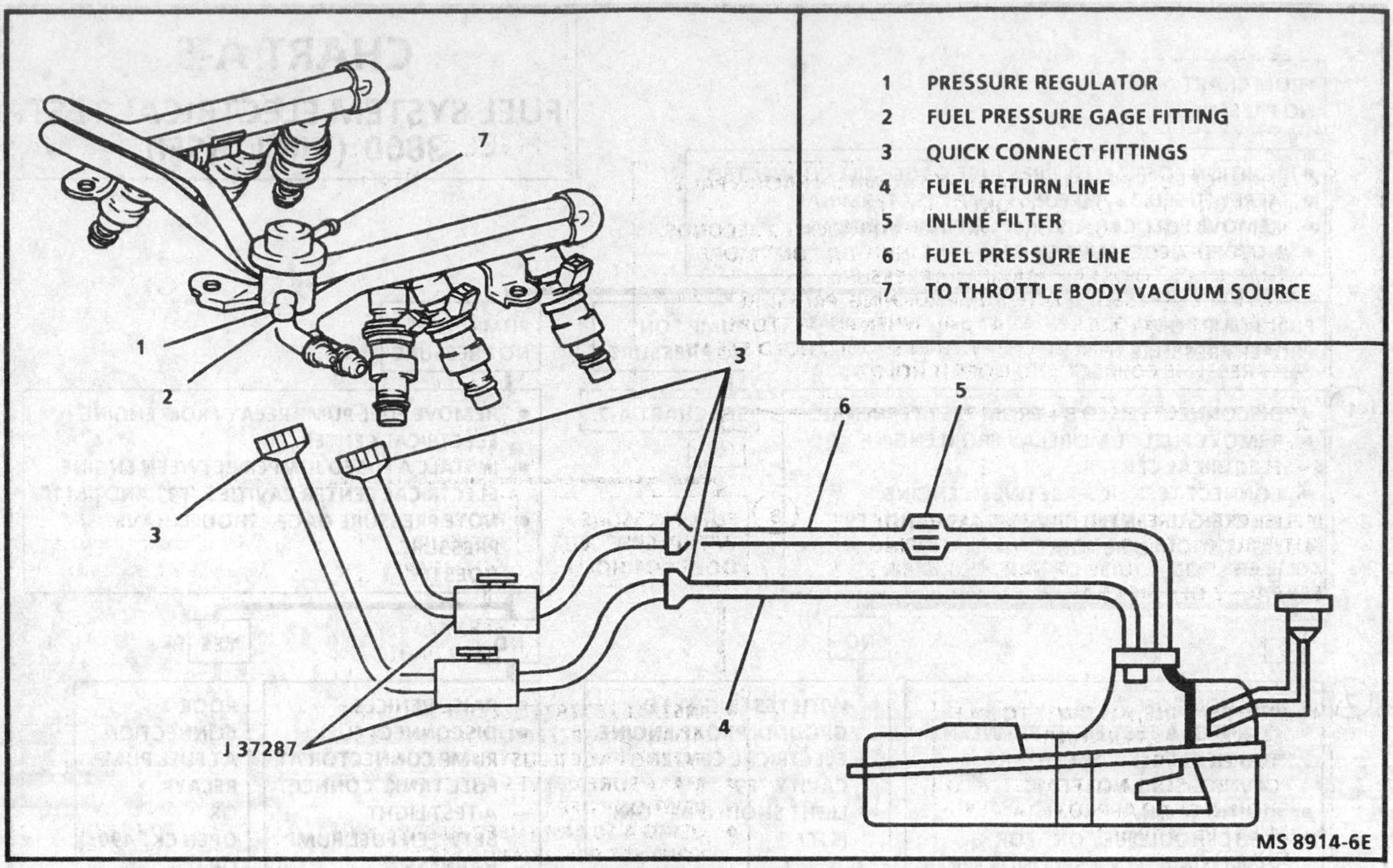
1 PRESSURE REGULATOR
2 FUEL PRESSURE GAGE FITTING
3 QUICK CONNECT FITTINGS
4 FUEL RETURN LINE
5 INLINE FILTER
6 FUEL PRESSURE LINE
7 TO THROTTLE BODY VACUUM SOURCE
J 37287
MS 8914-6E

CHART A-7

(Page 1 of 3)
FUEL SYSTEM PRESSURE TEST
3800 (VIN L) (SFI)

System Description:

An electric fuel pump, attached to the fuel sender assembly (inside the fuel tank) supplies fuel through an in-line filter to the fuel rail assembly. The pump is designed to provide fuel at a pressure above the regulated pressure needed by the injectors. A pressure regulator, an integral part of the fuel rail assembly, keeps fuel available to the injectors at a regulated pressure. Unused fuel is returned to the fuel tank by a separate line. The fuel pump "test" connector is located in the engine compartment. When the engine is stopped, the pump can be turned "ON" by applying battery voltage to the "test" connector.

Chart Test Description: Number(s) below refer to circled number(s) on the diagnostic chart.

1. Connect fuel pressure gage as shown in illustration. Wrap a shop towel around the fuel pressure connection to absorb any small amount of fuel leakage that may occur when installing the gage. With ignition "ON" and fuel pump running, pressure should be 284-325 kPa (41-47 psi). This pressure is controlled by spring pressure within the regulator assembly.
2. When the engine is idling, manifold pressure is low (high vacuum) and is applied to the pressure regulator diaphragm. Vacuum will offset spring pressure and result in lower fuel pressure. Fuel pressure at idle will vary somewhat depending on barometric pressure but, should be less than pressure noted in Step (1).
3. A system that does not hold pressure is caused by one of the following:
   - Leaking fuel pump check ball.
   - Leaking fuel pulse dampener.
   - Leaking valve/seat within pressure regulator.
   - Leaking injector(s).
4. A leaking injector can best be determined by checking for a fouled or saturated spark plug(s). If a leaking injector cannot be determined by this method, the following procedure should be used.
   - Remove fuel rail but leave fuel lines connected. Follow the procedures in "Fuel Metering System," Section "6E3-C2" of this manual.
   - Lift fuel rail out just enough to leave injector nozzles in the ports.

CAUTION: To reduce the risk of fire and personal injury that may result from fuel spray on the engine, make sure fuel rail is positioned over injector ports and injector retaining clips are intact.

   - Pressure the fuel system and observe injector.

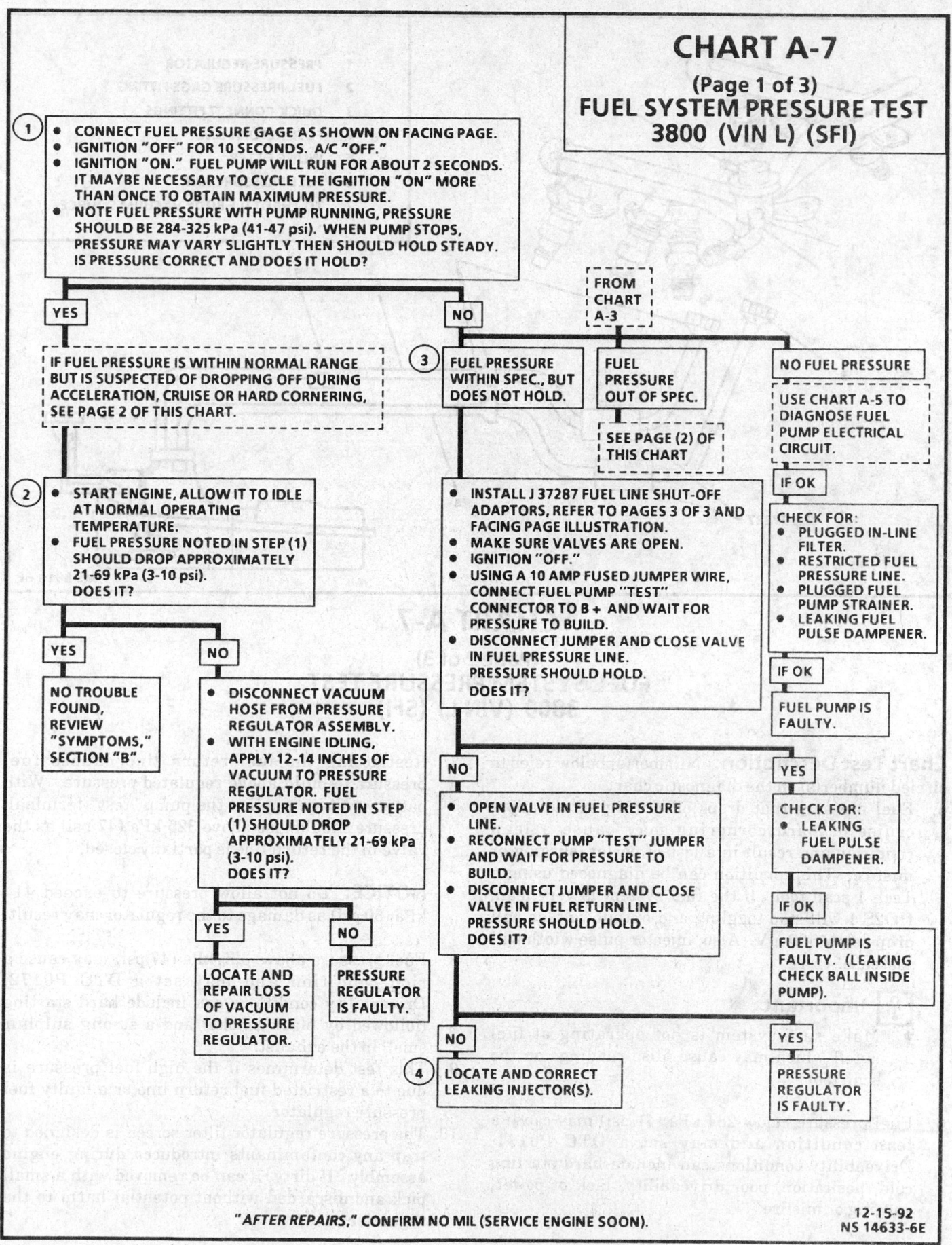

CHART A-7

(Page 1 of 3)
FUEL SYSTEM PRESSURE TEST
3800 (VIN L) (SFI)

(1)
- CONNECT FUEL PRESSURE GAGE AS SHOWN ON FACING PAGE.
- IGNITION "OFF" FOR 10 SECONDS. A/C "OFF."
- IGNITION "ON." FUEL PUMP WILL RUN FOR ABOUT 2 SECONDS. IT MAYBE NECESSARY TO CYCLE THE IGNITION "ON" MORE THAN ONCE TO OBTAIN MAXIMUM PRESSURE.
- NOTE FUEL PRESSURE WITH PUMP RUNNING, PRESSURE SHOULD BE 284-325 kPa (41-47 psi). WHEN PUMP STOPS, PRESSURE MAY VARY SLIGHTLY THEN SHOULD HOLD STEADY. IS PRESSURE CORRECT AND DOES IT HOLD?

YES

IF FUEL PRESSURE IS WITHIN NORMAL RANGE BUT IS SUSPECTED OF DROPPING OFF DURING ACCELERATION, CRUISE OR HARD CORNERING, SEE PAGE 2 OF THIS CHART.

(2)
- START ENGINE, ALLOW IT TO IDLE AT NORMAL OPERATING TEMPERATURE.
- FUEL PRESSURE NOTED IN STEP (1) SHOULD DROP APPROXIMATELY 21-69 kPa (3-10 psi). DOES IT?

YES

NO TROUBLE FOUND, REVIEW "SYMPTOMS," SECTION "B".

NO

- DISCONNECT VACUUM HOSE FROM PRESSURE REGULATOR ASSEMBLY.
- WITH ENGINE IDLING, APPLY 12-14 INCHES OF VACUUM TO PRESSURE REGULATOR. FUEL PRESSURE NOTED IN STEP (1) SHOULD DROP APPROXIMATELY 21-69 kPa (3-10 psi). DOES IT?

YES

LOCATE AND REPAIR LOSS OF VACUUM TO PRESSURE REGULATOR.

NO

PRESSURE REGULATOR IS FAULTY.

NO

FROM CHART A-3

(3) FUEL PRESSURE WITHIN SPEC., BUT DOES NOT HOLD.

- INSTALL J 37287 FUEL LINE SHUT-OFF ADAPTORS, REFER TO PAGES 3 OF 3 AND FACING PAGE ILLUSTRATION.
- MAKE SURE VALVES ARE OPEN.
- IGNITION "OFF."
- USING A 10 AMP FUSED JUMPER WIRE, CONNECT FUEL PUMP "TEST" CONNECTOR TO B + AND WAIT FOR PRESSURE TO BUILD.
- DISCONNECT JUMPER AND CLOSE VALVE IN FUEL PRESSURE LINE. PRESSURE SHOULD HOLD. DOES IT?

NO

- OPEN VALVE IN FUEL PRESSURE LINE.
- RECONNECT PUMP "TEST" JUMPER AND WAIT FOR PRESSURE TO BUILD.
- DISCONNECT JUMPER AND CLOSE VALVE IN FUEL RETURN LINE. PRESSURE SHOULD HOLD. DOES IT?

NO

(4) LOCATE AND CORRECT LEAKING INJECTOR(S).

YES

PRESSURE REGULATOR IS FAULTY.

YES

CHECK FOR:
- LEAKING FUEL PULSE DAMPENER.

IF OK

FUEL PUMP IS FAULTY. (LEAKING CHECK BALL INSIDE PUMP).

FUEL PRESSURE OUT OF SPEC.

SEE PAGE (2) OF THIS CHART

NO FUEL PRESSURE

USE CHART A-5 TO DIAGNOSE FUEL PUMP ELECTRICAL CIRCUIT.

IF OK

CHECK FOR:
- PLUGGED IN-LINE FILTER.
- RESTRICTED FUEL PRESSURE LINE.
- PLUGGED FUEL PUMP STRAINER.
- LEAKING FUEL PULSE DAMPENER.

IF OK

FUEL PUMP IS FAULTY.

"AFTER REPAIRS," CONFIRM NO MIL (SERVICE ENGINE SOON).

12-15-92
NS 14633-6E

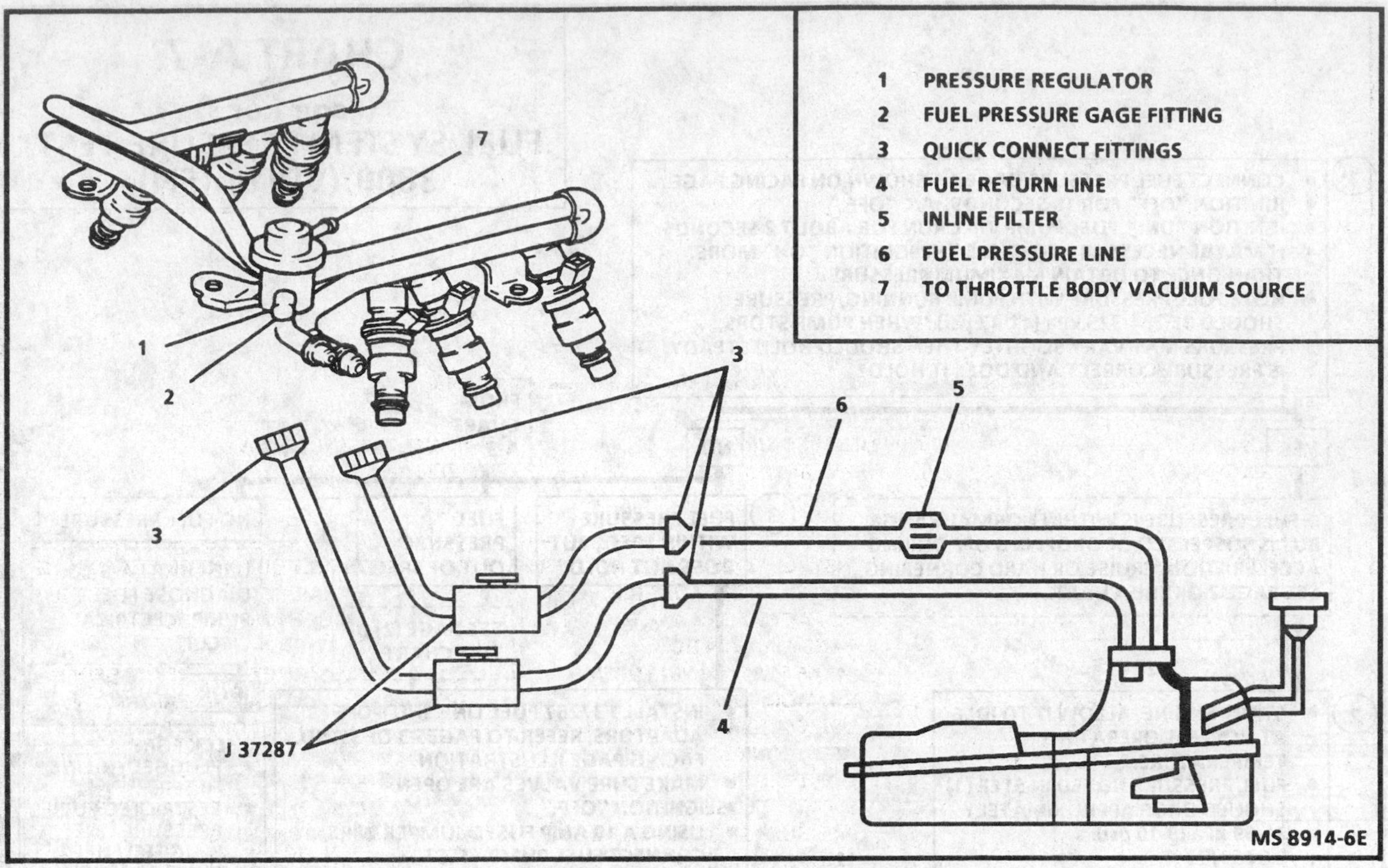

1 PRESSURE REGULATOR
2 FUEL PRESSURE GAGE FITTING
3 QUICK CONNECT FITTINGS
4 FUEL RETURN LINE
5 INLINE FILTER
6 FUEL PRESSURE LINE
7 TO THROTTLE BODY VACUUM SOURCE
1
2
3
3
4
5
6
7
J 37287
MS 8914-6E

CHART A-7

(Page 2 of 3)

FUEL SYSTEM PRESSURE TEST
3800 (VIN L) (SFI)

Chart Test Description: Number(s) below refer to circled number(s) on the diagnostic chart.

5. Fuel pressure that drops off during acceleration, cruise or hard cornering may cause a lean condition and result in a loss of power, surging or misfire. This condition can be diagnosed using a Tech 1 scan tool. If the fuel system is very lean, HO2S 1 will stop toggling and output voltage will drop below 500 mV. Also, injector pulse width will increase.

! Important

- Make sure system is not operating at fuel cutoff which may cause false readings on the scan tool.

6. Fuel pressure below 284 kPa (41 psi) may cause a lean condition and may set a DTC P0171. Driveability conditions can include hard starting cold, hesitation, poor driveability, lack of power, surging or misfire.

7. Restricting the fuel return line causes fuel pressure to build above regulated pressure. With battery voltage applied the pump "test" terminal, pressure should rise above 325 kPa (47 psi) as the valve in the return line is partially closed.

NOTICE: Do not allow pressure to exceed 414 kPa (60 psi) as damage to the regulator may result.

8. Fuel pressure above 325 kPa (47 psi) may cause a rich condition and may set a DTC P0172. Driveability conditions can include hard starting (followed by black smoke) and a strong sulphur smell in the exhaust.
9. This test determines if the high fuel pressure is due to a restricted fuel return line or a faulty fuel pressure regulator.
10. The pressure regulator filter screen is designed to trap any contaminants introduced during engine assembly. If dirty, it can be removed with a small pick and discarded without potential harm to the regulator.

CHART A-7

(Page 2 of 3)
FUEL SYSTEM PRESSURE TEST
3800 (VIN L) (SFI)

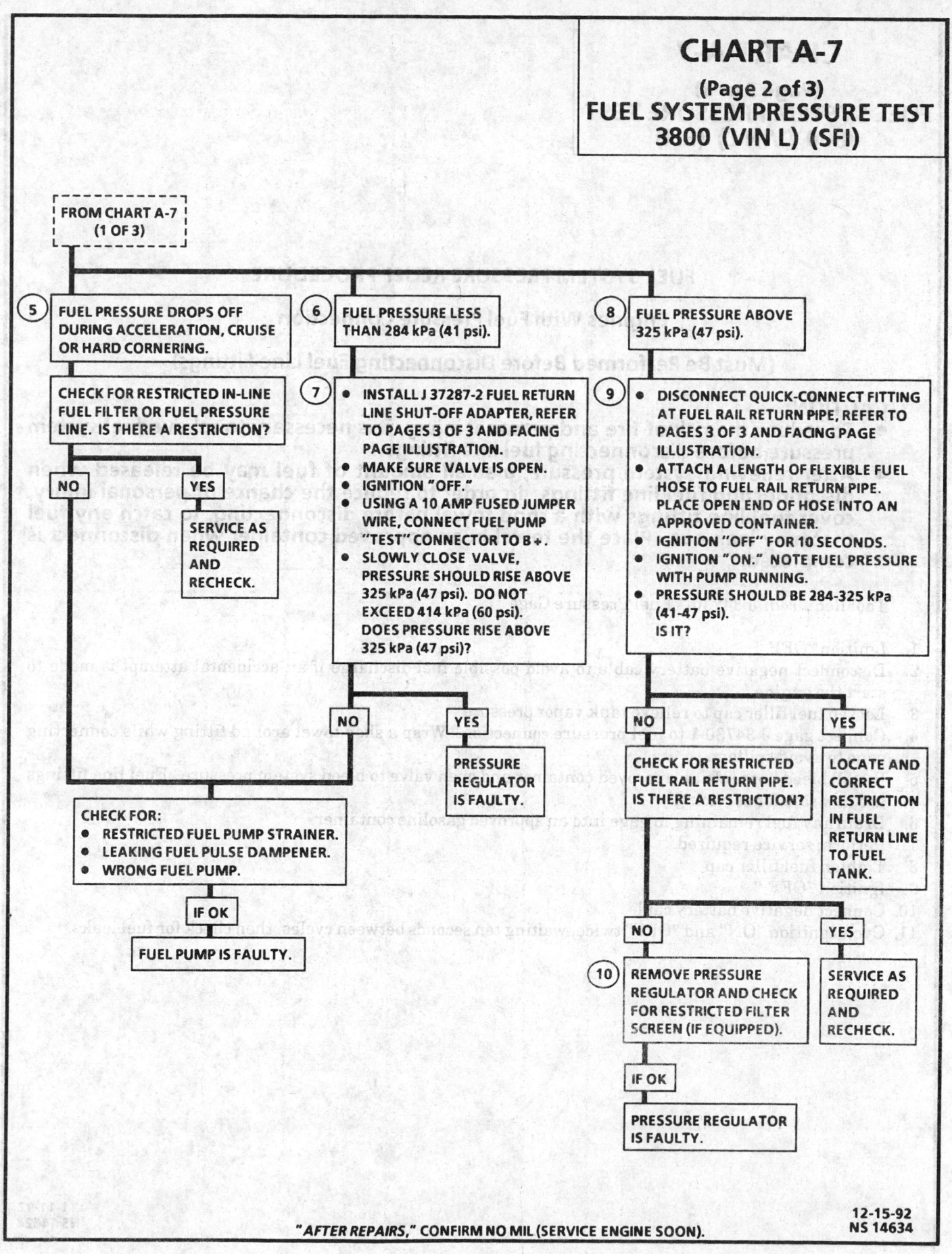

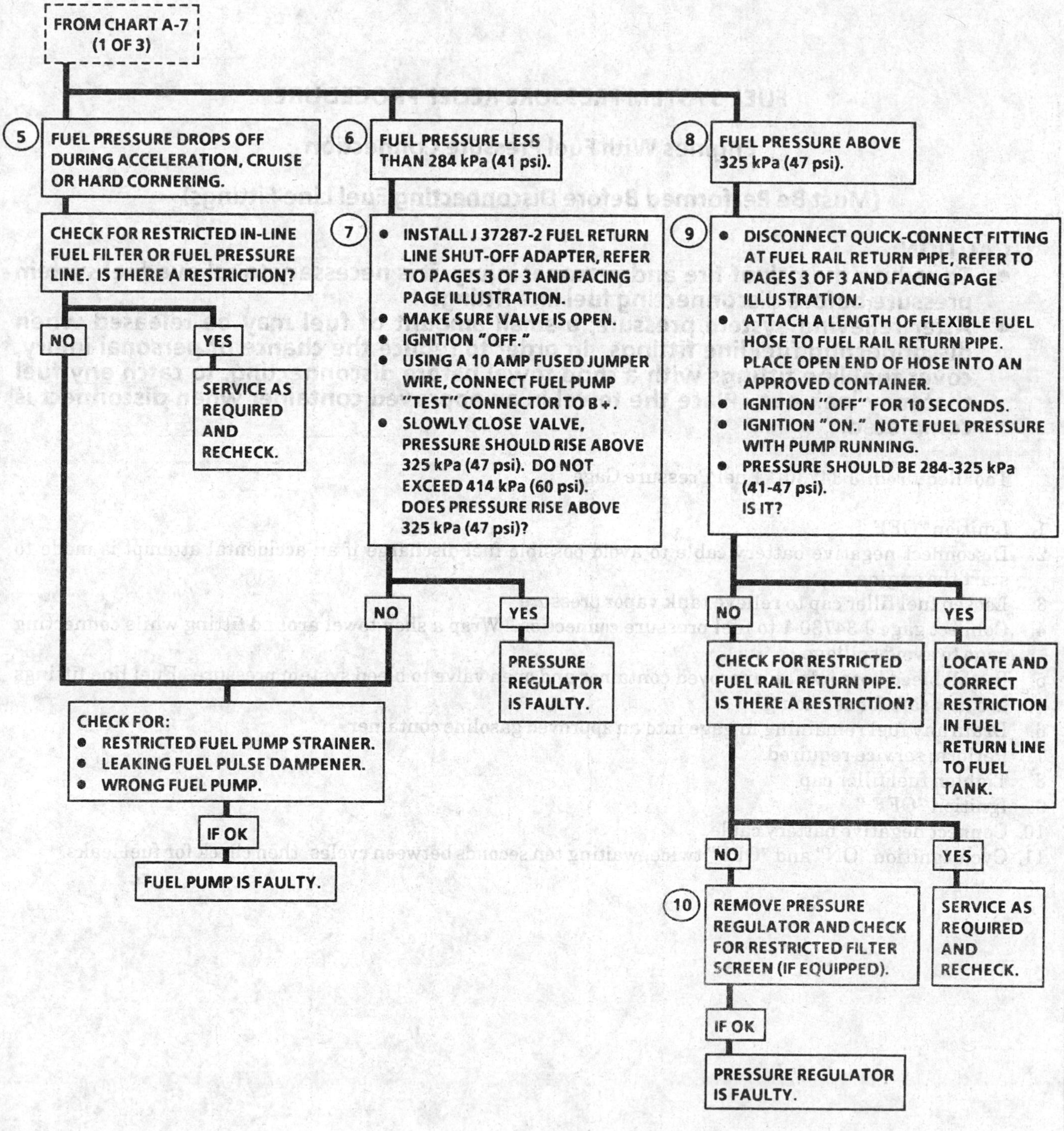
FROM CHART A-7 (1 OF 3)
5
FUEL PRESSURE DROPS OFF DURING ACCELERATION, CRUISE OR HARD CORNERING.
CHECK FOR RESTRICTED IN-LINE FUEL FILTER OR FUEL PRESSURE LINE. IS THERE A RESTRICTION?
NO
YES
SERVICE AS REQUIRED AND RECHECK.
6
FUEL PRESSURE LESS THAN 284 kPa (41 psi).
7
• INSTALL J 37287-2 FUEL RETURN LINE SHUT-OFF ADAPTER, REFER TO PAGES 3 OF 3 AND FACING PAGE ILLUSTRATION.
• MAKE SURE VALVE IS OPEN.
• IGNITION "OFF."
• USING A 10 AMP FUSED JUMPER WIRE, CONNECT FUEL PUMP "TEST" CONNECTOR TO B+.
• SLOWLY CLOSE VALVE, PRESSURE SHOULD RISE ABOVE 325 kPa (47 psi). DO NOT EXCEED 414 kPa (60 psi). DOES PRESSURE RISE ABOVE 325 kPa (47 psi)?
NO
YES
PRESSURE REGULATOR IS FAULTY.
CHECK FOR:
• RESTRICTED FUEL PUMP STRAINER.
• LEAKING FUEL PULSE DAMPENER.
• WRONG FUEL PUMP.
IF OK
FUEL PUMP IS FAULTY.
8
FUEL PRESSURE ABOVE 325 kPa (47 psi).
9
• DISCONNECT QUICK-CONNECT FITTING AT FUEL RAIL RETURN PIPE, REFER TO PAGES 3 OF 3 AND FACING PAGE ILLUSTRATION.
• ATTACH A LENGTH OF FLEXIBLE FUEL HOSE TO FUEL RAIL RETURN PIPE. PLACE OPEN END OF HOSE INTO AN APPROVED CONTAINER.
• IGNITION "OFF" FOR 10 SECONDS.
• IGNITION "ON." NOTE FUEL PRESSURE WITH PUMP RUNNING.
• PRESSURE SHOULD BE 284-325 kPa (41-47 psi). IS IT?
NO
YES
CHECK FOR RESTRICTED FUEL RAIL RETURN PIPE. IS THERE A RESTRICTION?
LOCATE AND CORRECT RESTRICTION IN FUEL RETURN LINE TO FUEL TANK.
NO
YES
10
REMOVE PRESSURE REGULATOR AND CHECK FOR RESTRICTED FILTER SCREEN (IF EQUIPPED).
SERVICE AS REQUIRED AND RECHECK.
IF OK
PRESSURE REGULATOR IS FAULTY.

"*AFTER REPAIRS,*" CONFIRM NO MIL (SERVICE ENGINE SOON).

12-15-92
NS 14634

CHART A-7

(Page 3 of 3)

FUEL SYSTEM PRESSURE TEST 3800 (VIN L) (SFI)

FUEL SYSTEM PRESSURE RELIEF PROCEDURE

Engines With Fuel Pressure Connection

(Must Be Performed Before Disconnecting Fuel Line Fittings)

CAUTION:

- **To reduce the risk of fire and personal injury, it is necessary to relieve fuel system pressure before disconnecting fuel line fittings.**
- **After relieving system pressure, a small amount of fuel may be released when disconnecting fuel line fittings. In order to reduce the chance of personal injury, cover fuel line fittings with a shop towel before disconnecting, to catch any fuel that may leak out. Place the towel in an approved container when disconnect is completed.**

Tool Required: J 34730-1 Fuel Pressure Gage

1. Ignition "OFF."
2. Disconnect negative battery cable to avoid possible fuel discharge if an accidental attempt is made to start the engine.
3. Loosen fuel filler cap to relieve tank vapor pressure.
4. Connect gage J 34730-1 to fuel pressure connection. Wrap a shop towel around fitting while connecting gage to avoid spillage.
5. Install bleed hose into an approved container and open valve to bleed system pressure. Fuel line fittings are now safe for servicing.
6. Drain any fuel remaining in gage into an approved gasoline container.
7. Perform service required.
8. Tighten fuel filler cap.
9. Ignition "OFF."
10. Connect negative battery cable.
11. Cycle ignition "ON" and "OFF" twice, waiting ten seconds between cycles, then check for fuel leaks.

11-11-92
NS 14624

CHART A-7
(Page 3 of 3)
FUEL SYSTEM PRESSURE TEST 3800 (VIN L) (SFI)

SERVICING QUICK-CONNECT FITTINGS

Important

- In order to install fuel system diagnostic equipment on vehicles equipped with plastic quick-connect fittings, fuel line separator tools must be used to disconnect the fittings. Using the separator tools to release the fittings will cause the plastic retainer to remain inside the female connector allowing diagnostic equipment to be connected.

Tools required:
J 37088-A tool set, fuel line quick-connect separator;
J 39504 tool set, fuel line quick-connect separator (restricted access).

Remove or Disconnect

1. Relieve fuel system pressure (see "Fuel System Pressure Relief").
2. If equipped, slide dust cover back to access quick-connect fitting.
3. Grasp both sides of fitting. Twist female connector 1/4 turn in each direction to loosen any dirt within fitting.

CAUTION: Safety glasses must be worn when using compressed air, as flying dirt particles may cause eye injury.

4. Using compressed air, blow dirt out of fitting.
5. Choose correct tool from J 37088 A or J 39504 tool set for size of fitting. Insert tool into female connector, then push/pull inward to release locking tabs.
6. Pull connection apart.

Clean and Inspect

NOTICE: If it is necessary to remove rust or burrs from fuel pipe, use emery cloth in a radial motion with the pipe end to prevent damage to O-ring sealing surface.

- Using a clean shop towel, wipe off male pipe end.
- Inspect both ends of fitting for dirt and burrs. Clean or replace components/assemblies as required.

Install or Connect

CAUTION: To Reduce the Risk of Fire and Personal Injury:
- **Before connecting fitting, always apply a few drops of clean engine oil to the male pipe end of engine fuel pipe, pressure gage adapter or fuel line shut-off adapter. This will ensure proper reconnection and prevent a possible fuel leak. (During normal operation, the O-rings located in the female connector will swell and may prevent proper reconnection if not lubricated.)**

1. Apply a few drops of clean engine oil to the male pipe end of engine fuel pipe, pressure gage adapter or fuel line shut-off adapter.
2. Push both sides of fitting together to cause the retaining tabs/fingers to snap into place.
3. Once installed, pull on both sides of fitting to make sure connection is secure.
4. If equipped, reposition dust cover over quick-connect fitting.

11-21-92
NS 14628

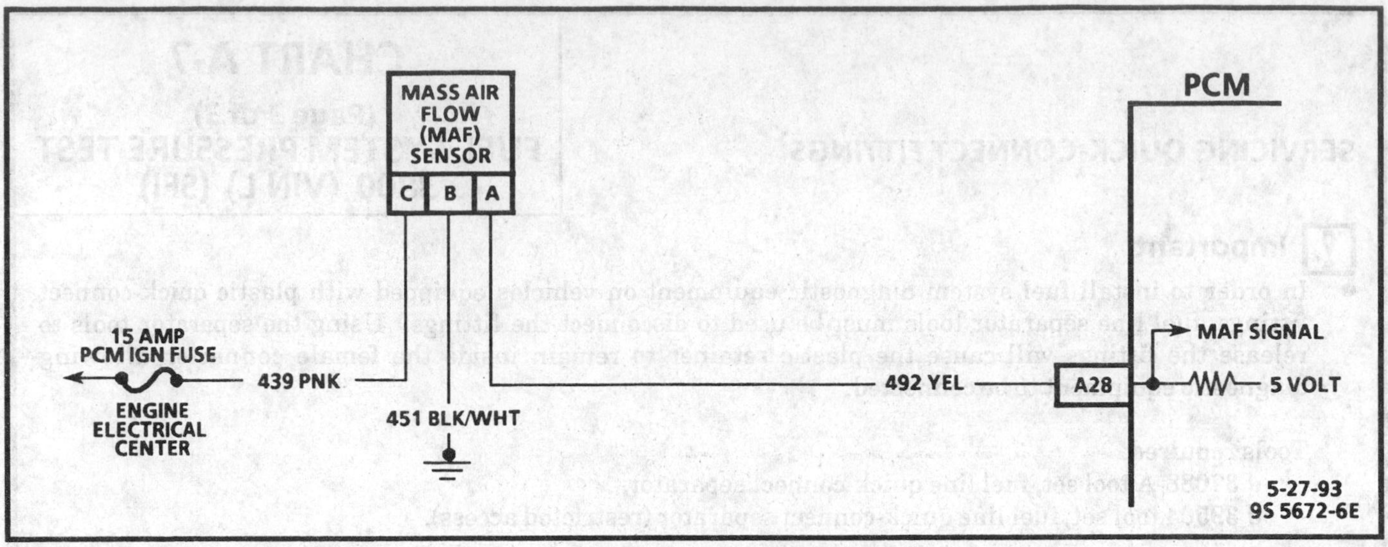
MASS AIR FLOW (MAF) SENSOR
C B A
PCM
MAF SIGNAL
15 AMP
PCM IGN FUSE
439 PNK
ENGINE
ELECTRICAL
CENTER
451 BLK/WHT
492 YEL
A28
5 VOLT
5-27-93
9S 5672-6E

DTC P0101

MASS AIR FLOW (MAF) SENSOR CIRCUIT
3800 (VIN L) (SFI)

Circuit Description:

The Mass Air Flow (MAF) sensor measures the flow of air which passes through it in a given time. The PCM uses this information to monitor the operating condition of the engine for fuel delivery calculations. A large quantity of air movement indicates acceleration, while a small quantity indicates deceleration or idle.

The MAF sensor produces a frequency signal which cannot be easily measured. The sensor can be diagnosed using the procedures on this chart.

DTC P0101 Will Set When:

- Engine running.
- No MAF signal for over 4 seconds.

Action Taken (PCM will default to): With DTC P0101 set, the PCM will use a default value for airflow based on throttle position and engine speed and some vehicle performance will return. The MIL (Service Engine Soon) will be illuminated.

DTC Chart Test Description: Number(s) below refer to circled number(s) on the diagnostic chart.

1. This step checks to see if PCM recognizes a problem.
2. A voltage reading at sensor harness connector terminal "A" of less than 4 or over 6 volts indicates a fault in CKT 492 or poor connection.
3. Verifies that both ignition feed voltage and a good ground circuit are available.

Diagnostic Aids: An intermittent may be caused by a poor connection, mis-routed harness, rubbed through wire insulation, or a wire broken inside the insulation.

Check for:

- Poor connection at PCM pin - Inspect harness connectors for backed out terminals, improper mating, broken locks, improperly formed or damaged terminals, and poor terminal to wire connection.
- Mis-routed harness - Inspect MAF sensor harness to insure that it is not too close to high voltage wires, such as spark plug leads.
- Damaged harness - Inspect harness for damage. If harness appears OK, observe Tech 1 while moving related connectors and wiring harness. A change in display would indicate the intermittent fault location.
- Plugged air intake filter - A wide-open throttle acceleration from a stop should cause the MAF reading on the Tech 1 to range from about 4-7 g/s at idle to 100 or greater at the time of the 1-2 shift. If not, check for restriction.

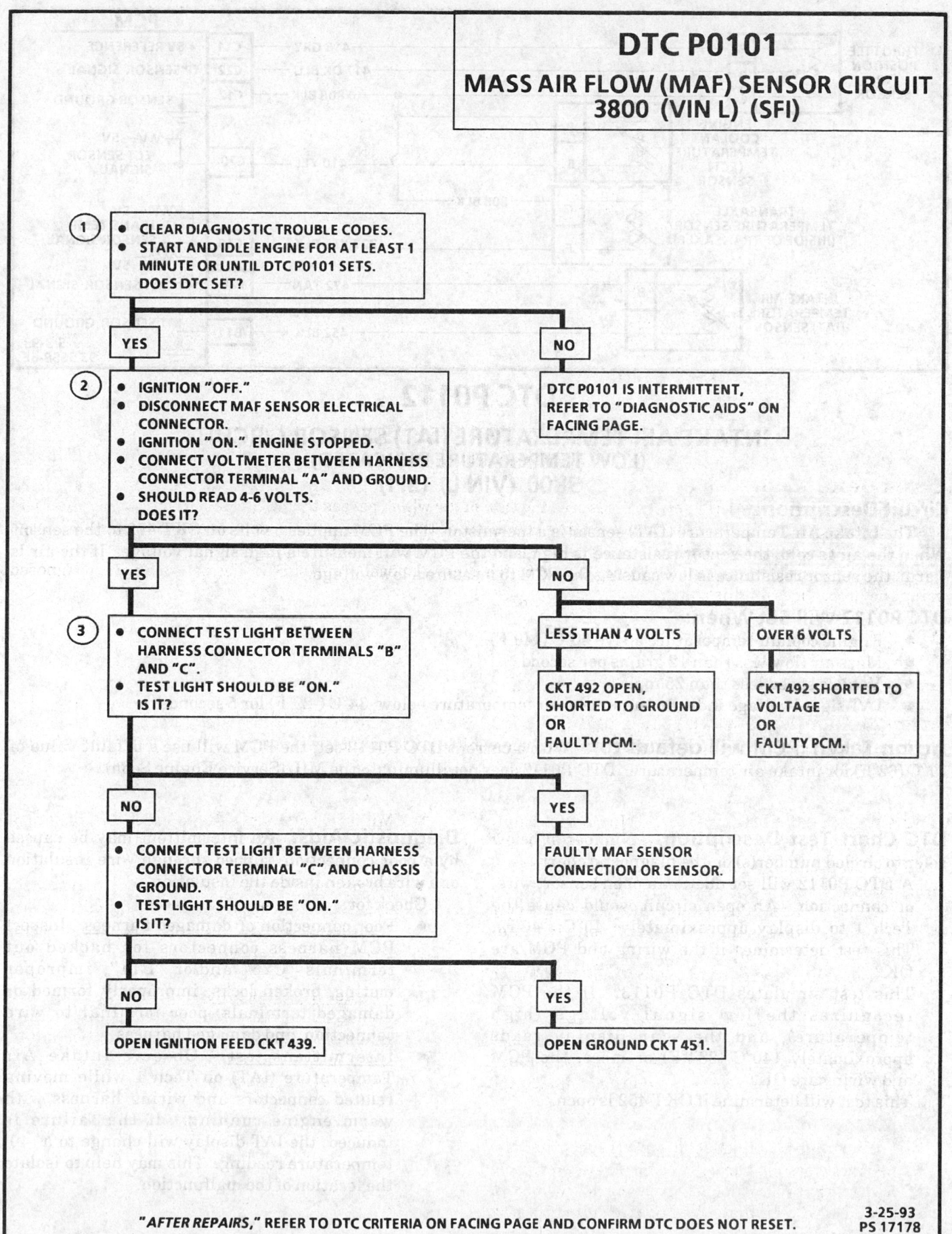

DTC P0101

MASS AIR FLOW (MAF) SENSOR CIRCUIT 3800 (VIN L) (SFI)

1
- CLEAR DIAGNOSTIC TROUBLE CODES.
- START AND IDLE ENGINE FOR AT LEAST 1 MINUTE OR UNTIL DTC P0101 SETS.

DOES DTC SET?

NO: DTC P0101 IS INTERMITTENT, REFER TO "DIAGNOSTIC AIDS" ON FACING PAGE.

YES:

2
- IGNITION "OFF."
- DISCONNECT MAF SENSOR ELECTRICAL CONNECTOR.
- IGNITION "ON." ENGINE STOPPED.
- CONNECT VOLTMETER BETWEEN HARNESS CONNECTOR TERMINAL "A" AND GROUND.
- SHOULD READ 4-6 VOLTS.

DOES IT?

NO:
- LESS THAN 4 VOLTS: CKT 492 OPEN, SHORTED TO GROUND OR FAULTY PCM.
- OVER 6 VOLTS: CKT 492 SHORTED TO VOLTAGE OR FAULTY PCM.

YES:

3
- CONNECT TEST LIGHT BETWEEN HARNESS CONNECTOR TERMINALS "B" AND "C".
- TEST LIGHT SHOULD BE "ON."

IS IT?

YES: FAULTY MAF SENSOR CONNECTION OR SENSOR.

NO:
- CONNECT TEST LIGHT BETWEEN HARNESS CONNECTOR TERMINAL "C" AND CHASSIS GROUND.
- TEST LIGHT SHOULD BE "ON."

IS IT?

NO: OPEN IGNITION FEED CKT 439.

YES: OPEN GROUND CKT 451.

"*AFTER REPAIRS,*" REFER TO DTC CRITERIA ON FACING PAGE AND CONFIRM DTC DOES NOT RESET.

3-25-93
PS 17178

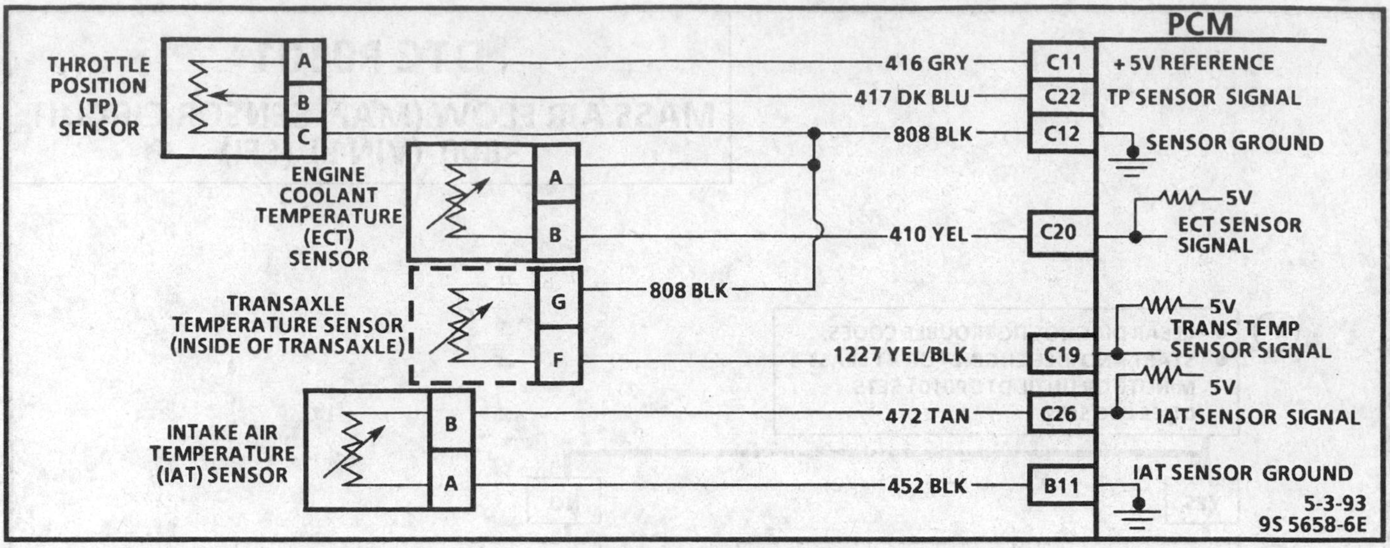
PCM
THROTTLE POSITION (TP) SENSOR
A
B
C
416 GRY
417 DK BLU
808 BLK
C11
C22
C12
+5V REFERENCE
TP SENSOR SIGNAL
SENSOR GROUND
ENGINE COOLANT TEMPERATURE (ECT) SENSOR
A
B
5V
410 YEL
C20
ECT SENSOR SIGNAL
TRANSAXLE TEMPERATURE SENSOR (INSIDE OF TRANSAXLE)
G
F
808 BLK
1227 YEL/BLK
C19
5V
TRANS TEMP SENSOR SIGNAL
5V
INTAKE AIR TEMPERATURE (IAT) SENSOR
B
A
472 TAN
C26
IAT SENSOR SIGNAL
452 BLK
B11
IAT SENSOR GROUND
5-3-93
9S 5658-6E

DTC P0112

INTAKE AIR TEMPERATURE (IAT) SENSOR CIRCUIT
(LOW TEMPERATURE INDICATED)
3800 (VIN L) (SFI)

Circuit Description:

The Intake Air Temperature (IAT) sensor is a thermistor. The PCM applies 5 volts on CKT 472 to the sensor. When the air is cold, the sensor resistance is high, and the PCM will measure a high signal voltage. If the air is warm, the sensor resistance is low causing the PCM to measure a low voltage.

DTC P0112 Will Set When:

- Engine coolant temperature above 60°C (140°F).
- Mass air flow less than 12 grams per second.
- Vehicle speed less than 25 mph.
- IAT signal voltage indicates an intake air temperature below -34°C (-29°F) for 5 seconds.

Action Taken (PCM will default to): With a current DTC P0112 set, the PCM will use a default value of 17°C (62°F) for intake air temperature. DTC P0112 does not illuminate the MIL (Service Engine Soon).

DTC Chart Test Description: Number(s) below refer to circled number(s) on the diagnostic chart.

1. A DTC P0112 will set due to an open sensor, wire, or connection. An open circuit would cause the Tech 1 to display approximately -40°C (-40°F). This test determines if the wiring and PCM are OK.
2. This test simulates DTC P0113. If the PCM recognizes the low signal voltage (high temperature), and the scan display reads approximately 140°C (284°F) or more, the PCM and wiring are OK.
3. This test will determine if CKT 452 is open.

Diagnostic Aids: An intermittent may be caused by a poor connection, rubbed through wire insulation or a wire broken inside the insulation.

Check for:

- Poor connection or damaged harness - Inspect PCM harness connectors for backed out terminals "C26" and/or "B11", improper mating, broken locks, improperly formed or damaged terminals, poor terminal to wire connection, and damaged harness.
- Intermittent test - Observe Intake Air Temperature (IAT) on Tech 1 while moving related connectors and wiring harness with warm engine running. If the failure is induced, the IAT display will change to a -40° temperature reading. This may help to isolate the location of the malfunction.

DTC P0112

INTAKE AIR TEMPERATURE (IAT) SENSOR CIRCUIT (LOW TEMPERATURE INDICATED) 3800 (VIN L) (SFI)

1
- INSTALL TECH 1.
- KEY "ON," ENGINE "OFF."
- OBSERVE "INTAKE AIR TEMP" ON TECH 1.
- SHOULD DISPLAY TEMPERATURE ABOVE -35°C (-31°F).

DOES IT?

YES: DTC IS INTERMITTENT - SEE "DIAGNOSTIC AIDS" ON FACING PAGE.

NO:

2
- DISCONNECT IAT SENSOR.
- JUMPER CKTs 472 AND 452 TOGETHER AT IAT SENSOR CONNECTOR.
- OBSERVE "INTAKE AIR TEMP" ON TECH 1.
- SHOULD DISPLAY APPROX. 140° C .

DOES IT?

YES: POOR IAT SENSOR CONNECTION OR FAULTY IAT SENSOR.

NO:

3
- JUMPER CKT 472 DIRECTLY TO GROUND.
- OBSERVE "INTAKE AIR TEMP" ON TECH 1.
- SHOULD DISPLAY APPROX. 140° C.

DOES IT?

NO: CHECK CKT 472 FOR AN OPEN OR POOR CONNECTION AT PCM TERMINAL "C26". IF OK, IT'S A FAULTY PCM.

YES: POOR CONNECTION AT PCM TERMINAL "B11" OR OPEN CKT 452.

"AFTER REPAIRS," REFER TO DTC CRITERIA ON FACING PAGE AND CONFIRM DTC DOES NOT RESET.

2-24-93
LS 9078-6E

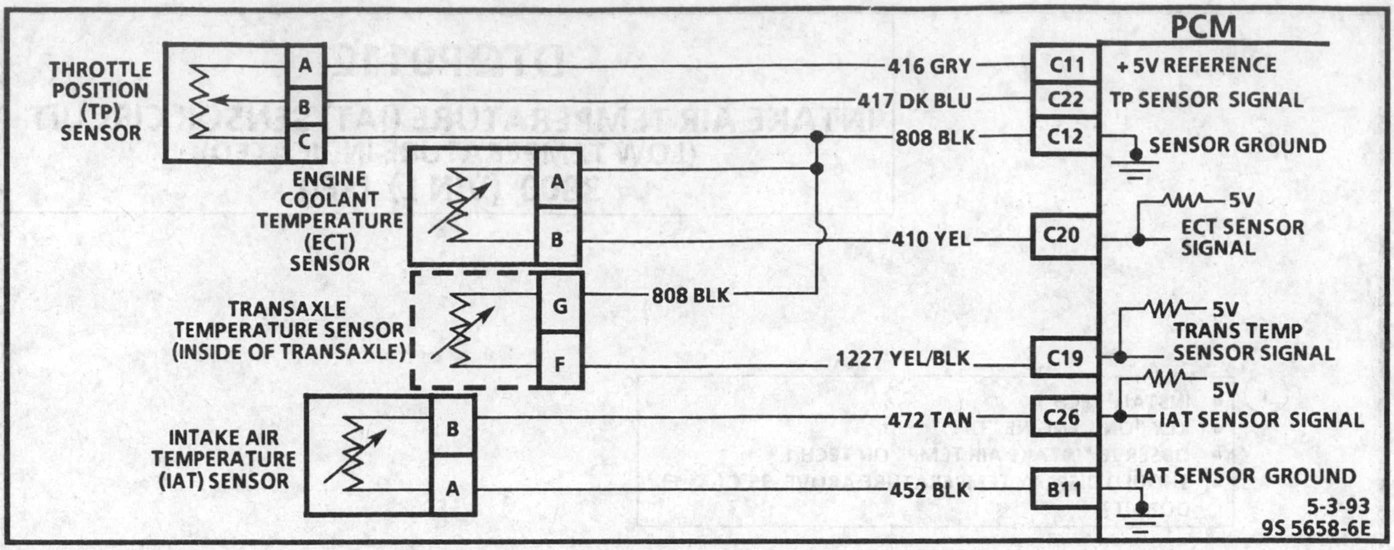

PCM
THROTTLE POSITION (TP) SENSOR
A
B
C
416 GRY
417 DK BLU
808 BLK
C11
C22
C12
+5V REFERENCE
TP SENSOR SIGNAL
SENSOR GROUND
ENGINE COOLANT TEMPERATURE (ECT) SENSOR
A
B
410 YEL
C20
5V
ECT SENSOR SIGNAL
TRANSAXLE TEMPERATURE SENSOR (INSIDE OF TRANSAXLE)
G
F
808 BLK
1227 YEL/BLK
C19
5V
TRANS TEMP SENSOR SIGNAL
INTAKE AIR TEMPERATURE (IAT) SENSOR
B
A
472 TAN
452 BLK
C26
B11
5V
IAT SENSOR SIGNAL
IAT SENSOR GROUND
5-3-93
9S 5658-6E

DTC P0113

INTAKE AIR TEMPERATURE (IAT) SENSOR CIRCUIT
(HIGH TEMPERATURE INDICATED)
3800 (VIN L) (SFI)

Circuit Description:

The Intake Air Temperature (IAT) sensor is a thermistor. The PCM applies a voltage (about 5 volts) on CKT 472 to the sensor. When air is cold, the sensor resistance is high and the PCM will measure a high signal voltage. If the air is warm, the sensor resistance is low causing the PCM to measure a low voltage.

DTC P0113 Will Set When:

- Signal voltage indicates an intake air temperature greater than 140°C (284°F).
- Vehicle speed is greater than 35 mph.
- Both of the above requirements are met for at least 5 seconds.

Action Taken (PCM will default to): With a current DTC P0113 set, the PCM will use a default value of 17°C (62°F) for intake air temperature. DTC P0113 does not illuminate the MIL (Service Engine Soon).

DTC Chart Test Description: Number(s) below refer to circled number(s) on the diagnostic chart.

1. A Tech 1 may be used to diagnose this fault since the PCM transmits "actual" values when the fault is present. A grounded circuit will cause the Tech 1 to display a temperature of approximately 147°C (297°F).
2. If the Tech 1 displays -40° with the IAT sensor disconnected, the PCM and wiring are OK and the IAT sensor must be replaced.

Diagnostic Aids: An intermittent may be caused by a poor connection, rubbed through wire insulation or a wire broken inside the insulation.

Check for:

- Poor connection or damaged harness - Inspect PCM harness for short to ground in CKT 472, improper mating, broken locks, improperly formed or damaged terminals, poor terminal to wire connection, and damaged harness.
- Intermittent test - Observe Intake Air Temperature (IAT) on Tech 1 while moving related connectors and wiring harness with warm engine running. If the failure is induced, the IAT display will change to a 147°C (297°F) temperature reading. This may help to isolate the location of the malfunction.

DTC P0113

INTAKE AIR TEMPERATURE (IAT) SENSOR CIRCUIT
(HIGH TEMPERATURE INDICATED)
3800 (VIN L) (SFI)

1
- INSTALL TECH 1.
- KEY "ON," ENGINE "OFF."
- OBSERVE "INTAKE AIR TEMP" ON TECH 1.
- SHOULD DISPLAY TEMPERATURE BELOW 140°C (284°F). DOES IT?

NO → go to step 2

YES → DTC P0113 IS INTERMITTENT. SEE "DIAGNOSTIC AIDS" ON FACING PAGE.

2
- DISCONNECT IAT SENSOR.
- OBSERVE "INTAKE AIR TEMP" ON TECH 1.
- SHOULD DISPLAY APPROXIMATELY -40°C (-40°F). DOES IT?

NO → CKT 472 SHORTED TO GROUND OR FAULTY PCM.

YES → FAULTY IAT SENSOR.

"*AFTER REPAIRS,*" REFER TO DTC CRITERIA ON FACING PAGE AND CONFIRM DTC DOES NOT RESET.

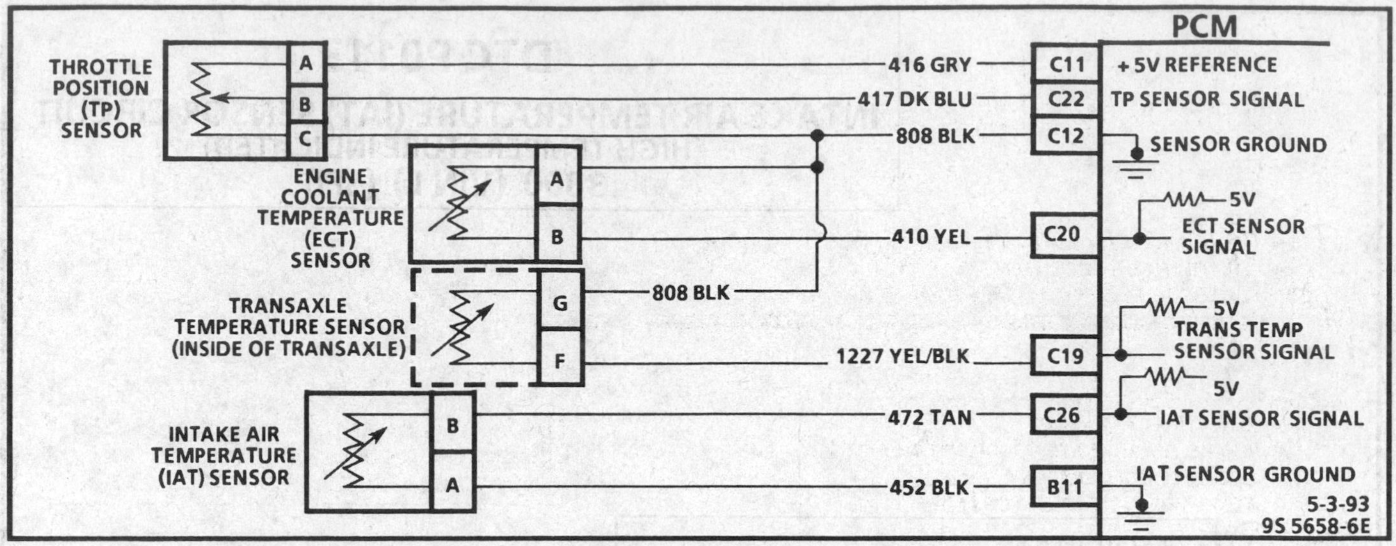
PCM
THROTTLE POSITION (TP) SENSOR
A
B
C
416 GRY
417 DK BLU
808 BLK
C11
C22
C12
+5V REFERENCE
TP SENSOR SIGNAL
SENSOR GROUND
ENGINE COOLANT TEMPERATURE (ECT) SENSOR
A
B
410 YEL
C20
5V
ECT SENSOR SIGNAL
TRANSAXLE TEMPERATURE SENSOR (INSIDE OF TRANSAXLE)
G
F
808 BLK
1227 YEL/BLK
C19
5V
TRANS TEMP SENSOR SIGNAL
INTAKE AIR TEMPERATURE (IAT) SENSOR
B
A
472 TAN
452 BLK
C26
B11
5V
IAT SENSOR SIGNAL
IAT SENSOR GROUND
5-3-93
9S 5658-6E

DTC P0117

ENGINE COOLANT TEMPERATURE (ECT) SENSOR CIRCUIT
(LOW TEMPERATURE INDICATED)
3800 (VIN L) (SFI)

Circuit Description:

The Engine Coolant Temperature (ECT) sensor uses a thermistor to control the signal voltage to the PCM. The PCM applies a voltage on CKT 410 to the sensor. When the engine is cold the sensor (thermistor) resistance is high; therefore, the PCM will see high signal voltage.

As the engine warms, the sensor resistance becomes less, and the voltage drops. At normal engine operating temperature (85°C to 95°C), the signal will measure about 1.5 to 2.0 volts.

DTC P0117 Will Set When:

- Engine is running over 3 seconds.
- Signal voltage indicates engine coolant temperature less than -39°C (-38°F) for at least 0.4 second.

Action Taken (PCM will default to): With a current DTC P0117 set, the PCM will turn both cooling fans "ON" and use a default engine coolant temperature value based on run time. The default value will rise to a maximum value of 90°C (194°F). The PCM will illuminate the MIL (Service Engine Soon).

DTC Chart Test Description: Number(s) below refer to circled number(s) on the diagnostic chart.

1. Determines if conditions necessary to set DTC P0117 exist.
2. This test simulates DTC P0118. If the PCM recognizes the low signal voltage (high temperature), and the scan display reads 130°C (266°F) or more, the PCM and wiring are OK.
3. This test will determine if CKT 410 is open.

Diagnostic Aids: A Tech 1 displays engine coolant temperature in degrees. After engine is started the temperature should rise steadily to about 90°C (194°F) then stabilize when thermostat opens.

An intermittent may be caused by a poor connection, rubbed through wire insulation or a wire broken inside the insulation.

Check for:

- Poor connection or damaged harness - Inspect PCM harness connectors for backed out terminal "C20" or "C12", improper mating, broken locks, improperly formed or damaged terminals, poor terminal to wire connection and damaged harness.
- Intermittent test - With Tech 1, monitor engine coolant temperature while moving related connectors and wiring harness. If the failure is induced, the display will change. This may help to isolate the location of the malfunction.
- Shifted sensor - The "Temperature To Resistance Value" scale may be used to test the engine coolant temperature sensor at various temperature levels to evaluate the possibility of a "shifted" (mis-scaled) sensor which may result in driveability complaints.
- A faulty connection, or an open in CKT 410 or 808 will result in a DTC P0117.

DTC P0117

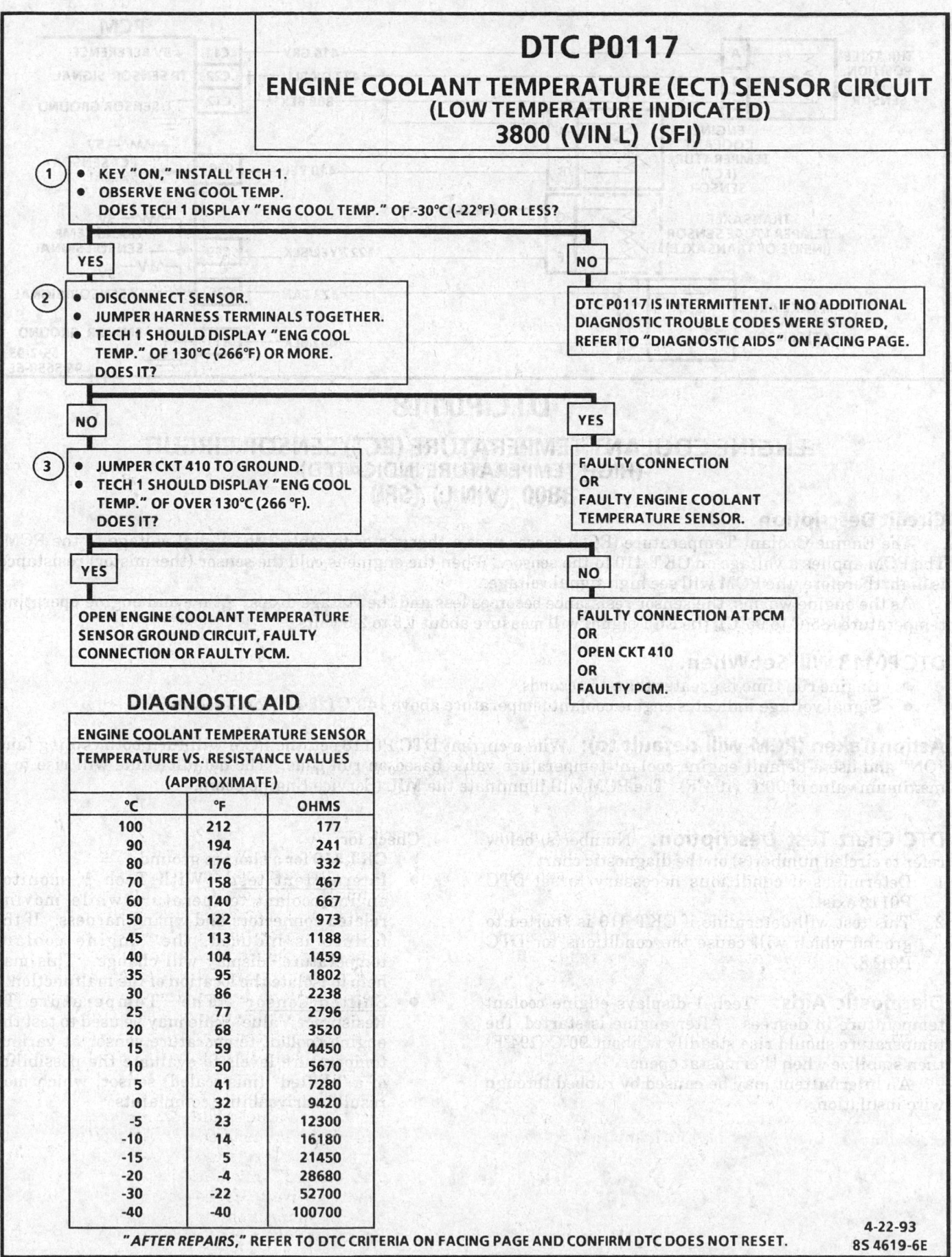

ENGINE COOLANT TEMPERATURE (ECT) SENSOR CIRCUIT
(LOW TEMPERATURE INDICATED)
3800 (VIN L) (SFI)

1
- KEY "ON," INSTALL TECH 1.
- OBSERVE ENG COOL TEMP.

DOES TECH 1 DISPLAY "ENG COOL TEMP." OF -30°C (-22°F) OR LESS?

YES → go to 2.

NO → DTC P0117 IS INTERMITTENT. IF NO ADDITIONAL DIAGNOSTIC TROUBLE CODES WERE STORED, REFER TO "DIAGNOSTIC AIDS" ON FACING PAGE.

2
- DISCONNECT SENSOR.
- JUMPER HARNESS TERMINALS TOGETHER.
- TECH 1 SHOULD DISPLAY "ENG COOL TEMP." OF 130°C (266°F) OR MORE.

DOES IT?

NO → go to 3.

YES → FAULTY CONNECTION OR FAULTY ENGINE COOLANT TEMPERATURE SENSOR.

3
- JUMPER CKT 410 TO GROUND.
- TECH 1 SHOULD DISPLAY "ENG COOL TEMP." OF OVER 130°C (266 °F).

DOES IT?

YES → OPEN ENGINE COOLANT TEMPERATURE SENSOR GROUND CIRCUIT, FAULTY CONNECTION OR FAULTY PCM.

NO → FAULTY CONNECTION AT PCM OR OPEN CKT 410 OR FAULTY PCM.

DIAGNOSTIC AID

ENGINE COOLANT TEMPERATURE SENSOR
TEMPERATURE VS. RESISTANCE VALUES
(APPROXIMATE)

°C	°F	OHMS
100	212	177
90	194	241
80	176	332
70	158	467
60	140	667
50	122	973
45	113	1188
40	104	1459
35	95	1802
30	86	2238
25	77	2796
20	68	3520
15	59	4450
10	50	5670
5	41	7280
0	32	9420
-5	23	12300
-10	14	16180
-15	5	21450
-20	-4	28680
-30	-22	52700
-40	-40	100700

"*AFTER REPAIRS*," REFER TO DTC CRITERIA ON FACING PAGE AND CONFIRM DTC DOES NOT RESET.

4-22-93
8S 4619-6E

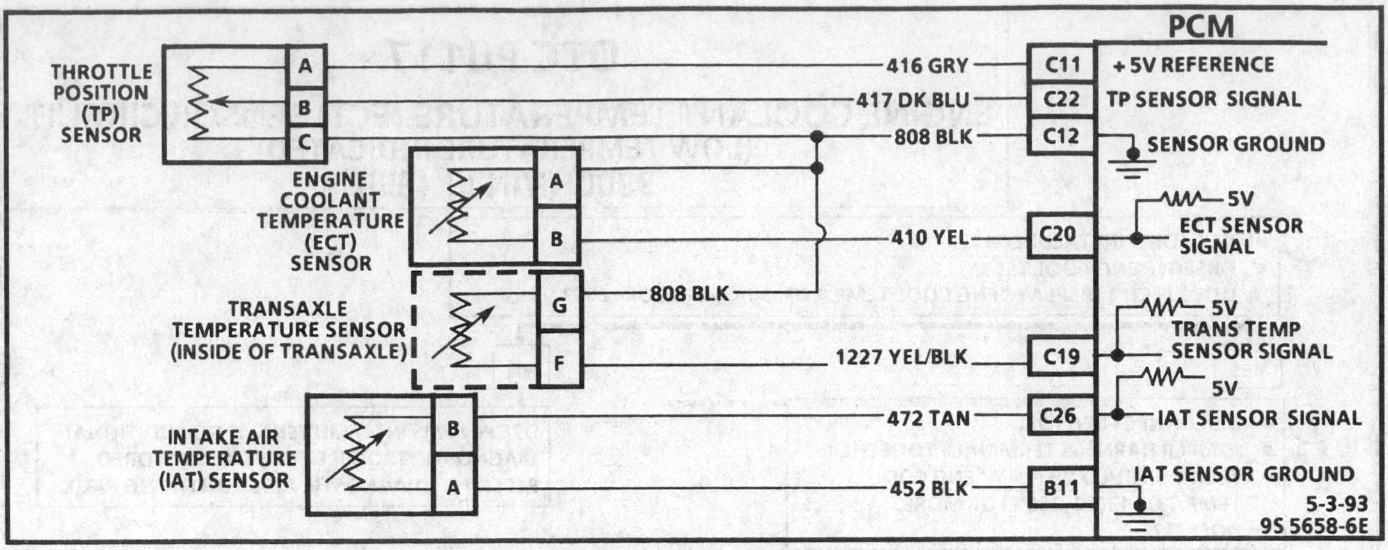
PCM
THROTTLE POSITION (TP) SENSOR
A
B
C
416 GRY
417 DK BLU
808 BLK
C11
C22
C12
+5V REFERENCE
TP SENSOR SIGNAL
SENSOR GROUND
ENGINE COOLANT TEMPERATURE (ECT) SENSOR
410 YEL
C20
5V
ECT SENSOR SIGNAL
TRANSAXLE TEMPERATURE SENSOR (INSIDE OF TRANSAXLE)
G
F
808 BLK
1227 YEL/BLK
C19
5V
TRANS TEMP SENSOR SIGNAL
INTAKE AIR TEMPERATURE (IAT) SENSOR
472 TAN
C26
5V
IAT SENSOR SIGNAL
452 BLK
B11
IAT SENSOR GROUND
5-3-93
9S 5658-6E

DTC P0118

ENGINE COOLANT TEMPERATURE (ECT) SENSOR CIRCUIT (HIGH TEMPERATURE INDICATED) 3800 (VIN L) (SFI)

Circuit Description:

The Engine Coolant Temperature (ECT) sensor uses a thermistor to control the signal voltage to the PCM. The PCM applies a voltage on CKT 410 to the sensor. When the engine is cold the sensor (thermistor) resistance is high; therefore, the PCM will see high signal voltage.

As the engine warms, the sensor resistance becomes less and the voltage drops. At normal engine operating temperature (85°C to 95°C), the ECT signal will measure about 1.5 to 2.0 volts.

DTC P0118 Will Set When:

- Engine run time is greater than 15 seconds.
- Signal voltage indicates engine coolant temperature above 140°C (284°F) for .4 second.

Action Taken (PCM will default to): With a current DTC P0118 set, the PCM will turn both cooling fans "ON" and use a default engine coolant temperature value based on run time. The default value will rise to a maximum value of 90°C (194°F). The PCM will illuminate the MIL (Service Engine Soon).

DTC Chart Test Description: Number(s) below refer to circled number(s) on the diagnostic chart.

1. Determines if conditions necessary to set DTC P0118 exist.
2. This test will determine if CKT 410 is shorted to ground which will cause the conditions for DTC P0118.

Diagnostic Aids: Tech 1 displays engine coolant temperature in degrees. After engine is started, the temperature should rise steadily to about 90°C (194°F) then stabilize when thermostat opens.

An intermittent may be caused by rubbed through wire insulation.

Check for:

- CKT 410 for a short to ground.
- Intermittent test - With Tech 1, monitor engine coolant temperature while moving related connectors and wiring harness. If the failure is induced, the "engine coolant temperature" display will change. This may help to isolate the location of the malfunction.
- Shifted sensor - The "Temperature To Resistance Value" scale may be used to test the engine coolant temperature sensor at various temperature levels to evaluate the possibility of a "shifted" (mis-scaled) sensor, which may result in driveability complaints.

DTC P0118

ENGINE COOLANT TEMPERATURE (ECT) SENSOR CIRCUIT

(HIGH TEMPERATURE INDICATED)

3800 (VIN L) (SFI)

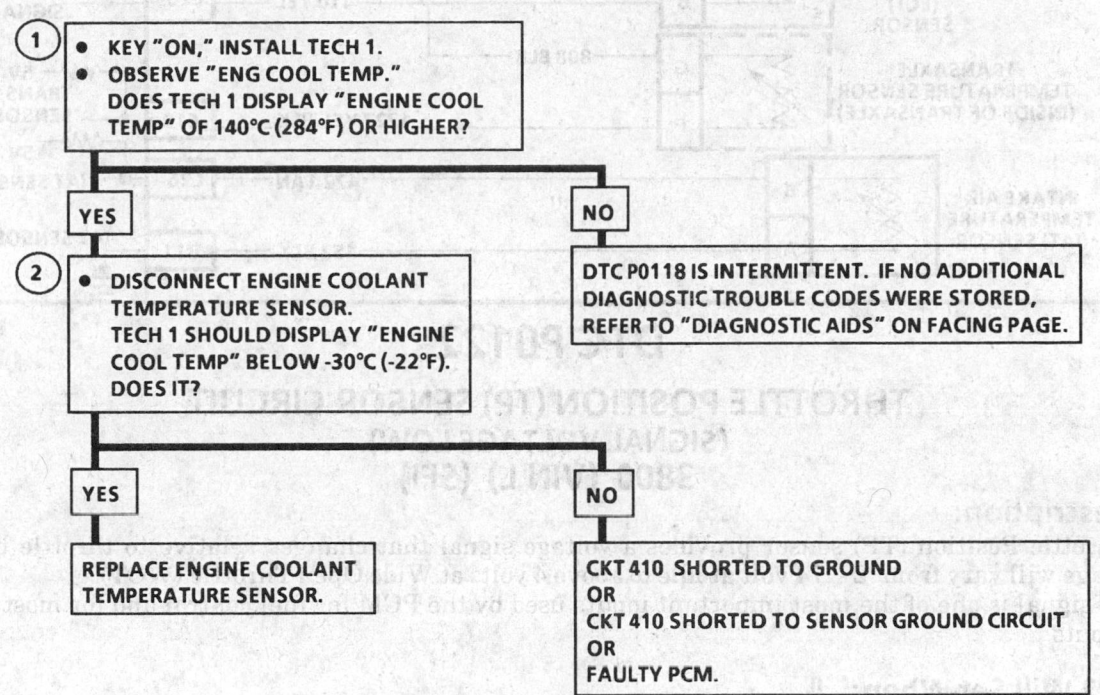

1
- KEY "ON," INSTALL TECH 1.
- OBSERVE "ENG COOL TEMP."

DOES TECH 1 DISPLAY "ENGINE COOL TEMP" OF 140°C (284°F) OR HIGHER?

YES → go to step 2.

NO → DTC P0118 IS INTERMITTENT. IF NO ADDITIONAL DIAGNOSTIC TROUBLE CODES WERE STORED, REFER TO "DIAGNOSTIC AIDS" ON FACING PAGE.

2
- DISCONNECT ENGINE COOLANT TEMPERATURE SENSOR.

TECH 1 SHOULD DISPLAY "ENGINE COOL TEMP" BELOW -30°C (-22°F). DOES IT?

YES → REPLACE ENGINE COOLANT TEMPERATURE SENSOR.

NO → CKT 410 SHORTED TO GROUND OR CKT 410 SHORTED TO SENSOR GROUND CIRCUIT OR FAULTY PCM.

DIAGNOSTIC AID

ENGINE COOLANT TEMPERATURE SENSOR

TEMPERATURE VS. RESISTANCE VALUES (APPROXIMATE)

°C	°F	OHMS
100	212	177
90	194	241
80	176	332
70	158	467
60	140	667
50	122	973
45	113	1188
40	104	1459
35	95	1802
30	86	2238
25	77	2796
20	68	3520
15	59	4450
10	50	5670
5	41	7280
0	32	9420
-5	23	12300
-10	14	16180
-15	5	21450
-20	-4	28680
-30	-22	52700
-40	-40	100700

4-21-93
NS 14302

"AFTER REPAIRS," REFER TO DTC CRITERIA ON FACING PAGE AND CONFIRM DTC DOES NOT RESET.

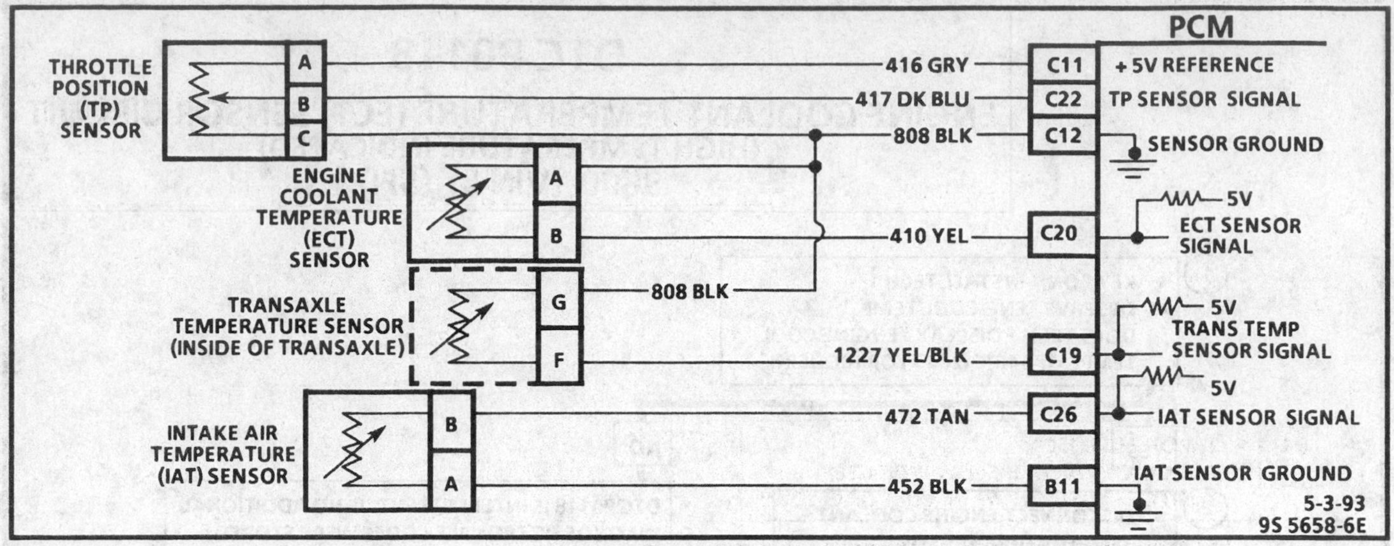
PCM
THROTTLE POSITION (TP) SENSOR
A
B
C
416 GRY
417 DK BLU
808 BLK
C11
C22
C12
+5V REFERENCE
TP SENSOR SIGNAL
SENSOR GROUND
ENGINE COOLANT TEMPERATURE (ECT) SENSOR
5V
410 YEL
C20
ECT SENSOR SIGNAL
TRANSAXLE TEMPERATURE SENSOR (INSIDE OF TRANSAXLE)
G
F
808 BLK
1227 YEL/BLK
C19
TRANS TEMP SENSOR SIGNAL
INTAKE AIR TEMPERATURE (IAT) SENSOR
472 TAN
C26
IAT SENSOR SIGNAL
452 BLK
B11
IAT SENSOR GROUND
5-3-93
9S 5658-6E

DTC P0122

THROTTLE POSITION (TP) SENSOR CIRCUIT
(SIGNAL VOLTAGE LOW)
3800 (VIN L) (SFI)

Circuit Description:

The Throttle Position (TP) sensor provides a voltage signal that changes relative to throttle blade angle. Signal voltage will vary from .2 - .74 volt at idle to above 4 volts at Wide Open Throttle (WOT).

The TP signal is one of the most important inputs used by the PCM for fuel control and for most of the PCM control outputs.

DTC P0122 Will Set When:

- Ignition "ON."
- TP sensor signal voltage is less than .16 volt for 4 seconds.

Action Taken (PCM will default to): If DTC P0122 is set, the PCM will not allow 4th gear, TCC or cruise control operation. The MIL (Service Engine Soon) is illuminated.

If CKT 417 is open or grounded when the vehicle engine is started, a high idle may result. The Tech 1 may read the following with CKT 417 open or grounded.
TP = .04 volt or less, RPM > 1000 in park, Desired idle = 725, IAC counts > 40, MIL (Service Engine Soon) "ON," DTC P0122 set.

If the intermittent is repaired without cycling the key "OFF," the Tech 1 may read the following:
TP = .42 volt, RPM > 1500 in park, Desired idle = 725, IAC counts > 55, MIL (Service Engine Soon) "OFF."

DTC Chart Test Description: Number(s) below refer to circled number(s) on the diagnostic chart.

1. Determines if conditions necessary to set DTC P0122 exist.
2. Simulates DTC P0123: (high voltage) If PCM recognizes the high signal voltage and sets DTC P0123, the PCM and wiring are OK.
3. Simulates a high signal voltage. Checks CKT 417 for an open.

Diagnostic Aids: The Tech 1 displays throttle position in volts. Voltage should increase at a steady rate as throttle is moved toward WOT.

An open or short to ground in CKT 416 or 417 will result in DTC P0122.

Check for:

- Poor connection or damaged harness - Inspect PCM harness connectors for backed out terminal "C11" and/or "C22", improper mating, broken locks, improperly formed or damaged terminals, poor terminal to wire connection, and damaged harness.
- Intermittent test - Monitor TP sensor voltage display while moving related connectors and wiring harness. If the failure is induced, the display will change. This may help to isolate the location of the malfunction.
- TP sensor scaling - Observe TP sensor voltage display while depressing accelerator pedal with engine stopped and ignition "ON." Display should vary from closed throttle TP sensor voltage when throttle is closed (.2 - .74 volt) to over 4.0 volts when throttle is held at Wide Open Throttle (WOT) position.

DTC P0122

THROTTLE POSITION (TP) SENSOR CIRCUIT
(SIGNAL VOLTAGE LOW)
3800 (VIN L) (SFI)

1
- THROTTLE CLOSED.
  DOES TECH 1 DATA DISPLAY INDICATE A THROTTLE POSITION OF .16 VOLT OR BELOW?

YES → go to step 2

NO →
- DTC P0122 IS INTERMITTENT.
  IF NO ADDITIONAL DTC(s) WERE STORED, REFER TO "DIAGNOSTIC AIDS" ON FACING PAGE.

2
- DISCONNECT THROTTLE POSITION SENSOR.
- JUMPER CKTs 416 AND 417 TOGETHER.
  TECH 1 DATA DISPLAY SHOULD INDICATE THROTTLE POSITION OVER 4.0 VOLTS.
  DOES IT?

NO → go to step 3

YES → REFER TO FACING PAGE FOR SPECIFIC INSTRUCTIONS.

3
- PROBE CKT 417 WITH A TEST LIGHT CONNECTED TO BATTERY VOLTAGE.
  TECH 1 DATA DISPLAY SHOULD INDICATE THROTTLE POSITION OVER 4.0V.
  DOES IT?

YES →
CKT 416 OPEN OR SHORTED TO GROUND
OR
POOR CONNECTION AT PCM
OR
FAULTY PCM.

NO →
CKT 417 OPEN OR SHORTED TO GROUND, OR SHORTED TO SENSOR GROUND CIRCUIT
OR
POOR CONNECTION AT PCM
OR
FAULTY PCM.

"*AFTER REPAIRS,*" REFER TO DTC CRITERIA ON FACING PAGE AND CONFIRM DTC DOES NOT RESET.

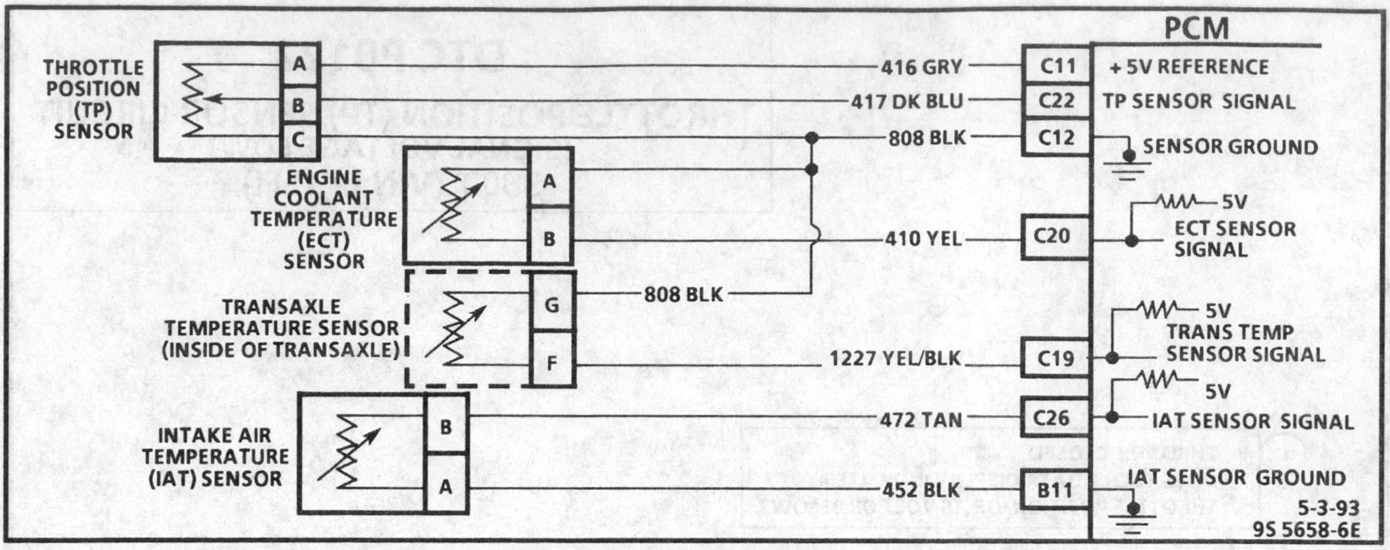
PCM
THROTTLE POSITION (TP) SENSOR
A
B
C
416 GRY
417 DK BLU
808 BLK
C11
C22
C12
+5V REFERENCE
TP SENSOR SIGNAL
SENSOR GROUND
ENGINE COOLANT TEMPERATURE (ECT) SENSOR
410 YEL
C20
5V
ECT SENSOR SIGNAL
TRANSAXLE TEMPERATURE SENSOR (INSIDE OF TRANSAXLE)
G
F
808 BLK
1227 YEL/BLK
C19
5V
TRANS TEMP SENSOR SIGNAL
INTAKE AIR TEMPERATURE (IAT) SENSOR
472 TAN
C26
5V
IAT SENSOR SIGNAL
452 BLK
B11
IAT SENSOR GROUND
5-3-93
9S 5658-6E

DTC P0123

THROTTLE POSITION (TP) SENSOR CIRCUIT
(SIGNAL VOLTAGE HIGH)
3800 (VIN L) (SFI)

Circuit Description:

The Throttle Position (TP) sensor provides a voltage signal that changes relative to throttle blade angle. Signal voltage will vary from .2 - .74 volt at idle to about 5 volts at Wide Open Throttle (WOT).

The TP sensor signal is one of the most important inputs used by the PCM for fuel control and for most of the PCM control outputs.

DTC P0123 Will Set When:

- TP sensor voltage is greater than 4.8 volts at any time.
  OR
- Engine is running and air flow is less than 15 gm/sec.
- TP sensor signal voltage is greater than 1.1 volts.
- DTC P0101 not present.
- All conditions met for 5 seconds.

Action Taken (PCM will default to): If DTC P0123 is set, the PCM will not allow cruise control, 4th gear or TCC operation. The MIL (Service Engine Soon) will be illuminated.

DTC Chart Test Description: Number(s) below refer to circled number(s) on the diagnostic chart.

1. With closed throttle, ignition "ON" or at idle, voltage at "C22" should be .2 - .74 volt.
2. With the TP sensor disconnected, the TP sensor voltage should go low and a DTC P0122 will set. This test verifies that the PCM and wiring are OK.
3. Probing CKT 808 with a test light checks the sensor ground circuit. A faulty sensor ground circuit will cause a DTC P0123.

Diagnostic Aids: The Tech 1 displays throttle position in volts. With closed throttle, ignition "ON" or at idle, voltage should be .2 - .74 volt. If not, refer to "Fuel Metering System," Section "6E3-C2" for replacement procedures.

Check for:

- Poor connection or damaged harness - Inspect PCM harness connectors for backed out terminal "C22" or "C12", improper mating, broken locks, improperly formed or damaged terminals, poor terminal to wire connection, and damaged harness.
- Intermittent test - Monitor TP sensor voltage on Tech 1 while moving related connectors and wiring harness. If the failure is induced, the display will change. This may help to isolate the location of the malfunction.
- TP sensor scaling - Observe TP sensor voltage display on Tech 1 while slowly depressing accelerator pedal with engine stopped and ignition "ON." Display should vary from closed throttle TP sensor voltage (.2 - .74 volt) when throttle is closed, to over 4.0 volts (4000 mV) when throttle is held at Wide Open Throttle (WOT) position. Typically, accelerator pedal travel only yields 4.1 or 4.2 volts maximum. If a TP sensor voltage of over 4.8 volts is observed at any point in normal accelerator pedal travel, replace TP sensor.

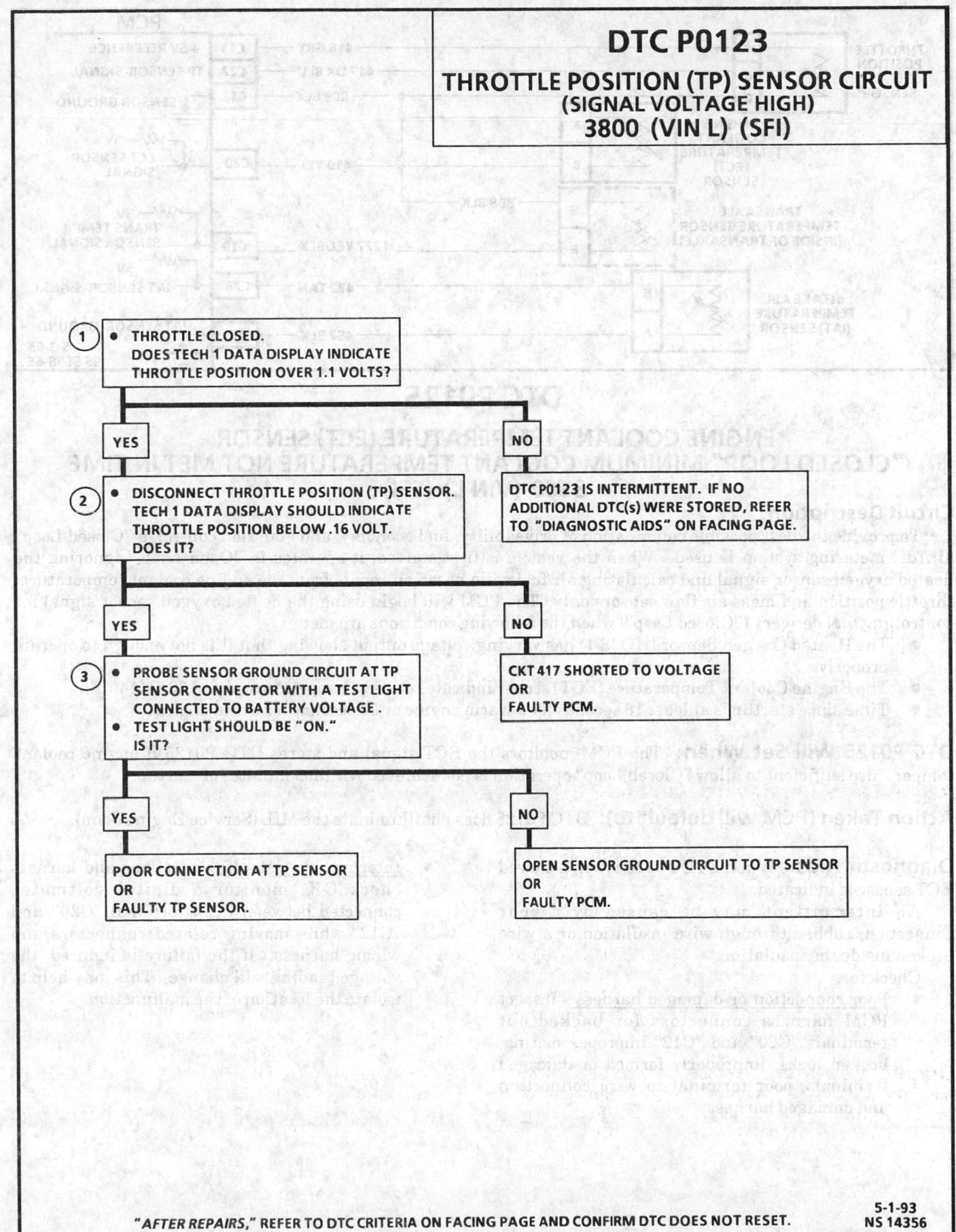

DTC P0123

THROTTLE POSITION (TP) SENSOR CIRCUIT
(SIGNAL VOLTAGE HIGH)
3800 (VIN L) (SFI)

1 • THROTTLE CLOSED. DOES TECH 1 DATA DISPLAY INDICATE THROTTLE POSITION OVER 1.1 VOLTS?

- **YES** → go to 2
- **NO** → DTC P0123 IS INTERMITTENT. IF NO ADDITIONAL DTC(s) WERE STORED, REFER TO "DIAGNOSTIC AIDS" ON FACING PAGE.

2 • DISCONNECT THROTTLE POSITION (TP) SENSOR. TECH 1 DATA DISPLAY SHOULD INDICATE THROTTLE POSITION BELOW .16 VOLT. DOES IT?

- **YES** → go to 3
- **NO** → CKT 417 SHORTED TO VOLTAGE OR FAULTY PCM.

3 • PROBE SENSOR GROUND CIRCUIT AT TP SENSOR CONNECTOR WITH A TEST LIGHT CONNECTED TO BATTERY VOLTAGE.
• TEST LIGHT SHOULD BE "ON." IS IT?

- **YES** → POOR CONNECTION AT TP SENSOR OR FAULTY TP SENSOR.
- **NO** → OPEN SENSOR GROUND CIRCUIT TO TP SENSOR OR FAULTY PCM.

"AFTER REPAIRS," REFER TO DTC CRITERIA ON FACING PAGE AND CONFIRM DTC DOES NOT RESET.

5-1-93
NS 14356

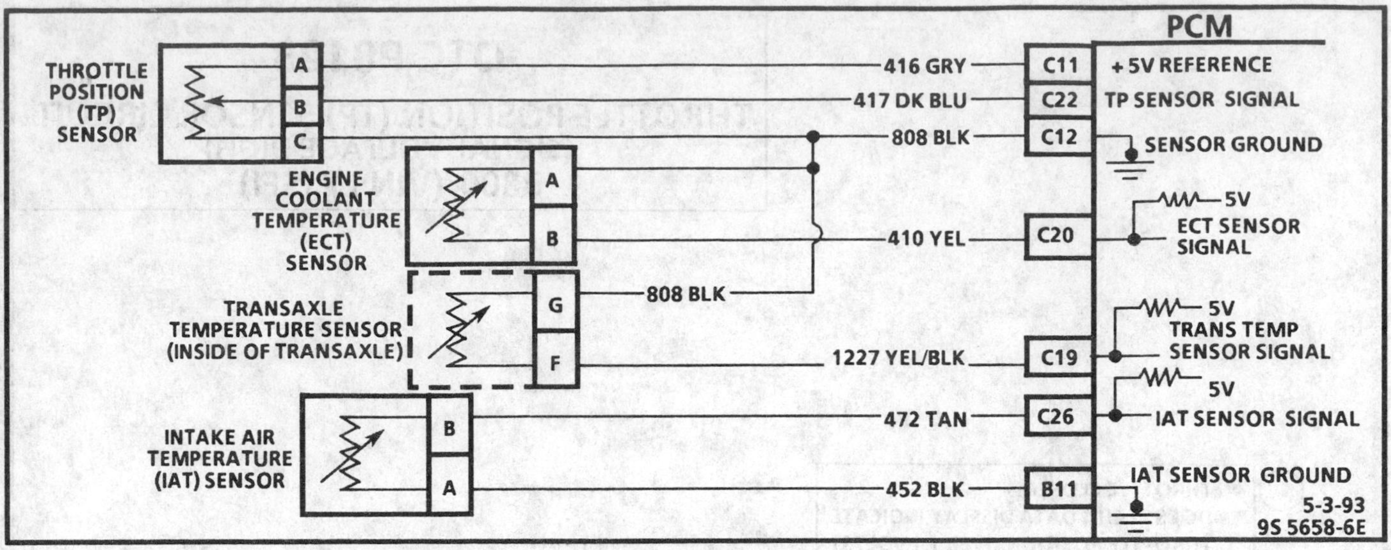
PCM
THROTTLE POSITION (TP) SENSOR
A
B
C
416 GRY
417 DK BLU
808 BLK
C11
C22
C12
+5V REFERENCE
TP SENSOR SIGNAL
SENSOR GROUND
ENGINE COOLANT TEMPERATURE (ECT) SENSOR
A
B
410 YEL
C20
5V
ECT SENSOR SIGNAL
TRANSAXLE TEMPERATURE SENSOR (INSIDE OF TRANSAXLE)
G
F
808 BLK
1227 YEL/BLK
C19
5V
TRANS TEMP SENSOR SIGNAL
5V
INTAKE AIR TEMPERATURE (IAT) SENSOR
B
A
472 TAN
452 BLK
C26
B11
IAT SENSOR SIGNAL
IAT SENSOR GROUND
5-3-93
9S 5658-6E

DTC P0125

ENGINE COOLANT TEMPERATURE (ECT) SENSOR - "CLOSED LOOP" MINIMUM COOLANT TEMPERATURE NOT MET IN TIME 3800 (VIN L) (SFI)

Circuit Description:

To provide the best possible combination of driveability, fuel economy, and emission control, a "Closed Loop" air/fuel metering system is used. When the vehicle is first started, it operates in "Open Loop," ignoring the heated oxygen sensor signal and calculating air/fuel ratio based on inputs from the engine coolant temperature, throttle position and mass air flow sensors only. The PCM will begin using the heated oxygen sensor signal for controlling fuel delivery ("Closed Loop") when the following conditions are met:

- The Heated Oxygen Sensor (HO2S 1) has varying voltage output showing that it is hot enough to operate properly.
- The Engine Coolant Temperature (ECT) sensor indicates coolant temperature above 60°C (140°F).
- Time since startup is at least 16 seconds for a warm engine or 50 seconds for a cold engine.

DTC P0125 Will Set When: The PCM monitors the ECT signal and stores DTC P0125 if engine coolant temperature sufficient to allow "Closed Loop" operation is not achieved within 9 minutes of startup.

Action Taken (PCM will default to): DTC P0125 does not illuminate the MIL (Service Engine Soon).

Diagnostic Aids: When DTC P0125 is set, a slewed ECT sensor is indicated.

An intermittent may be caused by a poor connection, rubbed through wire insulation or a wire broken inside the insulation.

Check for:

- Poor connection or damaged harness - Inspect PCM harness connectors for backed out terminals "C20" and "C12" improper mating, broken locks, improperly formed or damaged terminals, poor terminal to wire connection and damaged harness.
- Intermittent test - If connections and harness check OK, monitor a digital voltmeter connected between PCM terminal "C20" and "C12" while moving related connectors and wiring harness. If the failure is induced, the voltage reading will change. This may help to isolate the location of the malfunction.

DTC P0125

ENGINE COOLANT TEMPERATURE (ECT) SENSOR - "CLOSED LOOP" MINIMUM COOLANT TEMPERATURE NOT MET IN TIME 3800 (VIN L) (SFI)

- ALLOW ENGINE TO COOL COMPLETELY.
- IGNITION "ON."
- OBSERVE COOLING FANS - SHOULD BE "OFF." IF NOT, REFER TO CHART C-12A, "COOLING FANS CHECK" IN SECTION "6E3-C".
- INSTALL TECH 1.
- COMPARE "INTAKE AIR TEMP" TO " ENG COOL TEMP" - SHOULD BE CLOSE. IF NOT, REFER TO DTC P0117 CHART.
- START AND RUN ENGINE WHILE MONITORING "ENG COOL TEMP" ON TECH 1.
- "ENG COOL TEMP" VALUE SHOULD RISE STEADILY TO ABOVE 19°C (66°F) WITHIN 9 MINUTES. DOES IT?

YES

SEE "DIAGNOSTIC AIDS" ON FACING PAGE.

NO

CHECK COOLING SYSTEM COOLANT LEVEL. IF OK, COMPARE "ENG COOL TEMP" DISPLAY ON TECH 1 TO ACTUAL COOLANT TEMPERATURE; IF NOT CLOSE, REPLACE ECT SENSOR. IF CLOSE, REFER TO SECTION "6B" FOR COOLING SYSTEM DIAGNOSIS.

4-7-93
NS 15826

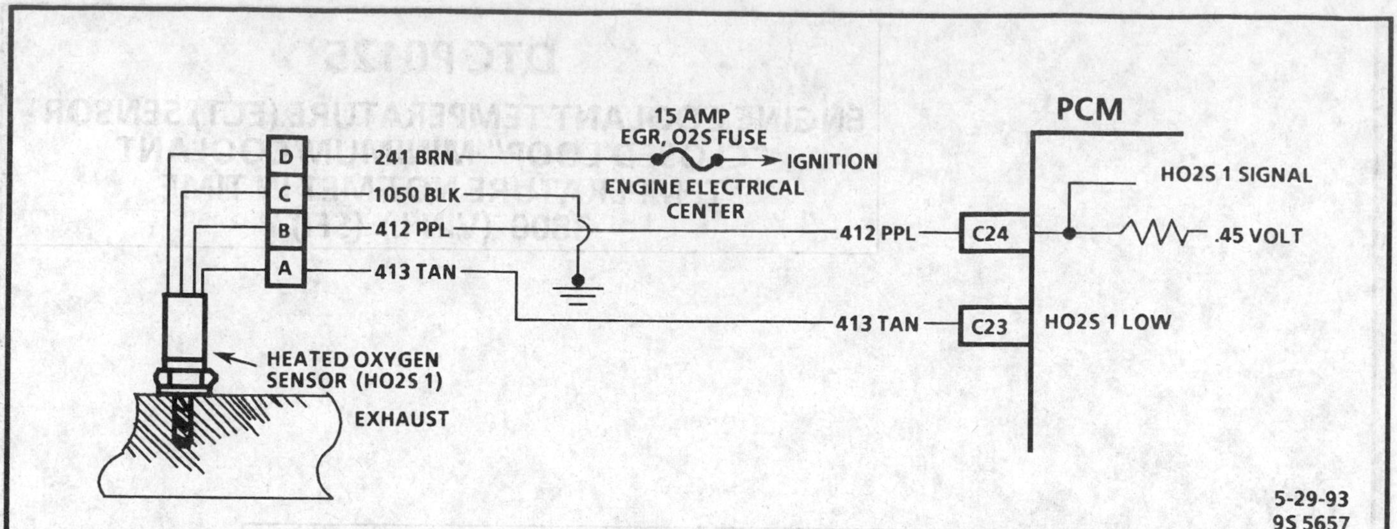

PCM
15 AMP
EGR, O2S FUSE
IGNITION
ENGINE ELECTRICAL
CENTER
D
C
B
A
241 BRN
1050 BLK
412 PPL
413 TAN
412 PPL
413 TAN
C24
C23
HO2S 1 SIGNAL
.45 VOLT
HO2S 1 LOW
HEATED OXYGEN
SENSOR (HO2S 1)
EXHAUST
5-29-93
9S 5657

DTC P0131

HEATED OXYGEN SENSOR (HO2S 1) CIRCUIT (LOW SIGNAL VOLTAGE) 3800 (VIN L) (SFI)

Circuit Description:

The PCM supplies a voltage of about .45 volt (450 mV) between terminals "C23" and "C24". (If measured with a 10 megohm digital voltmeter, this may read as low as .32 volt.) The Heated Oxygen Sensor (HO2S 1) varies the voltage within a range of about 1 volt (1000 mV) if the exhaust is rich, down to about .10 volt (100 mV) if exhaust is lean.

The sensor is like an open circuit and produces no voltage when it is below about 360°C (600°F). DTC P0131, P0132 or an open sensor circuit or cold sensor causes "Open Loop" operation.

DTC P0131 Will Set When:

- The HO2S 1 signal voltage on CKT 412 remains below 250 mV for up to 4.5 minutes.
- The system is operating in "Closed Loop."

Action Taken (PCM will default to): A current DTC P0131 set will cause the system to operate in "Open Loop." With DTC P0131 set, the MIL (Service Engine Soon) will be illuminated.

DTC Chart Test Description: Number(s) below refer to circled number(s) on the diagnostic chart.

1. Running the engine at 1200 RPM keeps the oxygen sensor hot to ensure the oxygen sensor remains active and can indicate the exhaust oxygen content accurately.
2. Opening the heated oxygen sensor circuit should result in a displayed voltage between 350 and 550 mV. If the display is still fixed below 350 mV, the fault is a short to ground in CKT 412 or a faulty PCM.

Diagnostic Aids: Using the Tech 1, observe the L.T. fuel trim values at different RPM and air flow conditions. The Tech 1 also displays the fuel trim cells, so the L.T. fuel trim values can be checked in each of the cells to determine when DTC P0131 may have been set. If the conditions for DTC P0131 exist, the L.T. fuel trim values will be around 158 or greater.

Check for:

- Heated oxygen sensor wire - Sensor pigtail may be mispositioned and contacting the exhaust manifold.
- Check for intermittent ground in wire between connector and sensor.
- Poor PCM to engine block ground.
- MAF sensor - A Mass Air Flow (MAF) sensor output that causes the PCM to sense a lower than normal air flow will cause the system to go lean. Disconnect the MAF sensor. If the lean condition is gone, check for an obstructed or damaged throttle body inlet screen and repair or replace throttle body as necessary. If inlet screen is OK, replace the MAF sensor.
- Lean injector(s) - Perform injector balance test CHART C-2A.
- Fuel contamination - Water, even in small amounts, near the in-tank fuel pump inlet can be delivered to the injectors. The water causes a lean exhaust and can set a DTC P0131.
- Fuel pressure - System will be lean if pressure is too low. It may be necessary to monitor fuel pressure while driving the vehicle at various road speeds and/or loads to confirm. Refer to "Fuel System Diagnosis," CHART A-7.
- Exhaust leaks - If there is an exhaust leak, the engine can cause outside air to be pulled into the exhaust and past the sensor.
- Vacuum or crankcase leaks can cause a lean condition and/or possibly a high idle.
- If the above are OK, it is a faulty heated oxygen sensor.

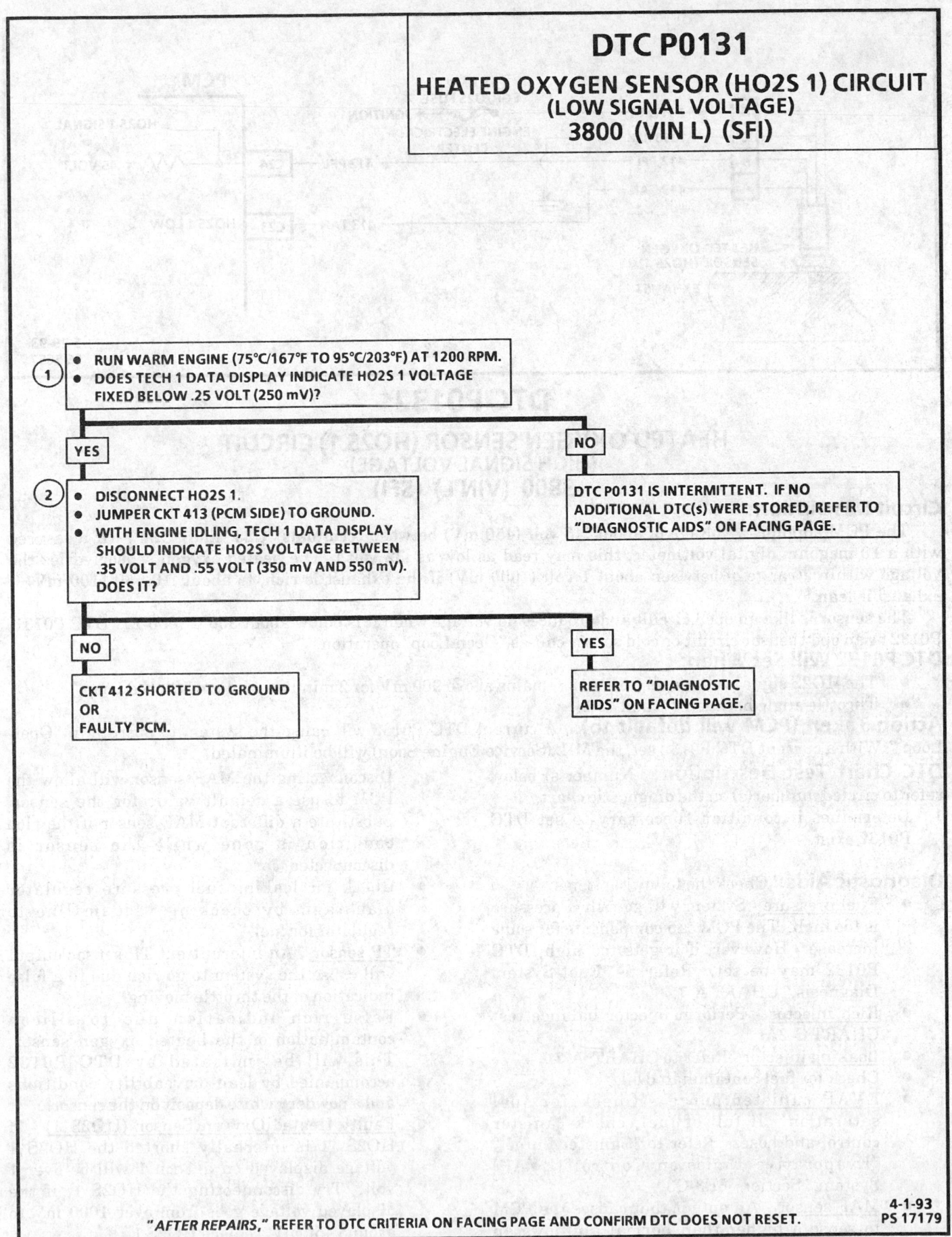

DTC P0131

HEATED OXYGEN SENSOR (HO2S 1) CIRCUIT (LOW SIGNAL VOLTAGE) 3800 (VIN L) (SFI)

1
- RUN WARM ENGINE (75°C/167°F TO 95°C/203°F) AT 1200 RPM.
- DOES TECH 1 DATA DISPLAY INDICATE HO2S 1 VOLTAGE FIXED BELOW .25 VOLT (250 mV)?

YES → step 2

NO → DTC P0131 IS INTERMITTENT. IF NO ADDITIONAL DTC(s) WERE STORED, REFER TO "DIAGNOSTIC AIDS" ON FACING PAGE.

2
- DISCONNECT HO2S 1.
- JUMPER CKT 413 (PCM SIDE) TO GROUND.
- WITH ENGINE IDLING, TECH 1 DATA DISPLAY SHOULD INDICATE HO2S VOLTAGE BETWEEN .35 VOLT AND .55 VOLT (350 mV AND 550 mV). DOES IT?

NO → CKT 412 SHORTED TO GROUND OR FAULTY PCM.

YES → REFER TO "DIAGNOSTIC AIDS" ON FACING PAGE.

"AFTER REPAIRS," REFER TO DTC CRITERIA ON FACING PAGE AND CONFIRM DTC DOES NOT RESET.

4-1-93
PS 17179

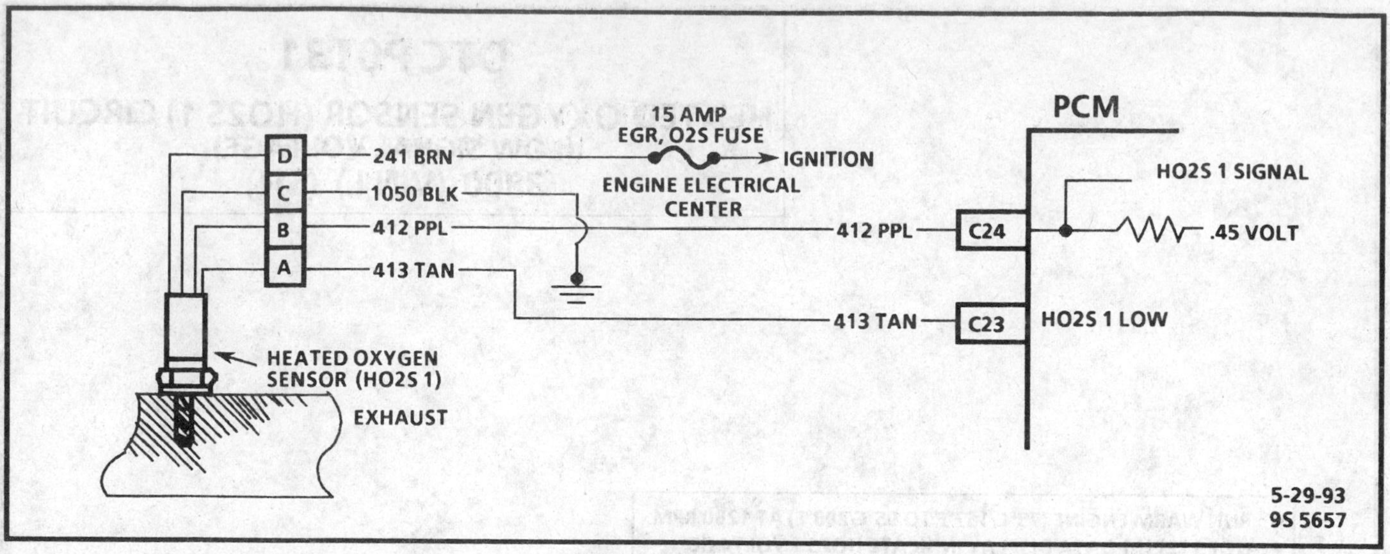
PCM
15 AMP
EGR, O2S FUSE
IGNITION
ENGINE ELECTRICAL
CENTER
D
C
B
A
241 BRN
1050 BLK
412 PPL
413 TAN
412 PPL
C24
HO2S 1 SIGNAL
.45 VOLT
413 TAN
C23
HO2S 1 LOW
HEATED OXYGEN
SENSOR (HO2S 1)
EXHAUST
5-29-93
9S 5657

DTC P0132

HEATED OXYGEN SENSOR (HO2S 1) CIRCUIT
(HIGH SIGNAL VOLTAGE)
3800 (VIN L) (SFI)

Circuit Description:

The PCM supplies a voltage of about .45 volt (450 mV) between terminals "C23" and "C24". (If measured with a 10 megohm digital voltmeter, this may read as low as .32 volt.) The heated oxygen sensor varies the voltage within a range of between about 1 volt (1000 mV) if the exhaust is rich, to about .10 volt (100 mV) if exhaust is lean.

The sensor is like an open circuit and produces no voltage when it is below about 360°C (600°F). DTC P0131, P0132 or an open sensor circuit or cold sensor causes "Open Loop" operation.

DTC P0132 Will Set When:

- The HO2S signal voltage on CKT 412 remains above 900 mV for 2 minutes while in "Closed Loop."
- Throttle angle between 2% and 40%.

Action Taken (PCM will default to): A current DTC P0132 will cause the system to operate in "Open Loop." With a current DTC P0132 set, the MIL (Service Engine Soon) will be illuminated.

DTC Chart Test Description: Number(s) below refer to circled number(s) on the diagnostic chart.

1. Determines if conditions necessary to set DTC P0132 exist.

Diagnostic Aids: Check the following items:

- Fuel pressure - System will go rich if pressure is too high. The PCM can compensate for some increase. However, if it gets too high, DTC P0132 may be set. Refer to "Fuel System Diagnosis," CHART A-7.
- Rich injector - Perform injector balance test CHART C-2A.
- Leaking injector - Refer to CHART A-7.
- Check for fuel contaminated oil.
- EVAP canister purge - Check for fuel saturation. If full of fuel, check canister control and hoses. Refer to "Canister Purge," "Evaporative Emission Control (EVAP) System," Section "6E3-C3".
- MAF sensor - An output that causes the PCM to sense a higher than normal air flow can cause the system to go rich. Disconnecting the MAF sensor will allow the PCM to use a default value for the sensor. Substitute a different MAF sensor if the rich condition is gone while the sensor is disconnected.
- Check for leaking fuel pressure regulator diaphragm by checking vacuum line to regulator for fuel.
- TP sensor - An intermittent TP sensor output will cause the system to go rich due to a false indication of the throttle moving.
- False rich indication due to silicon contamination of the heated oxygen sensor. This will be indicated by DTC P0132 accompanied by lean driveability conditions and a powdery white deposit on the sensor.
- Faulty Heated Oxygen Sensor (HO2S 1) - If HO2S 1 is internally shorted the HO2S 1 voltage displayed on a Tech 1 will be over 1 volt. Try disconnecting the HO2S 1; if the displayed voltage goes from over 1000 mV to around 450 mV, replace HO2S 1.

DTC P0132

HEATED OXYGEN SENSOR (HO2S 1) CIRCUIT (HIGH SIGNAL VOLTAGE) 3800 (VIN L) (SFI)

1

- RUN WARM ENGINE (75°C/167°F TO 95°C/203°F) AT 1200 RPM.
- DOES TECH 1 DATA DISPLAY INDICATE HO2S 1 VOLTAGE FIXED ABOVE .9 VOLT (900 mV)?

YES

- DISCONNECT HO2S 1 AND JUMPER HARNESS CKTs 412 AND 413 TO GROUND.
- TECH 1 DATA DISPLAY SHOULD INDICATE HO2S 1 VOLTAGE BELOW .35 VOLT (350 mV). DOES IT?

YES

REFER TO "DIAGNOSTIC AIDS" ON FACING PAGE.

NO

REPLACE PCM.

NO

DTC P0132 IS INTERMITTENT. IF NO ADDITIONAL DTC(s) WERE STORED, REFER TO "DIAGNOSTIC AIDS" ON FACING PAGE.

"AFTER REPAIRS," REFER TO DTC CRITERIA ON FACING PAGE AND CONFIRM DTC DOES NOT RESET.

5-1-93
PS 17180

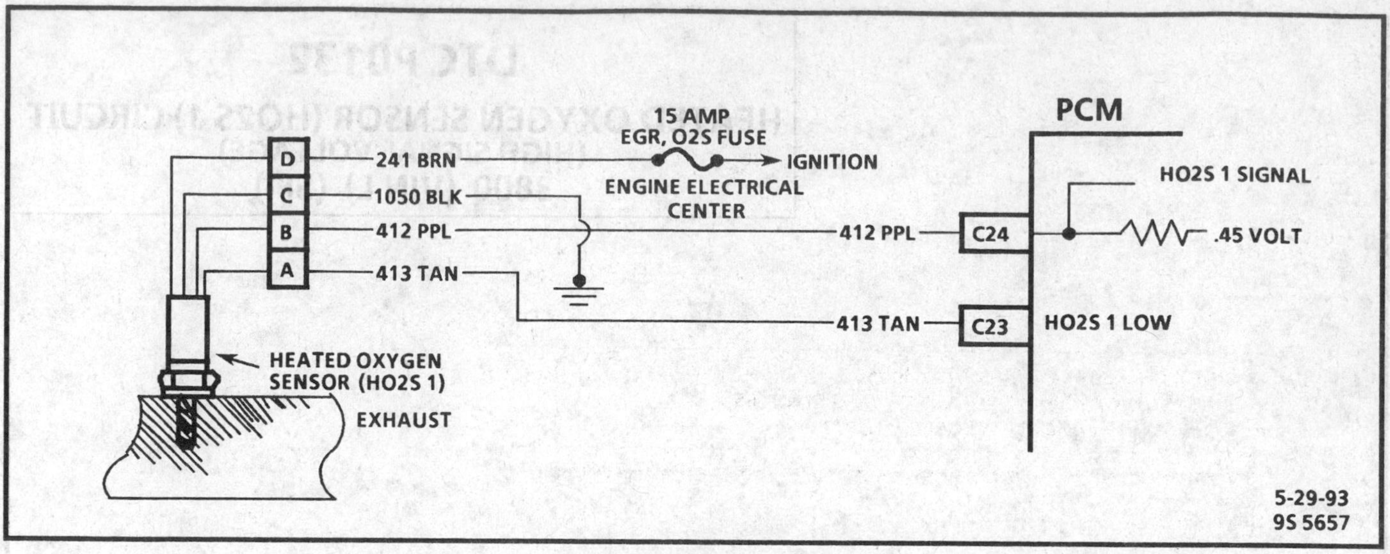
PCM
15 AMP
EGR, O2S FUSE
IGNITION
ENGINE ELECTRICAL
CENTER
D
C
B
A
241 BRN
1050 BLK
412 PPL
413 TAN
412 PPL
413 TAN
C24
C23
HO2S 1 SIGNAL
.45 VOLT
HO2S 1 LOW
HEATED OXYGEN
SENSOR (HO2S 1)
EXHAUST
5-29-93
9S 5657

DTC P0134

HEATED OXYGEN SENSOR (HO2S 1) CIRCUIT
(OPEN CIRCUIT)
3800 (VIN L) (SFI)

Circuit Description:

The PCM supplies a voltage of about .45 volt between terminals "C24" and "C23". (If measured with a 10 megohm digital voltmeter, this may read as low as .32 volt.) The Heated Oxygen Sensor (HO2S 1) varies the voltage within a range of about 1 volt if the exhaust is rich, down through about .10 volt if exhaust is lean.

The sensor is like an open circuit and produces no voltage when it is below 360°C (600°F). An open oxygen sensor circuit or cold oxygen sensor causes "Open Loop" operation.

DTC P0134 Will Set When:

- Engine coolant temperature above 43°C (110°F).
- Engine run time more than 40 seconds.
- HO2S 1 signal voltage is steady between 350 mV and 557 mV.
- Throttle angle above 3%.
- All conditions must be met for about 30 seconds.

Action Taken (PCM will default to): With a current DTC P0134 set, the system will operate in "Open Loop." The MIL (Service Engine Soon) will be illuminated.

DTC Chart Test Description: Number(s) below refer to circled number(s) on the diagnostic chart.

1. If the conditions for setting DTC P0134 exist, the system will not go into "Closed Loop."
2. This will determine if the sensor or the wiring is the cause of DTC P0134.
3. This test checks the continuity of CKT 413.

Diagnostic Aids: An intermittent may be caused by a poor connection, rubbed through wire insulation, or a wire broken inside the insulation.

Check for:

- Poor connection or damaged harness - Inspect harness connectors for backed out terminals, improper mating, broken locks, improperly formed or damaged terminals, poor terminal to wire connection, and damaged harness.
- Faulty HO2S 1 heater or heater circuit - With the ignition "ON," engine "OFF," the HO2S 1 voltage displayed on a Tech 1 should gradually drop to below .25 volt, indicating that the heater is working properly. If not, disconnect the HO2S 1 and connect a test light between terminals "C" and "D". If the test light does not light, repair open CKT 1050 or 241. If the test light lights, replace HO2S 1.
- Intermittent test - With Tech 1, monitor HO2S 1 signal voltage while moving related connectors and wiring harness, with warm engine running at part throttle in "Closed Loop." If the failure is induced, the HO2S 1 signal voltage reading will change from its normal fluctuating voltage (above 600 mV and below 300 mV) to a fixed value around 450 mV. This may help to isolate the location of the malfunction.

DTC P0134
HEATED OXYGEN SENSOR (HO2S 1) CIRCUIT
(OPEN CIRCUIT)
3800 (VIN L) (SFI)

1 ENGINE AT NORMAL OPERATING TEMPERATURE (ABOVE 80°C/176°F).
- RUN ENGINE ABOVE 1200 RPM FOR TWO MINUTES.
- DOES TECH 1 INDICATE "CLOSED LOOP"?

NO → go to 2

YES → DTC P0134 IS INTERMITTENT. IF NO ADDITIONAL DIAGNOSTIC TROUBLE CODES WERE STORED, REFER TO "DIAGNOSTIC AIDS" ON FACING PAGE.

2
- DISCONNECT HEATED OXYGEN SENSOR (HO2S 1) ELECTRICAL CONNECTOR.
- JUMPER HARNESS CKTs 412 AND 413 (PCM SIDE) TO GROUND.
- TECH 1 DATA DISPLAY SHOULD INDICATE HO2S 1 VOLTAGE BELOW .2 VOLT (200 mV) WITH ENGINE RUNNING. DOES IT?

NO → go to 3

YES → FAULTY HO2S 1 CONNECTION OR FAULTY HO2S 1.

3
- REMOVE JUMPERS AND RECONNECT HO2S 1.
- KEY "OFF."
- DISCONNECT BLUE PCM CONNECTOR "C".
- PROBE PCM HARNESS CONNECTOR TERMINAL "C23" WITH A TEST LIGHT TO B+.
- TEST LIGHT SHOULD BE "ON." IS IT?

YES → OPEN CKT 412 OR POOR CONNECTION AT PCM OR FAULTY PCM.

NO → OPEN CKT 413.

4-7-93
PS 17198

"AFTER REPAIRS," REFER TO DTC CRITERIA ON FACING PAGE AND CONFIRM DTC DOES NOT RESET.

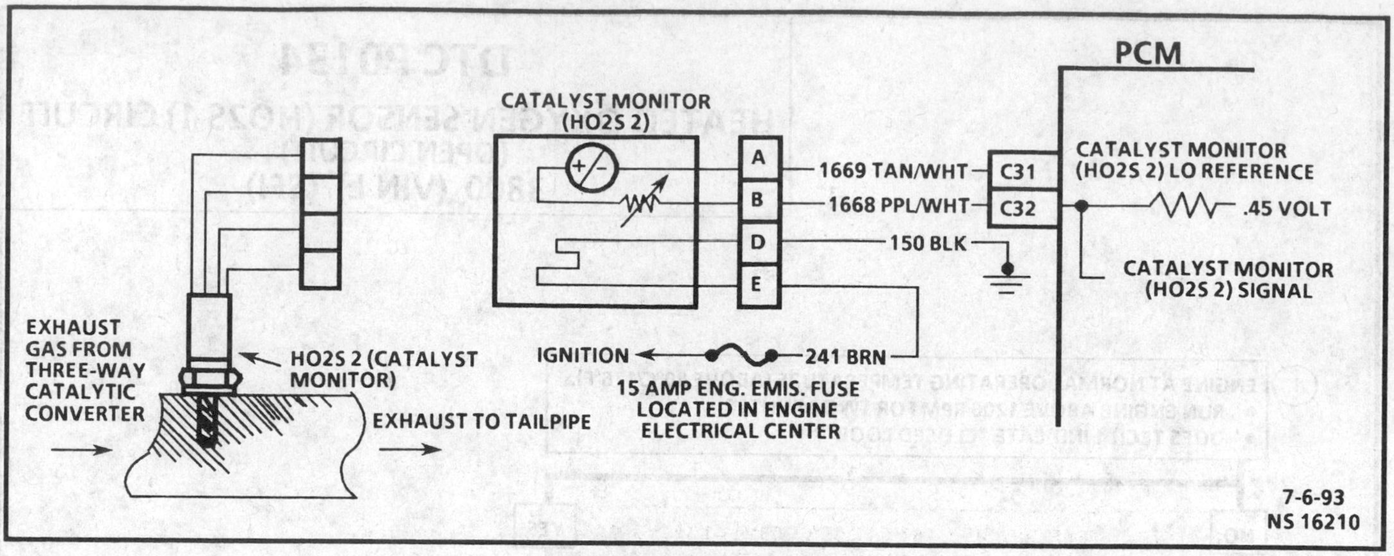
PCM
CATALYST MONITOR
(HO2S 2)
A
B
D
E
1669 TAN/WHT
1668 PPL/WHT
150 BLK
C31
C32
CATALYST MONITOR
(HO2S 2) LO REFERENCE
.45 VOLT
CATALYST MONITOR
(HO2S 2) SIGNAL
EXHAUST
GAS FROM
THREE-WAY
CATALYTIC
CONVERTER
HO2S 2 (CATALYST
MONITOR)
IGNITION
241 BRN
15 AMP ENG. EMIS. FUSE
LOCATED IN ENGINE
ELECTRICAL CENTER
EXHAUST TO TAILPIPE
7-6-93
NS 16210

DTC P0137
HO2S 2 (CATALYST MONITOR)
(LOW SIGNAL VOLTAGE)
3800 (VIN L) (SFI)

Circuit Description:

In order to control emissions of Hydrocarbons (HC), Carbon Monoxide (CO) and Oxides of Nitrogen (NOx), a three-way catalytic converter is used. The catalyst within the converter promotes a chemical reaction which oxidizes the HC and CO present in the exhaust gas, converting them into harmless water vapor and carbon dioxide. The catalyst also reduces NOx, converting it to nitrogen. The PCM has the capability to monitor this process using HO2S 2. HO2S 2, located in the exhaust stream past the three-way catalytic converter, produces an output signal which indicates the oxygen storage capacity of the catalyst; this in turn indicates the catalyst's ability to convert exhaust emissions effectively. If the catalyst is functioning correctly, the HO2S 2 signal will be far less active than that produced by HO2S 1. If a problem exists which causes the PCM to monitor an excessively low HO2S 2 signal voltage for an extended period of time, the PCM will set DTC P0137, indicating a possible short to ground in CKT 1668.

DTC P0137 Will Set When:

- Throttle angle between 2% and 40%.
- HO2S 2 signal voltage below 0.1 volt (100 mV).
- Above conditions for over 4 1/2 minutes.

Action Taken (PCM will default to): DTC P0137 does not illuminate the MIL (Service Engine Soon).

DTC Chart Test Description: Number(s) below refer to circled number(s) on the diagnostic chart.

1. Determines if conditions necessary for setting DTC P0137 exist.
2. Opening CKT 1668 and completing CKT 1669 to ground should cause the Tech 1 to display the PCM-supplied bias voltage (.35 - .55 volt). If the signal voltage is still low, CKT 1668 is shorted to ground or the PCM is faulty.

Diagnostic Aids: An intermittent may be caused by rubbed through wire insulation or a wire contacting the exhaust.

Check for:

- Poor connection or damaged harness - Inspect harness for short to ground in CKT 1668, improper mating, broken locks, improperly formed or damaged terminals, poor terminal to wire connection, and damaged harness.
- Intermittent test - Observe HO2S 2 on Tech 1 while moving related connectors and wiring harness with the key "ON." If the failure is induced, the HO2S 2 display will change. This may help isolate the location of the malfunction.

DTC P0137

HO2S 2 (CATALYST MONITOR)
(LOW SIGNAL VOLTAGE)
3800 (VIN L) (SFI)

1
- RUN WARM ENGINE (75°C/167°F TO 95°C/203°F) AT 1200 RPM.
- DOES TECH 1 DATA DISPLAY INDICATE HO2S 2 VOLTAGE FIXED BELOW 0.1 VOLT (100 mV)?

NO → DTC P0137 IS INTERMITTENT. IF NO ADDITIONAL DTC(s) WERE STORED, REFER TO "DIAGNOSTIC AIDS" ON FACING PAGE.

YES →

2
- DISCONNECT HO2S 2 ELECTRICAL CONNECTOR AND JUMPER CKT 1669 TO ENGINE GROUND.
- WITH ENGINE IDLING, TECH 1 DATA DISPLAY SHOULD INDICATE HO2S 2 VOLTAGE BETWEEN .35 VOLT AND .55 VOLT (350 mV AND 550 mV).
DOES IT?

NO → CHECK CKT 1668 FOR A SHORT TO GROUND. IF OK, REPLACE PCM.

YES →
- ENSURE THAT HO2S 2 WIRING IS NOT CONTACTING EXHAUST.
- CHECK HO2S 2 PIGTAIL FOR DAMAGE.
- CHECK EXHAUST BETWEEN THREE-WAY CATALYTIC CONVERTER AND FLANGE AND THREE-WAY CATALYTIC CONVERTER FOR LEAKS, CORROSION, OR LOOSE OR MISSING HARDWARE AND REPAIR AS NECESSARY.

IF OK, REFER TO "DIAGNOSTIC AIDS" ON FACING PAGE.

4-22-93
NS 14348

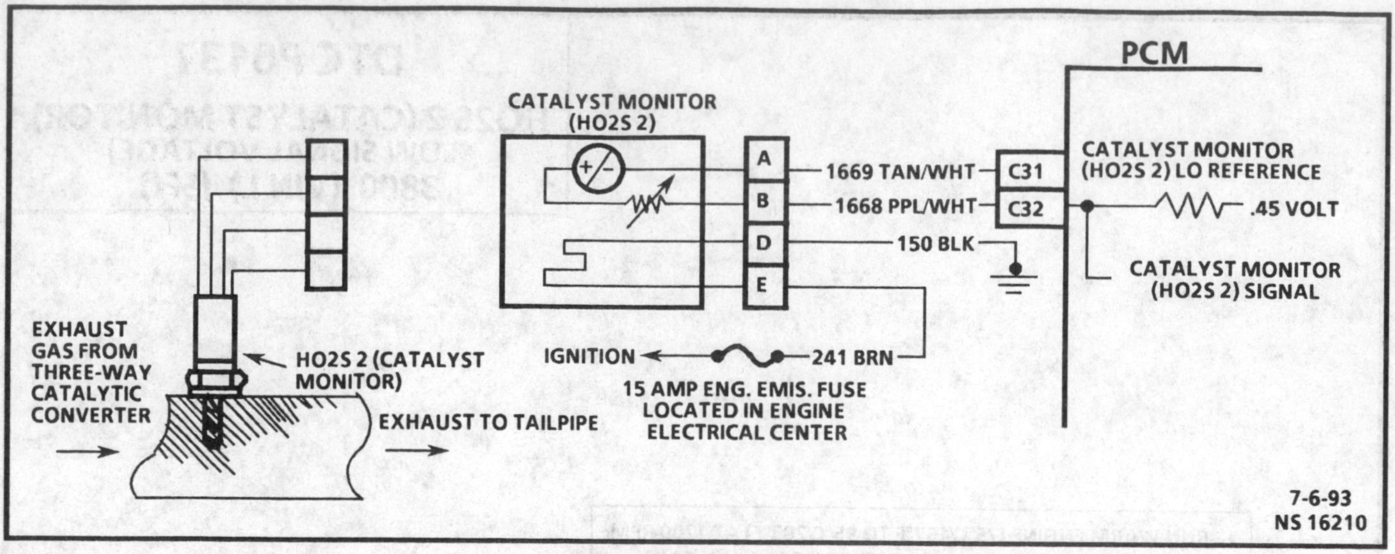
PCM
CATALYST MONITOR
(HO2S 2)
A
B
D
E
1669 TAN/WHT
1668 PPL/WHT
150 BLK
C31
C32
CATALYST MONITOR
(HO2S 2) LO REFERENCE
.45 VOLT
CATALYST MONITOR
(HO2S 2) SIGNAL
EXHAUST
GAS FROM
THREE-WAY
CATALYTIC
CONVERTER
HO2S 2 (CATALYST
MONITOR)
IGNITION
241 BRN
15 AMP ENG. EMIS. FUSE
LOCATED IN ENGINE
ELECTRICAL CENTER
EXHAUST TO TAILPIPE
7-6-93
NS 16210

DTC P0138

HO2S 2 (CATALYST MONITOR)
(HIGH SIGNAL VOLTAGE)
3800 (VIN L) (SFI)

Circuit Description:

In order to control emissions of Hydrocarbons (HC), Carbon Monoxide (CO) and Oxides of Nitrogen (NOx), a three-way catalytic converter is used. The catalyst within the converter promotes a chemical reaction which oxidizes the HC and CO present in the exhaust gas, converting them into harmless water vapor and carbon dioxide. The catalyst also reduces NOx, converting it to nitrogen. The PCM has the capability to monitor this process using HO2S 2. HO2S 2, located in the exhaust stream past the three-way catalytic converter, produces an output signal which indicates the oxygen storage capacity of the catalyst; this in turn indicates the catalyst's ability to convert exhaust emissions effectively. If the catalyst is functioning correctly, the HO2S 2 signal will be far less active than that produced by HO2S 1. If a problem exists which causes the PCM to detect high HO2S 2 signal voltage for an extended period of time, the PCM will set DTC P0138.

DTC P0138 Will Set When:

- Throttle angle between 2% and 40%.
- HO2S 2 signal voltage below 0.9 volt (900 mV).
- Above conditions for over 4 1/2 minutes.

Action Taken (PCM will default to): DTC P0138 does not illuminate the MIL (Service Engine Soon).

DTC Chart Test Description: Number(s) below refer to circled number(s) on the diagnostic chart.

1. Determines if conditions necessary for setting DTC P0138 exist.
2. Disconnecting HO2S 2 and jumpering CKTs 1668 and 1669 to ground should cause the Tech 1 to display HO2S 2 voltage below .2 volt (200 mV). If the signal voltage is still high, the PCM is faulty.

Diagnostic Aids: Check for:

- Rich exhaust - If DTC P0131, P0132, or P0134 are present, diagnose these DTC(s) prior to DTC P0138. An overly rich exhaust may load the catalyst causing high HO2S 2 signal voltages.
- False rich indication due to silicon contamination of HO2S 2. This will be indicated by DTC P0138 accompanied by a powdery white deposit on the sensor.
- Faulty HO2S 2 (catalyst monitor) - If HO2S 2 is internally shorted the HO2S 2 voltage displayed on a Tech 1 will be over 1 volt. Try disconnecting the HO2S 2 and jumpering CKT 1669 to engine ground; if the displayed voltage goes from over 1000 mV to around 450 mV, replace HO2S 2.
- Intermittent test - Observe HO2S 2 on Tech 1 while moving related connectors and wiring harness with key "ON." If the failure is induced, the HO2S 2 display will change. This may help to isolate the location of the malfunction.
- Damaged harness - Inspect PCM harness for a short to voltage in CKT 1668.

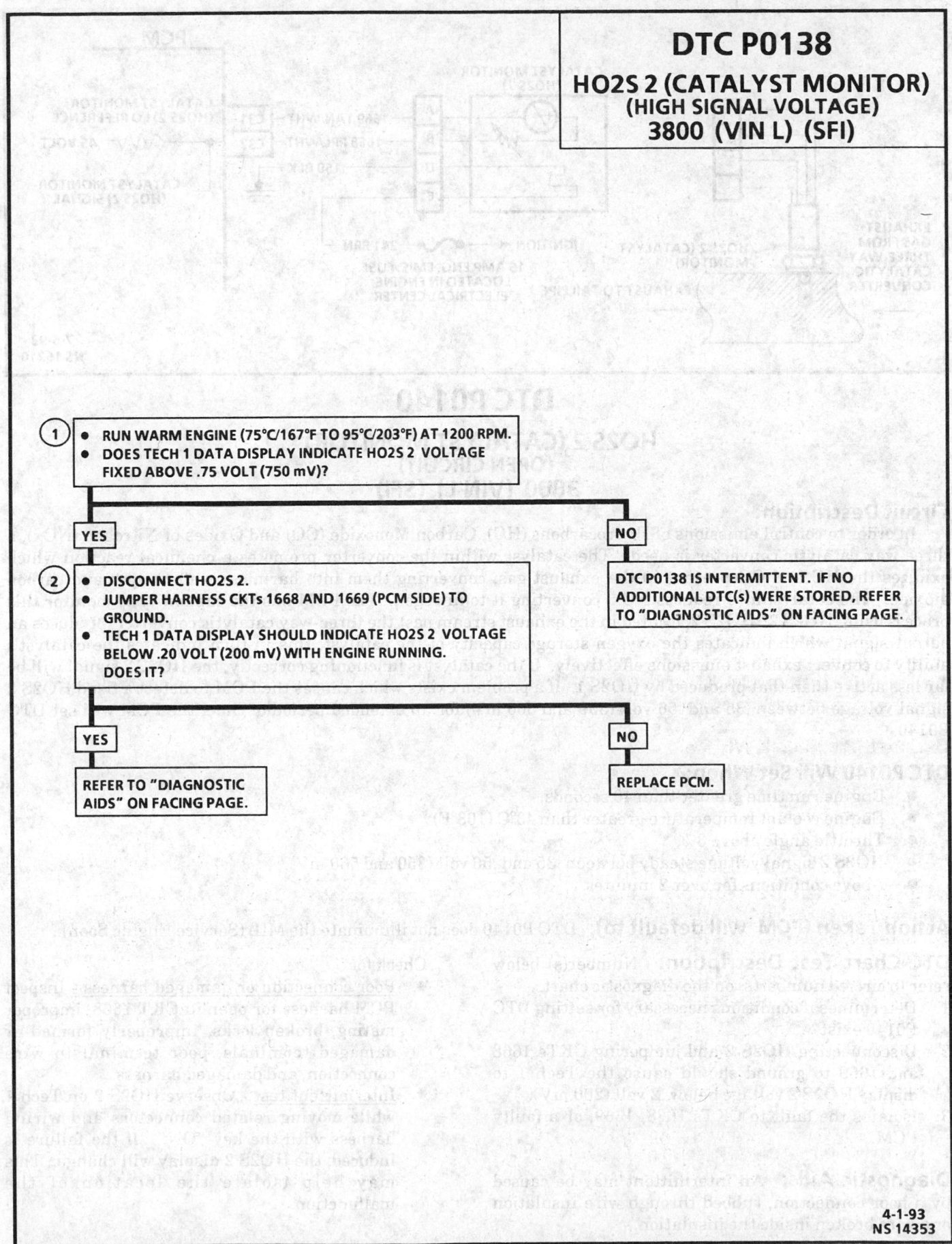

DTC P0138

HO2S 2 (CATALYST MONITOR)
(HIGH SIGNAL VOLTAGE)
3800 (VIN L) (SFI)

(1)
- RUN WARM ENGINE (75°C/167°F TO 95°C/203°F) AT 1200 RPM.
- DOES TECH 1 DATA DISPLAY INDICATE HO2S 2 VOLTAGE FIXED ABOVE .75 VOLT (750 mV)?

YES → go to step 2.

NO → DTC P0138 IS INTERMITTENT. IF NO ADDITIONAL DTC(s) WERE STORED, REFER TO "DIAGNOSTIC AIDS" ON FACING PAGE.

(2)
- DISCONNECT HO2S 2.
- JUMPER HARNESS CKTs 1668 AND 1669 (PCM SIDE) TO GROUND.
- TECH 1 DATA DISPLAY SHOULD INDICATE HO2S 2 VOLTAGE BELOW .20 VOLT (200 mV) WITH ENGINE RUNNING. DOES IT?

YES → REFER TO "DIAGNOSTIC AIDS" ON FACING PAGE.

NO → REPLACE PCM.

4-1-93
NS 14353

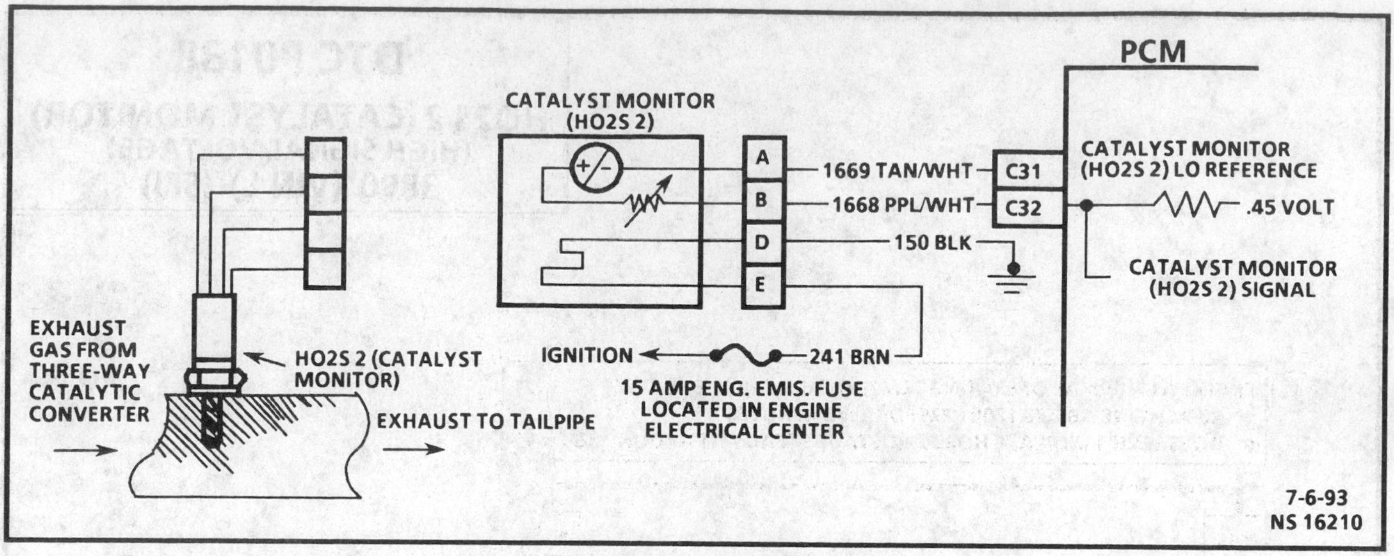
PCM
CATALYST MONITOR
(HO2S 2)
A
B
D
E
1669 TAN/WHT
1668 PPL/WHT
150 BLK
C31
C32
CATALYST MONITOR
(HO2S 2) LO REFERENCE
.45 VOLT
CATALYST MONITOR
(HO2S 2) SIGNAL
EXHAUST
GAS FROM
THREE-WAY
CATALYTIC
CONVERTER
HO2S 2 (CATALYST
MONITOR)
EXHAUST TO TAILPIPE
IGNITION
241 BRN
15 AMP ENG. EMIS. FUSE
LOCATED IN ENGINE
ELECTRICAL CENTER
7-6-93
NS 16210

DTC P0140

HO2S 2 (CATALYST MONITOR)
(OPEN CIRCUIT)
3800 (VIN L) (SFI)

Circuit Description:

In order to control emissions of Hydrocarbons (HC), Carbon Monoxide (CO) and Oxides of Nitrogen (NOx), a three-way catalytic converter is used. The catalyst within the converter promotes a chemical reaction which oxidizes the HC and CO present in the exhaust gas, converting them into harmless water vapor and carbon dioxide. The catalyst also reduces NOx, converting it to nitrogen. The PCM has the capability to monitor this process using HO2S 2. HO2S 2, located in the exhaust stream past the three-way catalytic converter, produces an output signal which indicates the oxygen storage capacity of the catalyst; this in turn indicates the catalyst's ability to convert exhaust emissions effectively. If the catalyst is functioning correctly, the HO2S 2 signal will be far less active than that produced by HO2S 1. If a problem exists which causes the PCM to detect a fixed HO2S 2 signal voltage between .35 and .56 volt (350 and 560 mV) for an extended period of time, the PCM will set DTC P0140.

DTC P0140 Will Set When:

- Engine run time greater than 40 seconds.
- Engine coolant temperature greater than 43°C (108°F).
- Throttle angle above 3%.
- HO2S 2 signal voltage steady between .35 and .56 volt (350 and 560 mV).
- Above conditions for over 2 minutes.

Action Taken (PCM will default to): DTC P0140 does not illuminate the MIL (Service Engine Soon).

DTC Chart Test Description: Number(s) below refer to circled number(s) on the diagnostic chart.

1. Determines if conditions necessary for setting DTC P0140 exist.
2. Disconnecting HO2S 2 and jumpering CKTs 1668 and 1669 to ground should cause the Tech 1 to display HO2S 2 voltage below .2 volt (200 mV).
3. Isolates the fault to CKTs 1668, 1669, or a faulty PCM.

Diagnostic Aids: An intermittent may be caused by a poor connection, rubbed through wire insulation or a wire broken inside the insulation.

Check for:

- Poor connection or damaged harness - Inspect PCM harness for open in CKT 1668, improper mating, broken locks, improperly formed or damaged terminals, poor terminal to wire connection, and damaged harness.
- Intermittent test - Observe HO2S 2 on Tech 1 while moving related connectors and wiring harness with the key "ON." If the failure is induced, the HO2S 2 display will change. This may help isolate the location of the malfunction.

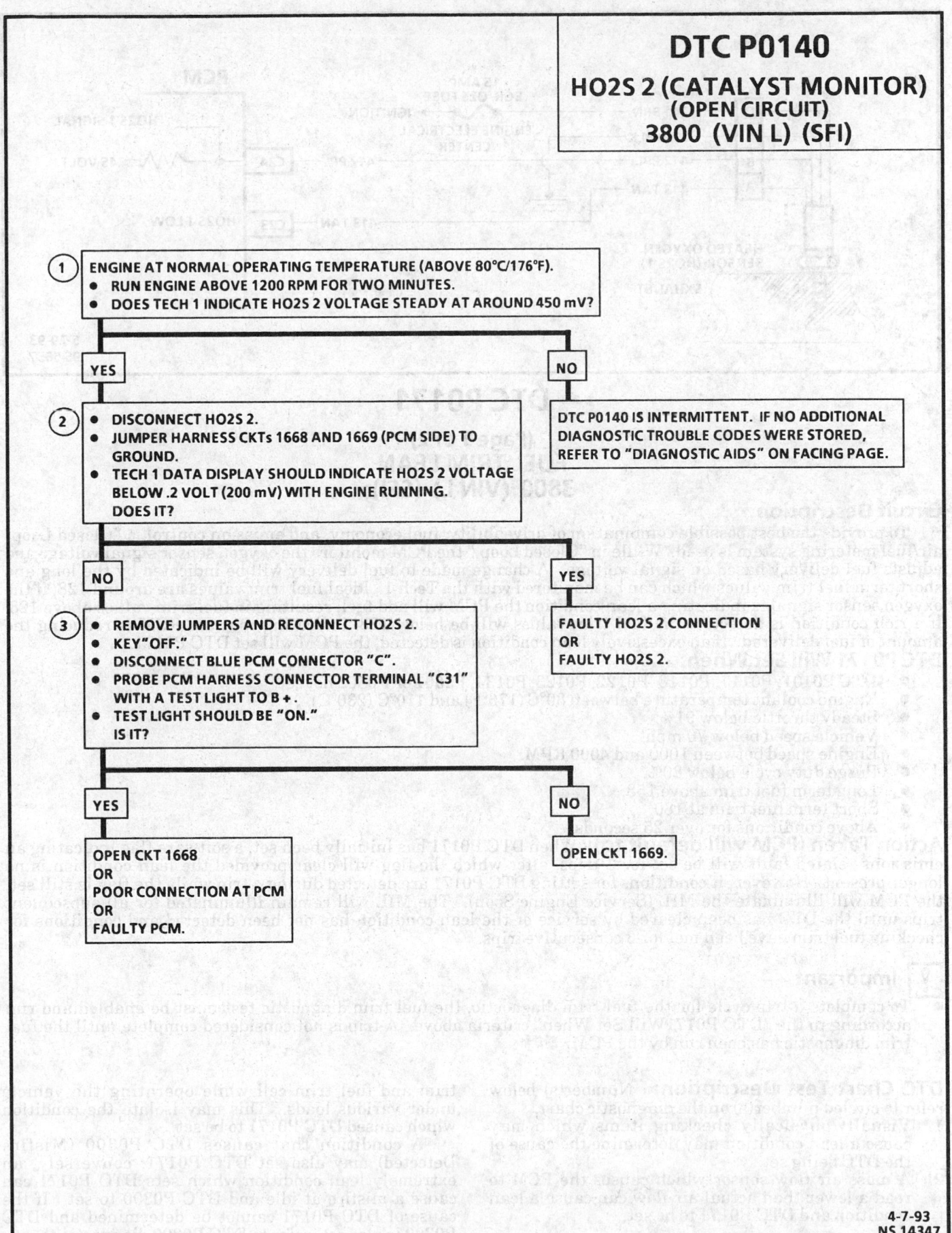

DTC P0140

HO2S 2 (CATALYST MONITOR) (OPEN CIRCUIT) 3800 (VIN L) (SFI)

1 ENGINE AT NORMAL OPERATING TEMPERATURE (ABOVE 80°C/176°F).
- RUN ENGINE ABOVE 1200 RPM FOR TWO MINUTES.
- DOES TECH 1 INDICATE HO2S 2 VOLTAGE STEADY AT AROUND 450 mV?

YES → go to 2

NO → DTC P0140 IS INTERMITTENT. IF NO ADDITIONAL DIAGNOSTIC TROUBLE CODES WERE STORED, REFER TO "DIAGNOSTIC AIDS" ON FACING PAGE.

2
- DISCONNECT HO2S 2.
- JUMPER HARNESS CKTs 1668 AND 1669 (PCM SIDE) TO GROUND.
- TECH 1 DATA DISPLAY SHOULD INDICATE HO2S 2 VOLTAGE BELOW .2 VOLT (200 mV) WITH ENGINE RUNNING. DOES IT?

NO → go to 3

YES → FAULTY HO2S 2 CONNECTION OR FAULTY HO2S 2.

3
- REMOVE JUMPERS AND RECONNECT HO2S 2.
- KEY "OFF."
- DISCONNECT BLUE PCM CONNECTOR "C".
- PROBE PCM HARNESS CONNECTOR TERMINAL "C31" WITH A TEST LIGHT TO B +.
- TEST LIGHT SHOULD BE "ON." IS IT?

YES → OPEN CKT 1668 OR POOR CONNECTION AT PCM OR FAULTY PCM.

NO → OPEN CKT 1669.

4-7-93
NS 14347

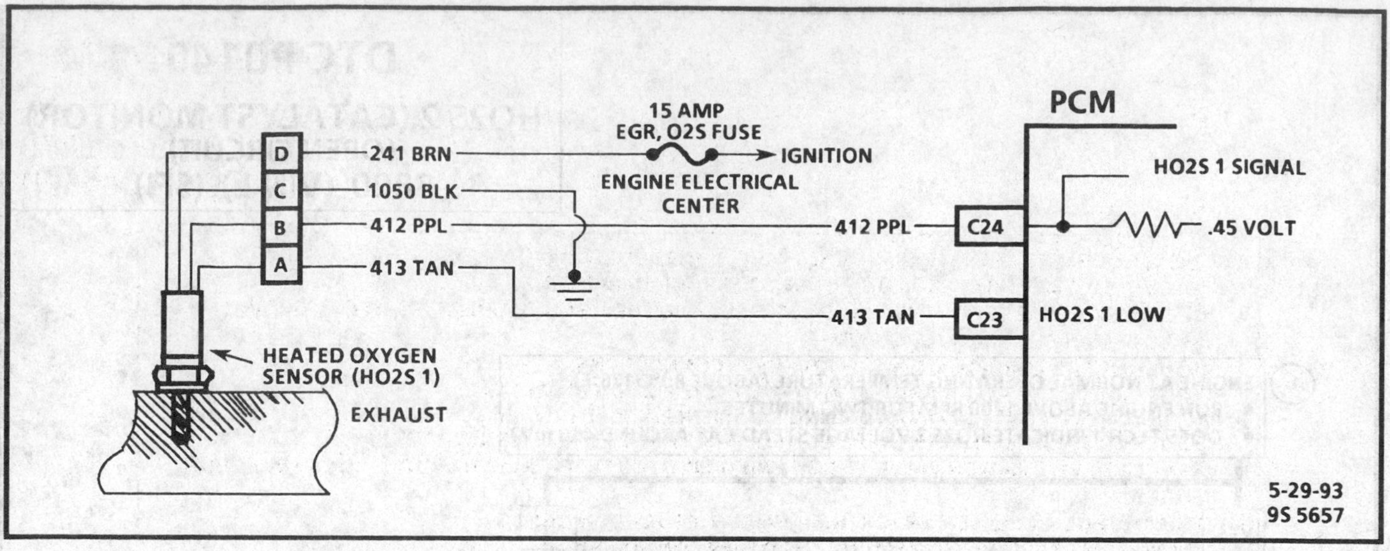
PCM
15 AMP
EGR, O2S FUSE
IGNITION
ENGINE ELECTRICAL
CENTER
D
C
B
A
241 BRN
1050 BLK
412 PPL
413 TAN
412 PPL
413 TAN
C24
C23
HO2S 1 SIGNAL
.45 VOLT
HO2S 1 LOW
HEATED OXYGEN
SENSOR (HO2S 1)
EXHAUST
5-29-93
9S 5657

DTC P0171

(Page 1 of 2)
FUEL TRIM LEAN
3800 (VIN L) (SFI)

Circuit Description:

To provide the best possible combination of driveability, fuel economy, and emission control, a "Closed Loop" air/fuel metering system is used. While in "Closed Loop," the PCM monitors the oxygen sensor signal voltage and adjusts fuel delivery based on signal voltage. A change made to fuel delivery will be indicated by the long and short term fuel trim values which can be monitored with the Tech 1. Ideal fuel trim values are around 128; if the oxygen sensor signal is indicating a lean condition the PCM will add fuel, resulting in fuel trim values above 128. If a rich condition is detected, the fuel trim values will be below 128, indicating that the PCM is reducing the amount of fuel delivered. If an excessively lean condition is detected, the PCM will set DTC P0171.

DTC P0171 Will Set When:

- DTC P0101, P0117, P0118, P0122, P0123, P0134, P0501 or P0502 not set.
- Engine coolant temperature between 80°C (176°F) and 110°C (230°C).
- Steady throttle below 91%.
- Vehicle speed below 70 mph.
- Engine speed between 1000 and 4000 RPM.
- Purge duty cycle below 80%.
- Long term fuel trim above 158.
- Short term fuel trim at 180.
- Above conditions for over 25 seconds.

Action Taken (PCM will default to): When DTC P0171 has initially been set, a software flag indicating an emissions-related fault will be set for 3 trips, after which the flag will clear provided the lean condition is no longer present. However, if conditions for setting DTC P0171 are detected during a trip while the flag is still set, the PCM will illuminate the MIL (Service Engine Soon). The MIL will remain illuminated for all subsequent trips until the DTC has been cleared by service or the lean condition has not been detected and conditions for checking fuel trim have been met for 3 consecutive trips.

! Important

- To complete a trip cycle for the fuel trim diagnostic, the fuel trim diagnostic test must be enabled and run according to the "DTC P0171Will Set When" criteria above. A trip is not considered complete until the fuel trim diagnostic has been run by the PCM.

DTC Chart Test Description: Number(s) below refer to circled number(s) on the diagnostic chart.

1. Visually/physically checking items which may cause a lean condition may determine the cause of the DTC being set.
2. A mass air flow sensor which causes the PCM to read a lower then actual air flow can cause a lean condition and DTC P0171 to be set.

Diagnostic Aids: If the problem cannot be isolated using the diagnostic charts, try monitoring L.T. fuel trim and fuel trim cell while operating the vehicle under various loads. This may isolate the condition which caused DTC P0171 to be set.

A condition that causes DTC P0300 (Misfire Detected) may also set DTC P0171; conversely, an extremely lean condition which sets DTC P0171 can cause a misfire at idle and DTC P0300 to set. If the cause of DTC P0171 cannot be determined and DTC P0300 is also set, refer to DTC P0300 diagnostic chart.

DTC P0171
(Page 1 of 2)
FUEL TRIM LEAN
3800 (VIN L) (SFI)

(1) PRELIMINARY CHECKS - VISUALLY/PHYSICALLY CHECK THE FOLLOWING ITEMS:
- EXHAUST SYSTEM FOR CORROSION, LOOSE OR MISSING HARDWARE.
- HEATED OXYGEN SENSOR IS INSTALLED SECURELY AND THE PIGTAIL HARNESS IS NOT CONTACTING EXHAUST MANIFOLD OR IGNITION WIRES.
- VACUUM HOSES FOR SPLITS, KINKS AND PROPER CONNECTIONS.
- THROTTLE BODY, INTAKE MANIFOLD AND EGR VALVE FOR VACUUM LEAKS.
- IAC; IF A HIGH OR UNSTEADY IDLE IS BEING EXPERIENCED, SCAN IDLE AIR CONTROL WITH THE TECH 1. IF IDLE AIR CONTROL DISPLAYS NEAR 0 COUNTS, USE CHART C-2B, IDLE AIR CONTROL VALVE CHECK.
- CRANKCASE VENTILATION VALVE, SPRING AND O-RING FOR PROPER INSTALLATION. REFER TO SECTION "6E3-C13".
- THROTTLE BODY INLET SCREEN FOR DAMAGE AND /OR FOREIGN OBJECTS.
- FUEL FOR EXCESSIVE WATER, ALCOHOL, OR OTHER CONTAMINANTS.
- PCM AND SENSOR GROUNDS ARE CLEAN, TIGHT AND IN THEIR PROPER LOCATIONS.

DID ANY OF THE ABOVE CHECKS ISOLATE A CONDITION REQUIRING REPAIR?

YES:
- REPAIR ITEMS FOUND IN STEP (1).
- OPERATE VEHICLE IN "CLOSED LOOP" WHILE MONITORING L.T. AND S.T. FUEL TRIM VALUES.
- L.T. FUEL TRIM SHOULD DECREASE BELOW 158. S.T. FUEL TRIM SHOULD DECREASE BELOW 180. DO THEY?

  - **NO:** CONTINUE WITH CHART STEP (2).
  - **YES:** LEAN CONDITION NOT PRESENT. IF A DRIVEABILITY SYMPTOM STILL EXISTS, REFER TO "SYMPTOMS," SECTION "B".

NO:

(2)
- DISCONNECT MASS AIR FLOW (MAF) SENSOR ELECTRICAL CONNECTOR.
- OPERATE VEHICLE IN "CLOSED LOOP" WHILE MONITORING L.T. AND S.T. FUEL TRIM VALUES.
- L.T. FUEL TRIM SHOULD DECREASE BELOW 158. S.T. FUEL TRIM SHOULD DECREASE BELOW 180. DO THEY?

YES: REPLACE MASS AIR FLOW SENSOR.

NO:
- CONNECT FUEL PRESSURE GAGE TO FITTING AT FUEL RAIL.
- IGNITION "OFF" FOR 10 SECONDS. A/C "OFF."
- IGNITION "ON." FUEL PUMP WILL RUN FOR ABOUT 2 SECONDS. IT MAYBE NECESSARY TO CYCLE THE IGNITION "ON" MORE THAN ONCE TO OBTAIN MAXIMUM PRESSURE.
- NOTE FUEL PRESSURE WITH PUMP RUNNING, PRESSURE SHOULD BE 284-325 kPa (41-47 psi). WHEN PUMP STOPS, PRESSURE MAY VARY SLIGHTLY THEN SHOULD HOLD STEADY. IS PRESSURE CORRECT AND DOES IT HOLD?

YES: SEE DTC P0171 (PAGE 2 OF 2).

NO: REFER TO "FUEL SYSTEM PRESSURE TEST," CHART A-7 FOR DIAGNOSIS.

4-21-93
PS 17049

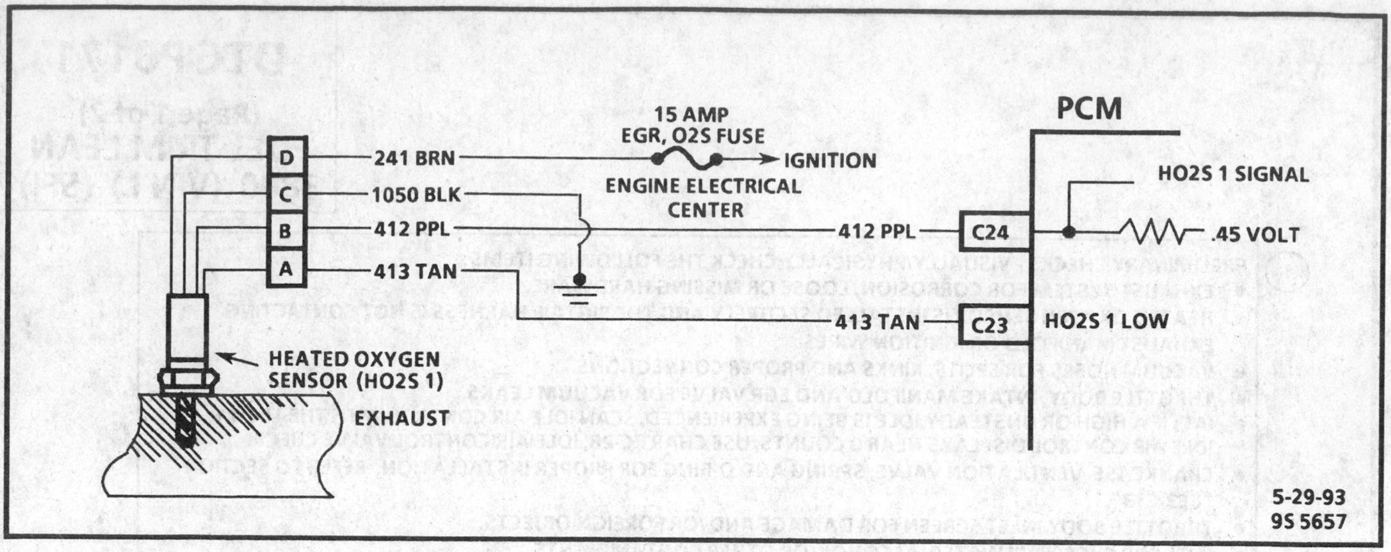

15 AMP
EGR, O2S FUSE
PCM
D
C
B
A
241 BRN
1050 BLK
412 PPL
413 TAN
IGNITION
ENGINE ELECTRICAL
CENTER
HO2S 1 SIGNAL
412 PPL
C24
.45 VOLT
413 TAN
C23
HO2S 1 LOW
HEATED OXYGEN
SENSOR (HO2S 1)
EXHAUST
5-29-93
9S 5657

DTC P0171

(Page 2 of 2)
FUEL TRIM LEAN
3800 (VIN L) (SFI)

Circuit Description:

To provide the best possible combination of driveability, fuel economy, and emission control, a "Closed Loop" air/fuel metering system is used. While in "Closed Loop," the PCM monitors the oxygen sensor signal voltage and adjusts fuel delivery based on signal voltage. A change made to fuel delivery will be indicated by the long and short term fuel trim values which can be monitored with the Tech 1. Ideal fuel trim values are around 128; if the oxygen sensor signal is indicating a lean condition the PCM will add fuel, resulting in fuel trim values above 128. If a rich condition is detected, the fuel trim values will be below 128, indicating that the PCM is reducing the amount of fuel delivered. If an excessively lean condition is detected, the PCM will set DTC P0171.

DTC P0171 Will Set When:

- DTC P0101, P0117, P0118, P0122, P0123, P0134, P0501 or P0502 not set.
- Engine coolant temperature between 80°C (176°F) and 110°C (230°C).
- Steady throttle below 91%.
- Vehicle speed below 70 mph.
- Engine speed between 1000 and 4000 RPM.
- Purge duty cycle below 80%.
- Long term fuel trim above 158.
- Short term fuel trim at 180.
- Above conditions for over 25 seconds.

Action Taken (PCM will default to): When DTC P0171 has initially been set, a software flag indicating an emissions-related fault will be set for 3 trips, after which the flag will clear provided the lean condition is no longer present. However, if conditions for setting DTC P0171 are detected during a trip while the flag is still set, the PCM will illuminate the MIL (Service Engine Soon). The MIL will remain illuminated for all subsequent trips until the DTC has been cleared by service or the lean condition has not been detected and conditions for checking fuel trim have been met for 3 consecutive trips.

[!] Important

- To complete a trip cycle for the fuel trim diagnostic, the fuel trim diagnostic test must be enabled and run according to the "DTC P0171Will Set When" criteria above. A trip is not considered complete until the fuel trim diagnostic has been run by the PCM.

DTC Chart Test Description: Number(s) below refer to circled number(s) on the diagnostic chart.

3. Checks for a fault in the EVAP purge system which may cause DTC P0171 to be set.

Diagnostic Aids: If the problem cannot be isolated using the diagnostic charts, try monitoring L.T. fuel trim and fuel trim cell while operating the vehicle under various loads. This may isolate the condition which caused DTC P0171 to be set.

A condition that causes DTC P0300 (Misfire Detected) may also set DTC P0171; conversely, an extremely lean condition which sets DTC P0171 can cause a misfire at idle and DTC P0300 to set. If the cause of DTC P0171 cannot be determined and DTC P0300 is also set, refer to DTC P0300 diagnostic chart.

DTC P0171
(Page 2 of 2)
FUEL TRIM LEAN
3800 (VIN L) (SFI)

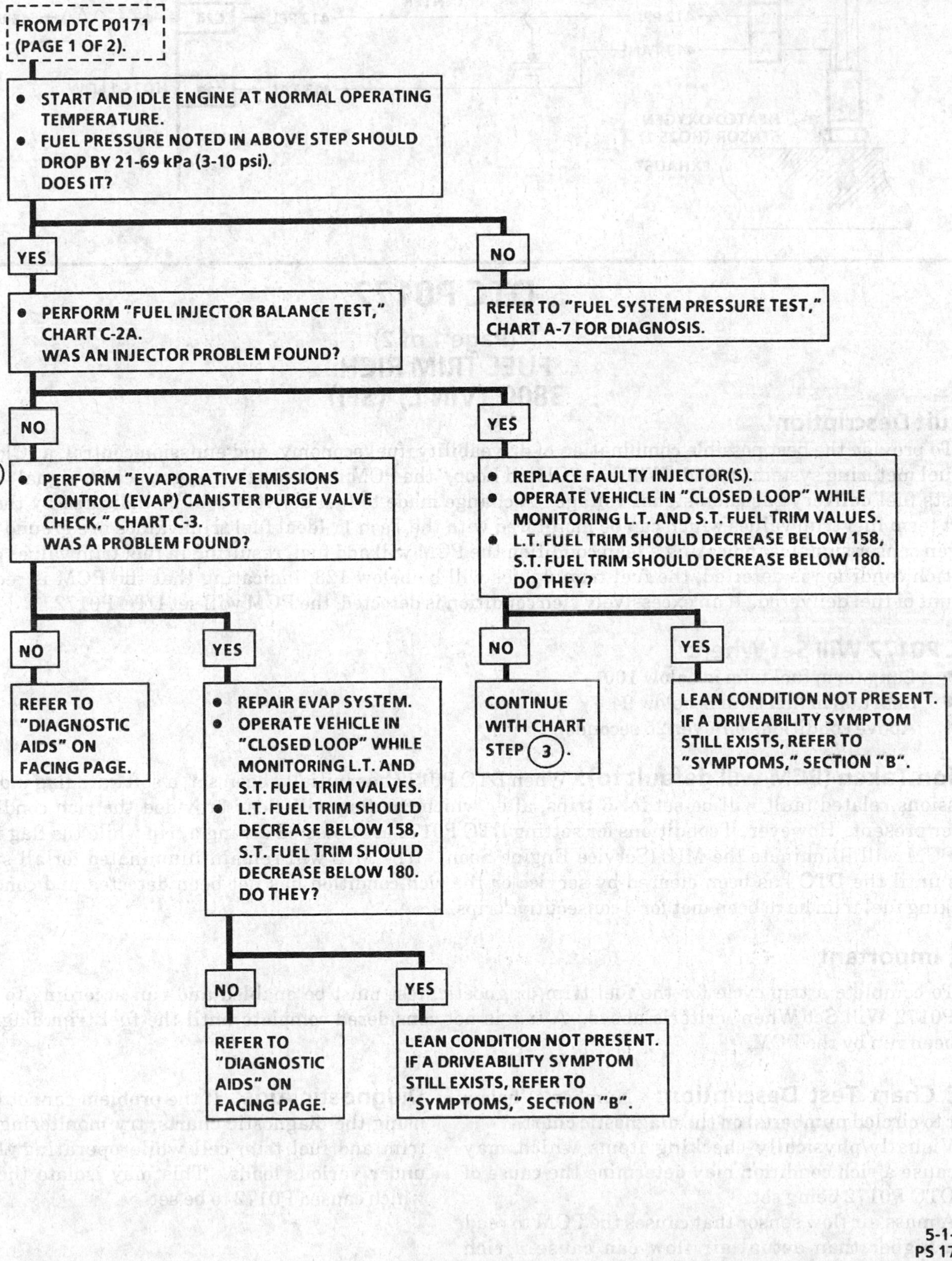
FROM DTC P0171 (PAGE 1 OF 2).
• START AND IDLE ENGINE AT NORMAL OPERATING TEMPERATURE.
• FUEL PRESSURE NOTED IN ABOVE STEP SHOULD DROP BY 21-69 kPa (3-10 psi). DOES IT?
YES
NO
• PERFORM "FUEL INJECTOR BALANCE TEST," CHART C-2A. WAS AN INJECTOR PROBLEM FOUND?
REFER TO "FUEL SYSTEM PRESSURE TEST," CHART A-7 FOR DIAGNOSIS.
NO
YES
3
• PERFORM "EVAPORATIVE EMISSIONS CONTROL (EVAP) CANISTER PURGE VALVE CHECK," CHART C-3. WAS A PROBLEM FOUND?
• REPLACE FAULTY INJECTOR(S).
• OPERATE VEHICLE IN "CLOSED LOOP" WHILE MONITORING L.T. AND S.T. FUEL TRIM VALUES.
• L.T. FUEL TRIM SHOULD DECREASE BELOW 158, S.T. FUEL TRIM SHOULD DECREASE BELOW 180. DO THEY?
NO
YES
NO
YES
REFER TO "DIAGNOSTIC AIDS" ON FACING PAGE.
• REPAIR EVAP SYSTEM.
• OPERATE VEHICLE IN "CLOSED LOOP" WHILE MONITORING L.T. AND S.T. FUEL TRIM VALVES.
• L.T. FUEL TRIM SHOULD DECREASE BELOW 158, S.T. FUEL TRIM SHOULD DECREASE BELOW 180. DO THEY?
CONTINUE WITH CHART STEP 3.
LEAN CONDITION NOT PRESENT. IF A DRIVEABILITY SYMPTOM STILL EXISTS, REFER TO "SYMPTOMS," SECTION "B".
NO
YES
REFER TO "DIAGNOSTIC AIDS" ON FACING PAGE.
LEAN CONDITION NOT PRESENT. IF A DRIVEABILITY SYMPTOM STILL EXISTS, REFER TO "SYMPTOMS," SECTION "B".

5-1-93
PS 17048

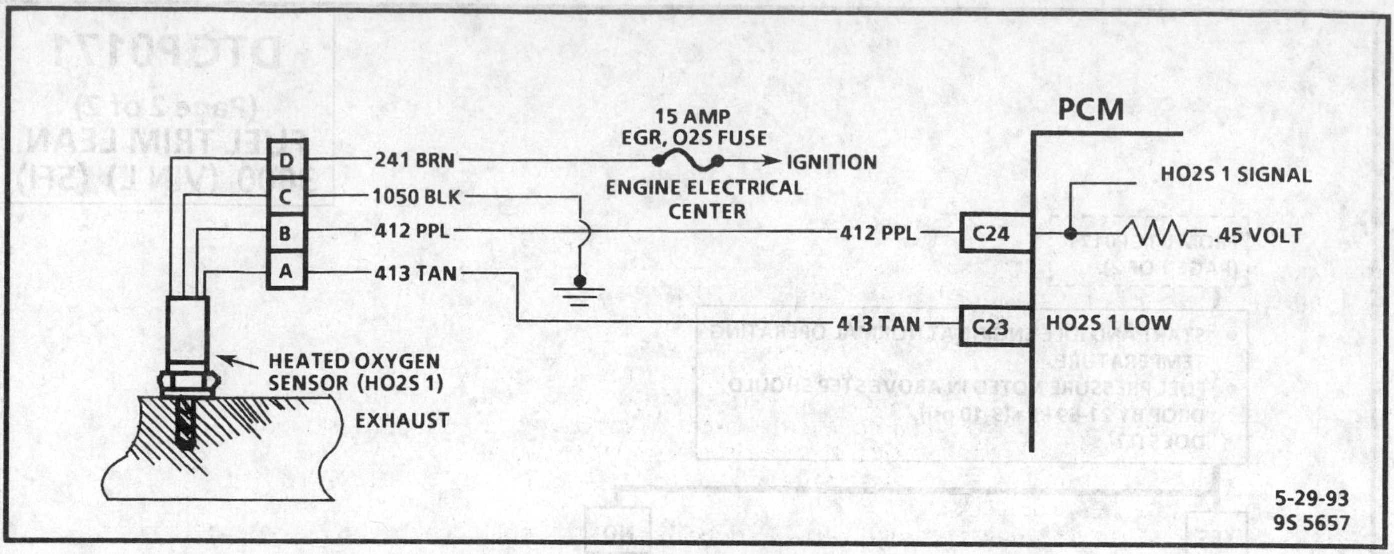
15 AMP
EGR, O2S FUSE
IGNITION
ENGINE ELECTRICAL
CENTER
PCM
D
C
B
A
241 BRN
1050 BLK
412 PPL
413 TAN
412 PPL
413 TAN
C24
C23
HO2S 1 SIGNAL
.45 VOLT
HO2S 1 LOW
HEATED OXYGEN
SENSOR (HO2S 1)
EXHAUST
5-29-93
9S 5657

DTC P0172

(Page 1 of 2)
FUEL TRIM RICH
3800 (VIN L) (SFI)

Circuit Description:

To provide the best possible combination of driveability, fuel economy, and emission control, a "Closed Loop" air/fuel metering system is used. While in "Closed Loop," the PCM monitors the oxygen sensor signal voltage and adjusts fuel delivery based on signal voltage. A change made to fuel delivery will be indicated by the long and short term fuel trim values which can be monitored with the Tech 1. Ideal fuel trim values are around 128; if the oxygen sensor signal is indicating a lean condition the PCM will add fuel, resulting in fuel trim values above 128. If a rich condition is detected, the fuel trim values will be below 128, indicating that the PCM is reducing the amount of fuel delivered. If an excessively rich condition is detected, the PCM will set DTC P0172.

DTC P0172 Will Set When:

- Long term fuel trim is below 100.
- Short term fuel trim is below 94.
- Above conditions for over 25 seconds.

Action Taken (PCM will default to): When DTC P0172 has initially been set, a software flag indicating an emissions-related fault will be set for 3 trips, after which the flag will clear provided the rich condition is no longer present. However, if conditions for setting DTC P0172 are detected during a trip while the flag is still set, the PCM will illuminate the MIL (Service Engine Soon). The MIL will remain illuminated for all subsequent trips until the DTC has been cleared by service or the rich condition has not been detected and conditions for checking fuel trim have been met for 3 consecutive trips.

? Important

- To complete a trip cycle for the fuel trim diagnostic, test must be enabled and run according to the "DTC P0172 Will Set When" criteria above. A trip is not considered complete until the fuel trim diagnostic has been run by the PCM.

DTC Chart Test Description: Number(s) below refer to circled number(s) on the diagnostic chart.

1. Visually/physically checking items which may cause a rich condition may determine the cause of DTC P0172 being set.
2. A mass air flow sensor that causes the PCM to read a higher than actual air flow can cause a rich condition and DTC P0172 to be set.

Diagnostic Aids: If the problem cannot be isolated using the diagnostic charts, try monitoring L. T. fuel trim and fuel trim cell while operating the vehicle under various loads. This may isolate the condition which caused P0172 to be set.

DTC P0172

(Page 1 of 2)

FUEL TRIM RICH
3800 (VIN L) (SFI)

1. PRELIMINARY CHECKS - VISUALLY/PHYSICALLY CHECK THE FOLLOWING:
   - AIR INTAKE DUCT FOR BEING COLLAPSED OR RESTRICTED; AIR FILTER FOR BEING PLUGGED.
   - THROTTLE BODY, CHECK FOR DAMAGE TO THE INLET SCREEN OR FOR FOREIGN OBJECTS PARTIALLY BLOCKING THE INLET SCREEN. REPAIR OR REPLACE THROTTLE BODY AS NECESSARY.
   - IAC; IF A LOW OR UNSTEADY IDLE IS BEING EXPERIENCED, SCAN IDLE AIR CONTROL WITH THE TECH 1. IF IDLE AIR CONTROL DISPLAYS OVER 100 COUNTS, USE CHART C-2B, IDLE AIR CONTROL VALVE CHECK. ALSO, CHECK FOR THROTTLE BODY COKING OR OBJECTS BLOCKING THE IAC PASSAGES.
   - FUEL PRESSURE REGULATOR. CHECK REGULATOR VACUUM HOSE FOR FUEL; IF FUEL IS PRESENT IN HOSE, REPLACE FUEL PRESSURE REGULATOR.
   - THROTTLE POSITION SENSOR. CHECK FOR LOOSE OR MISSING MOUNTING BOLTS. ALSO, MONITOR "THROT POSITION" WITH TECH 1 WHILE SLOWLY OPENING THROTTLE - "THROT POSITION" SHOULD INCREASE STEADILY AND EVENLY FROM CLOSED THROTTLE TP VOLTAGE (.2 - .74 VOLT) TO OVER 4 VOLTS. IF NOT, REPLACE TP SENSOR.

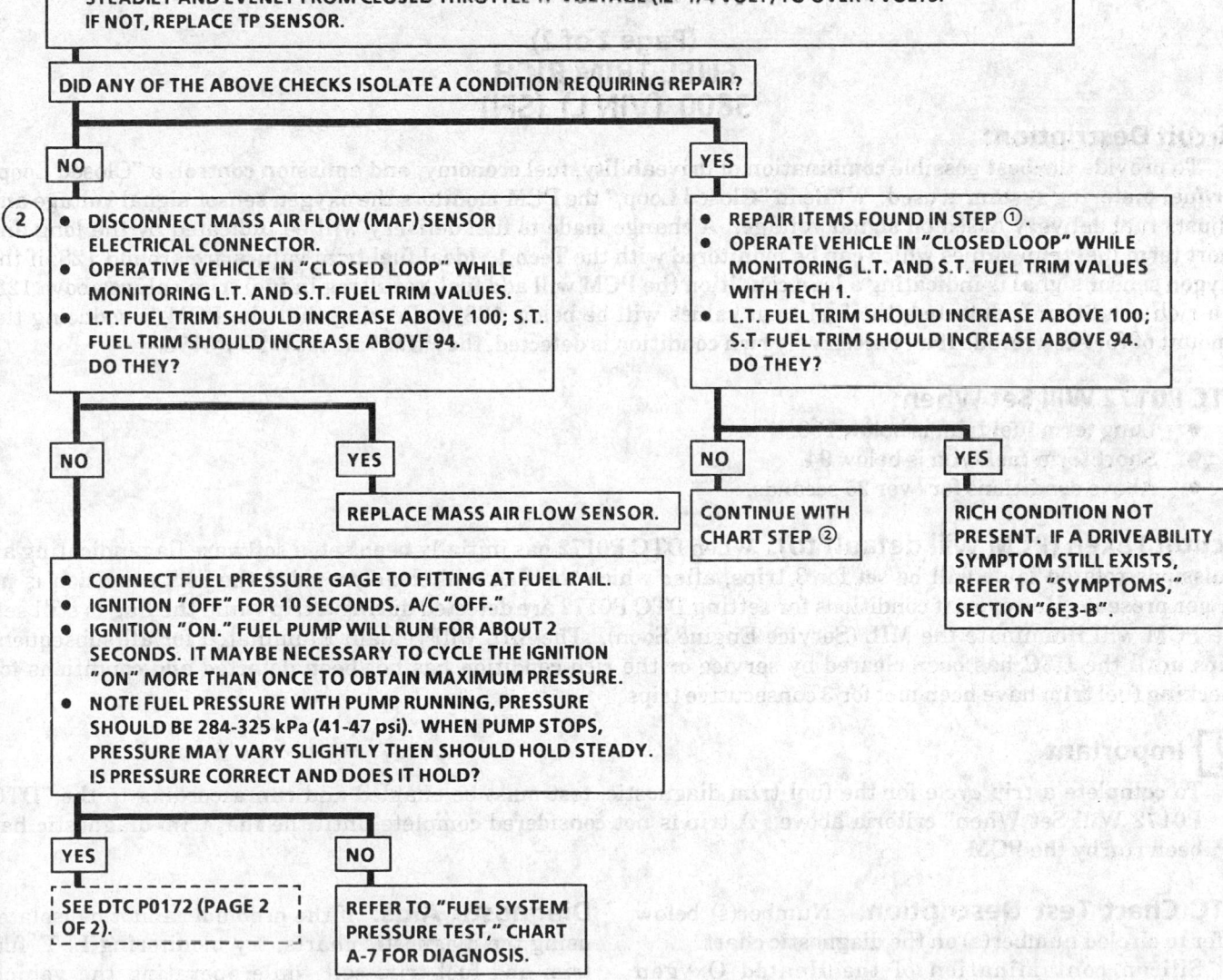

DID ANY OF THE ABOVE CHECKS ISOLATE A CONDITION REQUIRING REPAIR?

NO

2.
   - DISCONNECT MASS AIR FLOW (MAF) SENSOR ELECTRICAL CONNECTOR.
   - OPERATIVE VEHICLE IN "CLOSED LOOP" WHILE MONITORING L.T. AND S.T. FUEL TRIM VALUES.
   - L.T. FUEL TRIM SHOULD INCREASE ABOVE 100; S.T. FUEL TRIM SHOULD INCREASE ABOVE 94. DO THEY?

- **NO**
  - CONNECT FUEL PRESSURE GAGE TO FITTING AT FUEL RAIL.
  - IGNITION "OFF" FOR 10 SECONDS. A/C "OFF."
  - IGNITION "ON." FUEL PUMP WILL RUN FOR ABOUT 2 SECONDS. IT MAYBE NECESSARY TO CYCLE THE IGNITION "ON" MORE THAN ONCE TO OBTAIN MAXIMUM PRESSURE.
  - NOTE FUEL PRESSURE WITH PUMP RUNNING, PRESSURE SHOULD BE 284-325 kPa (41-47 psi). WHEN PUMP STOPS, PRESSURE MAY VARY SLIGHTLY THEN SHOULD HOLD STEADY. IS PRESSURE CORRECT AND DOES IT HOLD?
    - **YES**: SEE DTC P0172 (PAGE 2 OF 2).
    - **NO**: REFER TO "FUEL SYSTEM PRESSURE TEST," CHART A-7 FOR DIAGNOSIS.
- **YES**: REPLACE MASS AIR FLOW SENSOR.

YES

- REPAIR ITEMS FOUND IN STEP ①.
- OPERATE VEHICLE IN "CLOSED LOOP" WHILE MONITORING L.T. AND S.T. FUEL TRIM VALUES WITH TECH 1.
- L.T. FUEL TRIM SHOULD INCREASE ABOVE 100; S.T. FUEL TRIM SHOULD INCREASE ABOVE 94. DO THEY?
  - **NO**: CONTINUE WITH CHART STEP ②
  - **YES**: RICH CONDITION NOT PRESENT. IF A DRIVEABILITY SYMPTOM STILL EXISTS, REFER TO "SYMPTOMS," SECTION "6E3-B".

4-29-93
PS 17047

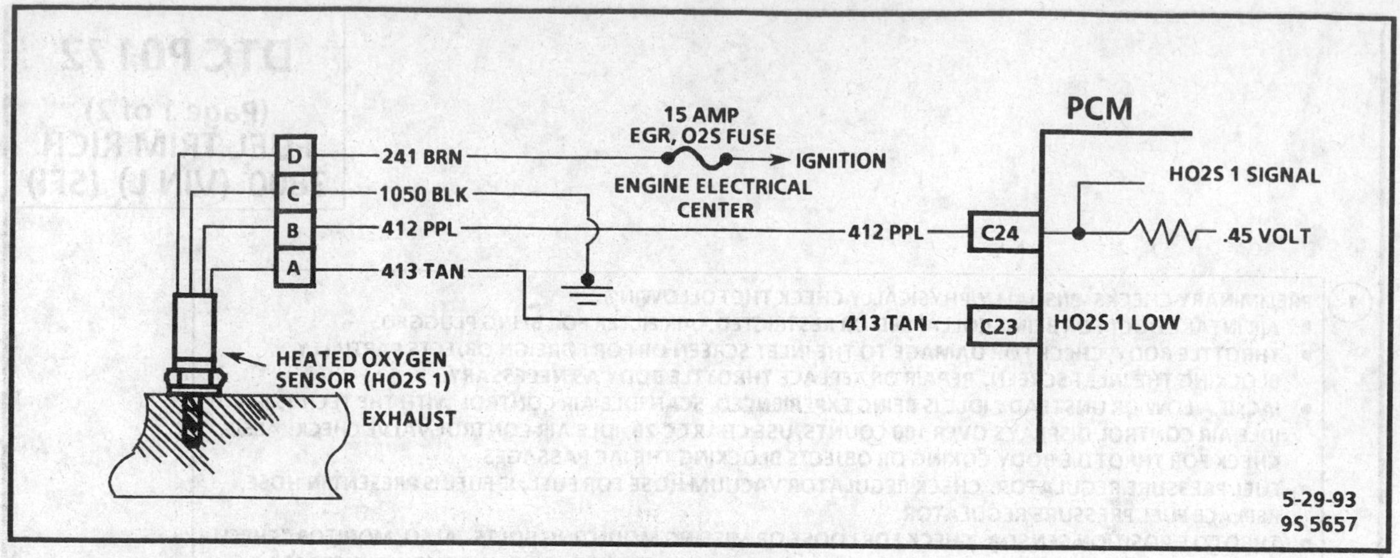
15 AMP
EGR, O2S FUSE
IGNITION
ENGINE ELECTRICAL
CENTER
PCM
HO2S 1 SIGNAL
D
C
B
A
241 BRN
1050 BLK
412 PPL
413 TAN
412 PPL
C24
.45 VOLT
413 TAN
C23
HO2S 1 LOW
HEATED OXYGEN
SENSOR (HO2S 1)
EXHAUST
5-29-93
9S 5657

DTC P0172

(Page 2 of 2)
FUEL TRIM RICH
3800 (VIN L) (SFI)

Circuit Description:

To provide the best possible combination of driveability, fuel economy, and emission control, a "Closed Loop" air/fuel metering system is used. While in "Closed Loop," the PCM monitors the oxygen sensor signal voltage and adjusts fuel delivery based on signal voltage. A change made to fuel delivery will be indicated by the long and short term fuel trim values which can be monitored with the Tech 1. Ideal fuel trim values are around 128; if the oxygen sensor signal is indicating a lean condition the PCM will add fuel, resulting in fuel trim values above 128. If a rich condition is detected, the fuel trim values will be below 128, indicating that the PCM is reducing the amount of fuel delivered. If an excessively rich condition is detected, the PCM will set DTC P0172.

DTC P0172 Will Set When:

- Long term fuel trim is below 100.
- Short term fuel trim is below 94.
- Above conditions for over 25 seconds.

Action Taken (PCM will default to): When DTC P0172 has initially been set, a software flag indicating an emissions-related fault will be set for 3 trips, after which the flag will clear provided the rich condition is no longer present. However, if conditions for setting DTC P0172 are detected during a trip while the flag is still set, the PCM will illuminate the MIL (Service Engine Soon). The MIL will remain illuminated for all subsequent trips until the DTC has been cleared by service or the rich condition has not been detected and conditions for checking fuel trim have been met for 3 consecutive trips.

Important

- To complete a trip cycle for the fuel trim diagnostic, test must be enabled and run according to the "DTC P0172 Will Set When" criteria above. A trip is not considered complete until the fuel trim diagnostic has been run by the PCM.

DTC Chart Test Description: Number(s) below refer to circled number(s) on the diagnostic chart.

3. Silicon contamination of the Heated Oxygen Sensor (HO2S 1) can cause a false rich indication to be seen by the PCM. The PCM will then reduce the amount of fuel delivered, possibly causing severe driveability symptoms.

Diagnostic Aids: If the problem cannot be isolated using the diagnostic charts, try monitoring L. T. fuel trim and fuel trim cell while operating the vehicle under various loads. This may isolate the condition which caused P0172 to be set.

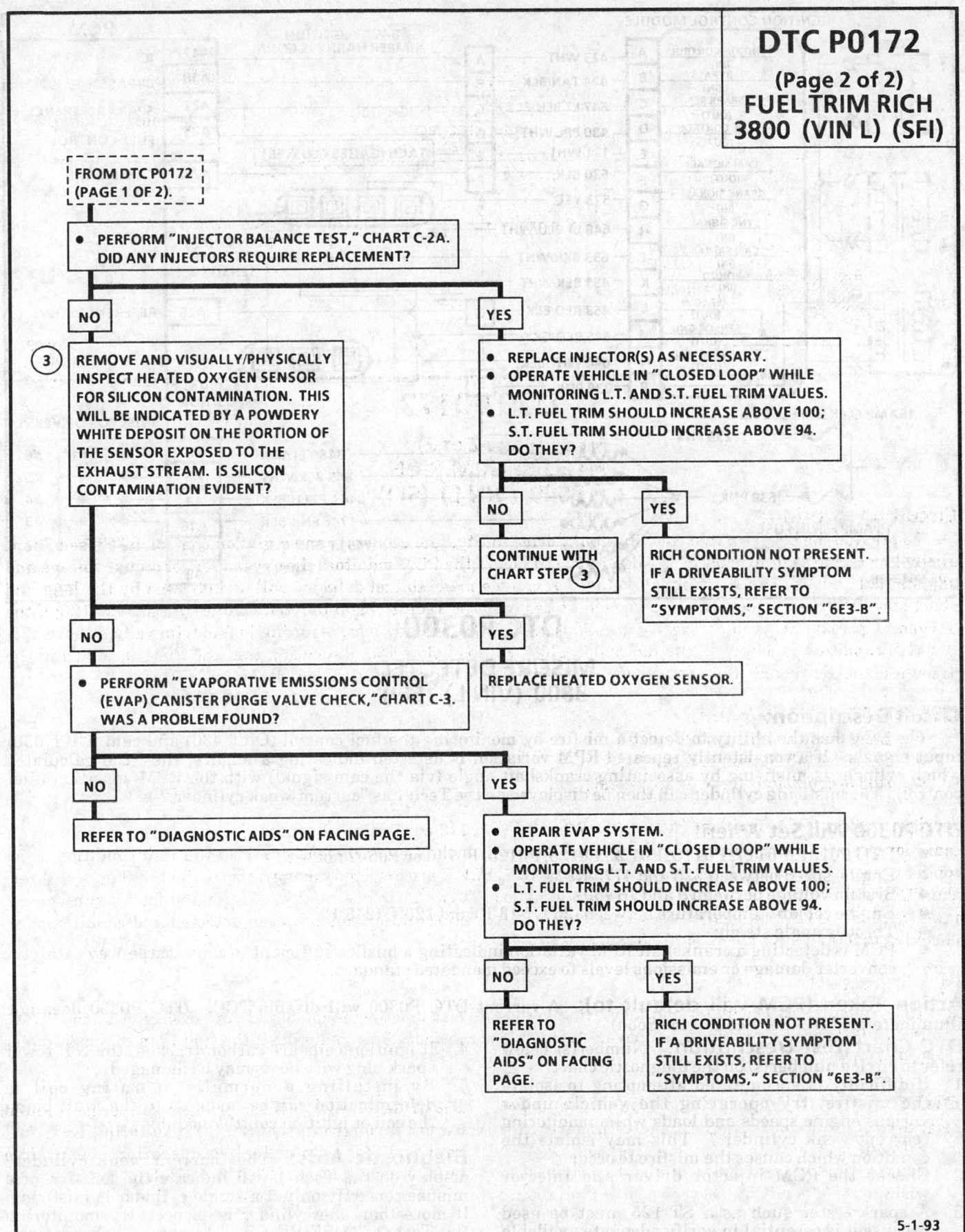

DTC P0172

(Page 2 of 2)
FUEL TRIM RICH
3800 (VIN L) (SFI)

FROM DTC P0172 (PAGE 1 OF 2).

- PERFORM "INJECTOR BALANCE TEST," CHART C-2A. DID ANY INJECTORS REQUIRE REPLACEMENT?

NO

(3) REMOVE AND VISUALLY/PHYSICALLY INSPECT HEATED OXYGEN SENSOR FOR SILICON CONTAMINATION. THIS WILL BE INDICATED BY A POWDERY WHITE DEPOSIT ON THE PORTION OF THE SENSOR EXPOSED TO THE EXHAUST STREAM. IS SILICON CONTAMINATION EVIDENT?

- **NO**
  - PERFORM "EVAPORATIVE EMISSIONS CONTROL (EVAP) CANISTER PURGE VALVE CHECK," CHART C-3. WAS A PROBLEM FOUND?
    - **NO**
      - REFER TO "DIAGNOSTIC AIDS" ON FACING PAGE.
    - **YES**
      - REPAIR EVAP SYSTEM.
      - OPERATE VEHICLE IN "CLOSED LOOP" WHILE MONITORING L.T. AND S.T. FUEL TRIM VALUES.
      - L.T. FUEL TRIM SHOULD INCREASE ABOVE 100; S.T. FUEL TRIM SHOULD INCREASE ABOVE 94. DO THEY?
        - **NO**
          - REFER TO "DIAGNOSTIC AIDS" ON FACING PAGE.
        - **YES**
          - RICH CONDITION NOT PRESENT. IF A DRIVEABILITY SYMPTOM STILL EXISTS, REFER TO "SYMPTOMS," SECTION "6E3-B".
- **YES**
  - REPLACE HEATED OXYGEN SENSOR.

YES

- REPLACE INJECTOR(S) AS NECESSARY.
- OPERATE VEHICLE IN "CLOSED LOOP" WHILE MONITORING L.T. AND S.T. FUEL TRIM VALUES.
- L.T. FUEL TRIM SHOULD INCREASE ABOVE 100; S.T. FUEL TRIM SHOULD INCREASE ABOVE 94. DO THEY?
  - **NO**
    - CONTINUE WITH CHART STEP (3)
  - **YES**
    - RICH CONDITION NOT PRESENT. IF A DRIVEABILITY SYMPTOM STILL EXISTS, REFER TO "SYMPTOMS," SECTION "6E3-B".

5-1-93
PS 17046

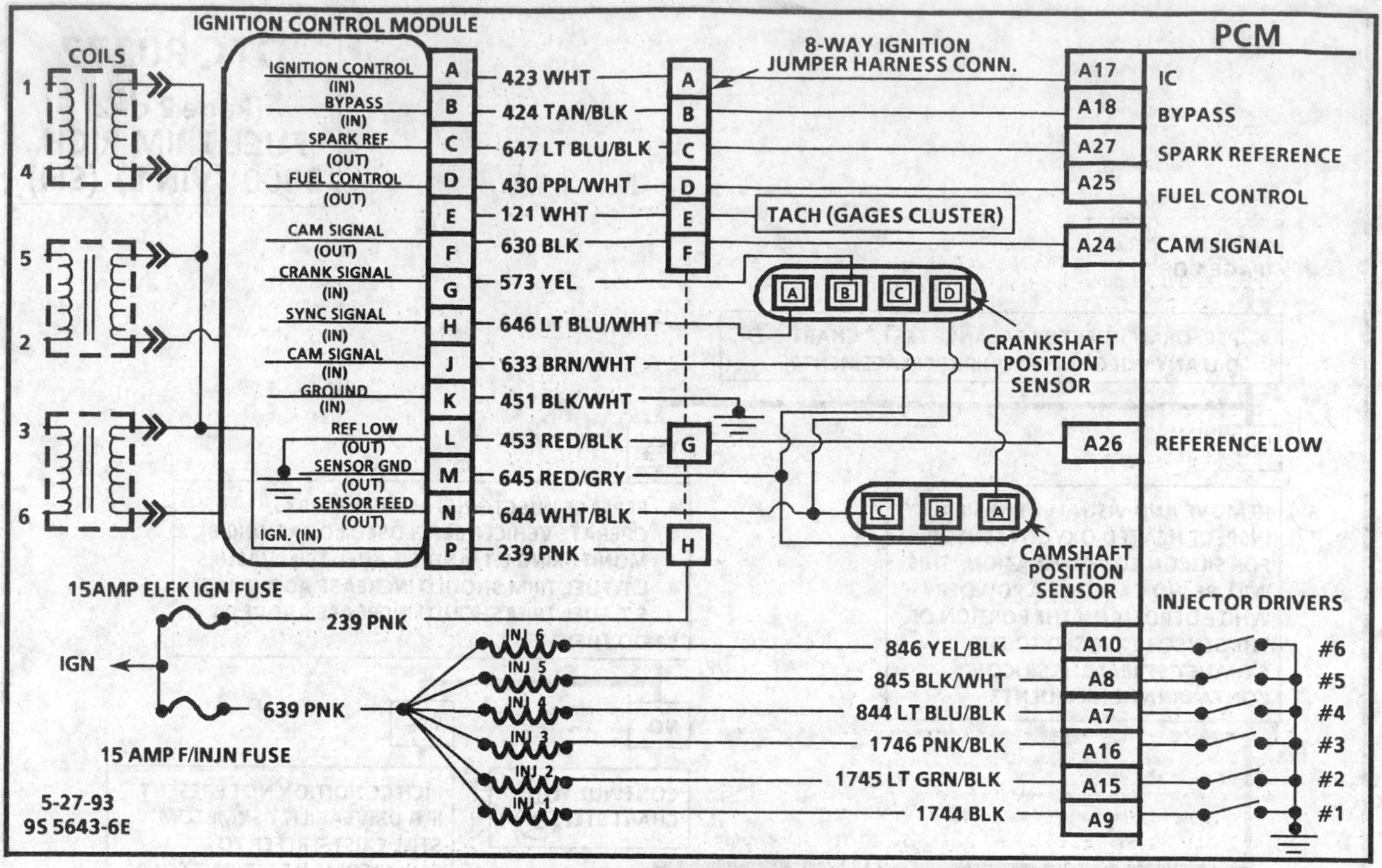
IGNITION CONTROL MODULE
PCM
COILS
1
4
5
2
3
6
IGNITION CONTROL (IN)
BYPASS (IN)
SPARK REF (OUT)
FUEL CONTROL (OUT)
CAM SIGNAL (OUT)
CRANK SIGNAL (IN)
SYNC SIGNAL (IN)
CAM SIGNAL (IN)
GROUND (IN)
REF LOW (OUT)
SENSOR GND (OUT)
SENSOR FEED (OUT)
IGN. (IN)
A
B
C
D
E
F
G
H
J
K
L
M
N
P
423 WHT
424 TAN/BLK
647 LT BLU/BLK
430 PPL/WHT
121 WHT
630 BLK
573 YEL
646 LT BLU/WHT
633 BRN/WHT
451 BLK/WHT
453 RED/BLK
645 RED/GRY
644 WHT/BLK
239 PNK
8-WAY IGNITION JUMPER HARNESS CONN.
TACH (GAGES CLUSTER)
A17
A18
A27
A25
A24
A26
IC
BYPASS
SPARK REFERENCE
FUEL CONTROL
CAM SIGNAL
REFERENCE LOW
CRANKSHAFT POSITION SENSOR
CAMSHAFT POSITION SENSOR
15AMP ELEK IGN FUSE
239 PNK
IGN
639 PNK
15 AMP F/INJN FUSE
INJ 6
INJ 5
INJ 4
INJ 3
INJ 2
INJ 1
846 YEL/BLK
845 BLK/WHT
844 LT BLU/BLK
1746 PNK/BLK
1745 LT GRN/BLK
1744 BLK
A10
A8
A7
A16
A15
A9
INJECTOR DRIVERS
#6
#5
#4
#3
#2
#1
5-27-93
9S 5643-6E

DTC P0300

MISFIRE DETECTED
3800 (VIN L) (SFI)

Circuit Description:

The PCM has the ability to detect a misfire by monitoring the fuel control (CKT 430) and cam (CKT 630) input signals. If a consistently repeated RPM variation is detected indicating a misfire, the PCM calculates which cylinder is misfiring by associating crankshaft angle (via the cam signal) with the RPM variation (fuel control). The misfiring cylinder can then be displayed on the Tech 1 as "current weak cylinder."

DTC P0300 Will Set When:

- DTC P0101, P0117, P0118, P0122, P0123, P0125, P0740 or P0502 not set.
- Engine speed between 525 and 4775 RPM.
- System voltage between 9 and 16 volts.
- Engine coolant temperature between -25°C (-13°F) and 120°C (248°F).
- Throttle angle steady.
- PCM is detecting a crankshaft RPM variation indicating a misfire sufficient to cause three-way catalytic converter damage or emissions levels to exceed mandated standard.

Action Taken (PCM will default to): A current DTC P0300 will disable TCC. DTC P0300 does not illuminate the MIL (Service Engine Soon).

DTC Chart Test Description: Number(s) below refer to circled number(s) on the diagnostic chart.

1. If difficulty is encountered attempting to isolate the misfire, try operating the vehicle under various engine speeds and loads while monitoring "current weak cylinder." This may isolate the condition which causes the misfire to occur.
2. Checks the PCM injector driver and injector wiring.
3. A spark tester such as a ST-125 must be used because it is essential to verify adequate available secondary voltage at the spark plug (25,000 volts). Spark should jump the tester gap on all 6 leads. This simulates a "load" condition.
4. If ignition coils are carbon tracked, the coil tower spark plug wire boots may be damaged.
5. By installing a normally operating coil, a determination can be made as to the fault being the coil or ignition control module.

Diagnostic Aids: The "current weak cylinder" display on the Tech 1 will indicate the location of a misfire correctly only if a single cylinder is misfiring. If more than one cylinder is suspect, try monitoring the Tech 1 "MISFIRE CYL" screen. Then continue with diagnostic chart Step 2, diagnosing cylinders which were displayed as misfiring.

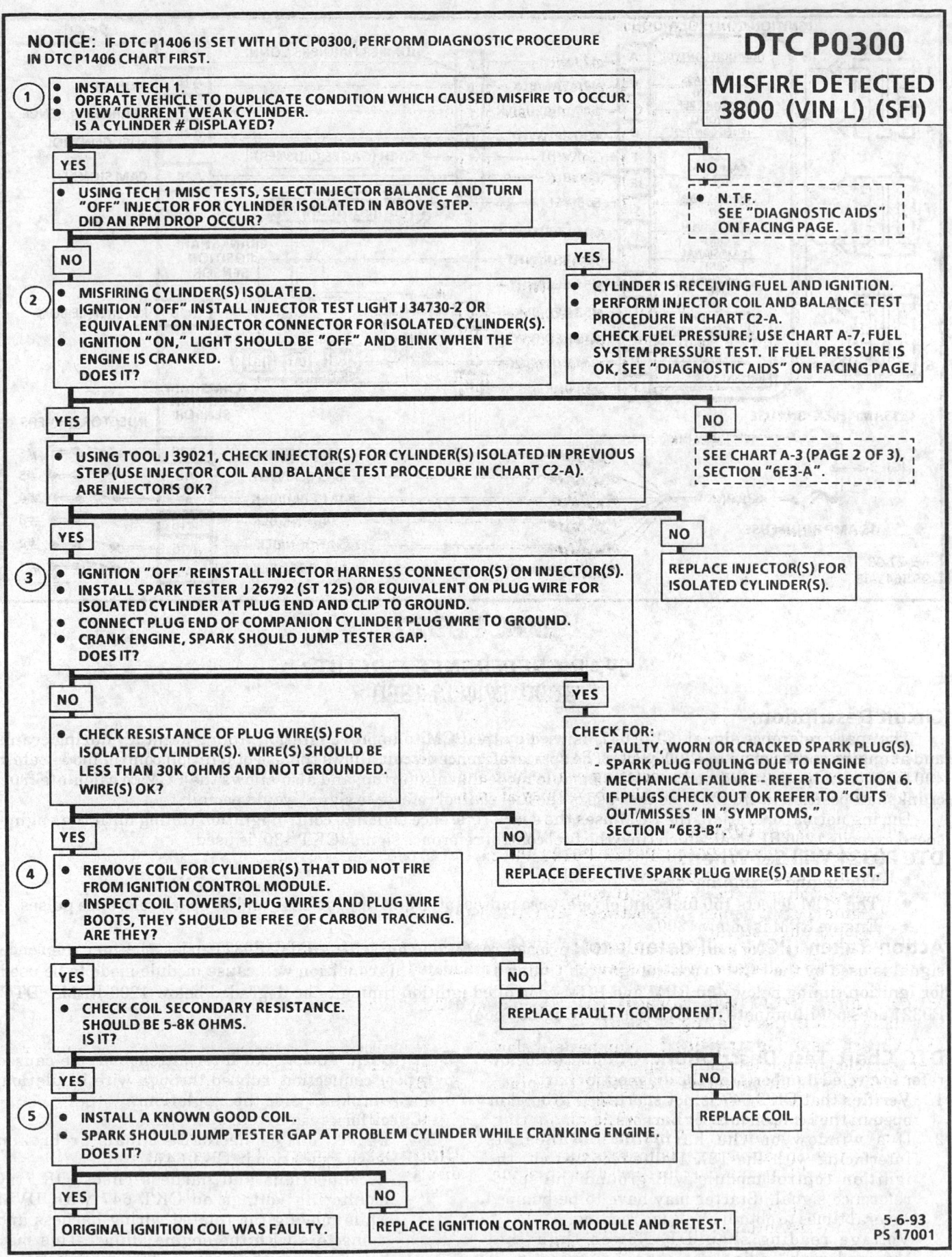

DTC P0300

MISFIRE DETECTED 3800 (VIN L) (SFI)

NOTICE: IF DTC P1406 IS SET WITH DTC P0300, PERFORM DIAGNOSTIC PROCEDURE IN DTC P1406 CHART FIRST.

(1)
- INSTALL TECH 1.
- OPERATE VEHICLE TO DUPLICATE CONDITION WHICH CAUSED MISFIRE TO OCCUR.
- VIEW "CURRENT WEAK CYLINDER.
  IS A CYLINDER # DISPLAYED?

YES
- USING TECH 1 MISC TESTS, SELECT INJECTOR BALANCE AND TURN "OFF" INJECTOR FOR CYLINDER ISOLATED IN ABOVE STEP.
  DID AN RPM DROP OCCUR?

NO
- N.T.F.
  SEE "DIAGNOSTIC AIDS" ON FACING PAGE.

(RPM DROP) NO

(2)
- MISFIRING CYLINDER(S) ISOLATED.
- IGNITION "OFF" INSTALL INJECTOR TEST LIGHT J 34730-2 OR EQUIVALENT ON INJECTOR CONNECTOR FOR ISOLATED CYLINDER(S).
- IGNITION "ON," LIGHT SHOULD BE "OFF" AND BLINK WHEN THE ENGINE IS CRANKED.
  DOES IT?

(RPM DROP) YES
- CYLINDER IS RECEIVING FUEL AND IGNITION.
- PERFORM INJECTOR COIL AND BALANCE TEST PROCEDURE IN CHART C2-A.
- CHECK FUEL PRESSURE; USE CHART A-7, FUEL SYSTEM PRESSURE TEST. IF FUEL PRESSURE IS OK, SEE "DIAGNOSTIC AIDS" ON FACING PAGE.

YES
- USING TOOL J 39021, CHECK INJECTOR(S) FOR CYLINDER(S) ISOLATED IN PREVIOUS STEP (USE INJECTOR COIL AND BALANCE TEST PROCEDURE IN CHART C2-A).
  ARE INJECTORS OK?

NO
SEE CHART A-3 (PAGE 2 OF 3), SECTION "6E3-A".

(INJECTORS OK) YES

(3)
- IGNITION "OFF" REINSTALL INJECTOR HARNESS CONNECTOR(S) ON INJECTOR(S).
- INSTALL SPARK TESTER J 26792 (ST 125) OR EQUIVALENT ON PLUG WIRE FOR ISOLATED CYLINDER AT PLUG END AND CLIP TO GROUND.
- CONNECT PLUG END OF COMPANION CYLINDER PLUG WIRE TO GROUND.
- CRANK ENGINE, SPARK SHOULD JUMP TESTER GAP.
  DOES IT?

(INJECTORS OK) NO
REPLACE INJECTOR(S) FOR ISOLATED CYLINDER(S).

(SPARK) NO
- CHECK RESISTANCE OF PLUG WIRE(S) FOR ISOLATED CYLINDER(S). WIRE(S) SHOULD BE LESS THAN 30K OHMS AND NOT GROUNDED.
  WIRE(S) OK?

(SPARK) YES
CHECK FOR:
- FAULTY, WORN OR CRACKED SPARK PLUG(S).
- SPARK PLUG FOULING DUE TO ENGINE MECHANICAL FAILURE - REFER TO SECTION 6.
  IF PLUGS CHECK OUT OK REFER TO "CUTS OUT/MISSES" IN "SYMPTOMS," SECTION "6E3-B".

(WIRES OK) YES

(4)
- REMOVE COIL FOR CYLINDER(S) THAT DID NOT FIRE FROM IGNITION CONTROL MODULE.
- INSPECT COIL TOWERS, PLUG WIRES AND PLUG WIRE BOOTS, THEY SHOULD BE FREE OF CARBON TRACKING.
  ARE THEY?

(WIRES OK) NO
REPLACE DEFECTIVE SPARK PLUG WIRE(S) AND RETEST.

YES
- CHECK COIL SECONDARY RESISTANCE.
  SHOULD BE 5-8K OHMS.
  IS IT?

NO
REPLACE FAULTY COMPONENT.

(RESISTANCE) YES

(5)
- INSTALL A KNOWN GOOD COIL.
- SPARK SHOULD JUMP TESTER GAP AT PROBLEM CYLINDER WHILE CRANKING ENGINE.
  DOES IT?

(RESISTANCE) NO
REPLACE COIL

YES
ORIGINAL IGNITION COIL WAS FAULTY.

NO
REPLACE IGNITION CONTROL MODULE AND RETEST.

5-6-93
PS 17001

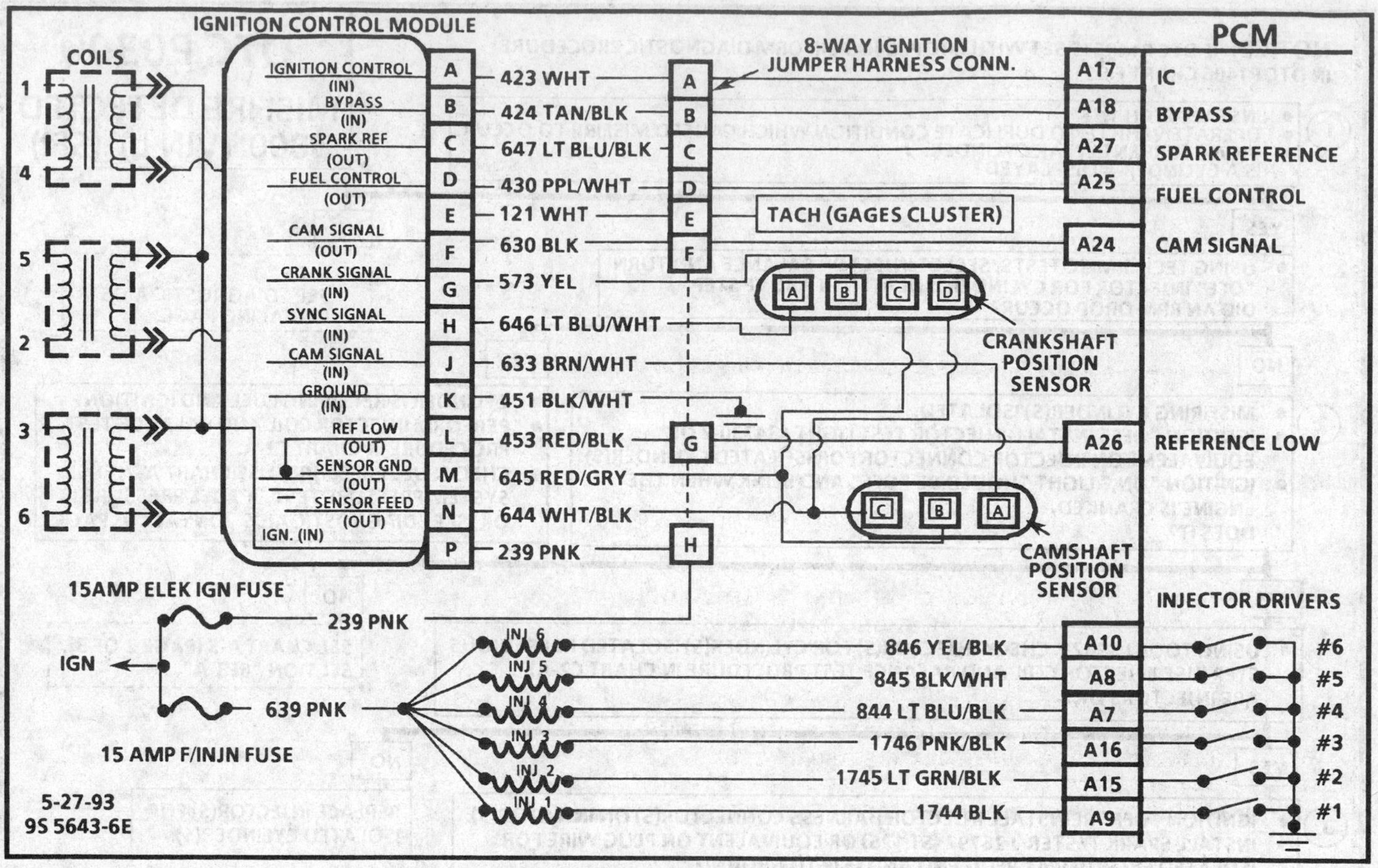
IGNITION CONTROL MODULE
COILS
PCM
8-WAY IGNITION JUMPER HARNESS CONN.
IGNITION CONTROL (IN)
BYPASS (IN)
SPARK REF (OUT)
FUEL CONTROL (OUT)
CAM SIGNAL (OUT)
CRANK SIGNAL (IN)
SYNC SIGNAL (IN)
CAM SIGNAL (IN)
GROUND (IN)
REF LOW (OUT)
SENSOR GND (OUT)
SENSOR FEED (OUT)
IGN. (IN)
423 WHT
424 TAN/BLK
647 LT BLU/BLK
430 PPL/WHT
121 WHT
630 BLK
573 YEL
646 LT BLU/WHT
633 BRN/WHT
451 BLK/WHT
453 RED/BLK
645 RED/GRY
644 WHT/BLK
239 PNK
TACH (GAGES CLUSTER)
A17 IC
A18 BYPASS
A27 SPARK REFERENCE
A25 FUEL CONTROL
A24 CAM SIGNAL
A26 REFERENCE LOW
CRANKSHAFT POSITION SENSOR
CAMSHAFT POSITION SENSOR
INJECTOR DRIVERS
15AMP ELEK IGN FUSE
IGN
15 AMP F/INJN FUSE
639 PNK
INJ 6
INJ 5
INJ 4
INJ 3
INJ 2
INJ 1
846 YEL/BLK
845 BLK/WHT
844 LT BLU/BLK
1746 PNK/BLK
1745 LT GRN/BLK
1744 BLK
A10
A8
A7
A16
A15
A9
#6
#5
#4
#3
#2
#1
5-27-93
9S 5643-6E

DTC P0321

SPARK REFERENCE CIRCUIT 3800 (VIN L) (SFI)

Circuit Description:

The spark reference signal (CKT 647) is used by the PCM to improve ignition timing accuracy during crank and at engine speeds of up to 1200 RPM. The spark reference circuit allows the use of ignition control mode below 400 RPM, eliminating the need to utilize module mode during startup, and also allows the PCM to calculate true crankshaft position in 1/6 the time that use of the fuel control reference signal would permit.

During normal operation, the PCM uses the spark reference signal to control ignition timing until the engine speed exceeds 1200 RPM, at which time the fuel control reference signal (CKT 430) is used.

DTC P0321 Will Set When:

- The engine is running.
- The PCM detects 150 fuel control reference pulses (50 crank revolutions), and no spark reference pulses.
- Engine RPM is below 1200.

Action Taken (PCM will default to): When conditions for setting DTC P0321 exist, the fuel reference signal is used by the PCM to control ignition timing advance. This condition will cause module mode to be used for ignition timing below 400 RPM and PCM-controlled ignition timing to be degraded below 1200 RPM. DTC P0321 does not illuminate the MIL (Service Engine Soon).

DTC Chart Test Description: Number(s) below refer to circled number(s) on the diagnostic chart.

1. Verifies that CKT 647 is not shorted to ground or open in the ignition jumper harness.
2. If a window on the harmonic balancer is interfacing with the 18X Hall-effect switch, the ignition control module will ground the spark reference signal. Starter may have to be bumped several times to obtain a voltage reading.
3. Voltage reading should be lower than that obtained with engine not running indicating a pulsed reference signal.

Diagnostic Aids: An intermittent may be caused by a poor connection, rubbed through wire insulation, or a wire broken inside the insulation.

Check for:

- Backed out connector terminals or broken down insulation in CKT 647.
- If connections and harness check OK, try monitoring voltage on CKT 647 with DVM while moving the related wiring harness and connectors with the engine idling. This may help to isolate the location of the malfunction.

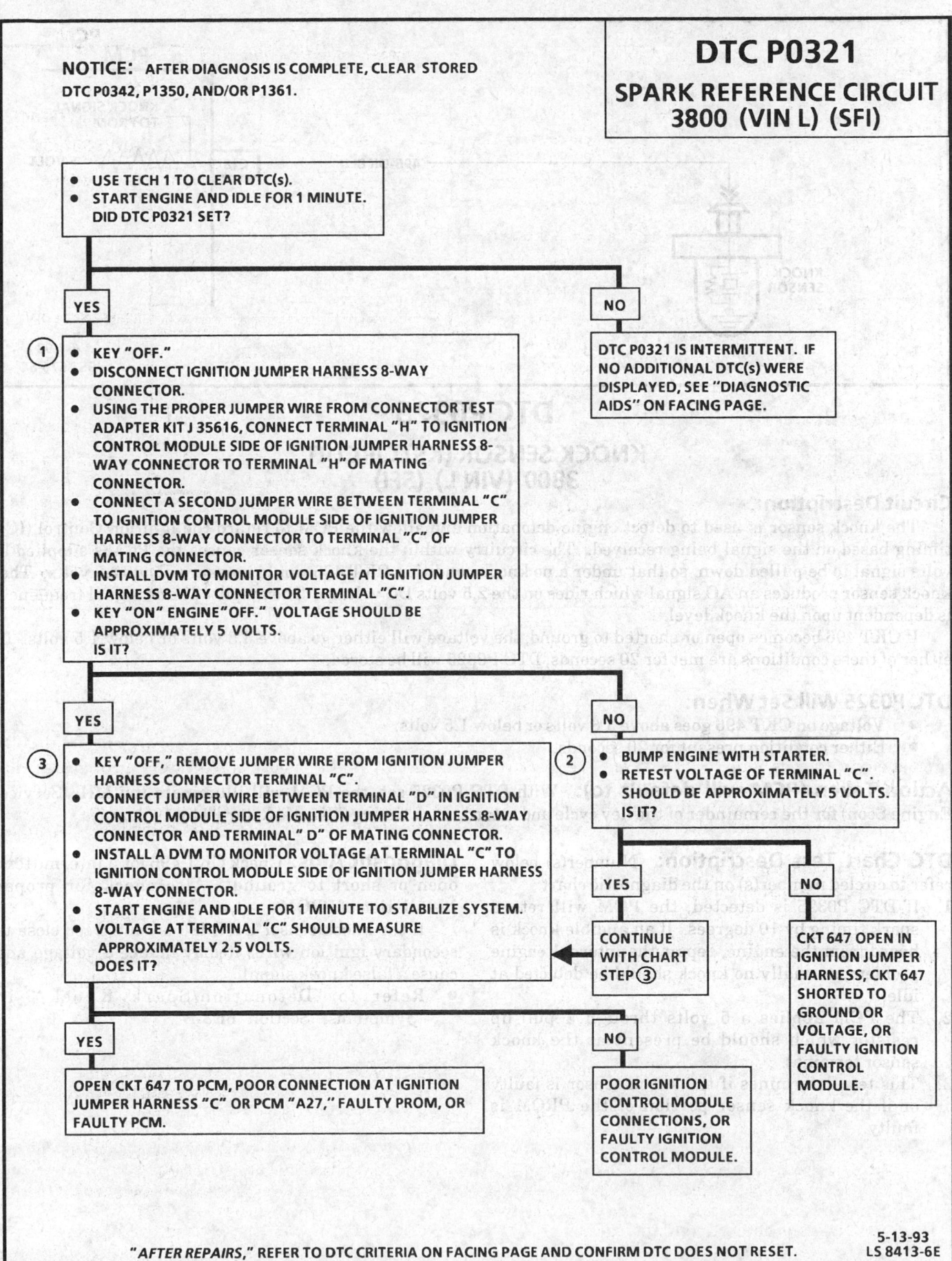

DTC P0321

SPARK REFERENCE CIRCUIT 3800 (VIN L) (SFI)

NOTICE: AFTER DIAGNOSIS IS COMPLETE, CLEAR STORED DTC P0342, P1350, AND/OR P1361.

- USE TECH 1 TO CLEAR DTC(s).
- START ENGINE AND IDLE FOR 1 MINUTE.

DID DTC P0321 SET?

NO: DTC P0321 IS INTERMITTENT. IF NO ADDITIONAL DTC(s) WERE DISPLAYED, SEE "DIAGNOSTIC AIDS" ON FACING PAGE.

YES:

(1)
- KEY "OFF."
- DISCONNECT IGNITION JUMPER HARNESS 8-WAY CONNECTOR.
- USING THE PROPER JUMPER WIRE FROM CONNECTOR TEST ADAPTER KIT J 35616, CONNECT TERMINAL "H" TO IGNITION CONTROL MODULE SIDE OF IGNITION JUMPER HARNESS 8-WAY CONNECTOR TO TERMINAL "H" OF MATING CONNECTOR.
- CONNECT A SECOND JUMPER WIRE BETWEEN TERMINAL "C" TO IGNITION CONTROL MODULE SIDE OF IGNITION JUMPER HARNESS 8-WAY CONNECTOR TO TERMINAL "C" OF MATING CONNECTOR.
- INSTALL DVM TO MONITOR VOLTAGE AT IGNITION JUMPER HARNESS 8-WAY CONNECTOR TERMINAL "C".
- KEY "ON" ENGINE "OFF." VOLTAGE SHOULD BE APPROXIMATELY 5 VOLTS.

IS IT?

YES:

(3)
- KEY "OFF," REMOVE JUMPER WIRE FROM IGNITION JUMPER HARNESS CONNECTOR TERMINAL "C".
- CONNECT JUMPER WIRE BETWEEN TERMINAL "D" IN IGNITION CONTROL MODULE SIDE OF IGNITION JUMPER HARNESS 8-WAY CONNECTOR AND TERMINAL "D" OF MATING CONNECTOR.
- INSTALL A DVM TO MONITOR VOLTAGE AT TERMINAL "C" TO IGNITION CONTROL MODULE SIDE OF IGNITION JUMPER HARNESS 8-WAY CONNECTOR.
- START ENGINE AND IDLE FOR 1 MINUTE TO STABILIZE SYSTEM.
- VOLTAGE AT TERMINAL "C" SHOULD MEASURE APPROXIMATELY 2.5 VOLTS.

DOES IT?

- **YES:** OPEN CKT 647 TO PCM, POOR CONNECTION AT IGNITION JUMPER HARNESS "C" OR PCM "A27," FAULTY PROM, OR FAULTY PCM.
- **NO:** POOR IGNITION CONTROL MODULE CONNECTIONS, OR FAULTY IGNITION CONTROL MODULE.

NO:

(2)
- BUMP ENGINE WITH STARTER.
- RETEST VOLTAGE OF TERMINAL "C". SHOULD BE APPROXIMATELY 5 VOLTS.

IS IT?

- **YES:** CONTINUE WITH CHART STEP (3)
- **NO:** CKT 647 OPEN IN IGNITION JUMPER HARNESS, CKT 647 SHORTED TO GROUND OR VOLTAGE, OR FAULTY IGNITION CONTROL MODULE.

"*AFTER REPAIRS*," REFER TO DTC CRITERIA ON FACING PAGE AND CONFIRM DTC DOES NOT RESET.

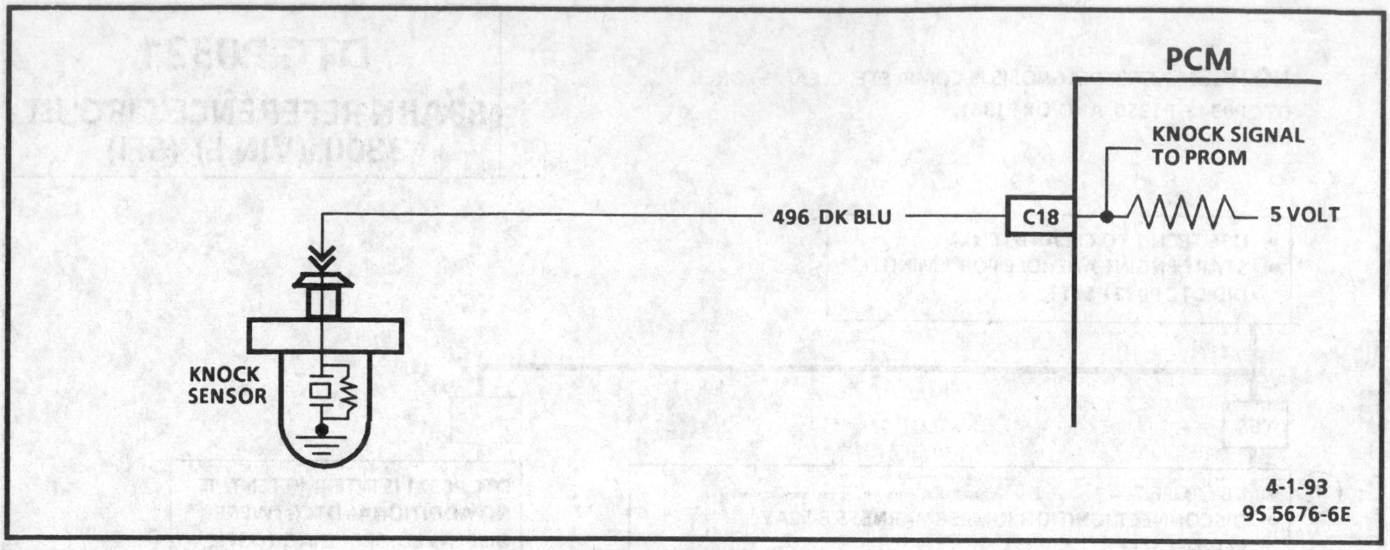
PCM
KNOCK SIGNAL TO PROM
496 DK BLU
C18
5 VOLT
KNOCK SENSOR
4-1-93
9S 5676-6E

DTC P0325

KNOCK SENSOR (KS) CIRCUIT
3800 (VIN L) (SFI)

Circuit Description:

The knock sensor is used to detect engine detonation and allow the PCM to retard the Ignition Control (IC) timing based on the signal being received. The circuitry within the knock sensor causes the PCM's supplied 5 volts signal to be pulled down, so that under a no knock condition CKT 496 would measure about 2.5 volts. The knock sensor produces an AC signal which rides on the 2.5 volts DC voltage. The amplitude and signal frequency is dependent upon the knock level.

If CKT 496 becomes open or shorted to ground, the voltage will either go above 3.5 volts or below 1.5 volts. If either of these conditions are met for 20 seconds, DTC P0325 will be stored.

DTC P0325 Will Set When:

- Voltage on CKT 496 goes above 3.6 volts or below 1.5 volts.
- Either condition present for 20 seconds.

Action Taken (PCM will default to): With DTC P0325 set, the PCM will illuminate the MIL (Service Engine Soon) for the remainder of the key cycle and retard spark timing ("Knock Retard") by 10 degrees.

DTC Chart Test Description: Number(s) below refer to circled number(s) on the diagnostic chart.

1. If DTC P0325 is detected, the PCM will retard spark timing by 10 degrees. If an audible knock is heard from the engine, repair the internal engine problem; normally no knock should be detected at idle.
2. The PCM applies a 5 volts through a pull-up resistor which should be present at the knock sensor terminal.
3. This test determines if the knock sensor is faulty or if the knock sensor portion of the PROM is faulty.

Diagnostic Aids: Check CKT 496 for a intermittent open or short to ground. Also check for proper installation of PROM.

If the knock sensor CKT 496 is routed too close to secondary ignition wires it may induce a voltage and cause a false knock signal.

- Refer to "Detonation/Spark Knock," in "Symptoms," Section "6E3-B".

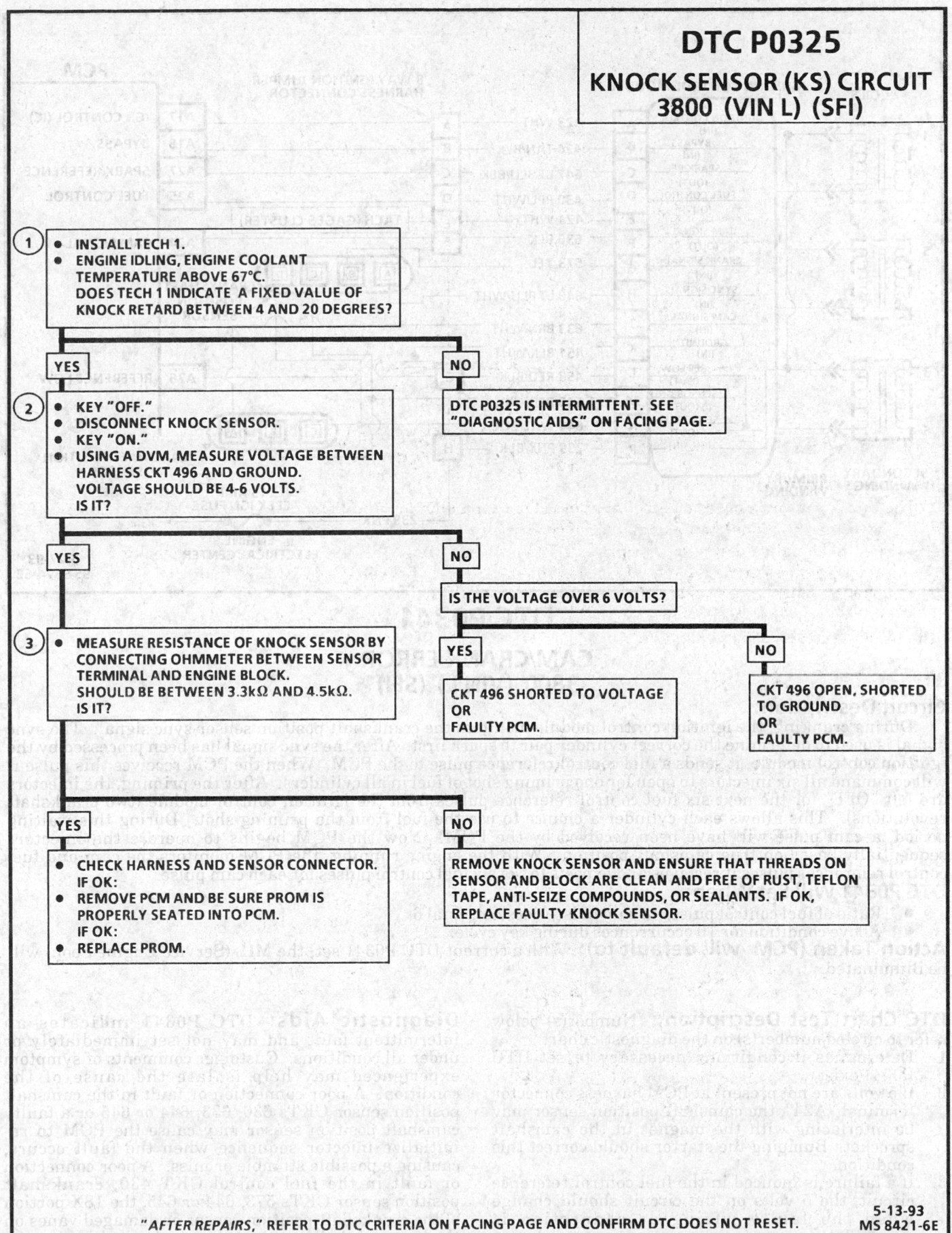

DTC P0325

KNOCK SENSOR (KS) CIRCUIT 3800 (VIN L) (SFI)

1
- INSTALL TECH 1.
- ENGINE IDLING, ENGINE COOLANT TEMPERATURE ABOVE 67°C.

DOES TECH 1 INDICATE A FIXED VALUE OF KNOCK RETARD BETWEEN 4 AND 20 DEGREES?

- **YES** → go to 2
- **NO** → DTC P0325 IS INTERMITTENT. SEE "DIAGNOSTIC AIDS" ON FACING PAGE.

2
- KEY "OFF."
- DISCONNECT KNOCK SENSOR.
- KEY "ON."
- USING A DVM, MEASURE VOLTAGE BETWEEN HARNESS CKT 496 AND GROUND.

VOLTAGE SHOULD BE 4-6 VOLTS. IS IT?

- **YES** → go to 3
- **NO** → IS THE VOLTAGE OVER 6 VOLTS?
  - **YES** → CKT 496 SHORTED TO VOLTAGE OR FAULTY PCM.
  - **NO** → CKT 496 OPEN, SHORTED TO GROUND OR FAULTY PCM.

3
- MEASURE RESISTANCE OF KNOCK SENSOR BY CONNECTING OHMMETER BETWEEN SENSOR TERMINAL AND ENGINE BLOCK.

SHOULD BE BETWEEN 3.3kΩ AND 4.5kΩ. IS IT?

- **YES** →
  - CHECK HARNESS AND SENSOR CONNECTOR. IF OK:
  - REMOVE PCM AND BE SURE PROM IS PROPERLY SEATED INTO PCM. IF OK:
  - REPLACE PROM.
- **NO** → REMOVE KNOCK SENSOR AND ENSURE THAT THREADS ON SENSOR AND BLOCK ARE CLEAN AND FREE OF RUST, TEFLON TAPE, ANTI-SEIZE COMPOUNDS, OR SEALANTS. IF OK, REPLACE FAULTY KNOCK SENSOR.

"AFTER REPAIRS," **REFER TO DTC CRITERIA ON FACING PAGE AND CONFIRM DTC DOES NOT RESET.**

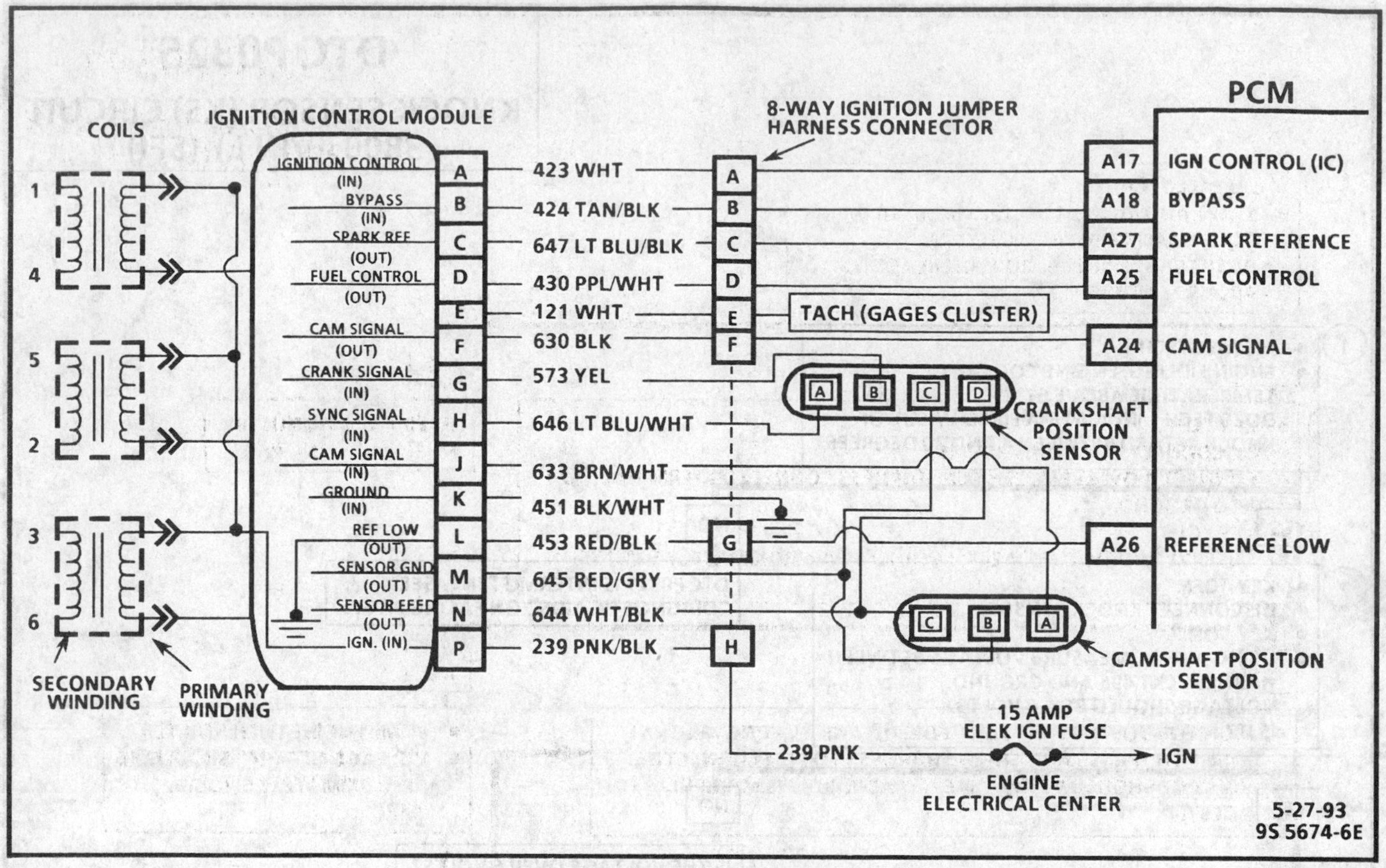
COILS
IGNITION CONTROL MODULE
8-WAY IGNITION JUMPER HARNESS CONNECTOR
PCM
IGNITION CONTROL (IN)
BYPASS (IN)
SPARK REF (OUT)
FUEL CONTROL (OUT)
CAM SIGNAL (OUT)
CRANK SIGNAL (IN)
SYNC SIGNAL (IN)
CAM SIGNAL (IN)
GROUND (IN)
REF LOW (OUT)
SENSOR GND (OUT)
SENSOR FEED (OUT)
IGN. (IN)
423 WHT
424 TAN/BLK
647 LT BLU/BLK
430 PPL/WHT
121 WHT
630 BLK
573 YEL
646 LT BLU/WHT
633 BRN/WHT
451 BLK/WHT
453 RED/BLK
645 RED/GRY
644 WHT/BLK
239 PNK/BLK
A17 IGN CONTROL (IC)
A18 BYPASS
A27 SPARK REFERENCE
A25 FUEL CONTROL
TACH (GAGES CLUSTER)
A24 CAM SIGNAL
CRANKSHAFT POSITION SENSOR
A26 REFERENCE LOW
CAMSHAFT POSITION SENSOR
SECONDARY WINDING
PRIMARY WINDING
15 AMP ELEK IGN FUSE
239 PNK
IGN
ENGINE ELECTRICAL CENTER
5-27-93
9S 5674-6E

DTC P0341

CAM/CRANK ERROR 3800 (VIN L) (SFI)

Circuit Description:

During cranking, the ignition control module monitors the crankshaft position sensor sync signal. The sync signal is used to determine the correct cylinder pair to spark first. After the sync signal has been processed by the ignition control module, it sends a fuel control reference pulse to the PCM. When the PCM receives this pulse it will command all six injectors to open for one priming shot of fuel in all cylinders. After the priming, the injectors are left "OFF" for the next six fuel control reference pulses from the ignition control module (two crankshaft revolutions). This allows each cylinder a chance to use the fuel from the priming shot. During this waiting period, a cam pulse will have been received by the PCM. Now the PCM begins to operate the injectors sequentially based on true camshaft position. With the engine running, the PCM monitors the cam and fuel control references pulses it receives and expects to see six fuel control pulses for each cam pulse.

DTC P0341 Will Set When:

- Ratio of fuel control pulses to cam pulses does not equal 6.
- Above condition for 10 occurrences during key cycle.

Action Taken (PCM will default to): With a current DTC P0341 set, the MIL (Service Engine Soon) will be illuminated.

DTC Chart Test Description: Number(s) below refer to circled number(s) on the diagnostic chart.

1. Determines if conditions necessary to set DTC P0341 exist.
2. If 5 volts are not present at PCM harness connector terminal "A24", the camshaft position sensor may be interfacing with the magnet in the camshaft sprocket. Bumping the starter should correct this condition.
3. If a failure is induced in the fuel control reference circuit, the 5 volts on the circuit should change when the faulty wiring or connection is manipulated.

Diagnostic Aids: DTC P0341 indicates an intermittent fault and may not set immediately or under all conditions. Customer comments of symptom experienced may help isolate the cause of the condition. A poor connection or fault in the camshaft position sensor CKTs 630, 633, 644 or 645 or a faulty camshaft position sensor may cause the PCM to re-initialize injector sequence when the fault occurs, causing a possible stumble or miss. A poor connection or fault in the fuel control CKT 430, crankshaft position sensor CKTs 573, 644 or 645, the 18X portion of the crankshaft position sensor or damaged vanes on the harmonic balancer interrupter rings will cause the PCM to stop pulsing the injectors when the fault occurs, causing an intermittent stumble or stall.

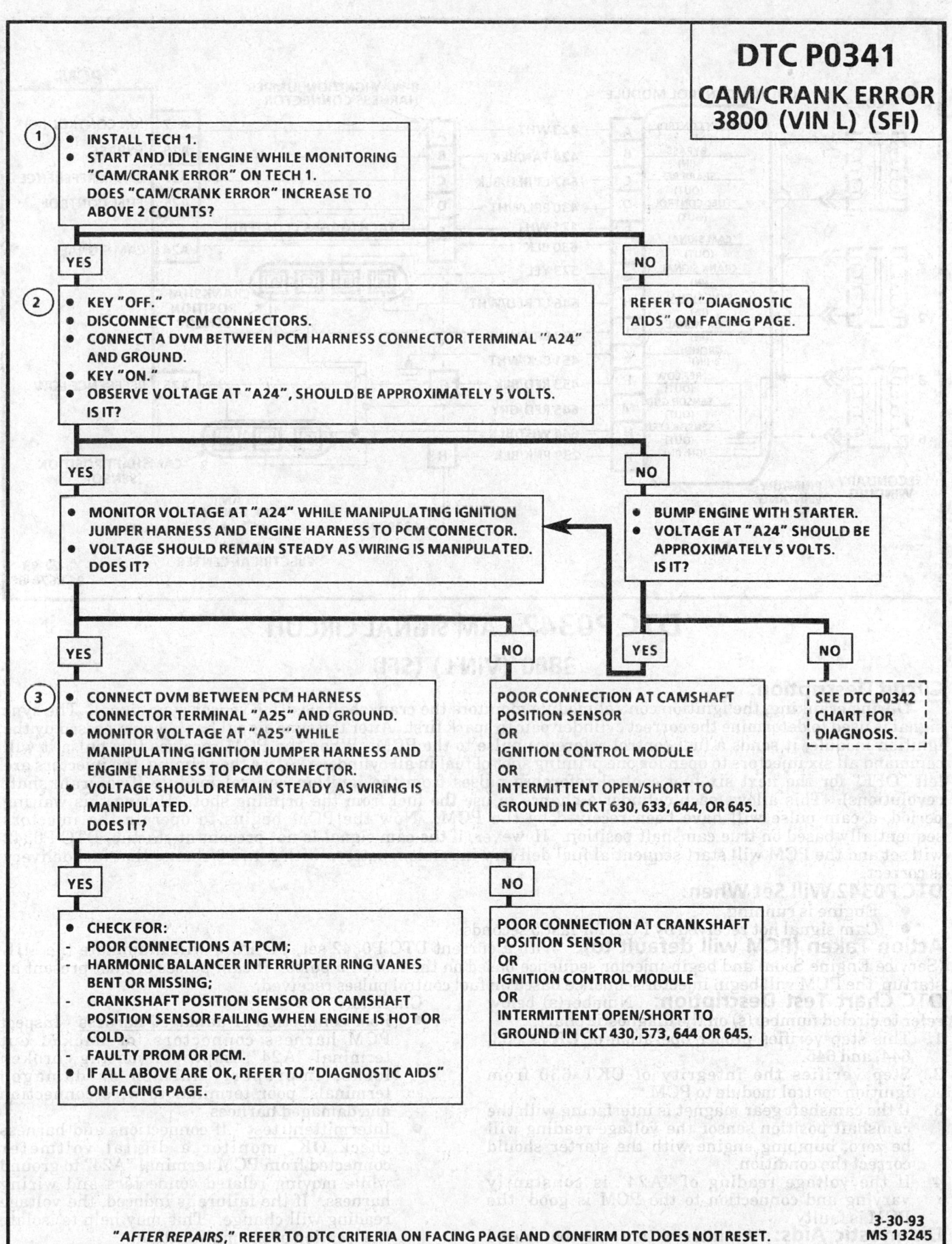

DTC P0341

CAM/CRANK ERROR 3800 (VIN L) (SFI)

1
- INSTALL TECH 1.
- START AND IDLE ENGINE WHILE MONITORING "CAM/CRANK ERROR" ON TECH 1.

DOES "CAM/CRANK ERROR" INCREASE TO ABOVE 2 COUNTS?

YES → step 2

NO → REFER TO "DIAGNOSTIC AIDS" ON FACING PAGE.

2
- KEY "OFF."
- DISCONNECT PCM CONNECTORS.
- CONNECT A DVM BETWEEN PCM HARNESS CONNECTOR TERMINAL "A24" AND GROUND.
- KEY "ON."
- OBSERVE VOLTAGE AT "A24", SHOULD BE APPROXIMATELY 5 VOLTS.

IS IT?

YES
- MONITOR VOLTAGE AT "A24" WHILE MANIPULATING IGNITION JUMPER HARNESS AND ENGINE HARNESS TO PCM CONNECTOR.
- VOLTAGE SHOULD REMAIN STEADY AS WIRING IS MANIPULATED.

DOES IT?

- **YES** → step 3
- **NO** → POOR CONNECTION AT CAMSHAFT POSITION SENSOR OR IGNITION CONTROL MODULE OR INTERMITTENT OPEN/SHORT TO GROUND IN CKT 630, 633, 644, OR 645.

NO
- BUMP ENGINE WITH STARTER.
- VOLTAGE AT "A24" SHOULD BE APPROXIMATELY 5 VOLTS.

IS IT?

- **YES** → go to "MONITOR VOLTAGE AT "A24" WHILE MANIPULATING..." above
- **NO** → SEE DTC P0342 CHART FOR DIAGNOSIS.

3
- CONNECT DVM BETWEEN PCM HARNESS CONNECTOR TERMINAL "A25" AND GROUND.
- MONITOR VOLTAGE AT "A25" WHILE MANIPULATING IGNITION JUMPER HARNESS AND ENGINE HARNESS TO PCM CONNECTOR.
- VOLTAGE SHOULD REMAIN STEADY AS WIRING IS MANIPULATED.

DOES IT?

YES
- CHECK FOR:
  - POOR CONNECTIONS AT PCM;
  - HARMONIC BALANCER INTERRUPTER RING VANES BENT OR MISSING;
  - CRANKSHAFT POSITION SENSOR OR CAMSHAFT POSITION SENSOR FAILING WHEN ENGINE IS HOT OR COLD.
  - FAULTY PROM OR PCM.
- IF ALL ABOVE ARE OK, REFER TO "DIAGNOSTIC AIDS" ON FACING PAGE.

NO
POOR CONNECTION AT CRANKSHAFT POSITION SENSOR OR IGNITION CONTROL MODULE OR INTERMITTENT OPEN/SHORT TO GROUND IN CKT 430, 573, 644 OR 645.

"*AFTER REPAIRS*," REFER TO DTC CRITERIA ON FACING PAGE AND CONFIRM DTC DOES NOT RESET.

3-30-93
MS 13245

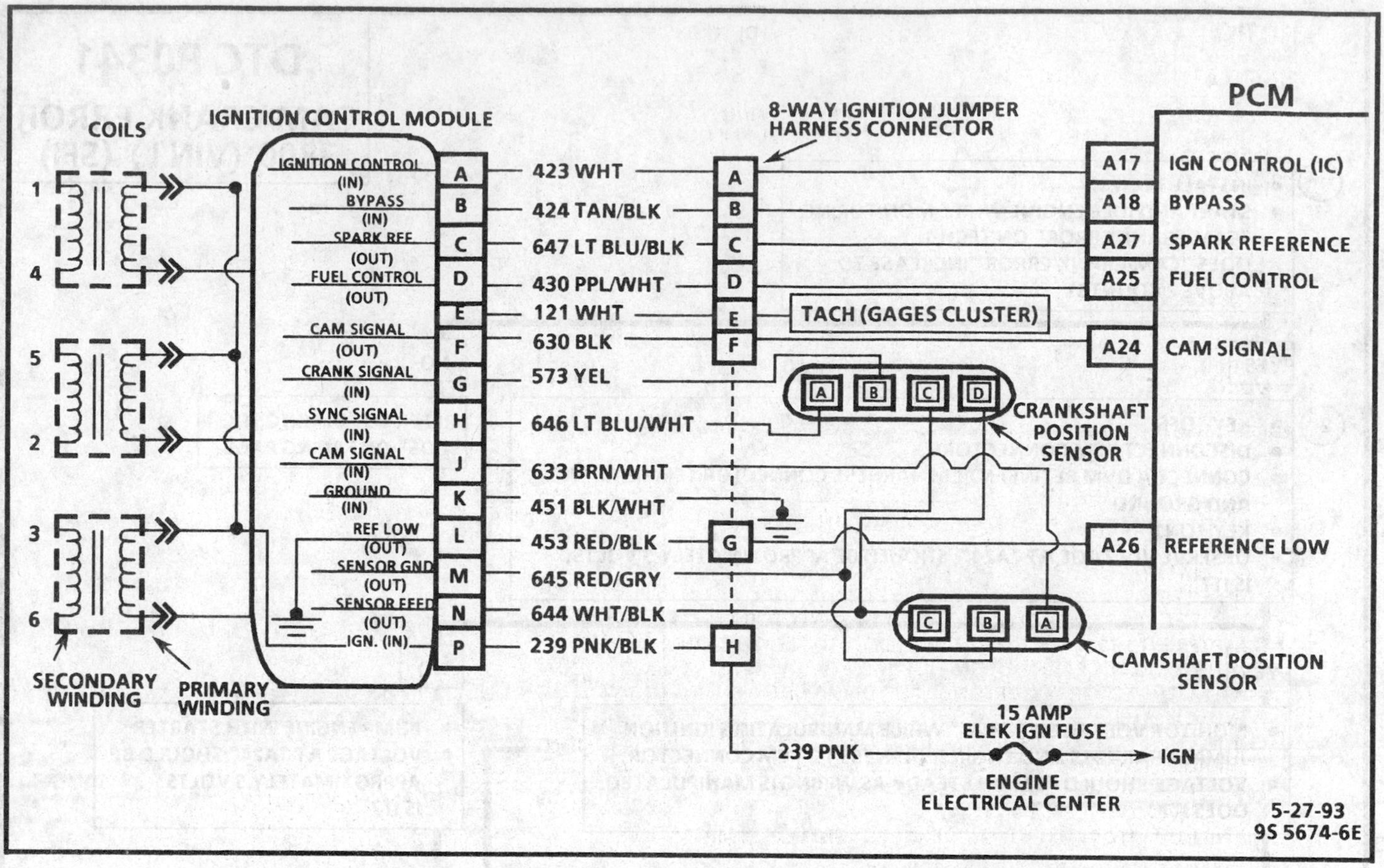
PCM
IGNITION CONTROL MODULE
COILS
8-WAY IGNITION JUMPER HARNESS CONNECTOR
IGNITION CONTROL (IN)
BYPASS (IN)
SPARK REF (OUT)
FUEL CONTROL (OUT)
CAM SIGNAL (OUT)
CRANK SIGNAL (IN)
SYNC SIGNAL (IN)
CAM SIGNAL (IN)
GROUND (IN)
REF LOW (OUT)
SENSOR GND (OUT)
SENSOR FEED (OUT)
IGN. (IN)
423 WHT
424 TAN/BLK
647 LT BLU/BLK
430 PPL/WHT
121 WHT
630 BLK
573 YEL
646 LT BLU/WHT
633 BRN/WHT
451 BLK/WHT
453 RED/BLK
645 RED/GRY
644 WHT/BLK
239 PNK/BLK
TACH (GAGES CLUSTER)
A17 IGN CONTROL (IC)
A18 BYPASS
A27 SPARK REFERENCE
A25 FUEL CONTROL
A24 CAM SIGNAL
A26 REFERENCE LOW
CRANKSHAFT POSITION SENSOR
CAMSHAFT POSITION SENSOR
SECONDARY WINDING
PRIMARY WINDING
15 AMP ELEK IGN FUSE
239 PNK
IGN
ENGINE ELECTRICAL CENTER
5-27-93
9S 5674-6E

DTC P0342 CAM SIGNAL CIRCUIT
3800 (VIN L) (SFI)

Circuit Description:

During cranking, the ignition control module monitors the crankshaft position sensor sync signal. The sync signal is used to determine the correct cylinder pair to spark first. After the sync signal has been processed by the ignition module, it sends a fuel control reference pulse to the PCM. When the PCM receives this pulse it will command all six injectors to open for one priming shot of fuel in all cylinders. After the priming, the injectors are left "OFF" for the next six fuel control reference pulses from the ignition control module (two crankshaft revolutions). This allows each cylinder a chance to use the fuel from the priming shot. During this waiting period, a cam pulse will have been received by the PCM. Now the PCM begins to operate the injectors sequentially based on true camshaft position. However, if the cam signal is not present at startup, DTC P0342 will set and the PCM will start sequential fuel delivery in random pattern with a 1 in 6 chance that fuel delivery is correct.

DTC P0342 Will Set When:

- Engine is running.
- Cam signal not received by PCM for last 5 seconds.

Action Taken (PCM will default to): With a current DTC P0342 set, the PCM will illuminate the MIL (Service Engine Soon) and begin injector sequence based on the last cam pulse. If cam pulses are not present at startup, the PCM will begin injector sequence based on fuel control pulses received.

DTC Chart Test Description: Number(s) below refer to circled number(s) on the diagnostic chart.

1. This step verifies proper operation of CKTs 633, 644, and 645.
2. Step verifies the integrity of CKT 630 from ignition control module to PCM.
3. If the camshaft gear magnet is interfacing with the camshaft position sensor the voltage reading will be zero; bumping engine with the starter should correct the condition.
4. If the voltage reading of "A24" is constantly varying and connection to the PCM is good, the PCM is faulty.

Diagnostic Aids: An intermittent may be caused by a poor connection, rubbed through wire insulation or a wire broken inside the insulation.

Check for:

- Poor connection or damaged harness - Inspect PCM harness connectors for backed out terminal "A24", improper mating, broken locks, improperly formed or damaged terminals, poor terminal to wire connection and damaged harness.
- Intermittent test - If connections and harness check OK, monitor a digital voltmeter connected from PCM terminal "A24" to ground while moving related connectors and wiring harness. If the failure is induced, the voltage reading will change. This may help to isolate the location of the malfunction.

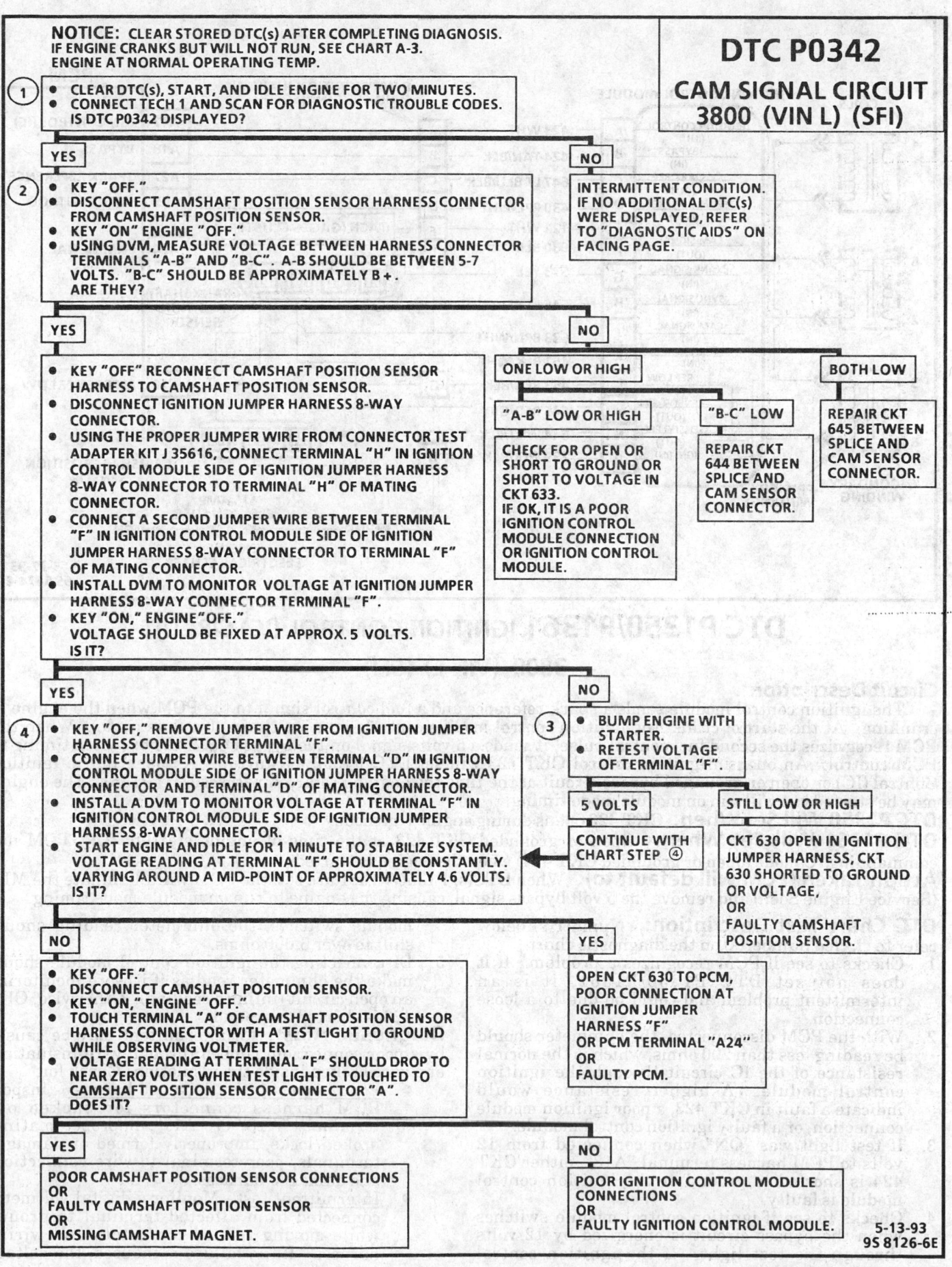

DTC P0342

CAM SIGNAL CIRCUIT 3800 (VIN L) (SFI)

NOTICE: CLEAR STORED DTC(s) AFTER COMPLETING DIAGNOSIS.
IF ENGINE CRANKS BUT WILL NOT RUN, SEE CHART A-3.
ENGINE AT NORMAL OPERATING TEMP.

(1)
- CLEAR DTC(s), START, AND IDLE ENGINE FOR TWO MINUTES.
- CONNECT TECH 1 AND SCAN FOR DIAGNOSTIC TROUBLE CODES.
  IS DTC P0342 DISPLAYED?

NO: INTERMITTENT CONDITION. IF NO ADDITIONAL DTC(s) WERE DISPLAYED, REFER TO "DIAGNOSTIC AIDS" ON FACING PAGE.

YES:

(2)
- KEY "OFF."
- DISCONNECT CAMSHAFT POSITION SENSOR HARNESS CONNECTOR FROM CAMSHAFT POSITION SENSOR.
- KEY "ON" ENGINE "OFF."
- USING DVM, MEASURE VOLTAGE BETWEEN HARNESS CONNECTOR TERMINALS "A-B" AND "B-C". A-B SHOULD BE BETWEEN 5-7 VOLTS. "B-C" SHOULD BE APPROXIMATELY B+.
  ARE THEY?

NO:
- **ONE LOW OR HIGH:**
  - **"A-B" LOW OR HIGH:** CHECK FOR OPEN OR SHORT TO GROUND OR SHORT TO VOLTAGE IN CKT 633. IF OK, IT IS A POOR IGNITION CONTROL MODULE CONNECTION OR IGNITION CONTROL MODULE.
  - **"B-C" LOW:** REPAIR CKT 644 BETWEEN SPLICE AND CAM SENSOR CONNECTOR.
- **BOTH LOW:** REPAIR CKT 645 BETWEEN SPLICE AND CAM SENSOR CONNECTOR.

YES:
- KEY "OFF" RECONNECT CAMSHAFT POSITION SENSOR HARNESS TO CAMSHAFT POSITION SENSOR.
- DISCONNECT IGNITION JUMPER HARNESS 8-WAY CONNECTOR.
- USING THE PROPER JUMPER WIRE FROM CONNECTOR TEST ADAPTER KIT J 35616, CONNECT TERMINAL "H" IN IGNITION CONTROL MODULE SIDE OF IGNITION JUMPER HARNESS 8-WAY CONNECTOR TO TERMINAL "H" OF MATING CONNECTOR.
- CONNECT A SECOND JUMPER WIRE BETWEEN TERMINAL "F" IN IGNITION CONTROL MODULE SIDE OF IGNITION JUMPER HARNESS 8-WAY CONNECTOR TO TERMINAL "F" OF MATING CONNECTOR.
- INSTALL DVM TO MONITOR VOLTAGE AT IGNITION JUMPER HARNESS 8-WAY CONNECTOR TERMINAL "F".
- KEY "ON," ENGINE "OFF."
  VOLTAGE SHOULD BE FIXED AT APPROX. 5 VOLTS.
  IS IT?

NO:

(3)
- BUMP ENGINE WITH STARTER.
- RETEST VOLTAGE OF TERMINAL "F".

- **5 VOLTS:** CONTINUE WITH CHART STEP (4)
- **STILL LOW OR HIGH:** CKT 630 OPEN IN IGNITION JUMPER HARNESS, CKT 630 SHORTED TO GROUND OR VOLTAGE, OR FAULTY CAMSHAFT POSITION SENSOR.

YES:

(4)
- KEY "OFF," REMOVE JUMPER WIRE FROM IGNITION JUMPER HARNESS CONNECTOR TERMINAL "F".
- CONNECT JUMPER WIRE BETWEEN TERMINAL "D" IN IGNITION CONTROL MODULE SIDE OF IGNITION JUMPER HARNESS 8-WAY CONNECTOR AND TERMINAL "D" OF MATING CONNECTOR.
- INSTALL A DVM TO MONITOR VOLTAGE AT TERMINAL "F" IN IGNITION CONTROL MODULE SIDE OF IGNITION JUMPER HARNESS 8-WAY CONNECTOR.
- START ENGINE AND IDLE FOR 1 MINUTE TO STABILIZE SYSTEM. VOLTAGE READING AT TERMINAL "F" SHOULD BE CONSTANTLY. VARYING AROUND A MID-POINT OF APPROXIMATELY 4.6 VOLTS.
  IS IT?

YES: OPEN CKT 630 TO PCM, POOR CONNECTION AT IGNITION JUMPER HARNESS "F" OR PCM TERMINAL "A24" OR FAULTY PCM.

NO:
- KEY "OFF."
- DISCONNECT CAMSHAFT POSITION SENSOR.
- KEY "ON," ENGINE "OFF."
- TOUCH TERMINAL "A" OF CAMSHAFT POSITION SENSOR HARNESS CONNECTOR WITH A TEST LIGHT TO GROUND WHILE OBSERVING VOLTMETER.
- VOLTAGE READING AT TERMINAL "F" SHOULD DROP TO NEAR ZERO VOLTS WHEN TEST LIGHT IS TOUCHED TO CAMSHAFT POSITION SENSOR CONNECTOR "A".
  DOES IT?

YES: POOR CAMSHAFT POSITION SENSOR CONNECTIONS OR FAULTY CAMSHAFT POSITION SENSOR OR MISSING CAMSHAFT MAGNET.

NO: POOR IGNITION CONTROL MODULE CONNECTIONS OR FAULTY IGNITION CONTROL MODULE.

5-13-93
9S 8126-6E

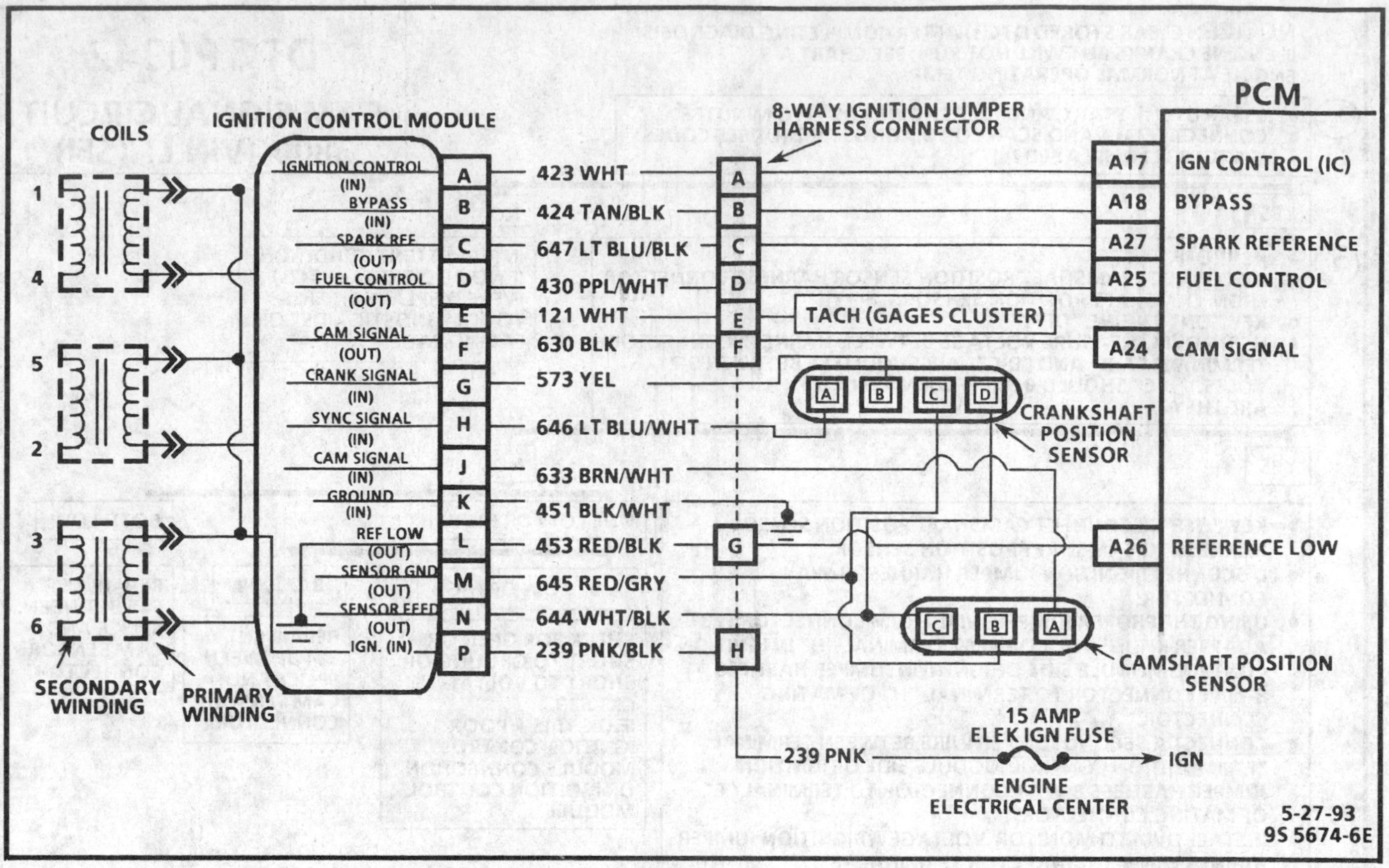
COILS
IGNITION CONTROL MODULE
8-WAY IGNITION JUMPER HARNESS CONNECTOR
PCM
IGNITION CONTROL (IN)
BYPASS (IN)
SPARK REF (OUT)
FUEL CONTROL (OUT)
CAM SIGNAL (OUT)
CRANK SIGNAL (IN)
SYNC SIGNAL (IN)
CAM SIGNAL (IN)
GROUND (IN)
REF LOW (OUT)
SENSOR GND (OUT)
SENSOR FEED (OUT)
IGN. (IN)
423 WHT
424 TAN/BLK
647 LT BLU/BLK
430 PPL/WHT
121 WHT
630 BLK
573 YEL
646 LT BLU/WHT
633 BRN/WHT
451 BLK/WHT
453 RED/BLK
645 RED/GRY
644 WHT/BLK
239 PNK/BLK
A17 IGN CONTROL (IC)
A18 BYPASS
A27 SPARK REFERENCE
A25 FUEL CONTROL
TACH (GAGES CLUSTER)
A24 CAM SIGNAL
CRANKSHAFT POSITION SENSOR
A26 REFERENCE LOW
CAMSHAFT POSITION SENSOR
15 AMP ELEK IGN FUSE
239 PNK
IGN
ENGINE ELECTRICAL CENTER
SECONDARY WINDING
PRIMARY WINDING
5-27-93
9S 5674-6E

DTC P1350/P1361 IGNITION CONTROL (IC) CIRCUIT
3800 (VIN L) (SFI)

Circuit Description:
The ignition control module sends a spark reference and a fuel control signal to the PCM when the engine is cranking. At the start of crank, the ignition control module controls ignition timing (module mode). When the PCM recognizes the second fuel control pulse, it sends a 5 volts signal on the bypass CKT 424 to switch timing to PCM control. An open in ignition control CKT 423 will set DTC P1350 at startup. An open in the Ignition Control (IC) or open or grounded bypass circuit at the time the engine is started will set DTC P1361. The engine may be started but will run on module mode timing.

DTC P1350 Will Set When: CKT 423 opens during engine run mode.

DTC P1361 Will Set When: Open or grounded CKT 423 at the time of engine startup. **OR** PCM not commanding IC mode (open or grounded CKT 424) when the engine is started.

Action Taken (PCM will default to): When DTC(s) P1350/P1361 are set, the PCM will illuminate the MIL (Service Engine Soon) and remove the 5 volt bypass signal, causing the engine to run on module mode timing.

DTC Chart Test Description: Number(s) below refer to circled number(s) on the diagnostic chart.

1. Checks to see if PCM recognizes a problem. If it does not set DTC P1350/P1361, it is an intermittent problem and could be due to a loose connection.
2. With the PCM disconnected, the ohmmeter should be reading less than 200 ohms, which is the normal resistance of the IC circuit through the ignition control module. A higher resistance would indicate a fault in CKT 423, a poor ignition module connection, or a faulty ignition control module.
3. If test light was "ON" when connected from 12 volts to PCM harness terminal "A18", either CKT 424 is shorted to ground or the ignition control module is faulty.
4. Checks to see if ignition control module switches when the bypass circuit is energized by 12 volts through the test light. If the ignition control module switches, the ohmmeter reading should shift to over 6,000 ohms.
5. Disconnecting the ignition control module should make the ohmmeter read as if it were monitoring an open circuit (infinite reading). Otherwise, CKT 423 is shorted to ground.

Diagnostic Aids: An intermittent may be caused by a poor connection, rubbed through wire insulation, or a wire broken inside the insulation. Check for:

- Poor connection or damaged harness - Inspect PCM harness connectors for backed out terminals "A18" or "A17", improper mating, broken locks, improperly formed or damaged terminals, poor terminal to wire connection, and damaged harness.
- Intermittent test - Monitor a digital voltmeter connected from affected terminal to ground while moving related connectors and wiring harness. If the failure is induced, the voltage reading will change.

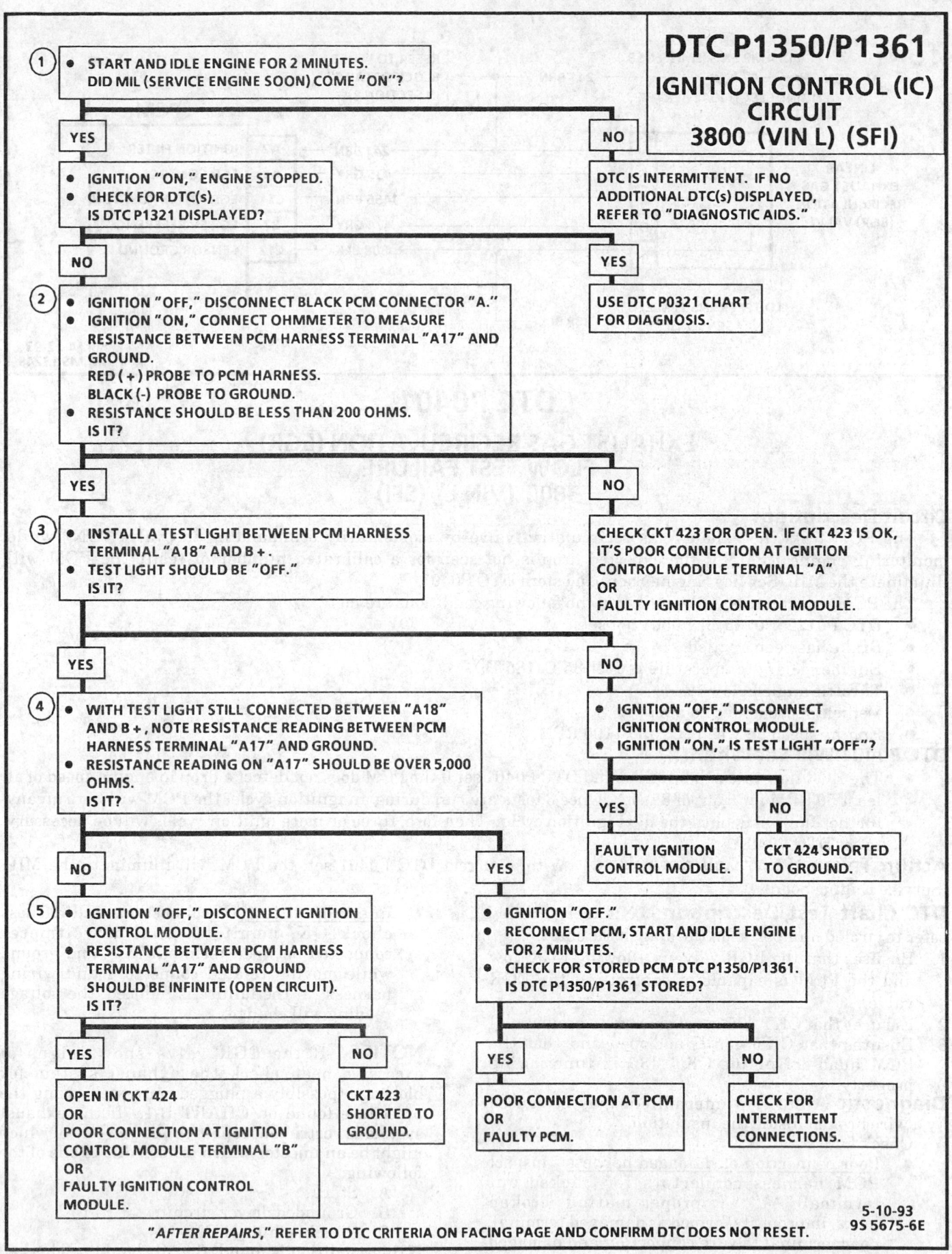

DTC P1350/P1361
IGNITION CONTROL (IC) CIRCUIT
3800 (VIN L) (SFI)

1
- START AND IDLE ENGINE FOR 2 MINUTES.
DID MIL (SERVICE ENGINE SOON) COME "ON"?

NO → DTC IS INTERMITTENT. IF NO ADDITIONAL DTC(s) DISPLAYED, REFER TO "DIAGNOSTIC AIDS."

YES →
- IGNITION "ON," ENGINE STOPPED.
- CHECK FOR DTC(s).
IS DTC P1321 DISPLAYED?

YES → USE DTC P0321 CHART FOR DIAGNOSIS.

NO →

2
- IGNITION "OFF," DISCONNECT BLACK PCM CONNECTOR "A."
- IGNITION "ON," CONNECT OHMMETER TO MEASURE RESISTANCE BETWEEN PCM HARNESS TERMINAL "A17" AND GROUND.
RED (+) PROBE TO PCM HARNESS.
BLACK (-) PROBE TO GROUND.
- RESISTANCE SHOULD BE LESS THAN 200 OHMS.
IS IT?

NO → CHECK CKT 423 FOR OPEN. IF CKT 423 IS OK, IT'S POOR CONNECTION AT IGNITION CONTROL MODULE TERMINAL "A" OR FAULTY IGNITION CONTROL MODULE.

YES →

3
- INSTALL A TEST LIGHT BETWEEN PCM HARNESS TERMINAL "A18" AND B+.
- TEST LIGHT SHOULD BE "OFF."
IS IT?

NO →
- IGNITION "OFF," DISCONNECT IGNITION CONTROL MODULE.
- IGNITION "ON," IS TEST LIGHT "OFF"?

  YES → FAULTY IGNITION CONTROL MODULE.

  NO → CKT 424 SHORTED TO GROUND.

YES →

4
- WITH TEST LIGHT STILL CONNECTED BETWEEN "A18" AND B+, NOTE RESISTANCE READING BETWEEN PCM HARNESS TERMINAL "A17" AND GROUND.
- RESISTANCE READING ON "A17" SHOULD BE OVER 5,000 OHMS.
IS IT?

NO →

5
- IGNITION "OFF," DISCONNECT IGNITION CONTROL MODULE.
- RESISTANCE BETWEEN PCM HARNESS TERMINAL "A17" AND GROUND SHOULD BE INFINITE (OPEN CIRCUIT).
IS IT?

  YES → OPEN IN CKT 424 OR POOR CONNECTION AT IGNITION CONTROL MODULE TERMINAL "B" OR FAULTY IGNITION CONTROL MODULE.

  NO → CKT 423 SHORTED TO GROUND.

YES →
- IGNITION "OFF."
- RECONNECT PCM, START AND IDLE ENGINE FOR 2 MINUTES.
- CHECK FOR STORED PCM DTC P1350/P1361.
IS DTC P1350/P1361 STORED?

  YES → POOR CONNECTION AT PCM OR FAULTY PCM.

  NO → CHECK FOR INTERMITTENT CONNECTIONS.

"*AFTER REPAIRS*," REFER TO DTC CRITERIA ON FACING PAGE AND CONFIRM DTC DOES NOT RESET.

5-10-93
9S 5675-6E

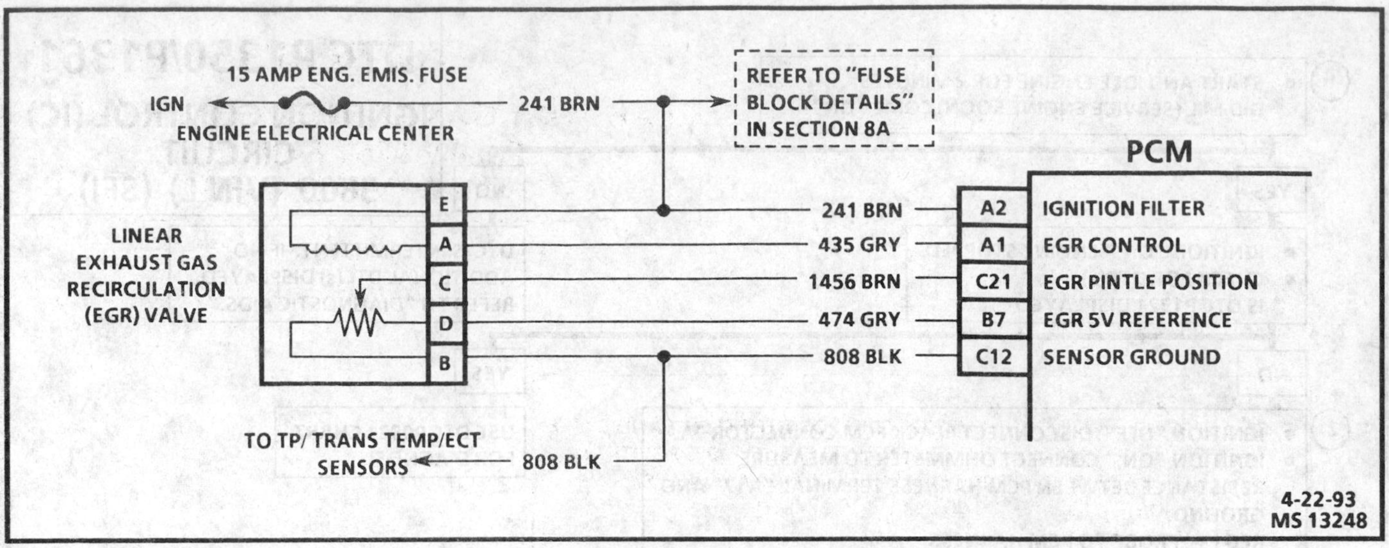
15 AMP ENG. EMIS. FUSE
IGN
241 BRN
ENGINE ELECTRICAL CENTER
REFER TO "FUSE BLOCK DETAILS" IN SECTION 8A
PCM
LINEAR EXHAUST GAS RECIRCULATION (EGR) VALVE
E
A
C
D
B
241 BRN
435 GRY
1456 BRN
474 GRY
808 BLK
A2
A1
C21
B7
C12
IGNITION FILTER
EGR CONTROL
EGR PINTLE POSITION
EGR 5V REFERENCE
SENSOR GROUND
TO TP/ TRANS TEMP/ECT SENSORS
808 BLK
4-22-93
MS 13248

DTC P0401

EXHAUST GAS RECIRCULATION (EGR) FLOW TEST FAILURE 3800 (VIN L) (SFI)

Circuit Description:

The PCM tests the exhaust gas recirculation valve by momentarily commanding the valve "ON" while monitoring engine RPM. If the expected drop is not seen for a calibrated number of tests, the PCM will illuminate the MIL (Service Engine Soon) and store DTC P0401.

The PCM will run the EGR tests when the following conditions are met:

- DTC P0122, P0123, or P0501 not set.
- Brake has been applied.
- Engine coolant temperature is over 85°C (185°F).
- Throttle angle below 1%.
- Vehicle speed above 25 mph.
- Engine speed between 900 and 1100 RPM.

DTC P0401 Will Set When:

- The EGR flow test will be failed and DTC P0401 set if the PCM does not detect a drop in engine speed of at least 50 RPM for 6 out of 8 tests. Once 3 tests are run during an ignition cycle, the PCM will not run any further flow tests until the next ignition cycle. Therefore, three or more ignition cycles will be necessary to set DTC P0401.

Action Taken (PCM will default to): With a currect DTC P0401 set, the PCM will illuminate the MIL (Service Engine Soon).

DTC Chart Test Description: Number(s) below refer to circled number(s) on the diagnostic chart.

1. Ensures that the EGR valve is allowing EGR flow and the PCM is capable of controlling the EGR valve.
2. Ensures that CKT 435 is not shorted to ground.
3. Ensures that CKT 435 is not open and that the PCM quad-driver for CKT 435 is functioning properly.

Diagnostic Aids: An intermittent may be caused by a wire broken inside the insulation.

Check for:

- Poor connection or damaged harness - Inspect PCM harness connectors for backed out terminal "A1", improper mating, broken locks, improperly formed or damaged terminal, poor terminal to wire connection and damaged harness.
- Intermittent test - If connections and harness check OK, monitor a digital voltmeter connected between terminal "A1" and ground while moving related connectors and wiring harness. If the failure is induced, the voltage reading will change.

NOTICE: If the EGR valve shows signs of excessive heat, check the exhaust system for blockage (possibly a plugged converter) using the procedure found on CHART B-1. If the exhaust system is restricted, repair the cause; one of which might be an injector which is open due to one of the following:

A. Stuck.
B. Grounded driver circuit.
C. Possible faulty PCM.

If this condition is found, the oil should be checked for possible fuel contamination.

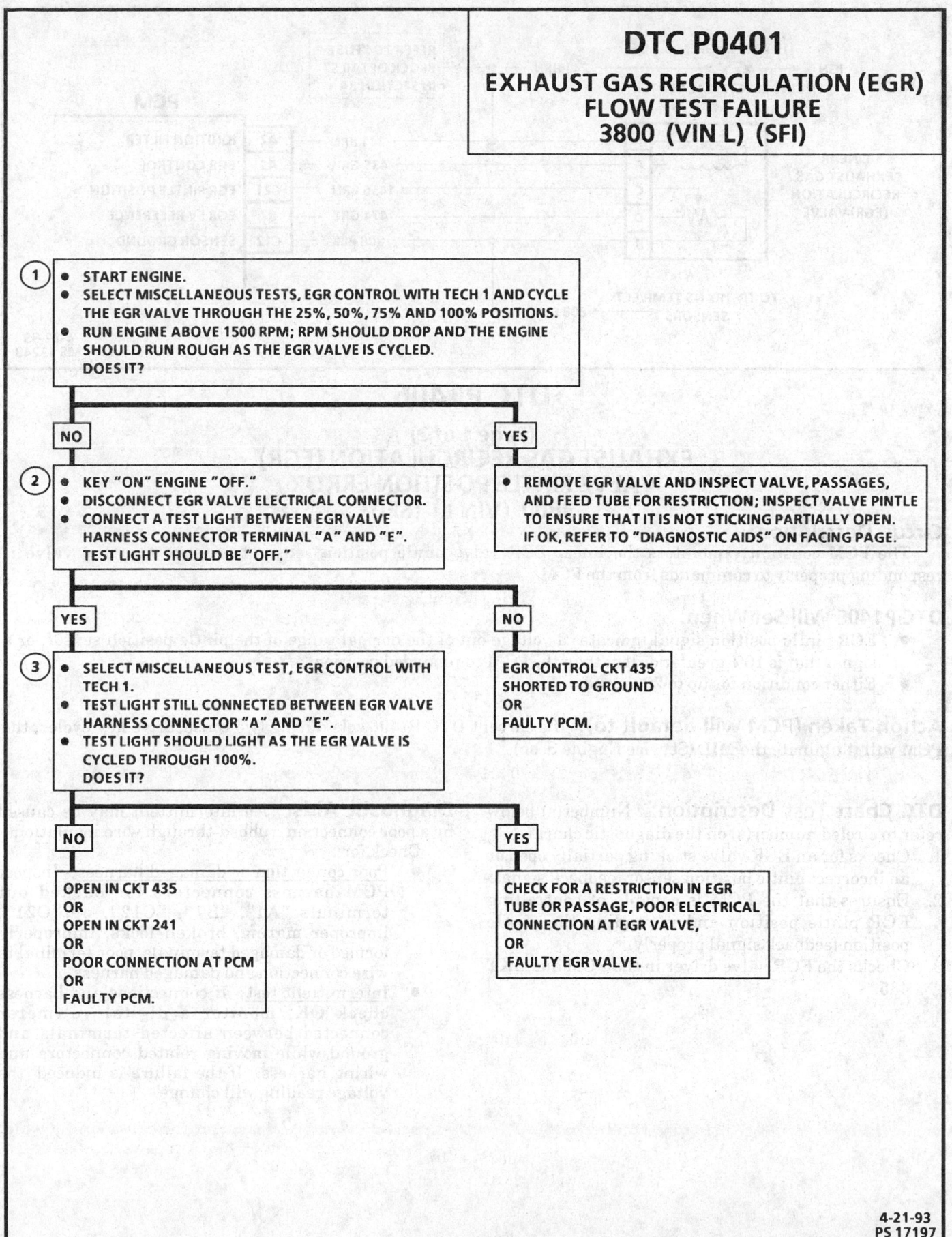

DTC P0401

EXHAUST GAS RECIRCULATION (EGR) FLOW TEST FAILURE 3800 (VIN L) (SFI)

(1)
- START ENGINE.
- SELECT MISCELLANEOUS TESTS, EGR CONTROL WITH TECH 1 AND CYCLE THE EGR VALVE THROUGH THE 25%, 50%, 75% AND 100% POSITIONS.
- RUN ENGINE ABOVE 1500 RPM; RPM SHOULD DROP AND THE ENGINE SHOULD RUN ROUGH AS THE EGR VALVE IS CYCLED.

DOES IT?

NO → (2)

YES →
- REMOVE EGR VALVE AND INSPECT VALVE, PASSAGES, AND FEED TUBE FOR RESTRICTION; INSPECT VALVE PINTLE TO ENSURE THAT IT IS NOT STICKING PARTIALLY OPEN. IF OK, REFER TO "DIAGNOSTIC AIDS" ON FACING PAGE.

(2)
- KEY "ON" ENGINE "OFF."
- DISCONNECT EGR VALVE ELECTRICAL CONNECTOR.
- CONNECT A TEST LIGHT BETWEEN EGR VALVE HARNESS CONNECTOR TERMINAL "A" AND "E". TEST LIGHT SHOULD BE "OFF."

YES → (3)

NO → EGR CONTROL CKT 435 SHORTED TO GROUND OR FAULTY PCM.

(3)
- SELECT MISCELLANEOUS TEST, EGR CONTROL WITH TECH 1.
- TEST LIGHT STILL CONNECTED BETWEEN EGR VALVE HARNESS CONNECTOR "A" AND "E".
- TEST LIGHT SHOULD LIGHT AS THE EGR VALVE IS CYCLED THROUGH 100%.

DOES IT?

NO → OPEN IN CKT 435 OR OPEN IN CKT 241 OR POOR CONNECTION AT PCM OR FAULTY PCM.

YES → CHECK FOR A RESTRICTION IN EGR TUBE OR PASSAGE, POOR ELECTRICAL CONNECTION AT EGR VALVE, OR FAULTY EGR VALVE.

4-21-93
PS 17197

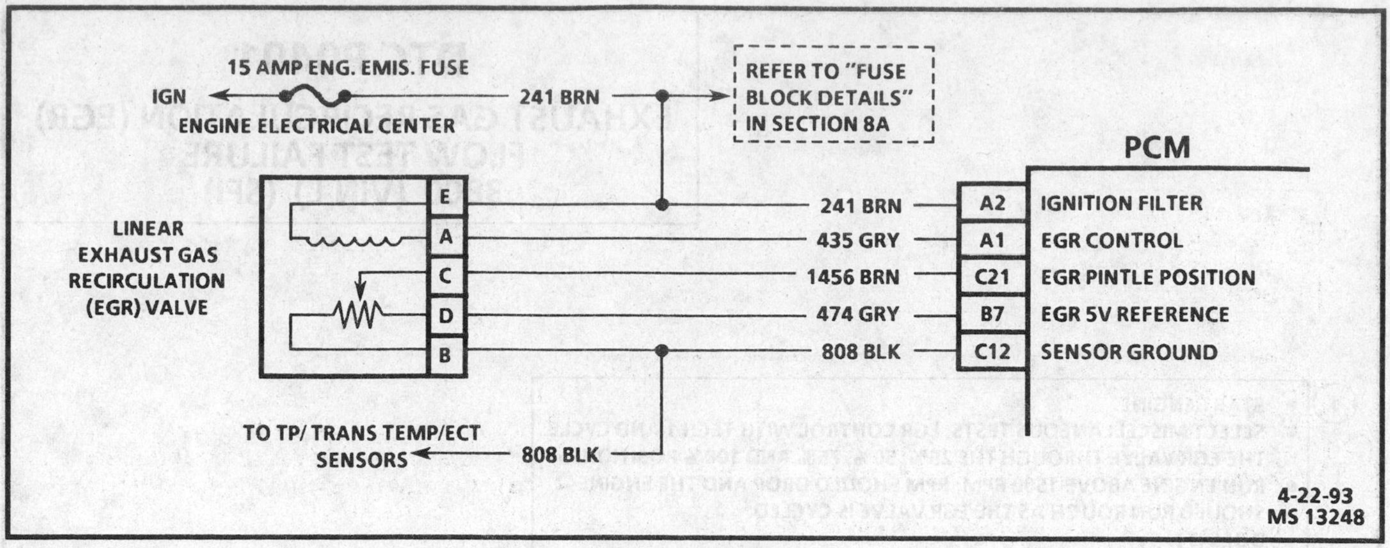
15 AMP ENG. EMIS. FUSE
IGN
241 BRN
ENGINE ELECTRICAL CENTER
REFER TO "FUSE BLOCK DETAILS" IN SECTION 8A
PCM
LINEAR EXHAUST GAS RECIRCULATION (EGR) VALVE
E
A
C
D
B
241 BRN
435 GRY
1456 BRN
474 GRY
808 BLK
A2
A1
C21
B7
C12
IGNITION FILTER
EGR CONTROL
EGR PINTLE POSITION
EGR 5V REFERENCE
SENSOR GROUND
TO TP/ TRANS TEMP/ECT SENSORS
808 BLK
4-22-93
MS 13248

DTC P1406

(Page 1 of 2)
EXHAUST GAS RECIRCULATION (EGR) VALVE PINTLE POSITION ERROR
3800 (VIN L) (SFI)

Circuit Description:

The PCM constantly monitors the linear EGR valve pintle position sensor to ensure that the valve is responding properly to commands from the PCM.

DTC P1406 Will Set When:

- EGR pintle position signal indicates a voltage out of the normal range of the pintle position sensor, or a signal that is 10% greater or less than the PCM commanded position.
- Either condition for up to 20 seconds.

Action Taken (PCM will default to): If a current DTC P1406 sets during two consecutive key cycles, the PCM will illuminate the MIL (Service Engine Soon).

DTC Chart Test Description: Number(s) below refer to circled number(s) on the diagnostic chart.

1. Checks for an EGR valve sticking partially open or an incorrect pintle position sensor feedback signal.
2. Ensures that the PCM is capable of controlling EGR pintle position and is reading the pintle position feedback signal properly.
3. Checks the EGR valve driver in the PCM and CKT 435.

Diagnostic Aids: An intermittent may be caused by a poor connection, rubbed-through wire insulation.

Check for:

- Poor connection or damaged harness - Inspect PCM harness connectors for backed out terminals "A1", "B7", "C12", or "C21", improper mating, broken locks, improperly formed or damaged terminals, poor terminal to wire connection and damaged harness.
- Intermittent test - If connections and harness check OK, monitor a digital voltmeter connected between affected terminals and ground while moving related connectors and wiring harness. If the failure is induced, the voltage reading will change.

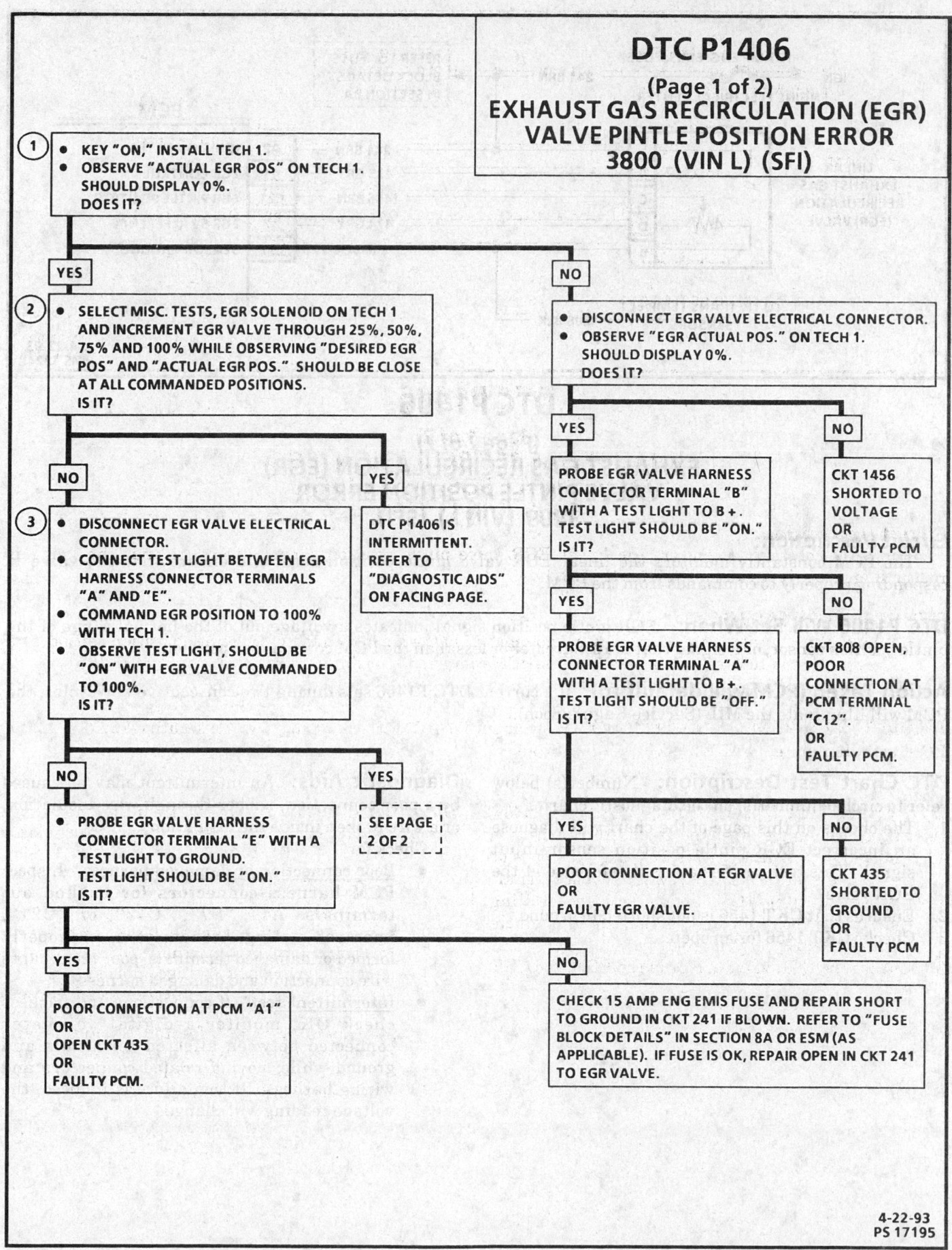

DTC P1406

(Page 1 of 2)

EXHAUST GAS RECIRCULATION (EGR) VALVE PINTLE POSITION ERROR 3800 (VIN L) (SFI)

1
- KEY "ON," INSTALL TECH 1.
- OBSERVE "ACTUAL EGR POS" ON TECH 1.

SHOULD DISPLAY 0%.
DOES IT?

YES

2
- SELECT MISC. TESTS, EGR SOLENOID ON TECH 1 AND INCREMENT EGR VALVE THROUGH 25%, 50%, 75% AND 100% WHILE OBSERVING "DESIRED EGR POS" AND "ACTUAL EGR POS." SHOULD BE CLOSE AT ALL COMMANDED POSITIONS.

IS IT?

NO

3
- DISCONNECT EGR VALVE ELECTRICAL CONNECTOR.
- CONNECT TEST LIGHT BETWEEN EGR HARNESS CONNECTOR TERMINALS "A" AND "E".
- COMMAND EGR POSITION TO 100% WITH TECH 1.
- OBSERVE TEST LIGHT, SHOULD BE "ON" WITH EGR VALVE COMMANDED TO 100%.

IS IT?

NO

- PROBE EGR VALVE HARNESS CONNECTOR TERMINAL "E" WITH A TEST LIGHT TO GROUND.

TEST LIGHT SHOULD BE "ON."
IS IT?

YES

POOR CONNECTION AT PCM "A1"
OR
OPEN CKT 435
OR
FAULTY PCM.

NO

CHECK 15 AMP ENG EMIS FUSE AND REPAIR SHORT TO GROUND IN CKT 241 IF BLOWN. REFER TO "FUSE BLOCK DETAILS" IN SECTION 8A OR ESM (AS APPLICABLE). IF FUSE IS OK, REPAIR OPEN IN CKT 241 TO EGR VALVE.

YES (from 3)

SEE PAGE 2 OF 2

YES (from 2)

DTC P1406 IS INTERMITTENT. REFER TO "DIAGNOSTIC AIDS" ON FACING PAGE.

NO (from 1)

- DISCONNECT EGR VALVE ELECTRICAL CONNECTOR.
- OBSERVE "EGR ACTUAL POS." ON TECH 1.

SHOULD DISPLAY 0%.
DOES IT?

NO

CKT 1456 SHORTED TO VOLTAGE
OR
FAULTY PCM

YES

PROBE EGR VALVE HARNESS CONNECTOR TERMINAL "B" WITH A TEST LIGHT TO B +.
TEST LIGHT SHOULD BE "ON."
IS IT?

NO

CKT 808 OPEN, POOR CONNECTION AT PCM TERMINAL "C12".
OR
FAULTY PCM.

YES

PROBE EGR VALVE HARNESS CONNECTOR TERMINAL "A" WITH A TEST LIGHT TO B +.
TEST LIGHT SHOULD BE "OFF."
IS IT?

YES

POOR CONNECTION AT EGR VALVE
OR
FAULTY EGR VALVE.

NO

CKT 435 SHORTED TO GROUND
OR
FAULTY PCM

4-22-93
PS 17195

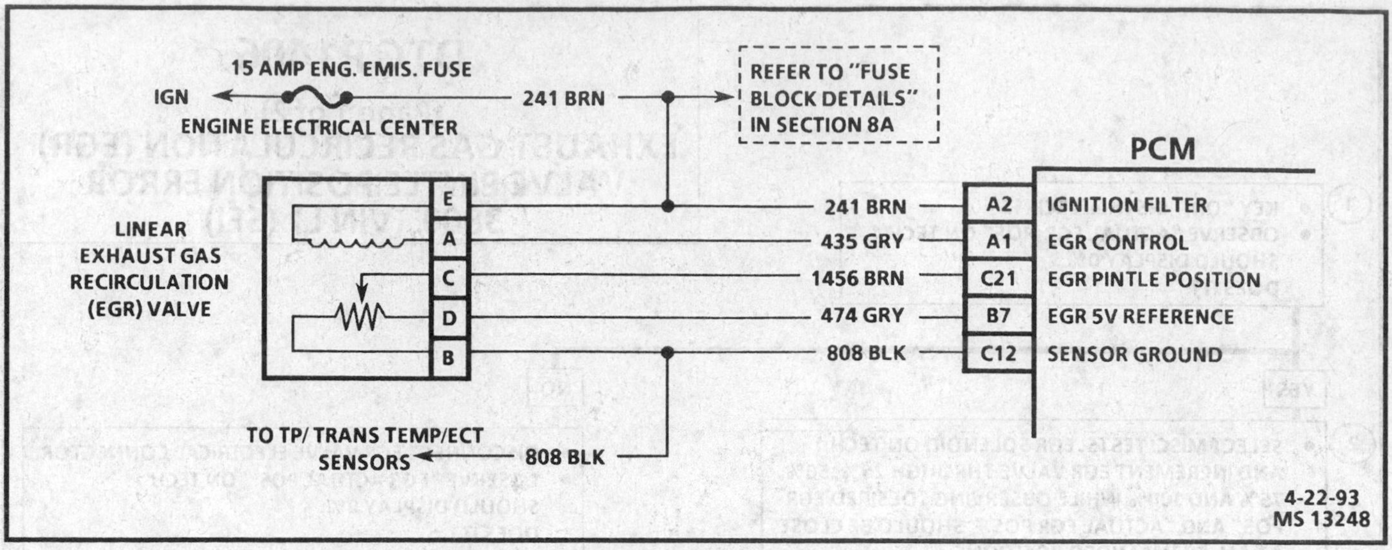
15 AMP ENG. EMIS. FUSE
IGN
241 BRN
ENGINE ELECTRICAL CENTER
REFER TO "FUSE BLOCK DETAILS" IN SECTION 8A
PCM
LINEAR EXHAUST GAS RECIRCULATION (EGR) VALVE
E
A
C
D
B
241 BRN
435 GRY
1456 BRN
474 GRY
808 BLK
A2
A1
C21
B7
C12
IGNITION FILTER
EGR CONTROL
EGR PINTLE POSITION
EGR 5V REFERENCE
SENSOR GROUND
TO TP/ TRANS TEMP/ECT SENSORS
808 BLK
4-22-93
MS 13248

DTC P1406

(Page 2 of 2)

EXHAUST GAS RECIRCULATION (EGR) VALVE PINTLE POSITION ERROR 3800 (VIN L) (SFI)

Circuit Description:

The PCM constantly monitors the linear EGR valve pintle position sensor to ensure that the valve is responding properly to commands from the PCM.

DTC P1406 Will Set When: EGR pintle position signal indicates a voltage out of the normal range of the pintle position sensor, or a signal that is 10% greater or less than the PCM commanded position.

Action Taken (PCM will default to): If a current DTC P1406 sets during two consecutive key cycles, the PCM will illuminate the MIL (Service Engine Soon).

DTC Chart Test Description: Number(s) below refer to circled number(s) on the diagnostic chart.

1. The checks on this page of the chart will diagnose an incorrect EGR pintle position sensor input signal. This test verifies a 5 volt reference at the EGR valve.
2. Ensures that CKT 1456 is not shorted to ground.
3. Checks CKT 1456 for an open.

Diagnostic Aids: An intermittent may be caused by a poor connection, rubber-through wire insulation, or a wire broken inside the insulation.

Check for:

- Poor connection or damaged harness - Inspect PCM harness connectors for backed out terminals "A1", "B7", "C12", or "C21", improper mating, broken locks, improperly formed or damaged terminals, poor terminal to wire connection and damaged harness.
- Intermittent test - If connections and harness check OK, monitor a digital voltmeter connected between affected terminals and ground while moving related connectors and wiring harness. If the failure is induced, the voltage reading will change.

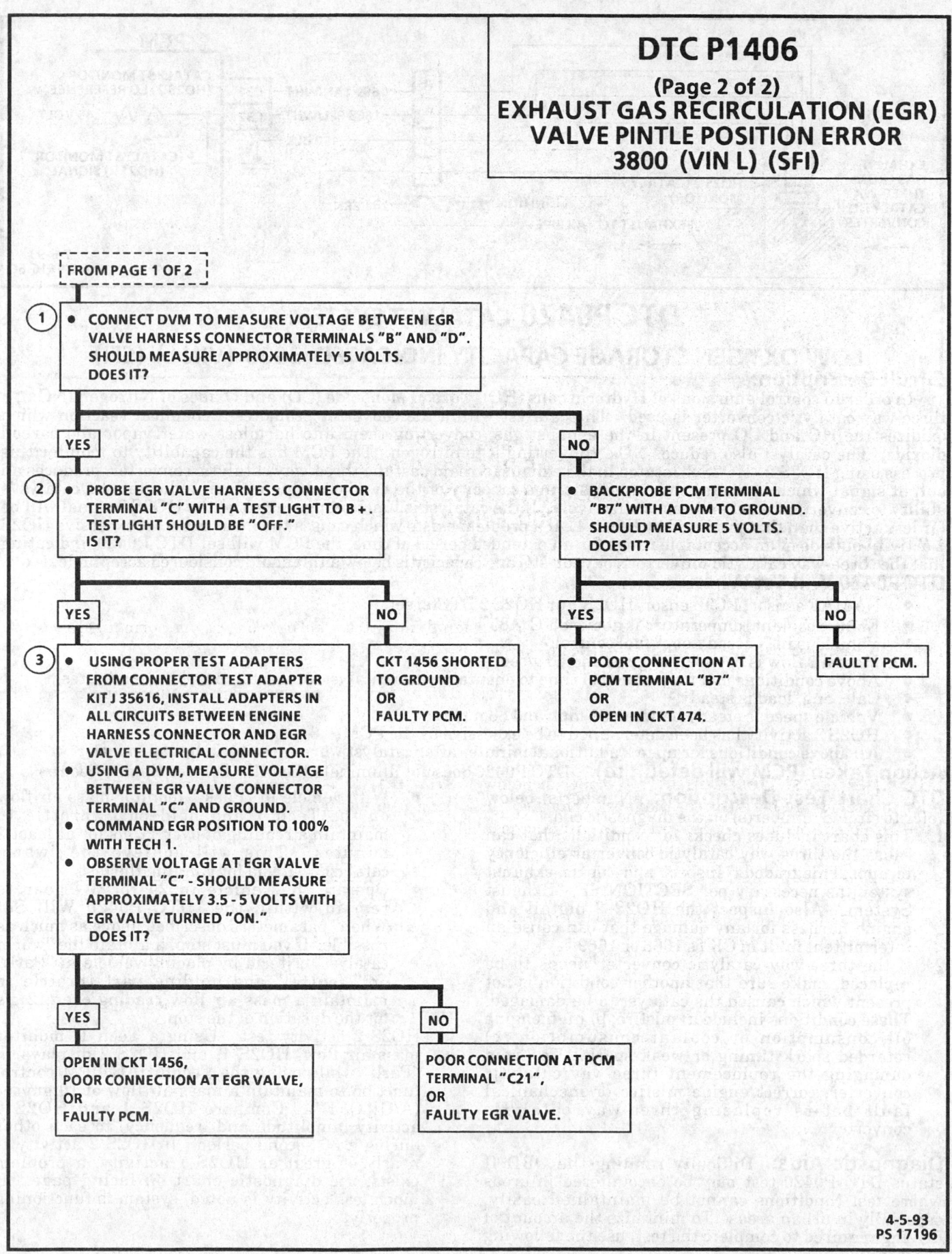

DTC P1406

(Page 2 of 2)
EXHAUST GAS RECIRCULATION (EGR) VALVE PINTLE POSITION ERROR 3800 (VIN L) (SFI)

FROM PAGE 1 OF 2

1
- CONNECT DVM TO MEASURE VOLTAGE BETWEEN EGR VALVE HARNESS CONNECTOR TERMINALS "B" AND "D". SHOULD MEASURE APPROXIMATELY 5 VOLTS. DOES IT?

YES →

2
- PROBE EGR VALVE HARNESS CONNECTOR TERMINAL "C" WITH A TEST LIGHT TO B+. TEST LIGHT SHOULD BE "OFF." IS IT?

YES →

3
- USING PROPER TEST ADAPTERS FROM CONNECTOR TEST ADAPTER KIT J 35616, INSTALL ADAPTERS IN ALL CIRCUITS BETWEEN ENGINE HARNESS CONNECTOR AND EGR VALVE ELECTRICAL CONNECTOR.
- USING A DVM, MEASURE VOLTAGE BETWEEN EGR VALVE CONNECTOR TERMINAL "C" AND GROUND.
- COMMAND EGR POSITION TO 100% WITH TECH 1.
- OBSERVE VOLTAGE AT EGR VALVE TERMINAL "C" - SHOULD MEASURE APPROXIMATELY 3.5 - 5 VOLTS WITH EGR VALVE TURNED "ON." DOES IT?

YES → OPEN IN CKT 1456, POOR CONNECTION AT EGR VALVE, OR FAULTY PCM.

NO → POOR CONNECTION AT PCM TERMINAL "C21", OR FAULTY EGR VALVE.

(From 2) NO → CKT 1456 SHORTED TO GROUND OR FAULTY PCM.

(From 1) NO →
- BACKPROBE PCM TERMINAL "B7" WITH A DVM TO GROUND. SHOULD MEASURE 5 VOLTS. DOES IT?

YES →
- POOR CONNECTION AT PCM TERMINAL "B7" OR OPEN IN CKT 474.

NO → FAULTY PCM.

4-5-93
PS 17196

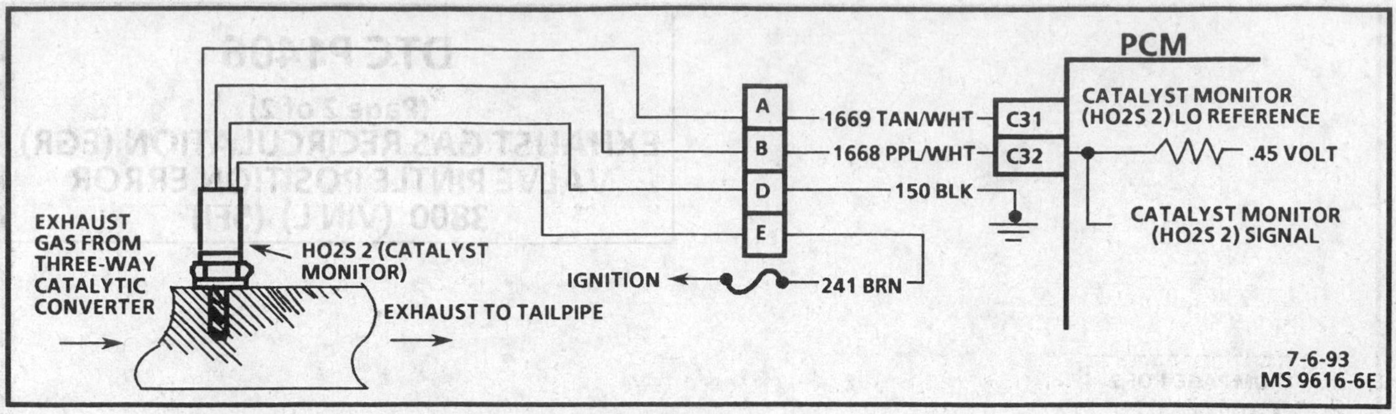
PCM
CATALYST MONITOR
(HO2S 2) LO REFERENCE
A
B
D
E
1669 TAN/WHT
1668 PPL/WHT
150 BLK
241 BRN
C31
C32
.45 VOLT
CATALYST MONITOR
(HO2S 2) SIGNAL
EXHAUST
GAS FROM
THREE-WAY
CATALYTIC
CONVERTER
HO2S 2 (CATALYST
MONITOR)
IGNITION
EXHAUST TO TAILPIPE
7-6-93
MS 9616-6E

DTC P0420 CATALYST SYSTEM - LOW OXYGEN STORAGE CAPACITY INDICATED 3800 (VIN L) (SFI)

Circuit Description:

In order to control emissions of Hydrocarbons (HC), Carbon Monoxide (CO) and Oxides of Nitrogen (NOx), a three-way catalytic converter is used. The catalyst within the converter promotes a chemical reaction which oxidizes the HC and CO present in the exhaust gas, converting them into harmless water vapor and carbon dioxide. The catalyst also reduces NOx, converting it to nitrogen. The PCM has the capability to monitor this process using HO2S 2. HO2S 2, located in the exhaust stream past the three-way catalytic converter, produces an output signal which indicates the oxygen storage capacity of the catalyst; this in turn indicates the catalyst's ability to convert exhaust emissions effectively. If the catalyst is functioning correctly, the HO2S 2 signal will be far less active than that produced by HO2S 1. If a problem exists which causes the PCM to detect excessive HO2S 2 activity outside of an acceptable range for an extended period of time, the PCM will set DTC P0420, indicating that the three-way catalytic converter's oxygen storage capacity is below a threshold considered acceptable.

DTC P0420 Will Set When:

- No MAF sensor, ECT sensor, HO2S 1 or HO2S 2 DTC(s) set.
- Engine coolant temperature is above 85°C (185°F).
- Vehicle is in "Closed Loop" fuel control.
- Mass air flow is between 12 g/sec and 40 g/sec.
- Above conditions met for a period of time to ensure a warm catalyst (at least 2 consecutive minutes).
- Calc. eng. load is steady.
- Vehicle speed is steady between 30 mph and 68 mph.
- HO2S 2 activity has been determined to be excessive by the PCM.
- All above conditions for up to 2 additional minutes after catalyst warmup criteria has been met.

Action Taken (PCM will default to): DTC P0420 does not illuminate the MIL (Service Engine Soon).

DTC Chart Test Description: Number(s) below refer to circled number(s) on the diagnostic chart.

1. This chart includes checks for conditions that can cause the three-way catalytic converter efficiency to appear degraded. Inspect and repair exhaust system as necessary per SECTION 6F, "Exhaust System." Also inspect the HO2S 2 pigtail and engine harness for any damage that can cause an intermittent fault in CKTs 1668 or 1669.
2. If the three-way catalytic converter needs to be replaced, make sure that another condition is not present which caused the catalyst to be damaged. These conditions include a) misfire; b) high engine oil consumption or coolant consumption; c) retarded spark timing or weak spark. To avoid damaging the replacement three-way catalytic converter, correct engine misfire or mechanical fault before replacing three-way catalytic converter.

Diagnostic Aids: Difficulty running the OBD II status DTC P0420 test may be encountered in areas where test conditions cannot be maintained easily, especially in urban areas. To minimize the amount of driving required to complete the test, use the following procedure:

- Allow engine to warm completely.
- With vehicle in "Park," monitor mass air flow on the Tech 1 and hold part throttle to maintain a reading of over 12 g/s for at least 2 minutes. This will achieve the "warm catalyst" criteria for running the test.
- Operate the vehicle in 2nd or 3rd gear to remain within the "DTC P0420 Will Set When" parameters described above as much as possible. If you must stop, maintain the "warm catalyst" criteria by placing vehicle in "Park" or "Neutral" and holding part throttle to maintain a mass air flow reading over 12 g/s for the duration of the stop.

HO2S 2 activity test: Using a Tech 1, monitor mass air flow, HO2S 1, and HO2S 2 displays in "Park" while using the Tech 1 IAC RPM control function to maintain a mass air flow of 10 gm/sec (A/C "OFF"). Compare HO2S 1 and HO2S 2 activity (amplitude and frequency) to each other during a 30 second period. If HO2S 2 activity is nearly as great as HO2S 1 activity, a problem exists; use diagnostic chart on facing page. If much less activity is noted, system is functioning properly.

DTC P0420

CATALYST SYSTEM - LOW OXYGEN STORAGE CAPACITY INDICATED 3800 (VIN L) (SFI)

NOTICE: IF ANY MAF SENSOR, HO2S 1 OR HO2S 2, VEHICLE SPEED SENSOR, OR ECT SENSOR DTC(s) ARE SET, DIAGNOSE THOSE DTC(s) BEFORE USING THIS CHART.

(1) VISUALLY/PHYSICALLY CHECK THE FOLLOWING:

- VERIFY THAT THREE-WAY CONVERTER IS PROPER ORIGINAL EQUIPMENT MANUFACTURER PART.
- THREE-WAY CATALYTIC CONVERTER FOR DAMAGE (DENTS, SEVERE DISCOLORATION CAUSED BY EXCESSIVE TEMPERATURES, HOLES, ETC). ALSO, ENSURE THAT INTERNAL CONVERTER RATTLE CAUSED BY DAMAGED CATALYST IS NOT PRESENT.
- EXHAUST SYSTEM BETWEEN THREE-WAY CATALYTIC CONVERTER AND REAR CONVERTER FLANGE FOR LEAKS, DAMAGE, OR LOOSE OR MISSING HARDWARE.
- HO2S 2. ENSURE THAT HO2S 2 IS SECURE AND THAT HO2S 2 PIGTAIL AND WIRING IS NOT DAMAGED OR CONTACTING EXHAUST.

WAS A PROBLEM FOUND?

NO

(2)
- CHECK ALL PCM AND SENSOR GROUNDS; CHECK CKTs 1668 AND 1669 FOR AN INTERMITTENT OPEN OR SHORT TO GROUND. IF OK, REPLACE THREE-WAY CATALYTIC CONVERTER.

Important

- IF THREE-WAY CATALYTIC CONVERTER NEEDS TO BE REPLACED, CHECK FOR A POSSIBLE MISFIRE (USE DTC P0300 CHART) OR AN ENGINE MECHANICAL PROBLEM (REFER TO SECTION 6A).

- SEE NOTICE BELOW TO VERIFY REPAIR.

YES

- REPAIR PROBLEM.
- SEE NOTICE BELOW TO VERIFY REPAIR.

NOTICE: AFTER REPAIRS ARE MADE, CLEAR PCM MEMORY BY DISCONNECTING BATTERY FOR AT LEAST 10 SECONDS, INSTALL TECH-1, SELECT DTC DISPLAY SCREEN, AND MONITOR OBDII TEST STATUS SCREEN WHILE OPERATING VEHICLE WITHIN THE "DTC P0420 WILL SET WHEN:" PARAMETERS LISTED ON FACING PAGE. IF DTC P0420 TEST DOES NOT RUN AND PASS AND DTC P0420 DIAGNOSTIC CHART HAS NOT BEEN COMPLETED, CONTINUE WITH DTC P0420 CHART. IF CHART HAS BEEN COMPLETED, AND DTC P0420 TEST STILL DOES NOT RUN AND PASS, REFER TO "DIAGNOSTIC AIDS" ON FACING PAGE.

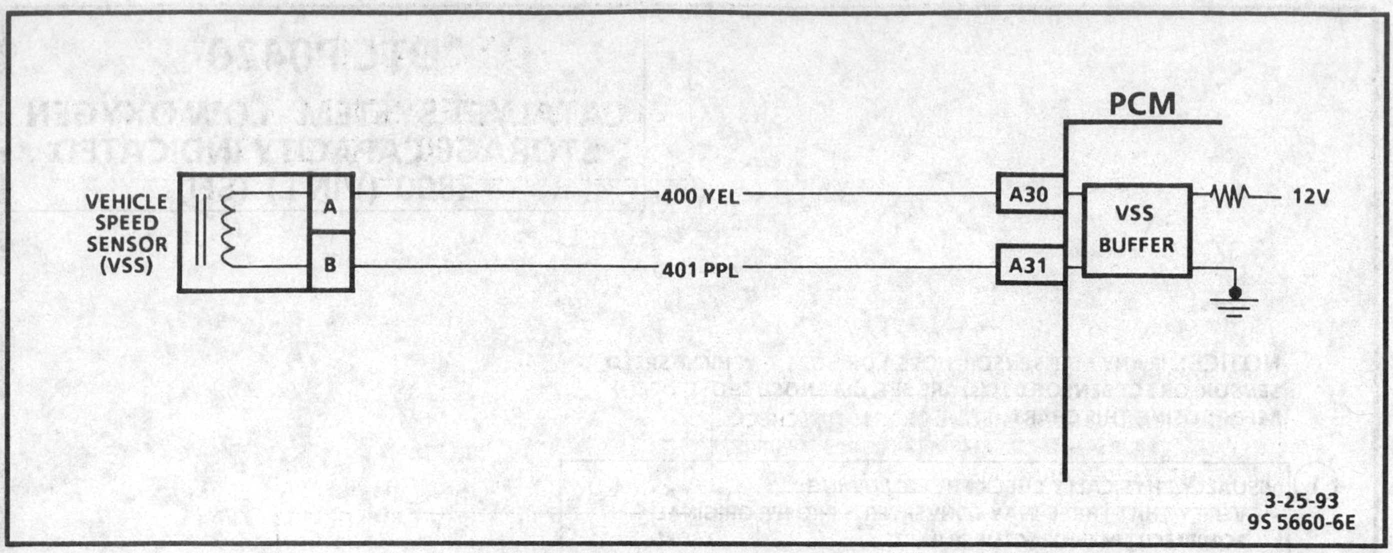
PCM
VEHICLE SPEED SENSOR (VSS)
A
B
400 YEL
401 PPL
A30
A31
VSS BUFFER
12V
3-25-93
9S 5660-6E

DTC P0501/P0502

VEHICLE SPEED SENSOR (VSS) CIRCUIT 3800 (VIN L) (SFI)

Circuit Description:

Vehicle speed information is provided to the PCM by the vehicle speed sensor in the transaxle. The voltage level and the number of pulses increases with vehicle speed. The PCM converts the pulsing voltage to mph, and the mph can be displayed with a Tech 1.

The function of the VSS buffer, used in past model years, has been incorporated into the PCM. The PCM supplies the necessary signal for the instrument panel (4004 pulses per mile) for operating the speedometer and the odometer.

DTC P0501 Will Set When:

- Vehicle speed goes from greater than 18 to 0 mph in less than 2 seconds, brake not applied.

DTC P0502 Will Set When:

- Engine is running.
- No DTC P0705.
- Transmission is out of park or neutral for more than 4 seconds.
- Engine speed is greater than 3250 RPM.
- Vehicle speed is less than 3 mph.
- All conditions met for 2 seconds.

Action Taken (PCM will default to): Cruise control operation will not be allowed with DTC P0501 or P0502 set. Also, the transaxle will be forced into 3rd gear with a 3-2 downshift available; TCC will not be allowed to engage. Additionally, the cluster speedometer may be inoperative. The MIL (Service Engine Soon) will be illuminated.

DTC Chart Test Description: Number(s) below refer to circled number(s) on the diagnostic chart.

1. The VSS signal generator only produces a signal if drive wheels are turning greater then 3 mph.
2. Before replacing the PCM, check the PROM for correct application.

Diagnostic Aids: Tech 1 should indicate a vehicle speed whenever the vehicle is moving greater than 3 mph.

DTC P0501 indicates an intermittent problem and may not set immediately or under all conditions. Check CKTs 400 and 401 for proper connections to be sure they are clean and tight and the harness is routed correctly. Refer to "Intermittents," in "Symptoms," Section "6E3-B".

DTC P0501/P0502
VEHICLE SPEED SENSOR (VSS) CIRCUIT
3800 (VIN L) (SFI)

- PERFORM ON-BOARD DIAGNOSTIC SYSTEM CHECK.
- IF DTC P0755 IS STORED ALONG WITH P0501/P0502, SEE DTC P0755 CHART FIRST.

(1)
- RAISE DRIVE WHEELS.

Important

- DO NOT PERFORM THIS TEST WITHOUT SUPPORTING THE LOWER CONTROL ARMS SO THAT THE DRIVE AXLES ARE IN A NORMAL HORIZONTAL POSITION. RUNNING THE VEHICLE IN GEAR WITH THE WHEELS HANGING DOWN AT FULL TRAVEL MAY DAMAGE THE DRIVE AXLES.

- WITH ENGINE IDLING IN GEAR, TECH 1 SHOULD DISPLAY MPH ABOVE 0. DOES IT?

NO

- IGNITION "OFF."
- DISCONNECT TECH 1 FROM DLC.
- START ENGINE AND IDLE IN GEAR.
- OBSERVE SPEEDOMETER. DOES SPEEDOMETER WORK?

NO

- KEY "OFF," DISCONNECT BLACK PCM CONNECTOR "A."
- CHECK CKT 400 AND CKT 401 FOR OPEN.
- CHECK CKT 400 FOR SHORT TO GROUND. ARE CIRCUITS OK?

YES

POOR CONNECTION AT VEHICLE SPEED SENSOR OR PCM
OR
FAULTY VEHICLE SPEED SENSOR OR FAULTY PCM.

NO

REPAIR CIRCUIT WHICH IS OPEN
OR
SHORTED TO GROUND.

YES (speedometer works)

(2) FAULTY PCM.

YES (Tech 1 displays MPH above 0)

DTC P0501/P0502 IS INTERMITTENT. IF NO ADDITIONAL DTCs WERE STORED, REFER TO "DIAGNOSTIC AIDS" ON FACING PAGE.

"*AFTER REPAIRS,*" REFER TO DTC CRITERIA ON FACING PAGE AND CONFIRM DTC DOES NOT RESET.

5-7-93
MS 8686-6E

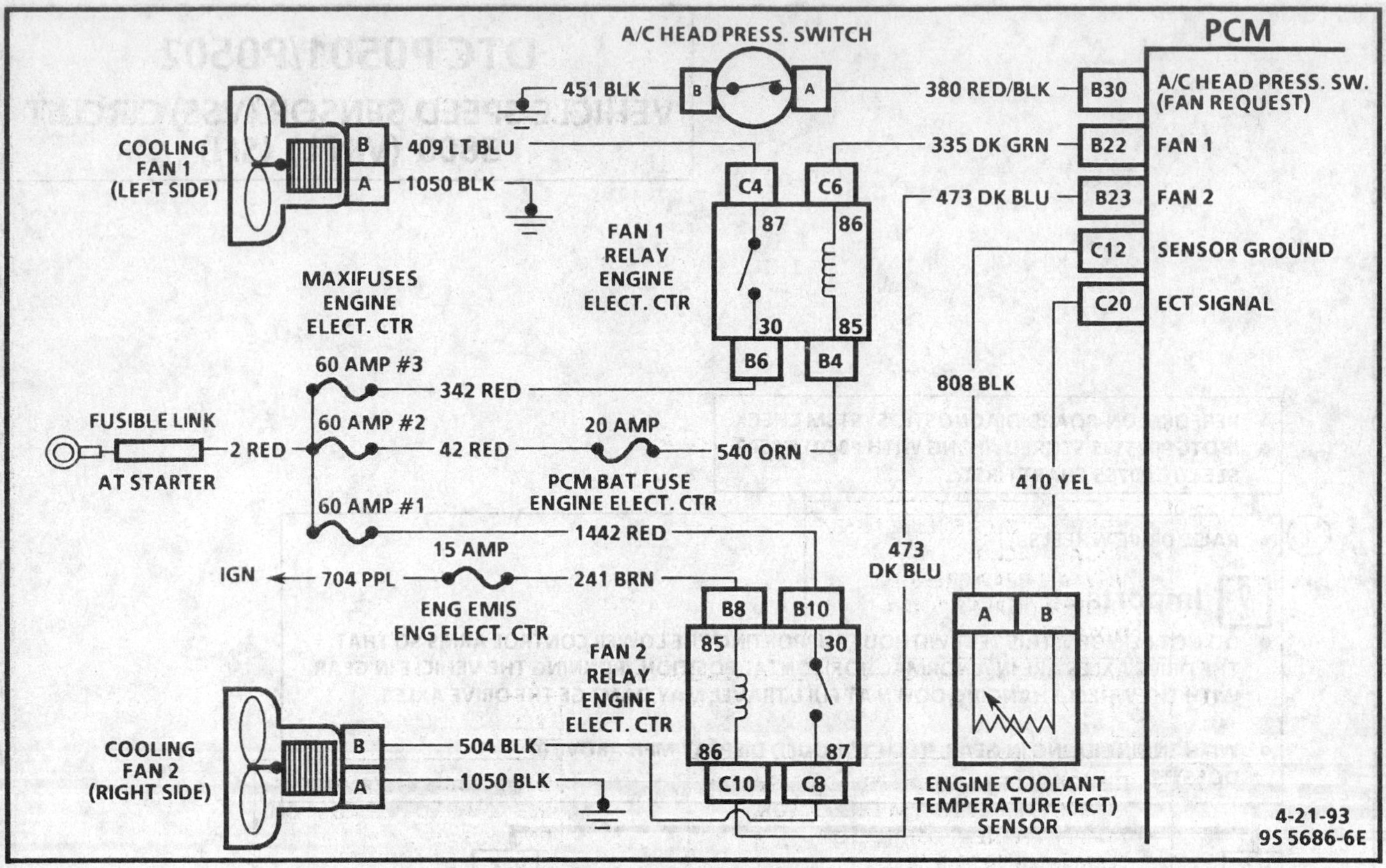
A/C HEAD PRESS. SWITCH
PCM
451 BLK
B
A
380 RED/BLK
B30
A/C HEAD PRESS. SW. (FAN REQUEST)
COOLING FAN 1 (LEFT SIDE)
409 LT BLU
1050 BLK
335 DK GRN
B22
FAN 1
C4
C6
473 DK BLU
B23
FAN 2
87
86
FAN 1 RELAY ENGINE ELECT. CTR
C12
SENSOR GROUND
MAXIFUSES ENGINE ELECT. CTR
C20
ECT SIGNAL
30
85
B6
B4
60 AMP #3
342 RED
808 BLK
FUSIBLE LINK
60 AMP #2
20 AMP
2 RED
42 RED
540 ORN
AT STARTER
PCM BAT FUSE ENGINE ELECT. CTR
410 YEL
60 AMP #1
1442 RED
15 AMP
473 DK BLU
IGN
704 PPL
241 BRN
ENG EMIS ENG ELECT. CTR
B8
B10
FAN 2 RELAY ENGINE ELECT. CTR
85
30
COOLING FAN 2 (RIGHT SIDE)
504 BLK
1050 BLK
86
87
C10
C8
ENGINE COOLANT TEMPERATURE (ECT) SENSOR
4-21-93
9S 5686-6E

DTC P1530
A/C HEAD PRESSURE SWITCH CIRCUIT
3800 (VIN L) (SFI)

Circuit Description:

The A/C head pressure switch opens at 210 psi (1448 kPa) ± 10. When the head pressure switch interrupts the ground at PCM CKT 380, both fans should run.

DTC P1530 Will Set When:

- The CKT 380 is grounded during the first 5 seconds of engine run time.
- Engine coolant temperature is less than 31°C (88°F).
- Intake air temperature is less than 28°C (82°F).
- RPM is less than 1800.
- No DTC P0101, P0112, P0113, P0117, or P0118 is set.
- All the above conditions must be met at the same time.

Action Taken (PCM will default to): If current DTC P1530 is set, both cooling fans will run anytime A/C is requested. DTC P1530 does not illuminate the MIL (Service Engine Soon).

DTC Chart Test Description: Number(s) below refer to circled number(s) on the diagnostic charts.

1. With the key "ON," engine not running, the A/C head pressure switch should be closed (CKT 380 grounded).
2. This test isolates the fault to the A/C head pressure switch or CKT 380 or 451.

Diagnostic Aids: An intermittent may be caused by a poor connection, rubbed through wire insulation, or a wire broken inside the insulation.

Check for:

- Poor connection or damaged harness - Inspect harness connectors for backed out terminals, improper mating, broken locks, improperly formed or damaged terminals, poor terminal to wire connection, and damaged harness.

DTC P1530

A/C HEAD PRESSURE SWITCH CIRCUIT 3800 (VIN L) (SFI)

1
- IGNITION "ON," ENGINE "OFF."
- INSTALL TECH 1.
- VIEW A/C HEAD PRESSURE.
- SHOULD DISPLAY "OK."

DOES IT?

YES → DTC P1530 IS INTERMITTENT. SEE "DIAGNOSTIC AIDS" ON FACING PAGE.

NO →

2
- DISCONNECT THE HEAD PRESSURE SWITCH WIRING HARNESS FROM THE SENSOR.
- JUMPER HARNESS CONNECTOR TERMINALS "A" TO "B".

DOES A/C HEAD PRESS. SWITCH TO OK?

YES → POOR CONNECTION AT A/C HEAD PRESSURE SWITCH OR FAULTY HEAD PRESSURE SWITCH.

NO → CHECK CKT 380 OR CKT 451 FOR AN OPEN. IF OK, IT'S A POOR CONNECTION AT THE PCM OR A FAULTY PCM.

"AFTER REPAIRS," REFER TO DTC CRITERIA ON FACING PAGE AND CONFIRM DTC DOES NOT RESET.

3-30-93
PS 17193

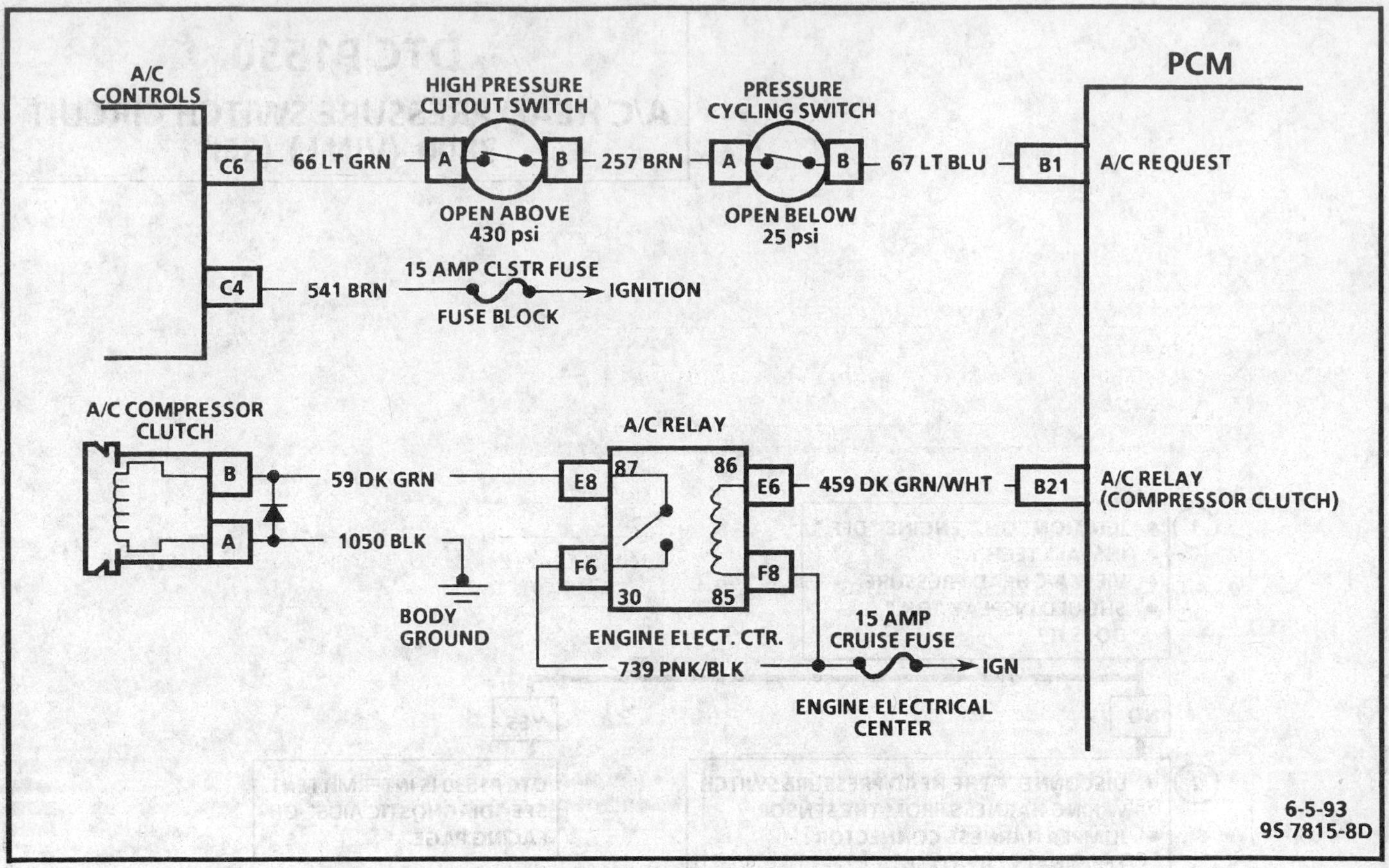
A/C CONTROLS
C6
66 LT GRN
HIGH PRESSURE CUTOUT SWITCH
A
B
OPEN ABOVE 430 psi
257 BRN
PRESSURE CYCLING SWITCH
A
B
OPEN BELOW 25 psi
67 LT BLU
B1
PCM
A/C REQUEST
C4
541 BRN
15 AMP CLSTR FUSE
FUSE BLOCK
IGNITION
A/C COMPRESSOR CLUTCH
B
A
59 DK GRN
1050 BLK
BODY GROUND
A/C RELAY
E8
87
86
E6
F6
30
85
F8
ENGINE ELECT. CTR.
459 DK GRN/WHT
B21
A/C RELAY (COMPRESSOR CLUTCH)
15 AMP CRUISE FUSE
739 PNK/BLK
IGN
ENGINE ELECTRICAL CENTER
6-5-93
9S 7815-8D

DTC P1531

LOW A/C REFRIGERANT CHARGE 3800 (VIN L) (SFI)

Circuit Description:

The PCM monitors the A/C request signal (CKT 67) and completes the ground for the A/C relay when an A/C mode is selected at the control head and refrigerant pressure is sufficient to close the A/C pressure cycling switch. If the refrigerant pressure is low and the A/C request signal causes the PCM to cycle the compressor too often, the PCM protects the compressor by disabling the A/C relay and storing DTC P1531.

DTC P1531 Will Set When: The A/C compressor cycles "ON" 10 or more times within 15 minutes, and compressor "ON" time for each cycle is less than 1.5 seconds.

Action Taken (PCM will default to): With a current DTC P1531 stored, the PCM will not allow the compressor to be turned "ON" until the next ignition cycle. If DTC P1531 is set during three ignition cycles, the A/C clutch will be disabled until the DTC P1531 is cleared from memory. DTC P1531 does not illuminate the MIL (Service Engine Soon).

Diagnostic Aids: An intermittent may be caused by a poor connection, rubbed through wire insulation or a wire broken inside the insulation.

Check for:

- Poor connection or damaged harness - Inspect harness connectors for backed out terminals, improper mating, broken locks, improperly formed or damaged terminals, poor terminal to wire connection, and damaged harness.

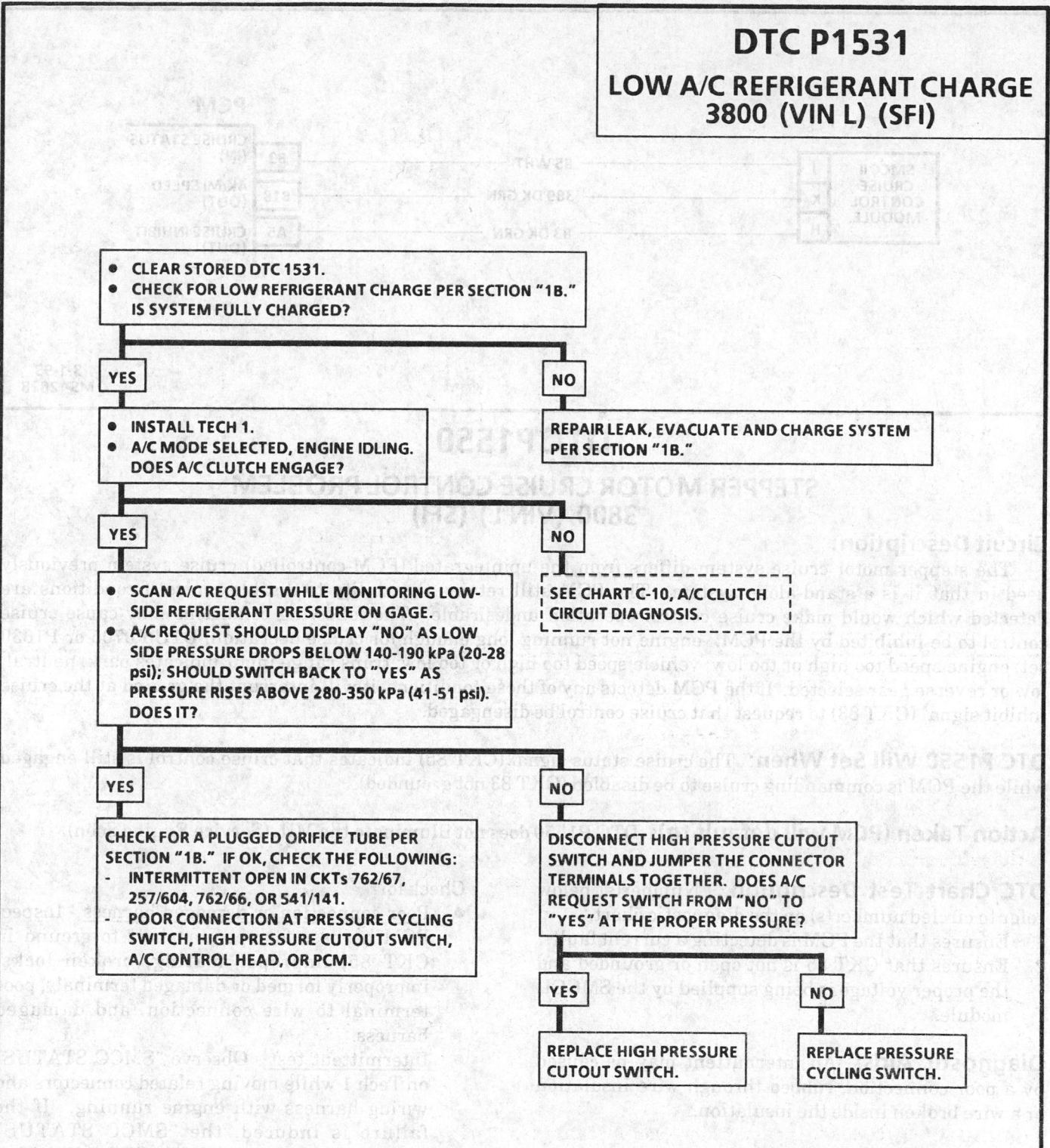

DTC P1531

LOW A/C REFRIGERANT CHARGE 3800 (VIN L) (SFI)

- CLEAR STORED DTC 1531.
- CHECK FOR LOW REFRIGERANT CHARGE PER SECTION "1B." IS SYSTEM FULLY CHARGED?

NO: REPAIR LEAK, EVACUATE AND CHARGE SYSTEM PER SECTION "1B."

YES:

- INSTALL TECH 1.
- A/C MODE SELECTED, ENGINE IDLING. DOES A/C CLUTCH ENGAGE?

NO: SEE CHART C-10, A/C CLUTCH CIRCUIT DIAGNOSIS.

YES:

- SCAN A/C REQUEST WHILE MONITORING LOW-SIDE REFRIGERANT PRESSURE ON GAGE.
- A/C REQUEST SHOULD DISPLAY "NO" AS LOW SIDE PRESSURE DROPS BELOW 140-190 kPa (20-28 psi); SHOULD SWITCH BACK TO "YES" AS PRESSURE RISES ABOVE 280-350 kPa (41-51 psi). DOES IT?

YES: CHECK FOR A PLUGGED ORIFICE TUBE PER SECTION "1B." IF OK, CHECK THE FOLLOWING:

- INTERMITTENT OPEN IN CKTs 762/67, 257/604, 762/66, OR 541/141.
- POOR CONNECTION AT PRESSURE CYCLING SWITCH, HIGH PRESSURE CUTOUT SWITCH, A/C CONTROL HEAD, OR PCM.

NO: DISCONNECT HIGH PRESSURE CUTOUT SWITCH AND JUMPER THE CONNECTOR TERMINALS TOGETHER. DOES A/C REQUEST SWITCH FROM "NO" TO "YES" AT THE PROPER PRESSURE?

- **YES:** REPLACE HIGH PRESSURE CUTOUT SWITCH.
- **NO:** REPLACE PRESSURE CYCLING SWITCH.

"*AFTER REPAIRS,*" REFER TO DTC CRITERIA ON FACING PAGE AND CONFIRM DTC DOES NOT RESET.

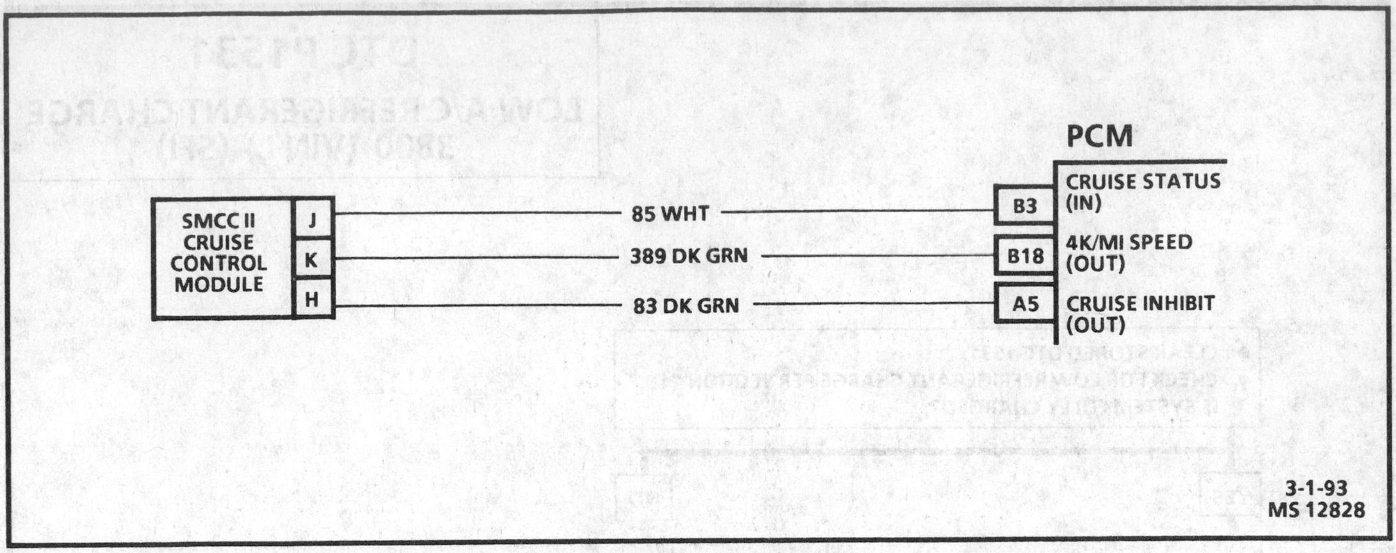
PCM
SMCC II CRUISE CONTROL MODULE
J
K
H
85 WHT
389 DK GRN
83 DK GRN
B3
B18
A5
CRUISE STATUS (IN)
4K/MI SPEED (OUT)
CRUISE INHIBIT (OUT)
3-1-93
MS 12828

DTC P1550

STEPPER MOTOR CRUISE CONTROL PROBLEM 3800 (VIN L) (SFI)

Circuit Description:

The stepper motor cruise system differs from the upintegrated (PCM-controlled) cruise system previously used in that it is a stand-alone system. The PCM still retains the ability to disable cruise if conditions are detected which would make cruise control operation undesirable. The following conditions may cause cruise control to be inhibited by the PCM: engine not running long enough for cruise operation; DTC P0705 or P1630 set; engine speed too high or too low; vehicle speed too high or too low; trans range input indicates park, neutral, low or reverse gear selected. If the PCM detects any of these conditions, it will interrupt the ground at the cruise inhibit signal (CKT 83) to request that cruise control be disengaged.

DTC P1550 Will Set When: The cruise status signal (CKT 85) indicates that cruise control is still engaged while the PCM is commanding cruise to be disabled (CKT 83 not grounded).

Action Taken (PCM will default to): DTC P1550 does not illuminate the MIL (Service Engine Soon).

DTC Chart Test Description: Number(s) below refer to circled number(s) on the diagnostic chart.

1. Ensures that the PCM is detecting a current fault.
2. Ensures that CKT 85 is not open or grounded and the proper voltage is being supplied by the SMCCII module.

Diagnostic Aids: An intermittent may be caused by a poor connection, rubbed through wire insulation or a wire broken inside the insulation.

Check for:

- Poor connection or damaged harness - Inspect PCM harness for open or short to ground in CKT 85, improper mating, broken locks, improperly formed or damaged terminals, poor terminal to wire connection, and damaged harness.
- Intermittent test - Observe "SMCC STATUS" on Tech 1 while moving related connectors and wiring harness with engine running. If the failure is induced, the "SMCC STATUS" display will change to "ENGAGED." This may help to isolate the location of the malfunction.

DTC P1550

STEPPER MOTOR CRUISE CONTROL PROBLEM 3800 (VIN L) (SFI)

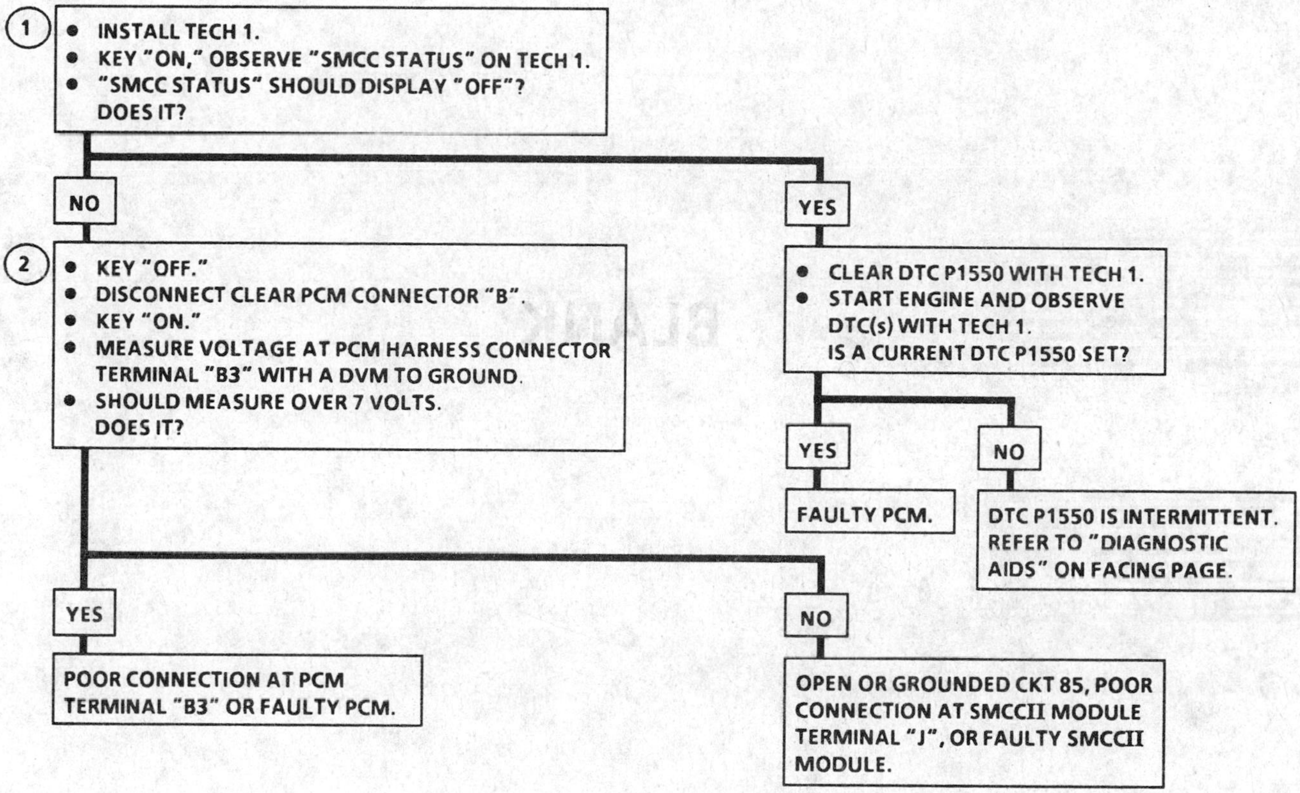
1
• INSTALL TECH 1.
• KEY "ON," OBSERVE "SMCC STATUS" ON TECH 1.
• "SMCC STATUS" SHOULD DISPLAY "OFF"? DOES IT?
NO
YES
2
• KEY "OFF."
• DISCONNECT CLEAR PCM CONNECTOR "B".
• KEY "ON."
• MEASURE VOLTAGE AT PCM HARNESS CONNECTOR TERMINAL "B3" WITH A DVM TO GROUND.
• SHOULD MEASURE OVER 7 VOLTS. DOES IT?
• CLEAR DTC P1550 WITH TECH 1.
• START ENGINE AND OBSERVE DTC(s) WITH TECH 1. IS A CURRENT DTC P1550 SET?
YES
NO
FAULTY PCM.
DTC P1550 IS INTERMITTENT. REFER TO "DIAGNOSTIC AIDS" ON FACING PAGE.
YES
NO
POOR CONNECTION AT PCM TERMINAL "B3" OR FAULTY PCM.
OPEN OR GROUNDED CKT 85, POOR CONNECTION AT SMCCII MODULE TERMINAL "J", OR FAULTY SMCCII MODULE.

3-8-93
MS 12830

BLANK

DTC 1623

PROM ERROR
(FAULTY OR INCORRECT PROM)
3800 (VIN L) (SFI)

CHECK THAT PROM IS CORRECTLY INSERTED IN THE SOCKET. IF OK, REPLACE PROM, CLEAR MEMORY AND RECHECK. IF DTC P1623 REAPPEARS, REPLACE PCM.

NOTICE: To prevent possible Electrostatic Discharge damage to the PCM or PROM, Do Not touch the component leads. Do Not remove integrated circuit from carrier.

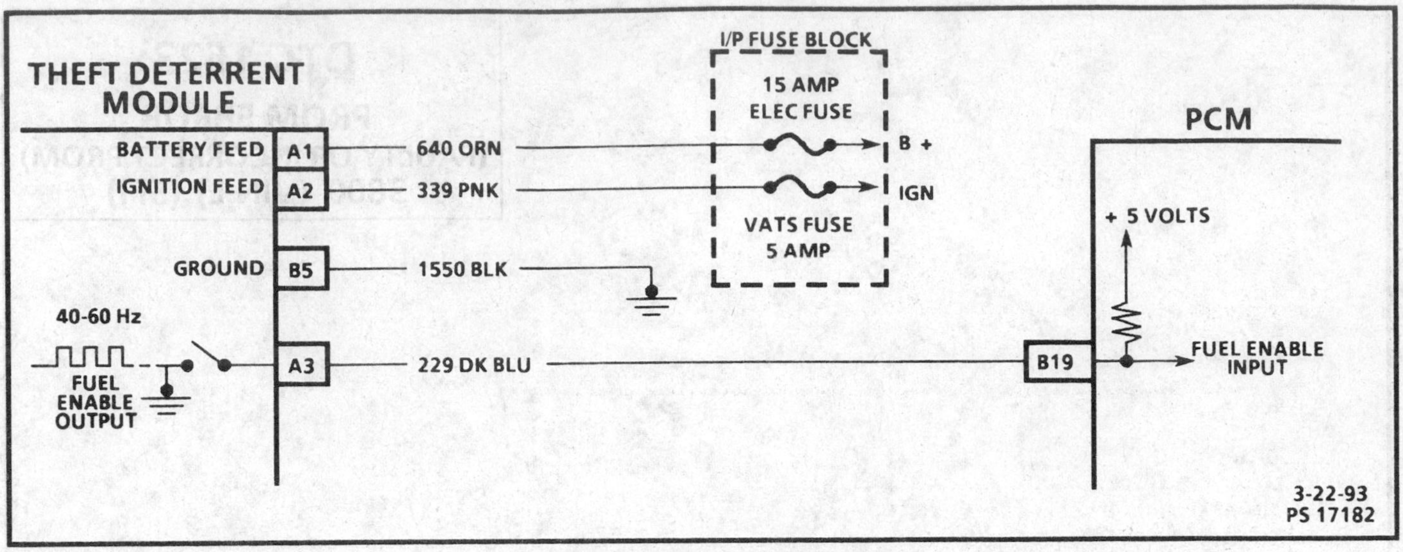
THEFT DETERRENT MODULE
BATTERY FEED
A1
IGNITION FEED
A2
GROUND
B5
40-60 Hz
FUEL ENABLE OUTPUT
A3
640 ORN
339 PNK
1550 BLK
229 DK BLU
I/P FUSE BLOCK
15 AMP ELEC FUSE
VATS FUSE 5 AMP
B +
IGN
PCM
+ 5 VOLTS
B19
FUEL ENABLE INPUT
3-22-93
PS 17182

DTC P1626/P1629

PASS-Key®II FUEL ENABLE CIRCUIT 3800 (VIN L) (SFI)

Circuit Description:

When the ignition is turned "ON," the theft deterrent module "reads" the key resistor pellet. If the proper resistance is recognized by the theft deterrent module, it sends a PWM fuel enable signal via CKT 229 to the PCM. The PCM looks for this signal during crank and allows fuel delivery by enabling the injectors when the signal is recognized.

DTC P1626 Will Set When: The fuel enable signal is lost after the engine has started.

DTC P1629 Will Set When: The fuel enable signal is not present during crank.

Action Taken (PCM Will default to): If the fuel enable signal is not seen during crank, the injectors will be disabled and the PCM will store DTC P1629, indicating a problem with the theft deterrent system or CKT 229. A current DTC P1629 will result in a "cranks but won't run" condition. DTC P1629 does not illuminate the MIL (Service Engine Soon). If the fuel enable signal is lost while the engine is running, the PCM will store DTC P1626 and the vehicle will run normally. As long as DTC P1626 is stored, the PCM will ignore any absence of the fuel enable signal and the vehicle will restart and run as long as the problem is isolated to the fuel enable circuit only. Refer to "Theft Deterrent Systems" in SECTION 8A for a complete description and diagnostic procedures. DTC P1626 does not illuminate the MIL (Service Engine Soon).

DTC Chart Test Description: Number(s) below refer to circled number(s) on the diagnostic chart.

1. If vehicle will not crank with DTC P1626 or P1629 stored, the problem affects the entire theft deterrent system and is not isolated to the fuel enable circuit. Refer to "Theft Deterrent System Diagnosis," in SECTION 8A when diagnosing DTC P1626 or P1629 accompanied by a no-crank.
2. The PCM supplies 5 volts to CKT 229 which the theft deterrent module pulses to ground when the correct key resistance is recognized. This test ensures that the PCM is supplying 5 volts and CKT 229 is not open or shorted to ground.
3. Checks the signal from the theft deterrent module. DC frequency on CKT 229 should measure around 50 hertz.
4. Checks for a faulty PCM or intermittent condition by clearing DTC P1626/P1629. Since the PCM ignores the absence of a fuel enable signal only when DTC P1626/P1629 is stored, the vehicle should not start if the problem is present and DTC P1626/P1629 has been cleared.

Diagnostic Aids: An intermittent DTC P1626/P1629 and/or a possible no-start can be caused by the following:

- Loss of power or ground to theft deterrent module - A loose ground or poor ignition or battery connection could cause an intermittent loss of the PASS-Key®II fuel enable signal and DTC P1626/P1629 to be set.
- Dirty, damaged, or loose connections or damaged harness - Check for any damage to the harness which could cause an intermittent open or short to ground, backed out terminals at the PCM and theft deterrent module connectors, broken locks, improperly formed or damaged terminals.

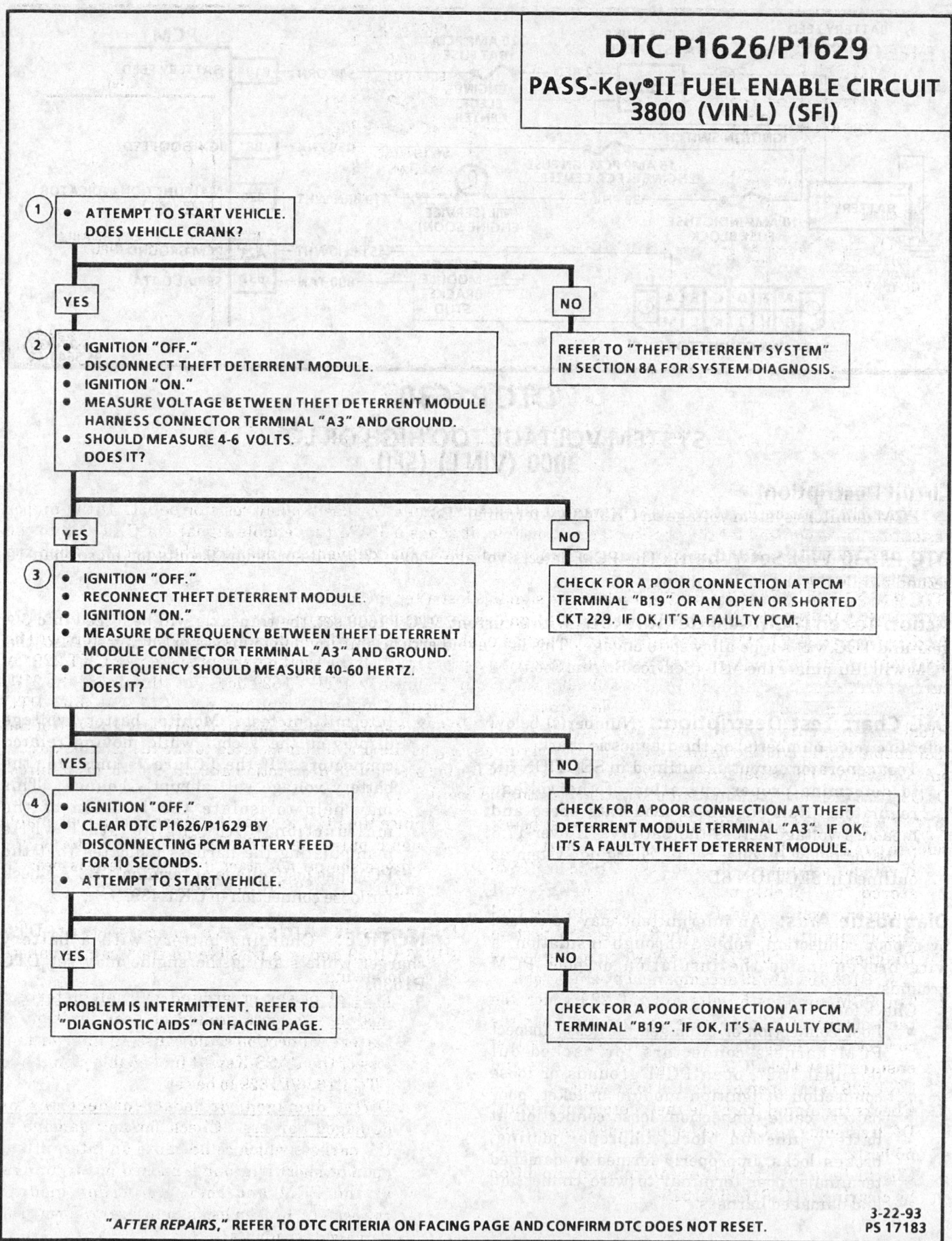

DTC P1626/P1629

PASS-Key®II FUEL ENABLE CIRCUIT 3800 (VIN L) (SFI)

1
- ATTEMPT TO START VEHICLE.
  DOES VEHICLE CRANK?

NO: REFER TO "THEFT DETERRENT SYSTEM" IN SECTION 8A FOR SYSTEM DIAGNOSIS.

YES:

2
- IGNITION "OFF."
- DISCONNECT THEFT DETERRENT MODULE.
- IGNITION "ON."
- MEASURE VOLTAGE BETWEEN THEFT DETERRENT MODULE HARNESS CONNECTOR TERMINAL "A3" AND GROUND.
- SHOULD MEASURE 4-6 VOLTS.
  DOES IT?

NO: CHECK FOR A POOR CONNECTION AT PCM TERMINAL "B19" OR AN OPEN OR SHORTED CKT 229. IF OK, IT'S A FAULTY PCM.

YES:

3
- IGNITION "OFF."
- RECONNECT THEFT DETERRENT MODULE.
- IGNITION "ON."
- MEASURE DC FREQUENCY BETWEEN THEFT DETERRENT MODULE CONNECTOR TERMINAL "A3" AND GROUND.
- DC FREQUENCY SHOULD MEASURE 40-60 HERTZ.
  DOES IT?

NO: CHECK FOR A POOR CONNECTION AT THEFT DETERRENT MODULE TERMINAL "A3". IF OK, IT'S A FAULTY THEFT DETERRENT MODULE.

YES:

4
- IGNITION "OFF."
- CLEAR DTC P1626/P1629 BY DISCONNECTING PCM BATTERY FEED FOR 10 SECONDS.
- ATTEMPT TO START VEHICLE.

YES: PROBLEM IS INTERMITTENT. REFER TO "DIAGNOSTIC AIDS" ON FACING PAGE.

NO: CHECK FOR A POOR CONNECTION AT PCM TERMINAL "B19". IF OK, IT'S A FAULTY PCM.

"AFTER REPAIRS," REFER TO DTC CRITERIA ON FACING PAGE AND CONFIRM DTC DOES NOT RESET.

3-22-93
PS 17183

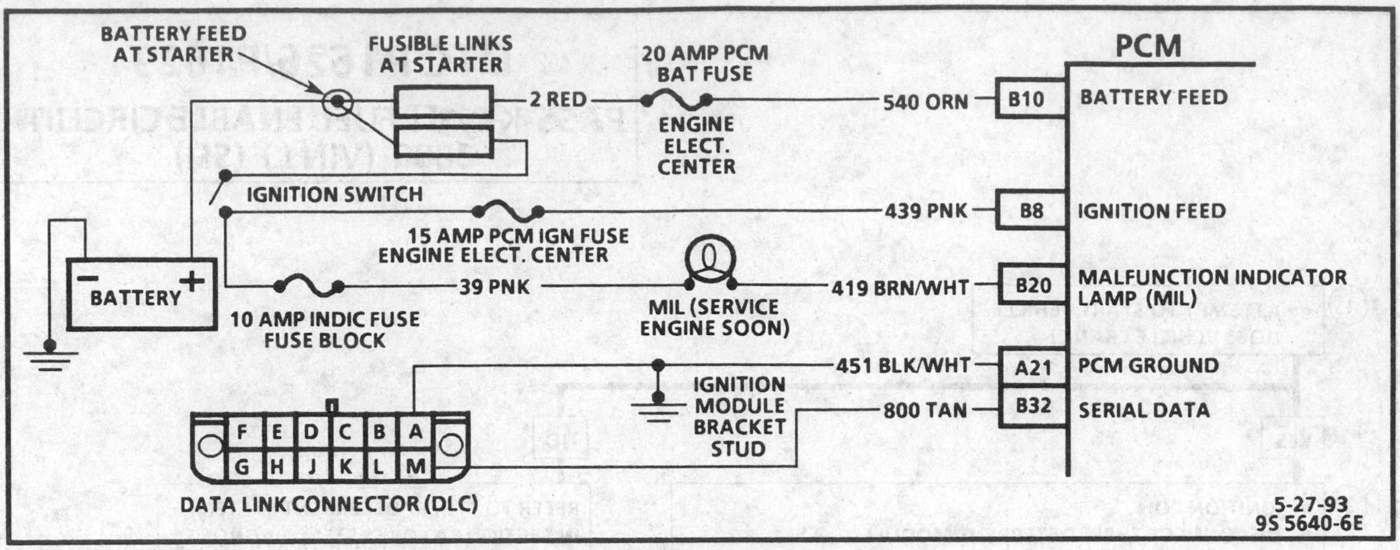
BATTERY FEED AT STARTER
FUSIBLE LINKS AT STARTER
2 RED
20 AMP PCM BAT FUSE
ENGINE ELECT. CENTER
540 ORN
B10
BATTERY FEED
PCM
IGNITION SWITCH
15 AMP PCM IGN FUSE ENGINE ELECT. CENTER
439 PNK
B8
IGNITION FEED
BATTERY
10 AMP INDIC FUSE FUSE BLOCK
39 PNK
MIL (SERVICE ENGINE SOON)
419 BRN/WHT
B20
MALFUNCTION INDICATOR LAMP (MIL)
451 BLK/WHT
A21
PCM GROUND
IGNITION MODULE BRACKET STUD
800 TAN
B32
SERIAL DATA
F E D C B A
G H J K L M
DATA LINK CONNECTOR (DLC)
5-27-93
9S 5640-6E

DTC P1630

SYSTEM VOLTAGE TOO HIGH OR LOW 3800 (VIN L) (SFI)

Circuit Description:

PCM monitors system voltage on CKT 439 to terminal "B8".

DTC P1630 Will Set When: The PCM detects voltage above 17.3 volts or below 9 volts for more than 10 seconds while the engine is running.

Action Taken (PCM will default to): With a current DTC P1630 set, the transaxle will be forced into 3rd gear and TCC will not be allowed to engage. This is to avoid erratic shifting due to improper voltages. Also, the PCM will illuminate the MIL (Service Engine Soon).

DTC Chart Test Description: Number(s) below refer to circled number(s) on the diagnostic chart.

1. Test generator output as outlined in SECTION 6D to determine proper operation of the voltage regulator. Run engine at moderate speed and measure voltage across the battery. If over 17.3 volts, or below 9 volts, repair charging system as outlined in SECTION 6D.

Diagnostic Aids: An intermittent may be caused by a poor connection, rubbed through insulation, a wire broken inside the insulation or poor PCM grounds.

Check for:

- Poor connection or damaged harness - Inspect PCM harness connectors for backed out terminal "B8", open PCM grounds or loose connection at ignition module bracket, poor battery cable connection, loose connection at battery junction block, improper mating, broken locks, improperly formed or damaged terminals, poor terminal to wire connection and damaged harness.
- Intermittent test - Monitor battery voltage display on the Tech 1 while moving related connectors. If the failure is induced, the battery voltage will abruptly change. This may help to isolate the location of the malfunction. An engine stall while manipulating the harness indicates that the PCM has lost voltage at terminal "B8". Check for loose connection in CKT 439.

NOTICE: Charging battery with a battery charger while starting the engine may set DTC P1630.

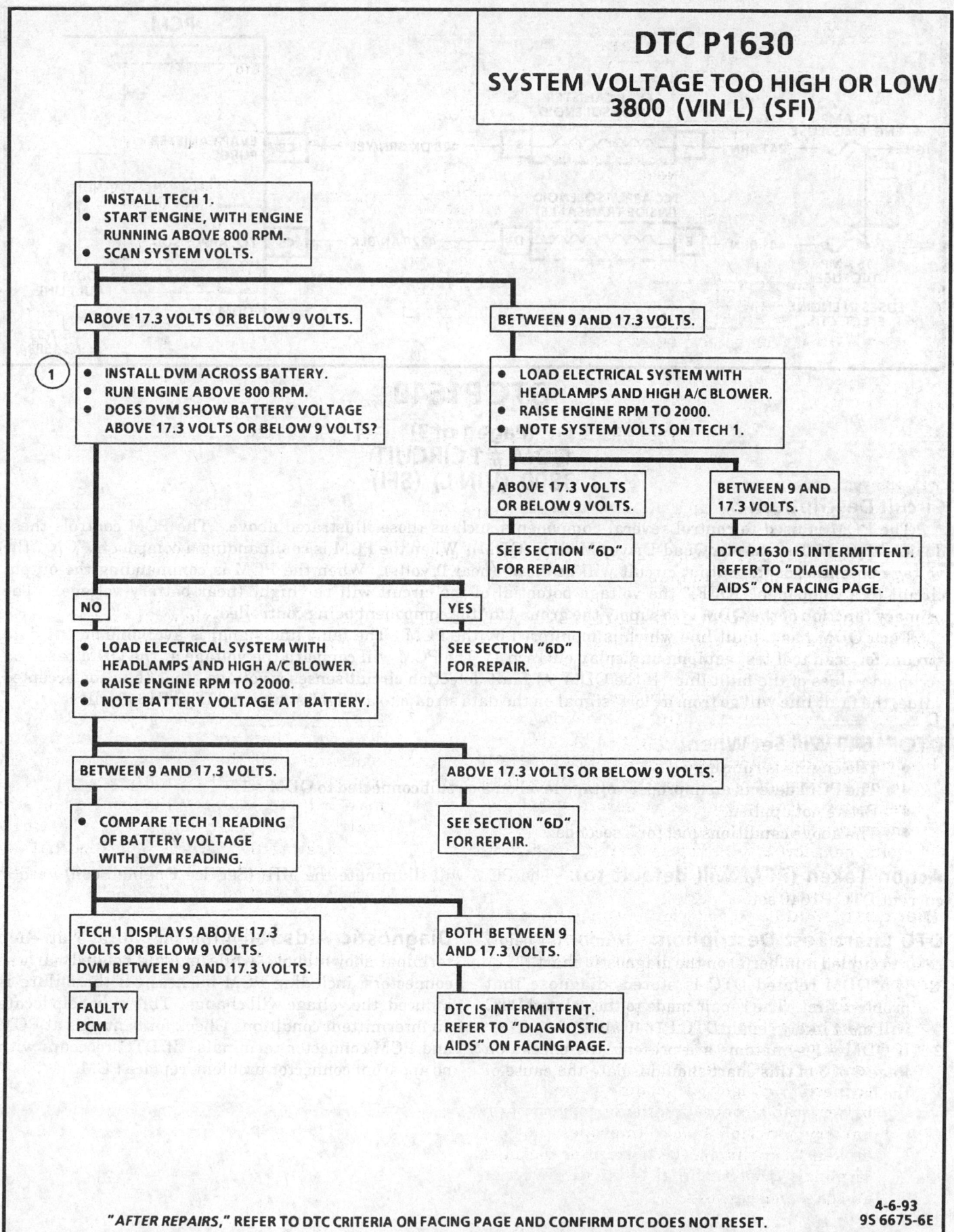

DTC P1630

SYSTEM VOLTAGE TOO HIGH OR LOW 3800 (VIN L) (SFI)

- INSTALL TECH 1.
- START ENGINE, WITH ENGINE RUNNING ABOVE 800 RPM.
- SCAN SYSTEM VOLTS.

ABOVE 17.3 VOLTS OR BELOW 9 VOLTS.

(1)
- INSTALL DVM ACROSS BATTERY.
- RUN ENGINE ABOVE 800 RPM.
- DOES DVM SHOW BATTERY VOLTAGE ABOVE 17.3 VOLTS OR BELOW 9 VOLTS?

NO

- LOAD ELECTRICAL SYSTEM WITH HEADLAMPS AND HIGH A/C BLOWER.
- RAISE ENGINE RPM TO 2000.
- NOTE BATTERY VOLTAGE AT BATTERY.

BETWEEN 9 AND 17.3 VOLTS.

- COMPARE TECH 1 READING OF BATTERY VOLTAGE WITH DVM READING.

TECH 1 DISPLAYS ABOVE 17.3 VOLTS OR BELOW 9 VOLTS. DVM BETWEEN 9 AND 17.3 VOLTS.

FAULTY PCM

BOTH BETWEEN 9 AND 17.3 VOLTS.

DTC IS INTERMITTENT. REFER TO "DIAGNOSTIC AIDS" ON FACING PAGE.

ABOVE 17.3 VOLTS OR BELOW 9 VOLTS.

SEE SECTION "6D" FOR REPAIR.

YES

SEE SECTION "6D" FOR REPAIR.

BETWEEN 9 AND 17.3 VOLTS.

- LOAD ELECTRICAL SYSTEM WITH HEADLAMPS AND HIGH A/C BLOWER.
- RAISE ENGINE RPM TO 2000.
- NOTE SYSTEM VOLTS ON TECH 1.

ABOVE 17.3 VOLTS OR BELOW 9 VOLTS.

SEE SECTION "6D" FOR REPAIR

BETWEEN 9 AND 17.3 VOLTS.

DTC P1630 IS INTERMITTENT. REFER TO "DIAGNOSTIC AIDS" ON FACING PAGE.

"*AFTER REPAIRS*," REFER TO DTC CRITERIA ON FACING PAGE AND CONFIRM DTC DOES NOT RESET.

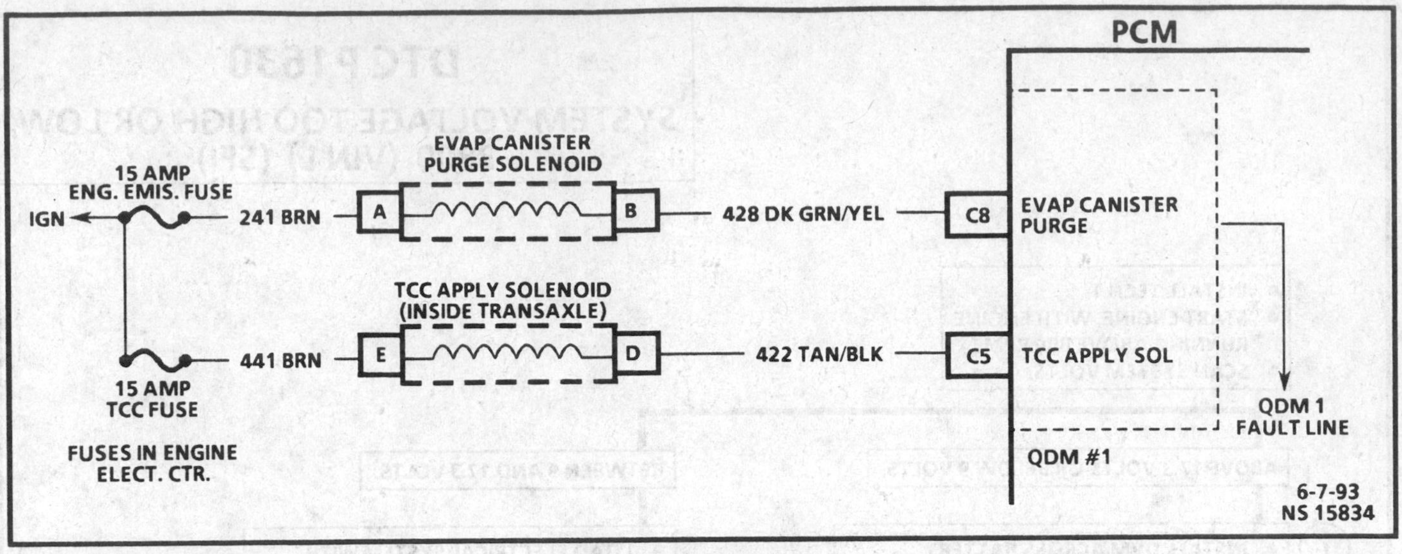
PCM
EVAP CANISTER
PURGE SOLENOID
15 AMP
ENG. EMIS. FUSE
IGN
241 BRN
A
B
428 DK GRN/YEL
C8
EVAP CANISTER
PURGE
TCC APPLY SOLENOID
(INSIDE TRANSAXLE)
441 BRN
E
D
422 TAN/BLK
C5
TCC APPLY SOL
15 AMP
TCC FUSE
QDM 1
FAULT LINE
FUSES IN ENGINE
ELECT. CTR.
QDM #1
6-7-93
NS 15834

DTC P1640

(Page 1 of 3)

QDM #1 CIRCUIT
3800 (VIN L) (SFI)

Circuit Description:

The PCM is used to control several components such as those illustrated above. The PCM controls these devices through the use of a Quad-Driver Module (QDM). When the PCM is commanding a component "ON," the voltage potential of the output circuit will be "low" (near 0 volts). When the PCM is commanding the output circuit to a component "OFF," the voltage potential of the circuit will be "high" (near battery voltage). The primary function of the QDM is to supply the ground for the component being controlled.

Each QDM has a fault line which is monitored by the PCM. The fault line signal is available on the data stream for scan tool test equipment display on Tech 1. The PCM will compare the voltage at the QDM based on accepted values of the fault line. If the QDM #1 fault detection circuit senses a voltage other than the accepted value, the fault line will go from a "low" signal on the data stream to a "high" signal and DTC P1640 will set.

DTC P1640 Will Set When:

- The engine is running.
- The PCM detects an improper voltage level on a circuit connected to QDM #1.
- Brake not applied.
- The above conditions met for 5 seconds.

Action Taken (PCM will default to): The PCM will illuminate the MIL (Service Engine Soon) with a current DTC P1640 set.

DTC Chart Test Description: Number(s) below refer to circled number(s) on the diagnostic chart.

1. If a QDM related DTC is stored, diagnose that problem first. The repair made to the related DTC will most likely repair DTC P1640 also.
2. If QDM #1 symptoms are present, the checks on Page 3 of 3 of this chart should isolate the cause of the fault.

Diagnostic Aids: Monitor the voltage at each terminal shown above while moving related harness connectors, including PCM harness. If the failure is induced, the voltage will change. This may help locate an intermittent condition. Check for bent pins at PCM and PCM connector terminals. If DTC reoccurs with no apparent connector problem, replace PCM.

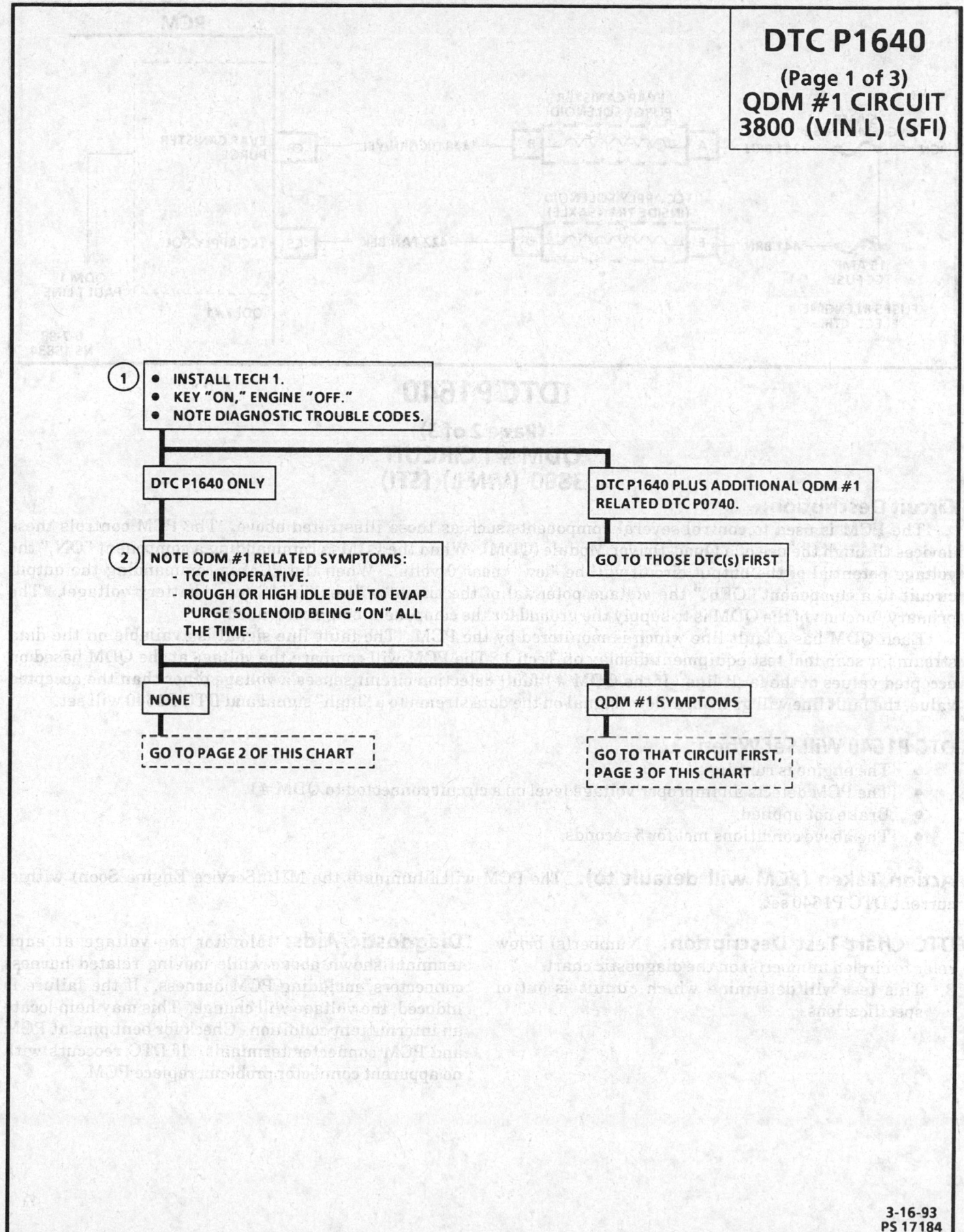

DTC P1640

(Page 1 of 3)
QDM #1 CIRCUIT
3800 (VIN L) (SFI)

1.
- INSTALL TECH 1.
- KEY "ON," ENGINE "OFF."
- NOTE DIAGNOSTIC TROUBLE CODES.

DTC P1640 ONLY

DTC P1640 PLUS ADDITIONAL QDM #1 RELATED DTC P0740.

GO TO THOSE DTC(s) FIRST

2. NOTE QDM #1 RELATED SYMPTOMS:
   - TCC INOPERATIVE.
   - ROUGH OR HIGH IDLE DUE TO EVAP PURGE SOLENOID BEING "ON" ALL THE TIME.

NONE

GO TO PAGE 2 OF THIS CHART

QDM #1 SYMPTOMS

GO TO THAT CIRCUIT FIRST, PAGE 3 OF THIS CHART

3-16-93
PS 17184

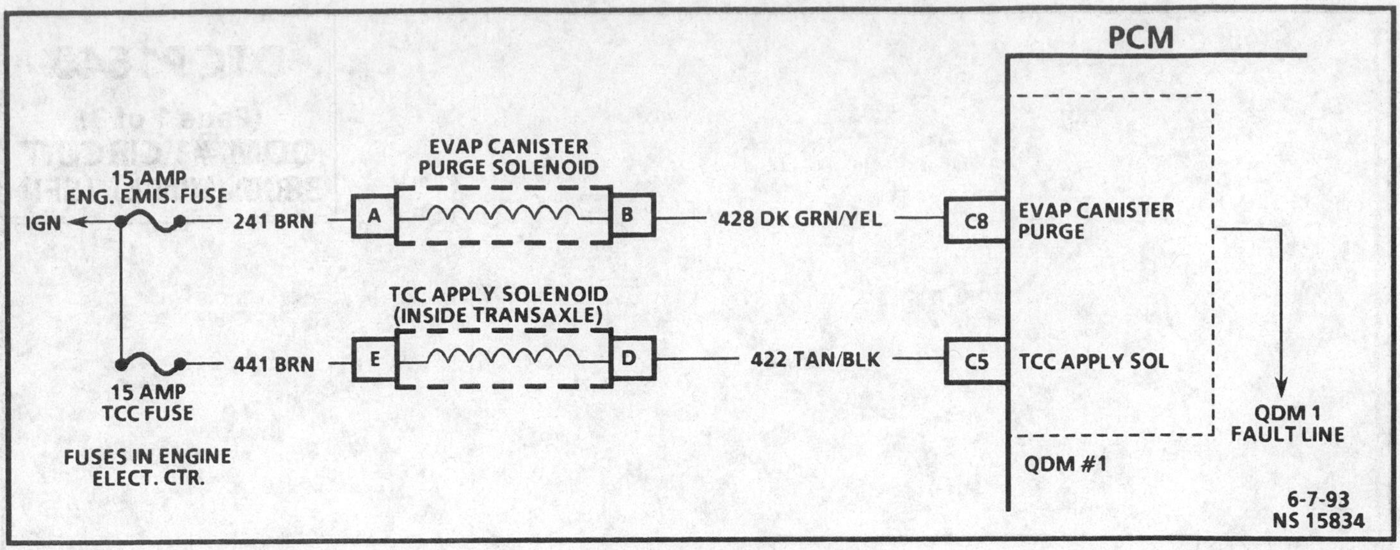
PCM
15 AMP
ENG. EMIS. FUSE
IGN
241 BRN
A
EVAP CANISTER
PURGE SOLENOID
B
428 DK GRN/YEL
C8
EVAP CANISTER
PURGE
TCC APPLY SOLENOID
(INSIDE TRANSAXLE)
441 BRN
E
D
422 TAN/BLK
C5
TCC APPLY SOL
15 AMP
TCC FUSE
QDM 1
FAULT LINE
FUSES IN ENGINE
ELECT. CTR.
QDM #1
6-7-93
NS 15834

DTC P1640

(Page 2 of 3)
QDM #1 CIRCUIT
3800 (VIN L) (SFI)

Circuit Description:

The PCM is used to control several components such as those illustrated above. The PCM controls these devices through the use of a Quad-Driver Module (QDM). When the PCM is commanding a component "ON," the voltage potential of the output circuit will be "low" (near 0 volts). When the PCM is commanding the output circuit to a component "OFF," the voltage potential of the circuit will be "high" (near battery voltage). The primary function of the QDM is to supply the ground for the component being controlled.

Each QDM has a fault line which is monitored by the PCM. The fault line signal is available on the data stream for scan tool test equipment display on Tech 1. The PCM will compare the voltage at the QDM based on accepted values of the fault line. If the QDM #1 fault detection circuit senses a voltage other than the accepted value, the fault line will go from a "low" signal on the data stream to a "high" signal and DTC P1640 will set.

DTC P1640 Will Set When:

- The engine is running.
- The PCM detects an improper voltage level on a circuit connected to QDM #1.
- Brake not applied.
- The above conditions met for 5 seconds.

Action Taken (PCM will default to): The PCM will illuminate the MIL (Service Engine Soon) with a current DTC P1640 set.

DTC Chart Test Description: Number(s) below refer to circled number(s) on the diagnostic chart.

3. This test will determine which circuit is out of specifications.

Diagnostic Aids: Monitor the voltage at each terminal shown above while moving related harness connectors, including PCM harness. If the failure is induced, the voltage will change. This may help locate an intermittent condition. Check for bent pins at PCM and PCM connector terminals. If DTC reoccurs with no apparent connector problem, replace PCM.

DTC P1640

(Page 2 of 3)
QDM #1 CIRCUIT
3800 (VIN L) (SFI)

(3)
- KEY "OFF."
- DISCONNECT BLUE PCM CONNECTOR "C".
- KEY "ON," ENGINE "OFF."
- DVM SET TO 2 AMP SCALE.
- PROBE PCM HARNESS CONNECTOR TERMINALS "C8" AND "C5."
  - RED LEAD (+) TO PCM HARNESS.
  - BLACK LEAD (-) TO GROUND.
- BOTH TERMINALS SHOULD MEASURE LESS THAN 1 AMP (BUT OVER .4 AMP). DO THEY?

YES

REFER TO "DIAGNOSTIC AIDS" ON FACING PAGE.

NO

SEE PAGE 3

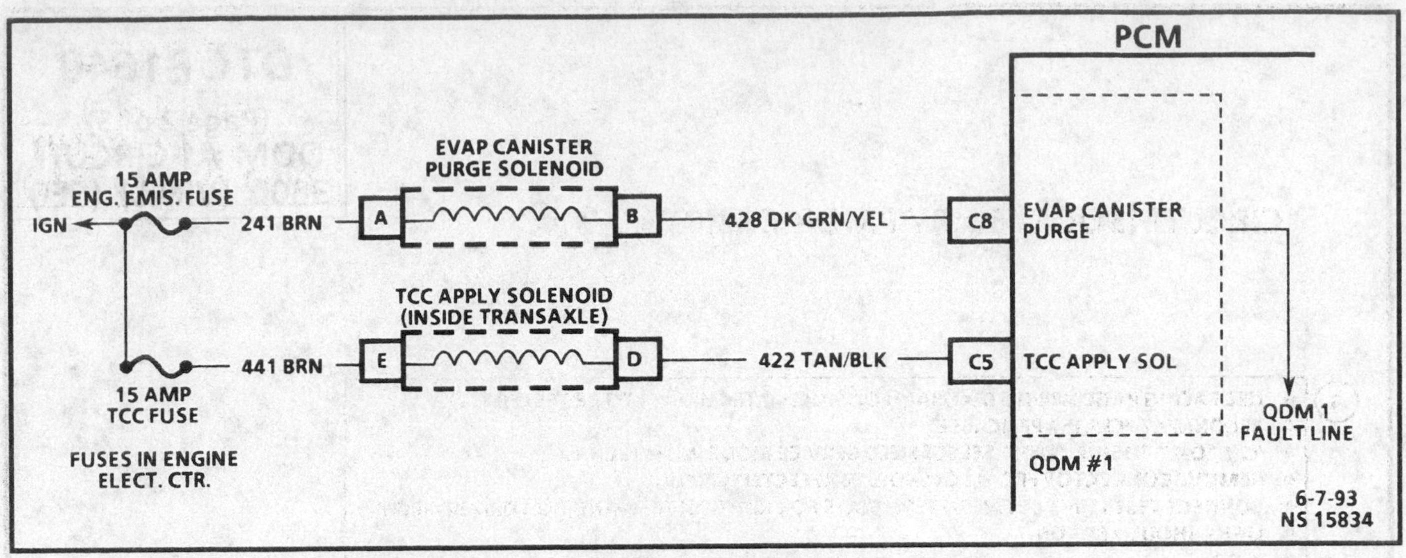
PCM
EVAP CANISTER
PURGE SOLENOID
15 AMP
ENG. EMIS. FUSE
IGN
241 BRN
A
B
428 DK GRN/YEL
C8
EVAP CANISTER
PURGE
TCC APPLY SOLENOID
(INSIDE TRANSAXLE)
441 BRN
E
D
422 TAN/BLK
C5
TCC APPLY SOL
15 AMP
TCC FUSE
QDM 1
FAULT LINE
FUSES IN ENGINE
ELECT. CTR.
QDM #1
6-7-93
NS 15834

DTC P1640

(Page 3 of 3)
QDM #1 CIRCUIT
3800 (VIN L) (SFI)

Circuit Description:

The PCM is used to control several components such as those illustrated above. The PCM controls these devices through the use of a Quad-Driver Module (QDM). When the PCM is commanding a component "ON," the voltage potential of the output circuit will be "low" (near 0 volts). When the PCM is commanding the output circuit to a component "OFF," the voltage potential of the circuit will be "high" (near battery voltage). The primary function of the QDM is to supply the ground for the component being controlled.

Each QDM has a fault line which is monitored by the PCM. The fault line signal is available on the data stream for scan tool test equipment display on Tech 1. The PCM will compare the voltage at the QDM based on accepted values of the fault line. If the QDM #1 fault detection circuit senses a voltage other than the accepted value, the fault line will go from a "low" signal on the data stream to a "high" signal and DTC P1640 will set.

DTC P1640 Will Set When:

- The engine is running.
- The PCM detects an improper voltage level on a circuit connected to QDM #1.
- Brake not applied.
- The above conditions met for 5 seconds.

Action Taken (PCM will default to): The PCM will illuminate the MIL (Service Engine Soon) with a current DTC P1640 set.

DTC Chart Test Description: Number(s) below refer to circled number(s) on the diagnostic chart.

4. This test will determine if the problem is the circuit or the component.
5. As the factory installed PCM is protected with an internal circuit breaker, it is highly unlikely that the PCM needs to be replaced.

Diagnostic Aids: Monitor the voltage at each terminal shown above while moving related harness connectors, including PCM harness. If the failure is induced, the voltage will change. This may help locate an intermittent condition. Check for bent pins at PCM and PCM connector terminals. If DTC reoccurs with no apparent connector problem, replace PCM.

DTC P1640

(Page 3 of 3)
QDM #1 CIRCUIT
3800 (VIN L) (SFI)

CIRCUIT ISOLATED BY PRIOR CHARTS

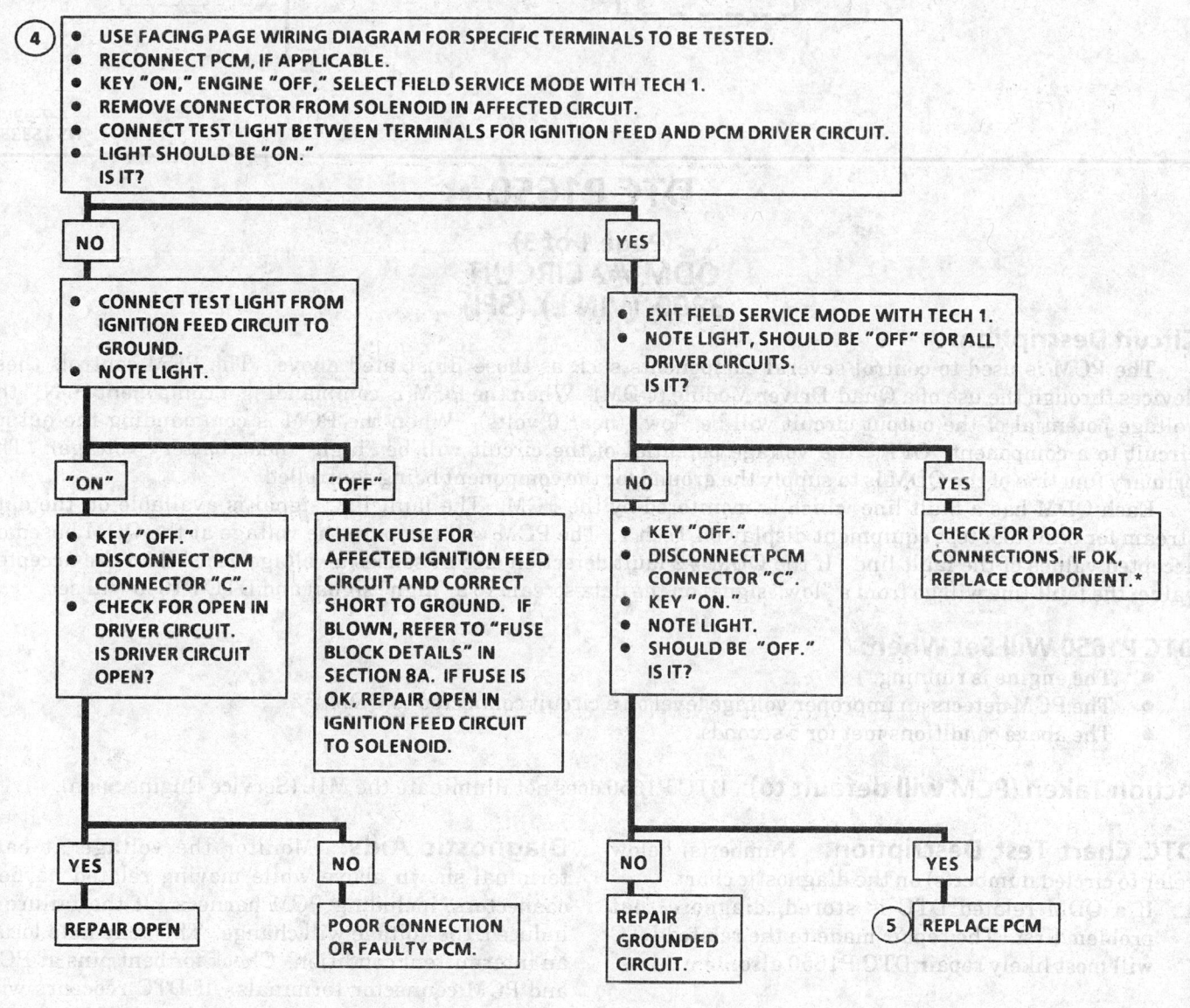

(4)
- USE FACING PAGE WIRING DIAGRAM FOR SPECIFIC TERMINALS TO BE TESTED.
- RECONNECT PCM, IF APPLICABLE.
- KEY "ON," ENGINE "OFF," SELECT FIELD SERVICE MODE WITH TECH 1.
- REMOVE CONNECTOR FROM SOLENOID IN AFFECTED CIRCUIT.
- CONNECT TEST LIGHT BETWEEN TERMINALS FOR IGNITION FEED AND PCM DRIVER CIRCUIT.
- LIGHT SHOULD BE "ON."

IS IT?

NO
- CONNECT TEST LIGHT FROM IGNITION FEED CIRCUIT TO GROUND.
- NOTE LIGHT.

"ON"
- KEY "OFF."
- DISCONNECT PCM CONNECTOR "C".
- CHECK FOR OPEN IN DRIVER CIRCUIT.

IS DRIVER CIRCUIT OPEN?

YES
REPAIR OPEN

NO
POOR CONNECTION OR FAULTY PCM.

"OFF"
CHECK FUSE FOR AFFECTED IGNITION FEED CIRCUIT AND CORRECT SHORT TO GROUND. IF BLOWN, REFER TO "FUSE BLOCK DETAILS" IN SECTION 8A. IF FUSE IS OK, REPAIR OPEN IN IGNITION FEED CIRCUIT TO SOLENOID.

YES
- EXIT FIELD SERVICE MODE WITH TECH 1.
- NOTE LIGHT, SHOULD BE "OFF" FOR ALL DRIVER CIRCUITS.

IS IT?

NO
- KEY "OFF."
- DISCONNECT PCM CONNECTOR "C".
- KEY "ON."
- NOTE LIGHT.
- SHOULD BE "OFF."

IS IT?

NO
REPAIR GROUNDED CIRCUIT.

YES
(5) REPLACE PCM

YES
CHECK FOR POOR CONNECTIONS. IF OK, REPLACE COMPONENT.*

* PCM IS PROTECTED BY AN INTERNAL CIRCUIT BREAKER. PCM REPLACEMENT IS NOT NECESSARY AFTER REPAIRING A SHORTED QUAD DRIVER CONTROLLED CIRCUIT OR COMPONENT.

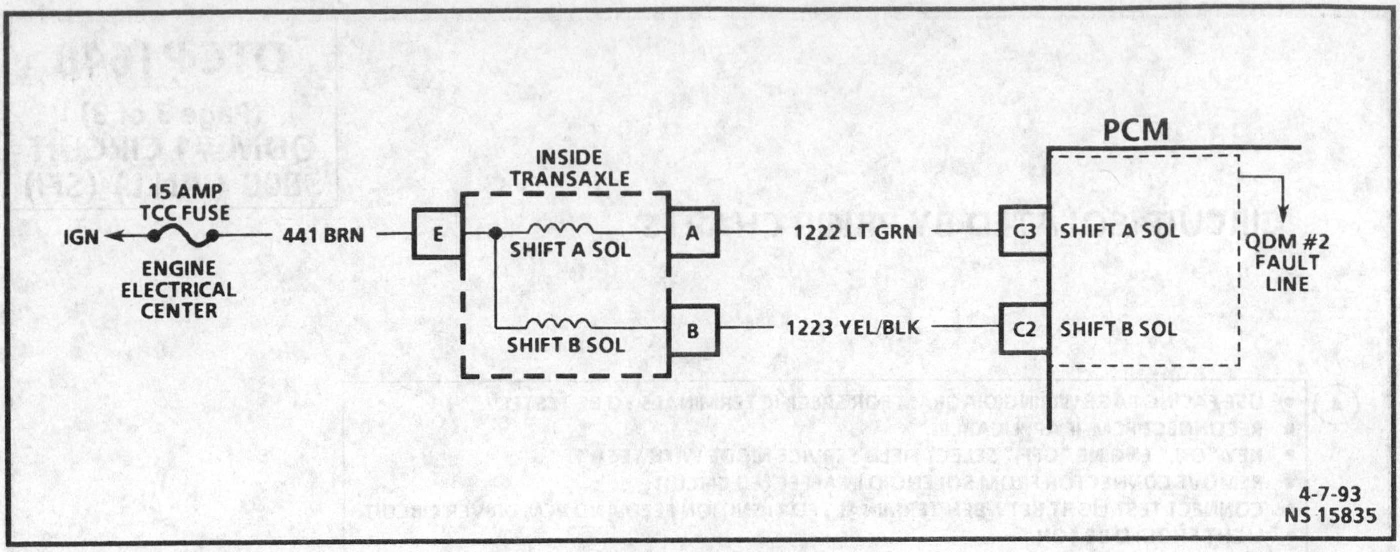

PCM
INSIDE TRANSAXLE
15 AMP TCC FUSE
IGN
441 BRN
E
SHIFT A SOL
A
1222 LT GRN
C3
SHIFT A SOL
QDM #2 FAULT LINE
ENGINE ELECTRICAL CENTER
SHIFT B SOL
B
1223 YEL/BLK
C2
SHIFT B SOL
4-7-93
NS 15835

DTC P1650

(Page 1 of 3)
QDM #2 CIRCUIT
3800 (VIN L) (SFI)

Circuit Description:

The PCM is used to control several components such as those illustrated above. The PCM controls these devices through the use of a Quad-Driver Module (QDM). When the PCM is commanding a component "ON," the voltage potential of the output circuit will be "low" (near 0 volts). When the PCM is commanding the output circuit to a component "OFF," the voltage potential of the circuit will be "high" (near battery voltage). The primary function of the QDM is to supply the ground for the component being controlled.

Each QDM has a fault line which is monitored by the PCM. The fault line signal is available on the data stream for scan tool test equipment display on Tech 1. The PCM will compare the voltage at the QDM based on accepted values of the fault line. If the QDM #2 fault detection circuit senses a voltage other than the accepted value, the fault line will go from a "low" signal on the data stream to a "high" signal and DTC P1650 will set.

DTC P1650 Will Set When:

- The engine is running.
- The PCM detects an improper voltage level on a circuit connected to QDM #2.
- The above conditions met for 5 seconds.

Action Taken (PCM will default to): DTC P1650 does not illuminate the MIL (Service Engine Soon).

DTC Chart Test Description: Number(s) below refer to circled number(s) on the diagnostic chart.

1. If a QDM related DTC is stored, diagnose that problem first. The repair made to the related DTC will most likely repair DTC P1650 also.

Diagnostic Aids: Monitor the voltage at each terminal shown above while moving related harness connectors, including PCM harness. If the failure is induced, the voltage will change. This may help locate an intermittent condition. Check for bent pins at PCM and PCM connector terminals. If DTC reoccurs with no apparent connector problem, replace PCM.

DTC P1650

(Page 1 of 3)

QDM #2 CIRCUIT

3800 (VIN L) (SFI)

(1)
- INSTALL TECH 1.
- KEY "ON," ENGINE "OFF."
- NOTE DIAGNOSTIC TROUBLE CODES.

- DTC P1650 ONLY.

GO TO PAGE 2 OF THIS CHART.

DTC P1650 PLUS ADDITIONAL QDM #2 RELATED DTC P0755.

GO TO DTC P0755 CHART FIRST.

6-2-93
NS 15819

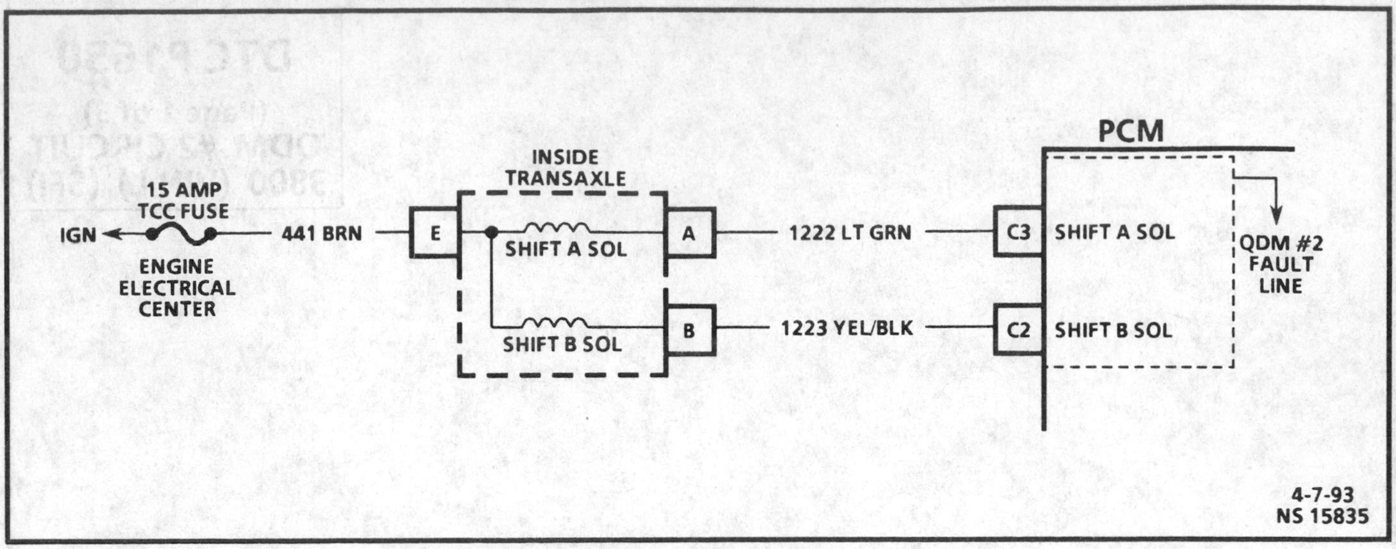
PCM
INSIDE TRANSAXLE
15 AMP TCC FUSE
IGN
441 BRN
E
SHIFT A SOL
A
1222 LT GRN
C3
SHIFT A SOL
QDM #2 FAULT LINE
ENGINE ELECTRICAL CENTER
SHIFT B SOL
B
1223 YEL/BLK
C2
SHIFT B SOL
4-7-93
NS 15835

DTC P1650

(Page 2 of 3)
QDM #2 CIRCUIT
3800 (VIN L) (SFI)

Circuit Description:

The PCM is used to control several components such as those illustrated above. The PCM controls these devices through the use of a Quad-Driver Module (QDM). When the PCM is commanding a component "ON," the voltage potential of the output circuit will be "low" (near 0 volts). When the PCM is commanding the output circuit to a component "OFF," the voltage potential of the circuit will be "high" (near battery voltage). The primary function of the QDM is to supply the ground for the component being controlled.

Each QDM has a fault line which is monitored by the PCM. The fault line signal is available on the data stream for scan tool test equipment display on Tech 1. The PCM will compare the voltage at the QDM based on accepted values of the fault line. If the QDM #2 fault detection circuit senses a voltage other than the accepted value, the fault line will go from a "low" signal on the data stream to a "high" signal and DTC P1650 will set.

DTC P1650 Will Set When:

- The engine is running.
- The PCM detects an improper voltage level on a circuit connected to QDM #2.
- The above conditions met for 5 seconds.

Action Taken (PCM will default to): DTC P1650 does not illuminate the MIL (Service Engine Soon).

DTC Chart Test Description: Number(s) below refer to circled number(s) on the diagnostic chart.

2. This test will determine which circuit is out of specification.

Diagnostic Aids: Monitor the voltage at each terminal shown above while moving related harness connectors, including PCM harness. If the failure is induced, the voltage will change. This may help locate an intermittent condition. Check for bent pins at PCM and PCM connector terminals. If DTC reoccurs with no apparent connector problem, replace PCM.

DTC P1650

(Page 2 of 3)

QDM #2 CIRCUIT 3800 (VIN L) (SFI)

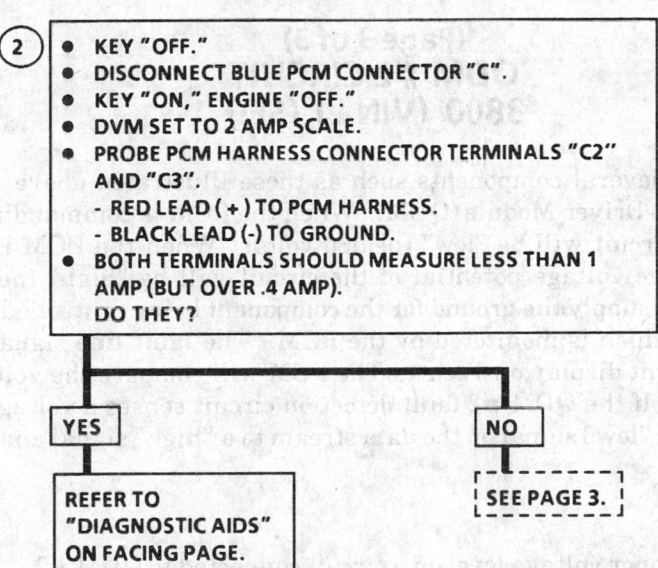

(2)
- KEY "OFF."
- DISCONNECT BLUE PCM CONNECTOR "C".
- KEY "ON," ENGINE "OFF."
- DVM SET TO 2 AMP SCALE.
- PROBE PCM HARNESS CONNECTOR TERMINALS "C2" AND "C3".
  - RED LEAD (+) TO PCM HARNESS.
  - BLACK LEAD (-) TO GROUND.
- BOTH TERMINALS SHOULD MEASURE LESS THAN 1 AMP (BUT OVER .4 AMP).

DO THEY?

YES → REFER TO "DIAGNOSTIC AIDS" ON FACING PAGE.

NO → SEE PAGE 3.

"AFTER REPAIRS," REFER TO DTC CRITERIA ON FACING PAGE AND CONFIRM DTC DOES NOT RESET.

4-22-93
NS 14359

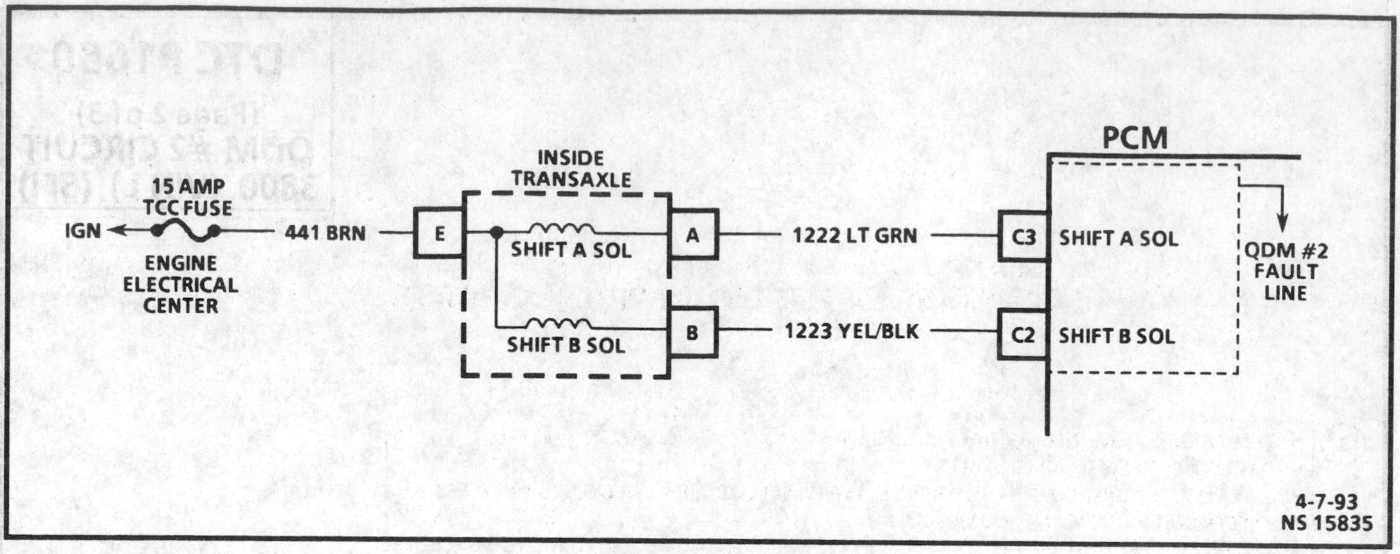
PCM
INSIDE
TRANSAXLE
15 AMP
TCC FUSE
IGN
441 BRN
E
A
SHIFT A SOL
1222 LT GRN
C3
SHIFT A SOL
QDM #2
FAULT
LINE
ENGINE
ELECTRICAL
CENTER
B
SHIFT B SOL
1223 YEL/BLK
C2
SHIFT B SOL
4-7-93
NS 15835

DTC P1650

(Page 3 of 3)
QDM #2 CIRCUIT
3800 (VIN L) (SFI)

Circuit Description:

The PCM is used to control several components such as those illustrated above. The PCM controls these devices through the use of a Quad-Driver Module (QDM). When the PCM is commanding a component "ON," the voltage potential of the output circuit will be "low" (near 0 volts). When the PCM is commanding the output circuit to a component "OFF," the voltage potential of the circuit will be "high" (near battery voltage). The primary function of the QDM is to supply the ground for the component being controlled.

Each QDM has a fault line which is monitored by the PCM. The fault line signal is available on the data stream for scan tool test equipment display on Tech 1. The PCM will compare the voltage at the QDM based on accepted values of the fault line. If the QDM #2 fault detection circuit senses a voltage other than the accepted value, the fault line will go from a "low" signal on the data stream to a "high" signal and DTC P1650 will set.

DTC P1650 Will Set When:

- The engine is running.
- The PCM detects an improper voltage level on a circuit connected to QDM #2.
- The above conditions met for 5 seconds.

Action Taken (PCM will default to): DTC P1650 does not illuminate MIL (Service Engine Soon).

DTC Chart Test Description: Number(s) below refer to circled number(s) on the diagnostic chart.

3. This test will determine if the problem is the circuit or the component.
4. As the factory installed PCM is protected with an internal circuit breaker, it is highly unlikely that the PCM need to be replaced.

Diagnostic Aids: Monitor the voltage at each terminal shown above while moving related harness connectors, including PCM harness. If the failure is induced, the voltage will change. This may help locate an intermittent condition. Check for bent pins at PCM and PCM connector terminals. If DTC reoccurs with no apparent connector problem, replace PCM.

DTC P1650
(Page 3 of 3)
QDM #2 CIRCUIT
3800 (VIN L) (SFI)

CIRCUIT ISOLATED FROM PRIOR CHARTS

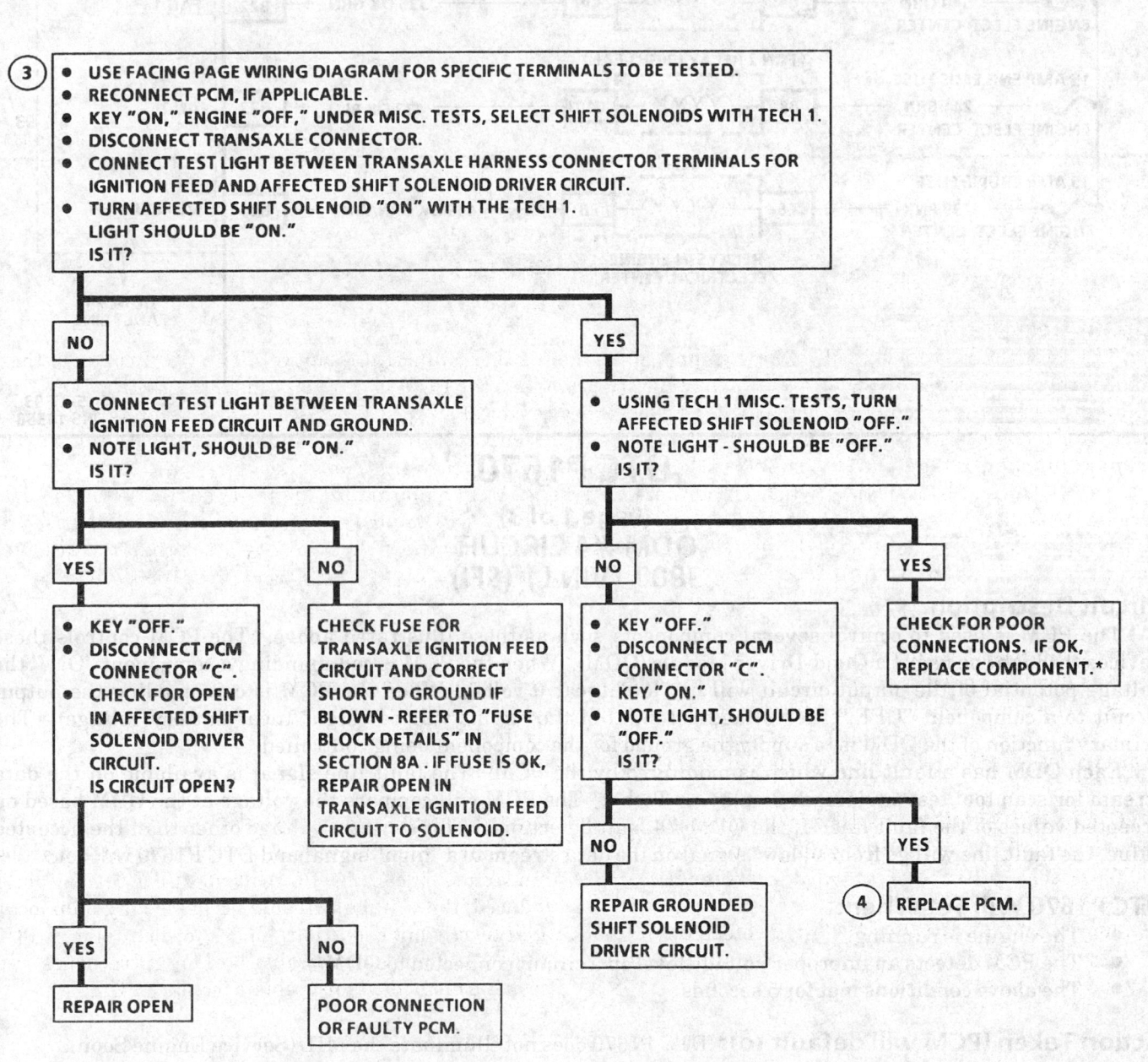

(3)
- USE FACING PAGE WIRING DIAGRAM FOR SPECIFIC TERMINALS TO BE TESTED.
- RECONNECT PCM, IF APPLICABLE.
- KEY "ON," ENGINE "OFF," UNDER MISC. TESTS, SELECT SHIFT SOLENOIDS WITH TECH 1.
- DISCONNECT TRANSAXLE CONNECTOR.
- CONNECT TEST LIGHT BETWEEN TRANSAXLE HARNESS CONNECTOR TERMINALS FOR IGNITION FEED AND AFFECTED SHIFT SOLENOID DRIVER CIRCUIT.
- TURN AFFECTED SHIFT SOLENOID "ON" WITH THE TECH 1. LIGHT SHOULD BE "ON." IS IT?

NO:
- CONNECT TEST LIGHT BETWEEN TRANSAXLE IGNITION FEED CIRCUIT AND GROUND.
- NOTE LIGHT, SHOULD BE "ON." IS IT?

  YES:
  - KEY "OFF."
  - DISCONNECT PCM CONNECTOR "C".
  - CHECK FOR OPEN IN AFFECTED SHIFT SOLENOID DRIVER CIRCUIT. IS CIRCUIT OPEN?

    YES: REPAIR OPEN

    NO: POOR CONNECTION OR FAULTY PCM.

  NO: CHECK FUSE FOR TRANSAXLE IGNITION FEED CIRCUIT AND CORRECT SHORT TO GROUND IF BLOWN - REFER TO "FUSE BLOCK DETAILS" IN SECTION 8A . IF FUSE IS OK, REPAIR OPEN IN TRANSAXLE IGNITION FEED CIRCUIT TO SOLENOID.

YES:
- USING TECH 1 MISC. TESTS, TURN AFFECTED SHIFT SOLENOID "OFF."
- NOTE LIGHT - SHOULD BE "OFF." IS IT?

  NO:
  - KEY "OFF."
  - DISCONNECT PCM CONNECTOR "C".
  - KEY "ON."
  - NOTE LIGHT, SHOULD BE "OFF." IS IT?

    NO: REPAIR GROUNDED SHIFT SOLENOID DRIVER CIRCUIT.

    YES: (4) REPLACE PCM.

  YES: CHECK FOR POOR CONNECTIONS. IF OK, REPLACE COMPONENT.*

* PCM IS PROTECTED BY AN INTERNAL CIRCUIT BREAKER. PCM REPLACEMENT IS NOT NECESSARY AFTER REPAIRING A SHORTED QUAD DRIVER CONTROLLED CIRCUIT OR COMPONENT.

5-18-93
NS 14352

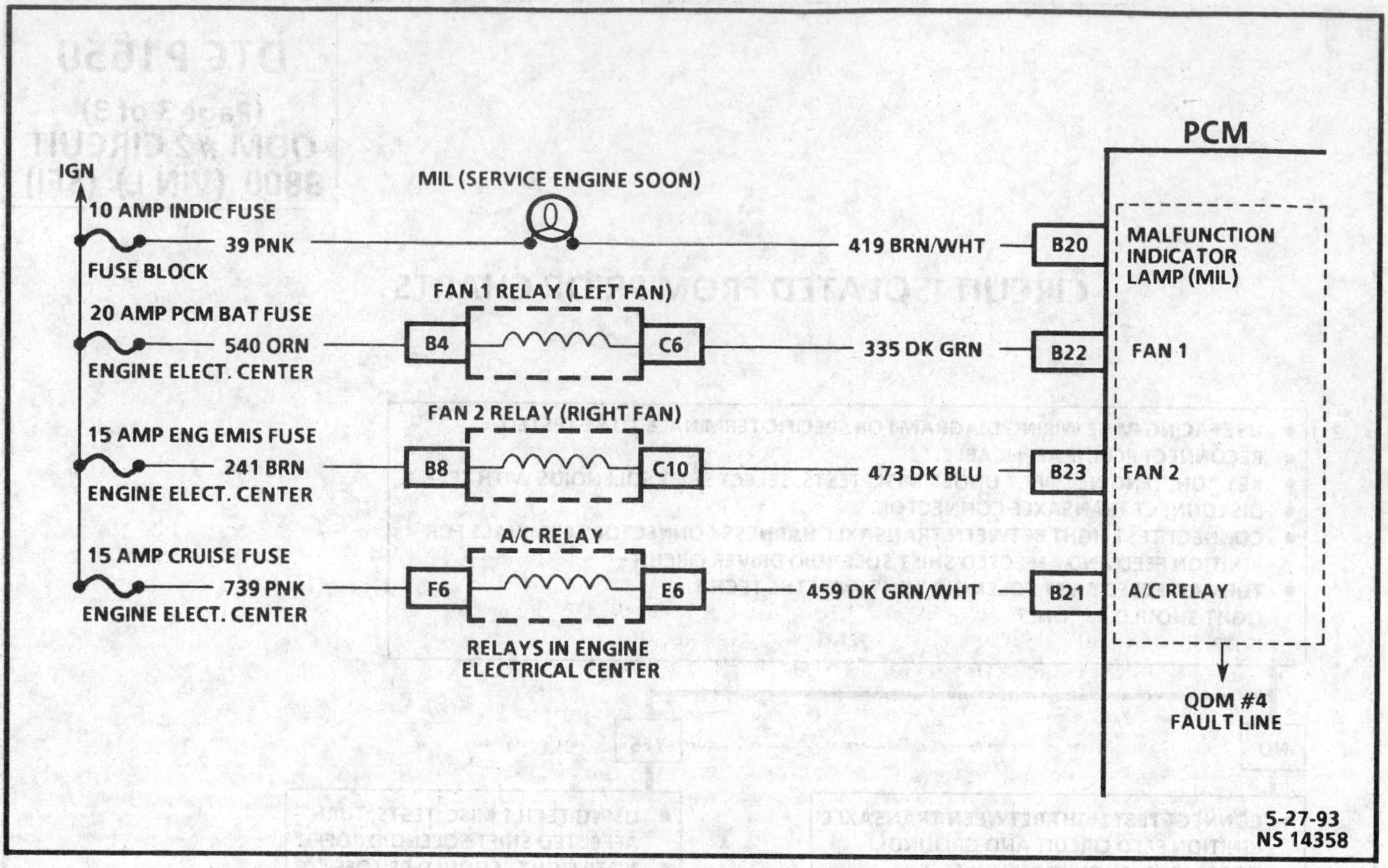
PCM
IGN
10 AMP INDIC FUSE
39 PNK
FUSE BLOCK
MIL (SERVICE ENGINE SOON)
419 BRN/WHT
B20
MALFUNCTION INDICATOR LAMP (MIL)
20 AMP PCM BAT FUSE
540 ORN
ENGINE ELECT. CENTER
FAN 1 RELAY (LEFT FAN)
B4
C6
335 DK GRN
B22
FAN 1
15 AMP ENG EMIS FUSE
241 BRN
ENGINE ELECT. CENTER
FAN 2 RELAY (RIGHT FAN)
B8
C10
473 DK BLU
B23
FAN 2
15 AMP CRUISE FUSE
739 PNK
ENGINE ELECT. CENTER
A/C RELAY
F6
E6
459 DK GRN/WHT
B21
A/C RELAY
RELAYS IN ENGINE ELECTRICAL CENTER
QDM #4 FAULT LINE
5-27-93
NS 14358

DTC P1670

(Page 1 of 3)
QDM #4 CIRCUIT
3800 (VIN L) (SFI)

Circuit Description:

The PCM is used to control several components such as those illustrated above. The PCM controls these devices through the use of a Quad-Driver Module (QDM). When the PCM is commanding a component "ON," the voltage potential of the output circuit will be "low" (near 0 volts). When the PCM is commanding the output circuit to a component "OFF," the voltage potential of the circuit will be "high" (near battery voltage). The primary function of the QDM is to supply the ground for the component being controlled.

Each QDM has a fault line which is monitored by the PCM. The fault line signal is available on the data stream for scan tool test equipment display on Tech 1. The PCM will compare the voltage at the QDM based on accepted values of the fault line. If the QDM #4 fault detection circuit senses a voltage other than the accepted value, the fault line will go from a "low" signal on the data stream to a "high" signal and DTC P1670 will set.

DTC P1670 Will Set When:

- The engine is running.
- The PCM detects an improper voltage level on a circuit connected to QDM #4.
- The above conditions met for 5 seconds.

Action Taken (PCM will default to): DTC P1670 does not illuminate the MIL (Service Engine Soon).

DTC Chart Test Description: Number(s) below refer to circled number(s) on the diagnostic chart.

1. If QDM #4 related symptoms are present the checks on Page 3 of 3 of this DTC chart should isolate the causes of the malfunction.

Diagnostic Aids: Monitor the voltage at each terminal shown above while moving related harness connectors, including PCM harness. If the failure is induced, the voltage will change. This may help locate an intermittent condition. Check for bent pins at PCM and PCM connector terminals. If DTC reoccurs with no apparent connector problem, replace PCM.

DTC P1670

(Page 1 of 3)

QDM #4 CIRCUIT
3800 (VIN L) (SFI)

(1) NOTE QDM #4 RELATED SYMPTOMS:
- MIL ("SERVICE ENGINE SOON") "ON" ALL THE TIME OR NOT "ON" AT KEY UP.
- A/C CLUTCH INOPERATIVE OR ENGAGED ALL THE TIME.
- COOLINGS FAN(S) "ON" ALL THE TIME OR NEVER "ON."

ARE QDM #4 RELATED SYMPTOMS PRESENT?

NO → GO TO PAGE 2 OF THIS CHART.

YES → GO TO THAT CIRCUIT FIRST, PAGE 3 OF THIS CHART.

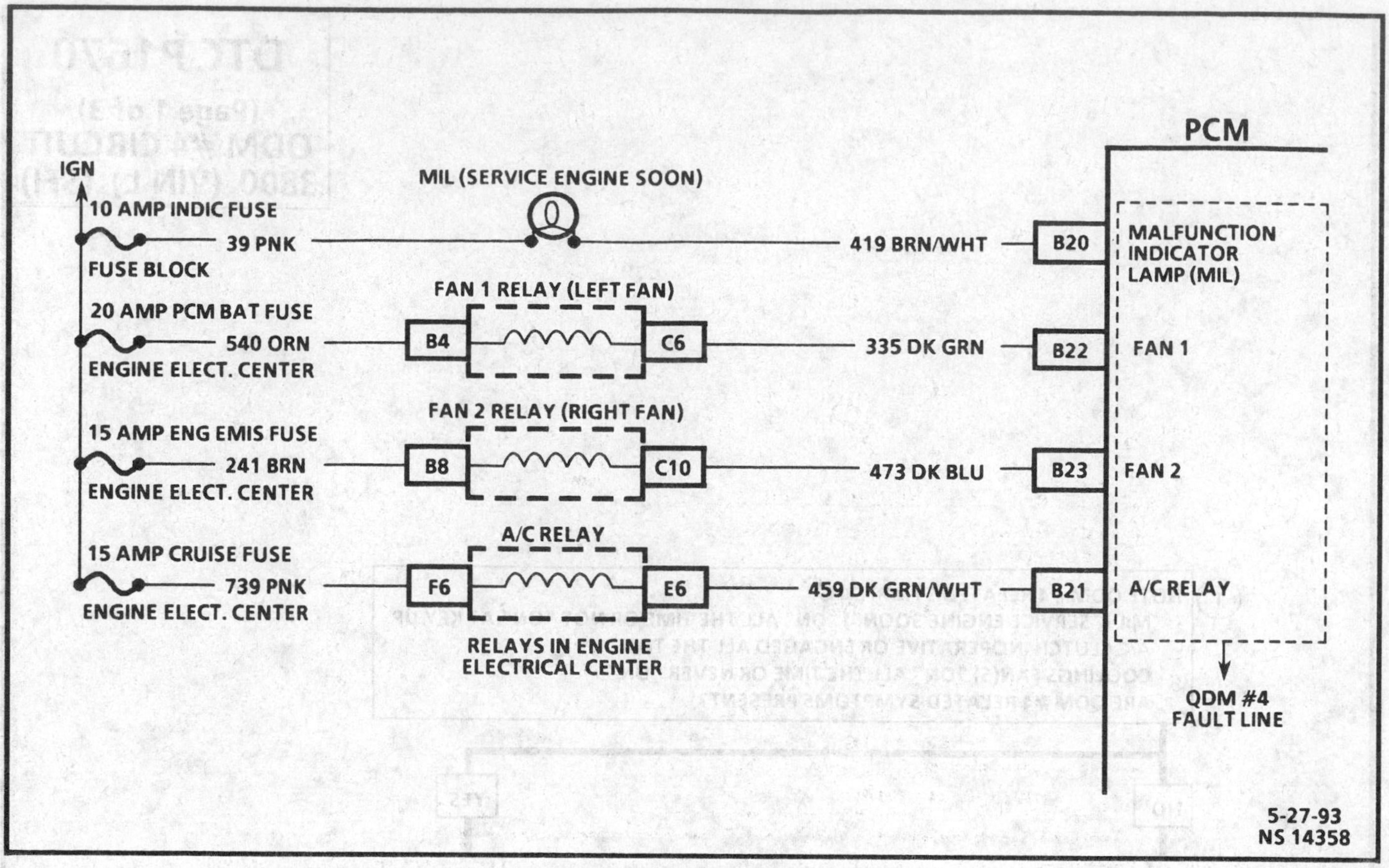
PCM
IGN
MIL (SERVICE ENGINE SOON)
10 AMP INDIC FUSE
39 PNK
419 BRN/WHT
B20
MALFUNCTION INDICATOR LAMP (MIL)
FUSE BLOCK
FAN 1 RELAY (LEFT FAN)
20 AMP PCM BAT FUSE
540 ORN
B4
C6
335 DK GRN
B22
FAN 1
ENGINE ELECT. CENTER
FAN 2 RELAY (RIGHT FAN)
15 AMP ENG EMIS FUSE
241 BRN
B8
C10
473 DK BLU
B23
FAN 2
ENGINE ELECT. CENTER
A/C RELAY
15 AMP CRUISE FUSE
739 PNK
F6
E6
459 DK GRN/WHT
B21
A/C RELAY
ENGINE ELECT. CENTER
RELAYS IN ENGINE ELECTRICAL CENTER
QDM #4 FAULT LINE
5-27-93
NS 14358

DTC P1670

(Page 2 of 3)
QDM #4 CIRCUIT
3800 (VIN L) (SFI)

Circuit Description:

The PCM is used to control several components such as those illustrated above. The PCM controls these devices through the use of a Quad-Driver Module (QDM). When the PCM is commanding a component "ON," the voltage potential of the output circuit will be "low" (near 0 volts). When the PCM is commanding the output circuit to a component "OFF," the voltage potential of the circuit will be "high" (near battery voltage). The primary function of the QDM is to supply the ground for the component being controlled.

Each QDM has a fault line which is monitored by the PCM. The fault line signal is available on the data stream for scan tool test equipment display on Tech 1. The PCM will compare the voltage at the QDM based on accepted values of the fault line. If the QDM #4 fault detection circuit senses a voltage other than the accepted value, the fault line will go from a "low" signal on the data stream to a "high" signal and DTC P1670 will set.

DTC P1670 Will Set When:

- The engine is running.
- The PCM detects an improper voltage level on a circuit connected to QDM #4.
- The above conditions met for 5 seconds.

Action Taken (PCM will default to): DTC P1670 does not illuminate the MIL (Service Engine Soon).

DTC Chart Test Description: Number(s) below refer to circled number(s) on the diagnostic chart.

2. This test will determine which circuit is out of specifications.

Diagnostic Aids: Monitor the voltage at each terminal shown above while moving related harness connectors, including PCM harness. If the failure is induced, the voltage will change. This may help locate an intermittent condition. Check for bent pins at PCM and PCM connector terminals. If DTC reoccurs with no apparent connector problem, replace PCM.

DTC P1670

(Page 2 of 3)

QDM #4 CIRCUIT 3800 (VIN L) (SFI)

(2) CIRCUIT NOT ISOLATED BY PRIOR STEPS.

- KEY "OFF."
- DISCONNECT PCM WHITE CONNECTOR.
- KEY "ON," ENGINE "OFF."
- DVM SET TO 2 AMP SCALE.
- PROBE PCM HARNESS TERMINALS "2-22," "2-23," AND "2-21."
  - RED LEAD (+) TO PCM HARNESS.
  - BLACK LEAD (-) TO GROUND.
- EACH TERMINAL SHOULD MEASURE LESS THAN .75 AMP (BUT NOT 0 AMP).

OK

SEE "DIAGNOSTIC AIDS" ON FACING PAGE.

NOT OK

SEE PAGE 3.

6-21-93
PS 18314

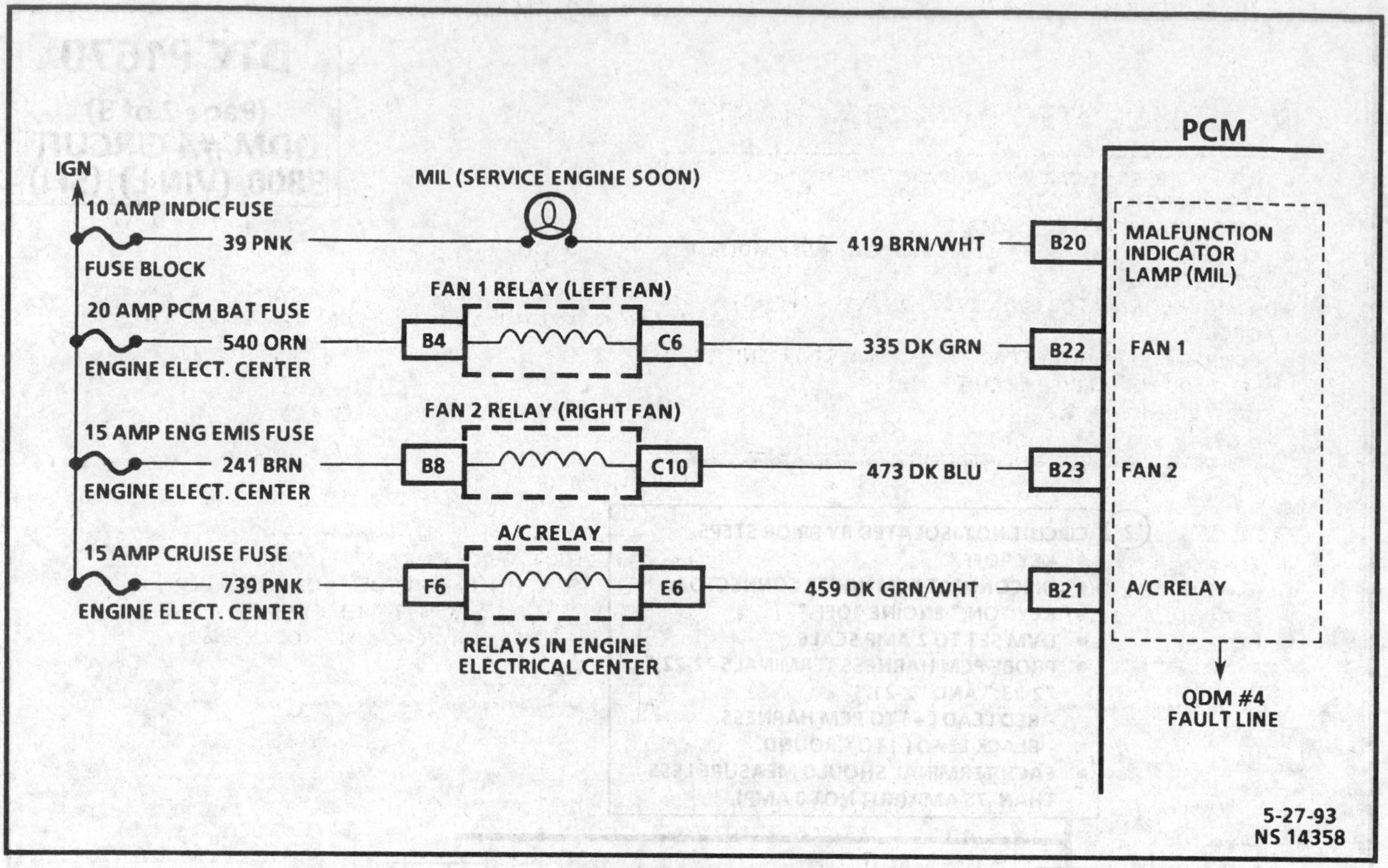
PCM
IGN
10 AMP INDIC FUSE
39 PNK
FUSE BLOCK
MIL (SERVICE ENGINE SOON)
419 BRN/WHT
B20
MALFUNCTION INDICATOR LAMP (MIL)
20 AMP PCM BAT FUSE
540 ORN
ENGINE ELECT. CENTER
FAN 1 RELAY (LEFT FAN)
B4
C6
335 DK GRN
B22
FAN 1
15 AMP ENG EMIS FUSE
241 BRN
ENGINE ELECT. CENTER
FAN 2 RELAY (RIGHT FAN)
B8
C10
473 DK BLU
B23
FAN 2
15 AMP CRUISE FUSE
739 PNK
ENGINE ELECT. CENTER
A/C RELAY
F6
E6
459 DK GRN/WHT
B21
A/C RELAY
RELAYS IN ENGINE ELECTRICAL CENTER
QDM #4 FAULT LINE
5-27-93
NS 14358

DTC P1670

(Page 3 of 3)
QDM #4 CIRCUIT
3800 (VIN L) (SFI)

Circuit Description:

The PCM is used to control several components such as those illustrated above. The PCM controls these devices through the use of a Quad-Driver Module (QDM). When the PCM is commanding a component "ON," the voltage potential of the output circuit will be "low" (near 0 volts). When the PCM is commanding the output circuit to a component "OFF," the voltage potential of the circuit will be "high" (near battery voltage). The primary function of the QDM is to supply the ground for the component being controlled.

Each QDM has a fault line which is monitored by the PCM. The fault line signal is available on the data stream for scan tool test equipment display on Tech 1. The PCM will compare the voltage at the QDM based on accepted values of the fault line. If the QDM #4 fault detection circuit senses a voltage other than the accepted value, the fault line will go from a "low" signal on the data stream to a "high" signal and DTC P1670 will set.

DTC P1670 Will Set When:

- The engine is running.
- The PCM detects an improper voltage level on a circuit connected to QDM #4.
- The above conditions met for 5 seconds.

Action Taken (PCM will default): DTC P1670 does not illuminate the MIL (Service Engine Soon).

DTC Chart Test Description: Number(s) below refer to circled number(s) on the diagnostic chart.

3. This test will determine if the problem is the circuit or the component.
4. As the factory installed PCM is protected with an internal circuit breaker, it is highly unlikely that the PCM needs to be replaced.

Diagnostic Aids: Monitor the voltage at each terminal shown above while moving related harness connectors, including PCM harness. If the failure is induced, the voltage will change. This may help locate an intermittent condition. Check for bent pins at PCM and PCM connector terminals. If DTC reoccurs with no apparent connector problem, replace PCM.

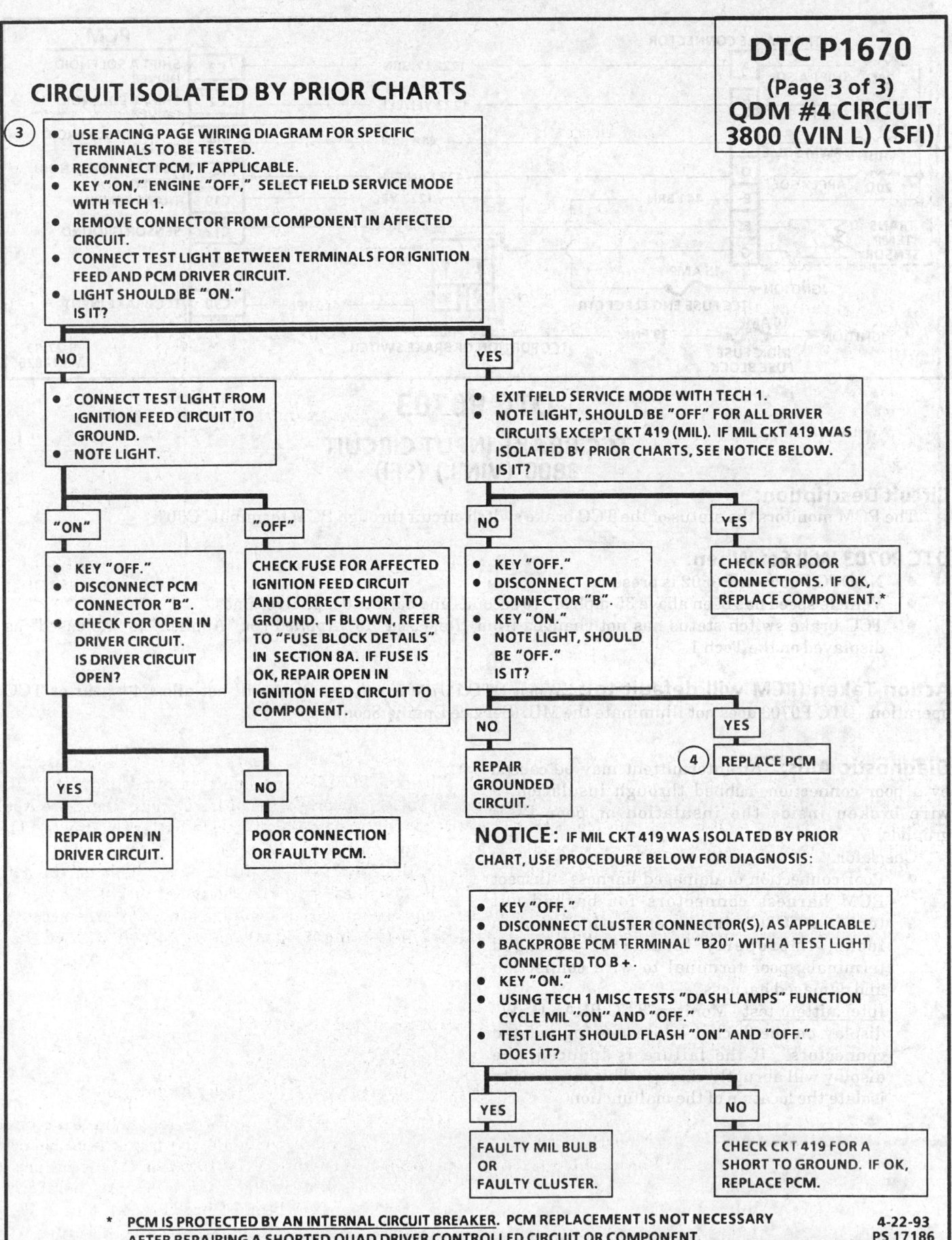

DTC P1670
(Page 3 of 3)
QDM #4 CIRCUIT 3800 (VIN L) (SFI)

CIRCUIT ISOLATED BY PRIOR CHARTS

(3)
- USE FACING PAGE WIRING DIAGRAM FOR SPECIFIC TERMINALS TO BE TESTED.
- RECONNECT PCM, IF APPLICABLE.
- KEY "ON," ENGINE "OFF," SELECT FIELD SERVICE MODE WITH TECH 1.
- REMOVE CONNECTOR FROM COMPONENT IN AFFECTED CIRCUIT.
- CONNECT TEST LIGHT BETWEEN TERMINALS FOR IGNITION FEED AND PCM DRIVER CIRCUIT.
- LIGHT SHOULD BE "ON."

IS IT?

NO
- CONNECT TEST LIGHT FROM IGNITION FEED CIRCUIT TO GROUND.
- NOTE LIGHT.

"ON"
- KEY "OFF."
- DISCONNECT PCM CONNECTOR "B".
- CHECK FOR OPEN IN DRIVER CIRCUIT.

IS DRIVER CIRCUIT OPEN?

YES: REPAIR OPEN IN DRIVER CIRCUIT.

NO: POOR CONNECTION OR FAULTY PCM.

"OFF": CHECK FUSE FOR AFFECTED IGNITION FEED CIRCUIT AND CORRECT SHORT TO GROUND. IF BLOWN, REFER TO "FUSE BLOCK DETAILS" IN SECTION 8A. IF FUSE IS OK, REPAIR OPEN IN IGNITION FEED CIRCUIT TO COMPONENT.

YES
- EXIT FIELD SERVICE MODE WITH TECH 1.
- NOTE LIGHT, SHOULD BE "OFF" FOR ALL DRIVER CIRCUITS EXCEPT CKT 419 (MIL). IF MIL CKT 419 WAS ISOLATED BY PRIOR CHARTS, SEE NOTICE BELOW.

IS IT?

NO
- KEY "OFF."
- DISCONNECT PCM CONNECTOR "B".
- KEY "ON."
- NOTE LIGHT, SHOULD BE "OFF."

IS IT?

NO: REPAIR GROUNDED CIRCUIT.

YES: (4) REPLACE PCM.

YES: CHECK FOR POOR CONNECTIONS. IF OK, REPLACE COMPONENT.*

NOTICE: IF MIL CKT 419 WAS ISOLATED BY PRIOR CHART, USE PROCEDURE BELOW FOR DIAGNOSIS:

- KEY "OFF."
- DISCONNECT CLUSTER CONNECTOR(S), AS APPLICABLE.
- BACKPROBE PCM TERMINAL "B20" WITH A TEST LIGHT CONNECTED TO B +.
- KEY "ON."
- USING TECH 1 MISC TESTS "DASH LAMPS" FUNCTION CYCLE MIL "ON" AND "OFF."
- TEST LIGHT SHOULD FLASH "ON" AND "OFF."

DOES IT?

YES: FAULTY MIL BULB OR FAULTY CLUSTER.

NO: CHECK CKT 419 FOR A SHORT TO GROUND. IF OK, REPLACE PCM.

* PCM IS PROTECTED BY AN INTERNAL CIRCUIT BREAKER. PCM REPLACEMENT IS NOT NECESSARY AFTER REPAIRING A SHORTED QUAD DRIVER CONTROLLED CIRCUIT OR COMPONENT.

4-22-93
PS 17186

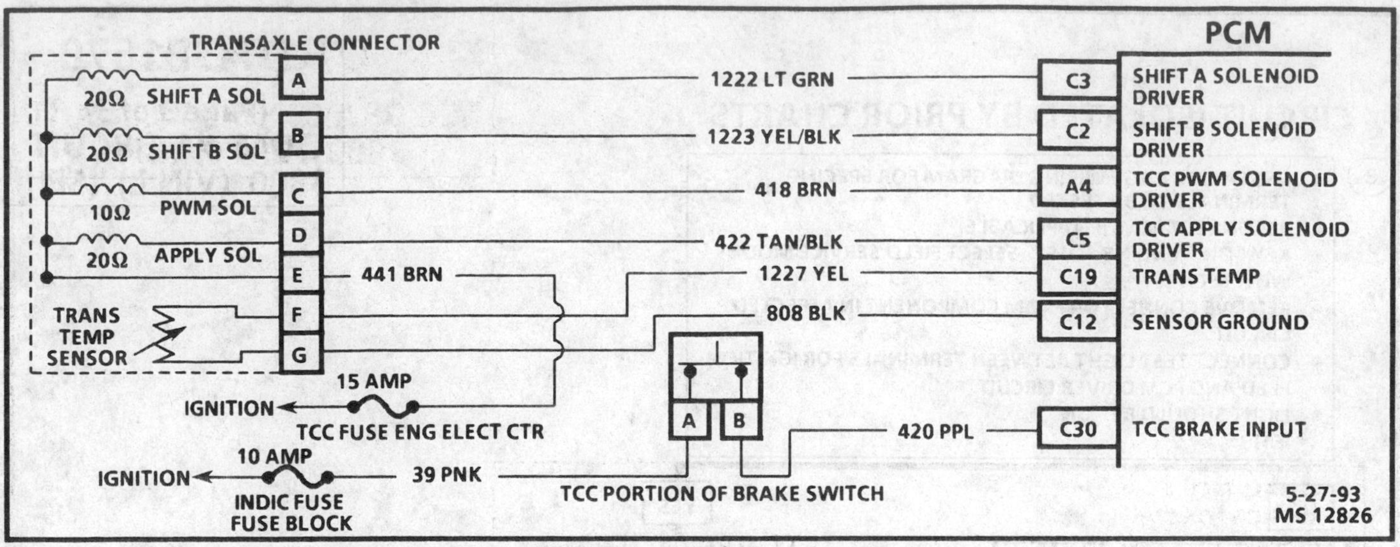
TRANSAXLE CONNECTOR
PCM
20Ω SHIFT A SOL
20Ω SHIFT B SOL
10Ω PWM SOL
20Ω APPLY SOL
TRANS TEMP SENSOR
A
B
C
D
E
F
G
1222 LT GRN
1223 YEL/BLK
418 BRN
422 TAN/BLK
441 BRN
1227 YEL
808 BLK
C3
C2
A4
C5
C19
C12
C30
SHIFT A SOLENOID DRIVER
SHIFT B SOLENOID DRIVER
TCC PWM SOLENOID DRIVER
TCC APPLY SOLENOID DRIVER
TRANS TEMP
SENSOR GROUND
TCC BRAKE INPUT
15 AMP
IGNITION
TCC FUSE ENG ELECT CTR
10 AMP
IGNITION
39 PNK
INDIC FUSE
FUSE BLOCK
420 PPL
TCC PORTION OF BRAKE SWITCH
5-27-93
MS 12826

DTC P0703

TCC BRAKE INPUT CIRCUIT
3800 (VIN L) (SFI)

Circuit Description:

The PCM monitors the status of the TCC brake switch circuit through PCM terminal "C30".

DTC P0703 Will Set When:

- No DTC P0501 or P0502 is present.
- Vehicle speed has been above 35 mph for 10 seconds and back to 0 mph five times.
- TCC brake switch status has not changed from "Released" to "Applied" or "Applied" to "Released" as displayed on the Tech 1.

Action Taken (PCM will default to): When DTC P0703 is set, the PCM will not allow 4th gear or TCC operation. DTC P0703 does not illuminate the MIL (Service Engine Soon).

Diagnostic Aids: An intermittent may be caused by a poor connection, rubbed through insulation, a wire broken inside the insulation or poor PCM grounds.

Check for:

- Poor connection or damaged harness - Inspect PCM harness connectors for backed out terminal "C30", improper mating, broken locks, improperly formed or damaged terminals, poor terminal to wire connection and damaged harness.
- Intermittent test - Monitor "TCC BRAKE SW" display on the Tech 1 while moving related connectors. If the failure is induced, the display will abruptly change. This may help to isolate the location of the malfunction.

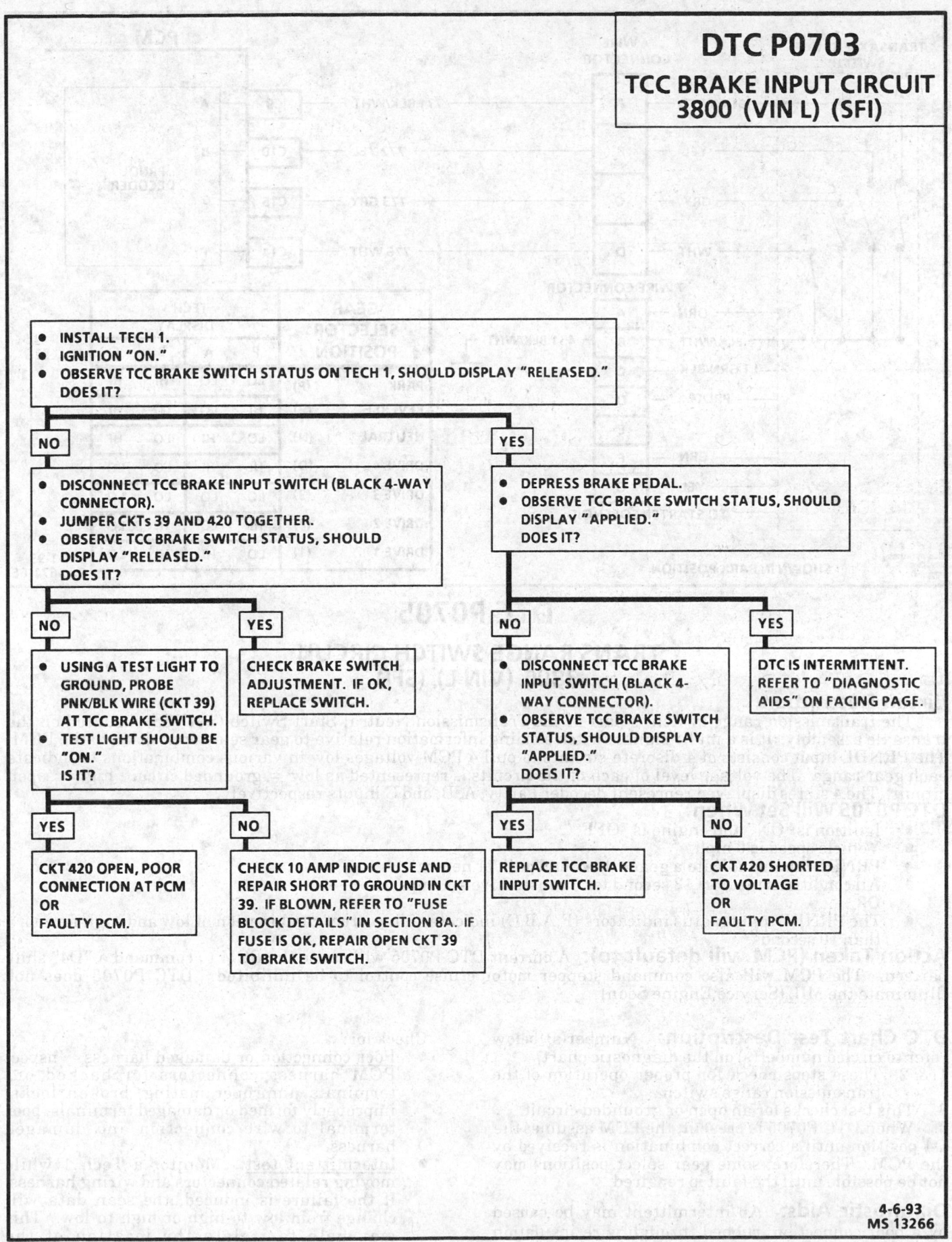

DTC P0703

TCC BRAKE INPUT CIRCUIT 3800 (VIN L) (SFI)

- INSTALL TECH 1.
- IGNITION "ON."
- OBSERVE TCC BRAKE SWITCH STATUS ON TECH 1, SHOULD DISPLAY "RELEASED." DOES IT?

NO

- DISCONNECT TCC BRAKE INPUT SWITCH (BLACK 4-WAY CONNECTOR).
- JUMPER CKTs 39 AND 420 TOGETHER.
- OBSERVE TCC BRAKE SWITCH STATUS, SHOULD DISPLAY "RELEASED." DOES IT?

NO

- USING A TEST LIGHT TO GROUND, PROBE PNK/BLK WIRE (CKT 39) AT TCC BRAKE SWITCH.
- TEST LIGHT SHOULD BE "ON." IS IT?

YES

CKT 420 OPEN, POOR CONNECTION AT PCM OR FAULTY PCM.

NO

CHECK 10 AMP INDIC FUSE AND REPAIR SHORT TO GROUND IN CKT 39. IF BLOWN, REFER TO "FUSE BLOCK DETAILS" IN SECTION 8A. IF FUSE IS OK, REPAIR OPEN CKT 39 TO BRAKE SWITCH.

YES

CHECK BRAKE SWITCH ADJUSTMENT. IF OK, REPLACE SWITCH.

YES

- DEPRESS BRAKE PEDAL.
- OBSERVE TCC BRAKE SWITCH STATUS, SHOULD DISPLAY "APPLIED." DOES IT?

NO

- DISCONNECT TCC BRAKE INPUT SWITCH (BLACK 4-WAY CONNECTOR).
- OBSERVE TCC BRAKE SWITCH STATUS, SHOULD DISPLAY "APPLIED." DOES IT?

YES

REPLACE TCC BRAKE INPUT SWITCH.

NO

CKT 420 SHORTED TO VOLTAGE OR FAULTY PCM.

YES

DTC IS INTERMITTENT. REFER TO "DIAGNOSTIC AIDS" ON FACING PAGE.

4-6-93
MS 13266

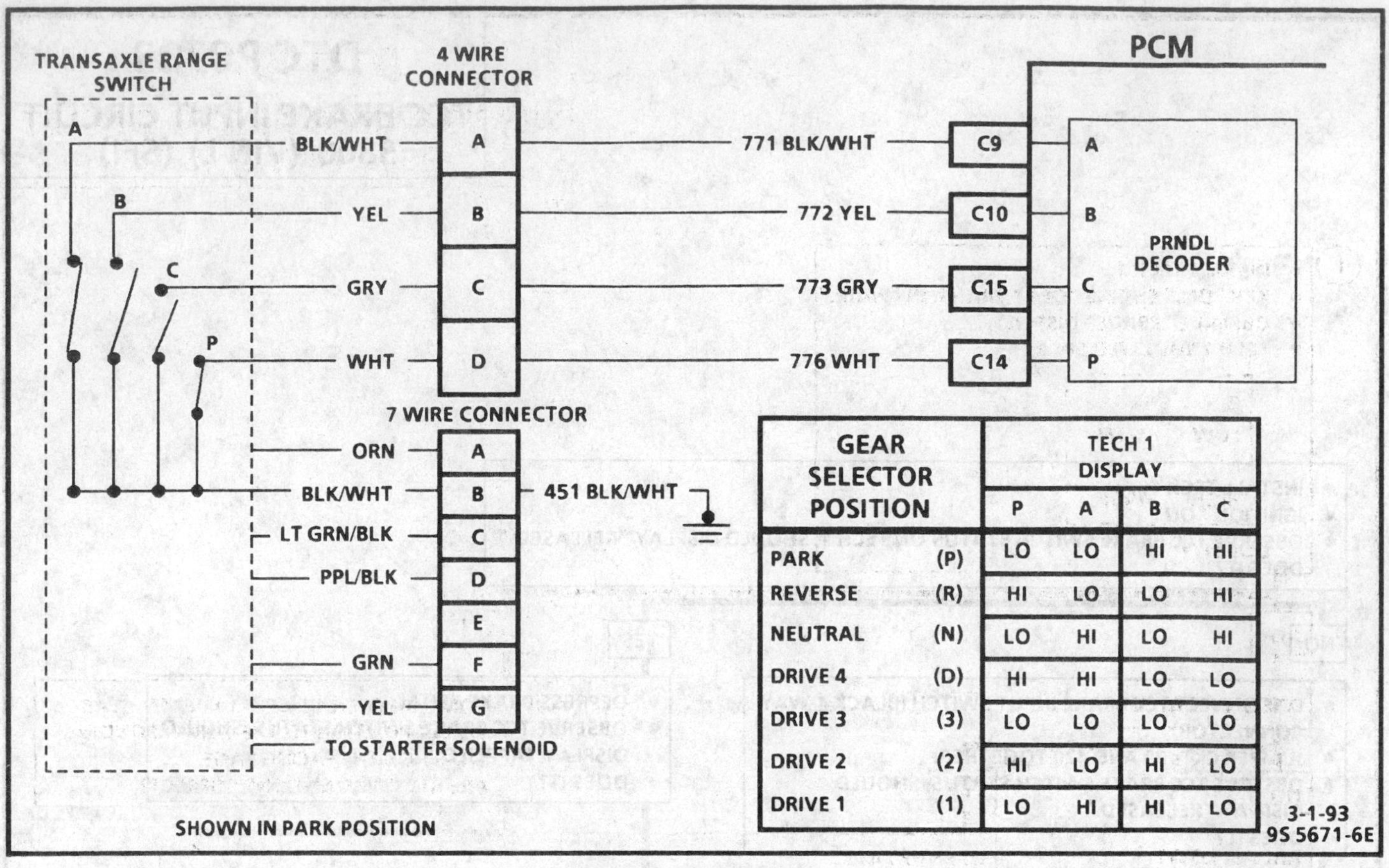
TRANSAXLE RANGE SWITCH
4 WIRE CONNECTOR
PCM
A
B
C
P
BLK/WHT
YEL
GRY
WHT
A
B
C
D
771 BLK/WHT
772 YEL
773 GRY
776 WHT
C9
C10
C15
C14
PRNDL DECODER
7 WIRE CONNECTOR
ORN
BLK/WHT
LT GRN/BLK
PPL/BLK
GRN
YEL
E
F
G
451 BLK/WHT
TO STARTER SOLENOID
SHOWN IN PARK POSITION
3-1-93
9S 5671-6E

GEAR SELECTOR POSITION		TECH 1 DISPLAY			
		P	A	B	C
PARK	(P)	LO	LO	HI	HI
REVERSE	(R)	HI	LO	LO	HI
NEUTRAL	(N)	LO	HI	LO	HI
DRIVE 4	(D)	HI	HI	LO	LO
DRIVE 3	(3)	LO	LO	LO	LO
DRIVE 2	(2)	HI	LO	HI	LO
DRIVE 1	(1)	LO	HI	HI	LO

DTC P0705

TRANS RANGE SWITCH CIRCUIT 3800 (VIN L) (SFI)

Circuit Description:

The transmission range switch is part of the Transmission Neutral Start Switch (TMNSS) mounted on the transaxle assembly. It is a multi-signal switch sending information relative to gear selector position to the PCM. The PRNDL input consists of 4 discrete circuits to pull 4 PCM voltages low in various combinations to indicate each gear range. The voltage level of each of the circuits is represented as low = grounded circuit, high = open circuit. The 4 states displayed represent decoder Parity, A, B, and C inputs respectively.

DTC P0705 Will Set When:

- Ignition is "ON" and engine is "OFF."
- Vehicle speed is 0 mph.
- PRNDL inputs indicate a gear other than park or neutral.
- All conditions met for .13 second for 3 consecutive startups.

OR

- The PRNDL input status indicators (P,A,B,C) indicate an incorrect combination of low and high for more than 10 seconds.

Action Taken (PCM will default to): A current DTC P0705 will cause the PCM to command a "D4" shift pattern. The PCM will also command stepper motor cruise control to be inhibited. DTC P0705 does not illuminate the MIL (Service Engine Soon).

DTC Chart Test Description: Number(s) below refer to circled number(s) on the diagnostic chart.

1. & 2. These steps check for proper operation of the transmission range switch.
3. This test checks for an open or grounded circuit.

When DTC P0705 is present, the PCM assumes the D4 position until a correct combination is received by the PCM. Therefore, some gear select positions may not be possible until the fault is repaired.

Diagnostic Aids: An intermittent may be caused by a poor connection, rubbed through wire insulation or a wire broken inside the insulation.

Check for:

- Poor connection or damaged harness - Inspect PCM harness connectors for backed out terminals, improper mating, broken locks, improperly formed or damaged terminals, poor terminal to wire connection and damaged harness.
- Intermittent test - Monitor a Tech 1 while moving related connectors and wiring harness. If the failure is induced, the scan data will change from low to high or high to low. This may help to isolate the location of the malfunction.

DTC P0705
TRANS RANGE SWITCH CIRCUIT
3800 (VIN L) (SFI)

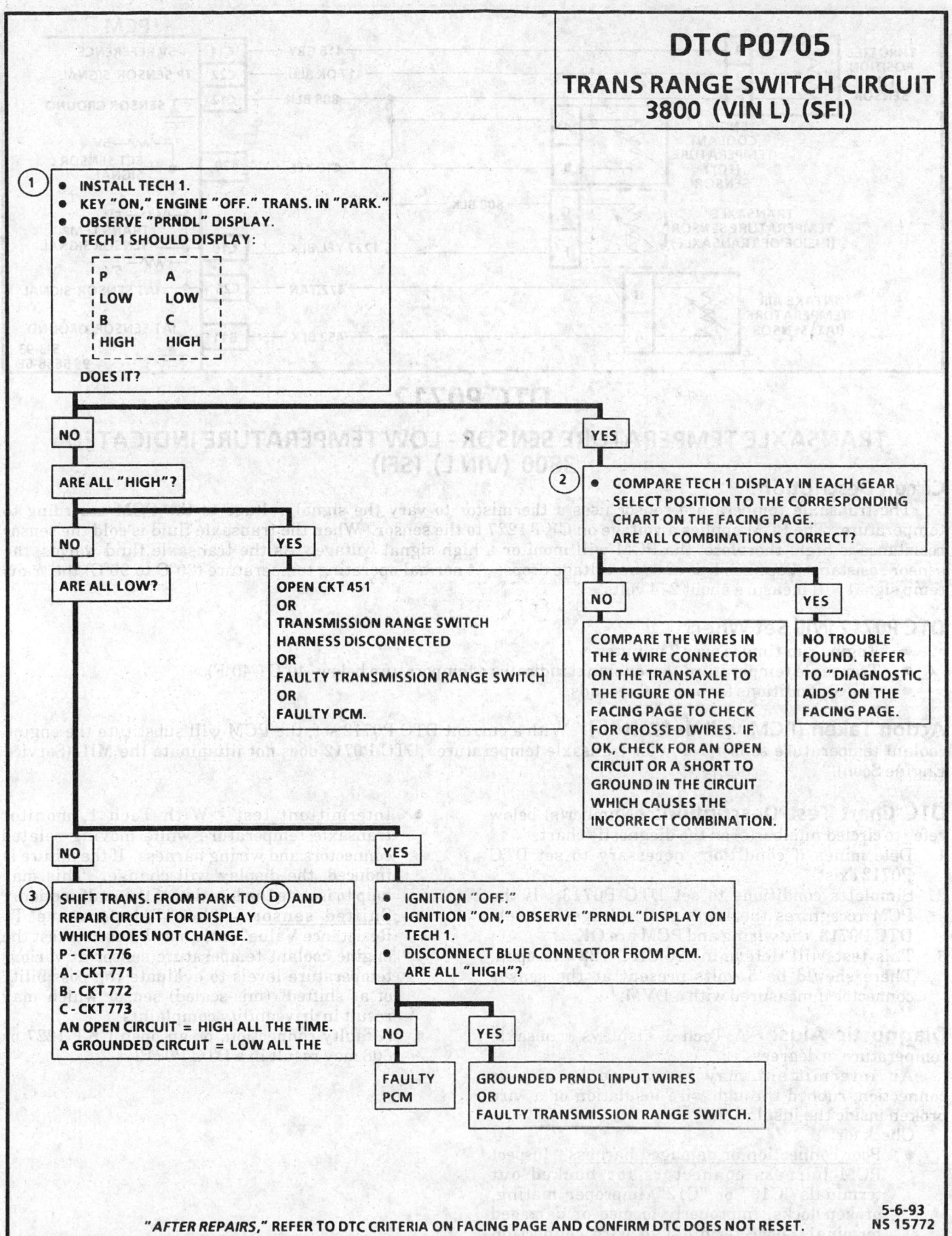

1
- INSTALL TECH 1.
- KEY "ON," ENGINE "OFF." TRANS. IN "PARK."
- OBSERVE "PRNDL" DISPLAY.
- TECH 1 SHOULD DISPLAY:

P	A
LOW	LOW
B	C
HIGH	HIGH

DOES IT?

NO → ARE ALL "HIGH"?
- **YES** → OPEN CKT 451 OR TRANSMISSION RANGE SWITCH HARNESS DISCONNECTED OR FAULTY TRANSMISSION RANGE SWITCH OR FAULTY PCM.
- **NO** → ARE ALL LOW?
  - **NO** → **3** SHIFT TRANS. FROM PARK TO (D) AND REPAIR CIRCUIT FOR DISPLAY WHICH DOES NOT CHANGE.
    - P - CKT 776
    - A - CKT 771
    - B - CKT 772
    - C - CKT 773

    AN OPEN CIRCUIT = HIGH ALL THE TIME.
    A GROUNDED CIRCUIT = LOW ALL THE
  - **YES** →
    - IGNITION "OFF."
    - IGNITION "ON," OBSERVE "PRNDL" DISPLAY ON TECH 1.
    - DISCONNECT BLUE CONNECTOR FROM PCM.

    ARE ALL "HIGH"?
    - **NO** → FAULTY PCM
    - **YES** → GROUNDED PRNDL INPUT WIRES OR FAULTY TRANSMISSION RANGE SWITCH.

YES → **2**
- COMPARE TECH 1 DISPLAY IN EACH GEAR SELECT POSITION TO THE CORRESPONDING CHART ON THE FACING PAGE.

ARE ALL COMBINATIONS CORRECT?
- **NO** → COMPARE THE WIRES IN THE 4 WIRE CONNECTOR ON THE TRANSAXLE TO THE FIGURE ON THE FACING PAGE TO CHECK FOR CROSSED WIRES. IF OK, CHECK FOR AN OPEN CIRCUIT OR A SHORT TO GROUND IN THE CIRCUIT WHICH CAUSES THE INCORRECT COMBINATION.
- **YES** → NO TROUBLE FOUND. REFER TO "DIAGNOSTIC AIDS" ON THE FACING PAGE.

"*AFTER REPAIRS*," REFER TO DTC CRITERIA ON FACING PAGE AND CONFIRM DTC DOES NOT RESET.

5-6-93
NS 15772

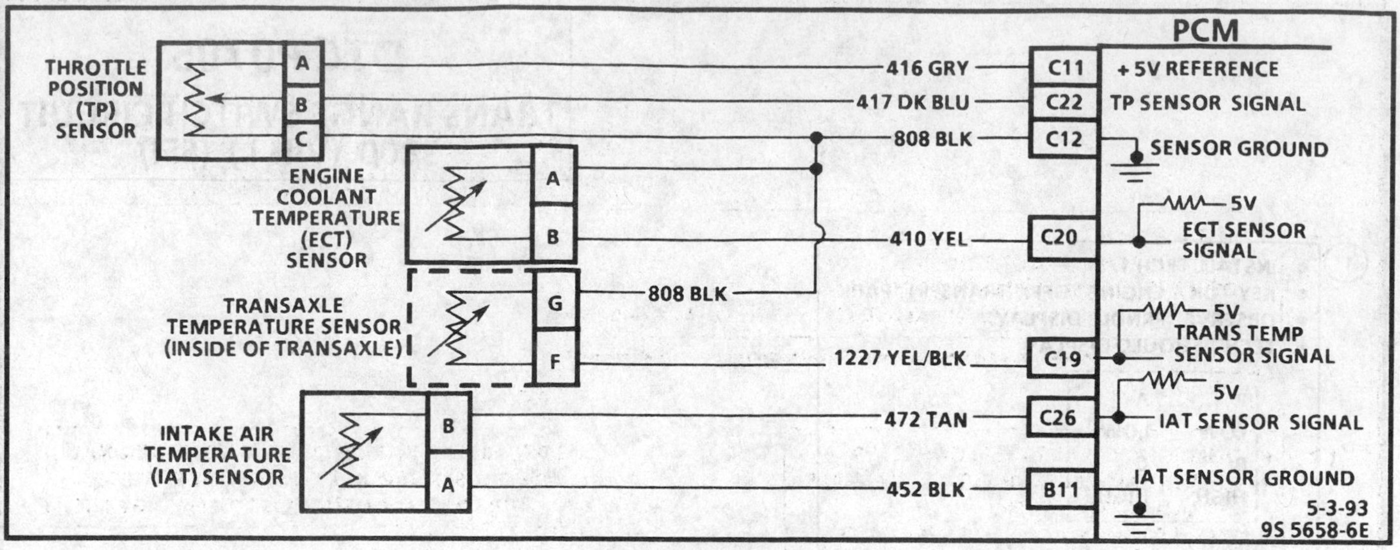
THROTTLE POSITION (TP) SENSOR
A
B
C
ENGINE COOLANT TEMPERATURE (ECT) SENSOR
TRANSAXLE TEMPERATURE SENSOR (INSIDE OF TRANSAXLE)
G
F
808 BLK
INTAKE AIR TEMPERATURE (IAT) SENSOR
416 GRY
417 DK BLU
808 BLK
410 YEL
1227 YEL/BLK
472 TAN
452 BLK
PCM
C11
C22
C12
C20
C19
C26
B11
+5V REFERENCE
TP SENSOR SIGNAL
SENSOR GROUND
5V
ECT SENSOR SIGNAL
5V
TRANS TEMP SENSOR SIGNAL
5V
IAT SENSOR SIGNAL
IAT SENSOR GROUND
5-3-93
9S 5658-6E

DTC P0712

TRANSAXLE TEMPERATURE SENSOR - LOW TEMPERATURE INDICATED 3800 (VIN L) (SFI)

Circuit Description:

The transaxle temperature sensor uses a thermistor to vary the signal voltage to the PCM according to temperature. The PCM applies a voltage on CKT 1227 to the sensor. When the transaxle fluid is cold the sensor resistance is high; therefore, the PCM will monitor a high signal voltage. As the transaxle fluid warms, the sensor resistance becomes less and the voltage drops. At normal operating temperature (20°C to 90°C) the trans temp signal will measure about 2- 4 volts.

DTC P0712 Will Set When:

- Engine run time is over 2 minutes.
- Transaxle temperature sensor signal indicates a temperature below -40°C (-40°F).
- Above conditions for over 1.6 seconds.

Action Taken (PCM will default to): With a current DTC P0712 set, the PCM will substitute the engine coolant temperature sensor value for transaxle temperature. DTC P0712 does not illuminate the MIL (Service Engine Soon).

DTC Chart Test Description: Number(s) below refer to circled number(s) on the diagnostic chart.

1. Determines if conditions necessary to set DTC P0712 exist.
2. Simulates conditions to set DTC P0713. If the PCM recognizes the low signal voltage and sets DTC P0713, the wiring and PCM are OK.
3. This test will determine if CKT 1227 is open. There should be 5 volts present at the sensor connector if measured with a DVM.

Diagnostic Aids: A Tech 1 displays transaxle temperature in degrees.

An intermittent may be caused by a poor connection, rubbed through wire insulation or a wire broken inside the insulation.

Check for:

- Poor connection or damaged harness - Inspect PCM harness connectors for backed out terminals "C19" or "C12", improper mating, broken locks, improperly formed or damaged terminals, poor terminal to wire connection and damaged harness.
- Intermittent test - With Tech 1, monitor transaxle temperature while moving related connectors and wiring harness. If the failure is induced, the display will change. This may help to isolate the location of the malfunction.
- Shifted sensor - The "Temperature To Resistance Value" scale may be used to test the engine coolant temperature sensor at various temperature levels to evaluate the possibility of a "shifted" (mis-scaled) sensor which may result in driveability complaints.
- A faulty connection, or an open CKT 1227 or 808 may result in a DTC P0712.

DTC P0712

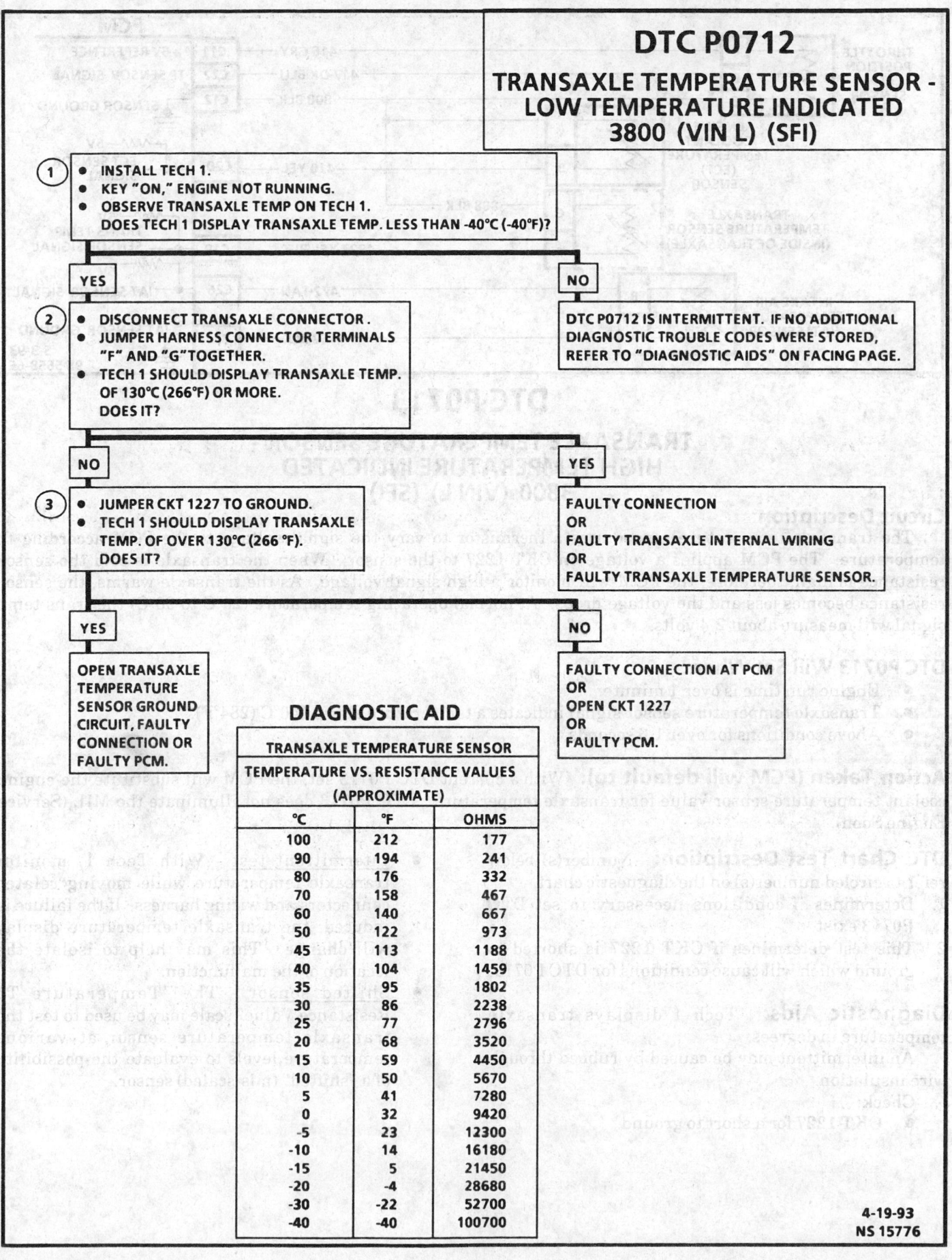

TRANSAXLE TEMPERATURE SENSOR - LOW TEMPERATURE INDICATED 3800 (VIN L) (SFI)

(1)
- INSTALL TECH 1.
- KEY "ON," ENGINE NOT RUNNING.
- OBSERVE TRANSAXLE TEMP ON TECH 1.

DOES TECH 1 DISPLAY TRANSAXLE TEMP. LESS THAN -40°C (-40°F)?

NO: DTC P0712 IS INTERMITTENT. IF NO ADDITIONAL DIAGNOSTIC TROUBLE CODES WERE STORED, REFER TO "DIAGNOSTIC AIDS" ON FACING PAGE.

YES:

(2)
- DISCONNECT TRANSAXLE CONNECTOR .
- JUMPER HARNESS CONNECTOR TERMINALS "F" AND "G" TOGETHER.
- TECH 1 SHOULD DISPLAY TRANSAXLE TEMP. OF 130°C (266°F) OR MORE.

DOES IT?

YES: FAULTY CONNECTION OR FAULTY TRANSAXLE INTERNAL WIRING OR FAULTY TRANSAXLE TEMPERATURE SENSOR.

NO:

(3)
- JUMPER CKT 1227 TO GROUND.
- TECH 1 SHOULD DISPLAY TRANSAXLE TEMP. OF OVER 130°C (266 °F).

DOES IT?

YES: OPEN TRANSAXLE TEMPERATURE SENSOR GROUND CIRCUIT, FAULTY CONNECTION OR FAULTY PCM.

NO: FAULTY CONNECTION AT PCM OR OPEN CKT 1227 OR FAULTY PCM.

DIAGNOSTIC AID

TRANSAXLE TEMPERATURE SENSOR

TEMPERATURE VS. RESISTANCE VALUES (APPROXIMATE)

°C	°F	OHMS
100	212	177
90	194	241
80	176	332
70	158	467
60	140	667
50	122	973
45	113	1188
40	104	1459
35	95	1802
30	86	2238
25	77	2796
20	68	3520
15	59	4450
10	50	5670
5	41	7280
0	32	9420
-5	23	12300
-10	14	16180
-15	5	21450
-20	-4	28680
-30	-22	52700
-40	-40	100700

4-19-93
NS 15776

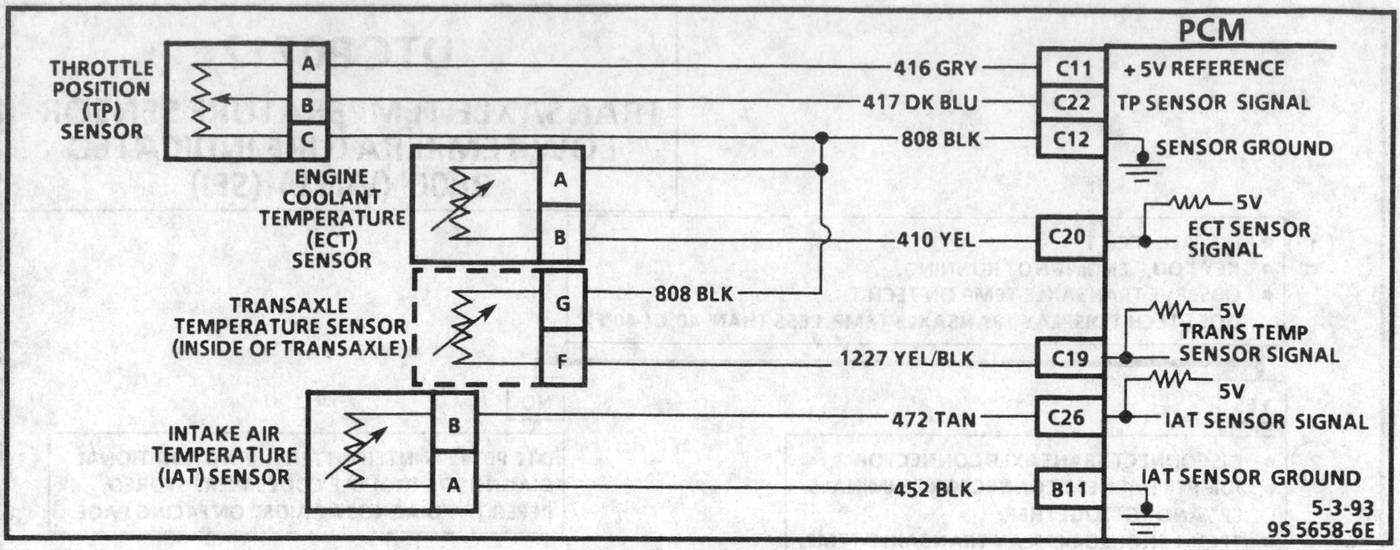
PCM
THROTTLE POSITION (TP) SENSOR
A
B
C
416 GRY
417 DK BLU
808 BLK
C11
C22
C12
+5V REFERENCE
TP SENSOR SIGNAL
SENSOR GROUND
ENGINE COOLANT TEMPERATURE (ECT) SENSOR
A
B
410 YEL
C20
5V
ECT SENSOR SIGNAL
TRANSAXLE TEMPERATURE SENSOR (INSIDE OF TRANSAXLE)
G
F
808 BLK
1227 YEL/BLK
C19
5V
TRANS TEMP SENSOR SIGNAL
INTAKE AIR TEMPERATURE (IAT) SENSOR
B
A
472 TAN
C26
5V
IAT SENSOR SIGNAL
452 BLK
B11
IAT SENSOR GROUND
5-3-93
9S 5658-6E

DTC P0713

TRANSAXLE TEMPERATURE SENSOR - HIGH TEMPERATURE INDICATED 3800 (VIN L) (SFI)

Circuit Description:

The transaxle temperature sensor uses a thermistor to vary the signal voltage to the PCM according to temperature. The PCM applies a voltage on CKT 1227 to the sensor. When the transaxle is cold the sensor resistance is high; therefore, the PCM will monitor a high signal voltage. As the transaxle warms, the sensor resistance becomes less and the voltage drops. At normal operating temperature (20°C to 90°C) the trans temp signal will measure about 2-4 volts.

DTC P0713 Will Set When:

- Engine run time is over 1 minute.
- Transaxle temperature sensor signal indicates a temperature above 140°C (284°F).
- Above conditions for over 1.6 seconds.

Action Taken (PCM will default to): With a current DTC P0713 set, the PCM will substitute the engine coolant temperature sensor value for transaxle temperature. DTC P0713 does not illuminate the MIL (Service Engine Soon).

DTC Chart Test Description: Number(s) below refer to circled number(s) on the diagnostic chart.

1. Determines if conditions necessary to set DTC P0713 exist.
2. This test determines if CKT 1227 is shorted to ground which will cause conditions for DTC P0713.

Diagnostic Aids: Tech 1 displays transaxle temperature in degrees.

An intermittent may be caused by rubbed through wire insulation.

Check:

- CKT 1227 for a short to ground.
- Intermittent test - With Tech 1, monitor transaxle temperature while moving related connectors and wiring harness. If the failure is induced, the transaxle temperature display will change. This may help to isolate the location of the malfunction.
- Shifted sensor - The "Temperature To Resistance Value" scale may be used to test the transaxle temperature sensor at various temperature levels to evaluate the possibility of a "shifted" (mis-scaled) sensor.

DTC P0713

TRANSAXLE TEMPERATURE SENSOR - HIGH TEMPERATURE INDICATED 3800 (VIN L) (SFI)

(1)
- INSTALL TECH 1.
- KEY "ON," ENGINE NOT RUNNING.
- OBSERVE TRANSAXLE TEMP ON TECH 1.

DOES TECH 1 DISPLAY TRANSAXLE TEMP OF 140°C (284°F) OR HIGHER?

YES → go to step 2.

NO → DTC P0713 IS INTERMITTENT. IF NO ADDITIONAL DIAGNOSTIC TROUBLE CODES WERE STORED, REFER TO "DIAGNOSTIC AIDS" ON FACING PAGE.

(2)
- DISCONNECT TRANSAXLE CONNECTOR. TECH 1 SHOULD DISPLAY TRANSAXLE TEMP BELOW -30°C (-22°F). DOES IT?

YES → FAULTY INTERNAL TRANSAXLE WIRING OR FAULTY TRANSAXLE TEMPERATURE SENSOR.

NO → CKT 1227 SHORTED TO GROUND OR CKT 1227 SHORTED TO SENSOR GROUND CIRCUIT OR FAULTY PCM.

DIAGNOSTIC AID

TRANSAXLE TEMPERATURE SENSOR

TEMPERATURE VS. RESISTANCE VALUES (APPROXIMATE)

°C	°F	OHMS
100	212	177
90	194	241
80	176	332
70	158	467
60	140	667
50	122	973
45	113	1188
40	104	1459
35	95	1802
30	86	2238
25	77	2796
20	68	3520
15	59	4450
10	50	5670
5	41	7280
0	32	9420
-5	23	12300
-10	14	16180
-15	5	21450
-20	-4	28680
-30	-22	52700
-40	-40	100700

4-19-93
NS 15777

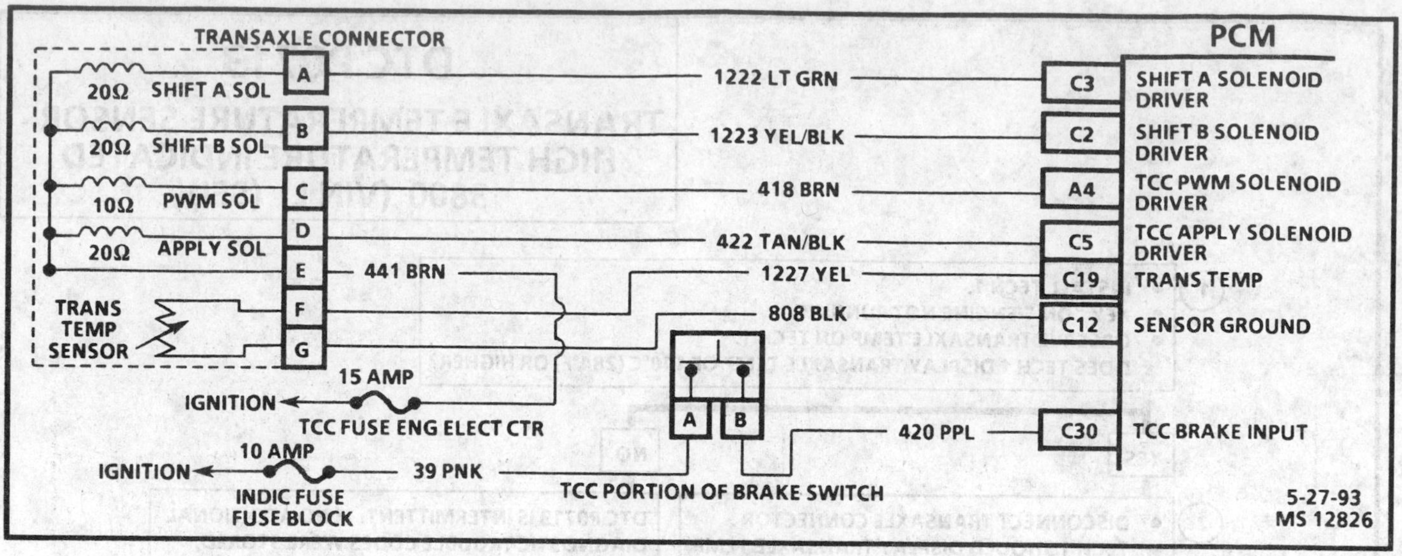
TRANSAXLE CONNECTOR
PCM
20Ω SHIFT A SOL
20Ω SHIFT B SOL
10Ω PWM SOL
20Ω APPLY SOL
TRANS TEMP SENSOR
A
B
C
D
E
F
G
1222 LT GRN
1223 YEL/BLK
418 BRN
422 TAN/BLK
441 BRN
1227 YEL
808 BLK
420 PPL
39 PNK
C3
C2
A4
C5
C19
C12
C30
SHIFT A SOLENOID DRIVER
SHIFT B SOLENOID DRIVER
TCC PWM SOLENOID DRIVER
TCC APPLY SOLENOID DRIVER
TRANS TEMP
SENSOR GROUND
TCC BRAKE INPUT
15 AMP
IGNITION
TCC FUSE ENG ELECT CTR
10 AMP
IGNITION
INDIC FUSE
FUSE BLOCK
TCC PORTION OF BRAKE SWITCH
5-27-93
MS 12826

DTC P0740

TORQUE CONVERTER CLUTCH (TCC) PROBLEM
3800 (VIN L) (SFI)

Circuit Description:

The purpose of the Torque Converter Clutch (TCC) feature is to eliminate the power loss of the torque converter when the vehicle is in a cruise condition. This allows the convenience of the automatic and the fuel economy of a manual transaxle. The heart of the system are two PCM controlled solenoids located inside the transaxle.

When the TCC apply solenoid coil is activated ("ON"), the Torque Converter Clutch (TCC) is applied which results in a straight through mechanical coupling from the engine to the wheels. When the apply solenoid coil is deactivated ("OFF"), the Torque Converter Clutch (TCC) is released which allows the torque converter to operate in the conventional manner (fluidic coupling between engine and transaxle).

The TCC PWM solenoid is used to vary hydraulic pressure to the converter clutch regulator valve, allowing a smoother engagement of the converter clutch.

DTC P0740 Will Set When:

- Vehicle is in 3rd or 4th gear.
- TCC is commanded "ON" by the PCM.
- Engine RPM/vehicle speed ratio indicates TCC is not locked.
- Above conditions for over 10 seconds.

Action Taken (PCM will default to): With a current DTC P0740 set, the PCM will not allow 4th gear operation. DTC P0740 does not illuminate the MIL (Service Engine Soon).

DTC Chart Test Description: Number(s) below refer to circled number(s) on the diagnostic chart.

1. Determines whether fault is caused by a bad solenoid or control circuit.
2. Checks availability of B+ on CKT 441.
3. Checks the PCM's ability to pulse the PWM solenoid "ON" and "OFF."
4. Electrical circuits have checked out. If there is a TCC engagement problem, refer to SECTION 7A.

Diagnostic Aids: The Tech 1 only indicates when the PCM has commanded the TCC driver "ON"; this does not confirm that the TCC is actually engaged. To determine if TCC is functioning properly, road test the vehicle. Engine RPM should decrease when the Tech 1 indicates the TCC has been turned "ON." If diagnosis indicates that all electrical circuits and components are OK, refer to "Automatic Transaxle Diagnosis," SECTION 7A for hydraulic and mechanical diagnosis.

DTC P0740

TORQUE CONVERTER CLUTCH (TCC) PROBLEM 3800 (VIN L) (SFI)

NOTICE: IF DTC P0740 AND P0755 ARE SET, REPAIR DTC P0755 FIRST.

SOLENOID RESISTANCE VS. TRANSAXLE TEMPERATURE TABLE

SOLENOID	RESISTANCE	
	AT 68°F (20°C)	AT 190°F (88°C)
SHIFT "A" & "B"	20-30Ω	23-50Ω
TCC APPLY	20-30Ω	23-50Ω
TCC PWM	10-15Ω	11-25Ω

* RESISTANCE VALUES INCREASE AT HIGHER TEMPERATURES AND DECREASE AT LOWER TEMPERATURES.

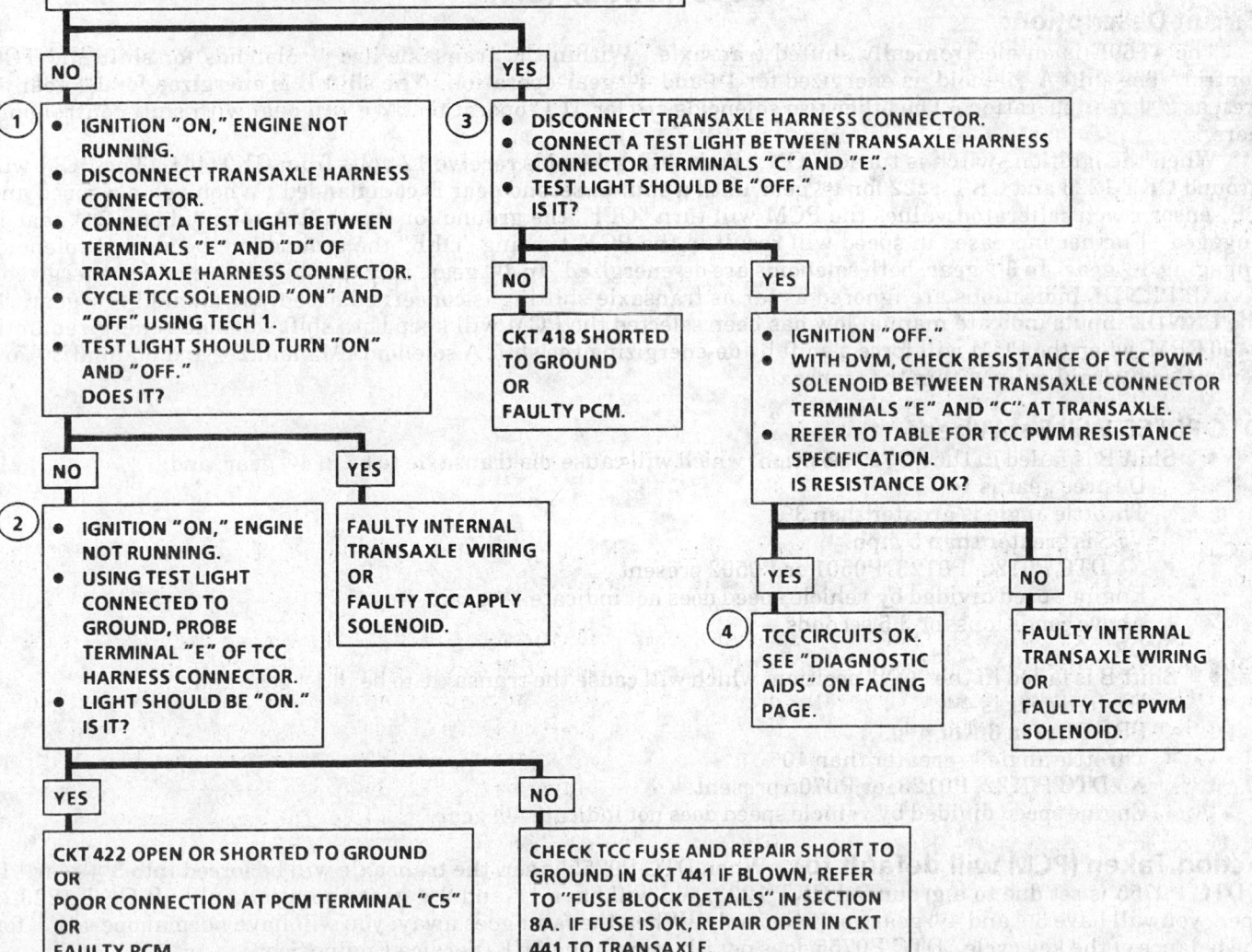

- INSTALL TECH 1.
- IGNITION "ON," ENGINE "OFF."
- SCAN TCC BRAKE SW. WITH TECH 1 WHILE APPLYING AND RELEASING BRAKE PEDAL. TECH 1 SHOULD INDICATE PROPER STATE OF BRAKE SWITCH. IF NOT, REFER TO DTC P0703 CHART FOR DIAGNOSIS. IF OK, CONTINUE.
- UNDER MISCELLANEOUS TEST, SELECT TRANSMISSION OUTPUT, TCC SOLENOID CONTROL.
- USING A STETHOSCOPE ON THE TRANSAXLE, YOU SHOULD BE ABLE TO HEAR THE TCC APPLY SOLENOID CLICK "ON" WHEN THE "↑" IS PRESSED AND CLICK "OFF" WHEN "↓" IS PRESSED.

DOES THE SOLENOID CLICK?

NO → (1)

YES → (3)

(1)
- IGNITION "ON," ENGINE NOT RUNNING.
- DISCONNECT TRANSAXLE HARNESS CONNECTOR.
- CONNECT A TEST LIGHT BETWEEN TERMINALS "E" AND "D" OF TRANSAXLE HARNESS CONNECTOR.
- CYCLE TCC SOLENOID "ON" AND "OFF" USING TECH 1.
- TEST LIGHT SHOULD TURN "ON" AND "OFF."

DOES IT?

- **NO** → (2)
- **YES** → FAULTY INTERNAL TRANSAXLE WIRING OR FAULTY TCC APPLY SOLENOID.

(2)
- IGNITION "ON," ENGINE NOT RUNNING.
- USING TEST LIGHT CONNECTED TO GROUND, PROBE TERMINAL "E" OF TCC HARNESS CONNECTOR.
- LIGHT SHOULD BE "ON."

IS IT?

- **YES** → CKT 422 OPEN OR SHORTED TO GROUND OR POOR CONNECTION AT PCM TERMINAL "C5" OR FAULTY PCM.
- **NO** → CHECK TCC FUSE AND REPAIR SHORT TO GROUND IN CKT 441 IF BLOWN, REFER TO "FUSE BLOCK DETAILS" IN SECTION 8A. IF FUSE IS OK, REPAIR OPEN IN CKT 441 TO TRANSAXLE.

(3)
- DISCONNECT TRANSAXLE HARNESS CONNECTOR.
- CONNECT A TEST LIGHT BETWEEN TRANSAXLE HARNESS CONNECTOR TERMINALS "C" AND "E".
- TEST LIGHT SHOULD BE "OFF."

IS IT?

- **NO** → CKT 418 SHORTED TO GROUND OR FAULTY PCM.
- **YES** →
  - IGNITION "OFF."
  - WITH DVM, CHECK RESISTANCE OF TCC PWM SOLENOID BETWEEN TRANSAXLE CONNECTOR TERMINALS "E" AND "C" AT TRANSAXLE.
  - REFER TO TABLE FOR TCC PWM RESISTANCE SPECIFICATION.

  IS RESISTANCE OK?

  - **YES** → **(4)** TCC CIRCUITS OK. SEE "DIAGNOSTIC AIDS" ON FACING PAGE.
  - **NO** → FAULTY INTERNAL TRANSAXLE WIRING OR FAULTY TCC PWM SOLENOID.

4-1-93
MS 13246

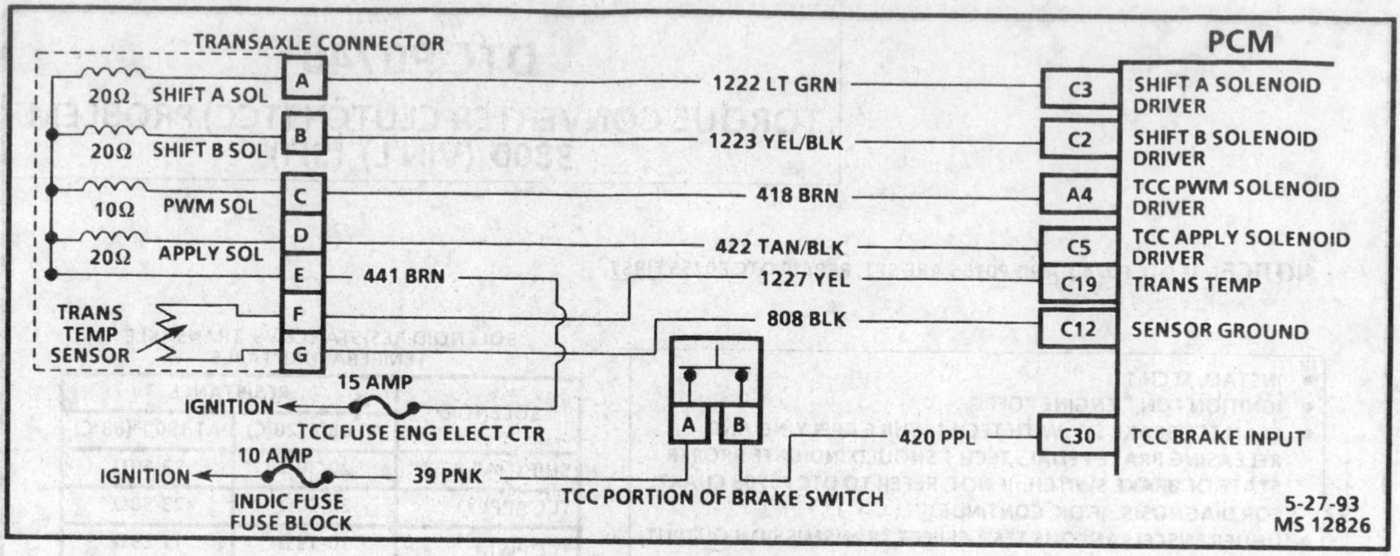
TRANSAXLE CONNECTOR
PCM
20Ω SHIFT A SOL
A
1222 LT GRN
C3
SHIFT A SOLENOID DRIVER
20Ω SHIFT B SOL
B
1223 YEL/BLK
C2
SHIFT B SOLENOID DRIVER
10Ω PWM SOL
C
418 BRN
A4
TCC PWM SOLENOID DRIVER
D
20Ω APPLY SOL
422 TAN/BLK
C5
TCC APPLY SOLENOID DRIVER
E
441 BRN
1227 YEL
C19
TRANS TEMP
TRANS TEMP SENSOR
F
808 BLK
C12
SENSOR GROUND
G
15 AMP
IGNITION
TCC FUSE ENG ELECT CTR
A
B
420 PPL
C30
TCC BRAKE INPUT
10 AMP
IGNITION
39 PNK
INDIC FUSE FUSE BLOCK
TCC PORTION OF BRAKE SWITCH
5-27-93
MS 12826

DTC P0755

TRANSAXLE SHIFT B SOLENOID PROBLEM 3800 (VIN L) (SFI)

Circuit Description:

The 4T60E is an electronically shifted transaxle. Within the transaxle are 4 solenoids for shift and TCC control. The shift A solenoid is energized for 1st and 4th gear operation. The shift B is energized for 1st gear as well as 2nd gear operation. The other two solenoids are for TCC operation. We will deal with shift control only here.

When the ignition switch is turned "ON," both shift solenoids receive 12 volts from CKT 441. The PCM will ground CKT 1223 and CKT 1222 for 1st gear until a shift to second gear is commanded. When vehicle speed and TP sensor reach calibrated values the PCM will turn "OFF" the ground for the shift A solenoid and 2nd gear is engaged. Further increases in speed will result in the PCM turning "OFF" the ground for the shift B solenoid, engaging 3rd gear. In 3rd gear, both solenoids are de-energized. In 4th gear, only the shift A solenoid is energized.

All PRNDL indications are ignored as far as transaxle shifting is concerned except for manual low gear. If the PRNDL inputs indicate manual low has been selected the PCM will keep both shift solenoids energized until 5400 RPM, when the PCM will force a shift by de-energizing the shift A solenoid. Manual 2nd and manual 3rd are controlled hydraulically within the transaxle.

DTC P0755 Will Set When:

- Shift B is failed in the "OFF" position, which will cause the transaxle to be in 4th gear, and:
  - Desired gear is 1st.
  - Throttle angle is greater than 3%.
  - VSS is greater than 5 mph.
  - No DTC P0122, P0123, P0501 or P0502 present.
  - Engine speed divided by vehicle speed does not indicate 1st gear.
  - Above conditions for 3.5 seconds.

  OR
- Shift B is failed in the "ON" position, which will cause the transaxle to be in 1st gear and:
  - Desired gear is 4th.
  - PRNDL is in 3rd or 4th.
  - Throttle angle is greater than 10%.
  - No DTC P0122, P0123, or P0705 present.
  - Engine speed divided by vehicle speed does not indicate 4th gear.

Action Taken (PCM will default to): When DTC P0755 is set, the transaxle will be forced into 3rd gear. If a DTC P0755 is set due to a grounded CKT 1223, you will have 1st and 2nd gear operation only. If CKT 1223 is open, you will have 3rd and 4th gear operation only. When the fault goes away, you will have normal operation for the balance of the key cycle. DTC P0755 does not illuminate the MIL (Service Engine Soon).

DTC P0755

TRANSAXLE SHIFT B SOLENOID PROBLEM 3800 (VIN L) (SFI)

NOTICE: DTC P0755 STORED WITH NO DTC P1650 INDICATES A PROBABLE HYDRAULIC OR MECHANICAL PROBLEM. REFER TO SECTION 7A.

NOTICE: IF DTC P0755 AND P0703 ARE STORED TOGETHER, CHECK TCC FUSE AND CKT 441 FOR AN OPEN.

SOLENOID RESISTANCE VS. TRANSAXLE TEMPERATURE TABLE

SOLENOID	RESISTANCE	
	AT 68°F (20°C)	AT 190°F (88°C)
SHIFT A & B	20-30Ω	23-50Ω
TCC APPLY	20-30Ω	23-50Ω
TCC PWM	10-15Ω	11-25Ω

* RESISTANCE VALUES INCREASE AT HIGHER TEMPERATURES AND DECREASE AT LOWER TEMPERATURES.

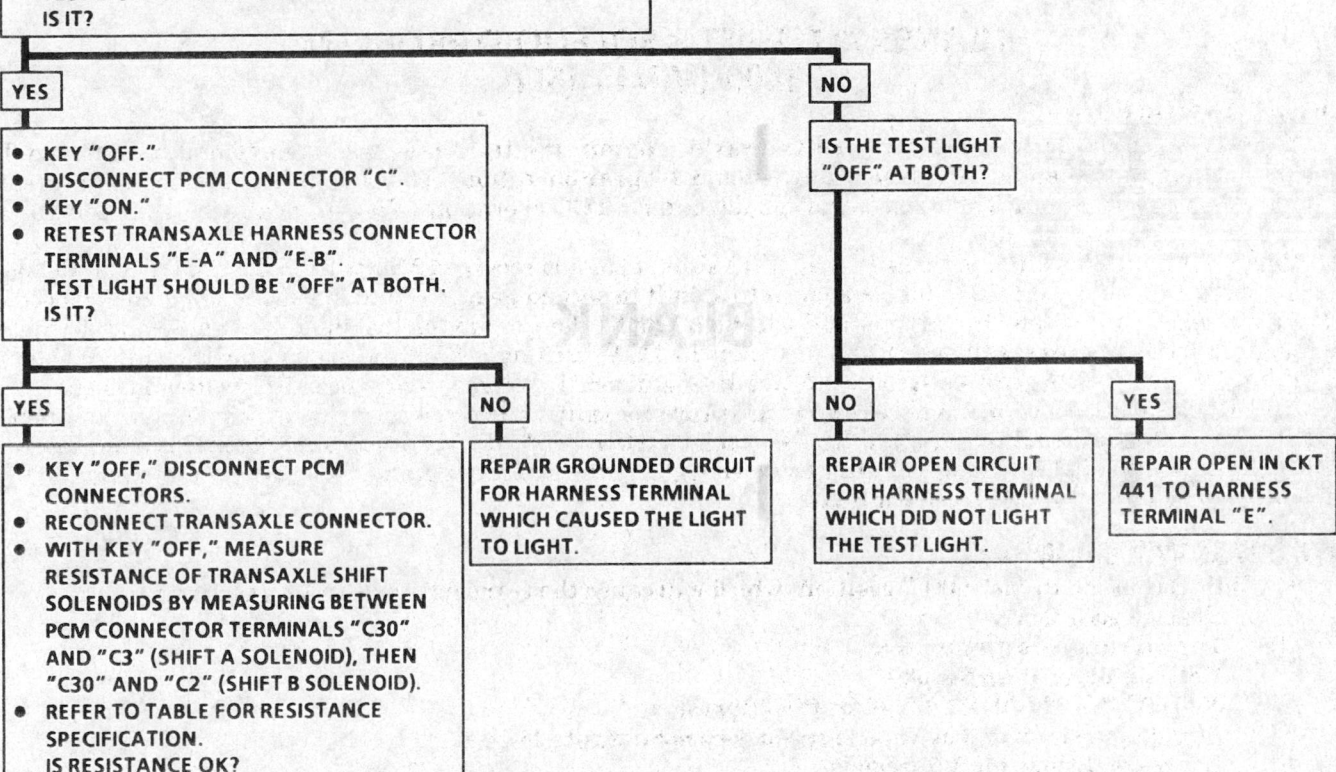

- KEY "ON," ENGINE "OFF."
- DISCONNECT TRANSAXLE CONNECTOR FROM TRANSAXLE.
- USING A TEST LIGHT, PROBE BETWEEN HARNESS TERMINALS "E-A" AND "E-B". TEST LIGHT SHOULD BE "ON" AT BOTH. IS IT?

YES

- KEY "OFF."
- DISCONNECT PCM CONNECTOR "C".
- KEY "ON."
- RETEST TRANSAXLE HARNESS CONNECTOR TERMINALS "E-A" AND "E-B". TEST LIGHT SHOULD BE "OFF" AT BOTH. IS IT?

YES

- KEY "OFF," DISCONNECT PCM CONNECTORS.
- RECONNECT TRANSAXLE CONNECTOR.
- WITH KEY "OFF," MEASURE RESISTANCE OF TRANSAXLE SHIFT SOLENOIDS BY MEASURING BETWEEN PCM CONNECTOR TERMINALS "C30" AND "C3" (SHIFT A SOLENOID), THEN "C30" AND "C2" (SHIFT B SOLENOID).
- REFER TO TABLE FOR RESISTANCE SPECIFICATION. IS RESISTANCE OK?

YES

CHECK CONNECTIONS AT TRANSAXLE CONNECTOR. IF OK, REPAIR TRANSAXLE HYDRAULIC OR MECHANICAL PROBLEM OR POSSIBLE STICKING SHIFT VALVE. REFER TO SECTION 7A.

NO

POOR CONNECTIONS AT TRANSAXLE, FAULTY TRANSMISSION INTERNAL WIRING OR FAULTY SOLENOID. SEE SECTION 7 (TRANSAXLE) FOR REPAIR.

NO (retest)

REPAIR GROUNDED CIRCUIT FOR HARNESS TERMINAL WHICH CAUSED THE LIGHT TO LIGHT.

NO (first test)

IS THE TEST LIGHT "OFF" AT BOTH?

NO

REPAIR OPEN CIRCUIT FOR HARNESS TERMINAL WHICH DID NOT LIGHT THE TEST LIGHT.

YES

REPAIR OPEN IN CKT 441 TO HARNESS TERMINAL "E".

"AFTER REPAIRS," REFER TO DTC CRITERIA ON FACING PAGE AND CONFIRM DTC DOES NOT RESET.

4-22-93
MS 13387

BLANK

SECTION B

SYMPTOMS

CONTENTS

IMPORTANT PRELIMINARY CHECKS

BEFORE USING THIS SECTION

Before using this section you should have performed the "Diagnostic Circuit Check" and determined that:

1. The PCM and MIL (Service Engine Soon) are operating correctly.
2. There are no diagnostic trouble codes stored.

SYMPTOM

Verify the customer complaint, and locate the correct symptom in the table of contents. Check the items indicated under that symptom.

VISUAL/PHYSICAL CHECK

Several of the symptom procedures call for a careful visual/physical check. The importance of this step cannot be stressed too strongly - it can lead to correcting a problem without further checks and can save valuable time. This check should include:

- PCM grounds and sensors for being clean, tight and in their proper location.
- Vacuum hoses for splits, kinks, and proper connections, as shown on "Vehicle Emission Control Information" label. Check thoroughly for any type of leak or restriction.
- Air leaks at throttle body mounting area and intake manifold sealing surfaces.
- Ignition wires for cracking, hardness, proper routing and carbon tracking.
- Wiring for proper connections, pinches and cuts.

INTERMITTENTS

Definition: Problem may or may not turn "ON" the MIL (Service Engine Soon) or store a DTC.

DO NOT use the diagnostic trouble code charts in "Engine Components/Wiring Diagrams/Diagnostic Charts," Section "6E3-A" for intermittent problems. The fault must be present to locate the problem. If a fault is intermittent, use of diagnostic trouble code charts may result in replacement of good parts.

- Most intermittent problems are caused by faulty electrical connections or wiring. Perform careful visual/physical check as described at start of "Symptoms," Section "6E3-B". Check for:
  - Poor mating of the connector halves or terminal not fully seated in the connector body (backed out).
  - Improperly formed or damaged terminal. All connector terminals in the problem circuit should be carefully replaced to ensure proper contact tension.
  - Poor terminal to wire connection. This requires removing the terminal from the connector body to check. Refer to "Introduction" in SECTION 6E, "Wiring Harness Service."

- If a visual/physical check does not find the cause of the problem, the vehicle can be driven with a voltmeter connected to a suspected circuit. A Tech 1 can also be used to help detect intermittent conditions. An abnormal voltage, or scan reading, when the problem occurs, indicates the problem may be in that circuit. If the wiring and connectors check OK, and a diagnostic trouble code was stored for a circuit having a sensor, except for DTC P0131, P0132, P0134, P0137, P0138, P0140, P0171, P0172 or P0420 substitute a known good sensor and recheck.

- Loss of diagnostic code memory. To check, disconnect TP sensor and idle engine until MIL (Service Engine Soon) comes "ON." DTC P0122 should be stored, and kept in memory when ignition is turned "OFF." If not, the PCM is faulty.

- An intermittent MIL (Service Engine Soon) with no stored diagnostic trouble code may be caused by:
  - Ignition coil shorted to ground and arcing at spark plug wires or plugs.
  - MIL (Service Engine Soon) wire to PCM shorted to ground (CKT 419).
  - PCM grounds, refer to PCM wiring diagrams.

- Check for an electrical system interference caused by a defective relay, PCM driven solenoid, or switch. They can cause a sharp electrical surge. Normally, the problem will occur when the faulty component is operated.

- Check for improper installation of electrical options such as lights, 2-way radios, car phones, CB antenna lead near PCM harness causing false readings and DTCs, etc.

- Check for open diode across A/C compressor clutch, located in the harness approximately 10 - 15 inches from the A/C compressor, and for other open diodes (refer to wiring diagrams).

- If problem has not been found, refer to "PCM Connector Symptom" charts at the end of "Symptoms," Section "6E3-B".

HARD START

Definition: Engine cranks OK, but does not start for a long time. Does eventually run, or may start but immediately dies.

PRELIMINARY CHECKS

- Perform the careful visual/physical checks as described at start of "Symptoms," Section "6E3-B".
- Make sure the driver is using the correct starting procedure.

SENSORS

- **CHECK:** Engine Coolant Temperature (ECT) sensor using a Tech 1, compare engine coolant temperature with Intake Air Temperature (IAT) on cold engine.
  - If engine coolant temperature readings are 5 degrees greater than or less than intake air temperature on a cold engine, check resistance in coolant sensor circuit or sensor itself. Compare ECT sensor resistance value to the "Diagnostic Aids" table on DTC P0117 chart.
- **CHECK:** TP sensor for binding or a high TP sensor voltage with the throttle closed (should read between .2 volt and .74 volt and 0% throttle angle).

FUEL SYSTEM

- **CHECK:** Fuel pump relay operation - pump should turn "ON" for 2 seconds when ignition is turned "ON." Use CHART A-5.
- **CHECK:** Fuel pressure, use CHART A-7.
- **CHECK:** For contaminated fuel and sufficient fuel quantity.

NOTICE: A faulty in-tank fuel pump check valve will allow the fuel in the lines to drain back to the tank after engine is stopped. To check for this condition, perform fuel system diagnosis CHART A-7.

IGNITION SYSTEM

- **CHECK:** For proper ignition voltage output with spark tester J 26792 (ST-125) or equivalent .
- **CHECK:** Spark plugs. Remove spark plugs, check for wet plugs, cracks, wear, improper gap, burned electrodes, or heavy deposits. Repair or replace as necessary.
- **CHECK:** Bare or shorted wires.
- **CHECK:** Loose ignition control module ground (mounting screws).

ADDITIONAL CHECKS

- **CHECK:** IAC operation - use CHART C-2B.
- **CHECK:** Basic engine problem. Refer to SECTION 6A.
- **CHECK:** Service Bulletins for PROM updates.
- **CHECK:** PCV valve stuck open.

SURGES AND/OR CHUGGLES

Definition: Engine power variation under steady throttle or cruise. Feels like the vehicle speeds up and slows down with no change in the acceleration pedal.

PRELIMINARY CHECKS

- Perform the careful visual checks as described at start of "Symptoms," Section "6E3-B".
- Be sure driver understands transmission torque converter clutch, and A/C compressor operation as explained in the owner's manual.

SENSORS

- **CHECK:** Heated Oxygen Sensor (HO2S 1). The heated oxygen sensor should respond quickly to different throttle positions; if it does not, check the heated oxygen sensor for silicon or other contaminants from fuel or use of improper RTV sealant. The sensor may have a white, powdery coating and a high but false signal voltage (rich exhaust indication). The PCM will then reduce the amount of fuel delivered to the engine, causing a severe driveability problem. Also, watch for green glycol contamination or cracking.

FUEL SYSTEM

NOTICE: To determine if the condition is caused by a rich or lean system, the vehicle should be driven at the speed of the complaint. Monitoring L.T. fuel trim and S.T. fuel trim will help identify a problem. Refer to "Typical Tech 1 Data Definitions," in "Engine Components/Wiring Diagrams/Diagnostics," Section "6E3-A" for an explanation of L.T. fuel trim and S.T. fuel trim. A poor PCM ground at the ignition control module mounting bracket may cause the S.T. fuel trim to read about 159.

- **CHECK:** Fuel pressure while condition exists. Use CHART A-7.
- **CHECK:** In-line fuel filter. Replace if restricted, dirty or plugged.

IGNITION SYSTEM

- **CHECK:** For adequate ignition voltage output using spark tester J 26792 (ST-125) or equivalent. Test one spark plug wire at a time.
- **CHECK:** Spark plugs. Remove spark plugs, check for wet plugs, cracks, wear, improper gap, burned electrodes, or heavy deposits. Repair or replace as necessary. Also, check condition of spark plug wires.

ADDITIONAL CHECKS

- **CHECK:** PCM grounds for being clean, tight and in their proper location.
- **CHECK:** Vacuum lines for kinks or leaks.
- **CHECK:** Generator output voltage. Repair if less than 9 or more than 17 volts.
- **CHECK:** Speedometer reading and the speed displayed on a Tech 1 should be equal.

LACK OF POWER, SLUGGISH OR SPONGY

Definition: Engine delivers less than expected power. Little or no increase in speed when accelerator pedal is pushed down part way.

PRELIMINARY CHECKS

- Perform the careful visual/physical checks as described at start of "Symptoms," Section "6E3-B".
- Compare customer's vehicle to similar unit. Make sure the customer has an actual problem.
- Remove air filter and check air filter for dirt, or for being plugged. Replace as necessary.

FUEL SYSTEM

- **CHECK:** Restricted fuel filter.
- **CHECK:** Fuel pressure, use CHART A-7.
- **CHECK:** Contaminated fuel.

IGNITION SYSTEM

- **CHECK:** Secondary voltage using a spark tester J 26792 (ST-125), or equivalent, to check for a weak coil, testing one spark plug wire at a time.
- **CHECK:** Knock sensor system for false retard due to mechanical noise.

ADDITIONAL CHECKS

- **CHECK:** PCM grounds for being clean, tight and in their proper locations. Refer to "PCM Wiring Diagrams."
- **CHECK:** Generator output voltage. Repair if less than 9 or more than 17 volts.
- **CHECK:** Exhaust system for possible restriction. Refer to CHART B-1.
  - Inspect exhaust system for damaged or collapsed pipes.
  - Inspect muffler for heat distress or possible internal failure.
- **CHECK:** Shift solenoid system and Torque Converter Clutch (TCC) for proper operation. Refer to "Torque Converter Clutch (TCC) and Shift Solenoid System," Section "6E3-C8" or SECTION 7A.

ENGINE MECHANICAL

- **CHECK:** Engine valve timing and compression.
- **CHECK:** Engine for incorrect or worn camshaft. Refer to SECTION 6A.

DETONATION/SPARK KNOCK

Definition: A mild to severe ping, usually worse under acceleration. The engine makes sharp metallic knocks that change with throttle opening.

PRELIMINARY CHECKS

- Perform the careful visual/physical checks as described at start of "Symptoms," Section "6E3-B".
- Transaxle range switch PRNDL inputs. Be sure scan indicates drive with gear selector in drive or overdrive.

NOTICE: If scan tool readings are normal (refer to facing page of "Diagnostic Circuit Check") and there are no engine mechanical faults, fill fuel tank with a known quality gasoline that has a minimum octane rating of 87 and re-evaluate vehicle performance.

- **CHECK:** TCC operation, TCC applying too soon. Use CHART C-8.

COOLING SYSTEM

- Check for obvious overheating problems:
  - Low engine coolant.
  - Loose water pump belt.
  - Restricted air flow to radiator, or restricted coolant flow.
  - Inoperative electric cooling fan circuit, use CHART C-12.
  - Correct coolant solution should be a 50/50 mix of GM #1052753 anti-freeze coolant (or equivalent) and water.

FUEL SYSTEM

NOTICE: To determine if the condition is caused by a rich or lean system, the vehicle should be driven at the speed of the complaint. Monitoring L.T. fuel trim will help identify problem.

- **CHECK:** Fuel pressure, use CHART A-7.

IGNITION SYSTEM

- **CHECK:** Spark plugs for proper heat range. Refer to "Owner's Manual."
- **CHECK:** Knock sensor system for proper operation, use CHART C-5.

ENGINE MECHANICAL

- **CHECK:** For excessive oil in the combustion chamber.
  - Valve oil seals for leaking.
- **CHECK:** Combustion chambers for excessive carbon buildup. Remove carbon with top engine cleaner and follow instructions on can.
- **CHECK:** Combustion chamber pressure by performing a compression test. See SECTION 6A.
- **CHECK:** For incorrect basic engine parts such as cam, heads, pistons, etc.

ADDITIONAL CHECKS

- **CHECK:** TCC operation, TCC applying too soon. Refer to CHART C-8.
- **CHECK:** EGR system, refer to CHART C-7.
- **CHECK:** For correct PROM. (See Service Bulletins.)

HESITATION, SAG, STUMBLE

Definition: Momentary lack of response as the accelerator is pushed down. Can occur at all vehicle speeds. Usually most severe when first trying to make the vehicle move, as from a stop sign. May cause engine to stall if severe enough.

PRELIMINARY CHECKS

- Perform the careful visual/physical checks as described at start of "Symptoms," Section "6E3-B".

SENSORS

- **CHECK:** TP sensor - Check TP sensor for binding or sticking. Voltage should increase at a steady rate as throttle is moved toward Wide Open Throttle (WOT).
- **CHECK:** Heated Oxygen Sensor (HO2S 1) ground.

FUEL SYSTEM

- **CHECK:** Fuel pressure, use CHART A-7.
- **CHECK:** Contaminated fuel.
- **CHECK:** EVAP canister purge system for proper operation. Use CHART C-3.
- **CHECK:** Fuel injectors. Perform injector balance test, use CHART C-2A.

IGNITION SYSTEM

- **CHECK:** Spark plugs for being fouled, or for there being faulty secondary wiring.
- **CHECK:** Ignition system ground (ignition control module mounting bolts).

ADDITIONAL CHECKS

- **CHECK:** For correct PROM. (See Service Bulletins.)
- **CHECK:** Engine thermostat functioning correctly and proper heat range.
- **CHECK:** Generator output voltage. Repair if less than 9 or more than 17 volts.
- **CHECK:** For air leaks between MAF sensor and the throttle body.

CUTS OUT, MISSES

(Page 1 of 2)

Definition: Steady pulsation or jerking that follows engine speed, usually more pronounced as engine load increases, not normally felt above 1500 RPM. The exhaust has a steady spitting sound at idle or low speed.

PRELIMINARY CHECKS

- Perform the careful visual/physical checks as described at start of "Symptoms," Section "6E3-B".

IGNITION SYSTEM

- Check for cylinder miss by:
  1. Start engine, allow engine to stabilize then disconnect IAC motor. Remove one injector connector at a time. If Tech 1 is available, it may be used to short out the cylinders rather than disconnecting injector connectors.
  2. If there is an RPM drop on all cylinders (equal to within 50 RPM), go to "Rough, Unstable, or Incorrect Idle, Stalling" symptom. Reconnect IAC valve.
  3. If there is no RPM drop on one or more cylinders, or excessive variation is drop, check for spark on the suspected cylinder(s) using a J 26792 (ST-125) spark tester or equivalent. If no spark, refer to "Electronic Ignition System," Section "6E3-C4". If there is a spark, remove spark plug(s) in these cylinders and check for:
     - Insulator cracks.
     - Wear.
     - Improper gap.
     - Burned electrodes.
     - Heavy deposits.
- **CHECK:** Spark plug wires by connecting ohmmeter to ends of each wire in question. If meter reads over 30,000 ohms, replace wire(s).
- **CHECK:** With engine running, spray coils and plug wires with fine water mist to check for faulty wires or coils.

FUEL SYSTEM

- **CHECK:** Fuel system - Plugged fuel filter, low pressure. Use CHART A-7.
- **CHECK:** Contaminated fuel.
- **CHECK:** Injector drivers. Disconnect all injector harness connectors. Connect J 34730-2 Injector Test Light or equivalent 6 volts test light between the harness terminal, of each injector connector and note light while cranking. If test light fails to blink at any connector, refer to CHART A-3 (Page 2 of 4).
- **CHECK:** Perform the injector coil and balance test. Refer to CHART C-2A.

CUTS OUT, MISSES

(Page 2 of 2)

Definition: Steady pulsation or jerking that follows engine speed, usually more pronounced as engine load increases, not normally felt above 1500 RPM. The exhaust has a steady spitting sound at idle or low speed.

ENGINE MECHANICAL

- **CHECK:** Compression. Perform compression check on questionable cylinder(s) found during checks on previous page. If compression is low, repair as necessary. Refer to SECTION 6A.
- **CHECK:** Base engine. Remove rocker covers. Check for bent pushrods, worn rocker arms, broken valve springs, worn or broken camshaft lobes and incorrect valve timing. Repair as necessary. Refer to SECTION 6A.

ADDITIONAL CHECKS

- **CHECK:** For vacuum leaks at intake manifold, throttle body, EGR feed tube, crankcase ventilation valve, etc.
- **CHECK:** For EMI interference. A missing condition can be caused by Electromagnetic Interference (EMI) on the reference circuit. EMI can usually be detected by monitoring engine RPM with a Tech 1. A sudden increase in displayed RPM with little change in actual engine RPM indicates EMI is present. If the problem exists, check routing of secondary wires, check ignition control module ground circuit.
- **CHECK:** Intake and exhaust manifold passage for casting flash.
- **CHECK:** For an intermittent camshaft position sensor or crankshaft position sensor fault by monitoring "Cam/Crank Error" on the Tech 1 data list; "Cam/Crank Error" will increase to above 2 counts while the engine is running if a fault exists. Use DTC P0341 chart for diagnosis of a "Cam/Crank Error" fault.
- **CHECK:** For a bent or missing vane on the crankshaft balancer interrupter rings.
- **CHECK:** EGR system. Use CHART C-7, "Exhaust Gas Recirculation (EGR) Flow Check."

ROUGH, UNSTABLE, OR INCORRECT IDLE, STALLING

Definition: Engine runs unevenly at idle. If severe, the engine or vehicle may shake. Engine idle speed may vary in RPM. Either condition may be severe enough to stall engine.

PRELIMINARY CHECKS

- Perform the careful visual/physical checks as described at start of "Symptoms," Section "6E3-B".
- **CHECK:** For vacuum leaks.
- **CHECK:** PCM grounds for being clean, tight and proper routing. See "PCM Wiring Diagrams."

FUEL SYSTEM

NOTICE: Monitoring L.T. fuel trim and S.T. fuel trim will help identify the cause of some problems. Refer to "Typical Tech 1 Data Definitions" for an explanation of L.T. fuel trim and S.T. fuel trim.

- **CHECK:** Injector balance. Refer to CHART C-2A.
- **CHECK:** For fuel in pressure regulator hose. If fuel is present, replace regulator assembly.
- **CHECK:** Evaporative Emission Control (EVAP) system, use CHART C-3.
- **CHECK:** The heated oxygen sensor should respond quickly to different throttle positions. If it does not, check the heated oxygen sensor for silicon contamination from fuel or use of improper RTV sealant. The sensor will have a white, powdery coating, and will indicate a high but false signal voltage (rich exhaust indication). The PCM will then reduce the amount of fuel delivered to the engine, causing a severe driveability problem.

IGNITION SYSTEM

- **CHECK:** Ignition system; wires, plugs, etc.

ENGINE MECHANICAL

- **CHECK:** Perform a cylinder compression check. Refer to SECTION 6.
- **CHECK:** For incorrect camshaft, worn camshaft or weak valve springs.

ADDITIONAL CHECKS

- **CHECK:** Throttle linkage for sticking or binding.
- **CHECK:** EGR system, use CHART C-7.
- **CHECK:** IAC operation, use CHART C-2B.
- **CHECK:** A/C signal to PCM, scan tool should indicate A/C is being requested whenever A/C is selected. If problem exists with A/C "ON," check A/C system operation CHART C-10.
- **CHECK:** PCV valve for proper operation. Refer to "Crankcase Ventilation System," Section "6E3-C13".
- **CHECK:** Service Bulletins for PROM updates.
- **CHECK:** For broken motor mounts.
- **CHECK:** Generator output voltage. Repair if less than 9 or more than 17 volts.

POOR FUEL ECONOMY

Definition: Fuel economy, as measured by an actual road test, is noticeably lower than expected. Also, economy is noticeably lower than it was on this vehicle at one time, as previously shown by an actual road test.

PRELIMINARY CHECKS

- Perform the careful visual checks as described at start of "Symptoms," Section "6E3-B".
- Visually (physically) check: Vacuum hoses for splits, kinks, and proper connections as shown on "Vehicle Emission Control Information" label.
- **CHECK:** Owner's driving habits.
  - Is A/C "ON" full time (Defroster mode "ON")?
  - Are tires at correct pressure?
  - Are excessively heavy loads being carried?
  - Is acceleration too much, too often?
- **CHECK:** Air cleaner element (filter) for dirty or being plugged.

IGNITION SYSTEM

- **CHECK:** Spark plugs. Check for wet plugs, cracks, wear, improper gap, burned electrodes, or heavy deposits. Repair or replace as necessary.

COOLING SYSTEM

- **CHECK:** Engine coolant level.
- **CHECK:** Engine thermostat for faulty part (always open) or for wrong heat range. Refer to SECTION 6B.

ENGINE MECHANICAL

- **CHECK:** Compression. Refer to SECTION 6A.

ADDITIONAL CHECKS

- **CHECK:** TCC operation. Use CHART C-8. The engine speed display on a Tech 1 should indicate an RPM drop when the TCC is commanded "ON."
- **CHECK:** For exhaust system restriction. Use CHART B-1.
- **CHECK:** For proper calibration of speedometer.
- **CHECK:** Induction system and crankcase for air leaks.

EXCESSIVE EXHAUST EMISSIONS OR ODORS

Definition: Vehicle fails an emission test. Vehicle has excessive "rotten egg" smell. Excessive odors do not necessarily indicate excessive emissions.

PRELIMINARY CHECKS

- Perform "On-Board Diagnostic System Check."

NOTICE: IF EMISSION TEST shows excessive CO and HC check items which cause vehicle to run RICH. Refer to "Diagnostic Aids" on facing page of DTC P0172.

NOTICE: IF EMISSION TEST shows excessive NOx, check EGR system (CHART C-7) and items which cause vehicle to run lean or too hot. Refer to "Diagnostic Aids" on the facing page of DTC P0171 chart.

COOLING SYSTEM

- If the scan tool indicates a very high engine coolant temperature and the system is running lean:
  - **CHECK:** Engine coolant level.
  - **CHECK:** Engine thermostat for faulty part (always open) or for incorrect heat range. Refer to SECTION 6B.
  - **CHECK:** Cooling fan operation, use CHART C-12.

FUEL SYSTEM

- **NOTICE:** If the system is running rich (L.T. fuel trim below 110 with canister purge solenoid disconnected), refer to "Diagnostic Aids" on facing page of DTC P0172. If the system is running lean (L.T. fuel trim above 150) refer to "Diagnostic Aids" on facing page of DTC P0171.

- **CHECK:** For properly installed fuel cap.
- **CHECK:** Fuel pressure. Use CHART A-7.
- **CHECK:** Injector balance test. Use CHART C-2A.
- **CHECK:** EVAP fuel canister for fuel loading. Use CHART C-3.

IGNITION SYSTEM

- **CHECK:** Spark plugs, plug wires, and ignition components. Refer to SECTION 6D.

ADDITIONAL CHECKS

- **CHECK:** For vacuum leaks.
- **CHECK:** For lead contamination of catalytic converter (look for the removal of fuel filler neck restrictor).
- **CHECK:** Carbon build-up. Remove carbon with top engine cleaner. Follow instructions on can.
- **CHECK:** Crankcase ventilation valve for being restricted or stuck or fuel in the crankcase.
- **CHECK:** For correct PROM (see Service Bulletins).

DIESELING, RUN-ON

Definition: Engine continues to run after key is turned "OFF."

PRELIMINARY CHECKS

- Perform the careful visual/physical checks as described at start of "Symptoms," Section "6E3-B".

FUEL SYSTEM

- **CHECK:** Ignition switch and switch adjustment.
- **CHECK:** For short to B + on CKT 3, CKT 39, CKT 139, CKT 239, CKT 339, CKT 439, CKT 539, CKT 639 or CKT 739. Refer to "Fuse Block Details" in SECTION 8A.

BACKFIRE

Definition: Fuel ignites in intake manifold, or in exhaust system, making loud popping noise.

PRELIMINARY CHECKS

- Perform the careful visual/physical checks as described at start of "Symptoms," Section "6E3-B".

IGNITION SYSTEM

- **CHECK:** Proper ignition coil output voltage with spark tester J 26792 (ST-125) or equivalent .
- **CHECK:** Spark plugs. Remove spark plugs, check for wet plugs, cracks, wear, improper gap, burned electrodes, or heavy deposits. Repair or rcplace as necessary.
- **CHECK:** Spark plug wires for crossfire, also inspect spark plug wires, and proper routing of plug wires.

NOTICE: If an intermittent condition exists in the ignition system, refer to "Electronic Ignition System," Section "6E3-C4" or SECTION 6D.

ENGINE MECHANICAL

- **CHECK:** Compression - Look for sticking or leaking valves.
- **CHECK:** Valve timing, refer to SECTION 6A.
- **CHECK:** Intake and exhaust manifold passages for casting flash.
- **CHECK:** Crankshaft balancer interrupter rings for bent or missing vanes.

FUEL SYSTEM

- **CHECK:** Perform fuel system diagnosis check, refer to CHART A-7.
- **CHECK:** Fuel injectors. Perform injector balance test, refer to CHART C-2A.

CHART B-1

RESTRICTED EXHAUST SYSTEM CHECK

CHECK AT HEATED OXYGEN SENSOR (HO2S 1):

1. Carefully remove heated oxygen sensor (HO2S 1).
2. Install exhaust backpressure tester (BT-8515 or BT-8603) or equivalent in place of heated oxygen sensor (HO2S 1) (see illustration).
3. After completing test described below, be sure to coat threads of (HO2S 1) with anti-seize compound P/N 5613695 or equivalent prior to re-installation.

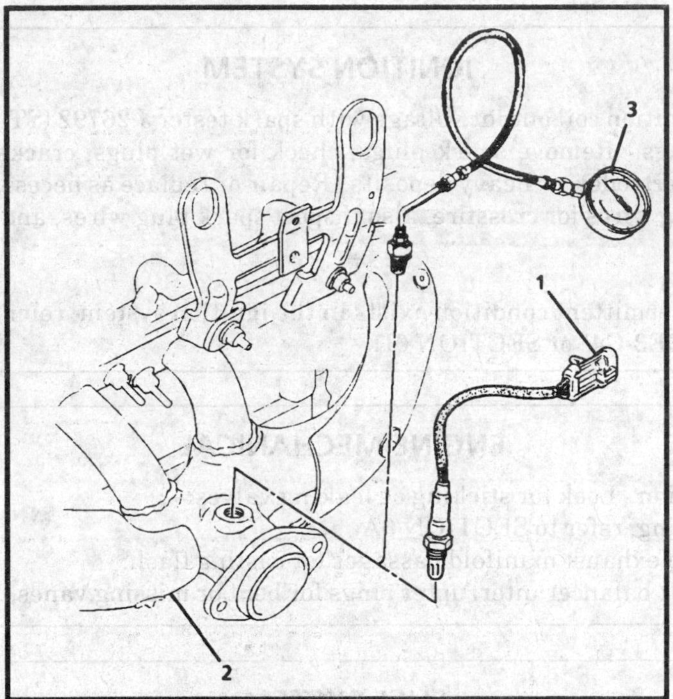
3
1
2

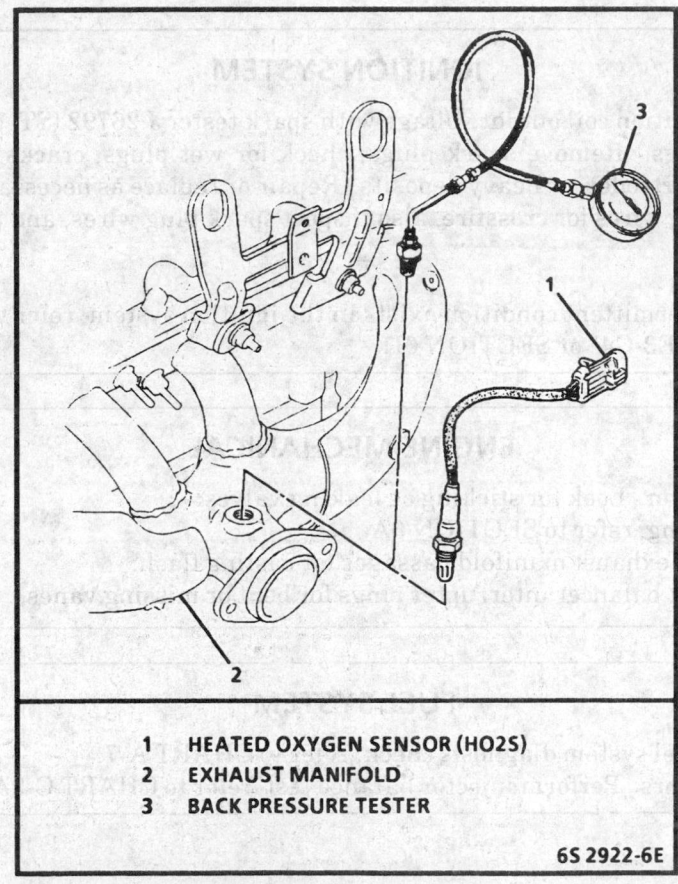

1 HEATED OXYGEN SENSOR (HO2S)
2 EXHAUST MANIFOLD
3 BACK PRESSURE TESTER

6S 2922-6E

DIAGNOSIS:

1. With the engine at normal operating temperature and running at 2500 RPM, observe the exhaust system backpressure reading on the gauge.
2. If the backpressure exceeds 1 1/4 psi (8.62 kPa), a restricted exhaust system is indicated.
3. Inspect the entire exhaust system for a collapsed pipe, heat distress, or possible internal muffler failure.
4. If there are no obvious reasons for the excessive backpressure, a restricted catalytic converter should be suspected, and replaced using current recommended procedures.

3-22-93
PS 17187

BLACK CONNECTOR "A"

PIN	FUNCTION	CKT #	WIRE COLOR	COMPONENT CONNECTOR CAVITY	DTC(s) AFFECTED	POSSIBLE SYMPTOMS FROM FAULTY CIRCUIT
A1	EGR CONTROL	435	GRY	LINEAR EGR "A"	P0401, P1406	(2) ROUGH IDLE, STALLING (1) EXCESSIVE NOx EMISSIONS
A2	IGNITION FILTER	241	BRN	ENG EMISS FUSE	P1406	(2) NO EGR, EXCESSIVE NOx
A3	N/C					
A4	TCC PWM SOLENOID	418	BRN	TRANSAXLE "B"	P0740	(1) HARSH TCC ENGAGEMENT (2) NO TCC ENGAGEMENT
A5	CRUISE INHIBIT	83	DK GRN	SMCC II MODULE "H"	NONE	(1) CRUISE CONTROL INOPERATIVE (2) CRUISE CONTROL ENGAGED WHEN REQUESTED "OFF" BY PCM
A6	N/C					
A7	INJECTOR #4	844	LT BLU/BLK	"B"	P0300	(3) ROUGH IDLE, POOR DRIVEABILITY
A8	INJECTOR #5	845	BLK/WHT	"B"	P0300	(3) ROUGH IDLE, POOR DRIVEABILITY
A9	INJECTOR #1	1744	BLK	"B"	P0300	(3) ROUGH IDLE, POOR DRIVEABILITY
A10	INJECTOR #6	846	YEL/BLK	"B"	P0300	(3) ROUGH IDLE, POOR DRIVEABILITY
A11	IAC "B" HIGH	1749	LT GRN/WHT	IAC "A"	NONE	(3) HIGH OR LOW IDLE, STALLING
A12	IAC "B" LOW	444	LT GRN/BLK	IAC "B"	NONE	(3) HIGH OR LOW IDLE, STALLING
A13	IAC "A" LOW	1748	LT BLU/BLK	IAC "D"	NONE	(3) HIGH OR LOW IDLE, STALLING
A14	IAC "A" HIGH	1747	LT BLU/WHT	IAC "C"	NONE	(3) HIGH OR LOW IDLE, STALLING
A15	INJECTOR #2	1745	LT GRN/BLK	"B"	P0300	(3) ROUGH IDLE, POOR DRIVEABILITY
A16	INJECTOR #3	1746	PNK/BLK	"B"	P0300	(3) ROUGH IDLE, POOR DRIVEABILITY
A17	IGNITION CONTROL (IC)	423	WHT	EI MODULE "A"	P1350 P1361	(3) MODULE MODE SPARK ADVANCE, REDUCED PERFORMANCE
A18	BYPASS	424	TAN/BLK	EI MODULE "B"	P1361	(3) MODULE MODE SPARK ADVANCE, REDUCED PERFORMANCE
A19	POWER GROUND	551	TAN/WHT	EI MODULE BRACKET STUD		(3) INTERMITTENT SYMPTOMS
A20	POWER GROUND	551	TAN/WHT	EI MODULE BRACKET STUD		(3) INTERMITTENT SYMPTOMS
A21	PCM GROUND	451	BLK/WHT	EI MODULE BRACKET STUD		(3) INTERMITTENT SYMPTOMS
A22	PCM GROUND	451	BLK/WHT	EI MODULE BRACKET STUD		(3) INTERMITTENT SYMPTOMS
A23	N/C					
A24	CAM SIGNAL	630	BLK	EI MODULE "F"	P0341 P0342	(3) P0341, STUMBLE, STALLING IF INTERMITTENT
A25	FUEL CONTROL	430	PPL/WHT	EI MODULE "D"	P0341	(3) P0341, STUMBLE, STALLING IF INTERMITTENT; OTHERWISE CRANKS BUT WON'T RUN
A26	REFERENCE LOW	453	RED/BLK	EI MODULE "G"	NONE	(3) INTERMITTENT SYMPTOMS
A27	SPARK REFERENCE	647	LT BLU/BLK	EI MODULE "C"	P0321	(3) EXTENDED CRANK
A28	MAF SIGNAL	492	YEL	MAF "A"	P0101	(3) REDUCED PERFORMANCE
A29	N/C					
A30	VSS HIGH	400	YEL	VSS "B"	P0501 P0502	(3) NO 4TH GEAR, NO TCC, NO CRUISE CONTROL, CLUSTER SPEEDO INOP
A31	VSS LOW	401	PPL	VSS "A"	P0501 P0502	(3) NO 4TH GEAR, NO TCC, NO CRUISE CONTROL, CLUSTER SPEEDO INOP
A32	N/C					

(1) OPEN CIRCUIT.
(2) GROUNDED CIRCUIT.
(3) OPEN/GROUNDED CIRCUIT.
* DEPENDS ON IPC OPTION, SEE SECTION 8A.

6-17-93
9S 8142-6E

PCM Connector Symptom Chart (1 of 3)

CLEAR CONNECTOR "B"

PIN	FUNCTION	CKT #	WIRE COLOR	COMPONENT CONNECTOR CAVITY	DTC(s) AFFECTED	POSSIBLE SYMPTOMS FROM FAULTY CIRCUIT
B1	A/C REQUEST	67	LT BLU	PRESSURE CYCLING SWITCH "B"	P1531	(3) A/C CLUTCH INOPERATIVE
B2	N/C					
B3	CRUISE STATUS	85	WHT	SMCC II MODULE "J"	P1550	(3) CRUISE CONTROL INOPERATIVE
B4	N/C					
B5	N/C					
B6	N/C					
B7	EGR 5V REFERENCE	474	GRY	LINEAR EGR "D"	P0122 P1406	(1) STALLS ON DECEL (2) P0122 SET, NO 4TH GEAR OR TCC
B8	IGNITION FEED	439	PNK/BLK	PCM IGN FUSE	NONE	(3) NO-START NO MIL (SERVICE ENGINE SOON)
B9	N/C					
B10	BATTERY FEED	540	ORN	PCM BATTERY FUSE	NONE	(3) NO-START NO MIL (SERVICE ENGINE SOON)
B11	IATS GROUND	452	BLK	IAT SENSOR "A"	P0112	NONE
B12	N/C					
B13	N/C					
B14	N/C					
B15	N/C					
B16	N/C					
B17	FUEL PUMP RELAY	465	DK GRN/WHT	ENG ELECT CTR "F11"	NONE	(3) EXTENDED CRANK
B18	4K/MI SPEED	389	DK GRN	SMCC II MODULE "K" IPC*	NONE	(3) CRUISE CONTROL AND SPEEDOMETER INOPERATIVE
B19	PASS-Key®II FUEL ENABLE	229	DK BLU	THEFT DETERRENT MODULE "A3"	P1626 P1629	(3) NO-START IF DTC 1629 SET
B20	MALFUNCTION INDICATION LAMP	419	BRN/WHT	*	P1670	(1) MIL (SERVICE ENGINE SOON) NEVER "ON" (2) MIL (SERVICE ENGINE SOON) ALWAYS "ON"
B21	A/C RELAY	459	DK GRN/WHT	ENG ELECT CTR "E6"	P1670	(1) A/C CLUTCH INOPERATIVE (2) A/C CLUTCH ALWAYS APPLIED
B22	LEFT FAN (FAN 1)	335	DK GRN	ENG ELECT CTR "C6"	P1670	(1) LEFT FAN NEVER "ON", INSUFFICIENT A/C COOLING (2) LEFT FAN ALWAYS "ON"
B23	RIGHT FAN (FAN 2)	473	DK BLU	ENG ELECT CTR "C10"	P1670	(1) RIGHT FAN NEVER "ON", INSUFFICIENT A/C COOLING (2) RIGHT FAN ALWAYS "ON"
B24	N/C					
B25	N/C					
B26	N/C					
B27	N/C					
B28	N/C					
B29	N/C					
B30	A/C HEAD PRESSURE SW (FAN REQUEST)	380	RED/BLK	A/C HEAD PRESSURE SWITCH "A"	P1530	(1) FANS ALWAYS "ON" (2) INSUFFICIENT A/C COOLING
B31	N/C					
B32	SERIAL DATA	800	TAN	DATA LINK CONNECTOR	NONE	(3) SCAN DATA NOT AVAILABLE FOR DISPLAY

(1) OPEN CIRCUIT.
(2) GROUNDED CIRCUIT.
(3) OPEN/GROUNDED CIRCUIT.
* DEPENDS ON IPC OPTION, SEE SECTION 8A.

4-27-93
9S 8143-6E

PCM Connector Symptom Chart (2 of 3)

BLUE CONNECTOR "C"

PIN	FUNCTION	CKT #	WIRE COLOR	COMPONENT CONNECTOR CAVITY	DTC(s) AFFECTED	POSSIBLE SYMPTOMS FROM FAULTY CIRCUIT
C1	N/C					
C2	SHIFT B SOLENOID	1223	YEL/BLK	TRANSAXLE "B"	P1650, P0755	(3) 3RD GEAR ONLY, NO TCC
C3	SHIFT A SOLENOID	1222	LT GRN	TRANSAXLE "A"	P1650	(1) SHIFT 1-4 ONLY (2) SHIFT 2-3 ONLY
C4	N/C					
C5	TCC APPLY SOLENOID	422	TAN/BLK	TRANSAXLE "D"	P1640, P0740	(1) NO TCC, NO 4TH GEAR (2) TCC ENGAGED, HARSH 2-3 SHIFT
C6	N/C					
C7	N/C					
C8	EVAP CANISTER PURGE	428	DK GRN/WHT	EVAP SOL."B"	P1640	(2) ROUGH IDLE, RICH EXHAUST
C9	PRNDL A	771	BLK/WHT	TRANS RANGE SWITCH "A"	P0705	(3) PCM COMMANDS "D4" SHIFT PATTERN
C10	PRNDL B	772	YEL	TRANS RANGE SWITCH "B"	P0705	(3) PCM COMMANDS "D4" SHIFT PATTERN
C11	TP SENSOR 5 VOLT REF	416	GRY	TP SENSOR "A"	P0122	(3) NO 4TH GEAR OR TCC
C12	SENSOR GROUND	808	BLK	ECT/TP/TRANS TEMP/EGR	P0117, P0123, P1406	(1) NO 4TH GEAR OR TCC, COOLING FANS ALWAYS "ON"
C13	N/C					
C14	PRNDL P	776	WHT	TRANS RANGE SWITCH "D"	P0705	(3) PCM COMMANDS "D4" SHIFT PATTERN
C15	PRNDL C	773	GRY	TRANS RANGE SWITCH "C"	P0705	(3) PCM COMMANDS "D4" SHIFT PATTERN
C-6	N/C					
C17	N/C					
C18	KNOCK SIGNAL	496	DK BLU	KNOCK SENSOR	P0325	(3) 10° SPARK RETARD, REDUCED PERFORMANCE
C19	TRANS TEMP SENSOR	1227	PPL	TRANSAXLE "F"	P0712, P0713	NONE
C20	ECT SIGNAL	410	YEL	ECT SENSOR "B"	P0117, P0118	(3) COOLING FANS "ON" ALL THE TIME
C21	EGR PINTLE POSITION	1456	BRN	LINEAR EGR "C"	P1406	(3) STALLS ON DECEL
C22	TP SENSOR	417	DK BLU	TP SENSOR "B"	P0122	(3) NO 4TH GEAR OR TCC
C23	HO2S 1 LOW	413	TAN	HO2S 1 "A"	P0134	(1) NO "CLOSED LOOP" FUEL CONTROL
C24	HO2S 1 SIGNAL	412	PPL	HO2S 1 "B"	P0131, P0132, P0134	(3) NO "CLOSED LOOP" FUEL CONTROL
C25	N/C					
C26	IAT SIGNAL	472	TAN	IAT SENSOR "B"	P0112, P0113	NONE
C27	N/C					
C28	N/C					
C29	N/C					
C30	TCC BRAKE SWITCH	420	PPL	TCC BRAKE SWITCH "B"	P0703	(3) NO 4TH GEAR OR TCC
C31	HO2S 2 LOW	1669	TAN/WHT	HO2S 2 "A"	P0140	NONE
C32	HO2S 2 SIGNAL	1668	PPL/WHT	HO2S 2 "B"	P0137, P0138, P0140	NONE

(1) OPEN CIRCUIT.
(2) GROUND CIRCUIT.
(3) OPEN/GROUNDED CIRCUIT.
* DEPENDS ON IPC OPTION, SEE SECTION 8A.

6-17-93
9S 8144-6E

PCM Connector Symptom Chart (3 of 3)

SECTION C

COMPONENT SYSTEMS

CAUTION: On vehicles equipped with Supplemental Inflatable Restraint (SIR), refer to "CAUTIONS" in Section 9J under "ON-VEHICLE SERVICE" and the "SIR Components and Wiring Location" view in Section 9J before performing service on or around SIR components or wiring. Failure to follow CAUTIONS could result in possible air bag deployment, personal injury, or otherwise unneeded SIR system repairs.

NOTICE: When fasteners are removed, always reinstall them at the same location from which they were removed. If a fastener needs to be replaced, use the correct part number fastener for that application. If the correct part number fastener is not available, a fastener of equal size and strength (or stronger) may be used. Fasteners that are not reused, and those requiring thread-locking compound will be called out. The correct torque value must be used when installing fasteners that require it. If the above conditions are not followed, parts or system damage could result.

Section "C" provides information on the following:

- General description of components and systems.
- On-vehicle service.
- Part names and group numbers.
- Diagnostic charts. These include a functional check of the system as well as diagnosis of any problem found in the functional check.

For locations of components, wiring diagrams, and PCM terminal end view, refer to the front of the Section "A" of the engine being diagnosed.

Following are the sub-section identification and the system covered:

FUNCTIONAL DIAGNOSTIC CHARTS

The diagnostic charts for each system are found after the On-Vehicle Service and Parts Information at the back of each section. Following are the charts found in this section.

SECTION C1

POWERTRAIN CONTROL MODULE (PCM) AND SENSORS

CONTENTS

GENERAL DESCRIPTION

POWERTRAIN CONTROL MODULE (PCM)

The Powertrain Control Module (PCM), located under the instrument panel, is the control center of the vehicle. It controls the following:

- Fuel metering system.
- Transaxle shifting.
- Ignition timing.

It constantly looks at the information from various sensors, and controls the systems that affect vehicle performance. The PCM also performs the diagnostic function of the system. It can recognize operational problems, alert the driver through the MIL (Service Engine Soon), and store diagnostic trouble codes which identify the problem areas to aid the technician in making repairs. Refer to "Introduction" in SECTION 6E, for more information on using the diagnostic function of the PCM.

3800 engines use a PCM (Figure C1-1). For service, the PCM consists of two parts: a controller (the PCM without a PROM) and an assembly called a PROM. (This stands for "Programmable Read-Only Memory.")

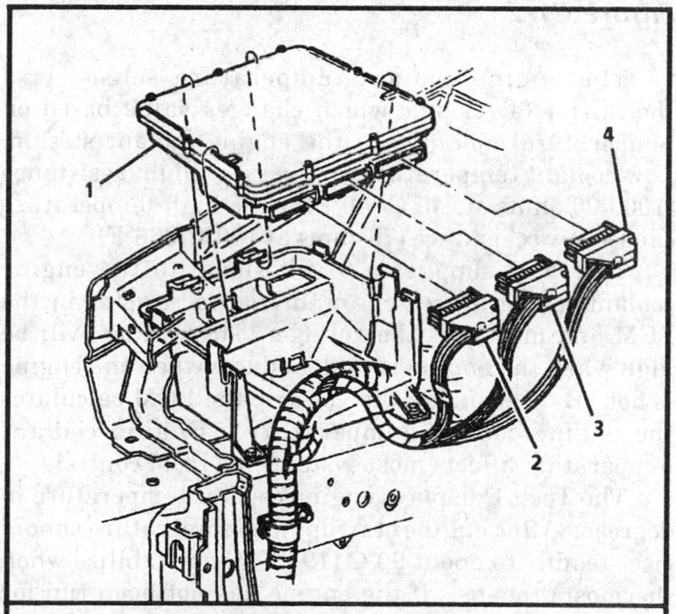
1
2
3
4
1 POWERTRAIN CONTROL MODULE (PCM)
2 CONNECTOR "A"
3 CONNECTOR "B"
4 CONNECTOR "C"
PS 17176

Figure C1-1 - Powertrain Control Module (PCM)

PROM

This assembly contains the functions of the PROM, PRNDL decoder, VSS buffer, and KS module used on past GM applications. It contains the calibrations needed for a specific vehicle based on axle ratio, tire size, and other vehicle characteristics.

PCM Function

The PCM supplies either 5 or 12 volts to power various sensors or switches. This is done through resistances in the PCM which are so high in value that a test light will not light when connected to the circuit. In some cases, even an ordinary shop voltmeter will not give an accurate reading because its resistance is too low. Therefore, a 10 megohm input impedance digital voltmeter is required to assure accurate voltage readings. Tool J 39200 meets this requirement.

The PCM controls output circuits such as the injectors, IAC, cooling fan relays, etc. by controlling the ground or power feed circuit through transistors or a device called a "Quad-Driver."

INFORMATION SENSORS/PCM INPUTS

All of the sensors and input switches can be diagnosed by the use of a Tech 1. Following is a short description of how the sensors and switches can be diagnosed by using a Tech 1. The Tech 1 can also be used to compare the values for a normal running engine with the engine you are diagnosing.

Engine Coolant Temperature (ECT) Sensor *Figure C1-2*

The engine coolant temperature sensor is a thermistor (a resistor which changes value based on temperature) mounted in the engine coolant stream. Low coolant temperature produces a high resistance (100,000 ohms at -40°C/-40°F) while high temperature causes low resistance (70 ohms at 130°C/266°F).

The PCM supplies a 5 volt signal to the engine coolant temperature sensor through a resistor in the PCM and measures the voltage. The voltage will be high when the engine is cold, and low when the engine is hot. By measuring the voltage, the PCM calculates the engine coolant temperature. Engine coolant temperature affects most systems the PCM controls.

The Tech 1 displays engine coolant temperature in degrees. After engine startup, the temperature should rise steadily to about 90°C (194°F) then stabilize when thermostat opens. If the engine has not been run for several hours (overnight), the engine coolant temperature and intake air temperature displays should be close to each other. A fault in the engine coolant sensor circuit should set DTC P0117 or DTC P0118. The DTC charts also contain a table to check for sensor resistance values relative to temperature.

Mass Air Flow (MAF) Sensor

The Mass Air Flow (MAF) sensor measures the amount of air which passes through it. The PCM uses this information to determine the operating condition of the engine, to control fuel delivery.

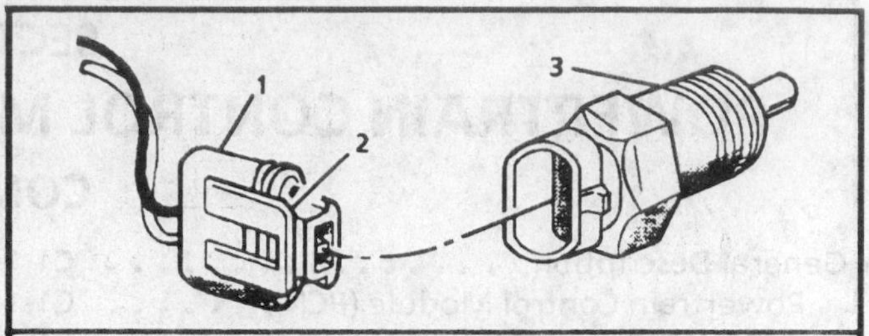
1
2
3

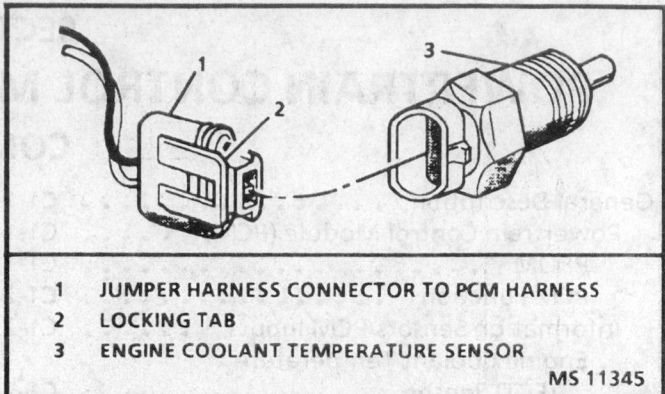

1 JUMPER HARNESS CONNECTOR TO PCM HARNESS
2 LOCKING TAB
3 ENGINE COOLANT TEMPERATURE SENSOR

MS 11345

Figure C1-2 - Engine Coolant Temperature Sensor

A large quantity of air indicates acceleration, while a small quantity indicates deceleration or idle.

The Tech 1 reads the MAF value and displays it in grams per second. It should read between 4-7 on a fully warmed up idling engine. Values should change rather quickly on acceleration, but values should remain fairly stable at any given RPM. A failure in the MAF sensor or circuit should set DTC P0401.

Intake Air Temperature (IAT) Sensor

The Intake Air Temperature (IAT) sensor is a thermistor which changes value based on the temperature of air entering the engine. Low temperature produces a high resistance (100,000 ohms at -40°C/-40°F), while high temperature causes low resistance (70 ohms at 130°C/266°F). The PCM supplies a 5 volt signal to the sensor through a resistor in the PCM and measures the voltage. The voltage will be high when the incoming air is cold, and low when the air is hot. By measuring the voltage, the PCM calculates the incoming air temperature.

The IAT sensor signal is used to adjust spark timing according to incoming air density.

The Tech 1 displays temperature of the air entering the engine, which should read close to ambient air temperature when engine is cold, and rise as underhood temperature increases. If the engine has not been run for several hours (overnight) the IAT sensor temperature and engine coolant temperature should read close to each other. A failure in the IAT sensor circuit should set DTC P0112 or DTC P0113.

Heated Oxygen Sensor (HO2S 1) *Figures C1-3 and C1-13*

The exhaust Heated Oxygen Sensor (HO2S 1) is mounted in the exhaust manifold where it can monitor the oxygen content of the exhaust gas stream.

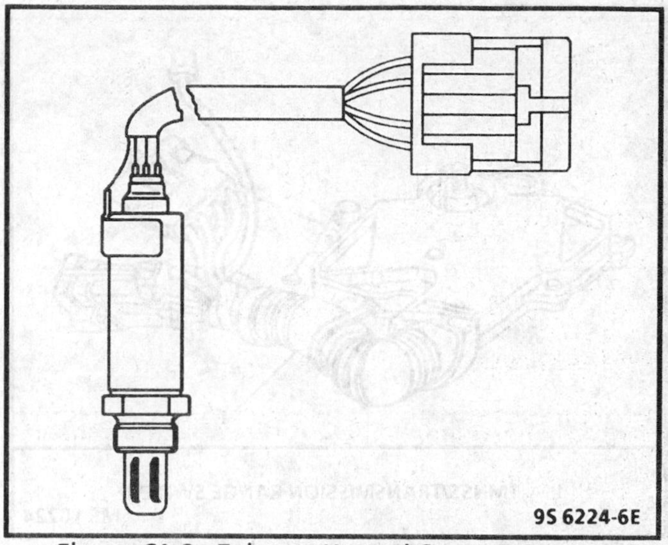
9S 6224-6E

Figure C1-3 - Exhaust Heated Oxygen Sensor (HO2S 1 and HO2S 2)

The oxygen content in the exhaust reacts with the sensor to produce voltage output. This voltage should constantly fluctuate from approximately 100 mV (high oxygen content - lean mixture) to 900 mV (low oxygen content - rich mixture). The heated oxygen sensor voltage can be monitored with a Tech 1.

By monitoring the voltage output of the oxygen sensor, the PCM calculates what fuel mixture command to give to the injector (lean mixture-low HO2S 1 voltage = rich command, rich mixture-high HO2S 1 voltage = lean command).

The heated oxygen sensor circuit, if open, should set a DTC P0134 and the Tech 1 will display a constant voltage between 350 - 550 mV. A constant voltage below 250 mV in the sensor circuit should set DTC P0131, while a constant voltage above 750 mV in the circuit should set DTC P0132. DTC P0131 and DTC P0132 could also be set as a result of fuel system problems. Refer to DTC charts for conditions that can cause a lean or rich system.

HO2S 2 (Catalyst Monitor) *Figures C1-3 and C1-12*

NOTICE: Early production vehicles may not be equipped with an HO2S 2. In this case, the HO2S 2 is replaced by a plug in the exhaust where the HO2S 2 would normally be located.

In order to control emissions of Hydrocarbons (HC), Carbon Monoxide (CO) and Oxides of Nitrogen (NOx), a three-way catalytic converter is used. The catalyst within the converter promotes a chemical reaction which oxidizes the HC and CO present in the exhaust gas, converting them into harmless water vapor and carbon dioxide. The catalyst also reduces NOx, converting it to nitrogen. The PCM has the capability to monitor this process using HO2S 2. HO2S 2, located in the exhaust stream past the three-way catalytic converter, produces an output signal which indicates the oxygen storage capacity of the catalyst; this in turn indicates the catalyst's ability to convert exhaust emissions effectively. A problem with the HO2S 2 electrical circuits should set DTC P0137, P0138 or P0140, depending on the specific condition. If the catalyst is functioning correctly, the HO2S 2 signal will be far less active than that produced by HO2S 1. If a problem exists which causes the PCM to detect excessive HO2S 2 activity outside of an acceptable range for an extended period of time, the PCM will set DTC P0420, indicating that the three-way catalytic converter's oxygen storage capacity is below a threshold considered acceptable.

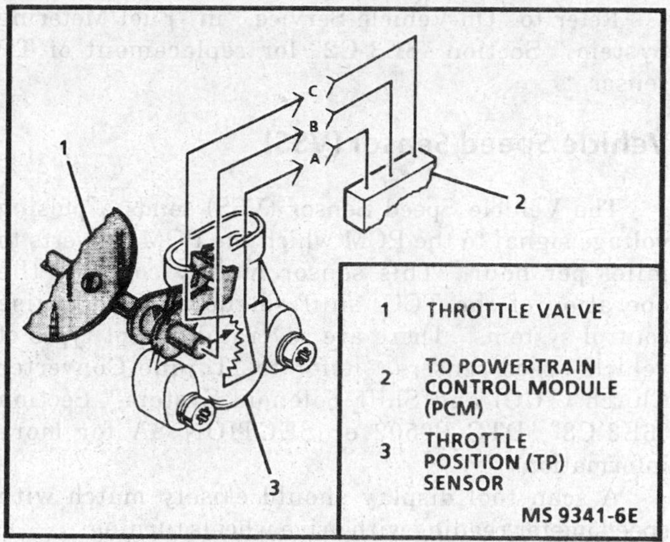
1
2
3
A
B
C
1 THROTTLE VALVE
2 TO POWERTRAIN CONTROL MODULE (PCM)
3 THROTTLE POSITION (TP) SENSOR
MS 9341-6E

Figure C1-4 - Throttle Position (TP) Sensor (Typical)

Throttle Position (TP) Sensor *Figure C1-4*

The Throttle Position (TP) sensor is a potentiometer connected to the throttle shaft on the throttle body. By monitoring the voltage on the signal line, the PCM calculates throttle position. As the throttle valve angle is changed (accelerator pedal moved), the TP sensor signal also changes.

At a closed throttle position, the output of the TP sensor is low. As the throttle valve opens, the output increases so that at Wide Open Throttle (WOT), the output voltage should be above 4 volts.

The PCM calculates fuel delivery based on throttle valve angle (driver demand). A broken or loose TP sensor may cause intermittent bursts of fuel from an injector and unstable idle because the PCM thinks the throttle is moving. A problem in the TP sensor 5 volts reference or signal circuits should set either a DTC P0122 or DTC P0123. A problem with the TP sensor ground circuit may set DTCs P0123 and P0117. Once a DTC is set, the PCM will use an artificial default value based on mass air flow for TP sensor and some vehicle performance will return. A high idle may result when either DTC P0122 or DTC P0123 is set.

Refer to "On-Vehicle Service," in "Fuel Metering System," Section "6E3-C2" for replacement of TP sensor.

Vehicle Speed Sensor (VSS)

The Vehicle Speed Sensor (VSS) sends a pulsing voltage signal to the PCM which the PCM converts to miles per hour. This sensor mainly controls the operation of the TCC, shift solenoids, and cruise control systems. There are several different types of vehicle speed sensors. Refer to "Torque Converter Clutch (TCC) and Shift Solenoid System," Section "6E3-C8", DTC P0502 or SECTION 8A for more information.

A scan tool display should closely match with speedometer reading with drive wheels turning.

Knock Sensor

Refer to "Knock Sensor (KS) System," Section "6E3-C5" for description of the knock sensor system.

A/C Request Signal

This signal tells the PCM when an A/C mode is selected, and the A/C pressure cycling switch is closed. The PCM uses this to adjust the idle speed before turning "ON" the A/C clutch.

If this signal is not available to the PCM, the A/C compressor will be inoperative.

Refer to "A/C Clutch Circuit Diagnosis," Section "6E3-C10" for A/C wiring diagrams and diagnosis of A/C electrical system.

Generator Control (CKT 225)

The PCM controls the vehicle charging system by applying B+ to the generator "L" terminal while the engine is running. Refer to SECTION 6D for further information on the vehicle charging system.

PRNDL Inputs

The PRNDL inputs from the transaxle range switch indicate to the PCM which gear the transaxle selector lever has selected. This information is used for timing, canister purge and IAC valve operation.

Important

- Vehicle should not be driven with transaxle range switch disconnected, as idle quality will be affected.

Refer to SECTION 7A for more information on the transaxle range switch/TMNSS.

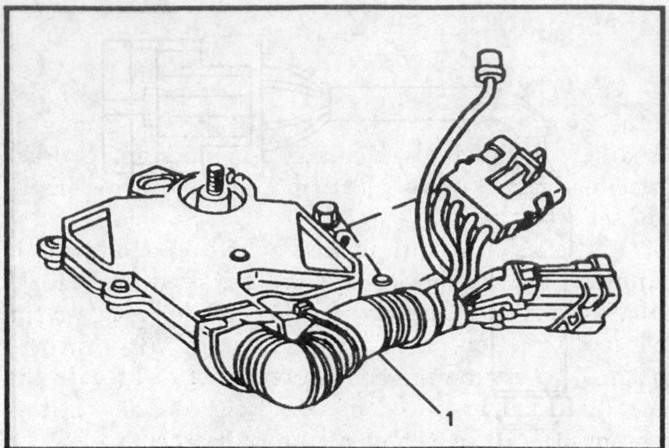
1

1 TMNSS/TRANSMISSION RANGE SWITCH

MS 10224

Figure C1-5 - TMNSS/Transmission Range Switch

Crankshaft Position Sensor

The crankshaft position sensor provides a signal through the ignition control module which the PCM uses as reference to calculate RPM and crankshaft position. Refer to "Electronic Ignition System," Section "6E3-C4" for additional information.

Fuel Control Reference PCM Input (CKT 430)

From the ignition control module, the PCM uses this signal to calculate engine RPM and crankshaft position. The PCM compares pulses on this circuit to reference ground CKT 453. The PCM also uses the pulses on this circuit to initiate injector pulses. If the PCM receives no pulses on this circuit, no fuel injection pulses will occur and the engine will not run.

Crankshaft Reference Ground (CKT 453)

This is a ground circuit for the digital RPM counter inside the PCM, but the wire is connected to engine ground _only_ through the ignition control module. Although this circuit is electrically connected to the PCM, *it is not connected to ground _at_ the PCM.* The PCM compares voltage pulses on the reference input CKT 430 to any on this circuit, ignoring pulses that ground on both. If the circuit is open, or connected to ground at the PCM, it may cause poor engine performance and possibly a MIL (Service Engine Soon) with no DTC.

Refer to "Electronic Ignition System," Section "6E3-C4" for further information.

Camshaft Position Sensor

The camshaft position sensor sends a signal to the PCM which uses it as a "sync pulse" to trigger the injectors in proper sequence. The cam signal is passed through the ignition control module. It is not processed in any way.

Cam Signal (CKT 630)

The PCM uses this signal to determine the position of the #1 piston during its power stroke. This signal is used by the PCM to calculate true Sequential Fuel Injection (SFI) mode of operation. A loss of this signal will set DTC P0342.

If the cam signal is lost while the engine is running, the fuel injection system will shift to a calculated sequential fuel injection mode based on the last fuel injection pulse, and the engine will continue to run. The engine can be restarted and will run in the calculated sequential mode as long as the fault is present with a 1 in 6 chance of being correct.

Refer to DTC P0342 for further information.

DIAGNOSIS

To read diagnostic trouble codes, use a Tech 1 tool.

To clear diagnostic trouble codes from memory:

- Ignition "OFF."
- Disconnect PCM power source for 30 seconds.

OR

- Diagnostic trouble codes may be cleared with the Tech 1 scan tool.

Since the PCM can have a failure which may affect only one circuit, following the diagnostic procedures in this section will determine which circuit has a problem and where it is.

If a diagnostic chart indicates that the PCM connections or PCM is the cause of a problem and the PCM is replaced, but does not correct the problem, one of the following may be the reason:

- There is a problem with the PCM terminal connections. The diagnostic chart will say PCM connections or PCM. The terminals may have to be removed from the connector in order to check them properly.
- PROM is not correct for the application. Incorrect components may cause a malfunction and may or may not set a DTC.
- The problem is intermittent. This means that the problem is not present at the time the system is being checked. In this case, refer to the "Symptoms," Section "6E3-B" portion of the manual and make a careful physical inspection of all portions of the system involved.
- Shorted solenoid, relay coil, or harness. Solenoids and relays are turned "ON" and "OFF" by the PCM using internal electronic switches called "drivers." Each driver is part of a group of four called "Quad-Drivers."

A shorted solenoid, relay coil, or harness will not damage the PCM but will cause the solenoid or relay to be inoperative.

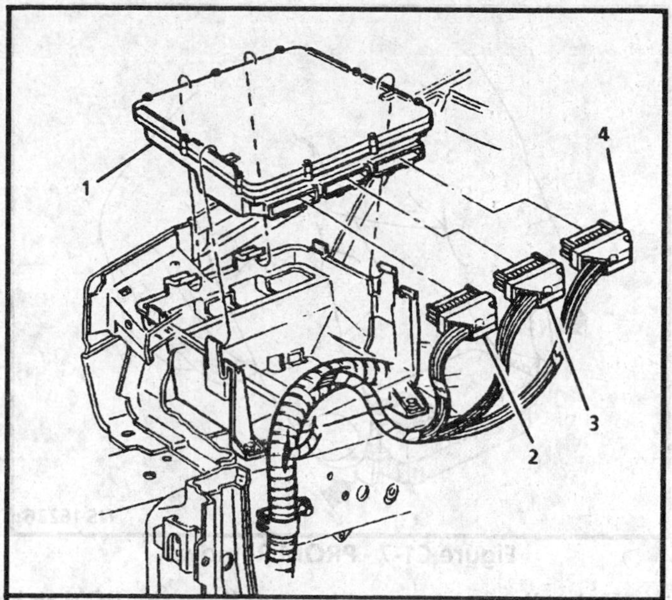
1
2
3
4

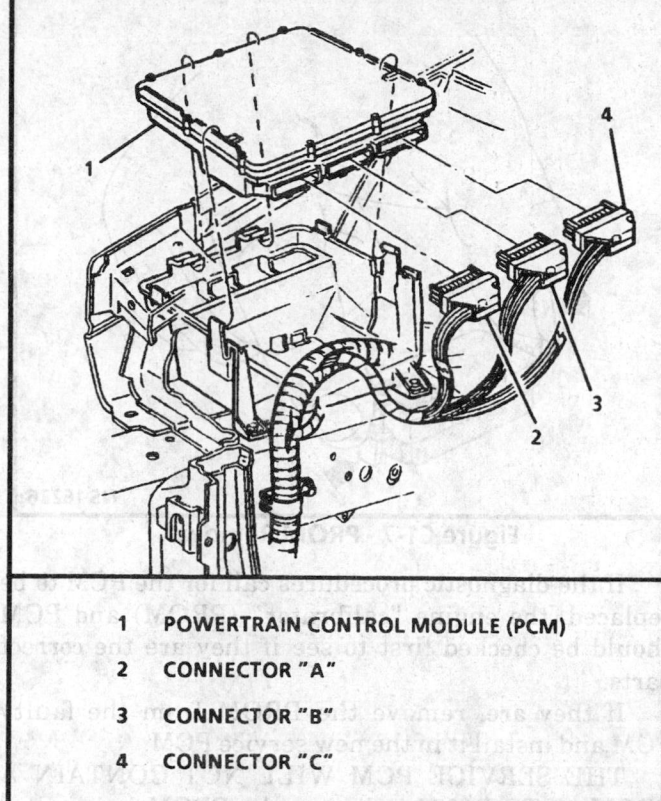

1 POWERTRAIN CONTROL MODULE (PCM)
2 CONNECTOR "A"
3 CONNECTOR "B"
4 CONNECTOR "C"

PS 17176

Figure C1-6 - PCM

J 34636 or BT-8405 testers, or equivalent, provide a fast, accurate means of checking for a shorted coil or a short to battery voltage.

- The PROM may be faulty. Although these rarely fail, it operates as part of the PCM. Therefore, it could be the cause of the problem. Substitute a known good PROM.
- The replacement PCM may be faulty. After the PCM is replaced, the system should be rechecked for proper operation. If the diagnostic chart again indicates the PCM is the problem, substitute a known good PCM. Although this is a rare condition, it could happen.

PROM

An incorrect or faulty PROM, which is installed in the PCM, may set DTC P1623.

ON-VEHICLE SERVICE

POWERTRAIN CONTROL MODULE (PCM)
Figure C1-6

Service of the PCM should normally consist of either replacement of the PCM or a PROM change.

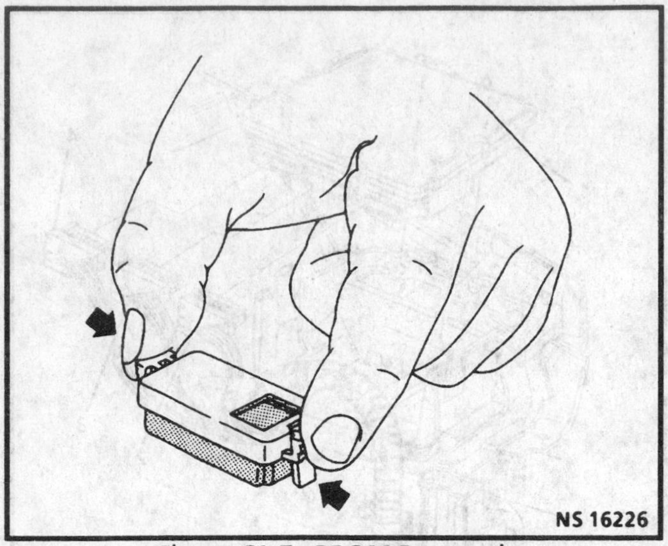
NS 16226

Figure C1-7 - PROM Removal

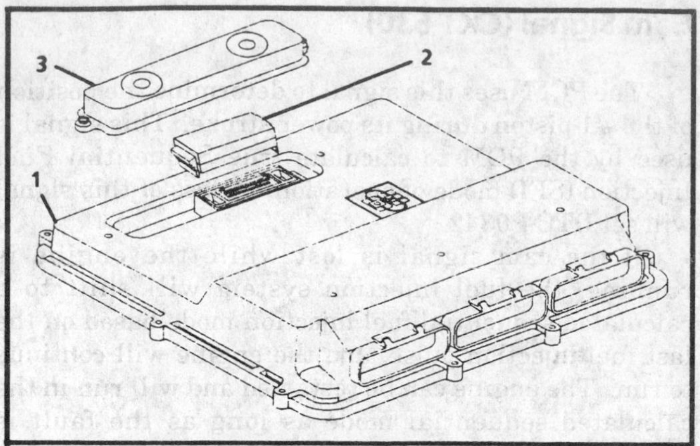
3
2
1

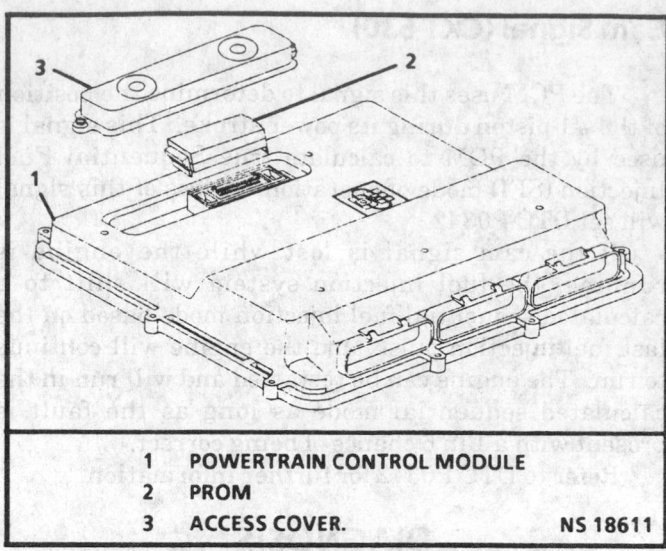

1 POWERTRAIN CONTROL MODULE
2 PROM
3 ACCESS COVER

NS 18611

Figure C1-8 - PCM and PROM

If the diagnostic procedures call for the PCM to be replaced, the engine "calibrator" (PROM) and PCM should be checked first to see if they are the correct parts.

If they are, remove the PROM from the faulty PCM and install it in the new service PCM.

THE SERVICE PCM WILL NOT CONTAIN A PROM. DTC P1623 indicates the PROM is installed improperly or has malfunctioned. When DTC P1623 is encountered, check the PCM installation for bent pins or pins not fully seated in the socket. If it is installed correctly and DTC P1623 still sets, replace the PROM.

NOTICE: To prevent possible Electrostatic Discharge damage to the PCM or PROM, Do Not touch the component leads, and Do Not remove integrated circuit from carrier.

Important

- When replacing the production PCM with a service PCM (controller), it is important to transfer the broadcast code and production PCM number to the service PCM label. Please do not record on PCM cover. This will allow positive identification of PCM parts throughout the service life of the vehicle.
- To prevent internal PCM damage, the ignition must be "OFF" when disconnecting or reconnecting power to PCM (for example, battery cable, PCM pigtail, PCM fuse, jumper cables, etc.).

PROM
Figure C1-7

Important

- The PROM is "keyed" to prohibit improper insertion. However, it is essential that the correct PROM be used with a specific vehicle model.

NOTICE: The ignition should always be "OFF" when installing or removing the PCM connectors.

LOCATION: Under access cover of PCM.

←→ Remove or Disconnect

1. Negative battery cable.
2. PCM from mounting hardware.
3. Harness connectors from PCM.
4. PCM from engine compartment.
5. PROM access cover.
6. Remove PROM by using thumb and first finger to gently squeeze each end of the blue PROM carrier (Figure C1-7) and pull upward.

→← Install or Connect

1. PROM in PCM.

Important

- Gently press on PROM until it is firmly seated in the socket.

2. PROM access cover.
3. Connectors to PCM.
4. PCM into vehicle.
5. Negative battery cable.

Functional Check

1. Perform on-board diagnostic system check.
2. Start engine and run for one minute.
3. Scan for DTCs using the Tech 1.
4. If DTC P0325, P1361, P1350 or P1623 occurs, or if the MIL (Service Engine Soon) is "ON" constantly with no diagnostic trouble codes, the PROM is not fully seated or is defective.
   - If it is necessary to remove the PROM, follow the previous removal instructions.

ENGINE COOLANT TEMPERATURE (ECT) SENSOR

Important

- Care must be taken when handling engine coolant temperature sensor. Damage to engine coolant temperature sensor will affect proper operation of the fuel injection system.

Remove or Disconnect

1. Drain radiator coolant.
2. Air induction tube.
3. Electrical connector.
4. Using a 19 mm deep well socket and 6 inch extension remove sensor.

Install or Connect

1. Coat engine coolant temperature sensor threads with sealer P/N 1052080 or equivalent.
2. Sensor in engine, torque to 30 N·m (22 lb. ft.).
3. Electrical connector.
4. Refill coolant, install air induction tube.
5. Negative battery cable.
6. Start engine check for leaks.
7. Recheck coolant level.

MAF SENSOR

The MAF sensor on this engine is attached to the throttle body assembly. To remove follow the steps listed below.

Remove or Disconnect

1. 3 wire electrical connector.
2. 3 screws holding MAF sensor to throttle body.

Install or Tighten

1. 3 screws holding MAF to throttle body.
2. Electrical connector.

IAT SENSOR

The IAT sensor is mounted in the air cleaner housing.

Remove or Disconnect

1. Electrical connector.
2. Carefully remove sensor (snaps into place).

Install or Connect

1. Sensor (snap into place).
2. Electrical connector.

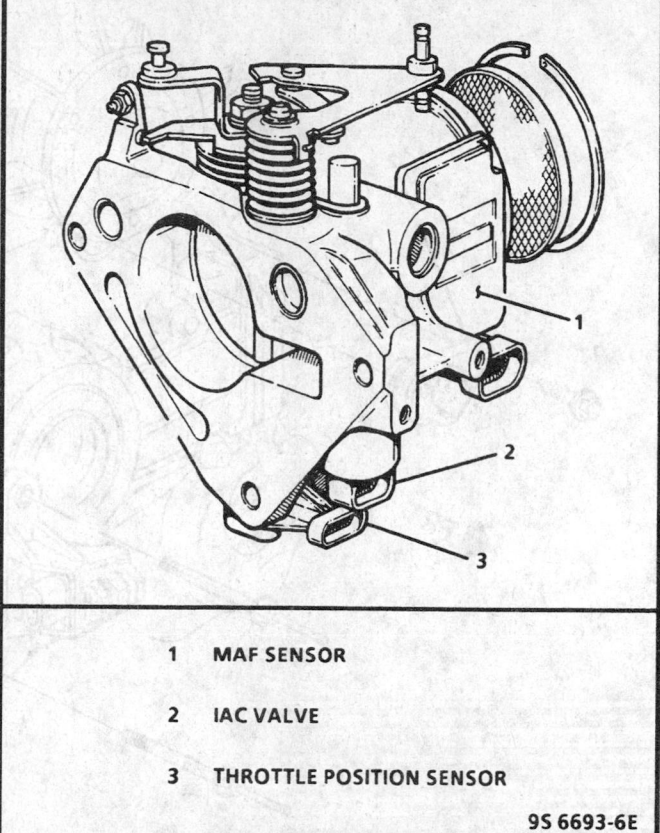

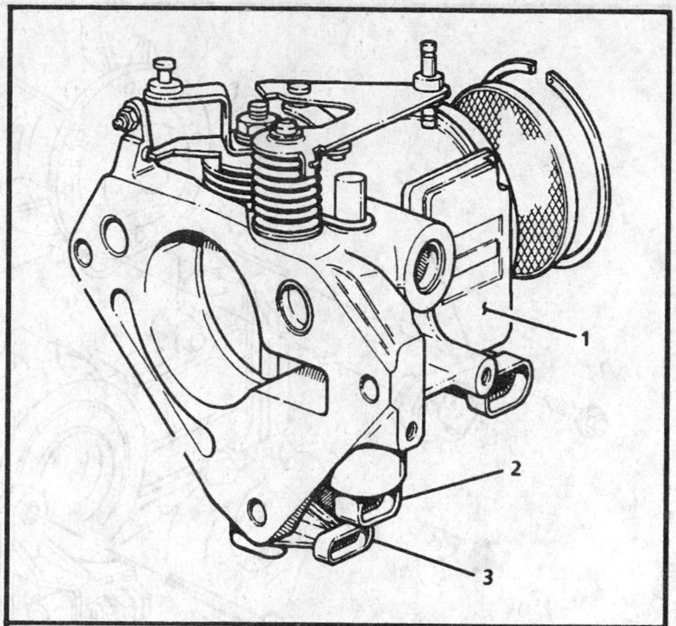
1
2
3

1 MAF SENSOR

2 IAC VALVE

3 THROTTLE POSITION SENSOR

9S 6693-6E

Figure C1-9 - Throttle Body with MAF

HEATED OXYGEN SENSOR/CATALYST MONITOR (HO2S 1 AND HO2S 2)

Figures C1-11 and C1-12

NOTICE: The Heated Oxygen Sensor and catalyst monitor (HO2S 1 and HO2S 2) each use a permanently attached pigtail and connector. This pigtail should not be removed from the heated oxygen sensor or catalyst monitor. Damage or removal of the pigtail or connector could affect proper operation of the heated oxygen sensor.

Important

- Take care when handling the heated oxygen sensor and catalyst monitor. The in-line electrical connector and louvered end must be kept free of grease, dirt or other contaminants. Also, avoid using cleaning solvents of any type. Do not drop or roughly handle the heated oxygen sensor/catalyst monitor. **A dropped sensor is a bad sensor.**

Remove or Disconnect

- The heated oxygen sensor/catalyst monitor may be difficult to remove when engine temperature is below 48°C (120°F). Excessive force may damage threads in exhaust manifold or exhaust pipe.

1. Electrical connector.
2. Carefully back out heated oxygen sensor/catalyst monitor.

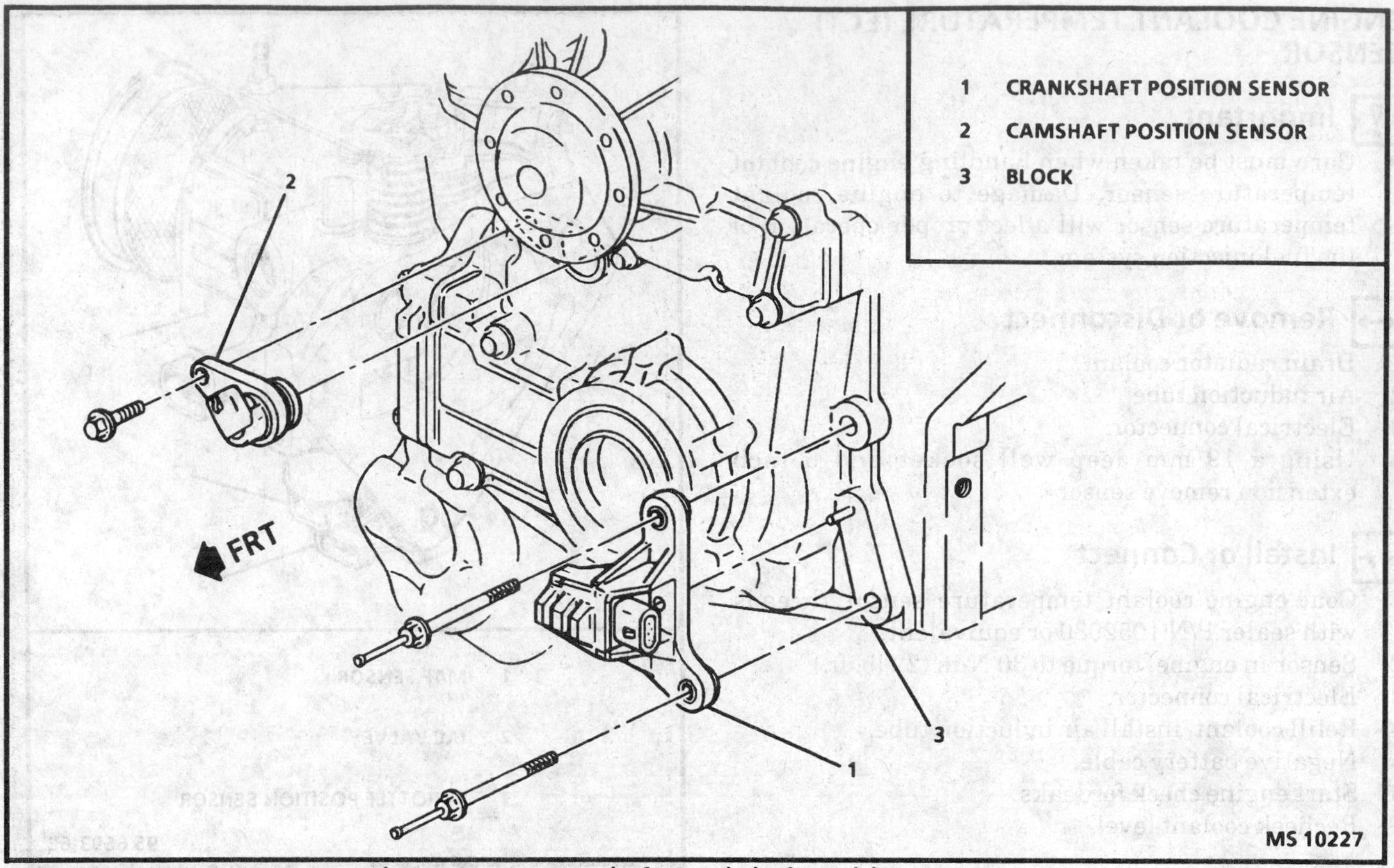
1 CRANKSHAFT POSITION SENSOR
2 CAMSHAFT POSITION SENSOR
3 BLOCK
2
FRT
3
1
MS 10227

Figure C1-10 - Camshaft/Crankshaft Position Sensors

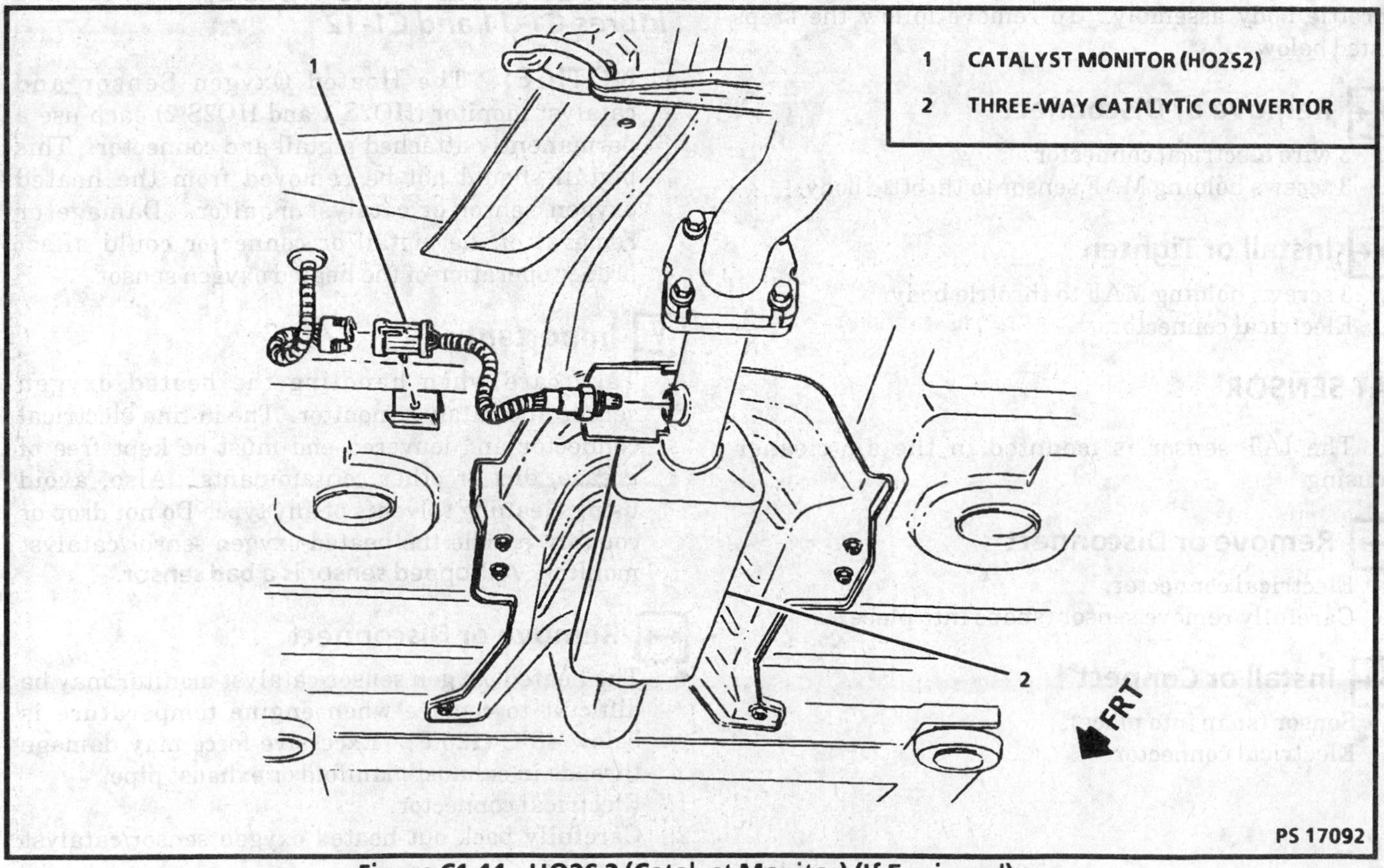
1 CATALYST MONITOR (HO2S2)
2 THREE-WAY CATALYTIC CONVERTOR
1
2
FRT
PS 17092

Figure C1-11 - HO2S 2 (Catalyst Monitor) (If Equipped)

Important

- A special anti-seize compound is used on the heated oxygen sensor threads. The compound consists of graphite suspended in fluid and glass beads. The graphite will burn away, but the glass beads will remain, making the sensor easier to remove. New or service sensors will already have the compound applied to the threads. If a sensor is removed from an engine and if for any reason is to be reinstalled, the threads must have anti-seize compound applied before reinstallation.

Install or Connect

1. Coat threads of heated oxygen sensor/catalyst monitor with anti-seize compound P/N 5613695, or equivalent if necessary.
2. Sensor and torque to 41 N·m (30 lb. ft.).
3. Electrical connector.

CAMSHAFT POSITION SENSOR

Remove or Disconnect

1. Negative battery cable.
2. Electrical connector from camshaft position sensor.
3. Camshaft position sensor retaining screw.
4. Camshaft position sensor.

Install or Connect

1. Camshaft position sensor.
2. Camshaft position sensor retaining screw, torque to 4-6 N·m (35-53 lb. in.).
3. Electrical connector.
4. Negative battery cable.

VSS

Refer to SECTION 7A for transaxle mounted VSS.

TRANSAXLE RANGE SWITCH

Refer to SECTION 7A for transaxle range switch. "On-Vehicle Service" and adjustment procedures are also listed there.

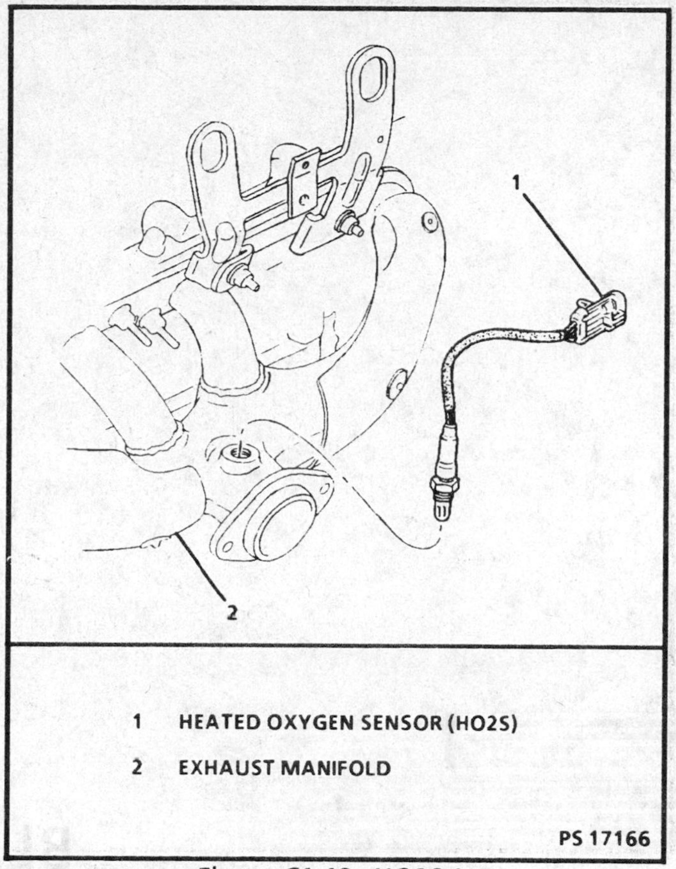
1
2
1 HEATED OXYGEN SENSOR (HO2S)
2 EXHAUST MANIFOLD
PS 17166

Figure C1-12 - HO2S 1

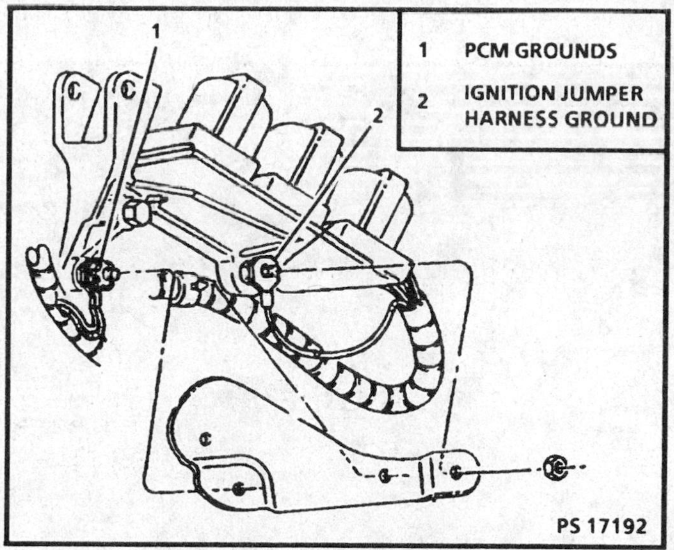
1
2
1 PCM GROUNDS
2 IGNITION JUMPER HARNESS GROUND
PS 17192

Figure C1-13 - PCM Grounds

BLANK

SECTION C2

FUEL METERING SYSTEM

CONTENTS

GENERAL DESCRIPTION

PURPOSE

The basic function of the fuel metering system is to control fuel delivery to the engine.

Fuel is delivered to the engine by individual fuel injectors mounted in the intake manifold near each cylinder.

The main control sensor is the Oxygen Sensor (O2S) which is located in the exhaust manifold. The oxygen sensor tells the PCM how much oxygen is in the exhaust gas and the PCM changes the air/fuel ratio to the engine by controlling the fuel injectors. The best mixture to minimize exhaust emissions is 14.7 to 1, which allows the catalytic converter to operate the most efficiently. Because of the constant measuring and adjusting of the air/fuel ratio, the fuel injection system is called a "Closed Loop" system.

MODES OF OPERATION

The PCM looks at voltages from several sensors to determine how much fuel should be delivered to the engine. The fuel is delivered under one of several conditions, called "modes." All the modes are controlled by the PCM and are described below.

Starting Mode

When the ignition is first turned "ON," the PCM turns "ON" the fuel pump relay for two seconds and the fuel pump builds up pressure. The PCM then checks the Engine Coolant Temperature (ECT) sensor, Throttle Position (TP) sensor, and fuel control signal to determine the proper air/fuel ratio for starting.

The PCM controls the amount of fuel delivered in the starting mode by changing how long the injectors are turned "ON" and "OFF." This is done by "pulsing" the injectors for very short times.

Clear Flood Mode

If the engine floods, it can be cleared by pushing the accelerator pedal down all the way. The PCM then completely turns "OFF" the fuel. No fuel is delivered from the injectors as long as the throttle stays wide open, and the engine speed is below 600 RPM. If the throttle position becomes less than 65%, the PCM returns to the starting mode.

Run Mode

The run mode has two conditions called "Open Loop" and "Closed Loop."

When the engine is first started, and RPM is above 400 RPM, the system is in "Open Loop" operation. In "Open Loop," the PCM will ignore the signal from the Oxygen Sensor (O2S), and calculate the air/fuel ratio based on inputs from the TP sensor, ECT sensor and MAF sensor.

The system will stay in "Open Loop" until the following conditions are met:

1. The O2S has varying voltage output showing that it is hot enough to operate properly. (This depends on temperature.)
2. The Engine Coolant Temperature (ECT) sensor is above a specified temperature.
3. A specific amount of time has elapsed after starting the engine.
4. Engine speed over 1200 RPM for at least 10 seconds.

The specific values for the above conditions are stored in the PROM. When these conditions are met, the system goes into "Closed Loop" operation. In "Closed Loop," the PCM will calculate the air/fuel ratio (injector "ON" time) based on the signal from the O2S. This allows the air/fuel ratio to stay very close to 14.7:1.

Acceleration Mode

When the driver pushes on the accelerator pedal, air flow into the cylinders increases rapidly, while fuel flow tends to lag behind. To prevent possible hesitation, the PCM increases the pulse width to the injectors to provide extra fuel during acceleration. The amount of fuel required is based on throttle position, manifold air pressure, and engine speed.

Deceleration Mode

When the driver releases the accelerator pedal, air flow into the engine is reduced. The corresponding changes in throttle position and manifold air pressure are relayed to the PCM, which reduces the injector pulse width to reduce fuel flow. If the deceleration is very rapid, or for long periods (such as long closed throttle coast-down), the PCM shuts "OFF" fuel completely to protect the catalytic converter.

Engine Speed/Vehicle Speed Fuel Disable Mode

The PCM monitors engine speed and shuts the fuel injectors "OFF" 5600 RPM. Fuel is turned back "ON" when engine speed decreases to below 5100 RPM.

The PCM also monitors vehicle speed and shuts fuel "OFF" at a speed which varies according to specific vehicle axle ratio and tire size and rating.

Battery Voltage Correction Mode

When battery voltage is low, the PCM will compensate for the weak spark by:

- Increasing the amount of fuel delivered;
- Increasing the idle RPM; and
- Increasing ignition dwell time.

Fuel Cutoff Mode

No fuel is delivered by the injector when the ignition is "OFF." This prevents dieseling. Also, fuel is not delivered if no reference pulses are seen (engine not running.) This prevents flooding.

FUEL METERING SYSTEM COMPONENTS

The fuel metering system is made up of the following parts:

- Fuel injectors.
- Throttle body.
- Fuel rail.
- Fuel pressure regulator.
- Idle Air Control (IAC) valve.
- Fuel pump.
- Fuel pump relay.

BASIC SYSTEM OPERATION

The fuel metering system starts with the fuel in the fuel tank. An electric fuel pump, located in the fuel tank with the gage sending unit, pumps fuel to the fuel rail through an in-line fuel filter. The pump is designed to provide fuel at a pressure above the pressure needed by the injectors. A pressure regulator in the fuel rail keeps fuel available to the injectors at a constant pressure. Unused fuel is returned to the fuel tank by a separate line. For further information on the fuel tank, in-line filter, and fuel lines, see SECTION 6C.

THROTTLE BODY UNIT

The throttle body has a throttle valve to control the amount of air delivered to the engine. The TP sensor and IAC valve are also mounted on the throttle body.

The throttle body contains vacuum ports located at, above, or below the throttle valve. These ports generate the vacuum signals needed by various components.

Engine coolant is directed through the coolant cavity in the throttle body, to warm the throttle valve and prevent icing.

FUEL RAIL

The fuel rail is mounted to the top of the engine. It distributes fuel to the individual injectors. Fuel is delivered to the input end of the rail by the fuel lines, goes through the rail, then to the pressure regulator. The regulator keeps the pressure to the injectors at a constant pressure. Remaining fuel is then returned to the fuel tank.

FUEL INJECTOR

The fuel injector is a solenoid operated device controlled by the PCM (see Figure C2-1). The PCM turns "ON" the solenoid which opens a valve to allow fuel delivery.

The fuel, under pressure, is injected in a conical spray pattern at the opening of the intake valve. Excess fuel not used by the injectors passes through the pressure regulator before being returned to the fuel tank.

An injector which is stuck partly open will cause loss of pressure after engine shut down, so long crank times would be noticed on some engines. Also, dieseling could occur because some fuel could be delivered to the engine after the ignition is turned "OFF."

PRESSURE REGULATOR

The pressure regulator (see Figure C2-2) is a diaphragm-operated relief valve with injector pressure on one side and manifold pressure on the other. The function of the regulator is to maintain the fuel pressure available to the injector at 3 times barometric pressure adjusted for engine load.

The pressure regulator is mounted on the fuel rail and is serviced separately.

If the pressure is too low, poor performance and DTC 44 could result. If the pressure is too high, excessive odor and a DTC 45 may result. CHART A-7 has information on diagnosing fuel pressure conditions.

IDLE AIR CONTROL (IAC) VALVE

The purpose of the Idle Air Control (IAC) valve (shown in Figure C2-3) is to control engine idle speed while preventing stalls due to changes in engine load. The IAC valve, mounted in the throttle body, controls bypass air around the throttle plate. By moving a conical valve, known as a pintle, IN (to decrease air flow) or OUT (to increase air flow), a controlled amount of air can move around the throttle plate.

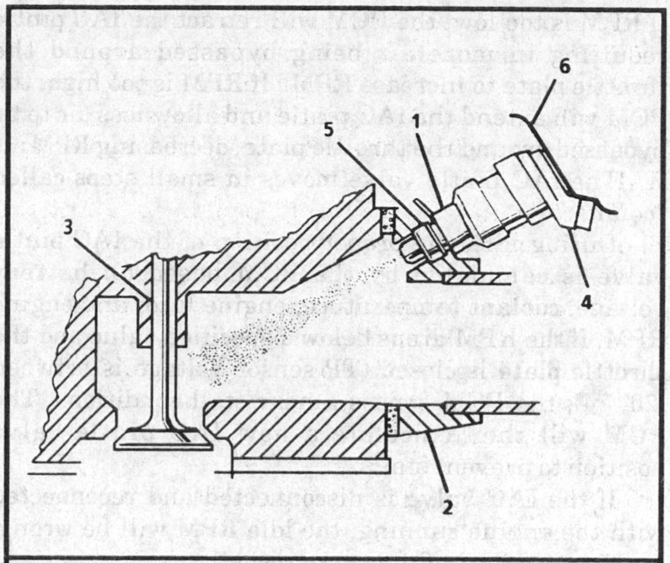
6
5
1
3
4
2

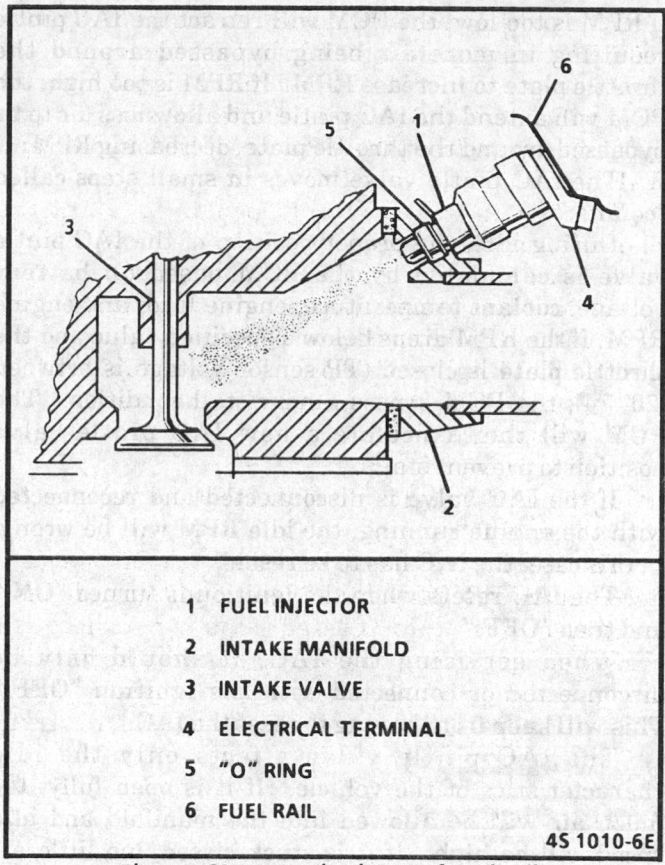

1 FUEL INJECTOR
2 INTAKE MANIFOLD
3 INTAKE VALVE
4 ELECTRICAL TERMINAL
5 "O" RING
6 FUEL RAIL

4S 1010-6E

Figure C2-1 - Fuel Injector (Typical)

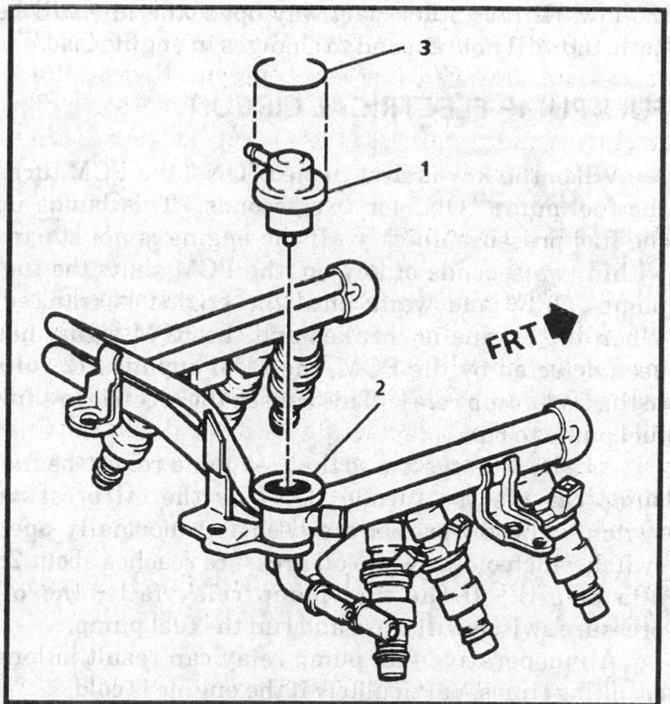
3
1
FRT
2

1 FUEL PRESSURE REGULATOR
2 REGULATOR HOUSING
3 SNAP RING

MS 7936-6E

Figure C2-2 - Fuel Pressure Regulator

If RPM is too low, the PCM will retract the IAC pintle resulting in more air being bypassed around the throttle plate to increase RPM. If RPM is too high, the PCM will extend the IAC pintle and allow less air to be bypassed around the throttle plate, decreasing RPM.

The IAC pintle valve moves in small steps called "counts."

During idle, the proper position of the IAC pintle valve is calculated by the PCM based on battery voltage, coolant temperature, engine load, and engine RPM. If the RPM drops below a specified value and the throttle plate is closed (TP sensor voltage is between .20-.74), the PCM senses a near stall condition. The PCM will then calculate a new IAC pintle valve position to prevent stalls.

If the IAC valve is disconnected and reconnected with the engine running, the idle RPM will be wrong. In this case, the IAC has to be reset.

The IAC resets when the ignition is turned "ON," and then "OFF."

When servicing the IAC, it should only be disconnected or connected with the ignition "OFF." This will keep from having to reset the IAC.

The IAC pintle valve affects only the idle characteristics of the vehicle. If it is open fully, too much air will be allowed into the manifold and idle speed will be high. If it is stuck closed, too little air will be allowed in the manifold, and idle speed will be too low. If it is stuck part way open, the idle will be high and will not respond to changes in engine load.

FUEL PUMP ELECTRICAL CIRCUIT

When the key is first turned "ON," the PCM turns the fuel pump "ON" for two seconds. This builds up the fuel pressure quickly. If the engine is not started within two seconds of key-up, the PCM shuts the fuel pump "OFF" and waits until the engine is cranked. When the engine is cranked and the RPM signal has been detected by the PCM, the PCM supplies 12 volts to the fuel pump relay. This causes the electric in-tank fuel pump to run.

As a backup system to the fuel pump relay, the fuel pump can also be turned "ON" by the oil pressure switch. The oil pressure switch is a normally open switch which closes when oil pressure reaches about 28 kPa (4 psi). If the fuel pump relay fails, the oil pressure switch will close and run the fuel pump.

An inoperative fuel pump relay can result in long cranking times, particularly if the engine is cold.

An inoperative fuel pump would cause a no start condition. A fuel pump which does not provide enough pressure can result in poor performance.

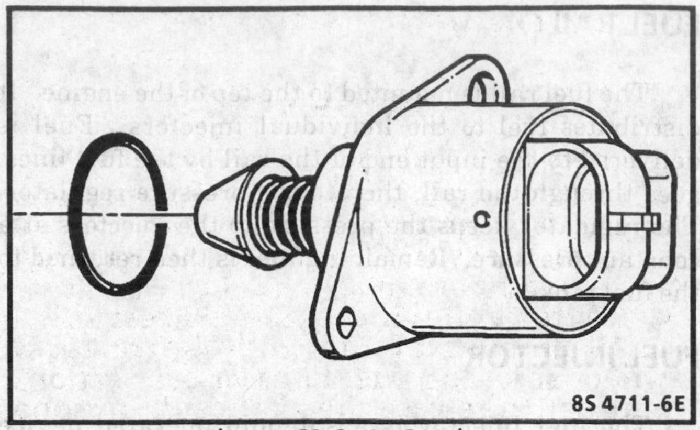
8S 4711-6E

Figure C2-3 - IAC Valve

DIAGNOSIS

FUEL METERING SYSTEM

Some failures of this system will result in an "Engine Cranks But Will Not Run." If this condition exists, see CHART A-3.

CHART A-3 will determine if the problem is caused by the ignition system, PCM or fuel pump circuit. If it's determined to be a fuel problem, CHART A-7 should be used. This includes the injectors, pressure regulator, fuel pump and fuel pump relay. The fuel system wiring schematic is covered on the facing page of CHART A-5. When a malfunction occurs in the fuel metering system, it usually results in either a rich or lean exhaust condition. If this condition is sensed by the oxygen sensor, the PCM will attempt to change the fuel calculation (injector pulse width) to compensate.

IDLE AIR CONTROL VALVE

The Tech 1 reads IAC position in counts. "0" counts indicates the PCM is commanding the IAC to be driven all the way in to a fully seated position. This is usually caused by a vacuum leak.

The higher the number of counts, the more air is being commanded to pass the IAC pintle. CHART C-2B should be used to diagnose the IAC system. Refer to "Rough, Unstable, or Incorrect Idle, Stalling" in "Symptoms," Section "6E3-B" for other possibilities for the cause of idle problems.

FUEL SYSTEM PRESSURE TEST

A fuel system pressure test is part of several of the diagnostic charts and symptom checks. To perform this test, use the procedure on the page opposite CHART A-7.

ON-VEHICLE SERVICE

PORT FUEL INJECTION COMPONENTS

CAUTION:
- **To reduce the risk of fire and personal injury, it is necessary to relieve the fuel system pressure before servicing fuel system components.**
- **After relieving system pressure, a small amount of fuel may be released when servicing fuel lines or connections. In order to reduce the chance of personal injury, cover fuel line fittings with a shop towel before disconnecting, to catch any fuel that may leak out. Place the towel in an approved container when disconnect is completed.**

Tool Required:
J 34730-1, Fuel Pressure Gage

1. Disconnect negative battery terminal to avoid possible fuel discharge if an accidental attempt is made to start the engine.
2. Loosen fuel filler cap to relieve tank vapor pressure.
3. Connect gage J 34730-1 to fuel pressure connection. Wrap a shop towel around fitting while connecting gage to avoid spillage.
4. Install bleed hose into an approved container and open valve to bleed system pressure. Fuel connections are now safe for servicing.
5. Drain any fuel remaining in gage into an approved container.

FUEL INJECTORS

Important
- Use care in removing injectors to prevent damage to the electrical connector pins on the injector and the nozzle. The fuel injector is serviced as a complete assembly only. The fuel injector is an electrical component and should not be immersed in any type of cleaner.

Remove or Disconnect
1. Remove electrical connections.
2. Fuel rail (see procedure below).
3. Injector retaining clips.
4. Injectors.

Install or Connect
1. Injectors using new O-ring. Coat O-rings with engine oil.
2. Injector retaining clips.
3. Fuel rail. Injectors are retained by the fuel rail.
4. Electrical connectors.

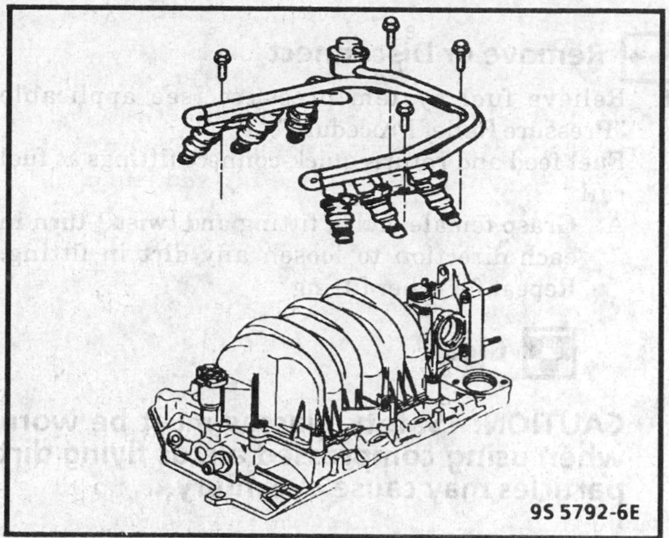
9S 5792-6E

Figure C2-4 - Fuel Rail and Injectors

Fuel Rail

Important
- When servicing the fuel rail assembly, precautions must be taken to prevent dirt and other contaminants from entering the fuel passages. It is recommended that fittings be capped, and holes plugged, during servicing.

Important
- Any time the fuel system is opened for service, the O-ring seals used with related component(s) should be replaced.

Cleaning and Inspection
- Before disassembly, the fuel rail assembly may be cleaned with a spray type engine cleaner, such as AC Delco X-30A or equivalent, following package instructions. The fuel rail should not be immersed in liquid solvent.

Tools Required:
J 37088-A, Fuel Line Quick-Connect Separators

CAUTION: To Reduce the Risk of Fire and Personal Injury: Do Not attempt to repair sections of nylon fuel pipes. If damaged, replace.

NOTICE: If nylon fuel feed or return pipes become kinked, and cannot be straightened, they must be replaced.

Remove or Disconnect

1. Relieve fuel system pressure (see applicable "Pressure Relief Procedure").
2. Fuel feed and return quick-connect fittings at fuel rail:
   A. Grasp female end of fitting and twist $\frac{1}{4}$ turn in each direction to loosen any dirt in fitting. Repeat for other fitting.

Clean

CAUTION: Safety glasses must be worn when using compressed air, as flying dirt particles may cause eye injury.

- Using compressed air, blow out dirt from quick-connect fittings before removing.

   B. Choose correct tool from J 37088-A tool set for size of fitting.
   C. Insert tool into female connector, push inward and pull connection apart.
   D. Repeat for other fitting.
3. Plug fuel feed and return pipes.

Clean and Inspect

NOTICE: If it is necessary to remove rust or burrs from the male tube ends of fuel rail inlet and outlet pipes: use emery cloth in a radial motion with the tube end to prevent damage to O-ring sealing surface.

- Using a clean shop towel, wipe off male tube ends.
- Inspect fuel feed/return quick-connect fittings and fuel rail inlet and outlet pipes for dirt or burrs. Clean or replace components/assemblies as required.

4. Injector electrical connectors.
5. Vacuum line from fuel pressure regulator.
6. Four bolts securing fuel rail assembly to intake manifold.
7. Fuel rail assembly from intake manifold. Cover all openings to avoid contamination.

CAUTION: To Reduce the Risk of Fire and Personal Injury:
• If nylon fuel lines are nicked, scratched or damaged during installation, they must be replaced.
• Before connecting quick-connect fittings, always apply a few drops of clean engine oil to the male tube ends of the fuel rail inlet and outlet pipes. This will ensure proper reconnection and prevent a possible fuel leak. (During normal operation, the O-rings located in the female connector will swell and may prevent proper reconnection if not lubricated.)

Install or Connect

1. Lightly coat injector O-rings with engine oil.
2. Fuel rail on intake manifold. Seat injectors into manifold by hand.
3. Four bolts securing fuel rail assembly to intake manifold.

Tighten

- Fuel rail retaining bolts to 10-20 N·m (7-14 lb. ft.).

4. Remove plugs from fuel feed and return pipes.
5. Apply a few drops of clean engine oil to the male tube ends of the fuel rail inlet and outlet pipes.
6. Connect fuel feed and return pipe quick-connect fittings:
   A. Push connectors together to cause the retaining tabs/fingers to snap into place.
   B. Once installed, pull on both ends of each connection to make sure it is secure.
7. Injector electrical connectors.
8. Vacuum line to fuel pressure regulator.

Inspect

- Turn ignition switch to "ON," position for two seconds, then turn to "OFF" for ten seconds. Again turn to "ON" position, and check for fuel leaks.

FUEL PRESSURE REGULATOR

Remove or Disconnect

1. Relieve fuel pressure (see procedure).
2. Clean dirt from regulator retaining ring.
3. Vacuum line from regulator.
4. Snap ring.
5. Using a shop towel to catch any spilled fuel, lift and twist pressure regulator to remove. Cover regulator housing to prevent contamination from entering fuel rail.

Install or Connect

1. New O-rings on regulator, if new regulator is not installed. Lubricate O-rings lightly with engine oil.
2. Regulator in regulator housing.
3. Snap ring.
4. Vacuum line on regulator.

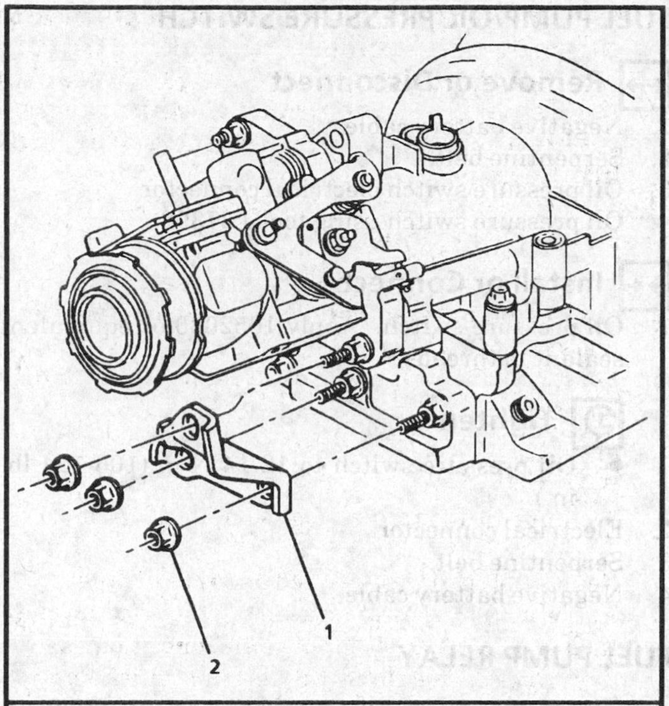
1
2
1 THROTTLE BODY SUPPORT
2 NUT (3)
NS 14119

Figure C2-5 - Throttle Body Support

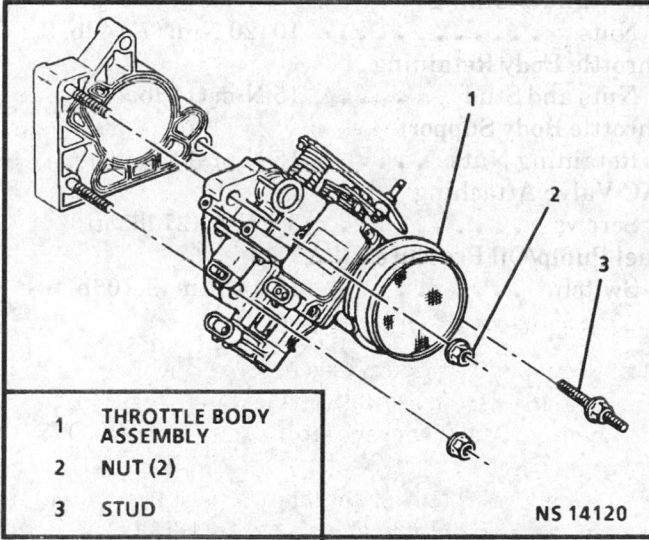

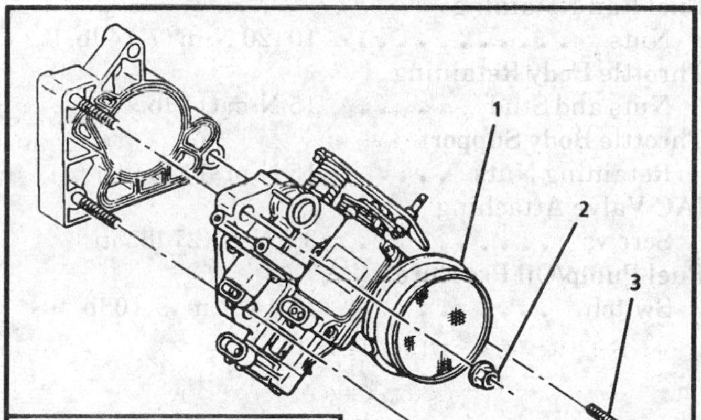
1
2
3
1 THROTTLE BODY ASSEMBLY
2 NUT (2)
3 STUD
NS 14120

Figure C2-6 - Throttle Body Service

THROTTLE BODY

THROTTLE BODY ASSEMBLY REMOVAL

Remove or Disconnect

1. Rear intake duct.
2. Drain radiator coolant.
3. Remove throttle and cruise cables.
4. Throttle cable bracket.
5. Disconnect IAC, TP sensor, and MAF sensor electrical connectors.
6. 3 nuts holding throttle body support to intake and throttle body; remove throttle body support.
7. Remove 2 nuts and stud holding throttle body to the intake manifold.
8. Remove throttle body assembly.

Clean

- Gasket surface on throttle body.

THROTTLE BODY ASSEMBLY INSTALLATION

Install or Connect

1. New gasket, if necessary.
2. Throttle body assembly.
3. Throttle body retaining nuts and stud.

Tighten

- Retaining nuts and stud to 15 N·m (11 lb. ft.).

4. Throttle body support and retaining nuts.

Tighten

- Retaining nuts to 15 N·m (11 lb. ft.).

5. Throttle cable bracket.
6. Throttle and cruise control cables.
7. IAC, TP and MAF sensor electrical connectors.
8. Air inlet duct.
9. Refill radiator to replace lost coolant.

THROTTLE POSITION (TP) SENSOR

Remove or Disconnect

1. Electrical connector.
2. TP sensor attaching screws.
3. TP sensor.

Install or Connect

1. With throttle valve in the normal closed idle position, install throttle position sensor on throttle body assembly, making sure TP sensor pickup lever is located ABOVE tang on throttle actuator lever.
2. TP sensor screws using a thread locking compound on the screws: Loctite 262, GM Part No. 1052624, or equivalent should be used.

IDLE AIR CONTROL VALVE

Remove or Disconnect

1. Electrical connector from Idle Air Control (IAC) valve.
2. IAC valve attaching screws.

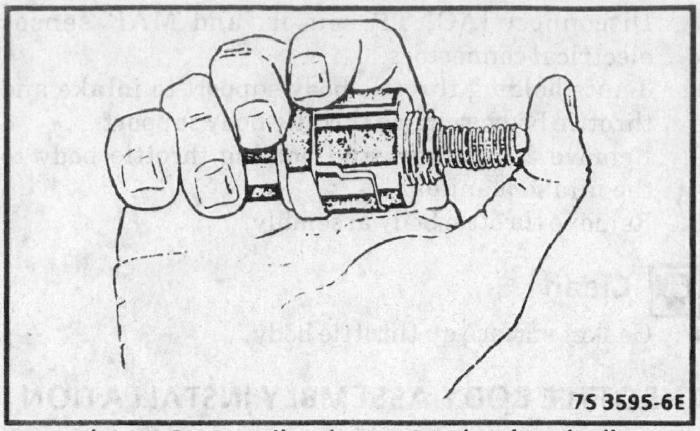
7S 3595-6E

Figure C2-7 - Adjusting IAC Valve (Typical)

Important

- Before installing new Idle Air Control (IAC) valve, measure the distance that the valve is extended. Measurement should be made from motor housing to end of cone. Distance should be no greater than 28mm (1-1/8 in.). If the cone is extended too far, adjustment is required or damage may occur to the valve when installed. Adjust IAC by manually compressing or extending the pintle to achieve the correct length (Figure C2-7).

Install or Connect

1. New IAC valve to throttle body. Use new O-ring gasket supplied with assembly.

   Tighten
   - IAC valve attaching screws to 3.0 N·m (27 lb. in.).
2. Electrical connector to Idle Air Control (IAC) valve.
3. Cycle ignition "ON" then "OFF" to reset IAC.
4. Start engine and allow engine to reach operating temperature.
5. The PCM will reset the IAC whenever the ignition switch is turned "ON," and then "OFF."

FUEL PUMP/OIL PRESSURE SWITCH

Remove or Disconnect

1. Negative battery cable.
2. Serpentine belt.
3. Oil pressure switch electrical connector.
4. Oil pressure switch using tool J 37398.

Install or Connect

1. Oil pressure switch. Apply 1052080 or equivalent sealant to threads.

   Tighten
   - Oil pressure switch to 12-14 N·m (106-124 lb. in.).
2. Electrical connector.
3. Serpentine belt.
4. Negative battery cable.

FUEL PUMP RELAY

The fuel pump relay is mounted in the engine electrical center. Other than checking for loose connectors, the only service possible is replacement.

TORQUE SPECIFICATIONS

Fuel Rail Retaining Nuts	10 -20 N·m (7-14 lb. ft.)
Throttle Body Retaining Nuts and Stud	15 N·m (11 lb. ft.)
Throttle Body Support Retaining Nuts	15 N·m (11 lb. ft.)
IAC Valve Attaching Screws	3.0 N·m (27 lb. in.)
Fuel Pump/Oil Pressure Switch	12-14 N·m (9-10 lb. ft.)

BLANK

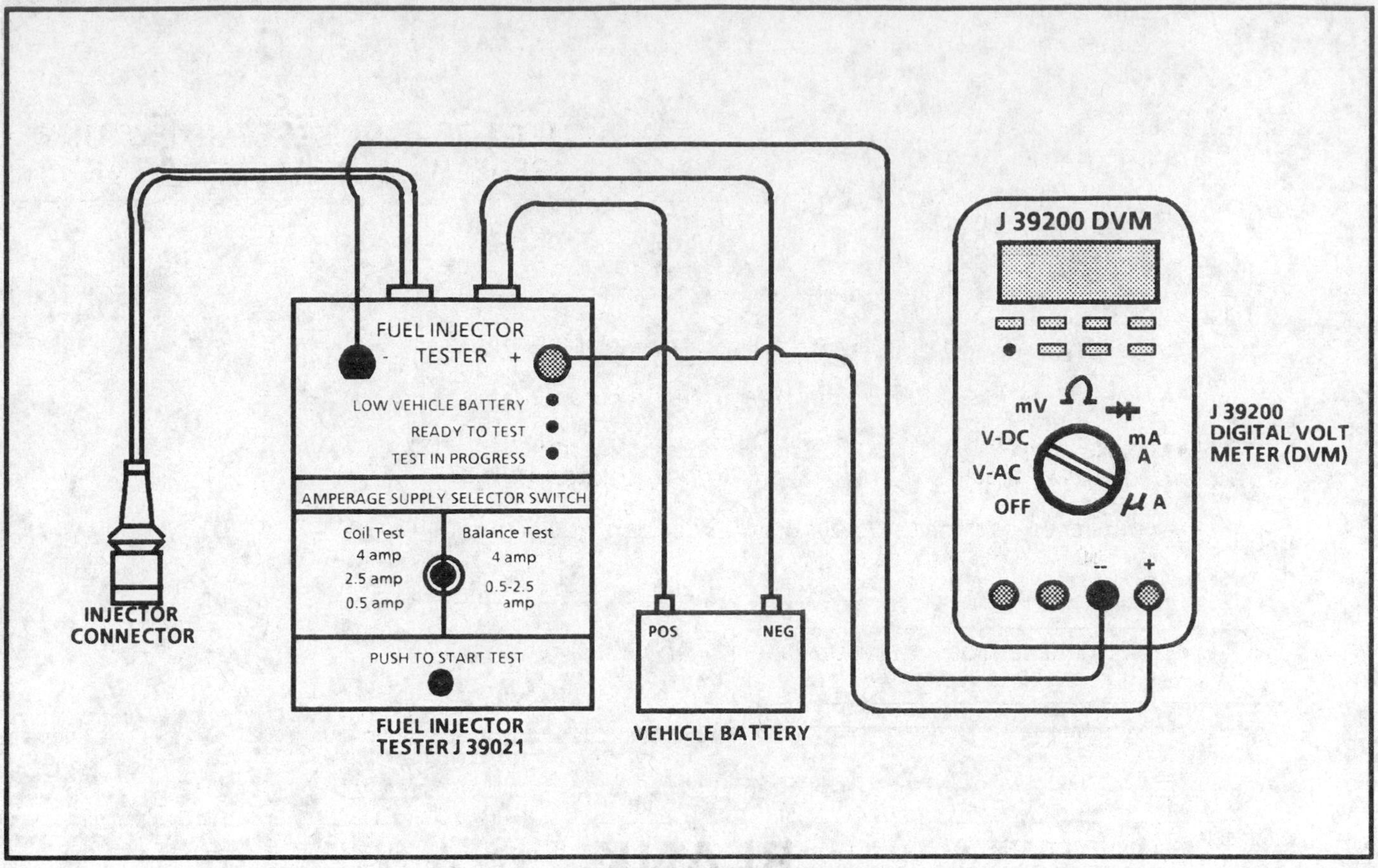
J 39200 DVM
mV
V-DC
V-AC
OFF
mA
A
μA
J 39200
DIGITAL VOLT
METER (DVM)
FUEL INJECTOR
- TESTER +
LOW VEHICLE BATTERY
READY TO TEST
TEST IN PROGRESS
AMPERAGE SUPPLY SELECTOR SWITCH
Coil Test
4 amp
2.5 amp
0.5 amp
Balance Test
4 amp
0.5-2.5 amp
PUSH TO START TEST
FUEL INJECTOR
TESTER J 39021
INJECTOR
CONNECTOR
POS
NEG
VEHICLE BATTERY

CHART C-2A

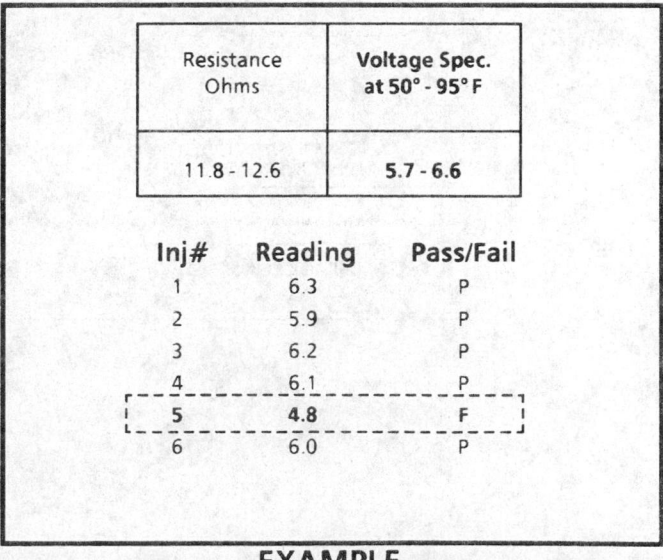

(Page 1 of 3)
INJECTOR COIL TEST PROCEDURE
3800 (VIN L) "W" CARLINE

Chart Test Description: Number(s) below refer to circled number(s) on the diagnostic chart.

1. This is the set-up step for performing the injector coil test. Also read instructions included with tools used for test.
2. Engine coolant temperature affects the tool's ability to detect a faulty injector. If engine coolant temperature is *NOT* between 50°F and 95°F the comparison chart (Page 2 of 3) must be used.
3. The first second of the voltage reading may be inaccurate due to initial current surge, therefore, record the lowest voltage displayed after the first second of test. The voltage reading should be within range (see example). The voltage reading may increase throughout the test as the injector windings warm and the resistance changes. An erratic voltage reading (one that jumps up and down) indicates an intermittent connection within the fuel injector.
4. To check the mechanical (fuel delivery) portion of the fuel injector, perform an injector balance test.

Resistance Ohms	**Voltage Spec. at 50° - 95° F**
11.8 - 12.6	**5.7 - 6.6**

Inj#	**Reading**	**Pass/Fail**
1	6.3	P
2	5.9	P
3	6.2	P
4	6.1	P
5	**4.8**	**F**
6	6.0	P

EXAMPLE

5-20-93
PS 17395

CHART C-2A

(Page 1 of 3)
INJECTOR COIL TEST PROCEDURE
3800 (VIN L) "W" CARLINE

(1)
- ENGINE "OFF."
- RELIEVE FUEL PRESSURE. (REFER TO "FUEL PRESSURE RELIEF" IN THIS SECTION.)
- ACCESS INJECTORS AS REQUIRED (REFER TO "ON-VEHICLE SERVICE" IN THIS SECTION.)
- CONNECT FUEL INJECTOR TESTER J 39021 TO VEHICLE BATTERY.
- SET AMPERAGE SUPPLY SELECTOR SWITCH TO THE "COIL TEST" 0.5 AMP POSITION.
- CONNECT LEADS FROM THE J 39200 DIGITAL VOLT METER (DVM) TO THE FUEL INJECTOR TESTER.
- SET DVM TO THE TENTHS SCALE (0.0).

(2)
- CHECK ENGINE COOLANT TEMPERATURE. IS IT BETWEEN 50° AND 95° F?

YES →

(3)
- CONNECT TESTER TO AN INJECTOR.
- PRESS THE "PUSH TO START TEST" BUTTON AND OBSERVE DVM. VOLTAGE MAY CLIMB DURING TEST. WATCH FOR ERRATIC READING (VOLTAGE JUMPS UP AND DOWN).
- RECORD LOWEST VOLTAGE DISPLAYED AFTER FIRST SECOND OF READING.
- REPEAT FOR EACH INJECTOR.
- DOES ANY INJECTOR VOLTAGE READING FALL OUTSIDE 5.7-6.6 VOLTS, OR DO ANY HAVE ERRATIC VOLTAGE READINGS?

YES → REPLACE FAULTY INJECTORS. → (4)

NO → (4)

(4)
- PERFORM "INJECTOR BALANCE TEST (PAGE 3 OF 3)".

NO (from 2) →
- PROCEED TO "CHART C-2A (PAGE 2 OF 3)".

3-24-93
PS 17396

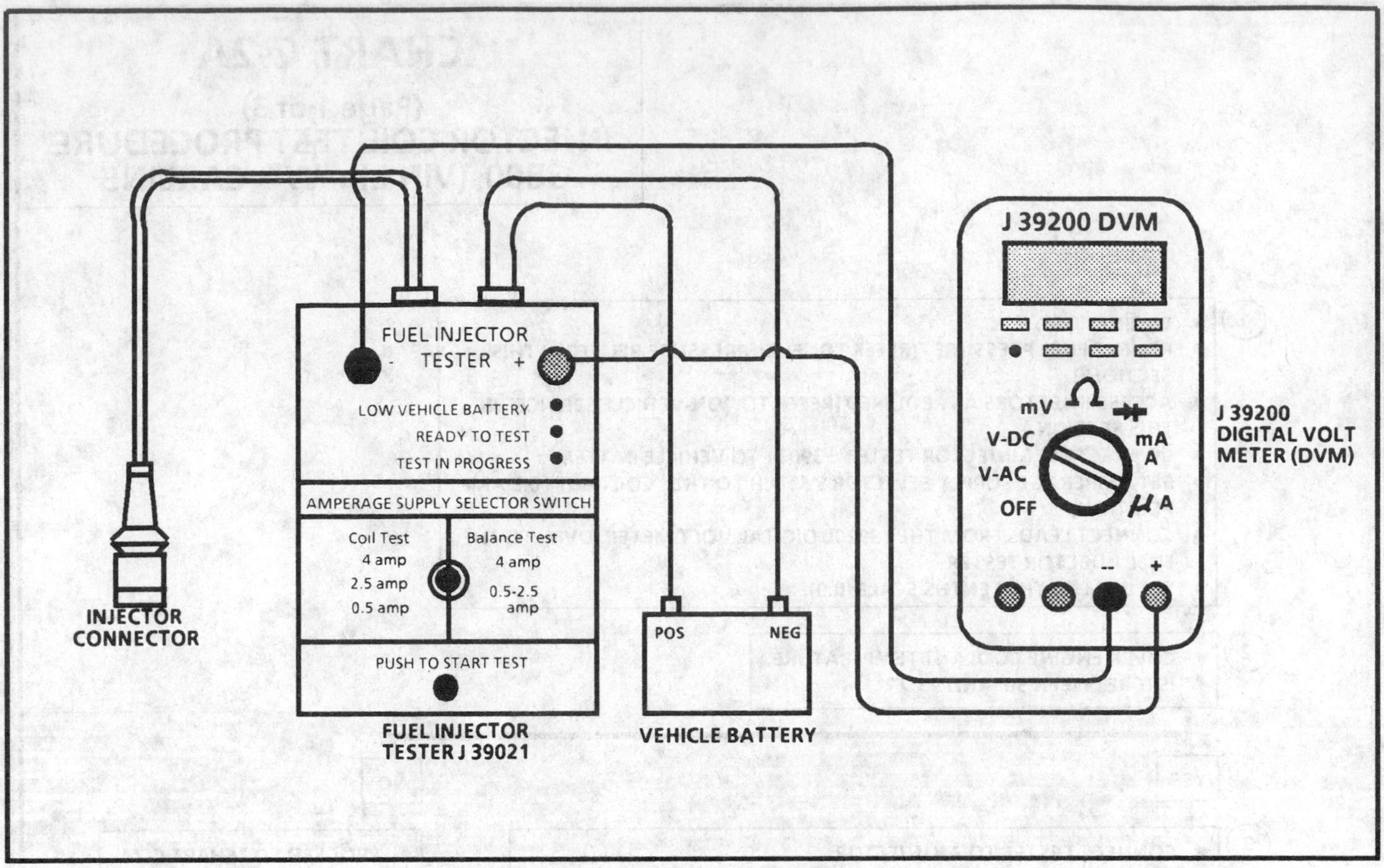
FUEL INJECTOR TESTER
-
+
LOW VEHICLE BATTERY
READY TO TEST
TEST IN PROGRESS
AMPERAGE SUPPLY SELECTOR SWITCH
Coil Test
4 amp
2.5 amp
0.5 amp
Balance Test
4 amp
0.5-2.5 amp
PUSH TO START TEST
FUEL INJECTOR TESTER J 39021
INJECTOR CONNECTOR
POS
NEG
VEHICLE BATTERY
J 39200 DVM
mV
Ω
V-DC
V-AC
OFF
mA
A
μA
J 39200 DIGITAL VOLT METER (DVM)

CHART C-2A

(Page 2 of 3)
INJECTOR COIL TEST PROCEDURE
3800 (VIN L) "W" CARLINE

Chart Test Description: Number(s) below refer to circled number(s) on the diagnostic chart.

1. The first second of the voltage reading may be inaccurate due to initial current surge, therefore, record the lowest voltage displayed after the first second of test. The voltage reading may increase throughout the test as the injector windings warm and the resistance changes. An erratic voltage reading (one that jumps up and down) indicates an intermittent connection within the fuel injector.
2. From recorded voltages (see example), identify the highest voltage reading recorded (other than those above 9.5 volts). Subtract all other voltages from the highest voltage recorded. The subtracted value for any injector must not exceed 0.6 volt.
3. To check the mechanical (fuel delivery) portion of the fuel injector, perform an injector balance test.

Highest Voltage Reading	7.1 Volts
Acceptable Subtracted Value Above/Below 50°-95°F.	0.6 Volt

Inj. No.	Voltage Reading	Subtracted Value	Pass/Fail
1	9.8	---	F
2	6.6	0.5	P
3	6.9	0.2	P
4	5.8	1.3	F
5	7.0	0.1	P
6	7.1	0.0	P

EXAMPLE

CHART C-2A
(Page 2 of 3)
INJECTOR COIL TEST PROCEDURE
3800 (VIN L) "W" CARLINE

FROM "CHART C-2A (PAGE 1 OF 3)"

(1)
- CONNECT TESTER TO AN INJECTOR.
- PRESS "PUSH TO START TEST" BUTTON AND OBSERVE DVM. VOLTAGE MAY CLIMB DURING TEST. WATCH FOR ERRATIC READING (VOLTAGE JUMPS UP AND DOWN).
- RECORD LOWEST VOLTAGE DISPLAYED AFTER THE FIRST SECOND OF READING.
- REPEAT FOR EACH INJECTOR.
- DOES ANY INJECTOR HAVE AN ERRATIC READING OR A READING ABOVE 9.5 VOLTS?

NO → go to (2)

YES
- DISREGARD INJECTOR(S) WITH VOLTAGE READING ABOVE 9.5 VOLTS OR ERRATIC READINGS (JUMPS UP AND DOWN) FROM CALCULATIONS. THESE INJECTORS ARE FAULTY AND MUST BE REPLACED.

(2)
- FROM RECORDED VOLTAGES, IDENTIFY THE HIGHEST VOLTAGE READING RECORDED (OTHER THAN THOSE ABOVE 9.5 VOLTS).
- SUBTRACT ALL OTHER VOLTAGES FROM THE HIGHEST VOLTAGE RECORDED.
- DOES ANY SUBTRACTED VALUE EXCEED 0.6 VOLTS?

YES

REPLACE ANY INJECTOR:
- WHOSE SUBTRACTED VALUE HAS EXCEEDED 0.6 VOLTS.
- WHOSE INITIAL READING WAS ABOVE 9.5 VOLTS.
- THAT HAD AN ERRATIC READING.

NO → go to (3)

(3) PERFORM "INJECTOR BALANCE TEST (PAGE 3 OF 3)".

3-24-93
PS 17398

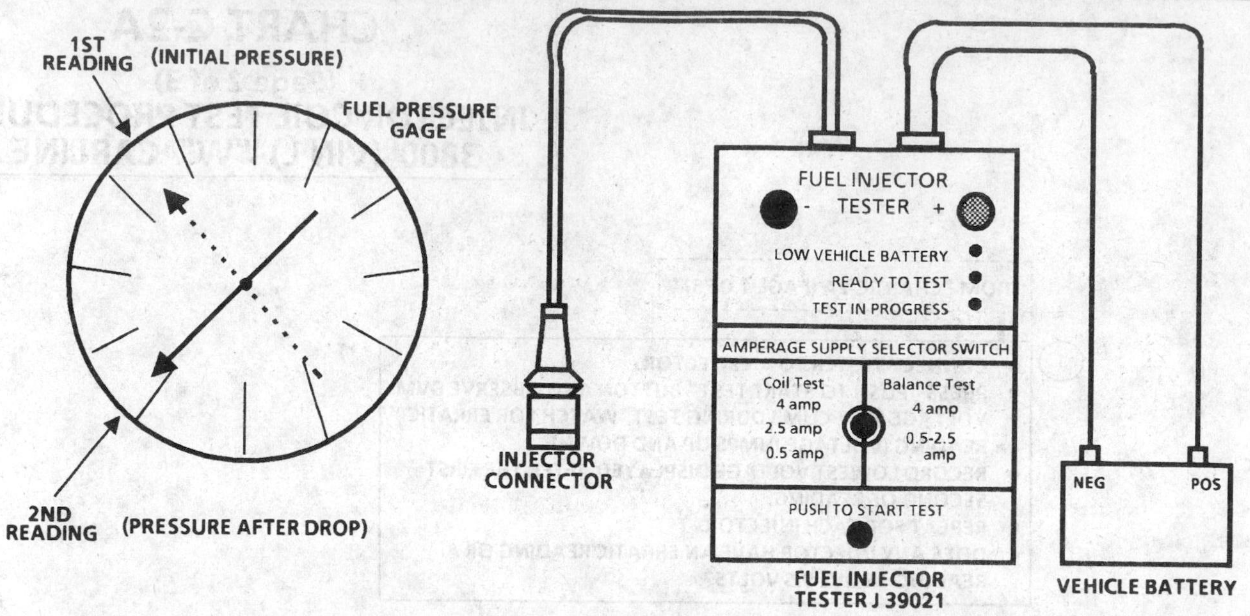

1ST READING (INITIAL PRESSURE)
FUEL PRESSURE GAGE
2ND READING (PRESSURE AFTER DROP)
INJECTOR CONNECTOR
FUEL INJECTOR TESTER - +
LOW VEHICLE BATTERY
READY TO TEST
TEST IN PROGRESS
AMPERAGE SUPPLY SELECTOR SWITCH
Coil Test 4 amp 2.5 amp 0.5 amp
Balance Test 4 amp 0.5-2.5 amp
PUSH TO START TEST
FUEL INJECTOR TESTER J 39021
NEG
POS
VEHICLE BATTERY

EXAMPLE

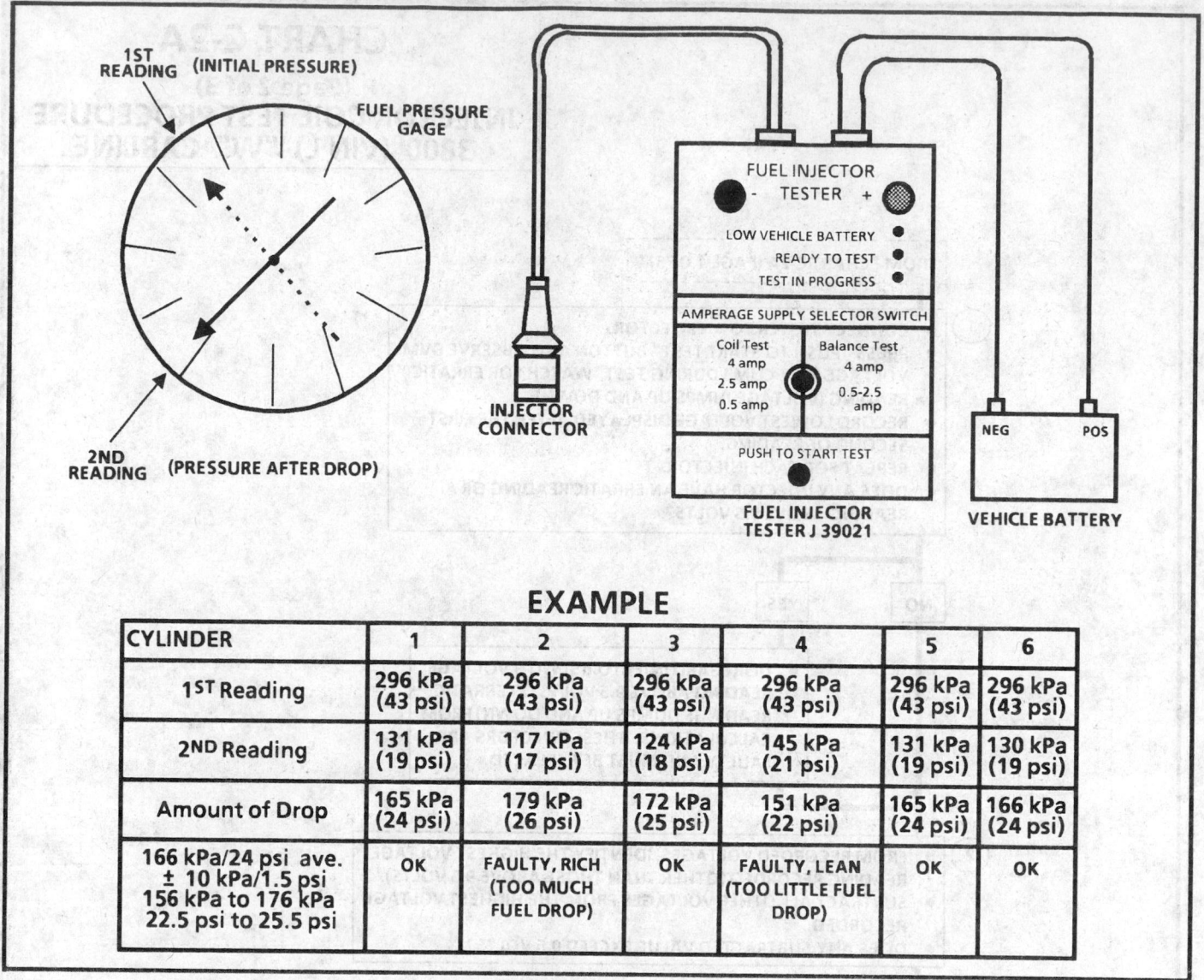

CYLINDER	1	2	3	4	5	6
1ST Reading	296 kPa (43 psi)	296 kPa (43 psi)	296 kPa (43 psi)	296 kPa (43 psi)	296 kPa (43 psi)	296 kPa (43 psi)
2ND Reading	131 kPa (19 psi)	117 kPa (17 psi)	124 kPa (18 psi)	145 kPa (21 psi)	131 kPa (19 psi)	130 kPa (19 psi)
Amount of Drop	165 kPa (24 psi)	179 kPa (26 psi)	172 kPa (25 psi)	151 kPa (22 psi)	165 kPa (24 psi)	166 kPa (24 psi)
166 kPa/24 psi ave. ± 10 kPa/1.5 psi 156 kPa to 176 kPa 22.5 psi to 25.5 psi	OK	FAULTY, RICH (TOO MUCH FUEL DROP)	OK	FAULTY, LEAN (TOO LITTLE FUEL DROP)	OK	OK

CHART C-2A

(Page 3 of 3)
INJECTOR BALANCE TEST PROCEDURE
3800 (VIN L) "W" CARLINE

Chart Test Description: Number(s) below refer to circled number(s) on the diagnostic chart.

1. Engine cool down period (10 minutes) is necessary to avoid irregular fuel pressure readings due to "Hot Soak" fuel boiling.
2. Energize tester one time and record pressure drop at the lowest point (Disregard any slight pressure variations).
3. If the pressure drop of all injectors is within 10 kPa (1.5 psi) of the average fuel pressure drop, the injectors are flowing properly. The actual amount of pressure drop is calculated by subtracting the second pressure reading from the first pressure reading.

ENGINE	FUEL PRESSURE RANGE
All engines EXCEPT 5.7L (VIN J) Corvette 3.1L (VIN W) Lumina VFV	284-325 kPa (41-47 psi)
5.7L (VIN J) Corvette 3.1L(VIN W) Lumina VFV	333-376 kPa (48-55 psi)

CHART C-2A

(Page 3 of 3)
INJECTOR BALANCE TEST PROCEDURE
3800 (VIN L) "W" CARLINE

CAUTION: TO REDUCE THE RISK OF FIRE AND PERSONAL INJURY, WRAP A SHOP TOWEL AROUND THE FUEL PRESSURE CONNECTION TO ABSORB ANY FUEL LEAKAGE THAT MAY OCCUR WHEN INSTALLING THE PRESSURE GAGE. PLACE TOWEL IN APPROVED CONTAINER.

NOTICE: The entire test should NOT be repeated more than once without running the engine to prevent flooding. (This includes any retest on faulty injectors.)

Important

The injector coil test should be performed prior to this test. Refer to Page 1 of 3.

(1)

- IF ENGINE IS AT OPERATING TEMPERATURE, ALLOW A 10 MINUTE "COOL DOWN" PERIOD.
- IGNITION "OFF."
- CONNECT FUEL PRESSURE GAGE.
- ENERGIZE FUEL PUMP USING AVAILABLE METHOD FOR VEHICLE (FUEL PUMP TEST CONNECTOR OR TECH 1 SCAN TOOL ENABLE).
- PLACE OPEN END OF BLEED HOSE INTO AN APPROVED GASOLINE CONTAINER AND BLEED AIR FROM FUEL GAGE.
- WITH FUEL PUMP RUNNING NOTE FUEL PRESSURE, PRESSURE SHOULD BE WITHIN SPECIFIED RANGE SHOWN ON FACING PAGE. IF NOT, REFER TO CHART A-7.
- TURN FUEL PUMP "OFF." WHEN PUMP STOPS, PRESSURE MAY VARY SLIGHTLY THEN SHOULD HOLD STEADY. IF NOT, REFER TO CHART A-7

(2)

- CONNECT FUEL INJECTOR TESTER TO AN INJECTOR.
  - SET AMPERAGE SUPPLY SELECTOR SWITCH TO THE "BALANCE TEST" 0.5 - 2.5 AMP POSITION.
- CYCLE FUEL PUMP "ON"/"OFF" TO PRESSURIZE FUEL SYSTEM.
- RECORD STABILIZED FUEL PRESSURE (1ST PRESSURE READING - SEE EXAMPLE ON FACING PAGE)
- ENERGIZE FUEL INJECTOR BY DEPRESSING "PUSH TO START TEST" BUTTON.
- NOTE FUEL PRESSURE THE INSTANT THE FUEL PRESSURE GAGE NEEDLE STOPS. RECORD FUEL PRESSURE READING (2ND PRESSURE READING - SEE EXAMPLE ON FACING PAGE).

(3)

- REPEAT STEP 2 ON ALL INJECTORS.
- SUBTRACT 2ND PRESSURE READING FROM 1ST PRESSURE READING TO OBTAIN PRESSURE DROP VALUES.
- ADD ALL PRESSURE DROP VALUES AND DIVIDE BY THE NUMBER OF FUEL INJECTORS TO GET THE AVERAGE PRESSURE DROP.
- ANY INJECTOR THAT HAS A 10 KPA (1.5 PSI) DIFFERENCE, EITHER MORE OR LESS FROM THE AVERAGE, IS CONSIDERED FAULTY.
- RETEST ANY INJECTOR THAT APPEARS FAULTY.
- ANY INJECTOR THAT FAILS THE RETEST IS FAULTY AND NEEDS TO BE REPLACED.
- IF NO PROBLEM IS FOUND, REVIEW "SYMPTOMS" SECTION "B".

3-24-93
PS 17400

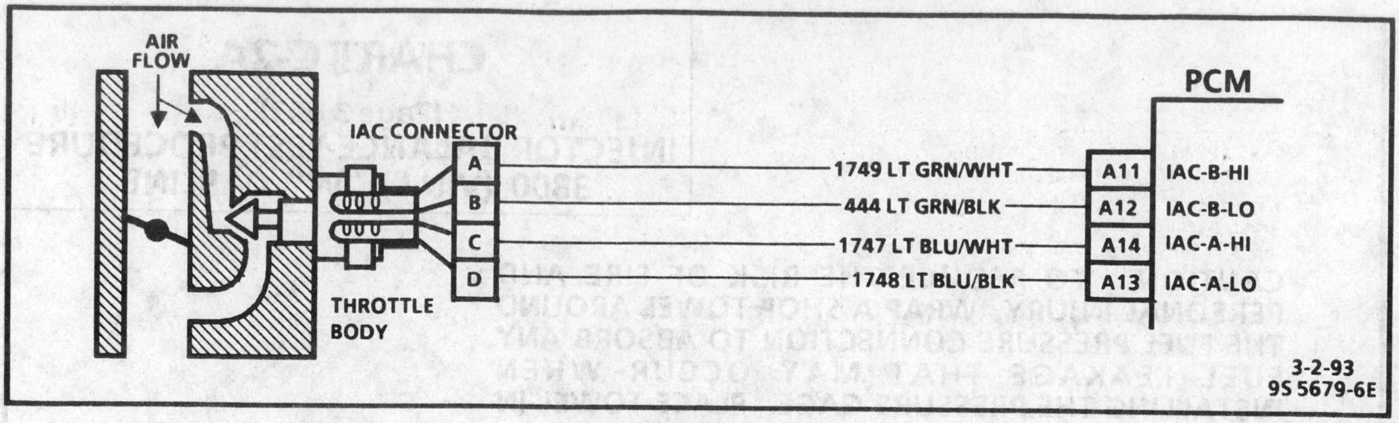
AIR FLOW
IAC CONNECTOR
A
B
C
D
THROTTLE BODY
1749 LT GRN/WHT
444 LT GRN/BLK
1747 LT BLU/WHT
1748 LT BLU/BLK
PCM
A11
A12
A14
A13
IAC-B-HI
IAC-B-LO
IAC-A-HI
IAC-A-LO
3-2-93
9S 5679-6E

CHART C-2B

IDLE AIR CONTROL (IAC) VALVE CHECK 3800 (VIN L) (SFI)

Circuit Description:

The PCM controls idle RPM with the IAC valve. To increase idle RPM, the PCM retracts the IAC pintle from the seat, allowing more air to bypass the throttle plate. To decrease RPM, it extends the IAC pintle valve in towards the seat, reducing air flow through the IAC valve port in the throttle body. A Tech 1 will read the PCM commands to the IAC valve in counts. The higher the counts, the more air allowed (higher idle). The lower the counts, the less air allowed (lower idle).

Chart Test Description: Number(s) below refer to circled number(s) on the diagnostic chart.

1. The Tech 1 is used to extend and retract the IAC valve. Valve movement is verified by an engine speed change.
2. This test checks all wires, connectors, and PCM.
3. This test checks for shorted or open IAC valve coils.

Diagnostic Aids: A slow, unstable idle may be caused by a system problem that cannot be overcome by the IAC.

NOTICE: If for some reason the air intake to the engine is restricted, the PCM will attempt to compensate by backing out the IAC pintle to maintain desired idle. This may result in IAC counts above 60. If the engine has another source of air to the intake, the PCM will compensate by extending the IAC pintle - scan IAC counts may reach zero as the PCM tries to maintain desired idle.

- System lean (high air/fuel ratio) - Idle speed may be too high or too low. Engine speed may vary up and down, disconnecting IAC does not help. May set DTC P0171.

  Tech 1 will read Heated Oxygen Sensor (HO2S) output less than 300 mV (.3 volt). Check for low regulated fuel pressure or water in fuel.
- System rich (low air/fuel ratio) - Idle speed too low. Scan IAC counts are usually above 80. System obviously rich and may exhibit black smoke exhaust. May set DTC P0172.

  Tech 1 will read Heated Oxygen Sensor (HO2S) signal fixed above 800 mV (.8 volt).

  Check:
  - High fuel pressure.
  - Injector leaking or sticking.
- Throttle body - Remove IAC and inspect bore for foreign material or evidence of IAC pintle dragging the bore.
- Refer to "Rough, Unstable, Incorrect Idle, or Stalling" in "Symptoms," Section "6E3-B".

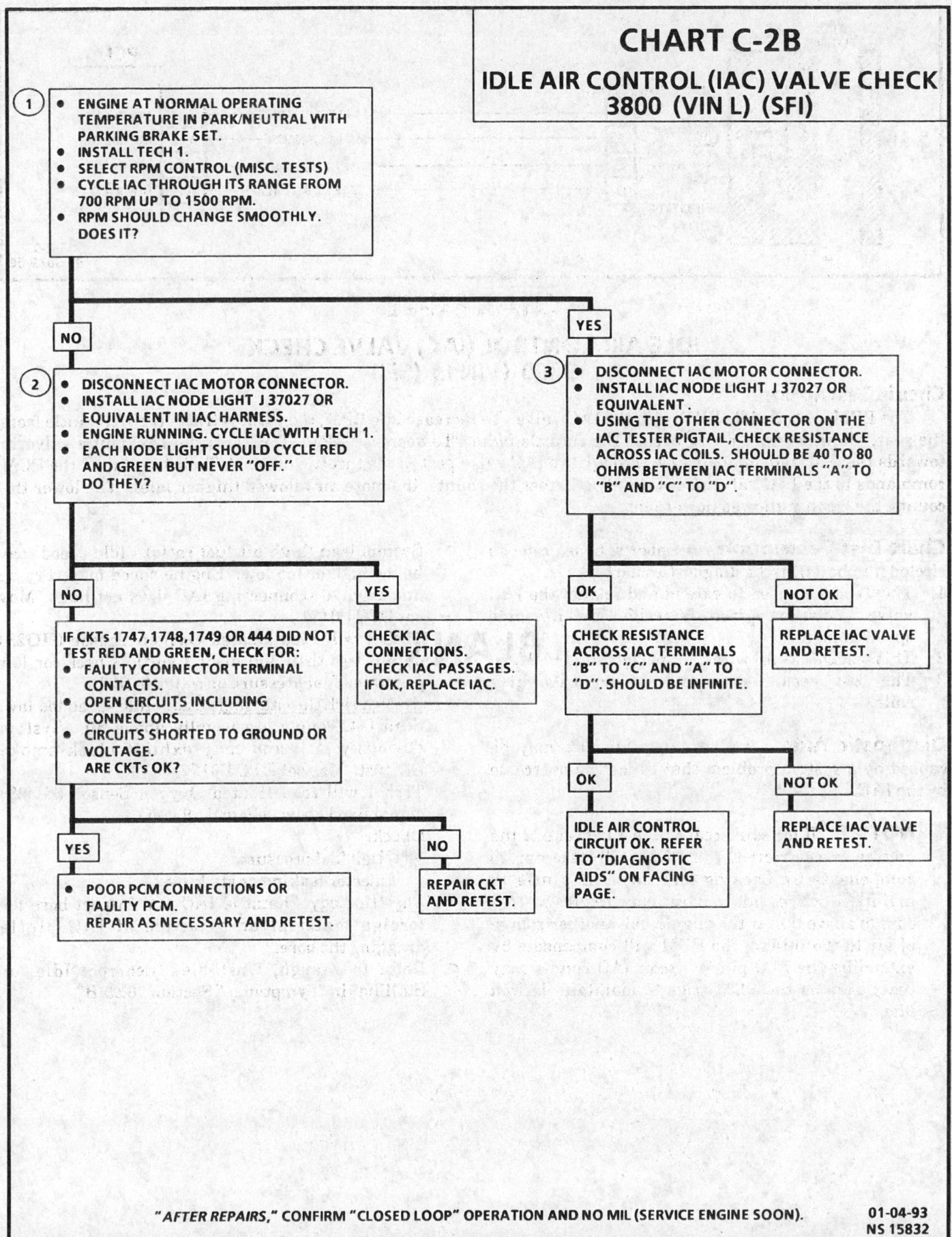

CHART C-2B

IDLE AIR CONTROL (IAC) VALVE CHECK
3800 (VIN L) (SFI)

1
- ENGINE AT NORMAL OPERATING TEMPERATURE IN PARK/NEUTRAL WITH PARKING BRAKE SET.
- INSTALL TECH 1.
- SELECT RPM CONTROL (MISC. TESTS)
- CYCLE IAC THROUGH ITS RANGE FROM 700 RPM UP TO 1500 RPM.
- RPM SHOULD CHANGE SMOOTHLY. DOES IT?

NO →

2
- DISCONNECT IAC MOTOR CONNECTOR.
- INSTALL IAC NODE LIGHT J 37027 OR EQUIVALENT IN IAC HARNESS.
- ENGINE RUNNING. CYCLE IAC WITH TECH 1.
- EACH NODE LIGHT SHOULD CYCLE RED AND GREEN BUT NEVER "OFF." DO THEY?

NO →

IF CKTs 1747,1748,1749 OR 444 DID NOT TEST RED AND GREEN, CHECK FOR:
- FAULTY CONNECTOR TERMINAL CONTACTS.
- OPEN CIRCUITS INCLUDING CONNECTORS.
- CIRCUITS SHORTED TO GROUND OR VOLTAGE.

ARE CKTs OK?

YES →
- POOR PCM CONNECTIONS OR FAULTY PCM.

REPAIR AS NECESSARY AND RETEST.

NO → REPAIR CKT AND RETEST.

YES → CHECK IAC CONNECTIONS. CHECK IAC PASSAGES. IF OK, REPLACE IAC.

YES →

3
- DISCONNECT IAC MOTOR CONNECTOR.
- INSTALL IAC NODE LIGHT J 37027 OR EQUIVALENT .
- USING THE OTHER CONNECTOR ON THE IAC TESTER PIGTAIL, CHECK RESISTANCE ACROSS IAC COILS. SHOULD BE 40 TO 80 OHMS BETWEEN IAC TERMINALS "A" TO "B" AND "C" TO "D".

OK →

CHECK RESISTANCE ACROSS IAC TERMINALS "B" TO "C" AND "A" TO "D". SHOULD BE INFINITE.

OK → IDLE AIR CONTROL CIRCUIT OK. REFER TO "DIAGNOSTIC AIDS" ON FACING PAGE.

NOT OK → REPLACE IAC VALVE AND RETEST.

NOT OK → REPLACE IAC VALVE AND RETEST.

"AFTER REPAIRS," CONFIRM "CLOSED LOOP" OPERATION AND NO MIL (SERVICE ENGINE SOON).

01-04-93
NS 15832

BLANK

SECTION C3

EVAPORATIVE EMISSION (EVAP) CONTROL SYSTEM

CONTENTS

GENERAL DESCRIPTION

PURPOSE

The basic Evaporative Emission (EVAP) Control system used on all vehicles is the charcoal canister storage method. This method transfers fuel vapor from the fuel tank to an activated carbon (charcoal) storage device (canister) to hold the vapors when the vehicle is not operating. When the engine is running, the fuel vapor is purged from the carbon element by intake air flow and consumed in the normal combustion process.

EVAPORATIVE SYSTEM

Gasoline vapors from the fuel tank flow into the tube labeled tank (Figure C3-1). These vapors are absorbed into the carbon. The canister is purged by PCM control when the engine is fully warmed up, IAT reading is over 9.5°C (50°F), and the engine has been running a specified amount of time. Air is drawn into the canister through the air inlet grid. The air mixes with the vapor and the mixture is drawn into the intake manifold.

OPERATION

The PCM operates a pulse width modulated solenoid valve, which controls vacuum to the charcoal canister.

The PCM pulses "ON" the solenoid valve and allows purge when:

- Engine is fully warmed up.
- After the engine has been running a specified time.
- IAT reading above 9.5°C (50°F).

RESULTS OF INCORRECT OPERATION

- Poor idle, stalling and poor driveability can be caused by:

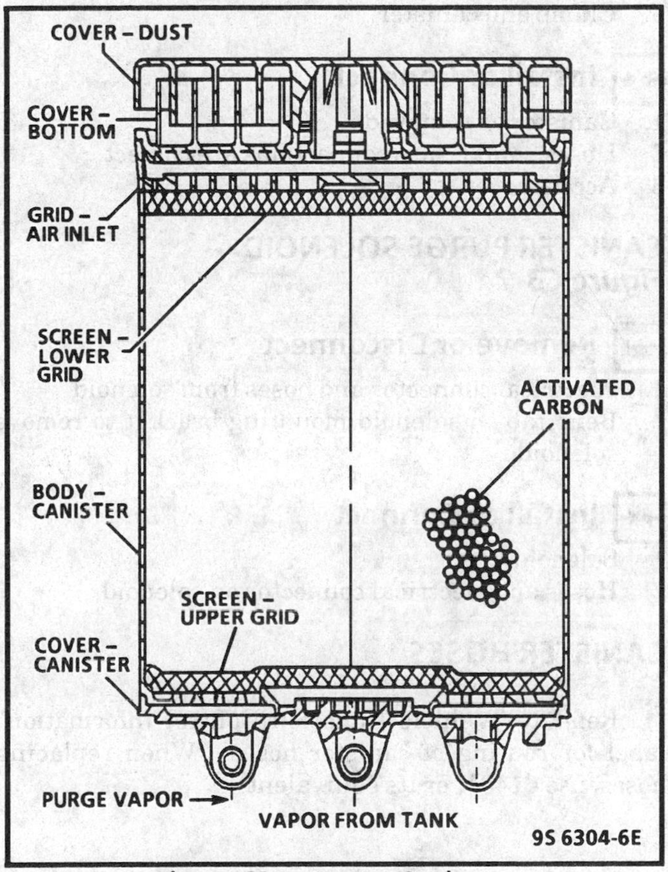

COVER - DUST
COVER - BOTTOM
GRID - AIR INLET
SCREEN - LOWER GRID
ACTIVATED CARBON
BODY - CANISTER
SCREEN - UPPER GRID
COVER - CANISTER
PURGE VAPOR
VAPOR FROM TANK
9S 6304-6E

Figure C3-1 - Vapor Canister

  - Malfunctioning purge solenoid.
  - Damaged canister.
  - Hoses split, cracked and/or not connected properly.

DIAGNOSIS

CANISTER PURGE SOLENOID

The canister purge solenoid operation is covered in CHART C-3 at the end of this section.

VISUAL CHECK OF CANISTER

- Cracked or damaged, replace canister.
- Fuel leaking from the canister, replace canister and check hoses and hose routing.

ON-VEHICLE SERVICE

FUEL VAPOR CANISTER

↔ Remove or Disconnect

1. Access cover at rear left wheel well.
2. Hoses from canister. Mark hoses to install on new canister.
3. Clamp and canister.

→← Install or Connect

1. Canister as removed.
2. Hoses. Make sure connections are correct.
3. Access cover.

CANISTER PURGE SOLENOID
Figure C3-2

↔ Remove or Disconnect

1. Electrical connector and hoses from solenoid.
2. Bend tab on solenoid mounting bracket to remove solenoid.

→← Install or Connect

1. Solenoid.
2. Hoses and electrical connector on solenoid.

CANISTER HOSES

Refer to "Vehicle Emission Control Information" label for routing of canister hoses. When replacing hoses, use 6148M or its equivalent.

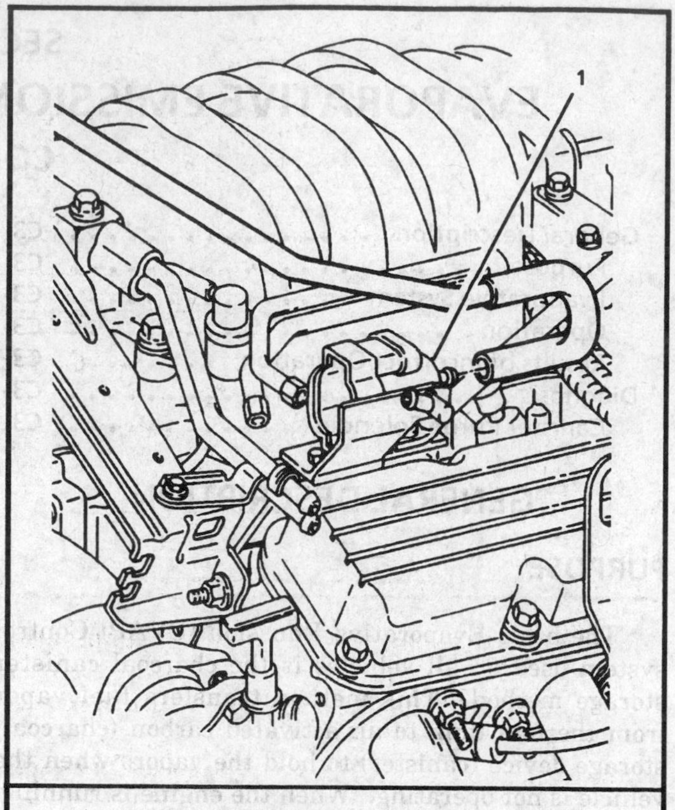
1
1 CANISTER PURGE SOLENOID
9S 6628-6E

Figure C3-2 - Canister Purge Solenoid

PARTS INFORMATION

PART NAME	GROUP
Canister, Fuel Vapor	3.130
Solenoid, Fuel Vapor Canister Purge	3.140

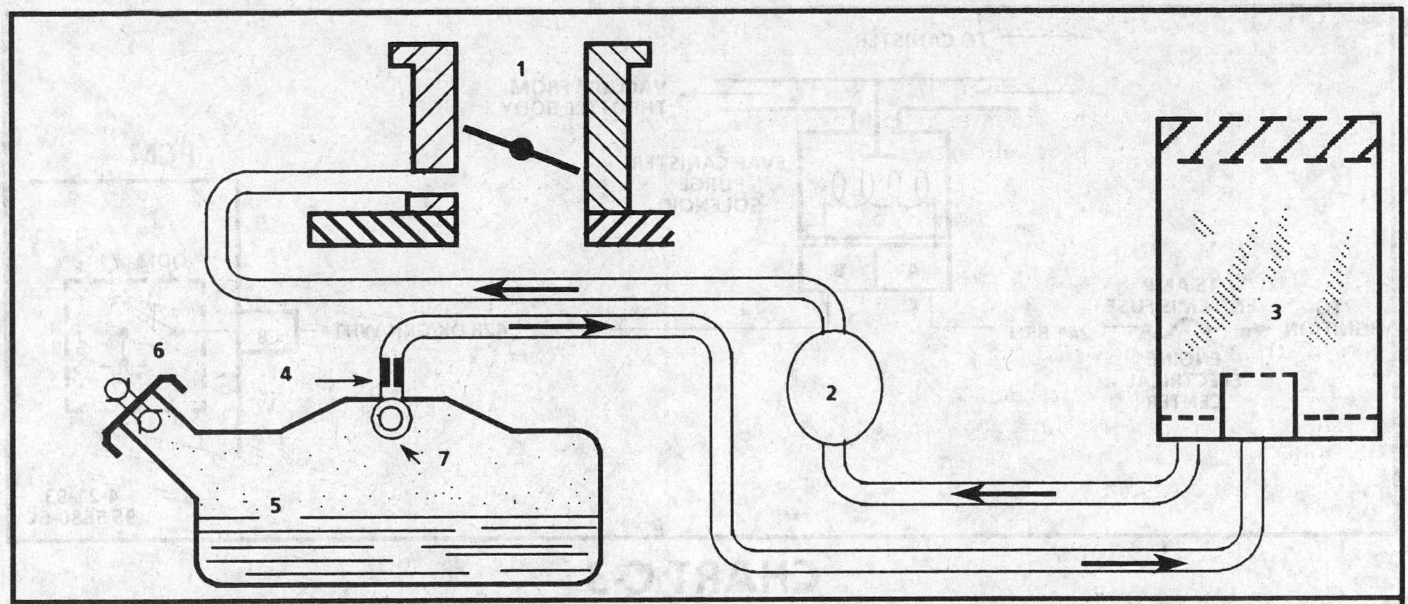
1
2
3
4
5
6
7

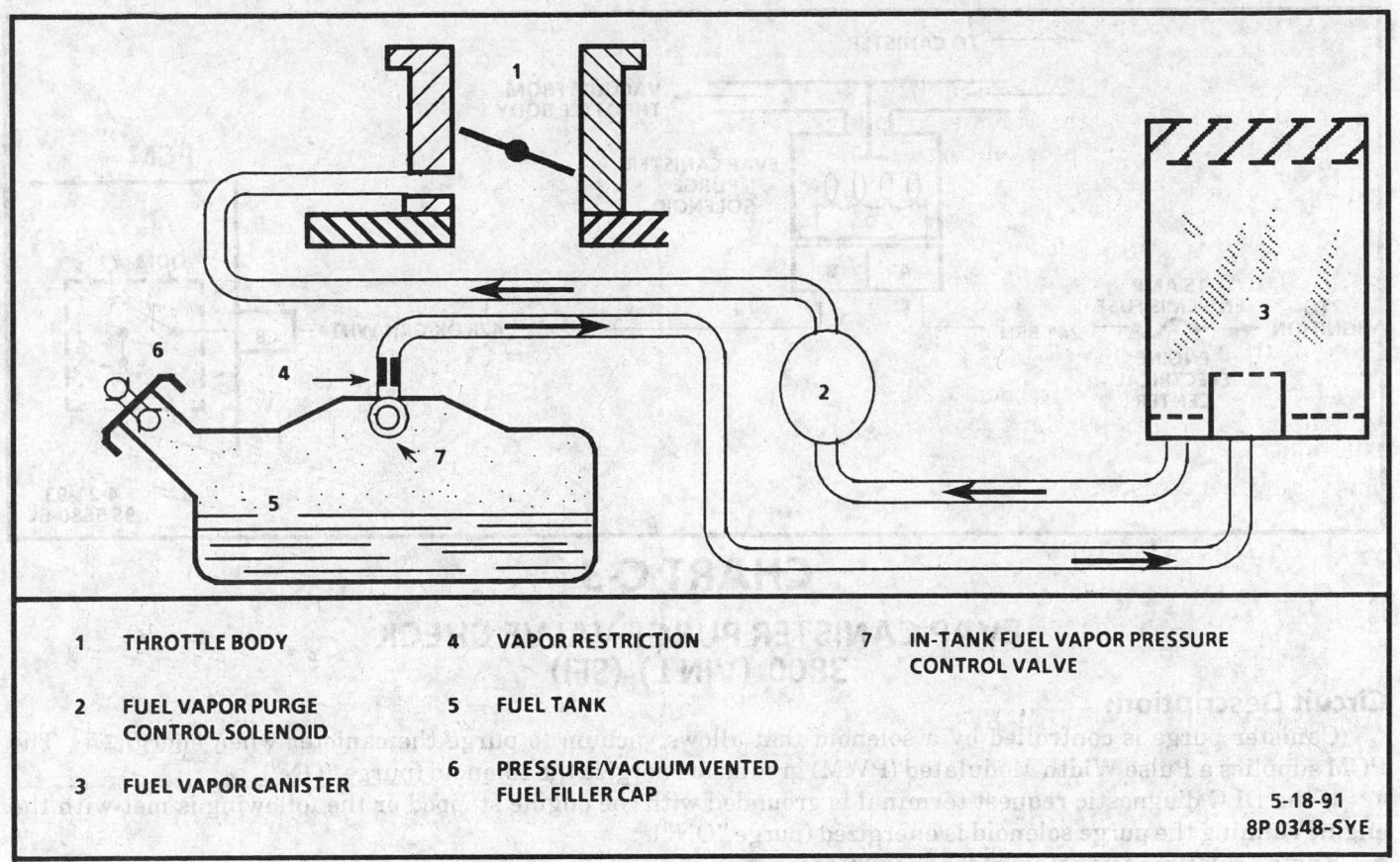

1 THROTTLE BODY
2 FUEL VAPOR PURGE CONTROL SOLENOID
3 FUEL VAPOR CANISTER
4 VAPOR RESTRICTION
5 FUEL TANK
6 PRESSURE/VACUUM VENTED FUEL FILLER CAP
7 IN-TANK FUEL VAPOR PRESSURE CONTROL VALVE

5-18-91
8P 0348-SYE

Figure C3-3 - Evaporative Emissions Control (EVAP) System Schematic

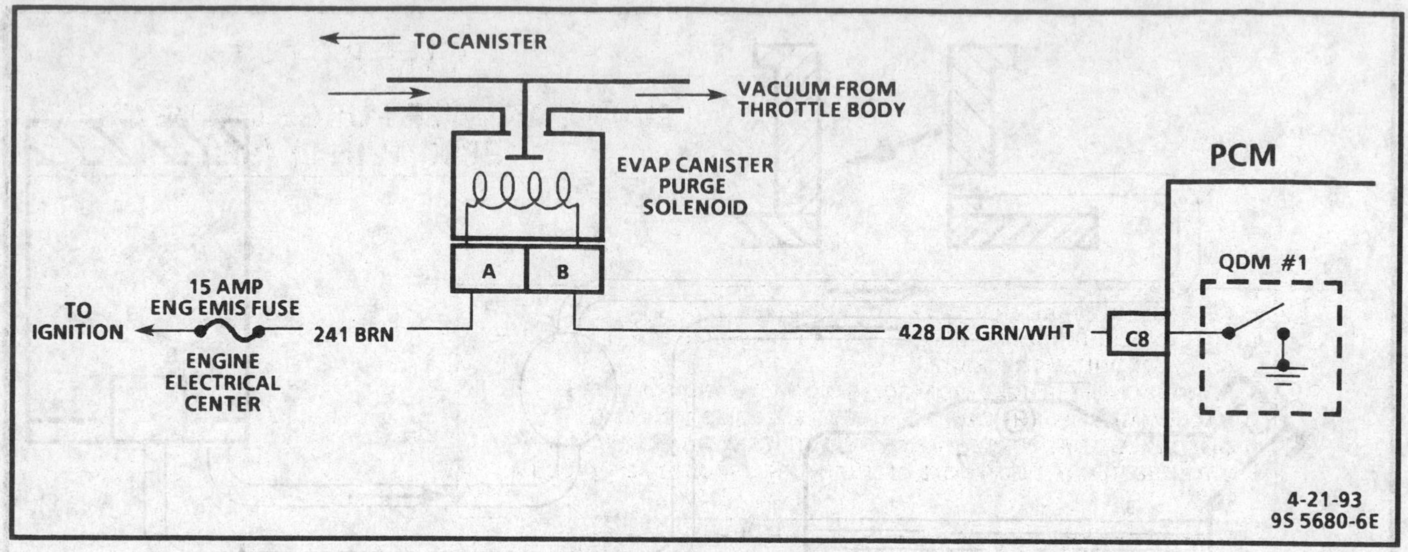
TO CANISTER
VACUUM FROM
THROTTLE BODY
EVAP CANISTER
PURGE
SOLENOID
PCM
A
B
QDM #1
15 AMP
ENG EMIS FUSE
TO
IGNITION
241 BRN
428 DK GRN/WHT
C8
ENGINE
ELECTRICAL
CENTER
4-21-93
9S 5680-6E

CHART C-3

EVAP CANISTER PURGE VALVE CHECK
3800 (VIN L) (SFI)

Circuit Description:

Canister purge is controlled by a solenoid that allows vacuum to purge the canister when energized. The PCM supplies a Pulse Width Modulated (PWM) ground to energize the solenoid (purge "ON").

If the DLC diagnostic request terminal is grounded with the engine stopped or the following is met with the engine running the purge solenoid is energized (purge "ON").

- Engine run time after start more than 20 seconds on a warm engine and 2.5 minutes on a cold engine.
- Engine coolant temperature above 60°C (158°F).
- Intake air temperature above 9.5°C (50°F).

Chart Test Description:

Number(s) below refer to circled number(s) on the diagnostic chart.

1. Checks to see if the EVAP canister purge solenoid is opened or closed. The solenoid is de-energized in this step, so it should be closed.
2. The Tech 1 is used to cycle the solenoid "ON" and "OFF" and check the operation of the solenoid.

CHART C-3

EVAP CANISTER PURGE VALVE CHECK 3800 (VIN L) (SFI)

(1)
- SET PARKING BRAKE AND BLOCK DRIVE WHEELS.
- CHECK VACUUM SOURCE. IF NO VACUUM, REPAIR CAUSE OF NO VACUUM. IF OK, CONTINUE WITH CHART.
- REMOVE CANISTER HOSE FROM SOLENOID VALVE AND CONNECT A VACUUM GAGE TO THE CANISTER SIDE OF THE SOLENOID VALVE.
- DISCONNECT EVAP PURGE SOLENOID ELECTRICAL CONNECTOR.
- WITH THE ENGINE IDLING NOTE VACUUM GAGE. SHOULD BE 0 VACUUM. IS IT?

NO: REPLACE SOLENOID.

YES:

(2)
- INSTALL TECH 1.
- RECONNECT SOLENOID ELECTRICAL CONNECTOR.
- UNDER MISC. TEST SELECT EVAP SOLENOID CONTROL.
- CYCLE THE PURGE SOLENOID "ON" AND "OFF." DOES THE VACUUM INCREASE AS THE SOLENOID IS CYCLED "ON" AND DECREASE WHEN IT IS CYCLED "OFF?"

YES: CHECK CANISTER AND HOSES FOR DAMAGE. IF OK, NO PROBLEM FOUND.

NO:

- DISCONNECT EVAP PURGE SOLENOID ELECTRICAL CONNECTOR.
- KEY "ON" ENGINE "OFF."
- INSTALL A TEST LIGHT BETWEEN HARNESS CONNECTOR TERMINAL "A" AND GROUND. TEST LIGHT SHOULD BE "ON." IS IT?

NO: REPAIR OPEN IN SOLENOID IGNITION FEED CIRCUIT.

YES:

- CONNECT A TEST LIGHT BETWEEN HARNESS CONNECTOR TERMINALS "A" AND "B". IS THE TEST LIGHT "ON?"

NO: CHECK FOR OPEN CKT 428. IF OK, POOR PCM CONNECTIONS, FAULTY SOLENOID, OR FAULTY PCM.

YES: CHECK CKT 428 FOR A SHORT TO GROUND. IF OK, REPLACE PCM.

"*AFTER REPAIRS,*" CONFIRM "CLOSED LOOP" OPERATION AND NO MIL (SERVICE ENGINE SOON).

11-2-92
MS 10623

BLANK

SECTION C4
ELECTRONIC IGNITION SYSTEM

CONTENTS

GENERAL DESCRIPTION

The electronic ignition system controls fuel combustion by providing a spark to ignite the compressed air/fuel mixture at the correct time. To provide optimum engine performance, fuel economy, and control of exhaust emissions, the PCM controls spark advance of the ignition system. Electronic ignition has several advantages over a mechanical distributor system.

- No moving parts.
- Less maintenance.
- Remote mounting capability.
- No mechanical load on the engine.
- More coil cool down time between firing events.
- Elimination of mechanical timing adjustments.
- Increased available ignition coil saturation time.

OPERATION

The electronic ignition system does not use the conventional distributor and coil. The ignition system consists of three ignition coils, an ignition control module, a dual Hall-effect crankshaft position sensor, an engine crankshaft balancer with interrupter rings attached to the rear, related connecting wires, and the Ignition Control (IC) and fuel metering portion of the PCM.

Conventional ignition coils have one end of the secondary winding connected to the engine ground. In this ignition system, neither end of the secondary winding is grounded. Instead, each end of a coil's secondary winding is attached to a spark plug. Each cylinder is paired with the cylinder that is opposite it (1-4, 2-5, 3-6).

These two plugs are on "companion" cylinders, i.e., on top dead center at the same time. When the coil discharges, both plugs fire at the same time to complete the series circuit. The cylinder on compression is said to be the "event" cylinder and the one on exhaust is the "waste" cylinder.

The cylinder on the exhaust stroke requires very little of the available energy to fire the spark plug. The remaining energy will be used as required by the cylinder on the compression stroke. The same process is repeated when the cylinders reverse roles. This method of ignition is called a "waste spark" ignition system.

Since the polarity of the ignition coil primary and secondary windings is fixed, one spark plug always fires with a forward current flow and its "companion" plug fires with a reverse current flow. This is different from a conventional ignition system that fires all the plugs with the same direction of current flow. Since it requires approximately 30% more voltage to fire a spark plug backwards, the ignition coil design is improved, with saturation time and primary current flow increased. This redesign of the system allows higher secondary voltage to be available from the ignition coils - greater than 40 kilovolts (*40,000 volts*) at any engine RPM. The voltage required by each spark plug is determined by the polarity and the cylinder pressure. The cylinder on compression requires more voltage to fire the spark plug than the one on exhaust.

It is possible for one spark plug to fire even though a plug wire from the same coil may be disconnected from its "companion" plug. The disconnected plug wire acts as one plate of a capacitor, with the engine being the other plate. These two "capacitor plates" are charged as a spark jumps across the gap of the connected spark plug. The "plates" are then discharged as the secondary energy is dissipated in an oscillating current across the gap of the still-connected spark plug. Secondary voltage requirements are very high with an "open" spark plug or wire. The ignition coil has enough reserve energy to fire the still-connected plug at idle, but possibly not under high engine load. A more noticeable misfire may be evident under load; both spark plugs may then be misfiring.

SYSTEM COMPONENTS

Crankshaft Position Sensor - Harmonic Balancer Interrupter Rings

The dual crankshaft position sensor, secured in an aluminum mounting bracket and bolted to the front left side of the engine timing chain cover, is partially behind the crankshaft balancer (Figure C4-1).

A 4-wire harness connector plugs into the sensor, connecting it to the ignition control module.

The dual crankshaft position sensor contains two Hall-effect switches with one shared magnet mounted between them. The magnet and each Hall-effect switch are separated by an air gap. A Hall-effect switch reacts like a solid-state switch, grounding a low-current signal voltage when a magnetic field is present. When the magnetic field is shielded from the switch by a piece of steel placed in the air gap between the magnet and the switch, the signal voltage is not grounded. If the piece of steel (called an interrupter) is repeatedly moved in and out of the air gap, the signal voltage will appear to go "ON-OFF-ON-OFF-ON-OFF." Compared to a conventional mechanical distributor, this "ON-OFF" signal is similar to the signal that a set of breaker points in the distributor would generate as the distributor shaft turned and the points opened and closed.

In the case of the electronic ignition system, the piece of steel is two concentric interrupter rings mounted to the rear of the crankshaft balancer (Figure C4-2). Each interrupter ring has blades and windows that, with crankshaft rotation, either block the magnetic field or allow it to reach one of the Hall-effect switches. The outer Hall-effect switch is called the 18X crankshaft position sensor, because the outer interrupter ring has 18 evenly-spaced same-width blades and windows. The 18X crankshaft position sensor produces 18 "ON-OFF" pulses per crankshaft revolution. The Hall-effect switch closest to the crankshaft, the 3X crankshaft position sensor, is so called because the inside interrupter ring has 3 unevenly-spaced, different-width blades and windows. The 3X crankshaft position sensor produces 3 different length "ON-OFF" pulses per crankshaft revolution (Figure C4-3).

When a 3X interrupter ring "window" is between the magnet and inner switch, the magnetic field will cause the 3X Hall-effect switch to ground the 3X signal voltage supplied from the ignition control module. The 18X interrupter ring and Hall-effect switch react similarly. The ignition control module interprets the 18X and 3X "ON-OFF" signals as an indication of crankshaft position, and must have both signals to "fire" the correct ignition coil.

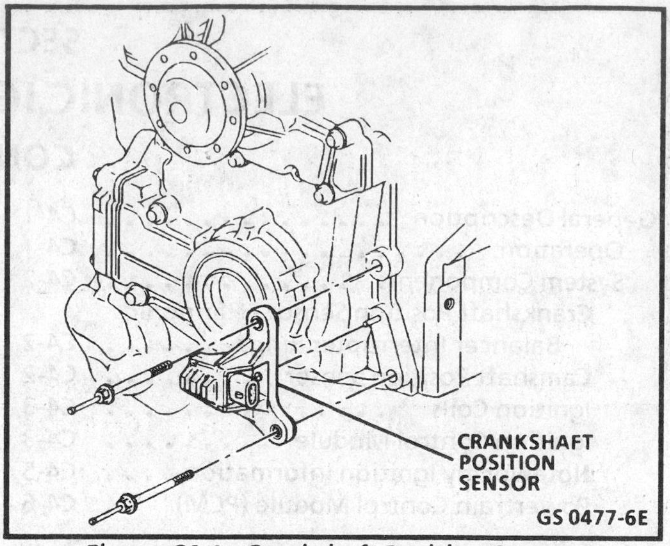
CRANKSHAFT
POSITION
SENSOR
GS 0477-6E

Figure C4-1 - Crankshaft Position Sensor

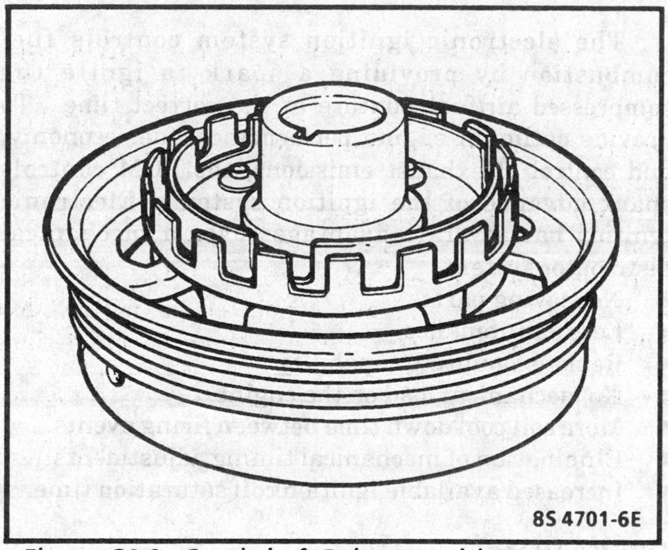
8S 4701-6E

Figure C4-2 - Crankshaft Balancer with Interrupter Rings

The ignition control module determines crankshaft position for correct ignition coil sequencing by counting how many 18X signal transitions occur, i.e.; "ON-OFF" <u>or</u> "OFF-ON," during a 3X pulse (Figure C4-3).

Camshaft Position Sensor

The camshaft position sensor (Figure C4-4) is located on the timing cover behind the water pump near the camshaft sprocket.

As the camshaft sprocket turns, a magnet in it activates the Hall-effect switch in the camshaft position sensor. When the Hall-effect switch is activated, it grounds the signal line to the PCM, pulling the cam signal line's applied voltage low. This is interpreted as a cam signal.

The cam signal is created as piston #1 is approximately 25° after top dead center on the power stroke.

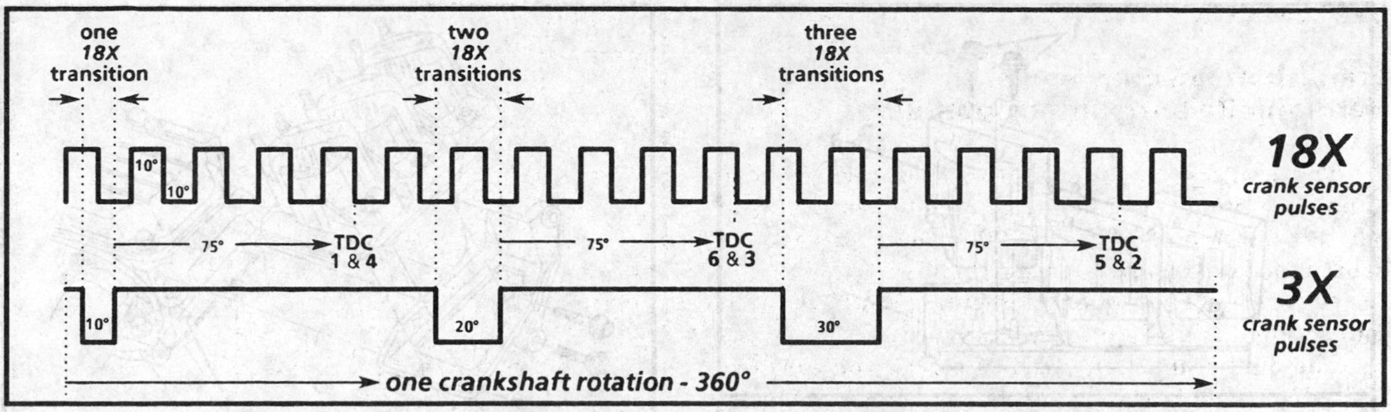
one
18X
transition
10°
10°
two
18X
transitions
three
18X
transitions
18X
crank sensor
pulses
75°
TDC
1 & 4
75°
TDC
6 & 3
75°
TDC
5 & 2
3X
crank sensor
pulses
10°
20°
30°
one crankshaft rotation - 360°

Figure C4-3 - *18X* and *3X* Crank Sensor Pulses for One Crankshaft Revolution

When the cam signal is not received by the PCM DTC P0342 will be set.

Ignition Coils

Three twin-tower ignition coils are individually mounted to the ignition control module (Figure C4-6). Each coil provides spark for two plugs simultaneously (waste spark distribution). Each coil is serviced separately.

Two terminals connect each coil pack to the module. Each coil is provided a fused ignition feed from the 15 amp ELEK IGN fuse. The other terminal at each coil is individually connected to the module, which will energize one coil at a time by completing and interrupting the primary circuit ground path to each coil at the proper time.

Ignition Control Module

The ignition control module performs several functions:

- It powers the dual crankshaft position sensor internal circuits.
- It supplies the voltage signals that each respective Hall-effect switch pulses to ground to generate the 3X and 18X crankshaft position sensor pulses.

1 CRANKSHAFT POSITION SENSOR
2 CAMSHAFT POSITION SENSOR
3 BLOCK
2
FRT
3
1
MS 10227

Figure C4-4 - Camshaft and Crankshaft Position Sensors

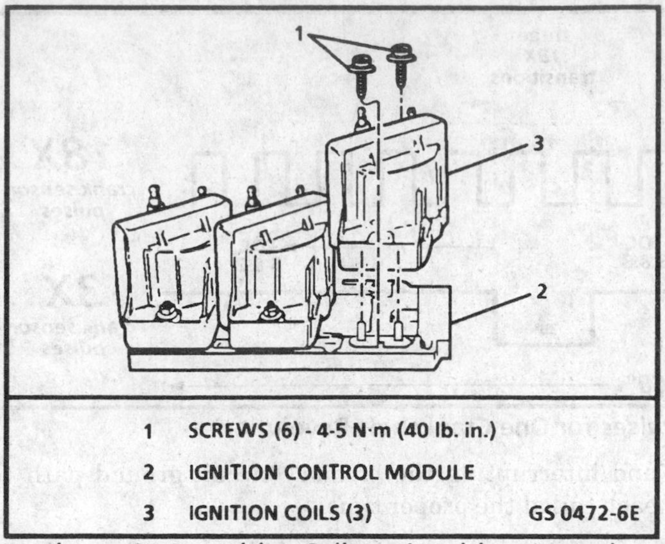
1
3
2
1 SCREWS (6) - 4-5 N·m (40 lb. in.)
2 IGNITION CONTROL MODULE
3 IGNITION COILS (3)
GS 0472-6E

Figure C4-5 - Ignition Coils and Ignition Control Module

- It determines the correct ignition coil firing sequence, based on how many 18X transitions occur during a 3X pulse (Figure C4-6). This coil sequencing occurs at startup. After the engine is running, the module remembers the sequence, and continues triggering the ignition coils in proper sequence.
- It determines whether or not the crankshaft is rotating in the proper direction, and cuts off fuel delivery and spark to prevent backfiring if reverse rotation is detected.
- It sends a "crankshaft reference" (fuel control) signal to the PCM. The PCM determines engine RPM from this signal. It is also used by the PCM to determine crankshaft position for Ignition Control (IC) spark advance calculations. *(The falling edge of each fuel control signal pulse occurs 70° before TDC of any cylinder.)*

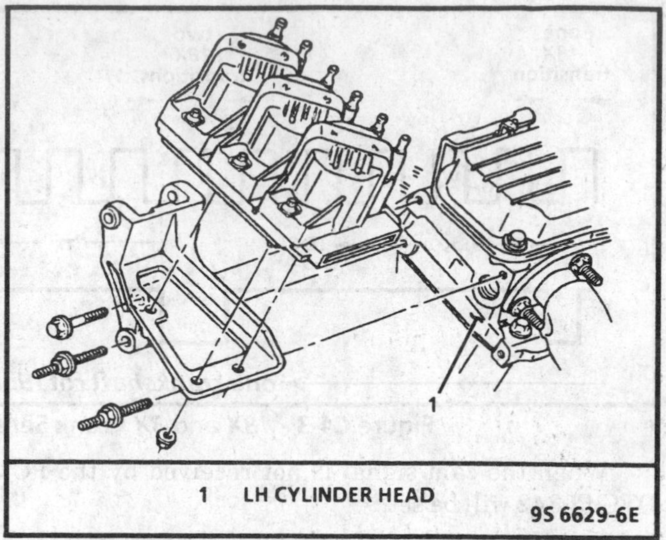
1
1 LH CYLINDER HEAD
9S 6629-6E

Figure C4-7 - Ignition Control Module and Coil Assembly

The fuel control signal sent to the PCM by the ignition module is an "ON-OFF" pulse occurring 3 times per crankshaft revolution (Figure C4-6). *This is neither the 3X nor the 18X crank sensor pulse, but both of these are required before the ignition control module will generate the fuel control signal.*

The ignition control module generates the fuel control signal by an internal "divide-by-6" circuit. This divider circuit divides the 18X crankshift positon sensor pulses by 6. The divider circuit is enabled, *or ready to begin dividing*, only after it receives a 3X crankshaft position sensor sync pulse. After beginning, the divider circuit does not need the 3X sync pulses to continue operating. If either the 18X crank or 3X sync pulses are missing at startup, the divider will not generate a fuel control signal pulses *(sent to the PCM)*, and no fuel injector pulses will occur.

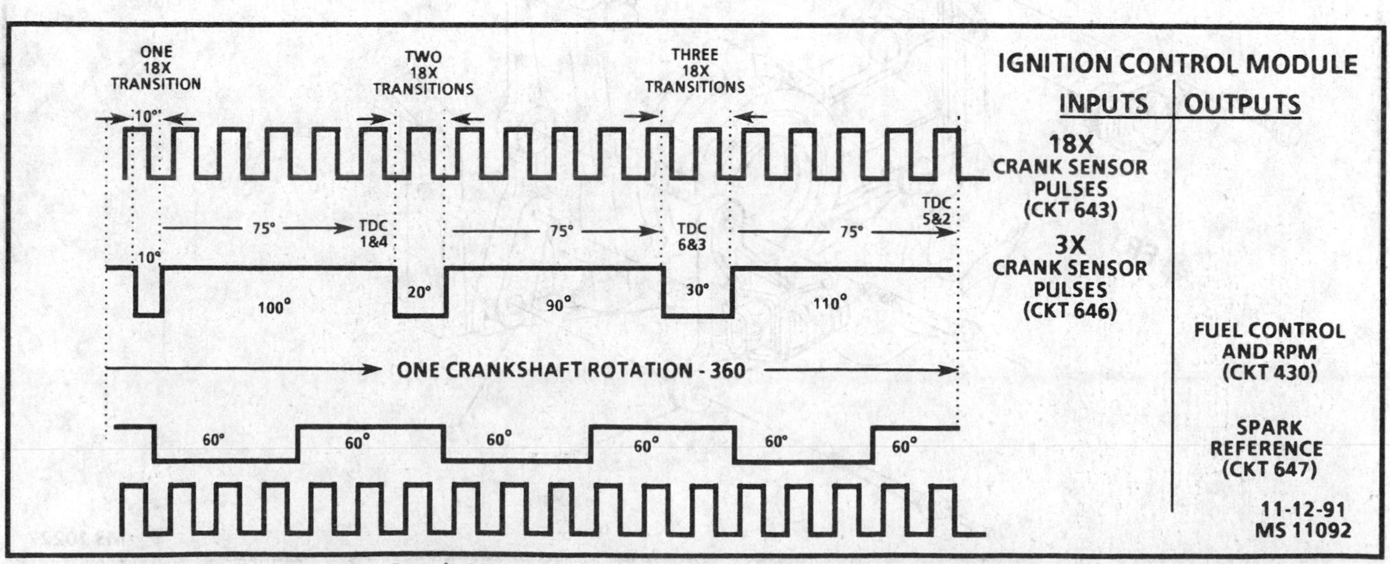
ONE 18X TRANSITION
TWO 18X TRANSITIONS
THREE 18X TRANSITIONS
10°
75°
TDC 1&4
75°
TDC 6&3
75°
TDC 5&2
10°
100°
20°
90°
30°
110°
ONE CRANKSHAFT ROTATION - 360
60°
60°
60°
60°
60°
60°
IGNITION CONTROL MODULE
INPUTS
OUTPUTS
18X CRANK SENSOR PULSES (CKT 643)
3X CRANK SENSOR PULSES (CKT 646)
FUEL CONTROL AND RPM (CKT 430)
SPARK REFERENCE (CKT 647)
11-12-91
MS 11092

Figure C4-6 - *18X* & *3X* Crank Sensor Pulses - and - Crankshaft Reference Signal Sent to the PCM

- Anytime the PCM does not apply 5 volts to the ignition control module "bypass" circuit, the ignition module controls ignition by triggering each of the three coils in the proper sequence at a pre-determined dwell, with spark advance fixed at 10° BTDC. This is called ***module mode*** ignition. The ignition control module provides proper ignition coil sequencing during both the module and IC modes.
- PCM applies 5 volts to the ignition module "bypass" circuit, signaling the module to allow the PCM to control the dwell and spark timing.

This is ***IC mode*** ignition. During IC mode, the PCM compensates for all driving conditions. Again, the ignition control module is responsible for proper ignition coil sequencing during both the module *and* IC modes.

Noteworthy Ignition Information

There are important considerations to point out when servicing the ignition system. This "*Noteworthy Information*" will list some of these, to help the technician in servicing the ignition system.

A. The ignition coils secondary voltage output capabilities are very high - more than 40,000 volts. **Avoid body contact with ignition high voltage secondary components when the engine is running, or personal injury may result!**

B. The dual Hall-effect 18X - 3X crankshaft position sensor is the most critical part of the ignition system. If the sensor is damaged so that the 18X or 3X crankshaft position sensor pulses are not generated, the engine will not start!

C. There are 4 circuit wires connecting the dual crankshaft position sensor to the ignition control module. If there is a problem with any of the four, the engine will not start *(no spark and no injector pulses)*. The circuits are:
   - +10 to 12 volt operating power supply for the Hall-effect switches from the ignition control module.
   - 18X crank pulse signal to the ignition control module.
   - 3X sync pulse signal to the ignition control module.
   - Ground circuit for both Hall-effect switches.

   Equally important is the crankshaft reference (fuel control) signal generated by the ignition control module. If the PCM does not receive this signal, it will not pulse the injectors.

D. If the 3X crankshaft position sensor sync pulses stop while the engine is running, the engine will keep running. However, it will not restart after being shut "OFF."

E. If the 18X crankshaft position sensor crank pulses stop while the engine is running, the engine will stop running and will not restart.

F. ***Crankshaft position sensor clearance is very important!*** The sensor must not contact the rotating interrupter rings at any time, or sensor damage will result. If the balancer interrupter rings are bent, the interrupter ring blades will act as a buzz saw, destroying the sensor.

G. *Ignition timing is not adjustable*. There are no timing marks on the crankshaft balancer or timing chain cover.

H. If crankshaft position sensor replacement is necessary, the crankshaft balancer must be removed first. The balancer is a press fit onto the crankshaft; removing the serpentine accessory drive belt and balancer attaching bolt will allow its removal with special tool J 38197. When reinstalled, proper torquing of the balancer attachment bolt is critical to ensure the balancer stays attached to the crankshaft.

I. If a crankshaft position sensor assembly is replaced, check the crankshaft balancer interrupter rings for any blades being bent. **If this is not checked closely and a bent blade exists, the new crankshaft position sensor can be destroyed by the bent blade with only one crankshaft revolution!**

J. Neither side of the the ignition coil primary or secondary windings is connected to engine ground. Although the ignition coil packs are secured to the ignition module, it is not an electrical connection to ground.

K. Be careful not to damage the high tension leads or boots *(dust caps)* when servicing the ignition system. Rotate each boot to dislodge it from the plug or coil tower before pulling it from either a spark plug or the ignition coil. **Never pierce a high tension lead or boot for any testing purposes!** Future problems are guaranteed if pinpoints or test lights are pushed through the insulation for testing.

L. The ignition control module is grounded to the engine block through 3 mounting studs used to secure the module to its mounting bracket. If servicing is required, ensure that good electrical contact is made between the module and its mounting bracket, including proper hardware and torque.

M. A conventional tachometer used to check RPM on a primary ignition "tach lead" will not work on this ignition system. To check RPM, use either of these:
   - A tachometer designed with an inductive pickup, used on the secondary side of an ignition system.
     These tachs are identified by a "clamp" that goes around a spark plug wire. Set the tach to "2-cycle" operation. The reason for 2-cycle? Spark plugs on this engine fire every time the piston is at the top of its stroke. If a "2-cycle" selection is not available, divide the indicated 4- cycle reading by 2.
   - Tech 1 diagnostic tool.

Powertrain Control Module (PCM)

The PCM is responsible for maintaining proper spark and fuel injection timing for all driving conditions.

To provide optimum driveability and emissions, the PCM monitors input signals from the following components in calculating Ignition Control (IC) spark timing:

- Ignition control module.
- Engine Coolant Temperature (ECT) sensor.
- Intake Air Temperature (IAT) sensor.
- Mass Air Flow (MAF) sensor.
- PRNDL input from transaxle range switch.
- Throttle Position (TP) sensor.
- Vehicle Speed Sensor (VSS).

MODES OF OPERATION

The ignition system uses the same four ignition module-*to*-PCM circuits as did previous Delco engine management systems using distributor-type ignition. Ignition Control (IC) spark timing is the PCM's method of controlling spark advance and ignition dwell when the ignition system is operating in the IC mode.

There are two "modes" of ignition system operation:

- **Module mode**
- **IC mode**

In the module mode, the ignition system operates independently of the PCM, with module mode spark advance always at 10° BTDC. The PCM has no control of the ignition system when in this mode. In fact, the PCM could be disconnected from the vehicle and the ignition system would still fire the spark plugs, as long as the other ignition system components were functioning. *(This would provide spark but no fuel injector pulses, and a no-start.)* The PCM switches to IC mode (PCM controlled spark advance) as soon as the engine begins cranking.

Once the change is made to IC mode, it will stay in effect until either: ① the engine is turned "OFF," ② the engine quits running, or ③ a PCM/IC fault is detected. If a PCM/IC fault is detected while the engine is running, the ignition system will switch to the module mode. The engine may quit running, but will restart and stay in the module mode with a noticeable driveability complaint.

In the IC mode, the ignition spark timing and ignition dwell time is fully controlled by the PCM. IC spark advance and ignition dwell is calculated by the PCM using the following inputs:

- Engine speed .... *(spark reference or fuel control reference)*
- Crankshaft position .... *(spark reference or fuel control reference)*
- Engine Coolant Temp. .... ECT sensor
- Throttle Position ...... TP sensor
- Knock Signal .... Knock sensor
- Park/Neutral Position ... PRNDL input
- Vehicle Speed .... VSS
- PCM and ignition system supply voltage.

The following describes the PCM to ignition control module circuits.

Fuel control reference PCM input (CKT 430) - From the ignition control module, the PCM uses this signal to calculate engine RPM and crankshaft position. The PCM compares pulses on this circuit to any that are on ground CKT 453, ignoring any pulses that appear on both. The PCM also uses the pulses on this circuit to initiate injector pulses. If the PCM receives no pulses on this circuit, no fuel injection pulses will occur and the engine will not run.

Spark reference (CKT 647) - The spark reference signal is used to accurately control spark timing at low RPM and allow IC operation during crank. Below 1200 RPM, the PCM is monitoring CKT 647 and using it as the reference for ignition timing advance. When engine speed exceeds 1200 RPM, the PCM begins using CKT 430, fuel control reference to control spark timing. If the spark control reference circuit is not received by the PCM while the engine is running, a DTC P0321 will be set and fuel control reference will be used to control spark advance under 1200 RPM, and module mode will be in effect at under 400 RPM. The engine will continue to run and start normally.

Reference low (CKT 453) - This is a ground circuit for the digital RPM counter inside the PCM, but the wire is connected to engine ground _only_ through the ignition module. Although this circuit is electrically connected to the PCM, *it is not connected to ground at the PCM*. The PCM compares voltage pulses on the reference input CKT 430 to those on this circuit, ignoring pulses that appear on both. If the circuit is open, or connected to ground at the PCM, it may cause poor engine performance and possibly a MIL (Service Engine Soon) with no DTC.

Bypass signal (CKT 424) - The PCM either allows the ignition control module to keep the spark advance at "module mode" 10° BTDC, or the PCM signals the ignition module that the PCM is going to control the spark advance *(IC mode)*. The ignition control module determines correct operating mode based on the level of voltage that the PCM sends to the ignition control module on the bypass circuit. The PCM provides 5 volts to the ignition control module if the PCM is going to control spark timing (*IC mode*). If the PCM does not turn "ON" the 5 volts, or if the ignition control module doesn't receive it, the module will keep control of spark timing (*module mode*). An open or grounded bypass control CKT 424 will set DTC P1361 and the ignition system will stay at module mode advance.

Ignition Control (IC) output (CKT 423) - The IC output circuitry of the PCM sends out timing pulses to the ignition control module on this circuit. When in the "module mode," the ignition control module grounds these pulses. When in the IC mode, these pulses are the ignition timing pulses used by the ignition control module to energize one of the ignition coils. *Proper sequencing of the 3 ignition coils, i.e.; which coil to "fire," is always the job of the ignition control module.* If CKT 423 is grounded when the engine is started, DTC P1361 will set and the ignition system will stay in the module mode. If CKT 423 becomes open or grounded during IC mode operation, DTC P1350 or P1361 may set and the engine will quit running but will restart following an ignition cycle. Upon restart, DTC P1361 will be set, and the ignition system will operate in "module mode."

Knock Sensor (KS) (CKT 496) - The KS system is comprised of a knock sensor and the PCM. The PCM monitors the KS signal (CKT 496) to determine when engine detonation occurs. When the knock sensor detects detonation, the PCM retards the timing (IC) to reduce detonation. Retarded timing can also be a result of excessive valve lifter, pushrod or other mechanical engine or transmission noise.

Cam signal (CKT 630) - The PCM uses this signal to determine the position of the #1 piston during its power stroke. This signal is used by the PCM to calculate true Sequential Fuel Injection (SFI) mode of operation. A loss of this signal will set DTC P0342. If the cam signal is lost while the engine is running the fuel injection system will shift to a calculated sequential fuel injection mode based on the last cam pulse, and the engine will continue to run. The engine can be re-started and will run in the calculated sequential mode as long as the fault is present with a 1 in 6 chance of being correct.

How DTCs P1350/P1361 are Determined

The IC output circuitry in the PCM issues IC output pulses _anytime_ crankshaft reference signal input pulses are being received. When the ignition system is operating in the module mode *(no voltage on the bypass control circuit)*, the ignition control module grounds the IC pulses coming from the PCM. The ignition module will remove the ground path for the IC pulses only after switching to the IC mode. *(The PCM commands the switching between module and IC modes, via the bypass control circuit of the ignition control module.)* The PCM monitors its own IC output, and expects to see no pulses on the IC circuit when it has not yet supplied the 5 volts on the bypass control circuit. When the second fuel control reference pulse at the start of crank is seen by the PCM, it applies 5 volts to the bypass control circuit and the IC pulses should no longer be grounded by the ignition module. The PCM constantly monitors its IC output, and should "see" the IC pulses only when operating in the IC mode.

If IC output CKT 423 is open, the PCM will detect IC output pulses while attempting to start the engine *(in the module mode)* due to the ignition control module not being able to ground the IC pulses. Three things will occur: ① DTC P1350 or P1361 will set, ② the PCM will not apply 5 volts to the bypass circuit, and ③ the engine will start and run in the module mode.

If IC output CKT 423 is grounded, the PCM would not detect a problem until the change to IC mode is commanded by the PCM. When the PCM applies 5 volts to the bypass control circuit, the ignition control module will switch to the IC mode. With IC CKT 423 grounded, there would be no IC pulses for the ignition control module to trigger the ignition coils, and the engine may falter. The PCM will quickly revert back to the module mode *(turn "OFF" the 5 volts on the bypass control)*, DTC P1361 will set, and the ignition system will operate in the module mode until the fault is corrected and the engine is stopped and restarted.

If bypass control CKT 424 is open -or- grounded, the ignition control module will not switch to the IC mode. In this case, the IC pulses will stay grounded in the ignition control module, and DTC P1361 will be set. The engine will start and run in the module mode.

Results of Incorrect Operation

An open or ground in the IC or bypass circuit will set DTC P1350 or P1361. If a fault occurs in the IC output circuit when the engine is running, the engine may falter or quit running but will restart and run in the module mode once the ignition has been cycled. A fault in either circuit will force the ignition system to operate on module mode timing (10° BTDC), which will result in reduced performance and fuel economy.

The PCM uses information from the engine coolant temperature sensor in addition to RPM to calculate the main spark advance values as follows:

High RPM	=	more advance
Cold engine	=	more advance
Low RPM	=	less advance
Hot engine	=	less advance

Therefore, detonation could be caused by high resistance in the engine coolant temperature sensor circuit. Poor performance could be caused by low resistance in the engine coolant temperature sensor circuit.

DIAGNOSIS

If the Engine Cranks But Will Not Run or immediately stalls, CHART A-3 must be used to determine if the failure is in the ignition system or the fuel system.

If DTC P0300, P0321, P0341, P0342 or P1350 or P1361 is set, the appropriate diagnostic trouble code chart must be used for diagnosis.

If a misfire is being experienced, CHART C-4 will provide a systematic diagnostic procedure.

ON-VEHICLE SERVICE

IGNITION COIL

↔ Remove or Disconnect

1. Spark plug wires.
2. 2 screws securing coil to ignition control module.
3. Coil assembly.

→← Install or Connect

1. Coil assembly.
2. 2 screws, torque to 4-5 N·m (40 lb. in.).
3. Spark plug wires.

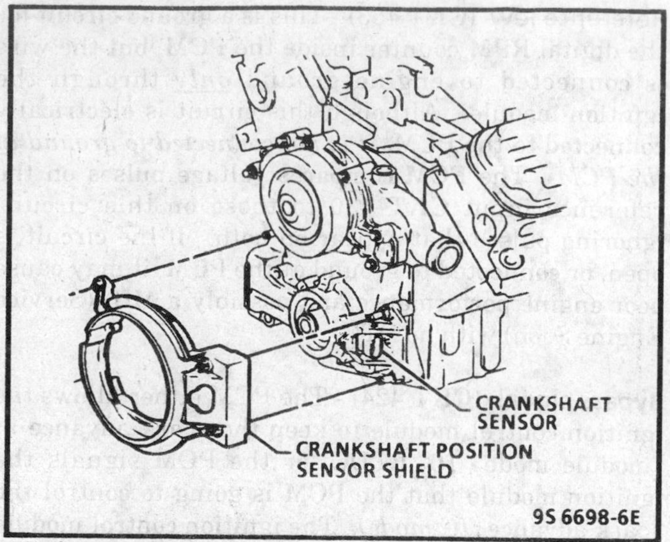
CRANKSHAFT SENSOR
CRANKSHAFT POSITION SENSOR SHIELD
9S 6698-6E

Figure C4-8 - Crankshaft Position Sensor Shield

IGNITION CONTROL MODULE

↔ Remove or Disconnect

1. 14-way connector at ignition control module.
2. Spark plug wires from coil assemblies.
3. 6 screws securing coil assemblies to ignition control module.
4. Disconnect coils from ignition control module.
5. Nuts and washers (3) securing ignition control module assembly to bracket.
6. Ignition control module.

→← Install or Connect

1. Coils to ignition control module.
2. 6 screws, torque to 4-5 N·m (40 lb. in.).
3. Nuts and washers securing assembly to bracket torque to 8 N·m (70 lb. in.).
4. Plug wires.
5. 14-way connector to module.

CRANKSHAFT POSITION SENSOR

↔ Remove or Disconnect

1. Negative battery cable.
2. Serpentine belts from crankshaft pulley.
3. Raise vehicle on hoist.
4. Right front tire and wheel assembly.
5. Right inner fender access cover.
6. Using 28 mm socket, remove crankshaft harmonic balancer retaining bolt.
7. Crankshaft harmonic balancer using special tool (J 38197).
8. Crankshaft position sensor shield (Figure C4-8) (Do Not use pry bar).
9. Sensor electrical connector.
10. Sensor from block face.

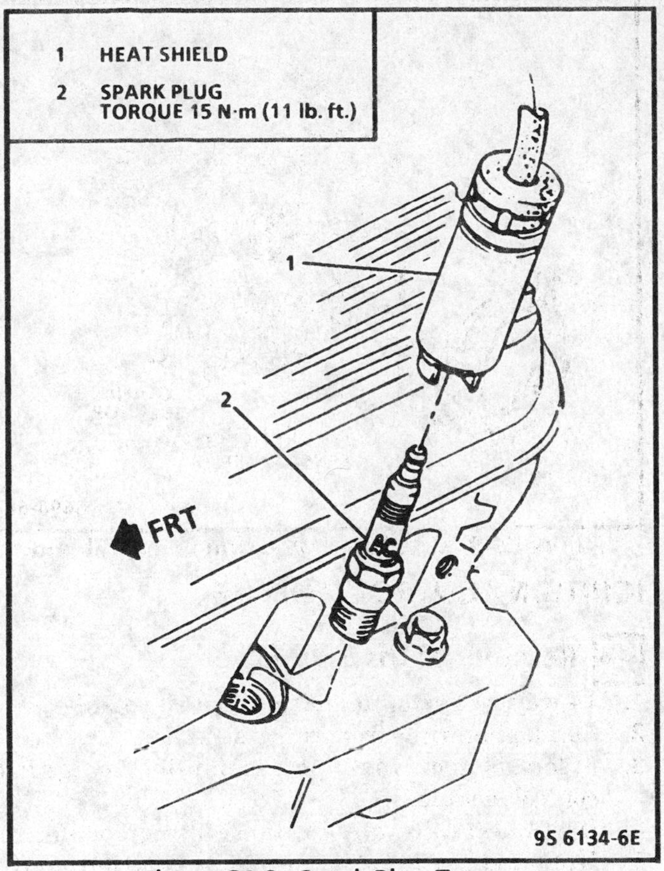
1 HEAT SHIELD
2 SPARK PLUG
TORQUE 15 N·m (11 lb. ft.)
FRT
9S 6134-6E

Figure C4-9 - Spark Plug Torque

Install or Connect

1. Crankshaft position sensor to block.
2. Bolts to hold sensor to block face, torque to 20-40 N·m (14-28 lb. ft.).
3. Crankshaft position sensor shield.
4. Electrical connector.
5. Balancer on crankshaft.
6. Apply thread sealer GM #1052080 or equivalent to threads of crankshaft balancer bolt. Torque bolt to 150 N·m + 76° (110 lb. ft. + 76°).
7. Inner fender shield.
8. Tire and wheel assembly. Torque lug nuts to 140 N·m (104 lb. ft.).
9. Lower vehicle.
10. Serpentine belt.
11. Negative battery cable.

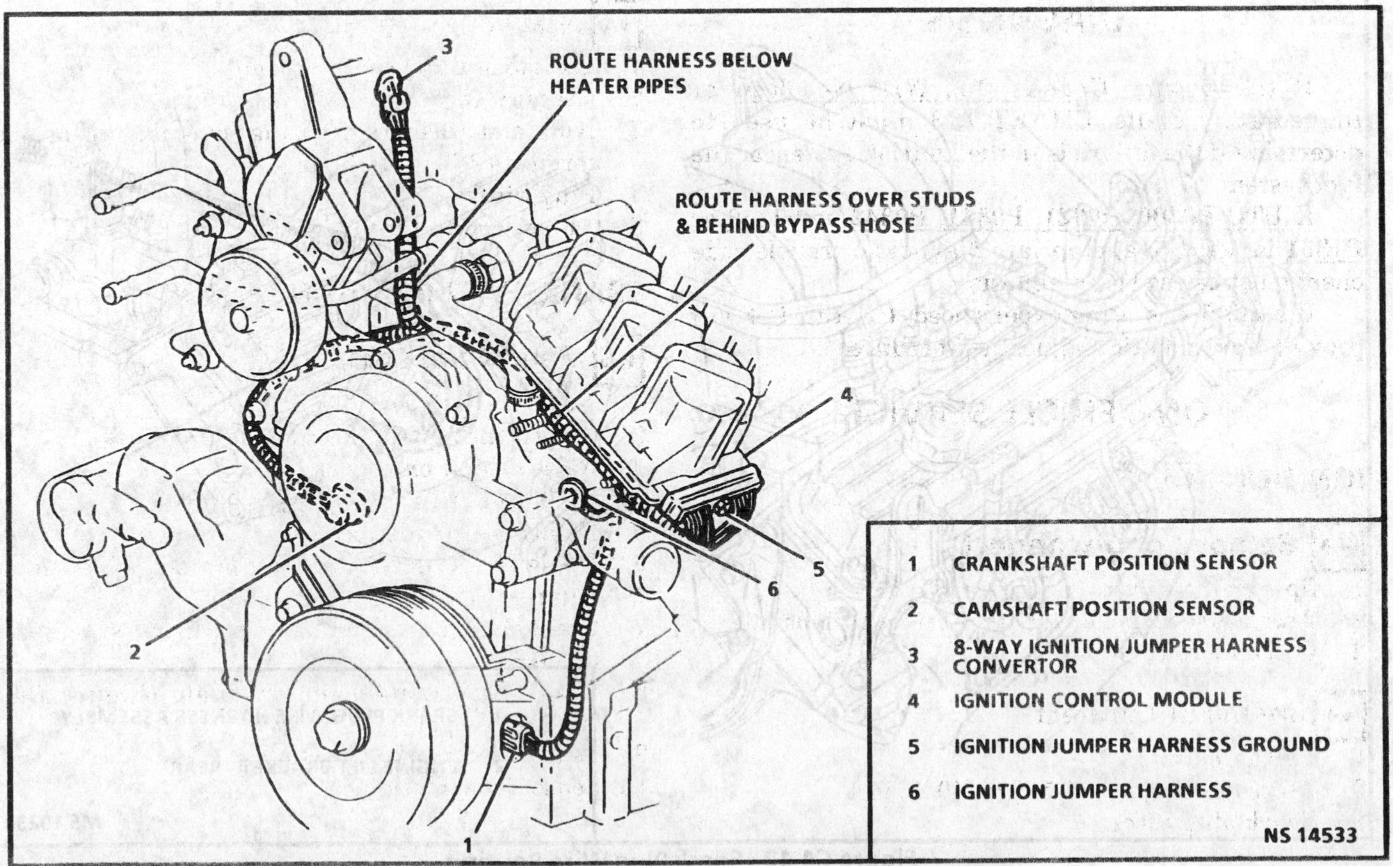
ROUTE HARNESS BELOW
HEATER PIPES
ROUTE HARNESS OVER STUDS
& BEHIND BYPASS HOSE
1 CRANKSHAFT POSITION SENSOR
2 CAMSHAFT POSITION SENSOR
3 8-WAY IGNITION JUMPER HARNESS CONVERTOR
4 IGNITION CONTROL MODULE
5 IGNITION JUMPER HARNESS GROUND
6 IGNITION JUMPER HARNESS
NS 14533

Figure C4-10 - Ignition Jumper Harness

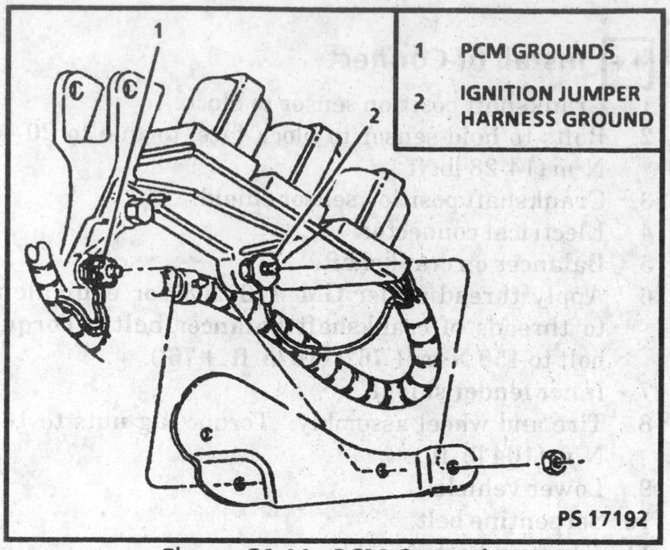
1
2
1 PCM GROUNDS
2 IGNITION JUMPER HARNESS GROUND
PS 17192

Figure C4-11 - PCM Grounds

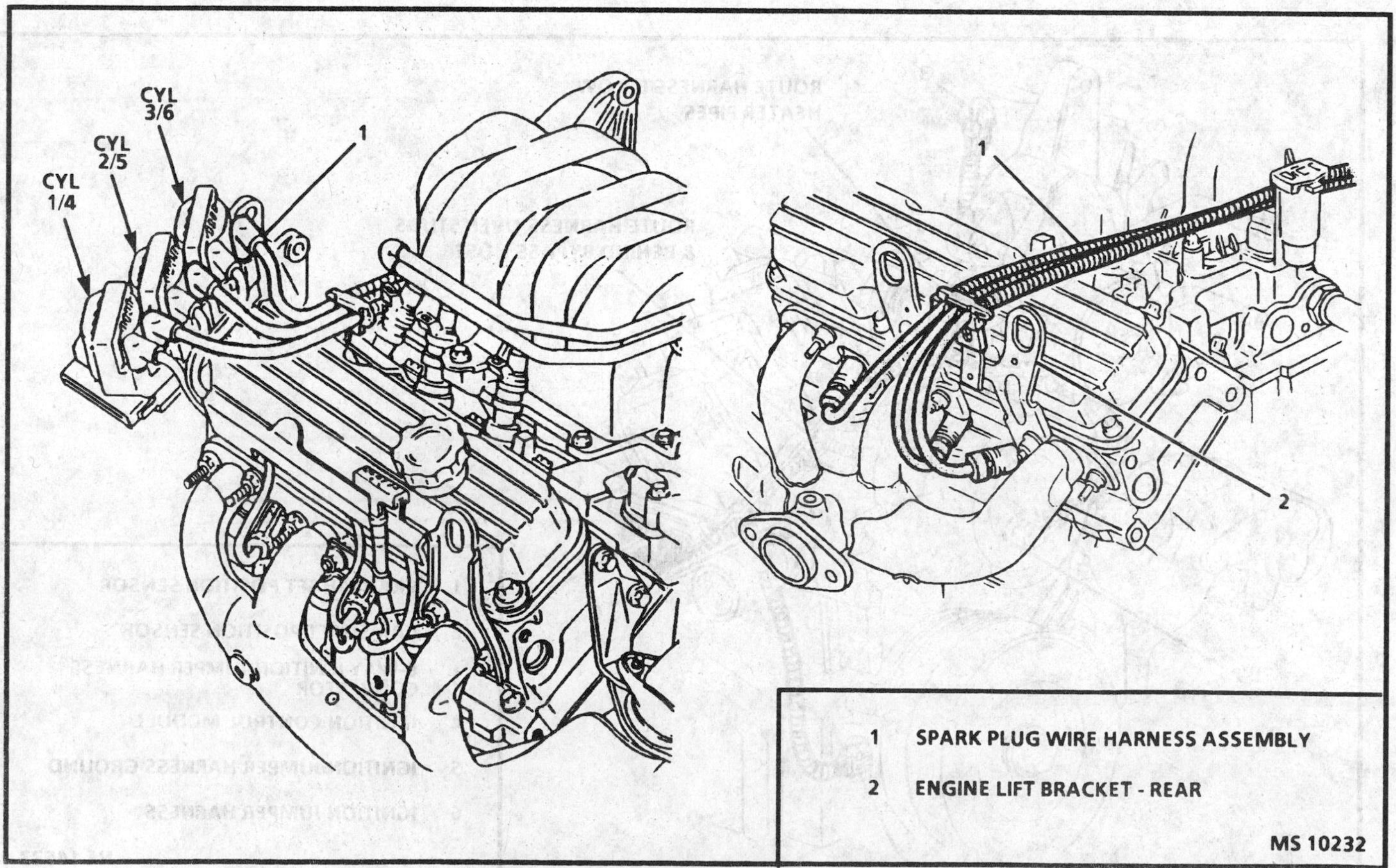
CYL 3/6
CYL 2/5
CYL 1/4
1
1
2
1 SPARK PLUG WIRE HARNESS ASSEMBLY
2 ENGINE LIFT BRACKET - REAR
MS 10232

Figure C4-12 - Spark Plug Wire Routing

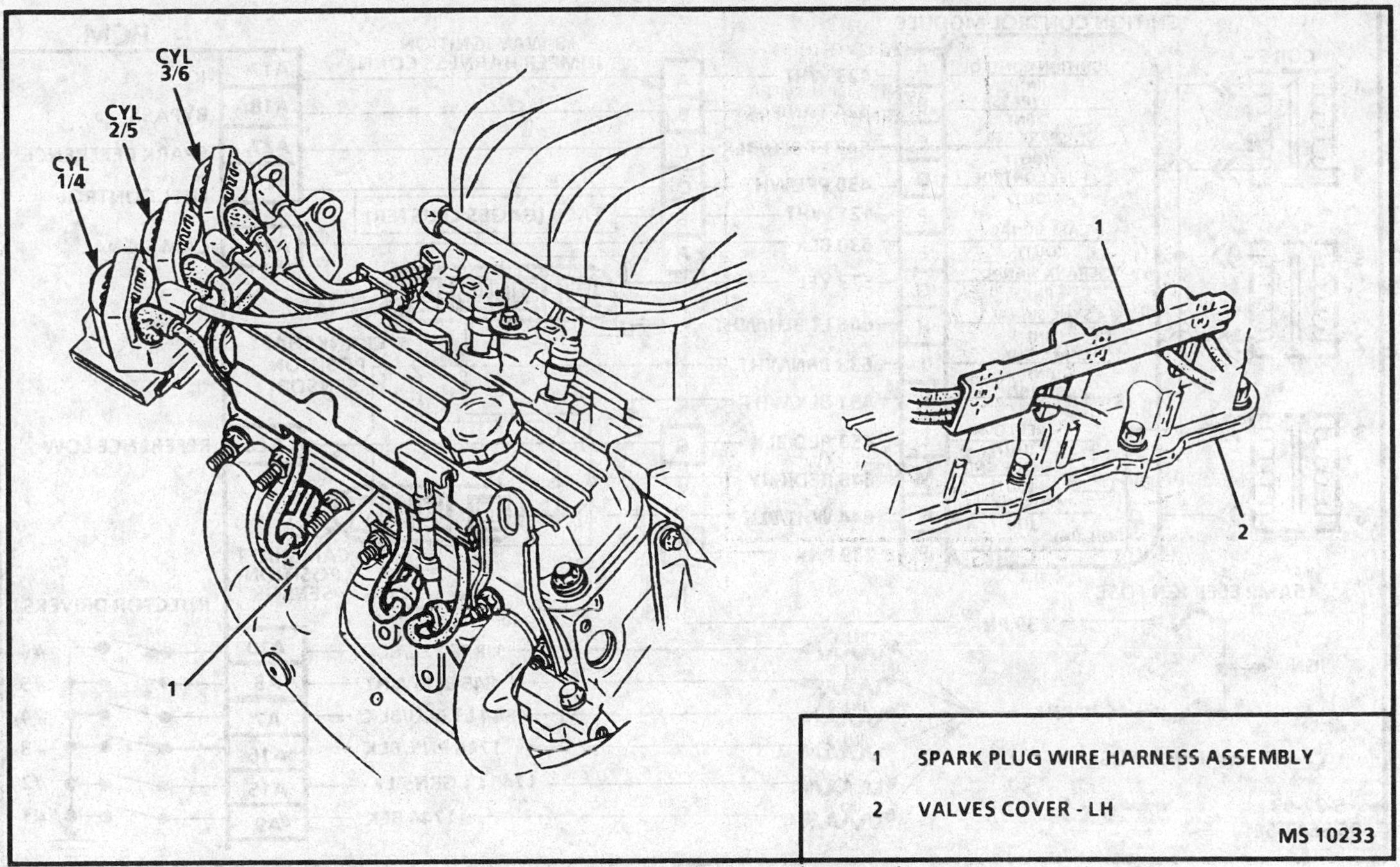
CYL 3/6
CYL 2/5
CYL 1/4
1
1
2
1 SPARK PLUG WIRE HARNESS ASSEMBLY
2 VALVES COVER - LH
MS 10233

Figure C4-13 - Spark Plug Wire Routing

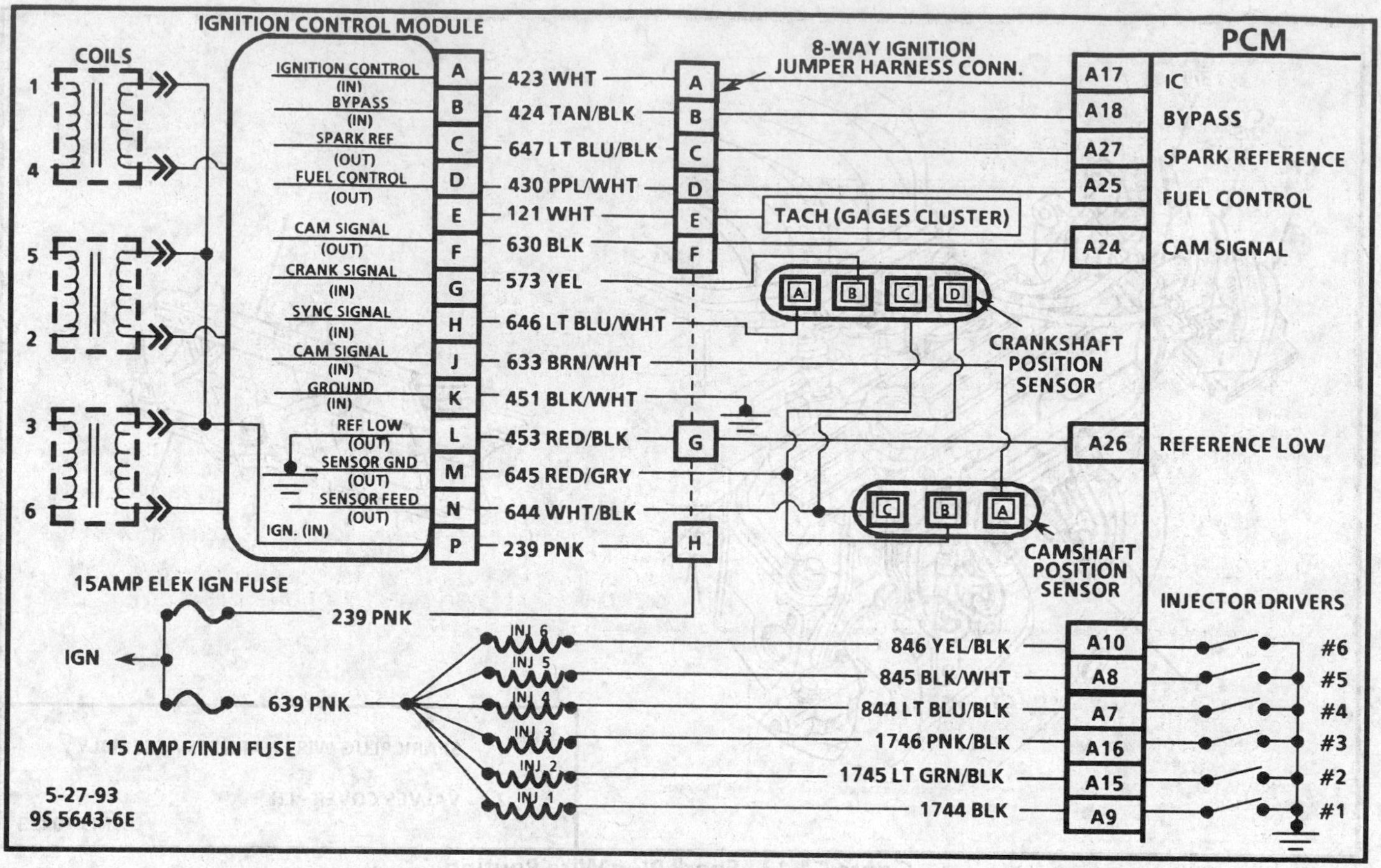
IGNITION CONTROL MODULE
COILS
PCM
IGNITION CONTROL (IN)
BYPASS (IN)
SPARK REF (OUT)
FUEL CONTROL (OUT)
CAM SIGNAL (OUT)
CRANK SIGNAL (IN)
SYNC SIGNAL (IN)
CAM SIGNAL (IN)
GROUND (IN)
REF LOW (OUT)
SENSOR GND (OUT)
SENSOR FEED (OUT)
IGN. (IN)
423 WHT
424 TAN/BLK
647 LT BLU/BLK
430 PPL/WHT
121 WHT
630 BLK
573 YEL
646 LT BLU/WHT
633 BRN/WHT
451 BLK/WHT
453 RED/BLK
645 RED/GRY
644 WHT/BLK
239 PNK
8-WAY IGNITION JUMPER HARNESS CONN.
TACH (GAGES CLUSTER)
A17 IC
A18 BYPASS
A27 SPARK REFERENCE
A25 FUEL CONTROL
A24 CAM SIGNAL
CRANKSHAFT POSITION SENSOR
A26 REFERENCE LOW
CAMSHAFT POSITION SENSOR
INJECTOR DRIVERS
15AMP ELEK IGN FUSE
IGN
639 PNK
15 AMP F/INJN FUSE
INJ 6
INJ 5
INJ 4
INJ 3
INJ 2
INJ 1
846 YEL/BLK
845 BLK/WHT
844 LT BLU/BLK
1746 PNK/BLK
1745 LT GRN/BLK
1744 BLK
A10
A8
A7
A16
A15
A9
#6
#5
#4
#3
#2
#1
5-27-93
9S 5643-6E

CHART C-4

MISFIRE DIAGNOSIS
3800 (VIN L) (SFI)

Circuit Description:

The ignition system uses a waste spark method of spark distribution. In this type of ignition system the ignition control module triggers the #1/4 coil pair resulting in both #1 and #4 spark plugs firing at the same time. #1 cylinder is on the compression stroke at the same time #4 is on the exhaust stroke, resulting in a lower energy requirement to fire #4 spark plug. This leaves the remaining high voltage to fire #1 spark plug.

Chart Test Description: Number(s) below refer to circled number(s) on the diagnostic chart.

1. An engine which runs OK at idle may misfire under load; monitoring "current weak cylinder" while operating the vehicle at different engine speeds and loads may isolate this condition.
2. Checks the PCM injector driver and injector wiring.
3. A spark tester such as a ST-125 must be used because it is essential to verify adequate available secondary voltage at the spark plug (25,000 volts). Spark should jump the tester gap on all 6 leads. This simulates a "load" condition.
4. If ignition coils are carbon tracked, the coil tower spark plug wire boots may be damaged.
5. By installing a normally operating coil, a determination can be made as to the fault being the coil or ignition control module.

Diagnostic Aids: A customer, under wide open throttle conditions, may experience fuel shut-off at high RPMs. RPM fuel shut-off point is PROM controlled, based on axle ratio. This could be interpreted as a misfire under load.

"Current weak cylinder" will correctly indicate the misfiring cylinder only if a single cylinder is misfiring. If a misfire cannot be isolated using "current weak cylinder" and more than one cylinder is suspect, try monitoring the Tech 1 "MISFIRE CYL" screen and diagnose any cylinders which are displayed misfiring.

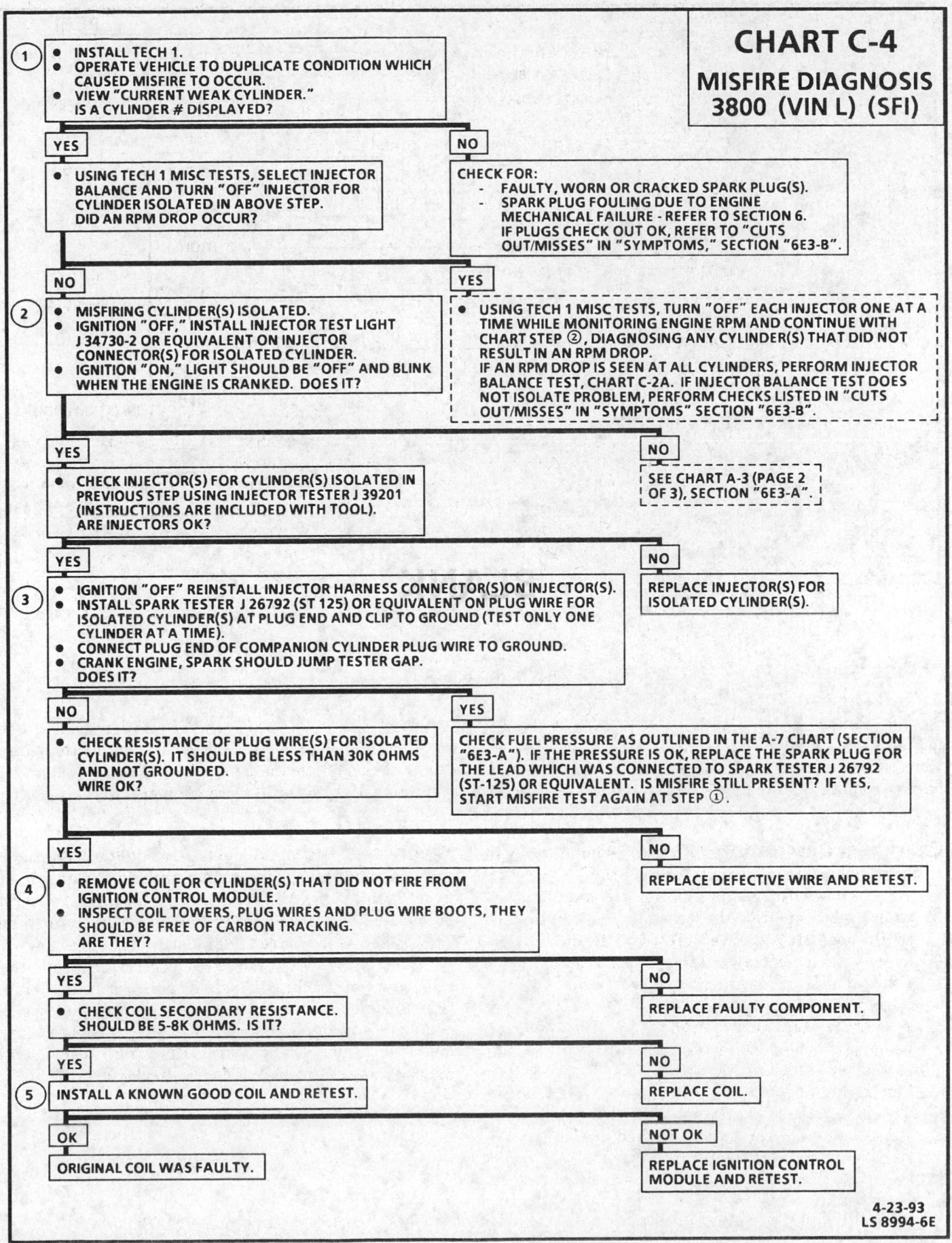

CHART C-4

MISFIRE DIAGNOSIS
3800 (VIN L) (SFI)

1
- INSTALL TECH 1.
- OPERATE VEHICLE TO DUPLICATE CONDITION WHICH CAUSED MISFIRE TO OCCUR.
- VIEW "CURRENT WEAK CYLINDER." IS A CYLINDER # DISPLAYED?

YES
- USING TECH 1 MISC TESTS, SELECT INJECTOR BALANCE AND TURN "OFF" INJECTOR FOR CYLINDER ISOLATED IN ABOVE STEP. DID AN RPM DROP OCCUR?

NO

CHECK FOR:
- FAULTY, WORN OR CRACKED SPARK PLUG(S).
- SPARK PLUG FOULING DUE TO ENGINE MECHANICAL FAILURE - REFER TO SECTION 6. IF PLUGS CHECK OUT OK, REFER TO "CUTS OUT/MISSES" IN "SYMPTOMS," SECTION "6E3-B".

NO

2
- MISFIRING CYLINDER(S) ISOLATED.
- IGNITION "OFF," INSTALL INJECTOR TEST LIGHT J 34730-2 OR EQUIVALENT ON INJECTOR CONNECTOR(S) FOR ISOLATED CYLINDER.
- IGNITION "ON," LIGHT SHOULD BE "OFF" AND BLINK WHEN THE ENGINE IS CRANKED. DOES IT?

YES
- USING TECH 1 MISC TESTS, TURN "OFF" EACH INJECTOR ONE AT A TIME WHILE MONITORING ENGINE RPM AND CONTINUE WITH CHART STEP ②, DIAGNOSING ANY CYLINDER(S) THAT DID NOT RESULT IN AN RPM DROP. IF AN RPM DROP IS SEEN AT ALL CYLINDERS, PERFORM INJECTOR BALANCE TEST, CHART C-2A. IF INJECTOR BALANCE TEST DOES NOT ISOLATE PROBLEM, PERFORM CHECKS LISTED IN "CUTS OUT/MISSES" IN "SYMPTOMS" SECTION "6E3-B".

YES
- CHECK INJECTOR(S) FOR CYLINDER(S) ISOLATED IN PREVIOUS STEP USING INJECTOR TESTER J 39201 (INSTRUCTIONS ARE INCLUDED WITH TOOL). ARE INJECTORS OK?

NO

SEE CHART A-3 (PAGE 2 OF 3), SECTION "6E3-A".

YES

3
- IGNITION "OFF" REINSTALL INJECTOR HARNESS CONNECTOR(S)ON INJECTOR(S).
- INSTALL SPARK TESTER J 26792 (ST 125) OR EQUIVALENT ON PLUG WIRE FOR ISOLATED CYLINDER(S) AT PLUG END AND CLIP TO GROUND (TEST ONLY ONE CYLINDER AT A TIME).
- CONNECT PLUG END OF COMPANION CYLINDER PLUG WIRE TO GROUND.
- CRANK ENGINE, SPARK SHOULD JUMP TESTER GAP. DOES IT?

NO

REPLACE INJECTOR(S) FOR ISOLATED CYLINDER(S).

NO
- CHECK RESISTANCE OF PLUG WIRE(S) FOR ISOLATED CYLINDER(S). IT SHOULD BE LESS THAN 30K OHMS AND NOT GROUNDED. WIRE OK?

YES

CHECK FUEL PRESSURE AS OUTLINED IN THE A-7 CHART (SECTION "6E3-A"). IF THE PRESSURE IS OK, REPLACE THE SPARK PLUG FOR THE LEAD WHICH WAS CONNECTED TO SPARK TESTER J 26792 (ST-125) OR EQUIVALENT. IS MISFIRE STILL PRESENT? IF YES, START MISFIRE TEST AGAIN AT STEP ①.

YES

4
- REMOVE COIL FOR CYLINDER(S) THAT DID NOT FIRE FROM IGNITION CONTROL MODULE.
- INSPECT COIL TOWERS, PLUG WIRES AND PLUG WIRE BOOTS, THEY SHOULD BE FREE OF CARBON TRACKING. ARE THEY?

NO

REPLACE DEFECTIVE WIRE AND RETEST.

YES
- CHECK COIL SECONDARY RESISTANCE. SHOULD BE 5-8K OHMS. IS IT?

NO

REPLACE FAULTY COMPONENT.

YES

5 INSTALL A KNOWN GOOD COIL AND RETEST.

NO

REPLACE COIL.

OK

ORIGINAL COIL WAS FAULTY.

NOT OK

REPLACE IGNITION CONTROL MODULE AND RETEST.

4-23-93
LS 8994-6E

BLANK

SECTION C5

KNOCK SENSOR (KS) SYSTEM

CONTENTS

GENERAL DESCRIPTION

PURPOSE

Varying octane levels in today's gasoline may cause detonation in some engines. Detonation is caused by an uncontrolled explosion (burn) in the combustion chamber. This uncontrolled explosion could produce a flame front opposite that of the normal flame front produced by the spark plug.

The "rattling" sound normally associated with detonation is the result of two or more opposing pressures (flame fronts) colliding within the combustion chamber. Though "light" detonation is sometimes considered normal, "heavy" detonation could result in engine damage.

To control spark knock, a Knock Sensor (KS) system is used. This system is designed to retard spark timing up to 10° to reduce spark knock in the engine. This allows the engine to use maximum spark advance to improve driveability and fuel economy.

OPERATION

The KS system has two major components:

- PROM.
- Knock sensor.

The knock sensor detects abnormal vibration (spark knocking) in the engine. The sensor is mounted in the engine block near the cylinders. The sensor produces an AC output voltage which increases with the severity of the knock. This signal voltage inputs to the PCM. The PCM then adjusts the Ignition Control (IC) timing to reduce spark knock.

DIAGNOSIS

The Tech 1 tool has two data displays to check for diagnosing this circuit. "KNOCK SIGNAL" is used to monitor the input signal from the knock sensor. This position will display "YES" when knock is being detected. "KNOCK RETARD" is the indication of how much the PCM is retarding the spark.

DTC P0325 is designed to diagnose the knock sensor and wiring, so problems encountered with this circuit should set the DTC.

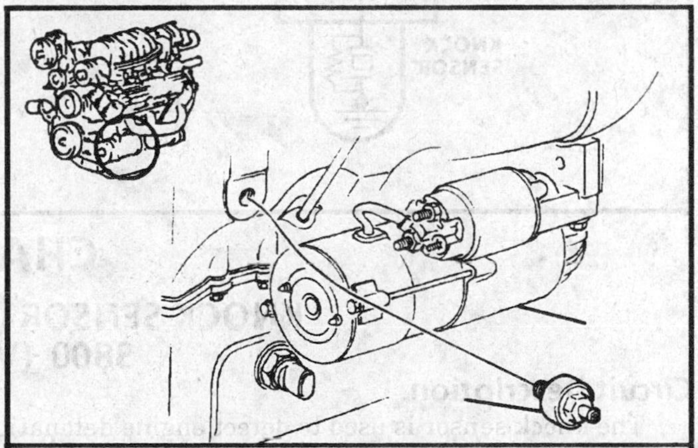

1 STARTER
2 KNOCK SENSOR

PS 17190

Figure C5-1 - Knock Sensor

However, if no DTC P0325 was set but the KS system is suspect because detonation was the customer's complaint, refer to CHART C-5.

ON-VEHICLE SERVICE

KNOCK SENSOR

↔ Remove or Disconnect

1. Knock sensor wiring harness connector from knock sensor.
2. Knock sensor from engine block.

→← Install or Connect

1. Knock sensor into engine block. Be sure threads are clean.
   - Tighten to 19 N·m (14 lb. ft.).

NOTICE: Overtorquing can damage the knock sensor.

2. Knock sensor wiring harness connector to the knock sensor.

PROM

Refer to "Powertrain Control Module (PCM) and Sensors," Section "6E3-C1" for replacement procedure.

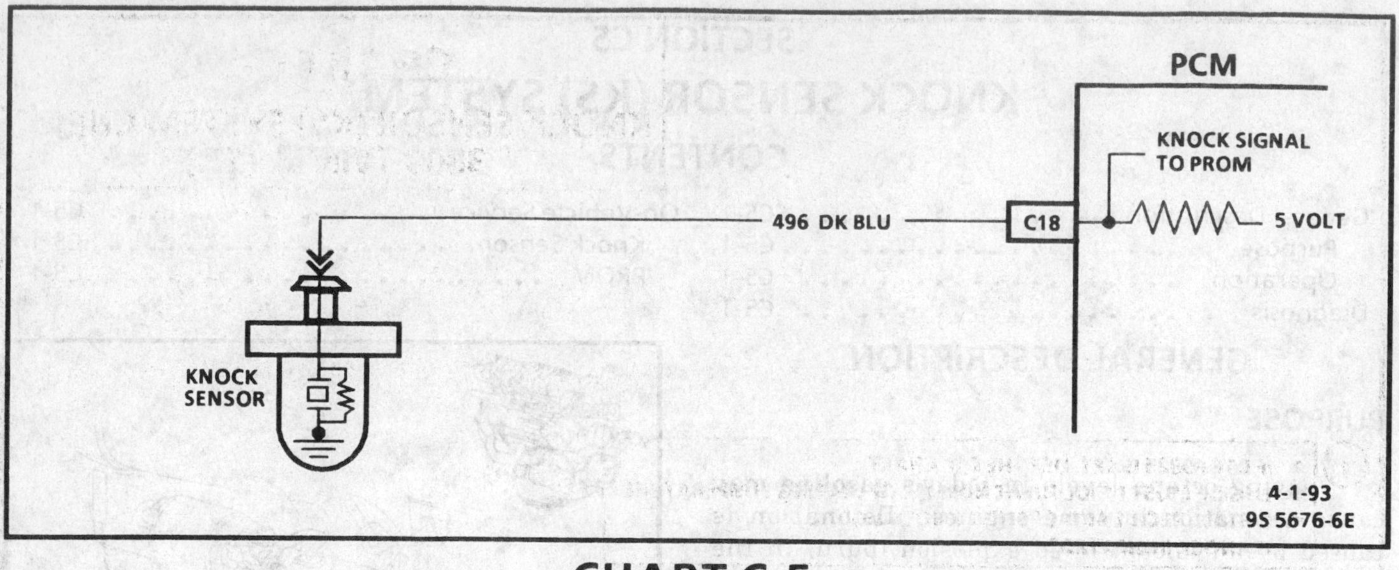
PCM
KNOCK SIGNAL TO PROM
496 DK BLU
C18
5 VOLT
KNOCK SENSOR
4-1-93
9S 5676-6E

CHART C-5

KNOCK SENSOR (KS) SYSTEM CHECK
3800 (VIN L) (SFI)

Circuit Description:

The knock sensor is used to detect engine detonation and allow the PCM to retard the ignition control timing based on the signal being received. The circuitry within the knock sensor causes the PCM supplied 5 volts signal to be pulled down so that under a no knock condition CKT 496 measures about 2.5 volts. The knock sensor produces an AC signal which rides on the 2.5 volts DC voltage. The amplitude and frequency are dependent upon the knock level.

The PROM used with this engine contains the functions which were part of the remotely mounted ESC modules used on past GM vehicles. When knock is being detected, the knock sensor portion of the PROM sends a signal to other parts of the PCM which retards the spark timing to reduce detonation.

Chart Test Description: Number(s) below refer to circled number(s) on the diagnostic chart.

1. With engine idling, there should not be a knock signal present at the PCM because detonation is not likely under a no load condition.
2. Tapping on the engine lift hook should simulate a knock signal and determine if the sensor is capable of detecting detonation. If no knock is detected, try tapping on engine block closer to sensor before replacing sensor.
3. If the engine has an internal problem which is creating a knock, the knock sensor may be responding to the internal failure.
4. This test determines if the knock sensor is faulty or if the knock sensor portion of the PROM is faulty. If it is determined that the PROM is faulty, be sure that it is properly installed and latched into place. If not properly installed, repair and retest.

Diagnostic Aids: While observing knock signal on the Tech 1, there should be an indication that knock is present when detonation can be heard. Detonation is most likely to occur under high engine load conditions.

If the KS CKT 496 is routed too close to secondary ignition wires, it may induce a voltage and cause a false knock signal.

- Refer to "Detonation/Spark Knock," in "Symptoms," Section "6E3-B".

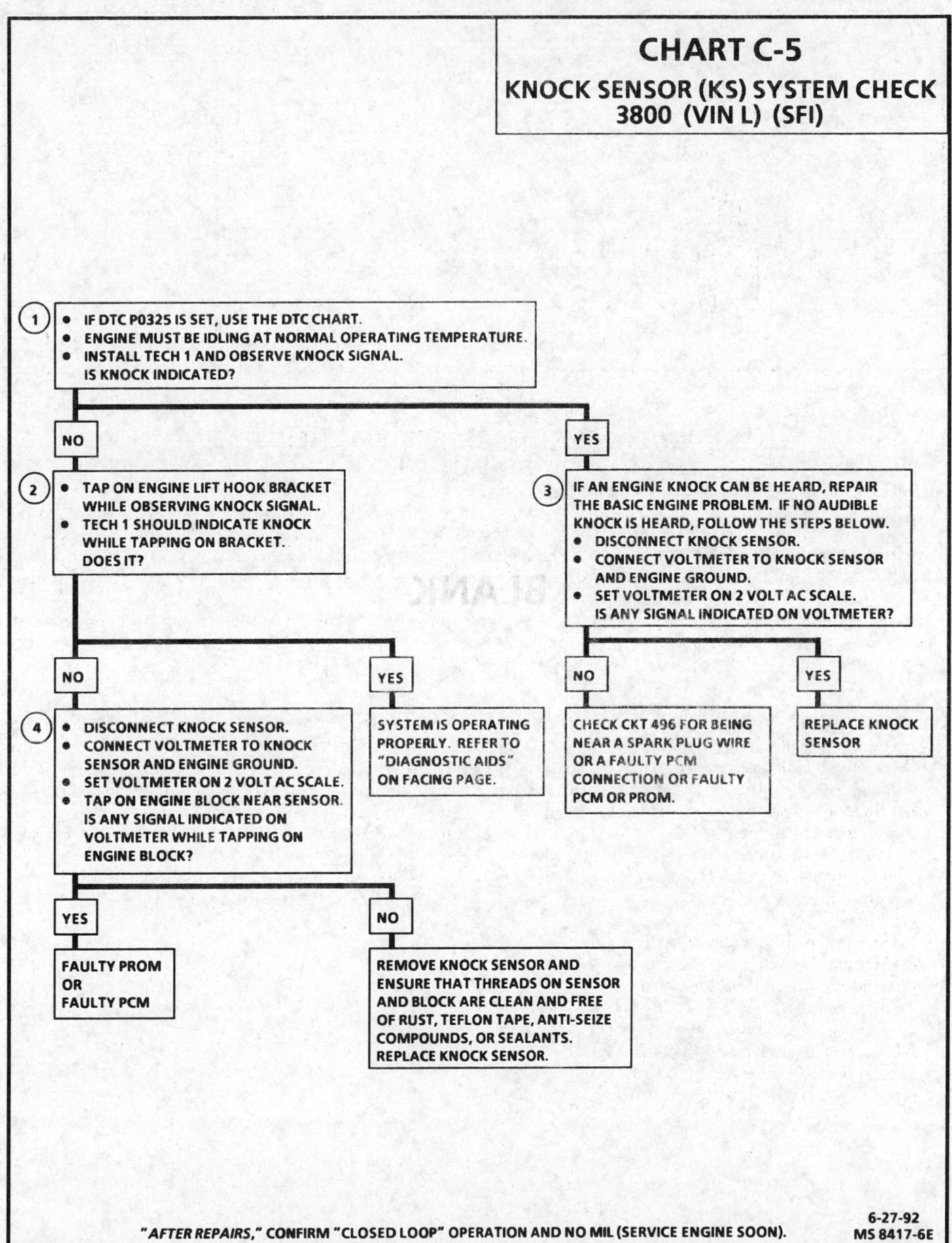

CHART C-5

KNOCK SENSOR (KS) SYSTEM CHECK
3800 (VIN L) (SFI)

1
- IF DTC P0325 IS SET, USE THE DTC CHART.
- ENGINE MUST BE IDLING AT NORMAL OPERATING TEMPERATURE.
- INSTALL TECH 1 AND OBSERVE KNOCK SIGNAL.

IS KNOCK INDICATED?

NO

2
- TAP ON ENGINE LIFT HOOK BRACKET WHILE OBSERVING KNOCK SIGNAL.
- TECH 1 SHOULD INDICATE KNOCK WHILE TAPPING ON BRACKET.

DOES IT?

NO

4
- DISCONNECT KNOCK SENSOR.
- CONNECT VOLTMETER TO KNOCK SENSOR AND ENGINE GROUND.
- SET VOLTMETER ON 2 VOLT AC SCALE.
- TAP ON ENGINE BLOCK NEAR SENSOR.

IS ANY SIGNAL INDICATED ON VOLTMETER WHILE TAPPING ON ENGINE BLOCK?

YES

FAULTY PROM OR FAULTY PCM

NO

REMOVE KNOCK SENSOR AND ENSURE THAT THREADS ON SENSOR AND BLOCK ARE CLEAN AND FREE OF RUST, TEFLON TAPE, ANTI-SEIZE COMPOUNDS, OR SEALANTS. REPLACE KNOCK SENSOR.

YES

SYSTEM IS OPERATING PROPERLY. REFER TO "DIAGNOSTIC AIDS" ON FACING PAGE.

YES

3
IF AN ENGINE KNOCK CAN BE HEARD, REPAIR THE BASIC ENGINE PROBLEM. IF NO AUDIBLE KNOCK IS HEARD, FOLLOW THE STEPS BELOW.
- DISCONNECT KNOCK SENSOR.
- CONNECT VOLTMETER TO KNOCK SENSOR AND ENGINE GROUND.
- SET VOLTMETER ON 2 VOLT AC SCALE.

IS ANY SIGNAL INDICATED ON VOLTMETER?

NO

CHECK CKT 496 FOR BEING NEAR A SPARK PLUG WIRE OR A FAULTY PCM CONNECTION OR FAULTY PCM OR PROM.

YES

REPLACE KNOCK SENSOR

"*AFTER REPAIRS*," CONFIRM "CLOSED LOOP" OPERATION AND NO MIL (SERVICE ENGINE SOON).

6-27-92
MS 8417-6E

BLANK

SECTION C7

EXHAUST GAS RECIRCULATION (EGR) SYSTEM

CONTENTS

GENERAL DESCRIPTION

PURPOSE

The Exhaust Gas Recirculation (EGR) system is used to lower Oxides of Nitrogen (NOx) emission levels caused by high combustion temperature. It does this by decreasing combustion temperature.

The main element of the system is the linear EGR valve. The EGR valve feeds small amounts of exhaust gas back into the combustion chamber. With the fuel/air mixture thus diluted, combustion temperatures are reduced.

OPERATION

Linear EGR Valve

The linear EGR valve is designed to accurately supply EGR to an engine independent of intake manifold vacuum. The valve controls EGR flow from the exhaust to the intake manifold through an orifice with a PCM controlled pintle. During operation, the PCM controls pintle position by monitoring the pintle position feedback signal. The feedback signal can be monitored with a Tech 1 as "ACTUAL EGR POS." "ACTUAL EGR POS" should always be near the commanded EGR position ("DESIRED EGR POS"). If a problem with the EGR system will not allow the PCM to control pintle position properly, DTC P1406 should set. The PCM also tests for EGR flow; if incorrect flow is detected, DTC P0401 should set. If DTCs P0401 and/or P1406 are encountered, refer to the diagnostic trouble code charts in Section "6E3-A".

The linear EGR valve is usually activated under the following conditions:

- Warm engine operation.
- Above idle speed.

LINEAR EGR CONTROL

The PCM monitors EGR position and adjusts pintle position accordingly. The PCM uses information from the following sensors to control the pintle position:

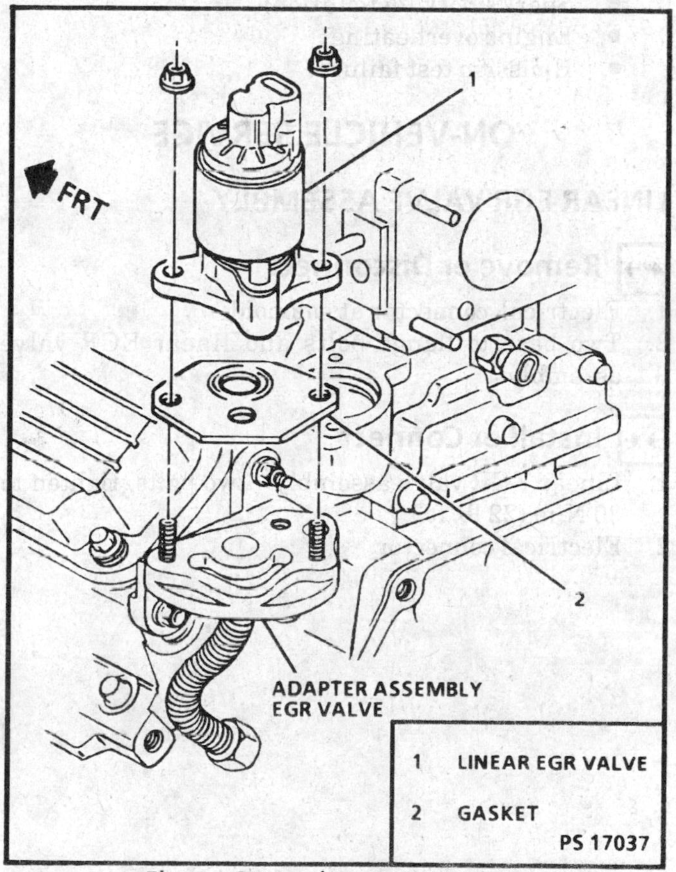

FRT
1
2
ADAPTER ASSEMBLY EGR VALVE
1 LINEAR EGR VALVE
2 GASKET
PS 17037

Figure C7-1 - Linear EGR Valve

- Engine Coolant Temperature (ECT) sensor.
- Throttle Position (TP) sensor.
- Mass Air Flow (MAF).

DIAGNOSIS

An EGR flow check diagnosis of the linear EGR system is covered in CHART C-7. If EGR diagnostic trouble codes P0401 and/or P1406 are encountered, refer to DTC charts in "Engine Components/Wiring Diagrams/Diagnostic Charts," Section "6E3-A" for diagnosis.

RESULTS OF INCORRECT EGR SYSTEM OPERATION

Too much EGR flow at idle, cruise, or cold operation may cause any of the following conditions to occur:

- Engine stalls after cold start.
- Engine stalls at idle after deceleration.
- Vehicle surges during cruise.
- Rough idle.
- DTC P0300 (misfire detected).

Too little or no EGR flow may allow combustion temperatures to get too high. This could cause:

- Spark knock (detonation).
- Engine overheating.
- Emission test failure.

ON-VEHICLE SERVICE

LINEAR EGR VALVE ASSEMBLY

←→ Remove or Disconnect

1. Electrical connector at solenoid.
2. Two base to flange bolts and linear EGR valve assembly.

→← Install or Connect

1. Linear EGR valve assembly - two bolts, tighten to 30 N·m (22 lb. ft.).
2. Electrical connector.

BLANK

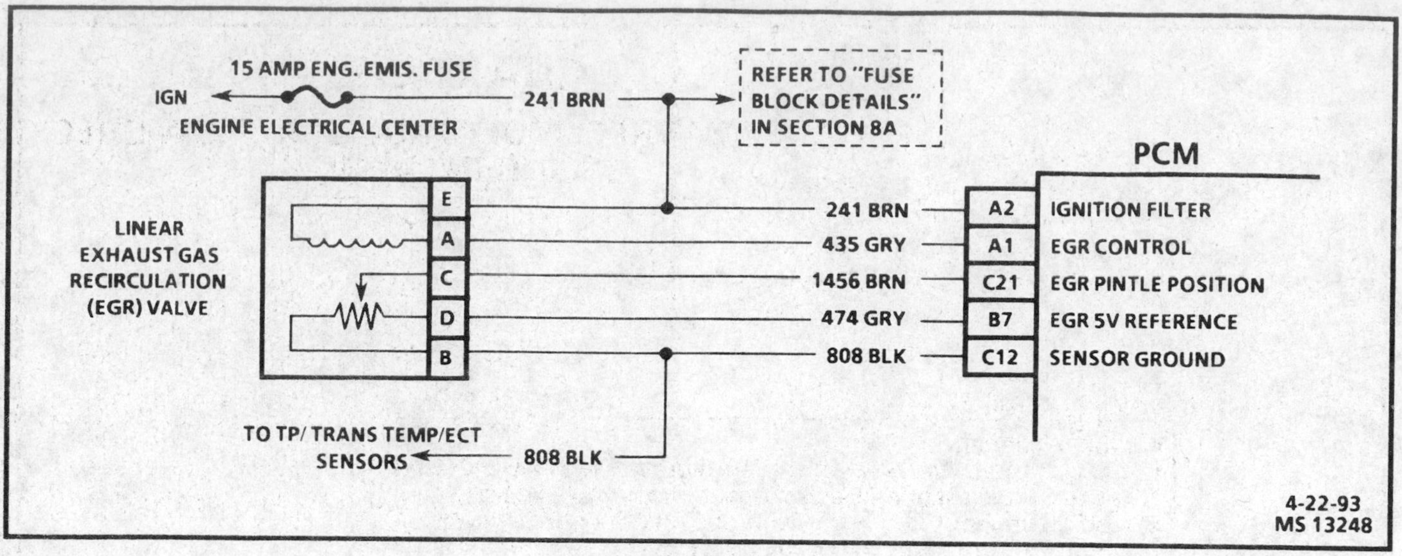
15 AMP ENG. EMIS. FUSE
IGN
ENGINE ELECTRICAL CENTER
241 BRN
REFER TO "FUSE BLOCK DETAILS" IN SECTION 8A
PCM
LINEAR EXHAUST GAS RECIRCULATION (EGR) VALVE
E
A
C
D
B
241 BRN
435 GRY
1456 BRN
474 GRY
808 BLK
A2
A1
C21
B7
C12
IGNITION FILTER
EGR CONTROL
EGR PINTLE POSITION
EGR 5V REFERENCE
SENSOR GROUND
TO TP/ TRANS TEMP/ECT SENSORS
808 BLK
4-22-93
MS 13248

CHART C-7

EXHAUST GAS RECIRCULATION (EGR) FLOW CHECK
3800 (VIN L) (SFI)

Circuit Description:

The linear Exhaust Gas Recirculation (EGR) valve is designed to accurately supply EGR to an engine independent of intake manifold vacuum. The valve controls EGR flow from the exhaust to the intake manifold through an orifice with a PCM-controlled pintle.

Chart Test Description: Number(s) below refer to circled number(s) on the diagnostic chart.

1. Ensures that the EGR valve is allowing EGR flow and the PCM is capable of controlling the EGR valve. The engine should run extremely rough and may even stall at the 75% and 100% positions.
2. Ensures that CKT 435 is not shorted to ground.
3. Ensures that CKT 435 is not open and that the PCM driver is functioning properly.

Diagnostic Aids:

- An intermittent may be caused by a poor connection, rubbed-through wire insulation, or a wire broken inside the insulation.

Check for:

- Poor connection or damaged harness. Inspect PCM harness connectors for backed out terminal "RA16", improper mating, broken locks, improperly formed or damaged terminals, poor terminal to wire connection and damaged harness.
- Intermittent test. If connections and harness check OK, disconnect PCM black connector "A" and monitor a digital voltmeter connected between PCM terminal "A1" and ground while moving related connectors and wiring harness. If the failure is induced, the voltage reading will change.
- Check for a restriction in EGR tube or passage. Also, ensure there is not excessive carbon buildup on EGR valve pintle and orifice.

NOTICE: If the linear EGR valve shows signs of excessive heat, check the exhaust system for blockage (possibly a plugged converter) using the procedure found on CHART B-1. If the exhaust system is restricted, repair the cause; possibly an ignition misfire or an injector which is open due to one of the following:

A. Stuck.
B. Grounded driver circuit.
C. Possibly defective PCM.

If this condition is found, the oil should be checked for possible fuel contamination.

CHART C-7

EXHAUST GAS RECIRCULATION (EGR) FLOW CHECK
3800 (VIN L) (SFI)

(1)
- START ENGINE.
- SELECT MISCELLANEOUS TESTS, EGR CONTROL WITH TECH 1 AND CYCLE THE EGR VALVE THROUGH THE 25%, 50%, 75% AND 100% POSITIONS.
- RUN ENGINE ABOVE 1500 RPM; RPM SHOULD DROP AND THE ENGINE SHOULD RUN ROUGH AS THE EGR VALVE IS CYCLED.
  DOES IT?

YES: NO TROUBLE FOUND, SEE "DIAGNOSTIC AIDS" ON FACING PAGE.

NO:

(2)
- KEY "ON," ENGINE "OFF."
- DISCONNECT EGR VALVE ELECTRICAL CONNECTOR.
- CONNECT A TEST LIGHT BETWEEN EGR VALVE HARNESS CONNECTOR TERMINAL "A" AND "E".
  TEST LIGHT SHOULD BE "OFF."

NO: EGR CONTROL CKT 435 SHORTED TO GROUND OR FAULTY PCM.

YES:

(3)
- SELECT MISCELLANEOUS TEST, EGR CONTROL WITH TECH 1.
- TEST LIGHT STILL CONNECTED BETWEEN EGR VALVE HARNESS CONNECTOR "A" AND "E".
- TEST LIGHT SHOULD LIGHT AS THE EGR VALVE IS CYCLED THROUGH 100%.
  DOES IT?

NO: OPEN IN CKT 435 OR OPEN IN CKT 241 OR POOR CONNECTION AT PCM OR FAULTY PCM.

YES: CHECK FOR A RESTRICTION IN EGR TUBE OR PASSAGE, POOR ELECTRICAL CONNECTION AT EGR VALVE, OR FAULTY EGR VALVE.

"*AFTER REPAIRS,*" CONFIRM "CLOSED LOOP" OPERATION AND NO MIL (SERVICE ENGINE SOON).

5-18-93
PS 17662

BLANK

SECTION C8

TORQUE CONVERTER CLUTCH (TCC) AND SHIFT SOLENOID SYSTEM

CONTENTS

GENERAL DESCRIPTION

PURPOSE

The Torque Converter Clutch (TCC) system uses two PCM controlled solenoids for engagement; a Pulse Width Modulated (PWM) solenoid valve, and an apply solenoid valve in the automatic transaxle to couple the engine flywheel to the output shaft of the transaxle through the torque converter. This reduces the slippage losses in the converter, increasing fuel economy.

TCC OPERATION

For the torque converter clutch to apply two conditions must be met:

- Internal transaxle fluid pressure must be correct. For information on internal transaxle operation, refer to SECTION 7A. This section will cover only the electrical operation of the TCC system.
- The PCM grounds switches internally to turn "ON" solenoids in the transaxle. This moves check balls, which will allow the torque converter clutch to apply, if the hydraulic pressure is correct as described above.
  The TCC "APPLY" solenoid controls the flow of transmission fluid to the TCC. The TCC Pulse Width Modulated (PWM) solenoid varies the hydraulic pressure at the converter clutch regulator valve to make locking and unlocking of TCC smoother.

The PCM controls the TCC apply and PWM solenoids after looking at several parameters:

- Vehicle Speed Sensor (VSS). Speed must be above a certain value before the clutch can apply.
- Engine Coolant Temperature (ECT) sensor. Engine must be warmed up before clutch can apply.

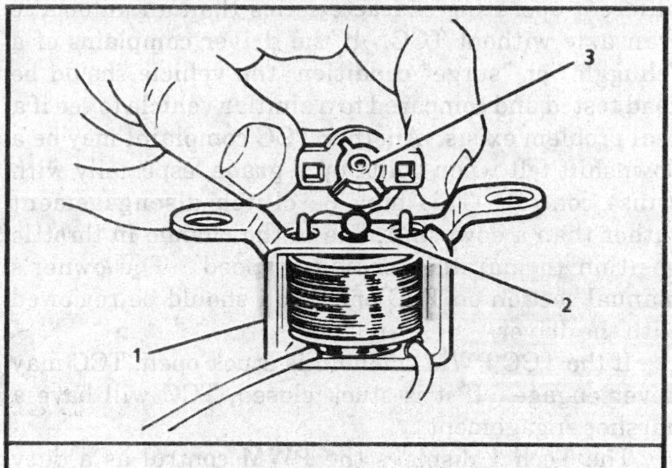

3
2
1
1 TCC SOLENOID
2 CHECK BALL
3 CHECK BALL SEAT
4S 0548-6E

Figure C8-1 - TCC Solenoid

- Throttle Position (TP) sensor. After the converter clutch applies, the PCM uses the information from the TP sensor to release the clutch when the vehicle is accelerating or decelerating at a certain rate.
- A TCC brake switch which opens a 12 volt signal to the PCM when the brake pedal is depressed.

SHIFT SOLENOIDS OPERATION

The 4T60E transaxles use two solenoids for shifting. Based on the N/V ratio (engine speed vs. vehicle speed) the PCM knows which gear the transaxle is operating in. The PCM uses this information along with other inputs such as TP sensor, RPM and air flow to determine the correct shift times for the transaxle.

TRANSAXLE TEMPERATURE SENSOR

The transaxle temperature sensor is a thermistor which changes value based on the temperature of the transaxle fluid. A high transaxle temperature may cause the vehicle to operate in "Hot Mode."

While in "Hot Mode," shift points may be altered, 4th gear disabled, and TCC forced "ON" in 2nd. A failure in the transaxle temperature sensor or associated wiring should cause a DTC P0712 or P0713 to set. With DTC P0712 or P0713 set, the PCM will substitute engine coolant temperature for transaxle temperature.

Results of Incorrect Operation

If the torque converter clutch does not apply, fuel economy may be lower than expected. If the vehicle speed sensor fails, the TCC will not apply.

The Torque Converter Clutch (TCC) system has different operating characteristics than an automatic transaxle without TCC. If the driver complains of a "chuggle" or "surge" condition, the vehicle should be road tested and compared to a similar vehicle to see if a real problem exists. Another TCC complaint may be a downshift felt when going up a grade, especially with cruise control. This may be clutch disengagement rather than a downshift, due to the change in throttle position to maintain cruising speed. The owner's manual section on TCC operation should be reviewed with the driver.

If the TCC PWM solenoid is stuck open, TCC may never engage. If it is stuck closed, TCC will have a harsher engagement.

The Tech 1 displays the PWM control as a duty cycle. 100% duty cycle is equal to 0 pressure/no TCC. 0% duty cycle is equal to full line pressure/TCC locked.

DIAGNOSIS

The diagnosis of the TCC system is covered in CHART C-8A. If the PCM detects a problem with the VSS signal, DTC P0501/P0502 should set. In this case, refer to DTC P0501/P0502 chart.

If the PCM doesn't switch the TCC "ON" when it should while driving, but the TCC solenoid activates using the Tech 1 under "Misc. Test," then sensors such as engine coolant temperature, vehicle speed, and throttle position should be checked.

Diagnosis of the shift solenoids is covered in CHART C-8B.

If any of the following diagnostic trouble codes are set, TCC may not be allowed to engage or may engage abnormally and transaxle shifting may be incorrect. Repair any existing diagnostic trouble codes and then re-check TCC or shift control.

DTC	Description
P0122	Throttle Position (TP) sensor circuit low
P0123	Throttle Position (TP) sensor circuit high
P0300	Misfire detected
P0501	Vehicle Speed Sensor (VSS) circuit problem (intermittent)
P0502	Vehicle Speed Sensor (VSS) circuit problem (hard failure)
P0703	TCC brake switch circuit problem
P0755	Transaxle shift "B" solenoid problem
P1630	System voltage high/low

F
A
D
B
E
G
C

A - SHIFT A SOLENOID (CKT 1222)
B - SHIFT B SOLENOID (CKT 1223)
C - TCC PWM SOLENOID (CKT 418)
D - TCC APPLY SOLENOID (CKT 422)
E - IGNITION FEED TO SHIFT SOLENOIDS (CKT 141)
F - TRANSAXLE TEMPERATURE SENSOR (CKT 1227)
G - SENSOR GROUND (CKT 818)

MS 9443

Figure C8-2 - Transaxle Harness Connector

ON-VEHICLE SERVICE

- Refer to SECTION 7A for TCC solenoids, shift solenoids and vehicle speed sensor.

TCC BRAKE SWITCH

Remove or Disconnect

1. Left hand hush panel.
2. Electrical connector(s).
3. Switch assembly.

Inspect

- Switch retainer for cracks.

Install or Connect

1. New switch assembly into retainer.
   A. Hold brake pedal depressed while installing switch or valve. Switch should bottom on retainer. Note that audible clicks can be heard as the threaded portion of the switch is pushed through the retainer.
   B. Slowly pull brake pedal fully rearward against pedal stop moving switch assembly rearward.
   C. Release brake pedal and pull back again to assure proper adjustment of switch.
   D. Visually reinspect retainer for cracks.
2. Electrical connector(s).
3. Left hand hush panel.

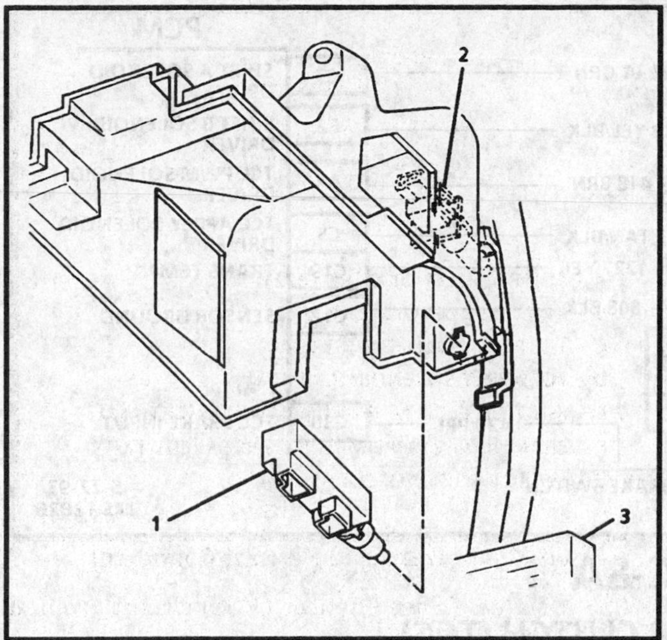
2
1
3

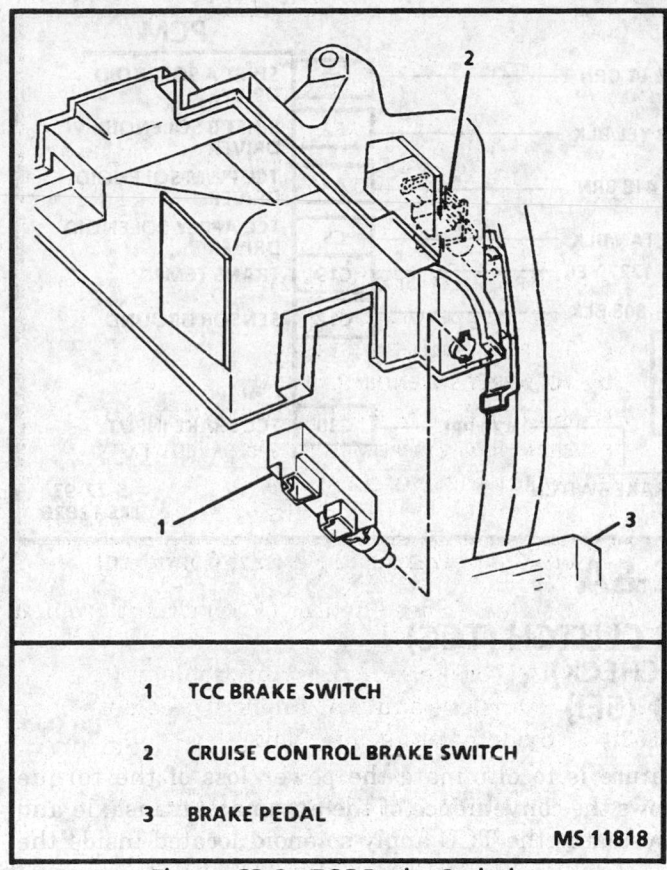

1 TCC BRAKE SWITCH

2 CRUISE CONTROL BRAKE SWITCH

3 BRAKE PEDAL

MS 11818

Figure C8-3 - TCC Brake Switch

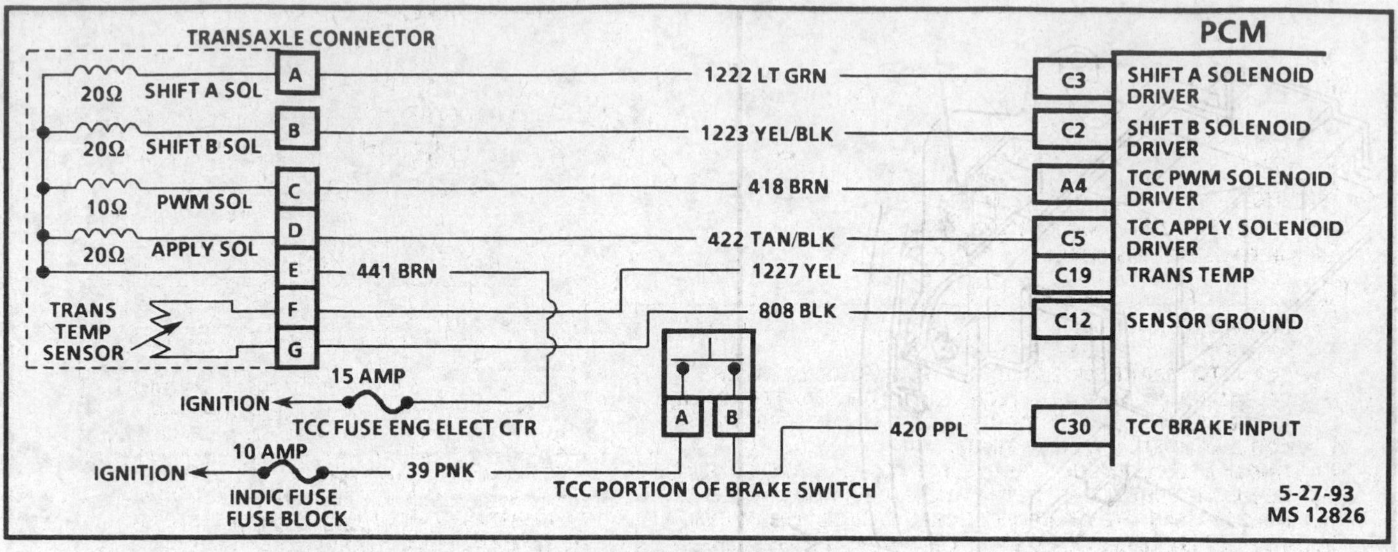
TRANSAXLE CONNECTOR
PCM
20Ω SHIFT A SOL
20Ω SHIFT B SOL
10Ω PWM SOL
20Ω APPLY SOL
TRANS TEMP SENSOR
A
B
C
D
E
F
G
1222 LT GRN
1223 YEL/BLK
418 BRN
422 TAN/BLK
441 BRN
1227 YEL
808 BLK
C3
C2
A4
C5
C19
C12
C30
SHIFT A SOLENOID DRIVER
SHIFT B SOLENOID DRIVER
TCC PWM SOLENOID DRIVER
TCC APPLY SOLENOID DRIVER
TRANS TEMP
SENSOR GROUND
TCC BRAKE INPUT
15 AMP
IGNITION
TCC FUSE ENG ELECT CTR
10 AMP
IGNITION
INDIC FUSE
FUSE BLOCK
39 PNK
420 PPL
TCC PORTION OF BRAKE SWITCH
5-27-93
MS 12826

CHART C-8A

TORQUE CONVERTER CLUTCH (TCC)
(FUNCTIONAL CHECK)
3800 (VIN L) (SFI)

Circuit Description:

The purpose of the Torque Converter Clutch (TCC) feature is to eliminate the power loss of the torque converter when the vehicle is in a cruise condition. This allows the convenience of the automatic transaxle and the fuel economy of a manual transaxle. The heart of the system is the TCC apply solenoid located inside the transaxle which is controlled by the PCM.

When the solenoid coil is activated ("ON"), the Torque Converter Clutch (TCC) is applied which results in a straight through mechanical coupling from the engine to the wheels. When the solenoid coil is deactivated ("OFF"), the Torque Converter Clutch (TCC) is released which allows the torque converter to operate in the conventional manner (fluid coupling between engine and transaxle).

The TCC PWM solenoid varies the hydraulic pressure at the converter clutch regulator valve to make locking and unlocking of TCC smoother. TCC will engage if:

- Engine warmed up.
- Vehicle speed above a calibrated value (about 28 mph 45 km/h).
- Throttle position sensor output not changing, indicating a steady road speed.
- Brake switch closed.
- Vehicle is in 3rd or 4th gear.

OR

- Vehicle is operating in "Hot Mode," which will cause the TCC to be engaged in 2nd gear.

Chart Test Description: Number(s) below refer to circled number(s) on the diagnostic chart.

> **NOTICE:** When connecting a test light or DVM to the connectors, use connector test adapter kit J 35616 or extension harness J 38835 to avoid damaging the connector terminals.

1. Determines whether fault is caused by a faulty solenoid or control circuit.
2. Checks availability of B+ on CKT 441.
3. Checks the PCM's capability to pulse the PWM solenoid "ON" and "OFF."
4. Electrical circuits have checked out. If there is a TCC engagement problem, refer to SECTION 7A.

Diagnostic Aids: The Tech 1 only indicates when the PCM has commanded the TCC solenoid driver "ON" and does not confirm that the TCC has engaged. To determine if TCC is functioning properly, road test the vehicle. Engine RPM should decrease when the Tech 1 indicates the TCC driver has turned "ON."

The TCC may engage in 2nd gear if the vehicle is operating in "Hot Mode." "Hot Mode" operation will be in effect when transaxle temperature exceeds 130°C (266°F).

CHART C-8A

TORQUE CONVERTER CLUTCH (TCC)
(FUNCTIONAL CHECK)
3800 (VIN L) (SFI)

NOTICE: IF ANY PCM DTC(s) ARE STORED, THEY MUST BE DIAGNOSED AND REPAIRS MADE PRIOR TO USING THIS CHART.

SOLENOID RESISTANCE VS. TRANSAXLE TEMPERATURE TABLE

SOLENOID	RESISTANCE	
	AT 68°F (20°C)	AT 190°F (88°C)
SHIFT A & B	20-30Ω	23-50Ω
TCC APPLY	20-30Ω	23-50Ω
TCC PWM	10-15Ω	11-25Ω

* RESISTANCE VALUES INCREASE AT HIGHER TEMPERATURES AND DECREASE AT LOWER TEMPERATURES.

- INSTALL TECH 1.
- IGNITION "ON," ENGINE "OFF."
- SCAN "TCC BRAKE SW." WITH TECH 1 WHILE APPLYING AND RELEASING BRAKE PEDAL - TECH 1 SHOULD INDICATE PROPER STATE OF BRAKE SWITCH. IF NOT, REFER TO DTC P0703 CHART FOR DIAGNOSIS. IF OK, CONTINUE.
- UNDER MISCELLANEOUS TEST SELECT TCC SOLENOID CONTROL.
- USING A STETHOSCOPE ON THE TRANSAXLE, YOU SHOULD BE ABLE TO HEAR THE TCC APPLY SOLENOID CLICK "ON" WHEN THE "↑" IS PRESSED AND CLICK "OFF" WHEN "↓" IS PRESSED.

DOES THE SOLENOID CLICK?

NO → (1)

YES → (3)

(1)
- IGNITION "ON," ENGINE "OFF."
- DISCONNECT TRANSAXLE HARNESS CONNECTOR.
- USING A TEST LIGHT, JUMPER TERMINALS "E" TO "D" OF TRANSAXLE HARNESS CONNECTOR.
- CYCLE TCC SOLENOID "ON" AND "OFF" USING TECH 1.

TEST LIGHT SHOULD TURN "ON" AND "OFF."
DOES IT?

- **NO** → (2)
- **YES** → FAULTY INTERNAL TRANSAXLE WIRING OR FAULTY TCC APPLY SOLENOID.

(2)
- IGNITION "ON," ENGINE "OFF."
- USING TEST LIGHT CONNECTED TO GROUND, PROBE TERMINAL "E" OF TRANSAXLE HARNESS CONNECTOR.

LIGHT SHOULD BE "ON."
IS IT?

- **YES** →
  - IGNITION "OFF."
  - DISCONNECT BLUE PCM CONNECTOR "C" AND CHECK CKT 422 FOR AN OPEN OR SHORT TO GROUND. IF CKT IS OK, IT IS A POOR CONNECTION AT PCM "C5" OR FAULTY PCM.
- **NO** → CHECK TCC FUSE AND REPAIR SHORT TO GROUND IN CKT 441 IF BLOWN - REFER TO "FUSE BLOCK DETAILS" IN SECTION 8A. IF FUSE IS OK, REPAIR OPEN IN CKT 441 TO TRANSAXLE.

(3)
- DISCONNECT TRANSAXLE HARNESS CONNECTOR.
- CONNECT A TEST LIGHT BETWEEN TRANSAXLE HARNESS CONNECTOR TERMINALS "C" AND "E".
- UNDER MISCELLANEOUS TESTS, SELECT TRANSMISSION TCC PWM SOLENOID ON THE TECH 1 AND TURN PWM SOLENOID "ON" AND "OFF."
- OBSERVE TEST LIGHT. THE TEST LIGHT SHOULD TURN "ON" WHEN THE PWM SOLENOID IS TURNED "ON," AND TURN "OFF" AS IT IS TURNED "OFF."

DOES IT?

- **NO** →
  - CONNECT A TEST LIGHT BETWEEN HARNESS TERMINAL "E" (CKT 441) AND GROUND. TEST LIGHT SHOULD BE "ON." IS IT?
    - **YES** → OPEN OR SHORT TO GROUND IN CKT 418 OR FAULTY PCM CONNECTION OR FAULTY PCM.
    - **NO** → OPEN IN CKT 441 TO TRANSAXLE CONNECTOR.
- **YES** →
  - IGNITION "OFF."
  - MEASURE RESISTANCE OF PWM SOLENOID BETWEEN TRANSAXLE CONNECTOR TERMINALS "C" AND "E" AT TRANSAXLE.
  - REFER TO TABLE FOR RESISTANCE SPECIFICATION.

  IS RESISTANCE OK?
    - **YES** → **(4)** CHECK FOR POOR CONNECTION IN CKT 418. IF OK, REFER TO AUTOMATIC TRANSAXLE DIAGNOSIS IN SECTION 7A FOR TRANSAXLE HYDRAULIC AND MECHANICAL DIAGNOSIS.
    - **NO** → FAULTY INTERNAL TRANSAXLE WIRING OR FAULTY TCC PWM SOLENOID.

3-30-93
MS 13265

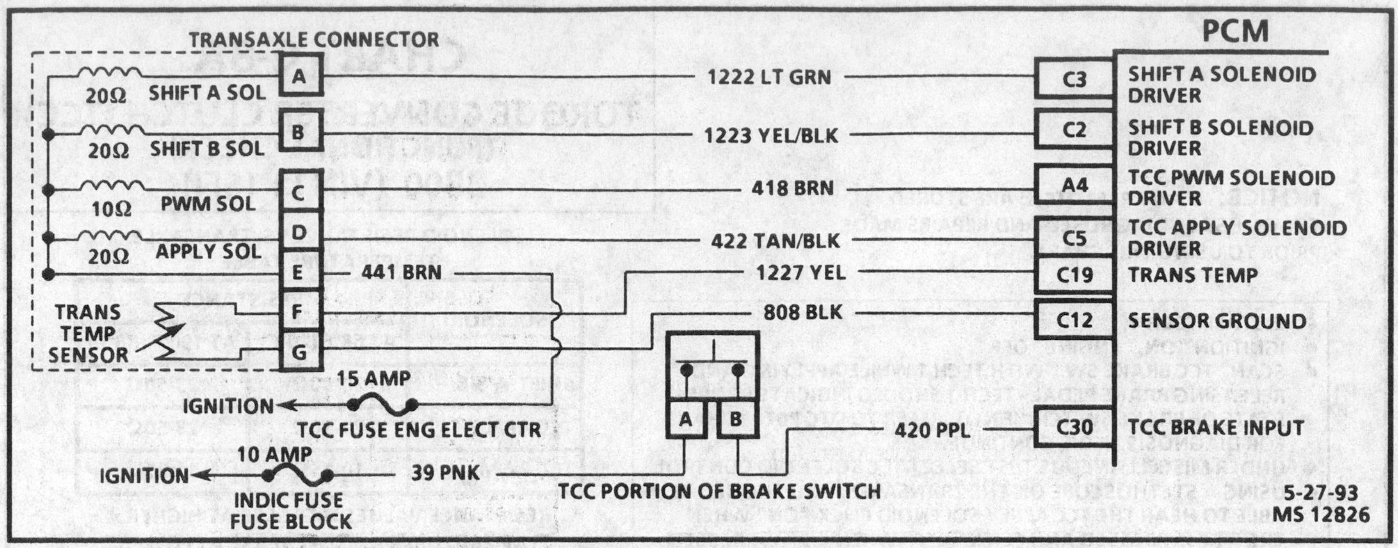
PCM
TRANSAXLE CONNECTOR
20Ω SHIFT A SOL
20Ω SHIFT B SOL
10Ω PWM SOL
20Ω APPLY SOL
TRANS TEMP SENSOR
A
B
C
D
E
F
G
1222 LT GRN
1223 YEL/BLK
418 BRN
422 TAN/BLK
441 BRN
1227 YEL
808 BLK
15 AMP
IGNITION
TCC FUSE ENG ELECT CTR
10 AMP
IGNITION
39 PNK
INDIC FUSE FUSE BLOCK
TCC PORTION OF BRAKE SWITCH
420 PPL
C3
SHIFT A SOLENOID DRIVER
C2
SHIFT B SOLENOID DRIVER
A4
TCC PWM SOLENOID DRIVER
C5
TCC APPLY SOLENOID DRIVER
C19
TRANS TEMP
C12
SENSOR GROUND
C30
TCC BRAKE INPUT
5-27-93
MS 12826

CHART C-8B

4T60E TRANSAXLE SHIFT SOLENOID FUNCTIONAL CHECK 3800 (VIN L) (SFI)

Circuit Description:

The 4T60E transaxle uses shift "A" and "B" solenoids to control transaxle shifting. Refer to table below for solenoid operating sequence.

The PCM monitors the TP sensor and vehicle speed vs. engine RPM to determine the correct shift points.

If the transaxle range switch PRNDL inputs indicate manual low position, the PCM will keep both shift solenoids energized until engine speed exceeds 5400 RPM, at which point the PCM will force a shift by de-energizing shift "A" solenoid. Manual 2nd and manual 3rd are controlled hydraulically within the transaxle.

SHIFT SOLENOID OPERATING SEQUENCE

COMMANDED GEAR	SHIFT A SOLENOID	SHIFT B SOLENOID
1st	CLOSED	CLOSED
2nd	OPEN	CLOSED
3rd	OPEN	OPEN
4th	CLOSED	OPEN

OPEN = DE-ENERGIZED

Diagnostic Aids: If the PCM, control circuitry, and shift solenoids are functioning properly and the transaxle still does not shift correctly, the problem may be hydraulic or mechanical. Refer to SECTION 7A. Also, check for "Hot Mode" operation. While in "Hot Mode," 4th gear may be disabled and transaxle shift timing altered. "Hot Mode" will be in effect when transaxle temperature exceeds 130°C (226°F).

CHART C-8B

4T60E TRANSAXLE SHIFT SOLENOID FUNCTIONAL CHECK 3800 (VIN L) (SFI)

SOLENOID RESISTANCE VS. TRANSAXLE TEMPERATURE TABLE

SOLENOID	RESISTANCE	
	AT 68°F (20°C)	AT 190°F (88°C)
SHIFT A & B	20-30Ω	23-50Ω
TCC APPLY	20-30Ω	23-50Ω
TCC PWM	10-15Ω	11-25Ω

* RESISTANCE VALUES INCREASE AT HIGHER TEMPERATURES AND DECREASE AT LOWER TEMPERATURES.

NOTICE: IF ANY DIAGNOSTIC TROUBLE CODES ARE STORED IN THE PCM'S MEMORY, THEY MUST BE REPAIRED BEFORE DIAGNOSING THE TRANSAXLE CIRCUITRY.

- KEY "ON," ENGINE "OFF."
- DISCONNECT THE TRANSAXLE ELECTRICAL CONNECTOR.
- CONNECT A TEST LIGHT BETWEEN HARNESS CONNECTOR TERMINALS "E-A" THEN "E-B".
- LIGHT SHOULD BE "ON" ON BOTH.
  IS IT?

YES

- INSTALL TECH 1 SCAN TOOL.
- UNDER MISC. TEST SELECT TRANSMISSION OUTPUT AND CYCLE SHIFT A SOLENOID AND SHIFT B SOLENOID "OFF" AND "ON."
- RETEST TERMINALS "E-A" (SHIFT "A") AND "E-B" (SHIFT "B"). DOES THE TEST LIGHT FLASH "ON" AND "OFF" RESPECTIVELY AS THE SOLENOIDS ARE CYCLED?

NO

IS THE LIGHT "OFF" ON BOTH?

YES

REPAIR OPEN IN CKT 441 TO HARNESS TERMINAL "E".

NO

CHECK FOR AN OPEN IN THE CIRCUIT WHICH DID NOT LIGHT THE TEST LIGHT. IF CIRCUIT IS OK, REPLACE PCM.

YES

- IGNITION "OFF."
- RECONNECT TRANSAXLE CONNECTOR.
- DISCONNECT PCM CONNECTORS.
- MEASURE THE RESISTANCE OF THE SHIFT SOLENOIDS BETWEEN PCM CONNECTOR TERMINALS "C30" AND "C3" (SHIFT A SOLENOID) THEN "C30" AND "C2" (SHIFT B SOLENOID).
- REFER TO TABLE FOR RESISTANCE SPECIFICATIONS.
  ARE BOTH RESISTANCES OK?

NO

CHECK THE CIRCUITS WHICH DID NOT FLASH FOR A SHORT TO GROUND. IF OK, REPLACE FAULTY PCM.

YES

ELECTRICAL CIRCUITS OK, SEE "AUTOMATIC TRANSAXLE DIAGNOSIS" IN SECTION 7A FOR TRANSAXLE HYDRAULIC AND MECHANICAL DIAGNOSIS.

NO

POOR CONNECTION AT TRANSAXLE
OR
FAULTY TRANSAXLE INTERNAL WIRING
OR
FAULTY SOLENOID. SEE SECTION 7 (TRANSAXLE) FOR REPAIR.

"*AFTER REPAIRS,*" CONFIRM "CLOSED LOOP" OPERATION AND NO MIL (SERVICE ENGINE SOON).

6-8-93
MS 13262

BLANK

SECTION C10
A/C CLUTCH CIRCUIT DIAGNOSIS

CONTENTS

GENERAL DESCRIPTION

In order to improve idle quality and Wide Open Throttle (WOT) performance, A/C compressor operation is controlled by the PCM.

OPERATION

This system consists of a pressure cycling switch, a high pressure cut-out switch, a control relay, the compressor clutch, the PCM, and the A/C control head or programmer.

The pressure cycling switch is closed when there is sufficient system pressure (depending on refrigerant charge and ambient temperature). When both the high pressure switch and the pressure cycling switch are closed, a complete circuit will exist between the A/C control head or programmer and PCM.

12 volts will be applied at the PCM by the A/C control head or programmer when the A/C selector is placed in the "ON" position and refrigerant pressure is sufficient to close the pressure cycling switch. The PCM will then energize the A/C clutch control relay. The PCM will also turn the left cooling fan (Fan 1) "ON" when A/C is requested. See "Electric Cooling Fans," Section "6E3-C12" for more information on cooling fan operation.

DIAGNOSIS

The A/C clutch control relay will not be allowed to energize if any of the following conditions are met:

- A/C not requested.
- Throttle angle greater than 90%.
- Engine speed greater than 4800 RPM.
- Engine coolant temperature greater than 121°C (250°F).

CHART C-10 should be used for diagnosing the electrical portion of the A/C circuit. When diagnosing the refrigerant portion of the A/C system, refer to SECTION 1B.

The Tech 1 will be used in diagnosing the system, as it has the ability to read the A/C request input to the PCM, as well as displaying when the PCM has commanded the A/C clutch "ON."

The Tech 1 has the ability to override the A/C request signal and energize the A/C control relay by using the misc tests function.

ON-VEHICLE SERVICE

For removal and replacement procedures of A/C components, refer to SECTION 1B.

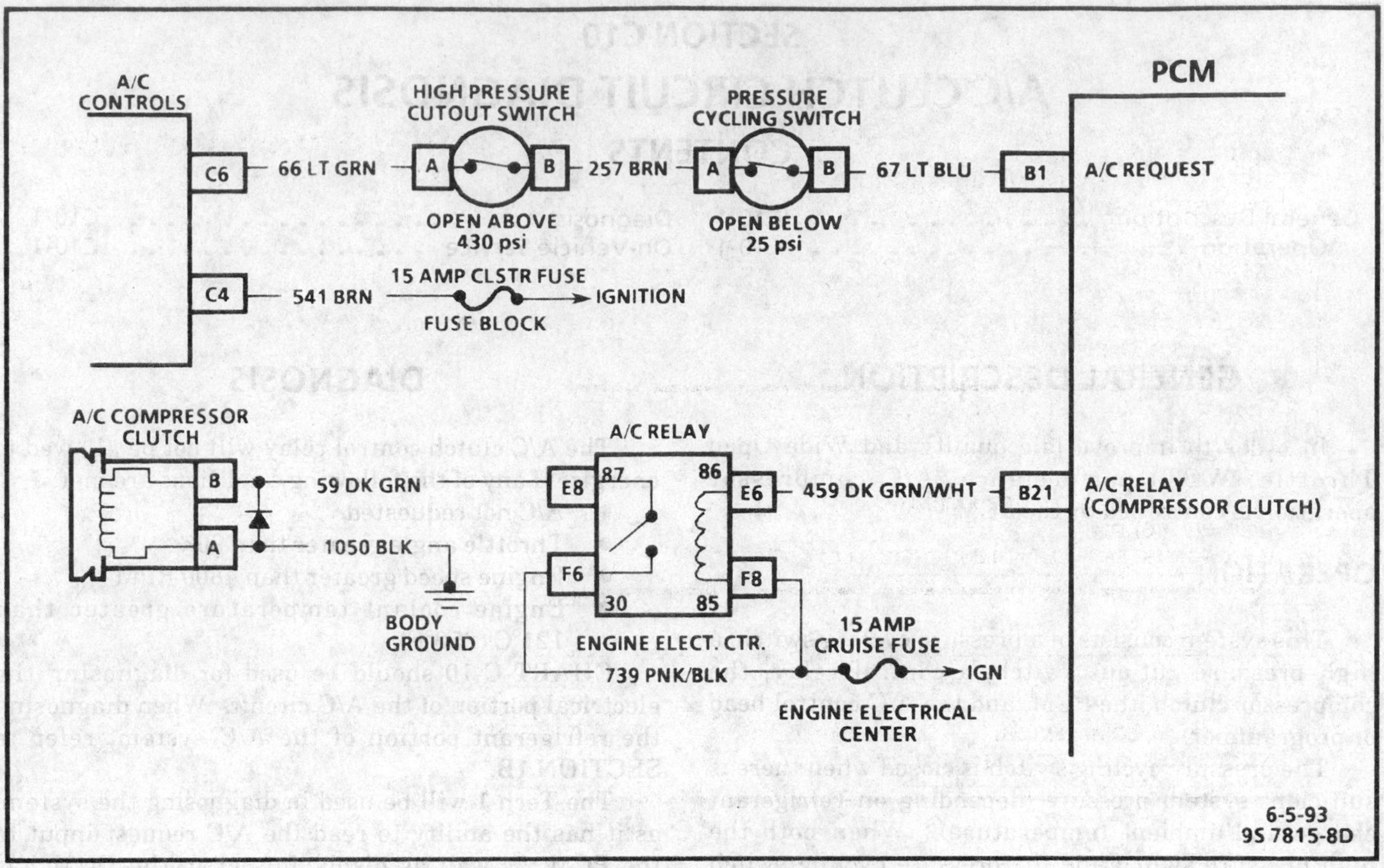
A/C CONTROLS
C6
66 LT GRN
HIGH PRESSURE CUTOUT SWITCH
A
B
257 BRN
OPEN ABOVE 430 psi
PRESSURE CYCLING SWITCH
A
B
67 LT BLU
OPEN BELOW 25 psi
PCM
B1
A/C REQUEST
C4
541 BRN
15 AMP CLSTR FUSE
IGNITION
FUSE BLOCK
A/C COMPRESSOR CLUTCH
B
A
59 DK GRN
1050 BLK
A/C RELAY
E8
87
86
E6
459 DK GRN/WHT
B21
A/C RELAY (COMPRESSOR CLUTCH)
F6
30
85
F8
BODY GROUND
ENGINE ELECT. CTR.
15 AMP CRUISE FUSE
739 PNK/BLK
IGN
ENGINE ELECTRICAL CENTER
6-5-93
9S 7815-8D

CHART C-10A

(Page 1 of 3)
A/C CLUTCH CIRCUIT DIAGNOSIS
3800 (VIN L) (SFI)

Circuit Description:

The A/C relay is PCM controlled to delay A/C clutch engagement .4 second after A/C is turned "ON." This allows the IAC to adjust engine RPM before the A/C clutch engages. The PCM also causes the relay to disengage the A/C clutch during WOT operation. The A/C relay is energized when the PCM provides a ground path for CKT 459. The PCM may apply the A/C clutch during cranking to prevent A/C slugging during startup.

Chart Test Description: Number(s) below refer to circled number(s) on the diagnostic chart.

1. A/C clutch should not be engaged with the engine running if an A/C mode is not selected at the control head.
2. Compressor clutch should apply if the conditions under the NOTICE at the top of the chart have been met.
3. Checks for an A/C request signal from the control head to the PCM.
4. Checks for an A/C request signal to the A/C high pressure cutout switch.

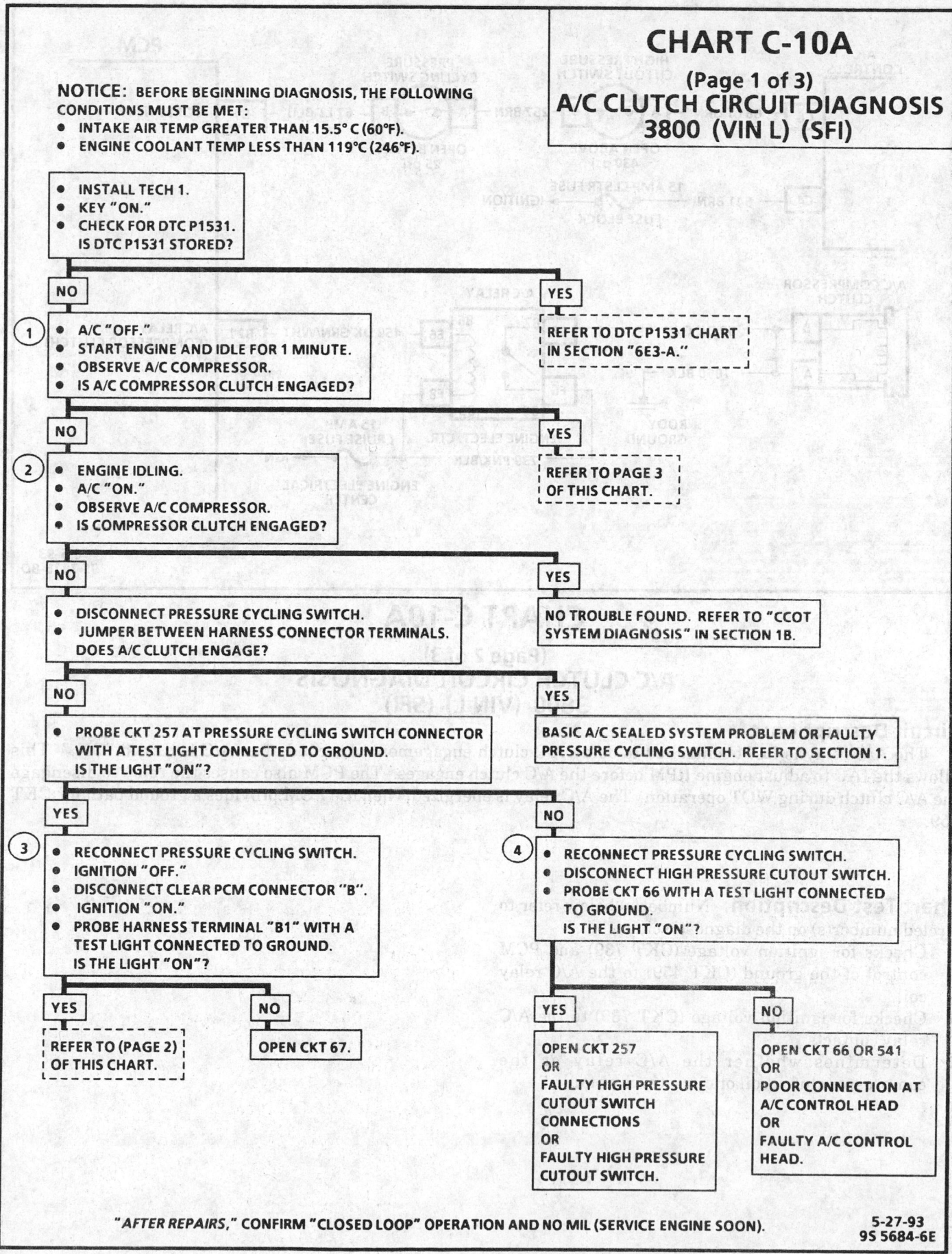

CHART C-10A

(Page 1 of 3)

A/C CLUTCH CIRCUIT DIAGNOSIS 3800 (VIN L) (SFI)

NOTICE: BEFORE BEGINNING DIAGNOSIS, THE FOLLOWING CONDITIONS MUST BE MET:

- INTAKE AIR TEMP GREATER THAN 15.5° C (60°F).
- ENGINE COOLANT TEMP LESS THAN 119°C (246°F).

- INSTALL TECH 1.
- KEY "ON."
- CHECK FOR DTC P1531.
  IS DTC P1531 STORED?

YES → REFER TO DTC P1531 CHART IN SECTION "6E3-A."

NO ↓

1
- A/C "OFF."
- START ENGINE AND IDLE FOR 1 MINUTE.
- OBSERVE A/C COMPRESSOR.
- IS A/C COMPRESSOR CLUTCH ENGAGED?

YES → REFER TO PAGE 3 OF THIS CHART.

NO ↓

2
- ENGINE IDLING.
- A/C "ON."
- OBSERVE A/C COMPRESSOR.
- IS COMPRESSOR CLUTCH ENGAGED?

YES → NO TROUBLE FOUND. REFER TO "CCOT SYSTEM DIAGNOSIS" IN SECTION 1B.

NO ↓

- DISCONNECT PRESSURE CYCLING SWITCH.
- JUMPER BETWEEN HARNESS CONNECTOR TERMINALS.
  DOES A/C CLUTCH ENGAGE?

YES → BASIC A/C SEALED SYSTEM PROBLEM OR FAULTY PRESSURE CYCLING SWITCH. REFER TO SECTION 1.

NO ↓

- PROBE CKT 257 AT PRESSURE CYCLING SWITCH CONNECTOR WITH A TEST LIGHT CONNECTED TO GROUND.
  IS THE LIGHT "ON"?

YES ↓

3
- RECONNECT PRESSURE CYCLING SWITCH.
- IGNITION "OFF."
- DISCONNECT CLEAR PCM CONNECTOR "B".
- IGNITION "ON."
- PROBE HARNESS TERMINAL "B1" WITH A TEST LIGHT CONNECTED TO GROUND.
  IS THE LIGHT "ON"?

YES → REFER TO (PAGE 2) OF THIS CHART.

NO → OPEN CKT 67.

NO ↓

4
- RECONNECT PRESSURE CYCLING SWITCH.
- DISCONNECT HIGH PRESSURE CUTOUT SWITCH.
- PROBE CKT 66 WITH A TEST LIGHT CONNECTED TO GROUND.
  IS THE LIGHT "ON"?

YES → OPEN CKT 257 OR FAULTY HIGH PRESSURE CUTOUT SWITCH CONNECTIONS OR FAULTY HIGH PRESSURE CUTOUT SWITCH.

NO → OPEN CKT 66 OR 541 OR POOR CONNECTION AT A/C CONTROL HEAD OR FAULTY A/C CONTROL HEAD.

"AFTER REPAIRS," CONFIRM "CLOSED LOOP" OPERATION AND NO MIL (SERVICE ENGINE SOON).

5-27-93
9S 5684-6E

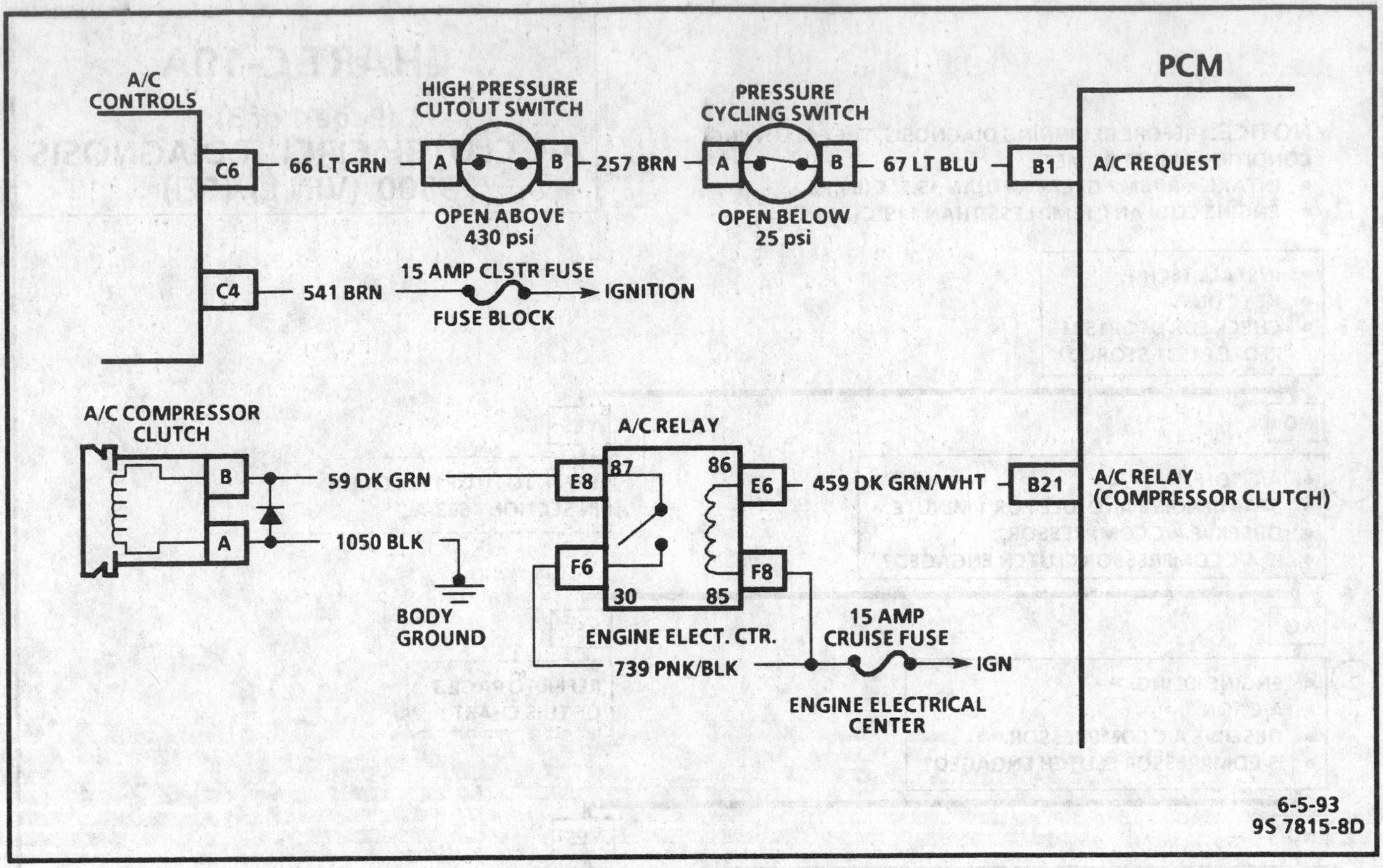
A/C CONTROLS
HIGH PRESSURE CUTOUT SWITCH
PRESSURE CYCLING SWITCH
PCM
C6
66 LT GRN
A
B
257 BRN
A
B
67 LT BLU
B1
A/C REQUEST
OPEN ABOVE 430 psi
OPEN BELOW 25 psi
C4
541 BRN
15 AMP CLSTR FUSE
IGNITION
FUSE BLOCK
A/C COMPRESSOR CLUTCH
A/C RELAY
B
59 DK GRN
E8
87
86
E6
459 DK GRN/WHT
B21
A/C RELAY (COMPRESSOR CLUTCH)
A
1050 BLK
F6
F8
30
85
BODY GROUND
ENGINE ELECT. CTR.
15 AMP CRUISE FUSE
739 PNK/BLK
IGN
ENGINE ELECTRICAL CENTER
6-5-93
9S 7815-8D

CHART C-10A

(Page 2 of 3)

A/C CLUTCH CIRCUIT DIAGNOSIS

3800 (VIN L) (SFI)

Circuit Description:

The A/C relay is PCM controlled to delay A/C clutch engagement .4 second after A/C is turned "ON." This allows the IAC to adjust engine RPM before the A/C clutch engages. The PCM also causes the relay to disengage the A/C clutch during WOT operation. The A/C relay is energized when the PCM provides a ground path for CKT 459.

Chart Test Description: Number(s) below refer to circled number(s) on the diagnostic chart.

5. Checks for ignition voltage (CKT 739) and PCM control of the ground (CKT 459) to the A/C relay coil.
6. Checks for ignition voltage (CKT 739) to the A/C relay contacts.
7. Determines whether the A/C relay or the compressor clutch coil or circuitry is at fault.

CHART C-10A

(Page 2 of 3)
A/C CLUTCH CIRCUIT DIAGNOSIS
3800 (VIN L) (SFI)

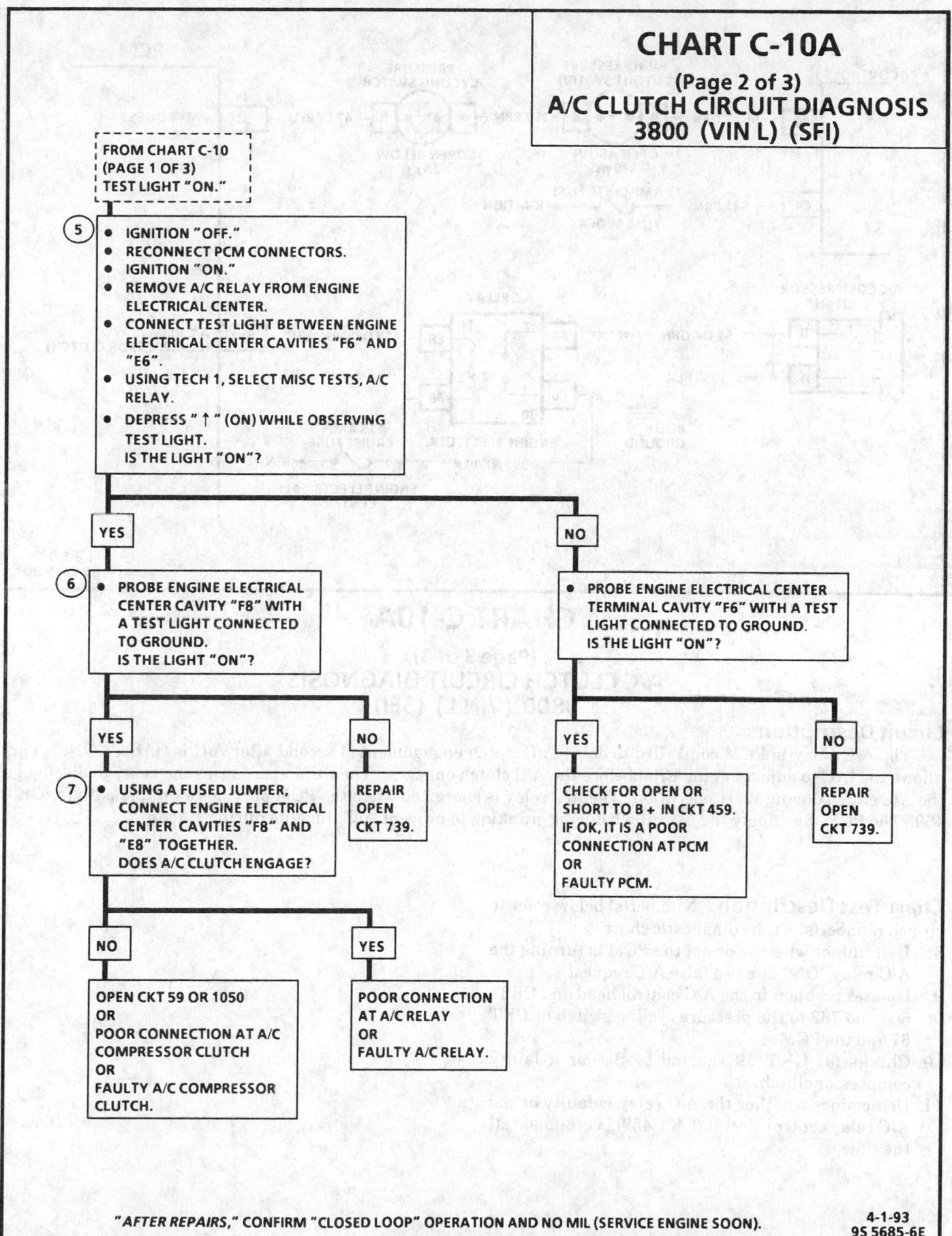

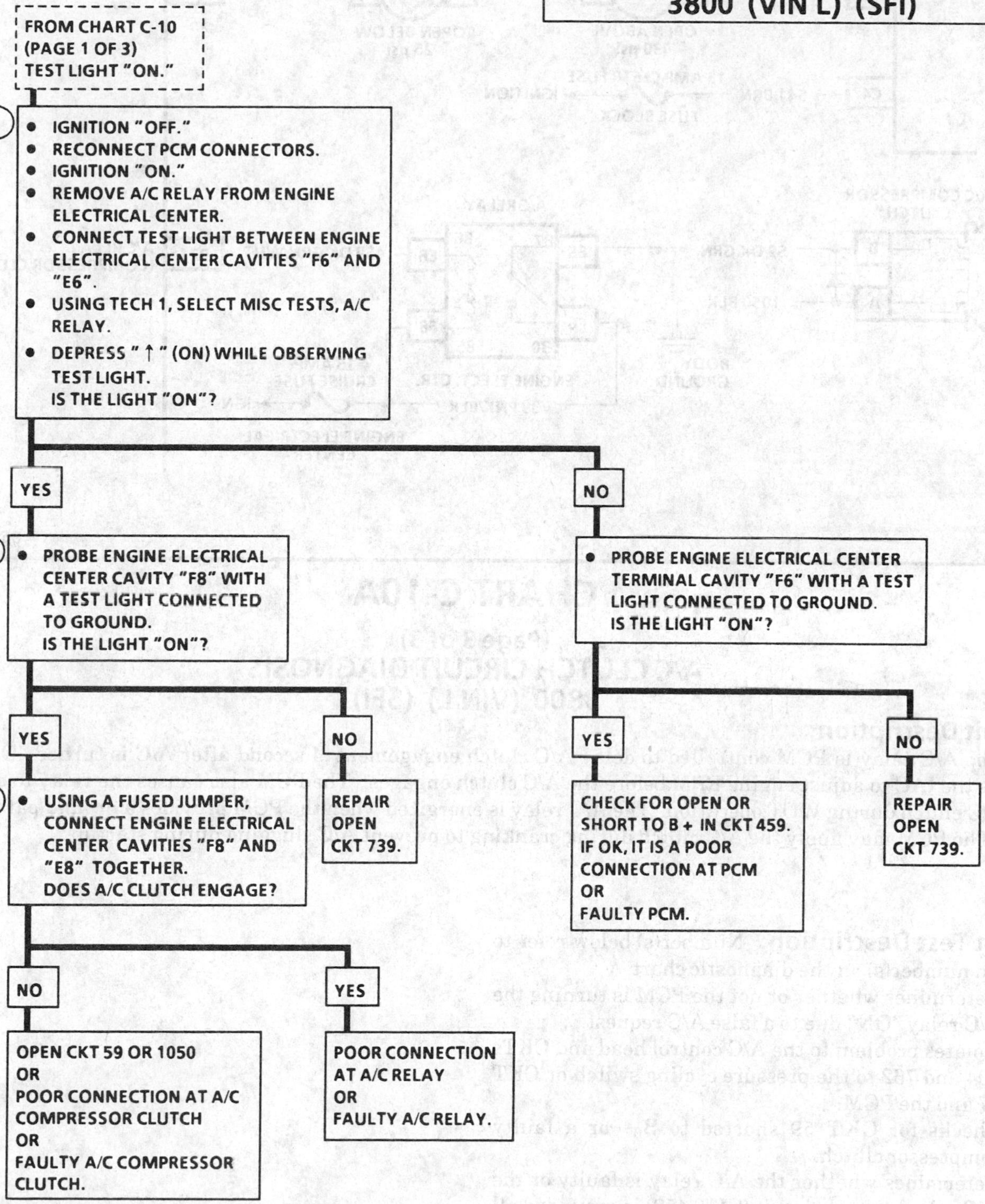
FROM CHART C-10
(PAGE 1 OF 3)
TEST LIGHT "ON."
5
• IGNITION "OFF."
• RECONNECT PCM CONNECTORS.
• IGNITION "ON."
• REMOVE A/C RELAY FROM ENGINE ELECTRICAL CENTER.
• CONNECT TEST LIGHT BETWEEN ENGINE ELECTRICAL CENTER CAVITIES "F6" AND "E6".
• USING TECH 1, SELECT MISC TESTS, A/C RELAY.
• DEPRESS " ↑ " (ON) WHILE OBSERVING TEST LIGHT.
IS THE LIGHT "ON"?
YES
NO
6
• PROBE ENGINE ELECTRICAL CENTER CAVITY "F8" WITH A TEST LIGHT CONNECTED TO GROUND.
IS THE LIGHT "ON"?
• PROBE ENGINE ELECTRICAL CENTER TERMINAL CAVITY "F6" WITH A TEST LIGHT CONNECTED TO GROUND.
IS THE LIGHT "ON"?
YES
NO
YES
NO
7
• USING A FUSED JUMPER, CONNECT ENGINE ELECTRICAL CENTER CAVITIES "F8" AND "E8" TOGETHER.
DOES A/C CLUTCH ENGAGE?
REPAIR OPEN CKT 739.
CHECK FOR OPEN OR SHORT TO B + IN CKT 459. IF OK, IT IS A POOR CONNECTION AT PCM OR FAULTY PCM.
REPAIR OPEN CKT 739.
NO
YES
OPEN CKT 59 OR 1050 OR POOR CONNECTION AT A/C COMPRESSOR CLUTCH OR FAULTY A/C COMPRESSOR CLUTCH.
POOR CONNECTION AT A/C RELAY OR FAULTY A/C RELAY.

"AFTER REPAIRS," **CONFIRM "CLOSED LOOP" OPERATION AND NO MIL (SERVICE ENGINE SOON).**

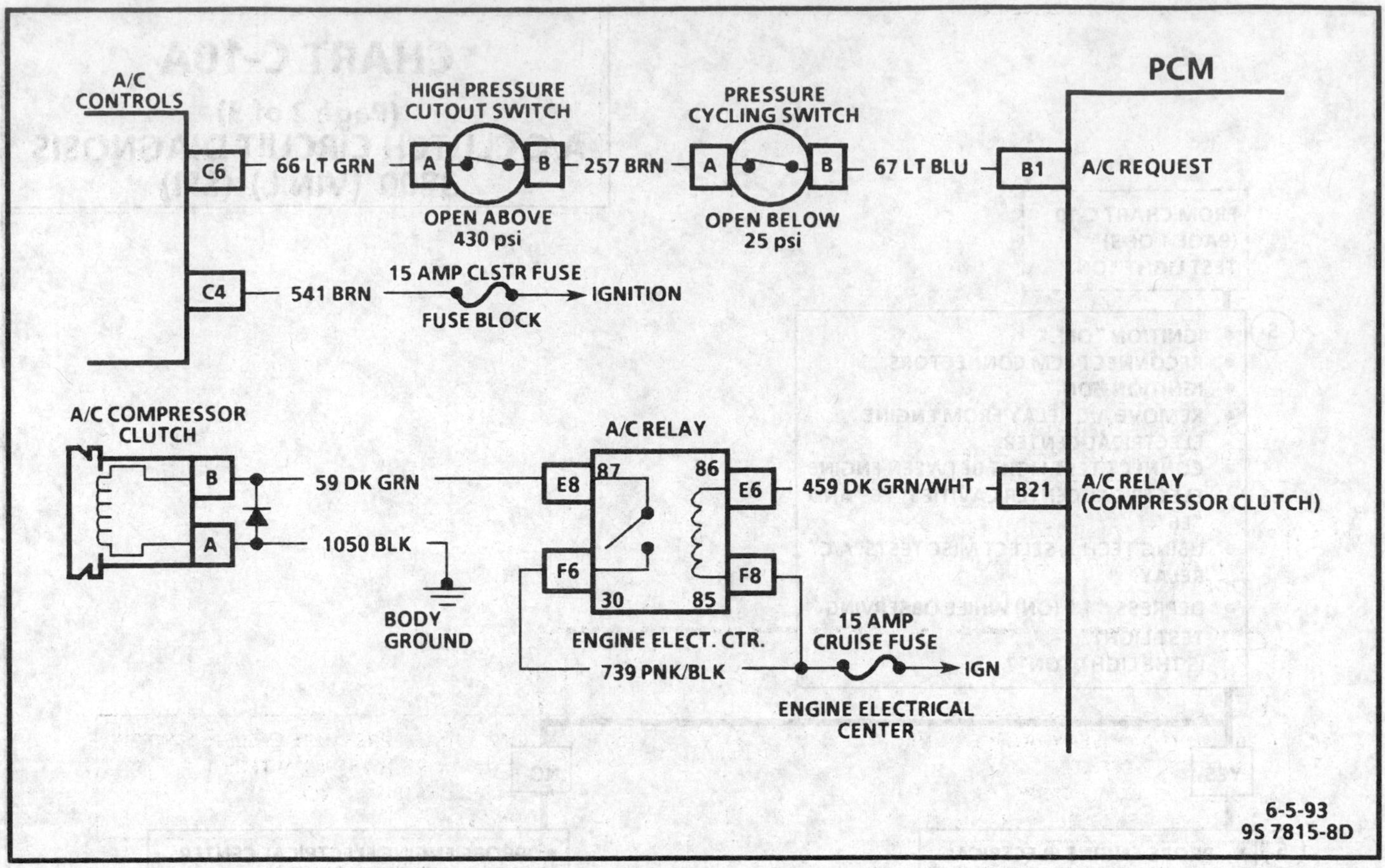
A/C CONTROLS
HIGH PRESSURE CUTOUT SWITCH
PRESSURE CYCLING SWITCH
PCM
C6
66 LT GRN
A
B
257 BRN
A
B
67 LT BLU
B1
A/C REQUEST
OPEN ABOVE 430 psi
OPEN BELOW 25 psi
15 AMP CLSTR FUSE
C4
541 BRN
IGNITION
FUSE BLOCK
A/C COMPRESSOR CLUTCH
A/C RELAY
B
59 DK GRN
E8
87
86
E6
459 DK GRN/WHT
B21
A/C RELAY (COMPRESSOR CLUTCH)
A
1050 BLK
F6
F8
30
85
BODY GROUND
ENGINE ELECT. CTR.
15 AMP CRUISE FUSE
739 PNK/BLK
IGN
ENGINE ELECTRICAL CENTER
6-5-93
9S 7815-8D

CHART C-10A

(Page 3 of 3)
A/C CLUTCH CIRCUIT DIAGNOSIS
3800 (VIN L) (SFI)

Circuit Description:

The A/C relay is PCM controlled to delay A/C clutch engagement .4 second after A/C is turned "ON." This allows the IAC to adjust engine RPM before the A/C clutch engages. The PCM also causes the relay to disengage the A/C clutch during WOT operation. The A/C relay is energized when the PCM provides a ground path for CKT 459. The PCM may apply the A/C clutch during cranking to prevent A/C slugging during startup.

Chart Test Description: Number(s) below refer to circled number(s) on the diagnostic chart.

8. Determines whether or not the PCM is turning the A/C relay "ON" due to a false A/C request.
9. Isolates problem to the A/C control head and CKTs 604 and 762 to the pressure cycling switch or CKT 67 and the PCM.
10. Checks for CKT 59 shorted to B+ or a faulty compressor clutch.
11. Determines whether the A/C relay is faulty or the A/C relay control circuit (CKT 459) is grounded all the time.

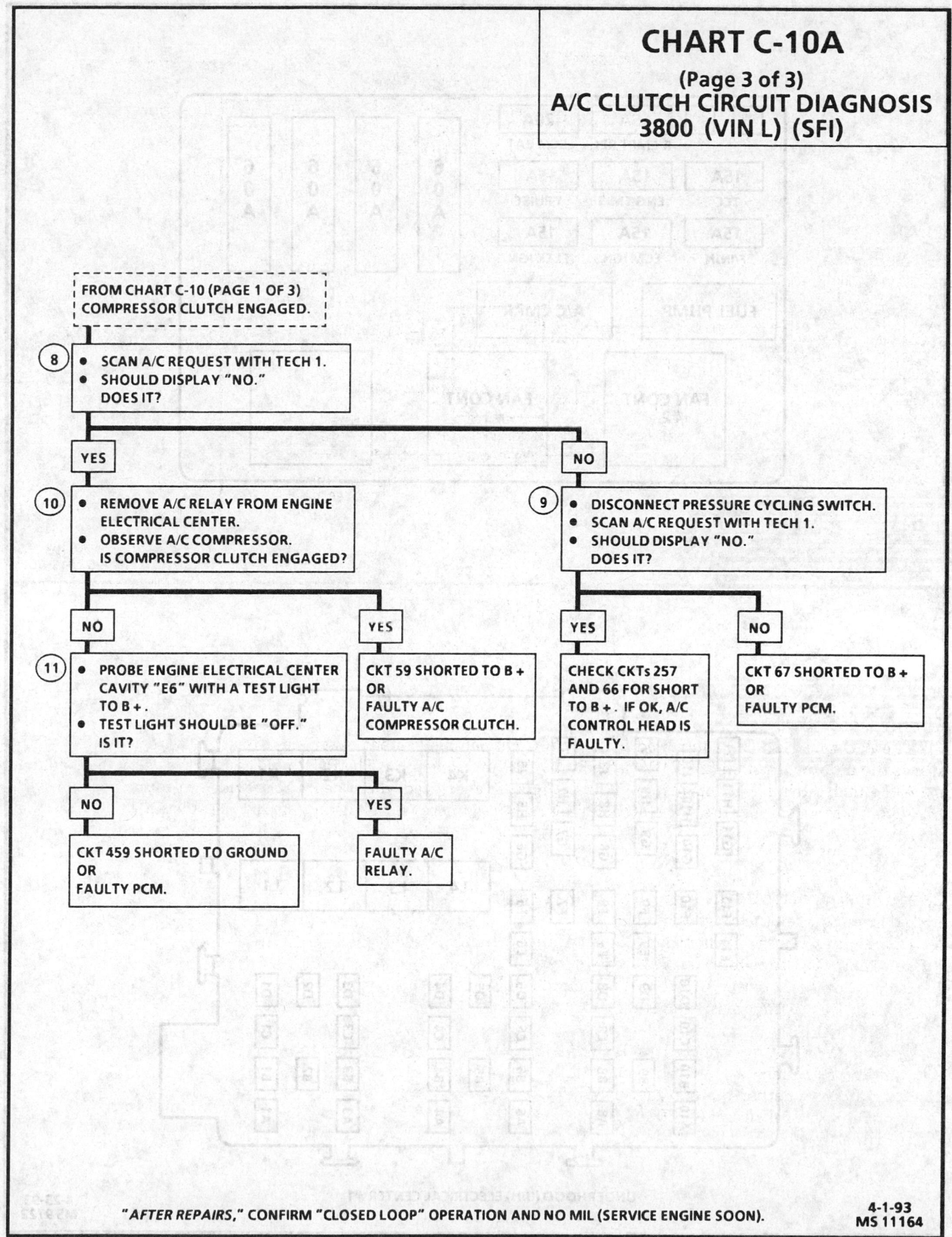

CHART C-10A

(Page 3 of 3)
A/C CLUTCH CIRCUIT DIAGNOSIS
3800 (VIN L) (SFI)

FROM CHART C-10 (PAGE 1 OF 3)
COMPRESSOR CLUTCH ENGAGED.

(8)
- SCAN A/C REQUEST WITH TECH 1.
- SHOULD DISPLAY "NO."
DOES IT?

YES

(10)
- REMOVE A/C RELAY FROM ENGINE ELECTRICAL CENTER.
- OBSERVE A/C COMPRESSOR.
IS COMPRESSOR CLUTCH ENGAGED?

NO

(11)
- PROBE ENGINE ELECTRICAL CENTER CAVITY "E6" WITH A TEST LIGHT TO B + .
- TEST LIGHT SHOULD BE "OFF."
IS IT?

NO

CKT 459 SHORTED TO GROUND
OR
FAULTY PCM.

YES

FAULTY A/C RELAY.

YES

CKT 59 SHORTED TO B +
OR
FAULTY A/C COMPRESSOR CLUTCH.

NO

(9)
- DISCONNECT PRESSURE CYCLING SWITCH.
- SCAN A/C REQUEST WITH TECH 1.
- SHOULD DISPLAY "NO."
DOES IT?

YES

CHECK CKTs 257 AND 66 FOR SHORT TO B + . IF OK, A/C CONTROL HEAD IS FAULTY.

NO

CKT 67 SHORTED TO B +
OR
FAULTY PCM.

"*AFTER REPAIRS,*" CONFIRM "CLOSED LOOP" OPERATION AND NO MIL (SERVICE ENGINE SOON).

4-1-93
MS 11164

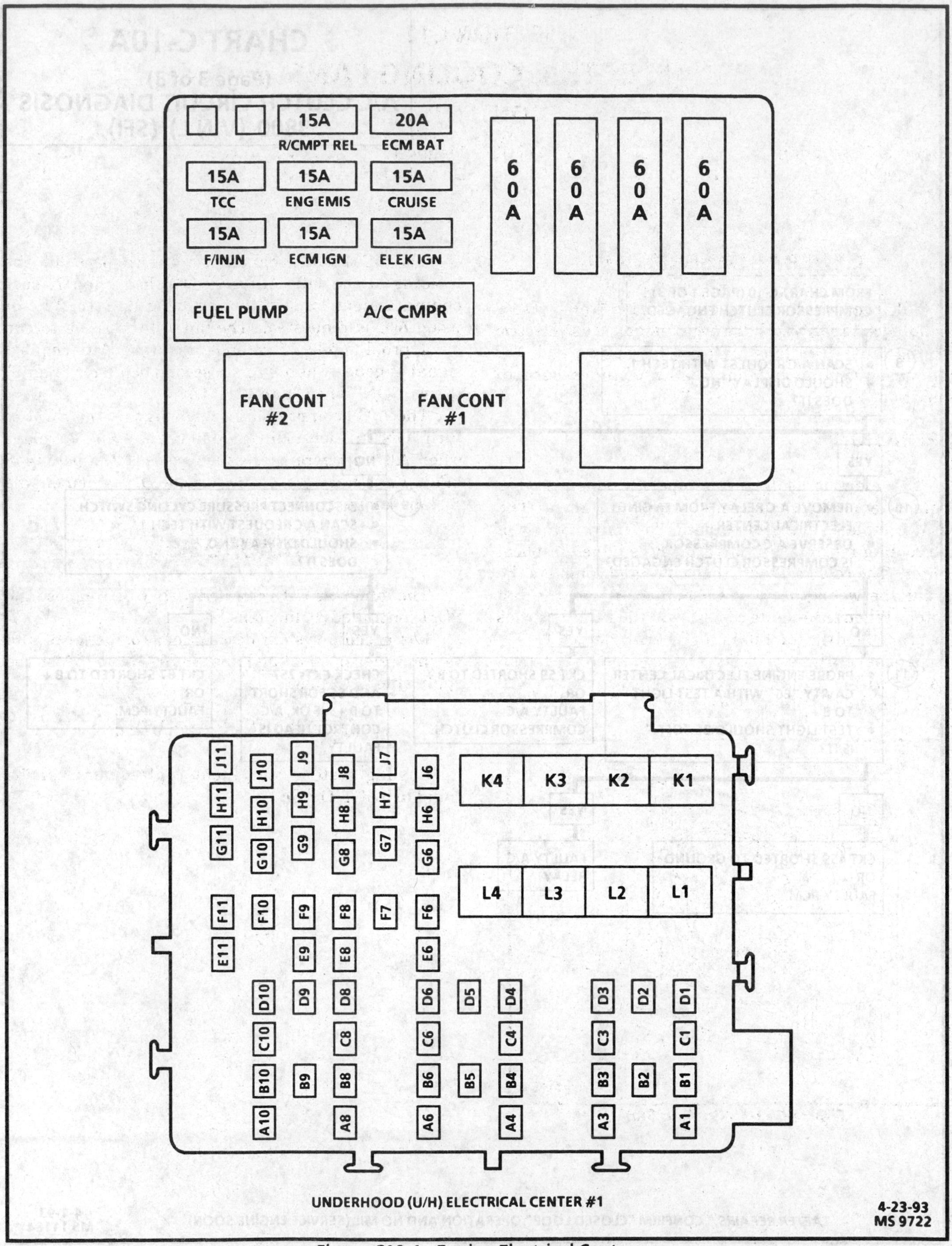
15A
R/CMPT REL
20A
ECM BAT
15A
TCC
15A
ENG EMIS
15A
CRUISE
15A
F/INJN
15A
ECM IGN
15A
ELEK IGN
60A
60A
60A
60A
FUEL PUMP
A/C CMPR
FAN CONT #2
FAN CONT #1
J11 J10 J9 J8 J7 J6
H11 H10 H9 H8 H7 H6
G11 G10 G9 G8 G7 G6
K4 K3 K2 K1
L4 L3 L2 L1
F11 F10 F9 F8 F7 F6
E11 E9 E8 E6
D10 D9 D8 D6 D5 D4 D3 D2 D1
C10 C8 C6 C4 C3 C1
B10 B9 B8 B6 B5 B4 B3 B2 B1
A10 A8 A6 A4 A3 A1
UNDERHOOD (U/H) ELECTRICAL CENTER #1
4-23-93
MS 9722

Figure C10-1 - Engine Electrical Center

SECTION C12

ELECTRIC COOLING FANS

CONTENTS

GENERAL DESCRIPTION

All front wheel drive vehicles with transversely mounted engines, and some other vehicles, use electric cooling fans. The fans are used for engine and A/C condenser cooling but only operate under certain conditions.

OPERATION

The electric cooling fans operate when engine coolant temperature exceeds a certain value. The PCM completes the ground paths for the windings of the cooling fan relays located in the engine electrical center. The relay contacts then close and complete the circuit between the 60 amp maxifuse and the fan motor. When the engine cools down, the PCM removes the ground for the fan relays and the fans stop.

Whenever there is a fan "ON" request the left fan (Fan 1) will be running. The left and right fans will run when "Fans 1 and 2" are called for.

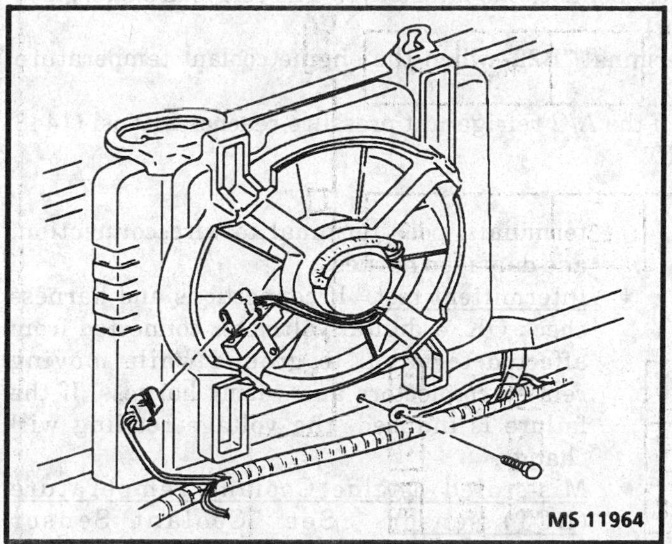
MS 11964

Figure C12-1 - Cooling Fan

The PCM will complete the ground path for the winding of the left fan (Fan 1) relay when it sees engine coolant temperature above 100°C (212°F) or when A/C is requested. The fan will continue to run for approximately 45 seconds after the A/C request signal is gone. There is a six second delay for "Fan 2" to turn "ON" when "Fan 1" is "ON."

The A/C head pressure switch signals the PCM to turn "ON" the left and right fan (Fans 1 and 2) relays when A/C refrigerant pressure exceeds 210 psi (1448 kPa). Fans 1 and 2 are also turned "ON" when engine coolant temperature is above 108°C (226°F).

DIAGNOSIS

The following C-12 circuit charts will diagnose the PCM controlled cooling fans.

For specific system description, components and wiring, refer to "Cooling Fans" in SECTION 8A or the applicable C-12 charts.

ON-VEHICLE SERVICE

Cooling system component replacement can be found in SECTION 6B.

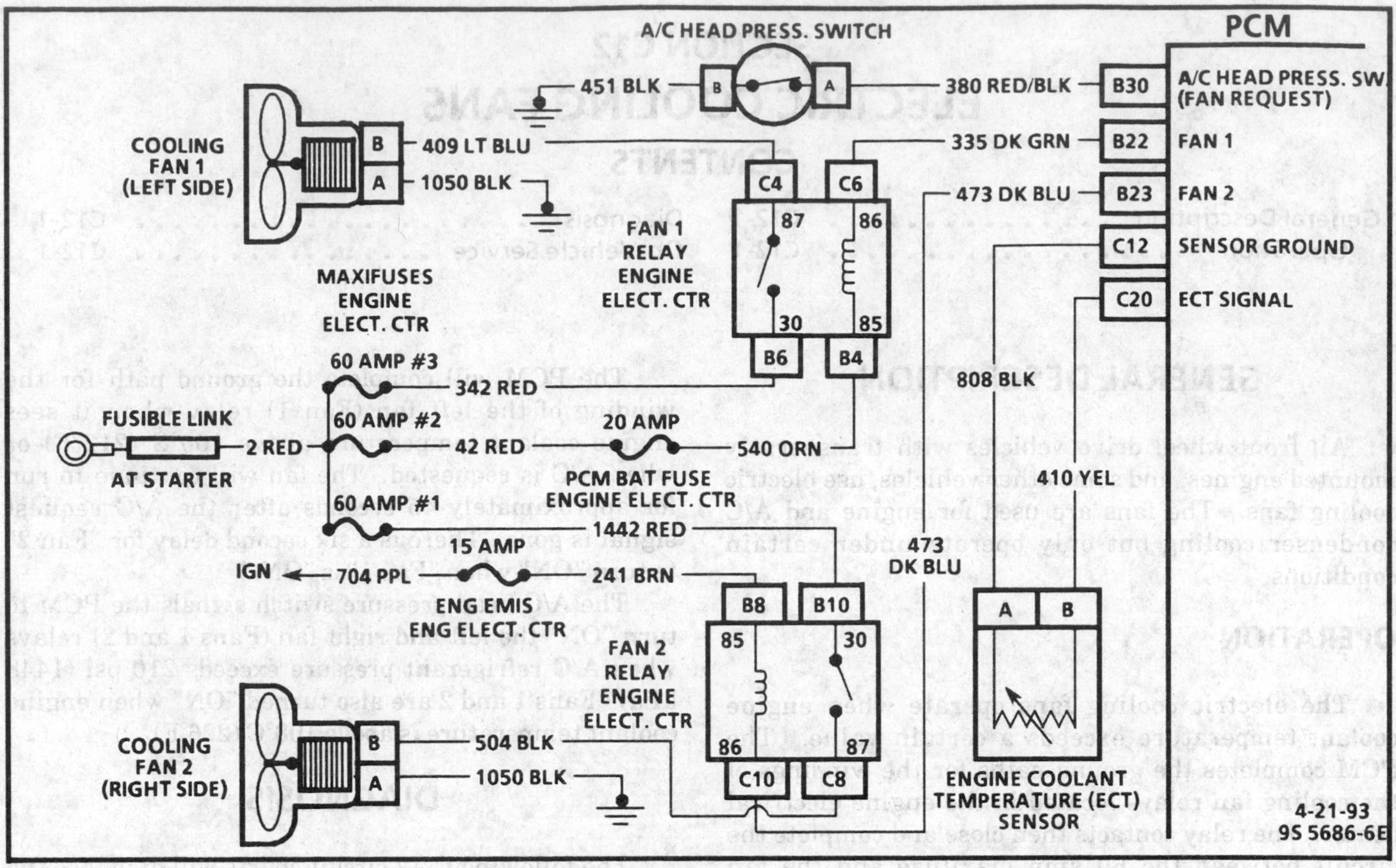
A/C HEAD PRESS. SWITCH
PCM
451 BLK
380 RED/BLK
B30
A/C HEAD PRESS. SW. (FAN REQUEST)
COOLING FAN 1 (LEFT SIDE)
409 LT BLU
1050 BLK
335 DK GRN
B22
FAN 1
C4
C6
473 DK BLU
B23
FAN 2
FAN 1 RELAY ENGINE ELECT. CTR
87
86
C12
SENSOR GROUND
MAXIFUSES ENGINE ELECT. CTR
C20
ECT SIGNAL
30
85
B6
B4
60 AMP #3
342 RED
808 BLK
FUSIBLE LINK AT STARTER
2 RED
60 AMP #2
42 RED
20 AMP
540 ORN
PCM BAT FUSE ENGINE ELECT. CTR
410 YEL
60 AMP #1
1442 RED
473 DK BLU
IGN
704 PPL
15 AMP
241 BRN
ENG EMIS ENG ELECT. CTR
B8
B10
FAN 2 RELAY ENGINE ELECT. CTR
85
30
A
B
COOLING FAN 2 (RIGHT SIDE)
504 BLK
1050 BLK
86
87
C10
C8
ENGINE COOLANT TEMPERATURE (ECT) SENSOR
4-21-93
9S 5686-6E

CHART C-12A
COOLING FAN(S) CHECK
3800 (VIN L) (SFI)

Circuit Description:

Power for the fan motors comes from 60 amp maxifuse elements to the fan relays. The relays are energized when current flows to ground through the PCM (Quad-Driver).

Fan 1 relay - The PCM energizes the relay through terminal "B22" when the engine coolant temperature reaches 100°C (212°F) or when A/C is requested.

Fan 2 relay - The Fan 2 relay is energized by the PCM if the A/C refrigerant pressure reaches 210 psi (1448 kPa) or the engine coolant temperature reaches 108°C (226°F).

Chart Test Description: Number(s) below refer to circled number(s) on the diagnostic chart.

1. Using the Tech 1 misc. tests, "Fan 1" control will cause the PCM to ground CKT 335, energizing the Fan 1 relay.
2. Selecting "Fan 2" with the Tech 1 allows control of CKT 473 and the Fan 2 relay.
3. Disconnecting the A/C head pressure switch should cause both fans to run.

Diagnostic Aids: An intermittent may be caused by a poor connection, rubbed through wire insulation, or a wire broken inside the insulation.

Check for:

- Poor connection or damaged harness. Inspect PCM harness connectors for backed out terminals "B22" or "B23", improper mating, broken locks, improperly formed or damaged terminals, poor terminal to wire connection, and damaged harness.
- Intermittent test. If connections and harness check OK, a digital voltmeter connected from affected terminal to ground while moving related connectors and wiring harness. If the failure is induced, the voltage reading will change.
- Mis-scaled Engine Coolant Temperature (ECT) sensor. See "Coolant Sensor Temperature vs. Resistance Values" table on DTC P0117 chart in "Engine Components/ Wiring Diagrams/Diagnostic Charts," Section "6E3-A".
- Basic cooling system problem. Refer to SECTION 6B for engine cooling and radiator diagnosis.

CHART C-12A

COOLING FAN(S) CHECK 3800 (VIN L) (SFI)

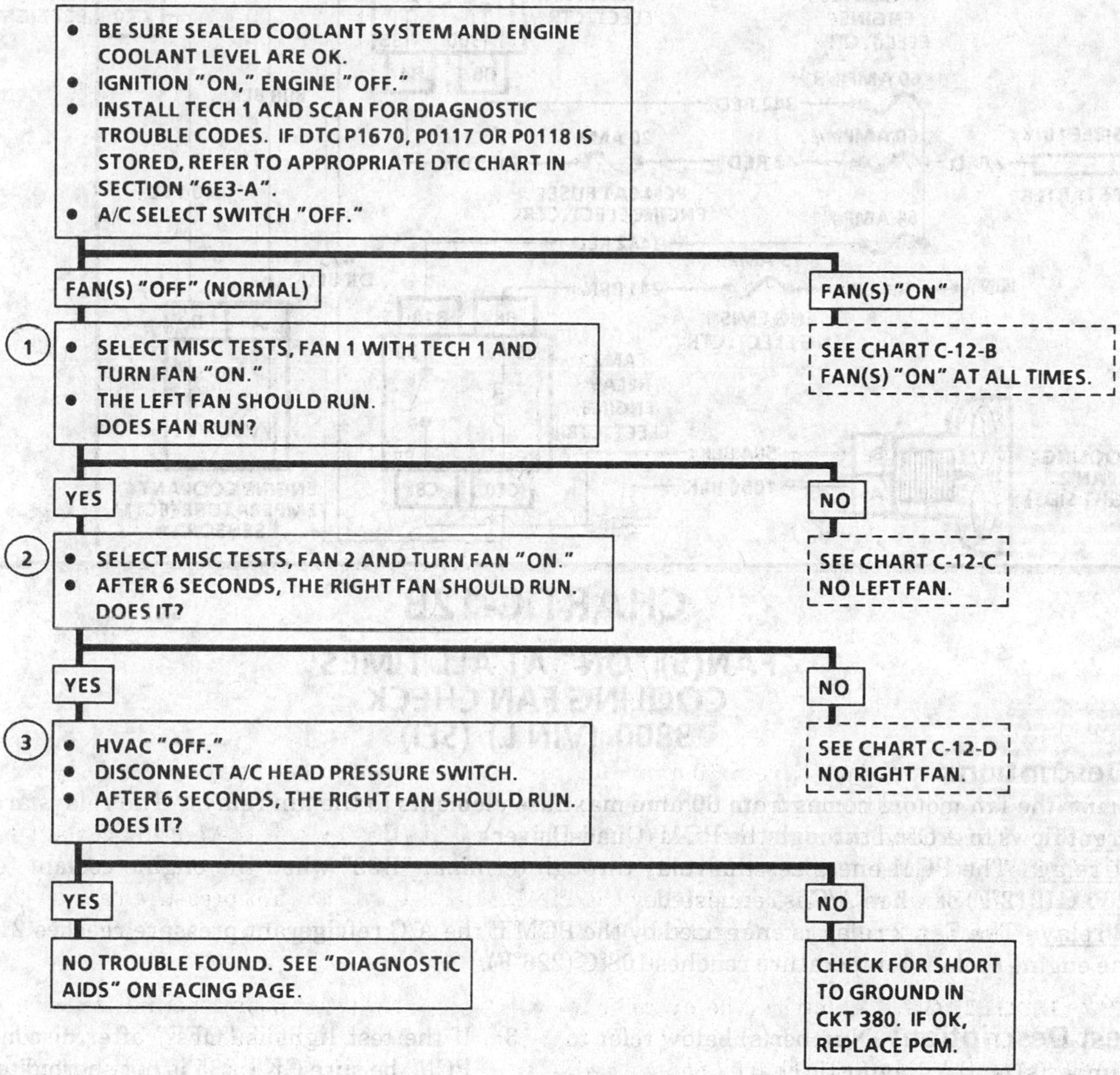
• BE SURE SEALED COOLANT SYSTEM AND ENGINE COOLANT LEVEL ARE OK.
• IGNITION "ON," ENGINE "OFF."
• INSTALL TECH 1 AND SCAN FOR DIAGNOSTIC TROUBLE CODES. IF DTC P1670, P0117 OR P0118 IS STORED, REFER TO APPROPRIATE DTC CHART IN SECTION "6E3-A".
• A/C SELECT SWITCH "OFF."
FAN(S) "OFF" (NORMAL)
FAN(S) "ON"
SEE CHART C-12-B FAN(S) "ON" AT ALL TIMES.
1
• SELECT MISC TESTS, FAN 1 WITH TECH 1 AND TURN FAN "ON."
• THE LEFT FAN SHOULD RUN. DOES FAN RUN?
YES
NO
SEE CHART C-12-C NO LEFT FAN.
2
• SELECT MISC TESTS, FAN 2 AND TURN FAN "ON."
• AFTER 6 SECONDS, THE RIGHT FAN SHOULD RUN. DOES IT?
YES
NO
SEE CHART C-12-D NO RIGHT FAN.
3
• HVAC "OFF."
• DISCONNECT A/C HEAD PRESSURE SWITCH.
• AFTER 6 SECONDS, THE RIGHT FAN SHOULD RUN. DOES IT?
YES
NO
NO TROUBLE FOUND. SEE "DIAGNOSTIC AIDS" ON FACING PAGE.
CHECK FOR SHORT TO GROUND IN CKT 380. IF OK, REPLACE PCM.

"AFTER REPAIRS," CONFIRM "CLOSED LOOP" OPERATION AND NO MIL (SERVICE ENGINE SOON).

6-3-93
MS 12831

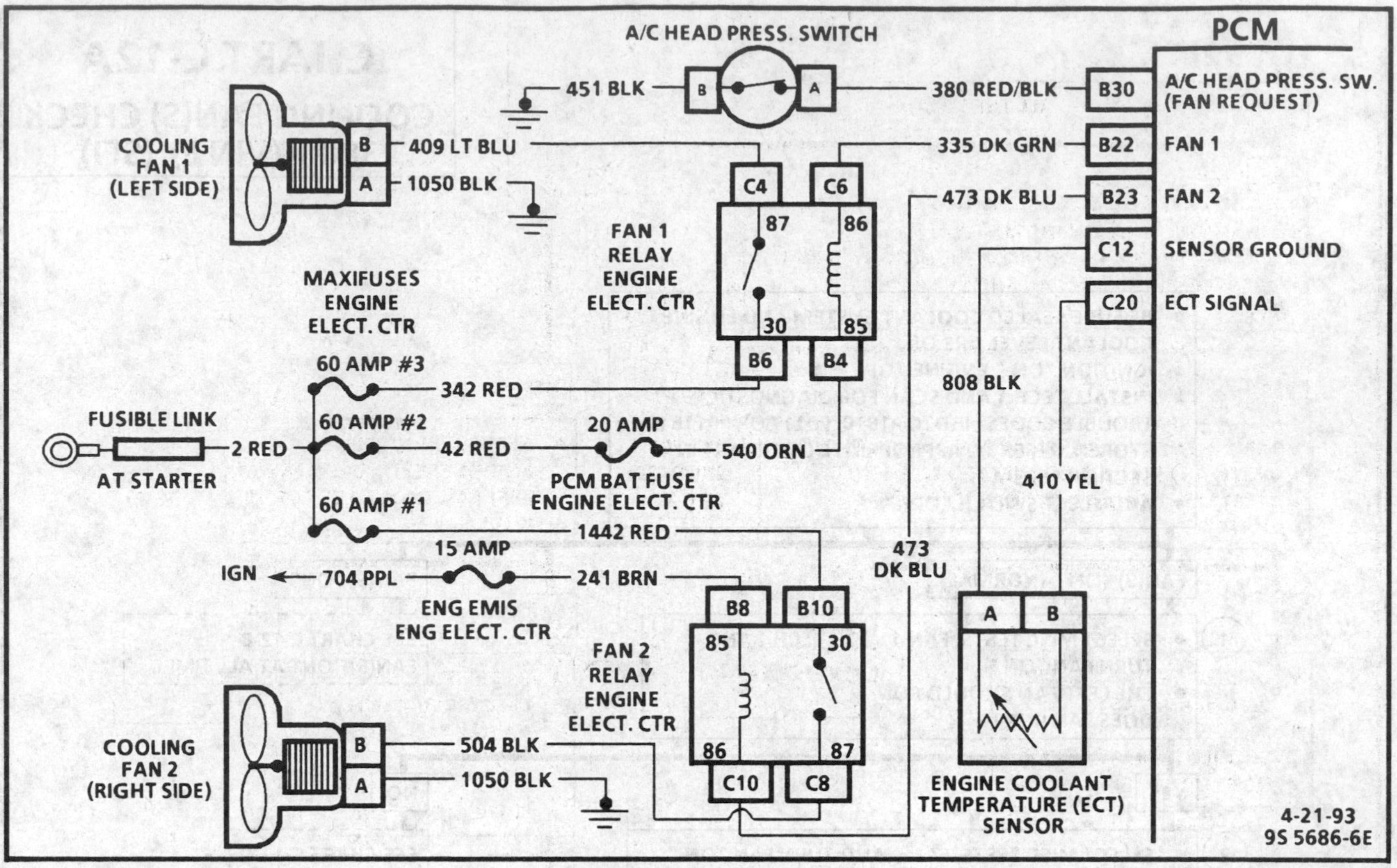

A/C HEAD PRESS. SWITCH
PCM
451 BLK
B
A
380 RED/BLK
B30
A/C HEAD PRESS. SW. (FAN REQUEST)
COOLING FAN 1 (LEFT SIDE)
409 LT BLU
1050 BLK
335 DK GRN
B22
FAN 1
C4
C6
473 DK BLU
B23
FAN 2
87
86
FAN 1 RELAY ENGINE ELECT. CTR
C12
SENSOR GROUND
MAXIFUSES ENGINE ELECT. CTR
C20
ECT SIGNAL
30
85
B6
B4
60 AMP #3
808 BLK
342 RED
FUSIBLE LINK
60 AMP #2
20 AMP
2 RED
42 RED
540 ORN
AT STARTER
PCM BAT FUSE ENGINE ELECT. CTR
410 YEL
60 AMP #1
1442 RED
15 AMP
473 DK BLU
IGN
704 PPL
241 BRN
ENG EMIS ENG ELECT. CTR
B8
B10
85
30
FAN 2 RELAY ENGINE ELECT. CTR
COOLING FAN 2 (RIGHT SIDE)
504 BLK
1050 BLK
86
87
C10
C8
ENGINE COOLANT TEMPERATURE (ECT) SENSOR
4-21-93
9S 5686-6E

CHART C-12B

FAN(S) "ON" AT ALL TIMES
COOLING FAN CHECK
3800 (VIN L) (SFI)

Circuit Description:

Power for the fan motors comes from 60 amp maxifuse elements to the fan relays. The relays are energized when current flows to ground through the PCM (Quad-Driver).

Fan 1 relay - The PCM energizes the relay through terminal "B22" when the engine coolant temperature reaches 100°C (212°F) or when A/C is requested.

Fan 2 relay - The Fan 2 relay is energized by the PCM if the A/C refrigerant pressure reaches 210 psi (1448 kPa) or the engine coolant temperature reaches 108°C (226°F).

Chart Test Description: Number(s) below refer to circled number(s) on the diagnostic chart.

1. Checks to see if CKT 473 is grounded all the time. A light indicates the wire is shorted to ground; the following steps will isolate the problem.
2. Checks to see if CKT 335 is grounded all the time, which would keep the relay closed at all times.
3. If the test light is "OFF" after disconnecting the PCM, be sure CKT 335 is not shorted to B+. If not shorted to B+, the PCM is shorted internally.
4. If the test light is "OFF" after disconnecting the PCM, be sure CKT 473 is not shorted to B+. If not shorted to B+, the PCM is shorted internally.

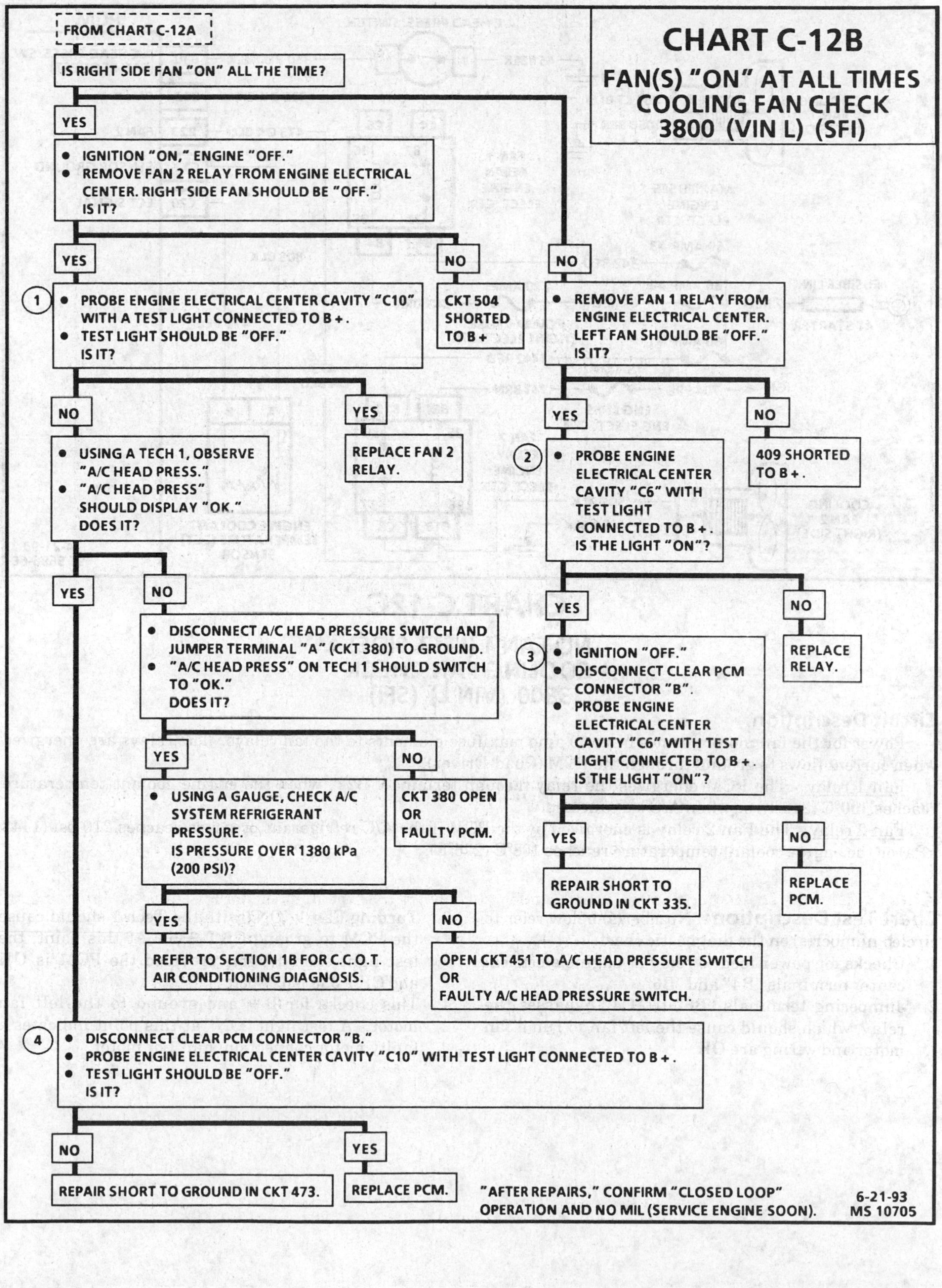
CHART C-12B
FAN(S) "ON" AT ALL TIMES
COOLING FAN CHECK
3800 (VIN L) (SFI)
FROM CHART C-12A
IS RIGHT SIDE FAN "ON" ALL THE TIME?
YES
• IGNITION "ON," ENGINE "OFF."
• REMOVE FAN 2 RELAY FROM ENGINE ELECTRICAL CENTER. RIGHT SIDE FAN SHOULD BE "OFF." IS IT?
YES
NO
CKT 504 SHORTED TO B +
NO
1
• PROBE ENGINE ELECTRICAL CENTER CAVITY "C10" WITH A TEST LIGHT CONNECTED TO B +.
• TEST LIGHT SHOULD BE "OFF." IS IT?
NO
YES
REPLACE FAN 2 RELAY.
• USING A TECH 1, OBSERVE "A/C HEAD PRESS."
• "A/C HEAD PRESS" SHOULD DISPLAY "OK." DOES IT?
YES
NO
• DISCONNECT A/C HEAD PRESSURE SWITCH AND JUMPER TERMINAL "A" (CKT 380) TO GROUND.
• "A/C HEAD PRESS" ON TECH 1 SHOULD SWITCH TO "OK." DOES IT?
YES
NO
• USING A GAUGE, CHECK A/C SYSTEM REFRIGERANT PRESSURE. IS PRESSURE OVER 1380 kPa (200 PSI)?
CKT 380 OPEN OR FAULTY PCM.
YES
NO
REFER TO SECTION 1B FOR C.C.O.T. AIR CONDITIONING DIAGNOSIS.
OPEN CKT 451 TO A/C HEAD PRESSURE SWITCH OR FAULTY A/C HEAD PRESSURE SWITCH.
• REMOVE FAN 1 RELAY FROM ENGINE ELECTRICAL CENTER. LEFT FAN SHOULD BE "OFF." IS IT?
YES
NO
409 SHORTED TO B +.
2
• PROBE ENGINE ELECTRICAL CENTER CAVITY "C6" WITH TEST LIGHT CONNECTED TO B +. IS THE LIGHT "ON"?
YES
NO
REPLACE RELAY.
3
• IGNITION "OFF."
• DISCONNECT CLEAR PCM CONNECTOR "B".
• PROBE ENGINE ELECTRICAL CENTER CAVITY "C6" WITH TEST LIGHT CONNECTED TO B +. IS THE LIGHT "ON"?
YES
NO
REPAIR SHORT TO GROUND IN CKT 335.
REPLACE PCM.
4
• DISCONNECT CLEAR PCM CONNECTOR "B."
• PROBE ENGINE ELECTRICAL CENTER CAVITY "C10" WITH TEST LIGHT CONNECTED TO B +.
• TEST LIGHT SHOULD BE "OFF." IS IT?
NO
YES
REPAIR SHORT TO GROUND IN CKT 473.
REPLACE PCM.
"AFTER REPAIRS," CONFIRM "CLOSED LOOP" OPERATION AND NO MIL (SERVICE ENGINE SOON).
6-21-93
MS 10705

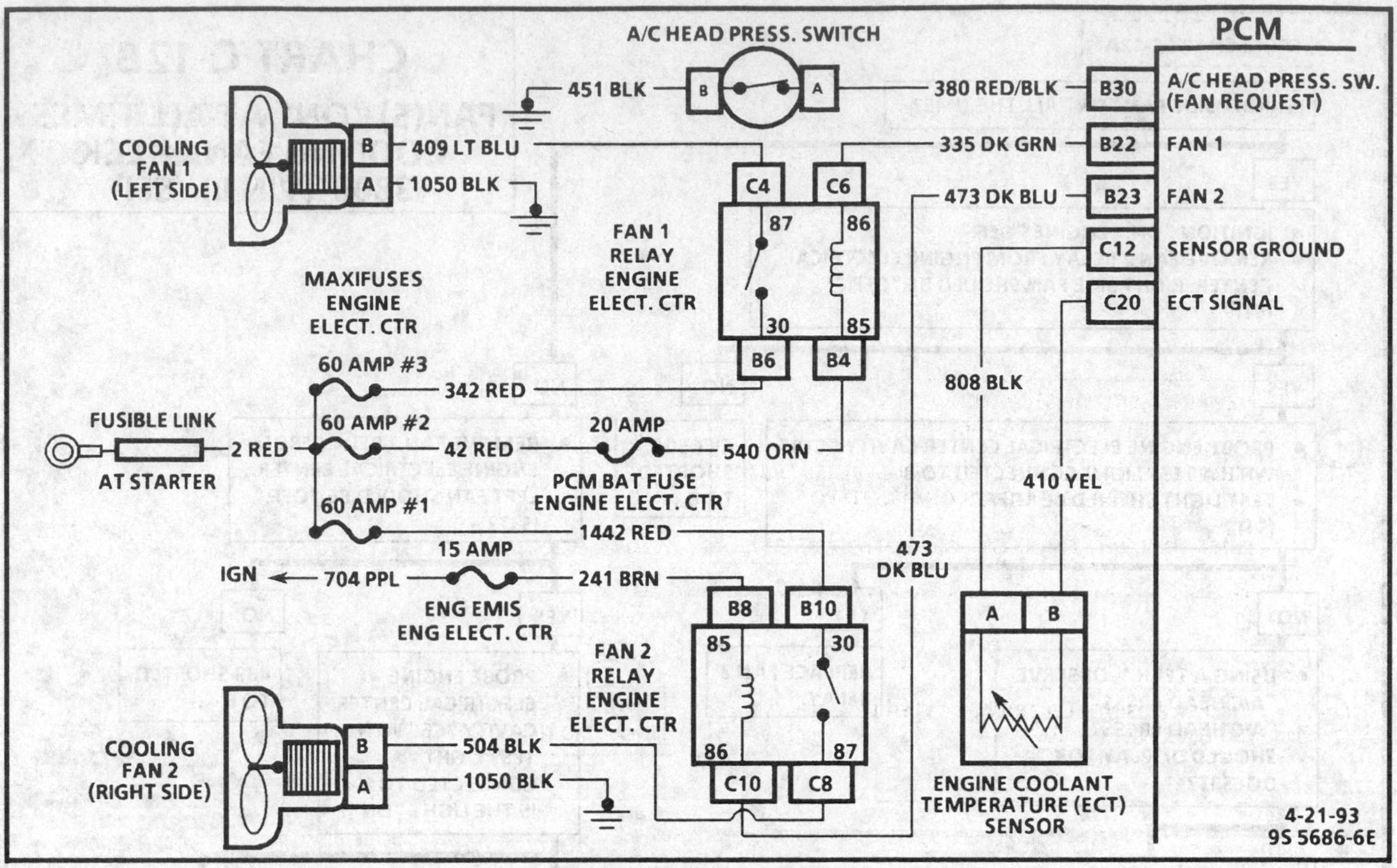
A/C HEAD PRESS. SWITCH
PCM
451 BLK
380 RED/BLK
B30
A/C HEAD PRESS. SW. (FAN REQUEST)
COOLING FAN 1 (LEFT SIDE)
409 LT BLU
1050 BLK
335 DK GRN
B22
FAN 1
473 DK BLU
B23
FAN 2
C4
C6
FAN 1 RELAY ENGINE ELECT. CTR
87
86
30
85
C12
SENSOR GROUND
C20
ECT SIGNAL
MAXIFUSES ENGINE ELECT. CTR
B6
B4
60 AMP #3
342 RED
808 BLK
FUSIBLE LINK
60 AMP #2
20 AMP
2 RED
42 RED
540 ORN
AT STARTER
PCM BAT FUSE ENGINE ELECT. CTR
410 YEL
60 AMP #1
1442 RED
15 AMP
473 DK BLU
IGN
704 PPL
241 BRN
ENG EMIS ENG ELECT. CTR
B8
B10
FAN 2 RELAY ENGINE ELECT. CTR
COOLING FAN 2 (RIGHT SIDE)
504 BLK
1050 BLK
C10
C8
ENGINE COOLANT TEMPERATURE (ECT) SENSOR
4-21-93
9S 5686-6E

CHART C-12C
NO FAN 1 (LEFT SIDE) COOLING FAN CHECK 3800 (VIN L) (SFI)

Circuit Description:

Power for the fan motors comes from 60 amp maxifuse elements to the fan relays. The relays are energized when current flows to ground through the PCM (Quad-Driver).

Fan 1 relay - The PCM energizes the relay through terminal "B22" when the engine coolant temperature reaches 100°C (212°F) or when A/C is requested.

Fan 2 relay - The Fan 2 relay is energized by the PCM if the A/C refrigerant pressure reaches 210 psi (1448 kPa) or the engine coolant temperature reaches 108°C (226°F).

Chart Test Description:

Number(s) below refer to circled number(s) on the diagnostic chart.

1. Checks for power feed to relay at engine electrical center terminals "B4" and "B6".
2. Jumpering terminals "B6" to "C4" bypasses the relay, which should cause the left fan to run if fan motor and wiring are OK.
3. Turning Fan 1 "ON" with the Tech 1 should cause the PCM to ground CKT 335. At this point, the test light should light, provided the PCM is OK and CKT 335 isn't open.
4. This checks for B+ and ground to the left fan motor. A test light "ON" at this point indicates a faulty motor connection, Fan 1 or motor.

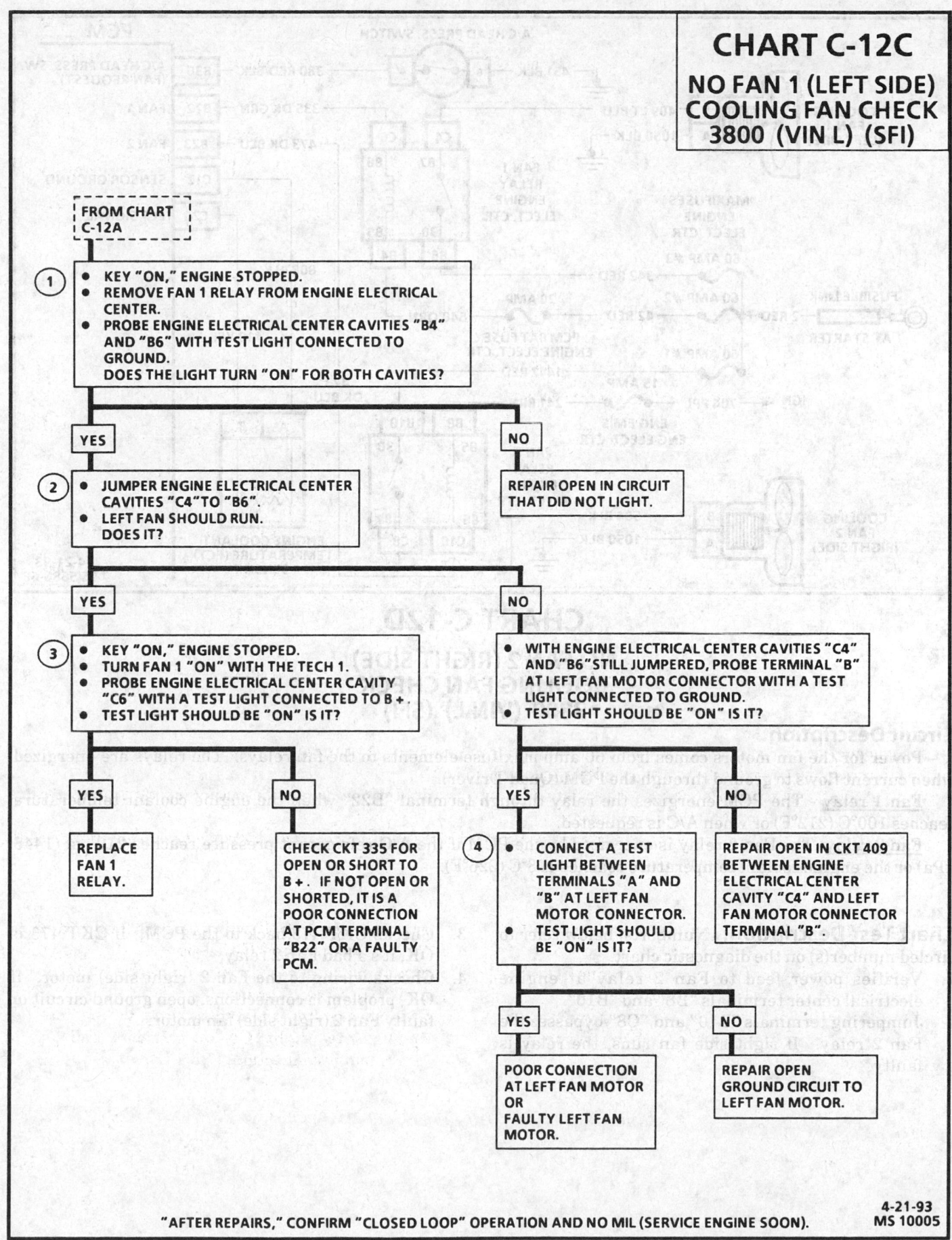

CHART C-12C

NO FAN 1 (LEFT SIDE) COOLING FAN CHECK 3800 (VIN L) (SFI)

FROM CHART C-12A

1
- KEY "ON," ENGINE STOPPED.
- REMOVE FAN 1 RELAY FROM ENGINE ELECTRICAL CENTER.
- PROBE ENGINE ELECTRICAL CENTER CAVITIES "B4" AND "B6" WITH TEST LIGHT CONNECTED TO GROUND.

DOES THE LIGHT TURN "ON" FOR BOTH CAVITIES?

- YES → go to 2
- NO → REPAIR OPEN IN CIRCUIT THAT DID NOT LIGHT.

2
- JUMPER ENGINE ELECTRICAL CENTER CAVITIES "C4" TO "B6".
- LEFT FAN SHOULD RUN.

DOES IT?

- YES → go to 3
- NO →
  - WITH ENGINE ELECTRICAL CENTER CAVITIES "C4" AND "B6" STILL JUMPERED, PROBE TERMINAL "B" AT LEFT FAN MOTOR CONNECTOR WITH A TEST LIGHT CONNECTED TO GROUND.
  - TEST LIGHT SHOULD BE "ON" IS IT?
    - YES → go to 4
    - NO → REPAIR OPEN IN CKT 409 BETWEEN ENGINE ELECTRICAL CENTER CAVITY "C4" AND LEFT FAN MOTOR CONNECTOR TERMINAL "B".

3
- KEY "ON," ENGINE STOPPED.
- TURN FAN 1 "ON" WITH THE TECH 1.
- PROBE ENGINE ELECTRICAL CENTER CAVITY "C6" WITH A TEST LIGHT CONNECTED TO B +.
- TEST LIGHT SHOULD BE "ON" IS IT?

- YES → REPLACE FAN 1 RELAY.
- NO → CHECK CKT 335 FOR OPEN OR SHORT TO B +. IF NOT OPEN OR SHORTED, IT IS A POOR CONNECTION AT PCM TERMINAL "B22" OR A FAULTY PCM.

4
- CONNECT A TEST LIGHT BETWEEN TERMINALS "A" AND "B" AT LEFT FAN MOTOR CONNECTOR.
- TEST LIGHT SHOULD BE "ON" IS IT?

- YES → POOR CONNECTION AT LEFT FAN MOTOR OR FAULTY LEFT FAN MOTOR.
- NO → REPAIR OPEN GROUND CIRCUIT TO LEFT FAN MOTOR.

"AFTER REPAIRS," CONFIRM "CLOSED LOOP" OPERATION AND NO MIL (SERVICE ENGINE SOON).

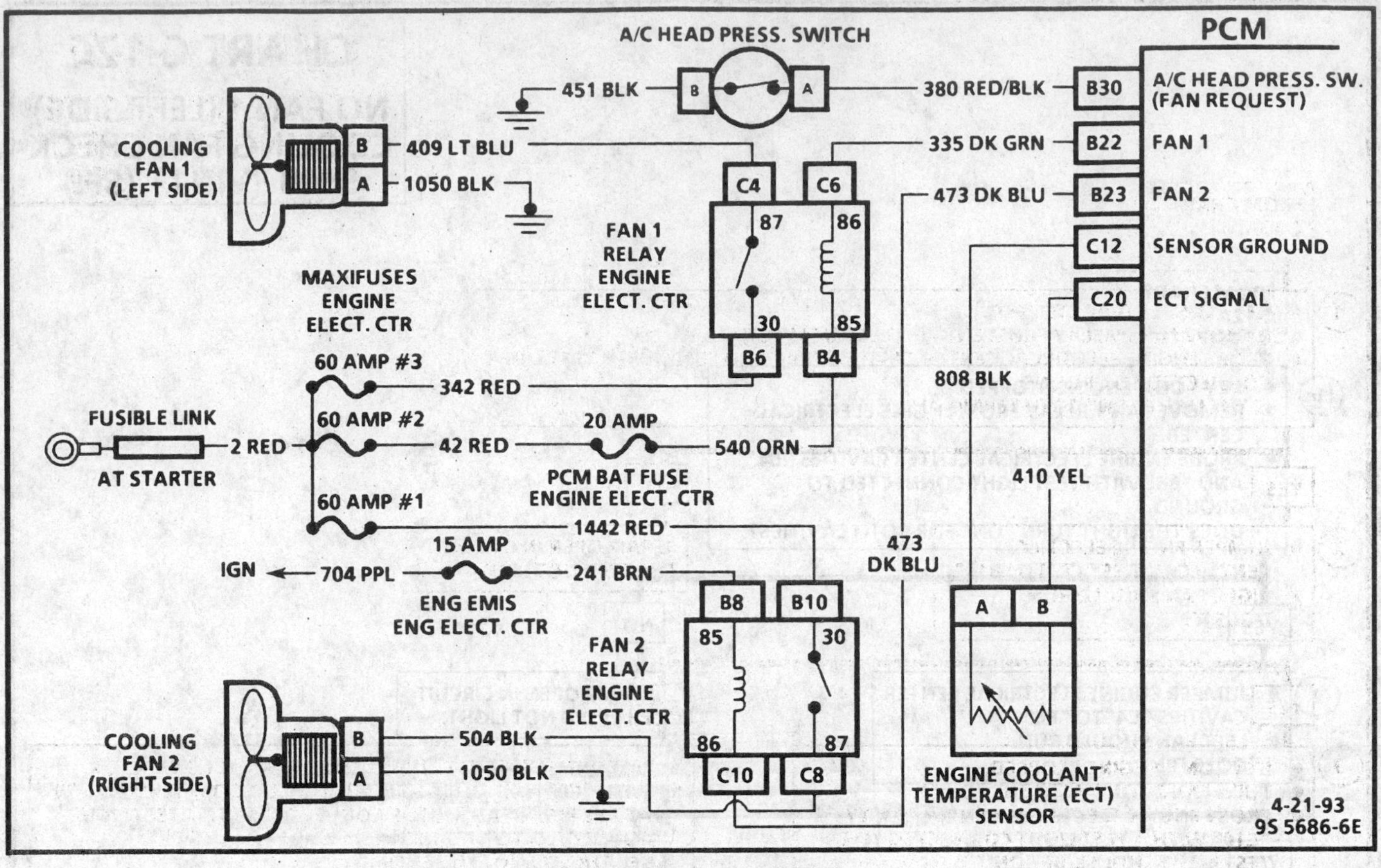
A/C HEAD PRESS. SWITCH
PCM
451 BLK
380 RED/BLK
B30
A/C HEAD PRESS. SW. (FAN REQUEST)
COOLING FAN 1 (LEFT SIDE)
409 LT BLU
1050 BLK
335 DK GRN
B22
FAN 1
473 DK BLU
B23
FAN 2
C4
C6
87
86
FAN 1 RELAY ENGINE ELECT. CTR
C12
SENSOR GROUND
MAXIFUSES ENGINE ELECT. CTR
C20
ECT SIGNAL
30
85
B6
B4
60 AMP #3
342 RED
808 BLK
FUSIBLE LINK
AT STARTER
2 RED
60 AMP #2
42 RED
20 AMP
540 ORN
PCM BAT FUSE ENGINE ELECT. CTR
410 YEL
60 AMP #1
1442 RED
15 AMP
473 DK BLU
IGN
704 PPL
241 BRN
ENG EMIS ENG ELECT. CTR
B8
B10
A
B
85
30
FAN 2 RELAY ENGINE ELECT. CTR
COOLING FAN 2 (RIGHT SIDE)
504 BLK
1050 BLK
86
87
C10
C8
ENGINE COOLANT TEMPERATURE (ECT) SENSOR
4-21-93
9S 5686-6E

CHART C-12D

NO FAN 2 (RIGHT SIDE) COOLING FAN CHECK 3800 (VIN L) (SFI)

Circuit Description:

Power for the fan motors comes from 60 amp maxifuse elements to the fan relays. The relays are energized when current flows to ground through the PCM (Quad-Driver).

Fan 1 relay - The PCM energizes the relay through terminal "B22" when the engine coolant temperature reaches 100°C (212°F) or when A/C is requested.

Fan 2 relay- The Fan 2 relay is energized by the PCM if the A/C refrigerant pressure reaches 210 psi (1448 kPa) or the engine coolant temperature reaches 108°C (226°F).

Chart Test Description: Number(s) below refer to circled number(s) on the diagnostic chart.

1. Verifies power feed to Fan 2 relay at engine electrical center terminals "B8" and "B10".
2. Jumpering terminals "B10" and "C8" bypasses the Fan 2 relay. If right side fan runs, the relay is faulty.
3. Checks CKT 473 back to the PCM. If CKT 473 is OK, it's a bad Fan 2 relay.
4. Checks wiring to the Fan 2 (right side) motor. If OK, problem is connections, open ground circuit or faulty Fan 2 (right side) fan motor.

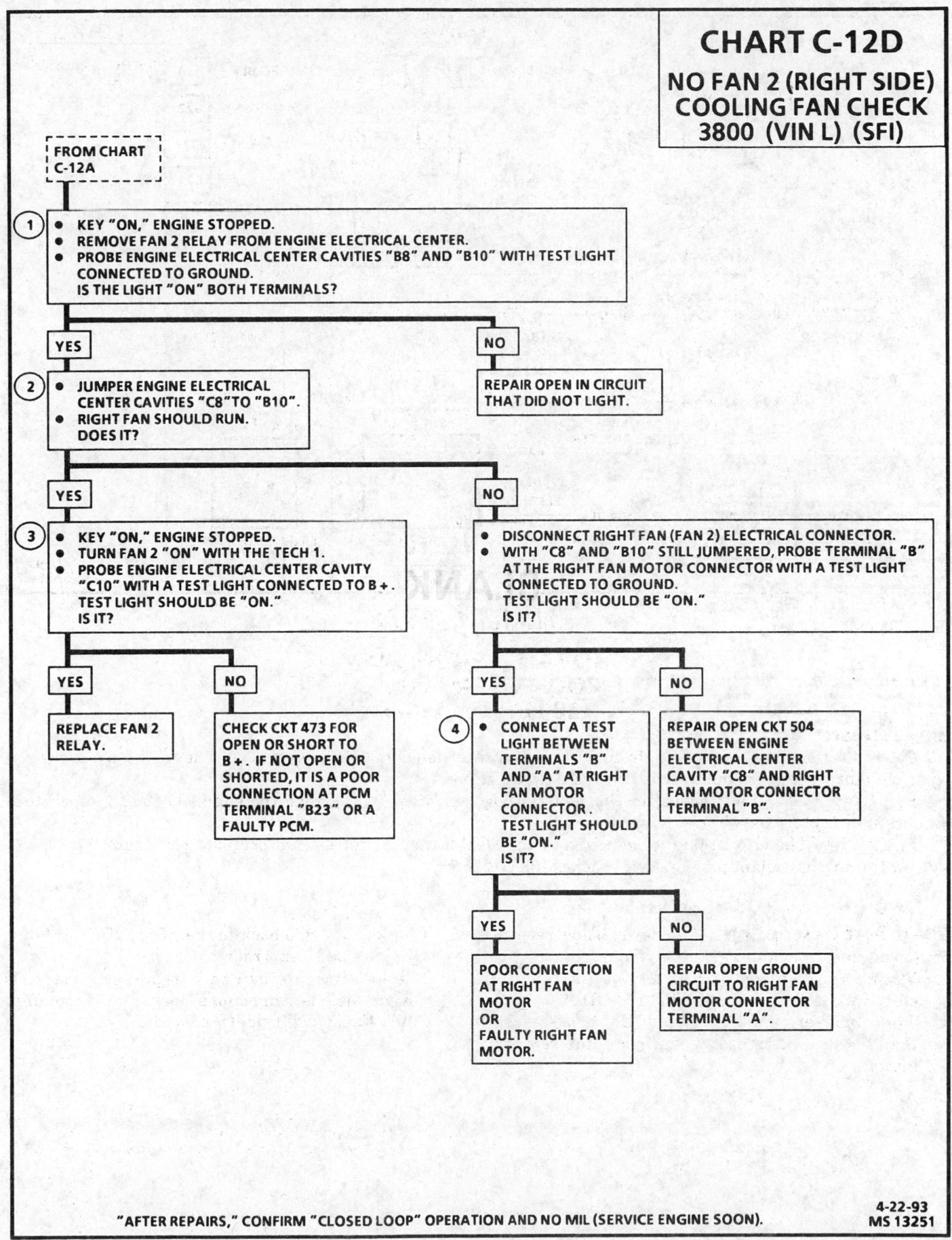

CHART C-12D

NO FAN 2 (RIGHT SIDE) COOLING FAN CHECK 3800 (VIN L) (SFI)

FROM CHART C-12A

1
- KEY "ON," ENGINE STOPPED.
- REMOVE FAN 2 RELAY FROM ENGINE ELECTRICAL CENTER.
- PROBE ENGINE ELECTRICAL CENTER CAVITIES "B8" AND "B10" WITH TEST LIGHT CONNECTED TO GROUND.

IS THE LIGHT "ON" BOTH TERMINALS?

YES → 2

NO → REPAIR OPEN IN CIRCUIT THAT DID NOT LIGHT.

2
- JUMPER ENGINE ELECTRICAL CENTER CAVITIES "C8" TO "B10".
- RIGHT FAN SHOULD RUN.

DOES IT?

YES → 3

NO →
- DISCONNECT RIGHT FAN (FAN 2) ELECTRICAL CONNECTOR.
- WITH "C8" AND "B10" STILL JUMPERED, PROBE TERMINAL "B" AT THE RIGHT FAN MOTOR CONNECTOR WITH A TEST LIGHT CONNECTED TO GROUND.

TEST LIGHT SHOULD BE "ON."
IS IT?

- YES → 4
- NO → REPAIR OPEN CKT 504 BETWEEN ENGINE ELECTRICAL CENTER CAVITY "C8" AND RIGHT FAN MOTOR CONNECTOR TERMINAL "B".

3
- KEY "ON," ENGINE STOPPED.
- TURN FAN 2 "ON" WITH THE TECH 1.
- PROBE ENGINE ELECTRICAL CENTER CAVITY "C10" WITH A TEST LIGHT CONNECTED TO B+.

TEST LIGHT SHOULD BE "ON."
IS IT?

- YES → REPLACE FAN 2 RELAY.
- NO → CHECK CKT 473 FOR OPEN OR SHORT TO B+. IF NOT OPEN OR SHORTED, IT IS A POOR CONNECTION AT PCM TERMINAL "B23" OR A FAULTY PCM.

4
- CONNECT A TEST LIGHT BETWEEN TERMINALS "B" AND "A" AT RIGHT FAN MOTOR CONNECTOR.

TEST LIGHT SHOULD BE "ON."
IS IT?

- YES → POOR CONNECTION AT RIGHT FAN MOTOR OR FAULTY RIGHT FAN MOTOR.
- NO → REPAIR OPEN GROUND CIRCUIT TO RIGHT FAN MOTOR CONNECTOR TERMINAL "A".

"AFTER REPAIRS," CONFIRM "CLOSED LOOP" OPERATION AND NO MIL (SERVICE ENGINE SOON).

4-22-93
MS 13251

BLANK

SECTION C13

CRANKCASE VENTILATION SYSTEM

CONTENTS

GENERAL DESCRIPTION

A crankcase ventilation system is used to consume crankcase vapors in the combustion process instead of venting them to atmosphere. Fresh air from the throttle body is supplied to the crankcase, mixed with blow-by gases and then passed through a crankcase ventilation valve into the intake manifold (Figure C13-1).

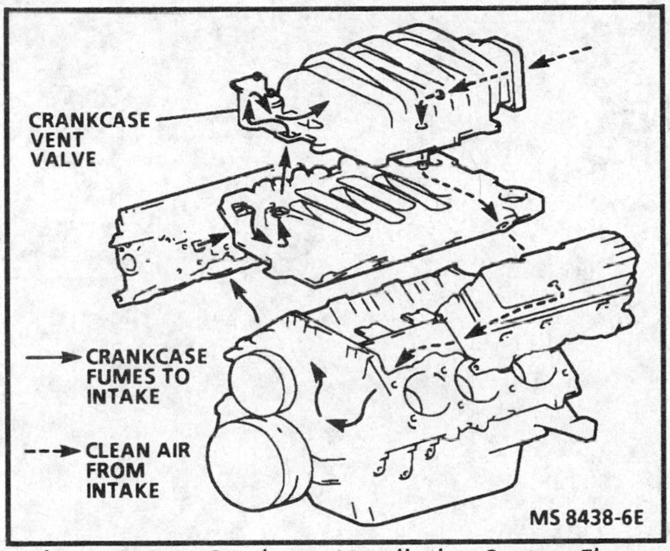

CRANKCASE VENT VALVE
CRANKCASE FUMES TO INTAKE
CLEAN AIR FROM INTAKE
MS 8438-6E

Figure C13-1 - Crankcase Ventilation System Flow

OPERATION

The primary control is through the crankcase ventilation valve (Figure C13-2) which meters the flow at a rate depending on inlet vacuum.

To maintain idle quality, the crankcase ventilation valve restricts the flow when inlet vacuum is high. If abnormal operating conditions arise, the system is designed to allow excessive amounts of blow-by gases to back flow through the crankcase vent into the throttle body to be consumed by normal combustion.

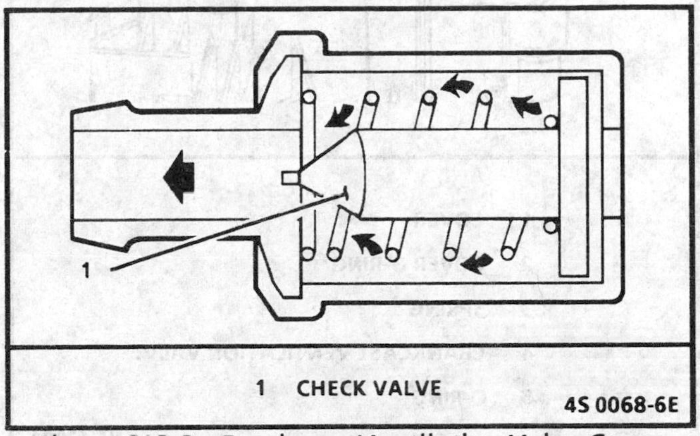

1
1 CHECK VALVE
4S 0068-6E

Figure C13-2 - Crankcase Ventilation Valve Cross Section

RESULTS OF INCORRECT OPERATION

- A plugged valve may cause:
  - Rough idle.
  - Stalling or slow idle speed.
  - Oil leaks.
  - Sludge in engine.
- A leaking valve would cause:
  - Rough idle.
  - Stalling.
  - High idle speed.

DIAGNOSIS

FUNCTIONAL CHECK OF CRANKCASE VENTILATION VALVE

If an engine is idling rough, check for a clogged crankcase ventilation valve. Replace as required. Use the following procedure:

1. Remove crankcase ventilation valve from intake manifold.
2. Shake valve and listen for the rattle of needle inside the valve. If valve does not rattle, replace valve.

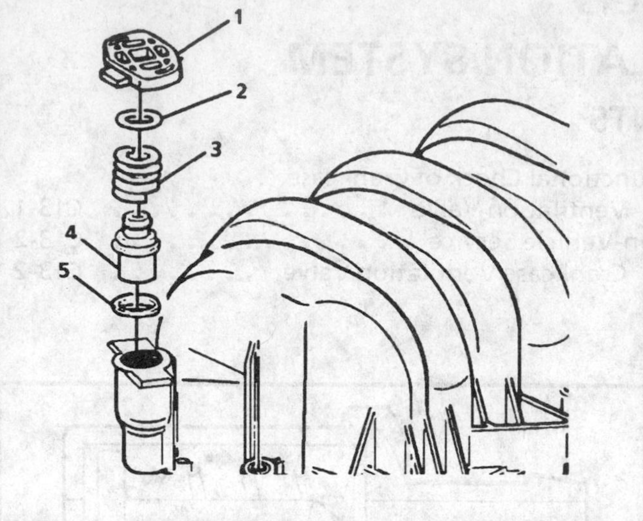
1
2
3
4
5

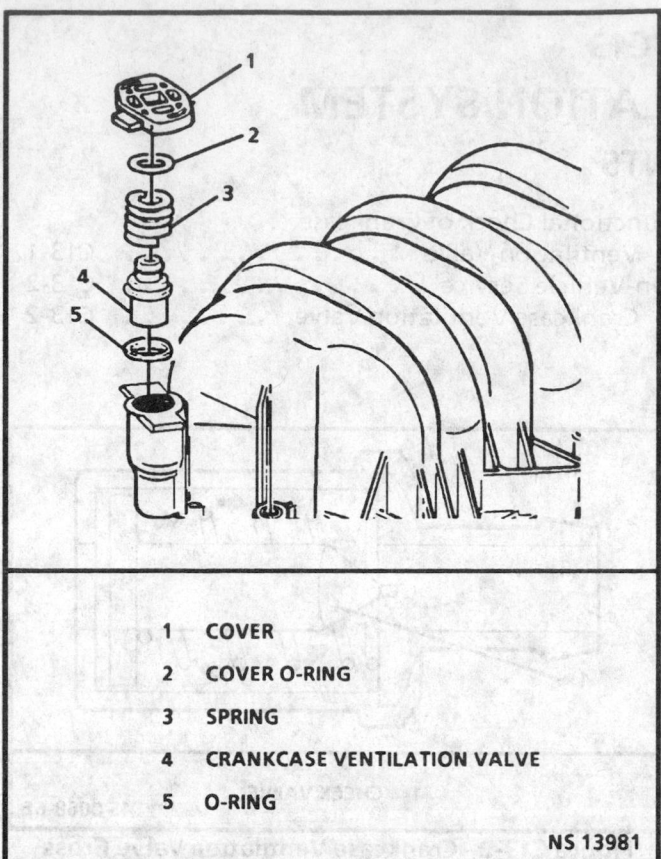

1 COVER
2 COVER O-RING
3 SPRING
4 CRANKCASE VENTILATION VALVE
5 O-RING

NS 13981

Figure C13-3 - Crankcase Ventilation Valve Location

With this system, any blow-by in excess of the system capacity (from a badly-worn engine, sustained heavy load, etc.) is exhausted into the intake manifold and is drawn into the engine.

Proper operation of the crankcase ventilation system is dependent upon a sealed engine. If oil sludging or dilution is noted, and the crankcase ventilation system is functioning properly, check engine for possible cause and correct to ensure that system will function as intended.

ON-VEHICLE SERVICE

CRANKCASE VENTILATION VALVE

←→ Remove or Disconnect

1. Remove sight shield from fuel rail and intake.
2. Press access cover down and rotate 1/4 turn counterclockwise.
3. Lift the cover and O-ring off slowly.
4. Remove spring and valve with O-ring from the intake manifold.

→← Install or Connect

1. Crankcase ventilation valve; replace O-ring if necessary.
2. Spring.
3. Cover and O-ring.
4. Cosmetic cover.

SECTION C14
AIR INDUCTION SYSTEM
CONTENTS

GENERAL DESCRIPTION

AIR INDUCTION SYSTEM

The air induction system draws outside air in through the forward mounted air cleaner. The air then enters the engine by flowing through the rear air intake duct, through the throttle body and into the plenum. The air is then directed into the plenum intake runners, cylinder heads and into the cylinder.

ON-VEHICLE SERVICE

NOTICE: When fasteners are removed, always reinstall them at the same location from which they were removed. If a fastener needs to be replaced use the correct part number fastener for that application. The correct torque value must be used, as specified, during reassembly to ensure proper retention of all parts, or damage to the part may result.

AIR FILTER ELEMENT

←→ Remove or Disconnect

1. Four screws from air cleaner assembly.
2. Air filter element.
3. Inspect air filter element for dust, dirt, water and replace if required. Refer to SECTION 0B.

→← Install or Connect

1. Air filter element.
2. Air cleaner cover and four screws.

AIR CLEANER ASSEMBLY

←→ Remove or Disconnect

1. Air filter element.
2. Clamp from rear air intake duct.
3. Air cleaner assembly.

→← Install or Connect

1. Position air cleaner assembly to front intake duct (Figure C14-1).
2. Clamp rear air intake duct to air cleaner assembly.
3. Air filter element.
4. Air cleaner cover and nut.

INTAKE AIR TEMPERATURE (IAT) SENSOR

NOTICE: Care must be taken when handling the Intake Air Temperature (IAT) sensor. Damage to the IAT sensor will affect proper operation of the fuel injection system.

←→ Remove or Disconnect

1. Air cleaner cover.
2. Air filter element.
3. Electrical connector.
4. Retaining clip from IAT sensor.
5. IAT sensor.

→← Install or Connect

1. Intake Air Temperature (IAT) sensor and clip in air cleaner assembly.
2. Electrical connector.
3. Air filter element.
4. Air cleaner cover and nut.

PARTS INFORMATION

PART NAME	GROUP
Clamps, Rear Air Intake Duct	3.417
Duct, Rear Air Intake	3.417
Duct Assembly, Front Air Intake	3.417
Element, Air Induction	3.410
Air Cleaner Kit	3.402
Nut, Air Cleaner Cover	8.920

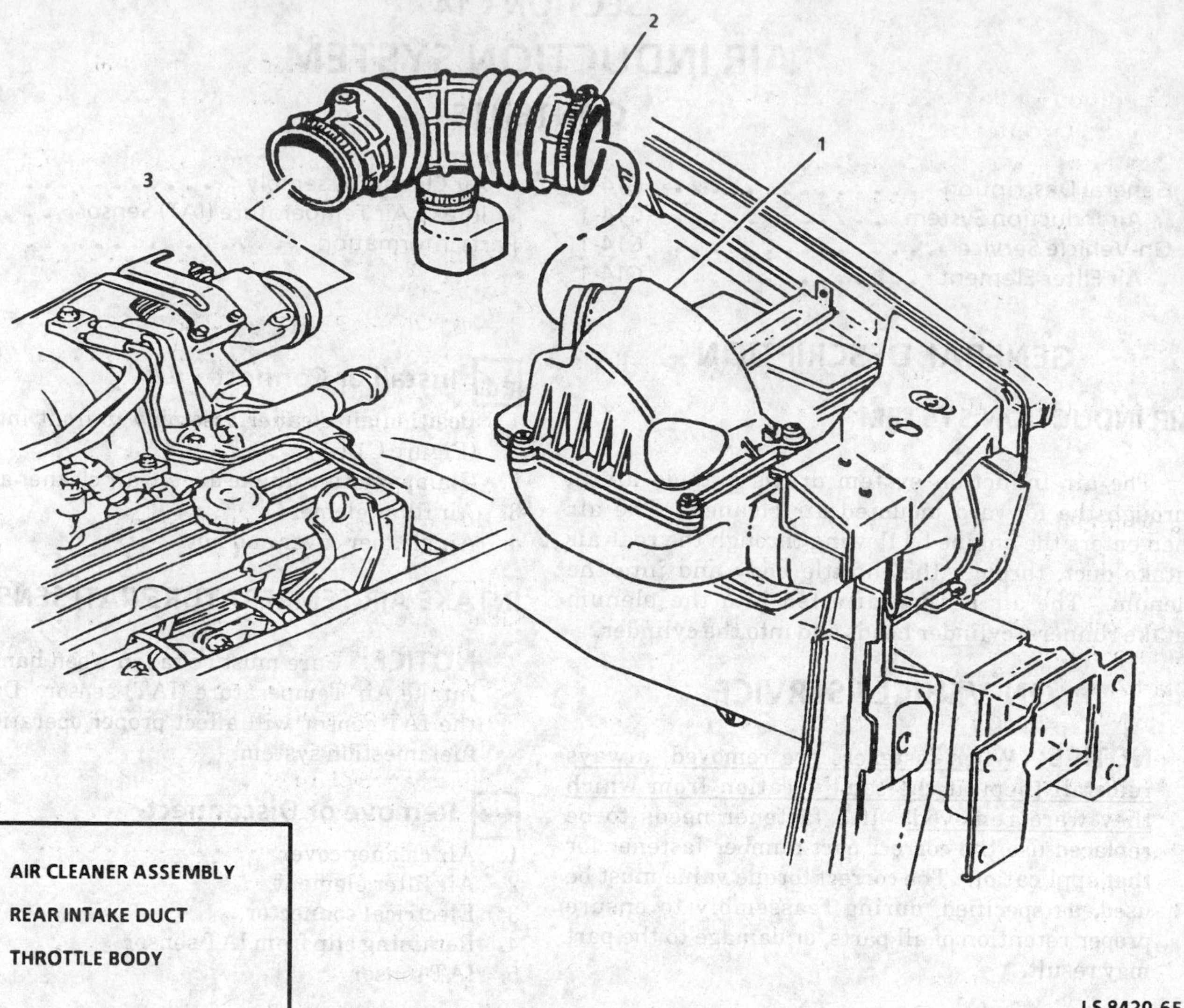
2
3
1
LS 8420-6E

1 AIR CLEANER ASSEMBLY
2 REAR INTAKE DUCT
3 THROTTLE BODY

Figure C14-1 - Air Induction System

SECTION 6F

EXHAUST SYSTEM

NOTICE: When fasteners are removed, always reinstall them at the same location from which they were removed. If a fastener needs to be replaced, use the correct part number fastener for that application. If the correct part number fastener is not available, a fastener of equal size and strength (or stronger) may be used. Fasteners that are not reused, and those requiring thread locking compound will be called out. The correct torque value must be used when installing fasteners that require it. If the above conditions are not followed, parts or system damage could result.

CONTENTS

GENERAL DESCRIPTION

When inspecting or replacing exhaust system components, make sure there is adequate clearance from all points on the underbody to prevent overheating of the floor pan and possible damage to the passenger compartment insulation and trim materials.

Check complete exhaust system and nearby body areas and rear compartment lid for broken, damaged, missing or mispositioned parts, open seams, holes, loose connections or other deterioration which could permit exhaust fumes to seep into the rear compartment or passenger compartment. Dust or water in the rear compartment may be an indication of a problem in one of these areas. Any faulty areas should be corrected immediately. To help insure continued integrity, the exhaust system pipe rearward of the muffler must be replaced whenever a new muffler is installed.

EXHAUST PIPE

The crossover pipe to exhaust pipe connection is of the flex joint type, thus eliminating the need for gaskets.

MUFFLER

The muffler is part of a welded exhaust system and is serviced as an assembly with the tail pipe on single exhaust systems.

HANGERS

Various types of hangers are used to support exhaust system(s). These include conventional rubber straps, rubber rings, and rubber blocks.

The installation of exhaust system supports is very important as improperly installed supports can cause annoying vibrations which can be difficult to diagnose.

CLAMPS

Two types of clamps are used for connecting exhaust system slip joints:

- Saddle/U-bolt
- Single nut compression

Coat slip joints with exhaust system sealer before assembling.

WELDED CONNECTIONS

When servicing a welded connection, it should be cut and the new connection clamped when installing replacement parts. Coat slip joints with exhaust system sealer before assembling.

THREE WAY CATALYTIC CONVERTER

The three way catalytic converter is an emission control device added to the exhaust system to reduce pollutants from the exhaust gas stream.

Important

- The three way catalytic converter requires the use of unleaded fuel only.

Periodic maintenance of the exhaust system is not required. If the vehicle is raised for other service, it is advisable to check the condition of the complete exhaust system.

DIAGNOSIS

NOISE

Rattles and noise vibrations in the exhaust system may be caused by misalignment of parts. When aligning the system, leave all bolts or nuts loose until all parts are properly aligned, then tighten, working from front to rear.

EXHAUST DIAGNOSIS

EXHAUST DIAGNOSIS

CONDITION	PROBABLE CAUSE	CORRECTION
Vibration or Rattling Noise from Exhaust System	1. Loose components (hangers, heat shields, etc.).	1. Tighten all loose fasteners to specifications.
	2. Misaligned components.	2. Align system. Check for bent or damaged hangers, mounting brackets or clamps.
Restricted Exhaust System (Excessive Back Pressure)	1. Kinked exhaust pipe(s).	1. Repair or replace as needed.
	2. Restriction in muffler.	2. Remove muffler and visually check. If restriction exists, replace muffler.
	3. End of tailpipe obstruction or crimped tailpipe.	3. Remove obstruction or straighten crimped tailpipe outlet. If damaged, replace muffler/tailpipe assembly.
	4. Plugged catalytic converter.	4. Replace catalytic converter. Refer to DRIVEABILITY AND EMISSIONS (SECTION 6E2 OR 6E3) to diagnose cause of restriction.
Exhaust Leakage and/or Excessive Noise	1. Improperly installed or misaligned components.	1. Align components and tighten connections to specifications.
	2. Loose connections at exhaust manifold or catalytic converter.	2. Tighten all fasteners to specifications.
	3. Exhaust manifold cracked or broken.	3. Replace exhaust manifold.
	4. Leakage at crossover pipe connections.	4. Tighten nuts and bolts to specifications.
	5. Damaged or worn seals.	5. Replace seals.
	6. Burned or rusted extension pipe.	6. Replace extension pipe (and muffler assembly if not previously serviced).
	7. Burned or rusted muffler.	7. Replace muffler/tailpipe assembly.
	8. Leakage at exhaust component joints or couplings (if previously serviced).	8. Tighten clamps to specifications, or replace clamps if damaged.

CPCW6F1

PERFORMANCE

Exhaust system performance complaints, such as excessive back pressure, are noticeable by their effect on engine performance. However, other faulty vehicle components, such as emission control devices, have similar effects on engine performance and may be characterized by the same symptoms or complaints. For further information, refer to SECTION 6E3.

ON-VEHICLE SERVICE

Four individual components of the single exhaust system can be serviced:

- Front exhaust pipe.
- Three way catalytic converter.
- Intermediate pipe.
- Muffler and tail pipe assembly.

FRONT EXHAUST PIPE

Figures 1 through 5

Remove or Disconnect

1. Raise vehicle and suitably support. Refer to SECTION 0A.
2. Support three way catalytic converter.

NOTICE: Cut(s) must be made as close to weld(s) as possible to ensure adequate overlap for clamping.

3. Cut front exhaust pipe at three way catalytic converter. Refer to Figures 1 and 2.
4. Bolts, springs and exhaust pipe from manifold.
5. Exhaust manifold seal from manifold.

Install or Connect

1. Clamp to three way catalytic converter. Do not tighten clamp.
2. Replacement pipe, by sliding pipe into three way catalytic converter opening. Refer to Figure 3.
3. Seal, pipe, springs and bolts to manifold.

Tighten

- Bolts to 32 N·m (24 lb. ft.).
- Clamp nut to 50 N·m (37 lb. ft.).

4. Lower vehicle.

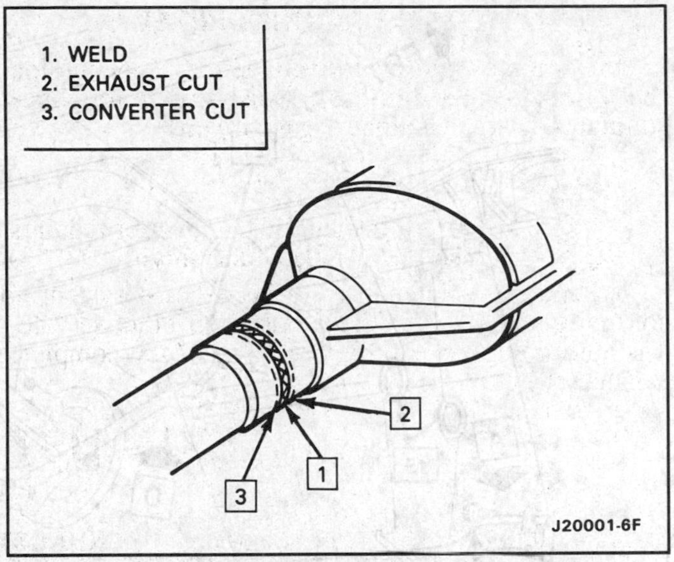
1. WELD
2. EXHAUST CUT
3. CONVERTER CUT
2
1
3
J20001-6F
Figure 1 Exhaust or Converter Cut Location

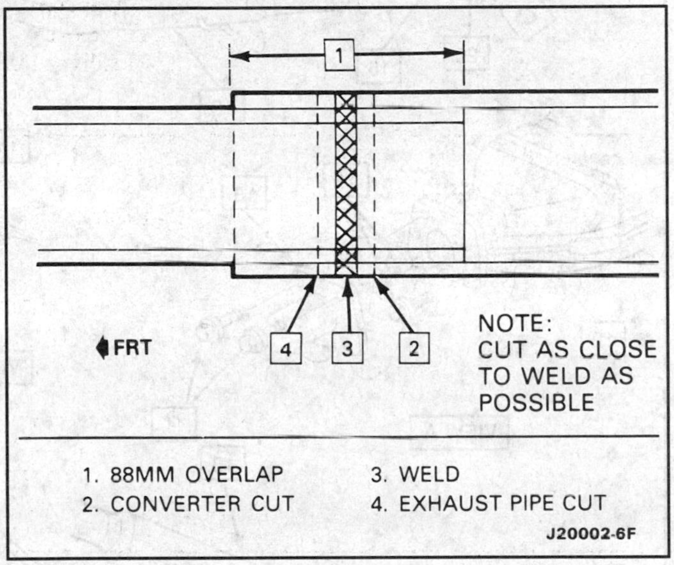
1
FRT
4
3
2
NOTE:
CUT AS CLOSE TO WELD AS POSSIBLE
1. 88MM OVERLAP
2. CONVERTER CUT
3. WELD
4. EXHAUST PIPE CUT
J20002-6F
Figure 2 Exhaust or Converter Cut Location

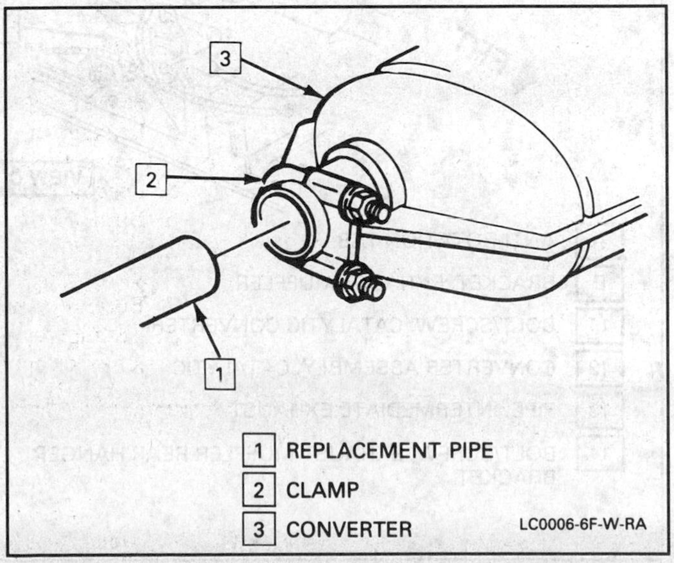
3
2
1
1 REPLACEMENT PIPE
2 CLAMP
3 CONVERTER
LC0006-6F-W-RA
Figure 3 Exhaust or Intermediate Pipe Installation

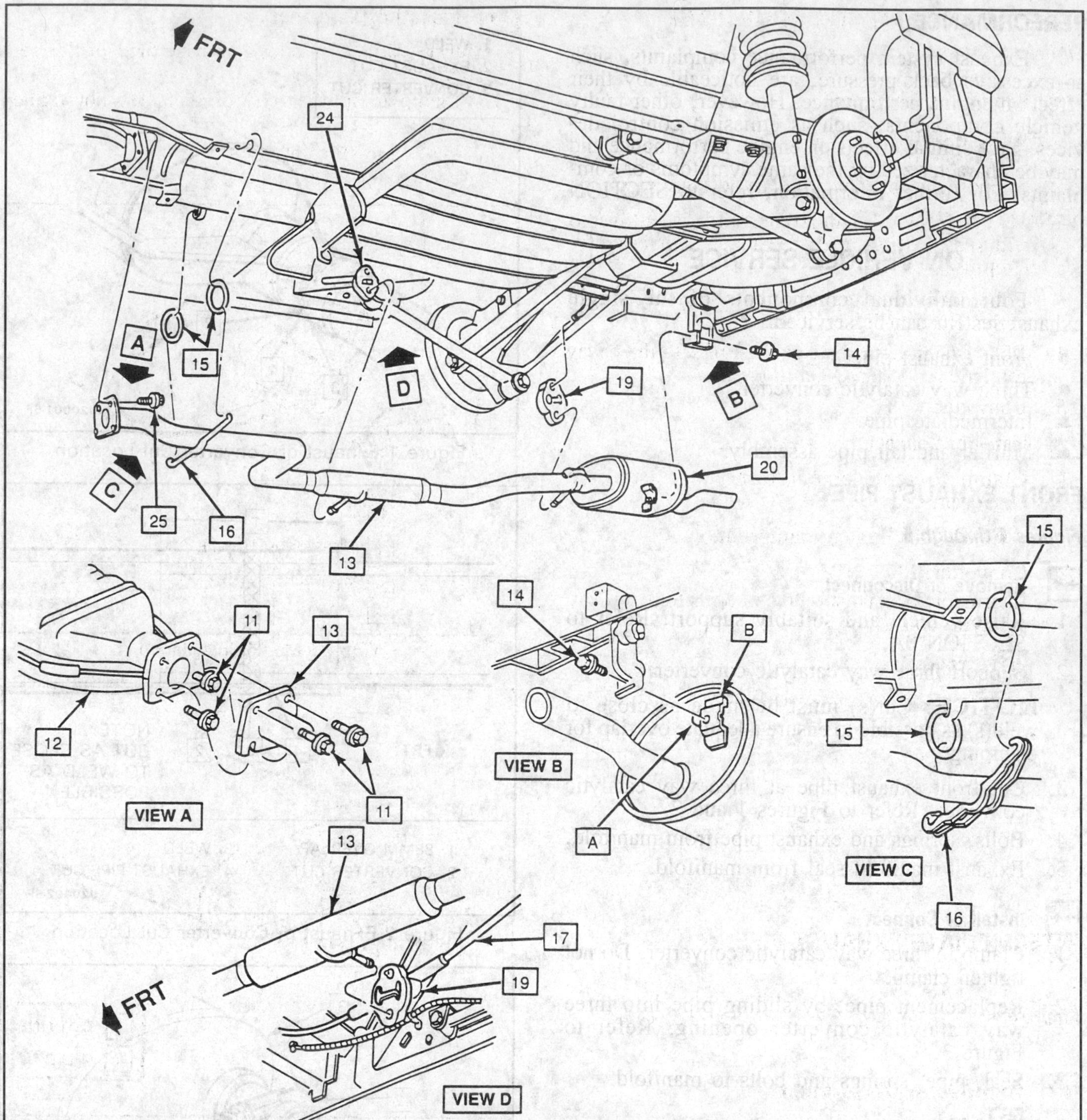

FRT
24
A
15
D
B
14
19
20
C
25
16
13
15
11
13
12
11
14
B
VIEW B
15
VIEW A
A
VIEW C
13
16
17
19
FRT
VIEW D
RC0020-6F-W-RP

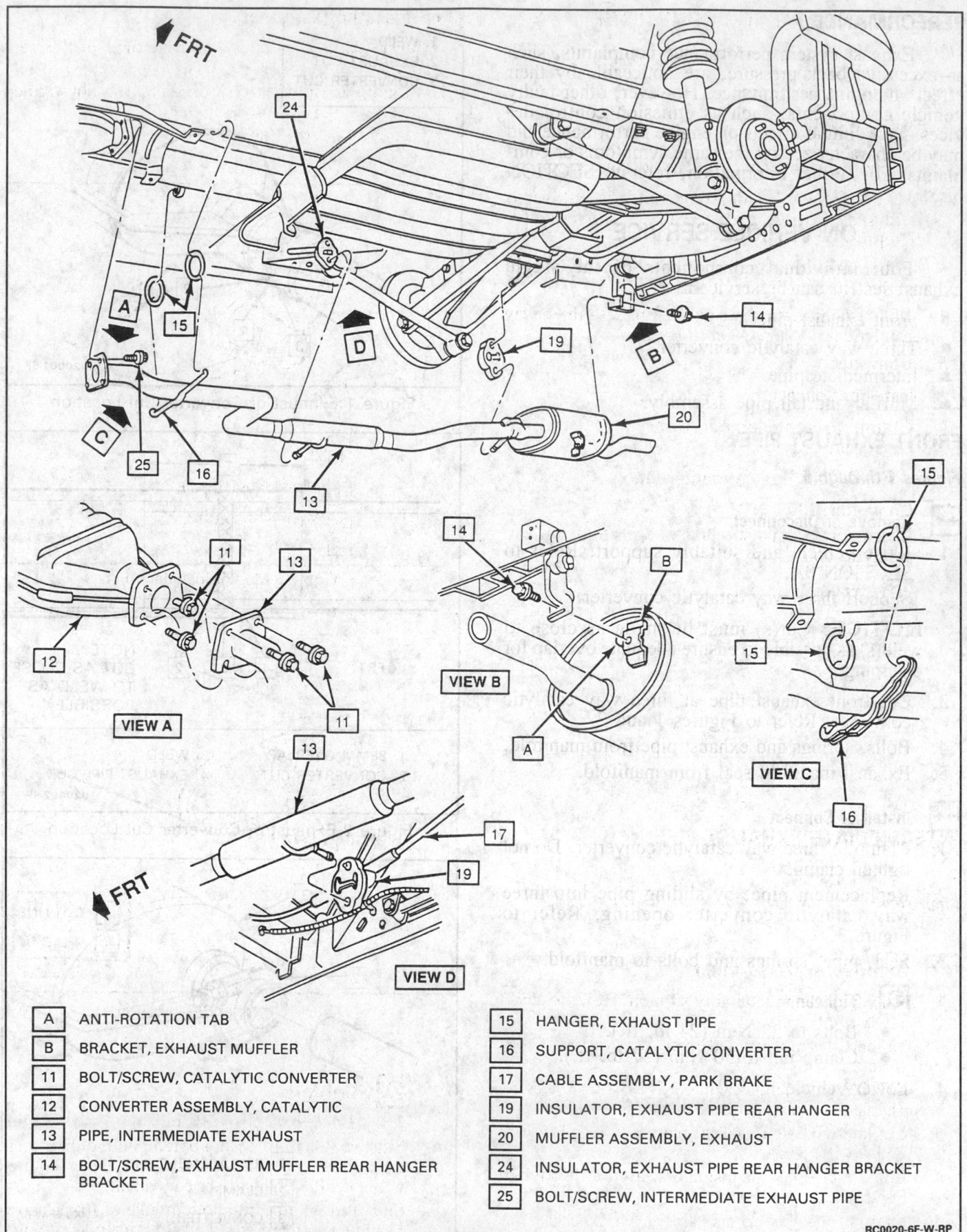

A	ANTI-ROTATION TAB	15	HANGER, EXHAUST PIPE
B	BRACKET, EXHAUST MUFFLER	16	SUPPORT, CATALYTIC CONVERTER
11	BOLT/SCREW, CATALYTIC CONVERTER	17	CABLE ASSEMBLY, PARK BRAKE
12	CONVERTER ASSEMBLY, CATALYTIC	19	INSULATOR, EXHAUST PIPE REAR HANGER
13	PIPE, INTERMEDIATE EXHAUST	20	MUFFLER ASSEMBLY, EXHAUST
14	BOLT/SCREW, EXHAUST MUFFLER REAR HANGER BRACKET	24	INSULATOR, EXHAUST PIPE REAR HANGER BRACKET
		25	BOLT/SCREW, INTERMEDIATE EXHAUST PIPE

Figure 4 Single Exhaust System

THREE WAY CATALYTIC CONVERTER

Figures 1 through 4

Remove or Disconnect

1. Raise vehicle and suitably support. Refer to SECTION 0A.
2. Support the three way catalytic converter.

NOTICE: Cut(s) must be made as close to weld(s) as possible to ensure adequate overlap for clamping.

3. Cut front exhaust pipe at three way catalytic converter. Refer to Figures 1 and 2.
4. Bolts from intermediate exhaust pipe to three way catalytic converter. Refer to Figure 4.
5. Converter.

Install or Connect

1. Clamp to replacement three way catalytic converter.
   - Do not tighten clamp nut.
2. Converter.
3. Intermediate exhaust pipe end bolts to three way catalytic converter.

Tighten

- Clamp nut to 50 N·m (37 lb. ft.).
- Bolts to three way catalytic converter to 47 N·m (35 lb. ft.).

4. Lower vehicle.

INTERMEDIATE EXHAUST PIPE

Figure 4

Remove or Disconnect

1. Raise vehicle and suitably support. Refer to SECTION 0A.
2. Support the muffler and three way catalytic converter.

NOTICE: Cut(s) must be made as close to weld(s) as possible to ensure adequate overlap for clamping.

3. Cut intermediate exhaust pipe at muffler. Refer to Figures 1, 2 and 3.
4. Bolts, hangers, and insulators, as used. Refer to Figure 4.
5. Intermediate exhaust pipe bolts from three way catalytic converter.
6. Intermediate exhaust pipe.

Install or Connect

NOTICE: See "Notice" on page 6F-1 of this section.

1. Clamp to muffler end of pipe. Do not tighten clamp.
2. Support intermediate pipe.
3. Bolts to converter.

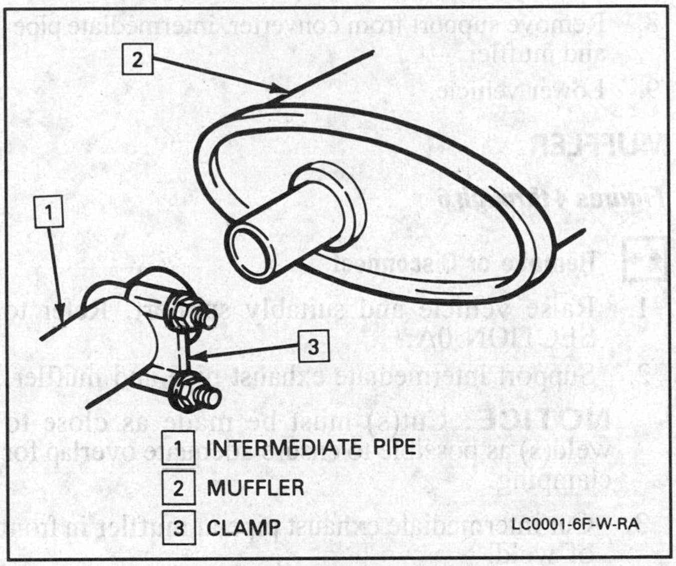
2
1
3
1 INTERMEDIATE PIPE
2 MUFFLER
3 CLAMP
LC0001-6F-W-RA

Figure 5 Muffler Installation

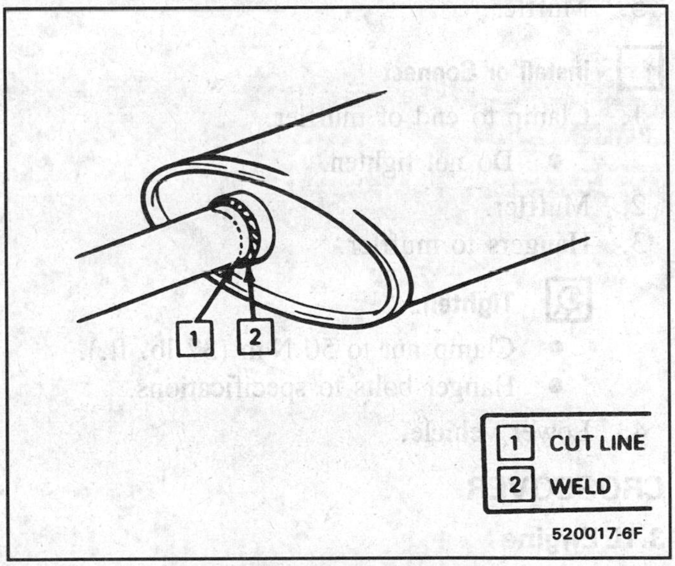
1
2
1 CUT LINE
2 WELD
520017-6F

Figure 6 Muffler Cut Location

Tighten

- Bolts to 47 N•m (35 lb. ft.).

4. Slide rod on muffler into bottom hole of rear insulator. Press until fully seated. Lubricate as required with GM P/N 9985406 or equivalent.
5. Slide rod on pipe into bottom hole of front insulator. Press until fully seated. Lubricate as required with GM P/N 9985406 or equivalent.

Important

- Park brake cable must route above and outboard of front insulator.

6. Hangers securely onto floor pan hook bracket.
7. Clamp nuts.

Tighten

- Nuts to 50 N•m (37 lb. ft.).

8. Remove support from converter, intermediate pipe and muffler.
9. Lower vehicle.

MUFFLER

Figures 4 through 6

Remove or Disconnect

1. Raise vehicle and suitably support. Refer to SECTION 0A.
2. Support intermediate exhaust pipe and muffler.

NOTICE: Cut(s) must be made as close to weld(s) as possible to ensure adequate overlap for clamping.

3. Cut intermediate exhaust pipe at muffler in front of weld.
4. Hangers from muffler.
5. Muffler.

Install or Connect

1. Clamp to end of muffler.
   - Do not tighten.
2. Muffler.
3. Hangers to muffler.

Tighten

- Clamp nut to 50 N·m (37 lb. ft.).
- Hanger bolts to specifications.

4. Lower vehicle.

CROSSOVER

3.1L Engine

Figure 7

Remove or Disconnect

1. Air cleaner and duct assembly. Refer to SECTION 6E3-C14.
2. Drain engine coolant. Refer to SECTION 6B.
3. Engine torque struts. Refer to SECTION 6A5A.
4. Rotate engine assembly. Refer to SECTION 6A5A.
5. Tie straps from heater outlet pipe and ignition wiring harness.
6. Upper radiator hose from engine. Refer to SECTION 6B.
7. Vacuum modulator pipe. Refer to SECTION 7A.
8. Heater outlet hose and thermostat bypass pipe. Refer to SECTION 1B.
9. Heat shield bolts.
10. Heat shield.
11. Crossover pipe bolts.
12. Crossover pipe.

Install or Connect

1. Crossover.
2. Bolts.

Tighten

- Bolts to 25 N•m (18 lb. ft.).

3. Heat shields.
4. Heat shield bolts.

Tighten

- Bolts to 10 N•m (89 lb. in.).

5. Heater outlet hose and thermostat bypass pipe. Refer to SECTION 1B.
6. Vacuum modulator pipe. Refer to SECTION 7A.
7. Tie straps at heater outlet pipe and ignition wiring harness.

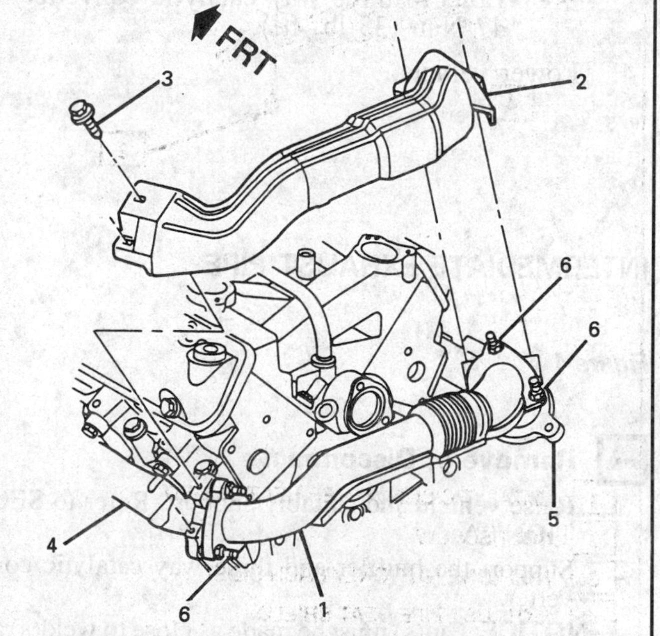
FRT
1
2
3
4
5
6
6
6
6

1 PIPE ASSEMBLY, EXHAUST CROSSOVER
2 SHIELD, EXHAUST CROSSOVER PIPE HEAT
3 BOLT/SCREW, EXHAUST CROSSOVER PIPE HEAT SHIELD
4 MANIFOLD ASSEMBLY, LEFT-HAND EXHAUST
5 MANIFOLD ASSEMBLY, RIGHT-HAND EXHAUST
6 BOLT/SCREW, EXHAUST CROSSOVER PIPE

PC3001-6F-W-RP

Figure 7 Crossover (3.1L Engine)

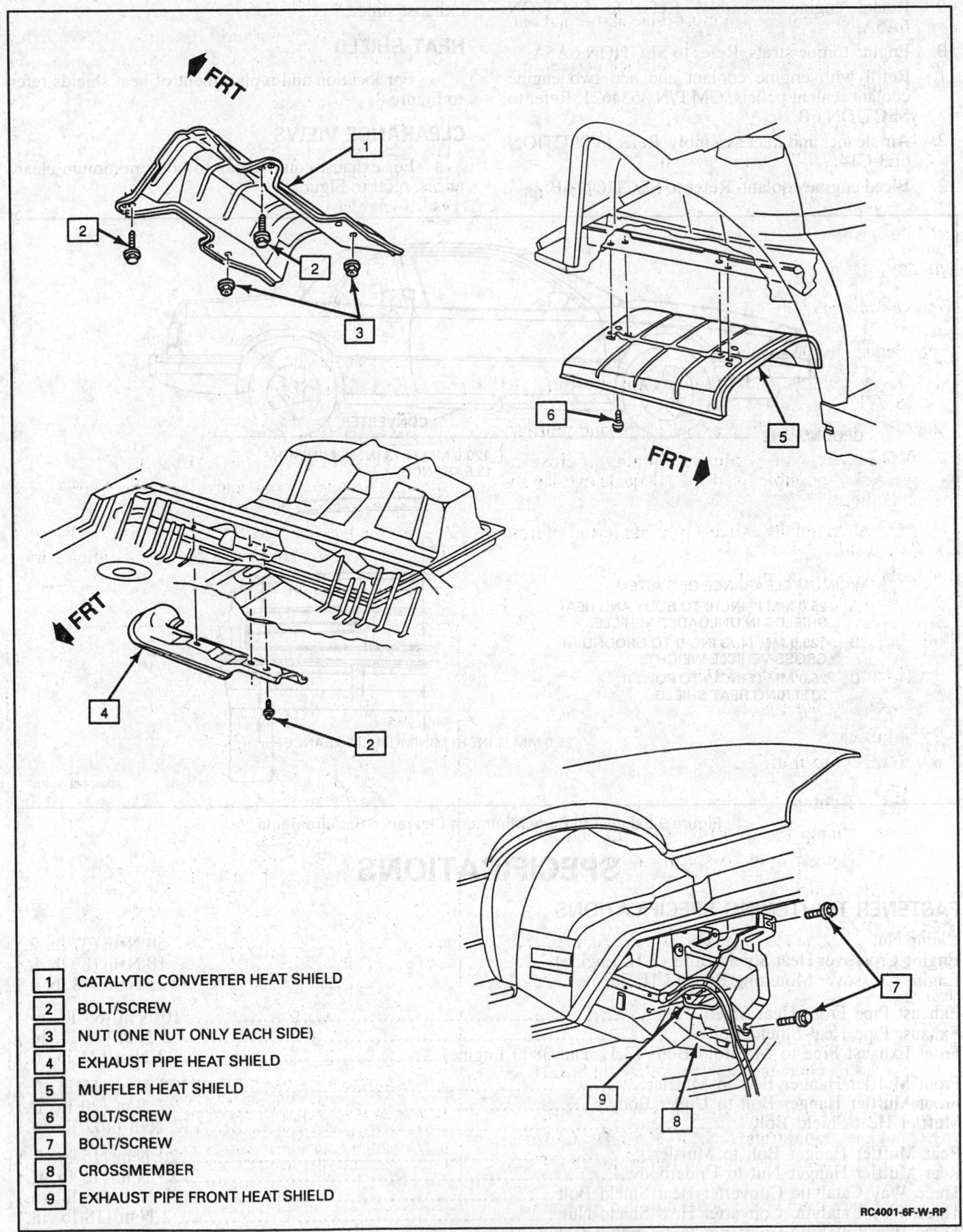

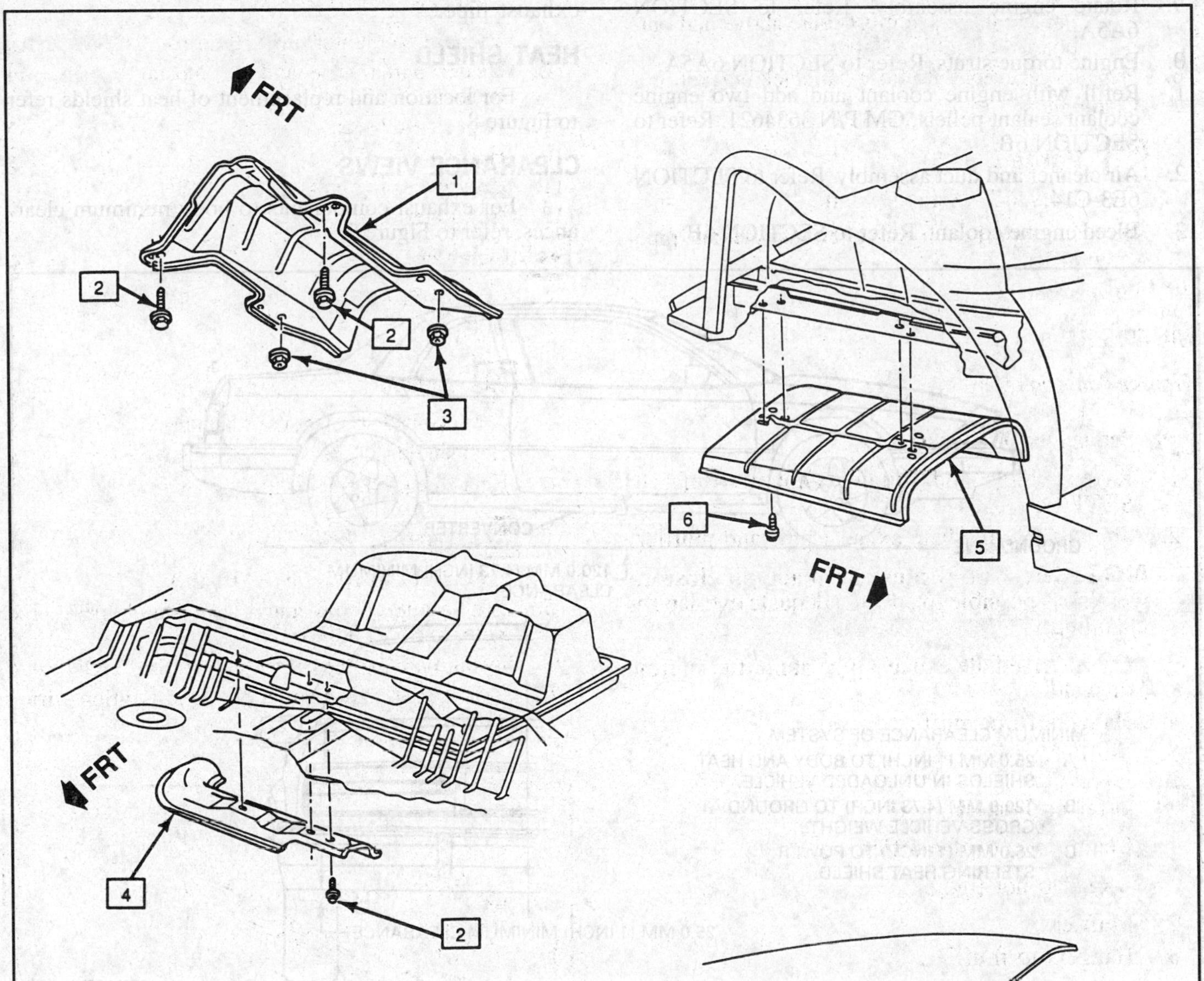
FRT
1
2
2
3
FRT
6
5
FRT
4
2
7
7
9
8
1 CATALYTIC CONVERTER HEAT SHIELD
2 BOLT/SCREW
3 NUT (ONE NUT ONLY EACH SIDE)
4 EXHAUST PIPE HEAT SHIELD
5 MUFFLER HEAT SHIELD
6 BOLT/SCREW
7 BOLT/SCREW
8 CROSSMEMBER
9 EXHAUST PIPE FRONT HEAT SHIELD
RC4001-6F-W-RP

Figure 8 Heat Shields

8. Upper radiator hose to engine. Refer to SECTION 6B.
9. Rotate engine assembly. Refer to SECTION 6A5A.
10. Engine torque struts. Refer to SECTION 6A5A.
11. Refill with engine coolant and add two engine coolant sealant pellets, GM P/N 3634621. Refer to SECTION 6B.
12. Air cleaner and duct assembly. Refer to SECTION 6E3-C14.
13. Bleed engine coolant. Refer to SECTION 6B.

3800 Engine

The 3800 engine no longer uses a crossover exhaust pipe.

HEAT SHIELD

For location and replacement of heat shields refer to Figure 8.

CLEARANCE VIEWS

For exhaust components to body minimum clearances, refer to Figure 9.

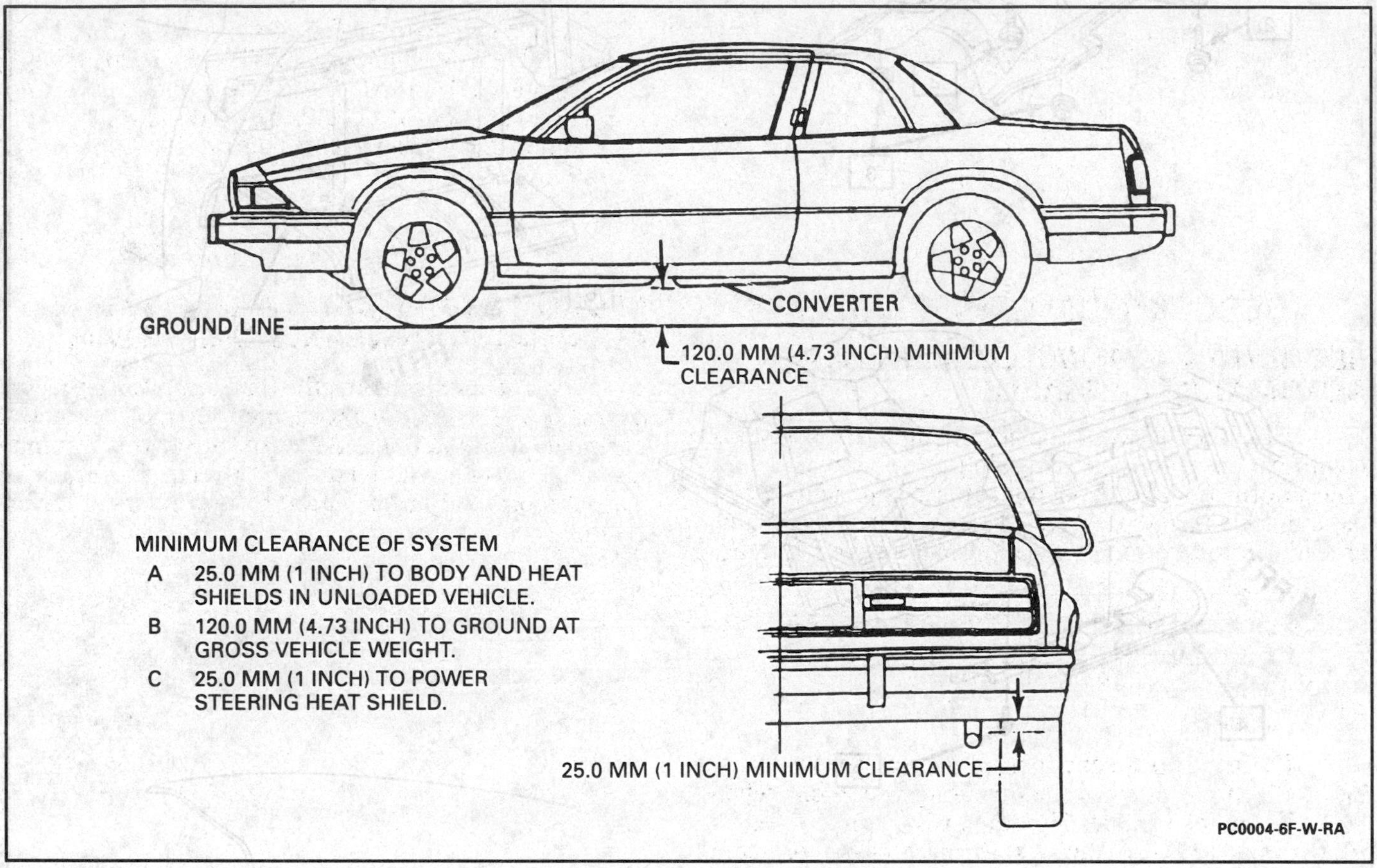
CONVERTER
GROUND LINE
120.0 MM (4.73 INCH) MINIMUM CLEARANCE
MINIMUM CLEARANCE OF SYSTEM
A 25.0 MM (1 INCH) TO BODY AND HEAT SHIELDS IN UNLOADED VEHICLE.
B 120.0 MM (4.73 INCH) TO GROUND AT GROSS VEHICLE WEIGHT.
C 25.0 MM (1 INCH) TO POWER STEERING HEAT SHIELD.
25.0 MM (1 INCH) MINIMUM CLEARANCE
PC0004-6F-W-RA

Figure 9 Exhaust to Body Minimum Clearance Requirements

SPECIFICATIONS

FASTENER TIGHTENING SPECIFICATIONS

Clamp Nut .... 50 N•m (37 lb. ft.)
Engine Crossover Heat Shield Bolts (3.1L Engine) .... 10 N•m (89 lb. ft.)
Engine Crossover Mounting Bolts (3.1L Engine) .... 25 N•m (18 lb. ft.)

Exhaust Pipe Front Heat Shield Nut .... 10 N·m (89 lb. in.)
Exhaust Pipe Heat Shield Bolt .... 2 N·m (18 lb. in.)
Front Exhaust Pipe to Manifold Bolts (3.1L and 3800 Engine) .... 32 N·m (24 lb. ft.)

Front Muffler Hanger Bolt to Muffler .... 20 N·m (15 lb. ft.)
Front Muffler Hanger Bolt to Under Body .... 27 N·m (20 lb. ft.)
Muffler Heat Shield Bolt .... 12 N·m (107 lb. in.)

Rear Muffler Hanger Bolt to Muffler .... 20 N·m (15 lb. ft.)
Rear Muffler Hanger Nut to Underbody .... 25 N·m (18 lb. ft.)
Three Way Catalytic Converter Heat Shield Bolt .... 2 N·m (18 lb. in.)
Three Way Catalytic Converter Heat Shield Nut .... 2 N·m (18 lb. in.)
Three Way Catalytic Converter to Intermediate Pipe Bolts .... 47 N·m (35 lb. ft.)

SECTION 7

AUTOMATIC TRANSAXLE GENERAL INFORMATION

CONTENTS

DESCRIPTION OF SECTION 7

SECTION 7A – ON-VEHICLE SERVICE – AUTOMATIC TRANSAXLE

This section contains information on transaxle identification, fluid level checking procedures and specific information for servicing some components while the transaxle is in the vehicle. This section also contains procedures for the removal and installation of the transaxle from the vehicle.

SECTION HYDRA-MATIC 7A5A1-4T60-E (3.1L) AND HYDRA-MATIC 7A5A2-4T60-E (3800L) AUTOMATIC TRANSAXLE DIAGNOSIS

These sections contain information that will assist in the diagnosis of transaxle operating conditions when the unit is in the vehicle. The diagnosis information covered is: road test procedures, shift speed charts, pressure check procedures, diagnosis charts, fluid flow diagrams, electrical wiring diagrams, fluid passage identification and torque converter clutch diagnosis.

SECTION HYDRA-MATIC 7A5B-4T60-E AUTOMATIC TRANSAXLE UNIT REPAIR

This section contains the disassembly, inspection, overhaul and assembly procedures for the mechanical components in the transaxle. Also included is information on the gaging of certain components, proper use of special tools, and torque specifications required for assembly.

SECTION 7A
AUTOMATIC TRANSAXLE

NOTICE: When fasteners are removed, always reinstall them at the same location from which they were removed. If a fastener needs to be replaced, use the correct part number fastener for that application. If the correct part number fastener is not available, a fastener of equal size and strength (or stronger) may be used. Fasteners that are not reused, and those requiring thread locking compound will be called out. The correct torque value must be used when installing fasteners that require it. If the above conditions are not followed, parts or system damage could result.

NOTICE: Do not use any type of grease to retain parts during assembly of this unit. Greases other than the recommended assembly lube will change transaxle fluid characteristics and cause undesirable shift conditions and/or filter clogging. It is recommended that TRANSJEL™ J 36850 or equivalent be used during assembly.

CONTENTS

GENERAL INFORMATION

The information contained in this section is common to all automatic transaxles. For complete Diagnosis and Unit Repair refer to the specific transaxle sections.

TRANSAXLE IDENTIFICATION INFORMATION

Figures 1 and 2

All automatic transaxles have a metal identification nameplate attached to the case exterior. The location of this nameplate is shown in Figure 1. The information on the nameplate will assist in the servicing and determination of replacement parts when ordered through a GM Parts Catalog.

Additional Transaxle identification is provided on the Service Parts Identification label. This label contains information on the regular production options (RPO) as well as standard and mandatory options, as shown in Figure 2.

This label is affixed to the inside of each vehicle at the assembly plant. Refer to SECTION 0A for label location and information.

TRANSAXLE DEFINITIONS

The following definitions are being provided to establish a common language and assist the user in describing transaxle related conditions. Some of these terms or conditions are used in the transaxle sections of this Service Manual.

Throttle Positions

- **Minimum Throttle** – the least amount of throttle opening required for an upshift.
- **Light Throttle**– approximately 1/4 of accelerator pedal travel.
- **Medium Throttle** – approximately 1/2 of accelerator pedal travel.
- **Heavy Throttle** – approximately 3/4 of accelerator pedal travel.
- **Wide Open Throttle (WOT)** – full travel of the accelerator pedal.
- **Full Throttle Detent Downshift** – a quick apply of the accelerator pedal to its full travel, forcing a downshift.
- **Zero Throttle Coastdown** – a full release of the accelerator pedal while the vehicle is in motion and in drive range.
- **Engine Braking** – a condition where the engine is used to slow the vehicle by manually downshifting during a zero throttle coastdown.

Shift Conditions

- **Bump** – a sudden and forceful apply of a clutch or band.
- **Chuggle** – a bucking or jerking condition that may be engine related. May be most noticeable when the converter clutch is engaged. Similar to the feel of towing a trailer.
- **Delayed** – a condition where a shift is expected but does not occur for a period of time. Samples of this condition could be described as clutch or band engagement does not occur as quickly as expected during a part throttle or wide open throttle apply of the accelerator or, when manually downshifting to a lower range. Also defined as "Late" or "Extended."
- **Double Bump ("Double Feel")** – two sudden and forceful applies of a clutch or band.
- **Early** – a condition where the shift occurs before the vehicle has reached a proper speed and tends to labor the engine after the upshift.
- **End Bump** – a firmer feel at the end of a shift as compared to the feel at the start of the shift. Also defined as "END FEEL" or, "SLIP BUMP."
- **Firm** – a noticeable quick apply of a clutch or band that is considered **normal** with a medium to heavy throttle shift. Should not be confused with "HARSH" or "ROUGH."
- **Flare** – a quick increase in engine rpm accompanied with a momentary loss of torque. This most generally occurs during a shift. Also defined as "SLIPPING."
- **Harsh ("Rough")** – a more noticeable apply of a clutch or band as compared to **"FIRM."** This condition is considered undesirable at any throttle position.
- **Hunting** – a repeating quick series of upshifts and downshifts that causes a noticeable change in engine rpm. An example could be described as a 4-3-4 shift pattern. Also defined as "BUSYNESS."

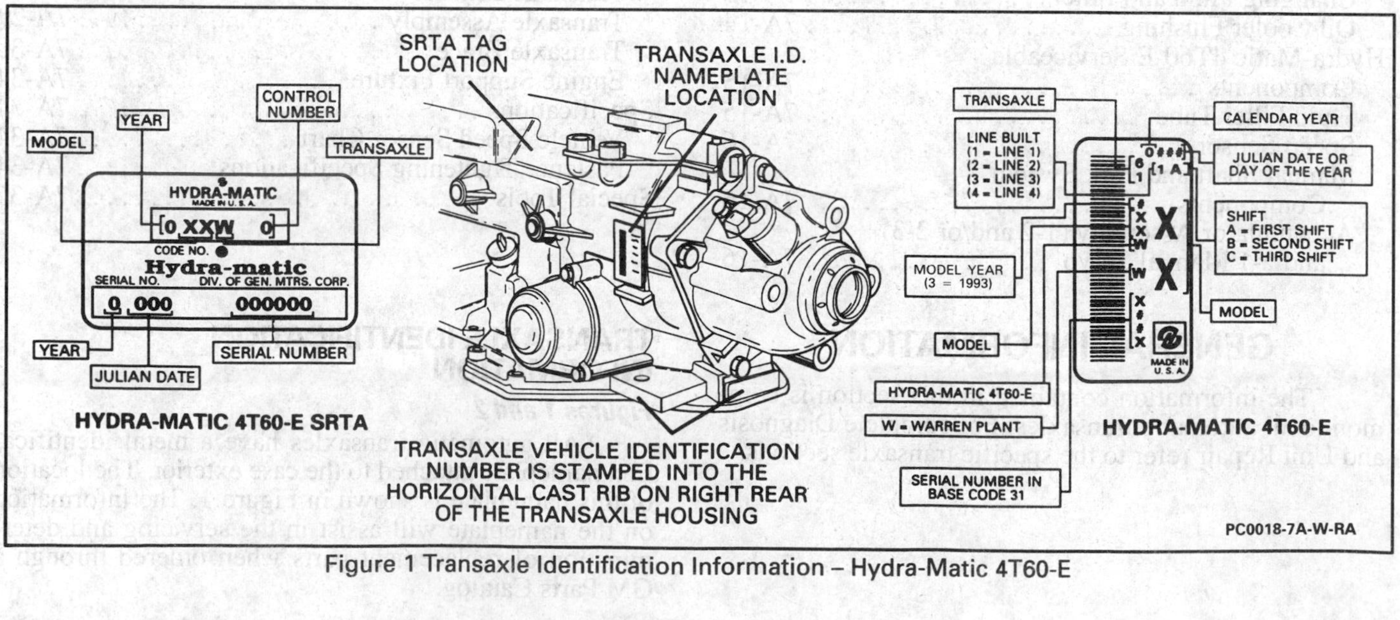
SRTA TAG LOCATION
TRANSAXLE I.D. NAMEPLATE LOCATION
CONTROL NUMBER
YEAR
MODEL
TRANSAXLE
HYDRA-MATIC
MADE IN U.S.A.
0 XXW 0
CODE NO.
Hydra-matic
SERIAL NO.
DIV. OF GEN. MTRS. CORP.
0 000
000000
YEAR
SERIAL NUMBER
JULIAN DATE
HYDRA-MATIC 4T60-E SRTA
TRANSAXLE VEHICLE IDENTIFICATION NUMBER IS STAMPED INTO THE HORIZONTAL CAST RIB ON RIGHT REAR OF THE TRANSAXLE HOUSING
TRANSAXLE
LINE BUILT (1 = LINE 1) (2 = LINE 2) (3 = LINE 3) (4 = LINE 4)
CALENDAR YEAR
JULIAN DATE OR DAY OF THE YEAR
SHIFT A = FIRST SHIFT B = SECOND SHIFT C = THIRD SHIFT
MODEL YEAR (3 = 1993)
MODEL
MODEL
MADE IN U.S.A.
HYDRA-MATIC 4T60-E
W = WARREN PLANT
HYDRA-MATIC 4T60-E
SERIAL NUMBER IN BASE CODE 31
PC0018-7A-W-RA

Figure 1 Transaxle Identification Information – Hydra-Matic 4T60-E

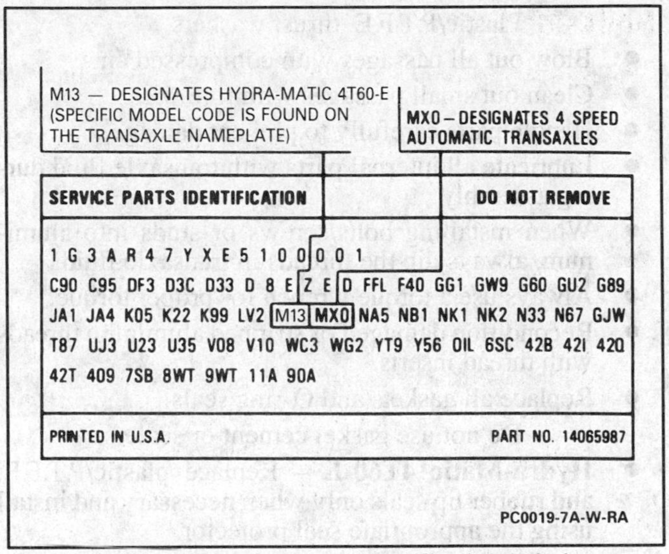
M13 — DESIGNATES HYDRA-MATIC 4T60-E (SPECIFIC MODEL CODE IS FOUND ON THE TRANSAXLE NAMEPLATE)
MXO – DESIGNATES 4 SPEED AUTOMATIC TRANSAXLES
SERVICE PARTS IDENTIFICATION
DO NOT REMOVE
1 G 3 A R 4 7 Y X E 5 1 0 0 0 0 1
C90 C95 DF3 D3C D33 D 8 E Z E D FFL F40 GG1 GW9 G60 GU2 G89
JA1 JA4 K05 K22 K99 LV2 M13 MXO NA5 NB1 NK1 NK2 N33 N67 GJW
T87 UJ3 U23 U35 V08 V10 WC3 WG2 YT9 Y56 OIL 6SC 42B 42I 42Q
42T 409 7SB 8WT 9WT 11A 90A
PRINTED IN U.S.A.
PART NO. 14065987
PC0019-7A-W-RA

Figure 2 Service Parts Identification Label

- **Initial Feel** – a distinct firmer feel at the start of a shift as compared to the finish of the shift.
- **Late** – a shift that occurs when the engine is at a higher than normal rpm for a given amount of throttle.
- **Shudder** – a repeating jerking sensation similar to "CHUGGLE" but more severe and rapid in nature. This condition may be most noticeable during certain ranges of vehicle speed. May also be used to define the condition after converter clutch engagement.
- **Slipping** – a noticeable increase in engine rpm without a vehicle speed increase. A slip usually occurs during or after initial clutch or band engagement.
- **Soft** – a slow, almost unnoticeable clutch apply with very little shift feel.
- **Surge** – a repeating engine related feeling of acceleration and deceleration that is less intense than "CHUGGLE."
- **Tie-Up** – a condition where two opposing clutches are attempting to apply at the same time causing the engine to labor with a noticeable loss of engine rpm.

Noise Conditions

- **Drive Link** – a whine or growl that increases and fades with vehicle speed and is most noticeable under light throttle acceleration. May also be noticeable in "PARK" or "NEUTRAL" operating ranges with the vehicle stationary.
- **Final Drive Noise** – a hum related to vehicle speed and is most noticeable under light throttle acceleration.
- **Gear Noise** – a whine, most noticeable in first gear and reverse that is related to vehicle speed. A gear noise condition may become less noticeable or go away after an upshift.
- **Pump Noise** – a high pitch whine that increases in intensity with engine rpm. This condition may also be noticeable in "PARK" and "NEUTRAL" operating ranges with the vehicle stationary.

PRELIMINARY CHECKING PROCEDURE

The condition of an automatic transaxle not operating properly may be influenced by one, or a combination of the following items:

- Fluid level high/low.
- Engine performance. Refer to SECTION 6 and SECTION 6E.
- Manual linkage adjustment.
- Internal fluid leaks. Refer to SECTION 7A-5B.
- Electrical system. Refer to SECTION 6E and SECTION 8A.
- Transaxle or other mechanical component. Refer to SECTION 7A-5B.
- Vacuum modulator. Refer to SECTION 7A-5B.

NOISE AND VIBRATION ANALYSIS

If noise or vibration is noticeable in "Park" (P) and "Neutral" (N) with engine at idle, but is less noticeable as RPM increases, the cause may be from poor engine performance.

A noise or vibration that is noticeable when the vehicle is in motion, MAY NOT be the result of the transaxle.

Inspect

- Tires for:
  - Uneven wear
  - Imbalance
  - Mixed sizes
  - Mixed radial and bias ply. Refer to SECTION 3E.
- Suspension components for:
  - Alignment and wear
  - Loose fasteners. Refer to SECTION 3C.
- Engine/Transaxle mounts for:
  - Damage. Refer to SECTION 6A5A or SECTION 6A7.
  - Loose bolts/screws.
- Transaxle case mounting holes for:
  - Missing bolts/screws, nuts, studs
  - Stripped threads
  - Cracks
- Flywheel for:
  - Missing or loose bolts/screws
  - Cracks
  - Imbalance. Refer to SECTION 6A5A or SECTION 6A7.
- Torque converter for:
  - Missing or loose bolts/screws or lugs
  - Missing or loose balance weights
  - Imbalance

TRANSAXLE FLUID LEVEL INFORMATION

Checking fluid level, color and condition at regular intervals will provide early diagnosis information about the transaxle. This information may then be used to correct a condition that, if not detected early, could result in major transaxle repairs.

When adding or changing fluid, use only DEXRON® -IIE or III. For maintenance information and servicing intervals, refer to SECTION 0B.

- Fluid level should be checked when it reaches normal operating temperatures of 88-93°C (190-200°F). This temperature is reached after approximately 24 km (15 miles) of highway driving.
- Fluid color
  - Should be dark red (may be light brown)

NOTICE: Do not overfill. Overfilling will cause foaming, loss of fluid, shift complaints and possible damage to the transaxle.

- Inaccurate fluid level readings will result if checked immediately after the vehicle has been operated:
  - In high ambient temperatures above 32°C (90°F)
  - At sustained high speeds
  - In heavy city traffic during hot weather
  - As a towing vehicle
  - In commercial service

TRANSAXLE FLUID LEVEL CHECKING PROCEDURE

Figure 3

1. Start engine and operate vehicle for 15 minutes or until a normal operating temperature is reached.
2. Park vehicle on level ground.
3. Apply parking brake and block wheels.
4. Move gear selector through all gear positions.
5. Move gear selector to "Park" (P).
6. Let vehicle idle for 3 minutes with accessories off.
7. Check fluid level, color and condition.

GENERAL SERVICE

PARTS CLEANING, INSPECTION AND REPLACEMENT

Important

- Use appropriate safety equipment such as:
  - Safety glasses
  - Safety shoes
  - Gloves
- Keep work area and tools clean.
- Clean transaxle exterior before removing parts.
- Do not use wipe cloths or rags.
- Do not use solvents on:
  - Rubber seals
  - Plastic/P.T.F.E. thrust washers
- Blow out all passages with compressed air.
- Clean out small passages with fine wire.
- Handle parts carefully to prevent damage.
- Lubricate all internal parts with transaxle fluid during assembly.
- When installing bolts/screws or studs into aluminum, always dip the threads in transaxle fluid.
- Always use a torque wrench for proper torque.
- Recondition damaged or stripped aluminum threads with thread inserts.
- Replace all gaskets and O-ring seals.
  - Do not use gasket cement or sealers.
- **Hydra-Matic 4T60-E** – Replace plastic/P.T.F.E. and rubber lip seals only when necessary and install using the appropriate seal protector.

Inspect

- Manual linkage for:
  - Wear at pivoting points
  - Bent or broken links and rods
- All seals, gaskets, O-rings and mating surfaces for:
  - Nicks
  - Cuts
  - Damage
- Snap rings for:
  - Expansion or compression
  - Distortion
  - Nicks
  - Proper ring to groove fit
- Bearings and thrust surfaces for:
  - Wear
  - Scoring
  - Pitting

FLYWHEEL/TORQUE CONVERTER VIBRATION TEST PROCEDURE

1. Start engine.
2. With engine at idle speed and the transaxle in "Park" (P) or "Neutral" (N), observe vibration.
3. Shut off engine.

Remove or Disconnect

1. Converter shield attaching bolts/screws.
2. Flywheel to torque converter attaching bolts/screws.
3. Rotate torque converter 120° (1/3 turn).

Install or Connect

NOTICE: Some engine/transaxle combinations cannot be balanced in this manner due to limited clearances between the torque converter bolts/screws and engine. Be sure bolts/screws do not bottom out in wheel nuts, or the torque converter cover could be dented and cause internal damage.

1. Flywheel to torque converter attaching bolts/screws.

Tighten

- Bolts/screws to 63 N•m (46 lb. ft.).

2. Converter shield bolts/screws.

Tighten

- Bolts/screws to 10 N•m (89 lb. in.).

Adjust

- Start engine and check for vibration. Repeat this procedure until the best possible balance is obtained.

FLUID LEAK DIAGNOSIS

Most fluid leaks can be located and repaired by visually finding the leak and replacing or repairing the necessary parts. On some occasions, a fluid leak may be difficult to locate or repair. The following procedure may help in locating and repairing most leaks.

Locating the Leak

1. Identify the fluid. Determine whether it is engine oil, automatic transaxle fluid, power steering fluid, etc.
2. To find where the fluid is leaking from: After running the vehicle 15 miles minimum to reach normal operating temperature, park the vehicle over a large sheet of paper. After a few minutes, you should be able to find the approximate location of the leak by the drippings on the paper.
3. Visually check around the suspected component. Check around all gasket mating surfaces for leaks. A mirror is useful for finding leaks in areas that are hard to reach.
4. If a leak still cannot be found, it may be necessary to clean the suspected area with a degreaser, steam or spray solvent. Clean the area well, then dry the area. Operate the vehicle for several miles at normal operating temperature and varying speeds. After operating the vehicle, visually inspect the suspected component. If you still cannot find the leak, try using the powder or black light and dye method.

Powder Method

1. Clean the suspected area.
2. Apply an aerosol-type powder (such as foot powder) to the suspected area.
3. Operate the vehicle under normal operating conditions.
4. Visually inspect the suspected component. You should be able to trace the leak path over the white powder surface to the source.

Black Light and Dye Method

A dye and black light kit is available for finding leaks. Refer to the manufacturer's directions when using the kit.

1. Pour specified amount of dye into leaking component.
2. Operate the vehicle under normal operating conditions as directed in the kit.
3. Direct the light toward the suspected area. The dyed fluid will appear as a brightly colored path leading to the source.
   - See kit directions for the color of the fluid and dye mix.

REPAIRING THE LEAK

Once the leak has been pinpointed and traced back to its source, the cause of the leak must be determined in order for it to be repaired properly. If a gasket is replaced, but the sealing flange is bent, the new gasket will not repair the leak. The bent flange must also be repaired. Before attempting to repair a leak, check to be sure that the following conditions are correct, as they may cause a leak.

Gaskets

1. Fluid level/pressure is too high.
2. Plugged vent or drain-back holes.
3. Improperly torqued fasteners or dirty/damaged threads.
4. Warped flanges or sealing surface.
5. Scratches, burrs or other damage to the sealing surface.
6. Damaged or worn gasket.
7. Cracking or porosity of the component.
8. Improper sealant used (where applicable).

Seals

1. Fluid level/pressure is too high.
2. Plugged vent or drain-back holes.
3. Damaged seal bore (scratched, burred or nicked).
4. Damaged or worn seal.
5. Improper installation.
6. Cracks in component.
7. Manual or output shaft surface scratched, nicked or damaged.
8. Loose or worn bearing causing excess seal wear.

Possible Points of Oil Leak

Figure 4

1. **Transaxle oil pan or side cover:**
   - Attaching bolts/screws not correctly torqued.
   - Improperly installed or damaged gasket.
   - Oil pan or valve body cover mounting face not flat.
2. **Case leak:**
   - Filler tube "multi-lip seal" damaged or missing.

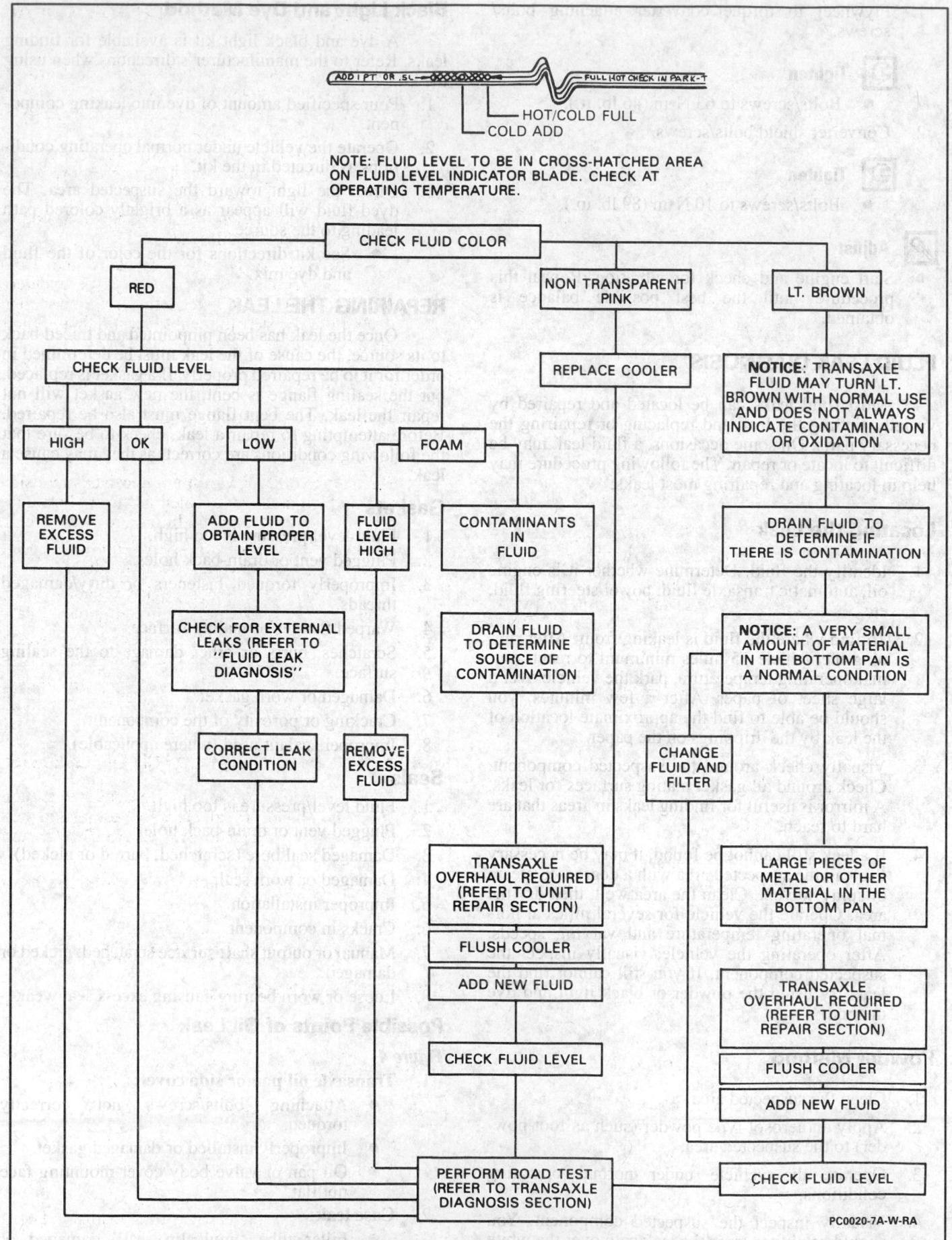

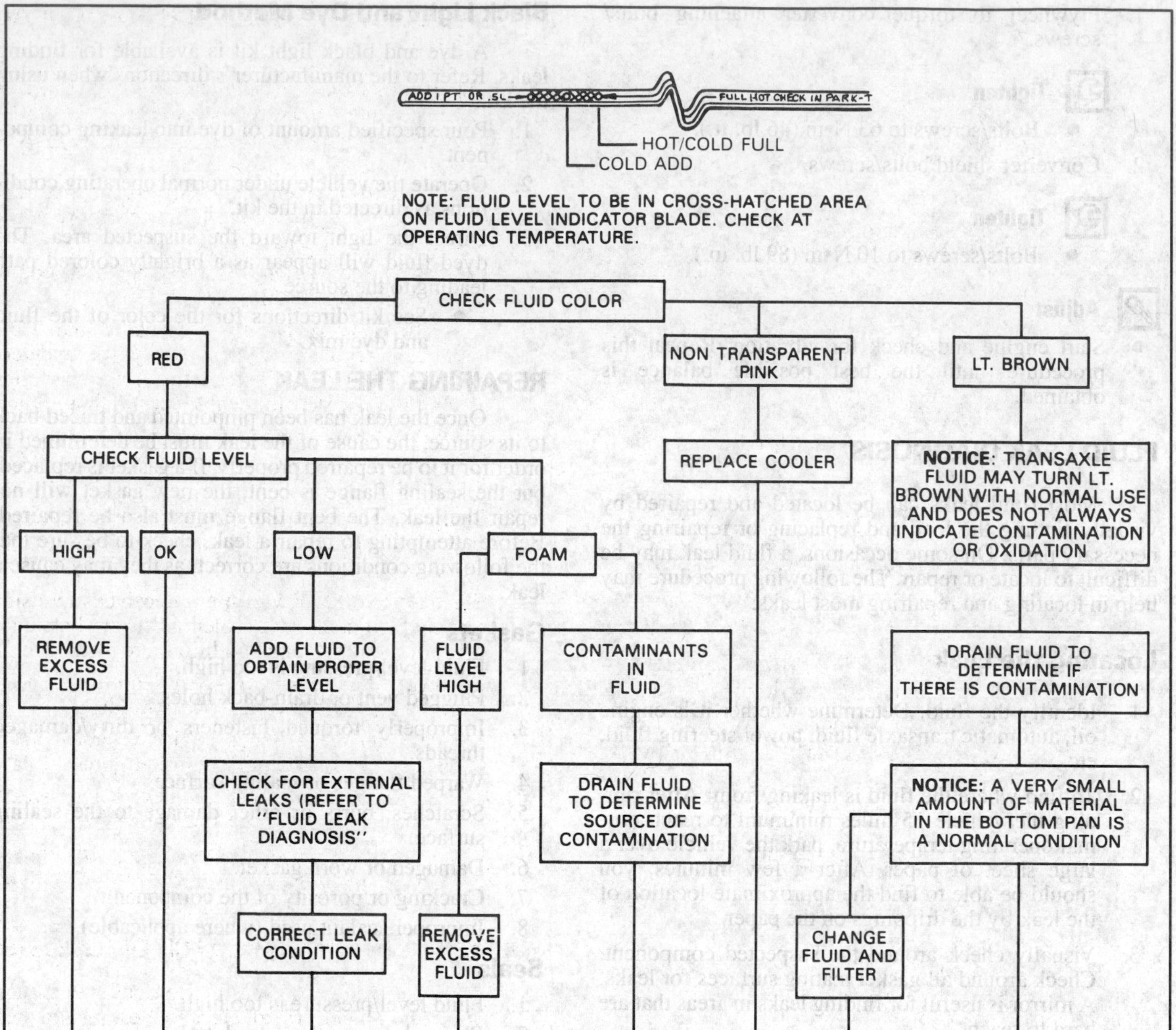
ADD 1 PT OR .5L
FULL HOT CHECK IN PARK
HOT/COLD FULL
COLD ADD
NOTE: FLUID LEVEL TO BE IN CROSS-HATCHED AREA ON FLUID LEVEL INDICATOR BLADE. CHECK AT OPERATING TEMPERATURE.
CHECK FLUID COLOR
RED
NON TRANSPARENT PINK
LT. BROWN
CHECK FLUID LEVEL
REPLACE COOLER
NOTICE: TRANSAXLE FLUID MAY TURN LT. BROWN WITH NORMAL USE AND DOES NOT ALWAYS INDICATE CONTAMINATION OR OXIDATION
HIGH
OK
LOW
FOAM
REMOVE EXCESS FLUID
ADD FLUID TO OBTAIN PROPER LEVEL
FLUID LEVEL HIGH
CONTAMINANTS IN FLUID
DRAIN FLUID TO DETERMINE IF THERE IS CONTAMINATION
CHECK FOR EXTERNAL LEAKS (REFER TO "FLUID LEAK DIAGNOSIS")
DRAIN FLUID TO DETERMINE SOURCE OF CONTAMINATION
NOTICE: A VERY SMALL AMOUNT OF MATERIAL IN THE BOTTOM PAN IS A NORMAL CONDITION
CORRECT LEAK CONDITION
REMOVE EXCESS FLUID
CHANGE FLUID AND FILTER
TRANSAXLE OVERHAUL REQUIRED (REFER TO UNIT REPAIR SECTION)
LARGE PIECES OF METAL OR OTHER MATERIAL IN THE BOTTOM PAN
FLUSH COOLER
ADD NEW FLUID
TRANSAXLE OVERHAUL REQUIRED (REFER TO UNIT REPAIR SECTION)
CHECK FLUID LEVEL
FLUSH COOLER
ADD NEW FLUID
PERFORM ROAD TEST (REFER TO TRANSAXLE DIAGNOSIS SECTION)
CHECK FLUID LEVEL
PC0020-7A-W-RA

Figure 3 Checking Fluid Color, Level and Condition

- Filler tube bracket improperly located.
- Governor cover and O-rings damaged or missing.
- Speed sensor seal damaged.
- Manual shaft seal damaged.
- Oil cooler connector fittings loose or damaged.
- Vacuum modulator loose or O-ring damaged or missing.
- Axle oil seals worn or damaged.
- Parking pawl shaft cup plug loose (if equipped).
- Governor pressure pipe plug loose.
- Line pressure pipe plug loose.
- Case-to-case cover gasket damaged (if equipped).
- Porous casting.

3. **Leaking at converter end:**
   - Converter seal damaged.
     – Seal lip cut (check converter hub for damage).
     – Bushing moved forward and damaged.
     – Garter spring missing from seal.
   - Converter leak in weld area.
     – **Hydra-Matic 4T60-E** – Refer to 7A-5B.
   - Porous casting (case, pump or drive sprocket support).
4. **Fluid comes out vent pipe or fill tube:**
   - Over-filled.
   - Water or coolant in fluid. Fluid will appear milky.
   - Case porous.
   - Incorrect fluid level indicator.
   - Plugged vent.
   - Drain back holes plugged.
   - Improperly positioned oil pump-to-case gasket (if equipped).

CASE POROSITY REPAIR

1. Clean the leak area with solvent and air-dry.

   CAUTION: Epoxy cement may cause skin irritations and eye damage. Read and follow all information on the container label as provided by the manufacturer.
2. Mix a sufficient amount of epoxy cement, GM p/n 1052533 (or equivalent), following the manufacturer's recommendations.
3. While the transaxle case is hot, apply epoxy cement with a clean, dry soldering acid brush.
4. Allow epoxy cement to cure for three hours before starting the engine.
5. Repeat fluid leak diagnosis procedures.

TORQUE CONVERTER CLUTCH ELECTRICAL CONTROLS

The Torque Converter Clutch (TCC) system uses controls that are internal as well as external to the transaxle. Internal control components of the TCC system include:

1. **TCC Solenoid Assembly** – Energizes to redirect transaxle fluid to the converter clutch apply valve in the control valve assembly.
2. **Fourth Clutch Switch** – Opens when transaxle is in fourth gear, to signal ECM.
3. **Control Valve Assembly** – Contains the TCC apply and regulator valves. Apply valve determines method of fluid feed to torque converter assembly in order to enable or disable clutch mechanism.

The external control components of the TCC system include:

1. **Brake Release Switch** – Releases the converter clutch to prevent engine stalling whenever the brakes are applied.
2. **Electronic Control Module** – Receives input signals and grounds TCC solenoid to apply clutch when proper operating conditions are met.
3. **Throttle Position Sensor** – Sends throttle position information to Electronic Control Module.
4. **Vacuum Sensor** – Sends engine vacuum (load) information to Electronic Control Module.
5. **Vehicle Speed Sensor** – Sends vehicle speed information to Electronic Control Module.
6. **Coolant Temperature Sensor** – Sends engine coolant temperature information to Electronic Control Module.

TORQUE CONVERTER CLUTCH DIAGNOSIS

To properly diagnosis the Torque Converter Clutch (TCC) system, first perform all electrical testing and then the hydraulic testing. Refer to SECTIONS 6E3-C8 and 7A-5A.

For electrical schematic of TCC system, refer to SECTION 8A.

ON-VEHICLE SERVICE

SHIFT CONTROL CABLE

Console Shift

Figures 5 through 7

↔ Remove or Disconnect

1. Air cleaner assembly.
2. Cable from transaxle lever and bracket.
3. Shift handle.
4. Console trim, storage box, courtesy lamp and console. Refer to SECTION 8C.
5. Cable retaining clips and cable at console.

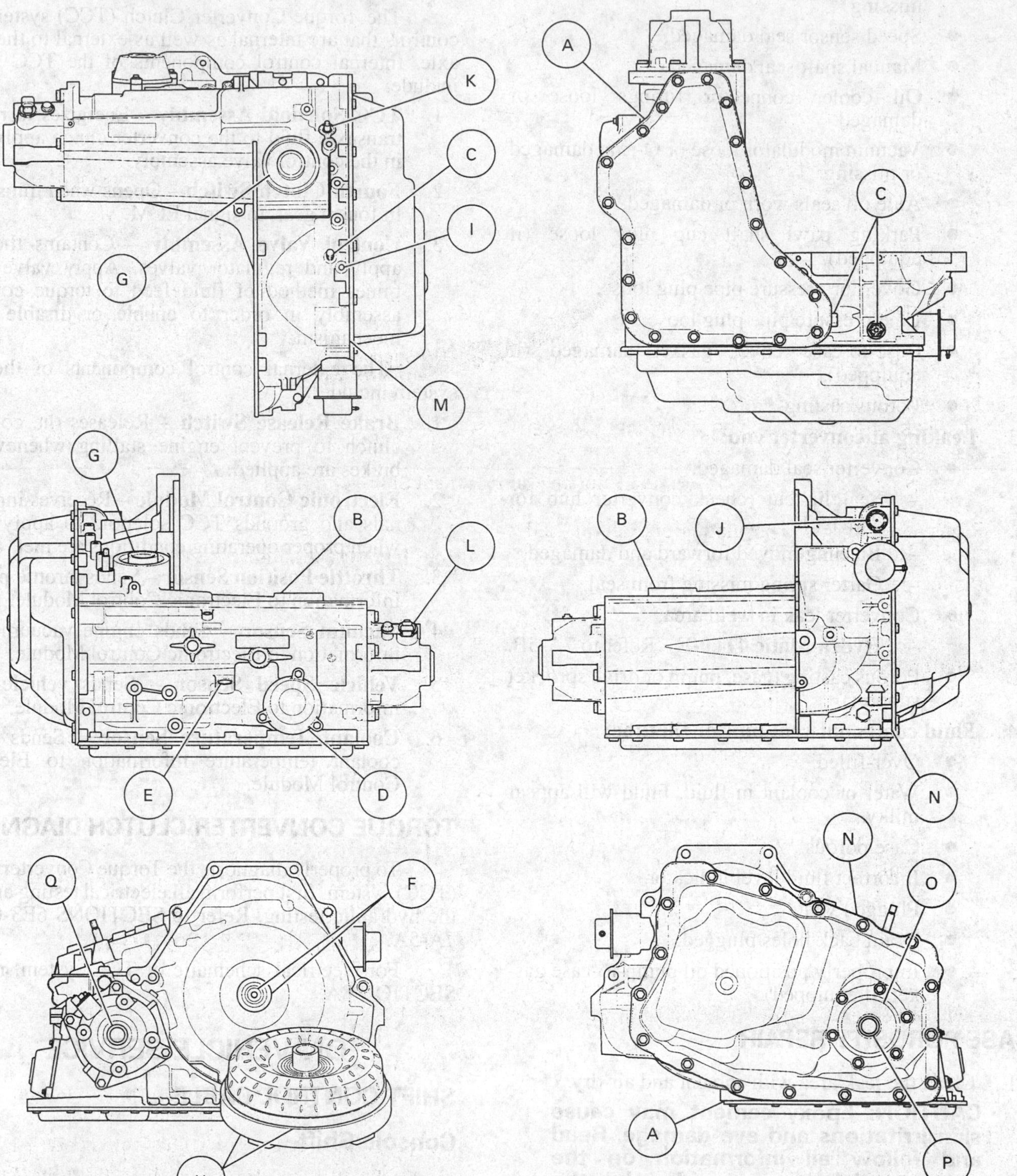
A
B
C
D
E
F
G
H
I
J
K
L
M
N
O
P
Q

A	BOTTOM PAN GASKET	G	REVERSE SERVO COVER	M	VACUUM MODULATOR TO CASE SEAL
B	CASE	H	CONVERTER	N	SIDE COVER TO CASE GASKET
C	LINE PRESSURE TAP TO COOLER CONNECTOR	I	VENT	O	SIDE COVER TO CHANNEL PLATE GASKET
D	FORWARD SERVO COVER SEAL	J	ELECTRICAL CONNECTOR SEAL	P	AXLE SEAL (LEFT HAND)
E	OIL FILL TUBE SEAL	K	MANUAL SHAFT SEAL	Q	AXLE SEAL (RIGHT HAND)
F	CONVERTER SEAL ASSEMBLY	L	VSS SEAL		

PH0133-4T60-E

Figure 4 Leak Points – Hydra-Matic 4T60-E

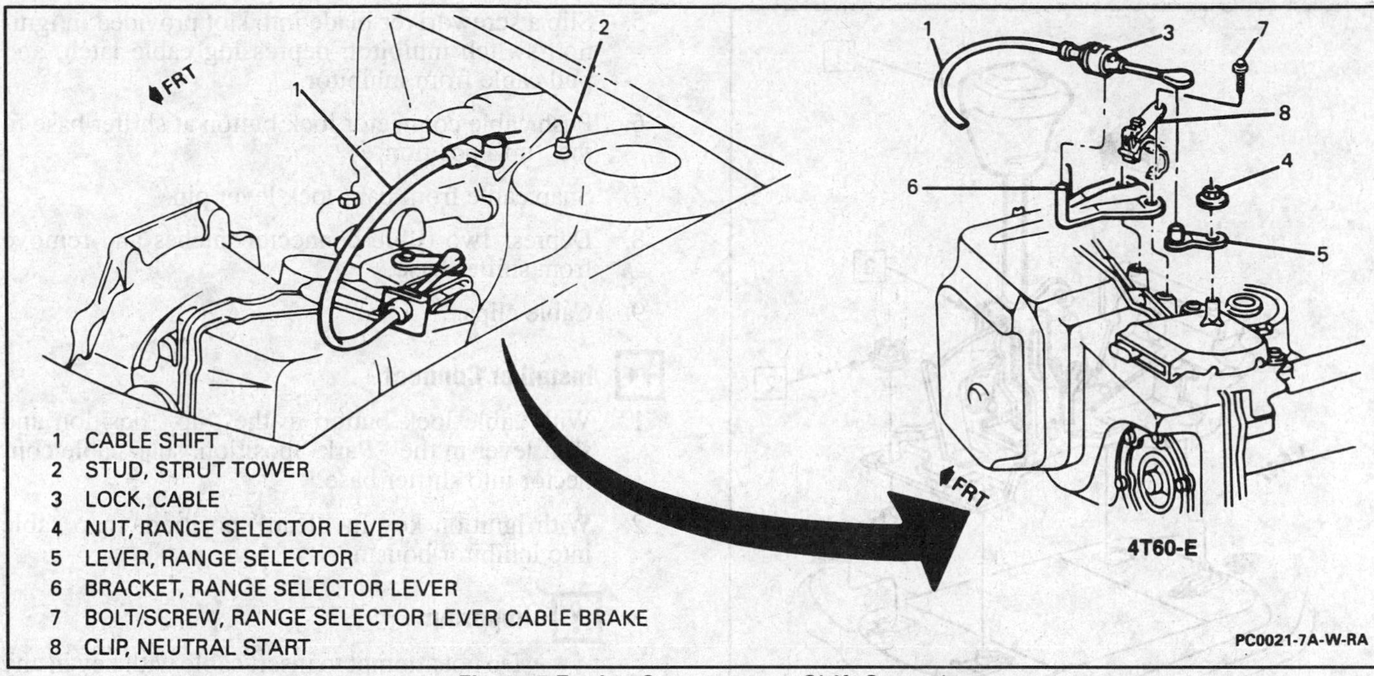
1 CABLE SHIFT
2 STUD, STRUT TOWER
3 LOCK, CABLE
4 NUT, RANGE SELECTOR LEVER
5 LEVER, RANGE SELECTOR
6 BRACKET, RANGE SELECTOR LEVER
7 BOLT/SCREW, RANGE SELECTOR LEVER CABLE BRAKE
8 CLIP, NEUTRAL START
FRT
4T60-E
PC0021-7A-W-RA

Figure 5 Engine Compartment Shift Control

6. Right and left sound insulators and shroud side panels. Refer to SECTION 8C.
7. Pull carpet back to expose cable.
8. Cable assembly through hole in cowl.

Install or Connect

1. Properly route and position cable.
2. Carpet into position, right and left sound insulators and shroud side panels. Refer to SECTION 8C.
3. Cable at console and retaining clips.
4. Console, courtesy lamp, storage box and console trim. Refer to SECTION 8C.
5. Shift handle.
6. Cable at transaxle lever and bracket.
7. Air cleaner assembly.

Adjust

- Cable. Refer to "Control Cable Adjustment" in this section.

Column Shift

Figures 5 and 8

Remove or Disconnect

1. Air cleaner assembly.
2. Cable from transaxle lever and bracket.
3. Cable from strut tower.
4. Left sound insulator. Refer to SECTION 8C.
5. Steering column trim panel.
6. Cable from shift control lever.
7. Cable from steering column bracket.
8. Cable assembly through hole in cowl.

Install or Connect

1. Properly route and position cable.
2. Cable to steering column bracket.
3. Cable to shift control lever.
4. Steering column trim panel.
5. Left sound insulator. Refer to SECTION 8C.
6. Cable to strut tower.
7. Cable to transaxle lever and bracket.
8. Air cleaner assembly.

Adjust

- Cable. Refer to "Control Cable Adjustment" in this section.

CONTROL CABLE ADJUSTMENT

Figure 5

Adjust

1. Apply park brake and block wheels.
2. Position steering column/floor console range selector lever into "Neutral" position.
3. Lift up range selector cable locking button.
4. Remove range selector cable end from transaxle range selector lever.
5. Position steering column/floor console range selector lever into "Low" position.
6. Position transaxle range selector lever into "Low" position.
   - Obtain "Low" position by rotating transaxle range selector lever toward front of vehicle until it stops.
7. Snap range selector cable end onto transaxle range selector lever.

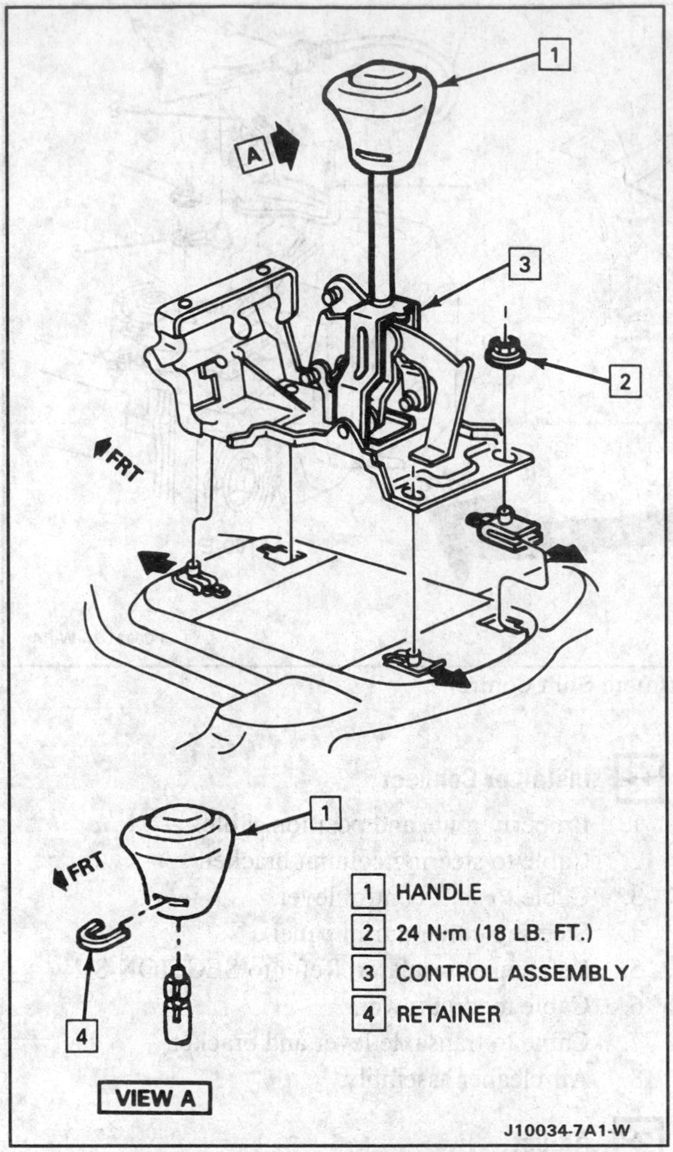
1
A
3
2
FRT
1
FRT
1 HANDLE
2 24 N·m (18 LB. FT.)
3 CONTROL ASSEMBLY
4 RETAINER
4
VIEW A
J10034-7A1-W
Figure 6 Console Shift Control

8. Press range selector cable locking button down. (Locked Position)
9. Position steering column/floor console range selector into "Park" position.
10. Remove wheel blocks and release park brake.

PARK/LOCK CONTROL CABLE

Figures 7 and 9

Remove or Disconnect

1. Air cleaner assembly.
2. Negative battery cable.
3. Place transaxle shift lever in "Park."
4. Turn ignition key to "Run" position.

Important

- Do not attempt to proceed to next step with key in any other position.

5. Slip a screwdriver blade into slot provided in ignition switch inhibitor, depressing cable latch, and pull cable from inhibitor.
6. Push cable connector lock button at shifter base to the "up" position.
7. Snap cable from park lock lever pin.
8. Depress two cable connector latches and remove from shifter base.
9. Cable clips.

Install or Connect

1. With cable lock button in the "up" position and shift lever in the "Park" position, snap cable connector into shifter base.
2. With ignition key in "Run" position, snap cable into inhibitor housing.

Important

- Do not attempt to insert cable with key in any other position.

3. Turn ignition key to "Lock."
4. Snap cable end onto shifter park lock lever pin.
5. Push cable connector nose forward to remove slack.
6. With no load applied to connector nose, snap cable connector lock button down.
7. Negative battery cable.
8. Air cleaner assembly.

Inspect

- Functional Operation
  - A. With the shift lever in "Park" and the key in "Lock" position, make sure that you cannot move the shifter lever to another position. Ignition key should be removable from column.
  - B. With key in "Run" and the shift lever in "Neutral," make sure that you cannot turn the key to "Lock."
  - C. If the above conditions are met, the system is properly adjusted. Proceed to Step E.
  - D. If the above conditions are not met, pull cable connector lock back to the "up" position and readjust as indicated in Steps 5 and 6 above, then push cable connector lock button down and recheck operation.
  - E. If key cannot be removed in "Park" position, snap connector lock button to "up" position and move cable connector nose rearward, until key can be removed from ignition.
  - F. Snap lock button down.
  - G. Reinstall cable into clips to provide correct routing.

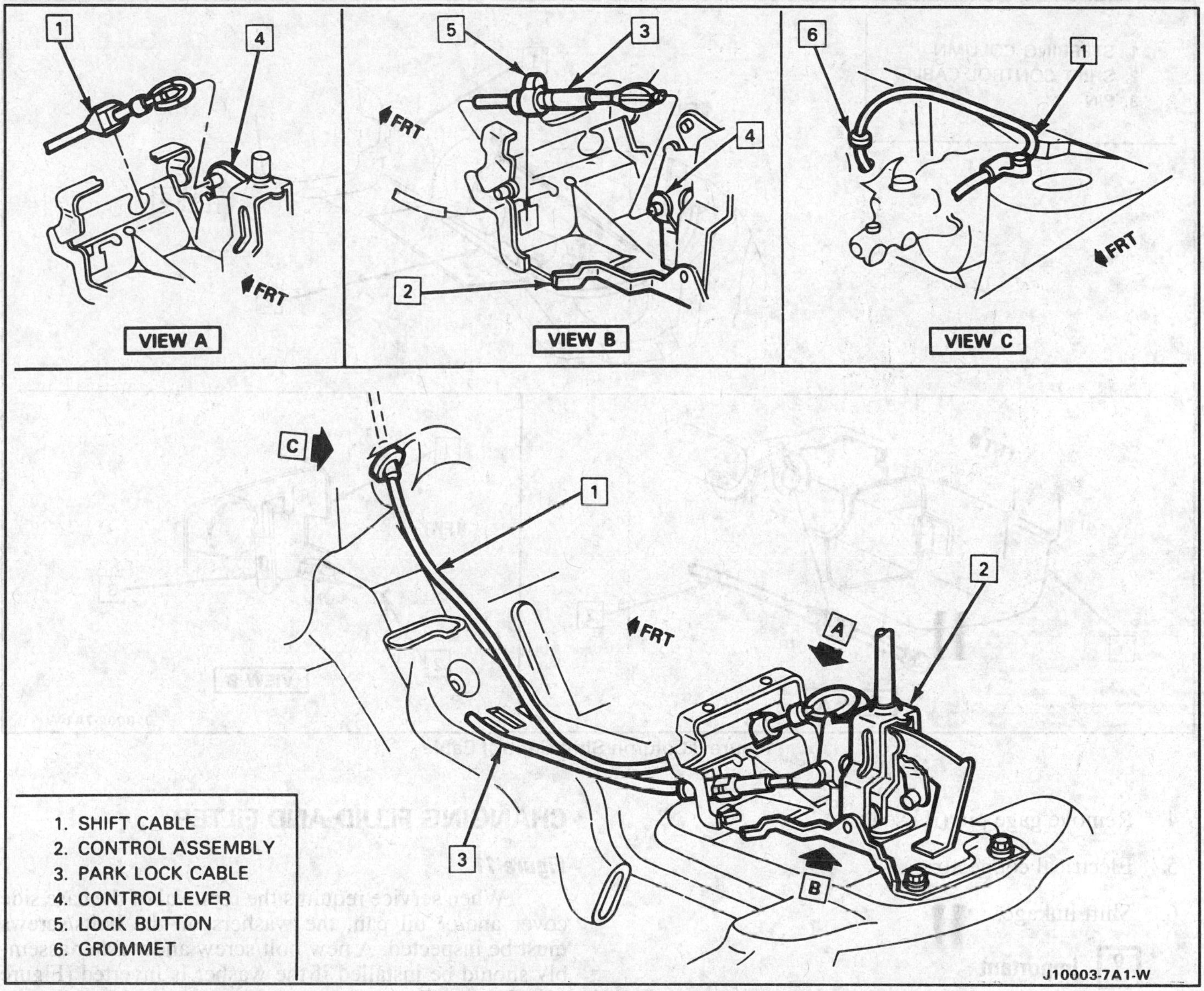
VIEW A
VIEW B
VIEW C
FRT
A
B
C
1. SHIFT CABLE
2. CONTROL ASSEMBLY
3. PARK LOCK CABLE
4. CONTROL LEVER
5. LOCK BUTTON
6. GROMMET
J10003-7A1-W

Figure 7 Console Shift Control Cables

NEUTRAL START SWITCH

Figure 10

Remove or Disconnect

1. Apply parking brake and block wheels.
2. Place vehicle in "Neutral."
3. Shift linkage.
4. Electrical connector.
5. Mounting bolts/screws.
6. Switch.

Install or Connect

1. Place shift shaft in "Neutral."
2. Align flats of shift shafts to flats in switch.
3. Mounting bolts/screws.

Important

- If bolt/screw holes do not align with mounting boss on transmission, verify shift shaft is in "Neutral" position. DO NOT ROTATE SWITCH. Switch is pinned in "Neutral" position.
- If switch has been rotated and pin broken or when using old switch, adjust as follows:
  - A. Assemble mounting bolts/screws loosely.
  - B. Align slot in support with slot in back and insert 2.34 mm diameter pin (or 3/32 inch drill bit) horizontally into both pieces.
  - C. Torque bolts/screws.

Tighten

- Mounting bolts/screws to 25 N•m (18 lb. ft.).

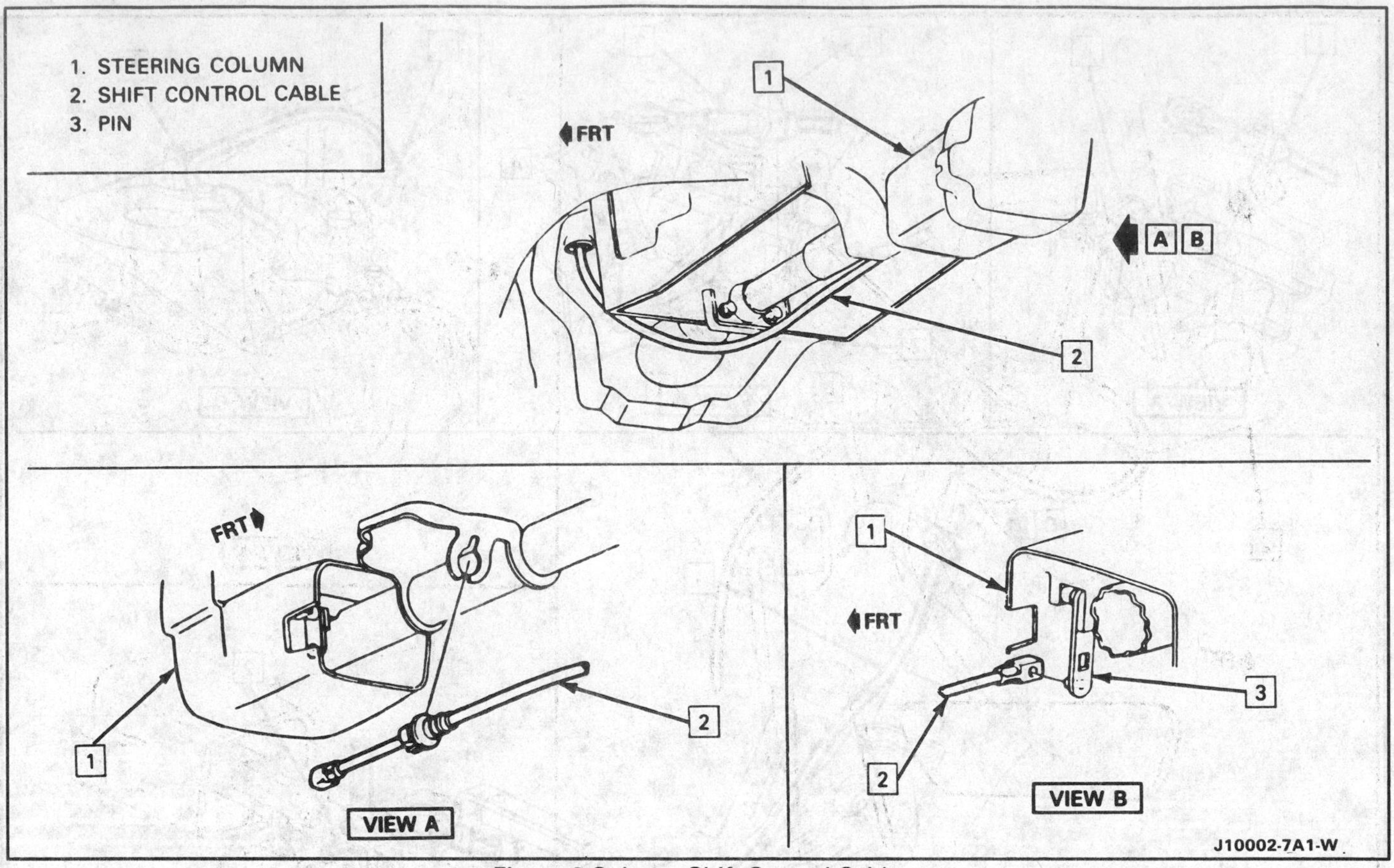
1. STEERING COLUMN
2. SHIFT CONTROL CABLE
3. PIN
FRT
A
B
1
2
3
VIEW A
VIEW B
J10002-7A1-W

Figure 8 Column Shift Control Cable

4. Remove gage pin (if used).
5. Electrical connector.
6. Shift linkage.

Important

- After switch installation, verify that engine will only start in "Park" or "Neutral." If engine will start in any other position, readjust switch.

Adjust

A. Place transmission control shifter assembly in the "Neutral" notch in detent plate.

B. Loosen switch attaching bolts/screws.

C. Rotate switch on shifter assembly to align service adjustment hole with carrier tang hole.

 – Insert 2.34 mm (3.32 inches) max. diameter gage pin to a depth of 15 mm (5/8 inch).

D. Tighten attaching bolts/screws to above specifications.

E. Remove gage pin.

7. Release parking brake and remove wheel blocks.

CHANGING FLUID AND FILTER

Figure 11

When service requires the removal of the case side cover and/or oil pan, the washers on the bolts/screws must be inspected. A new bolt/screw and washer assembly should be installed if the washer is inverted (Figure 11).

NOTICE: Do not overfill. Overfilling causes foaming and loss of fluid through the vent and may damage the automatic transaxle.

Remove or Disconnect

1. Raise vehicle and suitably support. Refer to SECTION 0A.
2. Place drain pan under transaxle oil pan.
3. Oil pan bolts/screws from front and sides.
4. Loosen rear oil pan bolts/screws approximately four turns.

NOTICE: Care must be taken not to damage mating surfaces of oil pan and case. Such damage may result in oil leaks in this area.

5. Lightly tap oil pan with rubber mallet or pry oil pan loose with a screwdriver and allow fluid to drain.
6. Remaining oil pan bolts/screws, pan and gasket.
7. Oil filter.
   - **Hydra-Matic 4T60-E** – Screen/filter. The lip ring seal pressed into the case should be removed only if replacement is necessary.

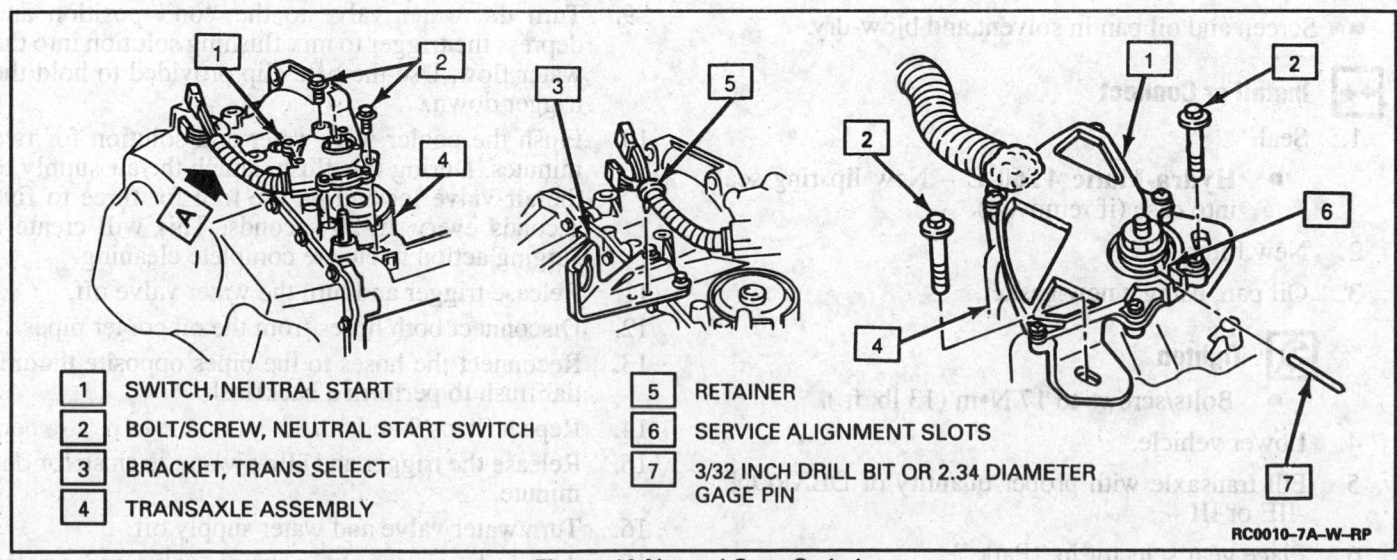

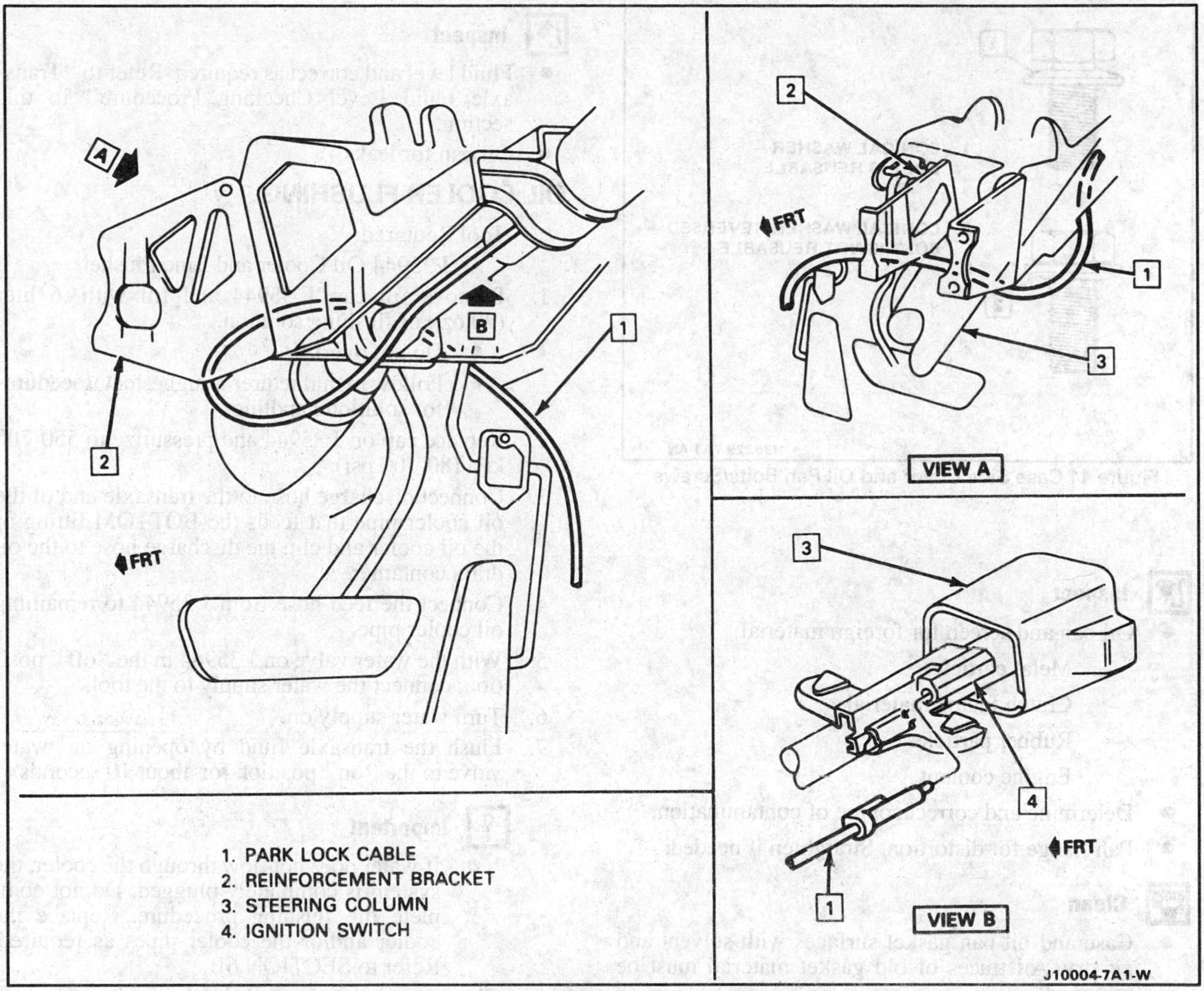
A
B
FRT
1
2
2
1
3
VIEW A
3
4
1
FRT
VIEW B
1. PARK LOCK CABLE
2. REINFORCEMENT BRACKET
3. STEERING COLUMN
4. IGNITION SWITCH
J10004-7A1-W

Figure 9 Park Lock Control Cable at Column

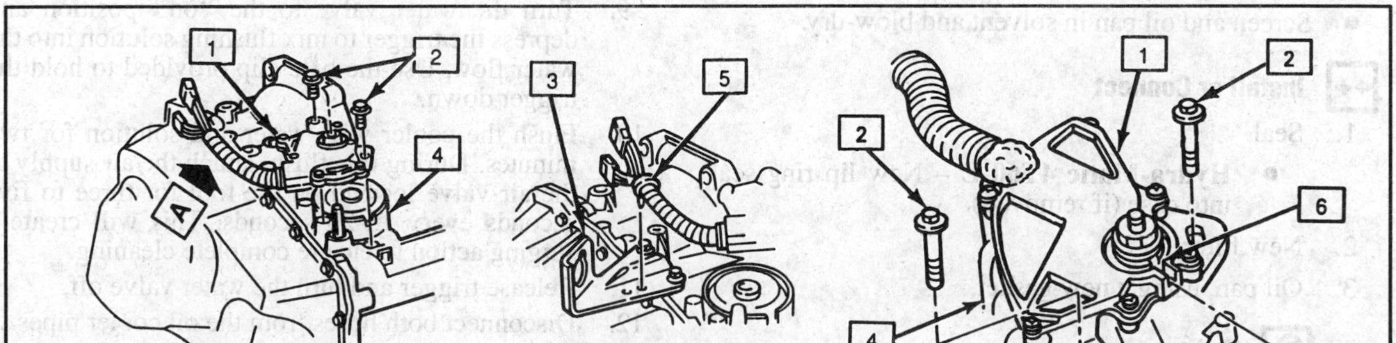
1
2
3
4
5
A
1
2
2
6
4
7
1 SWITCH, NEUTRAL START
2 BOLT/SCREW, NEUTRAL START SWITCH
3 BRACKET, TRANS SELECT
4 TRANSAXLE ASSEMBLY
5 RETAINER
6 SERVICE ALIGNMENT SLOTS
7 3/32 INCH DRILL BIT OR 2.34 DIAMETER GAGE PIN
RC0010-7A-W-RP

Figure 10 Neutral Start Switch

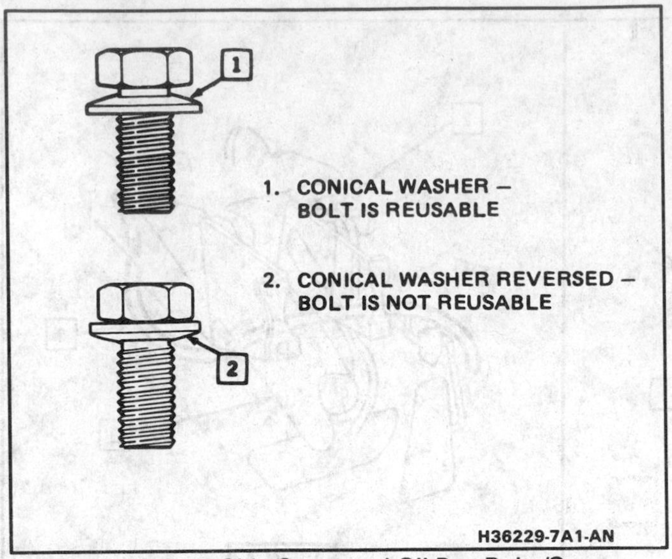
1. CONICAL WASHER – BOLT IS REUSABLE
2. CONICAL WASHER REVERSED – BOLT IS NOT REUSABLE
H36229-7A1-AN

Figure 11 Case Side Cover and Oil Pan Bolts/Screws

Inspect

- Oil pan and screen for foreign material:
  - Metal particles
  - Clutch facing material
  - Rubber particles
  - Engine coolant
- Determine and correct source of contamination.
- Pan flange for distortion. Straighten if needed.

Clean

- Case and oil pan gasket surfaces with solvent and air dry. All traces of old gasket material must be removed.

NOTICE: If the case and oil pan flanges are not dry and free of any oil film, leakage may result.

- Screen and oil pan in solvent and blow-dry.

Install or Connect

1. Seal.
   - **Hydra-Matic 4T60-E** – New lip ring seal into case (if removed).
2. New filter.
3. Oil pan, using a new gasket.

   Tighten
   - Bolts/screws to 17 N•m (13 lb. ft.).
4. Lower vehicle.
5. Fill transaxle with proper quantity of DEXRON® -IIE or III.
6. Place gear selector in "Park."
7. Start engine and run at slow idle. Do not race the engine.

Inspect

- Fluid level and correct as required. Refer to "Transaxle Fluid Level Checking Procedure" in this section.
- Oil pan for leaks.

OIL COOLER FLUSHING

Tool Required:
J 35944 Oil Cooler and Line Flusher

1. Remove fill cap J 35944 and fill with .6 liter (20 oz.) of flushing solution.
   - Do not overfill.
   - Follow manufacturer's suggested procedures for solution handling.
2. Replace cap on J 35944 and pressurize to 550-700 kPa (80-100 psi).
3. Connect discharge hose to the transaxle end of the oil cooler pipe that feeds the BOTTOM fitting of the oil cooler and clip the discharge hose to the oil drain container.
4. Connect the feed hose from J 35944 to remaining oil cooler pipe.
5. With the water valve on J 35944 in the "off" position, connect the water supply to the tool.
6. Turn water supply on.
7. Flush the transaxle fluid by opening the water valve to the "on" position for about 10 seconds.

   Important
   - If water does not flow through the cooler, the system is completely plugged. Do not complete the flushing procedure. Replace the cooler and/or the cooler pipes as required. Refer to SECTION 6B.
8. Close the water valve and clip the discharge hose to the 5-gallon pail. Cover the pail with a shop towel to prevent splashing.
9. Turn the water valve to the "on" position and depress the trigger to mix flushing solution into the water flow. Use the bale clip provided to hold the trigger down.
10. Flush the cooler with water and solution for two minutes. During this flush, attach the air supply to the air valve located on the tool for three to five seconds every 15-20 seconds. This will create a surging action to ensure complete cleaning.
11. Release trigger and turn the water valve off.
12. Disconnect both hoses from the oil cooler pipes.
13. Reconnect the hoses to the pipes opposite the initial flush to perform a backflush.
14. Repeat Steps 9 and 10.
15. Release the trigger and allow water to rinse for one minute.
16. Turn water valve and water supply off.
17. Attach the air supply to the air valve and dry the system out with air until no moisture is seen leaving the discharge hose.

18. Connect cooler feed pipe to the transaxle.
19. Reconnect discharge hose to cooler return pipe and clip hose to oil drain container.
20. After filling the transaxle with fluid, start the engine and run for 30 seconds. This will remove any residual moisture from the oil cooler. A minimum of two quarts of fluid should flow during the 30-second period. If fluid flow is insufficient, check the fluid flow from the transaxle by disconnecting the feed line at the cooler and observe the flow with the engine running.
    - If flow from the transaxle is insufficient, inspect transaxle for cause.
    - If flow from the transaxle is sufficient, inspect cooler pipes and fittings and repeat cooler flushing procedure. If flow through cooler is still insufficient, replace the cooler. Refer to SECTION 6B.
21. Remove the discharge hose and connect the cooler pipe.

Adjust

- Fluid level.

HYDRA-MATIC 4T60-E SERVICEABLE COMPONENTS

The following parts can be serviced with transaxle in the vehicle.

- Fluid filler tube.
- Speed sensor.
- Pan and/or gasket.
- Fluid filter and/or seal.
- Scavenger oil scoop.
- Accumulator assembly (1-2 and 2-3) and 2-1 manual servo.
- Thermo element.
- Vacuum modulator and/or O-ring.
- Reverse servo assembly.
- Forward servo assembly.
- Case side cover pan and/or gaskets.
- Pump.
- Valve body.
- Solenoids and wiring harness.
- Case extension housing.
- Final drive components.
- Oil cooler pipes and/or fittings.
- Auxiliary oil cooler.
- Transaxle mount.
- Transaxle bracket.
- Drive axle oil seal.

FLUID FILLER TUBE

Figure 12

Remove or Disconnect

1. Indicator assembly.
2. Raise and suitably support vehicle.
3. Front exhaust manifold pipe. Refer to SECTION 6F.
4. Steering gear heat shield.
5. Bolt/screw from bracket assembly.
6. Tube assembly.

Install or Connect

NOTICE: See "Notice" on page 7A-1 of this section.

1. Position tube assembly.

Important

- When installing tube assembly, do not place seal on tube assembly or seal will be damaged.

2. Bolt/screw.

Tighten

- Bolt/screw to 13 N•m (115 lb. in.).

3. Steering gear heat shield.
4. Front exhaust manifold pipe. Refer to SECTION 6F.
5. Lower vehicle.
6. Indicator assembly.

Adjust

- Fluid level.

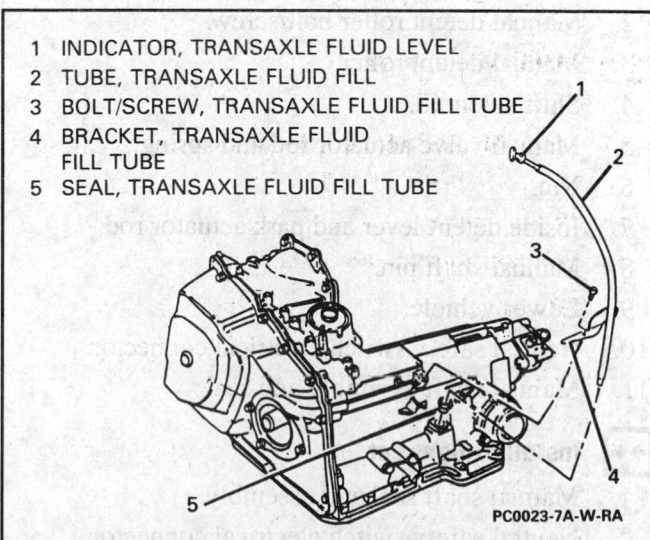

1 INDICATOR, TRANSAXLE FLUID LEVEL
2 TUBE, TRANSAXLE FLUID FILL
3 BOLT/SCREW, TRANSAXLE FLUID FILL TUBE
4 BRACKET, TRANSAXLE FLUID FILL TUBE
5 SEAL, TRANSAXLE FLUID FILL TUBE

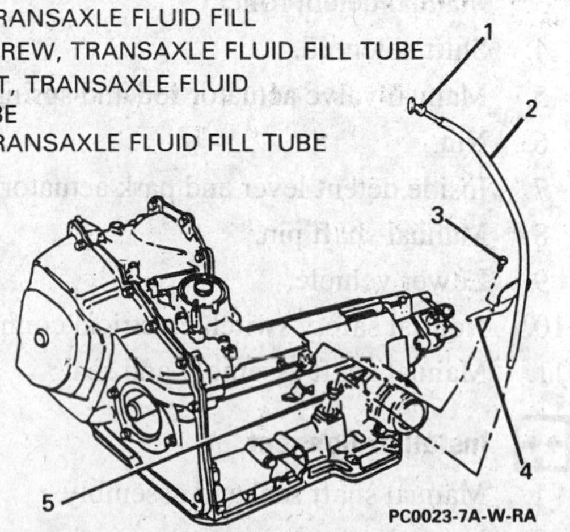
1
2
3
4
5
PC0023-7A-W-RA

Figure 12 Fluid Filler Tube and Indicator – Hydra-Matic 4T60-E

SPEED SENSOR

Figure 13

Remove or Disconnect

1. Raise vehicle and suitably support. Refer to SECTION 0A.
2. Right front tire and wheel. Refer to SECTION 3E.
3. Engine splash shield.
4. Drive axle shield.
5. Speed sensor electrical connector.
6. Bolt/screw.
7. Speed sensor from extension case.
8. O-ring from speed sensor.

Install or Connect

1. O-ring to speed sensor.
2. Speed sensor to extension case.
3. Bolt/screw.

Tighten

- Bolt/screw to 11 N•m (97 lb. in.).

4. Speed sensor electrical connector.
5. Drive axle shield.
6. Engine splash shield.
7. Right front tire and wheel. Refer to SECTION 3E.
8. Lower vehicle.

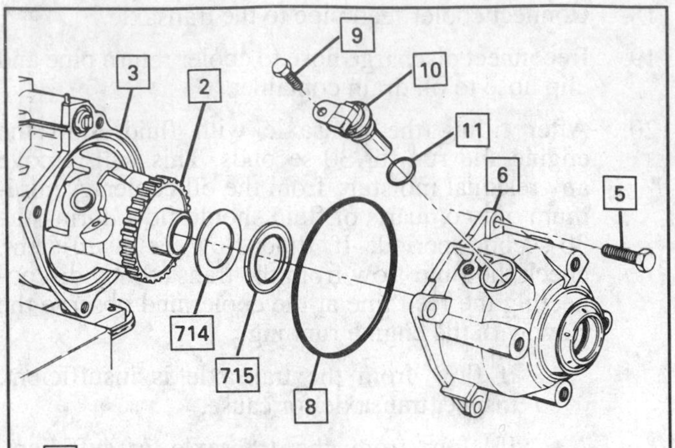

9
10
3
2
11
6
5
714
715
8

2	ROTOR, SPEED SENSOR
3	CASE, TRANSMISSION
5	BOLT, CASE EXTENSION
6	EXTENSION, CASE
8	SEAL, EXTENSION TO CASE
9	BOLT, SPEED SENSOR
10	SPEED SENSOR ASSEMBLY, COMPLETE
11	SEAL, O-RING SPEED SENSOR
714	WASHER, DIFFERENTIAL CARRIER/CASE (THRUST)
715	BEARING ASSEMBLY, THRUST (DIFFERENTIAL CARRIER/CASE)

MC0015-7A-W-RA

Figure 13 Speed Sensor Assembly – Hydra-Matic 4T60-E

MANUAL SHAFT AND PARK SYSTEM COMPONENTS

Remove or Disconnect

1. Case side cover pan. Refer to "Case Side Cover Pan and/or Gaskets" in this section.
2. Manual detent roller bolt/screw.
3. Manual detent roller.
4. Shift solenoid.
5. Manual valve actuator rod and spring.
6. Nut.
7. Inside detent lever and park actuator rod.
8. Manual shaft pin.
9. Lower vehicle.
10. Neutral safety switch electrical connector.
11. Manual shaft assembly and seal.

Install or Connect

1. Manual shaft seal and assembly.
2. Neutral safety switch electrical connector.
3. Raise vehicle and suitably support. Refer to SECTION 0A.
4. Manual shaft pin.
5. Inside detent lever and park actuator rod.
6. Nut.

Tighten

- Nut to 32 N•m (24 lb. ft.).

7. Manual valve actuator rod and spring.
8. Shift solenoid.
9. Manual detent roller.
10. Manual detent roller bolt/screw.

Tighten

- Bolt/screw to 11 N•m (97 lb. in.).

11. Case side cover pan. Refer to "Case Side Cover Pan and/or Gaskets" in this section.

ACCUMULATOR ASSEMBLY (1-2 AND/OR 2-3) AND 2-1 MANUAL SERVO

Figure 14

Remove or Disconnect

1. Raise vehicle and suitably support. Refer to SECTION 0A.
2. Pan. Refer to "Pan And/Or Gasket" in this section.
3. Filter.
4. Accumulator attaching bolts/screws.

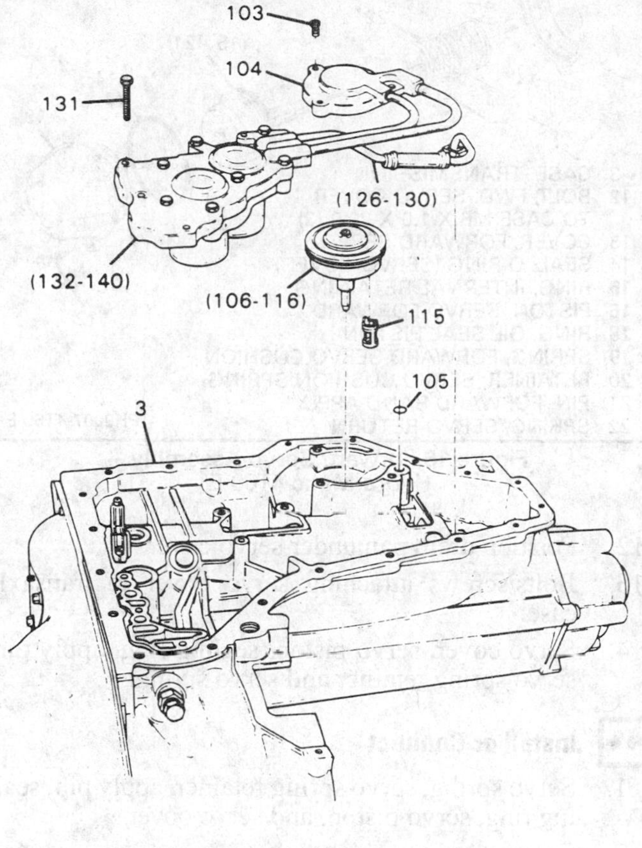
103
104
131
(126-130)
(132-140)
(106-116)
115
105
3
MH0010-4T60-E

3 CASE, TRANSMISSION
103 BOLT, 2/1 MANUAL SERVO COVER
104 COVER, 2/1 MANUAL SERVO BODY
105 SEAL, SQUARE CUT (2/1 SERVO)
106 CLIP, RETAINING (BOTTOM)
107 SEAL, LIP
108 PISTON, 2/1 MANUAL SERVO
109 SPRING, 2/1 MANUAL SERVO CUSHION
110 RETAINER, INT. SERVO SPRING MANUAL CUSHION
111 PIN, 2/1 MANUAL APPLY
112 SPRING, 2/1 MANUAL SERVO RETURN
113 SEAL, O-RING
114 BODY, 2/1 MANUAL SERVO
115 FILTER, 2/1 SERVO
116 CLIP, RETAINING (TOP)
126 PIPE, LUBE OIL
127 CLAMP, HOSE
128 HOSE, LUBE OIL
129 RETAINER, LUBE PIPE CLIP
130 PIPE & WASHER ASSEMBLY
131 BOLT, M6 X 1.0 X 30 (2)
132 COVER, ACCUMULATOR
133 GASKET, ACCUMULATOR COVER
134 PLATE, ACCUMULATOR SPACER
135 PIN, 2-3 ACCUMULATOR
136 PISTON, 1-2 & 2-3 ACCUMULATOR
137 RING, OIL SEAL ACCUMULATOR PISTON
138A SPRING, 2-3 ACCUMULATOR (INNER)
138B SPRING, 2-3 ACCUMULATOR (OUTER)
139 SPRING, 1-2 ACCUMULATOR
140 HOUSING, ACCUMULATOR (MACHINED)

Figure 14 Removing 1-2/2-3 Accumulator Assembly – Hydra-Matic 4T60-E

5. Accumulator assembly, 2-1 manual servo piston assembly, filter and seal.
   - To disassemble and inspect the accumulator and 2-1 manual servo assemblies, refer to 7A-5B.

Install or Connect

1. 2-1 manual servo piston assemblies, filter and seal.
2. Accumulator assemblies and attaching bolts/screws.

Tighten

- Bolts/screws to 11 N•m (97 lb. in.).

3. Filter seal, if removed.
4. Pan. Refer to "Pan And/Or Gasket" in this section.
5. Lower vehicle.

Adjust

- Fluid level.

REVERSE SERVO ASSEMBLY

Figure 15

Remove or Disconnect

1. Air cleaner assembly.
2. Exhaust crossover pipe. Refer to SECTION 6F.
3. Depress servo cover.
4. Snap ring, servo cover, servo piston, sealing ring, apply pin and servo spring.

Install or Connect

1. Jack up the drivers side of the car (channel plate side) so it is higher than the differential side. This will ensure that the reverse band will be in the proper location and not cocked to the channel plate side of the case.

Important

- If this procedure is not followed, the transaxle will not have reverse gear due to the servo pin missing the band.

2. Servo spring, apply pin, sealing ring, servo piston, servo cover and snap ring.
3. Exhaust crossover pipe. Refer to SECTION 6F.
4. Air cleaner assembly.

FORWARD SERVO ASSEMBLY

Figure 16

Tools Required:

J 28467-A Engine Support Fixture
J 28467-90 Engine Support Fixture Adapter
J 36462 Engine Support Adapter Leg

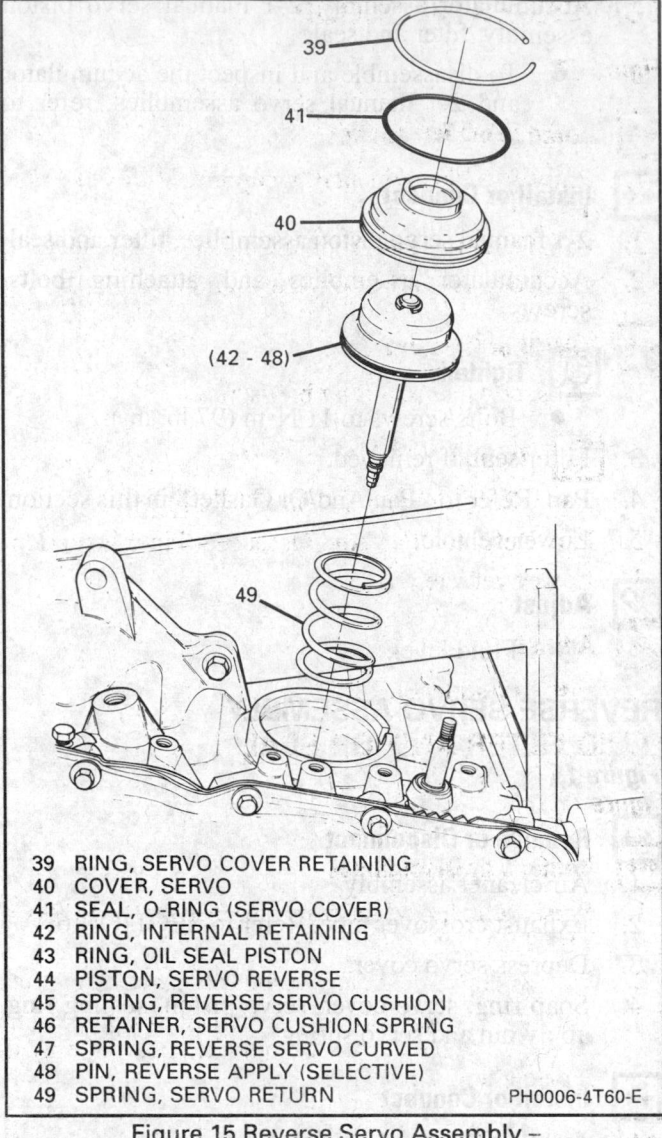

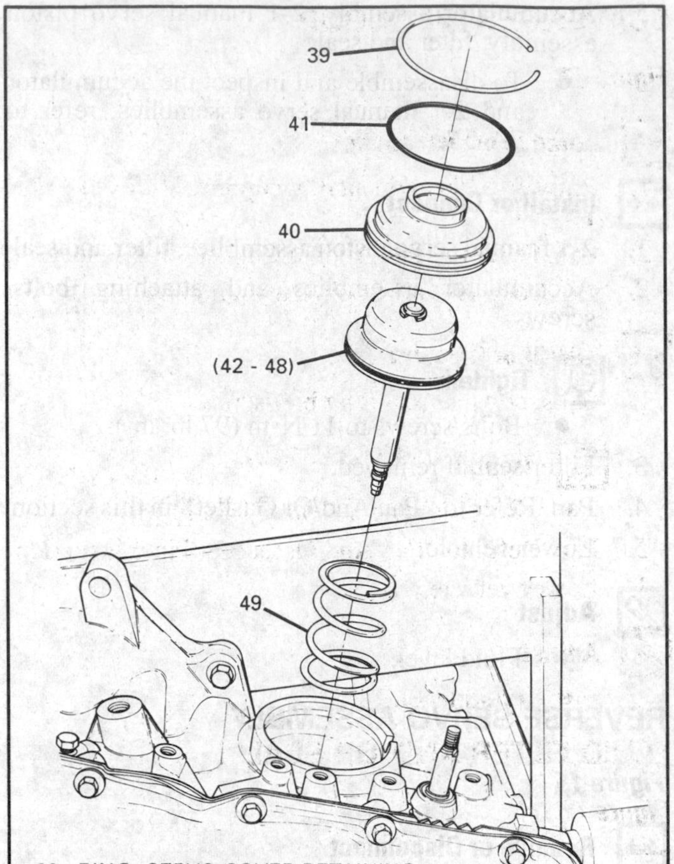
39
41
40
(42 - 48)
49
39 RING, SERVO COVER RETAINING
40 COVER, SERVO
41 SEAL, O-RING (SERVO COVER)
42 RING, INTERNAL RETAINING
43 RING, OIL SEAL PISTON
44 PISTON, SERVO REVERSE
45 SPRING, REVERSE SERVO CUSHION
46 RETAINER, SERVO CUSHION SPRING
47 SPRING, REVERSE SERVO CURVED
48 PIN, REVERSE APPLY (SELECTIVE)
49 SPRING, SERVO RETURN
PH0006-4T60-E

Figure 15 Reverse Servo Assembly – Hydra-Matic 4T60-E

Remove or Disconnect

1. Install J 28467-A, J 28467-90 and J 36462.
2. Raise vehicle and suitably support. Refer to SECTION 0A.
3. Power steering rack and pinion heat shield.
4. Power steering rack and pinion and hang from exhaust pipe flange. Refer to SECTION 3B.
5. Transaxle mount. Refer to "Transaxle Mount" in this section.
6. Engine mount. Refer to SECTION 6A5A or SECTION 6A7.
7. Support rear of frame with jackstand.
8. Loosen front frame bolts/screws. Refer to SECTION 10-3.
9. Rear frame bolts/screws. Refer to SECTION 10-3.
10. Lower frame from jackstand.
11. Power steering lines from right side of frame. Refer to SECTION 3B.

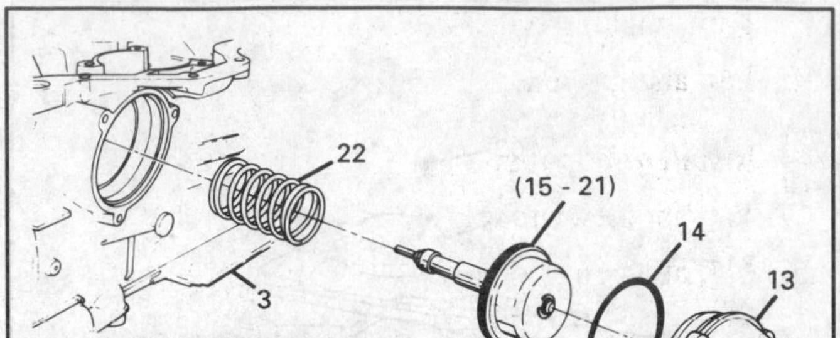
22
(15 - 21)
14
13
3
12
3 CASE, TRANSMISSION
12 BOLT, FWD. SERVO COVER TO CASE M6 X 1.0 X 20.0 (3)
13 COVER, FORWARD SERVO
14 SEAL, O-RING (SERVO COVER)
15 RING, INTERNAL RETAINING
16 PISTON, SERVO FORWARD
18 RING, OIL SEAL PISTON
19 SPRING, FORWARD SERVO CUSHION
20 RETAINER, SERVO CUSHION SPRING
21 PIN, FORWARD BAND APPLY
22 SPRING, SERVO RETURN
PH0007-4T60-E

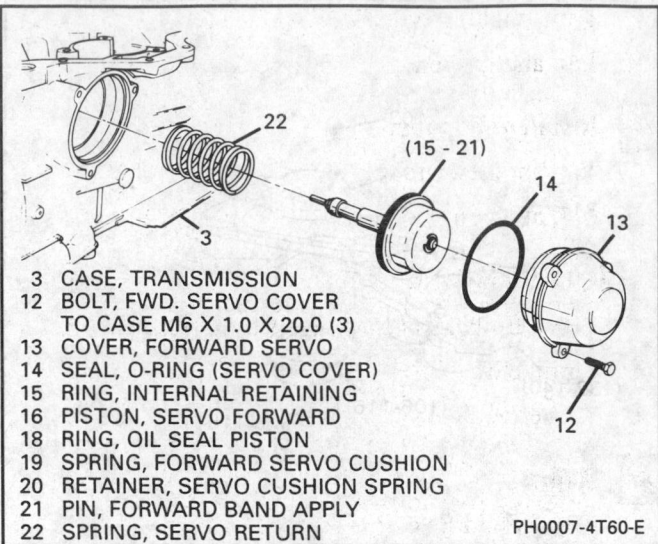

Figure 16 Forward Servo Assembly – Hydra-Matic 4T60-E

12. Position drain pan under servo cover.
13. Bolts/screws attaching servo cover to transaxle case.
14. Servo cover, servo piston, sealing ring, apply pin, servo spring retainer and servo spring.

Install or Connect

1. Servo spring, servo spring retainer, apply pin, sealing ring, servo piston, and servo cover.
2. Servo cover attaching bolts/screws.

Tighten

- Bolts/screws to 10 N•m (89 lb. in.).

3. Power steering lines to right side of frame. Refer to SECTION 3B.
4. Raise frame using jackstand.
5. Frame bolts/screws. Refer to SECTION 10-3.
6. Remove support from rear of frame.
7. Engine mount. Refer to SECTION 6A5A or SECTION 6A7.
8. Transaxle mount. Refer to "Transaxle Mount" in this section.
9. Power steering rack and pinion. Refer to SECTION 3B.
10. Power steering rack and pinion heat shield.
11. Lower vehicle.
12. Remove J 28467-A, J 28467-90 and J 36462.

PAN AND/OR GASKET

Figure 17

Remove or Disconnect

1. Raise vehicle and suitably support. Refer to SECTION 0A.
2. Position drain pan under vehicle.
3. Loosen pan bolts/screws and drain fluid.

4. Pan attaching bolts/screws.
5. Pan and gasket.

Install or Connect

1. Pan and new gasket.
2. Pan attaching bolts/screws.

Tighten

- Bolts/screws to 17 N•m (13 lb. ft.).

3. Drain pan.
4. Lower vehicle.

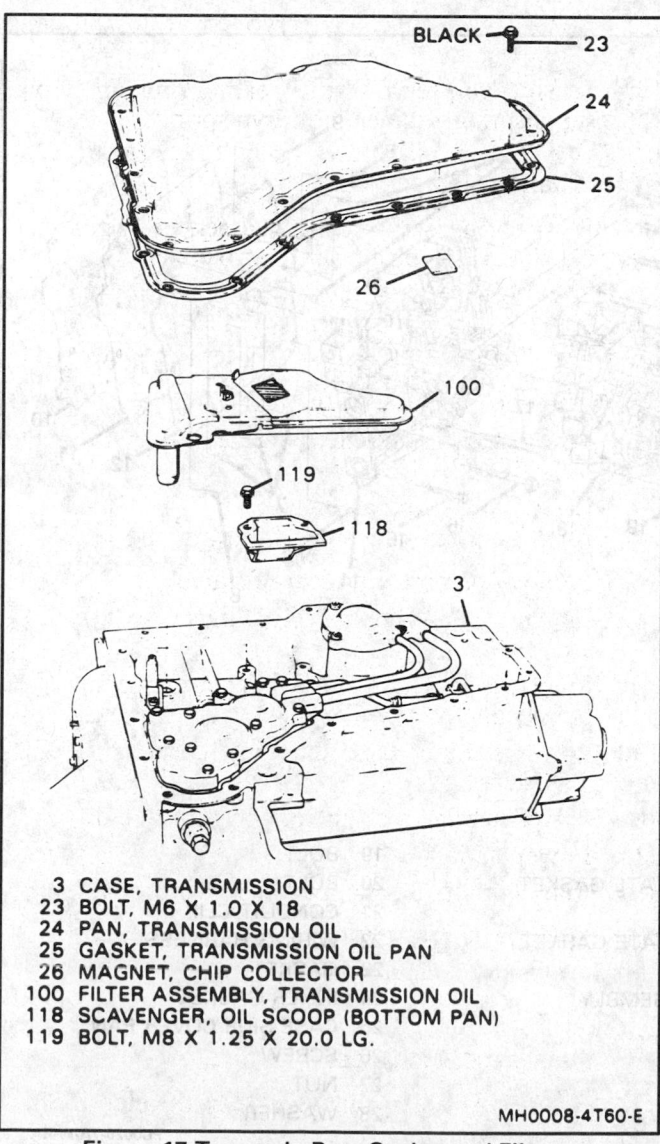

Adjust

- Fluid level.

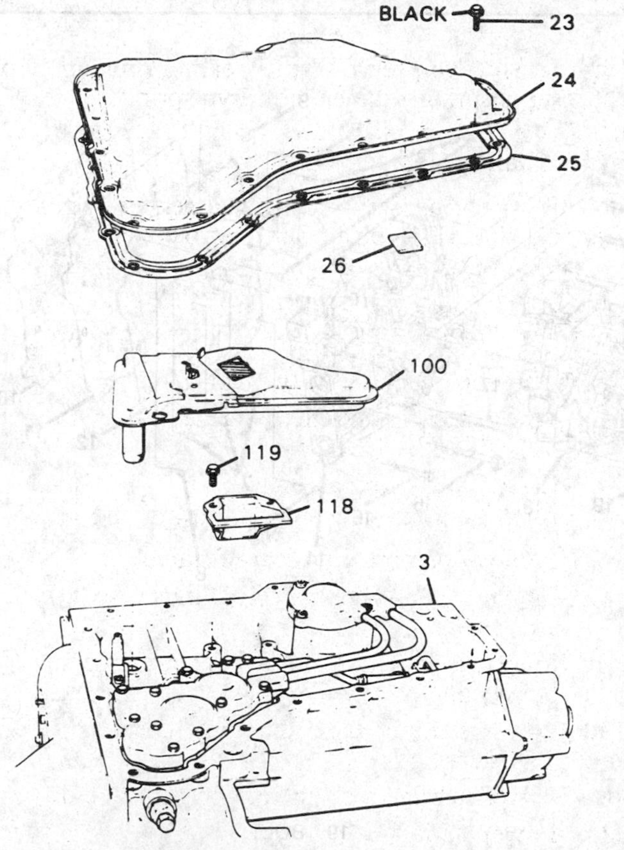
BLACK
23
24
25
26
100
119
118
3
3 CASE, TRANSMISSION
23 BOLT, M6 X 1.0 X 18
24 PAN, TRANSMISSION OIL
25 GASKET, TRANSMISSION OIL PAN
26 MAGNET, CHIP COLLECTOR
100 FILTER ASSEMBLY, TRANSMISSION OIL
118 SCAVENGER, OIL SCOOP (BOTTOM PAN)
119 BOLT, M8 X 1.25 X 20.0 LG.
MH0008-4T60-E

Figure 17 Transaxle Pan, Gasket and Filter – Hydra-Matic 4T60-E

SCAVENGER OIL SCOOP

Figure 17

Remove or Disconnect

1. Raise vehicle and suitably support. Refer to SECTION 0A.
2. Pan. Refer to "Pan And/Or Gasket" in this section.
3. Oil scoop retaining bolt/screw and oil scoop.

Install or Connect

1. Oil scoop and retaining bolt/screw.

Tighten

- Bolt/screw to 8 N•m (71 lb. in.).

2. Pan. Refer to "Pan And/Or Gasket" in this section.
3. Lower vehicle.

Adjust

- Fluid level.

FLUID FILTER AND/OR SEAL

Figure 17

Remove or Disconnect

1. Raise vehicle and suitably support. Refer to SECTION 0A.
2. Pan. Refer to "Pan And/Or Gasket" in this section.
3. Fluid filter and/or lip ring seal. The lip ring seal is pressed into the case and should be removed only if replacement is necessary.

Install or Connect

1. New fluid level and/or lip ring seal.
2. Pan. Refer to "Pan And/Or Gasket" in this section.
3. Lower vehicle.

Adjust

- Fluid level.

VALVE BODY

Figures 18 through 20

Remove or Disconnect

1. Case side cover pan. Refer to "Case Side Cover Pan And/Or Gaskets" in this section.
2. Pump. Refer to "Pump" in this section.
3. Valve body bolts/screws.
4. Valve body, keeping the spacer plate with the transaxle.
5. Spacer plate and gasket.
   - For checkball locations, refer to Figures 19 and 20.

Install or Connect

NOTICE: Do not use any type of grease to retain or hold parts during assembly of this unit. Greases other than the recommended assembly lube will change transaxle fluid characteristics and cause undesirable shift conditions and/or filter clogging.

1. Retain checkballs in their proper locations with TRANSJEL™ J 36850.
2. Spacer plate and gasket.
3. Valve body and gasket.
4. Valve body bolts/screws.

Tighten

- Valve body-to-case bolts/screws to 24 N•m (18 lb. ft.).
- Remaining bolts/screws to 11 N•m (97 lb. in.).

Important

- Do not use impact type tools on the valve body or pump assembly.

5. Pump. Refer to "Pump" in this section.
6. Case side cover pan. Refer to "Case Side Cover Pan And/Or Gaskets" in this section.

Adjust

- Fluid level.

CHANNEL PLATE

Remove or Disconnect

1. Valve body. Refer to "Valve Body" in this section.
2. Manual shaft assembly. Refer to "Manual Shaft and Park System Components" in this section.
3. Bolts/screws.
4. Channel plate.

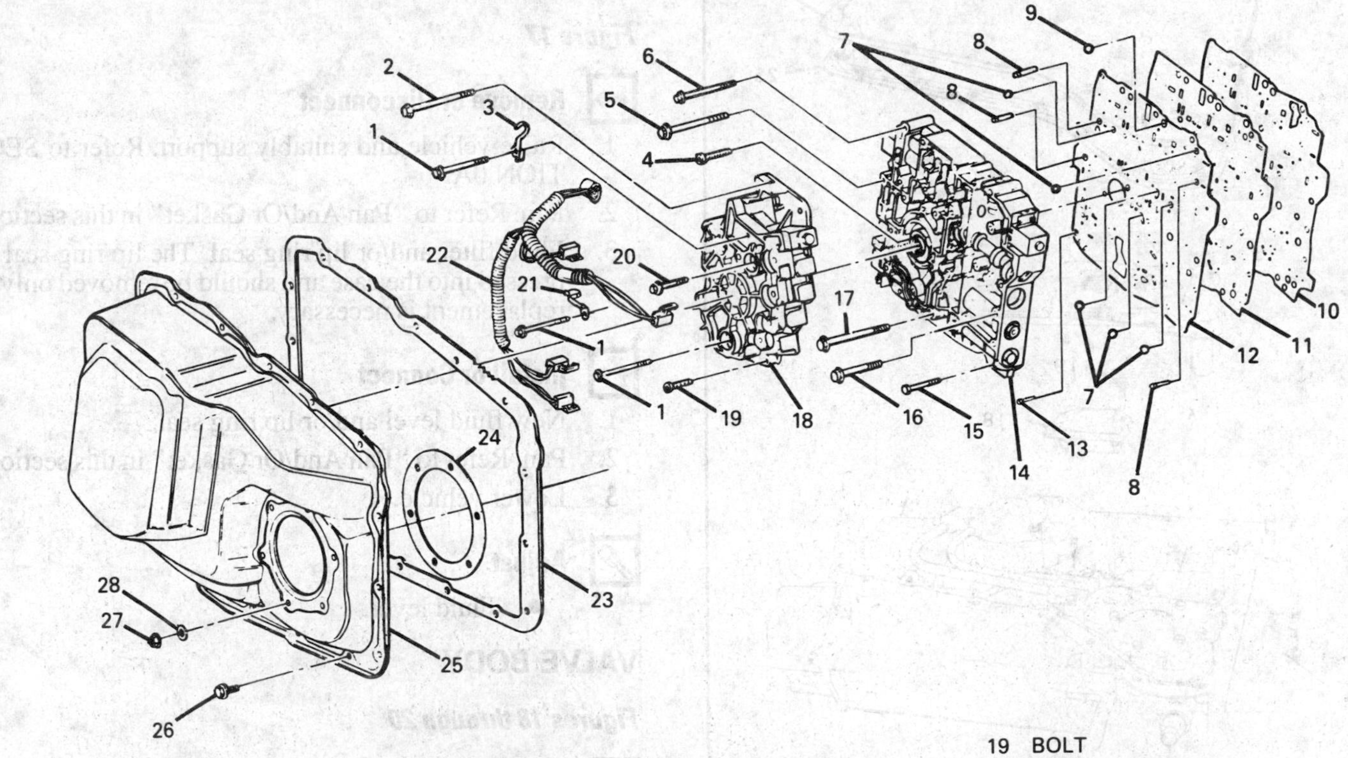
1
2
3
4
5
6
7
8
9
10
11
12
13
14
15
16
17
18
19
20
21
22
23
24
25
26
27
28

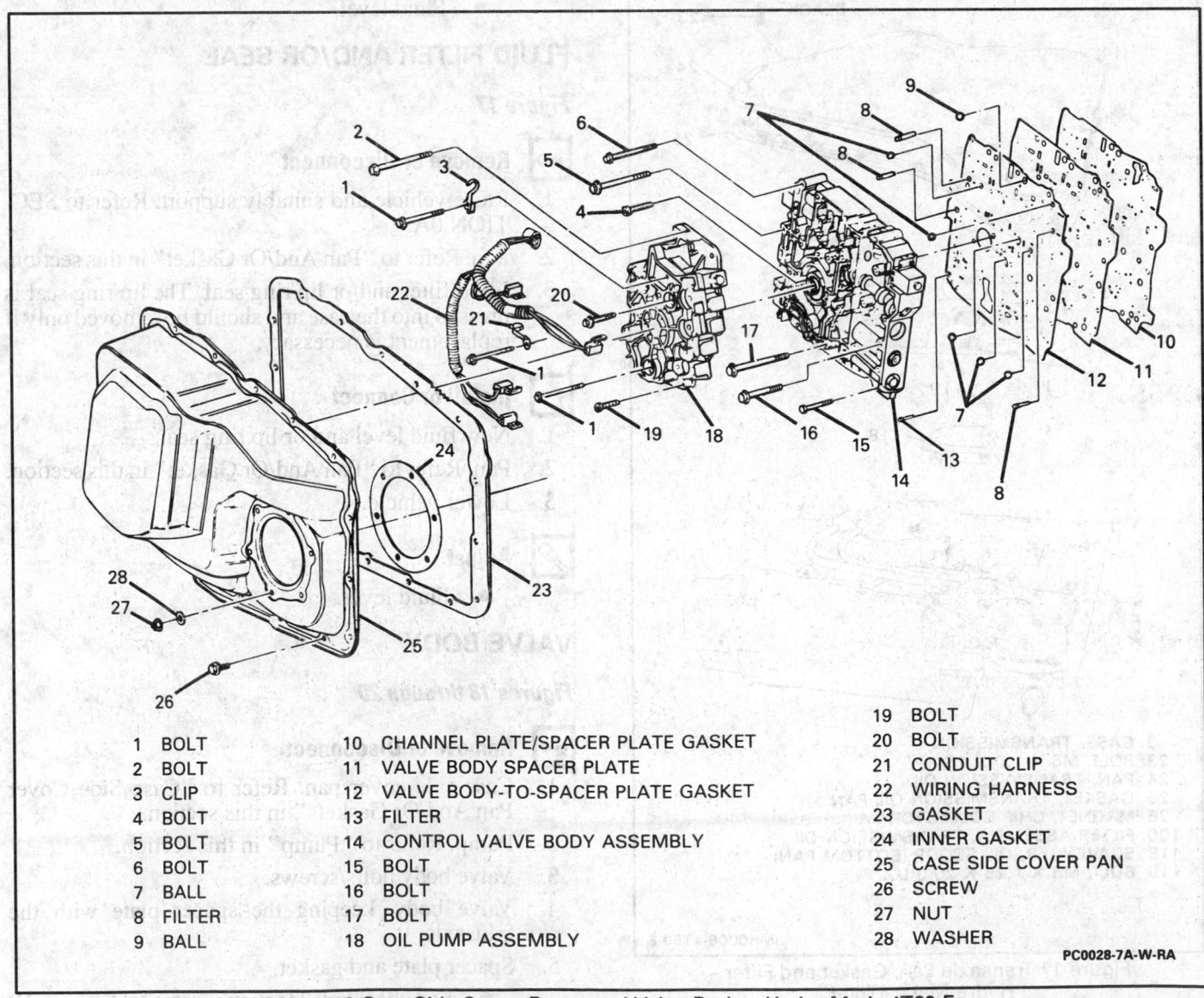

1	BOLT	10	CHANNEL PLATE/SPACER PLATE GASKET	19	BOLT
2	BOLT	11	VALVE BODY SPACER PLATE	20	BOLT
3	CLIP	12	VALVE BODY-TO-SPACER PLATE GASKET	21	CONDUIT CLIP
4	BOLT	13	FILTER	22	WIRING HARNESS
5	BOLT	14	CONTROL VALVE BODY ASSEMBLY	23	GASKET
6	BOLT	15	BOLT	24	INNER GASKET
7	BALL	16	BOLT	25	CASE SIDE COVER PAN
8	FILTER	17	BOLT	26	SCREW
9	BALL	18	OIL PUMP ASSEMBLY	27	NUT
				28	WASHER

PC0028-7A-W-RA

Figure 18 Case Side Cover, Pump and Valve Body – Hydra-Matic 4T60-E

5. Clutch pack assembly.
6. Seal.

Install or Connect

1. Seal.
2. Clutch pack assembly.
3. Channel plate.
4. Bolts/screws.

Tighten

- Bolts/screws to 24 N•m (18 lb. ft.).

5. Manual shaft assembly. Refer to "Manual Shaft and Park System Components" in this section.
6. Valve body. Refer to "Valve Body" in this section.

CLUTCH ASSEMBLY

Remove or Disconnect

1. Channel plate. Refer to "Clutch Assembly" in this section.
2. Hub and shaft assembly.
3. Drive sprocket, washer and driveline.
4. Clutch assembly.

Install or Connect

1. Clutch assembly.
2. Drive sprocket, washer and driveline.
3. Hub and shaft assembly.
4. Channel plate. Refer to "Clutch Assembly" in this section.

CASE SIDE COVER PAN AND/OR GASKETS

Figure 18

Tools Required:

J 28467-A Engine Support Fixture
J 28467-90 Engine Support Fixture Adapter
J 36462 Engine Support Adapter Leg

Remove or Disconnect

1. Air cleaner assembly.
2. Crossover pipe. Refer to SECTION 6F.
3. Shift cable clip at lever and mount bracket.
4. Install J 28467-A, J 28467-90 and J 36462.
5. Raise vehicle and suitably support. Refer to SECTION 0A.
6. Left front wheel. Refer to SECTION 3E.
7. Left inner fender splash shield.
8. Transaxle mount. Refer to "Transaxle Mount" in this section.
9. Loosen engine mount nuts at frame. Refer to SECTION 6A5A or SECTION 6A7.

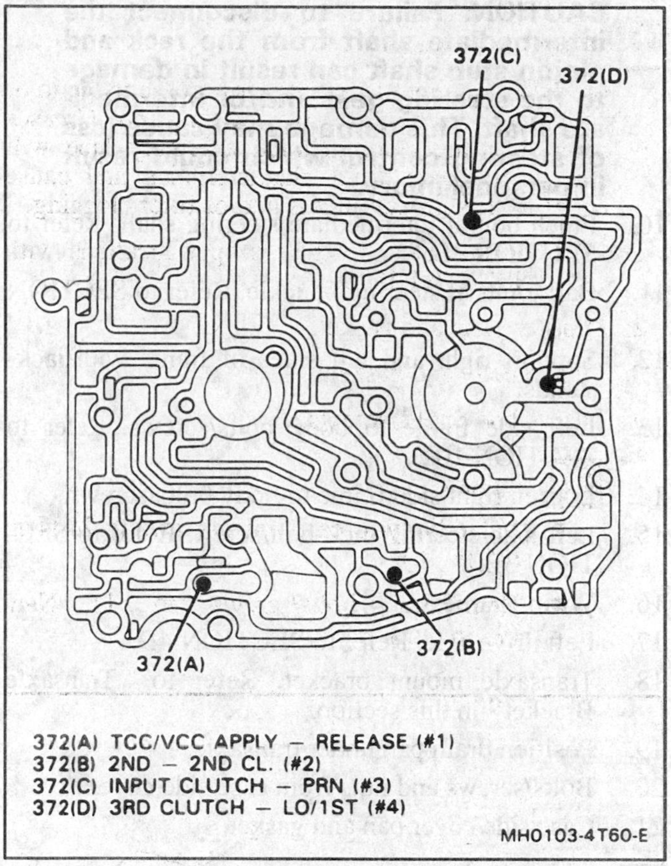
372(C)
372(D)
372(A)
372(B)
372(A) TCC/VCC APPLY – RELEASE (#1)
372(B) 2ND – 2ND CL. (#2)
372(C) INPUT CLUTCH – PRN (#3)
372(D) 3RD CLUTCH – LO/1ST (#4)
MH0103-4T60-E

Figure 19 Channel Plate Checkball Locations – Hydra-Matic 4T60-E

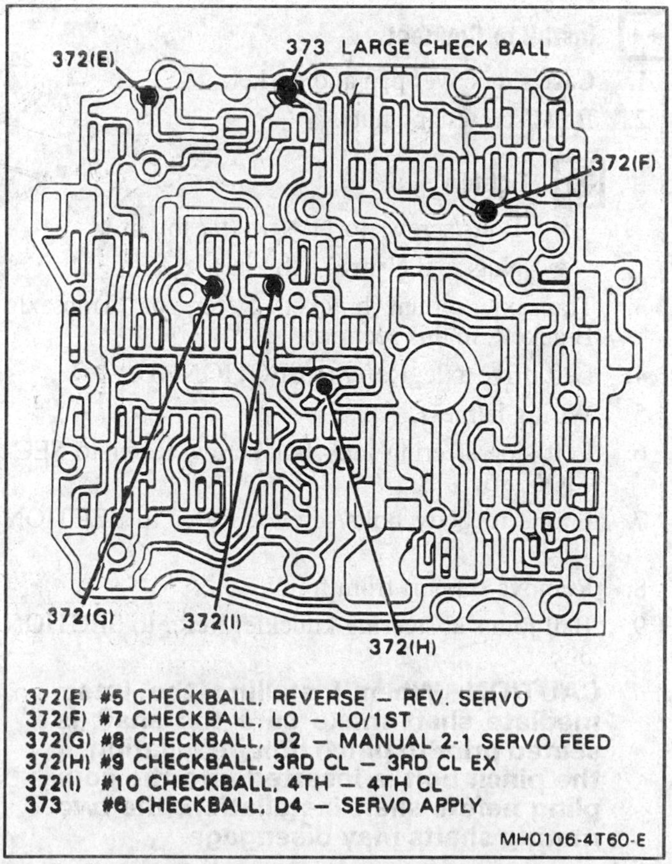
372(E)
373 LARGE CHECK BALL
372(F)
372(G)
372(I)
372(H)
372(E) #5 CHECKBALL, REVERSE – REV. SERVO
372(F) #7 CHECKBALL, LO – LO/1ST
372(G) #8 CHECKBALL, D2 – MANUAL 2-1 SERVO FEED
372(H) #9 CHECKBALL, 3RD CL – 3RD CL EX
372(I) #10 CHECKBALL, 4TH – 4TH CL
373 #6 CHECKBALL, D4 – SERVO APPLY
MH0106-4T60-E

Figure 20 Control Valve Assembly Checkball Locations – Hydra-Matic 4T60-E

CAUTION: Failure to disconnect the intermediate shaft from the rack and pinion stub shaft can result in damage to the steering gear and/or intermediate shaft. This damage may cause loss of steering control which could result in personal injury.

10. Pinch bolt at intermediate steering shaft. Refer to SECTION 3B.
11. Ball joints at steering knuckle. Refer to SECTION 3C.
12. Support right and left sides of frame with jack-stands.
13. Left side frame to body bolts/screws. Refer to SECTION 10-3.
14. Loosen right side frame to body bolts/screws.
15. Left side steering rack bolt/screw. Refer to SECTION 3B.
16. Wiring harness.
17. Left drive axle. Refer to SECTION 4D.
18. Transaxle mount bracket. Refer to "Transaxle Bracket" in this section.
19. Position drain pan under transaxle.
20. Bolts/screws and nuts from case side cover.
21. Case side cover pan and gasket.

Clean

- Case and side cover gasket surfaces.

Install or Connect

1. Case side cover pan and gasket.
2. Bolts/screws and nuts.

Tighten

- Bolts/screws to 11 N•m (97 lb. in.).
- Nuts to 8 N•m (71 lb. in.).

3. Transaxle mount bracket. Refer to "Transaxle Bracket" in this section.
4. Left drive axle. Refer to SECTION 4D.
5. Wiring harness.
6. Left side steering rack bolt/screw. Refer to SECTION 3B.
7. Frame to body bolts/screws. Refer to SECTION 10-3.
8. Remove support from frame.
9. Ball joints at steering knuckle. Refer to SECTION 3C.

CAUTION: When installing the intermediate shaft make sure the shaft is seated prior to pinch bolt installation. If the pinch bolt is inserted into the coupling before shaft installation, the two mating shafts may disengage.

10. Pinch bolt at intermediate steering shaft. Refer to SECTION 3B.
11. Engine mount at frame. Refer to SECTION 6A5A or SECTION 6A7.
12. Transaxle mount. Refer to "Transaxle Mount" in this section.
13. Left inner fender splash shield.
14. Left front wheel. Refer to SECTION 3E.
15. Lower vehicle.
16. Remove J 28467-A, J 28467-90 and J 36462.
17. Shift cable clip at lever and mount bracket.
18. Crossover pipe. Refer to SECTION 6F.
19. Air cleaner assembly.

WEIR OIL RESERVOIR

Remove or Disconnect

1. Case side cover pan. Refer to "Case Side Cover Pan and/or Gaskets" in this section.
2. Weir oil reservoir.

Install or Connect

1. Weir oil reservoir.
2. Case side cover pan. Refer to "Case Side Cover Pan and/or Gaskets" in this section.

CASE EXTENSION HOUSING

Remove or Disconnect

1. Air cleaner and duct assembly.
2. Left tire and wheel. Refer to SECTION 3E.
3. Powertrain rear mount and bracket. Refer to SECTION 6A5A or SECTION 6A7.
4. Vehicle speed sensor. Refer to "Speed Sensor" in this section.
5. Case extension housing bolts/screws.
6. Case extension housing with O-ring and axle seal.

Install or Connect

1. Case extension housing with axle seal and O-ring.
2. Case extension housing bolts/screws.

Tighten

- Bolts/screws to 43 N•m (32 lb. ft.).

3. Vehicle speed sensor. Refer to "Speed Sensor" in this section.
4. Powertrain rear mount and bracket. Refer to SECTION 6A5A or SECTION 6A7.
5. Left tire and wheel. Refer to SECTION 3E.
6. Air cleaner and duct assembly.

FINAL DRIVE COMPONENT REPLACEMENT

Tools Required:

J 28467-A Engine Support Fixture
J 28467-90 Engine Support Fixture Adapter
J 36462 Engine Support Adapter Leg

Remove or Disconnect

1. Electrical cooling fans. Refer to SECTION 6B.
2. Serpentine drive belt. Refer to SECTION 6A5A or SECTION 6A7.
3. Drain cooling system. Refer to SECTION 6B.
4. Heater hose pipe at intake manifold.
5. Position J 28467-A, J 28467-90, and J 36462. Refer to "Engine Support Fixture" in this section.
6. Raise vehicle and suitably support. Refer to SECTION 0A.
7. Front tire and wheel assemblies. Refer to SECTION 3E.
8. Upper half of right engine splash shield.
9. Catalytic converter. Refer to SECTION 6F.
10. Frame assembly. Refer to SECTION 10-3.
11. Lower vehicle.
12. Lower powertrain 3 inches using engine support fixture.
13. Both drive axles and support them to the body. Refer to SECTION 4D.
14. Case extension housing. Refer to "Case Extension Housing" in this section.
15. Output shaft snap ring. Refer to 7A-5B.
16. Carrier and differential assembly.

Disassemble

- Parking, sun, planetary, differential pinion and side gears if necessary. Refer to 7A-5B.

Assemble

- Parking, sun, planetary, differential pinion and side gears if disassembled. Refer to 7A-5B.

Install or Connect

1. Carrier and differential assembly.
2. Output shaft snap ring.
3. Case extension housing. Refer to "Case Extension Housing" in this section.

Measure

- Final drive end play. Refer to 7A-5B.

4. Both drive axles. Refer to SECTION 4D.
5. Raise powertrain 3 inches using engine support fixture.
6. Raise vehicle.
7. Frame assembly. Refer to SECTION 10-3.
8. Catalytic converter. Refer to SECTION 6F.
9. Upper half of right engine splash shield.
10. Front tire and wheel assemblies. Refer to SECTION 3E.
11. Lower vehicle.
12. Remove J 28467-A and J 36462. Refer to "Engine Support Fixture" in this section.
13. Heater hose pipe at intake manifold.
14. Refill cooling system. Refer to SECTION 6B.
15. Serpentine drive belt. Refer to SECTION 6A5A or SECTION 6A7.
16. Electric cooling fans. Refer to SECTION 6B.

PUMP

Figure 18

Remove or Disconnect

1. Case side cover pan. Refer to "Case Side Cover Pan And/Or Gaskets" in this section.
2. Electrical wiring harness, as needed.

NOTICE: Do not remove the three bolts/screws which hold the pump assembly together.

3. Pump bolts/screws.

Inspect

- For pump inspection. Refer to 7A-5B.

Install or Connect

1. Pump to valve body.
2. Bolts/screws.

Tighten

- Top two bolts/screws and bottom rear bolt/screw to 24 N•m (18 lb. ft.).
- Remaining bolts/screws to 11 N•m (97 lb. in.).

3. Electrical wiring harness.
4. Case side cover pan. Refer to "Case Side Cover Pan And/Or Gaskets" in this section.

Adjust

- Fluid level.

THERMO ELEMENT

Figures 21 and 22

Tool Required:

J 34094-A Thermo Element Height Gage

Remove or Disconnect

1. Oil pan. Refer to "Pan And/Or Gasket" in this section.
2. Thermo element retainer and element.

Install or Connect

1. Set thermo pin height with J 34094-A.
2. New element plate.
3. Pin and washer assemblies.
   - Set height of pin furthest from accumulators first using J 34094-A.

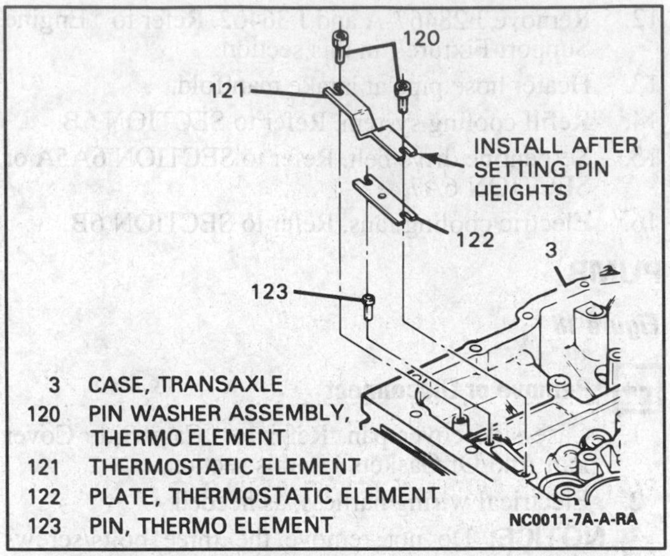
120
121
INSTALL AFTER SETTING PIN HEIGHTS
122
3
123
3 CASE, TRANSAXLE
120 PIN WASHER ASSEMBLY, THERMO ELEMENT
121 THERMOSTATIC ELEMENT
122 PLATE, THERMOSTATIC ELEMENT
123 PIN, THERMO ELEMENT
NC0011-7A-A-RA

Figure 21 Thermo Element – Hydra-Matic 4T60-E

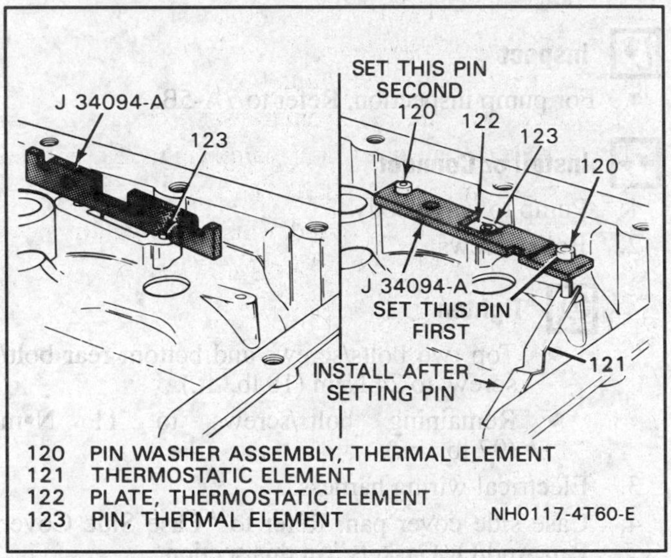
J 34094-A
123
SET THIS PIN SECOND
120
122
123
120
J 34094-A
SET THIS PIN FIRST
INSTALL AFTER SETTING PIN
121
120 PIN WASHER ASSEMBLY, THERMAL ELEMENT
121 THERMOSTATIC ELEMENT
122 PLATE, THERMOSTATIC ELEMENT
123 PIN, THERMAL ELEMENT
NH0117-4T60-E

Figure 22 Thermo Element Setting – Hydra-Matic 4T60-E

4. Thermo element.
5. Oil pan, new gasket and attaching bolts/screws. Refer to "Pan And/Or Gasket" in this section.

Adjust

- Fluid level.

VACUUM MODULATOR SYSTEM

The vacuum modulator system on the Hydra-Matic 4T60-E transaxle controls shift feel (may be soft or firm shifts) by sensing changes in engine load, which is indicated by engine vacuum. The modulator does this by controlling main line pressure boost. The vacuum modulator system may be suspect for firm or slipping shift conditions.

VACUUM MODULATOR DIAGNOSIS

For proper operation, the Hydra-Matic 4T60-E transaxle requires 44-57 kPa (13-17 in. Hg) of engine vacuum at hot engine idle checked at the modulator with the transaxle in DRIVE. An incorrect vacuum supply to the modulator or a malfunctioning modulator may cause some or all of the listed conditions:

- Harsh upshifts and downshifts.
- Harsh Park to Reverse engagement.
- Harsh Neutral to Drive engagement.
- Soft upshifts and downshifts.
- Harsh or firm light throttle upshifts.
- Second gear starts.
- Slips in Low, Drive and Reverse.
- Harsh 3-2 coastdown shifts.
- Rough 4-3 and 3-2 manual downshifts.
- Slipping in Drive or Reverse.
- Pressure regulator valve hydraulic buzz.
- Engine burning transaxle fluid.

An incorrect engine vacuum signal at the modulator can be caused by a pinched, cut, plugged or disconnected vacuum line. Also, engine mechanical and operating conditions related to the fuel, ignition, exhaust or emission systems may result in incorrect engine vacuum or poor transmission performance.

To check for proper vacuum, disconnect the vacuum supply line at the modulator and install a vacuum gage to the line. If there is less than 44-57 kPa (13-17 in. Hg) of vacuum at hot engine idle with the transaxle in "Drive," locate the cause and correct as required. The gage reading must respond quickly (only 1/10th of a second delay) to throttle movement because vacuum is supplied through a .031 inch orifice in order to stabilize line pressure when shifting the transaxle between forward and reverse ranges.

If there is enough engine vacuum available to the modulator, remove the modulator assembly and modulator valve. Inspect the valve for nicks or scoring. Connect a hand-operated vacuum pump to the modulator. Pump the device until 51-68 kPa (15-20 in. Hg) of vacuum is reached. At the same time, observe the modulator plunger; it should be drawn in as the vacuum pump is operated. After reaching 51-68 kPa (15-20 in. Hg), the vacuum should not bleed down for at least 30 seconds. If modulator checks ok, perform the next test.

If the following conditions are met:

- Vacuum signal within specifications
- Modulator functioning properly
- Modulator valve undamaged

Then the shift problem is not vacuum-related. At this time, an oil pressure check should be performed as outlined in the Hydra-Matic 4T60-E diagnosis section. Note the pressures and, if out of specification, refer to the appropriate diagnosis.

Vacuum Diaphragm Check

Inspect

- Turn the modulator so that the vacuum connector faces down. If any liquid (transaxle fluid, water condensate or gasoline) drains out, the modulator should be replaced.

Atmospheric Leak Check

Inspect

1. Apply soap solution to vacuum connector and crimped seam.
2. Attach a short piece of hose to the vacuum connector.
3. Blow into hose and check for leaks.

NOTICE: Do not use compressed air. Pressures in excess of 41 kPa (6 psi) may damage the modulator.

Load Check

Figure 23

Tool Required:
J 36619 Modulator Comparison Gage

Inspect

1. Install a known good modulator of the same type on one side of J 36619.
2. Install the modulator to be tested on the other side of J 36619.
3. Holding the assembly level, slowly push the two modulators together.
   - If the gage line remains blue, the modulator is not acceptable,
   - If the gage line is white, the modulator is acceptable.

Sleeve Alignment Check

Inspect

1. Roll modulator on a flat surface. Observe sleeve for concentricity with the modulator can.
2. Plunger for freedom of movement.

Causes of Improper Vacuum at Modulator

1. Engine.
   - Loose vacuum fittings or improperly routed hoses/lines
   - Vacuum-operated accessory leak (hoses, vacuum valve, etc).
   - Engine exhaust system restricted
2. Vacuum line to modulator.
   - Leaks
   - Loose fitting
   - Restricted or incorrect size orifice
   - Carbon build-up at modulator vacuum fitting
   - Pinched line
   - Grease in pipe (delayed or no upshift-cold)

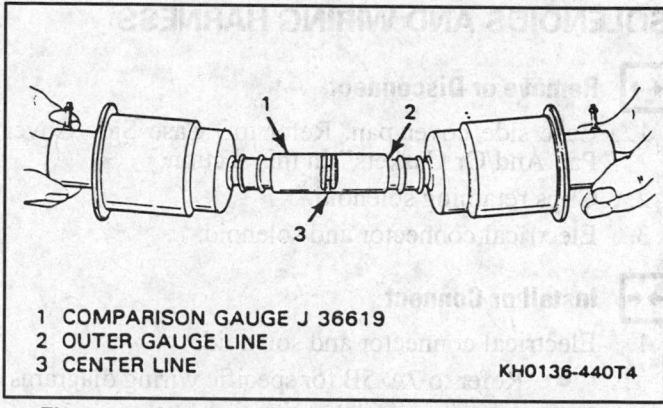

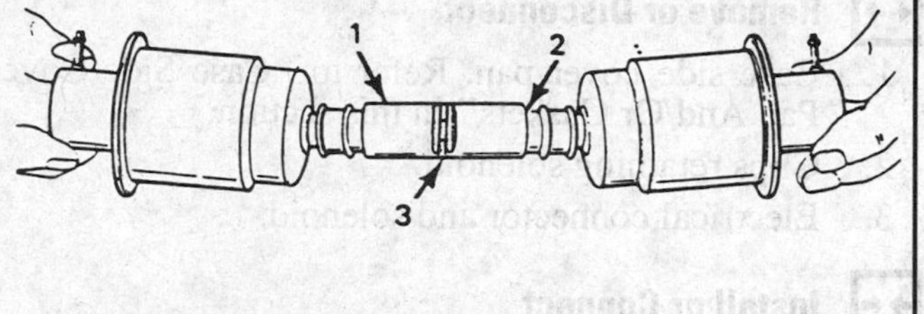
1
2
3
1 COMPARISON GAUGE J 36619
2 OUTER GAUGE LINE
3 CENTER LINE
KH0136-440T4

Figure 23 Checking Modulator – Hydra-Matic 4T60-E

VACUUM MODULATOR AND/OR O-RING

Figure 24

Remove or Disconnect

1. Air cleaner assembly.
2. Vacuum line at modulator.
3. Electrical connector from transaxle case.
4. Attaching bolt/screw and clamp at modulator base.
5. Vacuum modulator and O-ring.
   - Use care to avoid losing modulator valve from transaxle case.

Install or Connect

1. Vacuum modulator and new O-ring.
2. Clamp and attaching bolt/screw.

Tighten

- Bolt/screw to 27 N•m (20 lb. ft.).

3. Electrical connector to transaxle case.
4. Vacuum line at modulator.
5. Air cleaner assembly.

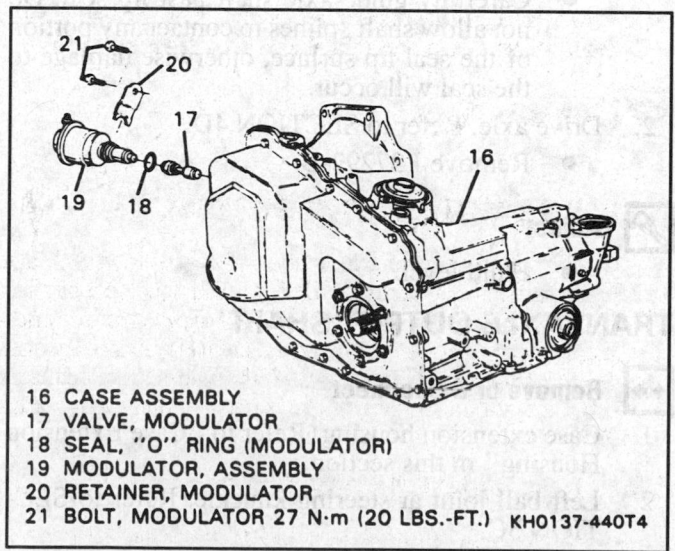

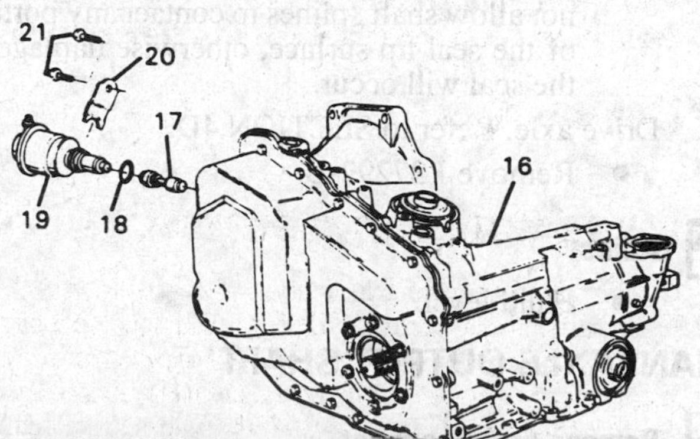
21
20
17
16
19
18
16 CASE ASSEMBLY
17 VALVE, MODULATOR
18 SEAL, "O" RING (MODULATOR)
19 MODULATOR, ASSEMBLY
20 RETAINER, MODULATOR
21 BOLT, MODULATOR 27 N·m (20 LBS.-FT.)
KH0137-440T4

Figure 24 Vacuum Modulator – Hydra-Matic 4T60-E

SOLENOIDS AND WIRING HARNESS

Remove or Disconnect

1. Case side cover pan. Refer to "Case Side Cover Pan And/Or Gaskets" in this section.
2. Clips retaining solenoid.
3. Electrical connector and solenoid.

Install or Connect

1. Electrical connector and solenoid.
   - Refer to 7A-5B for specific wiring diagrams.
2. Retaining clips.
3. Case side cover pan. Refer to "Case Side Cover Pan And/Or Gaskets" in this section.

Adjust

- Fluid level.

DRIVE AXLE OIL SEAL

Tools Required:

J 34115 Axle Seal Installer

J 37292-B Axle Seal Protector

Remove or Disconnect

1. Drive axle. Refer to SECTION 4D.
2. Pry out seal with a screwdriver or other suitable tool.
   - Do not damage seal bore.

Install or Connect

1. New seal using J 34115. Lubricate seal lip with a light wipe of transaxle fluid.
   - Install J 37292-B in seal.

   Important

   - Carefully guide axle shaft past lip seal. Do not allow shaft splines to contact any portion of the seal lip surface, otherwise damage to the seal will occur.
2. Drive axle. Refer to SECTION 4D.
   - Remove J 37292-B.

Adjust

- Fluid level.

TRANSAXLE OUTPUT SHAFT

Remove or Disconnect

1. Case extension housing. Refer to "Case Extension Housing" in this section.
2. Left ball joint at steering knuckle. Refer to SECTION 3C.
3. Drive axle at transaxle. Refer to SECTION 4D.
4. Output shaft retaining clip at differential.
5. Output shaft through left wheel opening.

Install or Connect

1. Output shaft through left wheel opening.
2. Output shaft retaining clip at differential.
3. Drive axle at transaxle. Refer to SECTION 4D.
4. Left ball joint at steering knuckle. Refer to SECTION 3C.
5. Case extension housing. Refer to "Case Extension Housing" in this section.

OIL COOLER PIPES

Figure 25

If replacement of transaxle cooler pipes is required, use only double-wrapped and brazed steel pipe meeting GM specification 123M or equivalent. Pipe should be double-flared.

NOTICE: Allow sufficient clearance around cooler pipes to prevent damage or wear which may cause fluid loss.

Remove or Disconnect

1. Electric engine cooling fan assemblies.
2. Transaxle oil cooler lower hose assembly and transaxle outer oil cooler pipe from pipe assemblies.
3. Bolt/screw.
4. Clip and retainer.
5. Pipe assemblies from radiator assembly.

Install or Connect

NOTICE: See "Notice" on page 7A-1 of this section.

Important

- Correct thread engagement is critical. Cross-threaded fittings can achieve proper tightness value and still leak.

1. Pipe assemblies to radiator assembly.

   Tighten

   - Pipe assemblies to 21 N•m (15 lb. ft.).
2. Retainer and clip.
3. Pipe assemblies to retainer and clip.
4. Bolt/screw.

   Tighten

   - Bolt/screw to 3 N•m (26 lb. in.).
5. Transaxle oil cooler lower hose assembly and transaxle outer oil cooler pipe to pipe assemblies.
6. Electric engine cooling fan assemblies.

Adjust

- Transaxle fluid level.

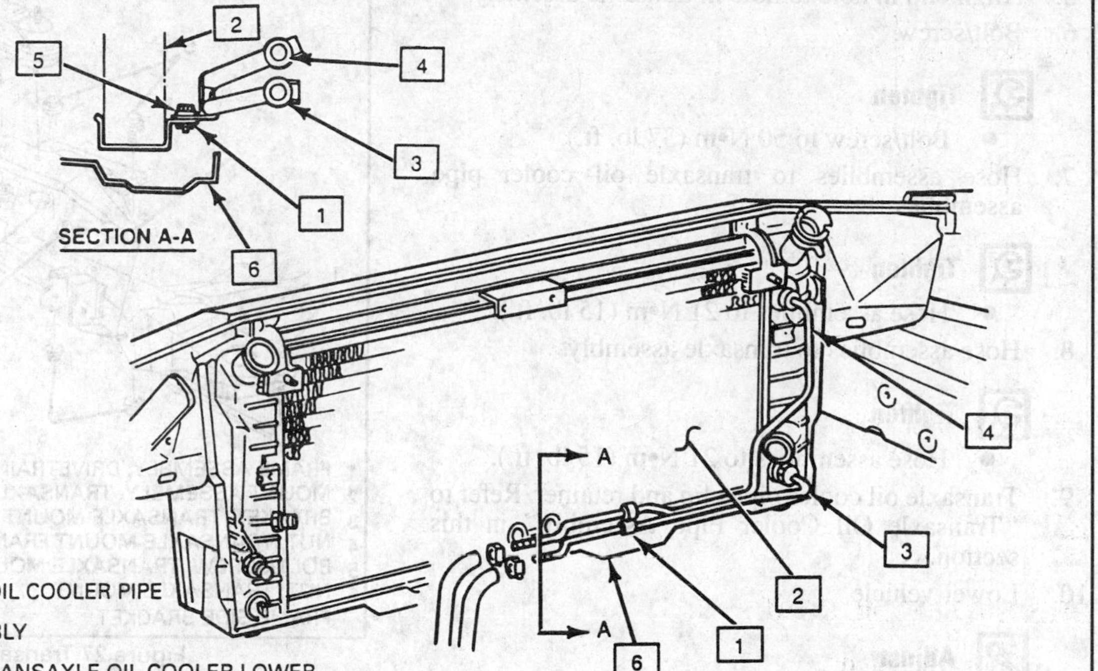
SECTION A-A
1
2
3
4
5
6
A
A
RC0001–7A–W–RP

1	CLIP, TRANSAXLE OIL COOLER PIPE
2	RADIATOR ASSEMBLY
3	PIPE ASSEMBLY, TRANSAXLE OIL COOLER LOWER
4	PIPE ASSEMBLY, TRANSAXLE OIL COOLER UPPER
5	BOLT/SCREW, TRANSAXLE OIL COOLER PIPE CLIP
6	RADIATOR TIE BAR ASSEMBLY

Figure 25 Transaxle Oil Cooler Pipes – Hydra-Matic 4T60-E

OIL COOLER HOSES

Figure 26

↔ Remove or Disconnect

1. Raise and suitably support vehicle.
2. Transaxle oil cooler pipe and retainer. Refer to "Transaxle Oil Cooler Pipe Assembly" in this section.
3. Hose assemblies from transaxle assembly.
4. Hose assemblies from transaxle oil cooler pipe assemblies.
5. Hose assemblies.

→← Install or Connect

NOTICE: See "Notice" on page 7A-1 of this section.

Important

- Correct thread engagement is critical. Cross-threaded fittings can achieve proper tightness value and still leak.

1. Position hose assemblies.
2. Hand start hose assemblies to transaxle oil cooler pipe assemblies.
3. Hand start hose assemblies to transaxle assembly.
4. Position clip around hose assemblies and squeeze clip closed.

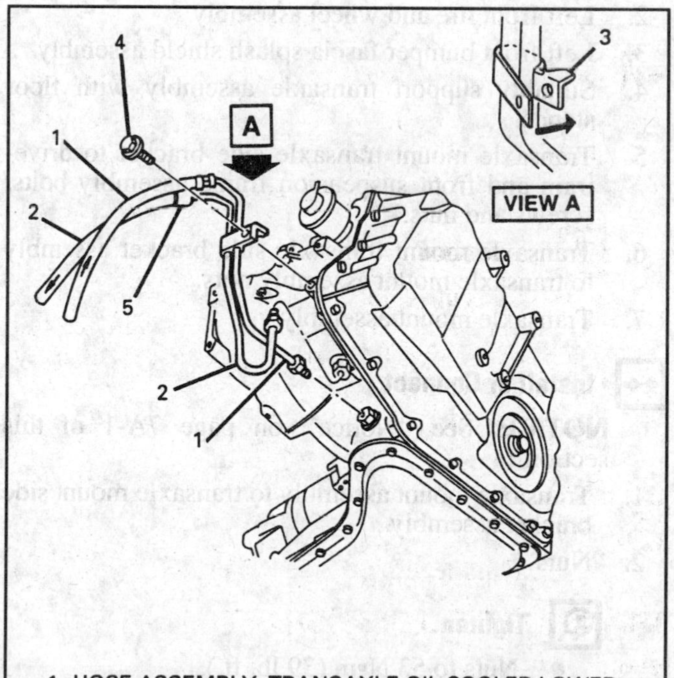
A
VIEW A
1
2
3
4
5
PC3004-7A-W-RP

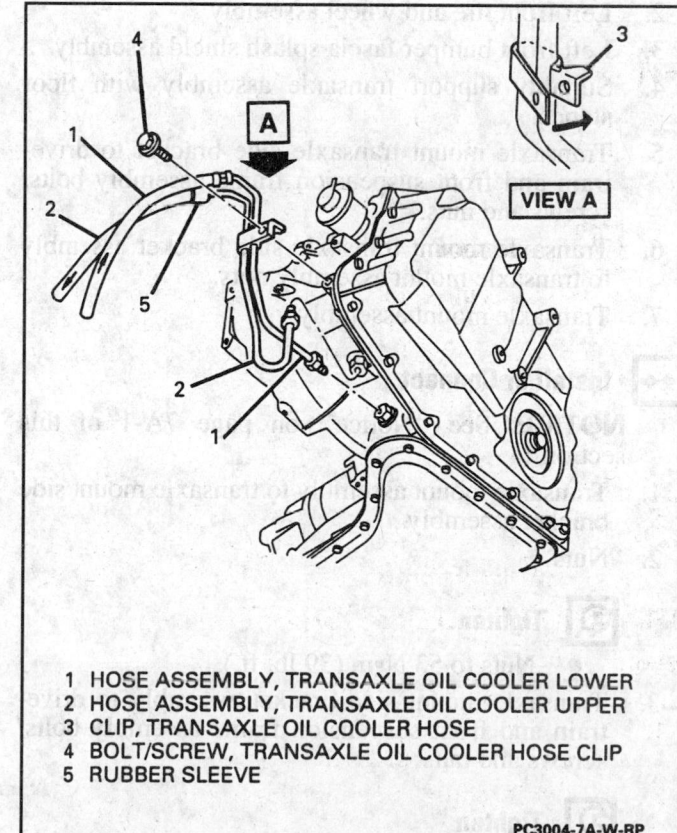

1 HOSE ASSEMBLY, TRANSAXLE OIL COOLER LOWER
2 HOSE ASSEMBLY, TRANSAXLE OIL COOLER UPPER
3 CLIP, TRANSAXLE OIL COOLER HOSE
4 BOLT/SCREW, TRANSAXLE OIL COOLER HOSE CLIP
5 RUBBER SLEEVE

Figure 26 Transaxle Oil Cooler Hoses

5. Align clip in hole to hole in transaxle assembly.
6. Bolt/screw.

Tighten

- Bolt/screw to 50 N•m (37 lb. ft.).

7. Hose assemblies to transaxle oil cooler pipe assemblies.

Tighten

- Hose assemblies to 21 N•m (15 lb. ft.).

8. Hose assemblies to transaxle assembly.

Tighten

- Hose assemblies to 21 N•m (15 lb. ft.).

9. Transaxle oil cooler pipe clip and retainer. Refer to "Transaxle Oil Cooler Pipe Assembly" in this section.
10. Lower vehicle.

Adjust

- Transaxle fluid level.

TRANSAXLE MOUNT

Figure 27

Remove or Disconnect

1. Raise and suitably support vehicle.
2. Left front tire and wheel assembly.
3. Left front bumper fascia splash shield assembly.
4. Suitably support transaxle assembly with floor stands.
5. Transaxle mount transaxle side bracket to drive-train and front suspension frame assembly bolts/screws and nuts.
6. Transaxle mount transaxle side bracket assembly to transaxle mount assembly nuts.
7. Transaxle mount assembly.

Install or Connect

NOTICE: See "Notice" on page 7A-1 of this section.

1. Transaxle mount assembly to transaxle mount side bracket assembly.
2. Nuts.

Tighten

- Nuts to 53 N•m (39 lb. ft.).

3. Transaxle mount side bracket assembly to drive-train and front suspension frame assembly bolts/screws and nuts.

Tighten

- Bolts/screws and nuts to 58 N•m (43 lb. ft.).

4. Remove support from transaxle assembly.

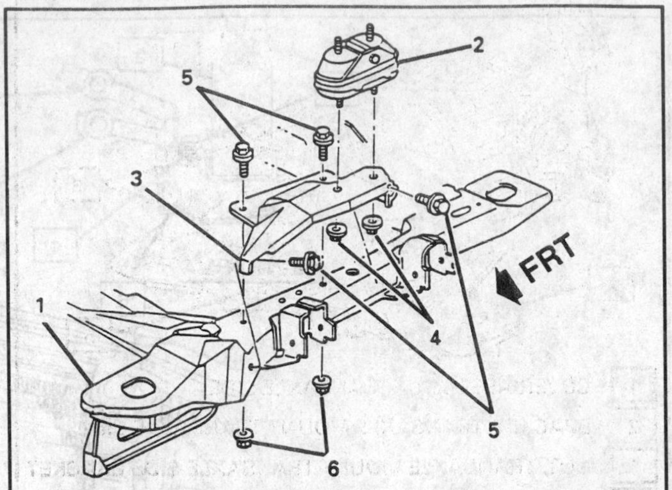

1
2
3
4
5
6
FRT
1 FRAME ASSEMBLY, DRIVETRAIN AND FRONT SUSPENSION
2 MOUNT ASSEMBLY, TRANSAXLE
3 BRACKET, TRANSAXLE MOUNT FRAME SIDE BRACKET
4 NUT, TRANSAXLE MOUNT FRAME SIDE
5 BOLT/SCREW, TRANSAXLE MOUNT FRAME SIDE BRACKET
6 NUT, TRANSAXLE MOUNT FRAME SIDE BRACKET
RC0002-7A-W-RP

Figure 27 Transaxle Mount

5. Left front bumper fascia splash shield assembly.
6. Left front tire and wheel assembly.
7. Lower vehicle.

TRANSAXLE BRACKET

Figure 28

Remove or Disconnect

1. Raise and suitably support vehicle.
2. Left front tire and wheel assembly.
3. Left front bumper fascia splash shield assembly.
4. Suitably support transaxle assembly with floor stands.
5. Transaxle mount transaxle side bracket to transaxle mount assembly nuts.
6. Bolts/screws.
7. Bracket.

Install or Connect

NOTICE: See "Notice" on page 7A-1 of this section.

1. Position bracket to transaxle assembly.
2. Hand start transaxle mount transaxle side bracket bolts/screws.
3. Bolts/screws.

Tighten

- Bolts/screws to 95 N•m (70 lb. ft.) starting with forward lower bolt/screw and working clockwise.

4. Remove support from transaxle assembly.
5. Transaxle mount transaxle side bracket to transaxle mount assembly nuts.

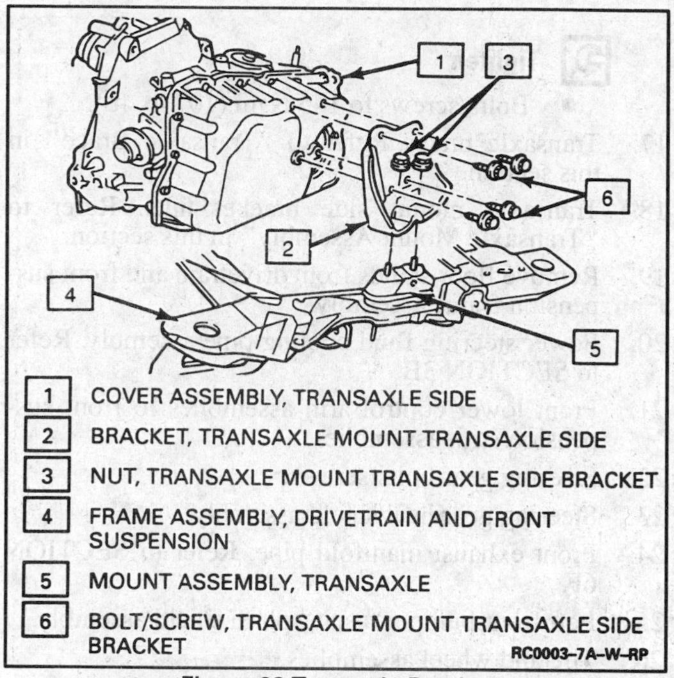
1
3
6
2
4
5
1 COVER ASSEMBLY, TRANSAXLE SIDE
2 BRACKET, TRANSAXLE MOUNT TRANSAXLE SIDE
3 NUT, TRANSAXLE MOUNT TRANSAXLE SIDE BRACKET
4 FRAME ASSEMBLY, DRIVETRAIN AND FRONT SUSPENSION
5 MOUNT ASSEMBLY, TRANSAXLE
6 BOLT/SCREW, TRANSAXLE MOUNT TRANSAXLE SIDE BRACKET
RC0003-7A-W-RP

Figure 28 Transaxle Bracket

Tighten

- Nuts to 53 N•m (39 lb. ft.).

6. Left front bumper fascia splash shield assembly.
7. Left front tire and wheel assembly.
8. Lower vehicle.

TRANSAXLE ASSEMBLY

Figures 29 through 34

Tools Required:

J 28467-A Engine Support Fixture
J 28467-90 Engine Support Fixture Adapter
J 35944 Oil Cooler and Line Flusher
J 36462 Engine Support Adapter Leg

Remove or Disconnect

1. Hood panel assembly.
2. Transaxle fluid level indicator assembly. Refer to "Fluid Filler Tube" in this section.
3. Engine mount strut brackets.
4. Electric engine cooling fan assemblies.
5. Install J 28467-A, J 28467-90 and J 36462.
6. Air intake duct assembly.
7. Automatic transaxle vacuum modulator pipe assembly. Refer to "Automatic Transaxle Vacuum Modulator Pipe and/or O-Ring" in this section.
8. Electrical connectors from transaxle assembly.
9. Transaxle range selector assembly from transaxle assembly.
10. Upper transaxle-to-engine bolts/screws.
11. Raise and suitably support vehicle.
12. Tire and wheel assembly.
13. Left front bumper fascia splash shield assembly.
14. Front exhaust manifold pipe. Refer to SECTION 6F.
15. Steering gear heat shield assembly.
16. Steering gear bolts/screws.
17. Front lower control arm assemblies from front suspension strut assemblies.
18. Power steering fluid cooling pipe assembly. Refer to SECTION 3B.
19. Suitably support drivetrain and front suspension frame assembly with floor stands.
20. Transaxle mount side bracket nuts. Refer to "Transaxle Mount" in this section.
21. Engine mount frame side nuts. Refer to SECTION 6A5A.
22. Transaxle brace. Refer to "Transaxle Brace" in this section.
23. Drivetrain and front suspension frame bolts/screws.
24. Drivetrain and front suspension frame assembly.
25. Electrical connector from vehicle speed sensor.
26. Front wheel driveshaft assemblies from transaxle assembly.
27. Transaxle converter cover assembly.
28. Starter motor assembly. Refer to SECTION 6D2.
29. Transaxle torque converter bolts/screws.

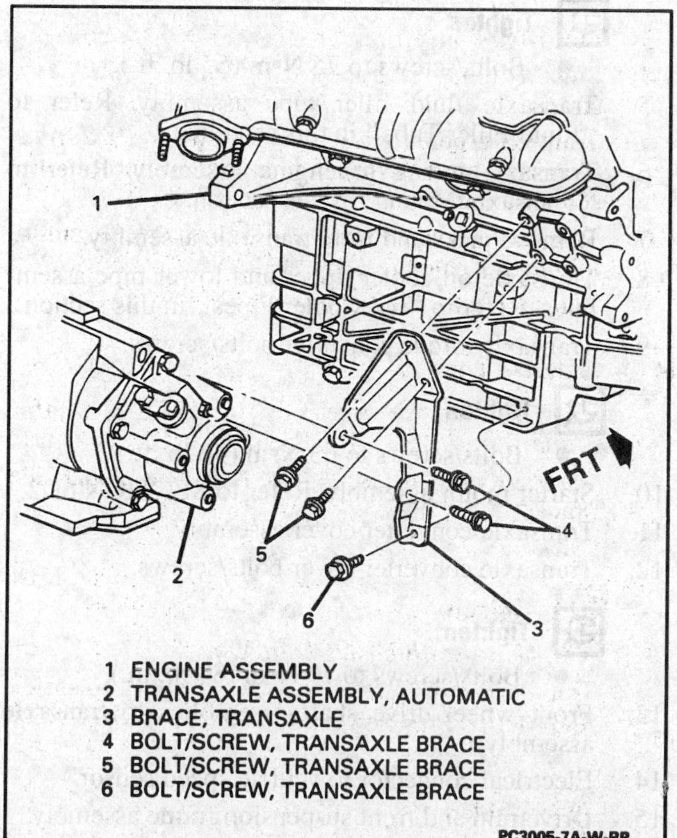
1
FRT
5
4
2
6
3
1 ENGINE ASSEMBLY
2 TRANSAXLE ASSEMBLY, AUTOMATIC
3 BRACE, TRANSAXLE
4 BOLT/SCREW, TRANSAXLE BRACE
5 BOLT/SCREW, TRANSAXLE BRACE
6 BOLT/SCREW, TRANSAXLE BRACE
PC3005-7A-W-RP

Figure 29 Transaxle Brace

30. Transaxle oil cooler upper and lower pipe assemblies. Refer to "Oil Cooler Pipes" in this section.
31. Install transaxle jack.
32. Transaxle mount assembly from engine assembly. Refer to "Transaxle Mount" in this section.
33. Transaxle fluid filler tube assembly. Refer to "Fluid Filler Tube" in this section.
34. Transaxle-to-engine bolt/screw.
35. Transaxle assembly.
36. Transaxle torque converter assembly from transaxle assembly.
37. Transaxle assembly from transaxle jack.

Important

- Transaxle oil cooler hose and pipe assemblies should be flushed with J 35944 or equivalent whenever the transaxle assembly is removed for overhaul or replacement of the transaxle torque converter assembly, transaxle pump or case assemblies.

Install or Connect

NOTICE: See "Notice" on page 7A-1 of this section.

1. Transaxle assembly to transaxle jack.
2. Transaxle torque converter assembly to transaxle assembly.
3. Transaxle assembly.
4. Lower rear transaxle-to-engine bolt/screw.

Tighten

- Bolts/screws to 75 N•m (55 lb. ft.).

5. Transaxle fluid filler tube assembly. Refer to "Fluid Filler Tube" in this section.
6. Transaxle mount to engine assembly. Refer to "Transaxle Mount" in this section.
7. Remove jackstand from transaxle assembly.
8. Transaxle oil cooler upper and lower pipe assemblies. Refer to "Oil Cooler Pipes" in this section.
9. Transaxle torque converter bolts/screws.

Tighten

- Bolts/screws to 63 N•m (46 lb. ft.).

10. Starter motor assembly. Refer to SECTION 6D2.
11. Transaxle converter cover assembly.
12. Transaxle converter cover bolts/screws.

Tighten

- Bolts/screws to 10 N•m (89 lb. in.).

13. Front wheel drive shaft assemblies to transaxle assembly.
14. Electrical connector to vehicle speed sensor.
15. Drivetrain and front suspension frame assembly.
16. Drivetrain and front suspension frame bolts/screws.

Tighten

- Bolts/screws to 145 N•m (107 lb. ft.).

17. Transaxle brace. Refer to "Transaxle Brace" in this section.
18. Transaxle mount side bracket nuts. Refer to "Transaxle Mount Assembly" in this section.
19. Remove floor stands from drivetrain and front suspension frame assembly.
20. Power steering fluid cooling pipe assembly. Refer to SECTION 3B.
21. Front lower control arm assemblies to front suspension strut assemblies.
22. Steering gear bolts/screws.
23. Steering gear heat shield assembly.
24. Front exhaust manifold pipe. Refer to SECTION 6F.
25. Left front bumper fascia splash shield assembly.
26. Tire and wheel assemblies.
27. Lower vehicle.
28. Upper transaxle-to-engine bolts/screws.

Tighten

- Bolts/screws to 75 N•m (55 lb. ft.).

29. Transaxle range selector assembly to transaxle assembly.
30. Electrical connectors to transaxle assembly.
31. Automatic transaxle vacuum modulator pipe assembly. Refer to "Automatic Transaxle Vacuum Modulator Pipe and/or O-ring" in this section.
32. Air intake duct assembly.
33. Remove J 28467-A, J 28467-90 and J 36462.
34. Electrical engine cooling fan assemblies.
35. Engine mount strut brackets.
36. Transaxle fluid level indicator assembly. Refer to "Fluid Filler Tube" in this section.
37. Hood panel assembly.

TRANSAXLE BRACE

Figure 29

Remove or Disconnect

1. Raise and suitably support vehicle.
2. Right front tire and wheel assembly.
3. Right front bumper fascia splash shield assembly.
4. Bolts/screws.
5. Transaxle brace.

Install or Connect

NOTICE: See "Notice" on page 7A-1 of this section.

1. Position transaxle brace to transaxle assembly and engine assembly.

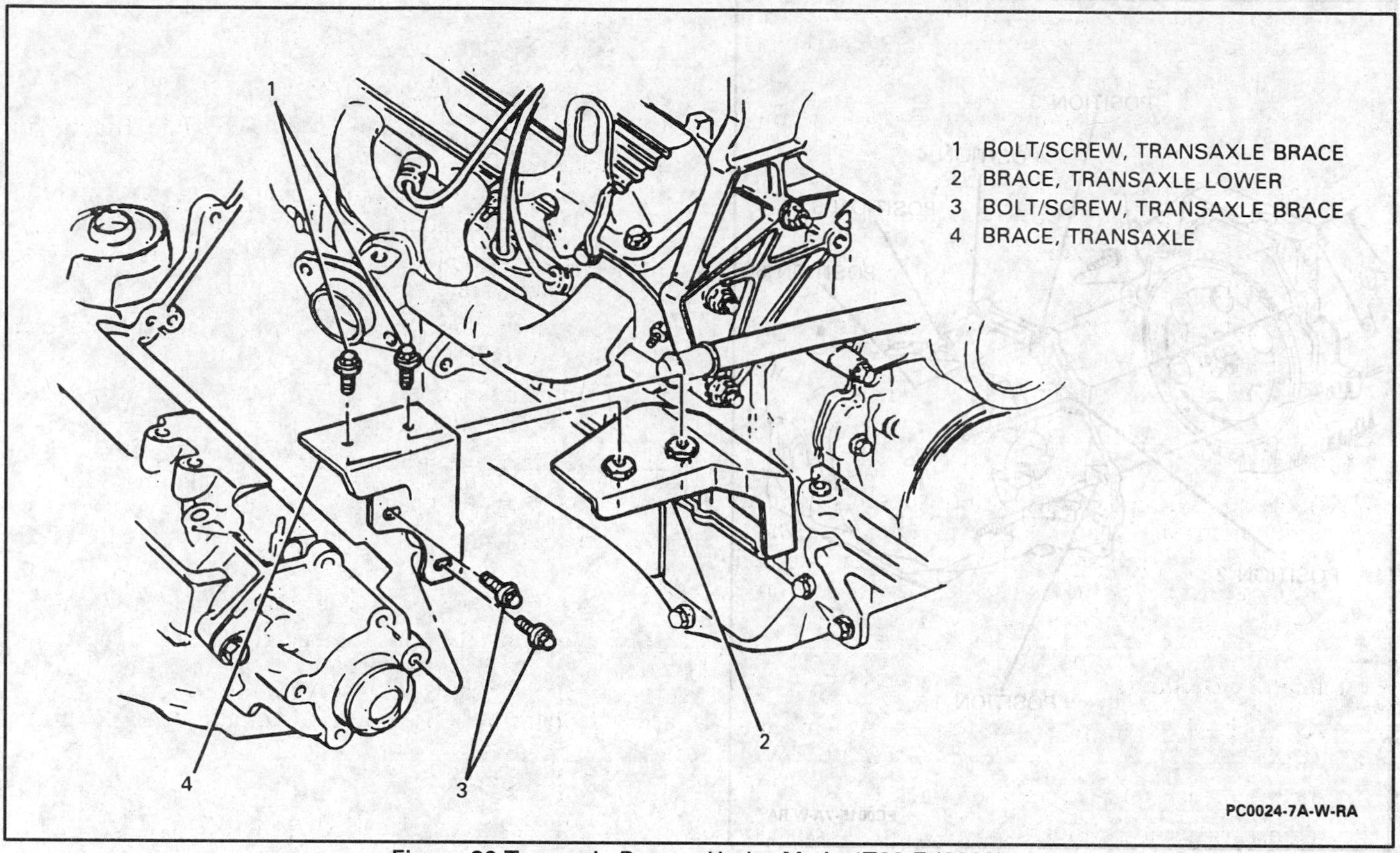
1
2
3
4
3
1 BOLT/SCREW, TRANSAXLE BRACE
2 BRACE, TRANSAXLE LOWER
3 BOLT/SCREW, TRANSAXLE BRACE
4 BRACE, TRANSAXLE
PC0024-7A-W-RA

Figure 30 Transaxle Brace – Hydra-Matic 4T60-E (3800)

Important

- Do not tighten transaxle brace bolts/screws out of sequence. Side load condition to transaxle assembly may occur.

2. Hand start bolts/screws to engine assembly and transaxle assembly.
3. Bolts/screws to engine assembly.

Tighten

- Bolts/screws to 47 N•m (35 lb. ft.).

4. Bolts/screws to transaxle assembly.

Tighten

- Bolts/screws to 47 N•m (35 lb. ft.).

5. Right front bumper fascia splash shield assembly.
6. Right front tire and wheel assembly.
7. Lower vehicle.

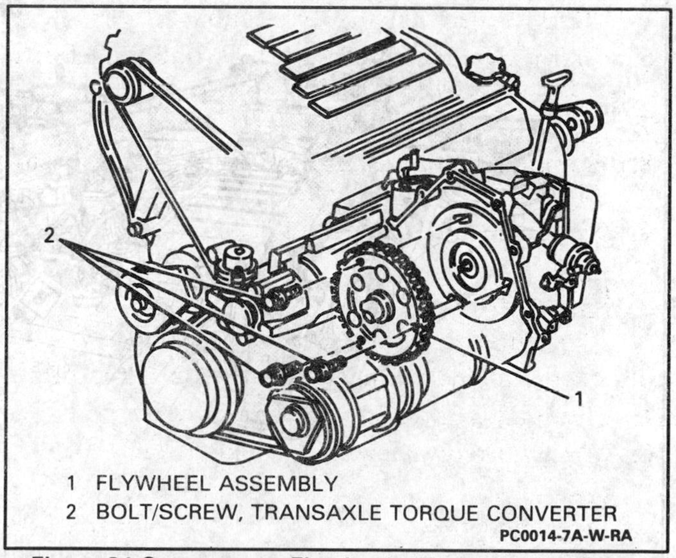
2
1
1 FLYWHEEL ASSEMBLY
2 BOLT/SCREW, TRANSAXLE TORQUE CONVERTER
PC0014-7A-W-RA

Figure 31 Converter to Flywheel – Hydra-Matic 4T60-E

ENGINE SUPPORT FIXTURE

Refer to Figures 33 and 34 for proper installation of the engine support fixutre J 28467-A.

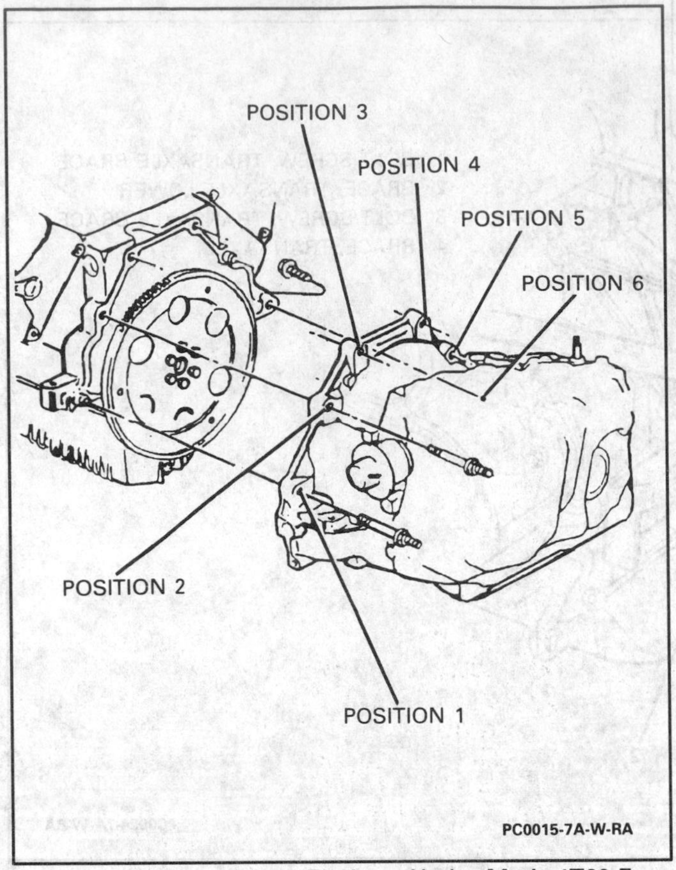
POSITION 3
POSITION 4
POSITION 5
POSITION 6
POSITION 2
POSITION 1
PC0015-7A-W-RA

Figure 32 Transaxle to Engine – Hydra-Matic 4T60-E

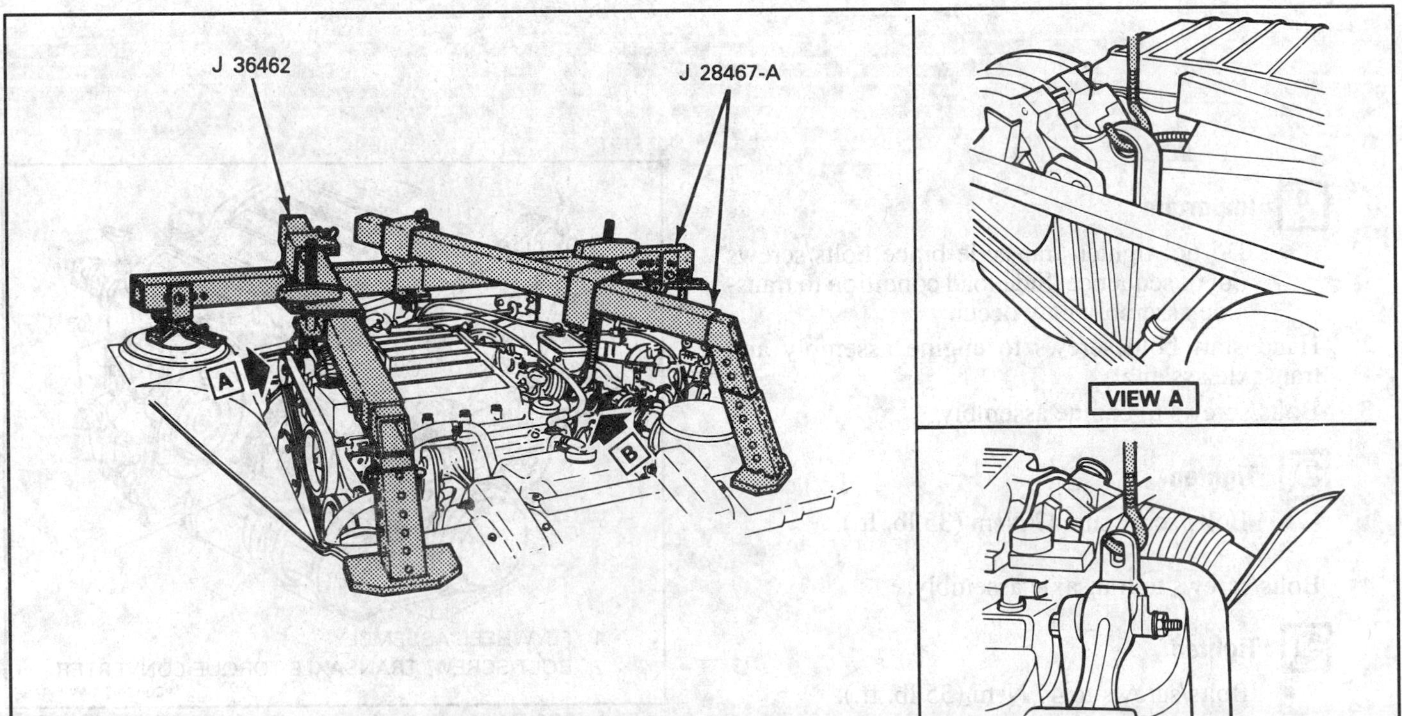
J 36462
J 28467-A
A
B
VIEW A
VIEW B
LC0005-7B-W-RA

Figure 33 Engine Support Fixture Installation – 3.1L Engine

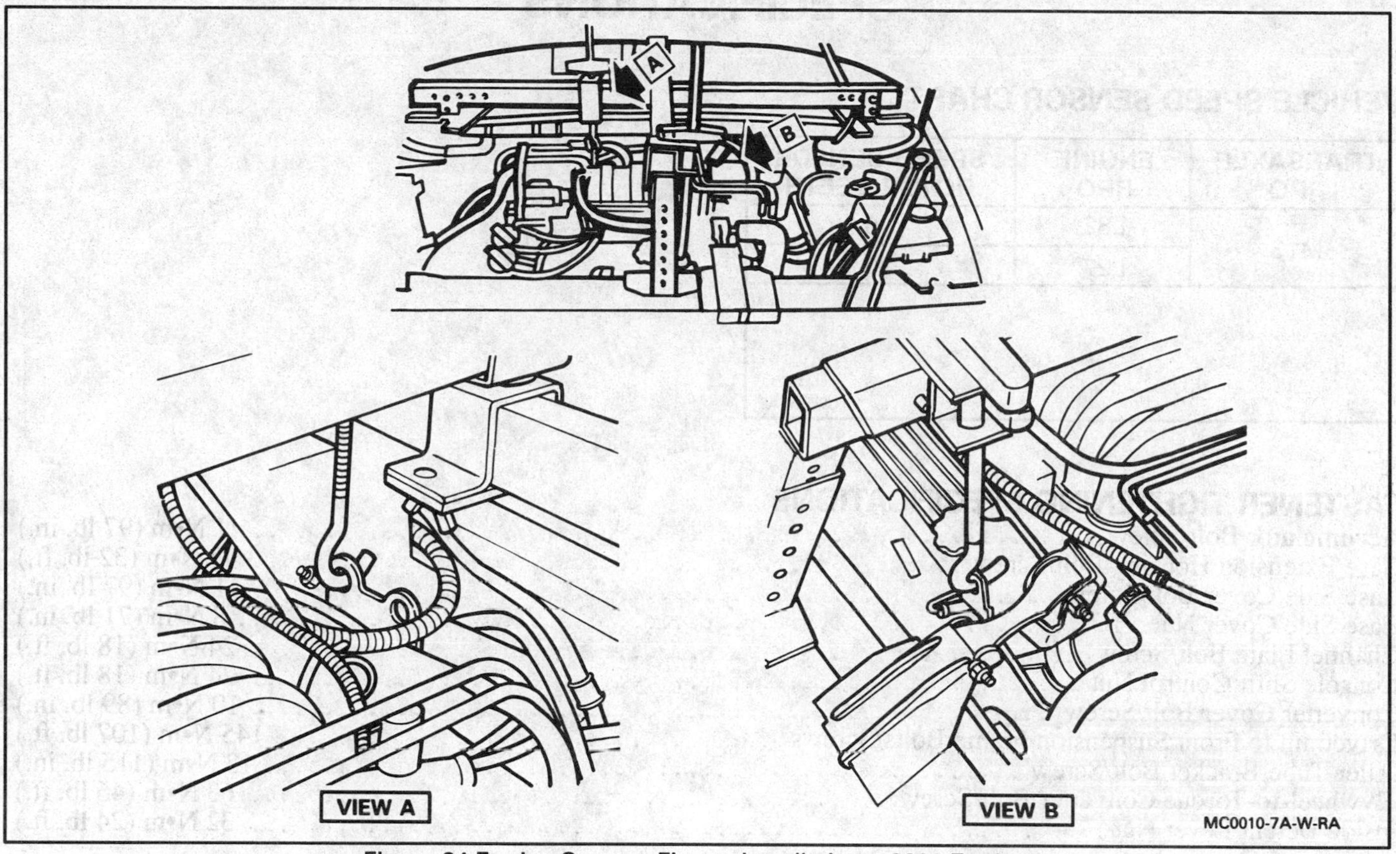
A
B
VIEW A
VIEW B
MC0010-7A-W-RA

Figure 34 Engine Support Fixture Installation – 3800 Engine

SPECIFICATIONS

VEHICLE SPEED SENSOR CHART

TRANSAXLE RPO	ENGINE RPO	SPEED SENSOR ROTOR TEETH
M13	L82	30
	L27	30

CPC W7A6

FASTENER TIGHTENING SPECIFICATIONS

Accumulator Bolt/Screw .... 11 N•m (97 lb. in.)
Case Extension Housing Bolt/Screw .... 43 N•m (32 lb. ft.)
Case Side Cover Bolt/Screw .... 11 N•m (97 lb. in.)
Case Side Cover Nut .... 8 N•m (71 lb. in.)
Channel Plate Bolt/Screw .... 24 N•m (18 lb. ft.)
Console Shift Control Nut .... 24 N•m (18 lb. ft.)
Converter Cover Bolt/Screw .... 10 N•m (89 lb. in.)
Drivetrain to Front Suspension Frame Bolts/Screws .... 145 N•m (107 lb. ft.)
Filler Tube Bracket Bolt/Screw .... 13 N•m (115 lb. in.)
Flywheel-to-Torque Converter Bolt/Screw .... 63 N•m (46 lb. ft.)
Inside Detent Lever Nut .... 32 N•m (24 lb. ft.)

Manual Detent Roller Bolt/Screw .... 11 N•m (97 lb. in.)
Neutral Start Switch Bolt/Screw .... 25 N•m (18 lb. ft.)
Oil Pan Bolt/Screw .... 17 N•m (13 lb. ft.)
Oil Scoop Bolt/Screw .... 8 N•m (71 lb. in.)
Pump Bolt/Screw (Top Two and Bottom Rear) .... 24 N•m (18 lb. ft.)
Pump Bolt/Screw (Remaining) .... 11 N•m (97 lb. in.)

Servo Cover Bolt/Screw .... 10 N•m (89 lb. in.)
Shift Control Cable Bracket Bolt/Screw .... 25 N•m (18 lb. ft.)
Shift Control Cable Bracket Nut .... 24 N•m (18 lb. ft.)
Shift Control Cable Lever Nut .... 20 N•m (15 lb. ft.)
Speed Sensor Bolt/Screw .... 11 N•m (97 lb. in.)

Transaxle Bracket-to-Transaxle Bolt/Screw .... 95 N•m (70 lb. ft.)
Transaxle Bracket-to-Mount Nut .... 53 N•m (39 lb. ft.)
Transaxle Mount Support Bolt/Screw .... 58 N•m (43 lb. ft.)
Transaxle Mount Support Nut .... 58 N•m (43 lb. ft.)
Transaxle Mount-to-Support Nut .... 53 N•m (39 lb. ft.)
Transaxle Oil Cooler Fitting-to-Radiator .... 21 N•m (15 lb. ft.)

Transaxle Oil Cooler Fitting-to-Transaxle .... 21 N•m (15 lb. ft.)
Transaxle Oil Cooler Hose Clamp .... 2 N•m (18 lb. in.)
Transaxle Oil Cooler Hose Clip Bolt/Screw .... 50 N•m (37 lb. ft.)
Transaxle Oil Cooler Pipe Clip Bolt/Screw .... 3 N•m (26 lb. in.)
Transaxle-to-Engine Bolt/Screw .... 75 N•m (55 lb. ft.)
Transaxle-to-Engine Brace Bolt/Screw .... 47 N•m (35 lb. ft.)

Vacuum Modulator Clamp Bolt/Screw .... 27 N•m (20 lb. ft.)
Vacuum Modulator Pipe Clip Nut .... 25 N•m (18 lb. ft.)
Valve Body-to-Case Bolt/Screw .... 24 N•m (18 lb. in.)
Valve Body Bolt/Screw (Remaining) .... 11 N•m (97 lb. ft.)

SPECIAL TOOLS

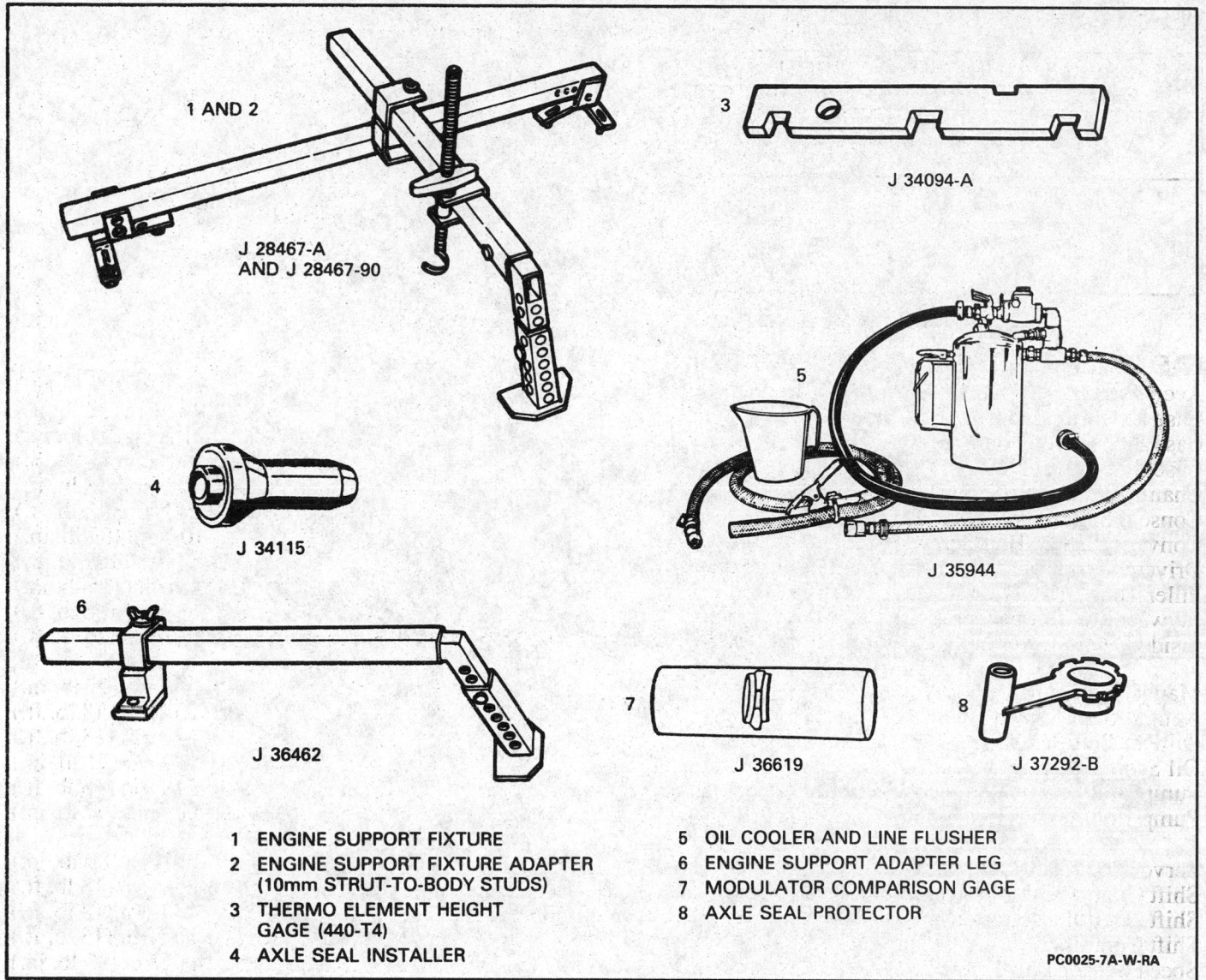

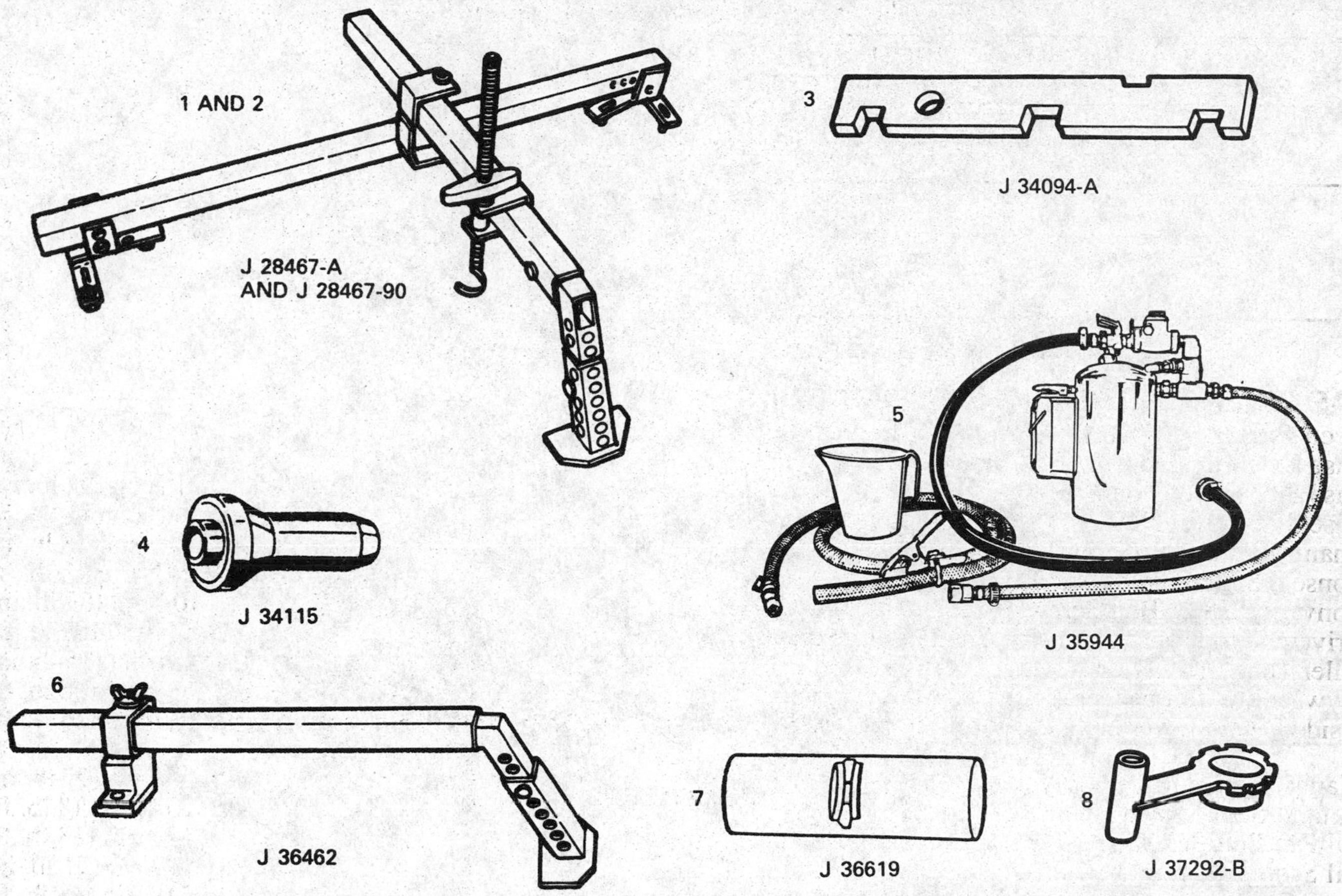
1 AND 2
J 28467-A
AND J 28467-90
3
J 34094-A
5
J 35944
4
J 34115
6
J 36462
7
J 36619
8
J 37292-B

1 ENGINE SUPPORT FIXTURE
2 ENGINE SUPPORT FIXTURE ADAPTER (10mm STRUT-TO-BODY STUDS)
3 THERMO ELEMENT HEIGHT GAGE (440-T4)
4 AXLE SEAL INSTALLER
5 OIL COOLER AND LINE FLUSHER
6 ENGINE SUPPORT ADAPTER LEG
7 MODULATOR COMPARISON GAGE
8 AXLE SEAL PROTECTOR

PC0025-7A-W-RA

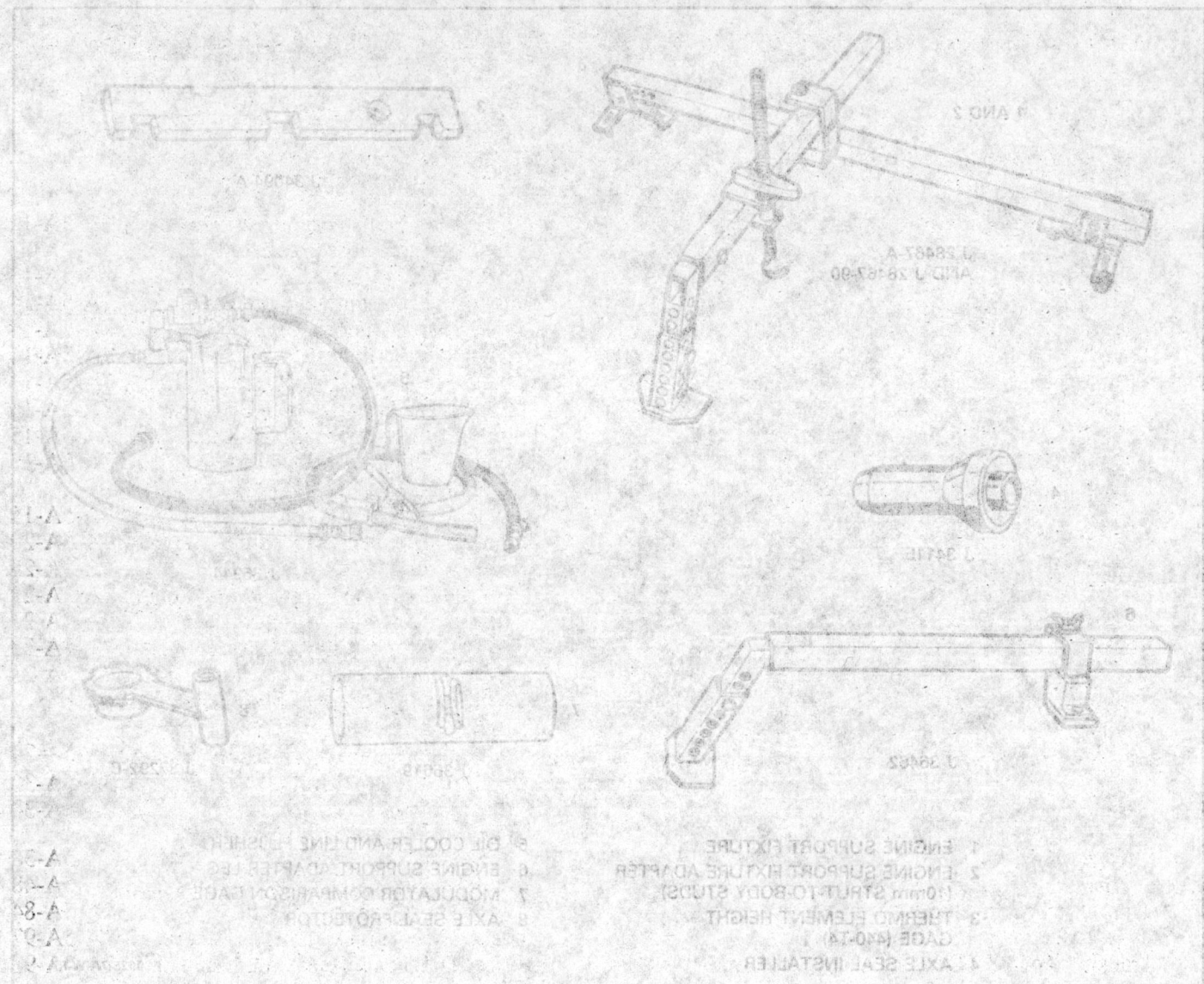

SECTION 7A-5A
HYDRA-MATIC 4T60-E
AUTOMATIC TRANSAXLE DIAGNOSIS
RPO M13

CONTENTS

TRANSAXLE DIAGNOSIS INFORMATION

QUICK CHECK PROCEDURE

Begin with the Quick Check Procedure (Figure 2) which provides a general outline of how to diagnose a HYDRA-MATIC 4T60-E. The Quick Check Procedure will indicate the proper path of diagnosing the transaxle by describing the basic checks and then referencing the locations of the specific checks.

Use on-board diagnostics or TECH 1 (or other scan tool) to see if any transaxle trouble codes have been set. Refer to the appropriate trouble tree (Section 6E) and repair the vehicle as directed. After repairing the vehicle, perform the road test and verify that the code has not set again.

If no trouble codes have been set and the condition is suspected to be hydraulic, take the vehicle on a road test. Refer to "Road Test Procedure" in this section.

GENERAL DESCRIPTION

The HYDRA-MATIC 4T60-E is a fully automatic front wheel drive transaxle. It provides four forward ranges including overdrive.

The major components of this unit are:

- Torque converter clutch is controlled by an electronic solenoid for the apply/release. The rate of apply/release is controlled either by a converter clutch regulator valve, or by a electronic Pulse Width Modulator (PWM) Solenoid, (model dependant).

- Sprocket and drive link assembly.
- Electronic shift solenoids to control shift points.
- Forward, manual 2/1 and reverse band assemblies that do not require selective band apply pins.
- Input, 3rd, 2nd, and 4th clutches – multiple disc assemblies.
- Compound planetary gear set.
- 3 one-way clutches: An input sprag, 3rd sprag and 2/1 roller clutch.
- Differential and final drive assembly with a bolt on case extension for on-car servicing.
- Variable vane type oil pump regulated by a vacuum modulator.

The transaxle can be operated in any one of the following seven modes:

P – Park position prevents the vehicle from rolling either forward or backward. (For safety reasons the parking brake should be used in addition to the park position).

R – Reverse allows the vehicle to be operated in a rearward direction.

N – Neutral allows the engine to be started and operated while driving the vehicle. If necessary this position may be selected if the engine must be restarted with the vehicle moving.

Ⓓ – Overdrive is used for all normal driving conditions. It provides four gear ratios plus converter clutch operation. Downshifts are available for safe passing by depressing the accelerator.

D – Drive position is used for city traffic, hilly terrain, and trailer towing. It provides three gear ranges. Again, downshifts are available by depressing the accelerator.

2 – Manual second is used to provide acceleration and engine braking. This range may be selected under 65 mph (104 km/h).

1 – Manual Lo is used to provide maximum engine braking. This range may also be selected at vehicle speeds under 40 mph (65 km/h).

GENERAL INFORMATION

HOW TO USE THIS SECTION

This section provides general information on transaxles, a detailed description of the operation of the HYDRA-MATIC 4T60-E and procedures for diagnosing the HYDRA-MATIC 4T60-E, beginning with the "Quick Check Procedure" in this section. After the cause of a condition is determined, refer to SECTION 7A, "ON-VEHICLE SERVICE" or the 7A-5B AUTOMATIC TRANSAXLE UNIT REPAIR for repair procedures.

TRANSAXLE DEFINITIONS AND ABBREVIATIONS

The following definitions and abbreviations are being provided to establish a common language and assist the user in describing transaxle related conditions. Some of these terms or conditions are used in the transaxle sections of this Service Manual.

Throttle Positions

- **Minimum Throttle** – the least amount of throttle opening required for an upshift.
- **Light Throttle** – approximately 1/4 of accelerator pedal travel.
- **Medium Throttle** – approximately 1/2 of accelerator pedal travel.
- **Heavy Throttle** – approximately 3/4 of accelerator pedal travel.
- **Wide Open Throttle (WOT)** – full travel of the accelerator pedal.
- **Full Throttle Detent Downshift** – a quick apply of the accelerator pedal to its full travel, forcing a downshift.
- **Zero Throttle Coastdown** – a full release of the accelerator pedal while the vehicle is in motion and in drive range.
- **Engine Braking** – a condition where the engine is used to slow the vehicle by manually downshifting during a zero throttle coastdown.

Shift Conditions

- **Bump** – a sudden and forceful apply of a clutch or band.
- **Chuggle** – a bucking or jerking condition that may be engine related. May be most noticeable when the converter clutch is engaged. Similar to the feel of towing a trailer.
- **Delayed** – condition where a shift is expected but does not occur for a period of time. Samples of this condition could be described as clutch or band engagement that does not occur as quickly as expected during a part throttle or wide open throttle apply of the accelerator or, when manually downshifting to a lower range. Also defined as 'LATE' or, 'EXTENDED.'
- **Double Bump ('Double Feel')** – two sudden and forceful applies of a clutch or band.
- **Early** – a condition where the shift occurs before the vehicle has reached a proper speed and tends to labor the engine after the upshift.

- **End Bump** – a firmer feel at the end of a shift as compared to the feel at the start of the shift. Also defined as 'END FEEL' or, 'SLIP BUMP'.
- **Firm** – a noticeably quick apply of a clutch or band that is considered normal with a medium to heavy throttle. Should not be confused with 'HARSH' or 'ROUGH'.
- **Flare** – a quick increase in engine rpm accompanied with a momentary loss of torque. This most generally occurs during a shift. Also defined as 'SLIPPING'.
- **Harsh ('ROUGH')** – a more noticeable apply of a clutch or band as compared with 'FIRM'. This condition is considered undesirable at any throttle position.
- **Hunting** – a repeating series of upshifts and downshifts that causes a noticeable change in engine rpm. An example could be described as a 4-3-4 shift pattern. Also defined as 'BUSYNESS'.
- **Initial Feel** – a distinct firmer feel at the start of a shift as compared to the finish of the shift.
- **Late** – a shift that occurs when the engine is at a higher than normal rpm for a given amount of throttle.
- **Shudder** – a repeating jerking sensation similar to 'CHUGGLE' but more severe and rapid in nature. This condition may be most noticeable during certain ranges of vehicle speed. May also be used to define the condition after converter clutch engagement.
- **Slipping** – a noticeable increase in engine rpm without a vehicle speed increase. A slip usually occurs during or after initial clutch or band apply.
- **Soft** – a slow, almost unnoticeable clutch or band apply with very little shift feel.
- **Surge** – a repeating engine related condition of acceleration and deceleration that is less intense than 'CHUGGLE'.
- **Tie-Up** – a condition where two opposing clutches and/or bands are attempting to apply at the same time causing the engine to labor with a noticeable loss of engine rpm.

Abbreviations

- PCM – Powertrain Control Module.
- TCC – Torque Converter Clutch.
- TCC Solenoid – Torque Converter Clutch Solenoid.
- A Solenoid – A Shift Solenoid.
- B Solenoid – B Shift Solenoid.
- TP Sensor – Throttle Position Sensor.
- ECT Sensor – Engine Coolant Temperature Sensor.
- VS Sensor – Vehicle Speed Sensor.
- CCDIC – Climate Control Driver Information Center.
- FWD – Front Wheel Drive.
- PWM Solenoid – Torque Converter Clutch Pulse Width Modulated Solenoid.

NOISE CONDITIONS

- **Drive Link Noise** – a whine or growl that increases or fades with engine rpm. Noise is not noticeable under light throttle acceleration or in 'DRIVE' or 'REVERSE' with the car stationary.
- **Final Drive Noise** – a hum related to car speed and is most noticeable under light throttle acceleration or zero throttle coast down.
- **Planetary Gear Noise** – a whine, most noticeable in first gear and reverse that is related to vehicle speed. A gear noise condition may become less noticeable or go away after an upshift.
- **Pump Noise** – a high pitch whine that increases intensity with engine rpm. This condition may also be noticeable in ALL operating ranges.
- **Torque Converter** – A whine usually noticed when a vehicle is stopped and transaxle is in "DRIVE" or REVERSE. The noise will increase with engine RPM. See "Torque Converter Evaluation" for further information.

GENERAL SERVICE PROCEDURES

Important

- Keep work area and tools clean.
- Always clean the exterior of the transaxle before removing any parts.
- Do not use wiping cloths or rags.
- Do not use solvent on:
  - Neoprene seals.
  - Composition faced clutch plates.
  - Thrust washers.
- Blow out all passages with compressed air. Probe small passages with tag wire.
- Handle parts with care to avoid nicks and scratches.

Inspect

- Linkage and pivot points for wear.
- Bearing and thrust surfaces for wear and scoring.
- Broken seal rings and damaged ring lands.
- Gaskets, mating surfaces, seals and O-rings for damage. Investigate and correct cause of damage.
- Do not remove Teflon oil seal rings unless damaged or performing a complete overhaul.
- Case for porosity. Refer to "CASE POROSITY REPAIR PROCEDURE" (SECTION 7A ON-VEHICLE).

Important

- Expand internal snap rings and compress external snap rings to assure proper seating.
- Lubricate all internal parts with transaxle fluid as they are being installed.
- When installing cap screws into aluminum parts:
  - Always use a torque wrench.
  - Always dip screw threads in transaxle fluid.
  - Stripped or damaged aluminum threads may be reconditioned with thread inserts. Refer to Section 6A.
- Replace all gaskets (except bottom pan gasket-reusable), seals and O-rings.
  - Always use seal protectors.
  - Do not use gasket cement or sealers on the oil pan and side cover.

FLUID LEAK DIAGNOSIS

1. Clean area thoroughly with solvent.
2. Remove the converter shield, if required.
3. Spray area with pressurized foot spray powder.
4. Start engine and run at fast idle.
5. Repair leaks and recheck as necessary.
   - Identify the type of oil. (Transaxle fluid contains a red dye.)
   - Leaking oil is generally carried toward the rear of the car by the air stream.
6. Drive car approximately 15 miles to warm up unit to operating temperature 88°C (190°F).
7. Inspect for leaks with engine running.
8. Turn engine off, check for leaks caused by drain back.

Possible Points of Oil Leak

1. Transaxle pan or valve body cover:
   - Attaching bolts not correctly torqued
   - Improperly installed or damaged gasket
   - Oil pan or valve body cover mounting face not flat
2. Case Leak:
   - Servo cover porosity or O-ring damage.
   - Filler pipe 'multi-lip seal' damaged or missing
   - Filler pipe bracket mislocated.
   - Electrical connector O-ring damaged.
   - Manual shaft seal damaged.
   - Oil cooler connector fittings loose or damaged.
   - Vacuum modulator O-ring damaged.
   - Axle oil seals worn or damaged.
   - Park lock out cup plug loose.
   - Line pressure pickup pipe plug loose.
   - Bottom pan or side cover gasket(s) damaged.
   - Porous casting.
3. Leak at converter end:
   - Converter seal damaged.
     - Seal lip cut. (Check converter hub for damage.)
     - Bushing moved forward and damaged.
     - Garter spring missing from seal.
   - Converter leak in weld area.
   - Porous casting. (Case or drive sprocket support.)
   - Turbine shaft oil seal worn or damaged.
4. Fluid comes out vent pipe:
   - Over-filled.
   - Water in fluid.
   - Case porous.
   - Incorrect dipstick.
   - Drain back holes plugged.
   - Mispositioned or damaged case to channel plate modulator gasket.
   - Incorrect thermal element height setting.

FLEXPLATE/TORQUE CONVERTER VIBRATION TEST PROCEDURE

- Start engine.
- With engine at idle speed and transaxle in 'PARK' (P) or 'NEUTRAL' (N), observe vibration.
- Key 'OFF'.

Remove or Disconnect

1. Flexplate shield attaching bolts.
2. Flexplate to torque converter attaching bolts.
3. Rotate torque converter 120 degrees (1/3 turn).

Install or Connect

1. Flexplate to torque converter attaching bolts.

   Tighten

   - Bolts to 62 N•m (46 lb. ft.).
2. Flexplate shield attaching bolts.
   - Start engine and check for vibration. Repeat procedure until best possible balance is obtained.

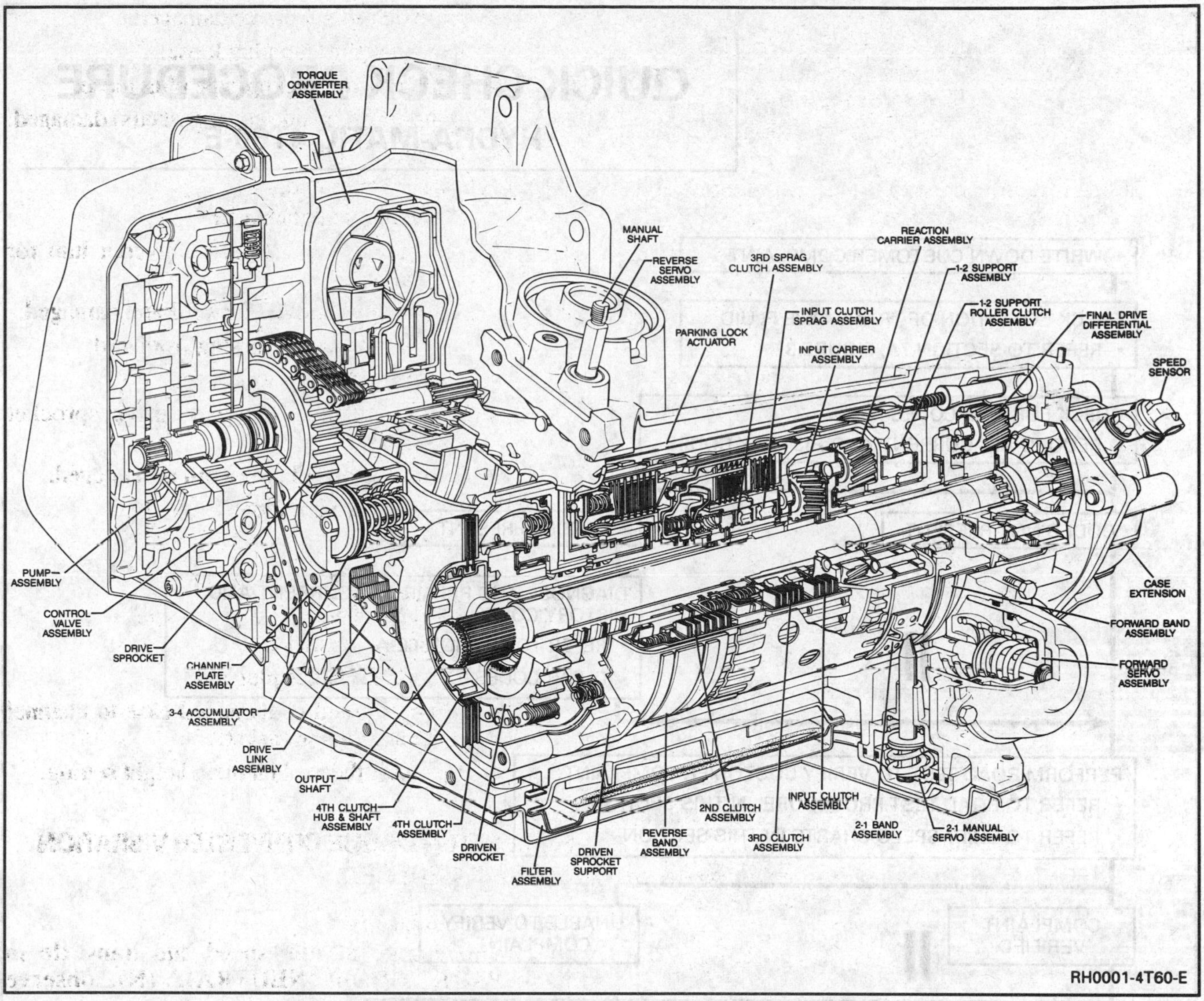
TORQUE CONVERTER ASSEMBLY
MANUAL SHAFT
REVERSE SERVO ASSEMBLY
3RD SPRAG CLUTCH ASSEMBLY
REACTION CARRIER ASSEMBLY
1-2 SUPPORT ASSEMBLY
1-2 SUPPORT ROLLER CLUTCH ASSEMBLY
FINAL DRIVE DIFFERENTIAL ASSEMBLY
SPEED SENSOR
INPUT CLUTCH SPRAG ASSEMBLY
PARKING LOCK ACTUATOR
INPUT CARRIER ASSEMBLY
PUMP ASSEMBLY
CONTROL VALVE ASSEMBLY
DRIVE SPROCKET
CHANNEL PLATE ASSEMBLY
3-4 ACCUMULATOR ASSEMBLY
DRIVE LINK ASSEMBLY
OUTPUT SHAFT
4TH CLUTCH HUB & SHAFT ASSEMBLY
4TH CLUTCH ASSEMBLY
DRIVEN SPROCKET
FILTER ASSEMBLY
DRIVEN SPROCKET SUPPORT
REVERSE BAND ASSEMBLY
2ND CLUTCH ASSEMBLY
INPUT CLUTCH ASSEMBLY
3RD CLUTCH ASSEMBLY
2-1 BAND ASSEMBLY
2-1 MANUAL SERVO ASSEMBLY
CASE EXTENSION
FORWARD BAND ASSEMBLY
FORWARD SERVO ASSEMBLY
RH0001-4T60-E

Figure 1 HYDRA-MATIC 4T60-E Automatic Transaxle

ROAD TEST PROCEDURE

- Perform the road test following the sequence given.
- Km/h (mph) shift points will vary with actual throttle position and driver habits.
- Compare the results of the test with shift speed chart information (Figure 4).

[!] Important

The shift speed charts have been updated to reference PERCENT THROTTLE OPENING to make shift speed measurement more uniform and accurate. On-board diagnostics must be used to monitor PERCENT THROTTLE OPENING.

With gear selector in "Overdrive" (D4):

1. Look at the shift speed chart contained in this section and choose a percent throttle angle of 5, 10 or 25.
2. Set up the on-board diagnostics or TECH 1 (or similar scan tool) to monitor PERCENT THROTTLE OPENING and VEHICLE SPEED.

[!] Important

- This test should only be performed when traffic and road conditions permit. Observe all traffic safety regulations.

3. Accelerate to the chosen throttle angle and hold the throttle steady.
4. As the transaxle upshifts, note the shift speed for:
   - 2nd gear
   - 3rd gear
   - 4th gear

- Shift speeds may vary due to slight hydraulic delays responding to electronic controls. A change from the original equipment tire size also affects shift speeds.

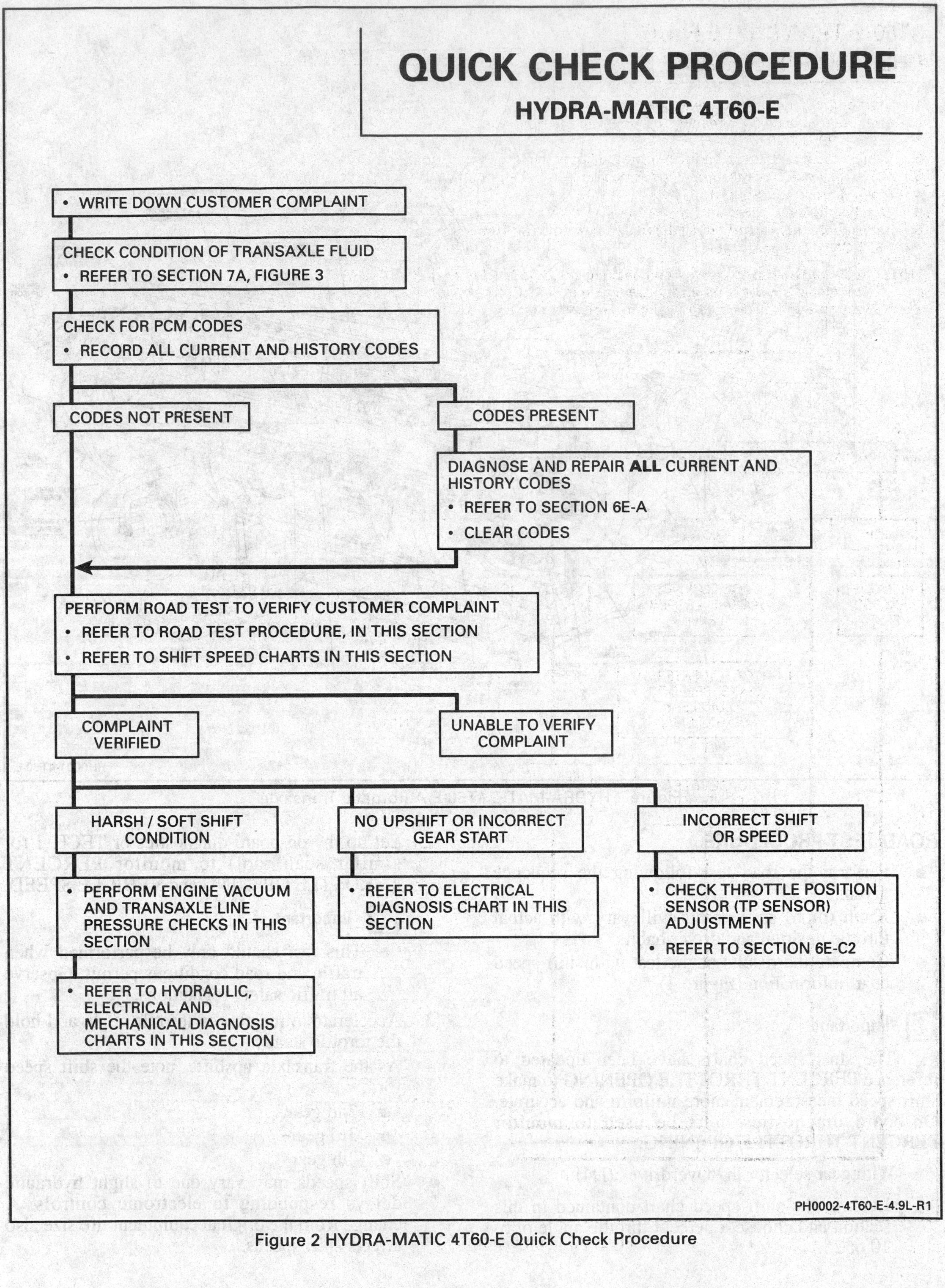
QUICK CHECK PROCEDURE
HYDRA-MATIC 4T60-E
• WRITE DOWN CUSTOMER COMPLAINT
CHECK CONDITION OF TRANSAXLE FLUID
• REFER TO SECTION 7A, FIGURE 3
CHECK FOR PCM CODES
• RECORD ALL CURRENT AND HISTORY CODES
CODES NOT PRESENT
CODES PRESENT
DIAGNOSE AND REPAIR ALL CURRENT AND HISTORY CODES
• REFER TO SECTION 6E-A
• CLEAR CODES
PERFORM ROAD TEST TO VERIFY CUSTOMER COMPLAINT
• REFER TO ROAD TEST PROCEDURE, IN THIS SECTION
• REFER TO SHIFT SPEED CHARTS IN THIS SECTION
COMPLAINT VERIFIED
UNABLE TO VERIFY COMPLAINT
HARSH / SOFT SHIFT CONDITION
NO UPSHIFT OR INCORRECT GEAR START
INCORRECT SHIFT OR SPEED
• PERFORM ENGINE VACUUM AND TRANSAXLE LINE PRESSURE CHECKS IN THIS SECTION
• REFER TO ELECTRICAL DIAGNOSIS CHART IN THIS SECTION
• CHECK THROTTLE POSITION SENSOR (TP SENSOR) ADJUSTMENT
• REFER TO SECTION 6E-C2
• REFER TO HYDRAULIC, ELECTRICAL AND MECHANICAL DIAGNOSIS CHARTS IN THIS SECTION
PH0002-4T60-E-4.9L-R1

Figure 2 HYDRA-MATIC 4T60-E Quick Check Procedure

4T60-E TRANSAXLE FLUID CHECKING PROCEDURE

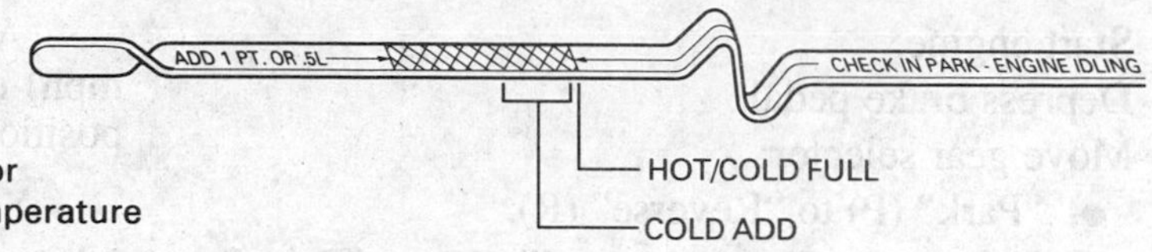
ADD 1 PT. OR .5L
CHECK IN PARK - ENGINE IDLING
HOT/COLD FULL
COLD ADD

1. Start engine and operate vehicle for 15 minutes or until the transaxle fluid reaches on operating temperature of 88 to 93°C (190 to 200°F).
2. Vehicle must be in park on level ground (Apply parking brake and block wheels).
3. Move gear selector through all gear positions while engine is idling and foot is applied to brake pedal.
4. Move gear selector back to **"PARK"**.
5. Check fluid level, color, and condition.
6. If it is necessary to add fluid, DEXRON®-III Automatic Transmissions Fluid is preferred, if unavailable DEXRON®-IIE is acceptable.

NOTE: It should be noted that when checking the fluid level in the HYDRA-MATIC 4T60-E, the fluid will be higher on the fluid level indicator when the transaxle is cold. Conversely, the fluid level will drop when checked at operating temperature. This is due to the case thermostatic element.

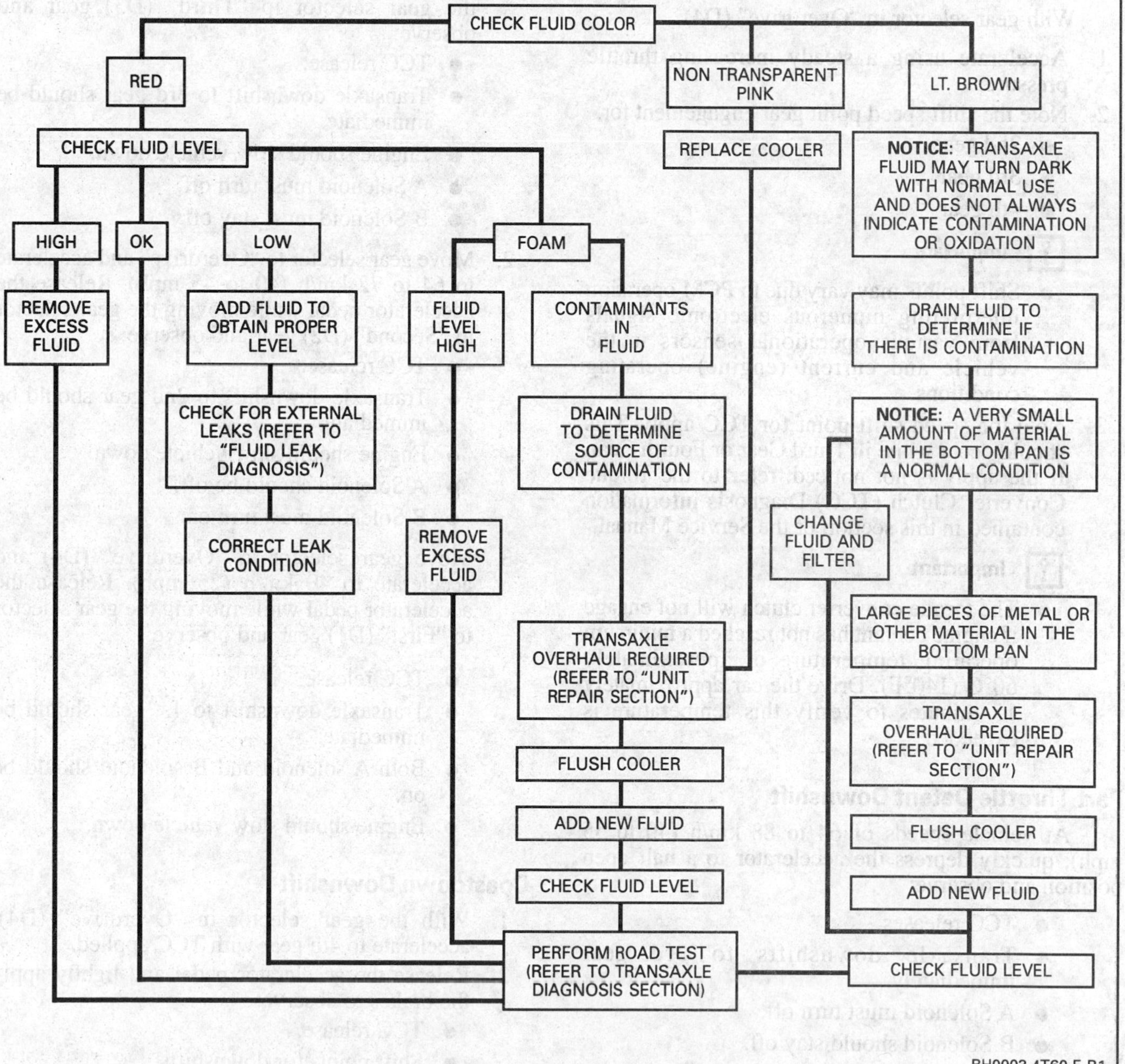
CHECK FLUID COLOR
RED
CHECK FLUID LEVEL
HIGH
OK
LOW
FOAM
REMOVE EXCESS FLUID
ADD FLUID TO OBTAIN PROPER LEVEL
FLUID LEVEL HIGH
CONTAMINANTS IN FLUID
CHECK FOR EXTERNAL LEAKS (REFER TO "FLUID LEAK DIAGNOSIS")
DRAIN FLUID TO DETERMINE SOURCE OF CONTAMINATION
CORRECT LEAK CONDITION
REMOVE EXCESS FLUID
TRANSAXLE OVERHAUL REQUIRED (REFER TO "UNIT REPAIR SECTION")
FLUSH COOLER
ADD NEW FLUID
CHECK FLUID LEVEL
PERFORM ROAD TEST (REFER TO TRANSAXLE DIAGNOSIS SECTION)
NON TRANSPARENT PINK
REPLACE COOLER
LT. BROWN
NOTICE: TRANSAXLE FLUID MAY TURN DARK WITH NORMAL USE AND DOES NOT ALWAYS INDICATE CONTAMINATION OR OXIDATION
DRAIN FLUID TO DETERMINE IF THERE IS CONTAMINATION
NOTICE: A VERY SMALL AMOUNT OF MATERIAL IN THE BOTTOM PAN IS A NORMAL CONDITION
CHANGE FLUID AND FILTER
LARGE PIECES OF METAL OR OTHER MATERIAL IN THE BOTTOM PAN
TRANSAXLE OVERHAUL REQUIRED (REFER TO "UNIT REPAIR SECTION")
FLUSH COOLER
ADD NEW FLUID
CHECK FLUID LEVEL
RH0003-4T60-E-R1

Figure 3 Fluid Level Checking Procedure

Garage Shift Check

1. Start engine.
2. Depress brake pedal.
3. Move gear selector:
   - "Park" (P) to "Reverse" (R).
   - "Reverse" (R) to "Neutral" (N) to "Drive" (D).
     - Gear selections should be immediate and not harsh.

Upshifts and Torque Converter Clutch (TCC) Apply

Figure 4

With gear selector in "Overdrive" (D4):

1. Accelerate using a steady increasing throttle pressure.
2. Note the shift speed point gear engagement for:
   - 2nd gear
   - 3rd gear
   - 4th gear

   Important

   - Shift points may vary due to PCM operation interpreting numerous electronic signals from various operational sensors in the vehicle and current (engine) operating conditions.
3. Note the speed shift point for TCC apply. This should occur while in Third Gear or Fourth Gear. If the apply is not noticed, refer to the Torque Converter Clutch (TCC) Diagnosis information contained in this section of the Service Manual.

   Important

   - The torque converter clutch will not engage if engine coolant has not reached a minimum operating temperature of approximately 60°C (140°F). Drive the car approximately 15 minutes to verify this temperature is exceeded.

Part Throttle Detent Downshift

At vehicle speeds of 64 to 88 km/h (40 to 55 mph), quickly depress the accelerator to a half open position and observe:

- TCC releases.
- Transaxle downshifts to 3rd gear immediately.
- A Solenoid must turn off.
- B Solenoid should stay off.

Full Throttle Detent Downshift

At vehicle speeds of 64 to 88 km/h (40 to 55 mph) quickly depress the accelerator to a wide open position and observe:

- TCC releases.
- Transaxle downshifts to 2nd gear immediately.
- B Solenoid must turn on.
- A Solenoid should stay off.

Manual Downshift

1. At vehicle speeds of 64 to 88 km/h (40 to 55 mph), release the accelerator pedal while moving the gear selector to "Third" (D3) gear and observe:
   - TCC release.
   - Transaxle downshift to 3rd gear should be immediate.
   - Engine should slow vehicle down.
   - A Solenoid must turn off.
   - B Solenoid must stay off.
2. Move gear selector to "Overdrive" and accelerate to 64 to 72 km/h (40 to 45 mph). Release the accelerator pedal while moving the gear selector to "Second" (D2) gear and observe:
   - TCC release.
   - Transaxle downshift to 2nd gear should be immediate.
   - Engine should slow vehicle down.
   - A Solenoid should be off.
   - B Solenoid must turn on.
3. Move gear selector to "Overdrive" (D4) and accelerate to 40 km/h (25 mph). Release the accelerator pedal while moving the gear selector to "First" (D1) gear and observe:
   - TCC release.
   - Transaxle downshift to 1st gear should be immediate.
   - Both A solenoid and B solenoid should be on.
   - Engine should slow vehicle down.

Coastdown Downshift

1. With the gear selector in "Overdrive" (D4), accelerate to 4th gear with TCC applied.
2. Release the accelerator pedal and lightly apply the brakes to observe:
   - TCC release.
   - Shift points for downshifts.

Manual Gear Range Selection

Manual Third (D3)

- With vehicle stopped, place gear selector in "Third" (D3) and accelerate to observe:
  - The first to second gear shift point.
  - The second to third gear shift point.

Manual Second (D2)

1. With vehicle stopped, place gear selector in "Second" (D2) and accelerate to observe:
   - The first to second gear shift point.
2. Accelerate to 40 km/h (25 mph) and observe:
   - That a second to third gear shift does not occur.
   - That TCC does not engage.

Manual First (D1)

- With vehicle stopped, place gear selector in "First" (D1) and accelerate to 24 km/h (15 mph) and observe:
  - That no upshift occurs.
  - That TCC does not engage.
  - Solenoids A and B must be on.

Reverse

1. With vehicle stopped, place gear selector in "Reverse" (R) and slowly accelerate to observe reverse gear operation.
   - A Solenoids and B solenoid must be on.

TRANSAXLE PRESSURE CHECK PROCEDURE

Figures 3 and 5

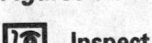

Inspect

Figure 3

- Fluid level.
- Manual linkage.
- Engine mechanical, emissions, electrical and fuel delivery systems.

Install or Connect

Figure 5

- Oil pressure gage.
- Tachometer.
- Hand operated vacuum device to the vacuum modulator.
  - J 23738-A or equivalent.

TRANSAXLE DIAGNOSIS

TRANSMISSION TEST BOX

Figures 6 through 9

A transmission test box, J 38791, and transaxle harness J 38791-60, is recommended to diagnose whether the cause of a problem is in the vehicle PCM, wiring harness, or in the transaxle.

Important

- Due to vehicle wiring harness and transaxle pin location changes from 1993 to 1994, it was necessary to design a new electrical wiring harness for the transmission test box J 38791. All 1994 vehicles must use J 38791-60 (transmission test box electrical connector) with J 38791 (transmission Test Box).
  Failure to comply may produce erroneous outputs and may cause internal damage to the transaxle.

The test box allows the technician to monitor vehicle electrical outputs through illumination of LED's, measure component resistance or perform other electrical checks through pin-out jacks, and control transaxle shifts or TCC operation while road testing the vehicle to conduct functional tests.

LED indicators on the test box monitor the presence of voltage at the PCM ignition input, brake switch, TCC apply solenoid, TCC modulate solenoid, and A Shift and B Shift solenoids. Pin-out jacks for these circuits are also provided just below each respective LED to facilitate probing with a digital volt ohmmeter when required. A gear selector switch and a converter clutch operation switch are located near the bottom of the face panel. A vehicle system ground pin-out jack is located at the bottom.

The test box is installed by connecting its harness connectors between the vehicle harness connector and the transaxle connector, routing the harness under the hood through the driver's door window into the passenger compartment, and inserting the ground connector into the cigarette lighter receptacle, (Figure 6).

1994 HYDRA-MATIC 4T60-E SHIFT SPEED CHART

1-2, 2-3 AND 3-4 SHIFT SPEEDS

MODEL		1-2 SHIFT SPEED IN % TPS ±3 MPH									2-3 SHIFT SPEED IN % TPS ±4 MPH									3-4 SHIFT SPEED IN % TPS ±5 MPH								
	TPS IN %	10	15	20	25	30	35	40	45	50	10	15	20	25	30	35	40	45	50	10	15	20	25	30	35	40	45	50

SHIFT SPEED INFORMATION NOT AVAILABLE AT TIME OF PUBLICATION

FINAL DRIVE / SPROCKETS RATIOS AND SHIFT SPEEDS

MODEL	RATIOS			1-2 MIN THROTTLE	2-3 MIN THROTTLE	3-4 MIN THROTTLE	3-2 DET DOWNSHIFT (Over 90 % TPS)	2-1 DET DOWNSHIFT (Over 90 % TPS)	1-2 W.O.T. (100 % TPS)	2-3 W.O.T. (100 % TPS)	3-4 W.O.T. (100 % TPS)	4-3 COAST DOWN	3-2 COAST DOWN	2-1 COAST DOWN
	FINAL DRIVE	SPROCKETS*	OVERALL											

SHIFT SPEED INFORMATION NOT AVAILABLE AT TIME OF PUBLICATION

NOTES:

1. ALL SPEEDS INDICATED ARE IN MILES PER HOUR. CONVERSION TO KM/h = MPH x 1.609.
2. SHIFT POINTS WILL VARY SLIGHTLY DUE TO ENGINE LOAD AND VEHICLE OPTIONS.
3. THE UPSHIFT SPEEDS FOR 1-2, 2-3 AND 3-4 ARE BASED ON THROTTLE POSITION SENSOR (TPS) DATA AS A REFERENCE – USE A TECH 1® OR OTHER SCAN TOOL THAT GIVES PERCENTAGE OF THROTTLE OPENING INSTEAD OF VOLTAGE TO MONITOR THIS DATA.
4. THE 1-2, 2-3 AND 3-4 SHIFT SPEED CHART INFORMATION IS BASED ON PERCENTAGE OF THROTTLE OPENING. THE CONVERSION FACTOR FOR THE OUPUT OF THE CADILLAC SELF-DIAGNOSTIC FEATURES FOR THE DRIVER INFORMATION CENTER (DIC) WOULD BE, PERCENT TPS X 0.819 TO GET THROTTLE ANGLE DATA. REFER TO SECTION 8D.
5. THE 3-2 AND 2-1 DETENT DOWNSHIFTS SPEEDS ARE THE MAXIMUM SPEEDS THAT A 3-2 OR 2-1 DETENT DOWNSHIFT (OVER 90 % TPS) WILL OCCUR. EUROPE AND JAPAN EXPORT VEHICLES WILL HAVE THE LOWER 2-1 DETENT VALVES.

* DESIGNATES THE NUMBER OF TEETH ON THE DRIVE/DRIVEN SPROCKETS, RESPECTIVELY.

RH0004-4T60-E

Figure 4 Shift Speed Chart

LINE PRESSURE CHECK PROCEDURE

Line pressure is controlled by pump output to the pressure regulator valve and is boosted in Reverse and **D1** by the reverse boost valve.

Also, line pressures should increase with throttle opening due to a decrease in engine vacuum supply to the vacuum modulator.

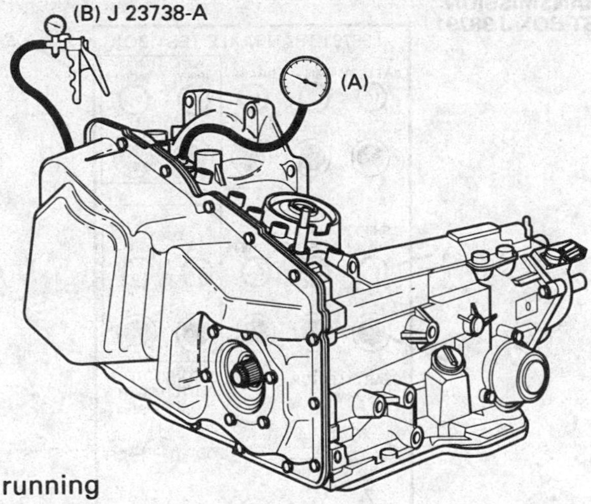
(B) J 23738-A
(A)

(A) ATTACH PRESSURE GAGE
(B) HAND OPERATED VACUUM PUMP

CHECK PRESSURES IN THE FOLLOWING MANNER:

Minimum Line Pressure Check

- Disconnect and plug vacuum supply at modulator.
- Apply 61 kPa (18 IN. Hg.) vacuum to modulator with pump (B).
- Set parking brake and apply vehicle brakes.
- Take pressure readings in all gear ranges with engine running at proper rpm.
- Compare pressures with information provided in the chart below.

Full Line Pressure Check

- Have 0 kPa (0 IN. Hg.) vacuum to modulator.
- Set parking brake and apply vehicle brakes.
- Take pressure readings in all gear ranges with engine running at proper rpm.
- Compare pressures with information provided in the chart below.

NOTICE: Total running time not to exceed 2 minutes.

CAUTION: Brakes must be applied at all times.

1994 TRANSAXLE LINE PRESSURE		RANGE	MODELS	kPa	PSI
	ZERO THROTTLE 1250 RPM 18 IN. HG. VACUUM	D4, D3, D2	AFW, KCW	512-596	74-86
			ATW, BLW, BNW, CBW, CWW, KLW, PAW, PCW, PFW, WFW, YDW	512-592	74-85
			KUW, WAW, YMW, YZW	422-475	61-69
		D1	AFW, ATW, BLW, BNW, CWW, KCW, KDW, PFW, YDW	921-1333	133-193
			CBW, KLW, PAW, PCW, WFW	1005-1289	146-187
			KUW, WAW, YMW, YZW	998-1276	145-185
		P, R, N	AFW, CWW, KCW, KDW, YDW	512-666	74-96
			CBW, KLW, PAW, PCW, WFW	542-696	78-101
			ATW, BLW, BNW, PFW	460-666	67-96
			KUW, WAW, YMW, YZW	423-536	61-77
	FULL THROTTLE 0 IN. HG. VACUUM	D4, D3, D2	AFW, ATW, BLW, BNW, CWW, KCW, KDW, PFW, YDW	1148-1400	166-203
			CBW, KLW, PAW, PCW, WFW	1153-1400	167-203
			KUW, WAW, YMW, YZW	1150-1390	166-201
		D1	AFW, ATW, BLW, BNW, CWW, KCW, KDW, PFW, YDW	921-1333	133-193
			CBW, KLW, PAW, PCW, WFW	1005-1289	145-187
			KUW, WAW, YMW, YZW	998-1276	144-185
		N, REV	AFW, ATW, BLW, BNW, CWW, KCW, KDW, PFW, YDW	1774-2164	257-314
			CBW, KLW, PAW, PCW, WFW	1540-1869	223-271
			KUW, WAW, YMW, YZW	1570-1898	227-275

IMPORTANT: ALTITUDE WILL AFFECT ENGINE VACUUM READINGS AS SHOWN IN THE FOLLOWING CHART:

ALTITUDE	ENGINE VACUUM
SEA LEVEL	48-76 kPa (14-22 IN. Hg.)
305 Meters (1000 Feet)	45-72 kPa (13-21 IN. Hg.)
610 Meters (2000 Feet)	42-69 kPa (12-20 IN. Hg.)
914 Meters (3000 Feet)	38-66 kPa (11-19 IN. Hg.)
1219 Meters (4000 Feet)	34-62 kPa (10-18 IN Hg.)
1524 Meters (5000 Feet)	31-58 kPa (9-17 IN. Hg.)

RH0005-4T60-E

Figure 5 Line Pressure Check Procedure Chart

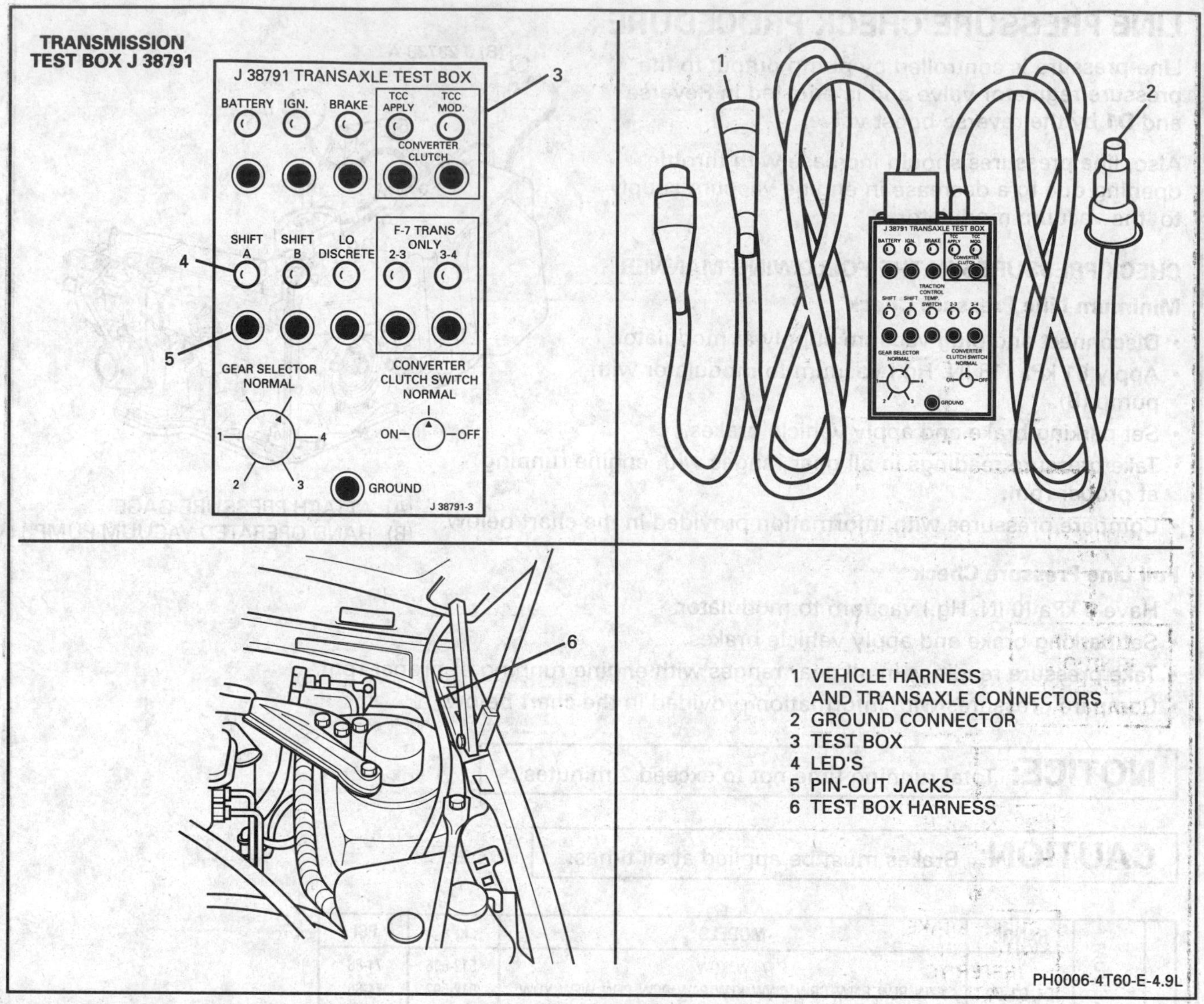
TRANSMISSION
TEST BOX J 38791
J 38791 TRANSAXLE TEST BOX
BATTERY
IGN.
BRAKE
TCC APPLY
TCC MOD.
CONVERTER CLUTCH
F-7 TRANS ONLY
SHIFT A
SHIFT B
LO DISCRETE
2-3
3-4
GEAR SELECTOR NORMAL
CONVERTER CLUTCH SWITCH NORMAL
ON
OFF
GROUND
J 38791-3
1 VEHICLE HARNESS AND TRANSAXLE CONNECTORS
2 GROUND CONNECTOR
3 TEST BOX
4 LED'S
5 PIN-OUT JACKS
6 TEST BOX HARNESS
PH0006-4T60-E-4.9L

Figure 6 Transmission Test Box

Using The Transmission Test Box

Figure 7

Important

- Before installing the Test Box, check the vehicle diagnostic system for PCM related codes. If any are present, refer to Section 6 for diagnosis and repair of these codes before diagnosing the transaxle.

1. Connect the test box.
   - A. Disconnect the vehicle transaxle wiring harness from the transaxle.
   - B. Connect the test box connectors into the vehicle harness and transaxle.
   - C. Route test box harness under the hood, through the driver's window. Use a tie strap if necessary to keep the test box harness away from the exhaust manifold or cooling fan (refer to Figure 6).
   - D. Insert the power/ground connector into the cigarette lighter receptacle in the passenger compartment. Observe that the battery LED comes ON.
   - E. Turn the ignition ON.
   - F. Set up the on-board diagnostics or TECH 1 (or other scan tool).

NOTICE: To avoid damage to the transaxle due to overstress, observe the following when using this tool:

- Do not start vehicle from a stop in 3rd or 4th gear setting.
- Do not shift to 1st gear setting above 40 km/h (25 mph).
- Do not brake torque vehicle with tool attached.
- Do not move converter clutch switch to the ON position when vehicle speed is less than 40 km/h (25 mph).
- Do not place vehicle shift selector in manual first or manual second.

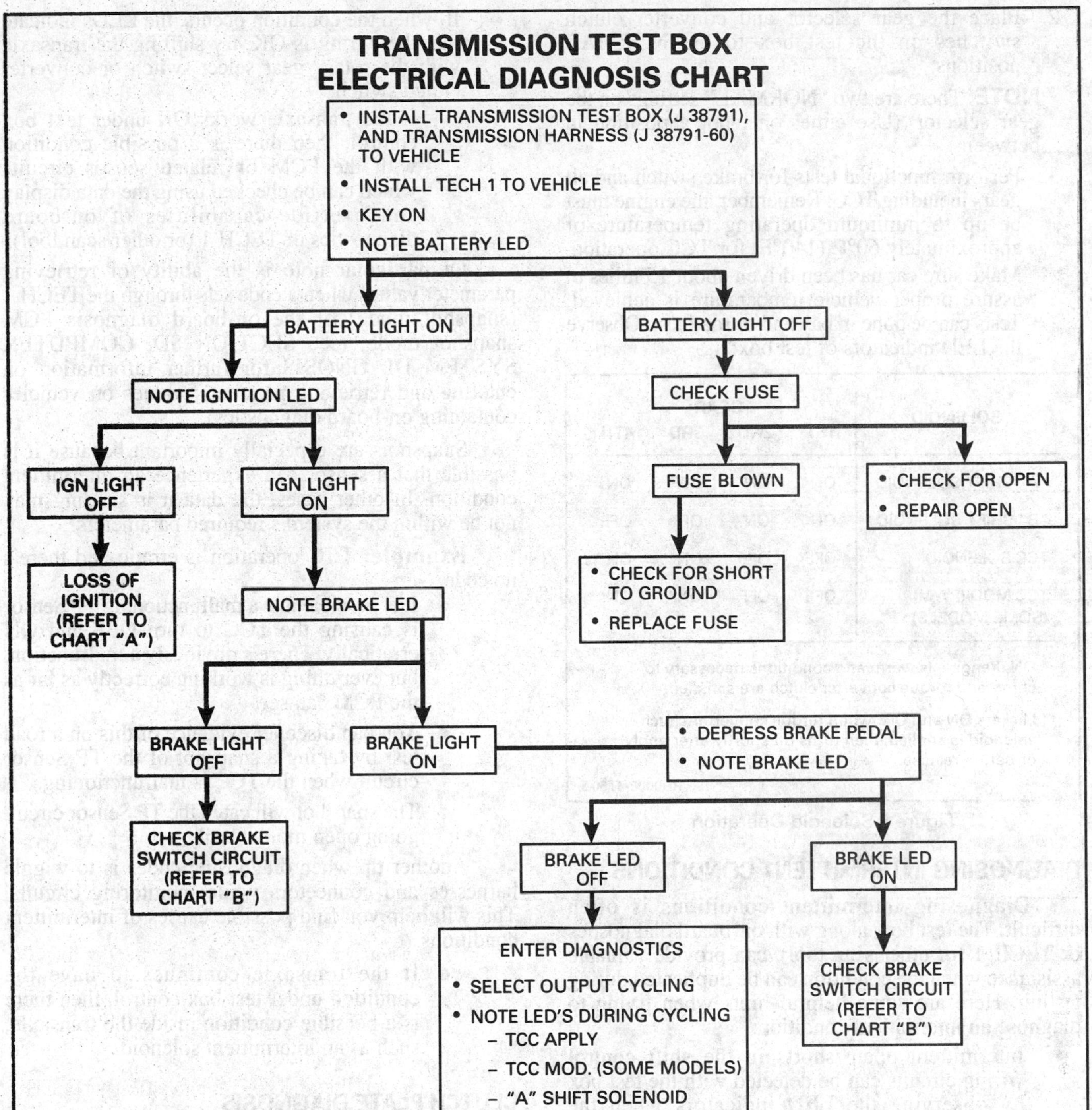
TRANSMISSION TEST BOX
ELECTRICAL DIAGNOSIS CHART
• INSTALL TRANSMISSION TEST BOX (J 38791), AND TRANSMISSION HARNESS (J 38791-60) TO VEHICLE
• INSTALL TECH 1 TO VEHICLE
• KEY ON
• NOTE BATTERY LED
BATTERY LIGHT ON
BATTERY LIGHT OFF
NOTE IGNITION LED
CHECK FUSE
IGN LIGHT OFF
IGN LIGHT ON
FUSE BLOWN
• CHECK FOR OPEN
• REPAIR OPEN
LOSS OF IGNITION (REFER TO CHART "A")
NOTE BRAKE LED
• CHECK FOR SHORT TO GROUND
• REPLACE FUSE
BRAKE LIGHT OFF
BRAKE LIGHT ON
• DEPRESS BRAKE PEDAL
• NOTE BRAKE LED
CHECK BRAKE SWITCH CIRCUIT (REFER TO CHART "B")
BRAKE LED OFF
BRAKE LED ON
ENTER DIAGNOSTICS
• SELECT OUTPUT CYCLING
• NOTE LED'S DURING CYCLING
– TCC APPLY
– TCC MOD. (SOME MODELS)
– "A" SHIFT SOLENOID
– "B" SHIFT SOLENOID
CHECK BRAKE SWITCH CIRCUIT (REFER TO CHART "B")
REFER TO HYDRAULIC, ELECTRICAL AND MECHANICAL DIAGNOSIS CHART (THIS SECTION)
ALL LED'S CYCLE
LED NOT CYCLING
REFER TO CHART
TCC APPLY C
TCC MOD. C
"A" SHIFT SOLENOID D
"B" SHIFT SOLENOID E
RH0007-4T60-E

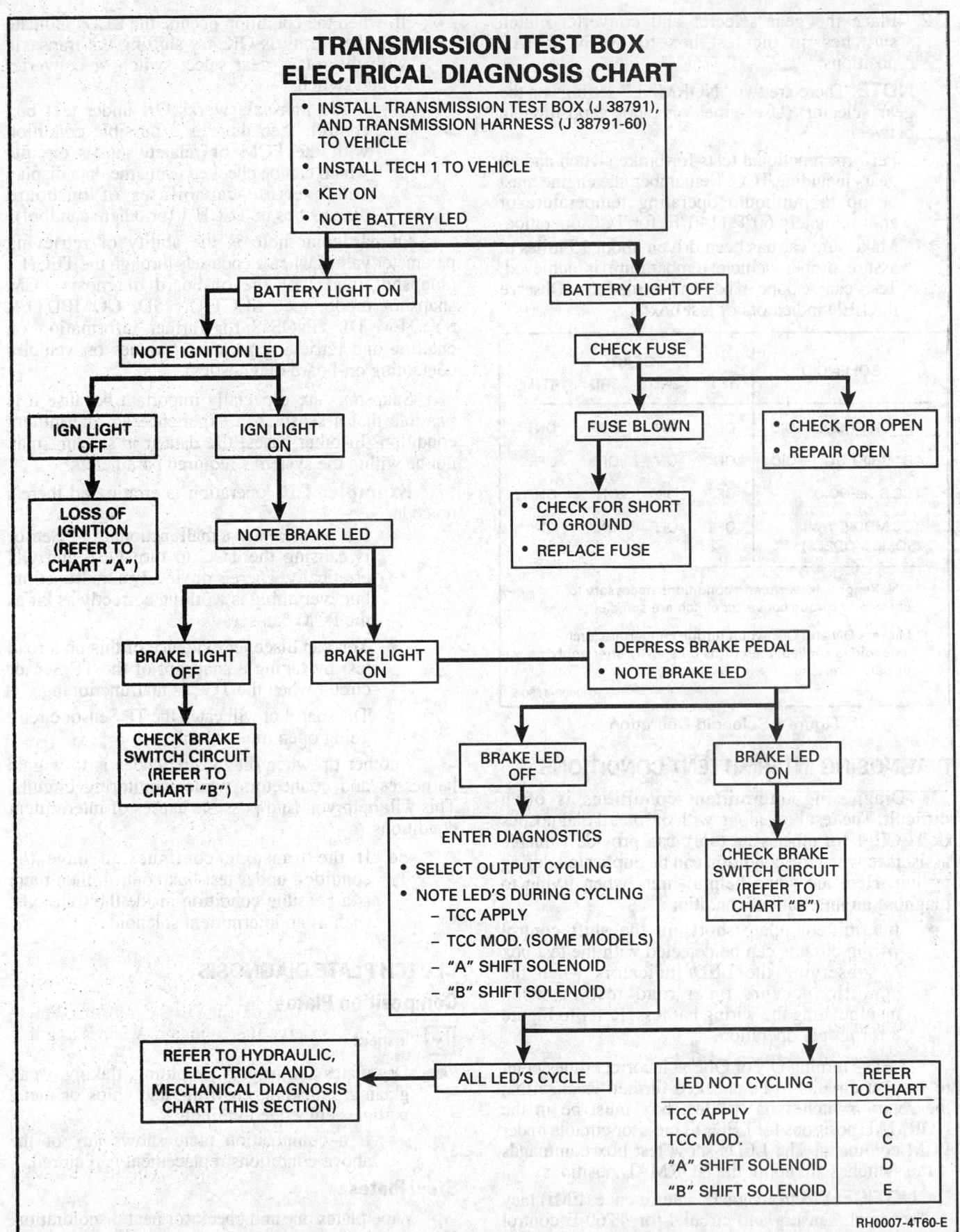

Figure 7 Transmission Test Box Electrical Diagnosis Chart

2. Place the gear selector and converter clutch switches on the test box to the NORMAL positions.

   NOTE: There are two "NORMAL" settings on the gear selector. (Use either one, not a position in between.)

3. Perform functional tests for brake switch and all gears including TCC. Remember, the engine must be up to minimum operating temperature of approximately 60°C (140°F) for TCC operation. Make sure car has been driven about 15 miles to assure proper vehicle temperature is achieved. Tests can be done in bay and/or road test. Observe the LED indicators of test box:

SOLENOID	GEAR			
	1ST	2ND	3RD	4TH
"A" SHIFT SOLENOID	ON	OFF	OFF	ON
"B" SHIFT SOLENOID	ON	ON	OFF	OFF
TCC SOLENOID	OFF	OFF	ON*	ON*
TCC MOD (PWM) (SOME MODELS)	OFF	OFF	ON**	ON**

* ON if engine is warm and conditions necessary to command torque converter clutch are satisfied.

** Flickers ON and OFF when torque converter clutch solenoid is applied, then turns off shortly after apply or before release.

RH0008-4T60-E

Figure 8 Solenoid Operation

DIAGNOSING INTERMITTENT CONDITIONS

Diagnosing intermittent conditions is often difficult. The test box, along with on-board diagnostics or TECH 1 (or other scan tool), can provide valuable assistance when the condition can be duplicated during testing. Here are some helpful hints when trying to diagnose an intermittent condition:

- Intermittent opens/shorts in the shift control wiring circuits can be detected with the test box by observing the LED indicators when the condition occurs on a road test or when manipulating the wiring harness. Refer to Figure 8 for proper operation.

LED's turning ON or OFF at incorrect times point to suspect circuits to be checked further. Realize that the rotary switches on the test box must be in the NORMAL positions for LEDs to monitor circuits under PCM command. The LEDs show test box commands if the switches are not in the NORMAL positions.

NOTICE: Electromagnetic interference (EMI) may act upon sensors and circuits for 4T60-E control and could affect shifting.

- If, when the condition occurs, the LEDs indicate that the wiring is OK, try shifting the transaxle with the rotary gear select switch or converter clutch switch.
  - If the transaxle works OK under text box control, then there is a possible condition with the PCM or related sensor circuits which can be checked using the data display and override capabilities of on-board diagnostics or TECH 1 (or other scan tool).

Of particular note is the ability of retrieving parameter values when a code sets through the TECH 1 (snapshot mode) or the on-board diagnosis PCM snapshot mode, (see SECTION 8D, COMPUTER SYSTEM DIAGNOSIS for further information on entering and retrieving parameter values on vehicles containing on-board diagnostics).

Snapshots are especially important because it is possible that a sensor can experience an intermittent condition. In other cases, the data it is sending may not be within the system's required parameters.

Example: TCC operation is erratic and there's no code.

- It is possible that a malfunctioning TP Sensor is causing the TCC to turn OFF and ON erratically. There's obviously a malfunction, but everything is working correctly as far as the PCM can see.
- You can discover evidence of this on a road test by taking a snapshot of the TP Sensor circuit when the TCC is malfunctioning.
- The snapshot will catch the TP Sensor circuit going open momentarily.

Another tip when diagnosing codes is to wiggle harnesses and connectors while monitoring circuits. This will help you find possible causes of intermittent conditions.

- If the transaxle continues to have the condition under test box control, then there is a possible condition inside the transaxle, such as an intermittent solenoid.

CLUTCH PLATE DIAGNOSIS

Composition Plates

Inspect

- Dry plates and inspect for pitting, flaking, wear, glazing, cracking, charring, and chips or metal particles embedded in lining.
  - If a composition plate shows any of the above conditions replacement is required.

Steel Plates

Wipe plates dry and check for heat discoloration. If the surfaces are smooth, even if color smear is indicated, the plate can be reused. If severe heat spot discoloration or surface scuffing is indicated, the plate must be replaced.

Important

- If there is evidence of extreme heat or burning in the area of the clutch, the springs should be replaced.

Causes of Burned Clutch Plates

Burned clutch plates can be caused by:

- Incorrect usage of clutch plates.
- Engine coolant in the transaxle fluid.
- Clutch piston cracked, seals damaged or missing.
- Low line pressure.
- Valve body face not flat, or porosity between channels, improperly installed valve bushing clips, or misplaced checks balls.
- Worn or damaged Teflon (rotating) seal rings.

ENGINE COOLANT IN TRANSAXLE

NOTICE: Antifreeze will deteriorate the "Viton" O-ring seals and the glue used to bond the clutch material to the pressure plate. Both conditions may cause transaxle damage.

If the Transaxle Oil Cooler Has Developed a Leak Allowing Engine Coolant to Enter the Transaxle:

- Disassemble transaxle and replace all rubber type seals. (The coolant will attack the seal material causing leakage.)
- Replace composition-faced clutch plate assemblies. (The facing material may become separated from the steel center portion.)
- Replace all nylon parts (washers).
- Replace the torque converter.
- Thoroughly clean and rebuild transaxle, using new gaskets and oil filter.
- Flush the cooler lines after the transaxle cooler has been properly repaired or replaced.

COOLER FLUSHING AND FLOWTEST

NOTICE: Cooler flushing **must** be performed whenever a transaxle is removed for service. It is essential to flush the cooler for SRTA installation, major overhaul, in any case of pump or torque converter replacement, or when fluid contamination is suspected. Use J 35944 to flush the cooler.

After filling the transaxle with fluid, start the engine and run for 30 seconds. This will remove any residual moisture from the oil cooler. A minimum of 2 quarts of fluid should flow during a 30 second period. To check the fluid flow, disconnect the return line at the transaxle and observe the flow with the engine running. If fluid flow is insufficient, check the fluid flow by disconnecting the feed line at the cooler and observe the flow with the engine running.

- Insufficient Flow from Cooler Return Line at Transaxle: check flow rate from feed line to cooler. Blockage exists in transaxle or cooler.
- Insufficient Flow from Transaxle Feed Line to Cooler: transaxle is cause of fluid flow problem.
- Sufficient flow from transaxle feed line to cooler but not at cooler return line to transaxle: inspect cooler pipes, fittings and repeat cooler flushing procedure. If the flow is still insufficient, replace the cooler.

TORQUE CONVERTER CLUTCH (TCC) DIAGNOSIS

The Torque Converter Clutch is applied by fluid pressure which is controlled by a solenoid located inside the Transaxle assembly. The solenoid is energized by completing an electrical circuit through a combination of switches and sensors.

Important

- Some vehicles contain a torque converter filled with a silicone fluid. This fluid is sealed between the cover and body of the clutch assembly. This is referred to as a VCC (Viscous Converter Clutch) type converter.

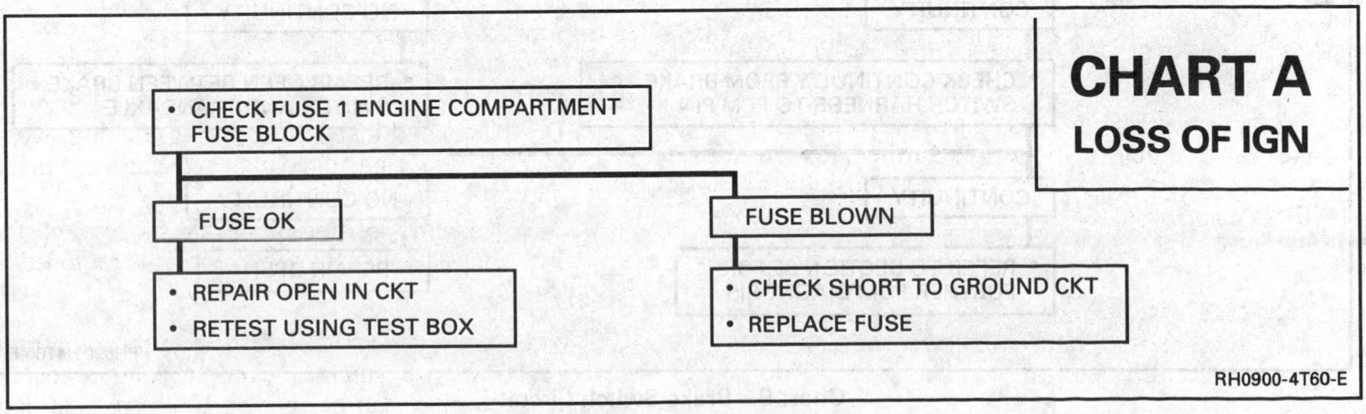
CHART A
LOSS OF IGN
• CHECK FUSE 1 ENGINE COMPARTMENT FUSE BLOCK
FUSE OK
FUSE BLOWN
• REPAIR OPEN IN CKT
• RETEST USING TEST BOX
• CHECK SHORT TO GROUND CKT
• REPLACE FUSE
RH0900-4T60-E

Chart A – Loss of Ignition

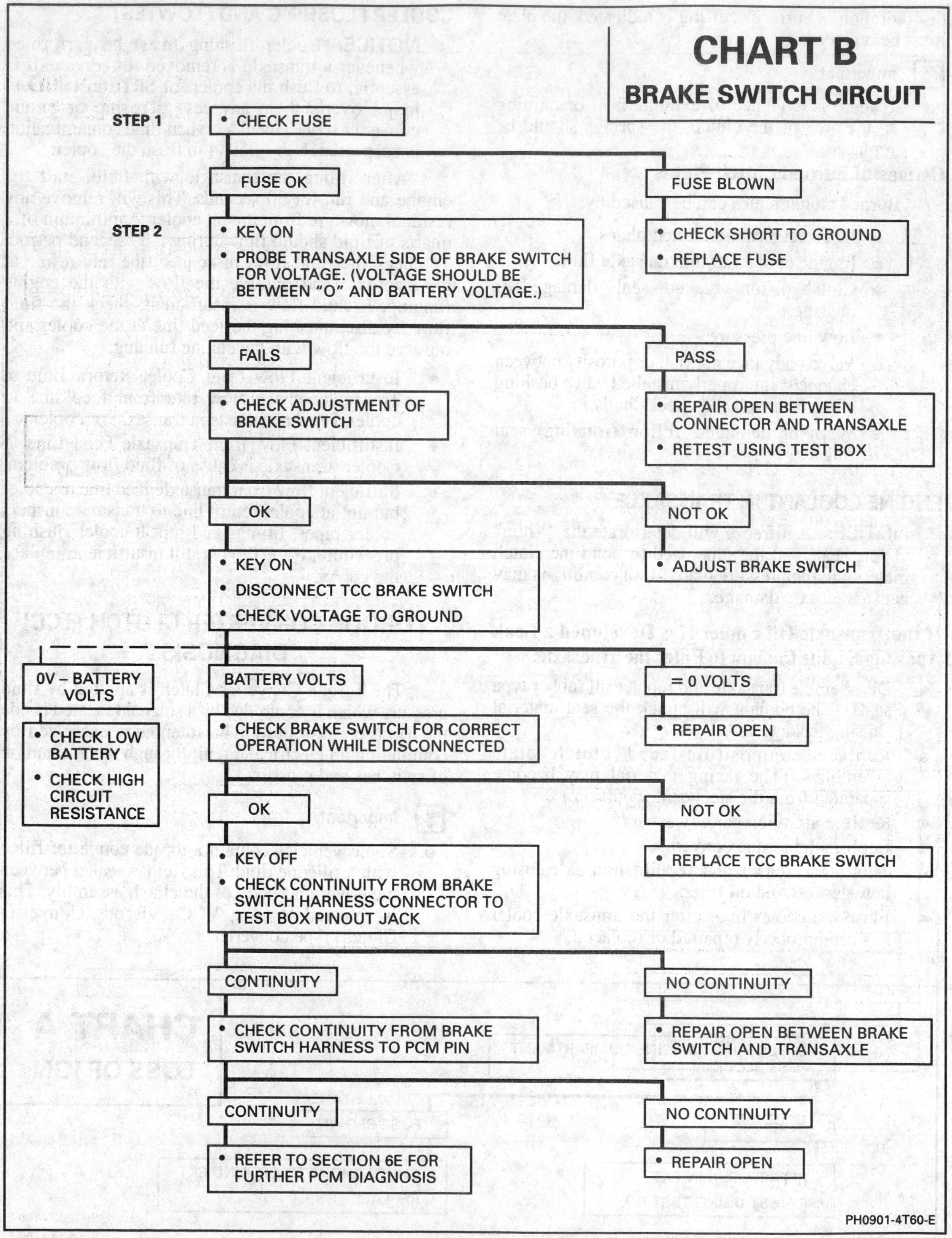
CHART B
BRAKE SWITCH CIRCUIT
STEP 1
• CHECK FUSE
FUSE OK
FUSE BLOWN
• CHECK SHORT TO GROUND
• REPLACE FUSE
STEP 2
• KEY ON
• PROBE TRANSAXLE SIDE OF BRAKE SWITCH FOR VOLTAGE. (VOLTAGE SHOULD BE BETWEEN "O" AND BATTERY VOLTAGE.)
FAILS
PASS
• CHECK ADJUSTMENT OF BRAKE SWITCH
• REPAIR OPEN BETWEEN CONNECTOR AND TRANSAXLE
• RETEST USING TEST BOX
OK
NOT OK
• ADJUST BRAKE SWITCH
• KEY ON
• DISCONNECT TCC BRAKE SWITCH
• CHECK VOLTAGE TO GROUND
0V – BATTERY VOLTS
BATTERY VOLTS
= 0 VOLTS
• CHECK LOW BATTERY
• CHECK HIGH CIRCUIT RESISTANCE
• CHECK BRAKE SWITCH FOR CORRECT OPERATION WHILE DISCONNECTED
• REPAIR OPEN
OK
NOT OK
• REPLACE TCC BRAKE SWITCH
• KEY OFF
• CHECK CONTINUITY FROM BRAKE SWITCH HARNESS CONNECTOR TO TEST BOX PINOUT JACK
CONTINUITY
NO CONTINUITY
• CHECK CONTINUITY FROM BRAKE SWITCH HARNESS TO PCM PIN
• REPAIR OPEN BETWEEN BRAKE SWITCH AND TRANSAXLE
CONTINUITY
NO CONTINUITY
• REFER TO SECTION 6E FOR FURTHER PCM DIAGNOSIS
• REPAIR OPEN
PH0901-4T60-E

Chart B – Brake Switch Circuit

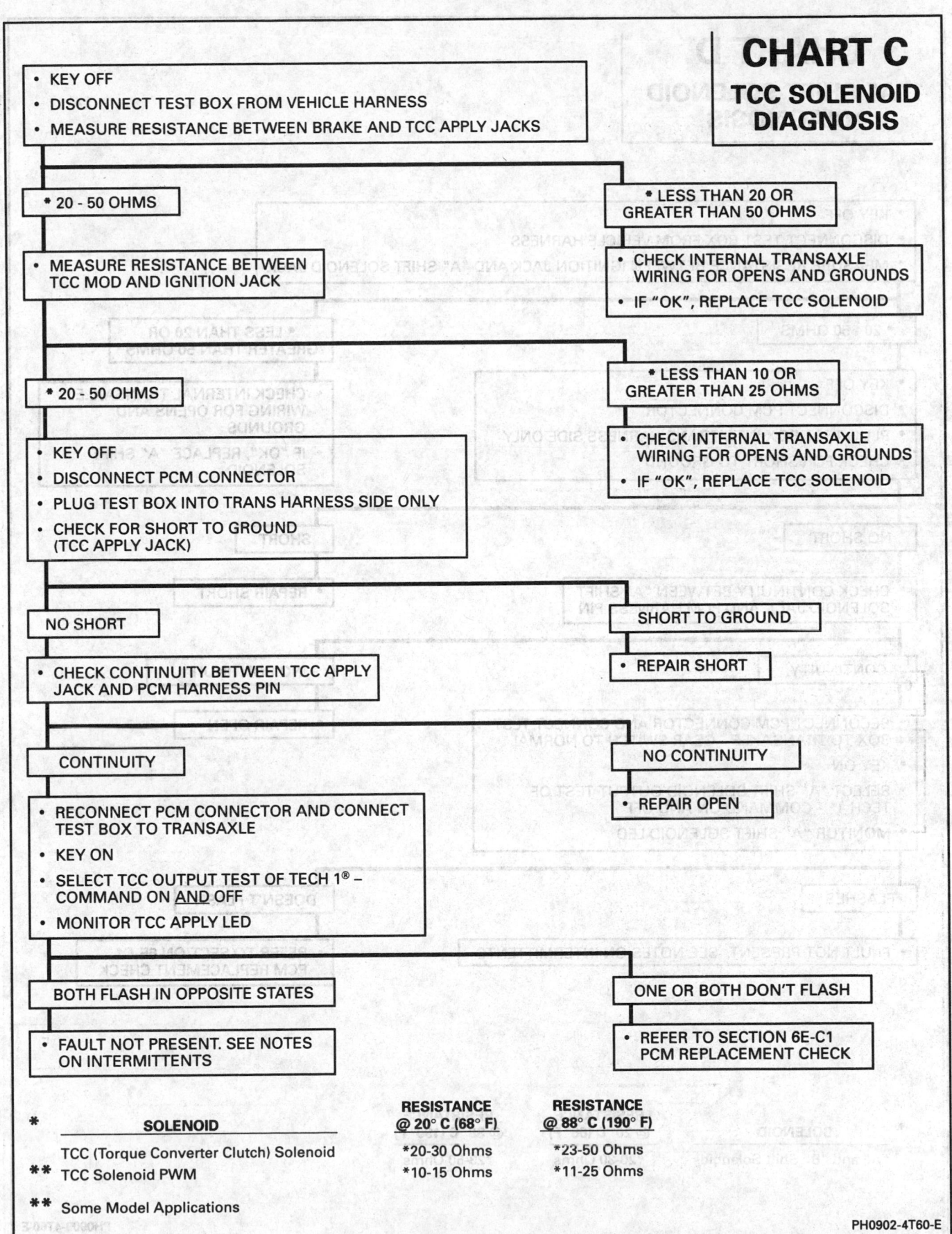

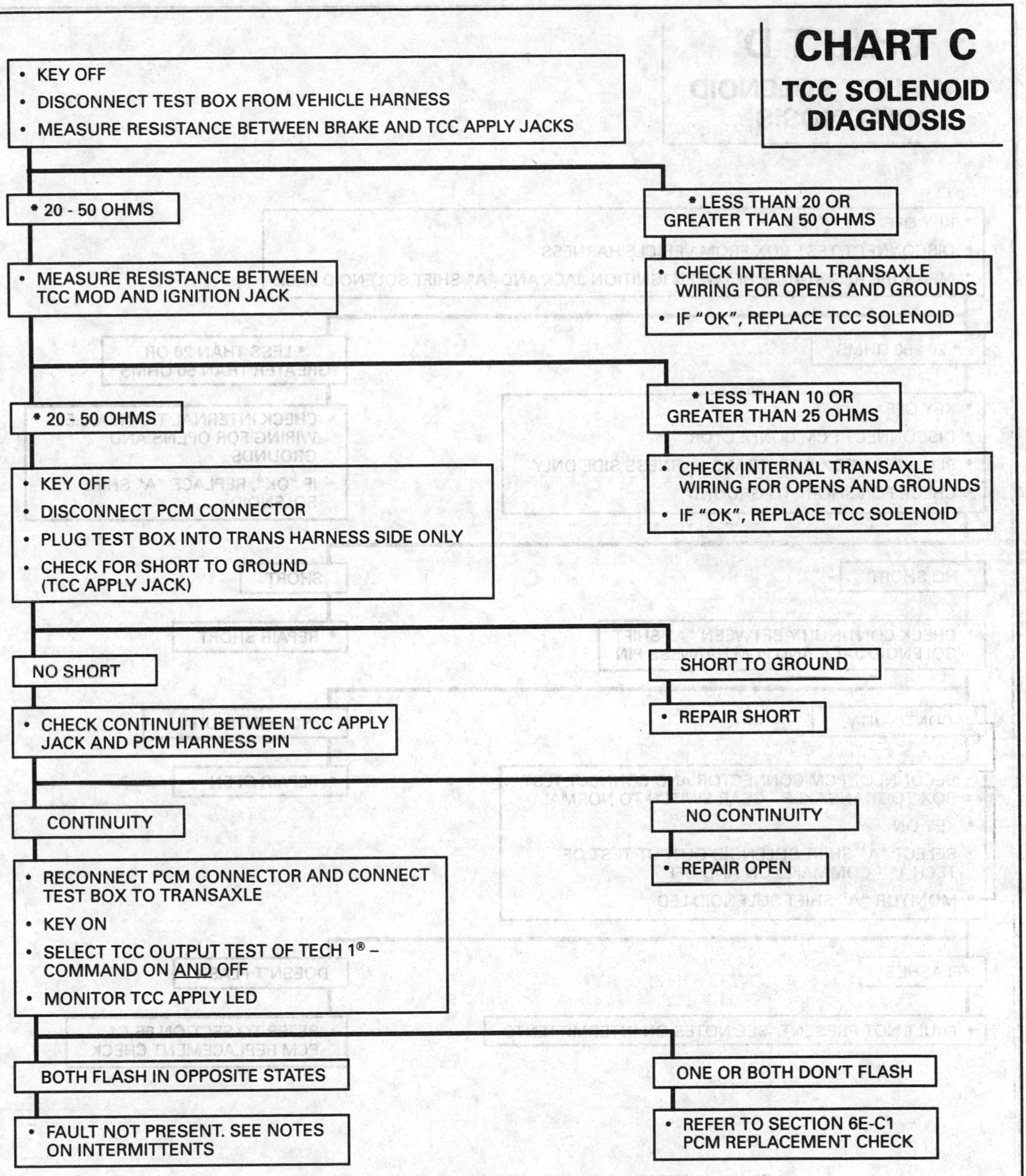
CHART C
TCC SOLENOID DIAGNOSIS
• KEY OFF
• DISCONNECT TEST BOX FROM VEHICLE HARNESS
• MEASURE RESISTANCE BETWEEN BRAKE AND TCC APPLY JACKS
* 20 - 50 OHMS
* LESS THAN 20 OR GREATER THAN 50 OHMS
• MEASURE RESISTANCE BETWEEN TCC MOD AND IGNITION JACK
• CHECK INTERNAL TRANSAXLE WIRING FOR OPENS AND GROUNDS
• IF "OK", REPLACE TCC SOLENOID
* LESS THAN 10 OR GREATER THAN 25 OHMS
* 20 - 50 OHMS
• CHECK INTERNAL TRANSAXLE WIRING FOR OPENS AND GROUNDS
• IF "OK", REPLACE TCC SOLENOID
• KEY OFF
• DISCONNECT PCM CONNECTOR
• PLUG TEST BOX INTO TRANS HARNESS SIDE ONLY
• CHECK FOR SHORT TO GROUND (TCC APPLY JACK)
NO SHORT
SHORT TO GROUND
• REPAIR SHORT
• CHECK CONTINUITY BETWEEN TCC APPLY JACK AND PCM HARNESS PIN
CONTINUITY
NO CONTINUITY
• REPAIR OPEN
• RECONNECT PCM CONNECTOR AND CONNECT TEST BOX TO TRANSAXLE
• KEY ON
• SELECT TCC OUTPUT TEST OF TECH 1® – COMMAND ON AND OFF
• MONITOR TCC APPLY LED
BOTH FLASH IN OPPOSITE STATES
ONE OR BOTH DON'T FLASH
• FAULT NOT PRESENT. SEE NOTES ON INTERMITTENTS
• REFER TO SECTION 6E-C1 PCM REPLACEMENT CHECK

* SOLENOID	RESISTANCE @ 20° C (68° F)	RESISTANCE @ 88° C (190° F)
TCC (Torque Converter Clutch) Solenoid	*20-30 Ohms	*23-50 Ohms
** TCC Solenoid PWM	*10-15 Ohms	*11-25 Ohms

** Some Model Applications

PH0902-4T60-E

Chart C – TCC Diagnosis

CHART D
"A" SHIFT SOLENOID DIAGNOSIS

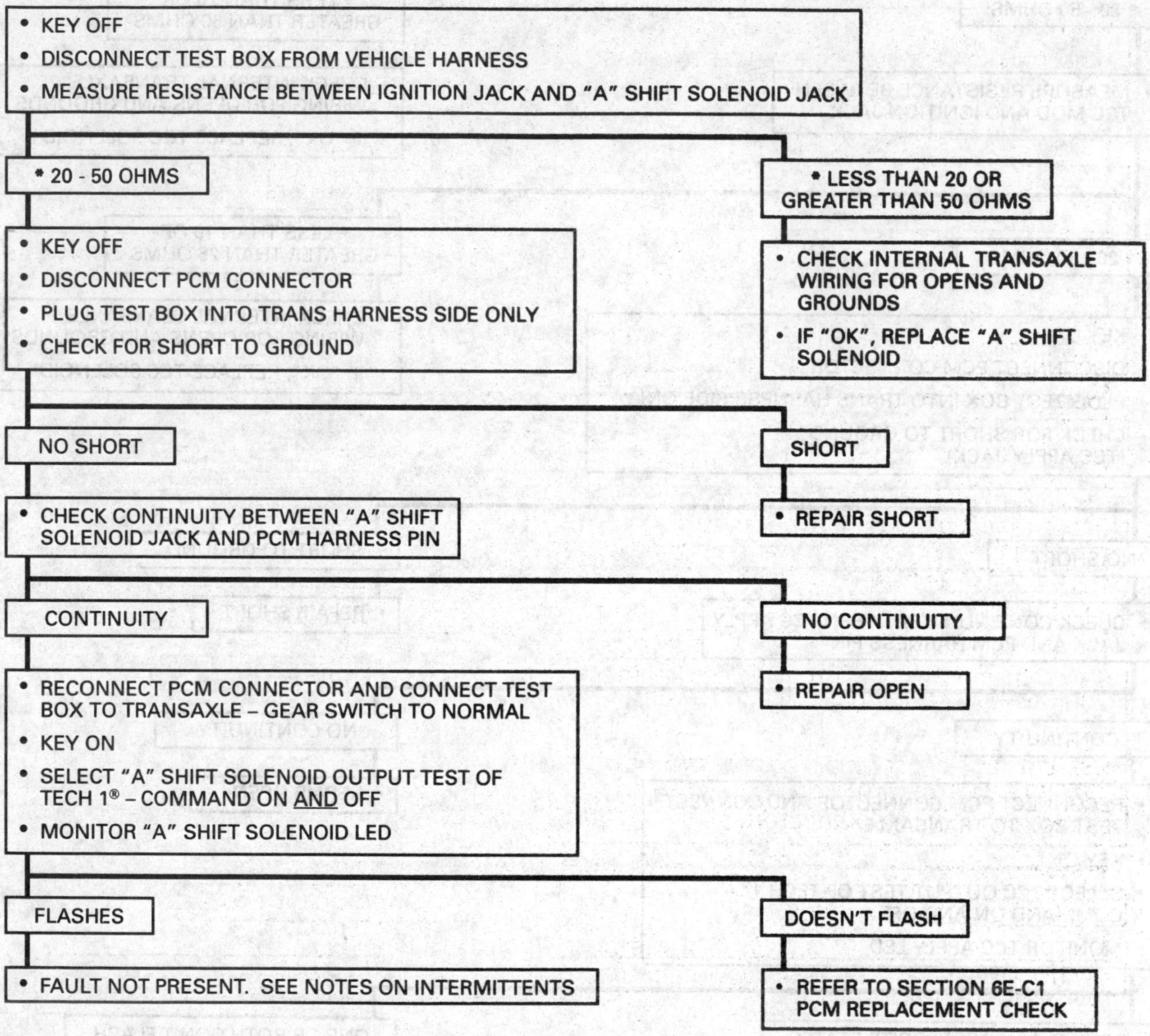
• KEY OFF
• DISCONNECT TEST BOX FROM VEHICLE HARNESS
• MEASURE RESISTANCE BETWEEN IGNITION JACK AND "A" SHIFT SOLENOID JACK
* 20 - 50 OHMS
* LESS THAN 20 OR GREATER THAN 50 OHMS
• KEY OFF
• DISCONNECT PCM CONNECTOR
• PLUG TEST BOX INTO TRANS HARNESS SIDE ONLY
• CHECK FOR SHORT TO GROUND
• CHECK INTERNAL TRANSAXLE WIRING FOR OPENS AND GROUNDS
• IF "OK", REPLACE "A" SHIFT SOLENOID
NO SHORT
SHORT
• CHECK CONTINUITY BETWEEN "A" SHIFT SOLENOID JACK AND PCM HARNESS PIN
• REPAIR SHORT
CONTINUITY
NO CONTINUITY
• RECONNECT PCM CONNECTOR AND CONNECT TEST BOX TO TRANSAXLE – GEAR SWITCH TO NORMAL
• KEY ON
• SELECT "A" SHIFT SOLENOID OUTPUT TEST OF TECH 1® – COMMAND ON AND OFF
• MONITOR "A" SHIFT SOLENOID LED
• REPAIR OPEN
FLASHES
DOESN'T FLASH
• FAULT NOT PRESENT. SEE NOTES ON INTERMITTENTS
• REFER TO SECTION 6E-C1 PCM REPLACEMENT CHECK

* SOLENOID	RESISTANCE @ 20° C (68° F)	RESISTANCE @ 88° C (190° F)
"A" and "B" Shift Solenoids	*20-30 Ohms	*23-50 Ohms

PH0903-4T60-E

Chart D – Shift A Diagnosis

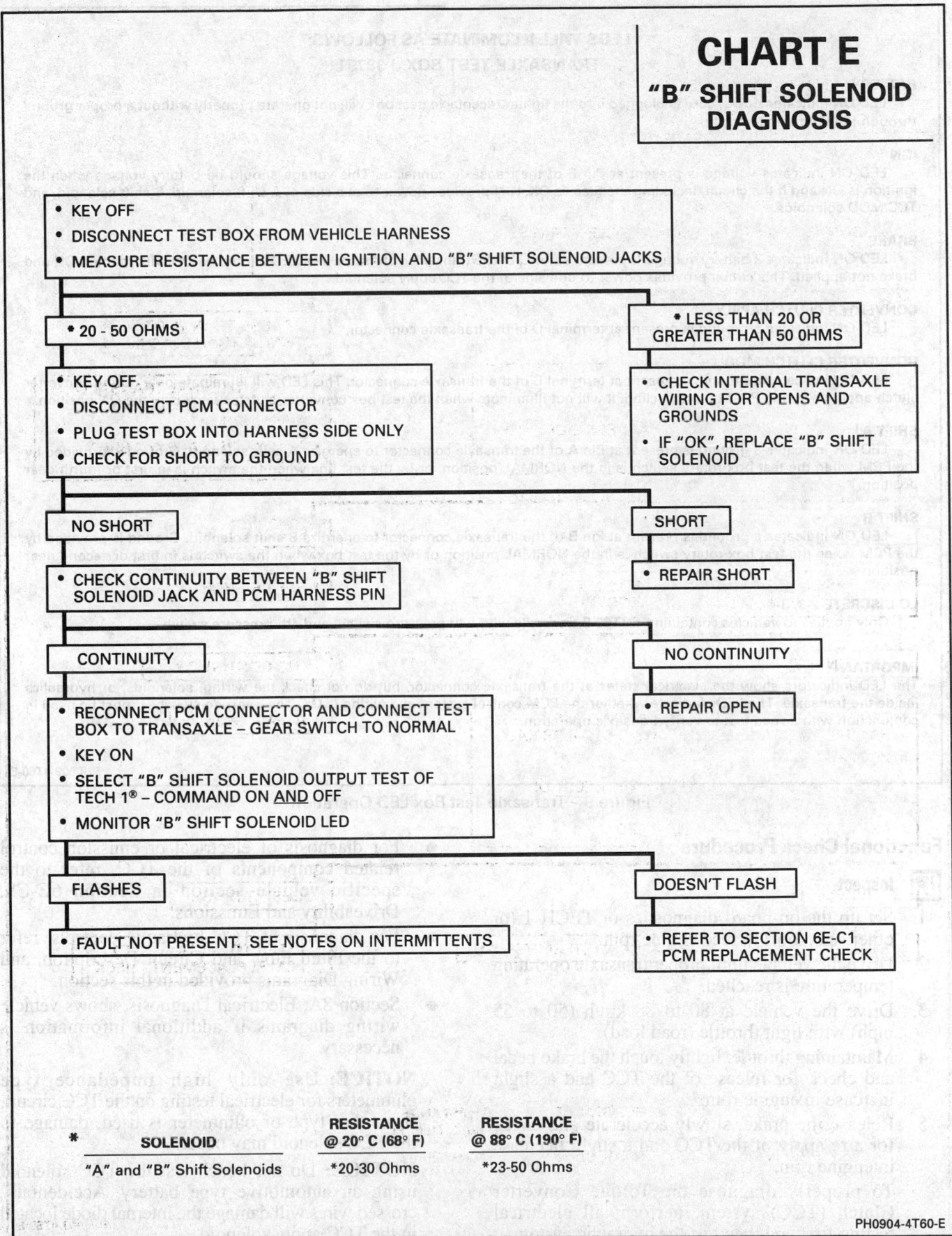

CHART E
"B" SHIFT SOLENOID DIAGNOSIS

- KEY OFF
- DISCONNECT TEST BOX FROM VEHICLE HARNESS
- MEASURE RESISTANCE BETWEEN IGNITION AND "B" SHIFT SOLENOID JACKS

*** 20 - 50 OHMS**

- KEY OFF
- DISCONNECT PCM CONNECTOR
- PLUG TEST BOX INTO HARNESS SIDE ONLY
- CHECK FOR SHORT TO GROUND

NO SHORT

- CHECK CONTINUITY BETWEEN "B" SHIFT SOLENOID JACK AND PCM HARNESS PIN

CONTINUITY

- RECONNECT PCM CONNECTOR AND CONNECT TEST BOX TO TRANSAXLE – GEAR SWITCH TO NORMAL
- KEY ON
- SELECT "B" SHIFT SOLENOID OUTPUT TEST OF TECH 1® – COMMAND ON AND OFF
- MONITOR "B" SHIFT SOLENOID LED

FLASHES

- FAULT NOT PRESENT. SEE NOTES ON INTERMITTENTS

DOESN'T FLASH

- REFER TO SECTION 6E-C1 PCM REPLACEMENT CHECK

NO CONTINUITY

- REPAIR OPEN

SHORT

- REPAIR SHORT

*** LESS THAN 20 OR GREATER THAN 50 OHMS**

- CHECK INTERNAL TRANSAXLE WIRING FOR OPENS AND GROUNDS
- IF "OK", REPLACE "B" SHIFT SOLENOID

* SOLENOID	RESISTANCE @ 20° C (68° F)	RESISTANCE @ 88° C (190° F)
"A" and "B" Shift Solenoids	*20-30 Ohms	*23-50 Ohms

PH0904-4T60-E

Chart E – Shift B Diagnosis

LEDS WILL ILLUMINATE AS FOLLOWS:
TRANSAXLE TEST BOX J 38791

BATTERY
LED ON indicates power cord is plugged into the lighter receptacle (test box will not operate properly without a proper ground through the lighter receptacle).

IGN
LED ON indicates voltage is present at Pin E of the transaxle connector. This voltage should be battery voltage when the ignition is ON and if the circuit, including the fuse, is OK. IGN provides power to one side of A shift solenoid, B shift solenoid, and TCC MOD solenoids.

BRAKE
LED ON indicates a battery voltage is present at Pin E of the transaxle connector. The LED should be ON with ignition ON and brake not applied. This circuit provides power to one side of the TCC apply solenoid.

CONVERTER CLUTCH APPLY
LED ON indicates a ground is present at terminal D of the transaxle connector.

CONVERTER CLUTCH MOD
LED ON indicates a ground is present at terminal C of the transaxle connector. This LED will illuminate only during converter clutch apply or during PCM output cycling. It will not illuminate when the test box converter clutch switch is in the ON position.

SHIFT A
LED ON indicates a ground is present at Pin A of the transaxle connector to energize A shift solenoid. Ground is provided by the PCM when the test box rotary switch is in the NORMAL position, or by the test box when the switch is in first or fourth gear position.

SHIFT B
LED ON indicates a ground is present at Pin B of the transaxle connector to energize B shift solenoid. Ground is provided by the PCM when the test box rotary switch is in the NORMAL position or by the test box when the switch is in first or second gear position.

LO DISCRETE 2-3, 3-4
Only applies to vehicles containing a 4T60-E transaxle with a lo pressure switch, and 4th pressure switch.

IMPORTANT!
The LED indicators show the electrical states at the transaxle connector, but do not check the wiring, solenoids, or hydraulics inside the transaxle. The LEDs indicate whether the PCM control system and wiring is OK. The override switches must be used in conjunction with a road test to verify transaxle operation.

RH0009-4T60-E

Figure 9 – Transaxle Test Box LED Operation

Functional Check Procedure

Inspect

1. Set up the on-board diagnostics or TECH 1 (or other scan tool) to read engine rpm.
2. Drive the vehicle until proper transaxle operating temperature is reached.
3. Drive the vehicle at 80 to 88 km/h (50 to 55 mph) with light throttle (road load).
4. Maintaining throttle, lightly touch the brake pedal and check for release of the TCC and a slight increase in engine rpm.
5. Release the brake, slowly accelerate and check for a re-apply of the TCC and a slight decrease in engine rpm.

   To properly diagnose the Torque Converter Clutch (TCC) system, perform all electrical testing first and then test the hydraulic system.

- For diagnosis of electrical or emission control related components of the TCC, refer to the specific vehicle section in Section 6E-C8, Driveability and Emissions.
- For diagnosis of TCC hydraulic controls, refer to the Fluid Flow and Circuit Description, and Wiring Diagrams provided in this section.
- Section 8A, Electrical Diagnosis, shows vehicle wiring diagrams if additional information is necessary.

NOTICE: Use only high impedance type ohmmeters for electrical testing on the TCC circuit. If another type of ohmmeter is used, damage to the TCC solenoid may occur.

NOTICE: Do not bench test the TCC solenoid using an automotive type battery. Accidentally crossed wires will damage the internal diode located in the TCC apply solenoid.

TORQUE CONVERTER EVALUATION

The torque converter **should** be replaced under any of the following conditions:

- External leaks in the hub weld area
- Converter hub is scored or damaged.
- Converter pilot is broken, damaged or fits poorly into crankshaft.
- Steel particles are found after flushing the cooler and cooler lines.
- Pump is damaged or steel particles are found in the converter.
- Vehicle has TCC shudder and/or no TCC apply. Replace only after all hydraulic and electrical diagnoses has been made. (Converter clutch material may be glazed.)
- Converter has an imbalance which cannot be corrected.
- Converter is contaminated with engine coolant containing antifreeze.
- Internal failure of stator roller clutch.
- Excess end play.
- Heavy clutch debris due to overheating (blue converter).
- Steel particles or clutch lining material found in fluid filter or on magnet when no internal parts in unit are worn or damaged – indicates that lining material came from converter.

The Torque Converter Should Not Be Replaced If:

- The oil has an odor, is discolored, and there is no evidence of metal or clutch facing particles.
- The threads in one or more of the converter bolt holes are damaged.
  - Correct with thread insert. (Refer to Section 6A).
- Transaxle failure did not display evidence of damaged or worn internal parts, steel particles or clutch plate lining material in unit and inside the fluid filter.
- Vehicle has been exposed to high mileage (only). The exception may be where the torque converter clutch dampener plate lining has seen excess wear by vehicles operated in heavy and/or constant traffic, such as taxi, delivery or police use.

Torque Converter Noise Evaluation

Torque converter whine is usually noticed when the vehicle is stopped and the transaxle is in "Drive" or "Reverse." The noise will increase when engine rpm is increased. The noise will stop when the vehicle is moving or when the torque converter clutch is applied because both halves of the converter are turning at the same speed.

Perform a stall test to make sure the noise is actually coming from the converter:

1. Place foot on brake.
2. Put gear selector in "Overdrive" (D4).
3. Depress accelerator to approximately 1200 rpm for no more than six seconds.

NOTICE: If the stall test is performed for more than six seconds, damage to the transaxle may occur.

A torque converter noise will increase under this load.

Important

- This noise should not be confused with pump whine noise which is usually noticeable in "Park", "Neutral" and all other gear ranges. Pump whine will vary with pressure ranges.

Torque Converter Stator

The torque converter stator roller clutch can malfunction in two different ways. It can either remain locked up at all times or freewheel in both directions.

If the stator is freewheeling at all times, the vehicle tends to have poor acceleration from standstill. The car may act normal at speeds above 50 to 55 km/h (30 to 35 mph). If poor acceleration is noted, it should first be determined that the exhaust system is not blocked, the engine timing is correct, and the transaxle is in "First" gear when starting out.

If the engine accelerates freely to high rpm in "Neutral" (N), it can be assumed that the engine and exhaust system are normal. Checking for poor performance in "Overdrive" (D4) and "Reverse" (R) will help determine if the stator is freewheeling at all times.

If the stator is locked up at all times, performance from a standstill appears normal. Engine rpm and acceleration is restricted or limited, however, at high speeds. The engine may overheat with this condition. Visual examination of the converter may reveal a blue color from overheating.

If the torque converter has been removed from the vehicle, the stator roller clutch can be checked by inserting a finger into the splined inner race of the roller clutch and trying to turn the race in both directions. The inner race should turn freely clockwise, but not turn counterclockwise.

TORQUE CONVERTER CLUTCH SHUDDER

The key to diagnosing torque converter clutch shudder is to note when it happens and under what conditions.

Torque converter clutch shudder should only occur during the APPLY and/or RELEASE of the converter clutch – NEVER after the torque converter clutch plate is fully applied.

WHILE TCC IS APPLYING OR RELEASING:

If the shudder occurs while the TCC is applying, the problem is within the transaxle or torque converter. Something is not allowing the clutch to become fully engaged, not allowing clutch to release, or is trying to release and apply the clutch at the same time. This could be caused by leaking turbine shaft seals, a restricted release orifice, a distorted clutch, damaged converter housing surface due to long converter bolts, or defective friction material.

If shudder occurs AFTER TCC HAS APPLIED (often with engine under load such as climbing a hill):

In this case, most of the time there is nothing wrong with the transaxle! As mentioned above, once the TCC has been applied, it is very unlikely that it will slip. Engine problems may go unnoticed under light throttle and load, but become noticeable when going up a hill or when accelerating due to the mechanical lock-up between engine and transaxle.

REMEMBER: Once TCC is applied, there is no torque converter (fluid coupling) assistance. Engine or driveline vibrations could be unnoticeable before TCC engagement.

The following components should be inspected to avoid misdiagnosis of TCC Shudder and possibly disassembling a transaxle and/or replacing a converter unnecessarily.

- Spark plugs – Inspect for cracks, high resistance or broken insulator.
- Plug wires – Lock in each end. If there is red dust (ozone) or black substance (carbon) present, then the wires are bad. Also look for a white discoloration of the wire indicating arcing during hard acceleration.
- Distributor cap and rotor – Look for broken or uncrimped parts.
- Coil – Look for black on bottom indicating arcing while engine is misfiring.
- Fuel injector – Filter may be plugged.
- Vacuum leak – Engine won't get correct amount of fuel. May run rich or lean depending on where the leak is.
- EGR valve – Valve may let in too much unburnable exhaust gas and cause engine to run lean.
- MAP/MAF sensor – Like vacuum leak, engine won't get correct amount of fuel for proper engine operation.
- Carbon on intake valve – Restricts proper flow of air/fuel mixture into cylinders.
- Flat cam – Valves don't open enough to let proper fuel/air mixture into cylinders.
- Oxygen sensor – May command engine too rich or too lean for too long.
- Fuel pressure – May be too low.
- Engine Mounts – Vibration of mounts can be multiplied by TCC engagement.
- Axle joints – Check for vibration.
- TP Sensor – TCC apply and release depends on TP Sensor in many engines. If TP Sensor is out of specification, TCC may remain applied during initial engine crowd.
- Cylinder balance – Bad piston rings or poorly sealed valves can cause low power in a cylinder.
- Fuel contamination – Causes poor engine performance.
- Check service bulletins for a PROM or EPROM update.

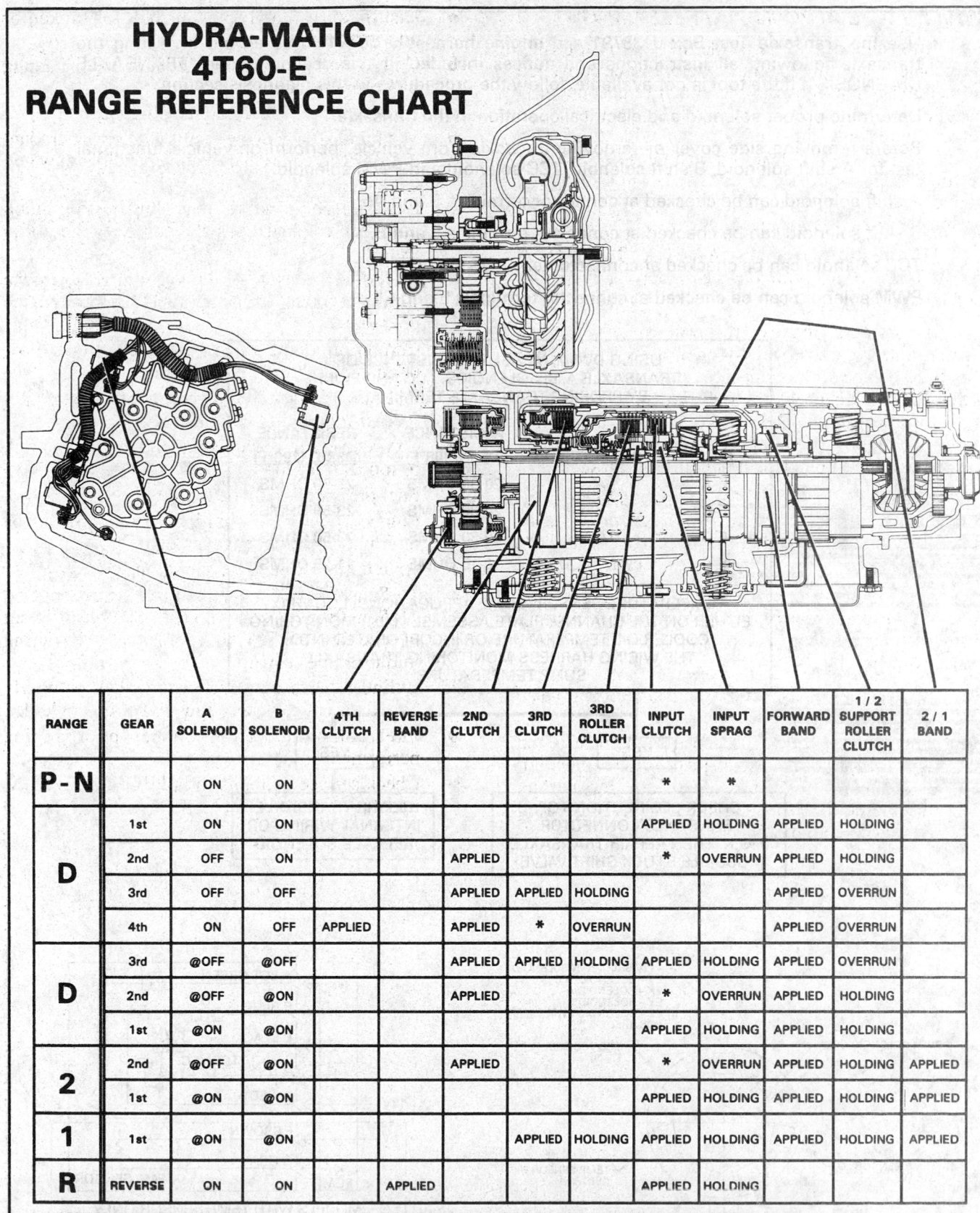

HYDRA-MATIC 4T60-E RANGE REFERENCE CHART

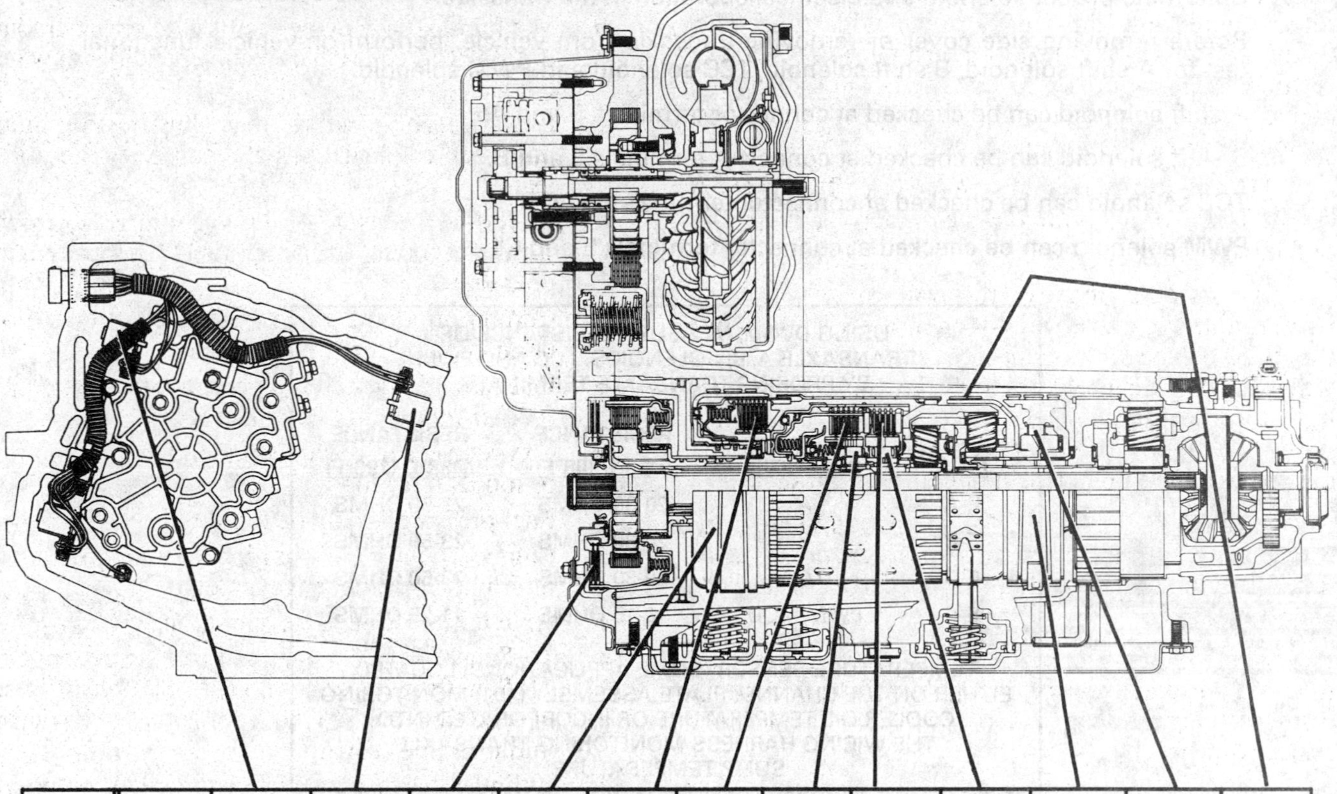

RANGE	GEAR	A SOLENOID	B SOLENOID	4TH CLUTCH	REVERSE BAND	2ND CLUTCH	3RD CLUTCH	3RD ROLLER CLUTCH	INPUT CLUTCH	INPUT SPRAG	FORWARD BAND	1/2 SUPPORT ROLLER CLUTCH	2/1 BAND
P-N		ON	ON						*	*			
D	1st	ON	ON						APPLIED	HOLDING	APPLIED	HOLDING	
	2nd	OFF	ON			APPLIED			*	OVERRUN	APPLIED	HOLDING	
	3rd	OFF	OFF			APPLIED	APPLIED	HOLDING			APPLIED	OVERRUN	
	4th	ON	OFF	APPLIED		APPLIED	*	OVERRUN			APPLIED	OVERRUN	
D	3rd	@OFF	@OFF			APPLIED	APPLIED	HOLDING	APPLIED	HOLDING	APPLIED	OVERRUN	
	2nd	@OFF	@ON			APPLIED			*	OVERRUN	APPLIED	HOLDING	
	1st	@ON	@ON						APPLIED	HOLDING	APPLIED	HOLDING	
2	2nd	@OFF	@ON			APPLIED			*	OVERRUN	APPLIED	HOLDING	APPLIED
	1st	@ON	@ON						APPLIED	HOLDING	APPLIED	HOLDING	APPLIED
1	1st	@ON	@ON				APPLIED	HOLDING	APPLIED	HOLDING	APPLIED	HOLDING	APPLIED
R	REVERSE	ON	ON		APPLIED				APPLIED	HOLDING			

*APPLIED BUT NOT EFFECTIVE

@ THE SOLENOID'S STATE FOLLOWS A SHIFT PATTERN WHICH DEPENDS UPON VEHICLE SPEED, THROTTLE POSITION AND SELECTED GEAR RANGE.

ON = SOLENOID ENERGIZED

OFF = SOLENOID DE-ENERGIZED

RH0010-4T60-E

Figure 10 Range Reference Chart

Use the Transaxle Test Box J 38791 and engine harness J 38791-60 as an aid in testing the transaxle following all instructions and notices included in this section under "TRANSAXLE DIAGNOSIS". If the tool is not available, follow the procedures in this diagnosis section.

Determine proper solenoid and electrical operation in the transaxle.

Before removing side cover or removing transaxle from vehicle, perform on-vehicle functional test for A shift solenoid, B shift solenoid, TCC solenoid and PWM solenoid.

A shift solenoid can be checked at connector terminals E and A.

B shift solenoid can be checked at connector terminals E and B.

TCC solenoid can be checked at connector terminals E and D.

PWM solenoid can be checked at connector terminals E and C.

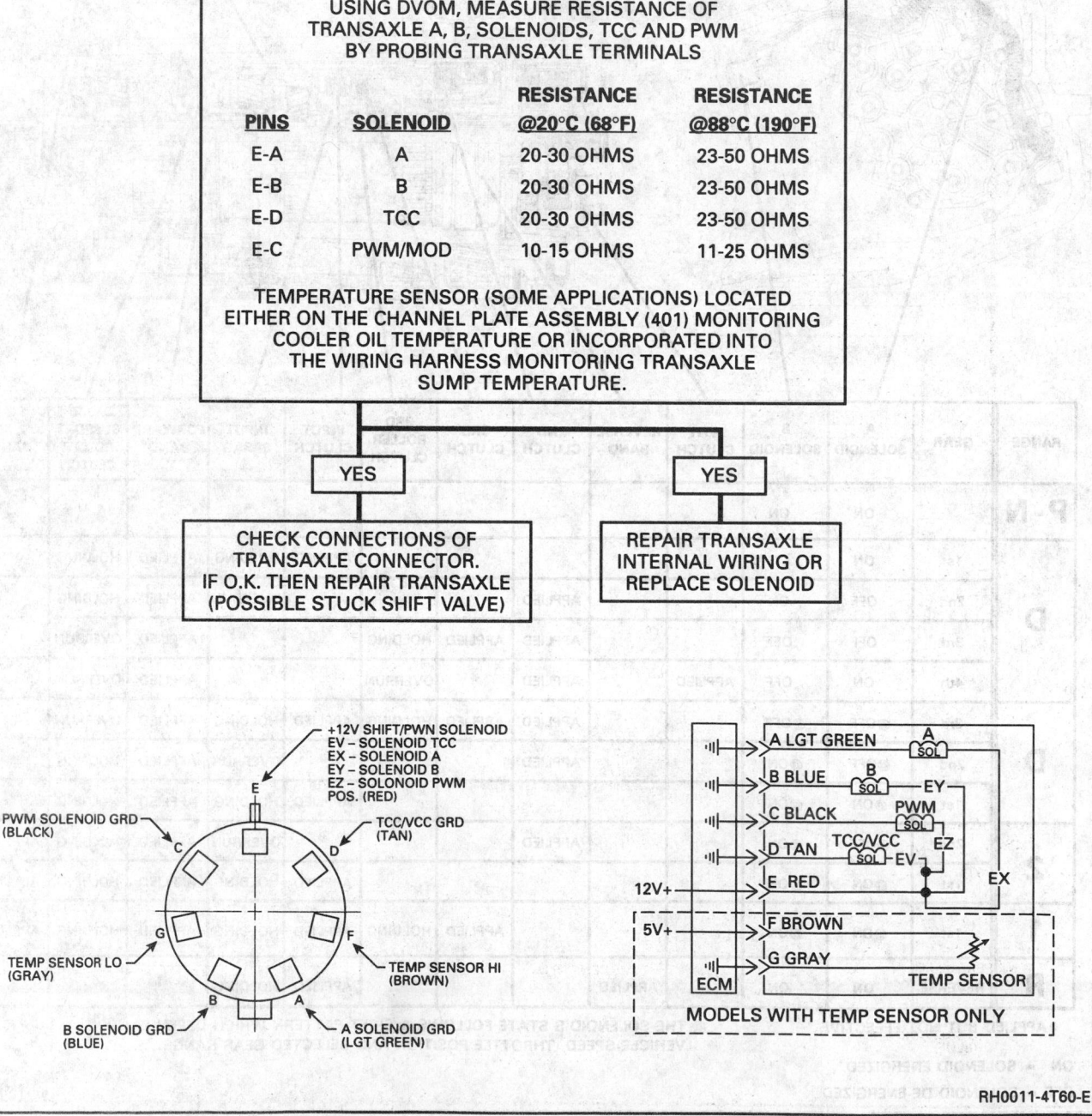

USING DVOM, MEASURE RESISTANCE OF TRANSAXLE A, B, SOLENOIDS, TCC AND PWM BY PROBING TRANSAXLE TERMINALS

PINS	SOLENOID	RESISTANCE @20°C (68°F)	RESISTANCE @88°C (190°F)
E-A	A	20-30 OHMS	23-50 OHMS
E-B	B	20-30 OHMS	23-50 OHMS
E-D	TCC	20-30 OHMS	23-50 OHMS
E-C	PWM/MOD	10-15 OHMS	11-25 OHMS

TEMPERATURE SENSOR (SOME APPLICATIONS) LOCATED EITHER ON THE CHANNEL PLATE ASSEMBLY (401) MONITORING COOLER OIL TEMPERATURE OR INCORPORATED INTO THE WIRING HARNESS MONITORING TRANSAXLE SUMP TEMPERATURE.

YES → CHECK CONNECTIONS OF TRANSAXLE CONNECTOR. IF O.K. THEN REPAIR TRANSAXLE (POSSIBLE STUCK SHIFT VALVE)

YES → REPAIR TRANSAXLE INTERNAL WIRING OR REPLACE SOLENOID

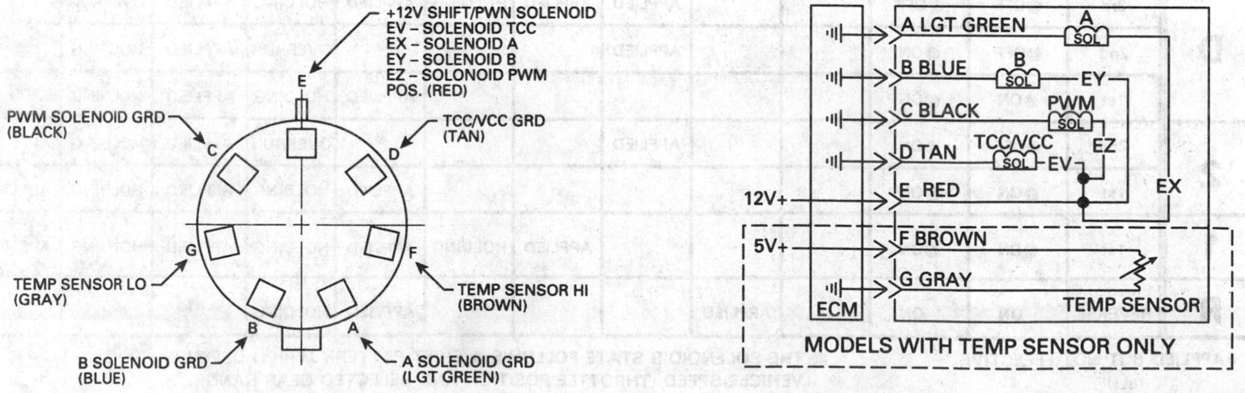
+12V SHIFT/PWN SOLENOID
EV – SOLENOID TCC
EX – SOLENOID A
EY – SOLENOID B
EZ – SOLONOID PWM
POS. (RED)
PWM SOLENOID GRD (BLACK)
TCC/VCC GRD (TAN)
TEMP SENSOR LO (GRAY)
TEMP SENSOR HI (BROWN)
B SOLENOID GRD (BLUE)
A SOLENOID GRD (LGT GREEN)
A B C D E F G
A LGT GREEN
B BLUE
C BLACK
D TAN
E RED
F BROWN
G GRAY
SOL
PWM
TCC/VCC
EX
EY
EZ
EV
12V+
5V+
ECM
TEMP SENSOR
MODELS WITH TEMP SENSOR ONLY
RH0011-4T60-E

Figure 11 Measuring Resistance of Shift Solenoids and TCC Solenoid Without Transmission Test Box

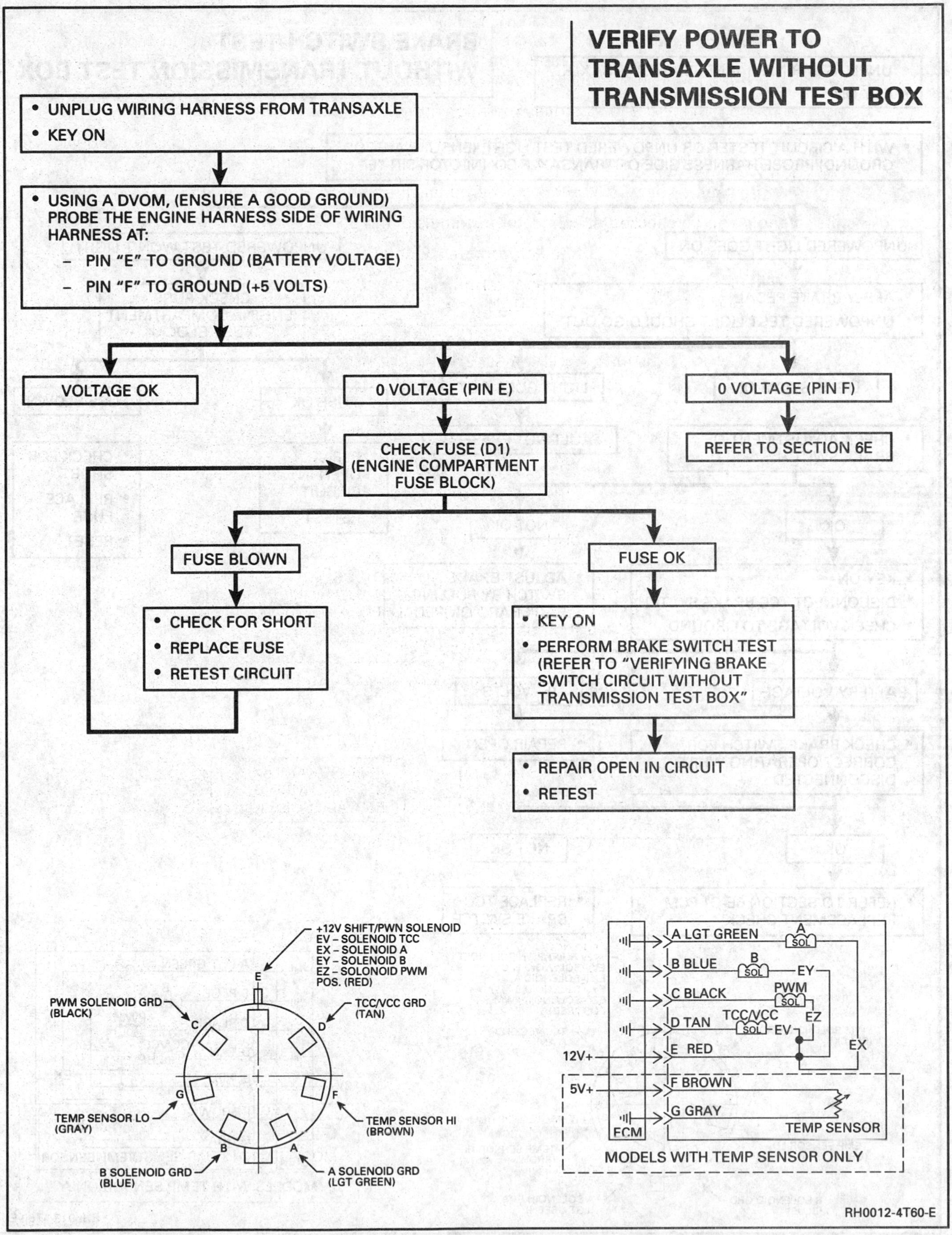
VERIFY POWER TO TRANSAXLE WITHOUT TRANSMISSION TEST BOX
• UNPLUG WIRING HARNESS FROM TRANSAXLE
• KEY ON
• USING A DVOM, (ENSURE A GOOD GROUND) PROBE THE ENGINE HARNESS SIDE OF WIRING HARNESS AT:
– PIN "E" TO GROUND (BATTERY VOLTAGE)
– PIN "F" TO GROUND (+5 VOLTS)
VOLTAGE OK
0 VOLTAGE (PIN E)
0 VOLTAGE (PIN F)
REFER TO SECTION 6E
CHECK FUSE (D1) (ENGINE COMPARTMENT FUSE BLOCK)
FUSE BLOWN
FUSE OK
• CHECK FOR SHORT
• REPLACE FUSE
• RETEST CIRCUIT
• KEY ON
• PERFORM BRAKE SWITCH TEST (REFER TO "VERIFYING BRAKE SWITCH CIRCUIT WITHOUT TRANSMISSION TEST BOX")
• REPAIR OPEN IN CIRCUIT
• RETEST
+12V SHIFT/PWN SOLENOID
EV – SOLENOID TCC
EX – SOLENOID A
EY – SOLENOID B
EZ – SOLONOID PWM
POS. (RED)
E
PWM SOLENOID GRD (BLACK)
C
TCC/VCC GRD (TAN)
D
G
TEMP SENSOR LO (GRAY)
F
TEMP SENSOR HI (BROWN)
B
B SOLENOID GRD (BLUE)
A
A SOLENOID GRD (LGT GREEN)
A LGT GREEN
A SOL
B BLUE
B SOL
EY
C BLACK
PWM SOL
D TAN
TCC/VCC SOL
EZ
EV
E RED
12V+
EX
F BROWN
5V+
G GRAY
ECM
TEMP SENSOR
MODELS WITH TEMP SENSOR ONLY
RH0012-4T60-E

Figure 12 Verifying Power to Transaxle Without Test Box J 38791

BRAKE SWITCH TEST WITHOUT TRANSMISSION TEST BOX

- UNPLUG WIRING HARNESS AT TRANSAXLE
- KEY ON

↓

- WITH A CIRCUIT TESTER OR UNPOWERED TEST LIGHT, (ENSURE A GOOD GROUND) PROBE HARNESS SIDE OF TRANSAXLE CONNECTOR PIN "E"

↓

UNPOWERED LIGHT GOES ON

- APPLY BRAKE PEDAL
- UNPOWERED TEST LIGHT SHOULD GO OUT

  - **LIGHT STAYS ON**
    - CHECK ADJUSTMENT OF BRAKE SWITCH
      - **OK**
        - KEY ON
        - DISCONNECT TCC BRAKE SWITCH
        - CHECK VOLTAGE TO GROUND
          - **BATTERY VOLTAGE**
            - CHECK BRAKE SWITCH FOR CORRECT OPERATING WHILE DISCONNECTED
              - **OK**
                - REFER TO SECTION 6E-C1 PCM REPLACEMENT CHECK
              - **NOT OK**
                - REPLACE TCC BRAKE SWITCH
          - **0 – VOLTS**
            - REPAIR OPEN
      - **NOT OK**
        - ADJUST BRAKE SWITCH BY PULLING BACK HARD ON PEDAL
  - **LIGHT GOES OUT**
    - FAULT NOT PRESENT

UNPOWERED TEST WON'T LIGHT

CHECK FUSE (ENGINE COMPARTMENT FUSE BLOCK)

- **FUSE OK**
  - REPAIR OPEN IN CIRCUIT
  - RETEST
- **FUSE BLOWN**
  - CHECK FOR SHORT
  - REPLACE FUSE
  - RESET

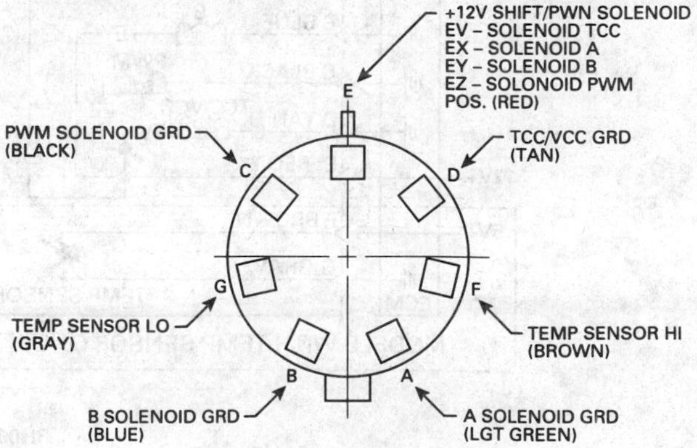
+12V SHIFT/PWN SOLENOID
EV – SOLENOID TCC
EX – SOLENOID A
EY – SOLENOID B
EZ – SOLONOID PWM
POS. (RED)
E
PWM SOLENOID GRD (BLACK)
C
TCC/VCC GRD (TAN)
D
G
F
TEMP SENSOR LO (GRAY)
TEMP SENSOR HI (BROWN)
B
A
B SOLENOID GRD (BLUE)
A SOLENOID GRD (LGT GREEN)

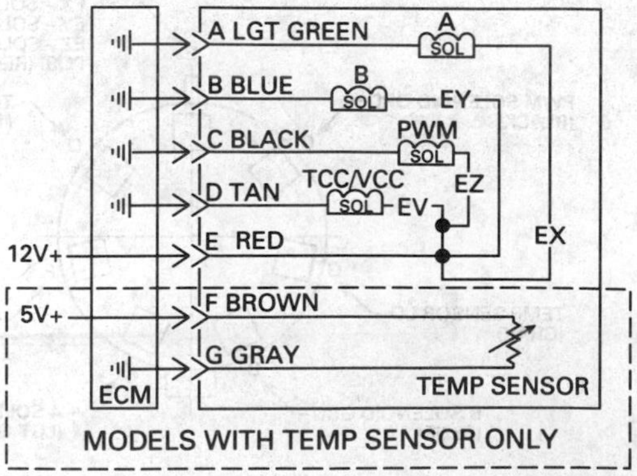
A LGT GREEN
A
SOL
B BLUE
B
SOL
EY
C BLACK
PWM
SOL
EZ
D TAN
TCC/VCC
SOL
EV
12V+
E RED
EX
5V+
F BROWN
G GRAY
TEMP SENSOR
ECM
MODELS WITH TEMP SENSOR ONLY

RH0013-4T60-E

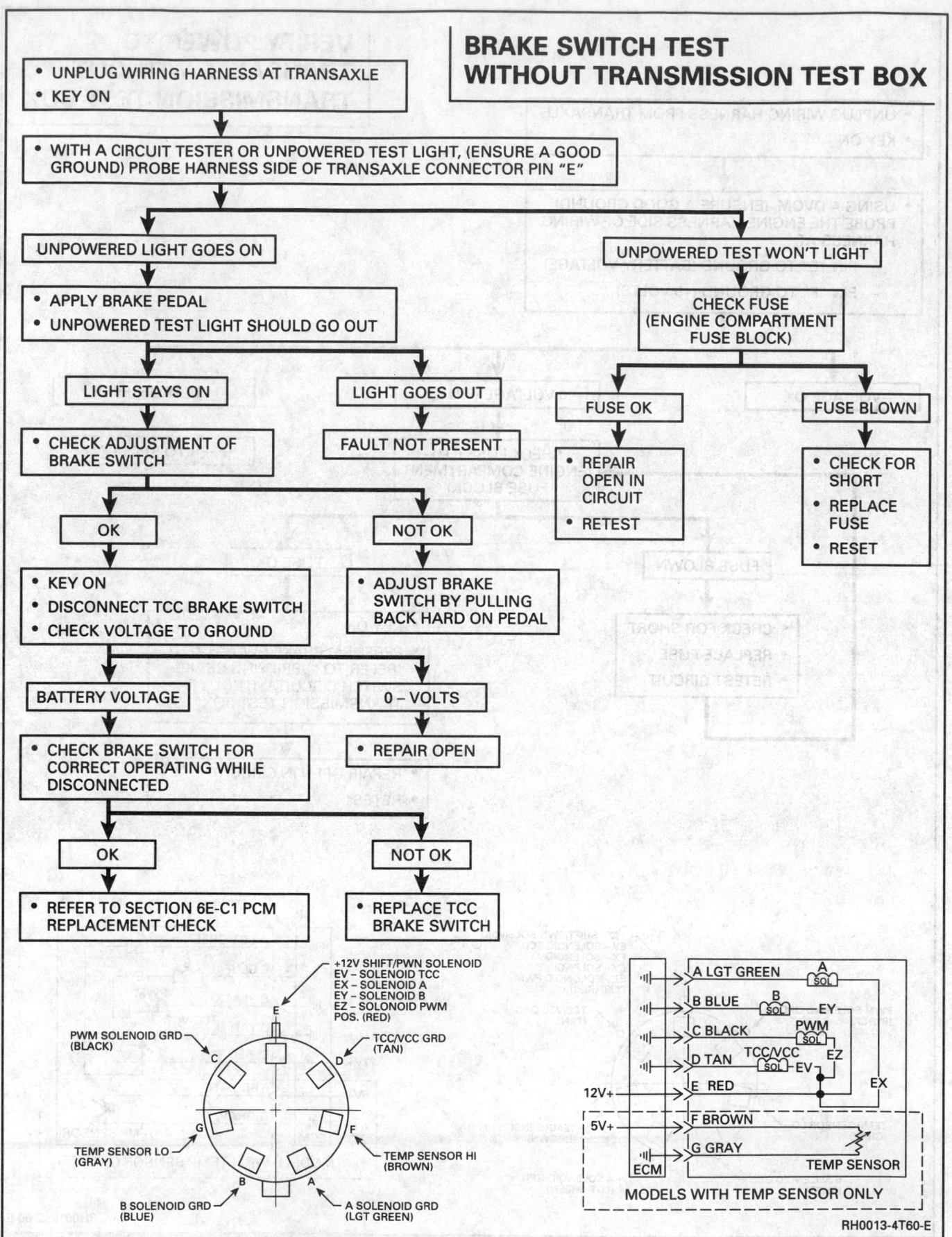

Figure 13 Brake Switch Test Without Test Box

TESTING "A" SHIFT SOLENOID OPERATION IN THE TRANSAXLE WITHOUT TRANSMISSION TEST BOX

- KEY OFF
- DISCONNECT ENGINE WIRING HARNESS AT TRANSAXLE
- SET DVOM TO OHMS (Ω) POSITION
- CHECK RESISTANCE OF A SHIFT SOLENOID CIRCUIT:
  - POSITIVE (RED) PROBE OF DVOM TO TRANSAXLE PIN "E"
  - NEGATIVE (BLK) PROBE OF DVOM TO TRANSAXLE PIN "A"

20-50 OHMS

- DISCONNECT PCM CONNECTOR
- CHECK CONTINUITY BETWEEN PIN "A" (ENGINE HARNESS) AND PCM CONNECTOR WIRING HARNESS PIN

CONTINUITY

- REFER TO SECTION 6E-C1 TO PCM REPLACEMENT CHECK

NO CONTINUITY

- REPAIR OPEN CKT
- RETEST

LESS THAN 20 OR GREATER THAN 50 OHMS

- CHECK INTERNAL TRANSAXLE WIRING HARNESS FOR OPENS AND GROUNDS
- IF WIRING HARNESS IS OK, REPLACE "A" SHIFT SOLENOID

* IF THE "A" SHIFT SOLENOID DOES NOT APPLY, CHECK JUMPER WIRE CONNECTIONS. IF NO SOLENOID APPLY STILL EXISTS, CHECK FOR THESE POSSIBLE CAUSES:

- LOOSE PINS IN TRANSAXLE CONNECTOR
- PINCHED OR BARE WIRE
- FOREIGN MATERIAL IN SOLENOID
- LOOSE OR DEFECTIVE CONNECTORS AT SOLENOIDS
- INOPERATIVE SOLENOIDS, BROKEN COIL IN SOLENOIDS

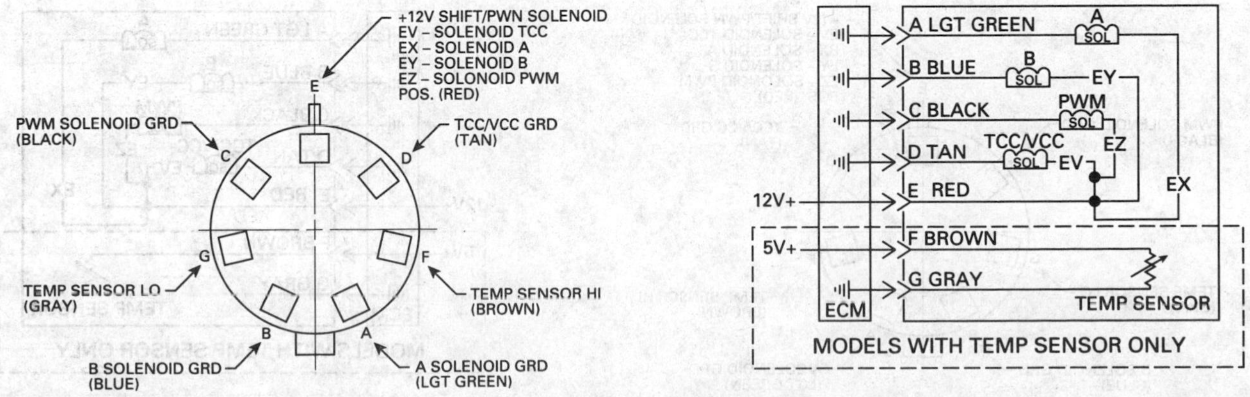
+12V SHIFT/PWN SOLENOID
EV – SOLENOID TCC
EX – SOLENOID A
EY – SOLENOID B
EZ – SOLONOID PWM
POS. (RED)
E
PWM SOLENOID GRD (BLACK)
C
TCC/VCC GRD (TAN)
D
G
F
TEMP SENSOR LO (GRAY)
TEMP SENSOR HI (BROWN)
B
A
B SOLENOID GRD (BLUE)
A SOLENOID GRD (LGT GREEN)
A LGT GREEN
A
SOL
B BLUE
B
SOL
EY
C BLACK
PWM
SOL
D TAN
TCC/VCC
SOL
EV
EZ
12V+
E RED
EX
5V+
F BROWN
G GRAY
ECM
TEMP SENSOR
MODELS WITH TEMP SENSOR ONLY

RH0014-4T60-E

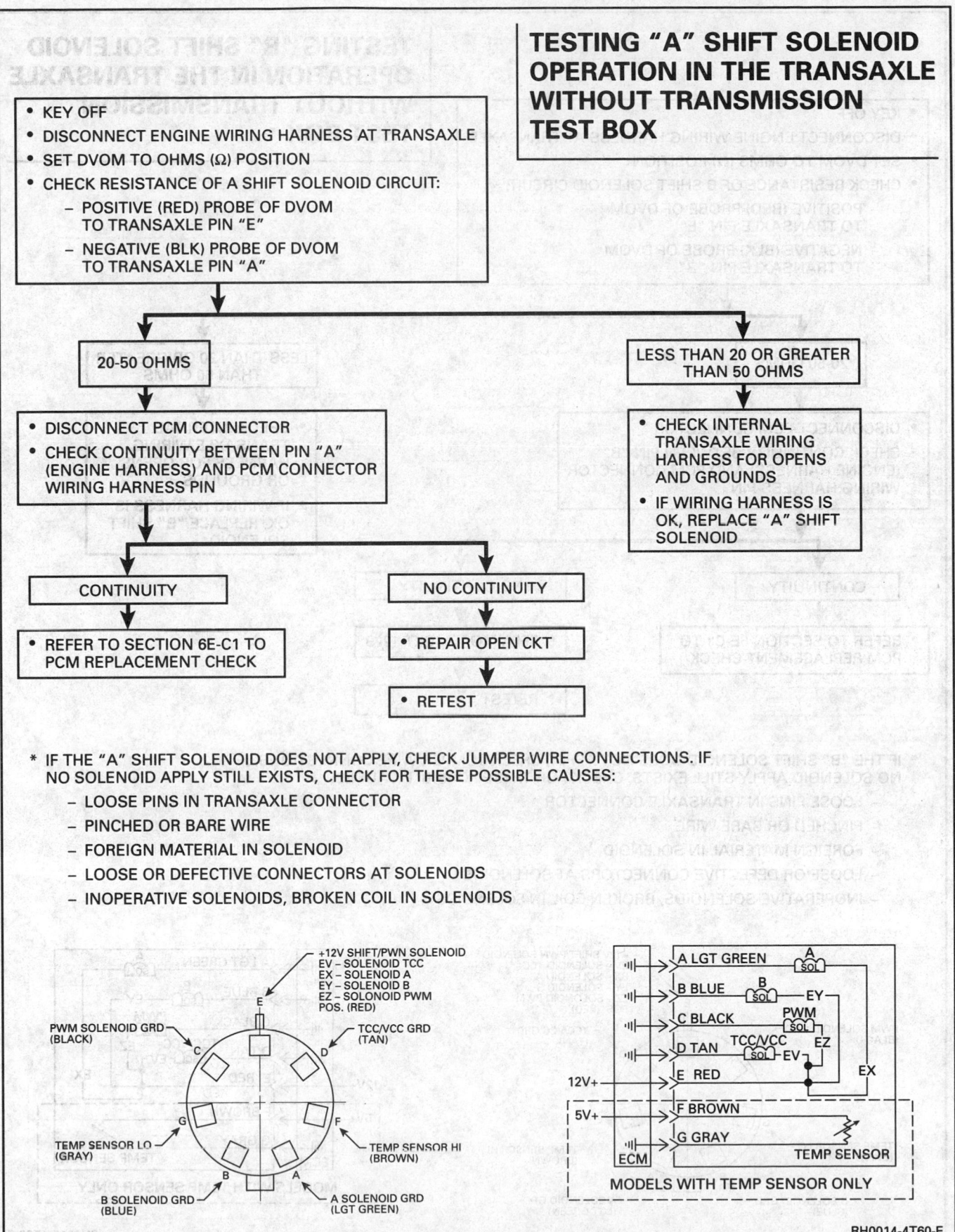

Figure 14 "A" Shift Solenoid Test Without Test Box

TESTING "B" SHIFT SOLENOID OPERATION IN THE TRANSAXLE WITHOUT TRANSMISSION TEST BOX

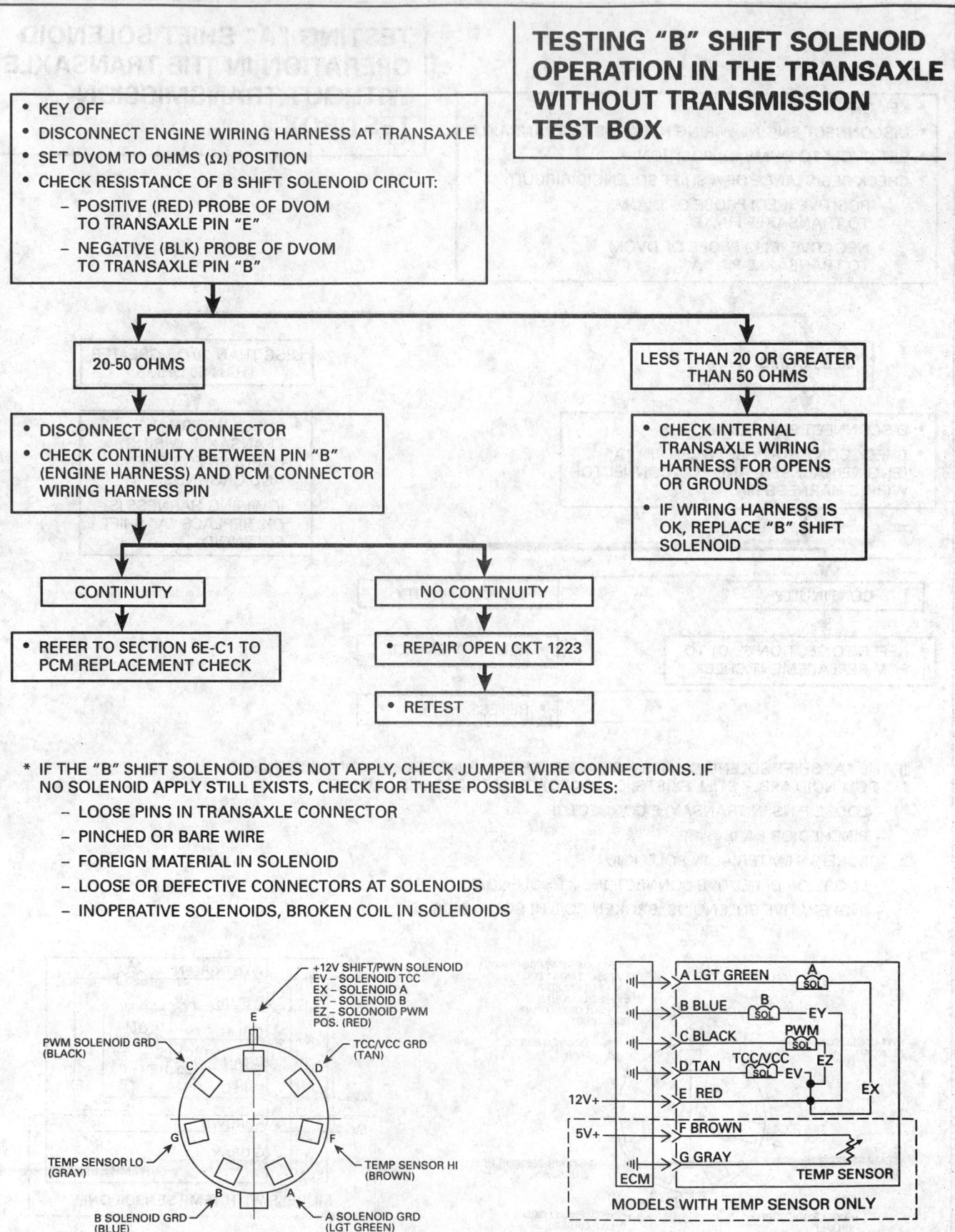

- KEY OFF
- DISCONNECT ENGINE WIRING HARNESS AT TRANSAXLE
- SET DVOM TO OHMS (Ω) POSITION
- CHECK RESISTANCE OF B SHIFT SOLENOID CIRCUIT:
  - POSITIVE (RED) PROBE OF DVOM TO TRANSAXLE PIN "E"
  - NEGATIVE (BLK) PROBE OF DVOM TO TRANSAXLE PIN "B"

20-50 OHMS

- DISCONNECT PCM CONNECTOR
- CHECK CONTINUITY BETWEEN PIN "B" (ENGINE HARNESS) AND PCM CONNECTOR WIRING HARNESS PIN

CONTINUITY

- REFER TO SECTION 6E-C1 TO PCM REPLACEMENT CHECK

NO CONTINUITY

- REPAIR OPEN CKT 1223
- RETEST

LESS THAN 20 OR GREATER THAN 50 OHMS

- CHECK INTERNAL TRANSAXLE WIRING HARNESS FOR OPENS OR GROUNDS
- IF WIRING HARNESS IS OK, REPLACE "B" SHIFT SOLENOID

* IF THE "B" SHIFT SOLENOID DOES NOT APPLY, CHECK JUMPER WIRE CONNECTIONS. IF NO SOLENOID APPLY STILL EXISTS, CHECK FOR THESE POSSIBLE CAUSES:

- LOOSE PINS IN TRANSAXLE CONNECTOR
- PINCHED OR BARE WIRE
- FOREIGN MATERIAL IN SOLENOID
- LOOSE OR DEFECTIVE CONNECTORS AT SOLENOIDS
- INOPERATIVE SOLENOIDS, BROKEN COIL IN SOLENOIDS

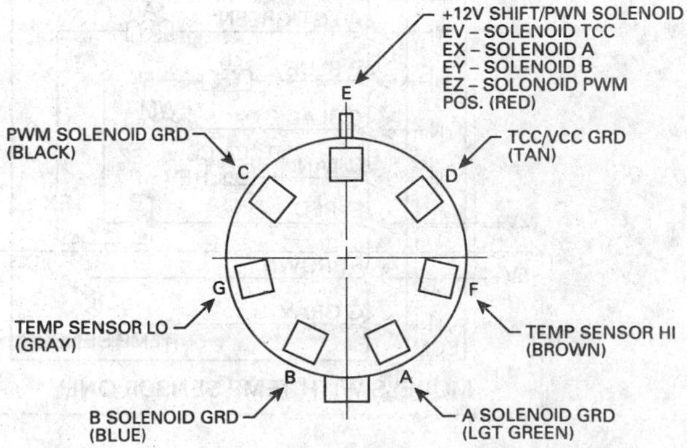
+12V SHIFT/PWN SOLENOID
EV – SOLENOID TCC
EX – SOLENOID A
EY – SOLENOID B
EZ – SOLENOID PWM
POS. (RED)
E
PWM SOLENOID GRD (BLACK)
C
TCC/VCC GRD (TAN)
D
G
F
TEMP SENSOR LO (GRAY)
TEMP SENSOR HI (BROWN)
B
A
B SOLENOID GRD (BLUE)
A SOLENOID GRD (LGT GREEN)

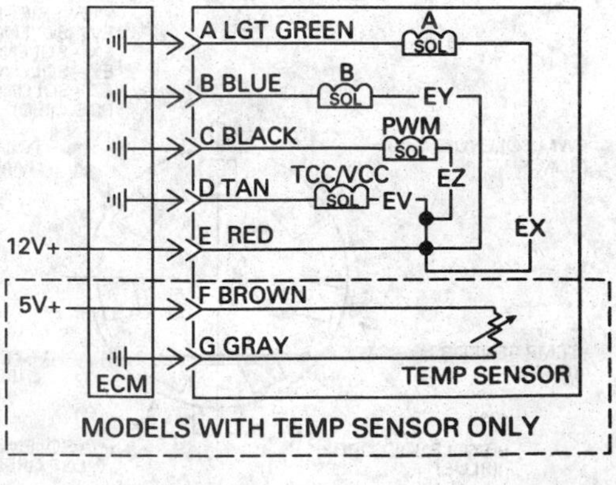
A LGT GREEN
A SOL
B BLUE
B SOL
EY
C BLACK
PWM SOL
D TAN
TCC/VCC SOL
EV
EZ
12V+
E RED
EX
5V+
F BROWN
G GRAY
ECM
TEMP SENSOR
MODELS WITH TEMP SENSOR ONLY

RH0015-4T60-E

Figure 15 "B" Shift Solenoid Test Without Test Box

TESTING "TCC" SOLENOID OPERATION IN THE TRANSAXLE WITHOUT TRANSMISSION TEST BOX

- KEY OFF
- DISCONNECT ENGINE WIRING HARNESS AT TRANSAXLE
- SET DVOM TO OHMS (Ω) POSITION
- CHECK RESISTANCE OF TCC SOLENOID CIRCUIT:
  - POSITIVE (RED) PROBE OF DVOM TO TRANSAXLE PIN "E"
  - NEGATIVE (BLK) PROBE OF DVOM TO TRANSAXLE PIN "D"

20-50 OHMS

- DISCONNECT PCM CONNECTOR
- CHECK CONTINUITY BETWEEN PIN "D" (ENGINE HARNESS) AND PCM CONNECTOR WIRING HARNESS PIN

CONTINUITY

- REFER TO SECTION 6E-C1 TO PCM REPLACEMENT CHECK

NO CONTINUITY

- REPAIR OPEN CKT
- RETEST

LESS THAN 20 OR GREATER THAN 50 OHMS

- * CHECK INTERNAL TRANSAXLE WIRING HARNESS FOR OPENS OR GROUNDS
- IF WIRING HARNESS IS OK, REPLACE TCC SOLENOID

* IF THE TCC SOLENOID DOES NOT APPLY, CHECK JUMPER WIRE CONNECTIONS. IF NO SOLENOID APPLY STILL EXISTS, CHECK FOR THESE POSSIBLE CAUSES:

- LOOSE PINS IN TRANSAXLE CONNECTOR
- PINCHED OR BARE WIRE
- FOREIGN MATERIAL IN SOLENOID
- LOOSE OR DEFECTIVE CONNECTORS AT SOLENOIDS
- INOPERATIVE SOLENOIDS, BROKEN COIL IN SOLENOIDS

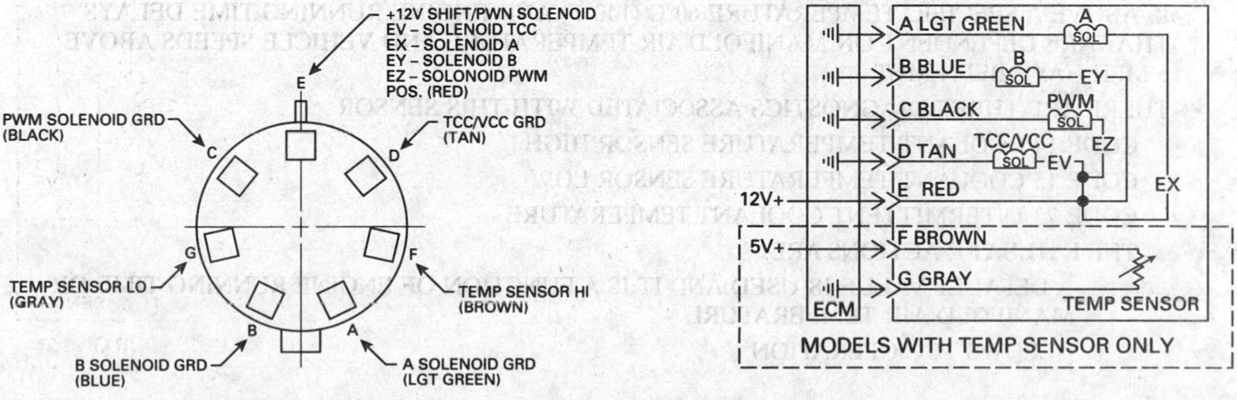
+12V SHIFT/PWN SOLENOID
EV – SOLENOID TCC
EX – SOLENOID A
EY – SOLENOID B
EZ – SOLONOID PWM
POS. (RED)
E
PWM SOLENOID GRD (BLACK)
C
TCC/VCC GRD (TAN)
D
G
F
TEMP SENSOR LO (GRAY)
TEMP SENSOR HI (BROWN)
B
A
B SOLENOID GRD (BLUE)
A SOLENOID GRD (LGT GREEN)
A LGT GREEN
A SOL
B BLUE
B SOL
EY
C BLACK
PWM SOL
D TAN
TCC/VCC SOL
EV
EZ
E RED
EX
12V+
5V+
F BROWN
G GRAY
ECM
TEMP SENSOR
MODELS WITH TEMP SENSOR ONLY

RH0016-4T60-E

Figure 16 "TCC" Solenoid Test Without Test Box

PCM INPUTS THAT AFFECT THE 4T60-E

THROTTLE POSITION SENSOR

- MEASURES THE THROTTLE POSITION AND INPUTS IT INTO THE PCM
- PROVIDES DATA TO DEVELOP THE SHIFT PATTERN
- THERE ARE FOUR DIAGNOSTIC CODES ASSOCIATED WITH THE TP SENSOR

  CODE 21 THROTTLE POSITION SENSOR TOO HIGH

  CODE 22 THROTTLE POSITION SENSOR TOO LOW

  CODE 55 THROTTLE POSITION SENSOR OUT OF ADJUSTMENT

  CODE 70 INTERMITTENT THROTTLE POSITION

  THE **FAILSAFE** ACTIONS FOR CODES 21 AND 22 ARE:

  - OFF MODE OF THE TCC
  - INHIBIT 4TH GEAR
  - USE DEFAULT VALUE FOR TP SENSOR IN SECOND AND THIRD GEAR MAY DISABLE THIRD GEAR

  THE **FAILSAFE** ACTION FOR CODE 55 IS:

  - USE DEFAULT VALUE FOR TP SENSOR

  IT WILL RECOVER UPON A VALID RANGE

VEHICLE SPEED SENSOR

- MEASURES THE SPEED OF THE FINAL DRIVE ASSEMBLY
- PROVIDES DATA TO DEVELOP THE SHIFT PATTERN
- GENERATES A VOLTAGE WAVEFORM AND ITS FREQUENCY DETERMINES VEHICLE SPEED
- THERE ARE TWO DIAGNOSTIC CODES ASSOCIATED WITH THE VSS SENSOR

  CODE 24 VEHICLE SPEED SENSOR

  - DETECTS WHEN THE SIGNAL IS TOO LOW

  CODE 75 INTERMITTENT SPEED SENSOR

  - DETECTS A LARGE DROP IN FREQUENCY

  THE **FAILSAFE** ACTIONS FOR CODE 24 ARE:

  - TCC WILL NOT OPERATE FOR THE IGNITION CYCLE
  - THIRD AND FOURTH GEARS WILL BE DISABLED UNDER MOST CONDITIONS

  IT WILL RECOVER WHEN VEHICLE SPEED IS ABOVE A SPECIFIC VALUE

ENGINE COOLANT TEMPERATURE

- MEASURES THE ENGINE COOLANT TEMPERATURE
- THE PCM WILL NOT COMMAND THE TCC UNTIL THE ENGINE COOLANT TEMPERATURE IS ABOVE A SPECIFIC TEMPERATURE 60°C (140°F) AND ENGINE RUNNING TIME DELAYS THAT ARE DEPENDENT ON MANIFOLD AIR TEMPERATURE AND VEHICLE SPEEDS ABOVE 5 MPH HAVE BEEN MET
- THERE ARE THREE DIAGNOSTICS ASSOCIATED WITH THIS SENSOR

  CODE 14 COOLANT TEMPERATURE SENSOR HIGH

  CODE 15 COOLANT TEMPERATURE SENSOR LOW

  CODE 73 INTERMITTENT COOLANT TEMPERATURE

  THE **FAILSAFE** ACTIONS ARE:

  - A DEFAULT VALUE IS USED AND IT IS A FUNCTION OF ENGINE RUNNING TIME OR MANIFOLD AIR TEMPERATURE
  - ALLOWS TCC OPERATION

RH0017-4T60-E

Figure 17 Failsafe Actions and PCM Inputs

CRUISE CONTROL

- WHEN ENGAGED ALTERS THE SHIFT PATTERN TO REDUCE THE NUMBER OF 3-4 AND 4-3 SHIFTS

  A TIME LIMIT MUST BE MET BETWEEN 3-2 AND A 2-3

  A TIME LIMIT MUST BE MET BETWEEN 4-3 AND A 3-4

ENGINE SPEED

- DETERMINED BY THE INJECTOR MODULE
- USED TO REGULATE THE PWM SOLENOID DUTY CYCLE

BRAKE SWITCH

- CONTROLS THE TCC SOLENOID AND INPUTS INTO THE PCM
- DISENGAGES THE TCC SOLENOID FROM THE POWER FEED SOURCE WHEN THE BRAKE IS APPLIED
- THERE IS ONE DIAGNOSTIC CODE ASSOCIATED WITH THIS SWITCH

  CODE 90 TCC BRAKE SWITCH PROBLEM

  - DETECTS WHEN A CHANGE OF STATE SHOULD HAVE OCCURRED AND IT DID NOT

  THE **FAILSAFE** ACTION IS:

  - NO CRUISE CONTROL

  IT WILL RECOVER ONCE THE SWITCH CHANGES STATE

PRNDL SWITCH

- IT IS MOUNTED ON THE MANUAL SHAFT LEVER AND IT GIVES TRANSMISSION RANGE BASED UPON LEVER POSITION
- INPUTS THE SELECTED TRANSMISSION RANGE INTO THE PCM
- CONTROLS SHIFT SOLENOID STATE
- IT IS AN ASSEMBLY OF FOUR SWITCHES THAT CONNECT TO GROUND
- THERE IS ONE DIAGNOSTIC CODE ASSOCIATED WITH THIS SWITCH

  CODE 91 PRNDL SWITCH PROBLEM

  - DETECTS THE 9 POSSIBLE FALSE COMBINATIONS
  - CHECKS THE P/N DISCRETE ON STARTING OR IN FOURTH GEAR

  THE **FAILSAFE** ACTIONS ARE:

  - USE THE D4 SHIFT SCHEDULES
  - TCC PWM SOLENOID WILL BE REGULATED INCORRECTLY IN D3

  RECOVERS UPON A VALID RANGE

  IF NOT PROPERLY ALIGNED BETWEEN D4 AND D3 NO TCC MAY OCCUR, SHOULD SET A CODE

  IF NOT PROPERLY ALIGNED OR IN WRONG RANGE MANUAL LO MAY NOT BE ATTAINABLE

RH0018-4T60-E

Figure 18 Failsafe Actions and PCM Inputs

TEMPERATURE SENSOR: (MODEL DEPENDANT)

- LOCATED ON EITHER THE CHANNEL PLATE ASM. (401) OR INCORPORATE INTO THE WIRING HARNESS AND CLIPS TO THE VALVE BODY SPACER PLATE
- THE SENSOR LOCATED ON THE CHANNEL PLATE MONITORS FLUID TEMPERATURE IN THE "COOLER" CIRCUIT. THE SENSOR CLIPPED ON THE SPACER PLATE ASM. MONITORS TRANSMISSION FLUID IN THE SIDE COVER
- BOTH SENSORS ARE NEGATIVE COEFFICIENT THERMISTORS THAT PROVIDE FLUID TEMPERATURE INFORMATION TO THE PCM. A 5 VOLT REFERENCE SIGNAL IS SENT TO THE SENSOR AND MEASURES THE VOLTAGE DROP IN THE CIRCUIT
- THE PCM USES THIS INFORMATION FOR DETERMINING SHIFT PATTERN WHEN TO ENGAGE OR DISENGAGE THE TCC – HOT MODE OPERATION
- HOT MODE OPERATION OCCURS WHEN THE TEMPERATURE OF THE TRANSAXLE FLUID REACHES 130°C (266°F)
- DURING HOT MODE OPERATION, THE PCM COMMANDS THE TRANSAXLE INTO A LOWER GEAR RANGE (3RD OR 2ND GEAR) AND CONTROLS THE TCC
- THERE ARE THREE DIAGNOSTIC CODES ASSOCIATED WITH THIS SENSOR

CODE 58 TRANSAXLE TEMPERATURE HIGH

- TRANSAXLE TEMPERATURE SENSOR VALUE IS 148°C FOR 5 SECONDS INDICATING A POSSIBLE SHORT TO GROUND

CODE 59 TRANSAXLE TEMPERATURE LOW

- TRANSAXLE TEMPERATURE SENSOR VALUE IS 40°C FOR 6 SECONDS INDICATING A POSSIBLE OPEN OR SHORT TO VOLTAGE IN THE CIRCUIT

CODE 79 TRANSAXLE OVER-TEMPERATURE

- NO SENSOR MALFUNCTION CODES. TRANSAXLE TEMPERATURE ABOVE 130°C (266°F). TRANSAXLE RETURNS TO NORMAL OPERATING MODE WHEN TEMPERATURE IS LESS THAN 120°C

RH0100-4T60-E

Figure 19 Failsafe Actions and PCM Inputs

4T60-E SOLENOIDS USED WITH THE HYDRA-MATIC 4T60-E

"A" SHIFT SOLENOID

- IS ELECTRONICALLY CONTROLLED BY A QDM LOCATED IN THE PCM
- IS AN ELECTRONIC, NORMALLY OPEN EXHAUST VALVE
- WHEN ACTIVATED, IT REDIRECTS THE EXHAUSTING FLUID TO ACT UPON THE 1-2 AND 3-4 SHIFT VALVES
- ON IN 1ST AND 4TH GEAR AND OFF IN 2ND AND 3RD GEAR
- THERE ARE NO DIAGNOSTIC CODES

"B" SHIFT SOLENOID

- IS ELECTRONICALLY CONTROLLED BY A QDM LOCATED IN THE PCM
- IS AN ELECTRONIC NORMALLY OPEN EXHAUST VALVE
- WHEN ACTIVATED, IT REDIRECTS THE EXHAUSTING FLUID TO ACT UPON THE 1-2, 2-3 AND3-4 SHIFT VALVES
- ON IN 1ST AND 2ND GEAR AND OFF IN 3RD AND 4TH GEAR
- THERE ARE NO DIAGNOSTIC CODES

TCC SOLENOID

- IS ELECTRONICALLY CONTROLLED BY A QDM LOCATED IN THE PCM
- IS AN ELECTRONIC NORMALLY OPEN EXHAUST VALVE
- WHEN ACTIVATED, IT REDIRECTS THE EXHAUSTING FLUID TO ACT UPON THE TCC SHIFT VALVE
- ON IN 3RD AND/OR 4TH GEAR
- SUPPLIED BY IGNITION
- THERE IS ONE DIAGNOSTIC CODE ASSOCIATED WITH THE SENSOR

  CODE 39 TCC ENGAGEMENT PROBLEM

  - DETECTS HIGH ENGINE RPM IN 4TH GEAR AFTER TCC HAS BEEN COMMANDED

  FAILSAFE ACTION IS:

  - DISABLE TCC FOR IGNITION CYCLE

  IT WILL RECOVER UPON NEXT IGNITION

TCC PWM SOLENOID

- REGULATES THE APPLY AND RELEASE OF THE TCC
- IS ELECTRONICALLY CONTROLLED BY A QDM LOCATED IN THE PCM
- THE QDM CONTROLS THE SOLENOID USING A DUTY CYCLE
- THERE IS ONE DIAGNOSTIC CODE ASSOCIATED WITH THIS SOLENOID

  CODE 39 TCC ENGAGEMENT PROBLEM

  - DETECTS HIGH ENGINE RPM IN 4TH GEAR AFTER TCC HAS BEEN COMMANDED

RH0019-4T60-E

Figure 20 Failsafe Actions and PCM Inputs

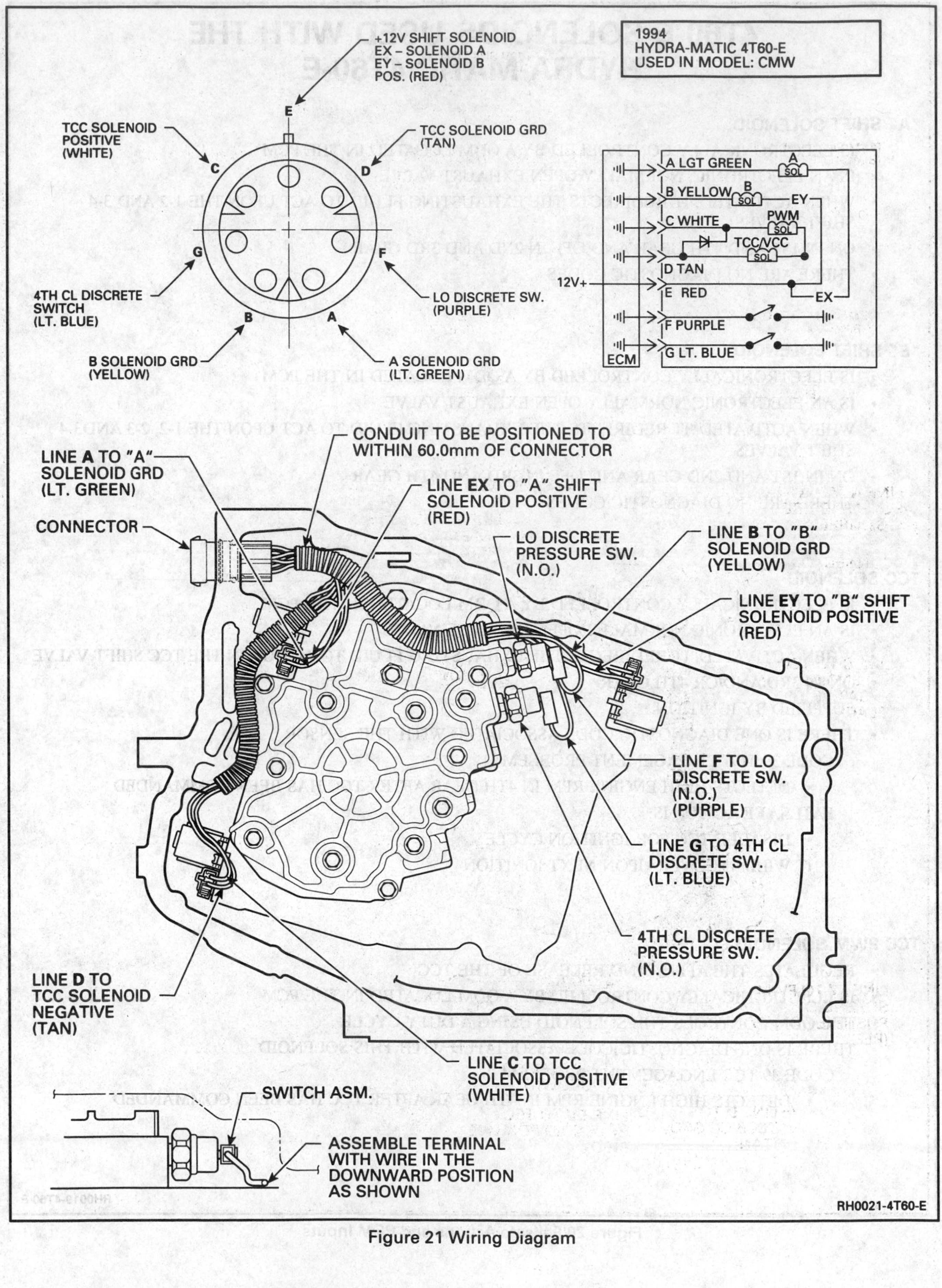
1994
HYDRA-MATIC 4T60-E
USED IN MODEL: CMW
+12V SHIFT SOLENOID
EX – SOLENOID A
EY – SOLENOID B
POS. (RED)
E
TCC SOLENOID POSITIVE (WHITE)
C
TCC SOLENOID GRD (TAN)
D
G
F
4TH CL DISCRETE SWITCH (LT. BLUE)
LO DISCRETE SW. (PURPLE)
B
A
B SOLENOID GRD (YELLOW)
A SOLENOID GRD (LT. GREEN)
A LGT GREEN
A SOL
B YELLOW
B SOL
EY
C WHITE
PWM SOL
TCC/VCC SOL
D TAN
12V+
E RED
EX
F PURPLE
G LT. BLUE
ECM
CONDUIT TO BE POSITIONED TO WITHIN 60.0mm OF CONNECTOR
LINE A TO "A" SOLENOID GRD (LT. GREEN)
LINE EX TO "A" SHIFT SOLENOID POSITIVE (RED)
CONNECTOR
LO DISCRETE PRESSURE SW. (N.O.)
LINE B TO "B" SOLENOID GRD (YELLOW)
LINE EY TO "B" SHIFT SOLENOID POSITIVE (RED)
LINE F TO LO DISCRETE SW. (N.O.) (PURPLE)
LINE G TO 4TH CL DISCRETE SW. (LT. BLUE)
4TH CL DISCRETE PRESSURE SW. (N.O.)
LINE D TO TCC SOLENOID NEGATIVE (TAN)
LINE C TO TCC SOLENOID POSITIVE (WHITE)
SWITCH ASM.
ASSEMBLE TERMINAL WITH WIRE IN THE DOWNWARD POSITION AS SHOWN
RH0021-4T60-E

Figure 21 Wiring Diagram

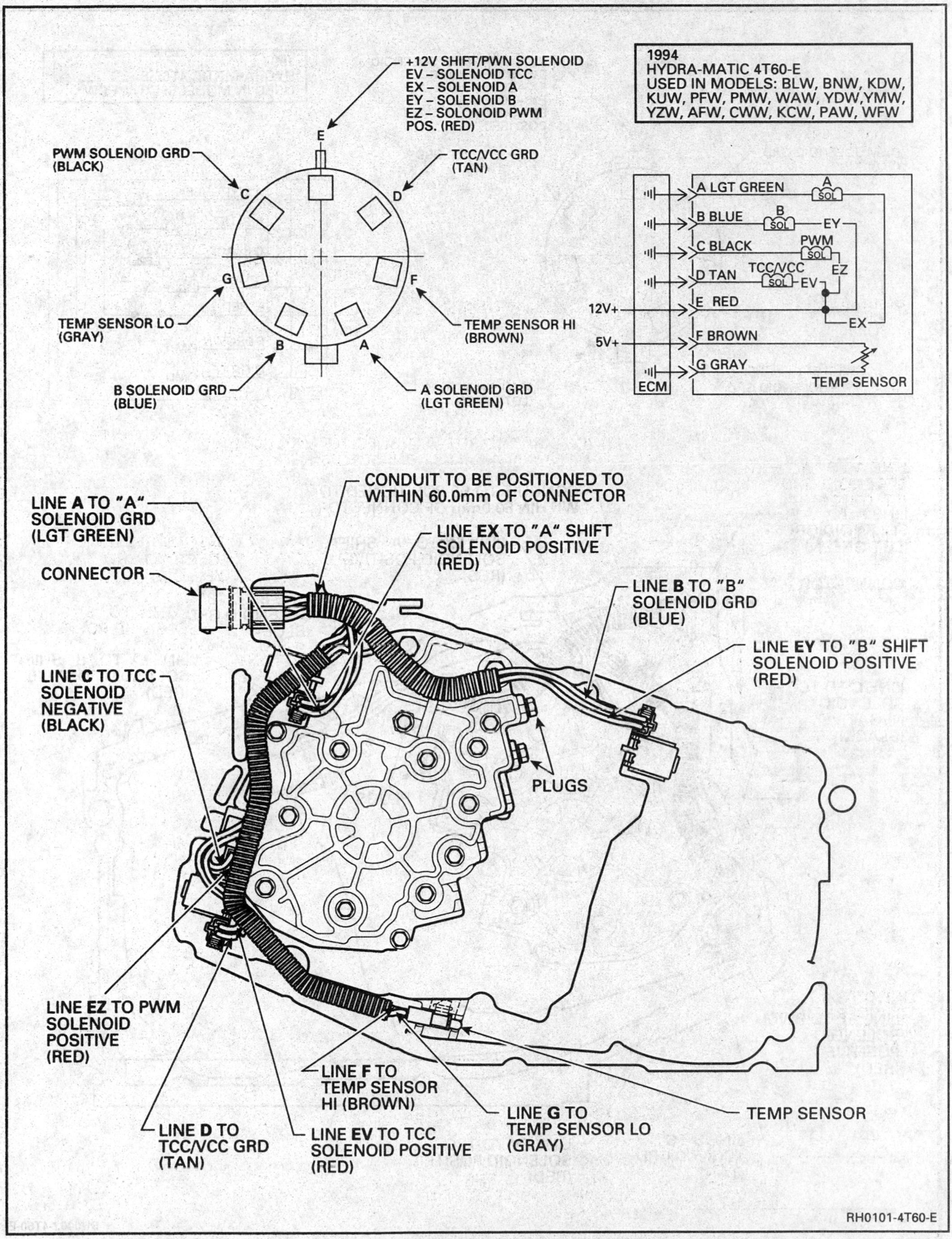

+12V SHIFT/PWN SOLENOID
EV – SOLENOID TCC
EX – SOLENOID A
EY – SOLENOID B
EZ – SOLONOID PWM
POS. (RED)
E
PWM SOLENOID GRD (BLACK)
C
TCC/VCC GRD (TAN)
D
G
F
TEMP SENSOR LO (GRAY)
TEMP SENSOR HI (BROWN)
B
A
B SOLENOID GRD (BLUE)
A SOLENOID GRD (LGT GREEN)
1994
HYDRA-MATIC 4T60-E
USED IN MODELS: BLW, BNW, KDW, KUW, PFW, PMW, WAW, YDW,YMW, YZW, AFW, CWW, KCW, PAW, WFW
A LGT GREEN
A SOL
B BLUE
B SOL
EY
C BLACK
PWM SOL
D TAN
TCC/VCC SOL
EV
EZ
12V+
E RED
EX
5V+
F BROWN
G GRAY
ECM
TEMP SENSOR
CONDUIT TO BE POSITIONED TO WITHIN 60.0mm OF CONNECTOR
LINE A TO "A" SOLENOID GRD (LGT GREEN)
LINE EX TO "A" SHIFT SOLENOID POSITIVE (RED)
CONNECTOR
LINE B TO "B" SOLENOID GRD (BLUE)
LINE EY TO "B" SHIFT SOLENOID POSITIVE (RED)
LINE C TO TCC SOLENOID NEGATIVE (BLACK)
PLUGS
LINE EZ TO PWM SOLENOID POSITIVE (RED)
LINE F TO TEMP SENSOR HI (BROWN)
LINE G TO TEMP SENSOR LO (GRAY)
TEMP SENSOR
LINE D TO TCC/VCC GRD (TAN)
LINE EV TO TCC SOLENOID POSITIVE (RED)
RH0101-4T60-E

Figure 22 Wiring Diagram

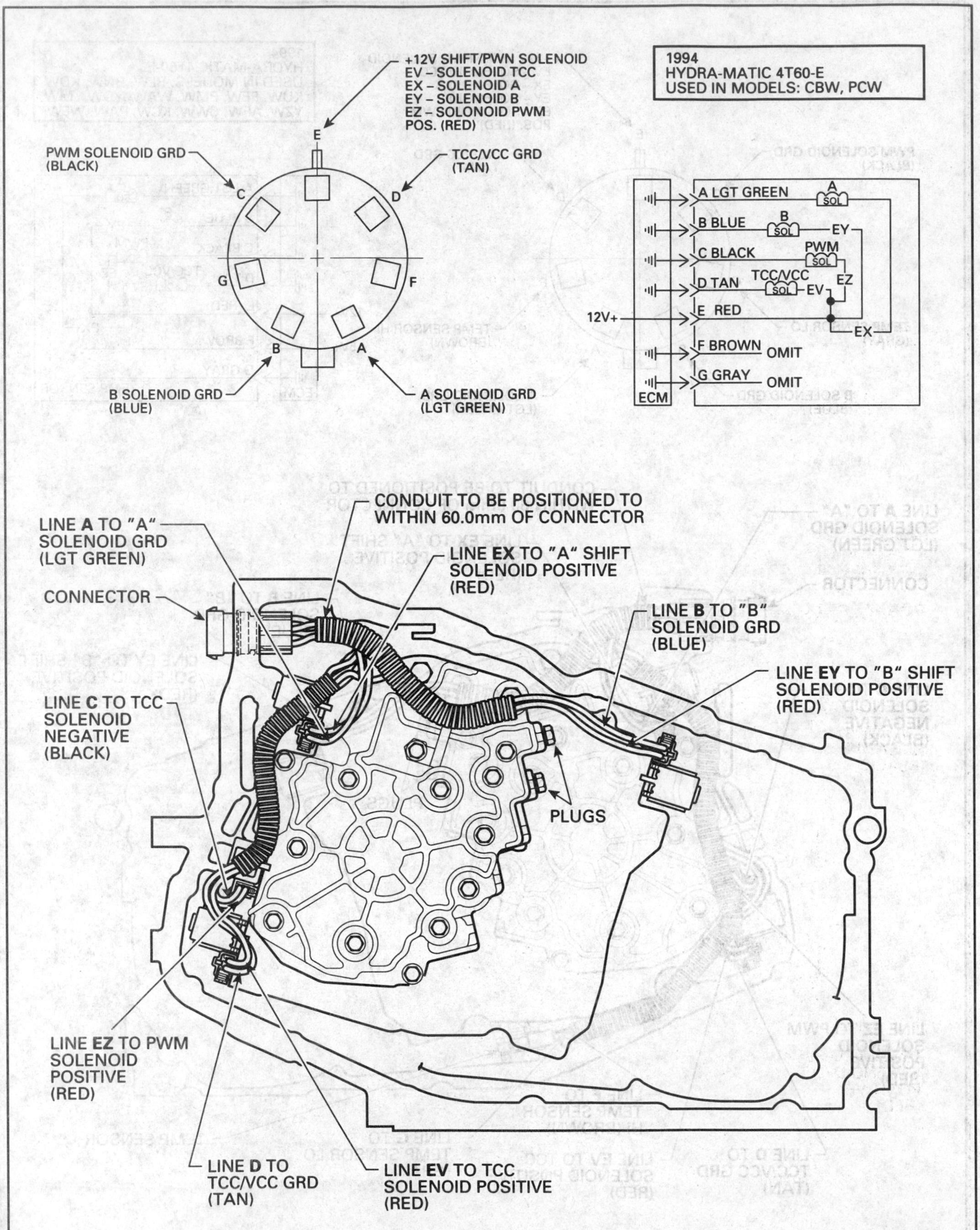
1994
HYDRA-MATIC 4T60-E
USED IN MODELS: CBW, PCW
+12V SHIFT/PWN SOLENOID
EV – SOLENOID TCC
EX – SOLENOID A
EY – SOLENOID B
EZ – SOLONOID PWM
POS. (RED)
E
PWM SOLENOID GRD
(BLACK)
TCC/VCC GRD
(TAN)
C
D
G
F
B
A
B SOLENOID GRD
(BLUE)
A SOLENOID GRD
(LGT GREEN)
A LGT GREEN
B BLUE
C BLACK
D TAN
E RED
F BROWN
G GRAY
SOL
PWM
TCC/VCC
EY
EZ
EV
EX
12V+
OMIT
OMIT
ECM
CONDUIT TO BE POSITIONED TO
WITHIN 60.0mm OF CONNECTOR
LINE A TO "A"
SOLENOID GRD
(LGT GREEN)
LINE EX TO "A" SHIFT
SOLENOID POSITIVE
(RED)
CONNECTOR
LINE B TO "B"
SOLENOID GRD
(BLUE)
LINE EY TO "B" SHIFT
SOLENOID POSITIVE
(RED)
LINE C TO TCC
SOLENOID
NEGATIVE
(BLACK)
PLUGS
LINE EZ TO PWM
SOLENOID
POSITIVE
(RED)
LINE D TO
TCC/VCC GRD
(TAN)
LINE EV TO TCC
SOLENOID POSITIVE
(RED)
RH0102-4T60-E

Figure 23 Wiring Diagram

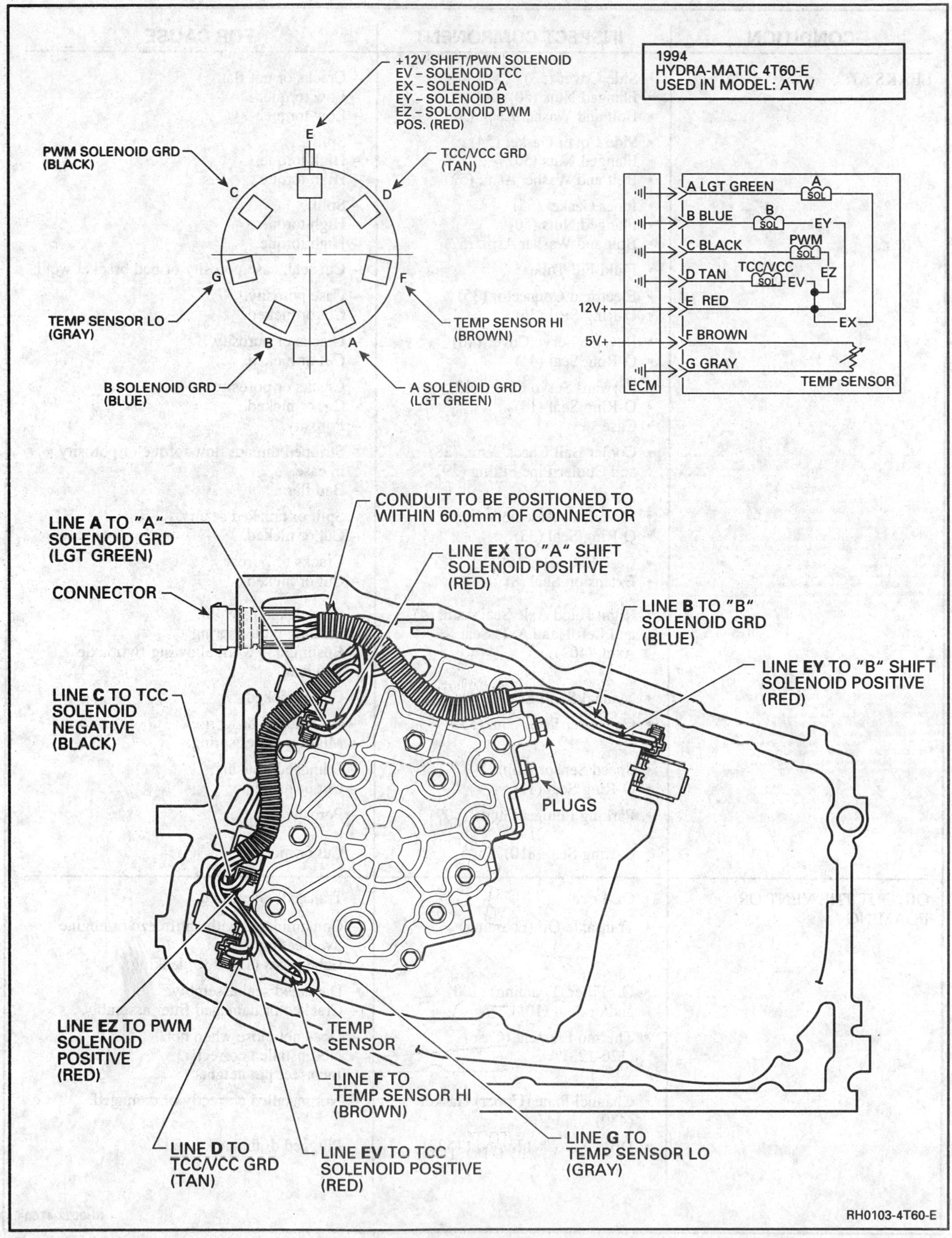
1994
HYDRA-MATIC 4T60-E
USED IN MODEL: ATW
+12V SHIFT/PWN SOLENOID
EV – SOLENOID TCC
EX – SOLENOID A
EY – SOLENOID B
EZ – SOLONOID PWM
POS. (RED)
PWM SOLENOID GRD
(BLACK)
TCC/VCC GRD
(TAN)
TEMP SENSOR LO
(GRAY)
TEMP SENSOR HI
(BROWN)
B SOLENOID GRD
(BLUE)
A SOLENOID GRD
(LGT GREEN)
E
C
D
G
F
B
A
A LGT GREEN
B BLUE
C BLACK
D TAN
E RED
F BROWN
G GRAY
12V+
5V+
ECM
A
SOL
B
SOL
EY
PWM
SOL
EZ
TCC/VCC
SOL
EV
EX
TEMP SENSOR
CONDUIT TO BE POSITIONED TO
WITHIN 60.0mm OF CONNECTOR
LINE A TO "A"
SOLENOID GRD
(LGT GREEN)
LINE EX TO "A" SHIFT
SOLENOID POSITIVE
(RED)
CONNECTOR
LINE B TO "B"
SOLENOID GRD
(BLUE)
LINE EY TO "B" SHIFT
SOLENOID POSITIVE
(RED)
LINE C TO TCC
SOLENOID
NEGATIVE
(BLACK)
PLUGS
LINE EZ TO PWM
SOLENOID
POSITIVE
(RED)
TEMP
SENSOR
LINE F TO
TEMP SENSOR HI
(BROWN)
LINE D TO
TCC/VCC GRD
(TAN)
LINE EV TO TCC
SOLENOID POSITIVE
(RED)
LINE G TO
TEMP SENSOR LO
(GRAY)
RH0103-4T60-E

Figure 24 Wiring Diagram

CONDITION	INSPECT COMPONENT	FOR CAUSE
LEAKS AT:	• Side Cover (53) • Flanged Nuts (50) • Bolt and Washer Asm. (52)	– Cracks or not flat. – Low torque. – Low torque.
	• Side Cover Gasket (54) • Flanged Nuts (50) • Bolt and Washer Asm. (52)	– Split. – High torque. – High torque.
	• Inner Gasket (55) • Flanged Nuts (50) • Bolt and Washer Asm. (52)	– Split. – High torque. – High torque.
	• Fluid Fill Tube	– Cut seal, case porosity or bad bracket weld.
	• Electrical Connector (35) • O-Ring Seal (36)	– Case porosity. – Cut or nicked.
	• Reverse Servo Cover (40) • O-Ring Seal (41)	– Cracks or porosity. – Cut or nicked.
	• Forward Servo Cover (13) • O-Ring Seal (14) • Case	– Cracks or porosity. – Cut or nicked. – Porosity.
	• Cooler Ball Check Asm. (28) and Cooler Pipe Fitting (29)	– Stripped threads, low torque or porosity in case. – Bad flare.
	• Modulator Assembly (32) • O-Ring Seal (33)	– Split or cracked seams. – Cut or nicked.
	• Case Extension (6) • Extension Seal (8)	– Cracks or porosity. – Cut or nicked.
	• Right Hand Axle Seal Asm. (4) and Left Hand Axle Seal Asm. (409)	– Cut, nicked or worn. – Missing garter spring. – Bushing (7) worn allowing right axle seal leak.
	• Manual Shaft Seal (806)	– Cut or nicked.
	• Converter Seal Asm. (525)	– Cut, nicked or worn. – Missing garter spring.
	• Speed Sensor Asm. (10) • O-Ring Seal (11)	– Damaged housing. – Cut or nicked.
	• Parking Plunger Guide (809)	– Porosity in case.
	• O-Ring Seal (810)	– Cut or nicked.
OIL OUT THE VENT OR FOAMING	• Oil Level	– Transaxle overfilled.
	• Transaxle Oil (Foaming)	– Contaminated with antifreeze or engine overheating. – Lube pipes (126-130) leaking.
	• Oil Filter (Foaming) (100) and/or Seal (101)	– Damaged seal assembly. – Cracked or damaged filter assembly.
	• Thermo Element (Case) (120-123)	– Does not close when hot. – Not installed correctly. – Incorrect pin heights.
	• Channel Plate (Upper) Gasket (430)	– Not installed correctly or damaged.
	• Drive Sprocket Support (522)	– Plugged drain back holes.

RH0022-4T60-E

Figure 25 Hydraulic, Electrical and Mechanical Diagnosis Chart

CONDITION	INSPECT COMPONENT	FOR CAUSE
HIGH OR LOW OIL PRESSURE (VERIFY WITH GAGE, ENGINE MUST BE PROPERLY TUNED) ENGINE MUST DEVELOP 13-18 HG. IN. OF VACUUM	• Oil Level	– High or low; correct as required.
	• Vacuum Line	– Leaking, pinched, disconnected or cut.
	• Modulator (32)	– Leaks or damaged diaphragm. (A bent modulator will not function correctly).
	• Modulator Valve (34)	– Nicked, scored or stuck.
	• Oil Pump Assembly	– Slide stuck, seals damaged, vanes damaged. – Pump drive shaft damaged.
	• Pressure Regulator Valve (313) or Springs (311 and 312)	– Nick or scored, springs damaged.
	• Pressure Relief Valve (321)	– Damaged spring, ball missing.
DELAYED ENGAGEMENT	• Fluid Level	– Low.
	• Cooler Checkball (28)	– Not seating, allowing converter drain back.
	• Reverse Servo Assembly	– Seal (43) cut or damaged.
	• Input Shaft and Housing Assembly	– Damaged retainer and ball asm. (633).
	• Forward Servo Assembly	– Seal (105) damaged or mislocated. – Seal (18) damaged or cut.
	• Input Clutch Outer Piston Seal	– Seal (635) damaged or cut/rolled.
SLIPS IN DRIVE	• Fluid Level	– Low - correct.
2ND GEAR START "A" SHIFT SOLENOID FOR "OFF" FAILURE	• Vacuum Line	– Pinched, slowing vacuum response.
	• Modulator (32)	– Damaged.
3RD GEAR START SEE 3RD GEAR ONLY	• Oil Pressure	– See Causes of Low Pressure.
	• Modulator Valve (34)	– Stuck or binding.
4TH GEAR START "B" SHIFT SOLENOID FOR "OFF" FAILURE OR TCC WIRES AND "B" SHIFT SOLENOID WIRES SWITCHED	• Forward Servo Assembly	– Damaged or missing cushion spring (19) or retainer (20).
	• Forward Servo Assembly (16)	– Seal (18) damaged.
	• Oil Filter (100)	– Plugged.
	• Filter Seal (101)	– Cut or damaged.
	• Forward Servo Seal (105)	– Leaking, damaged or missing seal or low torque of bolts (103).
	• Torque Converter (1)	– Stator roller clutch not holding.
	• Bolt (380)	– Low torque allowing leakage for driven sprocket support.
	• Input Clutch Assembly	– Leaks at ball capsule (633) or seals. – Seals damaged (634 and 635).
	• Pump Assembly	– Slide sticking. – Leak at slide seals.
	• "A" Shift Solenoid or "TCC"	– Malfunctioned or mislocated.
NO DRIVE IN DRIVE RANGE (INSTALL PRESSURE GAGE)	• Oil Level	– Low (correct).
	• Oil Pressure	– Low (See Causes of Low Pressure).

RH0023-4T60-E

Figure 26 Hydraulic, Electrical and Mechanical Diagnosis Chart

CONDITION	INSPECT COMPONENT	FOR CAUSE
NO DRIVE IN DRIVE RANGE (INSTALL PRESSURE GAGE) (Cont.)	• Manual Linkage	– Misadjusted or disconnected.
	• "A" Shift Solenoid or "TCC"	– Malfunctioned or mislocated.
	• Forward Servo Assembly	– Piston or seal damaged.
	• 1/2 Roller Clutch	– Damaged.
	• Drive Axles	– Disengaged.
	• Oil Pump Assembly	– Damaged. (See Causes of Low Oil Pressure.) – Pump drive shaft (227) damaged.
	• #3 Checkball	– Missing.
	• Torque Converter (1)	– Stator roller clutch (vehicle moves, but is very sluggish). – Converter not bolted to flex plate.
	• Drive Link Assembly	– Damaged or broken drive link chain. – Sprockets damaged.
	• Input Clutch Assembly	– Burned, clutch plates or missing. – Damaged piston seals or piston. – Housing checkball assembly leaking. – Input shaft seals damaged. – Input shaft feed passages blocked.
	• Input Sprag and Input Sun Gear Assembly	– Improper assembly. – Sprag damaged - roll over.
	• Input Carrier and Reaction Carrier Assembly	– Pinions damaged. – Internal gear damaged. – Sun gear damaged.
	• Output Shaft (510)	– Damaged, misassembled with axles.
	• Forward Band Assembly (688)	– Burned. – Band apply pin (21) mislocated with band. (Will still move in Manual Lo and Manual 2nd.)
	• Parking Pawl (694)	– Spring broken, pawl remains engaged.
	• Final Drive Assembly or Final Drive Sun Gear Shaft (689)	– Damaged side gear, gears, pinion, internal gear.
FIRST SPEED ONLY NO 1-2 SHIFT	• Control Valve Assembly (300)	– 1-2 Shift valve (318) stuck or binding. – Spacer plate (370) or gaskets (364 and 371) mispositioned or damaged.
	• Driven Sprocket Support (609)	– Oil seal rings (612 and 613) damaged.
	• 2nd Clutch Assembly (617)	– Clutch plates damaged. – Piston or seals damaged. – Parts misassembled.
	• Reverse Reaction Drum (669)	– Splines damaged.
1-2 SHIFT FEEL – HARSH OR SOFT	• Oil Pressure	– (See Causes of High or Low Oil Pressure.)
	• 1-2 Accumulator Piston (136 and 137) and Cover (132)	– Cover bolts (131) improperly torqued. – Piston or seal damaged. – Spring damaged. – Gaskets (133) mispositioned, damaged or low torque of bolts (131).

RH0024-4T60-E

Figure 27 Hydraulic, Electrical and Mechanical Diagnosis Chart

CONDITION	INSPECT COMPONENT	FOR CAUSE
1-2 SHIFT FEEL – HARSH OR SOFT (Cont.)	• Control Valve Asm. (300) • No. 2 Checkball	– 1-2 Accumulator valve (341) stuck. – Mislocated.
SOFT/SLIPPING	• Driven Sprocket Support (609)	– Rolled or twisted seal (612) for driven sprocket support ring. – Worn sleeve in 2nd clutch housing (616 or 619).
SLIPS ON TURNS	• Fluid Level • Filter (100)	– Low. – Cracked or damaged.
SHUDDER 1-2 SHIFT	• 2nd Clutch (616-627) • Driven Sprocket Support (609)	– Worn (fiber) plates (624). – Leaking check valve ball (618). – Cut seal (620). – Damaged (steel) plates (625). – Mispositioned snap ring (627 or 622). – Damaged seal rings (612 and 613). – (See Causes of Low Oil Pressure.)
1-2 SHIFT SPEED – HIGH OR LOW	• Refer To Shift Speed Chart and Section 6E • Check Service Bulletins If An Update To PROM • Incorrect Tooth Count On VS Sensor Rotor • Wrong PROM • Wrong Final Drive Ratio or Model	
1ST AND 2ND GEAR ONLY (1-2-2-1) POSSIBLE CODES: — 26 OR 56 QUAD DRIVER MODULE CIRCUIT (DEPENDING ON VEHICLE APPLICATION) — 36 TRANSAXLE SHIFT CONTROL PROBLEM	• "B" Shift Solenoid For "ON" Failure	– Foreign material in solenoid. – PCM signal grounded. – Pinched solenoid return wire to ground.
1ST AND 4TH GEAR ONLY EXTENDED 1ST GEAR BY PASSING 2ND AND 3RD THEN SHIFT TO 4TH POSSIBLE CODES: — 26 OR 56 QUAD DRIVER MODULE CIRCUIT (DEPENDING ON VEHICLE APPLICATION)	• "A" Shift Solenoid For "ON" Failure	– Foreign material in solenoid. – PCM signal grounded. – Pinched solenoid return wire to ground.

RH0025-4T60-E

Figure 28 Hydraulic, Electrical and Mechanical Diagnosis Chart

CONDITION	INSPECT COMPONENT	FOR CAUSE
2ND AND 3RD GEAR ONLY POSSIBLE CODES: — 26 OR 56 QUAD DRIVER MODULE CIRCUIT (DEPENDING ON VEHICLE APPLICATION)	• "A" Shift Solenoid For "OFF" Failure	– Insufficient force of solenoid. – Foreign material, plugging filter [374(A)]. – PCM not grounding. – O-ring failure. – No supply voltage to "A" Shift Solenoid. – Wires not connected to solenoid.
NO 2-3 SHIFT (1st, 2nd and 4th SPEED ONLY)	• Control Valve Asm. (300)	– 2-3 Shift valve (357) stuck. – 3-2 Manual downshift valve (356) stuck.
	• Channel Plate Gasket (429)	– Mispositioned or damaged.
	• Driven Sprocket Support (609)	– Blocked 3rd clutch passage..
	• Input Housing and Shaft Asm.	– Seals (628) damaged. – Blocked oil passages.
NO 2-3 SHIFT (1st, 2nd and 4th SPEED ONLY) (Cont.)	• 3rd Clutch Assembly	– Clutch plates burned. – Damaged piston or seals. – Damaged checkball assembly (piston).
	• 3rd Roller Clutch Assembly	– Damaged cage. – Rollers out of cage. – Damaged springs. – Misassembled on input sun gear shaft. – No third gear and no engine braking in Manual Lo.
2-3 SHIFT FEEL – HARSH OR SOFT	• See Causes Of High or Low Oil Pressure	
	• No. 4 Checkball	– Mislocated for a soft shift.
	• No. 9 Checkball	– Missing for a harsh shift.
	• 2-3 Accumulator Piston, Gaskets and Seals	– Missing springs [138(A) and 138(B)], cut seal (137), damaged gaskets (133) and low torque of bolts (131).
2-3 SHIFT SPEED – HIGH OR LOW	• Refer To Shift Speed Chart and Section 6E • Wrong PROM • Check Service Bulletins If An Update To PROM	
3RD GEAR ONLY (2ND GEAR POSSIBLE THROUGH MANUAL GEAR RANGE) POSSIBLE CODES: — 36 TRANSAXLE SHIFT CONTROL PROBLEM	• PCM and Transaxles Wiring	– Loose connector. – Corroded connector. – Defective PCM.
— 16 BATTERY VOLTAGE HIGH OR LOW — 36 TRANSAXLE SHIFT CONTROL PROBLEM	• Generator and Wiring	– Loose connector. – Corroded connector. – Defective generator.

RH0026-4T60-E

Figure 29 Hydraulic, Electrical and Mechanical Diagnosis Chart

CONDITION	INSPECT COMPONENT	FOR CAUSE
3RD GEAR ONLY (Cont.) (2ND GEAR POSSIBLE THROUGH MANUAL GEAR RANGE) POSSIBLE CODES: — 24 SPEED SENSOR	• Speed Sensor and Wiring	– Loose connector. – Corroded connector. – Defective speed sensor.
— 26 OR 56 QUAD DRIVER MODULE CIRCUIT (DEPENDING ON VEHICLE APPLICATION)	• PCM and Wiring "A" and "B" Shift Solenoids	– Loose connector. – Corroded connector. – Defective quad driver.
4TH GEAR START	• "B" Shift Solenoid	– Solenoid mislocated from control valve assembly.
3RD AND 4TH GEAR OPERATION (4-3-3-4) 2ND GEAR DOWNSHIFTS ATTAINABLE THROUGH MANUAL GEAR RANGES POSSIBLE CODES: (SOME MODELS) — 26 OR 56 QUAD DRIVER MODULE CIRCUIT (DEPENDING ON VEHICLE APPLICATION) — 36 TRANSAXLE SHIFT CONTROL PROBLEM	• "B" Shift Solenoid For "Off" Failure	– Foreign material, plugging filter [374(B)]. – Insufficient force of solenoid. – O-ring failure. – Open wire from "B" Shift Solenoid to PCM. – PCM not grounding. – No supply voltage to "B" Shift Solenoid. – Wires not connected to "B" Shift Solenoid.
NO 3-4 SHIFT	• Control Valve Assembly (300)	– 3-4 Shift valve (362) stuck. – 4-3 Manual downshift valve (360) stuck.
	• 4th Clutch Shaft (504)	– Spline damage.
	• 4th Clutch Assembly (500-502)	– Clutch plates burned. – Piston or seals damaged. – Clutch plates or piston mislocated.
	• Shift Cable Adjustment	
3-4 SHIFT FEEL – HARSH OR SOFT	• See Causes Of High or Low Oil Pressure	
	• Accumulator Cover (421) and Piston (428 and 427)	– Damaged seals (427 or 422). – Missing springs (423, 424 or 425).
	• #10 Checkball	– Missing.
	• Control Valve Assembly (300)	– 3-4 Accumulator valve (350) stuck.
	• 3-4 Accumulator Spring Package	– 3-4 Accumulator spring (423) present.
3-4 SHIFT SPEED – HIGH OR LOW	• Refer To Shift Speed Chart and Section 6E	
	• Check Service Bulletins If An Update To PROM	
	• Wrong PROM	

RH0027-4T60-E

Figure 30 Hydraulic, Electrical and Mechanical Diagnosis Chart

CONDITION	INSPECT COMPONENT	FOR CAUSE
NO REVERSE	• Oil Pressure (See Causes Of High or Low Pressure)	
	• Reverse Servo (17, 39-49)	– Misassembled. – Piston or seal damaged. – Missing cushion spring (45) or retainers (46).
	• Oil Pump Assembly (See No Drive)	
	• Drive Link Assembly (See No Drive)	
	• Reverse Band (615)	– Burned, damaged, or mislocated with band apply pin.
	• Input Clutch (See No Drive)	
	• "A" Shift Solenoid or "TCC"	– Solenoid misfunctioned or walked out.
	• Reverse Reaction Drum (669)	– Splines damaged.
	• Input Sprag (See No Drive)	
	• Input and Reaction Carriers (See No Drive)	– (See No Drive).
LOCKED UP IN REVERSE OR DRIVE	• Final Drive Internal Gear (693)	– Deformed/dented parking pawl (694).
	• Reverse Servo Pin and Bore	– Pin to bore (servo alignment).
SLIPS IN REVERSE (ALSO SEE SLIPS IN DRIVE)	• Oil Pressure	– See Causes of Low Pressure.
	• Reverse Servo Assembly	– Damaged seal (43).
	• Reverse Reaction Drum (669)	– Damaged splines.
NO PARK RANGE	• Final Drive Internal Gear (693 and 694)	– Park pawl spring. – Parking pawl. – Parking gear.
	• Actuator Assembly (800)	– Spring damage.
	• Shift Cable Adjustment	
HARSH NEUTRAL TO REVERSE OR HARSH NEUTRAL TO DRIVE	• Modulator (32), and/or Lines	– Loss of vacuum due to damaged lines or modulator.
	• Reverse Servo Cushion Spring	– Broken or wrong spring.
	• Control Valve Asm. (300)	– No. 5 Checkball missing - results in harsh reverse. – No. 6 Checkball missing - results in harsh drive.
	• Forward Servo Cushion Spring (19)	– Broken or wrong spring.
	• Spacer Plate (370)	– Thermal element does not close when warm, causing harsh Neutral to Drive.
2ND GEAR STARTS HARSH ENGAGEMENT OR	• Control Valve Asm. (300)	– Stuck 1-2 shift valve (318).
	• 2nd Clutch Housing and Drum	– Drum surface scored or hot spots caused by

RH0028-4T60-E

Figure 31 Hydraulic, Electrical and Mechanical Diagnosis Chart

CONDITION	INSPECT COMPONENT	FOR CAUSE
ENGAGEMENT SHUDDER IN REVERSE	Assembly (617) • Reverse Band Assembly (615) • No. 5 Checkball • Servo Cushion Spring (45)	band slippage. – Burned fiber material. – Missing or mislocated. – Wrong spring or damaged.
NO ENGINE BRAKING IN MANUAL 2ND OR LO	• 2-1 Manual Band (680) • Apply Pin (111) • Seals (113 and 107) • Gaskets (133) • Bolts (131)	– Burned or glazed fiber material. – Not engaging 2-1 manual band. – Cut or damaged. – Missing filter (115) allowing foreign material to damage seal and bore. – Damaged. – Low torque.
CONVERTER CLUTCH DOES NOT RELEASE	• TCC Solenoid • Control Valve Asm. (300) • TCC Screen [374(C)]	– TCC solenoid (315) does not exhaust. – Converter clutch valve (335) stuck in apply position. – Missing, allowing foreign material to stick TCC solenoid on.
TCC STUCK ON IN 3RD AND 4TH GEAR	• TCC Solenoid For "On" Failure	– Foreign material. – Pinched solenoid wire to ground. – PCM signal grounded.
TCC APPLIES WITH MAX PRESSURE – HARSH APPLY	• TCC PWM For "Off" Failure	– Foreign material in PWM solenoid. – No PCM signal. – Insufficient force of PCM. – O-rings failure. – Open wire. – No supply voltage to PWM solenoid.
CONVERTER CLUTCH APPLY, ROUGH, SLIPS, OR SHUDDERS	• Control Valve Asm (300) • Turbine Shaft (518) • Channel Plate (401) • Drive Sprocket Support (522) • Torque Converter	– Converter clutch regulator valve (332 or 334) stuck. – Seals damaged or missing. – Converter clutch blow off checkball (420) not seated or damaged. – Converter clutch regulator valve. – Worn bushing (523). – Worn or glazed fiber material. (Replace converter.)
4-3 DOWNSHIFT — HARSH	• Control Valve Asm. (300) • 3-4 Accumulator Seal • 3-4 Accumulator Valve	– No. 10 Checkball missing. – Cut seal (427). – Valve stuck (350).
3-2 DOWNSHIFT — HARSH	• Control Valve Asm. (300) • 2-3 Accumulator Valve	– No. 9 Checkball missing. – Valve stuck (343).

RH0029-4T60-E

Figure 32 Hydraulic, Electrical and Mechanical Diagnosis Chart

CONDITION	INSPECT COMPONENT	FOR CAUSE
2-1 DOWNSHIFT — HARSH	• Spacer Plate (370)	– Wrong spacer plate.
	• 1-2 Accumulator Seal	– Cut seal (137).
	• 1-2 Accumulator Valve	– Valve stuck (341).
NO CONVERTER CLUTCH APPLY	• Verify Proper PCM Operation and Vehicle Wiring	– Improper operation or wiring.
	• Wiring Harness (224)	– Connector damaged or loose. – Pinched wires. – TCC Solenoid (315) inoperative.
	• Control Valve Asm. (300)	– Converter clutch valve (335) stuck. – Converter clutch regulator valve (332 or 334) stuck.
	• TCC Solenoid (315)	– Solenoid O-ring (316) leaking.
	• Solenoid Screen [374(C)]	– Blocked.
	• Torque Converter (1)	– Inspect - Refer to Transaxle Unit Repair Section and Section 6E.
	• Turbine Shaft (518)	– Seals (519 or 520) damaged.
	• Oil Pump Drive Shaft (227)	– Damaged seal (228).
	• Channel Plate (401)	– Converter clutch blow off checkball not seated or damaged. – No. 1 Checkball [372(A)] missing.
NO TCC POSSIBLE CODES: ALSO, SEE TORQUE CONVERTER CLUTCH "COLD DRIVEABILITY" OF SECTION 7A1	• TCC Solenoid For "Off" Failure	– Foreign material, plugging filter [374(D)]. – Insufficient force. – O-ring failure. – No PCM signal. – Open wire. – No supply voltage to TCC solenoid. – Improperly molded solenoid housing causing solenoid to separate from control valve assembly.
	• TCC Solenoid For "On" Failure	– Foreign material. – Pinched wire. – PCM signal grounded.
— 90 BRAKE SWITCH CIRCUIT (MODEL DEPENDANT)	• Brake Switch (No TCC Apply)	– No supply voltage. – Connector corroded – Switch contact corrosion. – Connector loosens. – Pinched wire.
— 91 PRNDL SWITCH PROBLEM (MODEL DEPENDANT)	• PRNDL Circuit Problem	– Connector loose. – Connector corroded. – Switch contact corrosion. – Pinched wire. – PRNDL connector wires A and B switched around if PRNDL indicates anything but D3 or D4.

RH0030-4T60-E

Figure 33 Hydraulic, Electrical and Mechanical Diagnosis Chart

CONDITION	INSPECT COMPONENT	FOR CAUSE
NO TCC (Cont.)		
POSSIBLE CODES:		
— 15 COOLANT TEMP LOW (TCC WILL COME ON WITH A CODE 15 AFTER ENGINE HAS BEEN DRIVEN AWHILE – ENGINE RUN TIMER ELAPSED)	• Coolant Temp Sensor Engine Up To Operating Temperature of 75°C (167°F)?	– Connector corroded. – Incorrect resistance. – Connector loose. – Pinched wire.
— 96 TORQUE CONVERTER OVER-STRESSED (MODEL DEPENDANT)	• See Section 8D	
— 26 OR 56 QUAD DRIVER MODULE CIRCUIT (DEPENDING ON VEHICLE APPLICATION)	• TCC PWM For “ON” Failure	– Foreign material. – Pinched wire. – PCM signal grounded.
— 38 BRAKE SWITCH CIRCUIT (MODEL DEPENDANT)	• Brake Switch (No TCC Apply)	– No supply voltage. – Connector corroded. – Switch contact corrosion. – Connector loosens. – Pinched wire.
— 31 PRNDL SWITCH PROBLEM (MODEL DEPENDANT)	• PRNDL Circuit Problem	– Connector loosens. – Connector corroded. – Switch contact corrosion. – Pinched wire. – PRNDL connector wires A and B switched around if PRNDL indicates anything but D3 or D4.

RH0104-4T60-E

Figure 34 Hydraulic, Electrical and Mechanical Diagnosis Chart

THIS PAGE LEFT INTENTIONALLY BLANK

4T60-E TRANSAXLE

FLUID FLOW

AND

CIRCUIT DESCRIPTION

RH0000-4T60-E

Fluid Flow and Circuit Descriptions

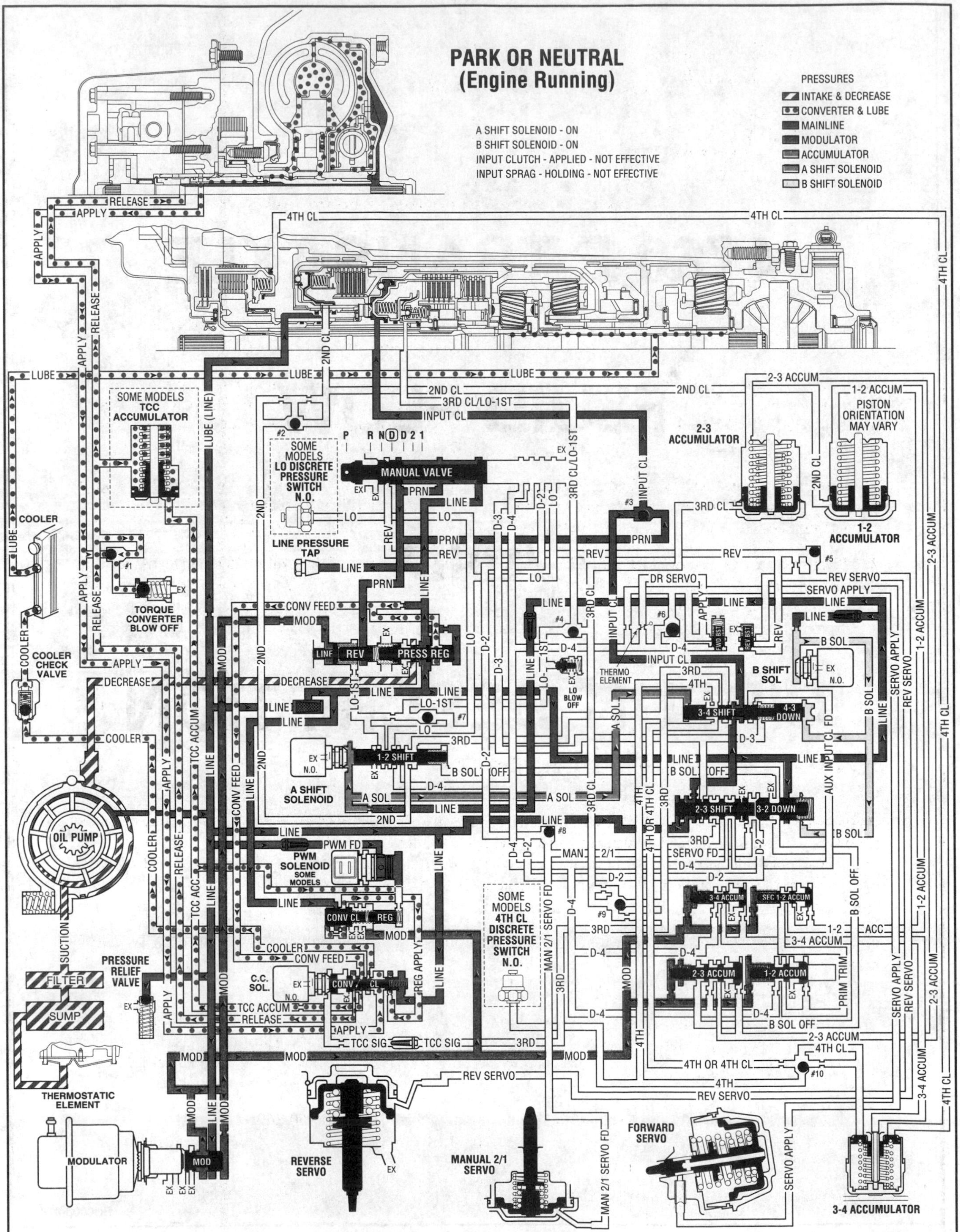
PARK OR NEUTRAL
(Engine Running)
A SHIFT SOLENOID - ON
B SHIFT SOLENOID - ON
INPUT CLUTCH - APPLIED - NOT EFFECTIVE
INPUT SPRAG - HOLDING - NOT EFFECTIVE
PRESSURES
INTAKE & DECREASE
CONVERTER & LUBE
MAINLINE
MODULATOR
ACCUMULATOR
A SHIFT SOLENOID
B SHIFT SOLENOID
RELEASE
APPLY
4TH CL
LUBE
2ND CL
3RD CL/LO-1ST
INPUT CL
2-3 ACCUM
1-2 ACCUM
PISTON ORIENTATION MAY VARY
2-3 ACCUMULATOR
1-2 ACCUMULATOR
SOME MODELS TCC ACCUMULATOR
SOME MODELS LO DISCRETE PRESSURE SWITCH N.O.
P R N D D 2 1
MANUAL VALVE
LINE PRESSURE TAP
COOLER
TORQUE CONVERTER BLOW OFF
COOLER CHECK VALVE
CONV FEED
MOD
REV
PRESS REG
DECREASE
1-2 SHIFT
A SHIFT SOLENOID
B SHIFT SOL
3-4 SHIFT
4-3 DOWN
2-3 SHIFT
3-2 DOWN
THERMO ELEMENT
LO BLOW OFF
DR SERVO
REV SERVO
SERVO APPLY
OIL PUMP
PWM SOLENOID SOME MODELS
CONV CL
REG
3-4 ACCUM
SEC 1-2 ACCUM
2-3 ACCUM
1-2 ACCUM
PRIM TRIM
SOME MODELS 4TH CL DISCRETE PRESSURE SWITCH N.O.
SUCTION
PRESSURE RELIEF VALVE
FILTER
SUMP
C.C. SOL.
REG APPLY
TCC ACCUM
TCC SIG
THERMOSTATIC ELEMENT
MODULATOR
REVERSE SERVO
MANUAL 2/1 SERVO
FORWARD SERVO
3-4 ACCUMULATOR
MAN 2/1 SERVO FD
4TH OR 4TH CL
AUX INPUT CL FD
B SOL OFF
EX

Figure 35 Park or Neutral Engine Running

PARK OR NEUTRAL ENGINE RUNNING

"A" SHIFT SOLENOID - ON

"B" SHIFT SOLENOID - ON

INPUT CLUTCH - APPLIED (NOT EFFECTIVE)

INPUT SPRAG - HOLDING (NOT EFFECTIVE)

In Park (P) range with the engine running, fluid is pulled from the sump, through the filter (100) and into the oil pump (200). Pump output is regulated by the pressure regulator valve (313) and a "decrease" passage which creates a calibrated output pressure called "line pressure". In PARK (P) range, line pressure is directed to the following components:

Pressure Regulator Valve (313): Regulates pump output in response to modulator pressure, PRN pressure at the reverse boost valve (310) and spring force from the pressure regulator valve springs (311, 312).

Manual Valve (404): Manually controlled through the gear selector lever, it directs line pressure from the pressure regulator valve (313) into the PRN passage in PARK, REVERSE or NEUTRAL. The manual valve (404) also provides for a hydraulic override of the electronic shift control system in the transaxle for manual third and manual second gear selection.

Modulator Valve (34): Controlled by the vacuum modulator, it regulates modulator pressure inversely to engine vacuum. Modulator pressure is directed to the line boost valve (304), 1-2 accumulator valve (341), secondary 1-2 accumulator valve (347), 2-3 accumulator valve (343) and 3-4 accumulator valve (350).

2-3 Shift Valve (357): In PARK range, line pressure passes through the 2-3 shift valve (357) and feeds the input clutch feed passage. Line pressure then passes through the 3-4 shift valve (362), around the No. 3 checkball (372, located in the channel plate) to apply the input clutch. Although the input clutch is applied and the input sprag is holding, they are not effective because neither the forward band assembly (688) or the reverse band assembly (615) are applied.

Converter Clutch Valve (335): Line pressure and spring force holds the valve against the converter clutch solenoid (315) allowing converter feed pressure to the release side of the converter clutch pressure plate. In this position, converter clutch apply pressure feeds into the cooler passage, through the cooler and into the lube circuit.

***Converter Clutch Regulator Valve (330):** Biased by modulator and TCC accumulator pressure, it uses line pressure to provide regulated apply fluid to the converter clutch valve (335).

Pulse Width Modulated (PWM) Solenoid (325): Electrically controlled by the Powertrain Control Module (PCM), it regulates PWM feed pressure into the PWM passage to the converter clutch regulator valve (330). This arrangement provides for precise control of regulated converter clutch apply pressure. Since the PWM solenoid (325) is not energized until 3rd gear operation, full line pressure passes through the solenoid to the converter clutch regulator valve (330).

"A" Shift Solenoid (315): Controlled by the Powertrain Control Module (PCM), it is energized (On) in PARK range. Line pressure moves the 1-2 shift valve (318) against spring pressure and directs line fluid into the "A" shift solenoid passage. "A" shift solenoid fluid is then directed to the 3-4 shift valve (362).

"B" Shift Solenoid (315): Controlled by the Powertrain Control Module (PCM), it is energized (On) in PARK range and directs line pressure into the "B" shift solenoid passage. "B" shift solenoid fluid is directed to: the 4-3 manual downshift valve (360) and moves the valve against spring pressure, and also the 3-2 manual downshift valve (356).

Pressure Relief Valve (321): Exhausts line pressure above 1,690-2480 kPa (450-360 psi).

Line Pressure Tap (38): Allows line pressure to be monitored with a gage.

* Applications that do not use a Pulse Width Modulator (PWM).

RH0032-4T60-E

Figure 36 Park or Neutral Engine Running – Legend

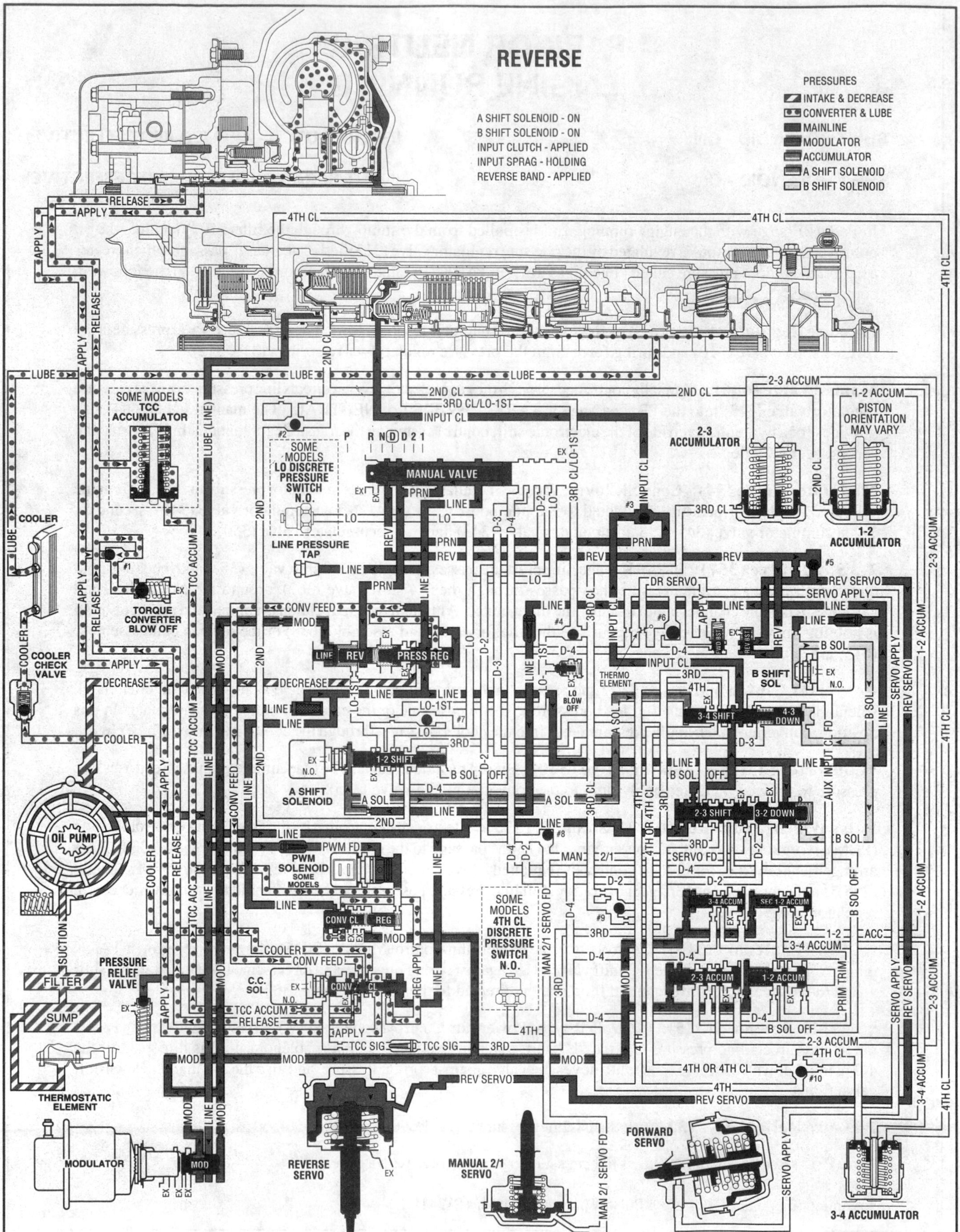
REVERSE
PRESSURES
INTAKE & DECREASE
CONVERTER & LUBE
MAINLINE
MODULATOR
ACCUMULATOR
A SHIFT SOLENOID
B SHIFT SOLENOID
A SHIFT SOLENOID - ON
B SHIFT SOLENOID - ON
INPUT CLUTCH - APPLIED
INPUT SPRAG - HOLDING
REVERSE BAND - APPLIED
SOME MODELS
TCC ACCUMULATOR
COOLER
TORQUE CONVERTER BLOW OFF
COOLER CHECK VALVE
SOME MODELS
LO DISCRETE PRESSURE SWITCH N.O.
LINE PRESSURE TAP
P R N D D 2 1
MANUAL VALVE
PRESS REG
1-2 SHIFT
A SHIFT SOLENOID
OIL PUMP
PWM SOLENOID
SOME MODELS
CONV CL REG
C.C. SOL
CONV CL
PRESSURE RELIEF VALVE
SUCTION
FILTER
SUMP
THERMOSTATIC ELEMENT
MODULATOR
REVERSE SERVO
MANUAL 2/1 SERVO
SOME MODELS
4TH CL DISCRETE PRESSURE SWITCH N.O.
FORWARD SERVO
3-4 ACCUMULATOR
2-3 ACCUMULATOR
1-2 ACCUMULATOR
PISTON ORIENTATION MAY VARY
B SHIFT SOL
THERMO ELEMENT
LO BLOW OFF
3-4 SHIFT
4-3 DOWN
2-3 SHIFT
3-2 DOWN
3-4 ACCUM
SEC 1-2 ACCUM
2-3 ACCUM
1-2 ACCUM

Figure 37 Reverse

REVERSE

"A" SHIFT SOLENOID - ON **INPUT CLUTCH - APPLIED** **REVERSE BAND - APPLIED**

"B" SHIFT SOLENOID - ON **INPUT SPRAG - HOLDING**

When the gear selector lever is moved to REVERSE (R), the manual valve allows line pressure to be fed through the PRN passage into the reverse fluid passage. Reverse fluid seats No. 5 checkball (372) and directs fluid to the reverse servo boost valve (365) and through the reverse servo feed orifice. Fluid passing through the orifice enters the reverse servo passage and forces the reverse servo piston (44) to overcome spring pressure to apply the reverse band (615). Depending on throttle position, engine manifold vacuum supply to the vacuum modulator can boost to full line pressure, 2100 kPa (305 psi) at 0 kPa (0" psi) engine manifold vacuum.

Manual Valve (404): Is moved manually to the right through the gear selector lever and allows line pressure to enter the reverse fluid passage through the PRN fluid passage.

No. 5 Checkball (373): Located in the valve body, (300), it blocks the reverse servo feed passage forcing reverse fluid through an orifice in the spacer plate (370) into the reverse servo passage. When the manual valve (404) is moved out of reverse, the checkball unseats allowing reverse servo fluid to exhaust through the ball seat instead of through the orifice.

Reverse Boost Valve (367): Opens under hard acceleration (high line pressure/high throttle position) to allow reverse fluid to by-pass the feed orifice and enter the reverse servo passage. This provides for a quick fill of the servo passage and quick apply of the reverse band to prevent band slippage during abusive shifts from Park or Neutral to Reverse.

Reverse Servo Assembly (39-49): Applies the reverse band (615) in response to reverse servo fluid pressure feeding into the servo cover (40) side of the reverse servo piston (44).

Reverse Band Assembly (615): Wraps around the second clutch housing (617) and holds the input carrier (672), through the reverse reaction drum (669), allowing the vehicle to move in reverse.

RH0034-4T60-E

Figure 38 Reverse – Legend

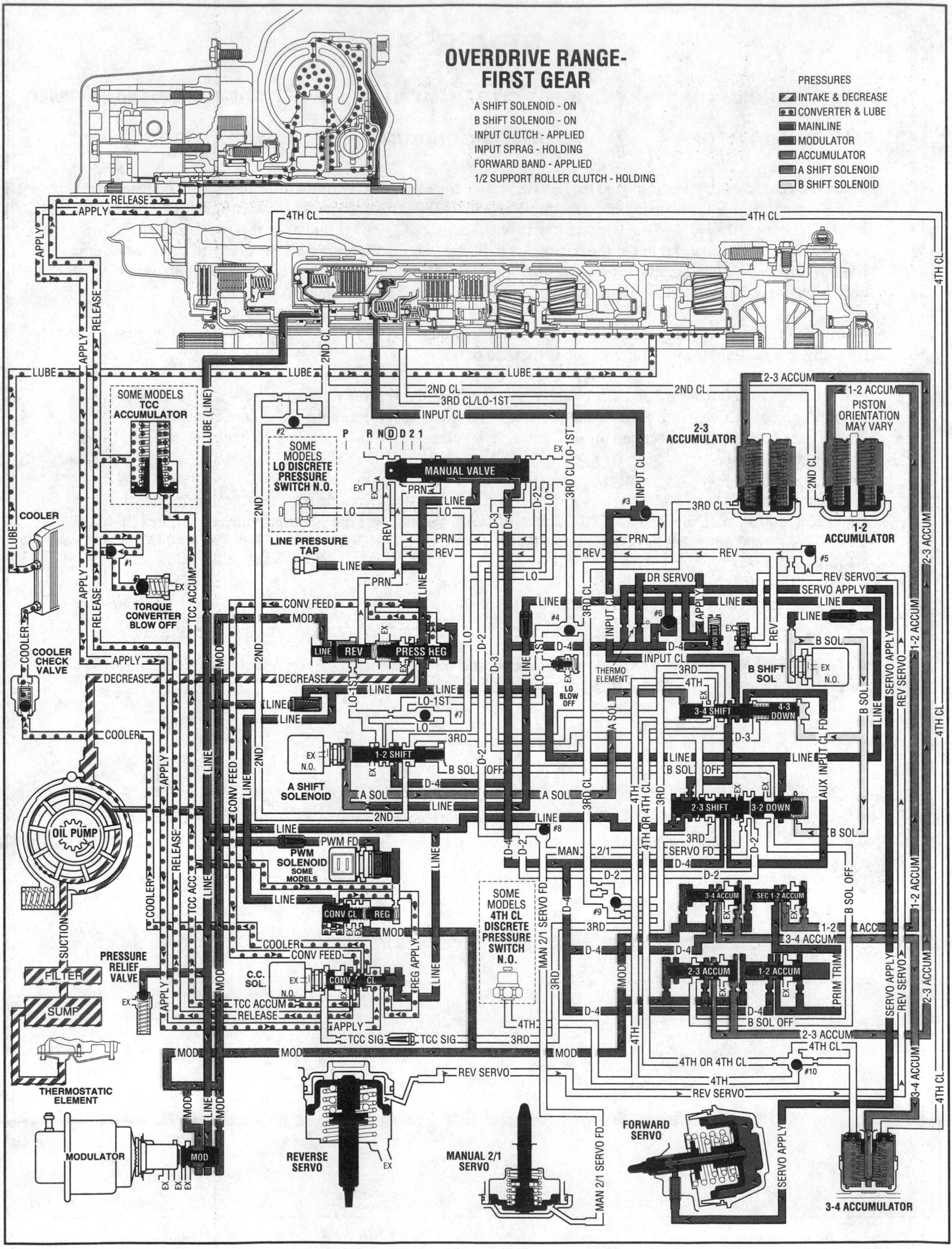
OVERDRIVE RANGE-
FIRST GEAR
A SHIFT SOLENOID - ON
B SHIFT SOLENOID - ON
INPUT CLUTCH - APPLIED
INPUT SPRAG - HOLDING
FORWARD BAND - APPLIED
1/2 SUPPORT ROLLER CLUTCH - HOLDING
PRESSURES
INTAKE & DECREASE
CONVERTER & LUBE
MAINLINE
MODULATOR
ACCUMULATOR
A SHIFT SOLENOID
B SHIFT SOLENOID
RELEASE
APPLY
4TH CL
LUBE
2ND CL
3RD CL/LO-1ST
INPUT CL
2-3 ACCUM
1-2 ACCUM
PISTON ORIENTATION MAY VARY
2-3 ACCUMULATOR
1-2 ACCUMULATOR
SOME MODELS TCC ACCUMULATOR
SOME MODELS LO DISCRETE PRESSURE SWITCH N.O.
P R N D D 2 1
MANUAL VALVE
LINE PRESSURE TAP
COOLER
TORQUE CONVERTER BLOW OFF
COOLER CHECK VALVE
CONV FEED
MOD
PRESS REG
DECREASE
DR SERVO
REV SERVO
SERVO APPLY
B SHIFT SOL
THERMO ELEMENT
LO BLOW OFF
3-4 SHIFT
4-3 DOWN
1-2 SHIFT
A SHIFT SOLENOID
2-3 SHIFT
3-2 DOWN
OIL PUMP
PWM SOLENOID SOME MODELS
CONV CL
REG
SOME MODELS 4TH CL DISCRETE PRESSURE SWITCH N.O.
3-4 ACCUM
SEC 1-2 ACCUM
2-3 ACCUM
1-2 ACCUM
SUCTION
FILTER
SUMP
PRESSURE RELIEF VALVE
C.C. SOL.
TCC ACCUM
TCC SIG
THERMOSTATIC ELEMENT
MODULATOR
REVERSE SERVO
MANUAL 2/1 SERVO
FORWARD SERVO
3-4 ACCUMULATOR

Figure 39 Overdrive Range – First Gear

OVERDRIVE RANGE - FIRST GEAR

"A" SHIFT SOLENOID - ON | **INPUT CLUTCH - APPLIED** | **FORWARD BAND - APPLIED**

"B" SHIFT SOLENOID - ON | **INPUT SPRAG - HOLDING** | **1/2 SUPPORT ROLLER CLUTCH - HOLDING**

When the gear selector lever is moved to the OVERDRIVE RANGE [D] the manual valve (404) moves and allows line pressure to fill the D-4 passage. D-4 pressure seats the No. 6 checkball (372) and sends fluid through the forward servo feed orifice into the servo apply passage. Servo apply fluid strokes the forward servo assembly (15-22) to apply the forward band (688). D-4 fluid also feeds the servo apply passage through the thermo element located on the spacer plate (370). D-4 fluid from the manual valve directs fluid to the following valves:

- 1-2 accumulator valve (341) into the primary trim passage to the secondary 1-2 accumulator valve (347) and into the 1-2 accumulator passage.
- 2-3 accumulator valve (343) and into the 2-3 accumulator passage.
- 3-4 accumulator valve (350) and into the 3-4 accumulator passage.
- 2-3 shift valve (357) and into the auxiliary input clutch feed passage.
- 1-2 shift valve (318)

Manual Valve (404): Is moved by the gear selector lever and allows line pressure to enter the D-4 passage.

No. 6 Checkball (372): Located in the valve body (300), blocks forward servo apply passage forcing D-4 pressure to the forward servo boost valve (367), the forward servo feed orifice and thermo element on the spacer plate (370). When the manual valve (404) is moved from Drive to Park or Neutral, the checkball unseats to allow for a quick exhaust of servo apply fluid and release of the forward band assembly (688).

Forward Servo Boost Valve (367): Opens under high line pressure (high throttle position) allowing D-4 fluid to by-pass the feed orifice and thermo element to enter the servo apply passage. This provides for a quick fill of the servo passage and quick apply of the forward band assembly (690) to prevent slippage during abusive shifts from Park or Neutral to Drive.

Forward Servo Assembly (15-22): Applies and holds the forward band (688) during all forward gear drive ranges.

Forward Band Assembly (688): Wraps around and holds the 1-2 support outer race (687) during all forward gear drive ranges.

1-2 Accumulator Valve (341): Fed by D-4 pressure, it regulates primary trim fluid pressure to the secondary 1-2 accumulator valve (347) in proportion to changes in modulator pressure.

Secondary 1-2 Accumulator Valve (347): Fed by primary trim fluid pressure, it regulates 1-2 accumulator pressure in proportion to modulator pressure. When primary trim reaches its breakpoint pressure, it is regulated lower by the secondary 1-2 accumulator valve.

2-3 Accumulator Valve (343): Fed by D-4 pressure, it regulates 2-3 accumulator pressure in proportion to modulator and "B" shift solenoid OFF pressure.

3-4 Accumulator Valve (350): Fed by D-4 pressure, it regulates 3-4 accumulator pressure in proportion to modulator pressure.

2-3 Shift Valve (357): Allows D-4 pressure to enter the auxiliary input clutch feed passage.

1-2 Shift Valve (318): Held against spring pressure by "A" shift solenoid pressure, D-4 fluid stops at this valve until a 1-2 shift is made.

RH0036-4T60-E

Figure 40 Overdrive Range – First Gear – Legend

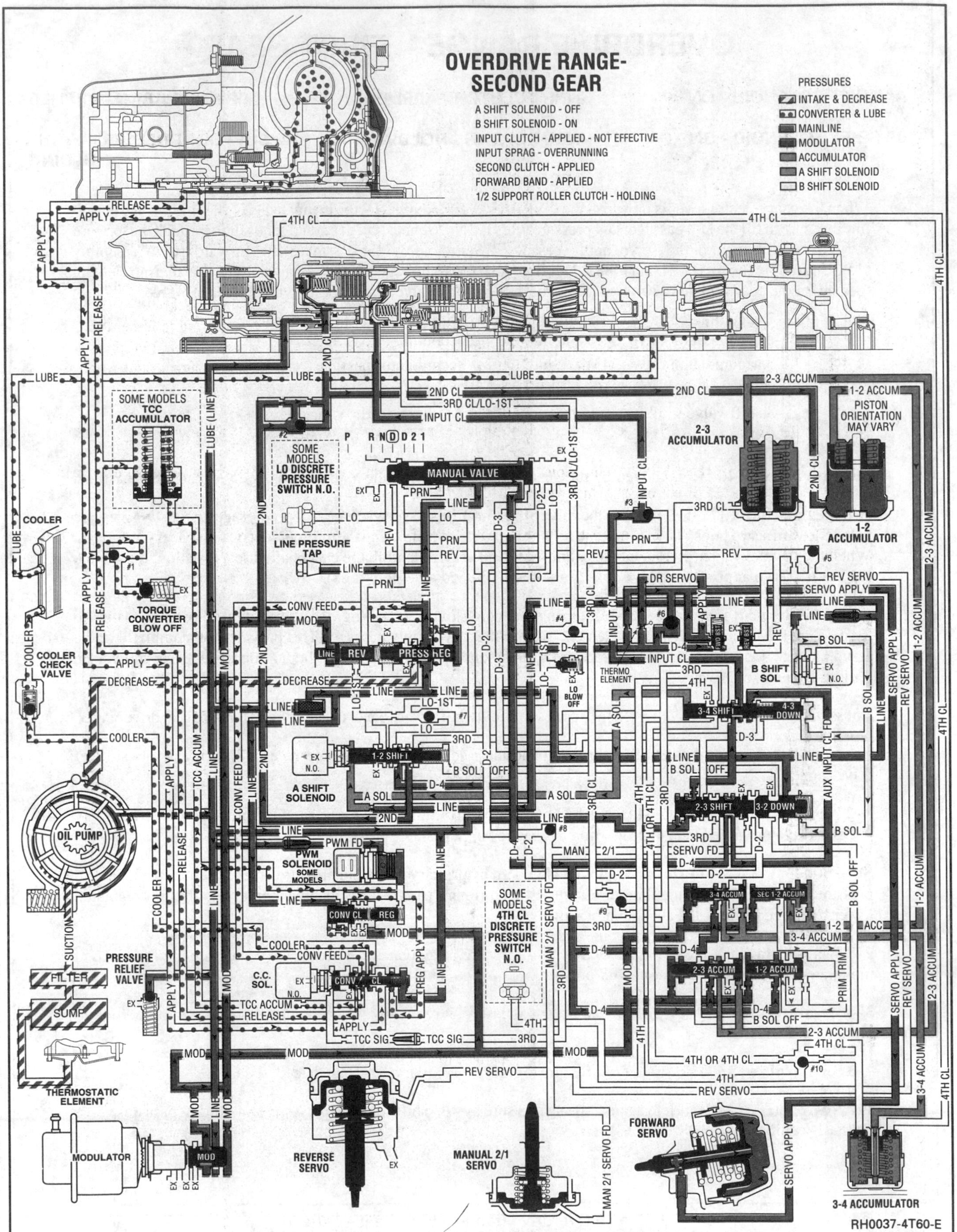
OVERDRIVE RANGE-
SECOND GEAR
A SHIFT SOLENOID - OFF
B SHIFT SOLENOID - ON
INPUT CLUTCH - APPLIED - NOT EFFECTIVE
INPUT SPRAG - OVERRUNNING
SECOND CLUTCH - APPLIED
FORWARD BAND - APPLIED
1/2 SUPPORT ROLLER CLUTCH - HOLDING
PRESSURES
INTAKE & DECREASE
CONVERTER & LUBE
MAINLINE
MODULATOR
ACCUMULATOR
A SHIFT SOLENOID
B SHIFT SOLENOID
SOME MODELS TCC ACCUMULATOR
COOLER
TORQUE CONVERTER BLOW OFF
COOLER CHECK VALVE
OIL PUMP
SUCTION
FILTER
SUMP
PRESSURE RELIEF VALVE
THERMOSTATIC ELEMENT
MODULATOR
SOME MODELS LO DISCRETE PRESSURE SWITCH N.O.
LINE PRESSURE TAP
MANUAL VALVE
P R N D D 2 1
REV
PRESS REG
1-2 SHIFT
A SHIFT SOLENOID
PWM SOLENOID SOME MODELS
CONV CL
REG
C.C. SOL.
REVERSE SERVO
MANUAL 2/1 SERVO
SOME MODELS 4TH CL DISCRETE PRESSURE SWITCH N.O.
LO BLOW OFF
THERMO ELEMENT
3-4 SHIFT
4-3 DOWN
B SHIFT SOL
2-3 SHIFT
3-2 DOWN
3-4 ACCUM
SEC 1-2 ACCUM
2-3 ACCUM
1-2 ACCUM
2-3 ACCUMULATOR
1-2 ACCUMULATOR
PISTON ORIENTATION MAY VARY
FORWARD SERVO
3-4 ACCUMULATOR
RH0037-4T60-E

Figure 41 Overdrive Range – Second Gear

OVERDRIVE RANGE - SECOND GEAR

"A" SHIFT SOLENOID - OFF

"B" SHIFT SOLENOID - ON

INPUT CLUTCH - APPLIED

INPUT SPRAG - OVERRUNNING

SECOND CLUTCH - APPLIED

FORWARD BAND - APPLIED

1/2 SUPPORT ROLLER CLUTCH - HOLDING

To obtain second gear, the PCM receives input signals from the Vehicle Speed Sensor (VS Sensor), Throttle Position Sensor (TP Sensor) and other engine sensors, to determine the precise moment to "de-energize" or "turn off current" to "A" shift solenoid (315). When this occurs, line pressure to the 1-2 shift valve (318) exhausts through the solenoid allowing spring pressure to move the valve. D-4 pressure at the valve during first gear operation can now enter the 2nd fluid passage. 2nd fluid feeds to the No. 2 checkball (372) and seats the checkball forcing the fluid through a feed orifice before applying the 2nd clutch. At the same time, 2nd clutch fluid is fed to the 1-2 accumulator piston (136) and strokes the piston up against spring pressure and 1-2 accumulator fluid pressure, cushioning 2nd clutch apply. 1-2 accumulator fluid is then forced through the 1-2 accumulator passage and exhausts at the 1-2 secondary accumulator valve (347).

"A" Shift Solenoid (315): De-energizes, allowing line pressure to exhaust through the solenoid.

1-2 Shift Valve (318): With "A" shift solenoid off, spring pressure moves the valve allowing D-4 pressure to enter the 2nd fluid passage directing 2nd fluid to the No. 2 checkball.

No. 2 Checkball (372): Located in the channel plate (400), 2nd fluid seats the checkball and is forced through an orifice into the 2nd clutch passage to apply the 2nd clutch.

1-2 Accumulator Piston (136): Cushions the apply of the 2nd clutch using 2nd clutch fluid to force the piston against spring force and 1-2 accumulator fluid.

Secondary 1-2 Accumulator Valve (347): Regulates the exhaust rate of 1-2 accumulator fluid during the apply of the 2nd clutch.

RH0038-4T60-E

Figure 42 Overdrive Range – Second Gear – Legend

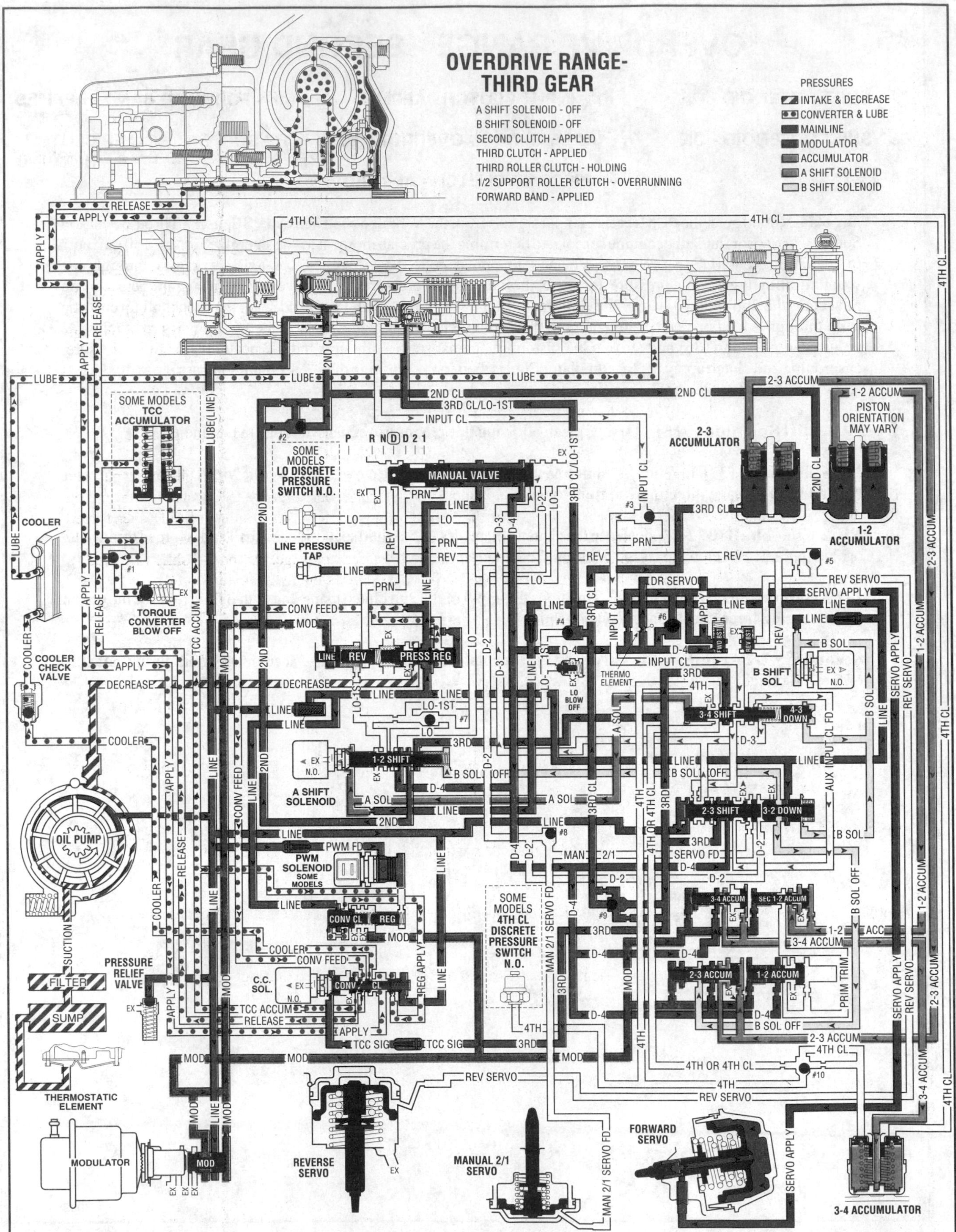
OVERDRIVE RANGE-
THIRD GEAR
A SHIFT SOLENOID - OFF
B SHIFT SOLENOID - OFF
SECOND CLUTCH - APPLIED
THIRD CLUTCH - APPLIED
THIRD ROLLER CLUTCH - HOLDING
1/2 SUPPORT ROLLER CLUTCH - OVERRUNNING
FORWARD BAND - APPLIED
PRESSURES
INTAKE & DECREASE
CONVERTER & LUBE
MAINLINE
MODULATOR
ACCUMULATOR
A SHIFT SOLENOID
B SHIFT SOLENOID
SOME MODELS TCC ACCUMULATOR
SOME MODELS LO DISCRETE PRESSURE SWITCH N.O.
LINE PRESSURE TAP
MANUAL VALVE
P R N D D 2 1
2-3 ACCUMULATOR
1-2 ACCUMULATOR
PISTON ORIENTATION MAY VARY
COOLER
TORQUE CONVERTER BLOW OFF
COOLER CHECK VALVE
REV
PRESS REG
LO BLOW OFF
THERMO ELEMENT
B SHIFT SOL
3-4 SHIFT
4-3 DOWN
1-2 SHIFT
A SHIFT SOLENOID
2-3 SHIFT
3-2 DOWN
OIL PUMP
PWM SOLENOID SOME MODELS
CONV CL
REG
C.C. SOL.
3-4 ACCUM
SEC 1-2 ACCUM
2-3 ACCUM
1-2 ACCUM
SOME MODELS 4TH CL DISCRETE PRESSURE SWITCH N.O.
PRESSURE RELIEF VALVE
FILTER
SUMP
THERMOSTATIC ELEMENT
MODULATOR
REVERSE SERVO
MANUAL 2/1 SERVO
FORWARD SERVO
3-4 ACCUMULATOR

Figure 43 Overdrive Range – Third Gear

OVERDRIVE RANGE - THIRD GEAR

"A" SHIFT SOLENOID - OFF

"B" SHIFT SOLENOID - OFF

SECOND CLUTCH - APPLIED

THIRD CLUTCH - APPLIED

THIRD ROLLER CLUTCH - HOLDING

1/2 SUPPORT ROLLER CLUTCH - OVERRUNNING

FORWARD BAND - APPLIED

To obtain third gear, the PCM receives input signals from the VS Sensor and TP Sensor in order to "de-energize" or "turn off current" supply to "B" shift solenoid (315) allowing "B" shift solenoid fluid to exhaust. When this occurs, spring force moves the 4-3 manual downshift valve (360), and, line pressure at the end of the 2-3 shift valve (357) moves the 3-2 manual downshift valve (356) against spring pressure. Line pressure also at the manual 3-2 downshift valve (356) enters the "B" shift solenoid off passage and assists in preventing the 1-2 shift valve (318) from moving. When the 2-3 shift valve (357) moves, D-4 fluid enters the 3rd fluid passage. The 3rd fluid passage feeds fluid to:

- the converter clutch solenoid (315), where it exhausts through the solenoid
- the 1-2 shift valve (318), and,
- to seat No. 9 checkball (372) forcing fluid through an orifice and into the 3rd clutch passage.

The 3rd clutch passage directs fluid to seat No. 4 checkball (372) sending fluid into the 3rd Clutch/Lo-1st passage to apply the 3rd clutch. 3rd clutch fluid pressure is also sent to the 2-3 accumulator piston (136) and forces the piston against the spring and 2-3 accumulator fluid to cushion the 3rd clutch apply. The 2-3 accumulator fluid is then forced to exhaust at the 2-3 accumulator valve (343). In third gear, the input clutch is released allowing input clutch apply fluid to exhaust through the 3-4 shift valve (362) into the input clutch feed passage. At the 2-3 shift valve (357), exhausting input clutch apply fluid is directed into the D-3 passage and out the manual valve (404).

"B" Shift Solenoid (315): De-energizes, allowing "B" shift solenoid fluid to exhaust through the solenoid. Spring pressure forces the 4-3 manual downshift valve (360) to move while line pressure moves the 2-3 shift valve (357) and 3-2 manual downshift valve (356).

No. 9 Checkball (372): Located in the valve body (300), forces 3rd fluid through a feed orifice and into the 3rd clutch passage.

No. 4 Checkball (372): Located in the channel plate (400), directs 3rd clutch fluid into the 3rd clutch/lo-1st passage to apply the 3rd clutch.

2-3 Shift Valve (357): When shifted, allows D-4 fluid to enter the 3rd passage to: stroke the 2-3 accumulator piston (136); apply the 3rd clutch; and, direct fluid to the converter clutch solenoid (315). The 2-3 shift valve also allows the input clutch apply fluid to exhaust into the D-3 passage and out at the manual valve (404).

2-3 Accumulator Piston (136): Cushions the apply of the 3rd clutch by using 3rd clutch fluid to force the piston against spring force and 2-3 accumulator fluid.

2-3 Accumulator Valve (343): Regulates the exhaust of 2-3 accumulator fluid during 3rd clutch apply.

RH0040-4T60-E

Figure 44 Overdrive Range – Third Gear – Legend

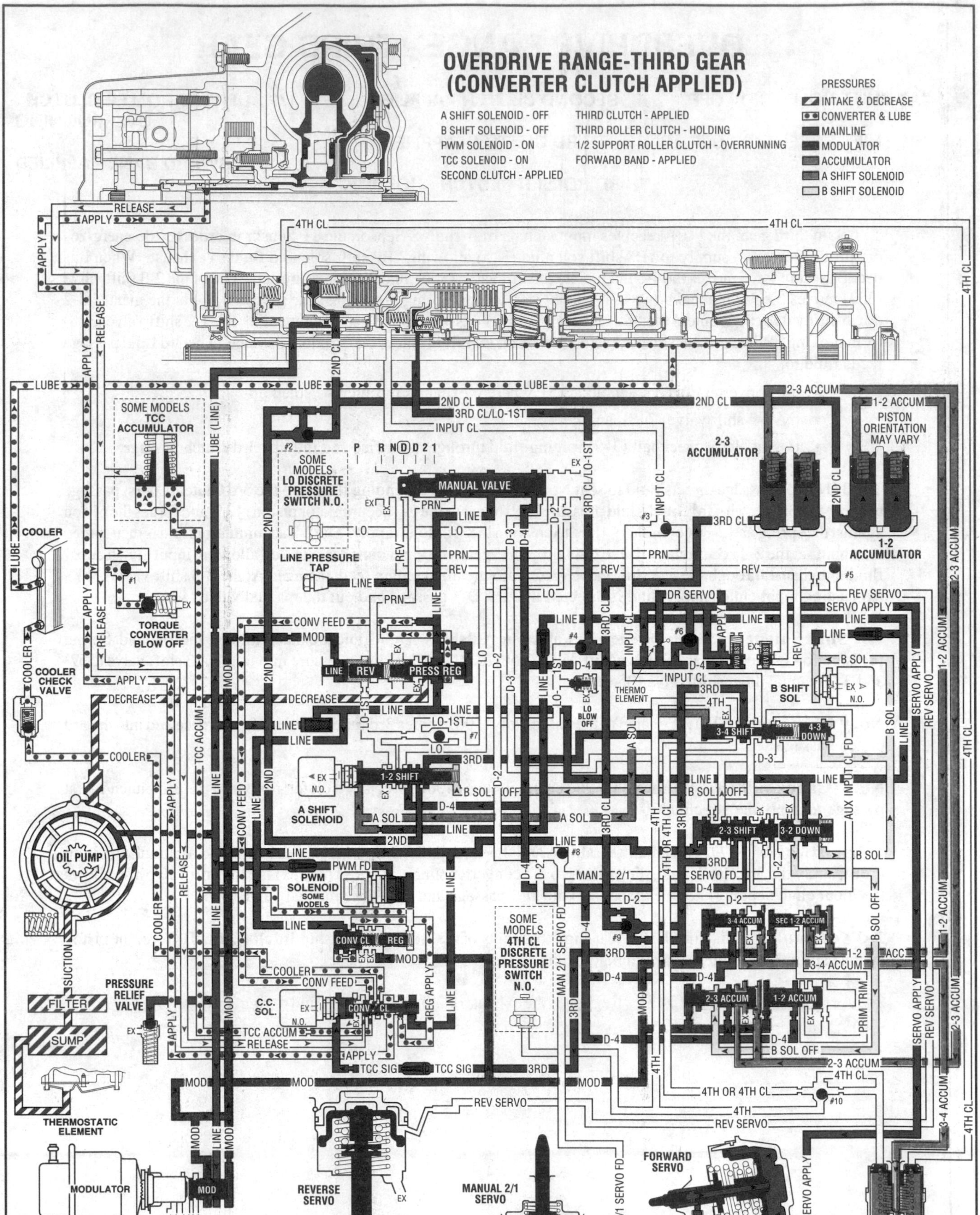
OVERDRIVE RANGE-THIRD GEAR
(CONVERTER CLUTCH APPLIED)
A SHIFT SOLENOID - OFF
B SHIFT SOLENOID - OFF
PWM SOLENOID - ON
TCC SOLENOID - ON
SECOND CLUTCH - APPLIED
THIRD CLUTCH - APPLIED
THIRD ROLLER CLUTCH - HOLDING
1/2 SUPPORT ROLLER CLUTCH - OVERRUNNING
FORWARD BAND - APPLIED
PRESSURES
INTAKE & DECREASE
CONVERTER & LUBE
MAINLINE
MODULATOR
ACCUMULATOR
A SHIFT SOLENOID
B SHIFT SOLENOID
SOME MODELS TCC ACCUMULATOR
SOME MODELS LO DISCRETE PRESSURE SWITCH N.O.
MANUAL VALVE
2-3 ACCUMULATOR
1-2 ACCUMULATOR
PISTON ORIENTATION MAY VARY
COOLER
LINE PRESSURE TAP
TORQUE CONVERTER BLOW OFF
COOLER CHECK VALVE
PRESS REG
THERMO ELEMENT
LO BLOW OFF
B SHIFT SOL
3-4 SHIFT
4-3 DOWN
1-2 SHIFT
A SHIFT SOLENOID
2-3 SHIFT
3-2 DOWN
OIL PUMP
PWM SOLENOID SOME MODELS
CONV CL
REG
SOME MODELS 4TH CL DISCRETE PRESSURE SWITCH N.O.
3-4 ACCUM
SEC 1-2 ACCUM
2-3 ACCUM
1-2 ACCUM
FILTER
PRESSURE RELIEF VALVE
SUMP
C.C. SOL.
THERMOSTATIC ELEMENT
MODULATOR
REVERSE SERVO
MANUAL 2/1 SERVO
FORWARD SERVO
3-4 ACCUMULATOR

Figure 45 Overdrive Range – Third Gear (TCC Applied)

OVERDRIVE RANGE - THIRD GEAR (CONVERTER CLUTCH APPLIED)

"A" SHIFT SOLENOID - OFF

"B" SHIFT SOLENOID - OFF

TCC SOLENOID - ON

SECOND CLUTCH - APPLIED

THIRD CLUTCH - APPLIED

THIRD ROLLER CLUTCH - HOLDING

1/2 SUPPORT ROLLER CLUTCH - OVERRUNNING

FORWARD BAND - APPLIED

The torque converter clutch applies during third gear operation after the PCM receives appropriate input signals from the VS Sensor, TP Sensor and engine temperature sensor. When the proper vehicle operating conditions have been met, the "on/off" TCC (315) is "energized". TCC signal fluid at the converter clutch solenoid (315) no longer exhausts and moves the converter clutch valve (335) against line pressure and spring force. With the valve in this position, the following occurs:

- release fluid from the converter clutch plate is allowed to exhaust
- converter feed pressure passes through the valve, enters the TCC accumulator passage and is sent to the TCC accumulator piston (416) and the converter clutch regulator valve (330)
- regulated apply fluid, from the converter clutch regulator valve (330), enters the apply passage

Apply fluid seats the No. 1 checkball (372) against release fluid and applies the converter clutch. Apply fluid is also at the torque converter blow off valve (417-20) to exhaust excess fluid pressure. Converter feed fluid at the converter clutch valve (335) is allowed to feed into the cooler passage where it passes through the cooler check valve (28), through the cooler and into the lube system of the transaxle.

TCC Accumulator Assembly (413-416): Absorbs converter feed fluid through the TCC accumulator passage and uses spring force to provide an increasing TCC accumulator bias pressure for the converter clutch regulator valve (330) during the apply of the torque converter clutch plate.

Converter Clutch Regulator Valve (330): Biased by modulator and TCC accumulator pressure, it uses line pressure to provide regulated apply fluid to the converter clutch valve (335).

Torque Converter Clutch Solenoid (315): When energized, TCC signal fluid shifts the converter clutch valve (335) against line pressure and spring force.

Converter Clutch Valve (335): When shifted, release fluid from the torque converter clutch exhausts. Converter feed fluid enters into the TCC accumulator passage to stroke the TCC accumulator piston (416) and also feeds into the cooler passage. Regulated apply fluid from the converter clutch regulator valve (330) can now enter the apply passage to the torque converter clutch.

No. 1 Checkball (372): Located in the channel plate (400), blocks release fluid while sending apply fluid to the torque converter clutch blow off valve (417-20).

Cooler Check Valve (28): Allows cooler fluid to pass through the cooler and provide lubrication for the transaxle. It also prevents converter drain back when the engine is off.

RH0042-4T60-E

Figure 46 Overdrive Range – Third Gear (TCC Applied) – Legend

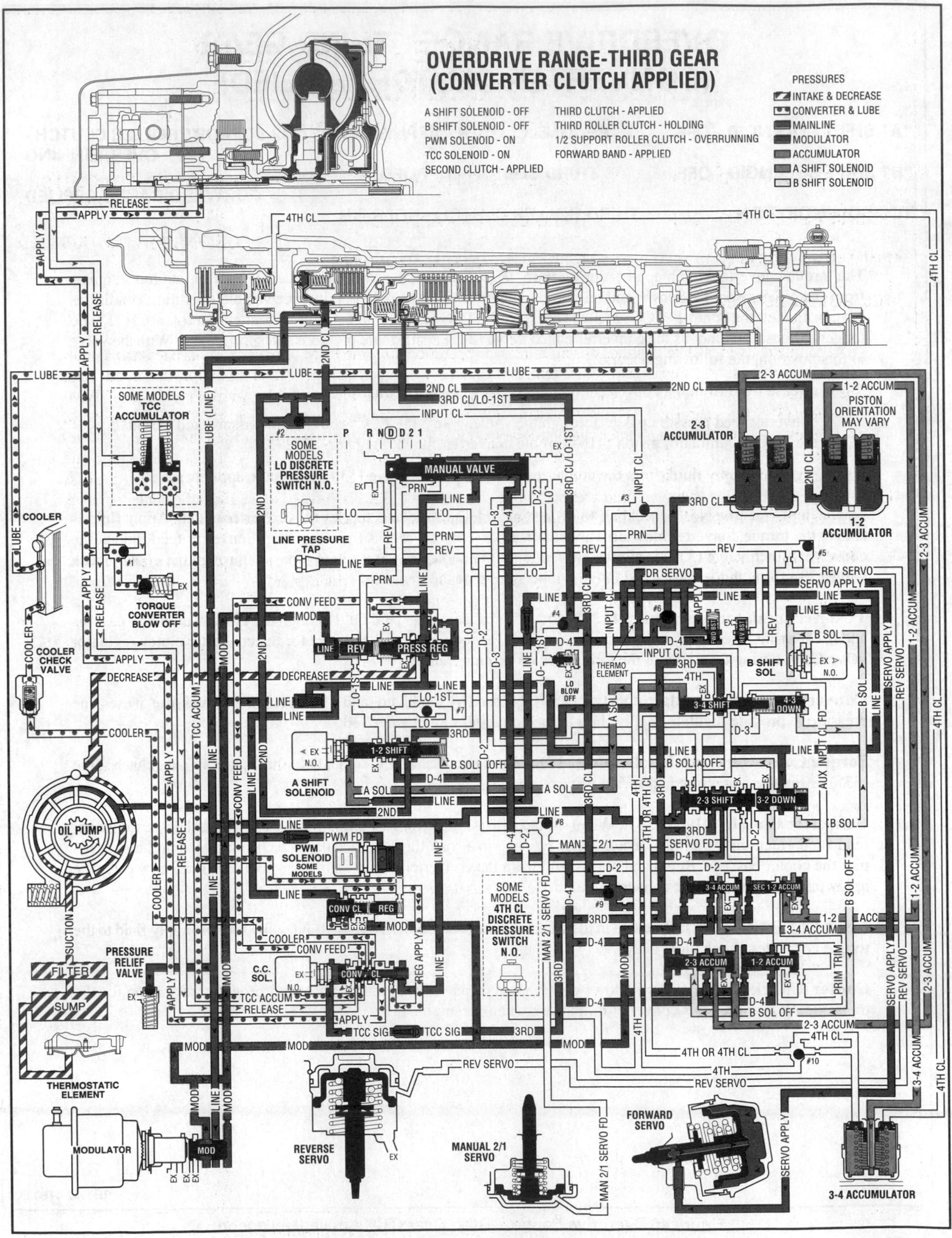
OVERDRIVE RANGE-THIRD GEAR
(CONVERTER CLUTCH APPLIED)
A SHIFT SOLENOID - OFF
B SHIFT SOLENOID - OFF
PWM SOLENOID - ON
TCC SOLENOID - ON
SECOND CLUTCH - APPLIED
THIRD CLUTCH - APPLIED
THIRD ROLLER CLUTCH - HOLDING
1/2 SUPPORT ROLLER CLUTCH - OVERRUNNING
FORWARD BAND - APPLIED
PRESSURES
INTAKE & DECREASE
CONVERTER & LUBE
MAINLINE
MODULATOR
ACCUMULATOR
A SHIFT SOLENOID
B SHIFT SOLENOID
RELEASE
APPLY
4TH CL
LUBE
2ND CL
3RD CL/LO-1ST
INPUT CL
2-3 ACCUM
1-2 ACCUM
PISTON ORIENTATION MAY VARY
2-3 ACCUMULATOR
1-2 ACCUMULATOR
SOME MODELS TCC ACCUMULATOR
SOME MODELS LO DISCRETE PRESSURE SWITCH N.O.
P R N D D 2 1
MANUAL VALVE
LINE PRESSURE TAP
COOLER
TORQUE CONVERTER BLOW OFF
COOLER CHECK VALVE
CONV FEED
MOD
LINE
REV
PRESS REG
DECREASE
LO BLOW OFF
THERMO ELEMENT
B SHIFT SOL
3-4 SHIFT
4-3 DOWN
1-2 SHIFT
A SHIFT SOLENOID
B SOL OFF
A SOL
2-3 SHIFT
3-2 DOWN
OIL PUMP
PWM SOLENOID SOME MODELS
CONV CL
REG
SOME MODELS 4TH CL DISCRETE PRESSURE SWITCH N.O.
3-4 ACCUM
SEC 1-2 ACCUM
2-3 ACCUM
1-2 ACCUM
C.C. SOL.
CONV CL
TCC ACCUM
TCC SIG
REG APPLY
SUCTION
PRESSURE RELIEF VALVE
FILTER
SUMP
THERMOSTATIC ELEMENT
MODULATOR
REVERSE SERVO
MANUAL 2/1 SERVO
FORWARD SERVO
3-4 ACCUMULATOR
REV SERVO
SERVO APPLY
MAN 2/1 SERVO FD
4TH OR 4TH CL
PRIM TRIM
AUX INPUT CL FD

Figure 47 Overdrive Range – Third Gear (TCC Applied)

OVERDRIVE RANGE - THIRD GEAR (CONVERTER CLUTCH APPLIED)

(MODELS CONTAINING PWM)

"A" SHIFT SOLENOID - OFF

"B" SHIFT SOLENOID - OFF

*PWM SOLENOID - ON

TCC SOLENOID - ON

SECOND CLUTCH - APPLIED

THIRD CLUTCH - APPLIED

THIRD ROLLER CLUTCH - HOLDING

1/2 SUPPORT ROLLER CLUTCH - OVERRUNNING

FORWARD BAND - APPLIED

The torque converter clutch applies during third gear operation after the PCM receives appropriate input signals from the VS Sensor, TP Sensor and engine temperature sensor. When the proper vehicle operating conditions have been met, the "on/off" converter clutch solenoid (315) [some models and the "pulse width modulated" (PWM) solenoid (325)] is "energized". The PWM solenoid duty cycle is "ramped" between 0 and 100% to regulate PWM fluid pressure to the converter clutch regulator valve (330). Regulated apply pressure is then sent to the converter clutch valve (335) into the apply passage. Apply fluid seats the No. 1 checkball (372) against release fluid and applies the converter clutch. Apply fluid is also at the torque converter blow off valve (417-20) to exhaust excess fluid pressure. Converter feed fluid at the converter clutch valve (335) is allowed to feed into the cooler passage, through the cooler check valve (28), through the cooler and into the lube system of the transaxle.

PWM Solenoid (325): Controlled by the PCM, it modifies the PWM duty cycle to vary the feed pressure in the PWM fluid passage to the converter clutch regulator valve (330). This arrangement provides for accurate control of the regulated converter clutch apply (and release) pressure.

Converter Clutch Regulator Valve (330): Provides regulated apply fluid to the converter clutch valve (335) into the apply fluid passage.

Converter Clutch Solenoid (315): When energized, TCC signal fluid shifts the converter clutch valve (335) against spring pressure.

Converter Clutch Valve (335): When shifted, directs regulated apply fluid into the apply passage; converter feed fluid into the cooler passage and, allows converter release fluid to exhaust.

No. 1 Checkball (372): Located in the channel plate (400), blocks release fluid while sending apply fluid to the torque converter clutch blow off valve (417-20).

Cooler Check Valve (28): Allows cooler fluid to pass through the cooler and provide lubrication for the transaxle. It also prevents converter drainback when the engine is off.

* SOME MODELS

RH0042-4T60-E-PWM

Figure 48 Overdrive Range – Third Gear (TCC Applied) – Legend

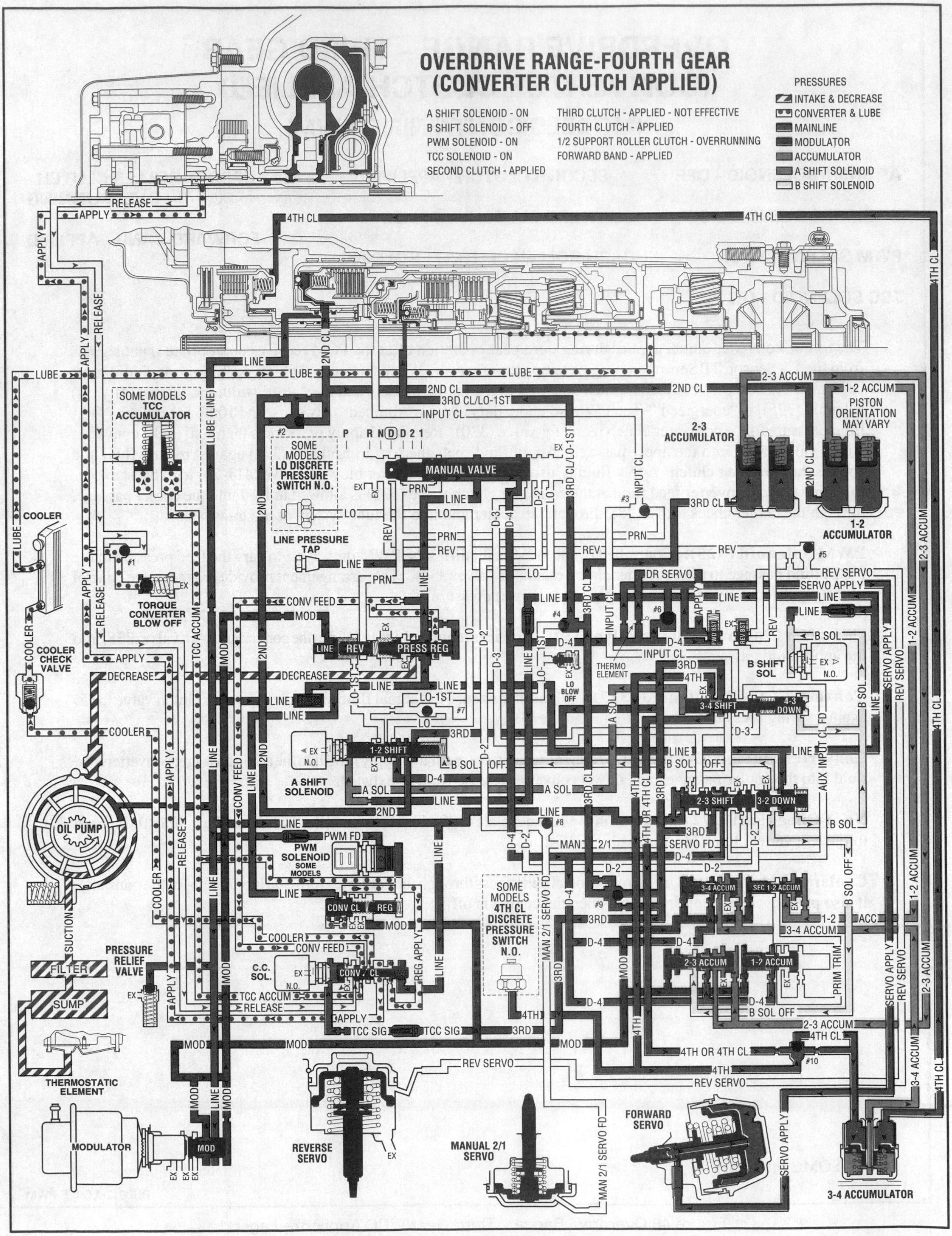
OVERDRIVE RANGE-FOURTH GEAR
(CONVERTER CLUTCH APPLIED)
A SHIFT SOLENOID - ON
B SHIFT SOLENOID - OFF
PWM SOLENOID - ON
TCC SOLENOID - ON
SECOND CLUTCH - APPLIED
THIRD CLUTCH - APPLIED - NOT EFFECTIVE
FOURTH CLUTCH - APPLIED
1/2 SUPPORT ROLLER CLUTCH - OVERRUNNING
FORWARD BAND - APPLIED
PRESSURES
INTAKE & DECREASE
CONVERTER & LUBE
MAINLINE
MODULATOR
ACCUMULATOR
A SHIFT SOLENOID
B SHIFT SOLENOID
RELEASE
APPLY
4TH CL
2ND CL
3RD CL/LO-1ST
INPUT CL
LINE
LUBE
SOME MODELS TCC ACCUMULATOR
SOME MODELS LO DISCRETE PRESSURE SWITCH N.O.
P R N D D 2 1
MANUAL VALVE
LINE PRESSURE TAP
2-3 ACCUM
1-2 ACCUM
PISTON ORIENTATION MAY VARY
2-3 ACCUMULATOR
1-2 ACCUMULATOR
COOLER
TORQUE CONVERTER BLOW OFF
COOLER CHECK VALVE
CONV FEED
MOD
PRESS REG
REV
DECREASE
THERMO ELEMENT
LO BLOW OFF
B SHIFT SOL
B SOL
EX
N.O.
3-4 SHIFT
4-3 DOWN
1-2 SHIFT
A SHIFT SOLENOID
B SOL OFF
A SOL
2-3 SHIFT
3-2 DOWN
AUX INPUT CL FD
OIL PUMP
PWM SOLENOID
SOME MODELS
PWM FD
CONV CL
REG
SOME MODELS 4TH CL DISCRETE PRESSURE SWITCH N.O.
MAN 2/1 SERVO FD
3-4 ACCUM
SEC 1-2 ACCUM
2-3 ACCUM
1-2 ACCUM
PRIM TRIM
SERVO APPLY
REV SERVO
SERVO FD
PRESSURE RELIEF VALVE
FILTER
SUMP
SUCTION
C.C. SOL.
TCC ACCUM
TCC SIG
4TH OR 4TH CL
THERMOSTATIC ELEMENT
MODULATOR
REVERSE SERVO
MANUAL 2/1 SERVO
FORWARD SERVO
3-4 ACCUMULATOR

Figure 49 Overdrive Range – Fourth Gear (TCC Applied)

OVERDRIVE RANGE - FOURTH GEAR (CONVERTER CLUTCH APPLIED)

"A" SHIFT SOLENOID - ON

"B" SHIFT SOLENOID - OFF

TCC SOLENOID - ON

SECOND CLUTCH - APPLIED

THIRD CLUTCH - APPLIED/ NOT EFFECTIVE

THIRD ROLLER CLUTCH - OVERRUNNING

FOURTH CLUTCH - APPLIED

1/2 SUPPORT ROLLER CLUTCH - OVERRUNNING

FORWARD BAND - APPLIED

To obtain fourth gear, the PCM receives input signals from the VS Sensor and TP Sensor in order to "energize" by providing a ground for "A" shift solenoid (315). When energized, line pressure is directed into the "A" shift solenoid passage to the 3-4 shift valve (362). "A" shift solenoid pressure shifts the valve against spring pressure allowing 3rd fluid to enter the 4th and 4th clutch fluid passages. 4th fluid is directed to:

- the 4th clutch discrete pressure switch (218) to close the switch
- seats No. 10 checkball (372) to force the fluid through a feed orifice to stroke the 3-4 accumulator piston (428) while applying the 4th clutch

3-4 accumulator fluid on the spring side of the piston is forced through the 3-4 accumulator pin (426) into the 3-4 accumulator passage and exhausts at the 3-4 accumulator valve (350).

"A" Shift Solenoid (315): Energizes to prevent fluid from exhausting out of the line passage and "A" shift solenoid passage.

1-2 Shift Valve (318): Is held against "A" shift solenoid by spring pressure and "B" shift solenoid off fluid pressure at the end of the valve.

3-4 Shift Valve (362): When shifted against spring force, it allows 3rd fluid to enter the 4th and 4th clutch fluid passages. 4th fluid seats No. 10 checkball (372) and is forced through a feed orifice before stroking the 3-4 accumulator piston (428) and applying the fourth clutch.

4th Clutch Discrete Switch (218): A normally open switch that closes when 4th fluid pressure is fed from the 3-4 shift valve (362). When the switch is closed it completes the circuit from the PCM to ground and provides information to the PCM that the transaxle is in Overdrive Range – Fourth Gear.

No. 10 Checkball (372): Located in the valve body (300), it forces 4th fluid through a feed orifice into the 4th clutch passage to stroke the 3-4 accumulator piston (428).

3-4 Accumulator Piston (428): Cushions the apply of the 4th clutch by using 4th clutch fluid to stroke the piston against spring force and 3-4 accumulator fluid.

3-4 Accumulator Valve (350): Controls the rate of exhaust of 3-4 accumulator fluid during 4th clutch apply.

RH0044-4T60-E

Figure 50 Overdrive Range – Fourth Gear (TCC Applied) – Legend

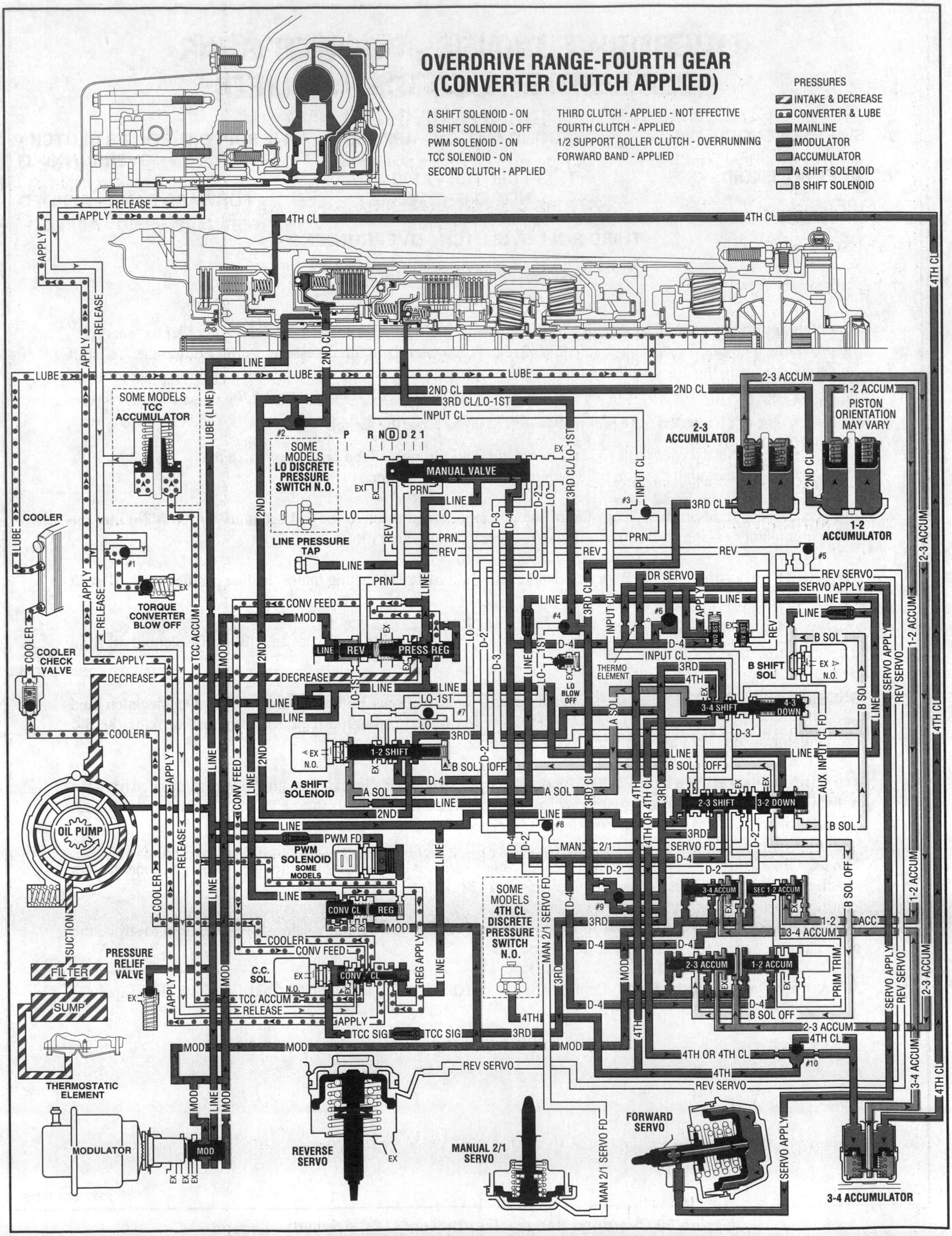
OVERDRIVE RANGE-FOURTH GEAR
(CONVERTER CLUTCH APPLIED)
A SHIFT SOLENOID - ON
B SHIFT SOLENOID - OFF
PWM SOLENOID - ON
TCC SOLENOID - ON
SECOND CLUTCH - APPLIED
THIRD CLUTCH - APPLIED - NOT EFFECTIVE
FOURTH CLUTCH - APPLIED
1/2 SUPPORT ROLLER CLUTCH - OVERRUNNING
FORWARD BAND - APPLIED
PRESSURES
INTAKE & DECREASE
CONVERTER & LUBE
MAINLINE
MODULATOR
ACCUMULATOR
A SHIFT SOLENOID
B SHIFT SOLENOID
MANUAL VALVE
OIL PUMP
COOLER
COOLER CHECK VALVE
TORQUE CONVERTER BLOW OFF
SOME MODELS TCC ACCUMULATOR
SOME MODELS LO DISCRETE PRESSURE SWITCH N.O.
LINE PRESSURE TAP
A SHIFT SOLENOID
B SHIFT SOL
PWM SOLENOID SOME MODELS
C.C. SOL.
PRESSURE RELIEF VALVE
FILTER
SUMP
THERMOSTATIC ELEMENT
MODULATOR
REVERSE SERVO
MANUAL 2/1 SERVO
FORWARD SERVO
SOME MODELS 4TH CL DISCRETE PRESSURE SWITCH N.O.
2-3 ACCUMULATOR
1-2 ACCUMULATOR
PISTON ORIENTATION MAY VARY
3-4 ACCUMULATOR
1-2 SHIFT
2-3 SHIFT
3-2 DOWN
3-4 SHIFT
4-3 DOWN
PRESS REG
CONV CL
REG
3-4 ACCUM
SEC 1-2 ACCUM
2-3 ACCUM
1-2 ACCUM
LO BLOW OFF
THERMO ELEMENT

Figure 51 Overdrive Range – Fourth Gear (TCC Applied)

OVERDRIVE RANGE - FOURTH GEAR (CONVERTER CLUTCH APPLIED)

(MODELS CONTAINING PWM)

"A" SHIFT SOLENOID - ON

"B" SHIFT SOLENOID - OFF

*PWM SOLENOID - ON

TCC SOLENOID - ON

SECOND CLUTCH - APPLIED

THIRD CLUTCH - APPLIED/ NOT EFFECTIVE

THIRD ROLLER CLUTCH - OVERRUNNING

FOURTH CLUTCH - APPLIED

1/2 SUPPORT ROLLER CLUTCH - OVERRUNNING

FORWARD BAND - APPLIED

To obtain fourth gear, the PCM receives input signals from the VS Sensor and TP Sensor in order to "energize" or "turn on current" supply to "A" shift solenoid (315). When energized, line pressure is directed into the "A" shift solenoid passage to the 3-4 shift valve (362). "A" shift solenoid pressure shifts the valve against spring pressure allowing 3rd fluid to enter the 4th and 4th clutch fluid passages. 4th fluid seats No. 10 checkball (372) and forces it through a feed orifice to stroke the 3-4 accumulator piston (428) while applying the 4th clutch. 3-4 accumulator fluid on the spring side of the piston is forced through the 3-4 accumulator pin (426) into the 3-4 accumulator passage and exhausts at the 3-4 accumulator valve (350).

"A" Shift Solenoid (315): Energizes to prevent fluid from exhausting out of the line passage and "A" shift solenoid passage.

1-2 Shift Valve (318): Is held against "A" shift solenoid by spring pressure and "B" shift solenoid off fluid pressure at the end of the valve.

3-4 Shift Valve (362): When shifted against spring force, it allows 3rd fluid to enter the 4th and 4th clutch fluid passages. 4th fluid seats No. 10 checkball (372) and is forced through a feed orifice before stroking the 3-4 accumulator piston (428) and applying the fourth clutch.

No. 10 Checkball (372): Located in the valve body (300), it forces 4th fluid through a feed orifice into the 4th clutch passage to stroke the 3-4 accumulator piston (428).

3-4 Accumulator Piston (428): Cushions the apply of the 4th clutch by using 4th clutch fluid to stroke the piston against spring force and 3-4 accumulator fluid.

3-4 Accumulator Valve (350): Controls the rate of exhaust of 3-4 accumulator fluid during 4th clutch apply.

* SOME MODELS

RH0045-4T60-E-PWM

Figure 52 Overdrive Range – Fourth Gear (TCC Applied) – Legend

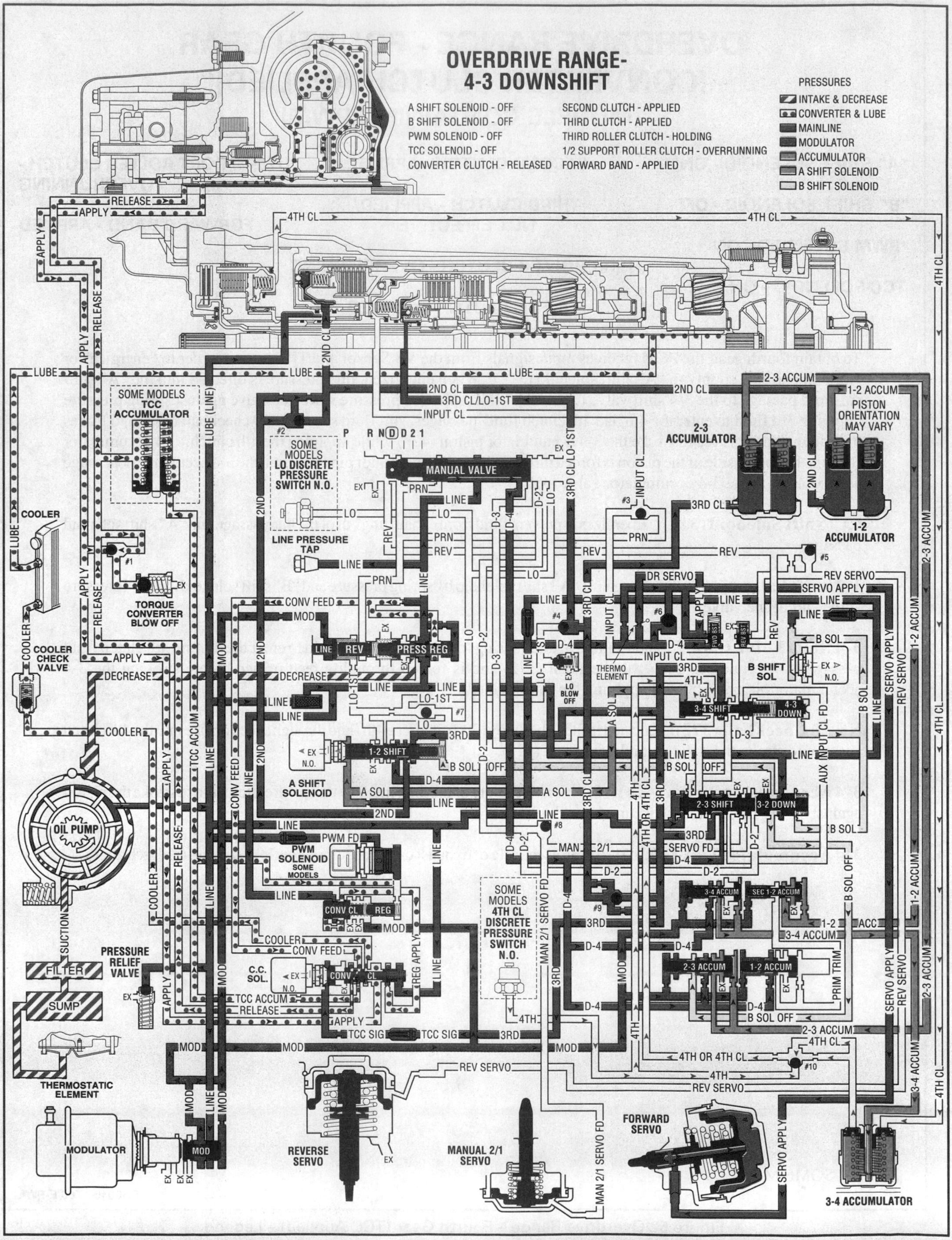
OVERDRIVE RANGE-
4-3 DOWNSHIFT
A SHIFT SOLENOID - OFF
B SHIFT SOLENOID - OFF
PWM SOLENOID - OFF
TCC SOLENOID - OFF
CONVERTER CLUTCH - RELEASED
SECOND CLUTCH - APPLIED
THIRD CLUTCH - APPLIED
THIRD ROLLER CLUTCH - HOLDING
1/2 SUPPORT ROLLER CLUTCH - OVERRUNNING
FORWARD BAND - APPLIED
PRESSURES
INTAKE & DECREASE
CONVERTER & LUBE
MAINLINE
MODULATOR
ACCUMULATOR
A SHIFT SOLENOID
B SHIFT SOLENOID
SOME MODELS TCC ACCUMULATOR
SOME MODELS LO DISCRETE PRESSURE SWITCH N.O.
LINE PRESSURE TAP
P R N D D 2 1
MANUAL VALVE
2-3 ACCUMULATOR
1-2 ACCUMULATOR
PISTON ORIENTATION MAY VARY
COOLER
TORQUE CONVERTER BLOW OFF
COOLER CHECK VALVE
PRESS REG
LO BLOW OFF
THERMO ELEMENT
B SHIFT SOL
3-4 SHIFT
4-3 DOWN
1-2 SHIFT
A SHIFT SOLENOID
2-3 SHIFT
3-2 DOWN
OIL PUMP
PWM SOLENOID SOME MODELS
CONV CL REG
SOME MODELS 4TH CL DISCRETE PRESSURE SWITCH N.O.
3-4 ACCUM
SEC 1-2 ACCUM
2-3 ACCUM
1-2 ACCUM
PRESSURE RELIEF VALVE
C.C. SOL.
FILTER
SUMP
THERMOSTATIC ELEMENT
MODULATOR
REVERSE SERVO
MANUAL 2/1 SERVO
FORWARD SERVO
3-4 ACCUMULATOR

Figure 53 Overdrive Range – 4-3 Downshift (TCC Released)

OVERDRIVE RANGE - 4-3 DOWNSHIFT (CONVERTER CLUTCH - RELEASED)

"A" SHIFT SOLENOID - OFF

"B" SHIFT SOLENOID - OFF

TCC SOLENOID - OFF

SECOND CLUTCH - APPLIED

THIRD CLUTCH - APPLIED

THIRD ROLLER CLUTCH - HOLDING

1/2 SUPPORT ROLLER CLUTCH - OVERRUNNING

FORWARD BAND - APPLIED

Under light throttle acceleration, the torque converter clutch will release when the input signals sent to the PCM from the VS Sensor, TP Sensor and 4th clutch discrete switch (218) have commanded a 4-3 downshift. When the appropriate signals are received, the torque converter clutch solenoid (315) is "de-energized" or "turned off". Line pressure and spring force at the converter clutch valve (335) moves the valve allowing TCC signal fluid to exhaust through the converter clutch solenoid (315). Converter feed fluid enters the release passage, seats No. 1 checkball (372) against apply fluid and feeds to the release side of the torque converter clutch plate. Apply fluid from the torque converter (1) is directed through the apply passage to the converter clutch valve (335) where it enters the cooler passage. TCC accumulator fluid, from the TCC accumulator piston (416), is directed: (1) through the converter clutch valve (335) and enters the release passage, and (2) to the converter clutch regulator valve (330) to control the release feel of the converter clutch plate.

A 4-3 shift occurs when the PCM "de-energizes" or "turns off current" to "A" shift solenoid (315) allowing "A" shift solenoid fluid at the 3-4 shift valve (362) to exhaust through the solenoid. Spring force at the 3-4 shift valve (362) moves the valve allowing 4th clutch apply fluid (at the 4th clutch) to be directed through the 3-4 accumulator assembly (421-428), seat No. 10 checkball (372) against 4th clutch (apply) fluid and exhaust at the 3-4 shift valve (362).

Torque Converter Clutch Solenoid (315): De-energizes, allowing the converter clutch valve (335) to move and TCC signal fluid to exhaust through the solenoid.

Converter Clutch Valve (335): When the torque converter clutch solenoid (315) is "off", converter feed fluid passes through the valve into the converter release passage and converter apply fluid is directed into the cooler passage. TCC accumulator fluid also exhausts into the release passage and acts as a bias on the converter clutch regulator valve (330).

Converter Clutch Regulator Valve (330): Uses filtered line fluid to supply regulated apply fluid to the converter clutch valve (335). Regulation is controlled by TCC accumulator and modulator fluid pressures.

TCC Accumulator Assembly (413-416): Spring force and release fluid pressure returns the TCC accumulator piston (416) to TCC "off" position.

No. 1 Checkball (372): Located in the channel plate (400), converter release fluid seats the checkball against apply fluid to allow release of the torque conveter clutch plate.

"A" Shift Solenoid (315): De-energizes, allowing "A" shift solenoid fluid at the 3-4 shift valve (362) to exhaust through the solenoid.

3-4 Shift Valve (362): When "A" shift solenoid fluid exhausts, spring force moves the valve allowing 4th clutch fluid to exhaust through the valve.

3-4 Accumulator Assembly (421-428): Allows 4th clutch exhaust fluid to pass through the accumulator assembly to No. 10 checkball (372).

No. 10 Checkball (372): Located in the valve body (300), forces 4th clutch fluid through an exhaust orifice to the 3-4 shift valve (362) where it exhausts.

4th Clutch Discrete Switch (218): "Opens" a circuit to the PCM to signal that the transaxle is no longer operating in Overdrive Range – Fourth Gear.

NOTE: Under light accelerating conditions, normally the torque converter clutch will release prior to the transaxle making a 4-3 downshift. However, depending on throttle angle, vehicle load and road conditions, torque converter clutch release and a 4-3 shift may occur at the same time.

RH0046-4T60-E

Figure 54 Overdrive Range – 4-3 Downshift (TCC Released) – Legend

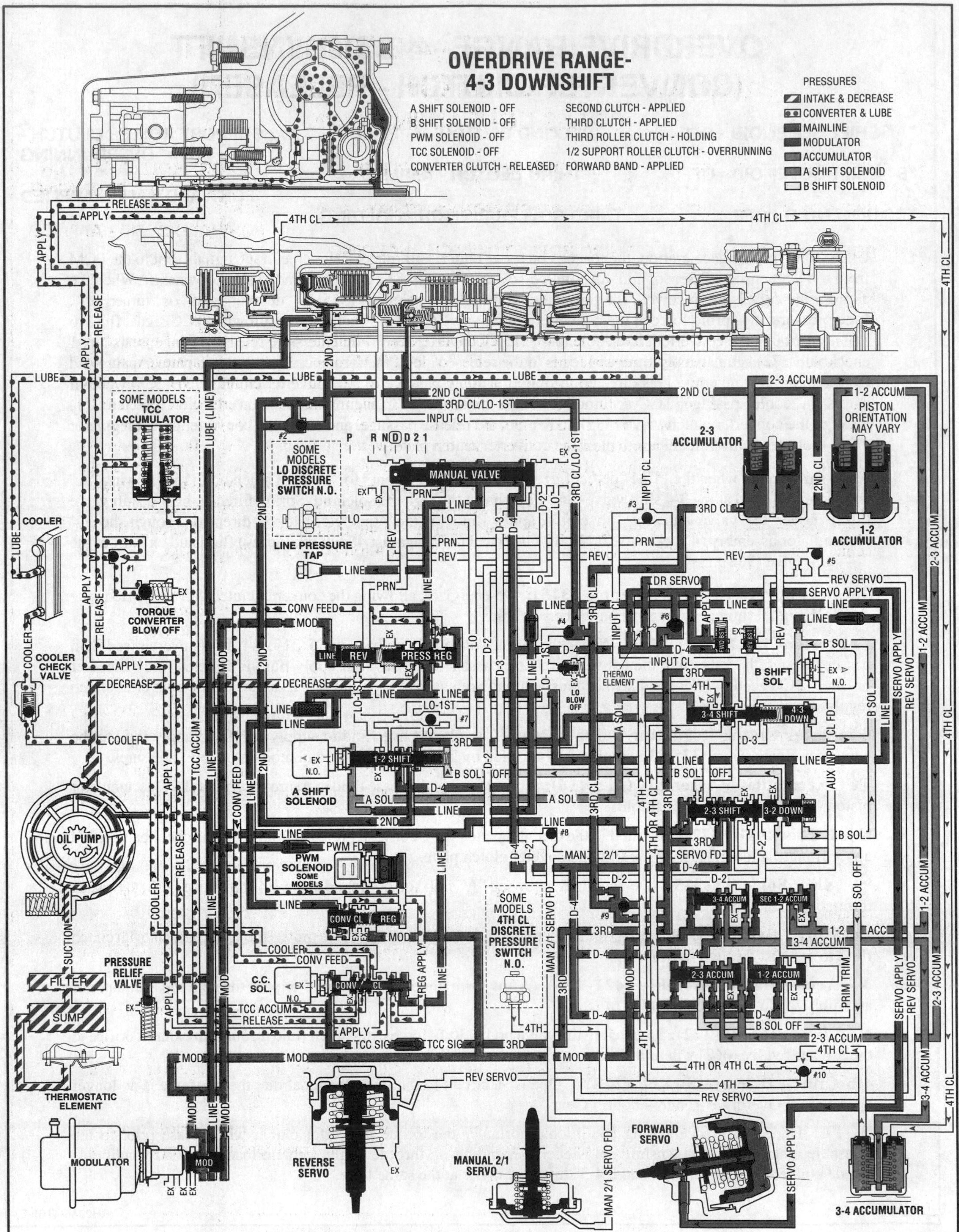
OVERDRIVE RANGE-
4-3 DOWNSHIFT
A SHIFT SOLENOID - OFF
B SHIFT SOLENOID - OFF
PWM SOLENOID - OFF
TCC SOLENOID - OFF
CONVERTER CLUTCH - RELEASED
SECOND CLUTCH - APPLIED
THIRD CLUTCH - APPLIED
THIRD ROLLER CLUTCH - HOLDING
1/2 SUPPORT ROLLER CLUTCH - OVERRUNNING
FORWARD BAND - APPLIED
PRESSURES
INTAKE & DECREASE
CONVERTER & LUBE
MAINLINE
MODULATOR
ACCUMULATOR
A SHIFT SOLENOID
B SHIFT SOLENOID
SOME MODELS TCC ACCUMULATOR
SOME MODELS LO DISCRETE PRESSURE SWITCH N.O.
LINE PRESSURE TAP
MANUAL VALVE
2-3 ACCUMULATOR
1-2 ACCUMULATOR
PISTON ORIENTATION MAY VARY
COOLER
TORQUE CONVERTER BLOW OFF
COOLER CHECK VALVE
PRESS REG
A SHIFT SOLENOID
1-2 SHIFT
OIL PUMP
PWM SOLENOID SOME MODELS
C.C. SOL.
B SHIFT SOL
3-4 SHIFT
4-3 DOWN
2-3 SHIFT
3-2 DOWN
THERMO ELEMENT
LO BLOW OFF
SOME MODELS 4TH CL DISCRETE PRESSURE SWITCH N.O.
PRESSURE RELIEF VALVE
FILTER
SUMP
SUCTION
THERMOSTATIC ELEMENT
MODULATOR
REVERSE SERVO
MANUAL 2/1 SERVO
FORWARD SERVO
3-4 ACCUMULATOR

Figure 55 Overdrive Range – 4-3 Downshift (TCC Released)

OVERDRIVE RANGE - 4-3 DOWNSHIFT (CONVERTER CLUTCH - RELEASED)

(MODELS CONTAINING PWM)

"A" SHIFT SOLENOID - OFF

"B" SHIFT SOLENOID - OFF

PWM SOLENOID - OFF

TCC SOLENOID - OFF

SECOND CLUTCH - APPLIED

THIRD CLUTCH - APPLIED

THIRD ROLLER CLUTCH - HOLDING

1/2 SUPPORT ROLLER CLUTCH - OVERRUNNING

FORWARD BAND - APPLIED

Under light throttle acceleration, the torque converter clutch is released when the PCM receives input signals from the VS Sensor and TP Sensor to regulate the "duty cycle" of the PWM solenoid in order to achieve a smooth disengagement of the converter clutch. Once this is achieved, the converter clutch solenoid (315) and the PWM solenoid (325) are "de-energized" or "turned off". Line pressure and spring force at the converter clutch valve (335) moves the valve to allow converter feed fluid to enter the release passage. Release pressure seats No. 1 checkball (372) against apply fluid and feeds to the release side of the torque converter clutch plate. Apply fluid in the torque converter (1) is directed through the apply passage to the converter clutch valve (335) where it enters the cooler passage. A 4-3 shift occurs when the PCM "de-energizes" or "turns off current" to "A" shift solenoid (315) allowing "A" shift solenoid fluid at the 3-4 shift valve (362) to exhaust through the solenoid. Spring force at the 3-4 shift valve (362) moves the valve allowing 4th clutch apply fluid (at the 4th clutch) to be directed through the 3-4 accumulator assembly (421-428), seat No. 10 checkball (372) against 4th clutch (apply) fluid passage and exhaust at the 3-4 shift valve (362).

PWM Solenoid (325): Controlled by the PCM, it modifies the PWM duty cycle to vary the feed pressure in the PWM fluid passage to the converter clutch regulator valve (330). When the PWM solenoid is "de-energized" or "turned off", full line pressure passes through the solenoid to the converter clutch regulator valve (330). This arrangement provides for accurate control of the regulated converter clutch apply and release pressure.

Converter Clutch Solenoid (315): De-energizes, allowing the converter clutch valve (335) to move and TCC signal fluid to exhaust through the solenoid.

Converter Clutch Valve (335): When the converter clutch solenoid (315) is "off", converter feed fluid passes through the valve into the converter release passage and converter apply fluid is directed into the cooler passage.

No. 1 Checkball (372): Located in the channel plate (400), converter release fluid seats the checkball against apply fluid to allow release of the torque converter clutch.

"A" Shift Solenoid (315): De-energizes, allowing "A" shift solenoid fluid at the 3-4 shift valve (362) to exhaust through the solenoid.

3-4 Shift Valve (362): When "A" shift solenoid fluid exhausts, spring force moves the valve allowing 4th clutch fluid to exhaust through the valve.

3-4 Accumulator Assembly (421-428): Allows 4th clutch exhaust fluid to pass through the accumulator assembly to No. 10 checkball (372).

No. 10 Checkball (372): Located in the valve body (300), forces 4th clutch fluid through an exhaust orifice to the 3-4 shift valve (362) where it exhausts.

NOTE: Under light accelerating conditions, normally the torque converter clutch will release prior to the transaxle making a 4-3 downshift. However, depending on throttle angle, vehicle load and road conditions, torque converter clutch release and a 4-3 shift may occur at the same time.

RH0046-4T60-E-PWM

Figure 56 Overdrive Range – 4-3 Downshift (TCC Released) – Legend

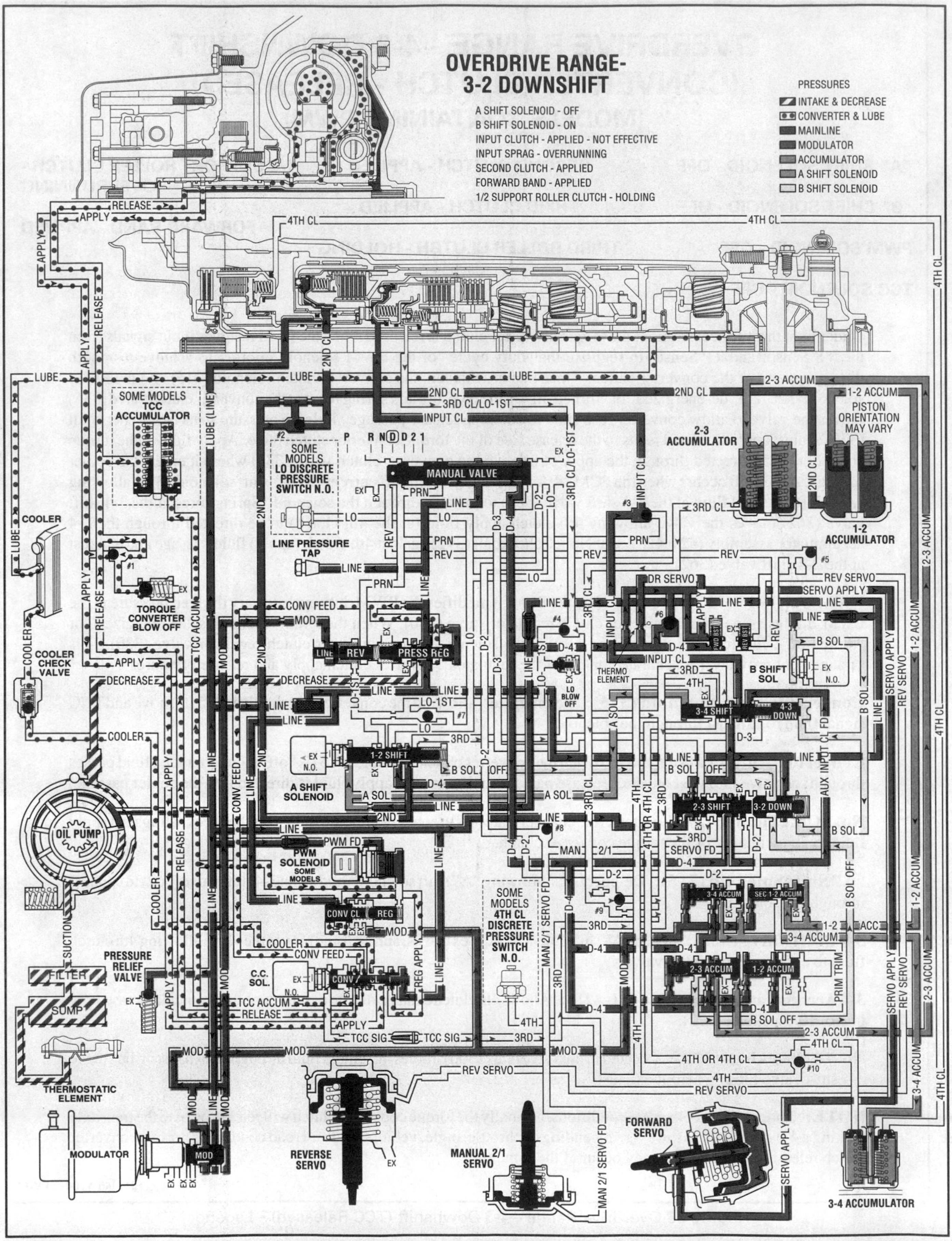
OVERDRIVE RANGE-
3-2 DOWNSHIFT
A SHIFT SOLENOID - OFF
B SHIFT SOLENOID - ON
INPUT CLUTCH - APPLIED - NOT EFFECTIVE
INPUT SPRAG - OVERRUNNING
SECOND CLUTCH - APPLIED
FORWARD BAND - APPLIED
1/2 SUPPORT ROLLER CLUTCH - HOLDING
PRESSURES
INTAKE & DECREASE
CONVERTER & LUBE
MAINLINE
MODULATOR
ACCUMULATOR
A SHIFT SOLENOID
B SHIFT SOLENOID
SOME MODELS TCC ACCUMULATOR
COOLER
TORQUE CONVERTER BLOW OFF
COOLER CHECK VALVE
OIL PUMP
FILTER
SUMP
PRESSURE RELIEF VALVE
THERMOSTATIC ELEMENT
MODULATOR
SOME MODELS LO DISCRETE PRESSURE SWITCH N.O.
LINE PRESSURE TAP
MANUAL VALVE
PRESS REG
1-2 SHIFT
A SHIFT SOLENOID
PWM SOLENOID SOME MODELS
C.C. SOL.
SOME MODELS 4TH CL DISCRETE PRESSURE SWITCH N.O.
REVERSE SERVO
MANUAL 2/1 SERVO
FORWARD SERVO
2-3 ACCUMULATOR
1-2 ACCUMULATOR
PISTON ORIENTATION MAY VARY
B SHIFT SOL
THERMO ELEMENT
LO BLOW OFF
3-4 SHIFT
4-3 DOWN
2-3 SHIFT
3-2 DOWN
3-4 ACCUM
SEC 1-2 ACCUM
2-3 ACCUM
1-2 ACCUM
3-4 ACCUMULATOR

Figure 57 Overdrive Range – 3-2 Downshift

OVERDRIVE RANGE - 3-2 DOWNSHIFT

"A" SHIFT SOLENOID - OFF

"B" SHIFT SOLENOID - ON

INPUT CLUTCH - APPLIED

INPUT SPRAG - OVERRUNNING

SECOND CLUTCH - APPLIED

1/2 SUPPORT ROLLER CLUTCH - HOLDING

FORWARD BAND - APPLIED

During all full throttle downshifts, engine manifold vacuum supply to the vacuum modulator (32) drops allowing the modulator valve (34) to move and increase modulator pressure to the line boost valve (304). At the same time, pump output increases through the higher engine speeds forcing a higher volume of fluid into the line circuit. The increased modulator fluid pressure and increased volume of fluid at the pressure regulator valve (313) creates higher line pressures for proper clutch and valve operation. A full throttle 3-2 downshift occurs when the PCM receives input signals from the VS Sensor and TP Sensor to "energize" or turn on "B" shift solenoid (315). Line pressure at the solenoid is forced into the "B" shift solenoid passage and is directed to the 4-3 manual downshift valve (360) and 3-2 manual downshift valve (356). "B" shift solenoid fluid forces the 3-2 manual downshift valve (356) to move also shifting the 2-3 shift valve (357). Line pressure at the 2-3 shift valve (357) is now directed into the input clutch feed passage, through the 3-4 shift valve (362) into the input clutch passage. Input clutch fluid seats #3 checkball (372) and applies the input clutch. The third clutch is released by allowing 3rd clutch/lo-lst fluid to exhaust to the #4 checkball (372) and into the 3rd clutch passage. 3rd clutch fluid is directed to #9 checkball (372) forcing it through the exhaust orifice and into the 3rd fluid passage to the 2-3 shift valve (357) where it exhausts.

Modulator Valve (34): Moves in response to engine manifold vacuum and increases modulator pressure to the line boost valve (304).

Line Boost Valve (304): Moves in response to modulator pressure to increase line pressure through the pressure regulator valve (313).

Pressure Regulator Valve (313): Increases line pressure in response to increased modulator pressure.

"B" Shift Solenoid (315): Energizes, allowing line pressure into the "B" shift solenoid passage to force a 3-2 downshift.

4-3 Manual Downshift Valve (360): Is shifted by "B" shift solenoid fluid and prevents the 3-4 shift valve (362) from moving.

3-2 Manual Downshift Valve (356): Is shifted by "B" shift solenoid fluid to downshift the 2-3 shift valve (357).

2-3 Shift Valve (357): When downshifted, it allows line pressure to enter into the input clutch feed passage and directs it to the 3-4 shift valve (362).

3-4 Shift Valve (362): Directs input clutch feed fluid into the input clutch passage and sends it to the #3 checkball (372).

#3 Checkball (372): Located in the channel plate (400), it is seated against the PRN passage to allow input clutch fluid to apply the input clutch.

#4 Checkball (372): Located in the channel plate (400), it directs 3rd clutch/lo-1st exhaust fluid into the 3rd clutch passage.

#9 Checkball (372): Located in the valve body (300), it directs 3rd clutch exhaust fluid into the 3rd fluid passage. 3rd fluid is sent to the 2-3 shift valve (357) where it exhausts.

RH0048-4T60-E

Figure 58 Overdrive Range – 3-2 Downshift – Legend

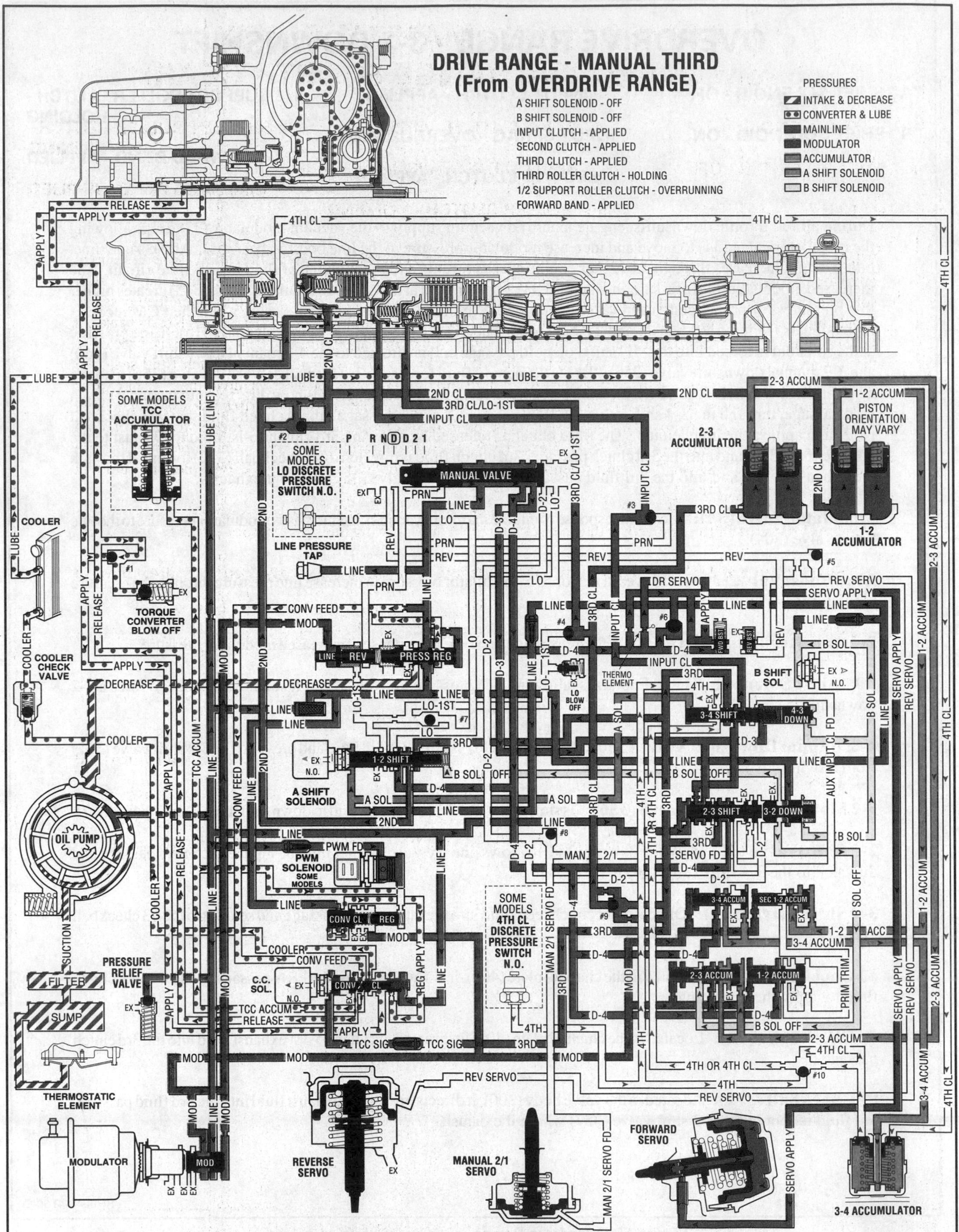
DRIVE RANGE - MANUAL THIRD
(From OVERDRIVE RANGE)
A SHIFT SOLENOID - OFF
B SHIFT SOLENOID - OFF
INPUT CLUTCH - APPLIED
SECOND CLUTCH - APPLIED
THIRD CLUTCH - APPLIED
THIRD ROLLER CLUTCH - HOLDING
1/2 SUPPORT ROLLER CLUTCH - OVERRUNNING
FORWARD BAND - APPLIED
PRESSURES
INTAKE & DECREASE
CONVERTER & LUBE
MAINLINE
MODULATOR
ACCUMULATOR
A SHIFT SOLENOID
B SHIFT SOLENOID
SOME MODELS TCC ACCUMULATOR
SOME MODELS LO DISCRETE PRESSURE SWITCH N.O.
LINE PRESSURE TAP
MANUAL VALVE
2-3 ACCUMULATOR
1-2 ACCUMULATOR
PISTON ORIENTATION MAY VARY
COOLER
TORQUE CONVERTER BLOW OFF
COOLER CHECK VALVE
THERMO ELEMENT
LO BLOW OFF
B SHIFT SOL
3-4 SHIFT
4-3 DOWN
1-2 SHIFT
A SHIFT SOLENOID
2-3 SHIFT
3-2 DOWN
OIL PUMP
PWM SOLENOID SOME MODELS
SOME MODELS 4TH CL DISCRETE PRESSURE SWITCH N.O.
3-4 ACCUM
SEC 1-2 ACCUM
2-3 ACCUM
1-2 ACCUM
PRESSURE RELIEF VALVE
FILTER
SUMP
C.C. SOL.
THERMOSTATIC ELEMENT
MODULATOR
REVERSE SERVO
MANUAL 2/1 SERVO
FORWARD SERVO
3-4 ACCUMULATOR

Figure 59 Drive Range – Manual Third (From Overdrive 4th Gear)

DRIVE RANGE - MANUAL THIRD (From OVERDRIVE RANGE FOURTH GEAR)

"A"SHIFT SOLENOID - OFF

"B" SHIFT SOLENOID - OFF

INPUT CLUTCH - APPLIED

SECOND CLUTCH - APPLIED

THIRD CLUTCH - APPLIED

THIRD ROLLER CLUTCH - HOLDING

1/2 SUPPORT ROLLER CLUTCH - OVERRUNNING

FORWARD BAND - APPLIED

When the gear selector lever is moved to the DRIVE RANGE (D), the manual valve (404) allows line pressure to enter the D-3 passage. D-3 fluid is then directed to the 3-4 shift valve (362) and moves the valve against "A" shift solenoid pressure. D-3 fluid is also sent to the 2-3 shift valve (357) where it enters the input clutch feed passage. Input clutch feed fluid passes through the 3-4 shift valve (362) into the input clutch passage, seats No. 3 checkball (372) against the PRN passage and applies the input clutch. 4th clutch apply fluid at the 4th clutch, is directed to the 3-4 accumulator assembly (421-428) to the No. 10 checkball (372). Exhausting 4th clutch fluid seats the No. 10 checkball (372) against the 4th passage directing fluid through an exhaust orifice up to the 3-4 shift valve (362) where it exhausts. Since D-3 fluid overrides "A" shift solenoid fluid at the 3-4 shift valve (362), a manual 4-3 downshift will result even if "A" shift solenoid is "energized" or "turned on" (Drive range 4th gear solenoid state is "A" shift solenoid on and "B" shift solenoid off). If the PCM receives the appropriate input signals from the VS Sensor and TP Sensor, "A" shift solenoid will "de-energize or "turn off" and "A" shift solenoid fluid will then exhaust through the solenoid.

Manual Valve (404): Is moved by the gear selector lever and allowing line pressure to enter the D-3 passage.

2-3 Shift Valve (357): Allows D-3 fluid to enter the input clutch feed passage and directs it to the 3-4 shift valve (362).

3-4 Shift Valve (362): Is downshifted when D-3 fluid is fed to the valve. In this position input clutch feed fluid enters the input clutch passage.

No. 3 Checkball (372): Located in the channel plate (400), it is seated against the PRN passage allowing input clutch fluid to apply the input clutch.

No. 10 Checkball (372): Located in the valve body (300), it is seated against 4th fluid allowing 4th clutch fluid to exhaust at the 3-4 shift valve (362).

"A" Shift Solenoid (315): When de-energized, it allows "A" shift solenoid fluid from the 3-4 shift valve (362) to exhaust through the solenoid. However, this event does not have to occur in order to achieve a manual 4-3 downshift.

RH0050-4T60-E

Figure 60 Drive Range – Manual Third (From Overdrive 4th Gear)– Legend

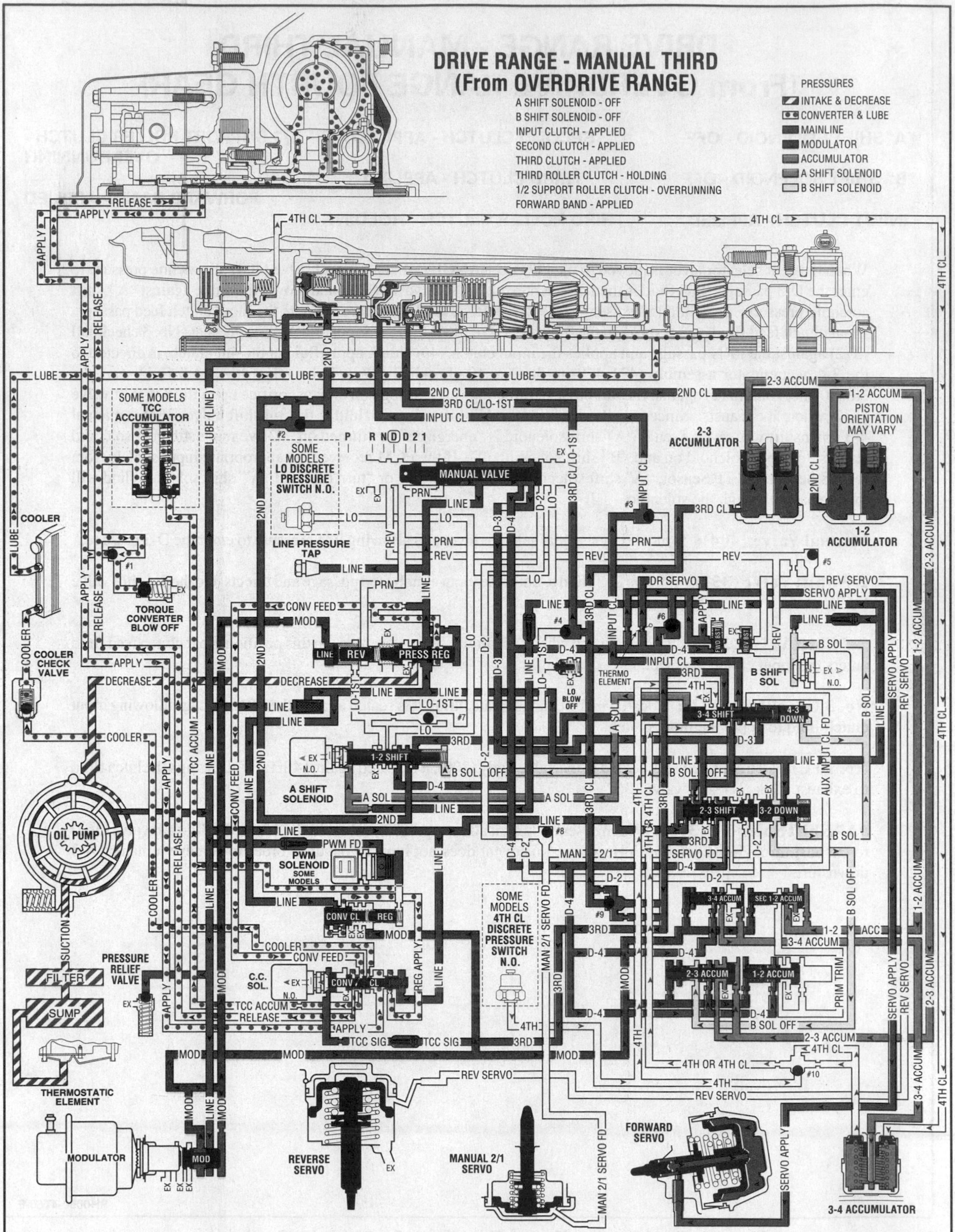
DRIVE RANGE - MANUAL THIRD
(From OVERDRIVE RANGE)
A SHIFT SOLENOID - OFF
B SHIFT SOLENOID - OFF
INPUT CLUTCH - APPLIED
SECOND CLUTCH - APPLIED
THIRD CLUTCH - APPLIED
THIRD ROLLER CLUTCH - HOLDING
1/2 SUPPORT ROLLER CLUTCH - OVERRUNNING
FORWARD BAND - APPLIED
PRESSURES
INTAKE & DECREASE
CONVERTER & LUBE
MAINLINE
MODULATOR
ACCUMULATOR
A SHIFT SOLENOID
B SHIFT SOLENOID
SOME MODELS TCC ACCUMULATOR
SOME MODELS LO DISCRETE PRESSURE SWITCH N.O.
LINE PRESSURE TAP
MANUAL VALVE
P R N D D 2 1
2-3 ACCUMULATOR
1-2 ACCUMULATOR
PISTON ORIENTATION MAY VARY
COOLER
TORQUE CONVERTER BLOW OFF
COOLER CHECK VALVE
REV
PRESS REG
THERMO ELEMENT
LO BLOW OFF
B SHIFT SOL
3-4 SHIFT
4-3 DOWN
1-2 SHIFT
A SHIFT SOLENOID
2-3 SHIFT
3-2 DOWN
OIL PUMP
PWM SOLENOID SOME MODELS
SOME MODELS 4TH CL DISCRETE PRESSURE SWITCH N.O.
3-4 ACCUM
SEC 1-2 ACCUM
2-3 ACCUM
1-2 ACCUM
CONV CL
REG
C.C. SOL.
CONV CL
PRESSURE RELIEF VALVE
FILTER
SUMP
SUCTION
THERMOSTATIC ELEMENT
MODULATOR
REVERSE SERVO
MANUAL 2/1 SERVO
FORWARD SERVO
3-4 ACCUMULATOR

Figure 61 Drive Range – Manual Third (From Overdrive 4th Gear)

DRIVE RANGE - MANUAL THIRD (From OVERDRIVE RANGE FOURTH GEAR)

(MODELS WITH PRESSURE SWITCHES)

"A" SHIFT SOLENOID - OFF

"B" SHIFT SOLENOID - OFF

INPUT CLUTCH - APPLIED

SECOND CLUTCH - APPLIED

THIRD CLUTCH - APPLIED

THIRD ROLLER CLUTCH - HOLDING

1/2 SUPPORT ROLLER CLUTCH - OVERRUNNING

FORWARD BAND - APPLIED

When the gear selector lever is moved to the DRIVE RANGE (D), the manual valve (404) allows line pressure to enter the D-3 passage. D-3 fluid is then directed to the 3-4 shift valve (362) and moves the valve against "A" shift solenoid pressure. D-3 fluid is also sent to the 2-3 shift valve (357) where it enters the input clutch feed passage. Input clutch feed fluid passes through the 3-4 shift valve (362) into the input clutch passage, seats No. 3 checkball (372) against the PRN passage and applies the input clutch. 4th clutch apply fluid at the 4th clutch, is directed through the 3-4 accumulator assembly (421-428) to the No. 10 checkball (372). Exhausting 4th clutch fluid seats the No. 10 checkball (372) against the 4th passage directing fluid through an exhaust orifice up to the 3-4 shift valve (362) where it exhausts. 4th fluid pressure at the 4th clutch discrete switch (218) also exhausts at the 3-4 shift valve (362) allowing the switch to open and signal the PCM that the transaxle is no longer operating in 4th gear.

Since D-3 fluid overrides "A" shift solenoid fluid at the 3-4 shift valve (362), a manual 4-3 downshift will result even if "A" shift solenoid is "energized" or"turned on" (Drive Range Fourth Gear solenoid state is "A" shift solenoid on and "B" shift solenoid off). If the PCM receives the appropriate input signals from the VS Sensor and TP Sensor, "A" shift solenoid will "de-energize" or "turn off" and "A" shift solenoid fluid will then exhaust through the solenoid.

Manual Valve (404): Is moved by the gear selector lever and allows line pressure to enter the D-3 passage.

2-3 Shift Valve (357): Allows D-3 fluid to enter the input clutch feed passage and directs it to the 3-4 shift valve (362).

3-4 Shift Valve (362): Is downshifted when D-3 fluid is fed to the valve. In this position input clutch feed fluid enters the input clutch passage.

No. 3 Checkball (372): Located in the channel plate (400), it is seated against the PRN passage allowing input clutch fluid to apply the input clutch.

No. 10 Checkball (372): Located in the valve body (300), it is seated against 4th fluid allowing 4th clutch fluid to exhaust at the 3-4 shift valve).

4th Clutch Discrete Switch (218): "Opens" a circuit to the PCM to signal that the transaxle is no longer operating in Overdrive Range – Fourth Gear.

"A" Shift Solenoid (315): When de-energized, it allows "A" shift solenoid fluid from the 3-4 shift valve (362) to exhaust through the solenoid. However, this event does not have to occur in order to achieve a manual 4-3 downshift.

NOTE: When a Manual Third Gear Range is selected (from Overdrive Range Fourth Gear) 4th fluid pressure at the 4th clutch discrete switch (218) exhausts allowing the switch to open. The PCM senses this change in vehicle operation and releases the torque converter clutch to help eliminate harsh manual D4 to D3 downshifts. The torque converter clutch will re-apply after the PCM senses that normal Third Gear operating conditions (such as vehicle speed, throttle position, etc.) have once again been met.

RH0050-4T60-E-PS

Figure 62 Drive Range – Manual Third (From Overdrive 4th Gear)– Legend

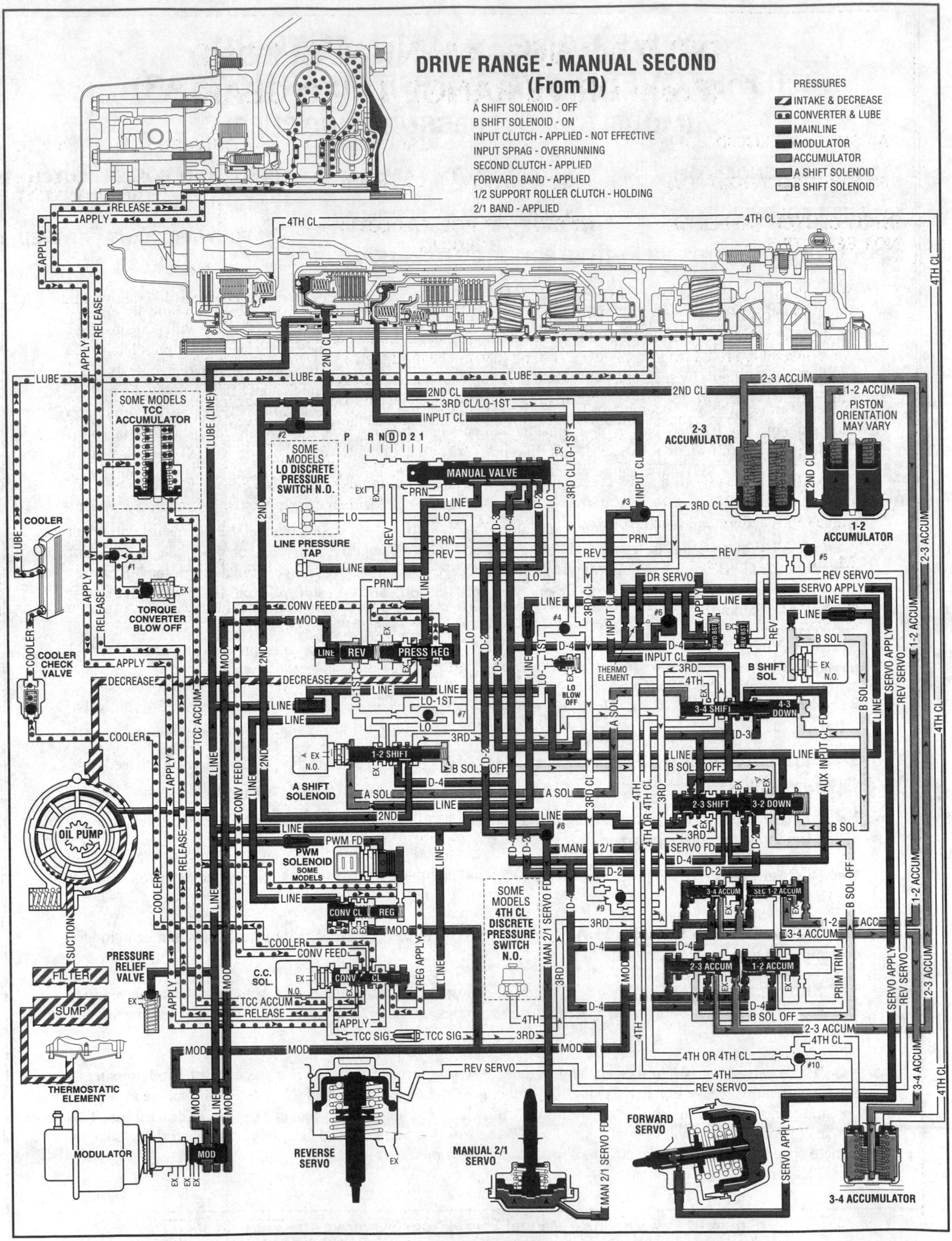
DRIVE RANGE - MANUAL SECOND
(From D)
A SHIFT SOLENOID - OFF
B SHIFT SOLENOID - ON
INPUT CLUTCH - APPLIED - NOT EFFECTIVE
INPUT SPRAG - OVERRUNNING
SECOND CLUTCH - APPLIED
FORWARD BAND - APPLIED
1/2 SUPPORT ROLLER CLUTCH - HOLDING
2/1 BAND - APPLIED
PRESSURES
INTAKE & DECREASE
CONVERTER & LUBE
MAINLINE
MODULATOR
ACCUMULATOR
A SHIFT SOLENOID
B SHIFT SOLENOID
RELEASE
APPLY
4TH CL
LUBE
2ND CL
3RD CL/LO-1ST
INPUT CL
2-3 ACCUM
1-2 ACCUM
PISTON ORIENTATION MAY VARY
2-3 ACCUMULATOR
1-2 ACCUMULATOR
SOME MODELS TCC ACCUMULATOR
SOME MODELS LO DISCRETE PRESSURE SWITCH N.O.
P R N D D 2 1
MANUAL VALVE
LINE PRESSURE TAP
COOLER
TORQUE CONVERTER BLOW OFF
COOLER CHECK VALVE
CONV FEED
MOD
REV
PRESS REG
DECREASE
LO BLOW OFF
THERMO ELEMENT
B SHIFT SOL
3-4 SHIFT
4-3 DOWN
1-2 SHIFT
A SHIFT SOLENOID
B SOL OFF
A SOL
2-3 SHIFT
3-2 DOWN
OIL PUMP
PWM SOLENOID SOME MODELS
CONV CL REG
SOME MODELS 4TH CL DISCRETE PRESSURE SWITCH N.O.
3-4 ACCUM
SEC 1-2 ACCUM
2-3 ACCUM
1-2 ACCUM
C.C. SOL.
CONV CL
PRESSURE RELIEF VALVE
SUCTION
FILTER
SUMP
TCC ACCUM
TCC SIG
THERMOSTATIC ELEMENT
MODULATOR
REV SERVO
REVERSE SERVO
MANUAL 2/1 SERVO
MAN 2/1 SERVO FD
FORWARD SERVO
SERVO APPLY
3-4 ACCUMULATOR
4TH OR 4TH CL
PRIM TRIM
AUX INPUT CL FD
DR SERVO
SERVO FD

Figure 63 Drive Range – Manual Second (From Drive Range 3rd Gear)

DRIVE RANGE - MANUAL SECOND (From DRIVE RANGE THIRD GEAR)

"A" SHIFT SOLENOID - OFF

"B" SHIFT SOLENOID - ON

INPUT CLUTCH - APPLIED/ NOT EFFECTIVE

INPUT SPRAG - OVERRUNNING

SECOND CLUTCH - APPLIED

1/2 SUPPORT ROLLER CLUTCH - HOLDING

FORWARD BAND - APPLIED

2/1 BAND - APPLIED

When the gear selector lever is moved to the MANUAL SECOND RANGE (2), the manual valve (404) allows line pressure to enter the D-2 passage. D-2 fluid seats #8 checkball (372) and is directed to the 2-3 shift valve (357) to shift the valve. When shifted, D-2 fluid enters the manual 2-1 servo feed passage and strokes the manual 2/1 servo assembly (104-116) to apply the 2/1 band (680). The third clutch is released by allowing 3rd clutch/lo-lst apply fluid to exhaust by seating #4 checkball (372) against the lo-lst passage and into the 3rd clutch passage. 3rd clutch fluid is then directed to #9 checkball (372) and seats it against the 3rd fluid passage forcing the fluid through an exhaust orifice into the 3rd fluid passage. 3rd fluid is then sent to the 2-3 shift valve (357) where it exhausts. Since D-2 fluid overrides line pressure at the 2-3 shift valve (357), a manual 3-2 downshift will result even if "B" shift solenoid is "de-energized" or "turned off" (drive range 3rd gear solenoid state is: "A" shift solenoid off and "B" shift solenoid off). If the PCM receives the appropriate input signals from the VS Sensor and TP Sensor, "B" shift solenoid will "energize" or "turn on". "B" shift solenoid fluid is then directed to the 4-3 manual downshift valve (360) and the 3-2 manual downshift valve (356).

Manual Valve (404): Is moved by the gear selector lever allowing line pressure to enter the D-2 passage.

#8 Checkball (372): Located in the valve body (300), is fed D-2 fluid from the manual valve (404) and directs it to the 2-3 shift valve (357).

2-3 Shift Valve (357): When shifted by D-2 fluid, it allows D-2 fluid to enter the manual 2-1 servo feed passage to stroke the manual 2/1 servo assembly (104-116) and allows 3rd fluid to exhaust.

Manual 2/1 Servo Assembly (104-116): Applies the 2/1 band (680) during manual second and manual first gear ranges.

#4 Checkball (372): Located in the channel plate (400), it directs 3rd clutch/lo-lst exhaust fluid into the 3rd clutch passage.

"B" Shift Solenoid (315): When energized, it allows line pressure to enter the "B" shift solenoid passage and sends it to the 4-3 manual downshift valve (360) and 3-2 manual downshift valve (356). However, this event does not have to occur in order to achieve a manual 3-2 downshift.

3-2 Manual Downshift Valve (356): Is shifted by "B" shift solenoid fluid and prevents the 2-3 shift valve (357) from upshifting.

RH0052-4T60-E

Figure 64 Drive Range – Manual Second (From Drive Range 3rd Gear) – Legend

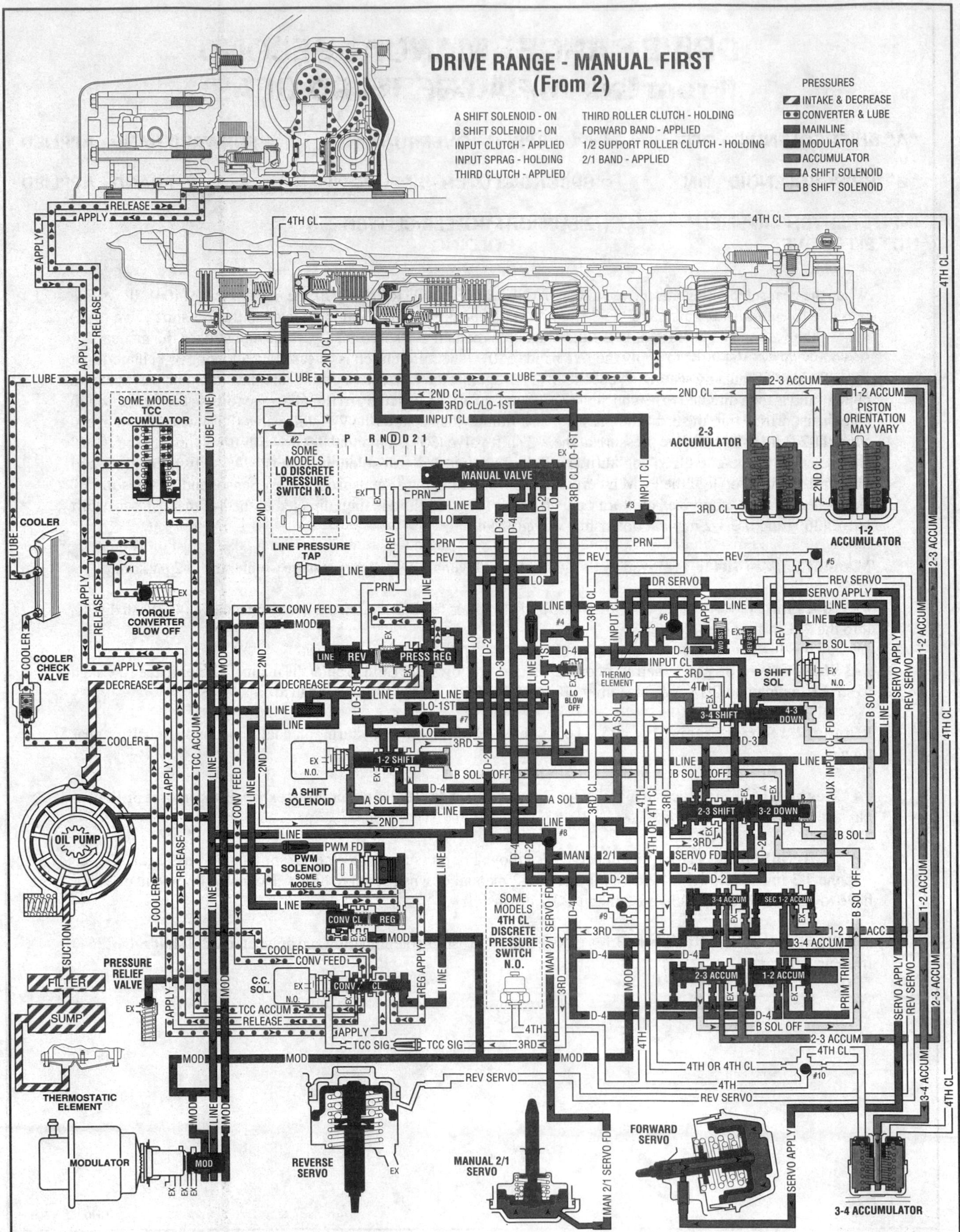
DRIVE RANGE - MANUAL FIRST
(From 2)
A SHIFT SOLENOID - ON
B SHIFT SOLENOID - ON
INPUT CLUTCH - APPLIED
INPUT SPRAG - HOLDING
THIRD CLUTCH - APPLIED
THIRD ROLLER CLUTCH - HOLDING
FORWARD BAND - APPLIED
1/2 SUPPORT ROLLER CLUTCH - HOLDING
2/1 BAND - APPLIED
PRESSURES
INTAKE & DECREASE
CONVERTER & LUBE
MAINLINE
MODULATOR
ACCUMULATOR
A SHIFT SOLENOID
B SHIFT SOLENOID
SOME MODELS TCC ACCUMULATOR
SOME MODELS LO DISCRETE PRESSURE SWITCH N.O.
LINE PRESSURE TAP
MANUAL VALVE
P R N D D 2 1
2-3 ACCUMULATOR
1-2 ACCUMULATOR
PISTON ORIENTATION MAY VARY
COOLER
TORQUE CONVERTER BLOW OFF
COOLER CHECK VALVE
PRESS REG
THERMO ELEMENT
B SHIFT SOL
LO BLOW OFF
3-4 SHIFT
4-3 DOWN
1-2 SHIFT
A SHIFT SOLENOID
2-3 SHIFT
3-2 DOWN
OIL PUMP
PWM SOLENOID SOME MODELS
CONV CL REG
3-4 ACCUM
SEC 1-2 ACCUM
2-3 ACCUM
1-2 ACCUM
SOME MODELS 4TH CL DISCRETE PRESSURE SWITCH N.O.
PRESSURE RELIEF VALVE
C.C. SOL.
FILTER
SUMP
SUCTION
THERMOSTATIC ELEMENT
MODULATOR
REVERSE SERVO
MANUAL 2/1 SERVO
FORWARD SERVO
3-4 ACCUMULATOR

Figure 65 Drive Range – Manual First (From Manual Second)

DRIVE RANGE - MANUAL FIRST (From MANUAL SECOND)

"A" SHIFT SOLENOID - ON

"B" SHIFT SOLENOID - ON

THIRD CLUTCH - APPLIED

THIRD ROLLER CLUTCH - HOLDING

INPUT CLUTCH - APPLIED

INPUT SPRAG - HOLDING

1/2 SUPPORT ROLLER CLUTCH - HOLDING

FORWARD BAND - APPLIED

2/1 BAND - APPLIED

When the gear selector lever is moved to the MANUAL FIRST RANGE (1), the manual valve (404) allows line pressure to enter the Lo passage. Lo fluid pressure is sent to No. 7 checkball (372) which seats against the lo-1st fluid passage. Based on PCM input signals from the VS Sensor, TP Sensor and lo-1st lockout speed calibration, "A" shift solenoid is "energized" or "turned on" allowing line pressure to enter the "A" shift solenoid passage. "A" shift solenoid fluid then holds the 1-2 shift valve (318) and is also directed to the 3-4 shift valve (362). The second clutch is released by 2nd clutch apply fluid exhausting to the No. 2 checkball (372), forcing it through the exhaust orifice into the 2nd fluid passage. 2nd fluid is then directed thorugh the 1-2 shift valve (318) and into the 3rd fluid passage where it exhausts at the 2-3 shift valve (357). Simultaneously, lo fluid is direced through the 1-2 shift valve (318) into the lo-1st fluid passage. Lo-1st fluid is sent to the pressure regulator valve (313) to boost line pressure and at the same time to the lo blow off valve (407). Lo-1st fluid also seats No. 4 checkball against the 3rd clutch passage and directs the fluid into the 3rd clutch/lo-lst passage to apply the 3rd clutch.

Manual Valve (404): Is moved by the gear selector lever and allows line pressure to enter the Lo fluid passage.

No. 7 Checkball (372): Located in the valve body (300), directs lo fluid to the 1-2 shift valve (318).

1-2 Shift Valve (318): When shifted against spring force, allows lo fluid to enter the lo-lst passage to the pressure regulator valve (313). During release of the 2nd clutch, exhausting 2nd fluid passes through the valve and enters the 3rd fluid passage.

Pressure Regulator Valve (313): Boosts line pressure using lo-lst fluid pressure.

Lo Blow Off Valve (407): A relief valve that will exhaust excess Lo fluid pressures above 448 kPa (65 psi) in the 3rd clutch apply circuit.

No. 4 Checkball (372): Located in the channel plate (400), it seats against 3rd clutch fluid allowing lo-lst fluid to enter the 3rd clutch fluid passage and apply the 3rd clutch.

"A" Shift Solenoid (315): Energizes, allowing line pressure to feed into the "A" shift solenoid passage and to the 3-4 shift valve (357).

No. 2 Checkball (372): Located in the channel plate (400), forces exhausting 2nd clutch apply fluid through an orifice into the 2nd clutch passage and to the 1-2 shift valve (318).

RH0054-4T60-E

Figure 66 Drive Range – Manual First (From Manual Second) – Legend

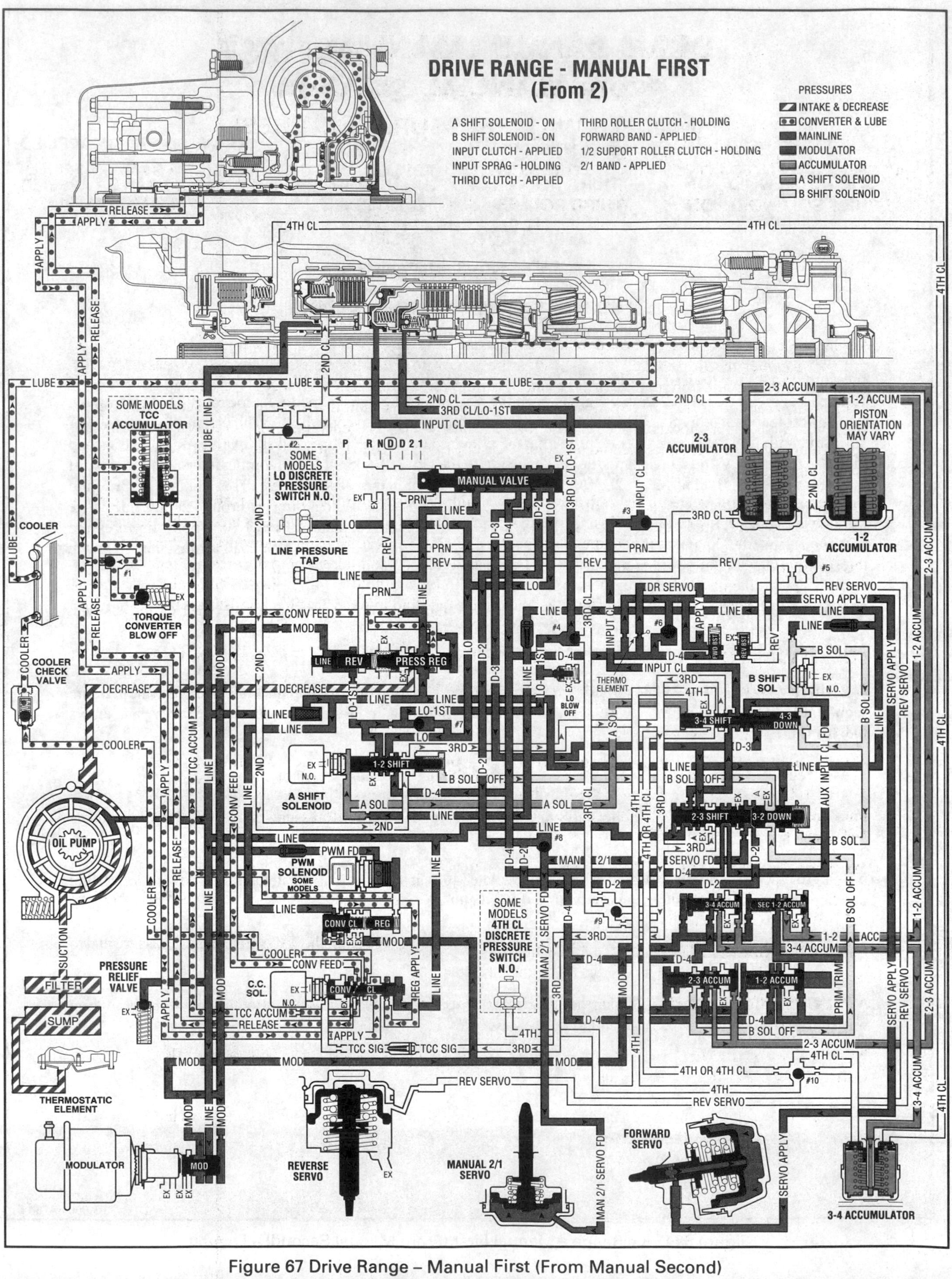

DRIVE RANGE - MANUAL FIRST
(From 2)
A SHIFT SOLENOID - ON
B SHIFT SOLENOID - ON
INPUT CLUTCH - APPLIED
INPUT SPRAG - HOLDING
THIRD CLUTCH - APPLIED
THIRD ROLLER CLUTCH - HOLDING
FORWARD BAND - APPLIED
1/2 SUPPORT ROLLER CLUTCH - HOLDING
2/1 BAND - APPLIED
PRESSURES
INTAKE & DECREASE
CONVERTER & LUBE
MAINLINE
MODULATOR
ACCUMULATOR
A SHIFT SOLENOID
B SHIFT SOLENOID
SOME MODELS TCC ACCUMULATOR
SOME MODELS LO DISCRETE PRESSURE SWITCH N.O.
LINE PRESSURE TAP
MANUAL VALVE
P R N D D 2 1
2-3 ACCUMULATOR
PISTON ORIENTATION MAY VARY
1-2 ACCUMULATOR
COOLER
TORQUE CONVERTER BLOW OFF
COOLER CHECK VALVE
PRESS REG
THERMO ELEMENT
LO BLOW OFF
B SHIFT SOL
3-4 SHIFT
4-3 DOWN
1-2 SHIFT
A SHIFT SOLENOID
2-3 SHIFT
3-2 DOWN
OIL PUMP
PWM SOLENOID SOME MODELS
CONV CL REG
C.C. SOL.
SOME MODELS 4TH CL DISCRETE PRESSURE SWITCH N.O.
3-4 ACCUM
SEC 1-2 ACCUM
2-3 ACCUM
1-2 ACCUM
SUCTION
PRESSURE RELIEF VALVE
FILTER
SUMP
THERMOSTATIC ELEMENT
MODULATOR
REVERSE SERVO
MANUAL 2/1 SERVO
FORWARD SERVO
3-4 ACCUMULATOR

Figure 67 Drive Range – Manual First (From Manual Second)

DRIVE RANGE - MANUAL FIRST (From MANUAL SECOND)

(MODELS WITH PRESSURE SWITCHES)

"A" SHIFT SOLENOID - ON
"B" SHIFT SOLENOID - ON
THIRD CLUTCH - APPLIED
THIRD ROLLER CLUTCH - HOLDING
INPUT CLUTCH - APPLIED
INPUT SPRAG - HOLDING
1/2 SUPPORT ROLLER CLUTCH - HOLDING
FORWARD BAND - APPLIED
2/1 BAND - APPLIED

When the gear selector lever is moved to the MANUAL FIRST RANGE (1), the manual valve (404) allows line pressure to enter the lo passage. Lo fluid pressure is sent to the lo discrete switch (218), closes it thereby completing the circuit from the PCM to ground. Lo fluid pressure is also sent to No. 7 checkball (372) which seats against the lo-1st fluid passage. Based on PCM input signals from the VS Sensor, TP Sensor, lo discrete switch (218), and lo-1st lockout speed calibration, "A" shift solenoid is "energized" or "turned on" allowing line pressure to enter the "A" shift solenoid passage. "A" shift solenoid fluid then holds the 1-2 shift valve (318) and is also directed to the 3-4 shift valve (362).

The second clutch is released by 2nd clutch apply fluid exhausting to the No. 2 checkball (372), forcing it through the exhaust orifice into the 2nd fluid passage. 2nd fluid is then directed through the 1-2 shift valve (318) and into the 3rd fluid passage where it exhausts at the 2-3 shift valve (357). Simultaneously, lo fluid is directed through the 1-2 shift valve (318) into the lo-1st fluid passage. Lo-1st fluid is sent to the pressure regulator valve (313) to boost line pressure and at the same time to the lo blow off valve (407). Lo-1st fluid also seats No. 4 checkball (372) against the 3rd clutch passage and directs the fluid into the 3rd clutch/lo-lst passage to apply the 3rd clutch.

Manual Valve (404): Is moved by the gear selector lever and allows line pressure to enter the lo fluid passage.

Lo Discrete Switch (218): A normally open switch that closes when lo fluid pressure is fed from the manual valve (404). When the switch is closed it completes the circuit from the PCM to ground and provides information to the PCM that the gear selector lever has been moved to Manual First Gear Range.

No. 7 Checkball (372): Located in the valve body (300), directs lo fluid to the 1-2 shift valve (318).

1-2 Shift Valve (318): When shifted against spring force, allows lo fluid to enter the lo-lst passage to the pressure regulator valve (313). During release of the 2nd clutch, exhausting 2nd fluid passes through the valve and enters the 3rd fluid passage.

Pressure Regulator Valve (313): Boosts line pressure using lo-lst fluid pressure.

Lo Blow Off Valve (407): A pressure relief valve that will exhaust excess lo fluid pressures above 448 kPa (65 psi) in the 3rd clutch apply circuit.

No. 4 Checkball (372): Located in the channel plate (400), it seats against 3rd clutch fluid allowing lo-lst fluid to enter the 3rd clutch fluid passage and apply the 3rd clutch.

"A" Shift Solenoid (315): Energizes, allowing line pressure to feed into the "A" shift solenoid passage and to the 3-4 shift valve (357).

No. 2 Checkball (372): Located in the channel plate (400), forces exhausting 2nd clutch apply fluid through an orifice into the 2nd clutch passage and to the 1-2 shift valve (318).

NOTE: The transaxle will shift to Manual First Gear Range only when the following conditions have been met:

- Manual First Gear Range is selected
- Solenoid state is operating for First Gear ("A" Shift Solenoid and "B" Shift Solenoid – ON)
- Lo Discrete Switch provides ground to PCM
- Vehicle speed is below 56 kmh (35 mph)

RH0054-4T60-E-PS

Figure 68 Drive Range – Manual First (From Manual Second) – Legend

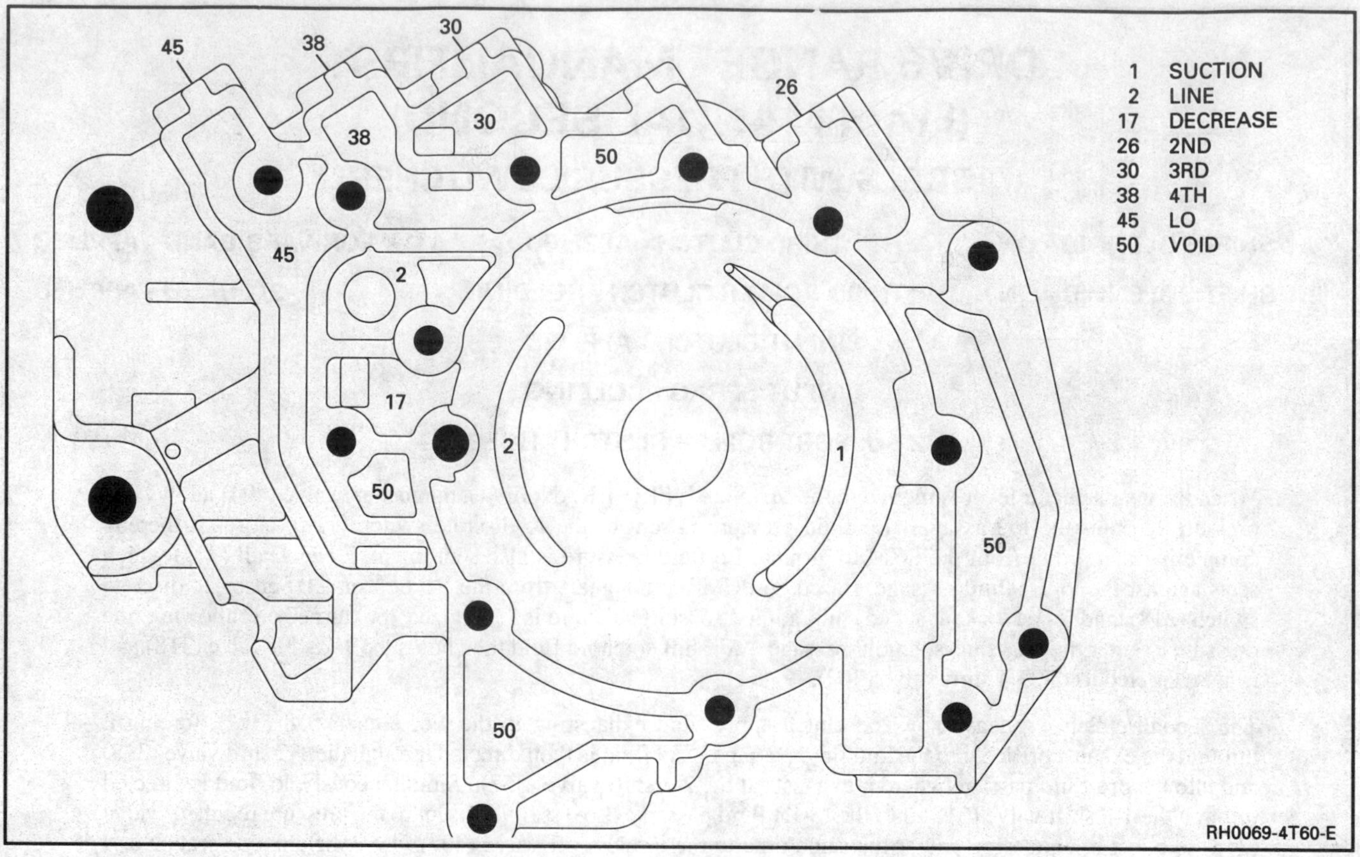
45
38
30
26
30
38
50
45
2
17
2
1
50
50
50
1 SUCTION
2 LINE
17 DECREASE
26 2ND
30 3RD
38 4TH
45 LO
50 VOID
RH0069-4T60-E

Figure 69 Oil Pump Passages

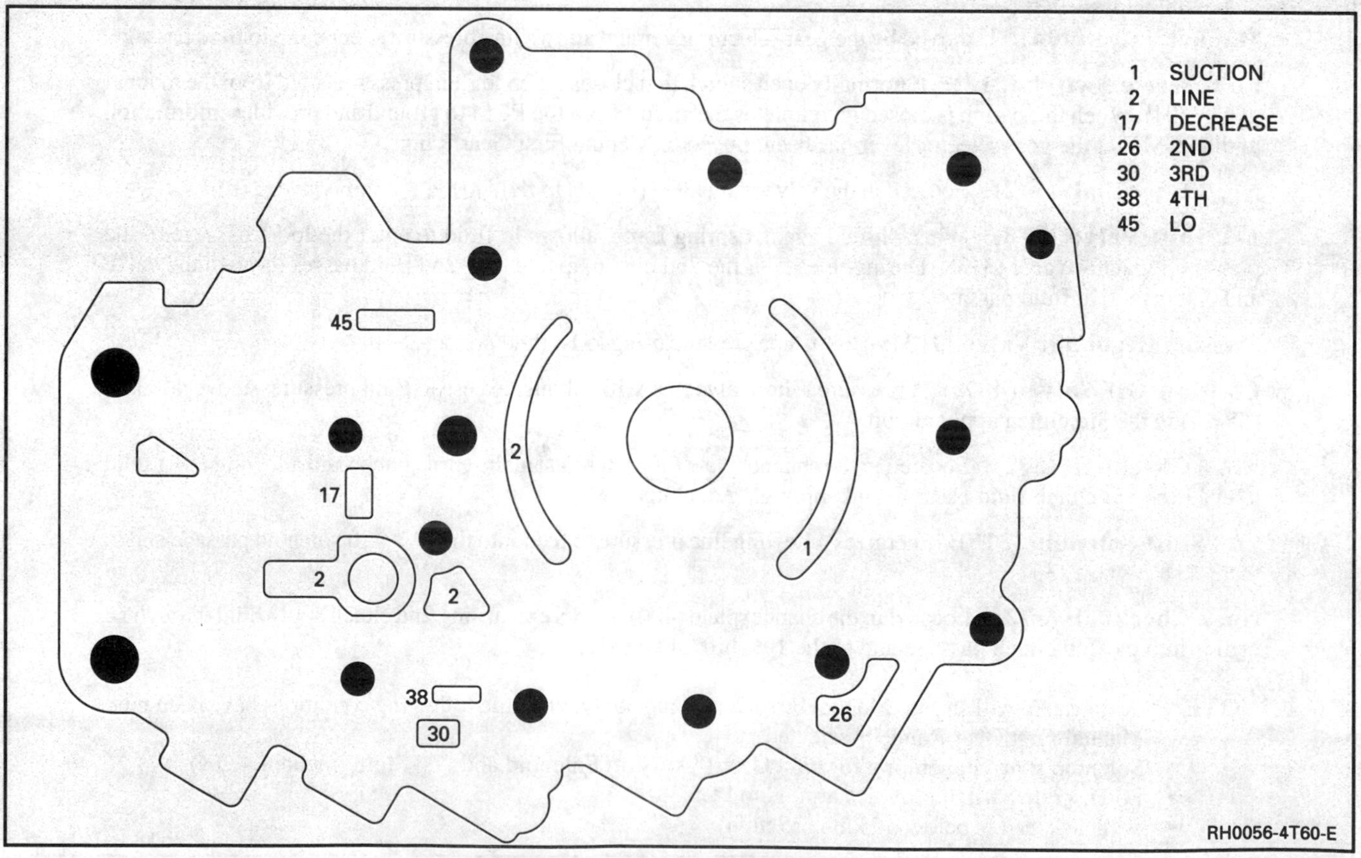
1 SUCTION
2 LINE
17 DECREASE
26 2ND
30 3RD
38 4TH
45 LO
45
2
17
1
2
2
38
30
26
RH0056-4T60-E

Figure 70 Oil Pump Passages

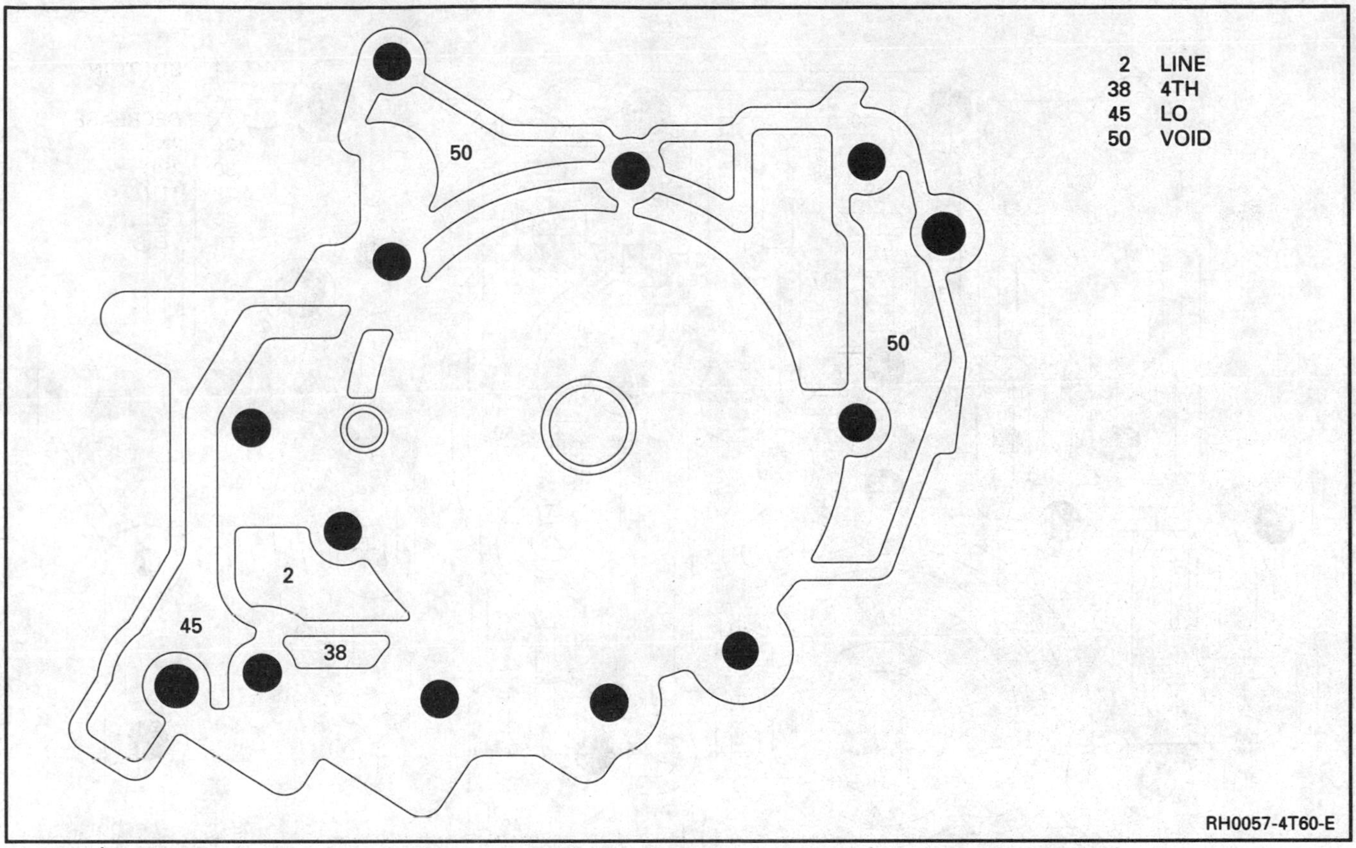
2 LINE
38 4TH
45 LO
50 VOID
50
50
2
45
38
RH0057-4T60-E

Figure 71 Oil Pump Passages

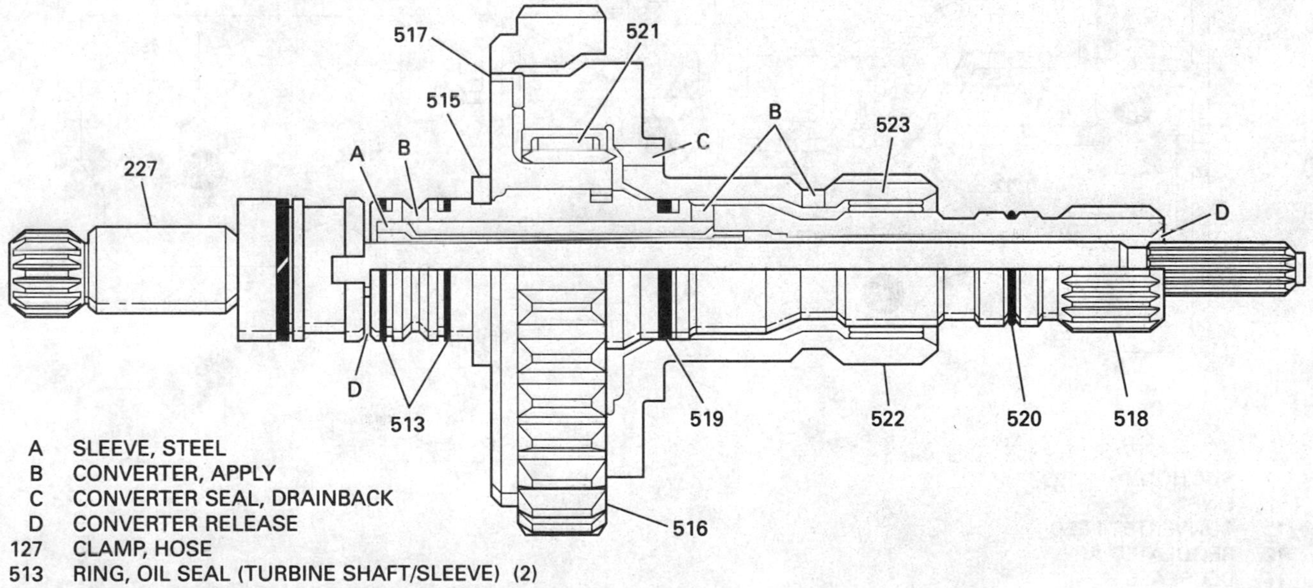
517
521
515
B
523
A
B
C
227
D
D
513
519
522
520
518
516

- A SLEEVE, STEEL
- B CONVERTER, APPLY
- C CONVERTER SEAL, DRAINBACK
- D CONVERTER RELEASE
- 127 CLAMP, HOSE
- 513 RING, OIL SEAL (TURBINE SHAFT/SLEEVE) (2)
- 515 RING, TURBINE SHAFT TO DRIVE SPROCKET (SNAP)
- 516 SPROCKET, DRIVE
- 517 WASHER, THRUST (DRIVE SPROCKET/SUPPORT)
- 518 SHAFT, TURBINE
- 519 RING, OIL SEAL (TURBINE SHAFT/SUPPORT)
- 520 SEAL, O-RING (TURBINE SHAFT/HUB) GREEN
- 521 BEARING ASM., DRIVE SUPPORT/SPROCKET (DRAWN CUP)
- 522 SUPPORT, DRIVE SPROCKET
- 523 BUSHING, DRIVE SPROCKET SUPPORT

RH0058-4T60-E

Figure 72 Pump Drive Shaft and Drive Sprocket Support

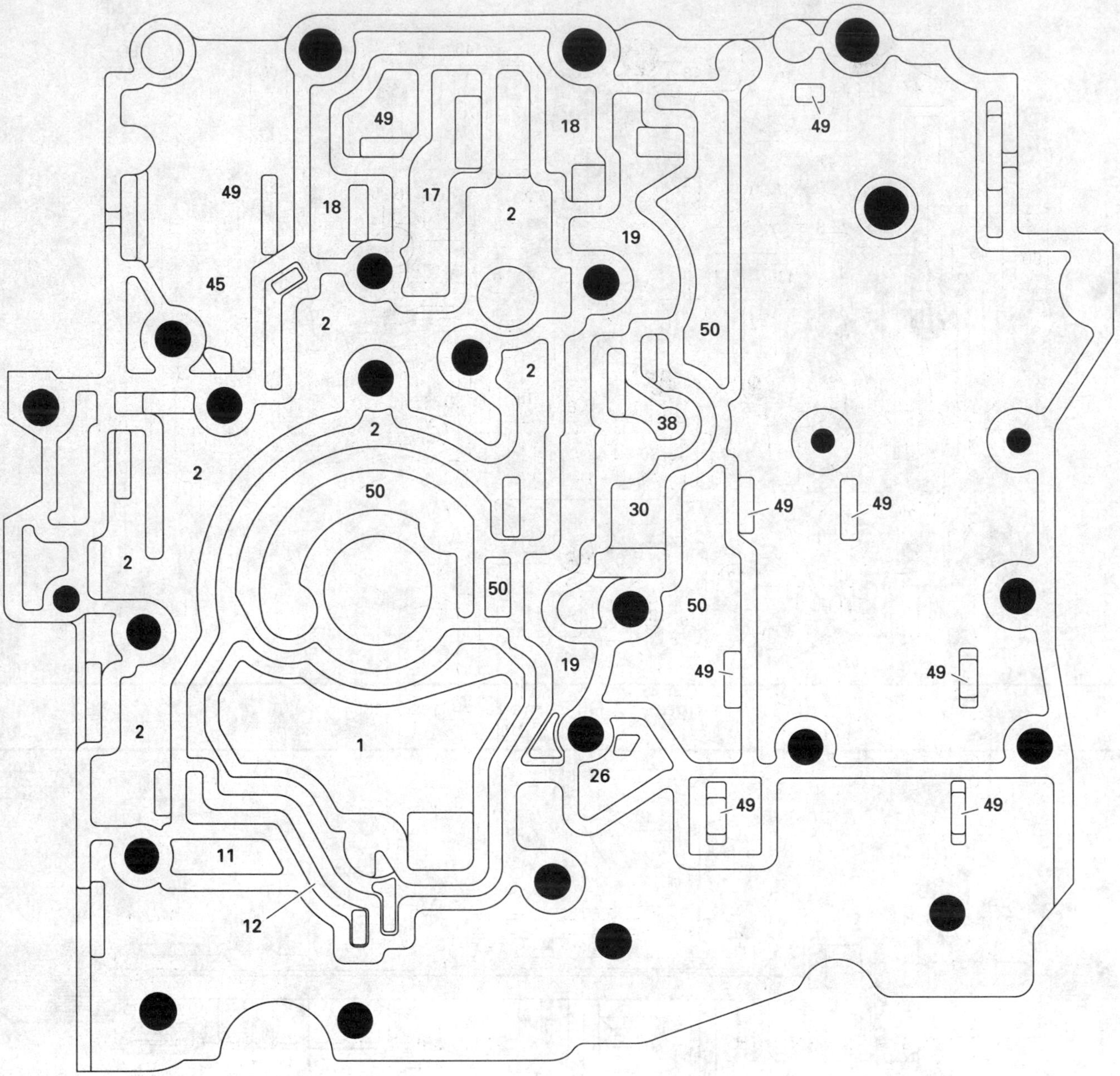
49
18
49
49
18
17
2
19
45
2
50
2
38
2
2
50
30
49
49
2
50
50
19
49
49
2
1
26
49
49
11
12

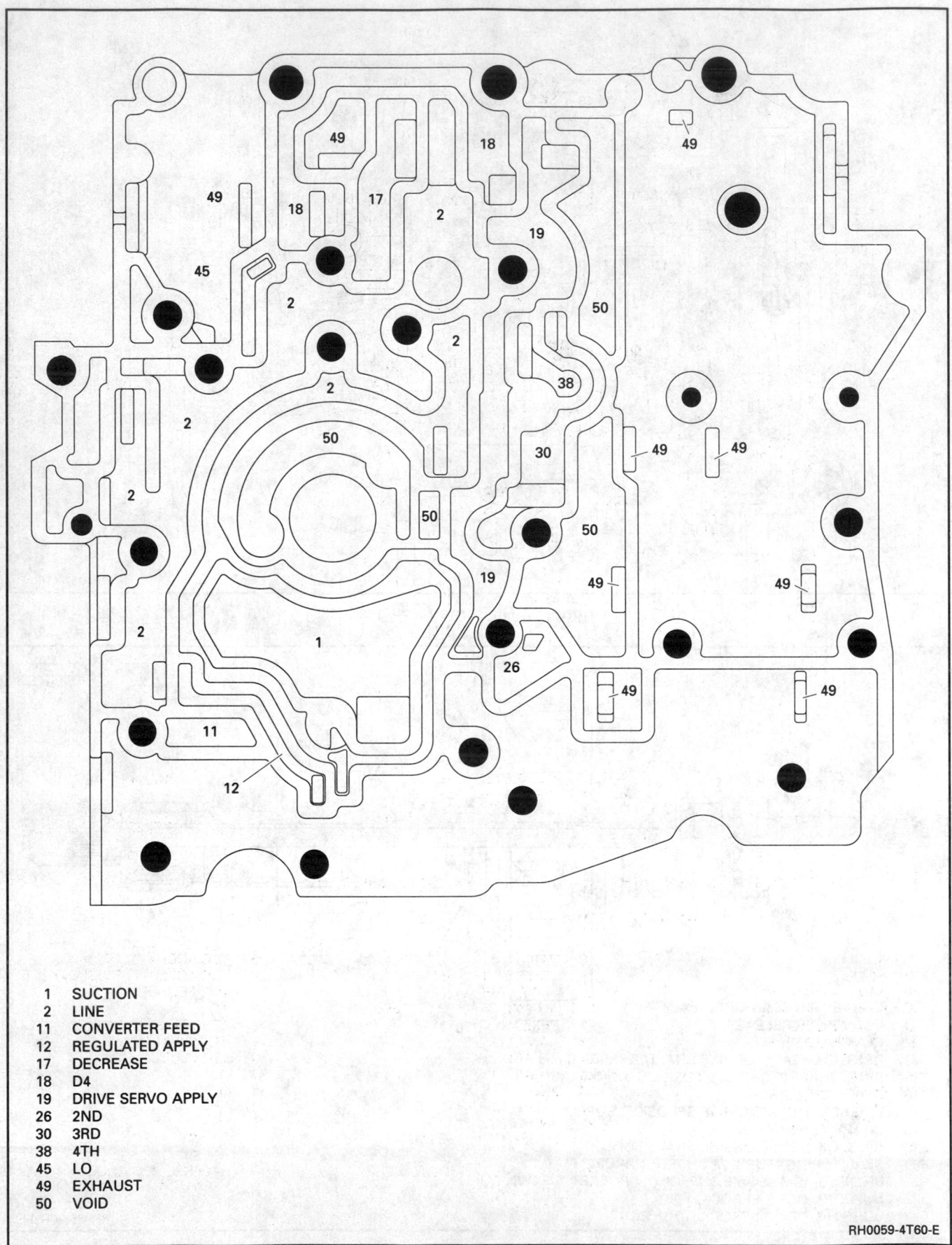

1 SUCTION
2 LINE
11 CONVERTER FEED
12 REGULATED APPLY
17 DECREASE
18 D4
19 DRIVE SERVO APPLY
26 2ND
30 3RD
38 4TH
45 LO
49 EXHAUST
50 VOID

RH0059-4T60-E

Figure 73 Control Valve Passages – Oil Pump Side

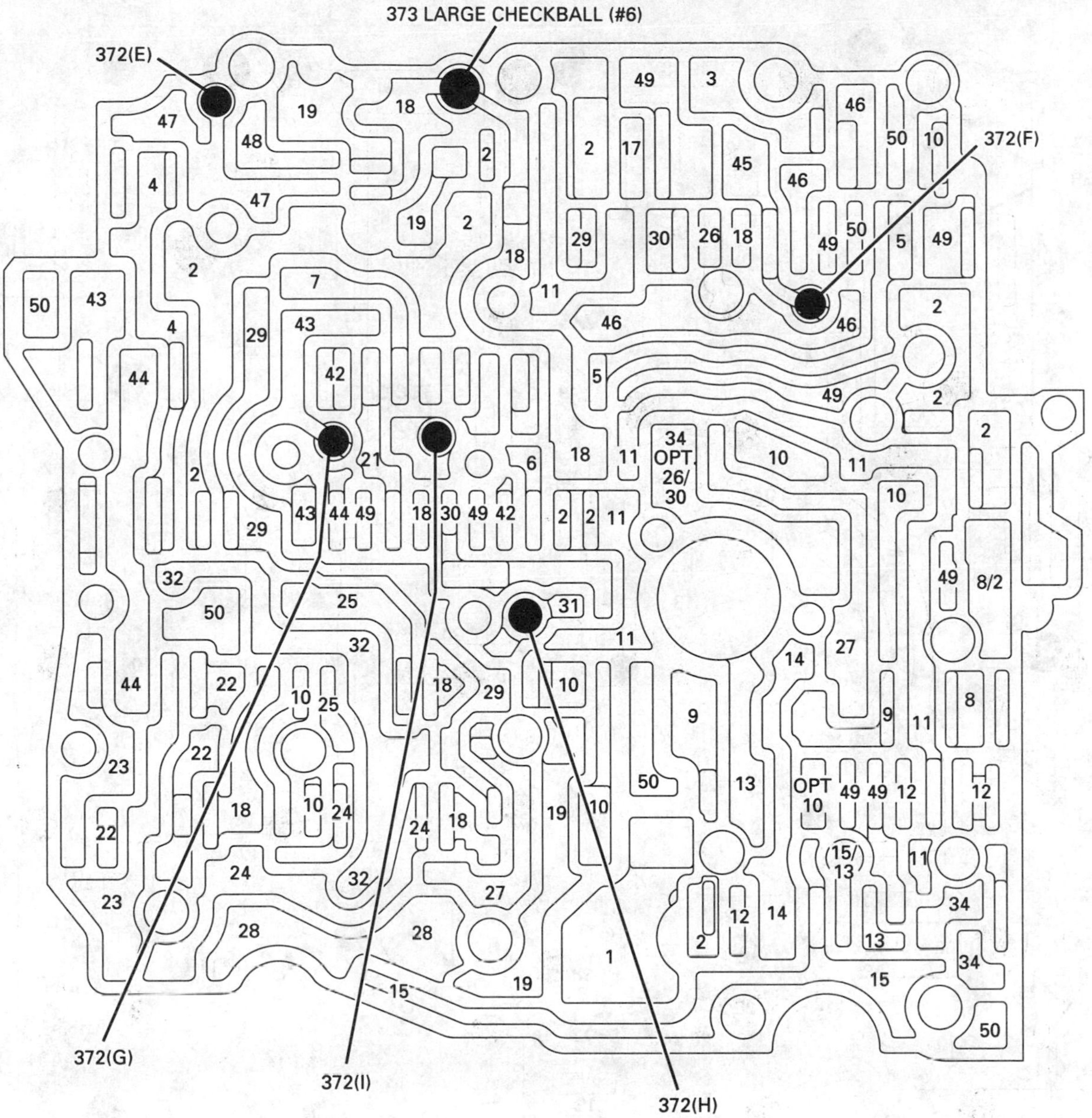
373 LARGE CHECKBALL (#6)
372(E)
372(F)
372(G)
372(I)
372(H)

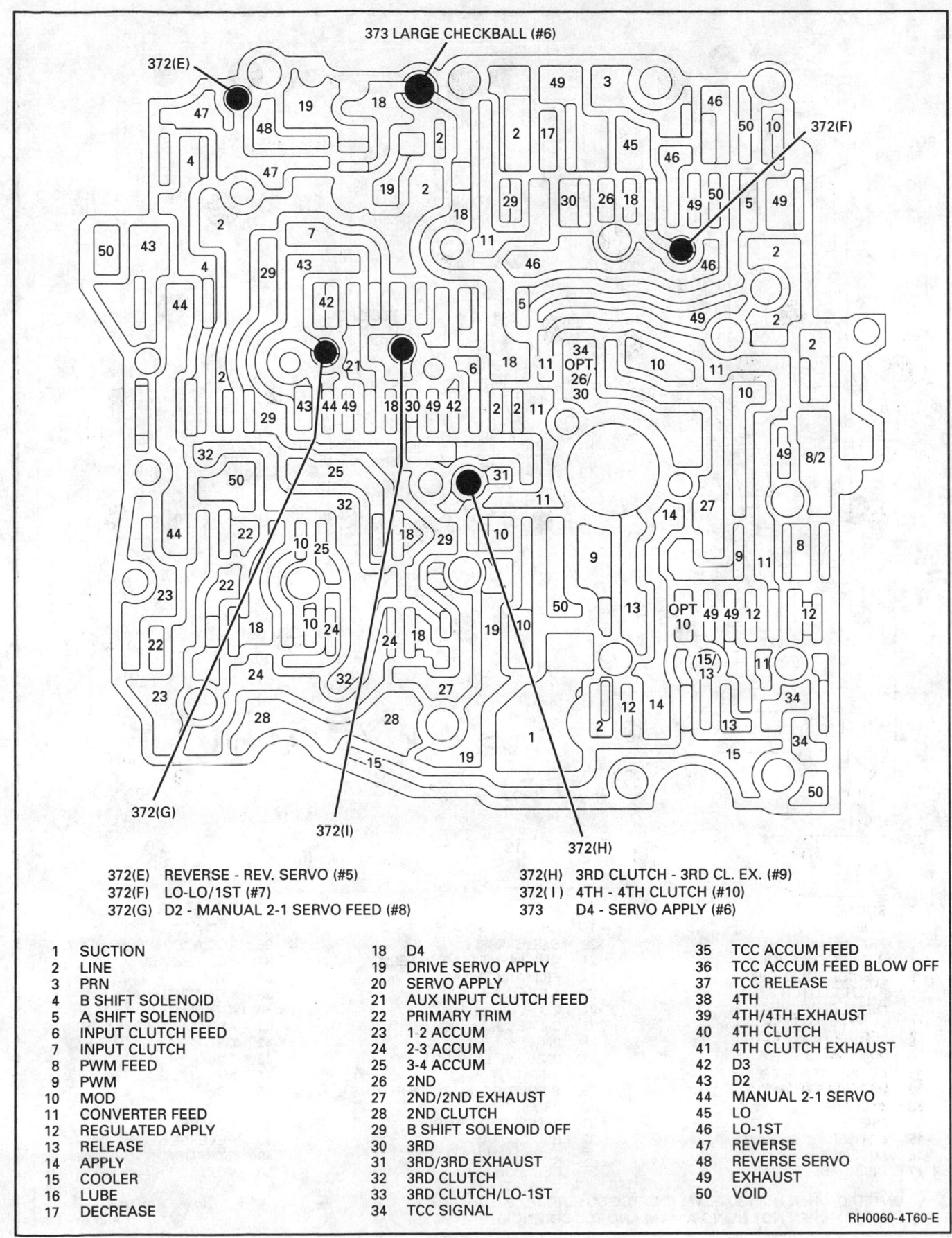

372(E)	REVERSE - REV. SERVO (#5)	372(H)	3RD CLUTCH - 3RD CL. EX. (#9)
372(F)	LO-LO/1ST (#7)	372(I)	4TH - 4TH CLUTCH (#10)
372(G)	D2 - MANUAL 2-1 SERVO FEED (#8)	373	D4 - SERVO APPLY (#6)

1	SUCTION	18	D4	35	TCC ACCUM FEED
2	LINE	19	DRIVE SERVO APPLY	36	TCC ACCUM FEED BLOW OFF
3	PRN	20	SERVO APPLY	37	TCC RELEASE
4	B SHIFT SOLENOID	21	AUX INPUT CLUTCH FEED	38	4TH
5	A SHIFT SOLENOID	22	PRIMARY TRIM	39	4TH/4TH EXHAUST
6	INPUT CLUTCH FEED	23	1-2 ACCUM	40	4TH CLUTCH
7	INPUT CLUTCH	24	2-3 ACCUM	41	4TH CLUTCH EXHAUST
8	PWM FEED	25	3-4 ACCUM	42	D3
9	PWM	26	2ND	43	D2
10	MOD	27	2ND/2ND EXHAUST	44	MANUAL 2-1 SERVO
11	CONVERTER FEED	28	2ND CLUTCH	45	LO
12	REGULATED APPLY	29	B SHIFT SOLENOID OFF	46	LO-1ST
13	RELEASE	30	3RD	47	REVERSE
14	APPLY	31	3RD/3RD EXHAUST	48	REVERSE SERVO
15	COOLER	32	3RD CLUTCH	49	EXHAUST
16	LUBE	33	3RD CLUTCH/LO-1ST	50	VOID
17	DECREASE	34	TCC SIGNAL		

RH0060-4T60-E

Figure 74 Control Valve Passages – Channel Plate Side

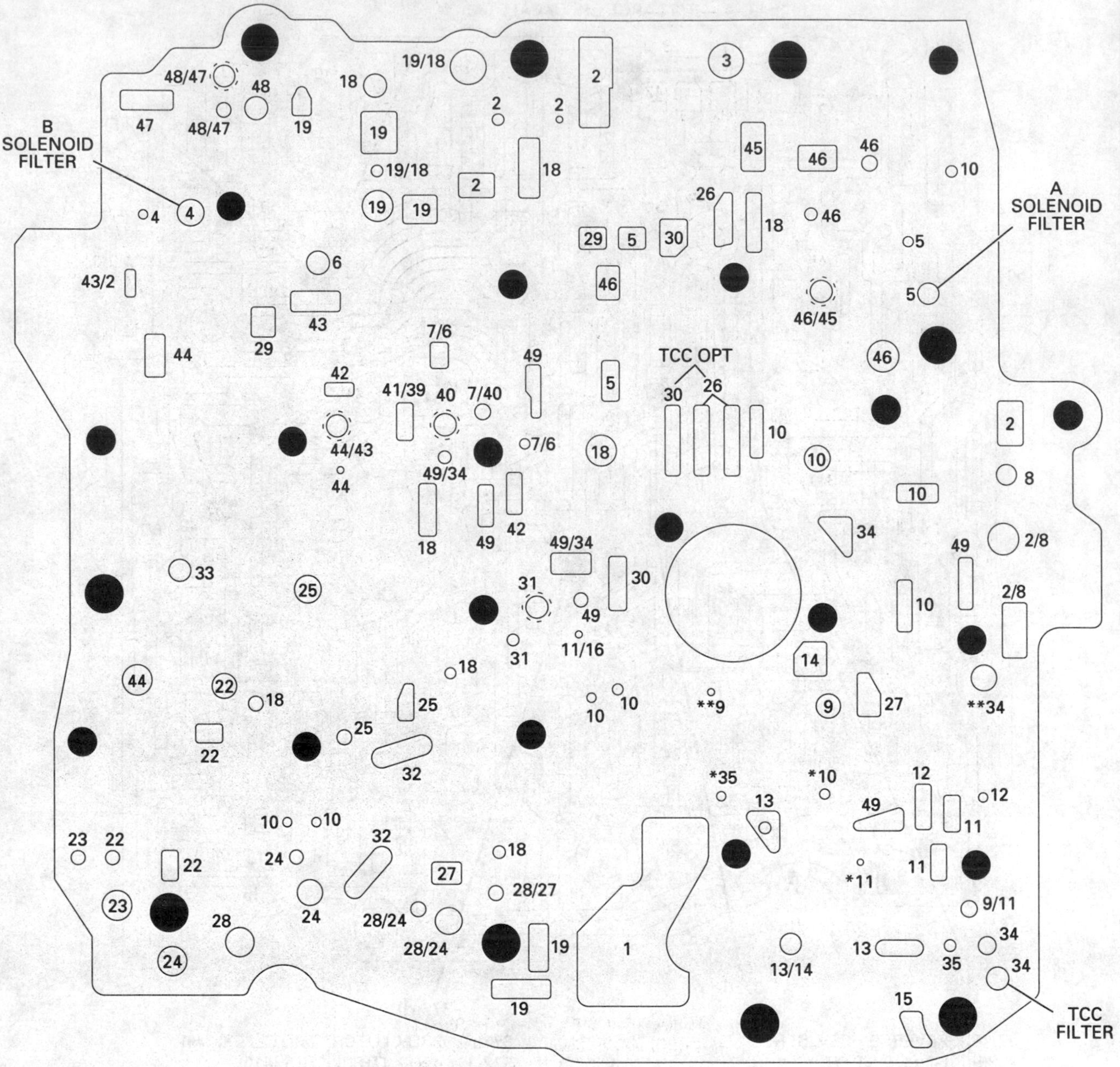
B SOLENOID FILTER
A SOLENOID FILTER
TCC OPT
TCC FILTER
48/47
48
47
19/18
18
19
2
3
45
46
10
26
29
5
30
4
6
43/2
43
44
7/6
49
42
41/39
40
7/40
44/43
49/34
33
25
31
11/16
14
9
27
**9
**34
*35
*10
12
13
11
*11
9/11
34
35
13/14
15
8
2/8
22
23
24
28
28/24
28/27
32
1

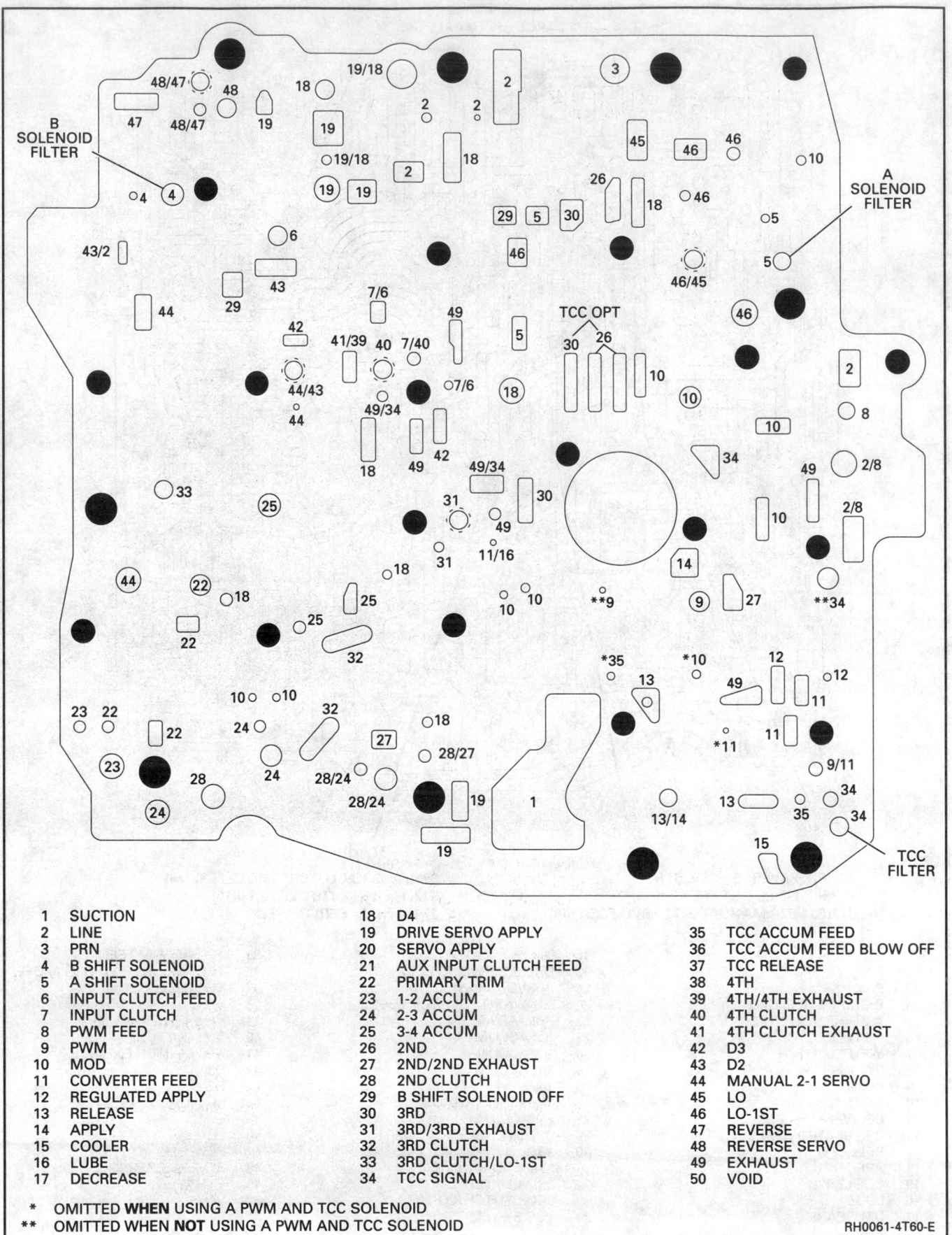

1 SUSPECTION
2 LINE
3 PRN
4 B SHIFT SOLENOID
5 A SHIFT SOLENOID
6 INPUT CLUTCH FEED
7 INPUT CLUTCH
8 PWM FEED
9 PWM
10 MOD
11 CONVERTER FEED
12 REGULATED APPLY
13 RELEASE
14 APPLY
15 COOLER
16 LUBE
17 DECREASE
18 D4
19 DRIVE SERVO APPLY
20 SERVO APPLY
21 AUX INPUT CLUTCH FEED
22 PRIMARY TRIM
23 1-2 ACCUM
24 2-3 ACCUM
25 3-4 ACCUM
26 2ND
27 2ND/2ND EXHAUST
28 2ND CLUTCH
29 B SHIFT SOLENOID OFF
30 3RD
31 3RD/3RD EXHAUST
32 3RD CLUTCH
33 3RD CLUTCH/LO-1ST
34 TCC SIGNAL
35 TCC ACCUM FEED
36 TCC ACCUM FEED BLOW OFF
37 TCC RELEASE
38 4TH
39 4TH/4TH EXHAUST
40 4TH CLUTCH
41 4TH CLUTCH EXHAUST
42 D3
43 D2
44 MANUAL 2-1 SERVO
45 LO
46 LO-1ST
47 REVERSE
48 REVERSE SERVO
49 EXHAUST
50 VOID

* OMITTED **WHEN** USING A PWM AND TCC SOLENOID
** OMITTED WHEN **NOT** USING A PWM AND TCC SOLENOID

RH0061-4T60-E

Figure 75 Typical Spacer Plate Passages

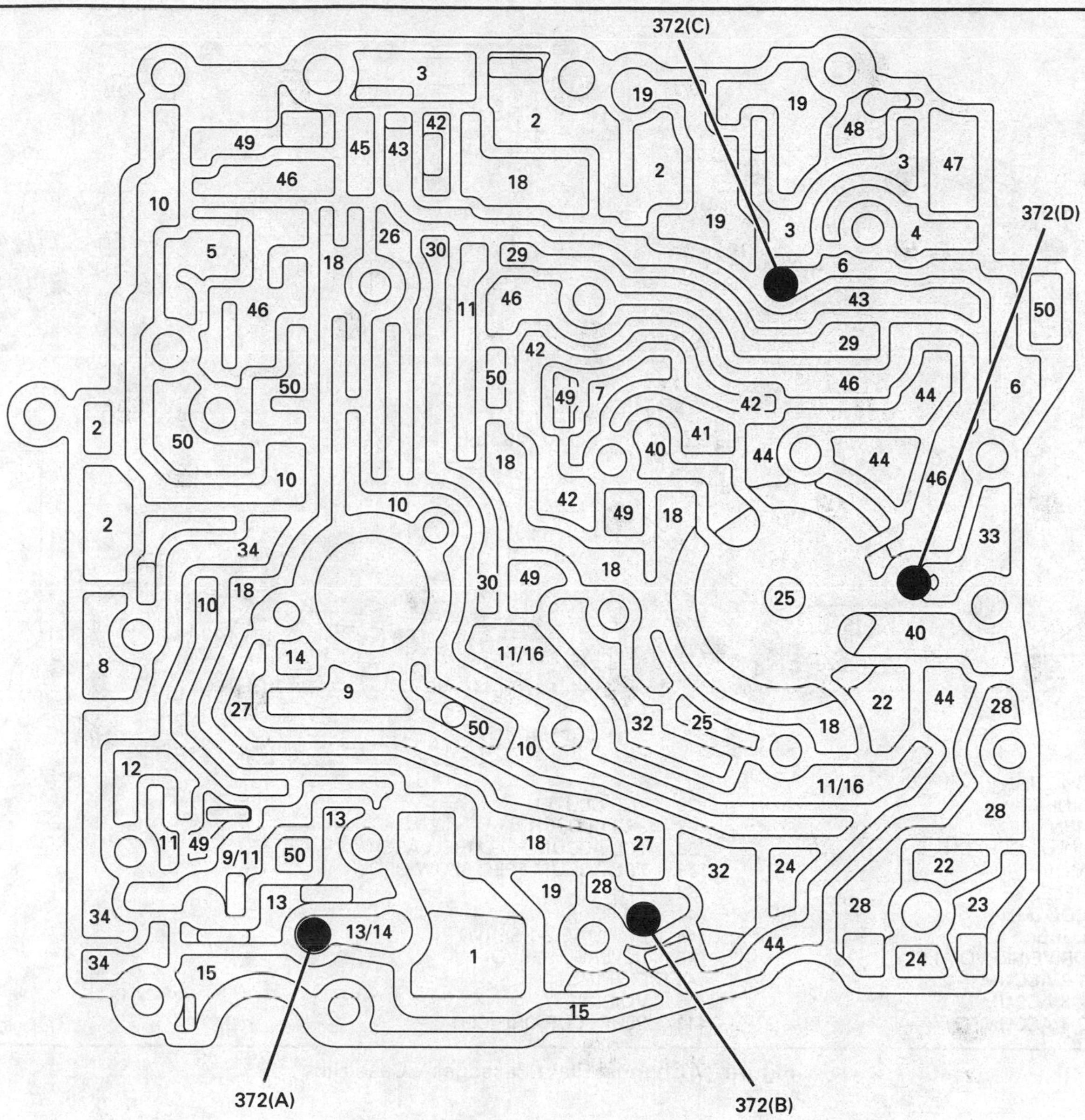
372(C)
372(D)
372(A)
372(B)

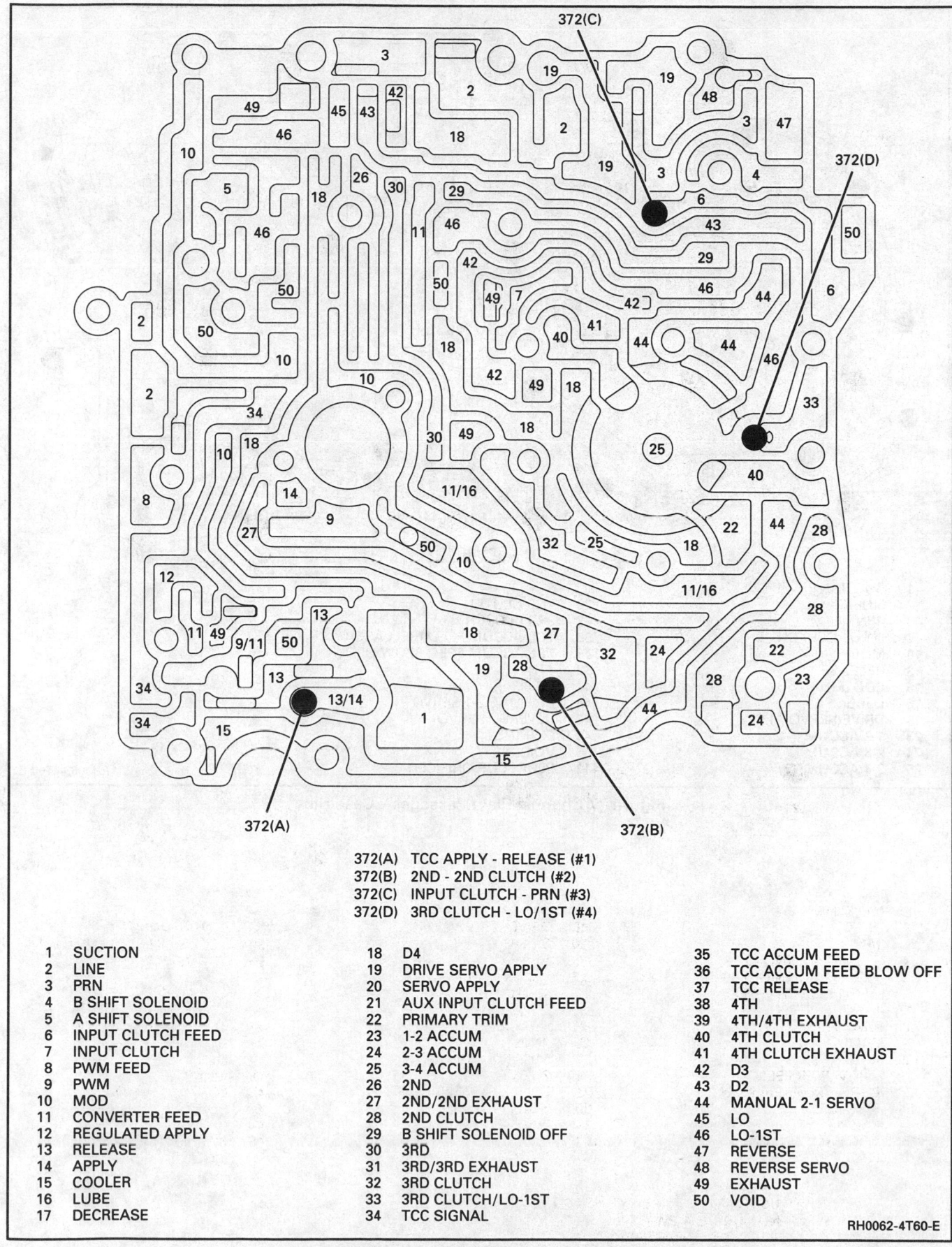

372(A) TCC APPLY - RELEASE (#1)
372(B) 2ND - 2ND CLUTCH (#2)
372(C) INPUT CLUTCH - PRN (#3)
372(D) 3RD CLUTCH - LO/1ST (#4)

1 SUCTION
2 LINE
3 PRN
4 B SHIFT SOLENOID
5 A SHIFT SOLENOID
6 INPUT CLUTCH FEED
7 INPUT CLUTCH
8 PWM FEED
9 PWM
10 MOD
11 CONVERTER FEED
12 REGULATED APPLY
13 RELEASE
14 APPLY
15 COOLER
16 LUBE
17 DECREASE
18 D4
19 DRIVE SERVO APPLY
20 SERVO APPLY
21 AUX INPUT CLUTCH FEED
22 PRIMARY TRIM
23 1-2 ACCUM
24 2-3 ACCUM
25 3-4 ACCUM
26 2ND
27 2ND/2ND EXHAUST
28 2ND CLUTCH
29 B SHIFT SOLENOID OFF
30 3RD
31 3RD/3RD EXHAUST
32 3RD CLUTCH
33 3RD CLUTCH/LO-1ST
34 TCC SIGNAL
35 TCC ACCUM FEED
36 TCC ACCUM FEED BLOW OFF
37 TCC RELEASE
38 4TH
39 4TH/4TH EXHAUST
40 4TH CLUTCH
41 4TH CLUTCH EXHAUST
42 D3
43 D2
44 MANUAL 2-1 SERVO
45 LO
46 LO-1ST
47 REVERSE
48 REVERSE SERVO
49 EXHAUST
50 VOID

RH0062-4T60-E

Figure 76 Channel Plate Passages – Control Valve Side

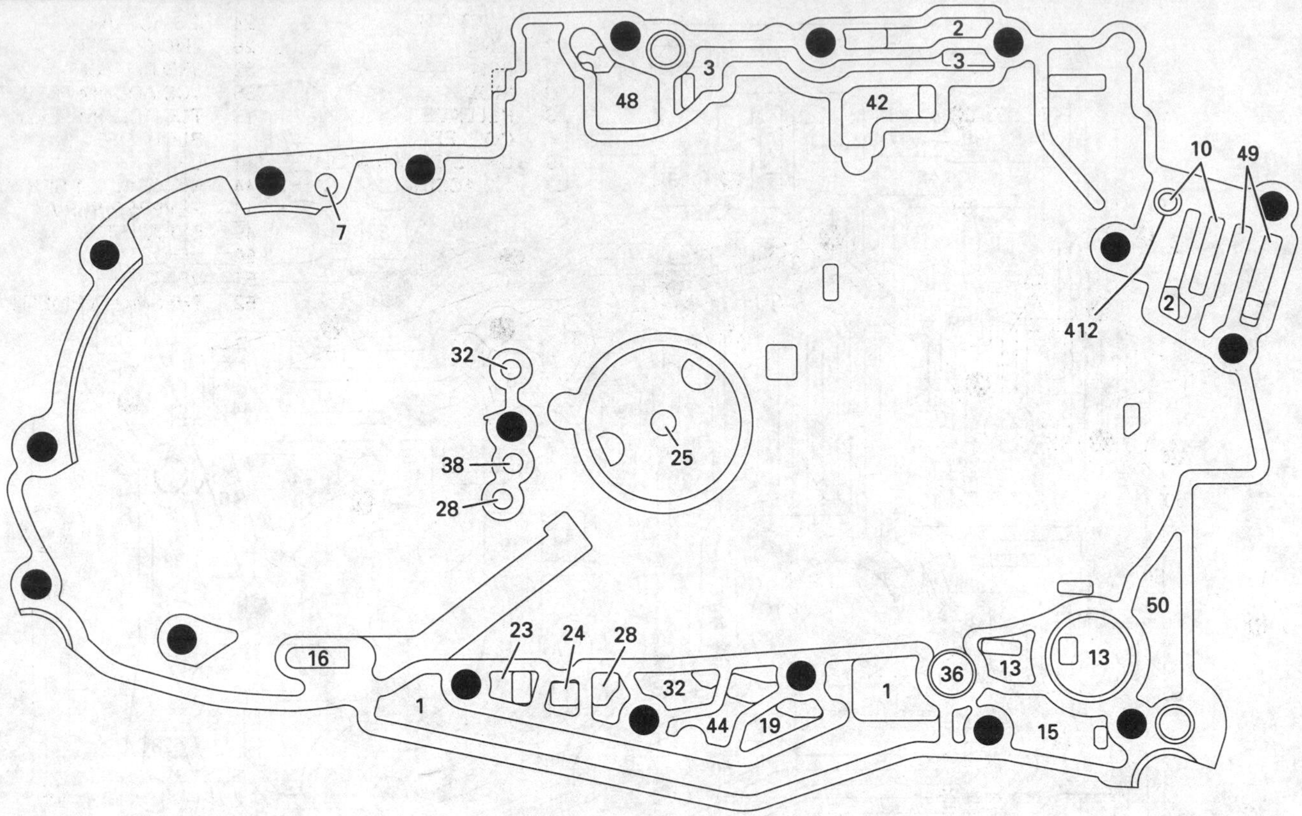
2
3
3
48
42
10
49
7
2
412
32
25
38
28
50
23
24
28
16
36
13
13
32
1
1
44
19
15

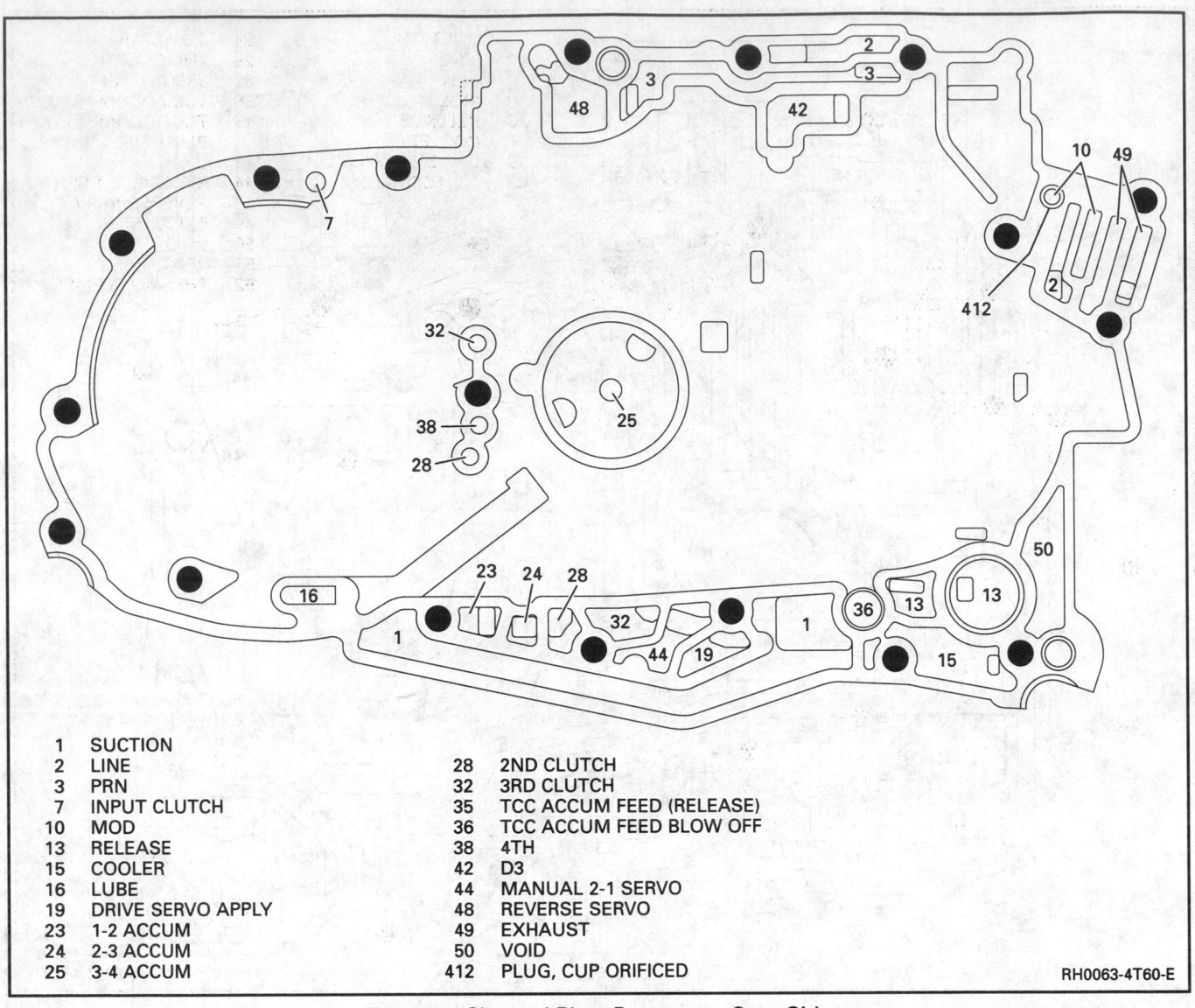

1	SUCTION
2	LINE
3	PRN
7	INPUT CLUTCH
10	MOD
13	RELEASE
15	COOLER
16	LUBE
19	DRIVE SERVO APPLY
23	1-2 ACCUM
24	2-3 ACCUM
25	3-4 ACCUM
28	2ND CLUTCH
32	3RD CLUTCH
35	TCC ACCUM FEED (RELEASE)
36	TCC ACCUM FEED BLOW OFF
38	4TH
42	D3
44	MANUAL 2-1 SERVO
48	REVERSE SERVO
49	EXHAUST
50	VOID
412	PLUG, CUP ORIFICED

RH0063-4T60-E

Figure 77 Channel Plate Passages – Case Side

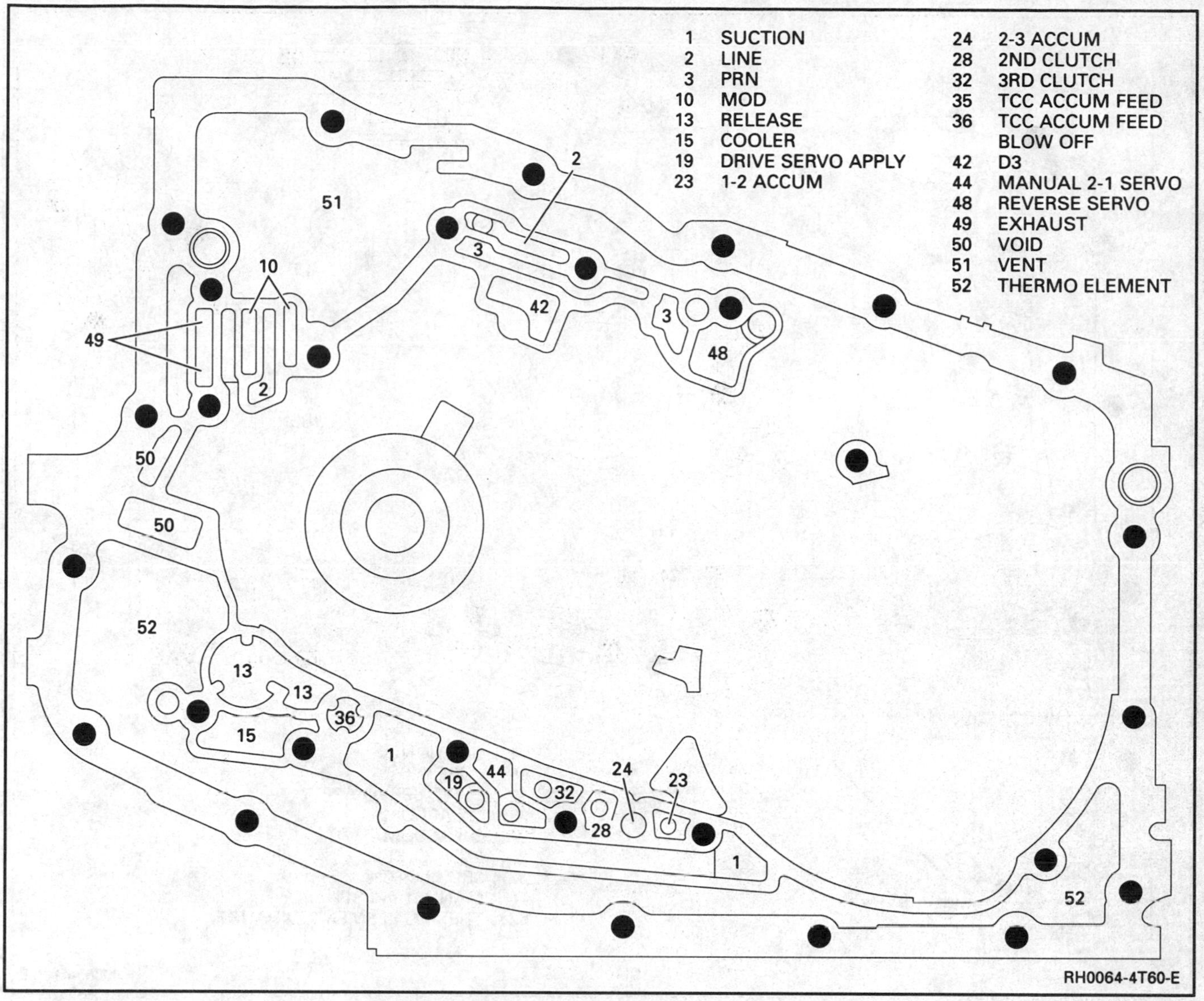
1 SUCTION
2 LINE
3 PRN
10 MOD
13 RELEASE
15 COOLER
19 DRIVE SERVO APPLY
23 1-2 ACCUM
24 2-3 ACCUM
28 2ND CLUTCH
32 3RD CLUTCH
35 TCC ACCUM FEED
36 TCC ACCUM FEED BLOW OFF
42 D3
44 MANUAL 2-1 SERVO
48 REVERSE SERVO
49 EXHAUST
50 VOID
51 VENT
52 THERMO ELEMENT
RH0064-4T60-E

Figure 78 Case Passages – Channel Plate Side

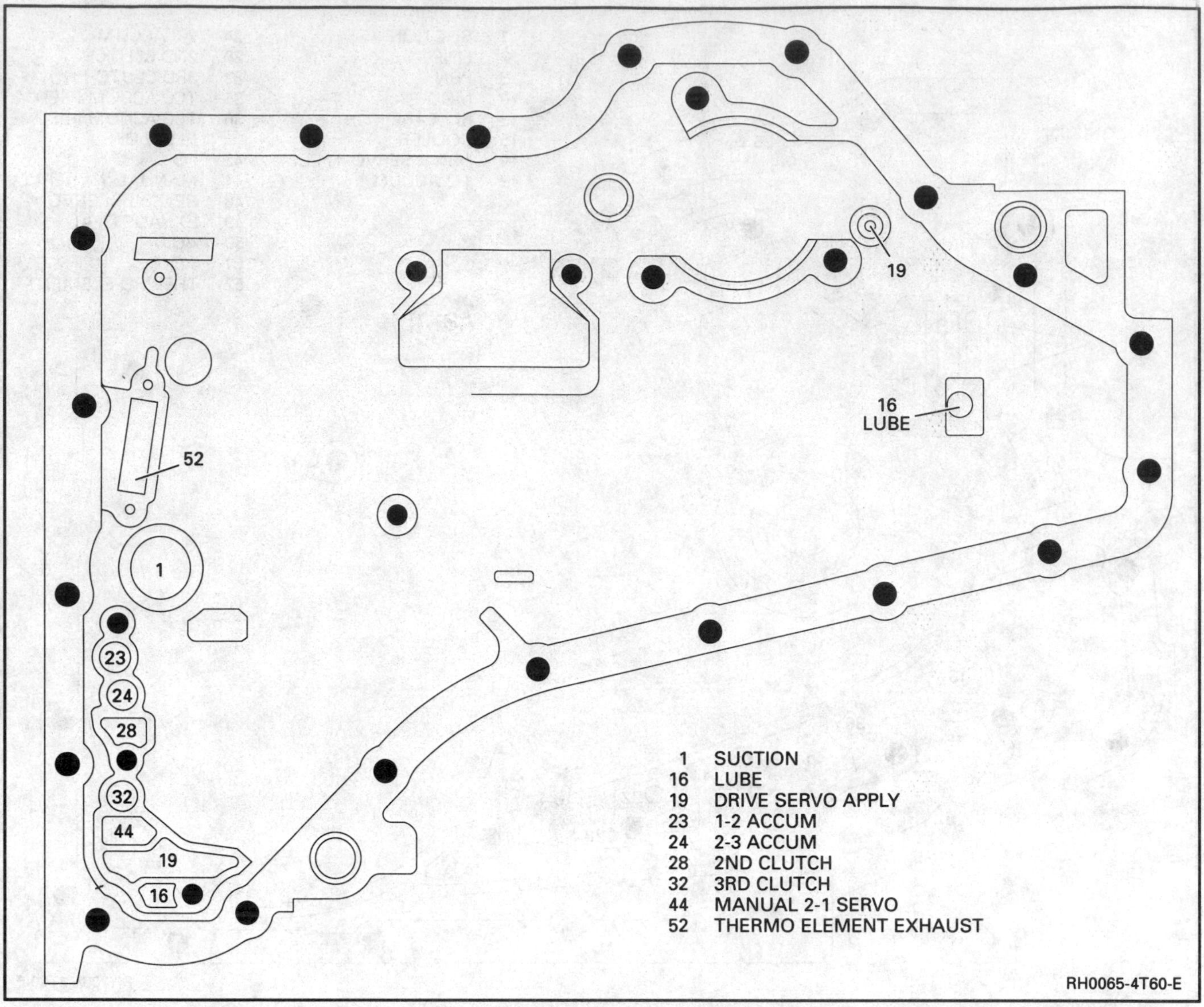
19
16
LUBE
52
1
23
24
28
32
44
19
16
1 SUCTION
16 LUBE
19 DRIVE SERVO APPLY
23 1-2 ACCUM
24 2-3 ACCUM
28 2ND CLUTCH
32 3RD CLUTCH
44 MANUAL 2-1 SERVO
52 THERMO ELEMENT EXHAUST
RH0065-4T60-E

Figure 79 Case Passages – Bottom

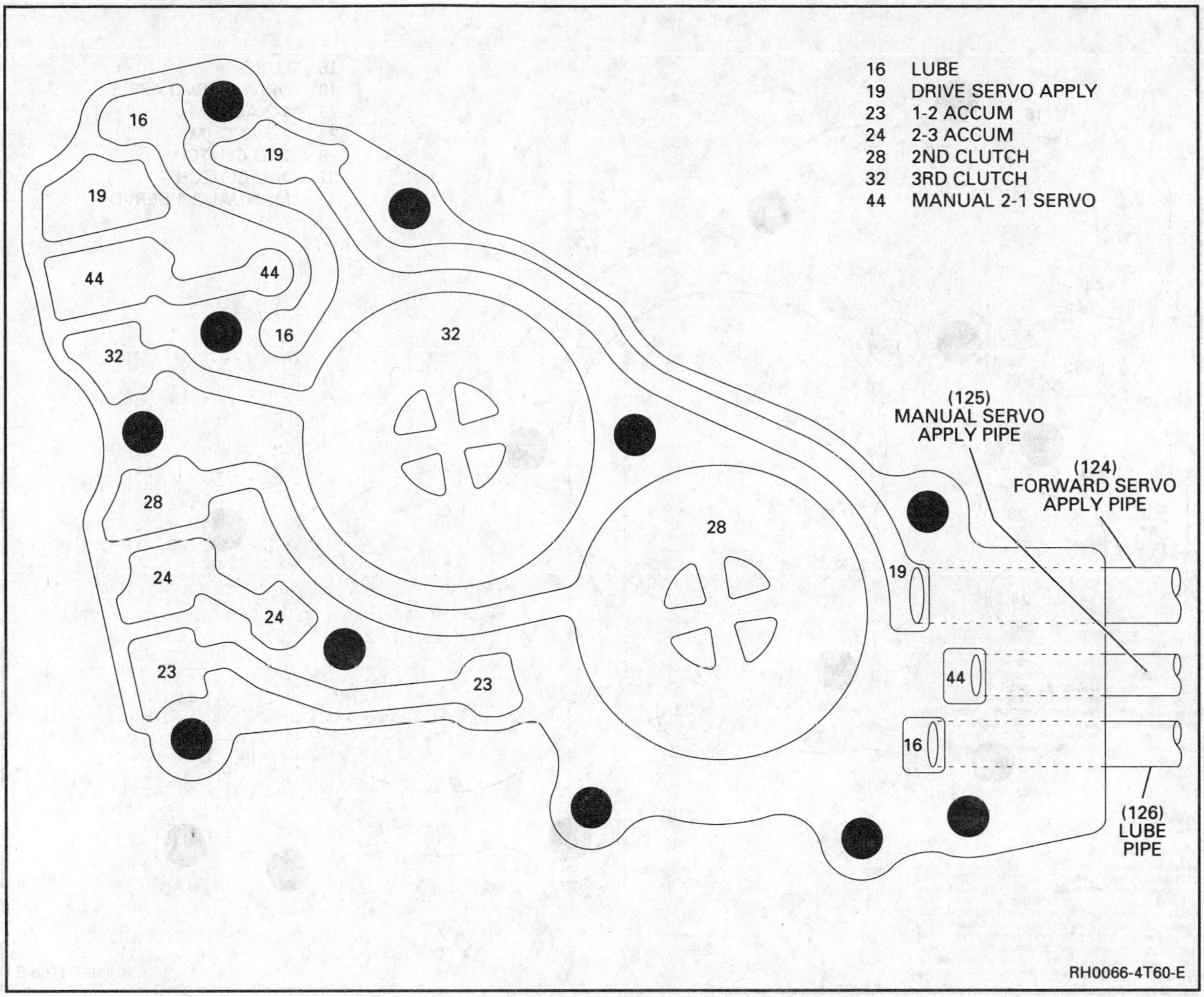
16 LUBE
19 DRIVE SERVO APPLY
23 1-2 ACCUM
24 2-3 ACCUM
28 2ND CLUTCH
32 3RD CLUTCH
44 MANUAL 2-1 SERVO
16
19
44
44
16
32
32
28
28
24
24
23
23
19
44
16
(125) MANUAL SERVO APPLY PIPE
(124) FORWARD SERVO APPLY PIPE
(126) LUBE PIPE
RH0066-4T60-E

Figure 80 1-2, 2-3 Accumulator Housing Passages

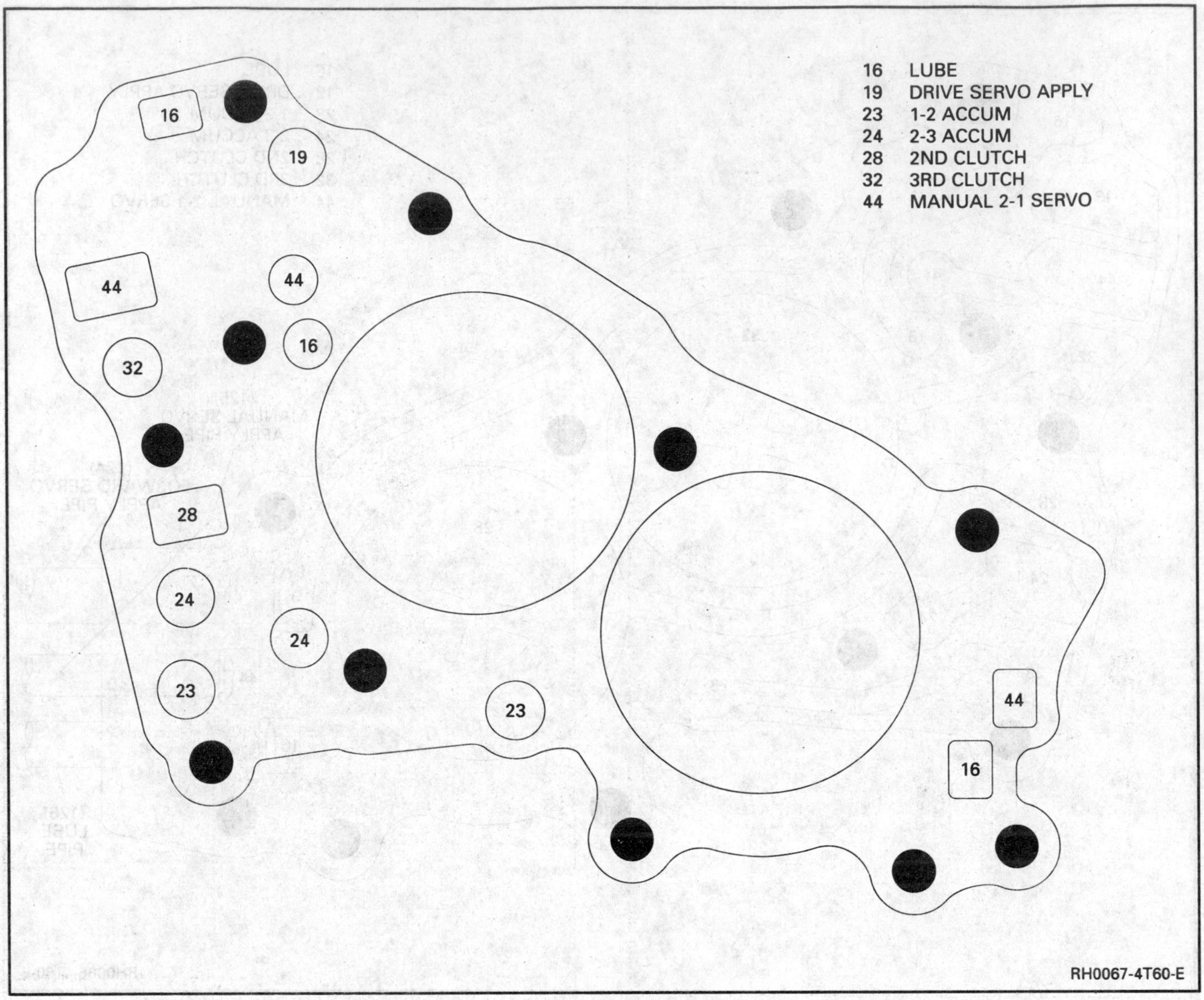
16 LUBE
19 DRIVE SERVO APPLY
23 1-2 ACCUM
24 2-3 ACCUM
28 2ND CLUTCH
32 3RD CLUTCH
44 MANUAL 2-1 SERVO
16
19
44
44
16
32
28
24
24
23
23
44
16
RH0067-4T60-E

Figure 81 1-2, 2-3 Accumulator Gasket Passages

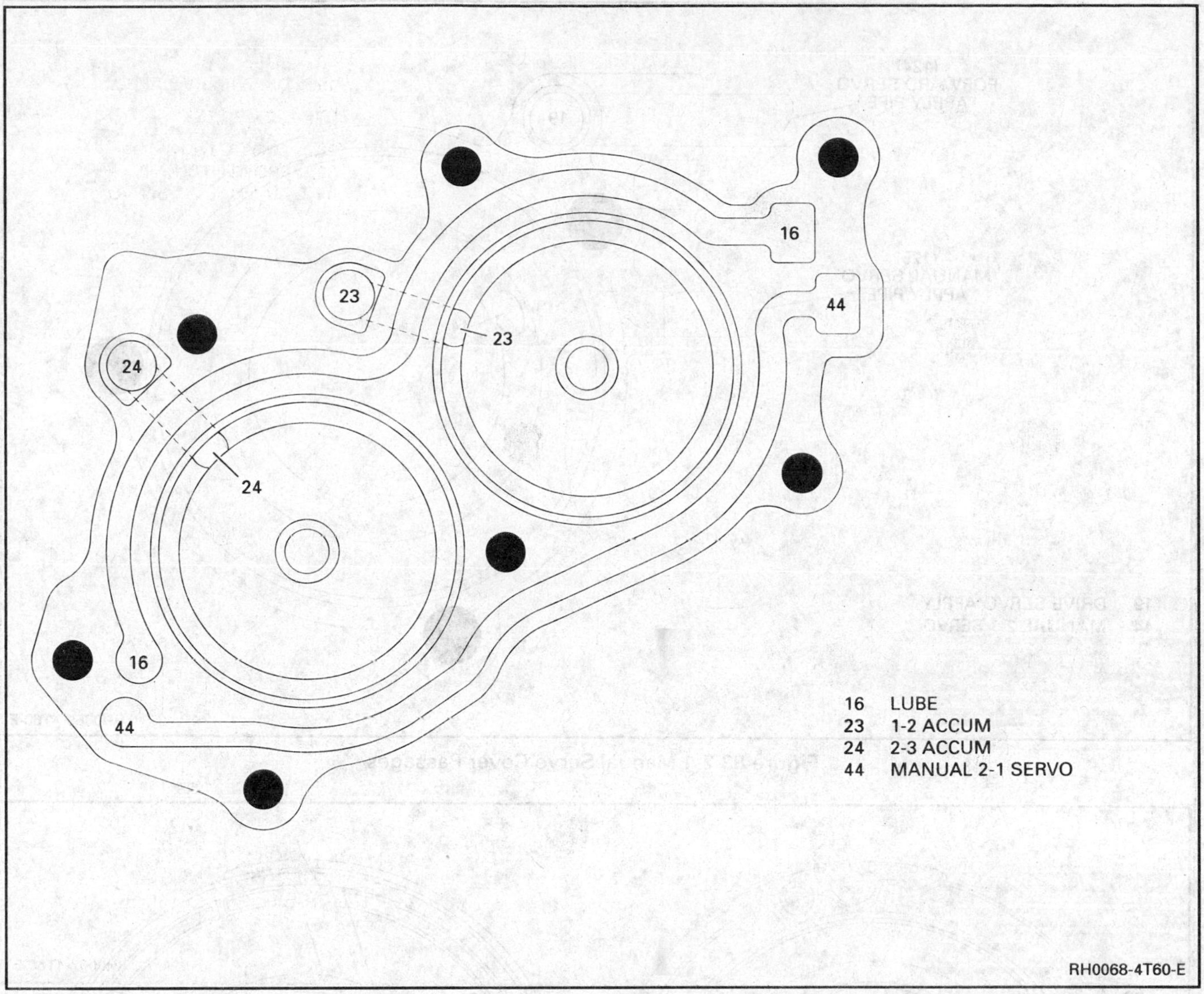
16
44
23
23
24
24
16
44
16 LUBE
23 1-2 ACCUM
24 2-3 ACCUM
44 MANUAL 2-1 SERVO
RH0068-4T60-E

Figure 82 1-2, 2-3 Accumulator Cover Passages

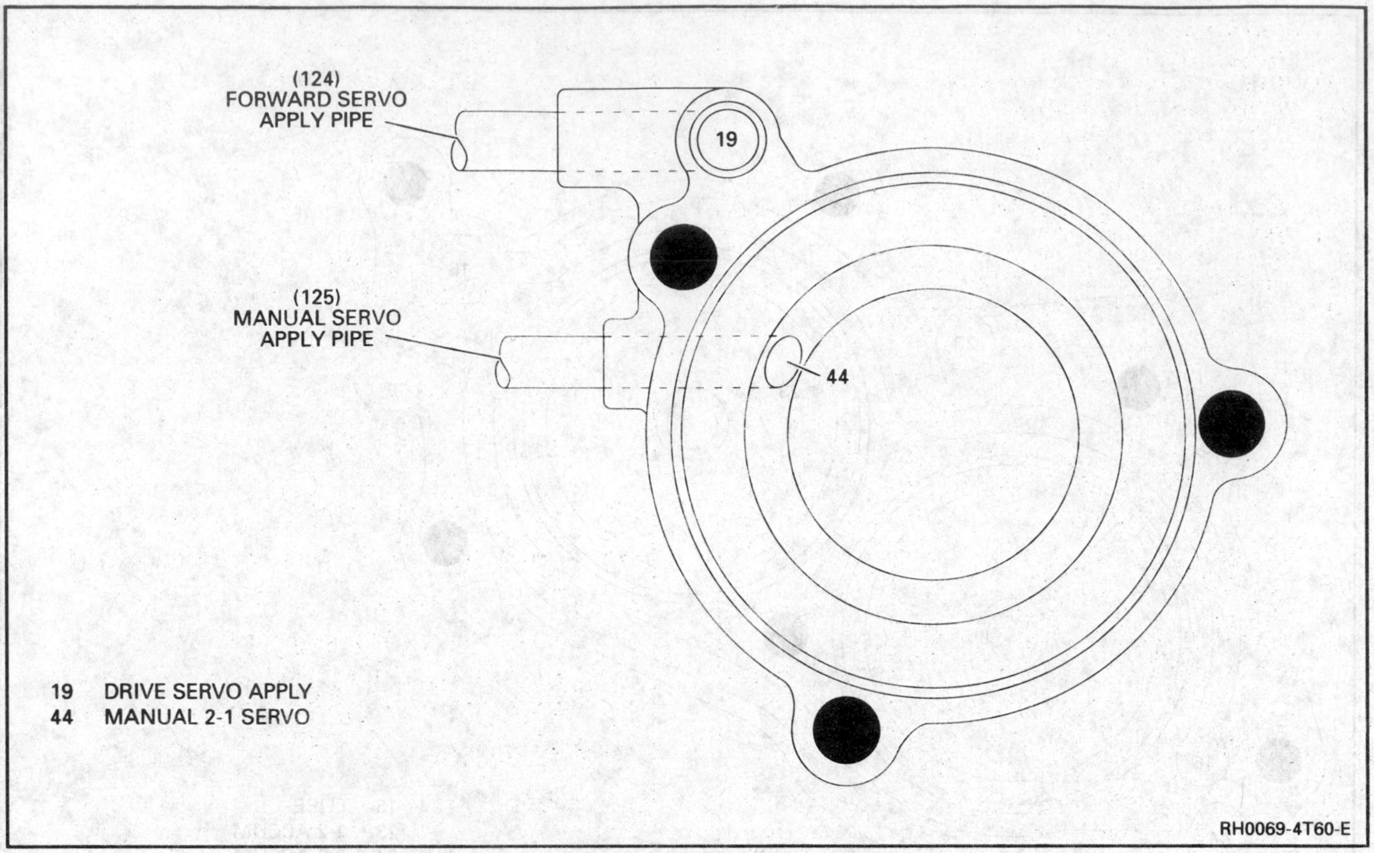
(124)
FORWARD SERVO
APPLY PIPE
19
(125)
MANUAL SERVO
APPLY PIPE
44
19 DRIVE SERVO APPLY
44 MANUAL 2-1 SERVO
RH0069-4T60-E

Figure 83 2-1 Manual Servo Cover Passages

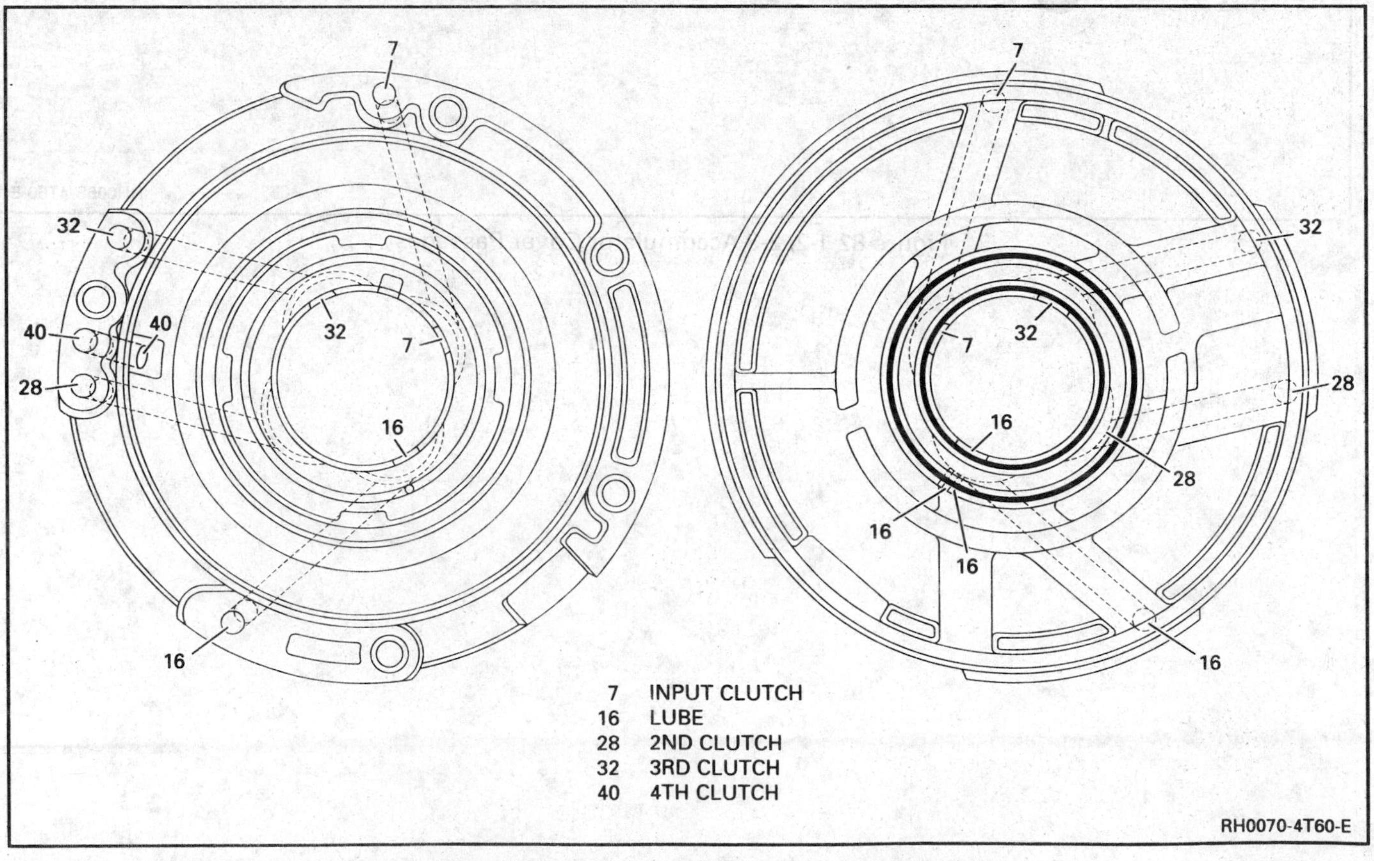
7
32
40
40
28
32
7
16
16
7
32
7
32
28
16
28
16
16
16
7 INPUT CLUTCH
16 LUBE
28 2ND CLUTCH
32 3RD CLUTCH
40 4TH CLUTCH
RH0070-4T60-E

Figure 84 Driven Sprocket Support Passages

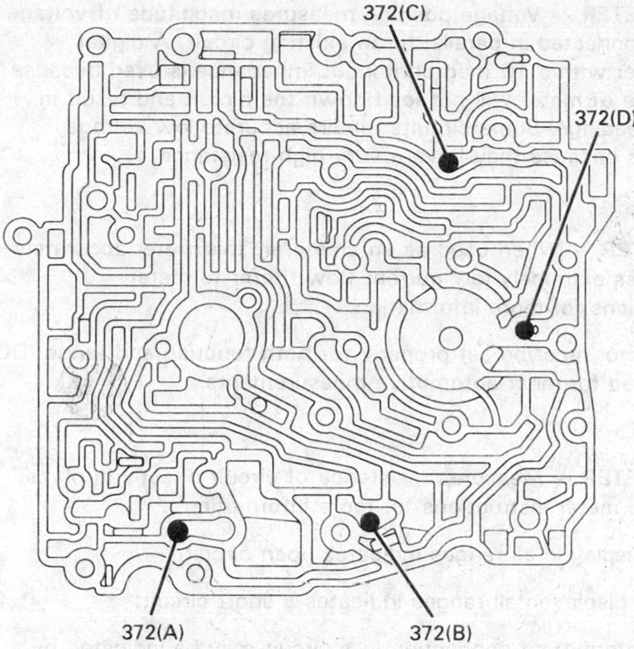
372(C)
372(D)
372(A)
372(B)

372(A) TCC APPLY - RELEASE (#1)
372(B) 2ND - 2ND CLUTCH (#2)
372(C) INPUT CLUTCH - PRN (#3)
372(D) 3RD CLUTCH - LO/1ST (#4)

CHANNEL PLATE SIDE

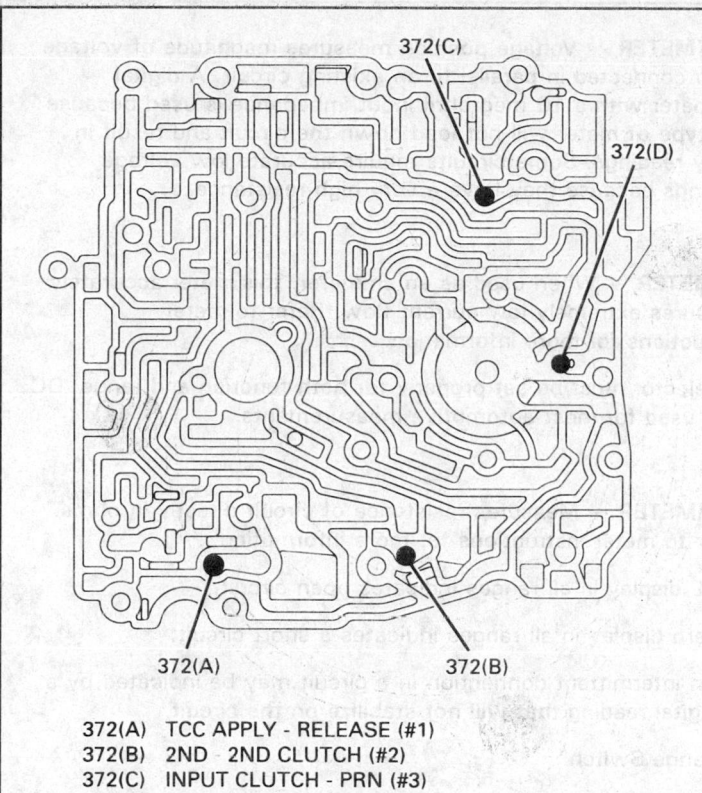

SHIFT CONDITIONS IS A CHECKBALL IS MISSING OR MISLOCATED FOR EACH CHECKBALL:

372(A) #1 NO CONVERTER CLUTCH APPLY

372(B) #2 1-2 SHIFT HARSH

372(C) #3 NO DRIVE IN DRIVE RANGES

372(D) #4 SOFT 2-3 SHIFT AND SLIPS IN 3RD GEAR UNDER LOAD

ALSO, MANUAL LO PRESSURE BOOST BELOW SPECIFICATION

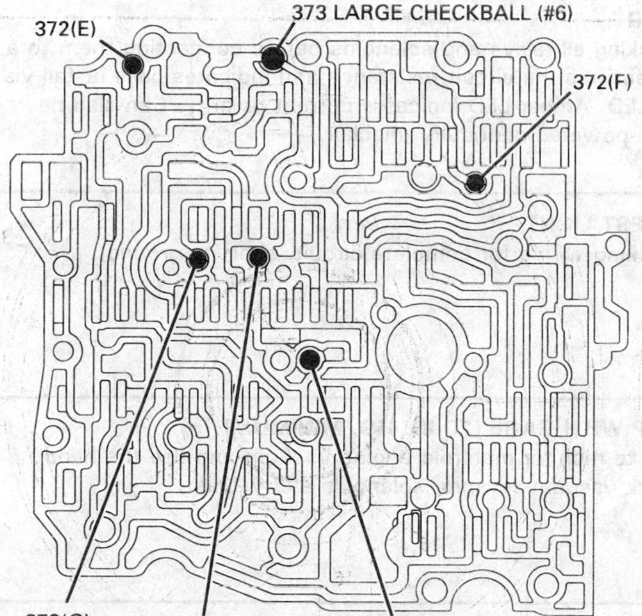
373 LARGE CHECKBALL (#6)
372(E)
372(F)
372(G)
372(I)
372(H)

372(E) REVERSE - REV. SERVO (#5)
372(F) LO-LO/1ST (#7)
372(G) D2 - MANUAL 2-1 SERVO FEED (#8)
372(H) 3RD CLUTCH - 3RD CL. EX. (#9)
372(I) 4TH - 4TH CLUTCH (#10)
373 D4 - SERVO APPLY (#6)

VALVE BODY SIDE

372(E) #5 HARSH NEUTRAL TO REVERSE

372(F) #7 HARSH APPLY OF 3RD CLUTCH FOR MANUAL LO AND MANUAL LO LOCK-OUT SPEED ABOVE 35 MPH

372(G) #8 HARSH APPLY OF 2-1 MANUAL BAND IN MANUAL 2ND AND LO

372(H) #9 2-3 SHIFT HARSH AND 3-2 SHIFT HARSH

372(I) #10 3-4 AND 4-3 SHIFT FEEL - HARSH

373 #6 HARSH NEUTRAL TO DRIVE

RH0071-4T60-E

Figure 85 Checkball Locations

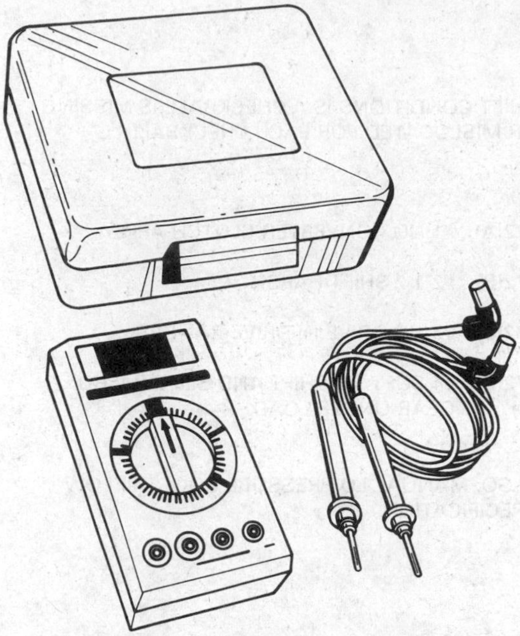

HIGH IMPEDANCE MULTIMETER
(DIGITAL VOLT-OHM METER DVOM)
J 39400

VOLTMETER — Voltage position measures magnitude of voltage when connected in parallel to an existing circuit. A digital voltmeter with a 10 meg ohm input impedance is used because this type of meter will not load down the circuit and result in faulty readings. Some circuits require accurate low voltage readings because they have a very high resistance.

AMMETER — When used as an ammeter, this meter accurately measures extremely low current flow. Refer to meter instructions for more information.

- Selector must be set properly for both function and range. DC is used for most automotive measurements.

OHMMETER — Measures resistance of circuit directly in ohms. Refer to meter instructions for more information.

- OL display in all ranges indicates open circuit.
- Zero display in all ranges indicates a short circuit.
- An intermittent connection in a circuit may be indicated by a digital reading that will not stabilize on the circuit.
- Range Switch.

☐ 200Ω — Reads ohms directly
2K, 20K, 200KΩ — Reads ohms in thousands
2M and 20MΩ — Reads ohms in millions

J 34636

CIRCUIT TESTER
Used for checking all relays and solenoids before connecting them to a new ECM. Measures the circuit resistance and indicates pass or fail via green or red LED. Amber LED indicates current polarity. Can also be used as a non-powered continuity checker.

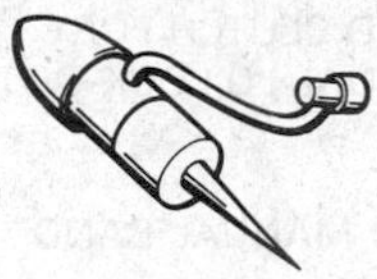

J 34142-A

UNPOWERED TEST LIGHT
Used for checking wiring for complete circuit, short to ground, or voltage.

J 23738

VACUUM PUMP WITH GAGE (20 IN. HG. MINIMUM)
Use the gage to monitor manifold engine vacuum and use the hand pump to check vacuum sensors, solenoids and valves.

Universal Pressure Gauge Set
(9 Ft. Hose; 0-300 PSI)

J 21867

UNIVERSAL PRESSURE GAUGE SET
(9 Ft. Hose; 0-300 PSI)
Used for checking line pressures, pump output (min., max.) in all gear ranges.

RH0072-4T60-E-R1

Figure 86 Electrical Diagnosis Tools

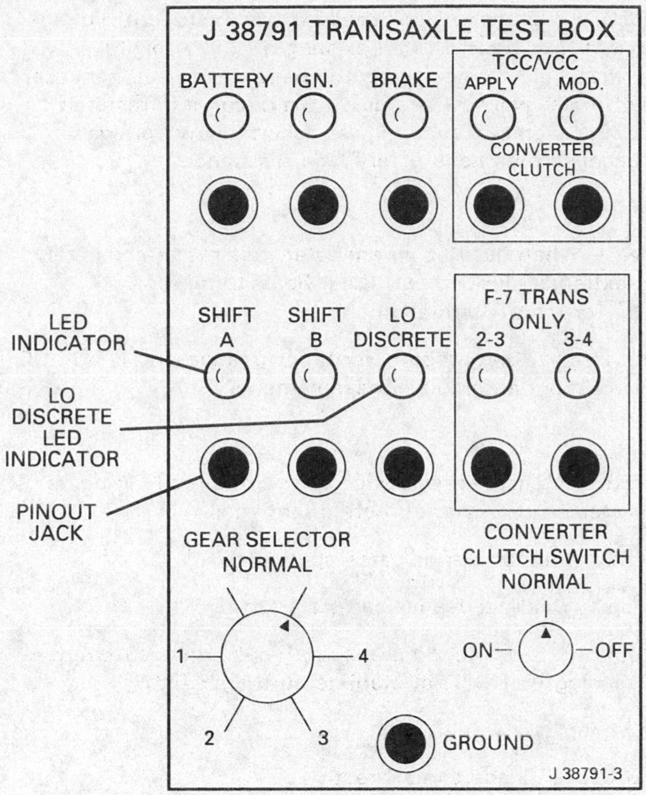
J 38791 TRANSAXLE TEST BOX
BATTERY
IGN.
BRAKE
TCC/VCC
APPLY
MOD.
CONVERTER CLUTCH
SHIFT A
SHIFT B
LO DISCRETE
F-7 TRANS ONLY
2-3
3-4
LED INDICATOR
LO DISCRETE LED INDICATOR
PINOUT JACK
GEAR SELECTOR NORMAL
1
2
3
4
CONVERTER CLUTCH SWITCH NORMAL
ON
OFF
GROUND
J 38791-3

TRANSMISSION TEST BOX J 38791

The Transmission Test Box J 38791 is another tool for 4T60-E diagnosis after all PCM codes have been repaired. The test box, when used properly, will assist in isolating the causeof a condition, whether it be related to the PCM, the wiring, or the transaxle itself.

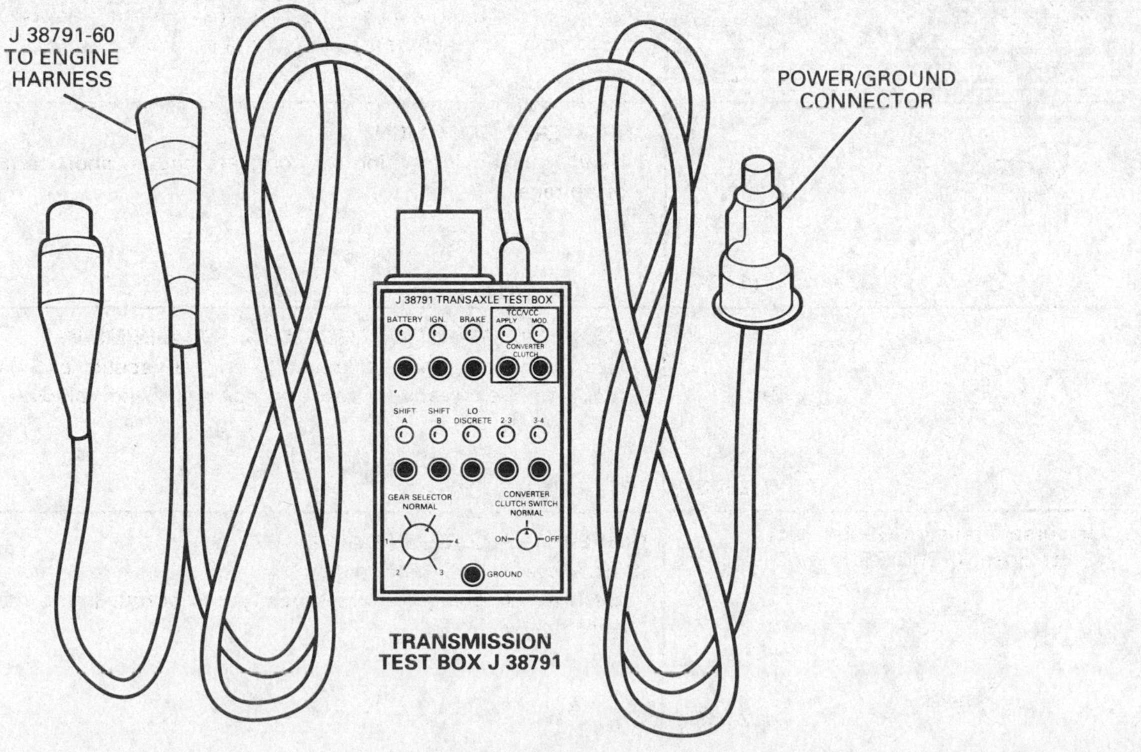
J 38791-60
TO ENGINE
HARNESS
POWER/GROUND
CONNECTOR
TRANSMISSION
TEST BOX J 38791

RH0073-4T60-E

Figure 87 Electrical Diagnosis Tools

SECTION 7A-5B
HYDRA-MATIC 4T60-E
AUTOMATIC TRANSAXLE UNIT REPAIR
RPO MT13

CAUTION: On vehicles equipped with Supplemental Inflatable Restraint (SIR), refer to CAUTIONS in Section 9J under "ON-VEHICLE SERVICE" and the SIR Component and Wiring Location view in Section 9J before performing service on or around SIR components or wiring. Failure to follow CAUTIONS could result in possible air bag deployment, personal injury, or otherwise unneeded SIR system repairs.

NOTICE: When fasteners are removed, always reinstall them at the same location from which they were removed. If a fastener needs to be replaced, use the correct part number fastener for that application. If the correct part number is not available, a fastener of equal size and strength (or stronger) may be used. Fasteners that are not reused, and those requiring thread locking compound will be called out. The correct torque value must be used when installing fasteners that require it. If the above conditions are not followed, parts or system damage could result.

CONTENTS

UNIT REPAIR

GENERAL SERVICE INFORMATION

- Make sure the work area is adequate and CLEAN for the layout and inspection of components.
- Replace Teflon® seal rings if cut, damaged or do not rotate freely in their groove or if performing complete overhaul.
- Inspect all seal ring grooves for debris, burrs or damage.
- Always lubricate bolt/screw threads with transmission fluid prior to installation into aluminum.
- Thrust washer and bearing surfaces may appear to be polished, this is a normal condition and should not be considered damaged.
- Do not over expand snap rings during disassembly or assembly.
- Replace **ALL** seals on components that have been disassembled.

Clean

- Thoroughly clean the exterior of the transaxle.

IMPORTANT: It is not recommended to use air powered tools to disassemble or assemble transmissions/transaxles. Improper bolt torques can contribute to transaxle repair conditions and this information, vital to diagnosis, can only be detected when using hand tools.

TRANSAXLE DISASSEMBLY

Figures 1 and 2

Tools Required:

J 28664-B Transaxle Support Fixture
J 3289-20 Fixture Base

Remove or Disconnect

Figure 1

- Torque converter assembly (1)

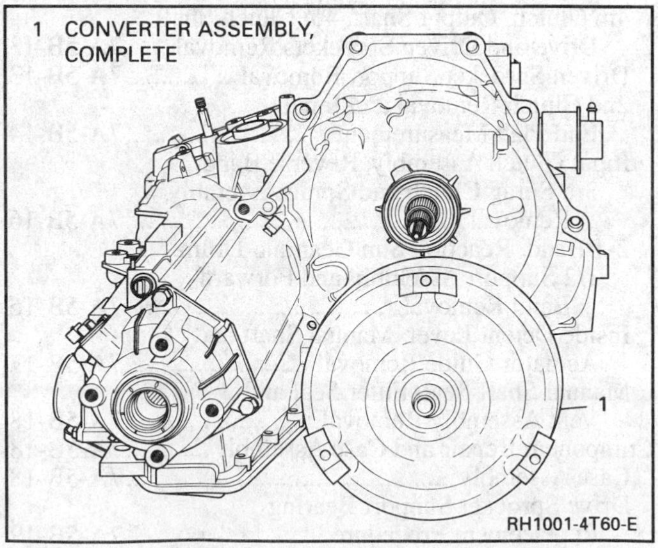
1 CONVERTER ASSEMBLY, COMPLETE
1
RH1001-4T60-E

Figure 1 Torque Converter Removal

Install or Connect

Figures 1 and 2

CAUTION: To avoid the possibility of personal injury and damage to the transaxle, install ALL the bolts for the support fixture and torque to 11 N•m (98 lb. in.).

1. J 28664-B support fixture onto transaxle.
2. Transaxle and fixture into base J 3289-20.
3. Position transaxle with case extension pointing downward to allow fluid drainage.
4. Insert pin into fixture base.

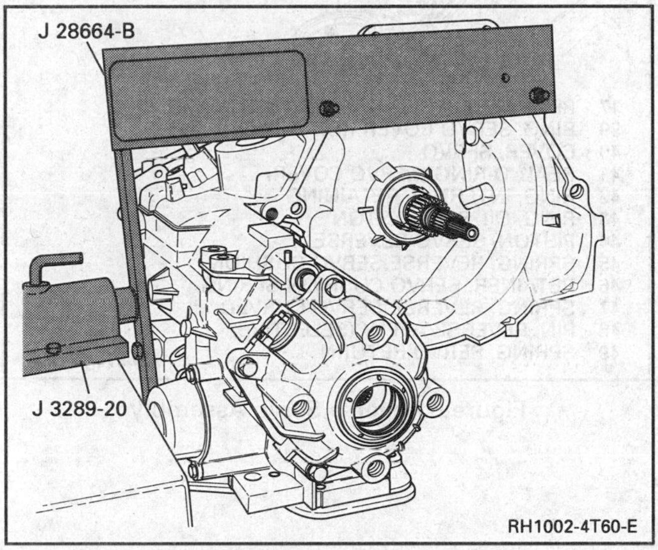
J 28664-B
J 3289-20
RH1002-4T60-E

Figure 2 4T60-E In Holding Fixture

Modulator Assembly

Figure 3

Remove or Disconnect

1. Bolt (30).
2. Modulator retainer (31).
3. Modulator (32) and O-ring (33).
   - May be stuck in bore.
4. Modulator valve (34) using a magnet.
   - May be stuck in bore.

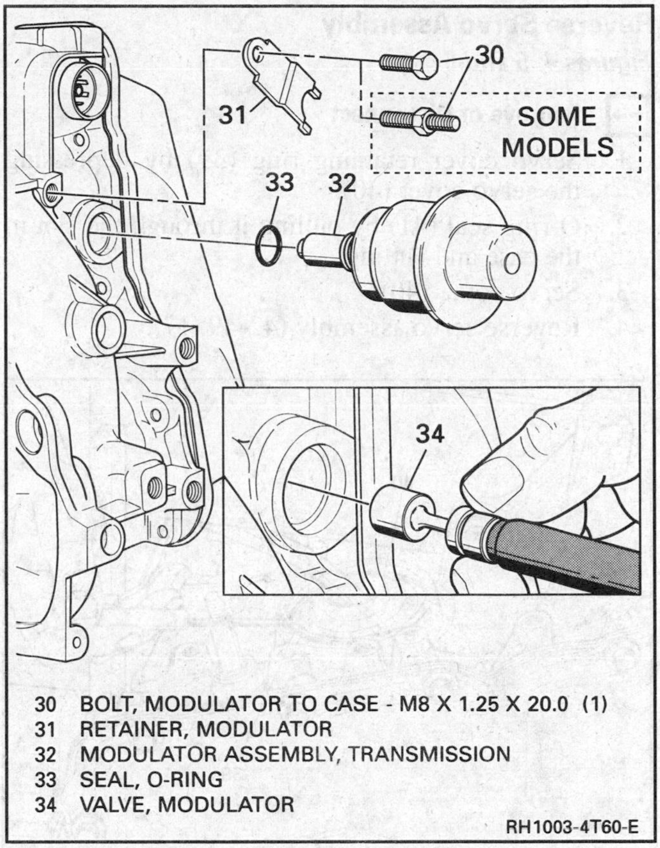
30
31
SOME MODELS
33
32
34
30 BOLT, MODULATOR TO CASE - M8 X 1.25 X 20.0 (1)
31 RETAINER, MODULATOR
32 MODULATOR ASSEMBLY, TRANSMISSION
33 SEAL, O-RING
34 VALVE, MODULATOR
RH1003-4T60-E

Figure 3 Modulator Assembly

Reverse Servo Assembly

Figures 4, 5 and 6

↔ Remove or Disconnect

1. Servo cover retaining ring (39) by depressing the servo cover (40).
2. O-ring seal (41) by pulling it through the slot in the case and cutting.
3. Servo cover (40).
4. Reverse servo assembly (42-49, 17).

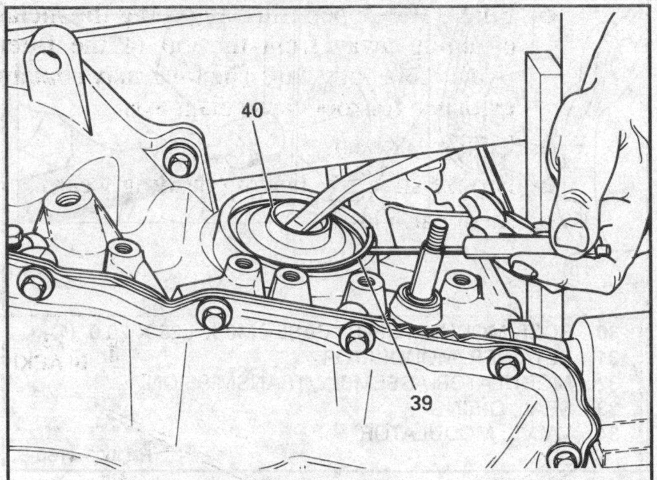
40
39

39 RING, SERVO COVER RETAINING
40 COVER, SERVO

MH1004-4T60-E

Figure 4 Removing Reverse Servo Assembly Retaining Ring

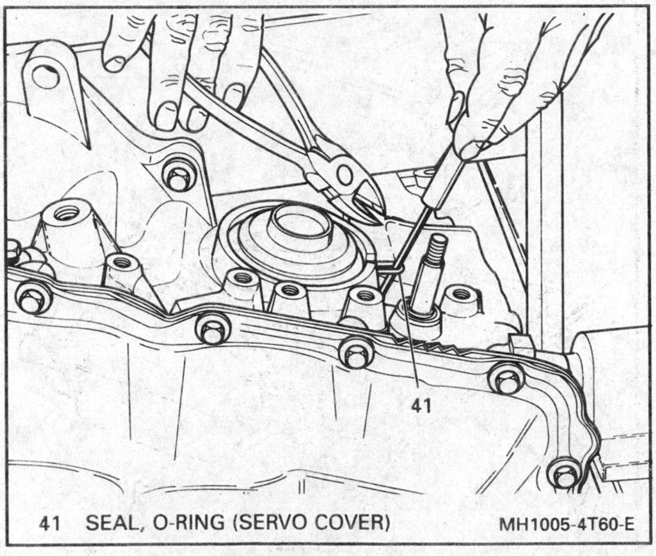
41

41 SEAL, O-RING (SERVO COVER)

MH1005-4T60-E

Figure 5 Removing O-Ring Seal

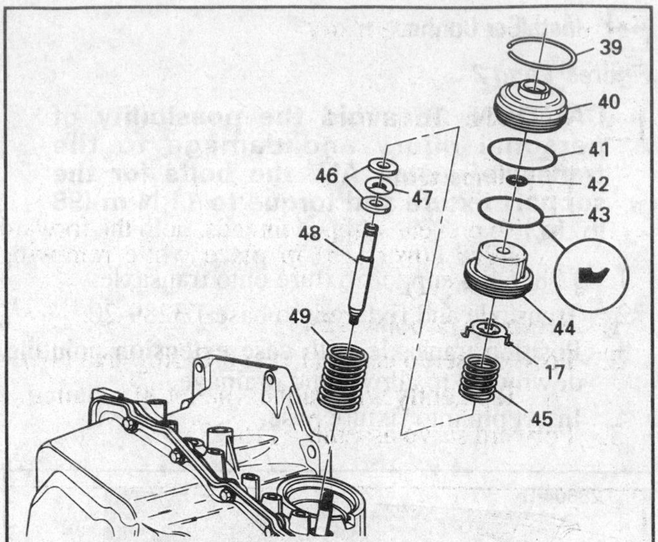
39
40
41
46
47
42
43
48
49
44
17
45

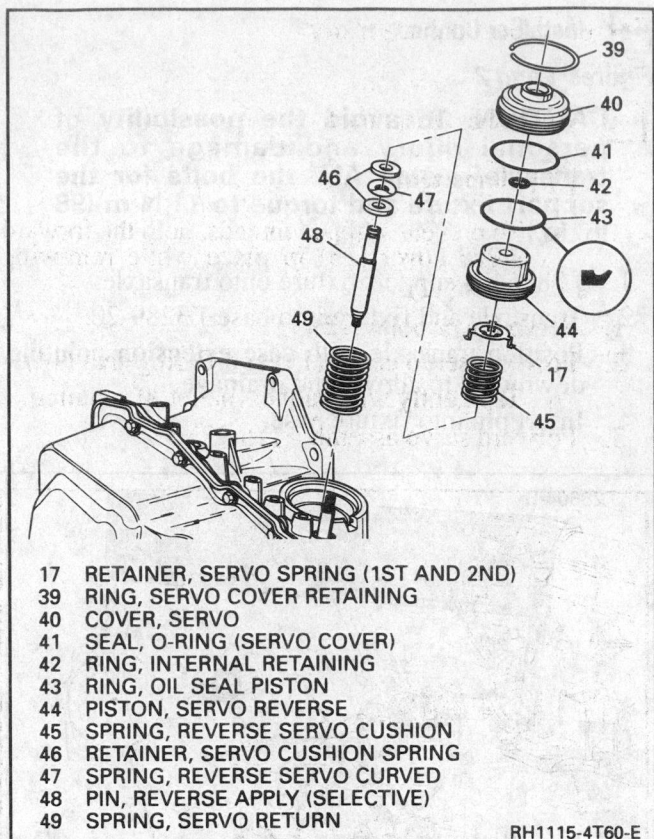

17 RETAINER, SERVO SPRING (1ST AND 2ND)
39 RING, SERVO COVER RETAINING
40 COVER, SERVO
41 SEAL, O-RING (SERVO COVER)
42 RING, INTERNAL RETAINING
43 RING, OIL SEAL PISTON
44 PISTON, SERVO REVERSE
45 SPRING, REVERSE SERVO CUSHION
46 RETAINER, SERVO CUSHION SPRING
47 SPRING, REVERSE SERVO CURVED
48 PIN, REVERSE APPLY (SELECTIVE)
49 SPRING, SERVO RETURN

RH1115-4T60-E

Figure 6 Reverse Servo Assembly

Forward Servo Assembly

Figure 7

Remove or Disconnect

Important

- To prevent stripped threads, hold the forward servo cover (13) in place while removing bolts (12).

1. Servo cover bolts (12).
2. Forward servo cover (13) and O-ring seal (14).
   - Tap gently with rubber mallet, if required.
3. Forward servo assembly (15-22).

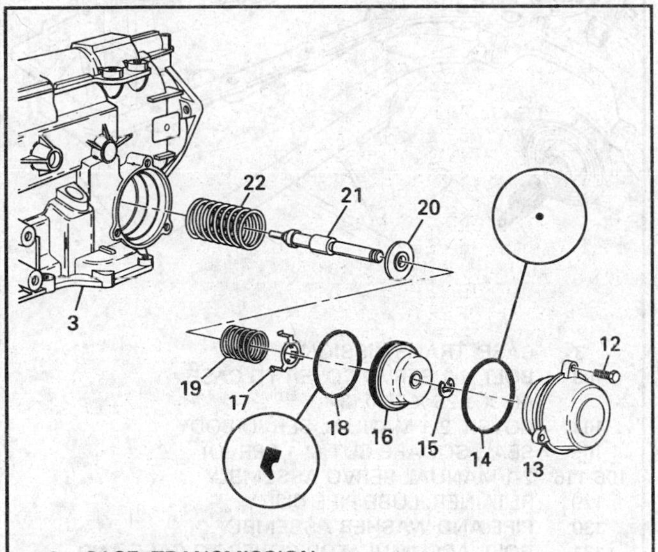
22
21
20
3
12
19
17
18
16
15
14
13

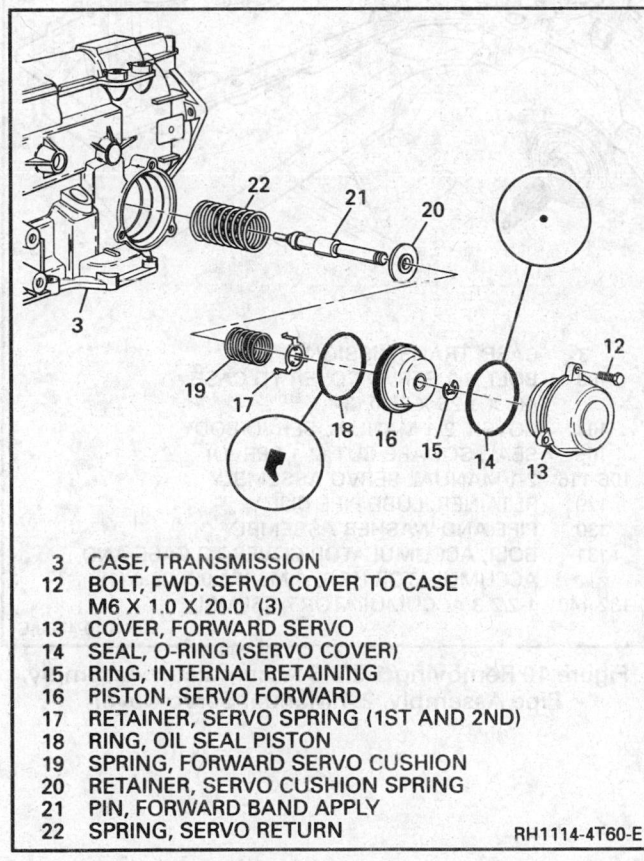

3 CASE, TRANSMISSION
12 BOLT, FWD. SERVO COVER TO CASE M6 X 1.0 X 20.0 (3)
13 COVER, FORWARD SERVO
14 SEAL, O-RING (SERVO COVER)
15 RING, INTERNAL RETAINING
16 PISTON, SERVO FORWARD
17 RETAINER, SERVO SPRING (1ST AND 2ND)
18 RING, OIL SEAL PISTON
19 SPRING, FORWARD SERVO CUSHION
20 RETAINER, SERVO CUSHION SPRING
21 PIN, FORWARD BAND APPLY
22 SPRING, SERVO RETURN

RH1114-4T60-E

Figure 7 Forward Servo Assembly

Oil Pan, Filter, Scavenger Scoop

Figure 8

Remove or Disconnect

1. Bolts (23), pan (24), magnet (26) and gasket (25). Gasket is reusable if seal rib is not broken.
2. Filter assembly (100) from case (3).
   - If filter is tight, pry gently with a screwdriver. Do not score or damage case surface.

Inspect

- Filter (100), open filter by prying the metal crimping away from the top of the filter (black) and pull apart. The filter may contain evidence for root cause diagnosis.
- Clutch material
- Bronze slivers indicating bushing wear.
- Steel particles

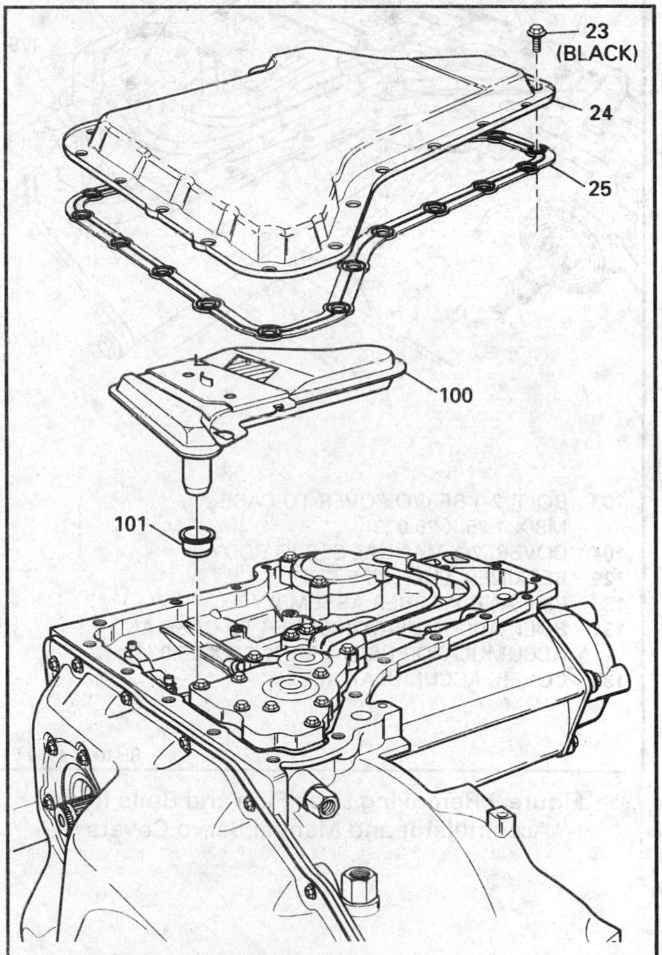
23
(BLACK)
24
25
100
101

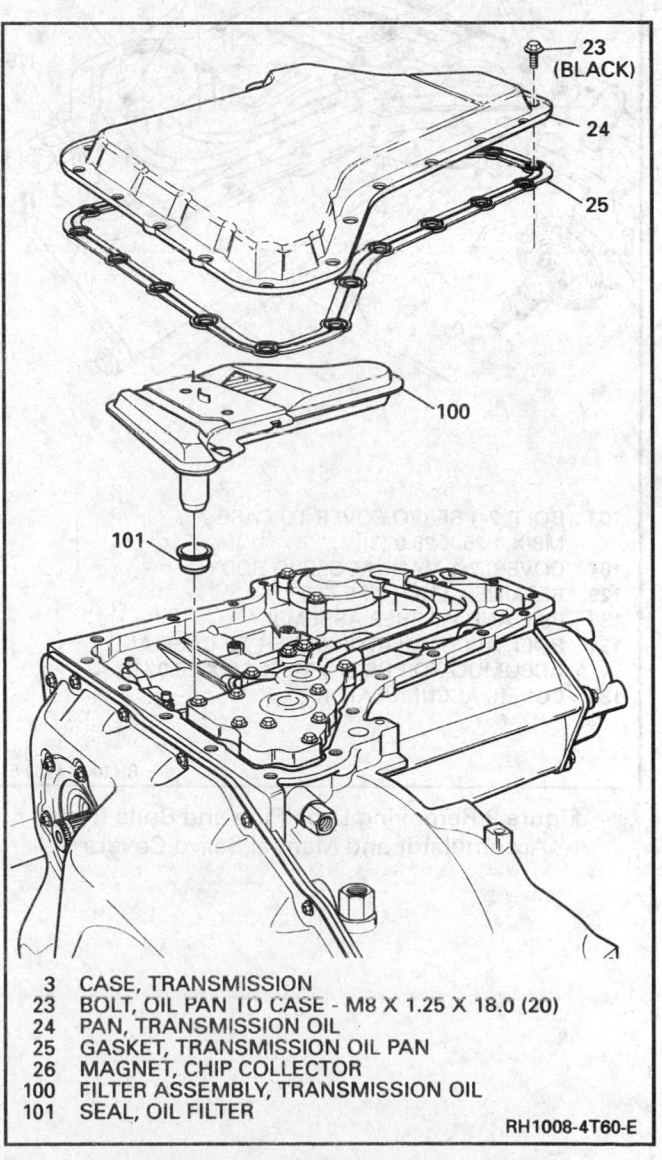

3 CASE, TRANSMISSION
23 BOLT, OIL PAN TO CASE - M8 X 1.25 X 18.0 (20)
24 PAN, TRANSMISSION OIL
25 GASKET, TRANSMISSION OIL PAN
26 MAGNET, CHIP COLLECTOR
100 FILTER ASSEMBLY, TRANSMISSION OIL
101 SEAL, OIL FILTER

RH1008-4T60-E

Figure 8 Oil Pan, Filter, Scavenger Scoop

1-2 and 2-3 Accumulator Assembly

Figures 9 and 10

Remove or Disconnect

1. Four bolts (131) from 1-2 and 2-3 accumulator cover (132).
2. Three bolts (103) from 2-1 manual servo cover (104).
3. Pry lube pipe retainer clip (129) from case.
4. Lube pipe (130) from final drive lube hole.
5. 1-2/2-3 accumulator assembly (132-140) pipe assembly (126-130) and 2-1 manual servo assembly (104-116) from case (3).
6. Forward servo apply O-ring (105) from case (3) – may be attached to 2-1 manual servo cover (104).

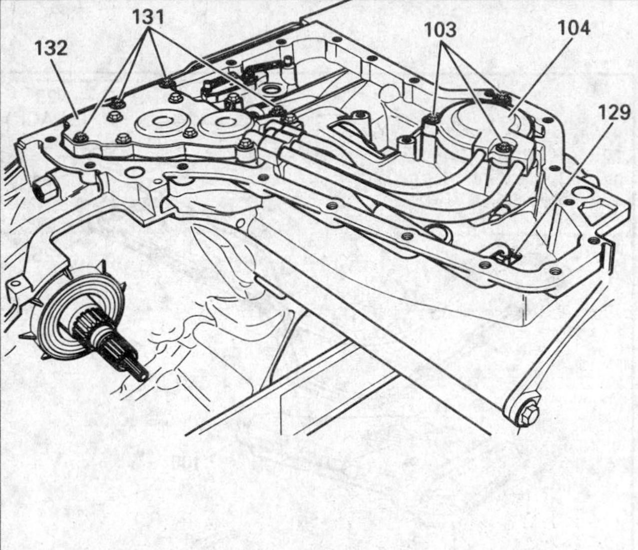

131
132
103
104
129

103	BOLT, 2-1 SERVO COVER TO CASE - M8 X 1.25 X 25.0 (3)
104	COVER, 2-1 MANUAL SERVO BODY
129	RETAINER, LUBE PIPE CLIP
130	PIPE AND WASHER ASSEMBLY
131	BOLT, ACCUMULATOR COVER TO CASE AND ACCUMULATOR HSG. - M6 X 1.0 X 28.0 (1)
132	COVER, ACCUMULATOR

RH1009-4T60-E

Figure 9 Removing Lube Pipe and Bolts from Accumulator and Manual Servo Covers

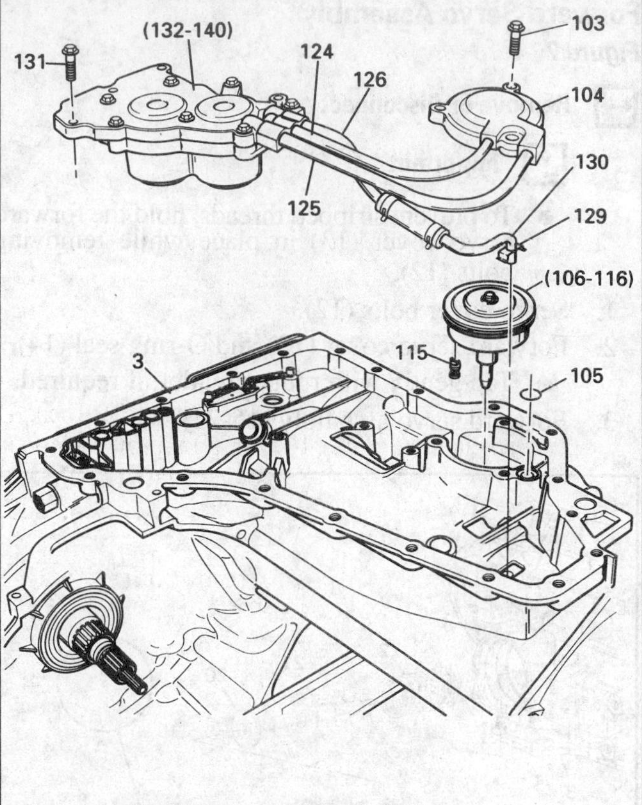

(132-140)
131
124
126
103
104
130
125
129
(106-116)
115
3
105

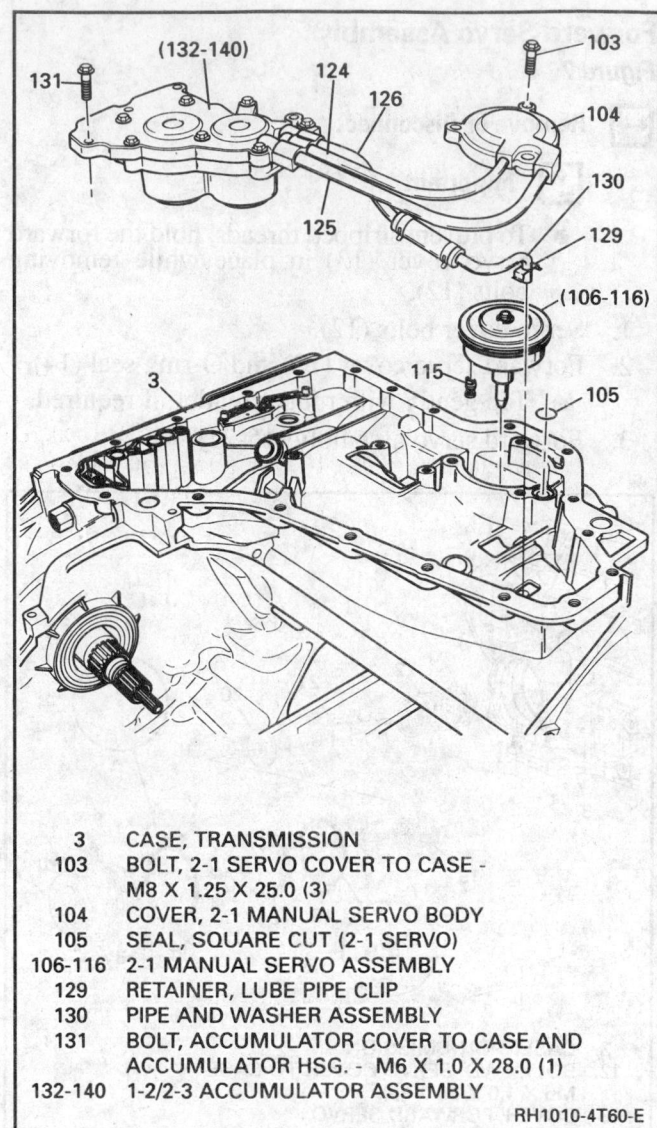

3	CASE, TRANSMISSION
103	BOLT, 2-1 SERVO COVER TO CASE - M8 X 1.25 X 25.0 (3)
104	COVER, 2-1 MANUAL SERVO BODY
105	SEAL, SQUARE CUT (2-1 SERVO)
106-116	2-1 MANUAL SERVO ASSEMBLY
129	RETAINER, LUBE PIPE CLIP
130	PIPE AND WASHER ASSEMBLY
131	BOLT, ACCUMULATOR COVER TO CASE AND ACCUMULATOR HSG. - M6 X 1.0 X 28.0 (1)
132-140	1-2/2-3 ACCUMULATOR ASSEMBLY

RH1010-4T60-E

Figure 10 Removing 1-2/2-3 Accumulator Assembly, Pipe Assembly, 2-1 Manual Servo Cover

Case Side Cover and Pump Assembly

Figures 11 through 14

↔ Remove or Disconnect

1. Bolts with conical washers (52).
2. Flanged nuts (50) and conical washers (51), case side cover pan (53).
3. Case side cover gasket (54) and inner case side cover gasket (55).
4. Wiring harness (224).
   - Use a screwdriver to unlock tabs at shift solenoids (315), pressure switch assembly (218) and temperature sensor (450) located on channel plate (401) or temperature sensor (391) located on the spacer plate (370).
5. Pump assembly attaching bolts (203, 204, 205, 206, 207).
6. Pump assembly (200) from control valve assembly (300).

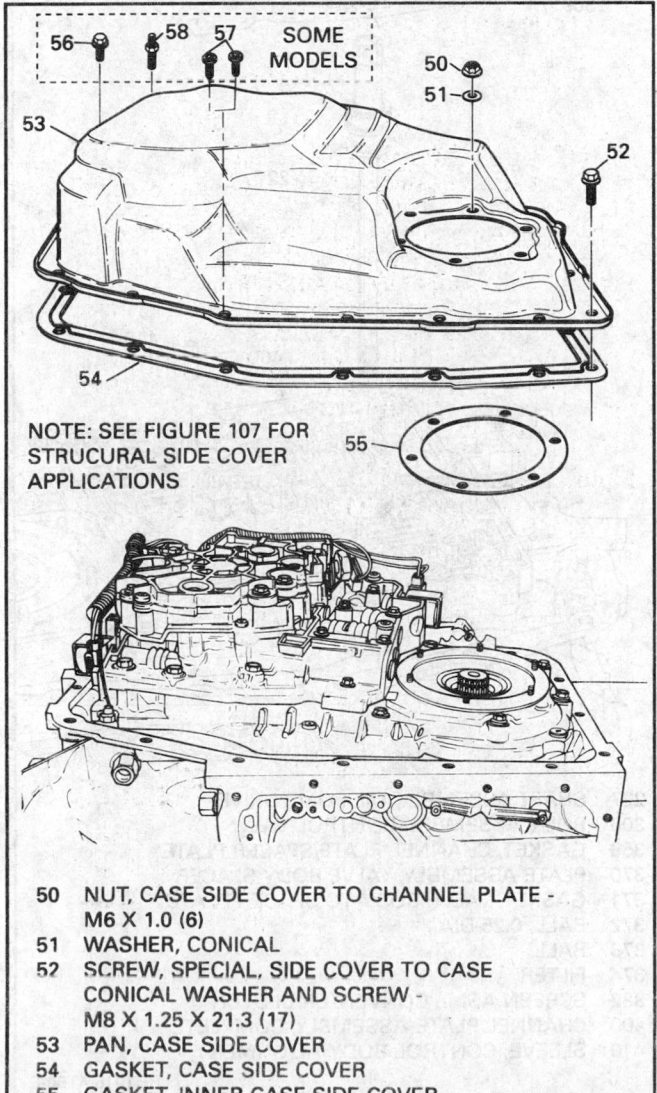

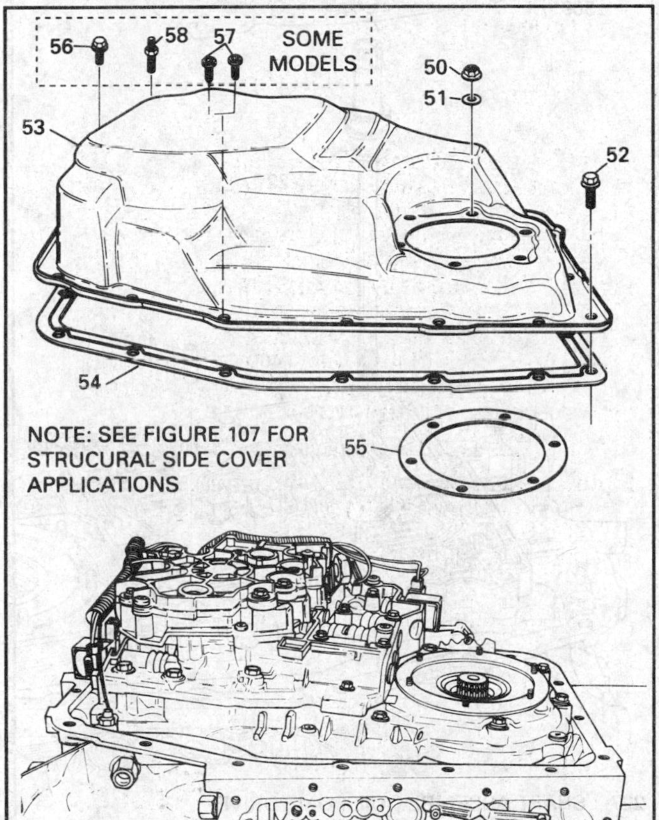
56
58
57
SOME MODELS
50
51
53
52
54
55
NOTE: SEE FIGURE 107 FOR STRUCURAL SIDE COVER APPLICATIONS

50 NUT, CASE SIDE COVER TO CHANNEL PLATE - M6 X 1.0 (6)
51 WASHER, CONICAL
52 SCREW, SPECIAL, SIDE COVER TO CASE CONICAL WASHER AND SCREW - M8 X 1.25 X 21.3 (17)
53 PAN, CASE SIDE COVER
54 GASKET, CASE SIDE COVER
55 GASKET, INNER CASE SIDE COVER

RH1011-4T60-E

Figure 11 Case Side Cover and Gaskets

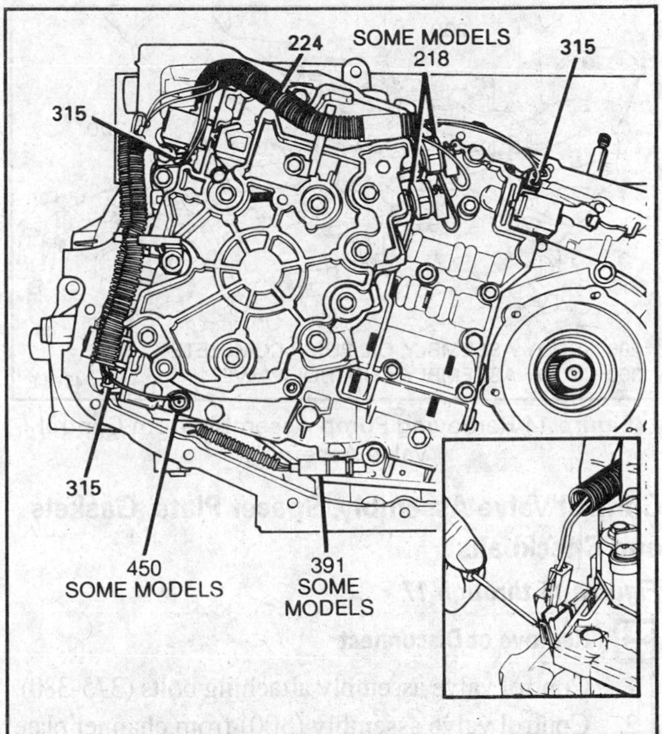
224
SOME MODELS
218
315
315
315
450
SOME MODELS
391
SOME MODELS

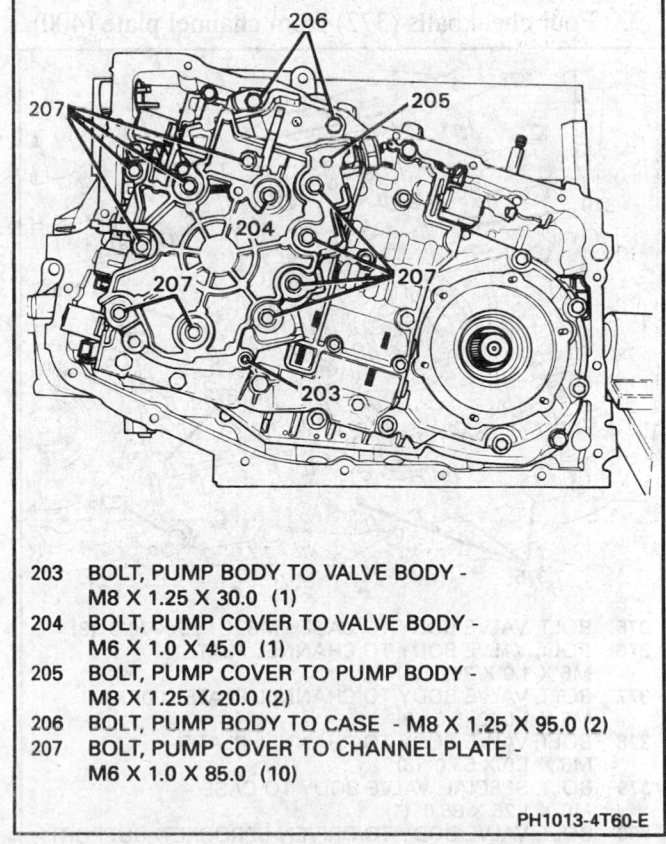

218 SWITCH ASEMBLY, PRESURE
224 HARNESS ASSEMBLY, WIRING
315 SOLENOID ASSEMBLY
450 SENSOR, TEMPERATURE

RH1012-4T60-E

Figure 12 Wiring Harness Assembly

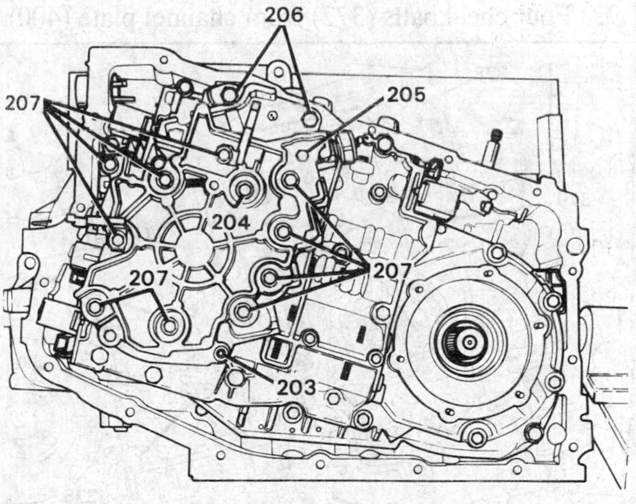
206
205
207
204
207
207
203

203 BOLT, PUMP BODY TO VALVE BODY - M8 X 1.25 X 30.0 (1)
204 BOLT, PUMP COVER TO VALVE BODY - M6 X 1.0 X 45.0 (1)
205 BOLT, PUMP COVER TO PUMP BODY - M8 X 1.25 X 20.0 (2)
206 BOLT, PUMP BODY TO CASE - M8 X 1.25 X 95.0 (2)
207 BOLT, PUMP COVER TO CHANNEL PLATE - M6 X 1.0 X 85.0 (10)

PH1013-4T60-E

Figure 13 Removing Pump Assembly Attaching Bolts

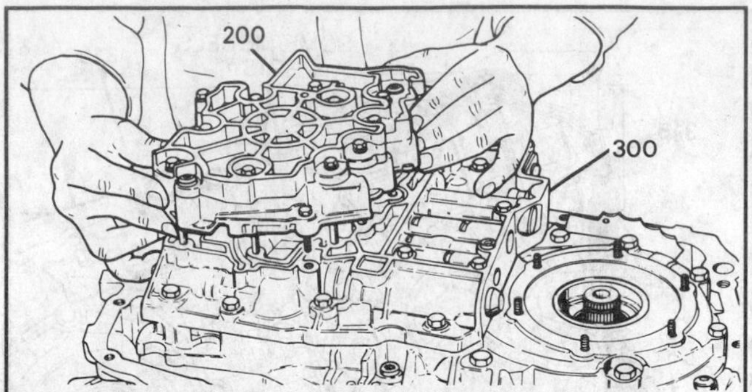
200
300

200 BODY ASSEMBLY, OIL PUMP COMPLETE
300 BODY ASSEMBLY, CONTROL VALVE

MH1014-4T60-E

Figure 14 Removing Pump Assembly from Control Valve Assembly

Control Valve Assembly, Spacer Plate, Gaskets and Checkballs

Figures 15 through 17

↔ Remove or Disconnect

1. Control valve assembly attaching bolts (375-380).
2. Control valve assembly (300) from channel plate (400).
3. Six checkballs (372, 373) from spacer plate (370).
4. Oil pump drive shaft (227).
5. Dowel pin sleeve (410).
6. Spacer plate (370) and gaskets (369, 371), four solenoid screens (374).
7. Four checkballs (372) from channel plate (400).

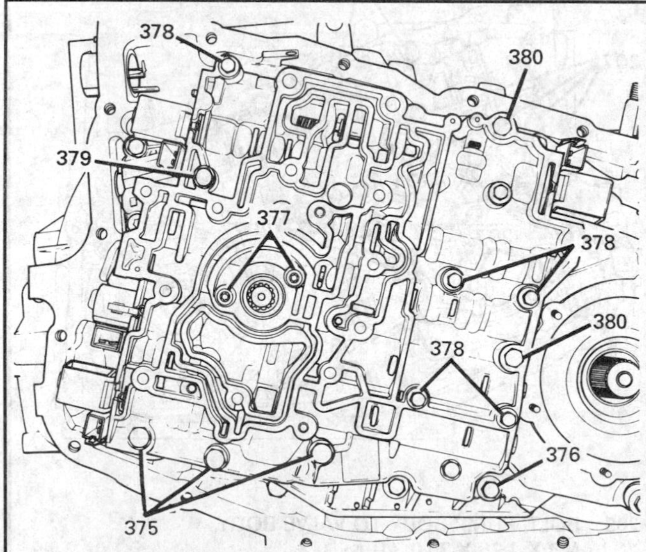
378
380
379
377
378
380
378
376
375

375 BOLT, VALVE BODY TO CASE - M8 X 1.25 X 70.0 (3)
376 BOLT, VALVE BODY TO CHANNEL PLATE - M6 X 1.0 X 35.0 (1)
377 BOLT, VALVE BODY TO CHANNEL PLATE (TORX) - M6 X 1.0 X 45.0 (2)
378 BOLT, VALVE BODY TO CHANNEL PLATE M6 X 1.0 X 55.0 (6)
379 BOLT, SPECIAL, VALVE BODY TO CASE - M8 X 1.25 X 85.0 (1)
380 BOLT, VALVE BODY TO DRIVEN SPROCKET SUPPORT - M8 X 1.25 X 90.0 (1)

PH1015-4T60-E

Figure 15 Control Valve Assembly Attaching Bolts

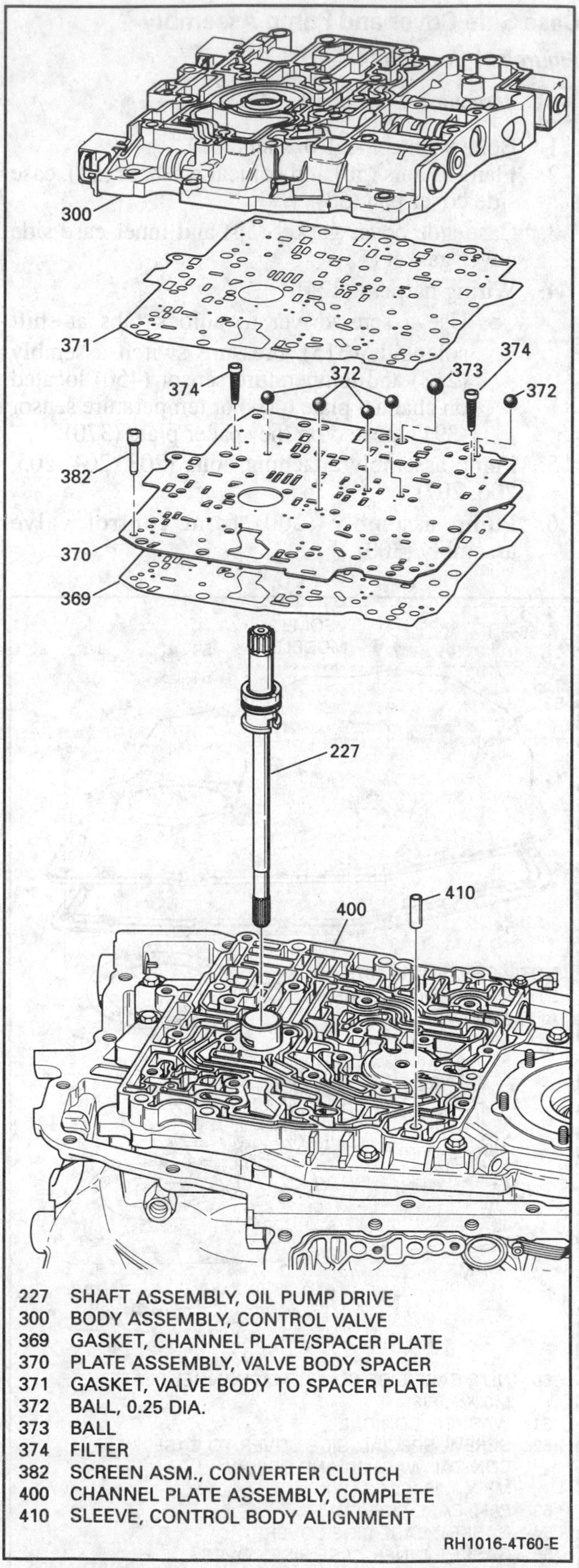
300
371
374
372
373
374
372
382
370
369
227
410
400

227 SHAFT ASSEMBLY, OIL PUMP DRIVE
300 BODY ASSEMBLY, CONTROL VALVE
369 GASKET, CHANNEL PLATE/SPACER PLATE
370 PLATE ASSEMBLY, VALVE BODY SPACER
371 GASKET, VALVE BODY TO SPACER PLATE
372 BALL, 0.25 DIA.
373 BALL
374 FILTER
382 SCREEN ASM., CONVERTER CLUTCH
400 CHANNEL PLATE ASSEMBLY, COMPLETE
410 SLEEVE, CONTROL BODY ALIGNMENT

RH1016-4T60-E

Figure 16 Removing Control Valve Assembly, Spacer Plate and Gasket

Case Extension and Speed Sensor

Figure 17

Remove or Disconnect

- Rotate transaxle so final drive case extension is as shown in Figure 17.

1. Speed sensor bolt (9), speed sensor (10) and O-ring (11).
2. Case extension bolts (5).
3. Case extension assembly (6).

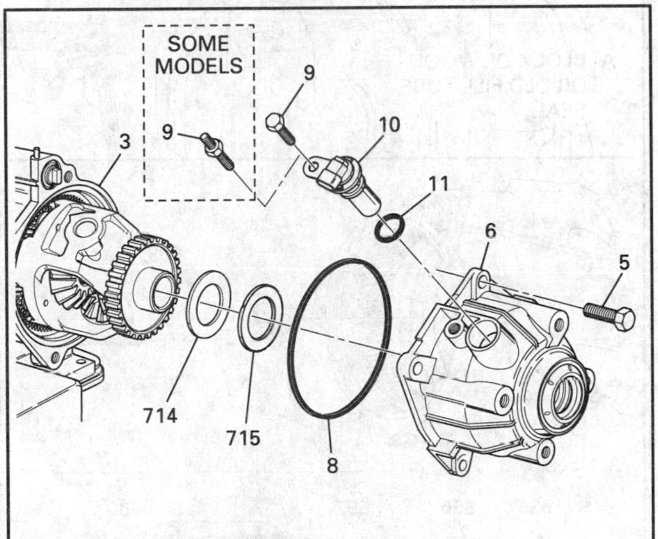
SOME MODELS
9
3
9
10
11
6
5
714
715
8

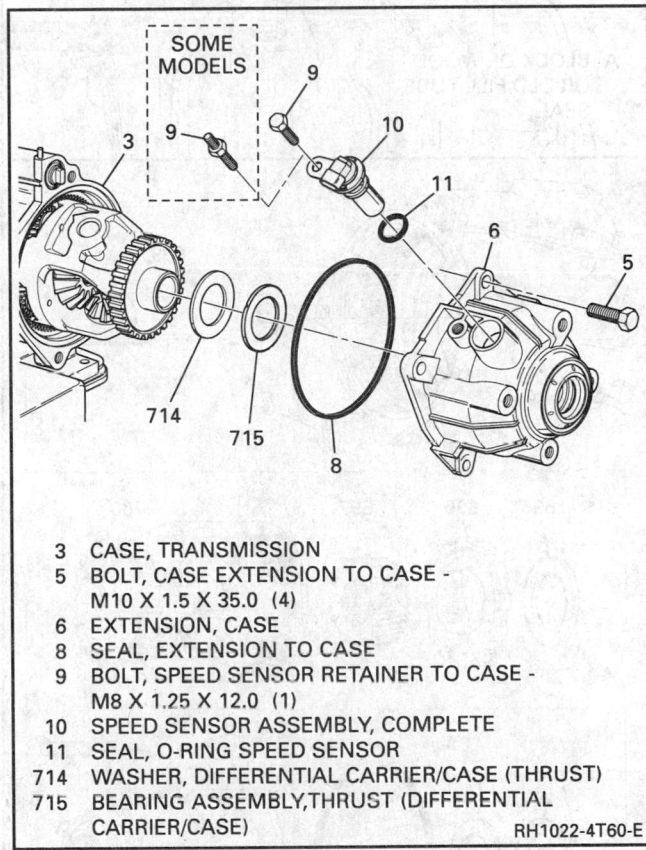

3 CASE, TRANSMISSION
5 BOLT, CASE EXTENSION TO CASE - M10 X 1.5 X 35.0 (4)
6 EXTENSION, CASE
8 SEAL, EXTENSION TO CASE
9 BOLT, SPEED SENSOR RETAINER TO CASE - M8 X 1.25 X 12.0 (1)
10 SPEED SENSOR ASSEMBLY, COMPLETE
11 SEAL, O-RING SPEED SENSOR
714 WASHER, DIFFERENTIAL CARRIER/CASE (THRUST)
715 BEARING ASSEMBLY,THRUST (DIFFERENTIAL CARRIER/CASE)

RH1022-4T60-E

Figure 17 Speed Sensor and Case Extension Removable

Output Shaft Snap Ring

Figures 18 and 19

Remove or Disconnect

Tool Required:

J 34757 Snap Ring Remover or long thin screwdrivers

1. Rotate output shaft (510) till snap ring (512) opening is visible.
2. Push snap ring (512) partially off shaft (510) with J 34757 then rotate shaft and remove snap ring with needle nose pliers. (The snap ring can also be removed with long thin screwdrivers).
3. Final drive.

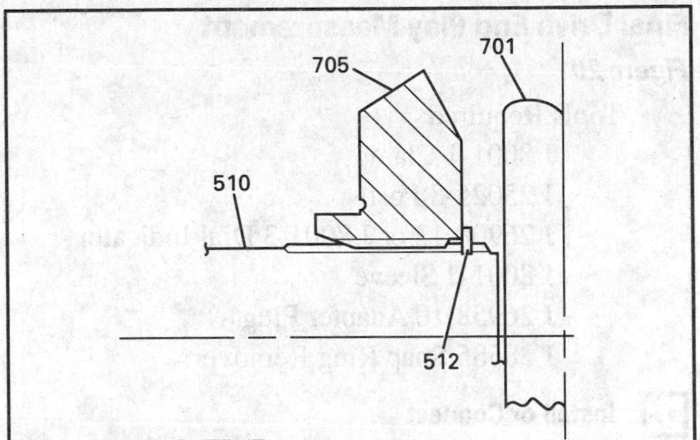
705
701
510
512

510 SHAFT, OUTPUT
512 RING, OUTPUT SHAFT/DIFFERENTIAL INBOARD (SNAP)
701 SHAFT, DIFFERENTIAL PINION
705 GEAR, DIFFERENTIAL SIDE

RH1023-4T60-E

Figure 18 Removable Output Shaft Snap Ring

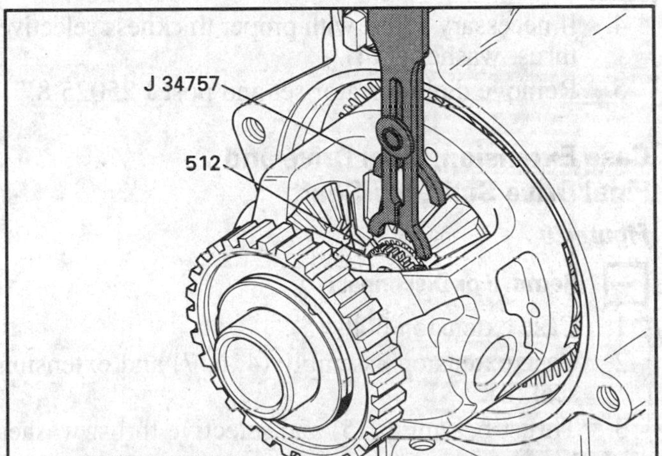
J 34757
512

512 RING, OUTPUT SHAFT/DIFFERENTIAL INBOARD (SNAP)

RH1024-4T60-E

Figure 19 Removing Output Shaft Snap Ring

Final Drive End Play Measurement

Figure 20

Tools Required:

- J 8001-1 Clamp
- J 25025-8 Post
- J 26900-12 or J 8001-3 Dial Indicator
- J 8001-2 Sleeve
- J 26958-10 Adapter Plug
- J 28585 Snap Ring Remover

Install or Connect

Figure 20

1. Position dial indicator set and zero out dial indicator – stem must contact J 26958-10.
2. Lift speed sensor rotor (713) with J 28585 for measurement.
3. Proper end play clearance is 0.12 to 0.62 mm (0.005-0.025 inch).
4. If necessary adjust with proper thickness selective thrust washer (714).
5. Remove dial indicator set and post J 25025-8.

Case Extension, Final Drive and Final Drive Sun Gear Shaft

Figure 20

Remove or Disconnect

1. Case extension bolts (5).
2. Case extension assembly (4, 6, 7) and extension seal (8).
3. Thrust bearing (715) and selective thrust washer (714).
4. Final drive assembly (700) from case.
5. Final drive sun gear (697), parking gear (696) and thrust bearing (695).
6. Final drive sun gear shaft (689).

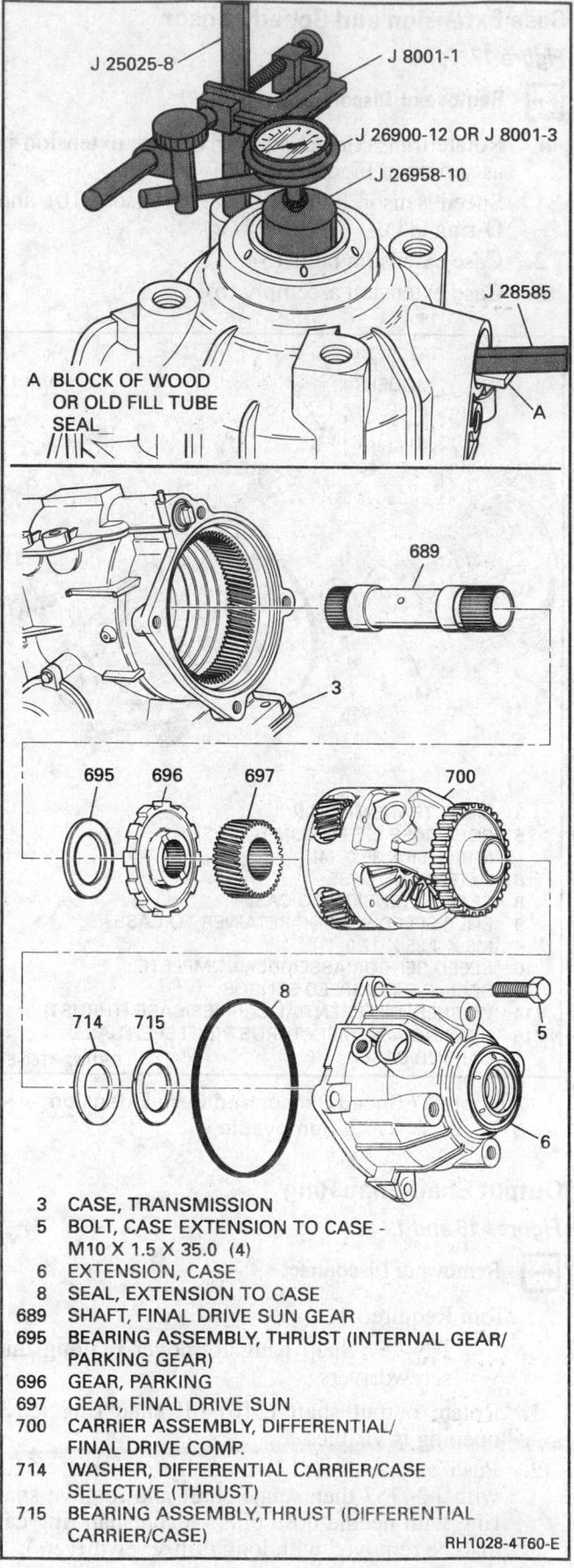

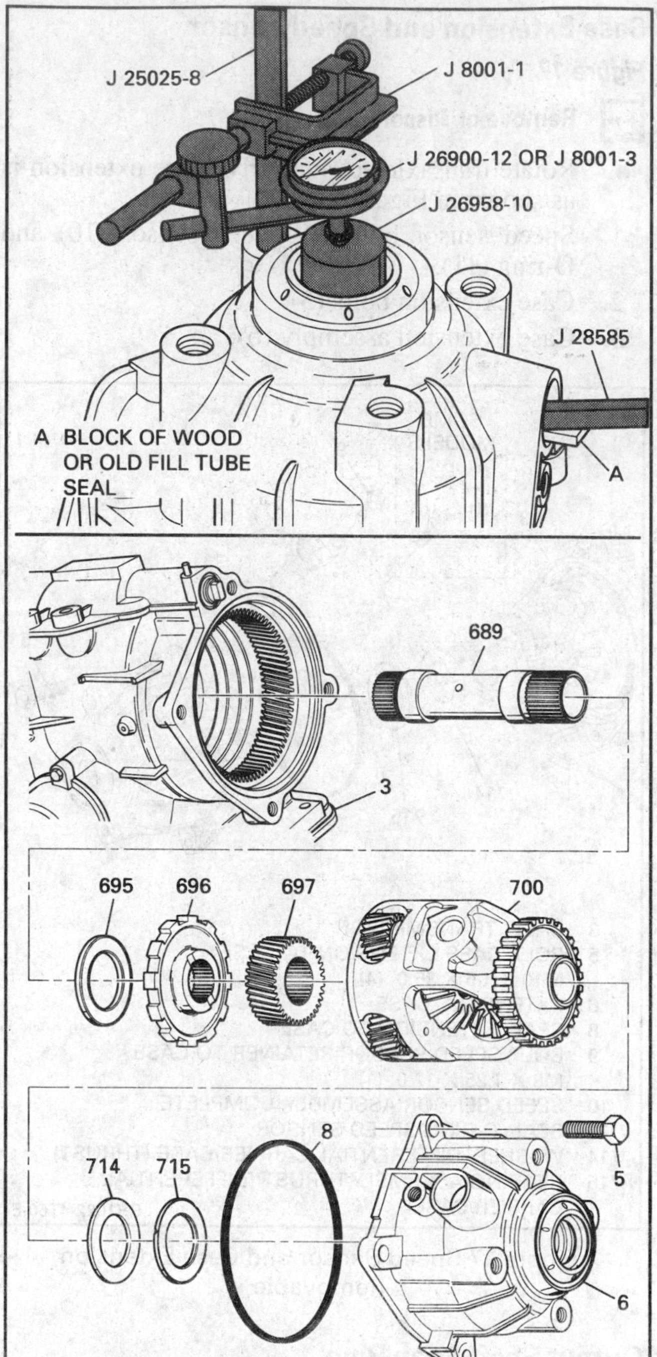
J 25025-8
J 8001-1
J 26900-12 OR J 8001-3
J 26958-10
J 28585
A BLOCK OF WOOD OR OLD FILL TUBE SEAL
A
689
3
695
696
697
700
8
714
715
5
6

3 CASE, TRANSMISSION
5 BOLT, CASE EXTENSION TO CASE - M10 X 1.5 X 35.0 (4)
6 EXTENSION, CASE
8 SEAL, EXTENSION TO CASE
689 SHAFT, FINAL DRIVE SUN GEAR
695 BEARING ASSEMBLY, THRUST (INTERNAL GEAR/ PARKING GEAR)
696 GEAR, PARKING
697 GEAR, FINAL DRIVE SUN
700 CARRIER ASSEMBLY, DIFFERENTIAL/ FINAL DRIVE COMP.
714 WASHER, DIFFERENTIAL CARRIER/CASE SELECTIVE (THRUST)
715 BEARING ASSEMBLY,THRUST (DIFFERENTIAL CARRIER/CASE)

RH1028-4T60-E

Figure 20 Final Drive End Play Measurement and Removal of Case Extension

Channel Plate, Oil Weir and Gaskets

Figures 21 and 22

Remove or Disconnect

1. Oil reservoir weir (27).
2. Bolt (805) from manual detent spring and roller assembly (804).
3. Manual valve link (402) from manual valve (404) – pull back spring (403).
4. Temp-sensor (do not **tap** or **pry** sensor).
5. Channel plate attaching bolts (434-436).
6. Channel plate assembly (400) from case (3).
7. Lower channel plate gasket (429) and upper channel plate gasket (430).
8. TCC accumulator spring (413) and pin (414) – may be in the case (3) (optional).
9. Thrust washer (514) – may be attached to channel plate assembly (400).
10. Dowel pins (526) from case – may be attached to channel plate (400).

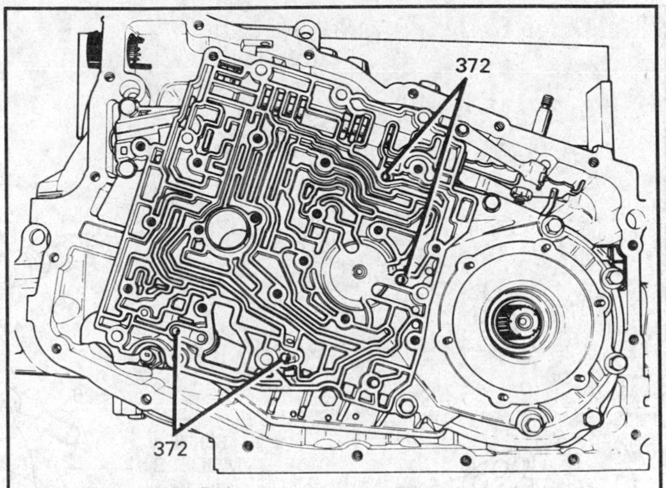
372
372

372 BALL, 0.25 DIA.

PH1017-4T60-E

Figure 21 Checkballs in Channel Plate

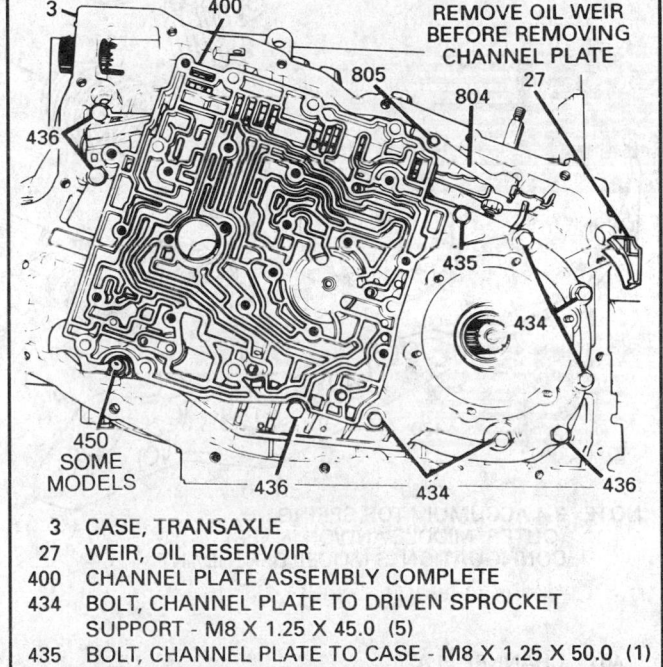

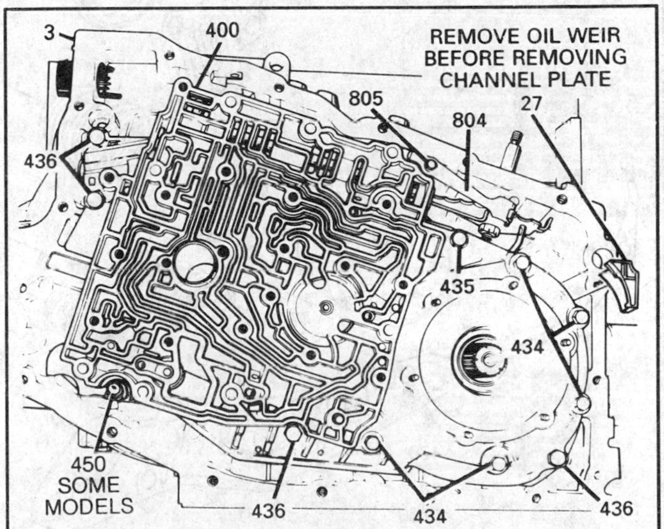
3
400
REMOVE OIL WEIR BEFORE REMOVING CHANNEL PLATE
805
27
804
436
435
434
450 SOME MODELS
436
434
436

3	CASE, TRANSAXLE
27	WEIR, OIL RESERVOIR
400	CHANNEL PLATE ASSEMBLY COMPLETE
434	BOLT, CHANNEL PLATE TO DRIVEN SPROCKET SUPPORT - M8 X 1.25 X 45.0 (5)
435	BOLT, CHANNEL PLATE TO CASE - M8 X 1.25 X 50.0 (1)
436	BOLT, CHANNEL PLATE TO CASE - M8 X 1.25 X 30.0 (4)
450	TEMP SENSOR, 1/8-27 DRYSEAL SAE-SHORT (1)
804	SPRING AND ROLLER ASSEMBLY, MANUAL DETENT
805	BOLT, MANUAL DETENT SPRING TO CHANNEL PLATE - M6 X 1.0 X 16.0 (1)

RH1018-4T60-E

Figure 22 Channel Plate Bolts and Manual Spring Bolt

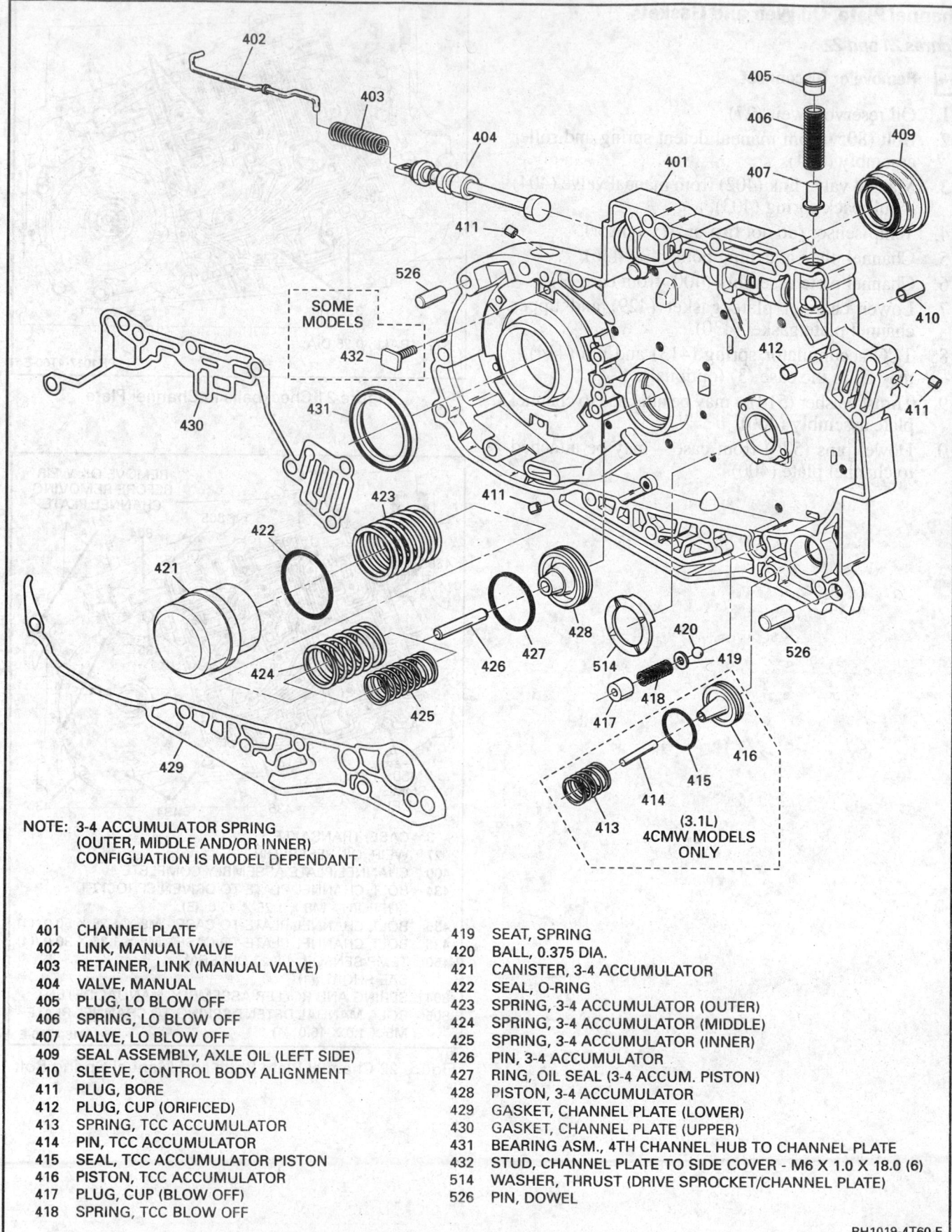

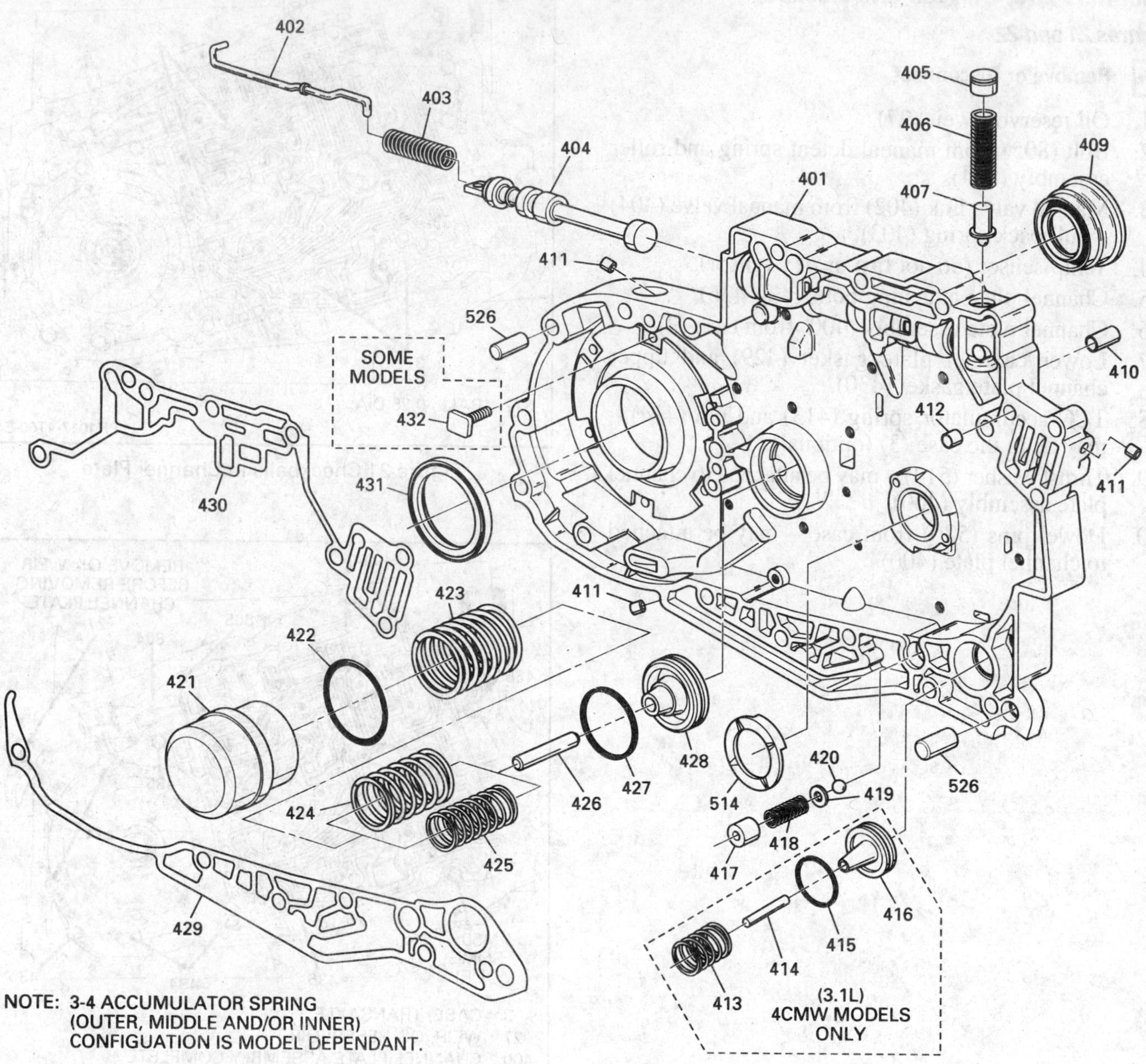
402
403
404
405
406
407
409
401
411
526
SOME MODELS
432
410
412
411
431
430
423
411
422
421
428
420
419
526
427
426
514
424
418
425
417
416
429
415
414
413
(3.1L) 4CMW MODELS ONLY
NOTE: 3-4 ACCUMULATOR SPRING (OUTER, MIDDLE AND/OR INNER) CONFIGUATION IS MODEL DEPENDANT.

401	CHANNEL PLATE	419	SEAT, SPRING
402	LINK, MANUAL VALVE	420	BALL, 0.375 DIA.
403	RETAINER, LINK (MANUAL VALVE)	421	CANISTER, 3-4 ACCUMULATOR
404	VALVE, MANUAL	422	SEAL, O-RING
405	PLUG, LO BLOW OFF	423	SPRING, 3-4 ACCUMULATOR (OUTER)
406	SPRING, LO BLOW OFF	424	SPRING, 3-4 ACCUMULATOR (MIDDLE)
407	VALVE, LO BLOW OFF	425	SPRING, 3-4 ACCUMULATOR (INNER)
409	SEAL ASSEMBLY, AXLE OIL (LEFT SIDE)	426	PIN, 3-4 ACCUMULATOR
410	SLEEVE, CONTROL BODY ALIGNMENT	427	RING, OIL SEAL (3-4 ACCUM. PISTON)
411	PLUG, BORE	428	PISTON, 3-4 ACCUMULATOR
412	PLUG, CUP (ORIFICED)	429	GASKET, CHANNEL PLATE (LOWER)
413	SPRING, TCC ACCUMULATOR	430	GASKET, CHANNEL PLATE (UPPER)
414	PIN, TCC ACCUMULATOR	431	BEARING ASM., 4TH CHANNEL HUB TO CHANNEL PLATE
415	SEAL, TCC ACCUMULATOR PISTON	432	STUD, CHANNEL PLATE TO SIDE COVER - M6 X 1.0 X 18.0 (6)
416	PISTON, TCC ACCUMULATOR	514	WASHER, THRUST (DRIVE SPROCKET/CHANNEL PLATE)
417	PLUG, CUP (BLOW OFF)	526	PIN, DOWEL
418	SPRING, TCC BLOW OFF		

RH1019-4T60-E

Figure 23 Channel Plate Components

Fourth Clutch, Output Shaft, Fourth Clutch Shaft, Drive and Driven Sprockets

Figures 24 and 25

Remove or Disconnect

1. Output Shaft (510).
2. Fourth clutch reaction plates (500, 502) and fiber plates (501).
3. Chain scavenging scoop (608).
4. Fourth clutch hub and shaft assembly (504).
5. Turbine shaft O-ring (520) from inside bell housing.
6. Drive sprocket (516), driven sprocket (506) and drive link (507) together – grasp sprockets and lift up.

Important

- The copper link should be facing up. If not, reassemble the drive link assembly with the sprockets the same way as found – either the copper link up or down so the set wear pattern remains the same to reduce noise.

7. Thrust washers (514, 505, 508) – may be attached to sprockets.
8. Wiring harness assembly (224) from case electrical connector (35).
   - Use a screwdriver to unlock tabs.

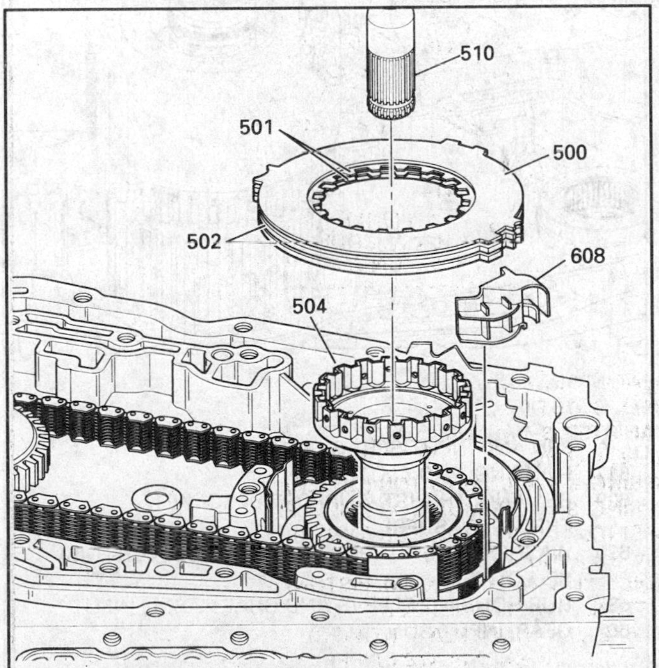
510
501
500
502
608
504

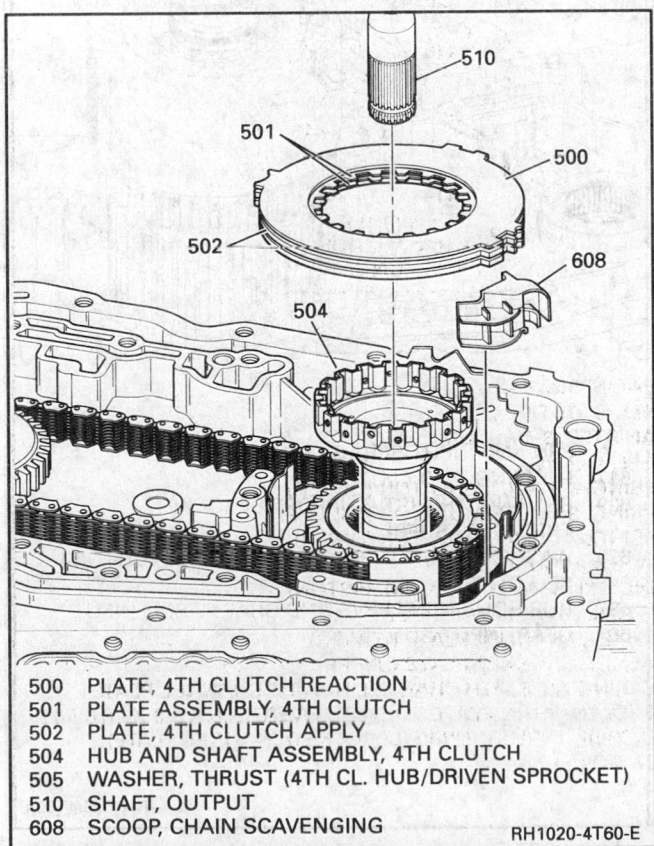

500 PLATE, 4TH CLUTCH REACTION
501 PLATE ASSEMBLY, 4TH CLUTCH
502 PLATE, 4TH CLUTCH APPLY
504 HUB AND SHAFT ASSEMBLY, 4TH CLUTCH
505 WASHER, THRUST (4TH CL. HUB/DRIVEN SPROCKET)
510 SHAFT, OUTPUT
608 SCOOP, CHAIN SCAVENGING
RH1020-4T60-E

Figure 24 Removing 4th Clutch Plates and 4th Clutch Hub

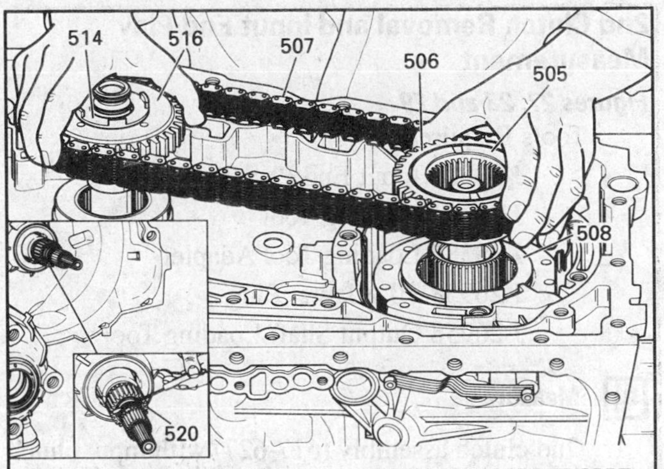
514
516
507
506
505
508
520

505 WASHER, THRUST (4TH CL. HUB/DRIVEN SPRKT SPRT)
506 SPROCKET, DRIVEN
507 LINK ASSEMBLY, DRIVE
508 WASHER, THRUST (DRIVEN AND 2ND CL. DRUM)
514 WASHER, THRUST (DRIVE SPROCKET/CHANNEL PLATE)
516 SPROCKET, DRIVE
520 SEAL, O-RING (TURBINE SHAFT/HUB)
RH1021-4T60-E

Figure 25 Removing Sprockets, Drive Link Assembly

Driven Sprocket Support

Figure 26

Remove or Disconnect

1. Partially screw two channel plate attaching bolts (434) into driven sprocket support (609).
2. Driven sprocket support (609) from case – grasp bolts and lift up.
3. Thrust washer (611) – may be on 2nd clutch housing (617).

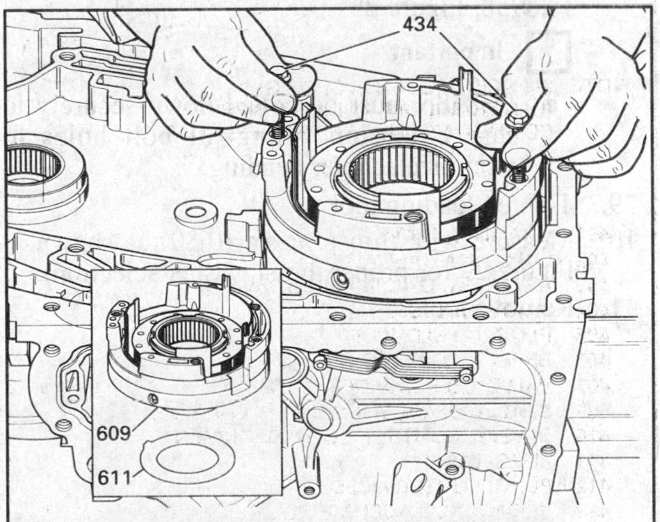
434
609
611

434 BOLT, CHANNEL PLATE TO DRIVEN SPROCKET SUPPORT, M8 X 45.0, (6)
609 SUPPORT, DRIVEN SPROCKET
611 WASHER, THRUST (DRIVEN SPROCKET SUPPORT/2ND CLUTCH DRUM)
RH1200-4T60-E

Figure 26 Removing Driven Sprocket Support

2nd Clutch Removal and Input End Play Measurement

Figures 27, 28 and 29

Tools Required:

J 33386 Input End Play Tool
J 33381 Loading Tool
J 38385 Loading Tool Adapter
J 26958-10 Adapter Plug
J 26958 Output Shaft Loading Tool

Measure

1. 2nd clutch assembly (617-627) with input clutch housing (632) – grasp splines of input shaft and lift straight up or use J 33381.
2. Separate the 2nd clutch housing (617) and the input clutch housing (632).
3. Remove thrust washer (630) and thrust bearing (629) from input housing (632).
4. Install input housing and shaft assembly (632) in case interlocking with roller clutch (650-653) and sprag (660-667).
5. Make sure input housing is all the way down.
6. Install J 33386.
7. Install differential thrust washer (714), thrust bearing assembly (715), case extension (6) and a couple bolts (5).

Tighten

- Bolt(s) to 30-41 N•m (23-31 lbs. ft.)

8. Install J 38385 to case with remaining bolts (5) so all the bolt holes are filled, J 26958-10 and J 26958. Figure 28.

Important

- J 38385 must be bolted down securely to case extension filling all bolt holes to minimize adapter bending.

9. Tighten loading tool.
10. Measure with thrust washer (630) as shown in Figure 29 for proper thrust washer selection.
11. Remove tools.

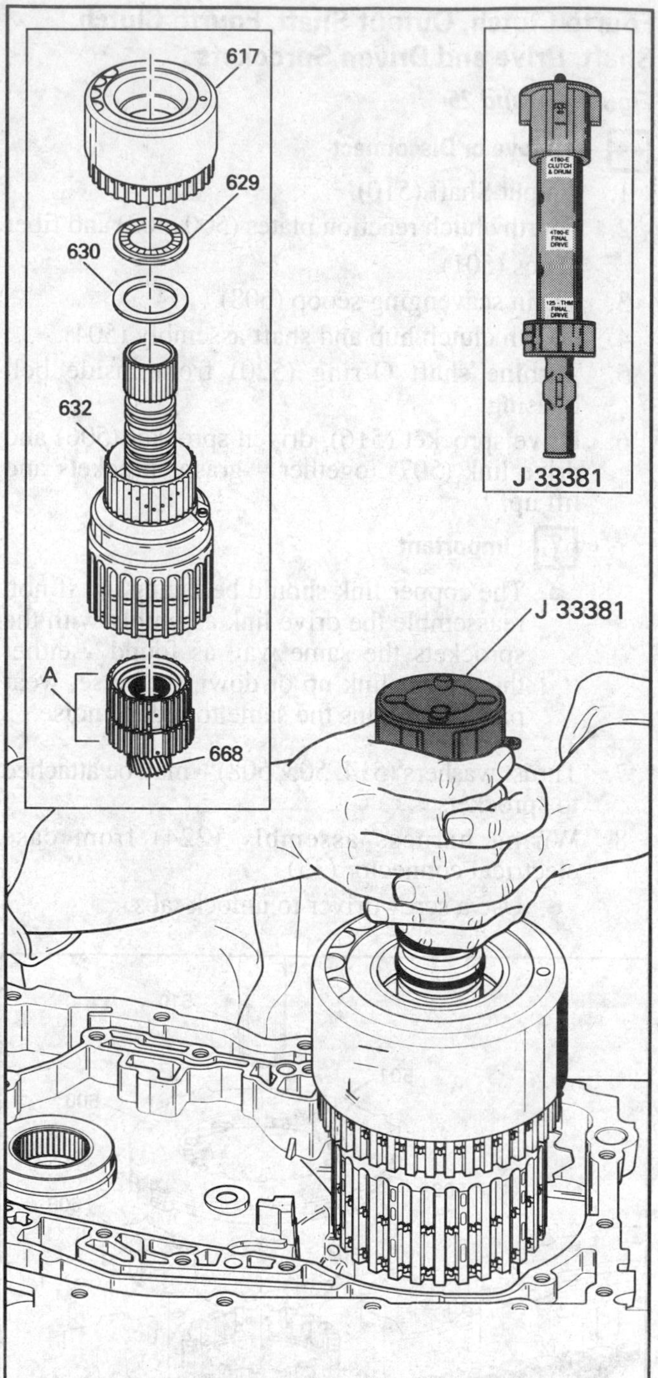
617
629
630
632
A
668
J 33381
J 33381

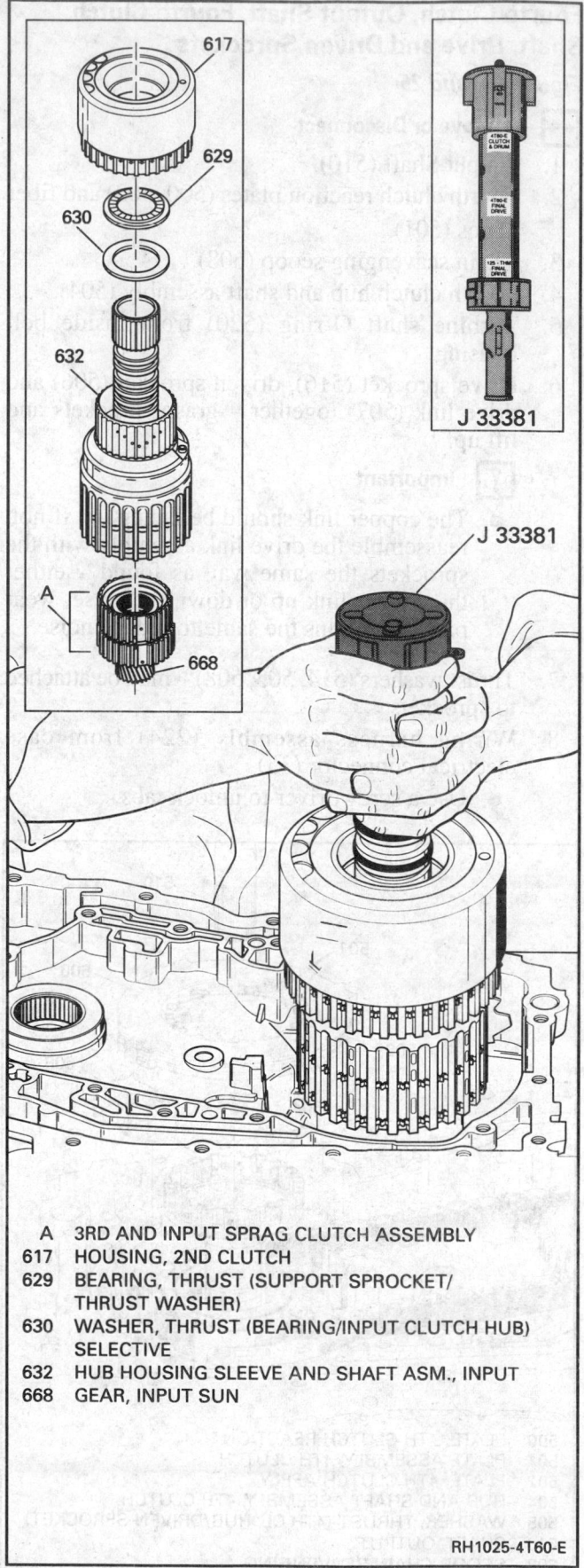

A 3RD AND INPUT SPRAG CLUTCH ASSEMBLY
617 HOUSING, 2ND CLUTCH
629 BEARING, THRUST (SUPPORT SPROCKET/ THRUST WASHER)
630 WASHER, THRUST (BEARING/INPUT CLUTCH HUB) SELECTIVE
632 HUB HOUSING SLEEVE AND SHAFT ASM., INPUT
668 GEAR, INPUT SUN

RH1025-4T60-E

Figure 27 Removing 2nd Clutch Housing and Input Clutch Housing

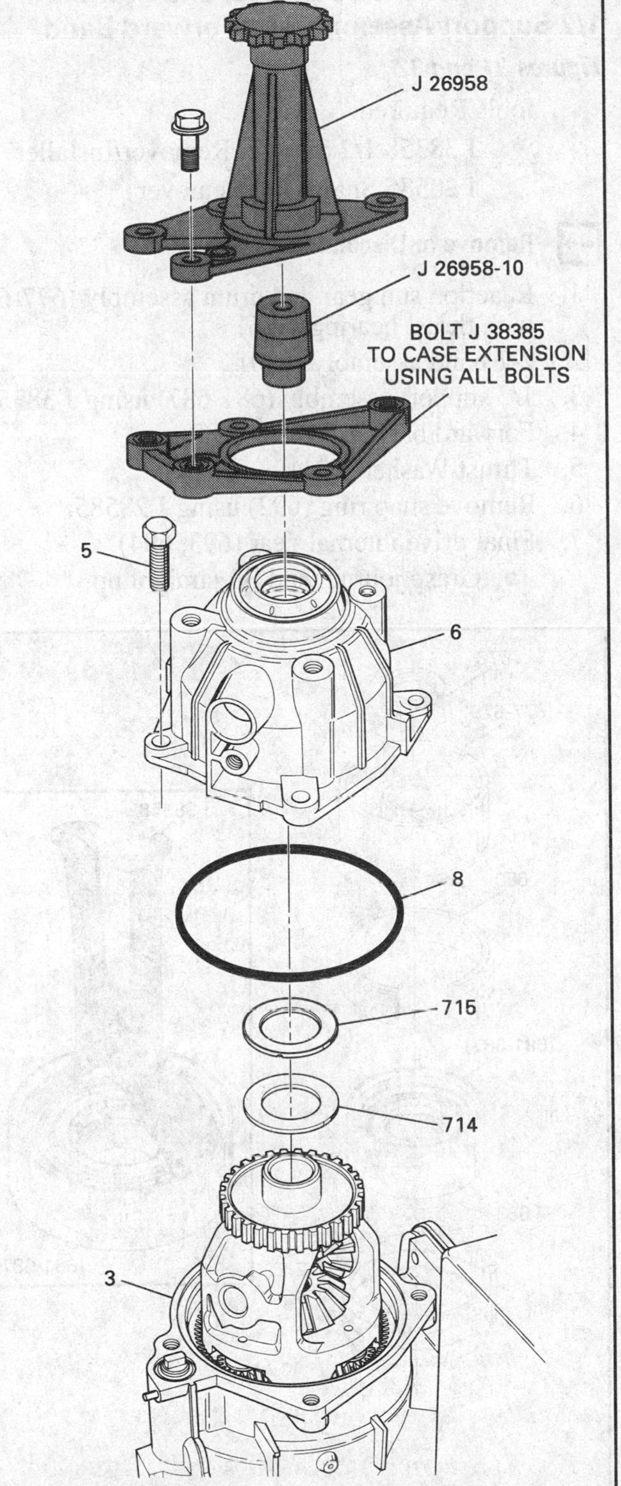

J 26958
J 26958-10
BOLT J 38385
TO CASE EXTENSION
USING ALL BOLTS
5
6
8
715
714
3

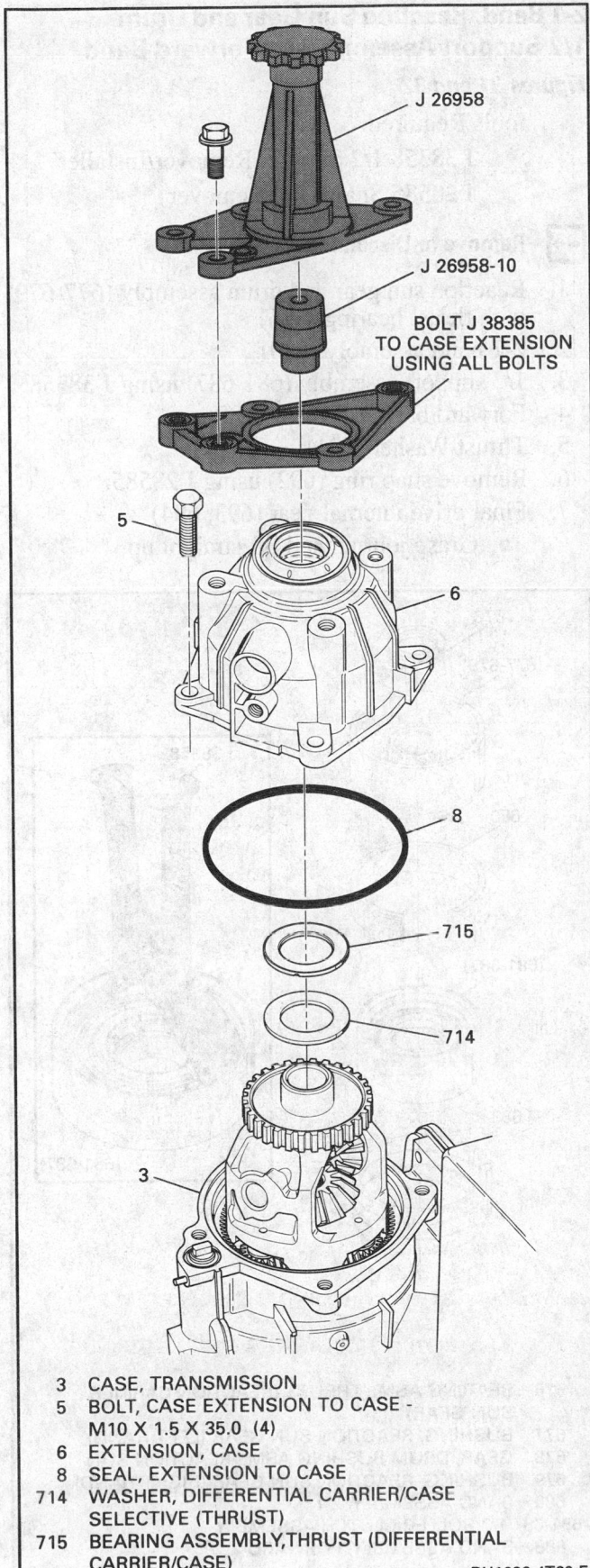

3 CASE, TRANSMISSION
5 BOLT, CASE EXTENSION TO CASE - M10 X 1.5 X 35.0 (4)
6 EXTENSION, CASE
8 SEAL, EXTENSION TO CASE
714 WASHER, DIFFERENTIAL CARRIER/CASE SELECTIVE (THRUST)
715 BEARING ASSEMBLY,THRUST (DIFFERENTIAL CARRIER/CASE)

RH1026-4T60-E

Figure 28 Case Extension and Input End Play Loading Tools Installation

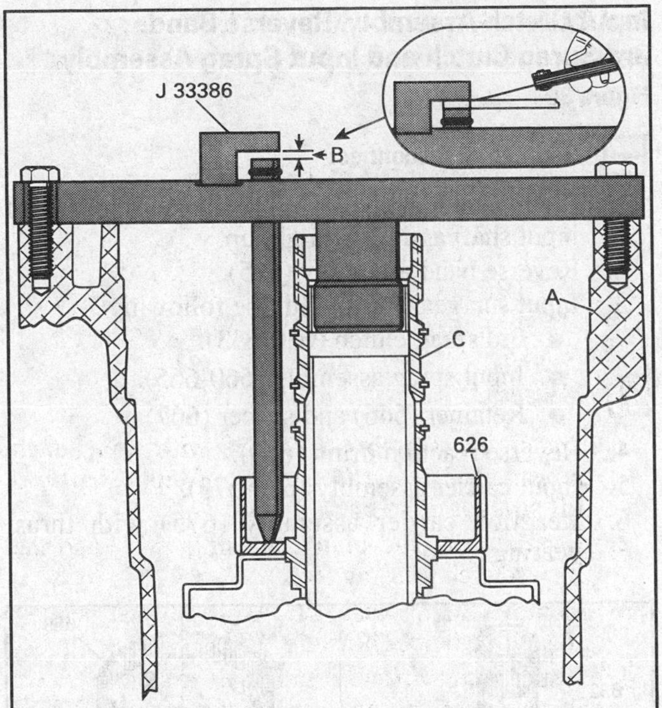

J 33386
B
A
C
626

A CASE
B INSERT SELECTIVE THRUST WASHER TO DETERMINE PROPER SIZE
C INPUT SHAFT
630 WASHER, THRUST (BEARING/INPUT CLUTCH HUB) SELECTIVE
632 HOUSING AND SHAFT ASSEMBLY, INPUT

If a .521 mm (.006") feeler gage or larger can be inserted between thrust washer and tool, use next size larger thrust washer.

GUIDE FOR SELECTIVE THRUST WASHER

I.D. NO.	DIMENSION		COLOR
	MM	INCHES	
1	2.90-3.00	(0.114-0.118)	ORANGE/GREEN
2	3.05-3.15	(0.120-0.124)	ORANGE/BLACK
3	3.20-3.30	(0.126-0.130)	ORANGE
4	3.35-3.45	(0.132-0.136)	WHITE
5	3.50-3.60	(0.138-0.142)	BLUE
6	3.65-3.75	(0.144-0.148)	PINK
7	3.80-3.90	(0.150-0.154)	BROWN
8	3.95-4.05	(0.156-0.159)	GREEN
9	4.10-4.20	(0.161-0.165)	BLACK
10	4.25-4.35	(0.167-0.171)	PURPLE
11	4.40-4.50	(0.173-0.177)	PURPLE/WHITE
12	4.55-4.65	(0.179-0.183)	PURPLE/BLUE
13	4.70-4.80	(0.185-0.189)	PURPLE/PINK
14	4.85-4.95	(0.191-0.195)	PURPLE/BROWN
15	5.00-5.10	(0.197-0.200)	PURPLE/GREEN

PH1027-4T60-E

Figure 29 Input End Play

Input Clutch Assembly, Reverse Band, 3rd Sprag Clutch and Input Sprag Assembly

Figure 30

↔ Remove or Disconnect

1. Input clutch housing (632) – grasp splines of input shaft and lift straight up.
2. Reverse band assembly (615).
3. Input sun gear (668) with the following:
   - 3rd sprag clutch (650-653).
   - Input sprag assembly (660-665).
   - Retainer (666) and spacer (667).
4. Reverse reaction drum (669).
5. Input carrier assembly (670-673).
6. Reaction carrier assembly (675) with thrust bearing (674).

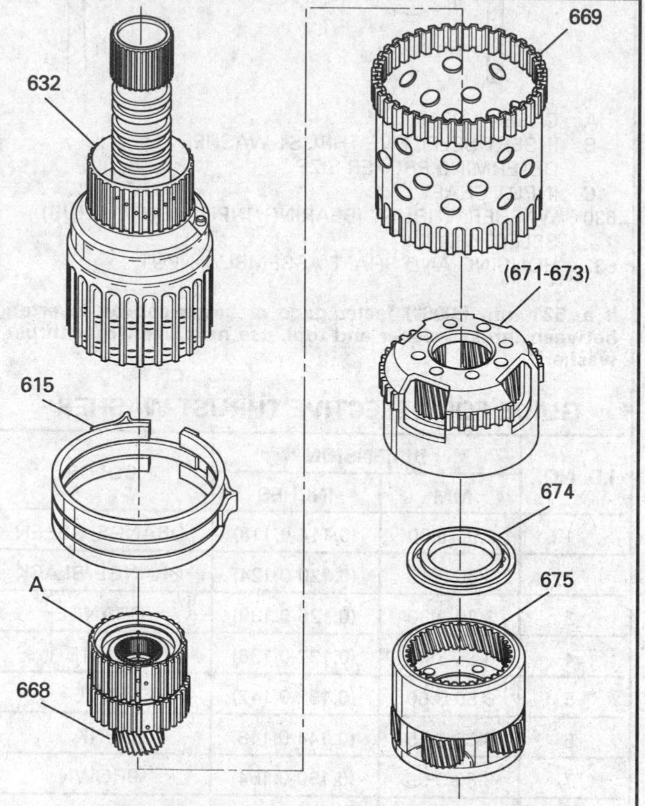
632
669
(671-673)
615
674
A
675
668

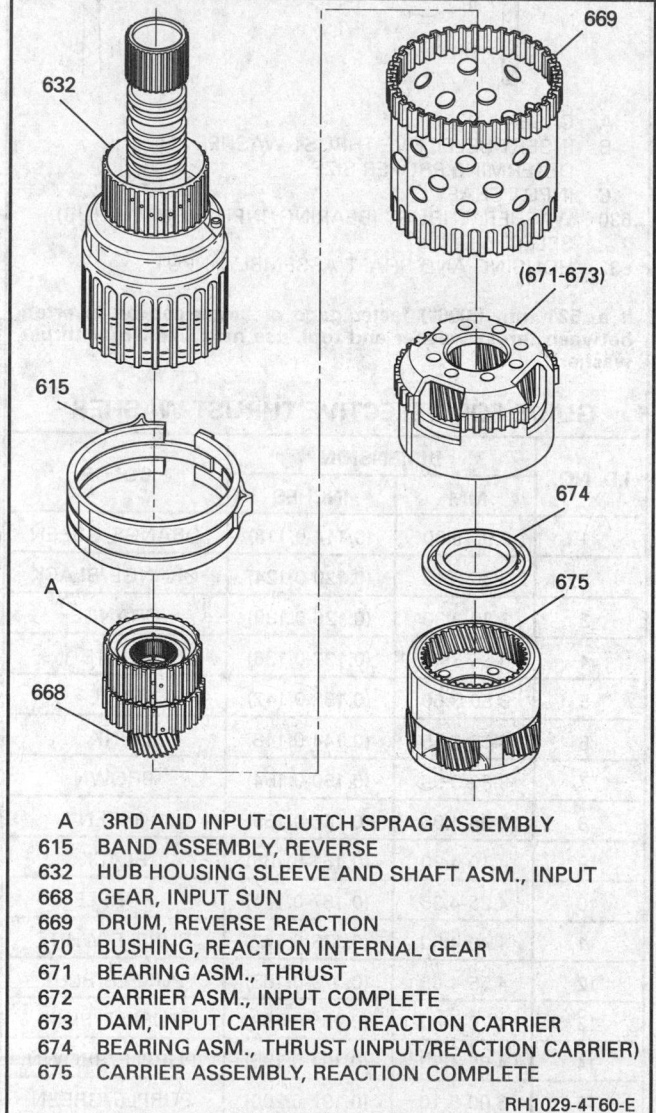

A 3RD AND INPUT CLUTCH SPRAG ASSEMBLY
615 BAND ASSEMBLY, REVERSE
632 HUB HOUSING SLEEVE AND SHAFT ASM., INPUT
668 GEAR, INPUT SUN
669 DRUM, REVERSE REACTION
670 BUSHING, REACTION INTERNAL GEAR
671 BEARING ASM., THRUST
672 CARRIER ASM., INPUT COMPLETE
673 DAM, INPUT CARRIER TO REACTION CARRIER
674 BEARING ASM., THRUST (INPUT/REACTION CARRIER)
675 CARRIER ASSEMBLY, REACTION COMPLETE

RH1029-4T60-E

Figure 30 Input Clutch, Reverse Band, 3rd Sprag Clutch and Input Sprag Clutch

2-1 Band, Reaction Sun Gear and Drum, 1/2 Support Assembly and Forward Band

Figures 31 and 32

Tools Required:

J 38358 1/2 Support Remover/Installer
J 28585 Snap Ring Remover

↔ Remove or Disconnect

1. Reaction sun gear and drum assembly (677-679) with thrust bearing (676).
2. 2-1 band assembly (680).
3. 1/2 support assembly (681-687) using J 38358.
4. Forward band assembly (688).
5. Thrust Washer (691).
6. Remove snap ring (692) using J 28585.
7. Final drive internal gear (693, 694).
   - Grasp journal and lift straight up.

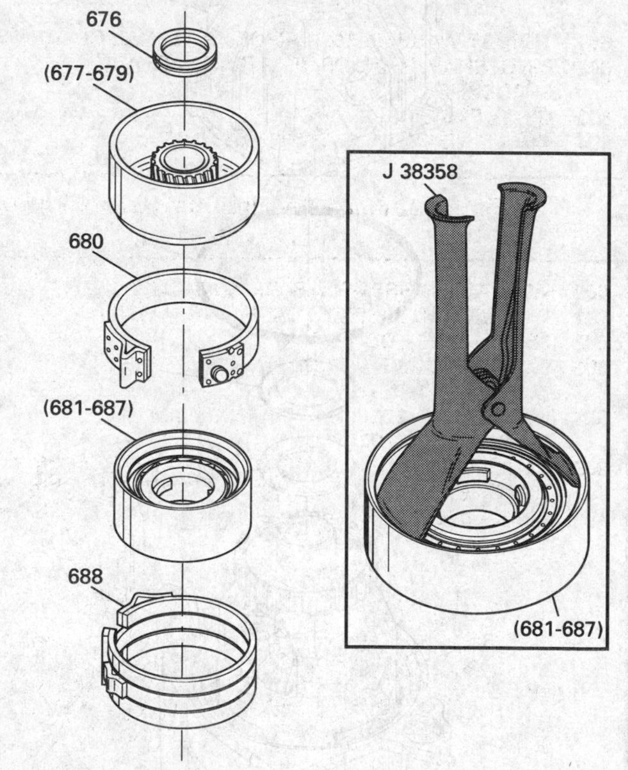
676
(677-679)
J 38358
680
(681-687)
688
(681-687)

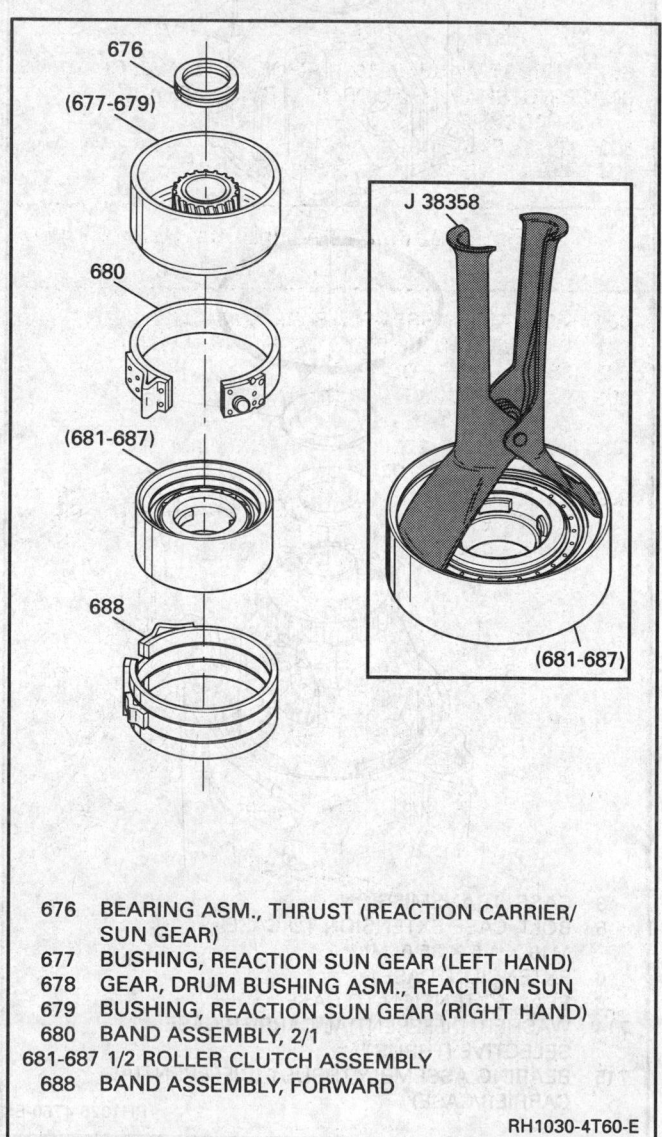

676 BEARING ASM., THRUST (REACTION CARRIER/ SUN GEAR)
677 BUSHING, REACTION SUN GEAR (LEFT HAND)
678 GEAR, DRUM BUSHING ASM., REACTION SUN
679 BUSHING, REACTION SUN GEAR (RIGHT HAND)
680 BAND ASSEMBLY, 2/1
681-687 1/2 ROLLER CLUTCH ASSEMBLY
688 BAND ASSEMBLY, FORWARD

RH1030-4T60-E

Figure 31 Removal of 1/2 Support

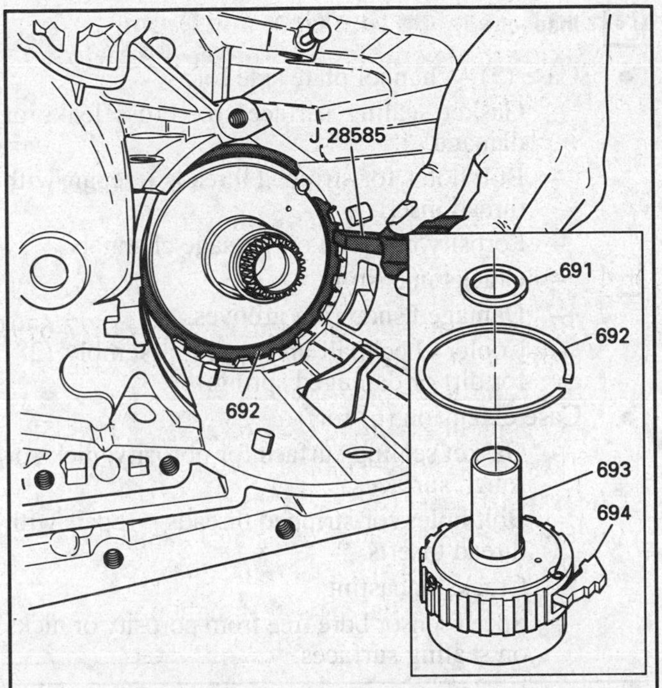
J 28585
691
692
692
693
694

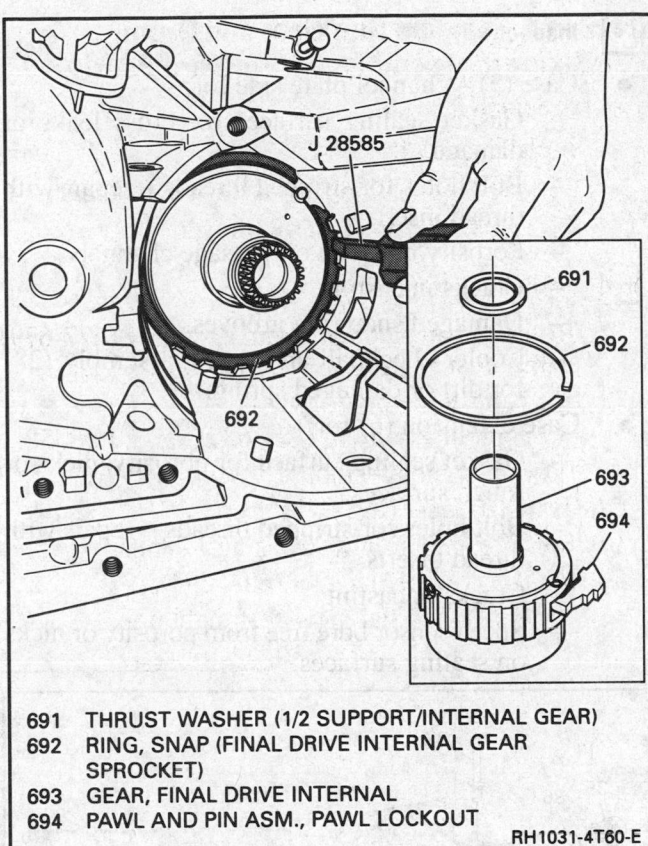

691 THRUST WASHER (1/2 SUPPORT/INTERNAL GEAR)
692 RING, SNAP (FINAL DRIVE INTERNAL GEAR SPROCKET)
693 GEAR, FINAL DRIVE INTERNAL
694 PAWL AND PIN ASM., PAWL LOCKOUT

RH1031-4T60-E

Figure 32 Final Drive Internal Gear

Inside Detent Lever, Manual Shaft and Actuator Guide

Figure 33

Remove or Disconnect

1. Hex nut (803) from manual shaft (807).
2. Inside detent lever (802) with parking lock actuator rod (800).
3. Manual shaft retaining pin (801) using diagonal cutting pliers.
   - Protect case with a piece of wood or rubber when removing pin.
4. Manual shaft (807) from case.
5. Actuator guide retaining pin (808) from case.
6. Actuator guide (809) from case.

800 ACTUATOR ASSEMBLY, PARKING LOCK
801 PIN, MANUAL SHIFT TO CASE
802 LEVER, INSIDE DETENT
803 NUT, MANUAL SHAFT/DETENT LEVER (HEX) - M10 X 1.5 (1)
804 SPRING AND ROLLER ASSEMBLY, MANUAL DETENT
805 MANUAL DETENT SPRING TO CHANNEL PLATE - M6 X 1.0 X 16.0 (1)

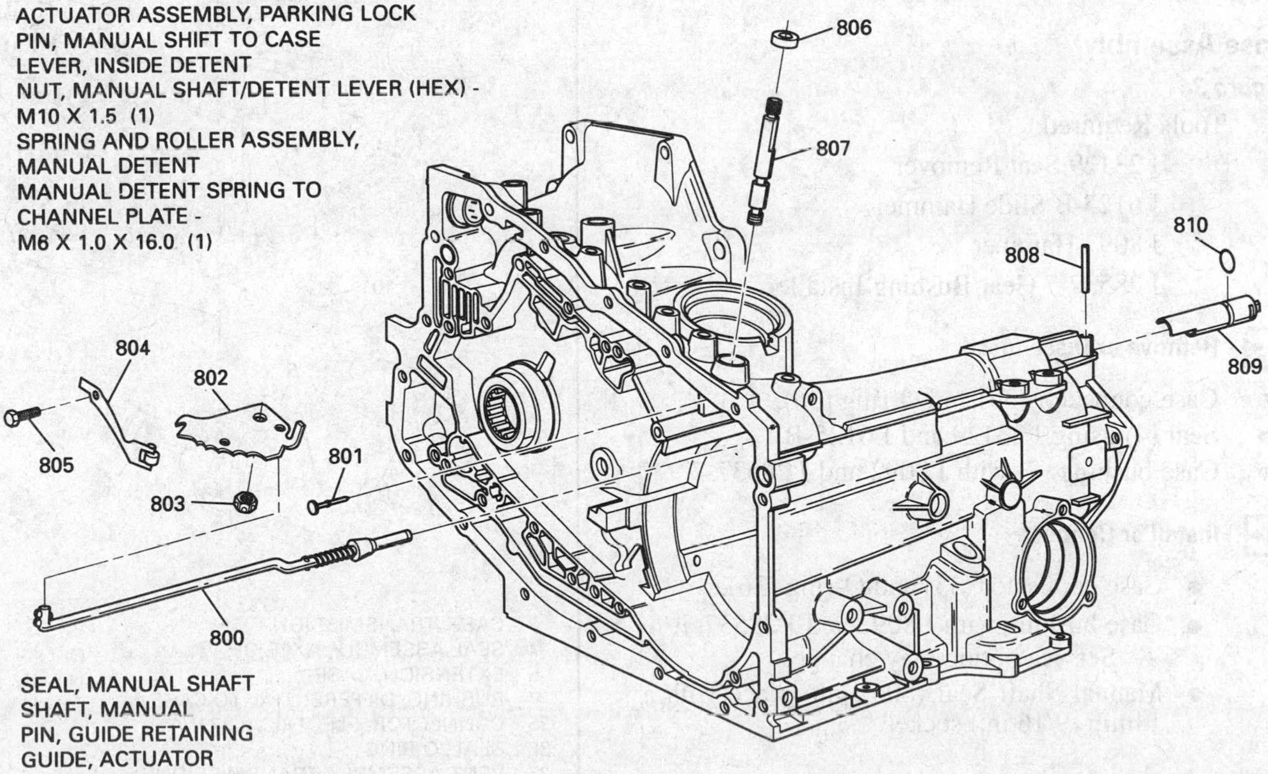
806
807
810
808
809
804
802
805
801
803
800

806 SEAL, MANUAL SHAFT
807 SHAFT, MANUAL
808 PIN, GUIDE RETAINING
809 GUIDE, ACTUATOR
810 SEAL, O-RING

PH1036-4T60-E

Figure 33 Manual Shaft and Park System Components

Manual Shaft Seal, Filter Seal and Vent Assembly

Figure 34

Tools Required:

J 6125-1B Slide Hammer

J 23129 Seal Remover

J 28585 Snap Ring Remover

Remove or Disconnect

- Manual shaft seal (806) with J 28585
- Vent assembly (37) – **ONLY if plugged or damaged**.
- Filter seal assembly (101) using J 23129 and J 6125-1B.

COMPONENT REPAIR AND CASE ASSEMBLY

NOTICE: The assembly of some components will require the use of an assembly lube. It is recommended that TRANSJEL™ J 36850 or equivalent be used during assembly.

NOTICE: Do not use any type of grease to retain or hold parts during assembly of this unit. Greases other than the recommended assembly lube will change transmission fluid characteristics and cause undesirable shift conditions and/or filter clogging.

Case Assembly

Figure 34

Tools Required:

J 23129 Seal Remover

J 6125-B Slide Hammer

J 8092 Hammer

J 28537-7 Gear Bushing Installer

Remove or Disconnect

- Case connector (35) and O-ring (36).
- Seal (4) using J 23129 and J 6125-B.
- Case bushing (7) with J 8092 and J 28537-7.

Install or Connect

- Case connector (35) and O-ring (36).
- Case bushing with J 8092 and J 28537-7.
  - Service option may change.
- Manual Shaft Seal (806) into place with a 14mm (9/16 in.) socket.

Clean

- Thoroughly with solvent and air dry.
  - DO NOT WIPE WITH CLOTH OR PAPER TOWELS.

Inspect

- Case (3) – channel plate side for:
  - Gasket sealing surfaces for cross leaks or damage.
  - Bolt holes for stripped threads – repair with thread insert.
  - Porosity between oil passage channels.
  - Cracks in casting.
  - Damaged snap ring grooves.
  - Cooler checkball and spring assembly (28) for dirt or damaged spring.
- Case extension (6) for:
  - Gasket sealing surface for porosity, nicks or rough surfaces.
  - Bolt holes for stripped threads – repair with thread inserts.
  - Cracks in casting.
  - Speed sensor bore free from porosity or nicks on sealing surfaces.

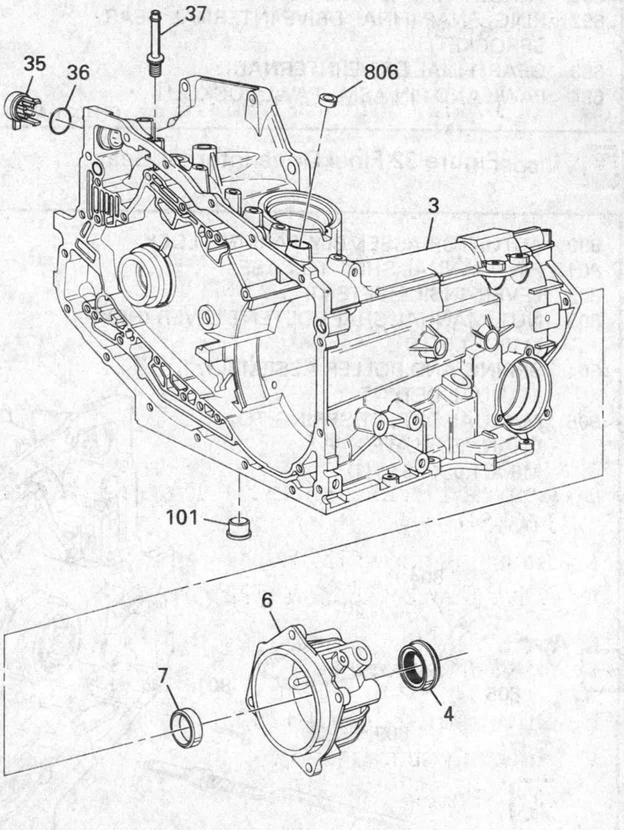

37
35
36
806
3
101
6
7
4

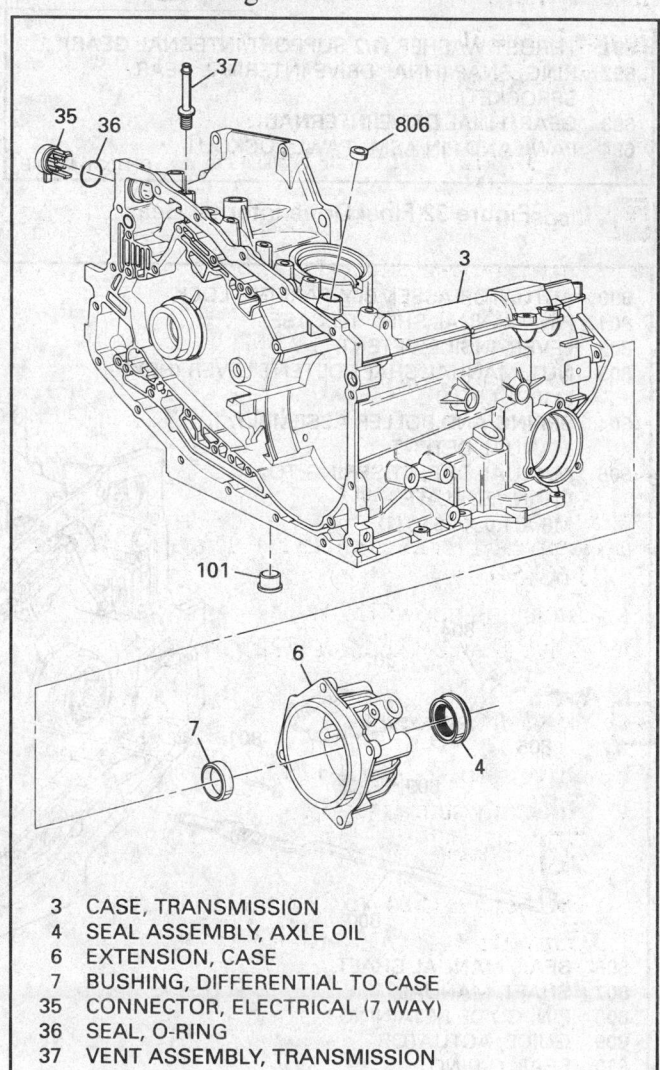

3 CASE, TRANSMISSION
4 SEAL ASSEMBLY, AXLE OIL
6 EXTENSION, CASE
7 BUSHING, DIFFERENTIAL TO CASE
35 CONNECTOR, ELECTRICAL (7 WAY)
36 SEAL, O-RING
37 VENT ASSEMBLY, TRANSMISSION
100 FILTER ASSEMBLY, TRANSMISSION OIL
806 SEAL, MANUAL SHAFT

RH1033-4T60-E

Figure 34 Manual Shaft Seal, Vent, Case Connector and Extension

Drive Sprocket Support Bearing Replacement Procedure

Figure 36

Tools Required:

J 26941 Bearing Puller
J 23907 Slide Hammer
J 28667 Bearing Installer
J 8092 Driver Handle

Remove or Disconnect

- Bearing (521) using J 26941 and J 23907.

Install or Connect

- Bearing (521) using J 28667 and J 8092.

Converter Seal and Drive Sprocket Support Replacement

Figures 35 and 36

Tools Required:

J 6125-1B Slide Hammer
J 23129 Axle Seal Remover

Inspect

- Drive sprocket support (522) for:
  - Spline damage.
  - Journal damage.
  - Bushing damage.
- Blocked converter drain down holes in case.

Remove or Disconnect

1. Converter helix seal (525) using J 23129 and J 6215-1B.
2. Attaching screws (524).
3. Drive sprocket support (522).

Install or Connect

1. Drive sprocket support (522).
2. Attaching screws (524).

   Tighten

   - Screws (524) to 24 N•m (18 lb. ft.)
3. Converter seal (525) using J 28540.

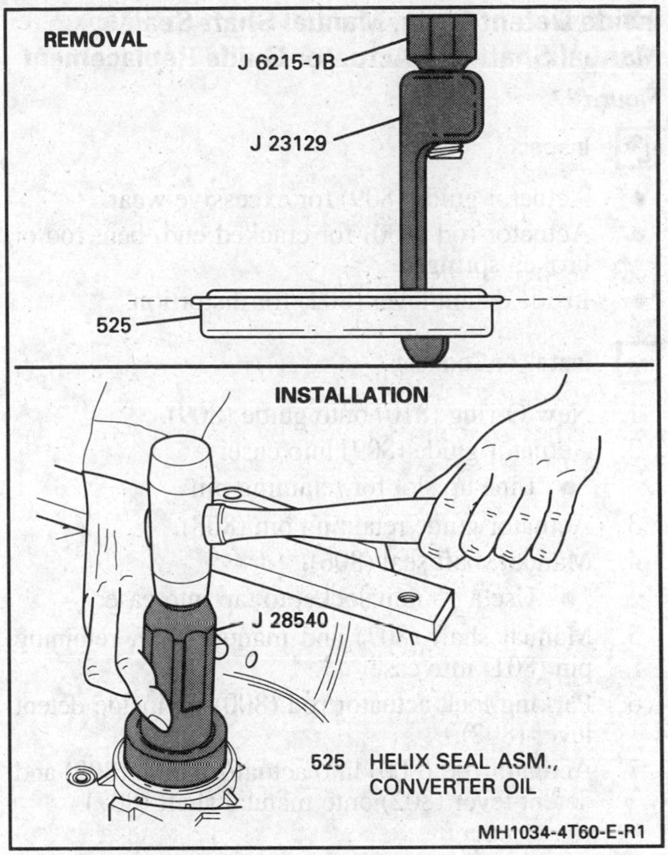
REMOVAL
J 6215-1B
J 23129
525
INSTALLATION
J 28540
525 HELIX SEAL ASM., CONVERTER OIL
MH1034-4T60-E-R1

Figure 35 Converter Seal Replacement

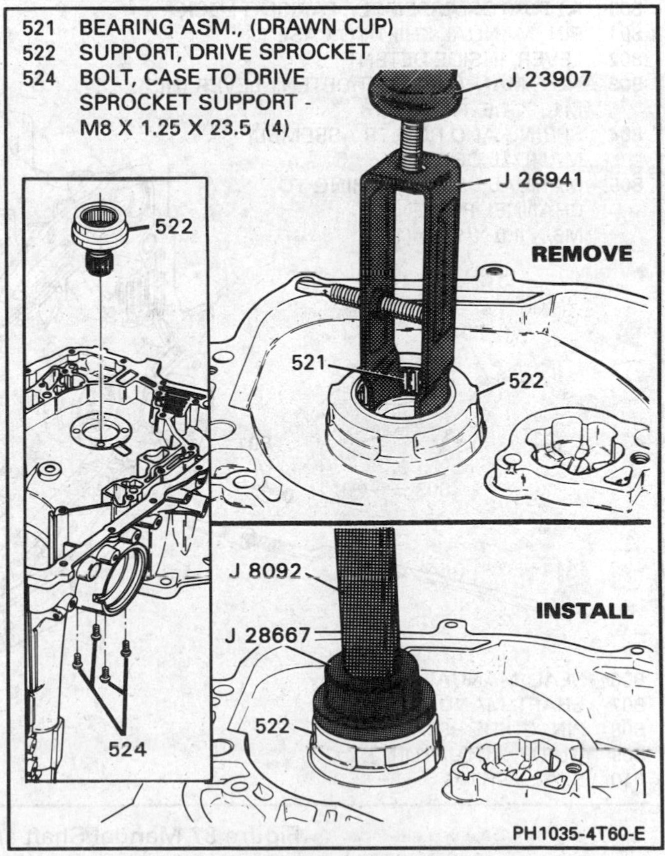
521 BEARING ASM., (DRAWN CUP)
522 SUPPORT, DRIVE SPROCKET
524 BOLT, CASE TO DRIVE SPROCKET SUPPORT - M8 X 1.25 X 23.5 (4)
J 23907
J 26941
522
REMOVE
521
522
J 8092
INSTALL
J 28667
522
524
PH1035-4T60-E

Figure 36 Drive Sprocket Support

Inside Detent Lever, Manual Shaft Seal, Manual Shaft and Actuator Guide Replacement

Figure 37

Inspect

- Actuator guide (809) for excessive wear.
- Actuator rod (800) for cracked end, bent rod or broken spring.
- Inside detent lever (802) for distortion.

Install or Connect

1. New O-ring (810) onto guide (809).
2. Actuator guide (809) into case.
   - Line up slot for retaining pin.
3. Actuator guide retaining pin (808).
4. Manual shaft seal (806).
   - Use a 15 mm socket to tap into case.
5. Manual shaft (807) and manual shaft retaining pin (801) into case.
6. Parking lock actuator rod (800) on inside detent lever (802).
7. Actuator rod (800) into actuator guide (809) and detent lever (802) onto manual shaft (807).
8. Retaining nut (803) on manual shaft.

Tighten

- Nut (803) to 32 N•m (24 lb. ft.).

Final Drive Assembly

Figure 38

Inspect

- Differential pinion gears (711) for damage to teeth.
- Differential pinion gear end play using a feeler gage – 0.24 to 0.63 mm (0.009 to 0.025).
- Speed sensor rotor (713) for damaged teeth.
- Parking gear (696) for damage to lugs or internal splines.
- Final drive sun gear (697) for damage to teeth or internal splines.
- Bearing assemblies (698) and (715) for damage.

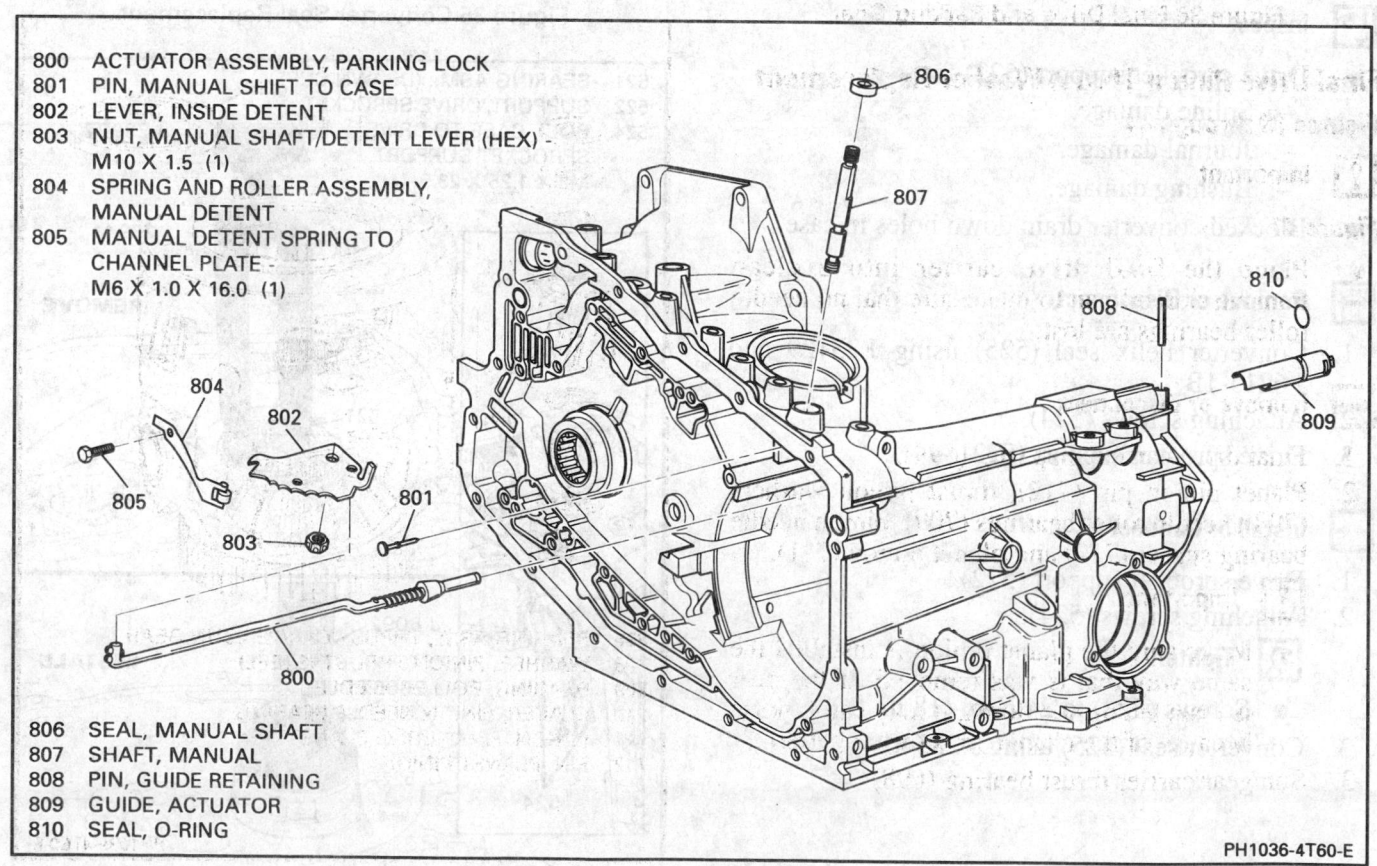

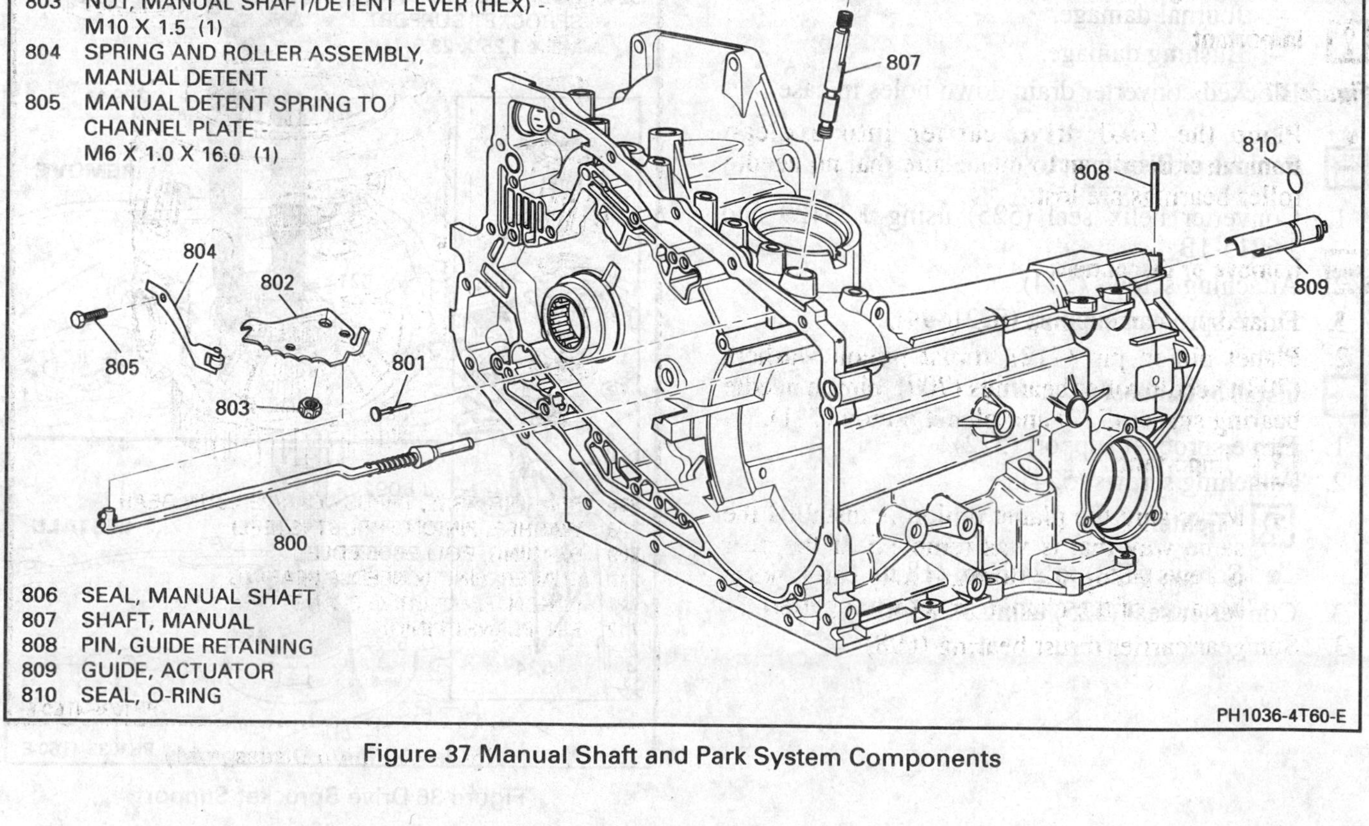
800 ACTUATOR ASSEMBLY, PARKING LOCK
801 PIN, MANUAL SHIFT TO CASE
802 LEVER, INSIDE DETENT
803 NUT, MANUAL SHAFT/DETENT LEVER (HEX) - M10 X 1.5 (1)
804 SPRING AND ROLLER ASSEMBLY, MANUAL DETENT
805 MANUAL DETENT SPRING TO CHANNEL PLATE - M6 X 1.0 X 16.0 (1)
806 SEAL, MANUAL SHAFT
807 SHAFT, MANUAL
808 PIN, GUIDE RETAINING
809 GUIDE, ACTUATOR
810 SEAL, O-RING
806
807
810
808
809
804
802
805
801
803
800
PH1036-4T60-E

Figure 37 Manual Shaft and Park System Components

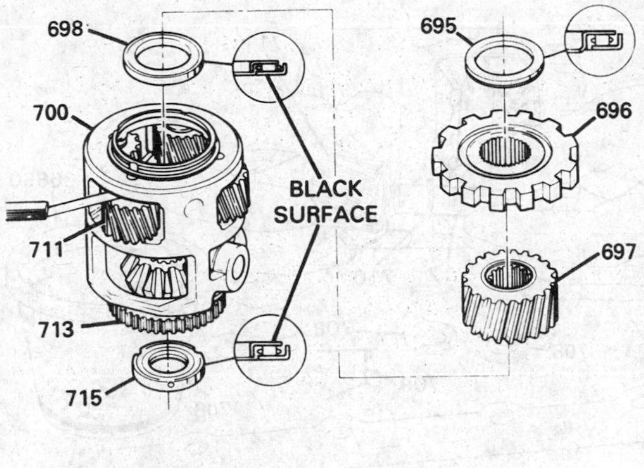
698
695
700
696
BLACK
SURFACE
711
697
713
715

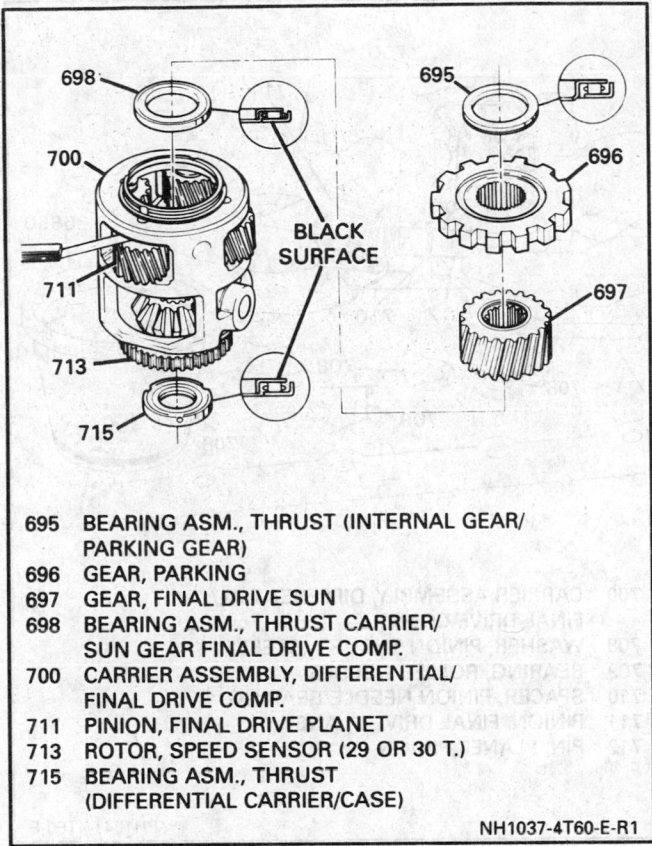

695 BEARING ASM., THRUST (INTERNAL GEAR/ PARKING GEAR)
696 GEAR, PARKING
697 GEAR, FINAL DRIVE SUN
698 BEARING ASM., THRUST CARRIER/ SUN GEAR FINAL DRIVE COMP.
700 CARRIER ASSEMBLY, DIFFERENTIAL/ FINAL DRIVE COMP.
711 PINION, FINAL DRIVE PLANET
713 ROTOR, SPEED SENSOR (29 OR 30 T.)
715 BEARING ASM., THRUST (DIFFERENTIAL CARRIER/CASE)

NH1037-4T60-E-R1

Figure 38 Final Drive and Parking Gear

Final Drive Pinion Thrust Washer Replacement

Figures 39 through 44

Important

Figure 41

- Place the final drive carrier into a clean transmission oil pan to make sure that no needle roller bearings are lost.

Remove or Disconnect

1. Final drive carrier snap ring (699).
2. Planet pinion pin (712), thrust pinion washers (708), needle roller bearings (709), pinion needle bearing spacer (710) and planet pinion (711).

   Important

   - Make sure the planet pinion is installed the same way that is was removed. If the gear is installed upside down, it may cause noise because of the change in set wear pattern.
3. Sun gear/carrier thrust bearing (698).

Inspect

Figures 40 and 41

- Needle bearings (709) and planet pinion pin (712) for excessive wear (polishing is normal).
- Planet pinion (711) for damage or wear.
- Thrust bearing (698) for damage or wear.

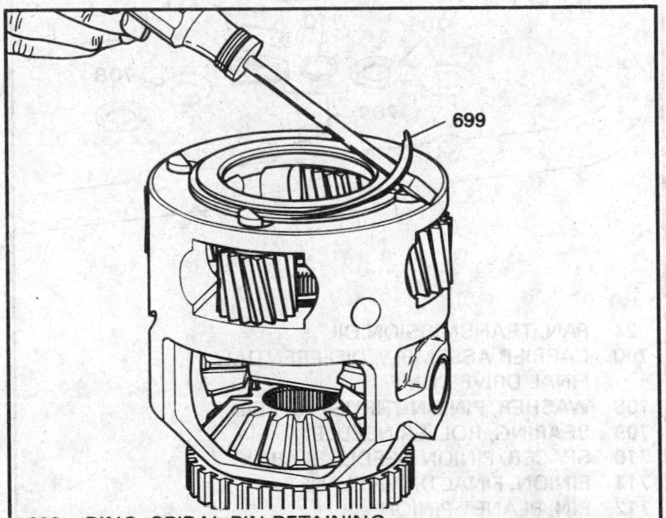
699

699 RING, SPIRAL PIN RETAINING

MH1038-4T60-E

Figure 39 Snap Ring Removal

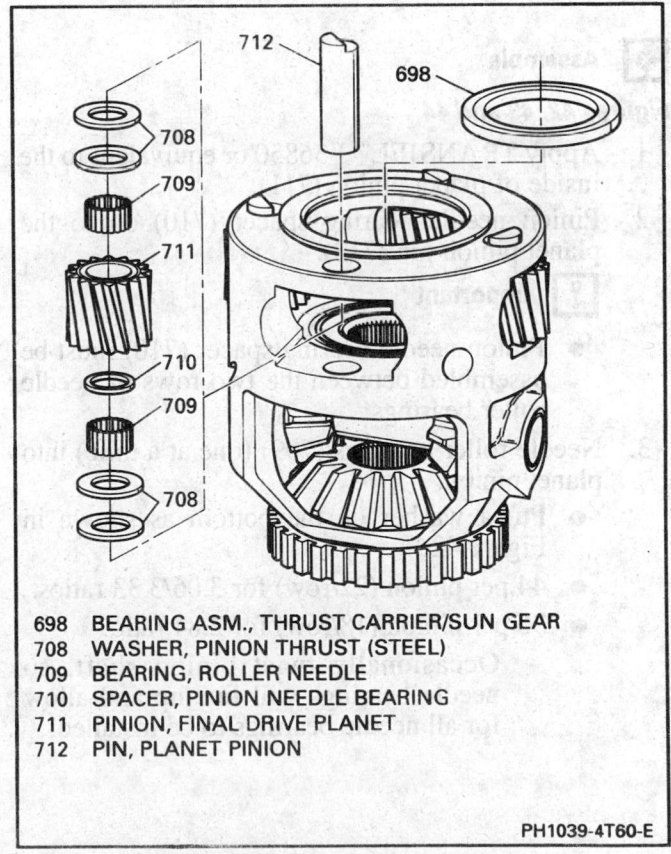

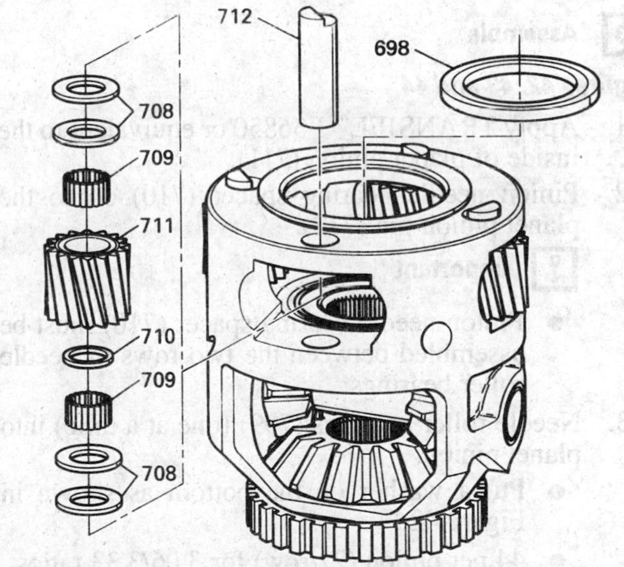
712
698
708
709
711
710
709
708

698 BEARING ASM., THRUST CARRIER/SUN GEAR
708 WASHER, PINION THRUST (STEEL)
709 BEARING, ROLLER NEEDLE
710 SPACER, PINION NEEDLE BEARING
711 PINION, FINAL DRIVE PLANET
712 PIN, PLANET PINION

PH1039-4T60-E

Figure 40 Pinion Disassembly

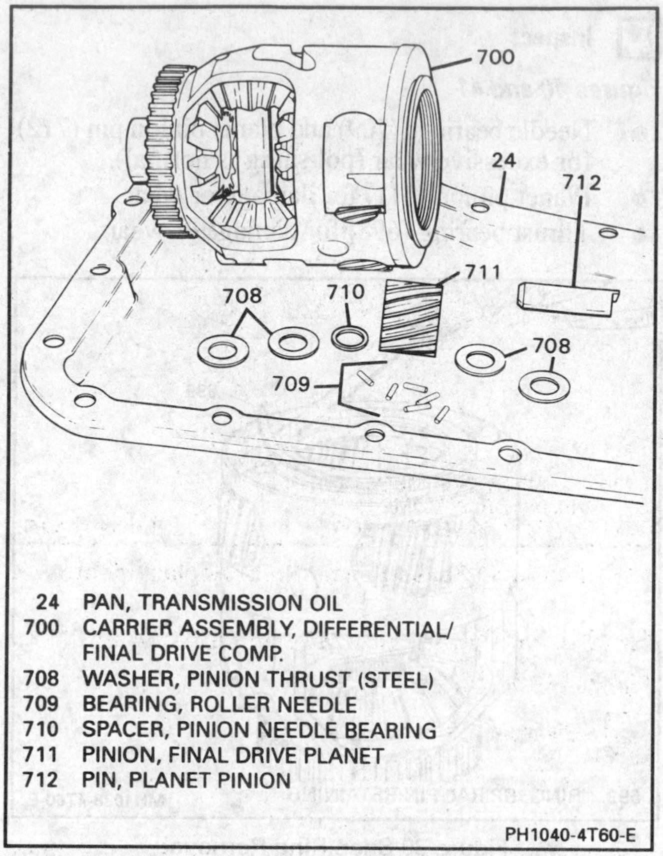
700
24
712
711
708
710
708
709
24 PAN, TRANSMISSION OIL
700 CARRIER ASSEMBLY, DIFFERENTIAL/ FINAL DRIVE COMP.
708 WASHER, PINION THRUST (STEEL)
709 BEARING, ROLLER NEEDLE
710 SPACER, PINION NEEDLE BEARING
711 PINION, FINAL DRIVE PLANET
712 PIN, PLANET PINION
PH1040-4T60-E

Figure 41 Pinion Components

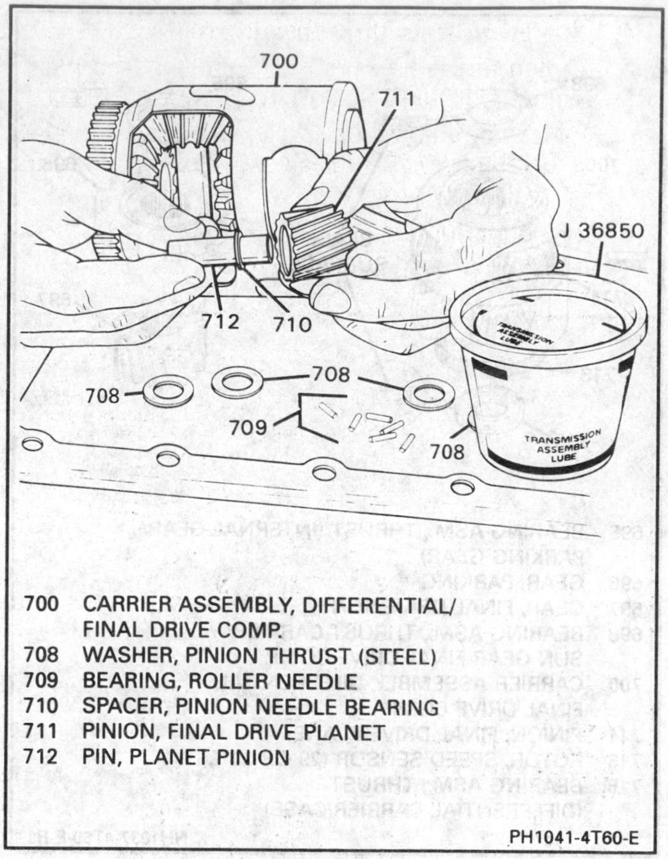
700
711
J 36850
712
710
708
708
709
708
TRANSMISSION ASSEMBLY LUBE
700 CARRIER ASSEMBLY, DIFFERENTIAL/ FINAL DRIVE COMP.
708 WASHER, PINION THRUST (STEEL)
709 BEARING, ROLLER NEEDLE
710 SPACER, PINION NEEDLE BEARING
711 PINION, FINAL DRIVE PLANET
712 PIN, PLANET PINION
PH1041-4T60-E

Figure 42 Needle Bearing Installation

Assemble

Figures 42, 43 and 44

1. Apply TRANSJEL™ J 36850 or equivalent to the inside of planet pinion (711).
2. Pinion needle bearing spacer (710) on to the planet pinion pin (712).

Important

- Pinion needle bearing spacer (710) must be assembled between the two rows of needle roller bearings.

3. Needle roller bearings (709) (one at a time) into planet pinion.
   - Put a washer on the bottom as shown in Figure 42.
   - 44 per pinion (22/row) for 3.06/3.33 ratios.
   - 36 per pinion (18/row) for 2.84 ratio.
     – Occasionally twist pinion shaft, so needle bearings will line up and allow for all needle bearings to be installed.

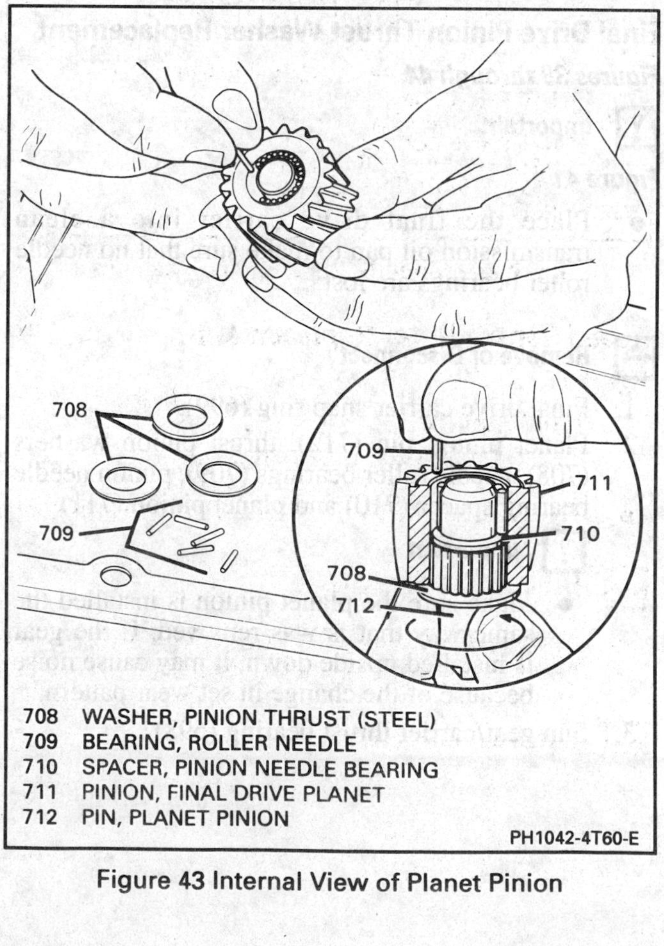
708
709
711
709
710
708
712
708 WASHER, PINION THRUST (STEEL)
709 BEARING, ROLLER NEEDLE
710 SPACER, PINION NEEDLE BEARING
711 PINION, FINAL DRIVE PLANET
712 PIN, PLANET PINION
PH1042-4T60-E

Figure 43 Internal View of Planet Pinion

4. Sun gear/carrier thrust bearing (698).
5. Pinion thrust washers (707 and 708) and planet pinion (711) into final drive carrier.
   - Two pinion thrust washers on side of planet pinion (711). Bronze washers towards the outside.
6. Planet pinion pin (712).
7. Final drive carrier snap ring (699).

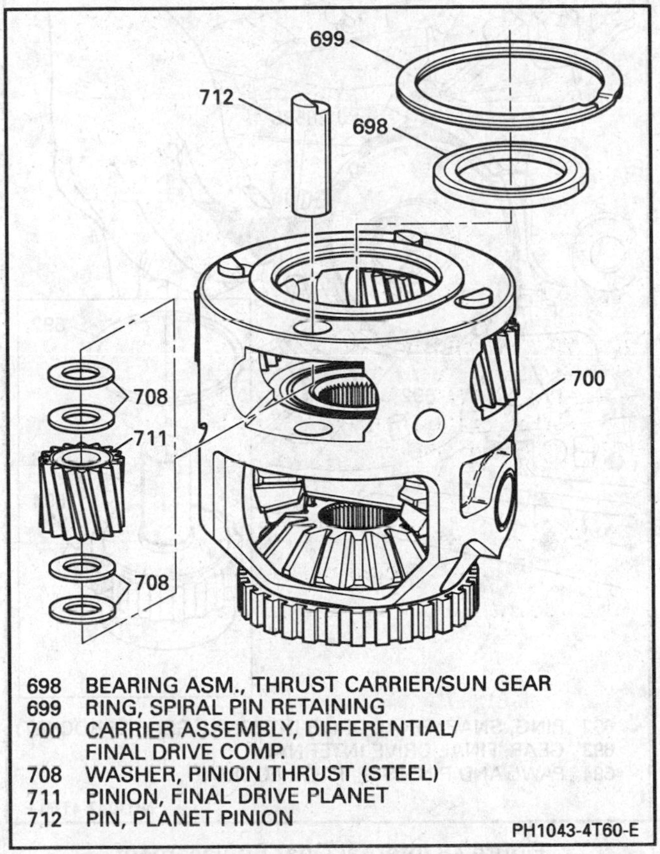
699
712
698
708
711
700
708
698 BEARING ASM., THRUST CARRIER/SUN GEAR
699 RING, SPIRAL PIN RETAINING
700 CARRIER ASSEMBLY, DIFFERENTIAL/ FINAL DRIVE COMP.
708 WASHER, PINION THRUST (STEEL)
711 PINION, FINAL DRIVE PLANET
712 PIN, PLANET PINION
PH1043-4T60-E

Figure 44 Planet Pinion and Pin Installation

Speed Sensor Rotor Replacement

Figure 45

Tool Required:
J 22888 Universal Puller

- DO NOT REMOVE UNLESS DAMAGED.

Remove or Disconnect

- Speed sensor rotor (713) use a thick flat washer to prevent damage to hub during removal.

Install or Connect

- Speed sensor rotor (713) in place with a plastic mallet.
  – It may help to warm the rotor before installation.

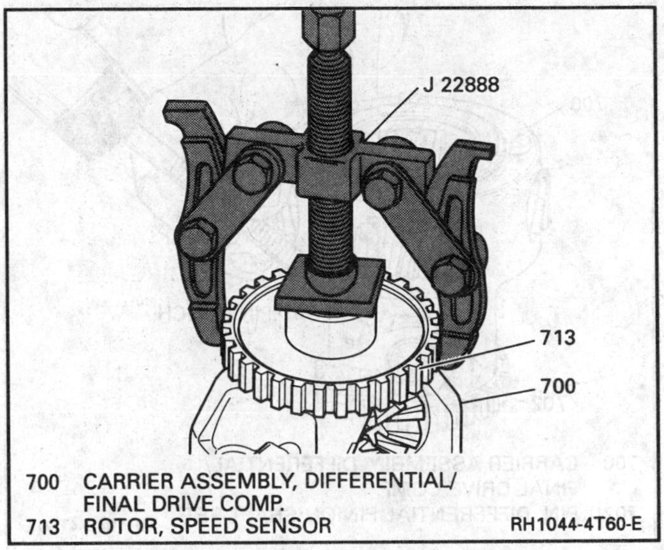
J 22888
713
700
700 CARRIER ASSEMBLY, DIFFERENTIAL/ FINAL DRIVE COMP.
713 ROTOR, SPEED SENSOR
RH1044-4T60-E

Figure 45 Speed Sensor Rotor Replacement

Final Drive Pinion/Side Gears Replacement

Figures 46 and 47

Disassemble

1. Retaining pin (702) using a pin punch.
2. Differential pinion shaft (701).
3. Differential pinion gears (704) and thrust washers (703).
4. Differential side gears (705) and thrust washers (706).

Inspect

1. Differential pinion shaft (701) for spalling or wear.
2. Thrust washers (703 and 706) for wear, cracks.

Assemble

1. Thrust washers (706) onto differential side gears (705) and install into carrier.
2. Thrust washers (703) onto pinion gears (704) – retain with TRANSJEL™ J 36850 or equivalent.
3. Differential pinion gears (704) with washers (703) into carrier (700).
4. Slide pinion shaft (701) through pinion gears for alignment, then remove.
5. Rotate pinion gears into position and install pinion shaft (701) through carrier.
6. Retaining pin (702) through pinion shaft (701) and carrier.
7. Stake retaining pin (702).

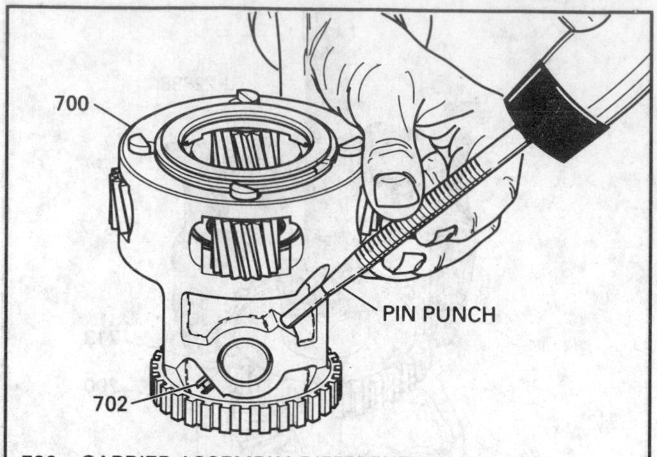
700
PIN PUNCH
702

700 CARRIER ASSEMBLY, DIFFERENTIAL/ FINAL DRIVE COMP.
702 PIN, DIFFERENTIAL PINION SHAFT RET.

MH1045-4T60-E

Figure 46 Retaining Pin Removal

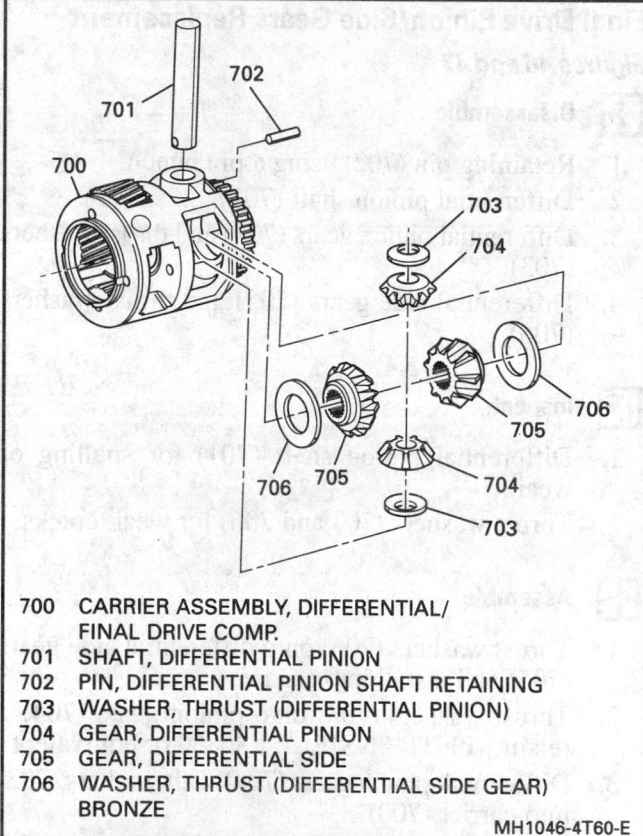

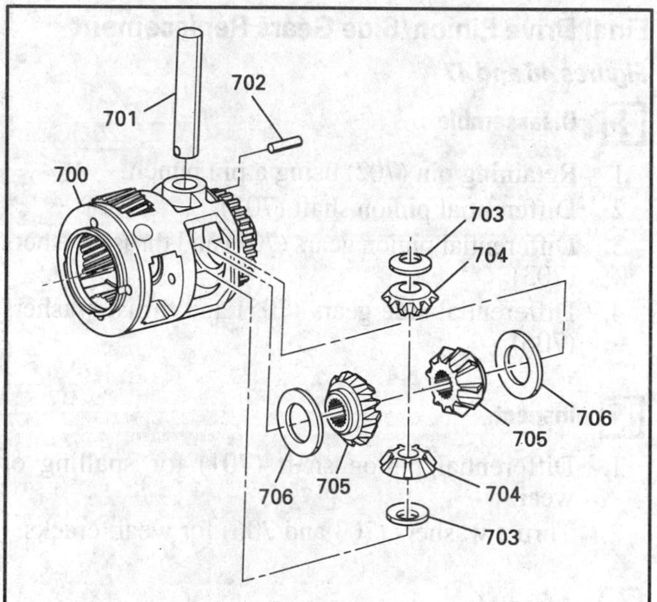
702
701
700
703
704
706
705
706
705
704
703

700 CARRIER ASSEMBLY, DIFFERENTIAL/ FINAL DRIVE COMP.
701 SHAFT, DIFFERENTIAL PINION
702 PIN, DIFFERENTIAL PINION SHAFT RETAINING
703 WASHER, THRUST (DIFFERENTIAL PINION)
704 GEAR, DIFFERENTIAL PINION
705 GEAR, DIFFERENTIAL SIDE
706 WASHER, THRUST (DIFFERENTIAL SIDE GEAR) BRONZE

MH1046-4T60-E

Figure 47 Pinion and Side Gear Replacement

Final Drive Internal Gear and Final Drive Assembly Replacement

Figures 48 and 49

Inspect

- Final drive internal gear for:
  - Scored bushings or off location.
  - Plugged lube holes.
  - Cracked or damaged case lugs.
  - Worn or broken gear teeth.
  - Burrs, crack or wear on parking pawl (694).
  - Broken or distorted parking pawl return spring.
- Thrust washer (714) for wear and thrust bearing (715) for damage.

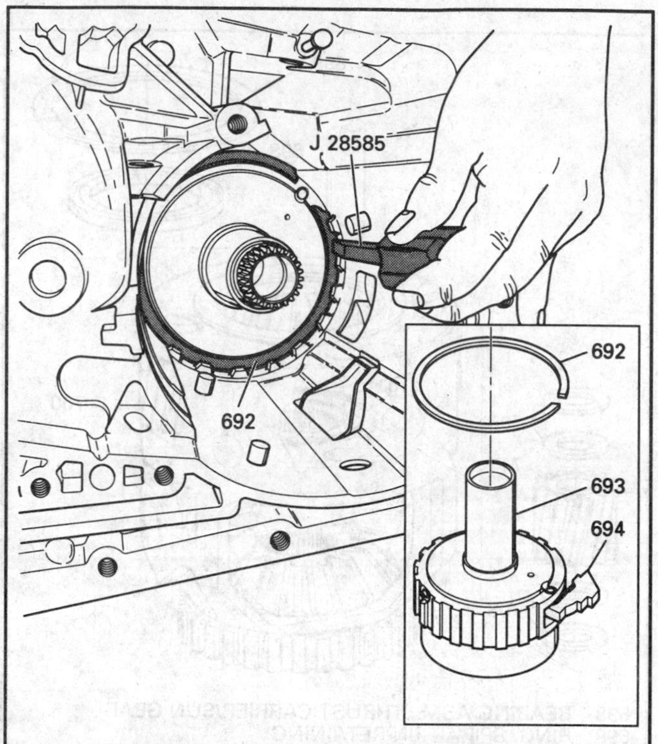
J 28585
692
692
693
694

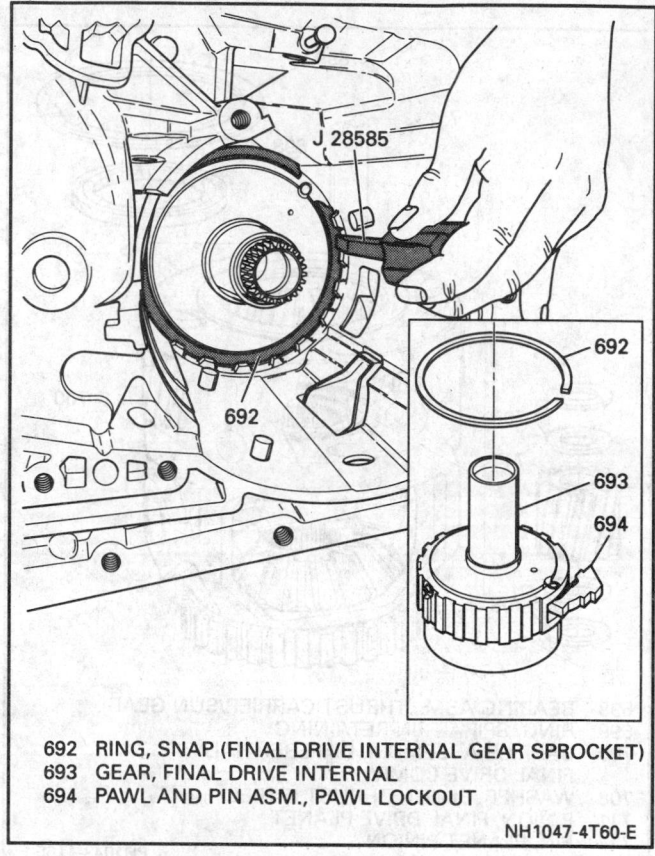

692 RING, SNAP (FINAL DRIVE INTERNAL GEAR SPROCKET)
693 GEAR, FINAL DRIVE INTERNAL
694 PAWL AND PIN ASM., PAWL LOCKOUT

NH1047-4T60-E

Figure 48 Internal Gear Replacement

Install or Connect

1. Final drive internal gear (693) into case (3).
2. Snap ring (692) into case (3).
3. Rotate transaxle and insert thrust bearing (695), parking gear (696), final drive sun gear (697) and thrust bearing (698) onto final drive internal gear (693).
   - The step on the final drive sun gear (697) internal spline area must be towards the parking gear (696).
4. Final drive assembly (700) into final drive internal gear (693).
5. Differential thrust washer (714) and thrust bearing (715) onto final drive assembly (700) – retain with TRANSJEL™ J 36850 or equivalent.
6. Case extension (6) with new seal (8) onto case.
   - Retain with two bolts for later removal.

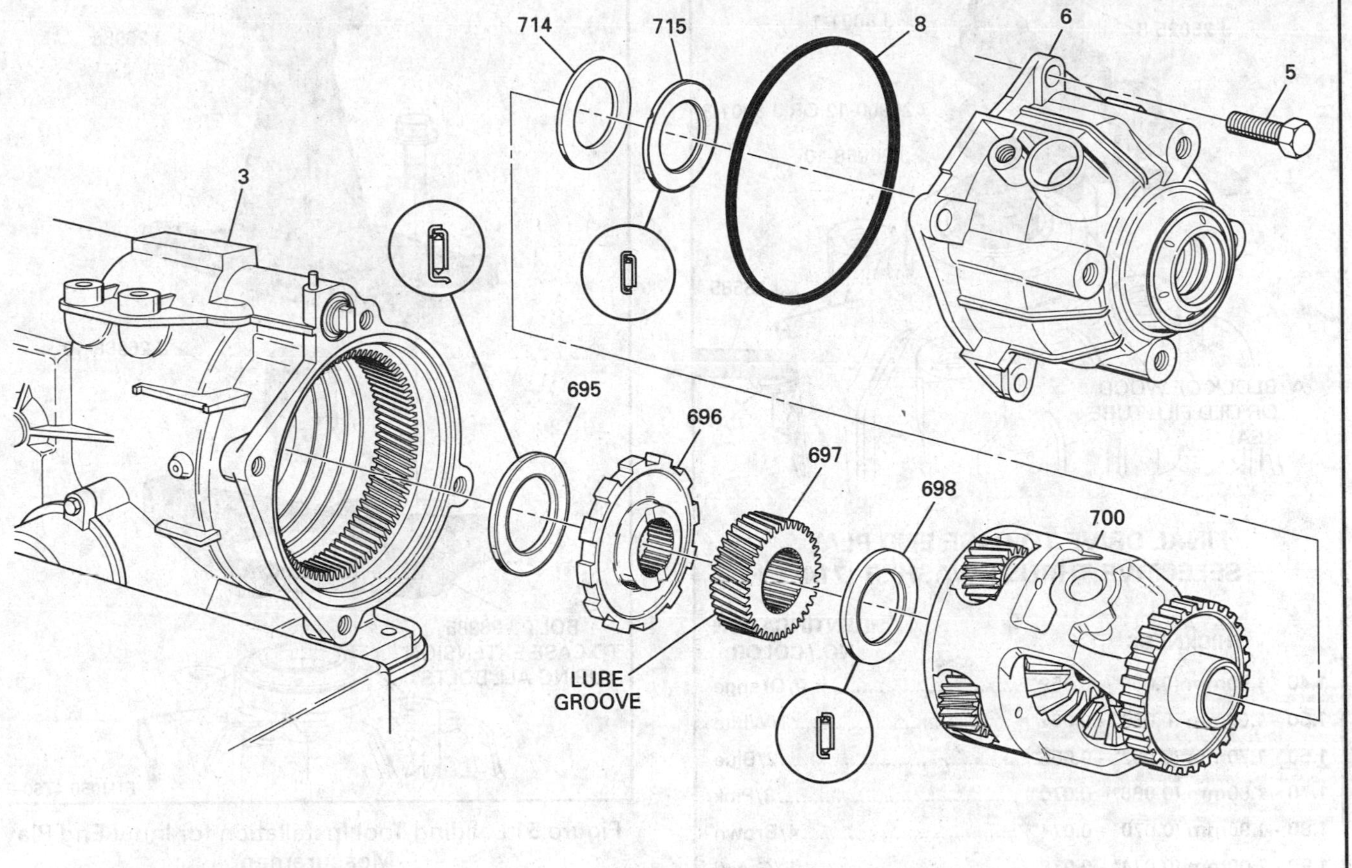
714
715
8
6
5
3
695
696
697
698
700
LUBE GROOVE

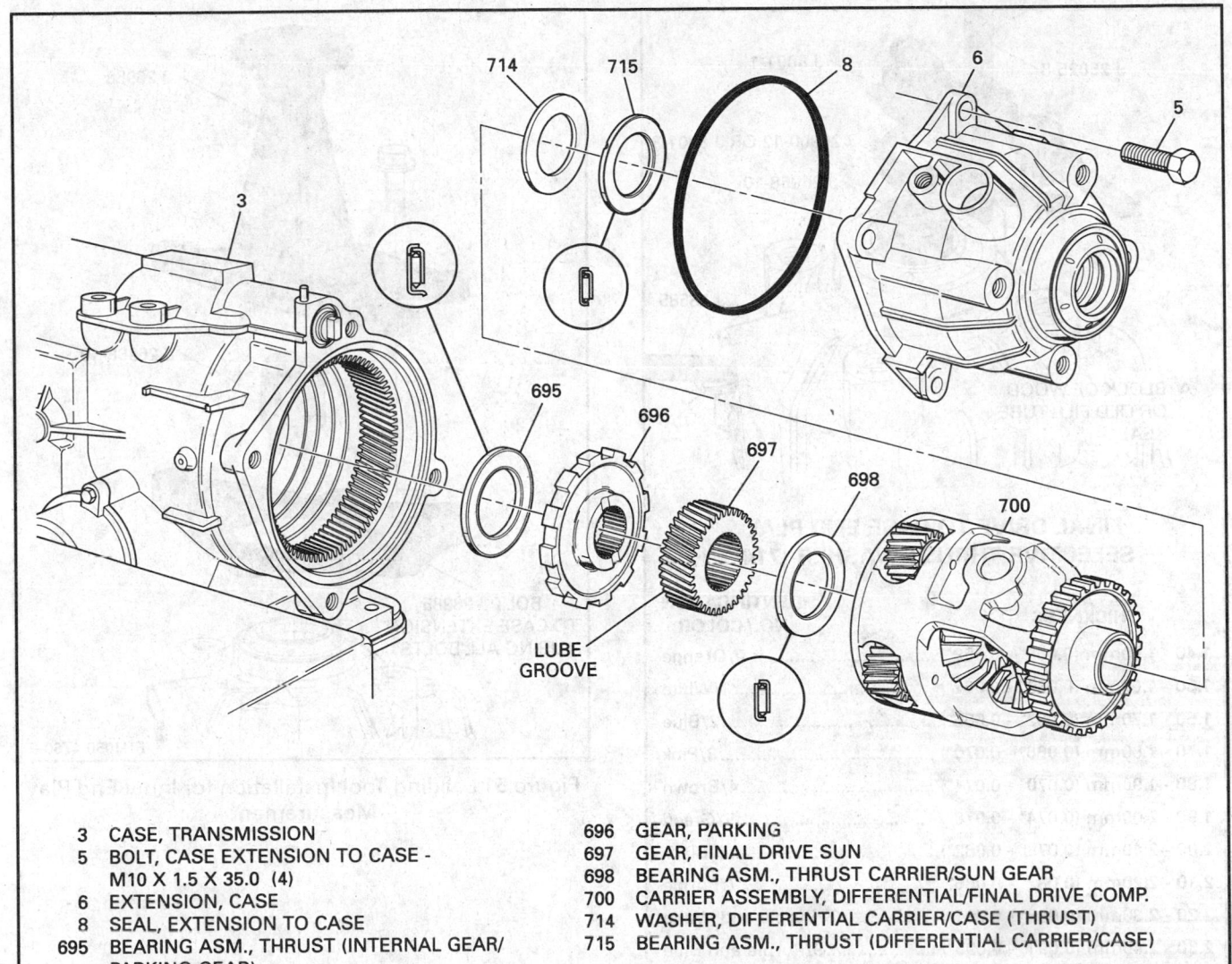

3 CASE, TRANSMISSION
5 BOLT, CASE EXTENSION TO CASE - M10 X 1.5 X 35.0 (4)
6 EXTENSION, CASE
8 SEAL, EXTENSION TO CASE
695 BEARING ASM., THRUST (INTERNAL GEAR/ PARKING GEAR)
696 GEAR, PARKING
697 GEAR, FINAL DRIVE SUN
698 BEARING ASM., THRUST CARRIER/SUN GEAR
700 CARRIER ASSEMBLY, DIFFERENTIAL/FINAL DRIVE COMP.
714 WASHER, DIFFERENTIAL CARRIER/CASE (THRUST)
715 BEARING ASM., THRUST (DIFFERENTIAL CARRIER/CASE)

RH1048-4T60-E

Figure 49 Final Drive and Case Extension Replacement

Final Drive End Play Measurement

Figures 50 and 51

Tools Required:

J 8001-1 Clamp
J 25025-8 Post
J 26900-12 or J 8001-3 Dial Indicator
J 8001-2 Sleeve
J 26958-10 Adapter Plug
J 38385 Loading Tool Adapter
J 26958 Output Shaft Loading Tool

Install or Connect

1. Position dial indicator set and zero out dial indicator.
   - Stem must contact J 26958-10.
2. Lift speed sensor rotor (713) with J 28585 for measurement.
   - Protect bore with a piece of rubber (spark plug boot).
3. Proper end play clearance is 0.12 to 0.62 mm (0.005 to 0.025 inch).
4. If necessary adjust with proper thickness selective thrust washer (714).
5. Remove dial indicator set and post (J 25025-8) and install J 38385 filling all bolt holes and J 26958 with adapter J 26938-10.

Important

- J 38385 must be bolted down securely to case extension filling all bolt holes to minimize adapter bending.

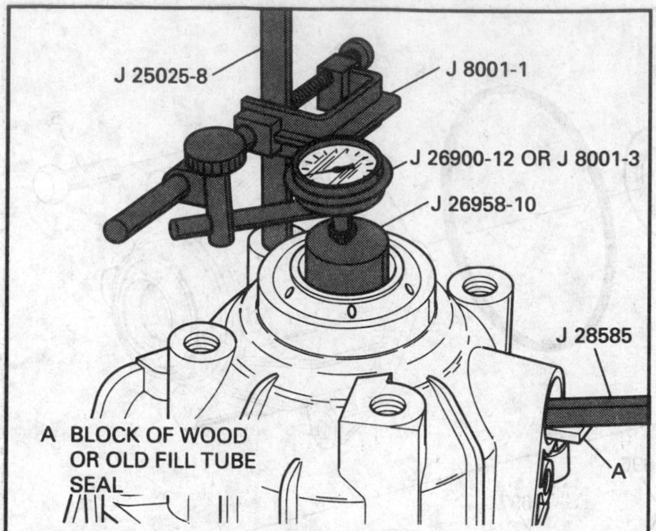
J 25025-8
J 8001-1
J 26900-12 OR J 8001-3
J 26958-10
J 28585
A BLOCK OF WOOD OR OLD FILL TUBE SEAL
A

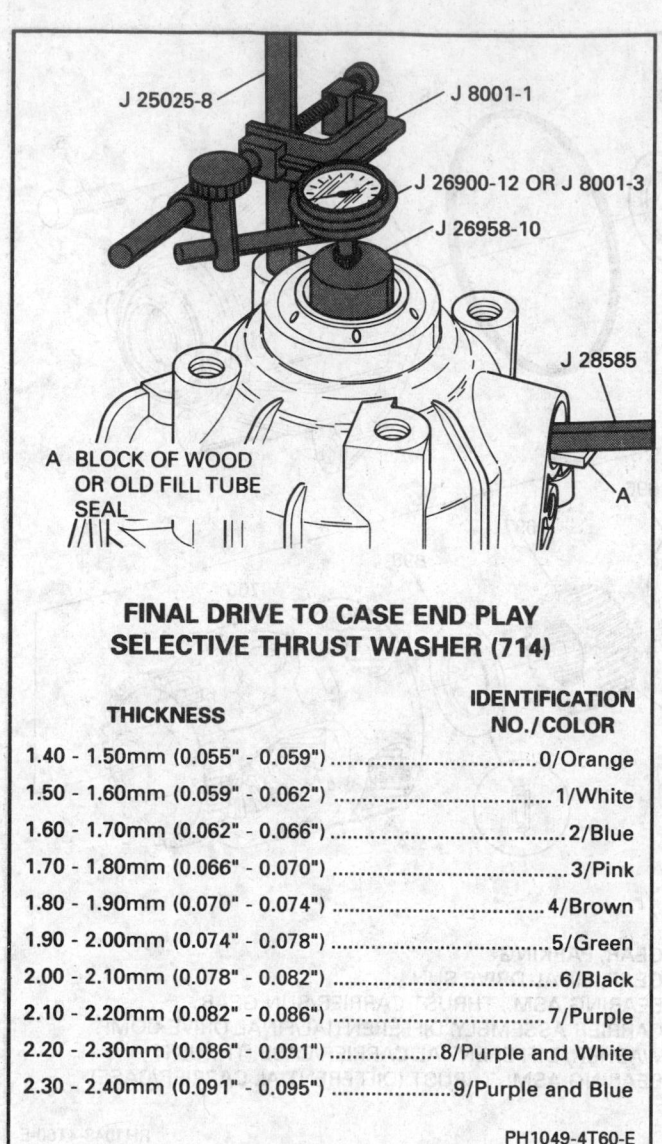

FINAL DRIVE TO CASE END PLAY SELECTIVE THRUST WASHER (714)

THICKNESS	IDENTIFICATION NO./COLOR
1.40 - 1.50mm (0.055" - 0.059")	0/Orange
1.50 - 1.60mm (0.059" - 0.062")	1/White
1.60 - 1.70mm (0.062" - 0.066")	2/Blue
1.70 - 1.80mm (0.066" - 0.070")	3/Pink
1.80 - 1.90mm (0.070" - 0.074")	4/Brown
1.90 - 2.00mm (0.074" - 0.078")	5/Green
2.00 - 2.10mm (0.078" - 0.082")	6/Black
2.10 - 2.20mm (0.082" - 0.086")	7/Purple
2.20 - 2.30mm (0.086" - 0.091")	8/Purple and White
2.30 - 2.40mm (0.091" - 0.095")	9/Purple and Blue

PH1049-4T60-E

Figure 50 Final Drive End Play Measurement

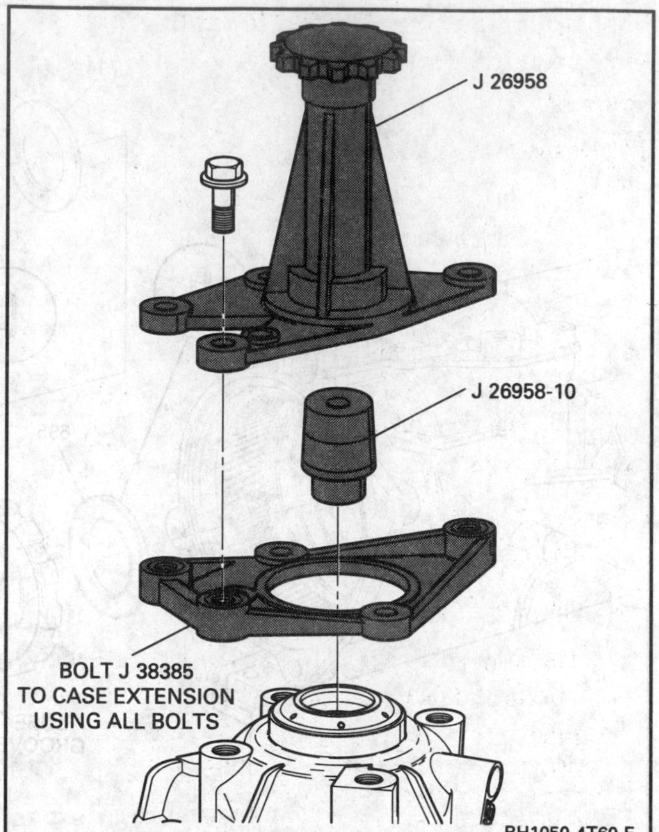
J 26958
J 26958-10
BOLT J 38385 TO CASE EXTENSION USING ALL BOLTS
RH1050-4T60-E

Figure 51 Loading Tool Installation for Input End Play Measurement

Final Drive Sun Gear Shaft, Thrust Bearing and Forward Band

Figure 52

Inspect

- Final drive sun gear shaft (689) for:
  - Damaged splines.
  - Cracks at lube holes.
  - Damaged bearing journals.
- Thrust bearing (691) for:
  - Missing or damaged rollers.
  - Damaged cage.
- Forward band assembly (688) for:
  - Cracked or separated friction material.
  - Friction material burnt.

Install or Connect

1. Thrust washer (691) onto final drive internal gear.
   - Inside race against final drive internal gear.
2. Final drive sun gear shaft (689) through final drive internal gear (693) splines must engage with the parking gear (696) and final drive sun gear (697).
3. Forward band (688) into case
   - Locate band on anchor pin.

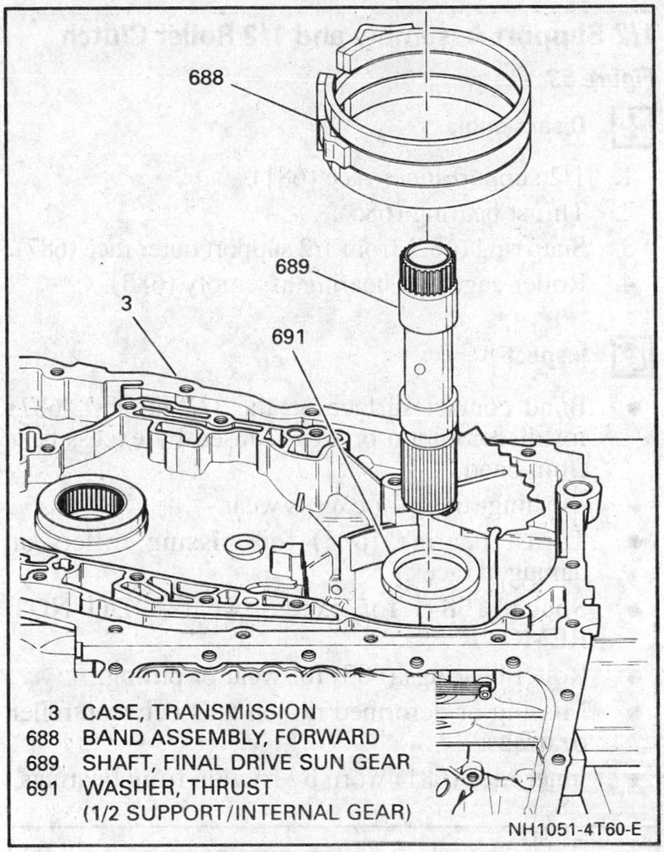
688
689
3
691
3 CASE, TRANSMISSION
688 BAND ASSEMBLY, FORWARD
689 SHAFT, FINAL DRIVE SUN GEAR
691 WASHER, THRUST
(1/2 SUPPORT/INTERNAL GEAR)
NH1051-4T60-E

Figure 52 Sun Gear Shaft, Thrust Bearing and Forward Band Installation

1/2 Support Assembly and 1/2 Roller Clutch

Figure 53

Disassemble

1. 1/2 support inner race (681).
2. Thrust bearing (685).
3. Snap ring (682) from 1/2 support outer race (687).
4. Roller cage and bearing assembly (683).

Inspect

- Band contact surface on the 1/2 support (687) for discoloration or wear caused by excess heat from band.
- Bushing (686) for excess wear.
- Thrust bearing (685) for missing rollers or damaged races.
- Spacer (684) for excess wear – DO NOT REMOVE.
- Roller bearings (683) for wear or pitting.
- Missing or deformed ribbon tabs between roller bearings.
- Inner race (681) worn by friction from bearings.

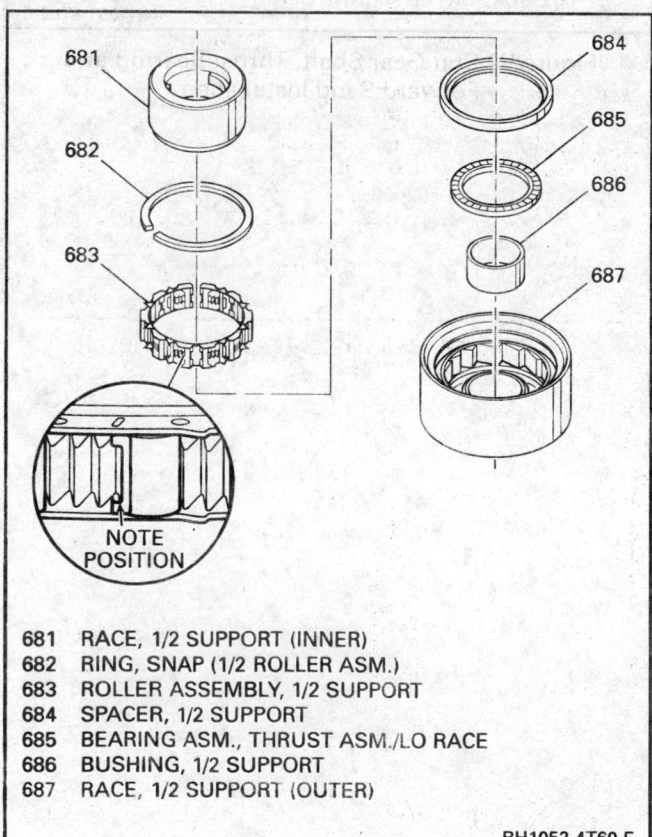

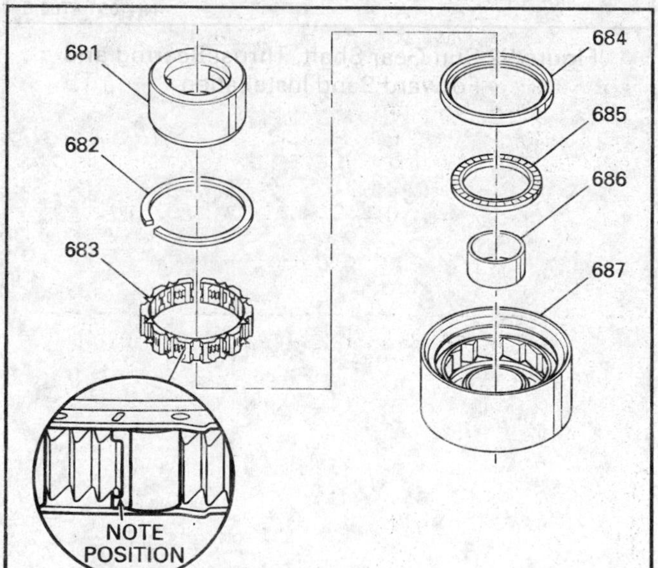
681
682
683
684
685
686
687
NOTE POSITION

681 RACE, 1/2 SUPPORT (INNER)
682 RING, SNAP (1/2 ROLLER ASM.)
683 ROLLER ASSEMBLY, 1/2 SUPPORT
684 SPACER, 1/2 SUPPORT
685 BEARING ASM., THRUST ASM./LO RACE
686 BUSHING, 1/2 SUPPORT
687 RACE, 1/2 SUPPORT (OUTER)

RH1052-4T60-E

Figure 53 Support Assembly

Assemble

1. Thrust bearing (685) into 1/2 support (687).
2. Roller cage assembly (683) into 1/2 support.
   - Note position of ribbon tab shoes for proper installation.
3. Snap ring (682) into 1/2 support.
4. Inner race (681) into 1/2 support assembly (687).
   - Use the reaction sun gear and drum assembly (678) to install.

Functional Check of 1/2 Support Assembly and 1/2 Roller Clutch

Figure 54

1. Position the 1/2 support assembly (681-687) on the bench as it would be installed in the transaxle.
2. While holding the outer race in the position shown, the inner race should rotate only **counterclockwise**.

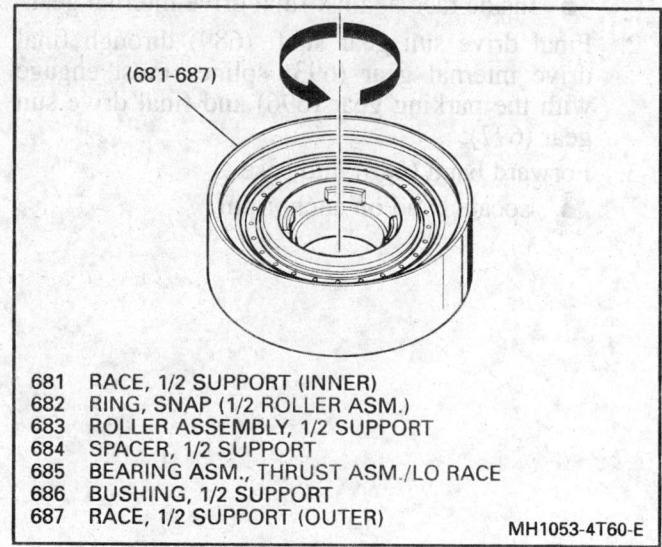

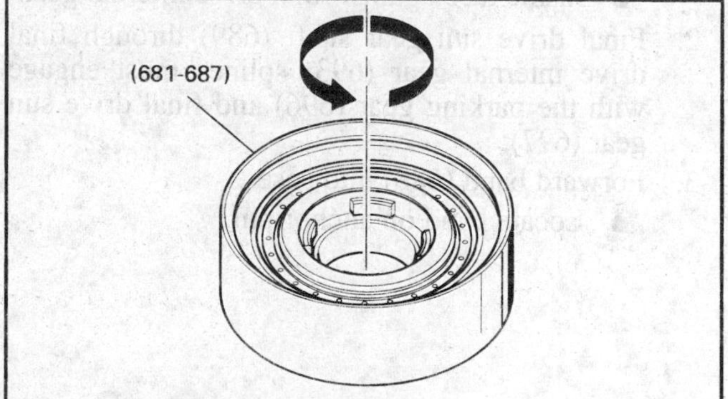
(681-687)

681 RACE, 1/2 SUPPORT (INNER)
682 RING, SNAP (1/2 ROLLER ASM.)
683 ROLLER ASSEMBLY, 1/2 SUPPORT
684 SPACER, 1/2 SUPPORT
685 BEARING ASM., THRUST ASM./LO RACE
686 BUSHING, 1/2 SUPPORT
687 RACE, 1/2 SUPPORT (OUTER)

MH1053-4T60-E

Figure 54 1/2 Roller Clutch Check

2-1 Manual Band and Reaction Gear and Sun Drum

Figure 55

Tool Required:

J 38358 1/2 Support Remover/Installer

Inspect

- 2-1 Manual band assembly (680) for:
  - Cracked or separated friction material.
  - Burnt friction material.
  - Cracks around apply lugs.
- Reaction sun gear and drum assembly (678) for:
  - Worn or scored bushings (677 and 679)
  - Damaged teeth on reaction sun gear.
  - Band contact surface on drum for discoloration or wear.
  - Sun gear to drum welds for cracks.

Install or Connect

1. 1/2 support assembly (681-687) with J 38358.
2. 2-1 manual band (680) into case.
   - Locate on band anchor pin.
3. Reaction sun gear and drum (678).
   - Lugs must engage with 1/2 support roller clutch inner race (681).

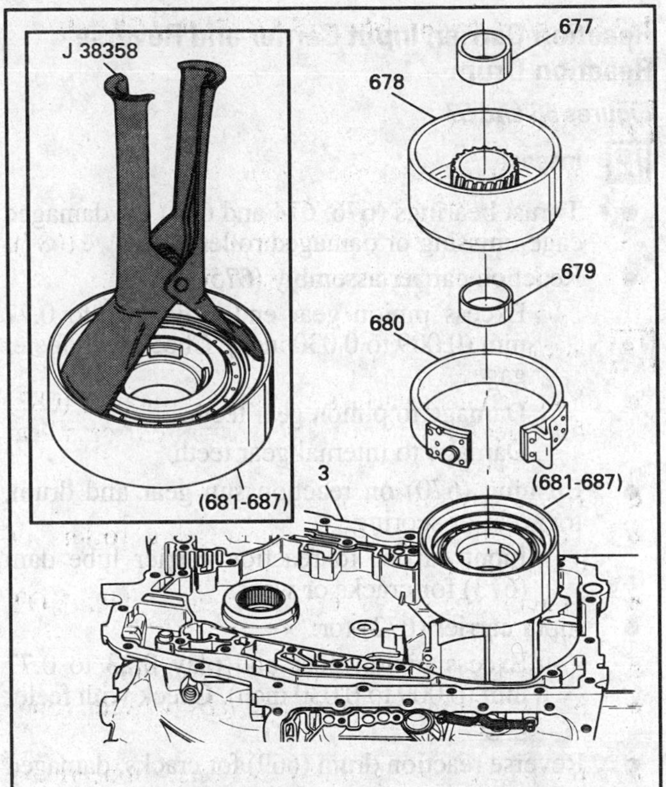
J 38358
677
678
679
680
3
(681-687)
(681-687)

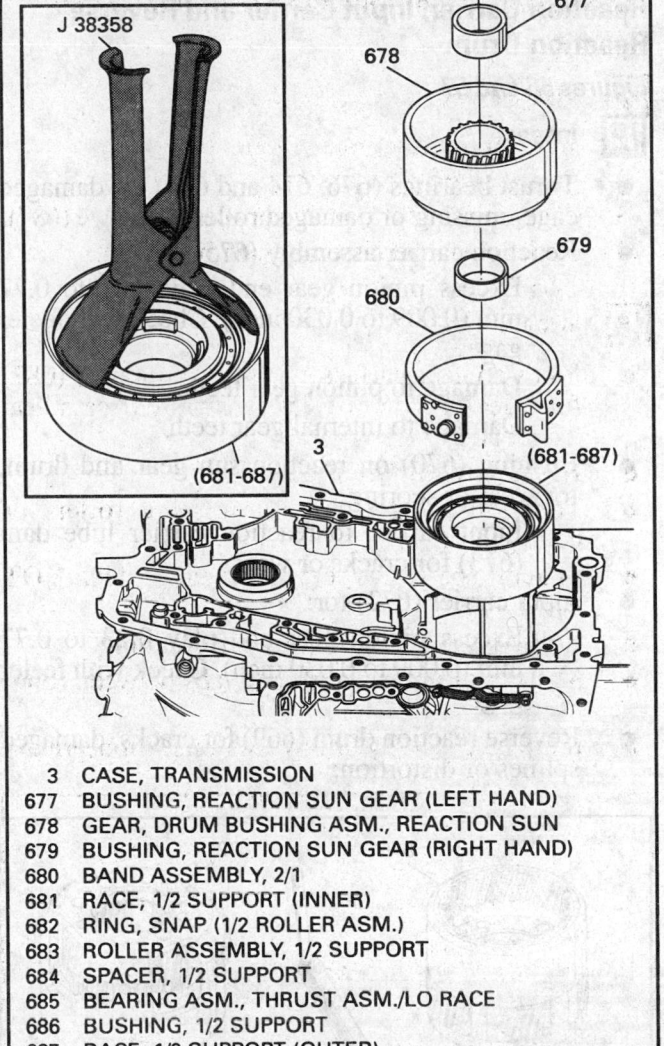

3	CASE, TRANSMISSION
677	BUSHING, REACTION SUN GEAR (LEFT HAND)
678	GEAR, DRUM BUSHING ASM., REACTION SUN
679	BUSHING, REACTION SUN GEAR (RIGHT HAND)
680	BAND ASSEMBLY, 2/1
681	RACE, 1/2 SUPPORT (INNER)
682	RING, SNAP (1/2 ROLLER ASM.)
683	ROLLER ASSEMBLY, 1/2 SUPPORT
684	SPACER, 1/2 SUPPORT
685	BEARING ASM., THRUST ASM./LO RACE
686	BUSHING, 1/2 SUPPORT
687	RACE, 1/2 SUPPORT (OUTER)

RH1054-4T60-E

Figure 55 Manual Band and Sun Drum

Reaction Carrier, Input Carrier and Reverse Reaction Drum

Figures 56 and 57

Inspect

- Thrust bearings (676, 674 and 671) for damaged cage, missing or damaged rollers.
- Reaction carrier assembly (675) for:
  - Excess pinion gear end play 0.23 to 0.77 mm (0.009 to 0.030 inch). Check with feeler gage.
  - Damage to pinion gear teeth.
  - Damage to internal gear teeth.
- Bushing (670) on reaction sun gear and drum, for wear or scoring.
  - Input carrier to reaction carrier lube dam (673) for cracks or wear.
- Input carrier (672) for:
  - Excess pinion gear end play 0.23 to 0.77 mm (0.009 to 0.030 inch). Check with feeler gage.
- Reverse reaction drum (669) for cracks, damaged splines or distortion.

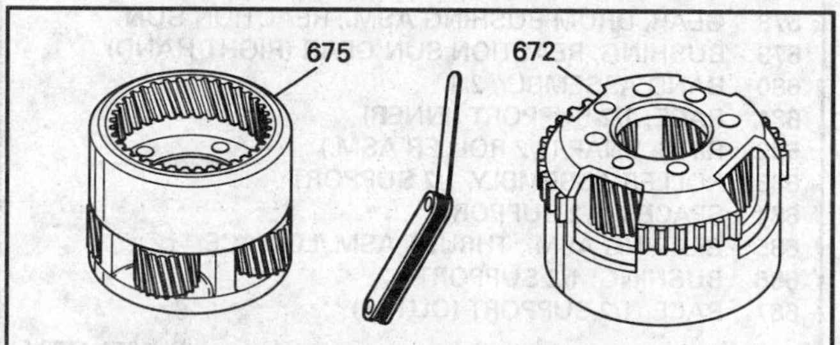
675
672

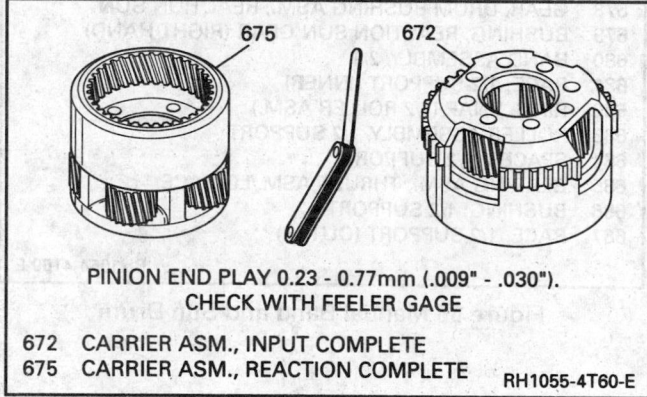

PINION END PLAY 0.23 - 0.77mm (.009" - .030"). CHECK WITH FEELER GAGE

672 CARRIER ASM., INPUT COMPLETE
675 CARRIER ASM., REACTION COMPLETE

RH1055-4T60-E

Figure 56 Pinion Gear End Play Check

Install or Connect

Figure 57

1. Thrust bearing (676) onto reaction carrier (675) with inner race next to carrier – retain with TRANSJEL™ J 36850 or equivalent.
2. Reaction carrier (675) into case – rotate until the pinions engage the reaction sun gear.
3. Thrust bearing (674) into input carrier (672) – retain with TRANSJEL™ J 36850 or equivalent.
4. Lube dam (673) into input carrier (672) – retain with TRANSJEL™ J 36850 or equivalent.
5. Input carrier (672) into case – rotate to verify carrier assenbly is fully seated.
6. Reverse reaction drum (669) engage splines with input carrier (672).

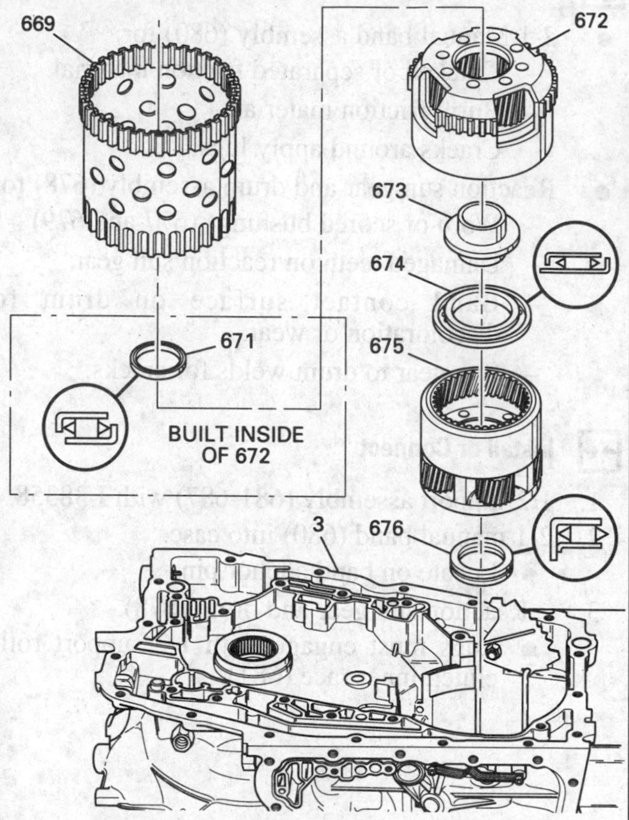
669
672
673
674
671
675
BUILT INSIDE OF 672
3
676

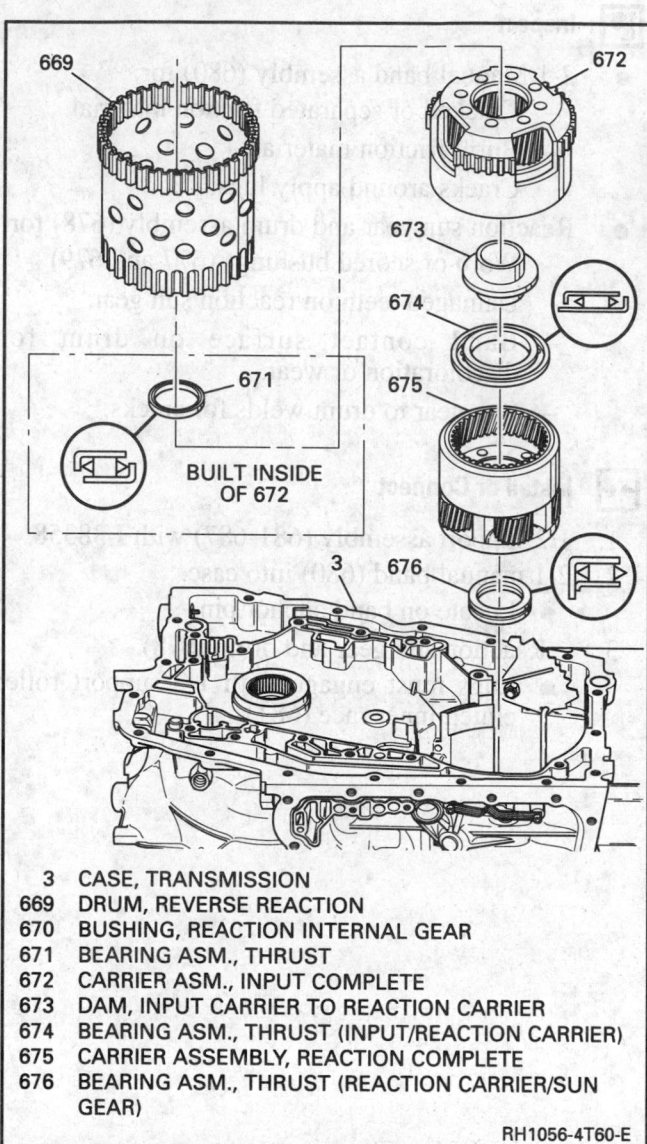

3 CASE, TRANSMISSION
669 DRUM, REVERSE REACTION
670 BUSHING, REACTION INTERNAL GEAR
671 BEARING ASM., THRUST
672 CARRIER ASM., INPUT COMPLETE
673 DAM, INPUT CARRIER TO REACTION CARRIER
674 BEARING ASM., THRUST (INPUT/REACTION CARRIER)
675 CARRIER ASSEMBLY, REACTION COMPLETE
676 BEARING ASM., THRUST (REACTION CARRIER/SUN GEAR)

RH1056-4T60-E

Figure 57 Reaction Carrier and Input Carrier Installation

3rd Sprag and Input Sprag assembly, Input Sun Gear and Input Sun Gear Spacer

3rd Sprag Assembly

Figure 58

Disassemble

- Spiral lock ring (717) from inner race and retainer assembly (661), (Use tapered blade screwdriver to remove spiral lock ring). Spiral lock ring (717) must be replaced when serviced.
- 3rd sprag assembly (653, 718-721) and input sprag assembly (665, 719, 722) from inner race and retainer assembly (661).
- Inner race and retainer assembly (661) and input sun gear spacer (667) from input sun gear (668).

3rd Sprag Clutch Assembly

Figure 58

Position 3rd sprag clutch assembly on the bench (lube dam side down) and push down on end bearing (719) until it contacts the bench.

Inspect

- 3rd sprag clutch outer race (653) for:
  - Worn or damaged splines.
  - Scoring on inside diameter of race.
  - Wear or cracks.
- Sprag elements for flat spots.
- Sprag cage for distortion or broken ribbon tabs.
- End bearings (719) and center bearing (721) for cracks.

Assemble

- Position 3rd sprag clutch outer race (653) on the bench (lube dam side down).
- Center bearing (721) into 3rd clutch outer race (653) and push into position.
- 3rd sprag assembly (720) into 3rd clutch outer race (653) - lip on sprag cage should be in the "up" position.
- End bearing (719) into 3rd clutch outer race (653). Set aside.

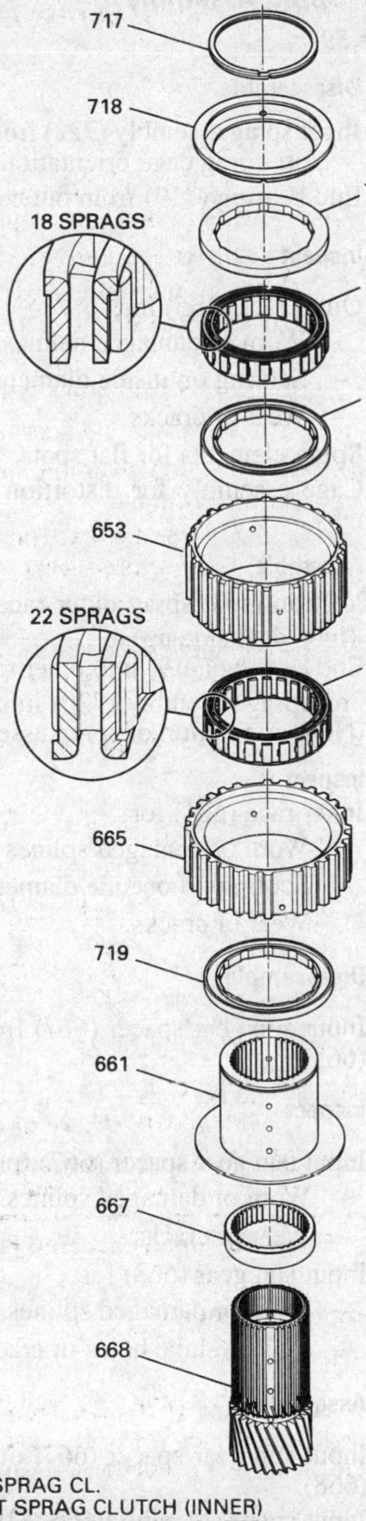
717
718
719
18 SPRAGS
720
721
653
22 SPRAGS
722
665
719
661
667
668

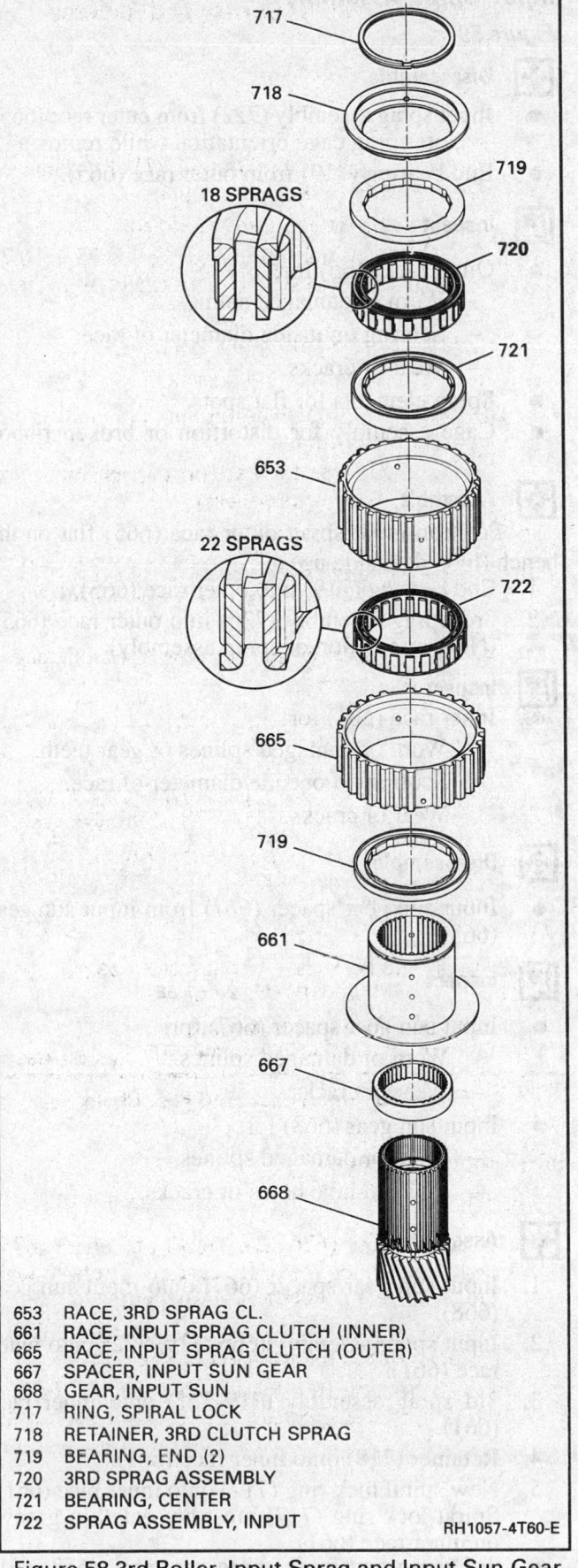

653 RACE, 3RD SPRAG CL.
661 RACE, INPUT SPRAG CLUTCH (INNER)
665 RACE, INPUT SPRAG CLUTCH (OUTER)
667 SPACER, INPUT SUN GEAR
668 GEAR, INPUT SUN
717 RING, SPIRAL LOCK
718 RETAINER, 3RD CLUTCH SPRAG
719 BEARING, END (2)
720 3RD SPRAG ASSEMBLY
721 BEARING, CENTER
722 SPRAG ASSEMBLY, INPUT

RH1057-4T60-E

Figure 58 3rd Roller, Input Sprag and Input Sun Gear Disassembly

Input Sprag Assembly

Figure 59

Disassemble

- Input sprag assembly (722) from outer race (665).
  – Note sprag cage orientation while removing.
- End bearing (719) from outer race (665).

Inspect

- Outer race (665) for:
  – Worn or damaged splines.
  – Scoring on inside diameter of race.
  – Wear or cracks.
- Sprag elements for flat spots.
- Cage assembly for distortion or broken ribbon tabs.

Assemble

Position input sprag outer race (665) flat on the bench (lube dam side up).

1. End bearing (719) into outer race (665).
2. 3rd Sprag assembly (720) into outer race (665). (Note orientation of sprag assembly).

Inspect

- Inner race (661) for:
  – Worn or damaged splines or gear teeth.
  – Scoring on outside diameter of race.
  – Wear or cracks.

Disassemble

- Input sun gear spacer (667) from input sun gear (668).

Inspect

- Input sun gear spacer (667) for:
  – Worn or damaged splines.
  – Wear or cracks.
- Input sun gear (668) for:
  – Worn or damaged splines.
  – Plugged lube holes or cracks.

Assemble

1. Input sun gear spacer (667) onto input sun gear (668).
2. Input sprag assembly (665, 719, 722) onto inner race (661).
3. 3rd sprag assembly (719-721) onto inner race (661).
4. Retainer (718) onto inner race (661).
5. New spiral lock ring (717) onto inner race (661). Spiral lock ring (717) must be seated in groove on inner race (661).
6. 3rd sprag and input sprag assembly (653, 661, 665, 717-722) onto input sun gear (668).

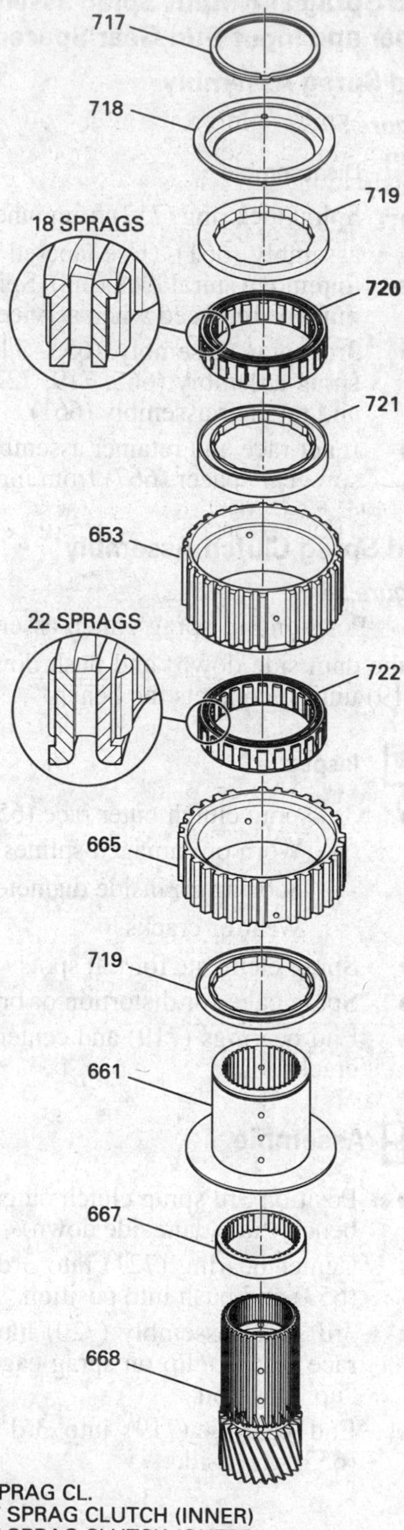

717
718
719
18 SPRAGS
720
721
653
22 SPRAGS
722
665
719
661
667
668

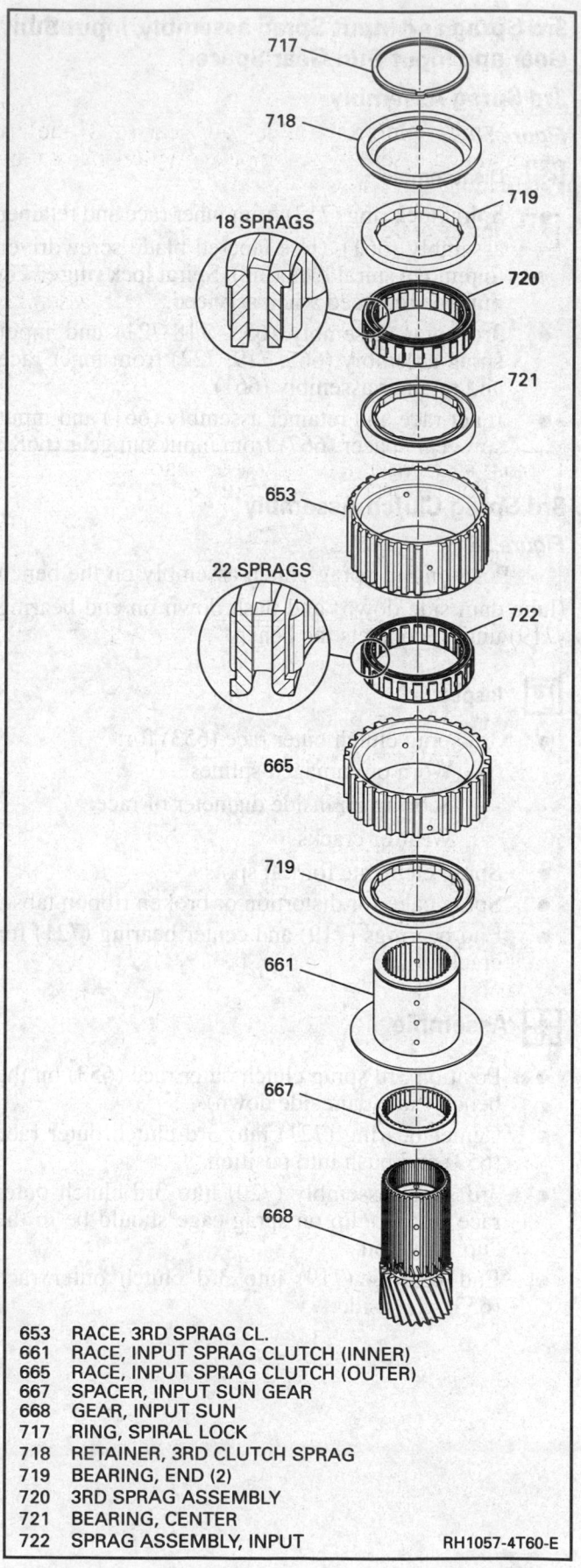

653 RACE, 3RD SPRAG CL.
661 RACE, INPUT SPRAG CLUTCH (INNER)
665 RACE, INPUT SPRAG CLUTCH (OUTER)
667 SPACER, INPUT SUN GEAR
668 GEAR, INPUT SUN
717 RING, SPIRAL LOCK
718 RETAINER, 3RD CLUTCH SPRAG
719 BEARING, END (2)
720 3RD SPRAG ASSEMBLY
721 BEARING, CENTER
722 SPRAG ASSEMBLY, INPUT

RH1057-4T60-E

Figure 59 Input Sprag and 3rd Sprag Assemblies

Functional Check of 3rd Sprag Clutch Assembly and Input Sprag Assembly

Figure 60

While holding the input sun gear (668) the 3rd sprag clutch assembly and input sprag assembly must rotate in the directions as shown.

Install or Connect

- Input sun gear (668) with input sprag assembly (665, 719, 722) and 3rd sprag clutch assembly (653, 717-721) and inner race and retainer assembly (661) into case.

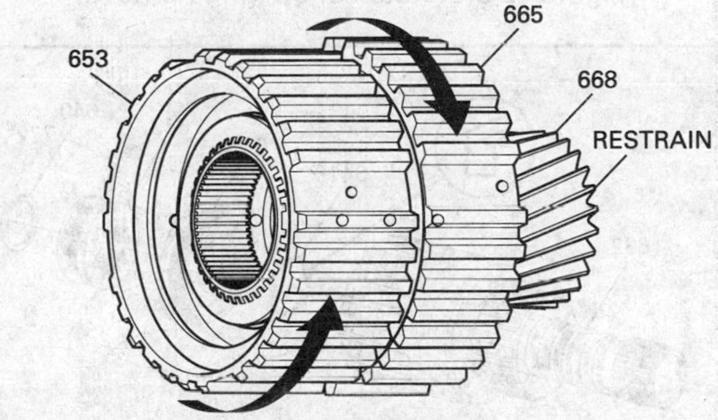
MUST FREEWHEEL IN DIRECTION OF ARROWS
AND HOLD IN OPPOSITE DIRECTION
665
653
668
RESTRAIN
653 RACE, 3RD SPRAG CLUTCH (OUTER)
665 RACE, INPUT SPRAG CLUTCH (OUTER)
668 GEAR, INPUT SUN
RH1059-4T60-E

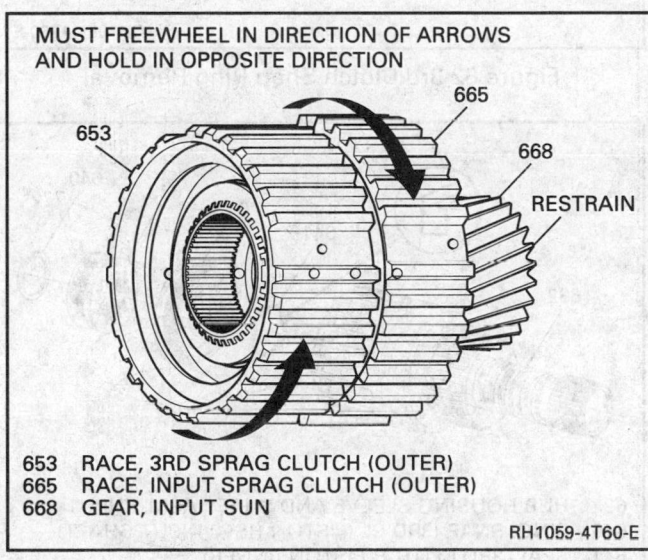

Figure 60 3rd Sprag Clutch and Input Sprag Check

Input Clutch and 3rd Clutch Assemblies

Figure 61

Disassemble

1. Snap ring (659).
2. Input clutch backing plate (658).
3. Input clutch plate assembly (656) and steel plate (657).
4. Input clutch wave plate (655) and apply plate (654).
5. Snap ring (649).
6. 3rd clutch backing plate (648).
7. Internal splined composition plates (647) and external splined composition plates (646).
8. 3rd clutch (waved) plate (645).
9. Thrust bearing (644).

3rd Clutch Piston and Input Clutch Piston Assemblies

Figures 62 through 65

Tools Required:

J 25018-A Adapter
J 28585 Snap Ring Pliers
J 21420-2 Disc
J 23327-2 Bolt and Nut
J 23327-1 Clutch Spring Compressor Bridge

Disassemble

1. Compress spring and retainer assembly (643) with J 23327 and J 25018-A.
2. Snap ring (640) – DO NOT OVER EXPAND.
3. Spring and retainer assembly (643).
4. Piston seal and ball capsule assembly (633) from input housing (632).
5. 3rd clutch inner piston seal (641) from shaft.
6. Compress 3rd clutch piston housing (639) and remove snap ring (640) (Figure 64).
7. 3rd clutch piston housing (639).
8. Input clutch spring and retainer assembly (637).
9. O-ring seal (638) from shaft.
10. Input clutch piston (636) and input clutch inner piston seal (634) from shaft.

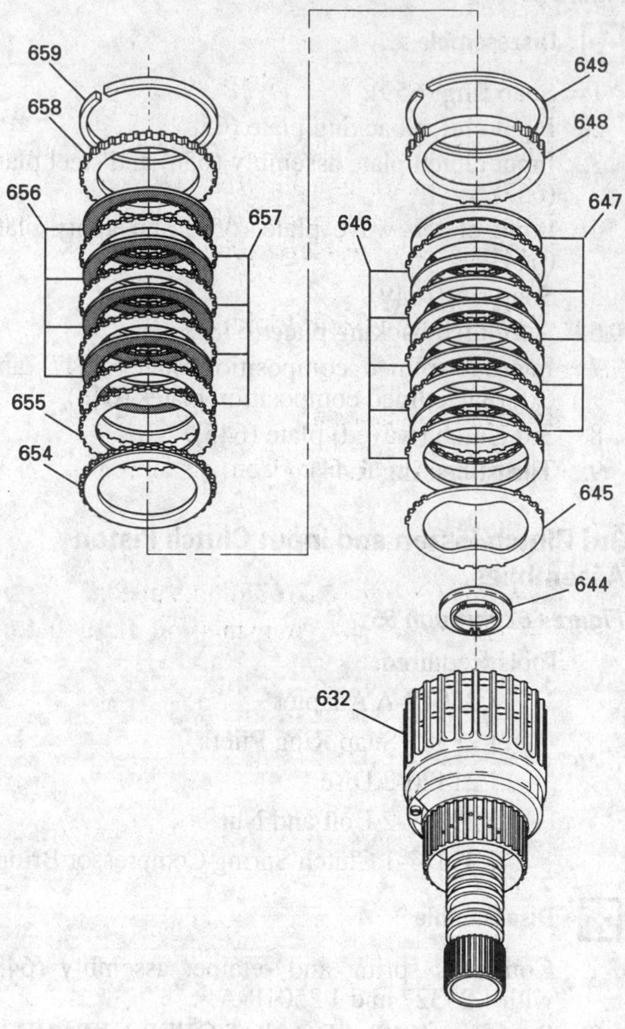
659
658
656
657
655
654
649
648
647
646
645
644
632

632 HUB HOUSING SLEEVE AND SHAFT ASM., INPUT
644 BEARING ASSEMBLY, THRUST
645 PLATE, 3RD CLUTCH (WAVED)
646 PLATE ASSEMBLY, 3RD CLUTCH (SPROCKET SUPPORT/SPLINE O.D.)
647 PLATE ASSEMBLY, 3RD CLUTCH (SPROCKET SUPPORT/SPLINE I.D.)
648 PLATE, BACKING
649 RING, SNAP
654 PLATE, INPUT CLUTCH APPLY
655 PLATE, INPUT CLUTCH, (WAVED)
656 PLATE ASM., INPUT CLUTCH (FIBER)
657 PLATE, INPUT CLUTCH (1.9 FLAT)
658 PLATE, CLUTCH BACKING (STEEL)
659 RING, SNAP

RH1060-4T60-E

Figure 61 Input and 3rd Clutch Assemblies

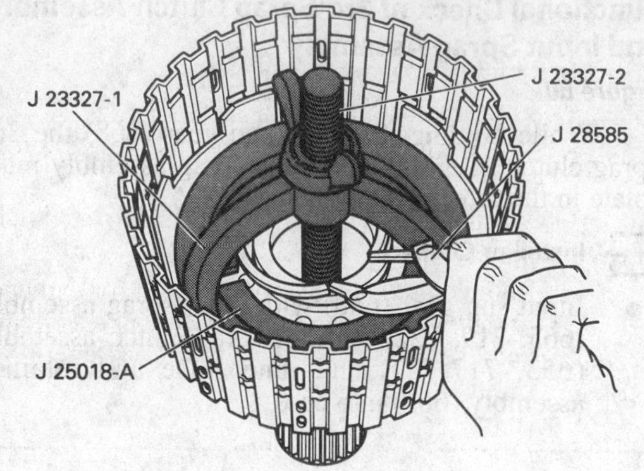
J 23327-2
J 23327-1
J 28585
J 25018-A

RH1061-4T60-E

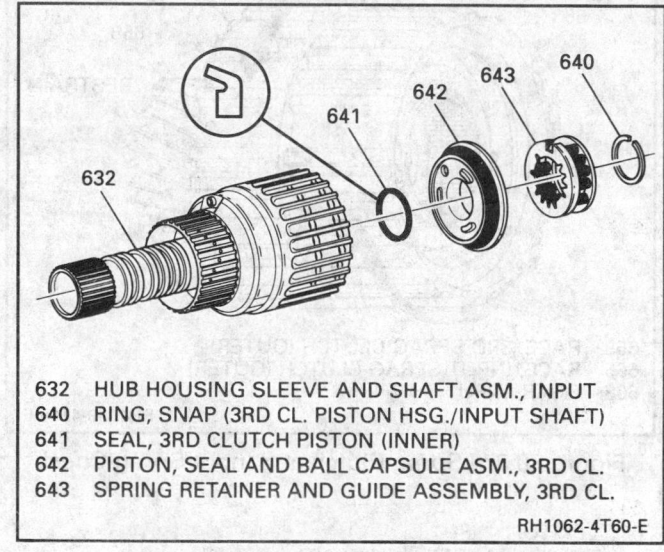

Figure 62 3rd Clutch Snap Ring Removal

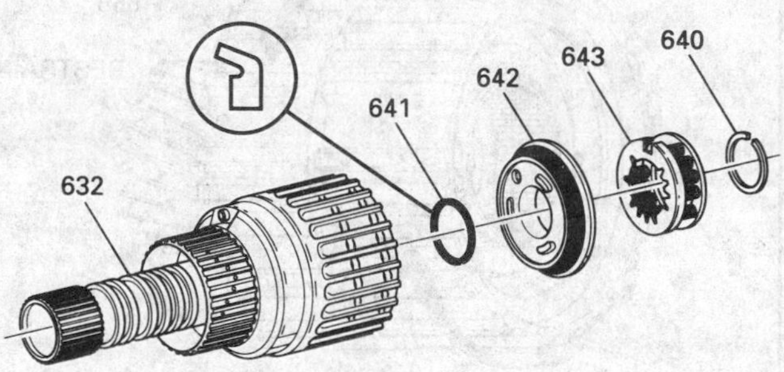
640
643
642
641
632

632 HUB HOUSING SLEEVE AND SHAFT ASM., INPUT
640 RING, SNAP (3RD CL. PISTON HSG./INPUT SHAFT)
641 SEAL, 3RD CLUTCH PISTON (INNER)
642 PISTON, SEAL AND BALL CAPSULE ASM., 3RD CL.
643 SPRING RETAINER AND GUIDE ASSEMBLY, 3RD CL.

RH1062-4T60-E

Figure 63 Removing 3rd Clutch Piston

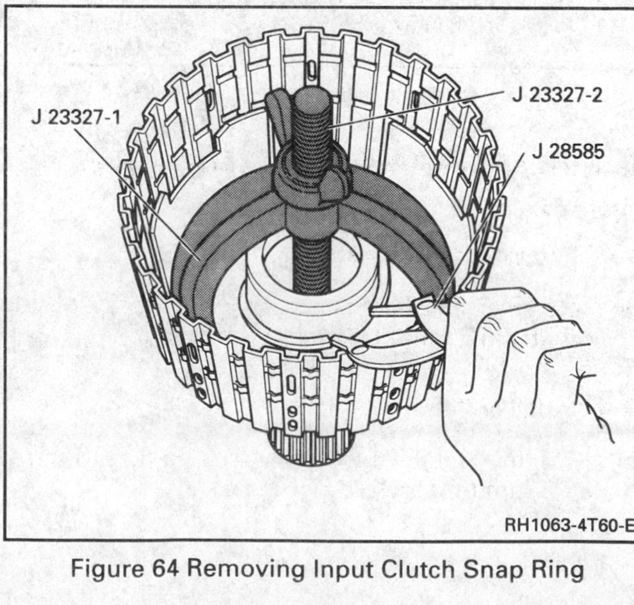
J 23327-2
J 23327-1
J 28585

RH1063-4T60-E

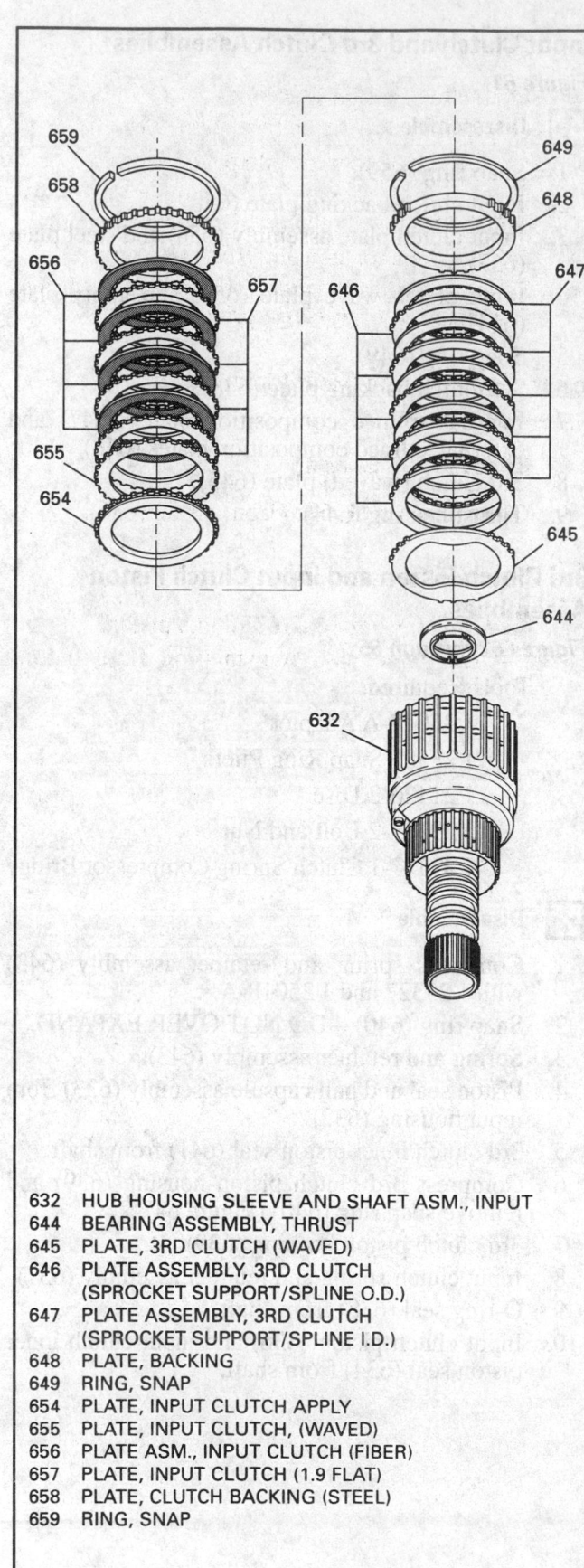

Figure 64 Removing Input Clutch Snap Ring

Inspect

- Input clutch housing (632) for:
  - Plugged feed passages.
  - Worn or damaged splines for driven sprocket.
  - Worn or damaged splines for second clutch plates.
  - Retainer and ball assembly (633) for damage or leaks – turn housing to seat checkball and use transmission fluid for leak check.
  - Welds for cracks.

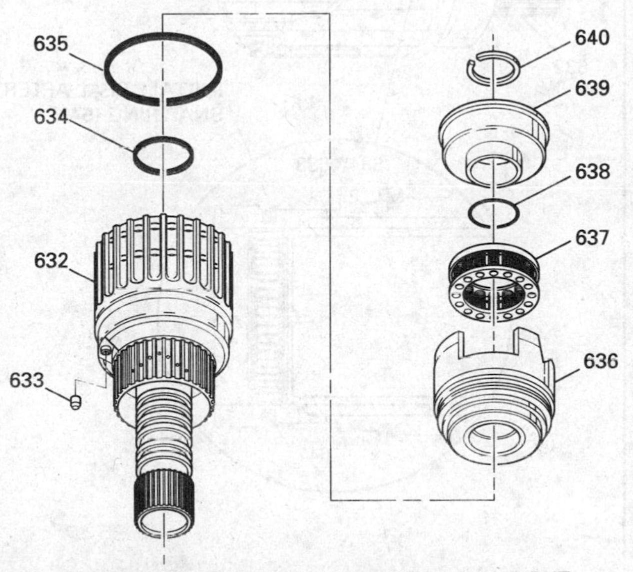
635
634
632
633
640
639
638
637
636

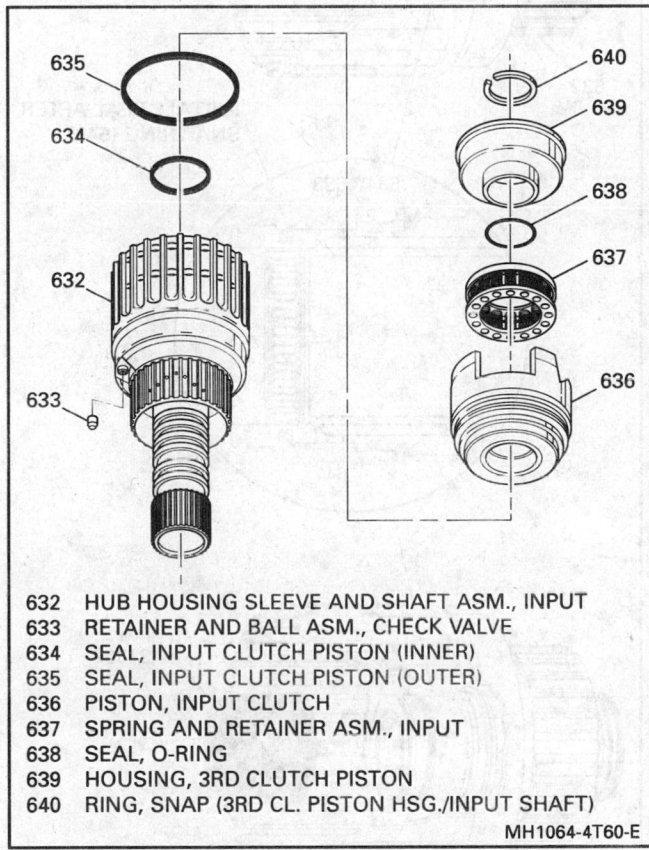

632 HUB HOUSING SLEEVE AND SHAFT ASM., INPUT
633 RETAINER AND BALL ASM., CHECK VALVE
634 SEAL, INPUT CLUTCH PISTON (INNER)
635 SEAL, INPUT CLUTCH PISTON (OUTER)
636 PISTON, INPUT CLUTCH
637 SPRING AND RETAINER ASM., INPUT
638 SEAL, O-RING
639 HOUSING, 3RD CLUTCH PISTON
640 RING, SNAP (3RD CL. PISTON HSG./INPUT SHAFT)

MH1064-4T60-E

Figure 65 Removing Input Clutch Piston

Retainer and Ball Assembly Replacement

Figure 65

Remove or Disconnect

- Retainer and ball assembly (633) from housing with a 6.25 mm (1/4 inch) drift.

Install or Connect

- Tap new retainer and ball assembly (633) with a 9.5 mm (3/8 inch) drift.

Inspect

- Input clutch piston (636) for:
  - Cracks or damage to seal grooves.
  - Clutch plate wear into piston lugs.
- Input clutch spring and retainer (637) for damaged cage and distorted or missing springs.
- 3rd clutch piston housing (639) for damage.
- Spring retainer and guide (643) for damaged cage and distorted or missing springs.

Input Clutch Piston Seal Replacement

Figure 67

Remove or Disconnect

- Outer piston seal (635) from piston (636).

Install or Connect

- New outer piston seal (635) onto piston.
  - Lubricate with transmission fluid before installation.

Input and 3rd Clutch Assemblies

Figures 66 through 72

Tools Required:

J 23327 Clutch Spring Compressor
J 25018-A Adapter
J 37361 Input Clutch Inner Piston Seal Protector
J 37362 3rd Clutch Inner Piston Seal Protector

Assemble

1. New input clutch inner piston seal (634) – lubricate with transmission fluid and install with J 37361.
2. New O-ring seal (638) on input shaft.
3. Input clutch piston (636) into input housing (632).
4. Spring and retainer assembly (637) into input clutch piston (636).
5. 3rd clutch piston housing (639) into input housing (632).
6. Compress 3rd clutch piston housing (639) with J 23327 and J 25018-A, install snap ring (640).
7. New 3rd clutch inner piston seal (641) – lubricate with transmission fluid and install with J 37362.
8. New 3rd clutch piston seal assembly (642) into housing (632) – lubricate with transmission fluid.
9. Spring retainer and guide assembly (643) – compress with J 23327 and J 25018-A then install snap ring (640).

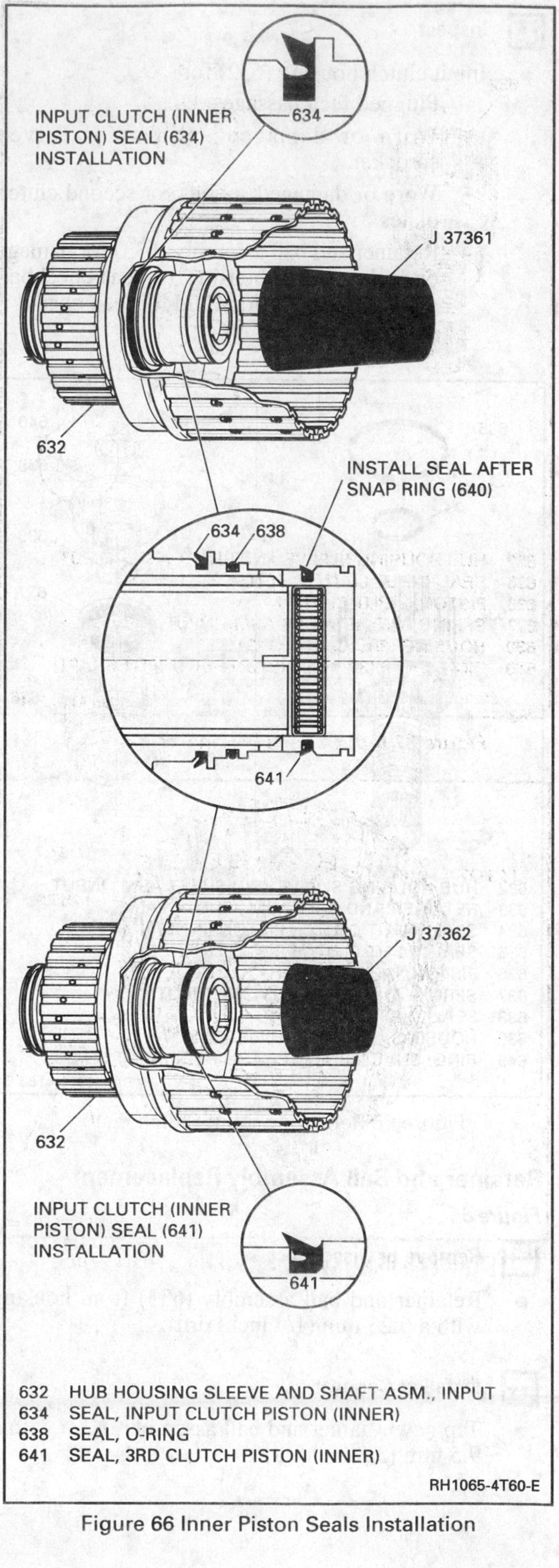

INPUT CLUTCH (INNER PISTON) SEAL (634) INSTALLATION
634
J 37361
632
INSTALL SEAL AFTER SNAP RING (640)
634
638
641
J 37362
632
INPUT CLUTCH (INNER PISTON) SEAL (641) INSTALLATION
641
632 HUB HOUSING SLEEVE AND SHAFT ASM., INPUT
634 SEAL, INPUT CLUTCH PISTON (INNER)
638 SEAL, O-RING
641 SEAL, 3RD CLUTCH PISTON (INNER)
RH1065-4T60-E

Figure 66 Inner Piston Seals Installation

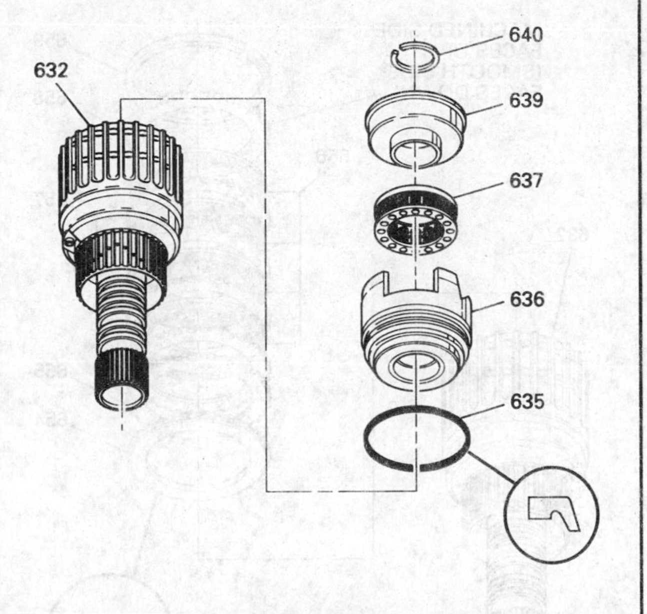
640
632
639
637
636
635

632 HUB HOUSING SLEEVE AND SHAFT ASM., INPUT
635 SEAL, INPUT CLUTCH PISTON (OUTER)
636 PISTON, INPUT CLUTCH
637 SPRING AND RETAINER ASM., INPUT
639 HOUSING, 3RD CLUTCH PISTON
640 RING, SNAP (3RD CL. PISTON HSG./INPUT SHAFT)

MH1066-4T60-E-R1

Figure 67 Input Clutch Piston Components

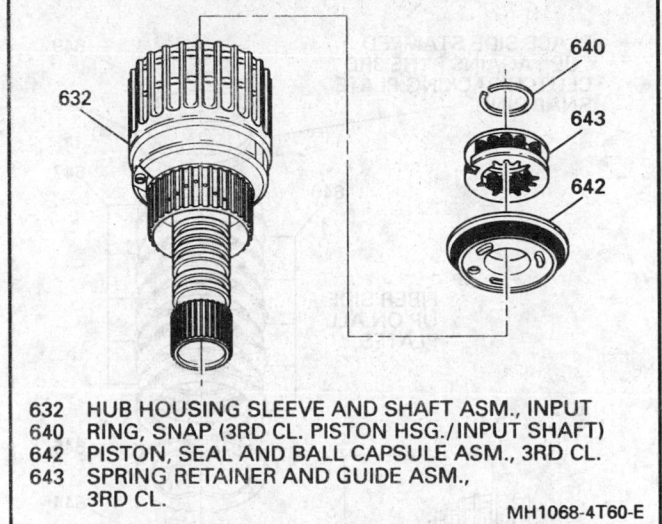

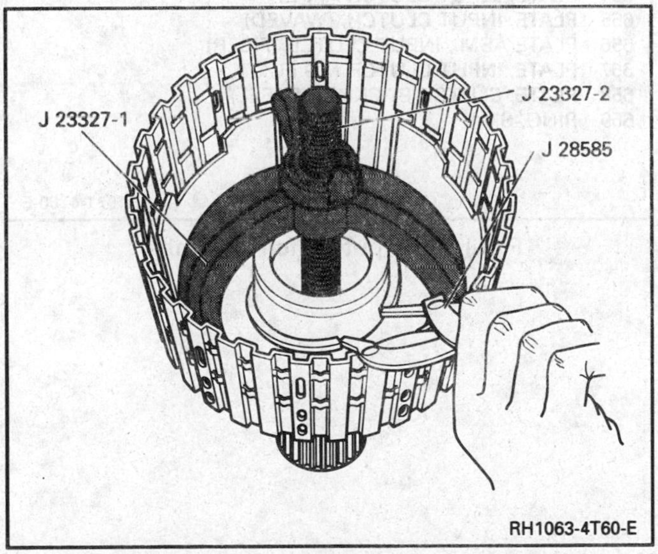
J 23327-1
J 23327-2
J 28585
RH1063-4T60-E

Figure 68 Input Clutch Snap Ring Installation

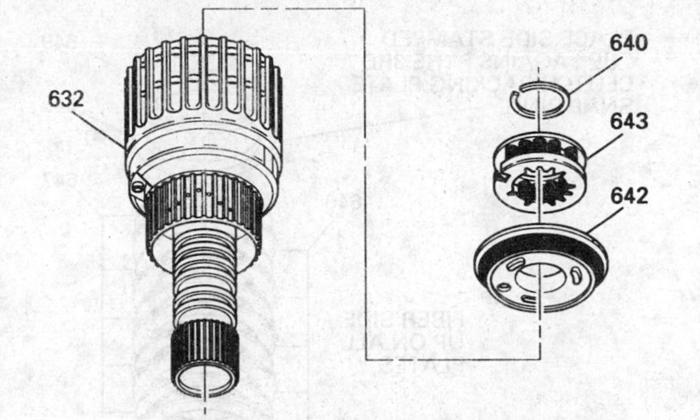
640
632
643
642

632 HUB HOUSING SLEEVE AND SHAFT ASM., INPUT
640 RING, SNAP (3RD CL. PISTON HSG./INPUT SHAFT)
642 PISTON, SEAL AND BALL CAPSULE ASM., 3RD CL.
643 SPRING RETAINER AND GUIDE ASM., 3RD CL.

MH1068-4T60-E

Figure 69 3rd Clutch Piston Components

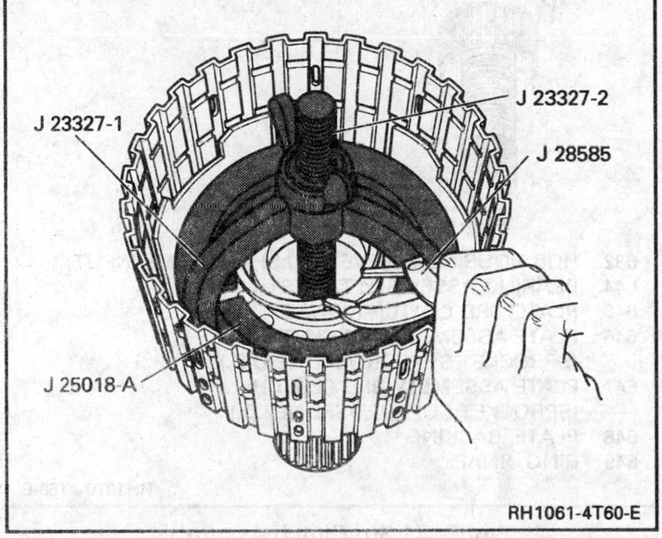
J 23327-2
J 23327-1
J 28585
J 25018-A
RH1061-4T60-E

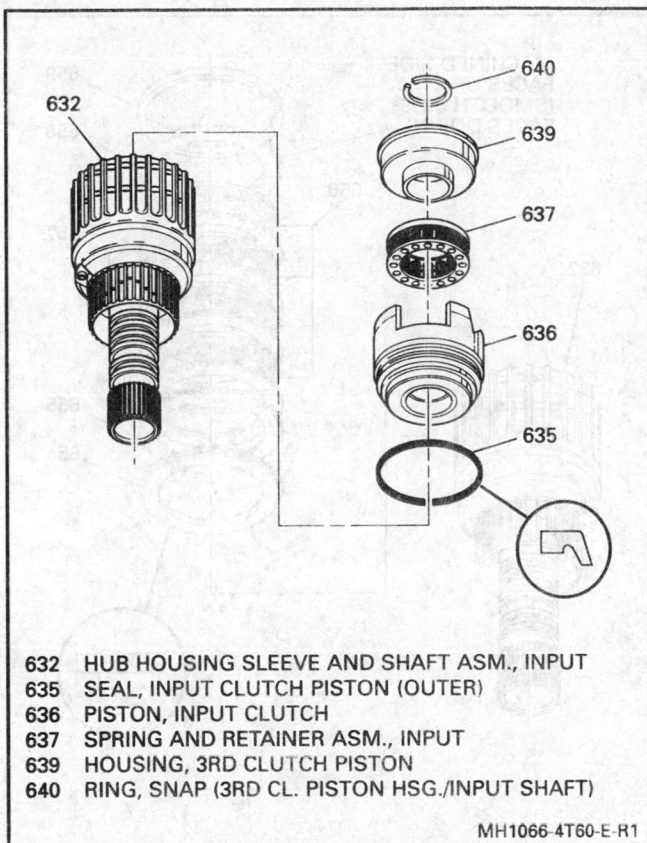

Figure 70 3rd Clutch Snap Ring Installation

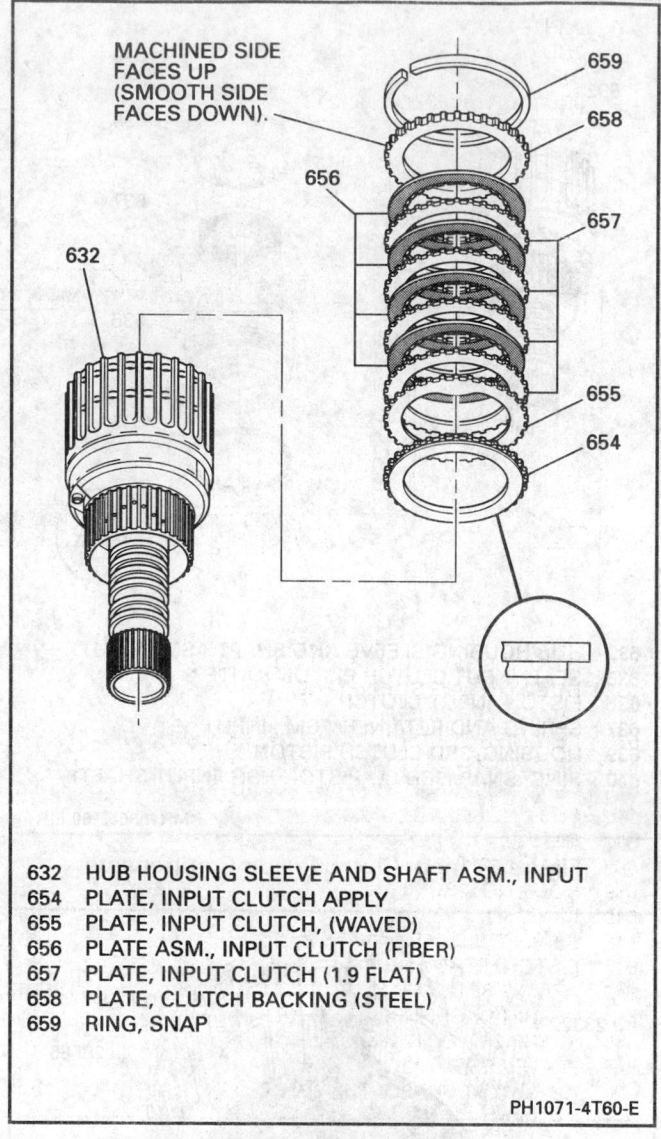

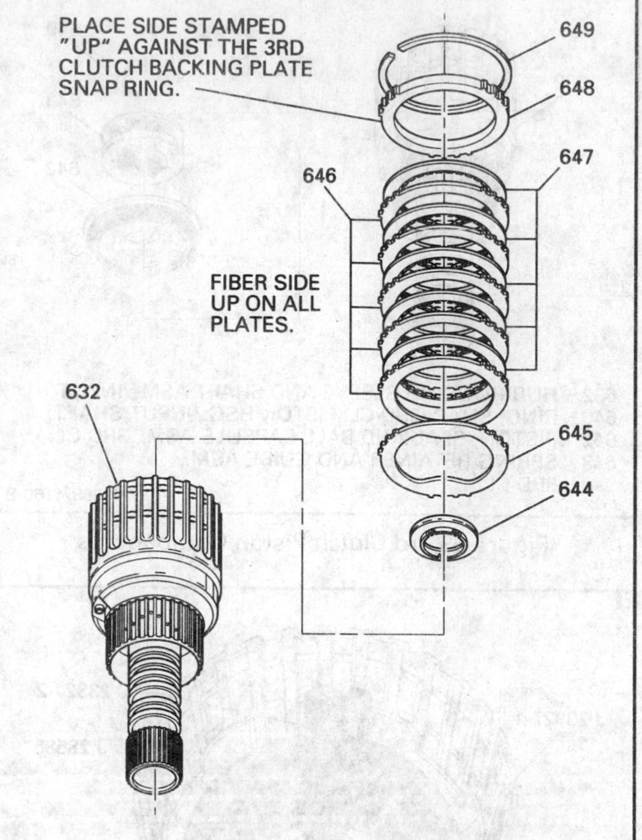
PLACE SIDE STAMPED "UP" AGAINST THE 3RD CLUTCH BACKING PLATE SNAP RING.
649
648
647
646
FIBER SIDE UP ON ALL PLATES.
632
645
644

632 HUB HOUSING SLEEVE AND SHAFT ASM., INPUT
644 BEARING ASSEMBLY, THRUST
645 PLATE, 3RD CLUTCH (WAVED)
646 PLATE ASSEMBLY, 3RD CLUTCH (SPROCKET SUPPORT/SPLINE O.D.)
647 PLATE ASSEMBLY, 3RD CLUTCH (SPROCKET SUPPORT/SPLINE I.D.)
648 PLATE, BACKING
649 RING, SNAP

RH1070-4T60-E

Figure 71 3rd Clutch Assembly

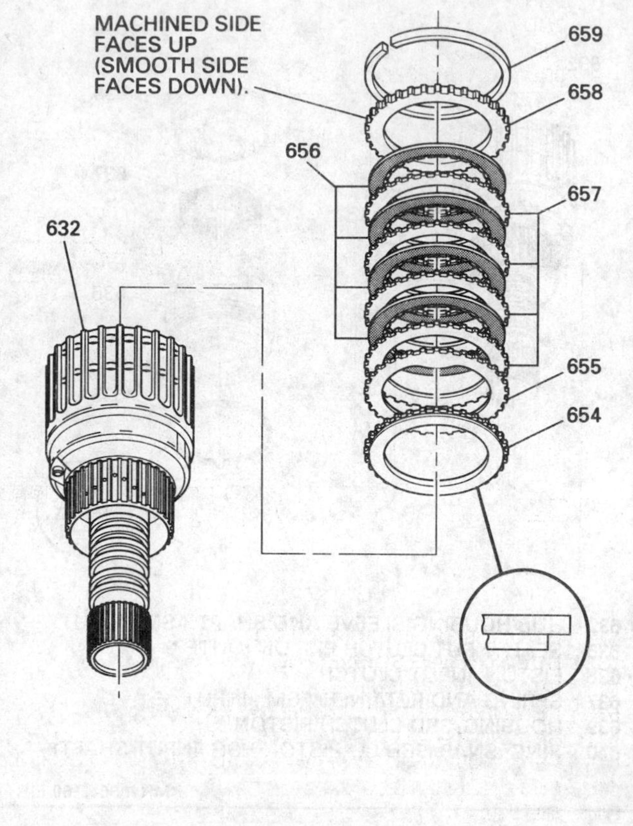
MACHINED SIDE FACES UP (SMOOTH SIDE FACES DOWN).
659
658
656
657
632
655
654

632 HUB HOUSING SLEEVE AND SHAFT ASM., INPUT
654 PLATE, INPUT CLUTCH APPLY
655 PLATE, INPUT CLUTCH, (WAVED)
656 PLATE ASM., INPUT CLUTCH (FIBER)
657 PLATE, INPUT CLUTCH (1.9 FLAT)
658 PLATE, CLUTCH BACKING (STEEL)
659 RING, SNAP

PH1071-4T60-E

Figure 72 Input Clutch Assembly

Assemble

Figure 71 and 72

1. Thrust bearing (644).
2. 3rd clutch (waved) plate (645).
3. 3rd clutch plate assemblies (646 and 647) beginning with external spline plate with steel side against wave plate (645) – alternate with internal splined plates (647).
4. 3rd clutch backing plate (648) – stepped side facing out.
5. Thin snap ring (649).
6. Input clutch apply plate (654) with notched side of teeth against snap ring (649).
7. Input clutch waved plate (655).
8. Input clutch steel plates (657) and input clutch plate assembly (658) beginning with a steel plate.
9. Input clutch backing plate (658) with tapered teeth side facing up.
10. Snap ring (659).

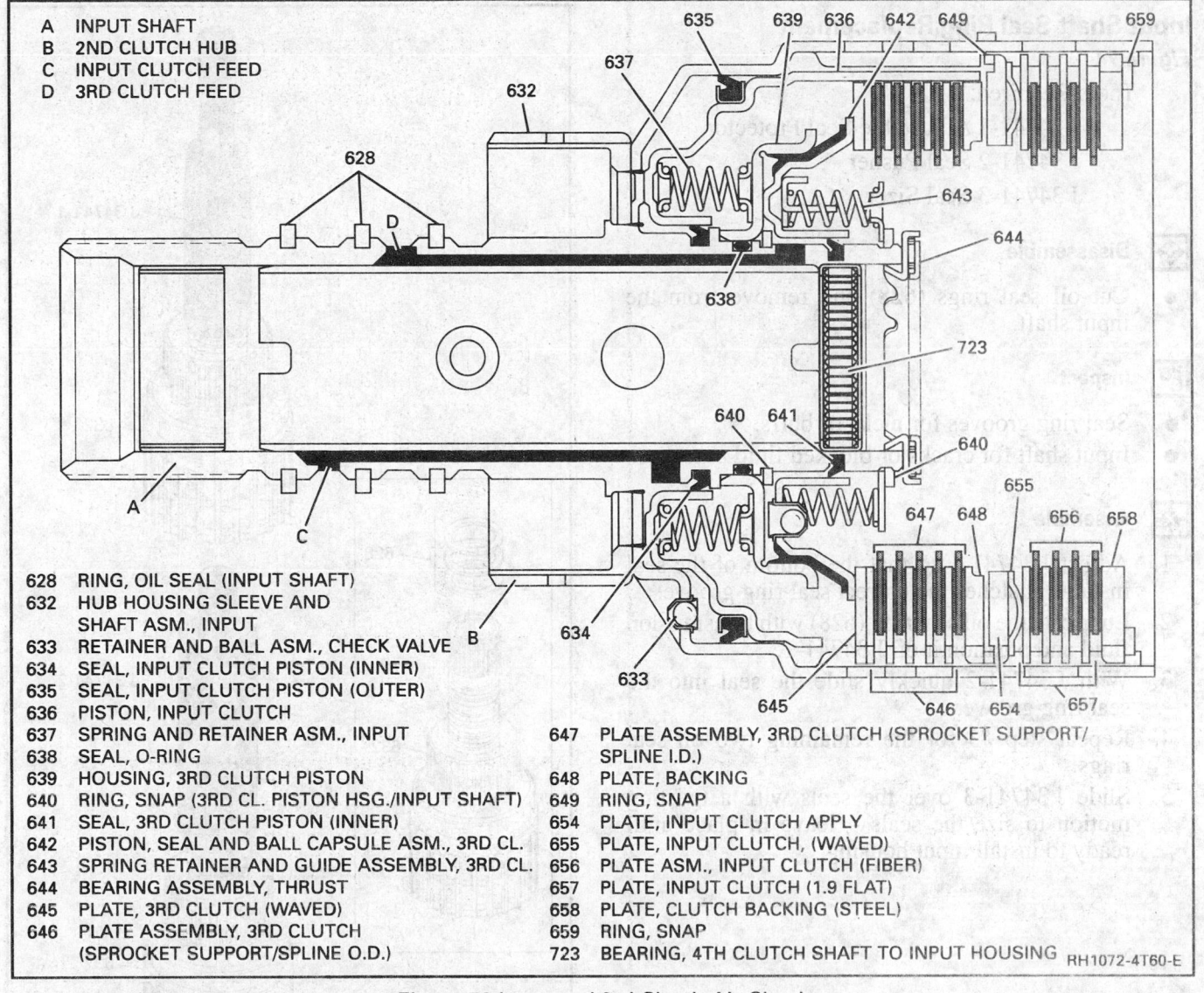

A INPUT SHAFT
B 2ND CLUTCH HUB
C INPUT CLUTCH FEED
D 3RD CLUTCH FEED

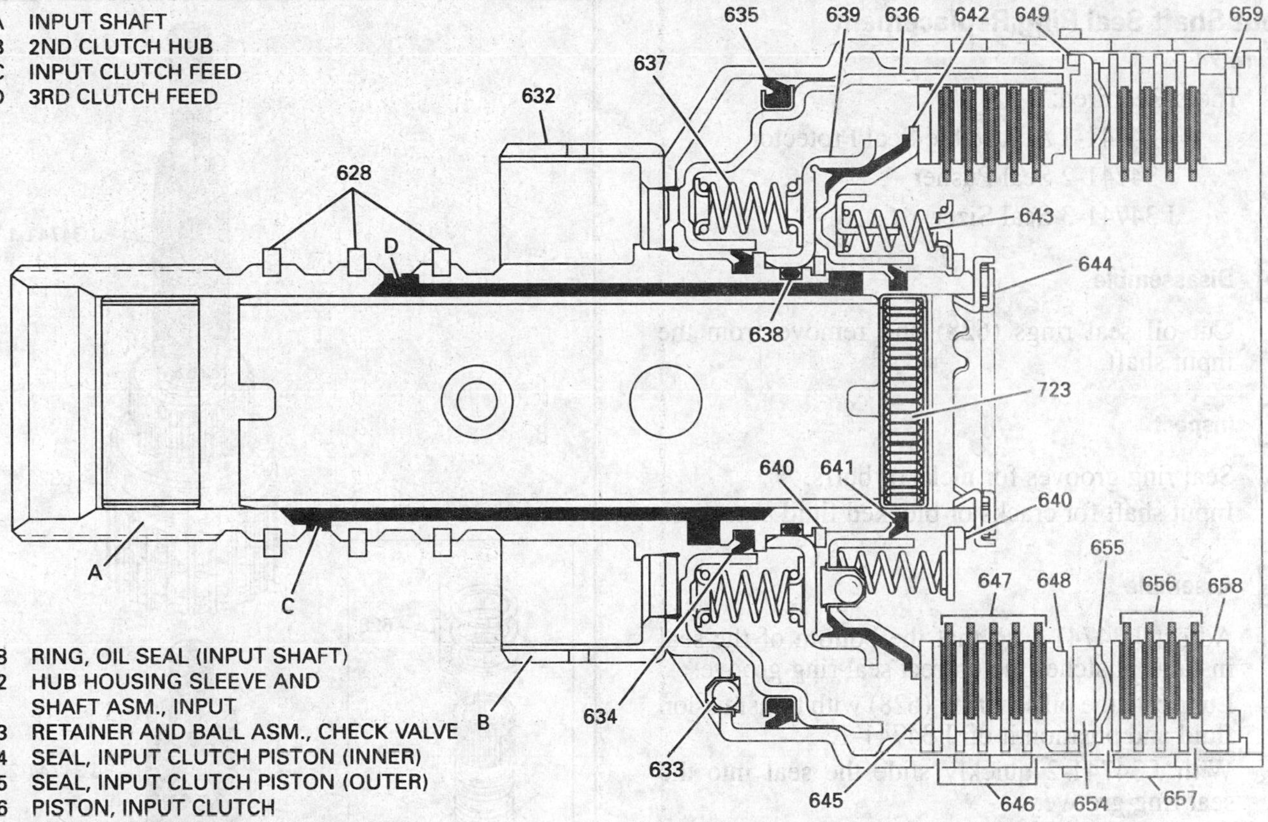

635
639
636
642
649
659
637
632
628
D
643
644
638
723
640
641
640
655
647
648
656
658
A
C
B
634
633
645
646
654
657

628 RING, OIL SEAL (INPUT SHAFT)
632 HUB HOUSING SLEEVE AND SHAFT ASM., INPUT
633 RETAINER AND BALL ASM., CHECK VALVE
634 SEAL, INPUT CLUTCH PISTON (INNER)
635 SEAL, INPUT CLUTCH PISTON (OUTER)
636 PISTON, INPUT CLUTCH
637 SPRING AND RETAINER ASM., INPUT
638 SEAL, O-RING
639 HOUSING, 3RD CLUTCH PISTON
640 RING, SNAP (3RD CL. PISTON HSG./INPUT SHAFT)
641 SEAL, 3RD CLUTCH PISTON (INNER)
642 PISTON, SEAL AND BALL CAPSULE ASM., 3RD CL.
643 SPRING RETAINER AND GUIDE ASSEMBLY, 3RD CL.
644 BEARING ASSEMBLY, THRUST
645 PLATE, 3RD CLUTCH (WAVED)
646 PLATE ASSEMBLY, 3RD CLUTCH (SPROCKET SUPPORT/SPLINE O.D.)
647 PLATE ASSEMBLY, 3RD CLUTCH (SPROCKET SUPPORT/SPLINE I.D.)
648 PLATE, BACKING
649 RING, SNAP
654 PLATE, INPUT CLUTCH APPLY
655 PLATE, INPUT CLUTCH, (WAVED)
656 PLATE ASM., INPUT CLUTCH (FIBER)
657 PLATE, INPUT CLUTCH (1.9 FLAT)
658 PLATE, CLUTCH BACKING (STEEL)
659 RING, SNAP
723 BEARING, 4TH CLUTCH SHAFT TO INPUT HOUSING

RH1072-4T60-E

Figure 73 Input and 3rd Clutch Air Check

Input Clutch and 3rd Clutch Assembly Functional Check

Figure 73

- With rubber tipped air nozzle apply maximum 138 kPa (20 psi) to hole “D” and listen for the 3rd clutch to apply.
- Apply maximum 138 kPa (20 psi) to hole “C” and listen for the input clutch to apply.

NOTICE: Extremely high pressures may roll over or damage seals.

Input Shaft Seal Ring Replacement

Figure 74

Tools Required:

J 34741-1 Adjustable Seal Protector

J 34741-2 Seal Pusher

J 34741-3 Seal Sizer

Disassemble

- Cut oil seal rings (628) and remove from the input shaft.

Inspect

- Seal ring grooves for nicks or burrs.
- Input shaft for cracks or blocked fluid passages.

Assemble

1. Adjust J 34741-1 so that the bottom of the seal installer matches the correct seal ring groove.
2. Lubricate the oil seal ring (628) with transmission fluid and position it on J 34741-1.
3. With J 34741-2 quickly slide the seal into the seal ring groove.
4. Repeat step #3 for the remaining two oil seal rings.
5. Slide J 34741-3 over the seals with a twisting motion to size the seals – leave in place until ready to install input housing.

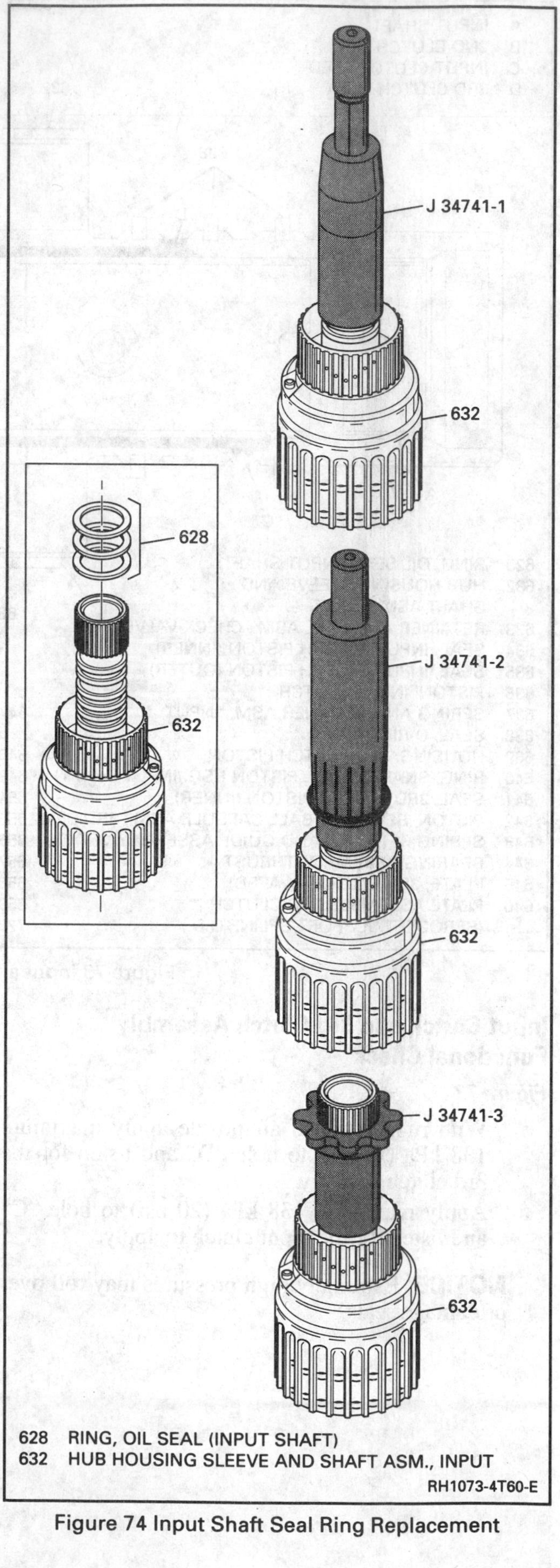
J 34741-1
632
628
632
J 34741-2
632
J 34741-3
632
628 RING, OIL SEAL (INPUT SHAFT)
632 HUB HOUSING SLEEVE AND SHAFT ASM., INPUT
RH1073-4T60-E

Figure 74 Input Shaft Seal Ring Replacement

2nd Clutch Assembly

Figure 75

Disassemble

1. Snap ring (627).
2. Backing support ring plate (626), 2nd clutch fiber plates (624) and 2nd clutch steel plates (625).
3. 2nd clutch apply plate (716) and waved plate (623).
4. Snap ring (622).
5. Apply ring and release spring assembly (621).
6. 2nd clutch piston (620).

Inspect

- Backing support ring plate (626) and 2nd clutch wave plate (623) for cracks or heat spots.
- 2nd clutch steel plates (625) and apply plate (716) for cracks or wear.
- 2nd clutch fiber plates (624) for wear, flaking, or lining separation.
- Apply ring and release spring assembly (621) for damage to ring cage, distorted or missing springs.
- 2nd clutch housing (617) for:
  - Leaking or damaged retainer and ball assembly (618) – turn drum assembly to seat checkball and use transmission fluid to check for leaks.
  - Scored or worn bushings (616 and 619).
  - Discolored band surface or wear on drum caused by excess heat.
  - Flatness of band surfacc on drum.
  - Damaged reverse reaction drum splines.
  - Warped or out of round.
  - Cracks in welds.

Retainer and Ball Assembly Replacement

Figure 75

Remove or Disconnect

- Retainer and ball assembly (618) from 2nd clutch housing (617) using a 6.25 mm (1/4 inch) drift.

Install or Connect

- Tap new retainer and ball assembly (618) into 2nd clutch housing (617) using a 9.5 mm (3/8 inch) drift.

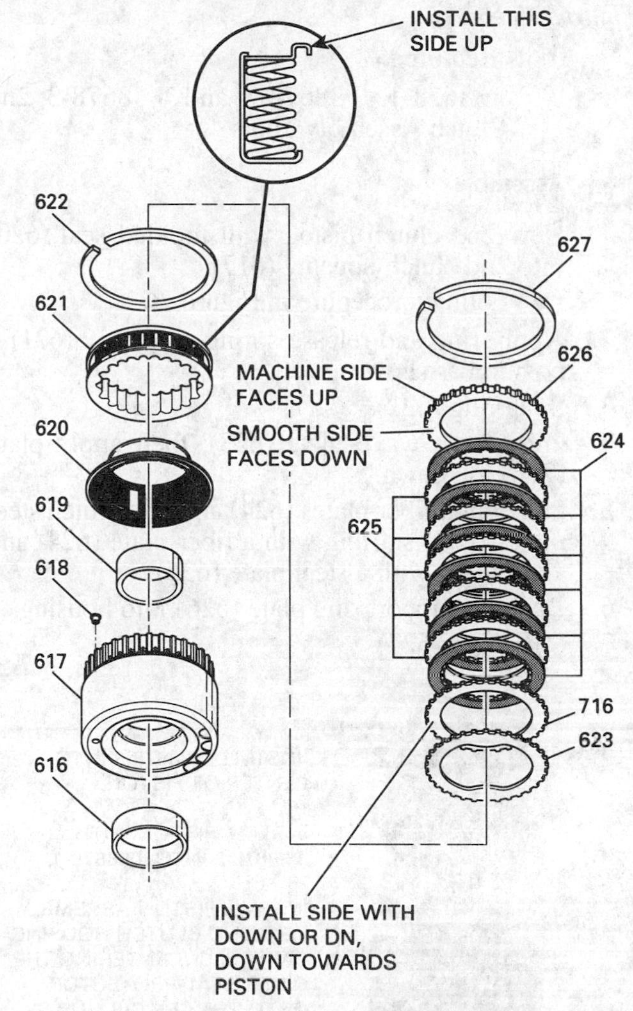
INSTALL THIS SIDE UP
622
627
621
626
MACHINE SIDE FACES UP
620
SMOOTH SIDE FACES DOWN
624
619
625
618
617
716
623
616
INSTALL SIDE WITH DOWN OR DN, DOWN TOWARDS PISTON

616 BUSHING, 75.5 O.D. X 8.0
617 HOUSING, 2ND CLUTCH
618 RETAINER AND BALL ASSEMBLY, CHECK VALVE (FORWARD CLUTCH)
619 BUSHING, 70.0 O.D. X 11.0
620 PISTON, 2ND CLUTCH W/MOLDED SEAL
621 APPLY RING AND RELEASE SPRING ASSEMBLY, 2ND CLUTCH
622 RING, SNAP
623 PLATE, 2ND CLUTCH (WAVED)
624 PLATE ASSEMBLY, 2ND CLUTCH (FIBER)
625 PLATE, 2ND CLUTCH REACTION (STEEL)
626 PLATE, BACKING SUPPORT RING (STEEL)
627 RING, SNAP 2ND CLUTCH (OUTER)
716 PLATE, 2ND CL. APPLY REACTION (TAPERED)

PH1074-4T60-E

Figure 75 2nd Clutch Assembly

2nd Clutch Piston Seal and Clutch Plate Replacement

Figures 75 and 76

Tools Required:

J 38678-1, J 38678-2 and J 38678-3 2nd Clutch Assembly Tools

Assemble

1. New 2nd clutch piston with molded seal (620) into 2nd clutch housing (617).
   - Follow procedure in Figure 76.
2. Apply ring and release spring assembly (621) – position as shown.
3. Snap ring (622).
4. 2nd clutch wave plate (623), then apply plate (716) as shown.
5. 2nd clutch fiber plates (624) and 2nd clutch steel plates (625) starting with a fiber plate (624) and alternating with a steel plate (625).
6. Backing support ring plate (626) into housing.
7. Snap ring (627).

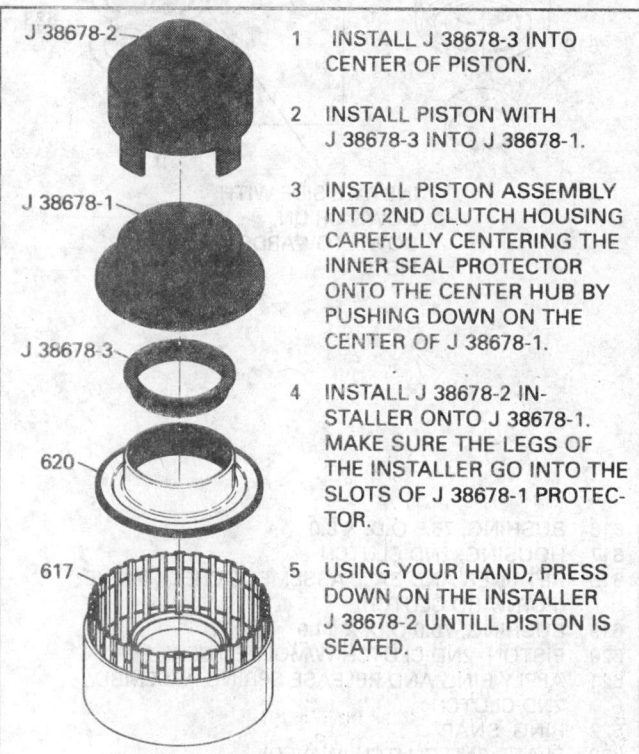

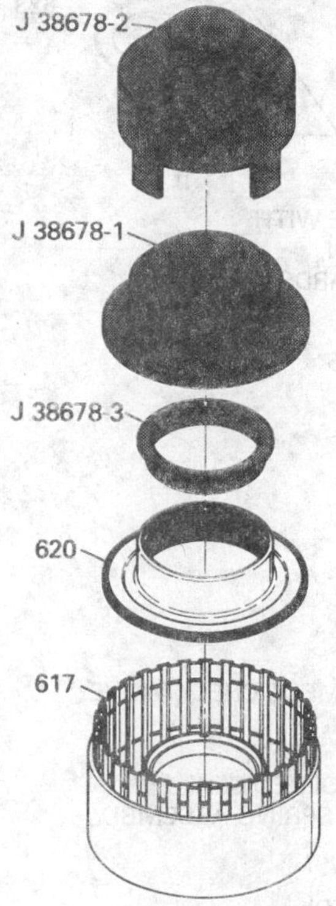
J 38678-2
J 38678-1
J 38678-3
620
617
1 INSTALL J 38678-3 INTO CENTER OF PISTON.
2 INSTALL PISTON WITH J 38678-3 INTO J 38678-1.
3 INSTALL PISTON ASSEMBLY INTO 2ND CLUTCH HOUSING CAREFULLY CENTERING THE INNER SEAL PROTECTOR ONTO THE CENTER HUB BY PUSHING DOWN ON THE CENTER OF J 38678-1.
4 INSTALL J 38678-2 INSTALLER ONTO J 38678-1. MAKE SURE THE LEGS OF THE INSTALLER GO INTO THE SLOTS OF J 38678-1 PROTECTOR.
5 USING YOUR HAND, PRESS DOWN ON THE INSTALLER J 38678-2 UNTILL PISTON IS SEATED.
617 HOUSING, 2ND CLUTCH
620 PISTON, 2ND CLUTCH W/MOLDED SEAL
RH1075-4T60-E

Figure 76 2nd Clutch Piston Installation

Driven Sprocket Support

Figures 77, 78 and 79

Tools Required:

Mechanical Press

J 4670-01 Clutch Spring Compressor

Disassemble

1. Snap ring (601) – compress 4th clutch piston return spring (602) to remove snap ring. Figure 76.
2. Piston return spring assembly (602) and fourth clutch piston (603) from driven sprocket support (609).

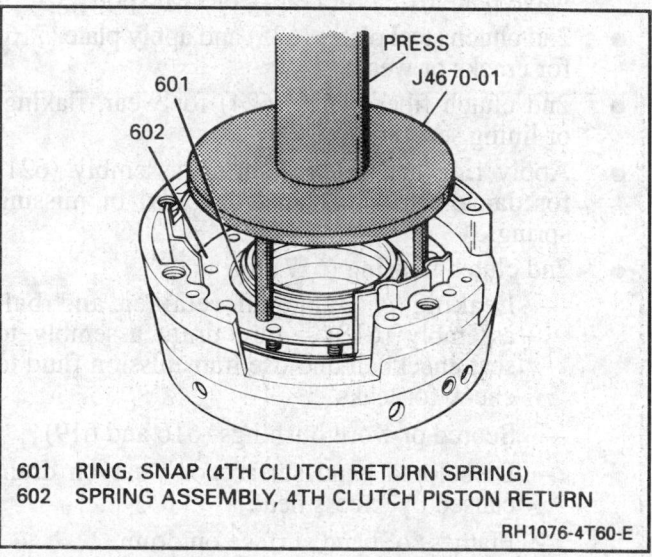

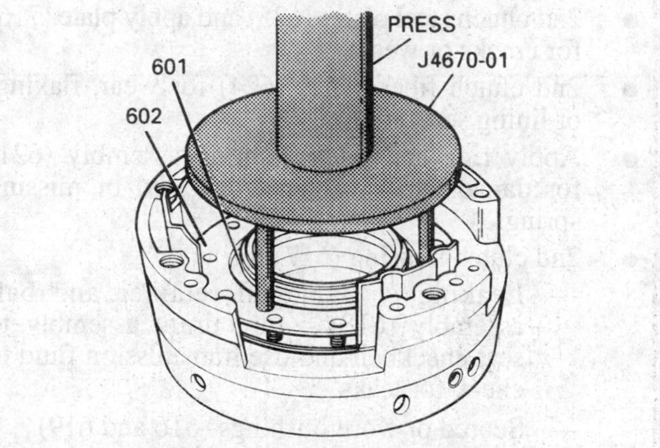
PRESS
J4670-01
601
602
601 RING, SNAP (4TH CLUTCH RETURN SPRING)
602 SPRING ASSEMBLY, 4TH CLUTCH PISTON RETURN
RH1076-4T60-E

Figure 77 Removing 4th Clutch Snap Ring

Inspect

- Driven sprocket support (609) for:
  - Worn or cut oil seal rings (613).
  - Rolled or cut four lobed seal rings (612).
  - Damage to piston seal surface in sprocket support.
  - Blocked or porous oil passages in support.
  - Leaking or missing cup plug.
- 4th clutch piston (603) for damage.
- Thrust washer (611) for cracks or distortion.
- 4th clutch piston return spring assembly (602) for distorted or missing springs – springs should be straight in cage.
- Bearing assembly (606) for foreign material, missing flat or damaged rollers.

Driven Sprocket Support Drawn Cup Bearing Replacement

Figure 78

Tools Required:

J 34129-B Bearing Remover
J 34126 Bearing Installer
J 8092 Handle

Disassemble

- Tap out drawn cup bearing (606) using J 34129-B.

Assemble

- Drawn cup bearing (606) with markings on edge up with J 34126 until bearing is seated flush or below support hub.

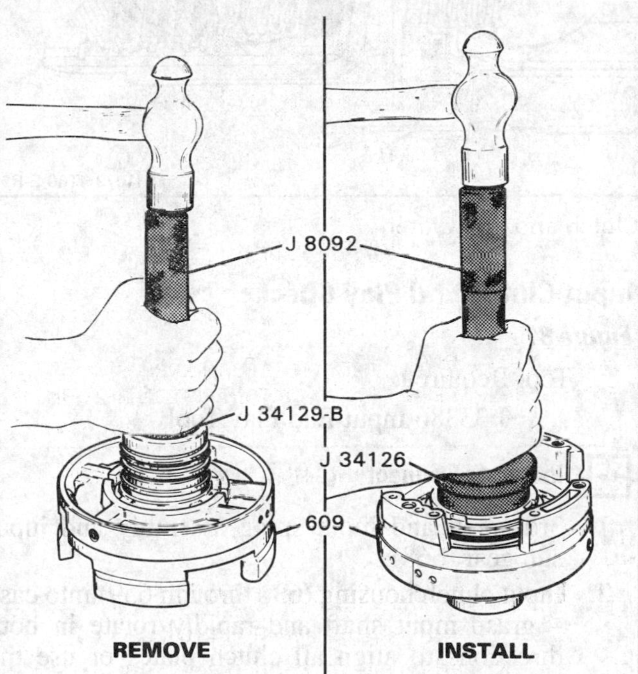
J 8092
J 34129-B
J 34126
609
REMOVE
INSTALL

609 SUPPORT DRIVEN SPROCKET

MH1077-4T60-E

Figure 78 Drawn Cup Bearing Replacement

4th Clutch Piston Seal, 4th Clutch and Driven Sprocket Support Assembly

Figure 79

Disassemble

- 4th clutch piston outer seal (604) from piston (603).
- 4th clutch piston inner seal (605) from sprocket support hub.
- Oil seal rings (613) and four lobed seal rings (612) from driven sprocket support.

Install or Connect

1. New 4th clutch piston outer seal (604) on piston (603) – lubricate with transmission fluid.
2. New 4th clutch piston inner seal (605) on sprocket support hub – lubricate with transmission fluid.
3. 4th clutch piston (603) into driven sprocket support (609) – position as shown.
4. 4th clutch piston return spring (602) onto piston.
5. Compress 4th clutch return spring with mechanical press and install snap ring (601).
6. New four lobed seal ring (612) and oil seal rings (613) – lubricate with transmission fluid.

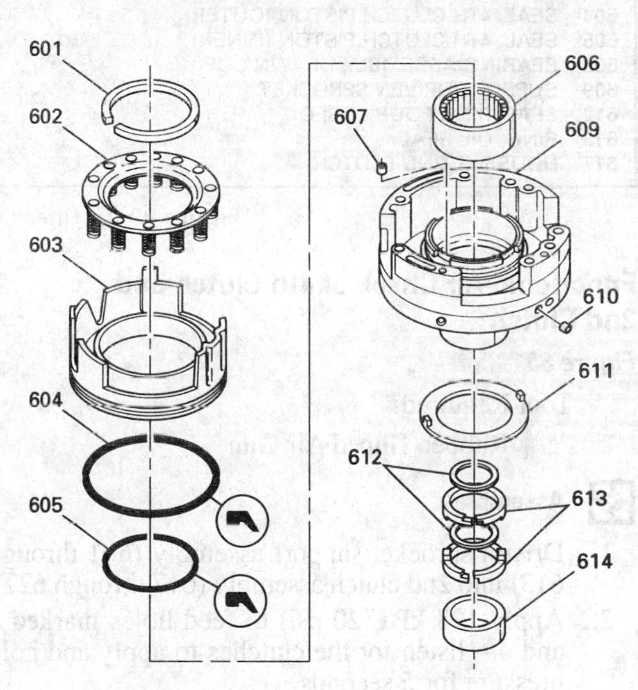
601
602
603
604
605
606
607
609
610
611
612
613
614

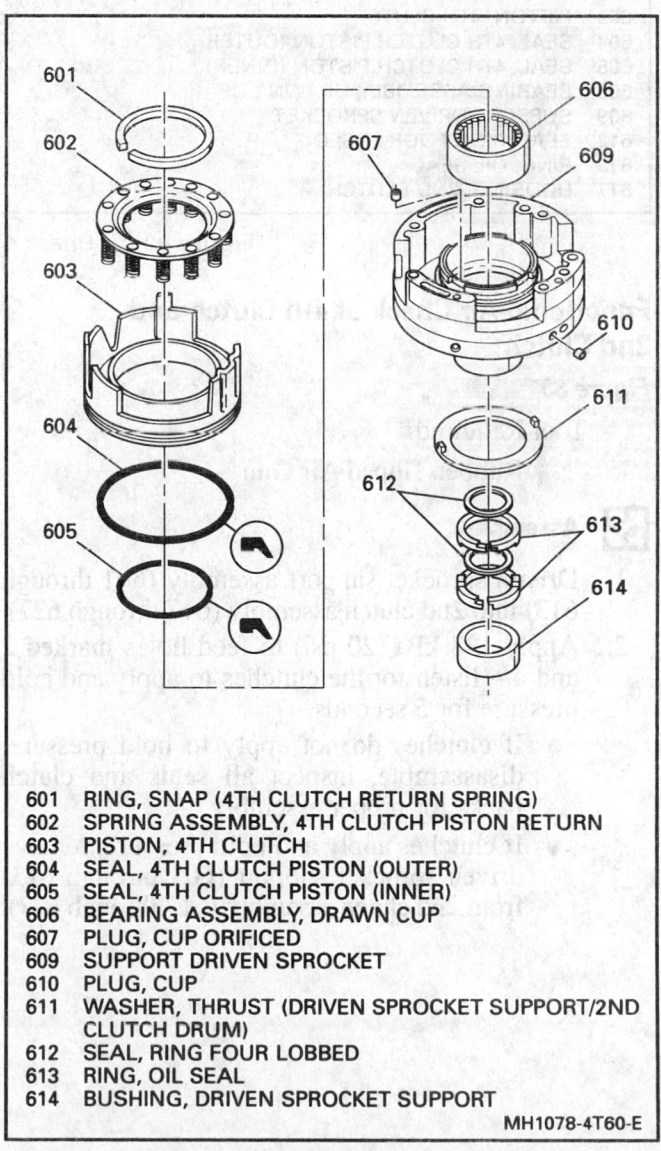

601 RING, SNAP (4TH CLUTCH RETURN SPRING)
602 SPRING ASSEMBLY, 4TH CLUTCH PISTON RETURN
603 PISTON, 4TH CLUTCH
604 SEAL, 4TH CLUTCH PISTON (OUTER)
605 SEAL, 4TH CLUTCH PISTON (INNER)
606 BEARING ASSEMBLY, DRAWN CUP
607 PLUG, CUP ORIFICED
609 SUPPORT DRIVEN SPROCKET
610 PLUG, CUP
611 WASHER, THRUST (DRIVEN SPROCKET SUPPORT/2ND CLUTCH DRUM)
612 SEAL, RING FOUR LOBBED
613 RING, OIL SEAL
614 BUSHING, DRIVEN SPROCKET SUPPORT

MH1078-4T60-E

Figure 79 Driven Sprocket Support Components

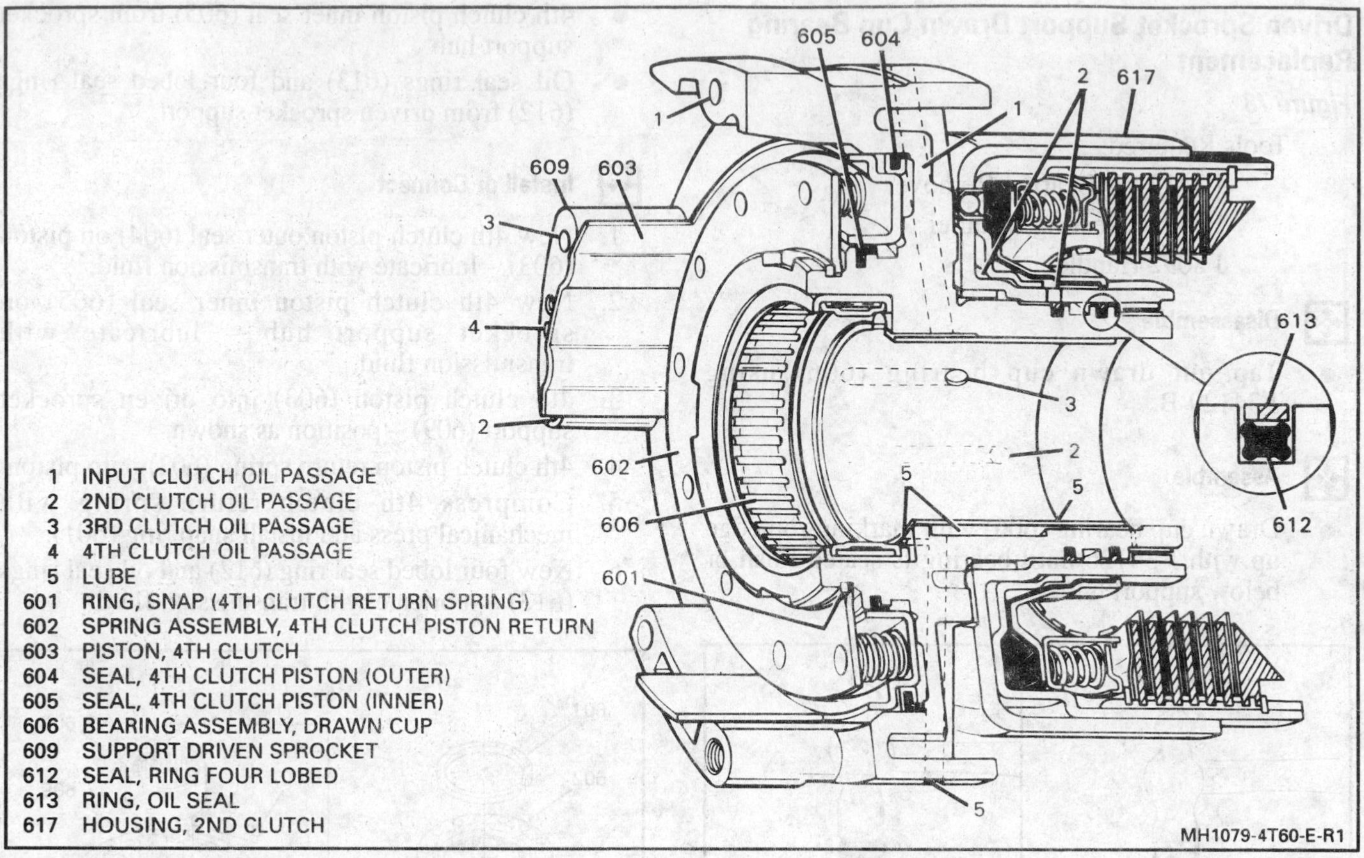
605
604
2
617
1
1
609
603
3
4
2
613
3
2
602
5
5
606
612
601
5
1 INPUT CLUTCH OIL PASSAGE
2 2ND CLUTCH OIL PASSAGE
3 3RD CLUTCH OIL PASSAGE
4 4TH CLUTCH OIL PASSAGE
5 LUBE
601 RING, SNAP (4TH CLUTCH RETURN SPRING)
602 SPRING ASSEMBLY, 4TH CLUTCH PISTON RETURN
603 PISTON, 4TH CLUTCH
604 SEAL, 4TH CLUTCH PISTON (OUTER)
605 SEAL, 4TH CLUTCH PISTON (INNER)
606 BEARING ASSEMBLY, DRAWN CUP
609 SUPPORT DRIVEN SPROCKET
612 SEAL, RING FOUR LOBED
613 RING, OIL SEAL
617 HOUSING, 2ND CLUTCH
MH1079-4T60-E-R1

Figure 80 Air Check of 4th Clutch and 2nd Clutch

Functional Air Check of 4th Clutch and 2nd Clutch

Figure 80

Tool Required:

Rubber Tipped Air Gun

Assemble

1. Driven sprocket support assembly (601 through 613) into 2nd clutch assembly (617 through 627).
2. Apply 138 kPa (20 psi) to feed holes marked 2 and 4 – listen for the clutches to apply and hold pressure for 5 seconds.
   - If clutches do not apply to hold pressure, disassemble, inspect all seals and clutch packs for proper assembly.
   - If clutches apply and hold pressure, remove driven sprocket support (601 through 613) from 2nd clutch assembly (617 through 627).

Input Clutch End Play Check

Figure 81

Tool Required:

J 33386 Input End Play Tool

Install or Connect

1. 3rd sprag and input sprag assembly and input sun gear (668).
2. Input clutch housing (631 through 659) into case – grasp input shaft and rapidly rotate in both directions to align all clutch plates or use the method in Figure 79.
   - Do not install the 2nd clutch assembly (617), thrust bearing (629) or thrust washer (630) at this time.
3. J 33386 input end play tool.

Measure

- With loading tool still installed and loaded.
- End play using the proper selective thrust washer (630) and a feeler gage.

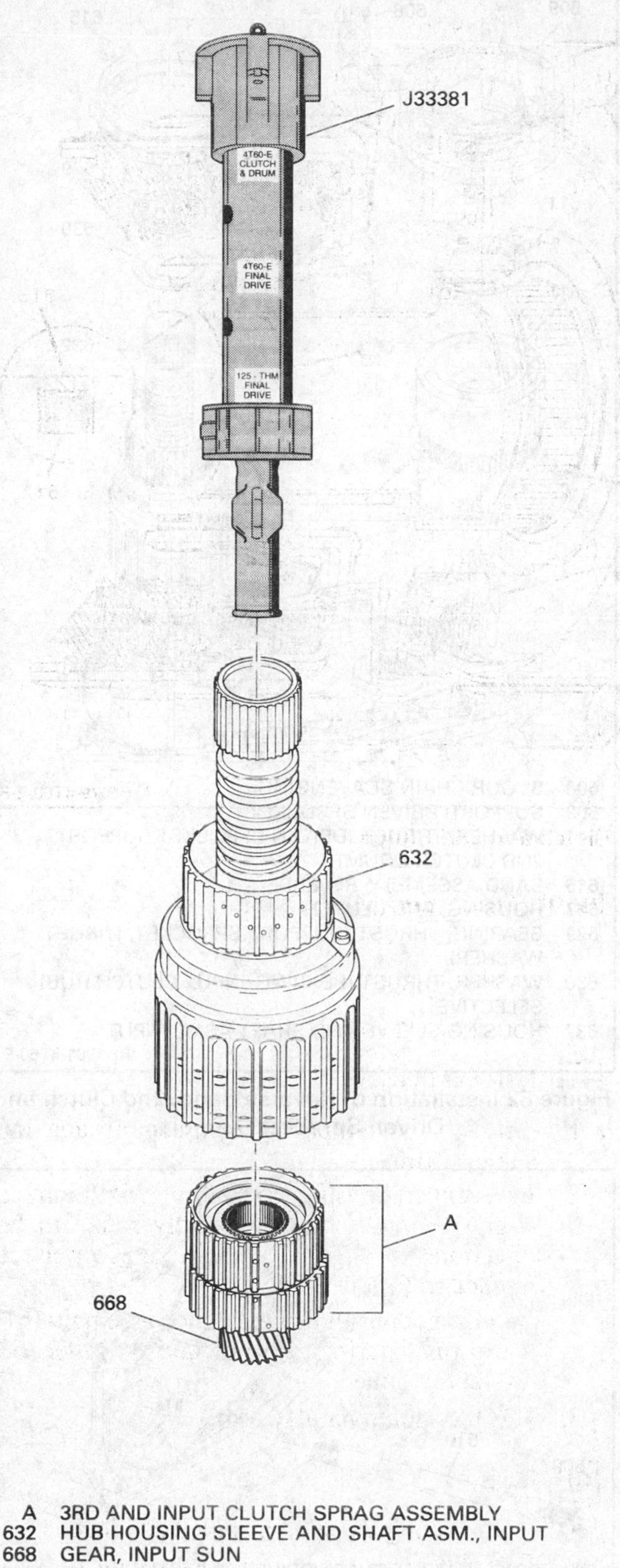
J33381
4T60-E CLUTCH & DRUM
4T60-E FINAL DRIVE
125 - THM FINAL DRIVE
632
A
668

A 3RD AND INPUT CLUTCH SPRAG ASSEMBLY
632 HUB HOUSING SLEEVE AND SHAFT ASM., INPUT
668 GEAR, INPUT SUN

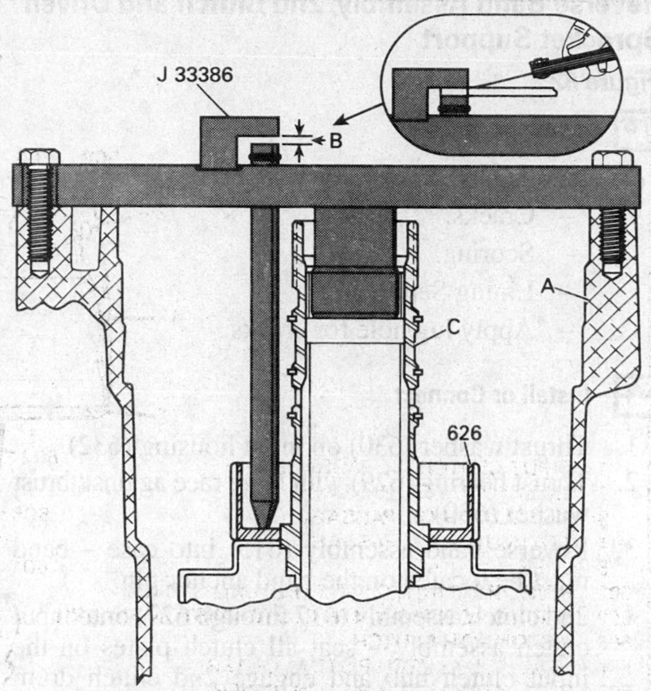
J 33386
B
A
C
626

A CASE
B INSERT SELECTIVE THRUST WASHER TO DETERMINE PROPER SIZE
C INPUT SHAFT
630 WASHER, THRUST (BEARING/INPUT CLUTCH HUB) SELECTIVE
632 HOUSING AND SHAFT ASSEMBLY, INPUT

If a .521 mm (.006") feeler gage or larger can be inserted between thrust washer and tool, use next size larger thrust washer.

GUIDE FOR SELECTIVE THRUST WASHER

I.D. NO.	DIMENSION		COLOR
	MM	INCHES	
1	2.90-3.00	(0.114-0.118)	ORANGE/GREEN
2	3.05-3.15	(0.120-0.124)	ORANGE/BLACK
3	3.20-3.30	(0.126-0.130)	ORANGE
4	3.35-3.45	(0.132-0.136)	WHITE
5	3.50-3.60	(0.138-0.142)	BLUE
6	3.65-3.75	(0.144-0.148)	PINK
7	3.80-3.90	(0.150-0.154)	BROWN
8	3.95-4.05	(0.156-0.159)	GREEN
9	4.10-4.20	(0.161-0.165)	BLACK
10	4.25-4.35	(0.167-0.171)	PURPLE
11	4.40-4.50	(0.173-0.177)	PURPLE/WHITE
12	4.55-4.65	(0.179-0.183)	PURPLE/BLUE
13	4.70-4.80	(0.185-0.189)	PURPLE/PINK
14	4.85-4.95	(0.191-0.195)	PURPLE/BROWN
15	5.00-5.10	(0.197-0.200)	PURPLE/GREEN

RH1080-4T60-E

Figure 81 Installing Input Housing and Thrust Washer Selection

Reverse Band Assembly, 2nd Clutch and Driven Sprocket Support

Figure 82

Inspect

- Reverse band assembly (615) for:
  - Cracks.
  - Scoring.
  - Lining Separation.
  - Apply lug hole for cracks.

Install or Connect

1. Thrust washer (630) on input housing (632).
2. Thrust bearing (629) with large race against thrust washer (630).
3. Reverse band assembly (615) into case – band must be located on the band anchor pin.
4. 2nd clutch assembly (617 through 627) onto input clutch assembly – seat all clutch plates on the input clutch hub and engage 2nd clutch drum with reverse reaction drum.
5. Thrust washer (611) to driven sprocket support (609) – retain with TRANSJEL™ J 36850 or equivalent.
6. Driven sprocket support (609) – when installed properly support should be approximately 1.0 mm (0.025 inch) below case surface.
7. Chain scavenging scoop (608).

Output Shaft

Figure 83

Inspect

- Output shaft (510) for:
  - Cracked or deformed bearing cage.
  - Damaged bushing journals.
  - Stripped splines.
  - Snap ring groove damage.
  - O-ring under non-removable snap ring (512) for damage.

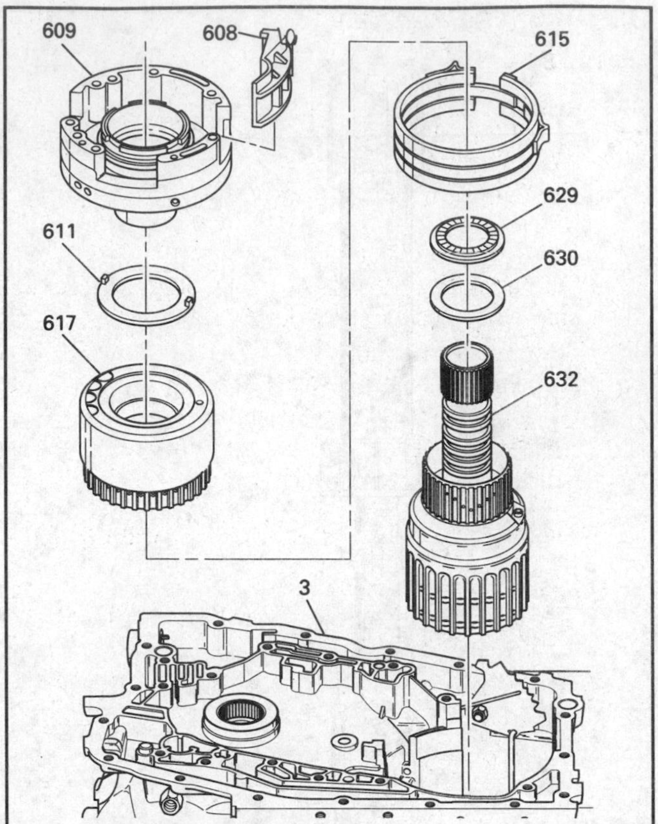
609
608
615
629
611
630
617
632
3

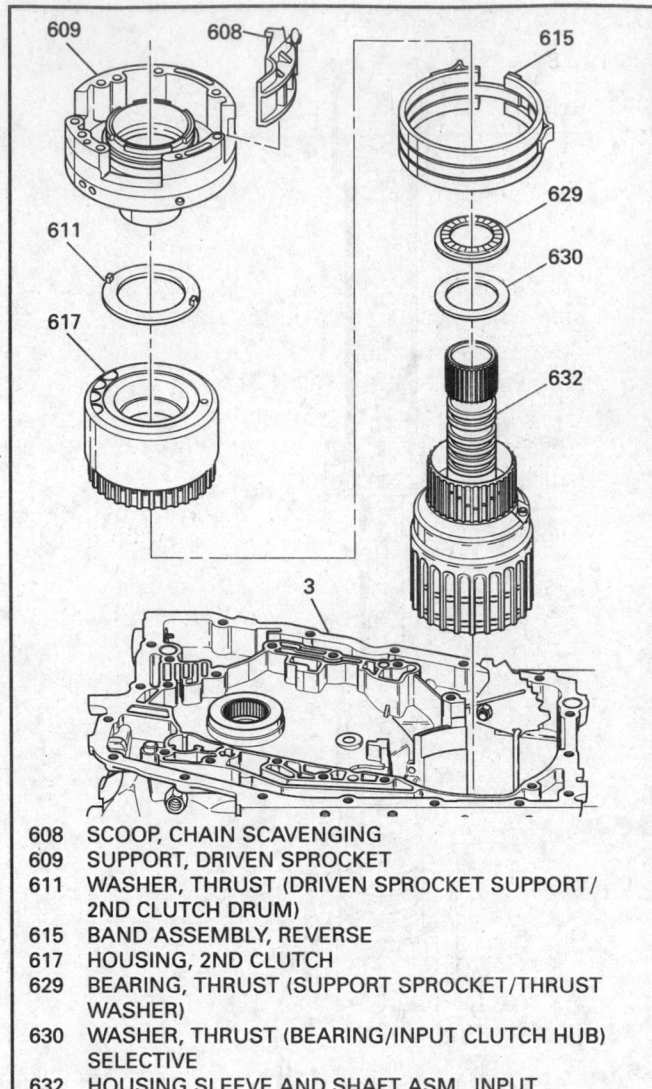

608 SCOOP, CHAIN SCAVENGING
609 SUPPORT, DRIVEN SPROCKET
611 WASHER, THRUST (DRIVEN SPROCKET SUPPORT/ 2ND CLUTCH DRUM)
615 BAND ASSEMBLY, REVERSE
617 HOUSING, 2ND CLUTCH
629 BEARING, THRUST (SUPPORT SPROCKET/THRUST WASHER)
630 WASHER, THRUST (BEARING/INPUT CLUTCH HUB) SELECTIVE
632 HOUSING SLEEVE AND SHAFT ASM., INPUT

RH1081-4T60-E

Figure 82 Installation of Reverse Band, 2nd Clutch and Driven Sprocket Support

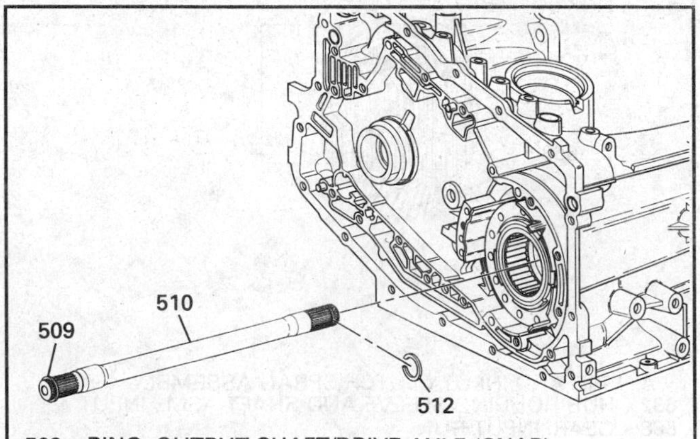
510
509
512

509 RING, OUTPUT SHAFT/DRIVE AXLE (SNAP)
510 SHAFT, OUTPUT
511 BEARING, INPUT SUN GEAR
512 RING, OUTPUT SHAFT/DIFFER. INBOARD (SNAP)

RH1082-4T60-E

Figure 83 Output Shaft

Output Shaft Snap Ring

Figures 84 and 85

Install or Connect

Tool Required:

J 34757 Snap Ring Remover/Installer

1. Remove bolts (5) and case extension (6).
2. Output shaft (510) into case through differential side gear (705) while holding final drive.
3. Snap ring (512) into J 34757.
4. Hold final drive and push snap ring onto output shaft with J 34757 – "Pop-on" or use screwdriver.
5. Ensure that the thrust washer (714) and thrust bearing (715) are in place. Figure 49.
6. Seal (8) case extension (6) and bolts (5).

Tighten

- Bolts (5) to 36 N•m (27 lb. ft.).

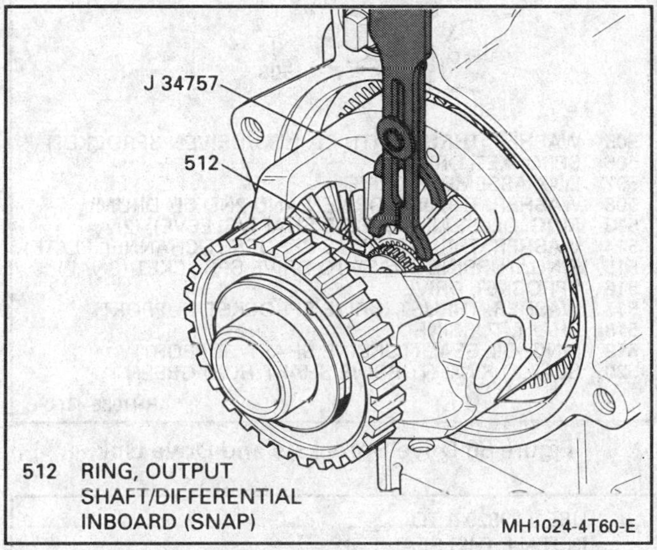
J 34757
512
512 RING, OUTPUT SHAFT/DIFFERENTIAL INBOARD (SNAP)
MH1024-4T60-E

Figure 84 Installing Output Shaft Snap Ring

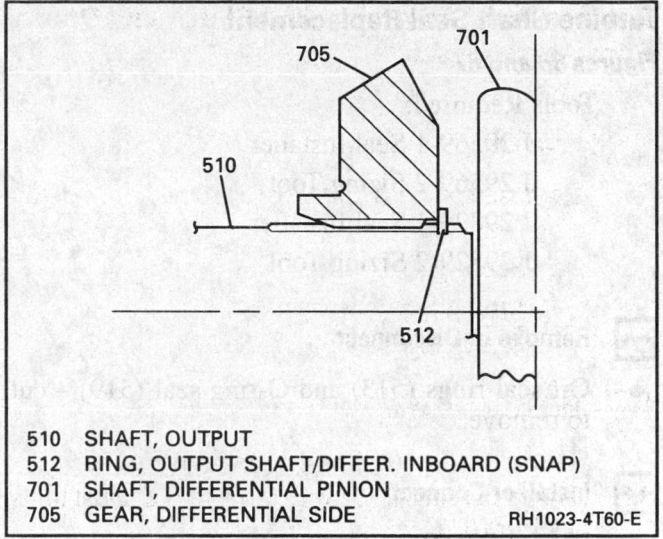

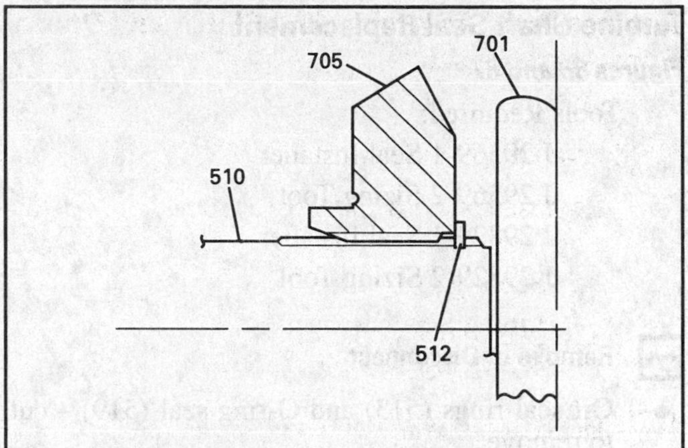
705
701
510
512
510 SHAFT, OUTPUT
512 RING, OUTPUT SHAFT/DIFFER. INBOARD (SNAP)
701 SHAFT, DIFFERENTIAL PINION
705 GEAR, DIFFERENTIAL SIDE
RH1023-4T60-E

Figure 85 Output Shaft Snap Ring

Drive Sprocket, Turbine Shaft, Driven Sprocket and Drive Link Assembly

Figure 86

Inspect

- Driven sprocket (506) for:
  - Worn or chipped teeth.
  - Same size for all teeth.
  - Stripped splines.
  - Damage to bearing surface.
- Thrust washers (505 and 508) for wear or cracks.
- Drive sprocket (516) for:
  - Worn or chipped teeth.
  - Same size for all teeth.
  - Stripped splines.
  - Damage to bearing surface.
- Turbine shaft (518) for:
  - Cracked sleeve.
  - Damaged bushing journals.
  - Stripped converter turbine splines.
  - Cut, worn or missing oil seal rings (513, 519).
  - Cut, worn or missing O-ring seal (520).
- Thrust washers (514 and 517) for wear or cracks.

Turbine Shaft Seal Replacement

Figures 86 and 87

Tools Required:

J 29569-1 Seal Installer
J 29569-2 Sizing Tool
J 29829-1 Seal Installer
J 29829-2 Sizing Tool

Remove or Disconnect

- Oil seal rings (513) and O-ring seal (519) – cut to remove.

Install or Connect

1. Place J 29569-1 over turbine shaft and coat with TRANSJEL™ or equivalent.
2. Slide turbine shaft seals (513) into position.
3. Size seals with J 29569-2.
4. Place J 29829-1 over turbine shaft and coat with TRANSJEL™ or equivalent.
5. Slide turbine shaft seal (519) into position.
6. Size with J 29829-2.

Install or Connect

1. Thrust washer (517) onto drive sprocket (516).
   - Retain with TRANSJEL™ or equivalent.
2. Thrust washer (508) onto driven sprocket support (609) – retain with TRANSJEL™ or equivalent.
3. Drive sprocket (516) and driven sprocket (506) into drive link (507).

   Important

   - Reassemble the drive link assembly with the sprockets the same way as found during disassembly – either with the black link up or down so the set wear pattern remains the same to reduce noise.
   - If installing a new drive link assembly, install it with the black link up.
4. Sprockets and drive link into case.
5. New O-ring (520) onto turbine shaft on the converter side of case.

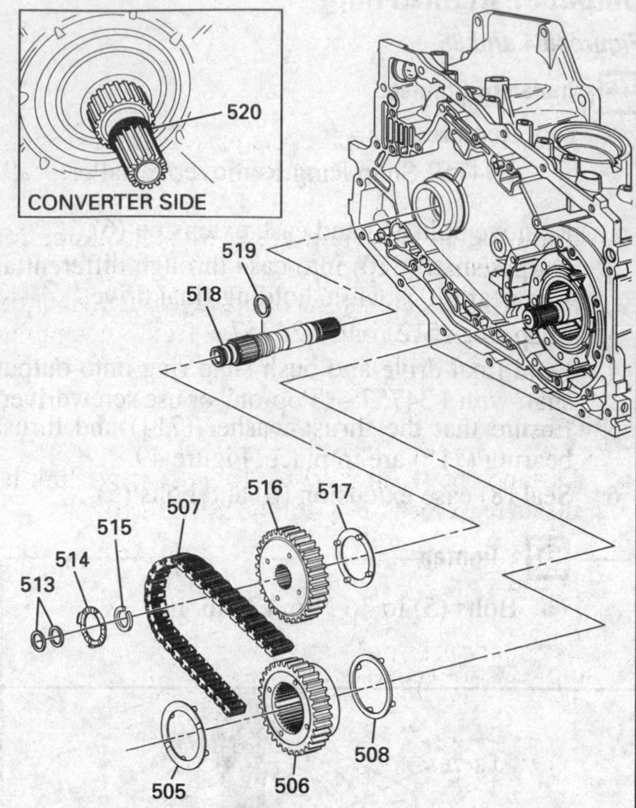
520
CONVERTER SIDE
519
518
516
517
507
515
514
513
508
505
506

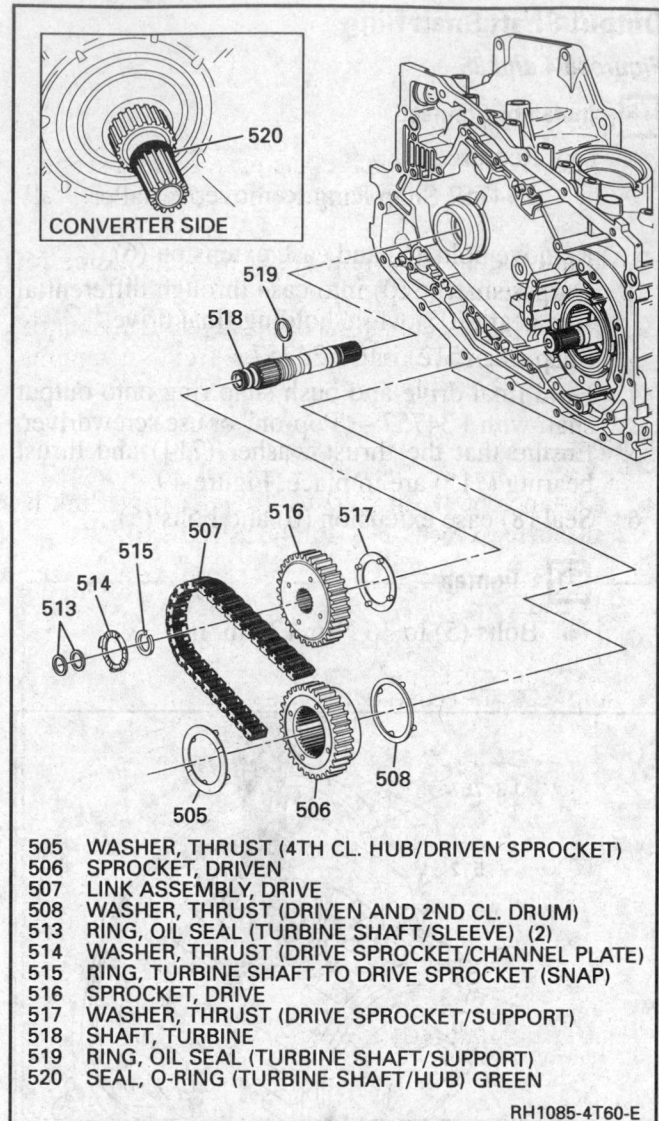

505 WASHER, THRUST (4TH CL. HUB/DRIVEN SPROCKET)
506 SPROCKET, DRIVEN
507 LINK ASSEMBLY, DRIVE
508 WASHER, THRUST (DRIVEN AND 2ND CL. DRUM)
513 RING, OIL SEAL (TURBINE SHAFT/SLEEVE) (2)
514 WASHER, THRUST (DRIVE SPROCKET/CHANNEL PLATE)
515 RING, TURBINE SHAFT TO DRIVE SPROCKET (SNAP)
516 SPROCKET, DRIVE
517 WASHER, THRUST (DRIVE SPROCKET/SUPPORT)
518 SHAFT, TURBINE
519 RING, OIL SEAL (TURBINE SHAFT/SUPPORT)
520 SEAL, O-RING (TURBINE SHAFT/HUB) GREEN

RH1085-4T60-E

Figure 86 Drive Sprockets and Drive Link

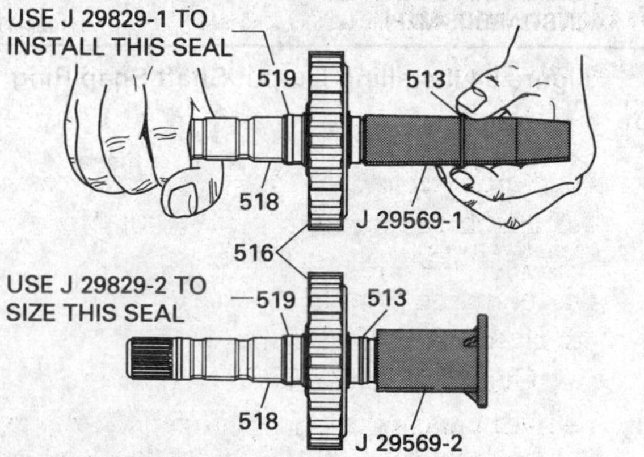
USE J 29829-1 TO
INSTALL THIS SEAL
519
513
518
J 29569-1
516
USE J 29829-2 TO
SIZE THIS SEAL
519
513
518
J 29569-2

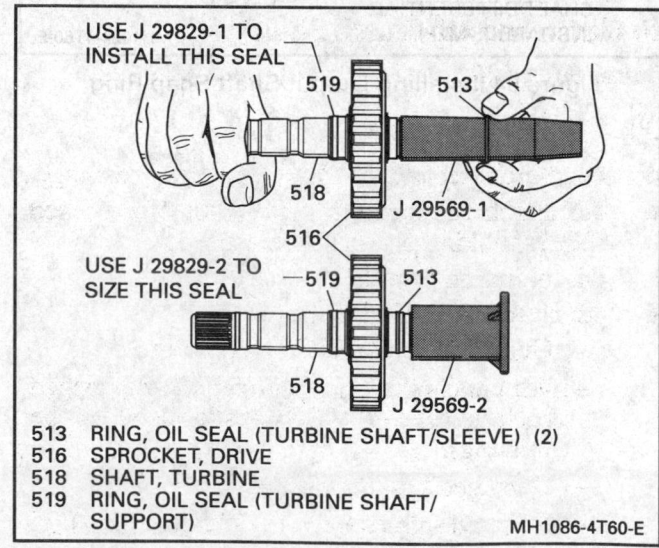

513 RING, OIL SEAL (TURBINE SHAFT/SLEEVE) (2)
516 SPROCKET, DRIVE
518 SHAFT, TURBINE
519 RING, OIL SEAL (TURBINE SHAFT/ SUPPORT)

MH1086-4T60-E

Figure 87 Turbine Seals

Drive Link Inspection

Figure 88

Inspect

1. Midway between sprockets push bottom section of drive link (507) towards top section until all slack is removed.
2. Mark the case at right angle to bottom side of link assembly (507).
3. Push link assembly in opposite direction until slack is removed and mark case from same point on link assembly.

Measure

- Distance between marks – Replace drive link if distance exceeds 27.4 mm (1 1/16 inch).

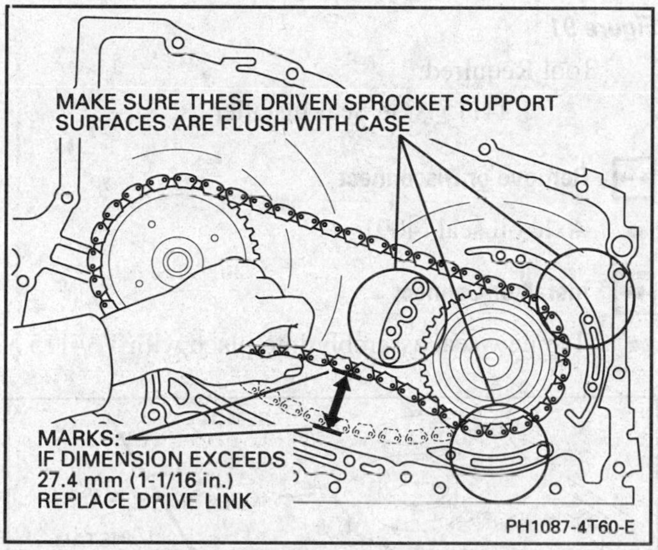
MAKE SURE THESE DRIVEN SPROCKET SUPPORT SURFACES ARE FLUSH WITH CASE
MARKS:
IF DIMENSION EXCEEDS 27.4 mm (1-1/16 in.) REPLACE DRIVE LINK
PH1087-4T60-E

Figure 88 Drive Link Inspection

4th Clutch and 4th Clutch Shaft

Figures 89 and 90

Inspect

- 4th clutch steel plates (500) for wear or damage.
- 4th clutch composition plates (501) for peened splines, flaking or worn fiber material.
- Discoloration from heat.
- 4th clutch shaft (504) for:
  - Cut or worn 4th clutch plate splines.
  - 4th clutch shaft bearing (503) for damaged rollers (one needle is supposed to be missing).
  - Damaged bushing journal.
  - Stripped splines for input sun gear (668).
  - Cracked or damaged hub or shaft.

Install or Connect

1. Thrust washer (505) on driven sprocket (506).
2. 4th clutch shaft (504) through driven sprocket (506).
3. 4th clutch apply plate (502) – identification mark towards sprocket (506).
4. 4th clutch plates starting with composition plate (501) and alternating with steel plate (500).

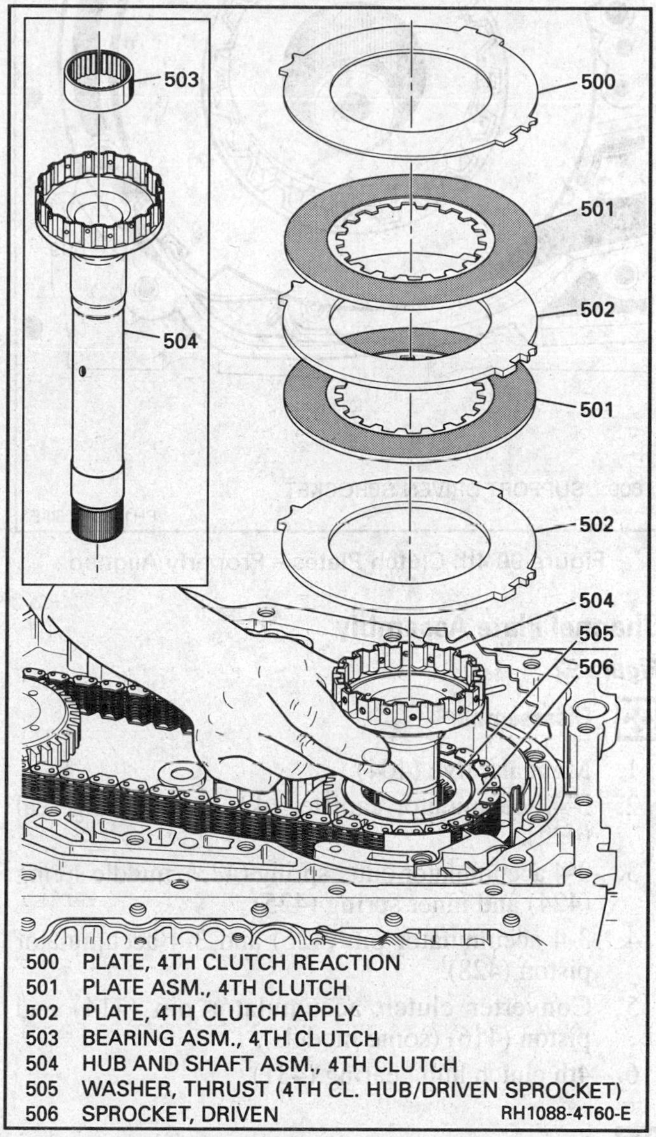
503
504
500
501
502
501
502
504
505
506
500 PLATE, 4TH CLUTCH REACTION
501 PLATE ASM., 4TH CLUTCH
502 PLATE, 4TH CLUTCH APPLY
503 BEARING ASM., 4TH CLUTCH
504 HUB AND SHAFT ASM., 4TH CLUTCH
505 WASHER, THRUST (4TH CL. HUB/DRIVEN SPROCKET)
506 SPROCKET, DRIVEN
RH1088-4T60-E

Figure 89 4th Clutch Assembly Installation

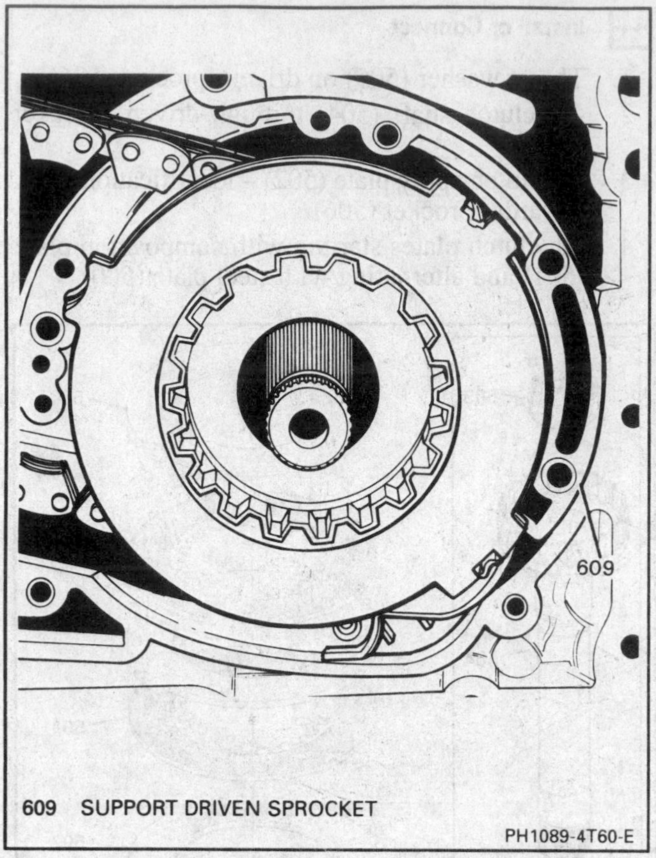
609
609 SUPPORT DRIVEN SPROCKET
PH1089-4T60-E

Figure 90 4th Clutch Plates – Properly Aligned

Channel Plate Assembly

Figure 92

Disassemble

1. Manual valve (404).
2. 3-4 accumulator canister (421) and O-ring seal (422).
3. 3-4 accumulator outer spring (423), middle spring (424) and inner spring (425).
4. 3-4 accumulator pin (426) and 3-4 accumulator piston (428).
5. Converter clutch accumulator pin (414) and piston (416) (some models).
6. 4th clutch hub bearing (431).

Inspect

- 3-4 accumulator piston (428) for:
  - Porosity.
  - Scored pin bore.
  - Nicked piston seal groove.
- 3-4 accumulator piston pin (426) for scoring and free movement in piston bore.
- 3-4 accumulator springs (423 through 425) for distorted or broken coils.
- 3-4 accumulator canister (421) for:
  - Porosity or cracks.
  - Rough or scored piston seal surface.
  - Cut O-ring (422).
- Converter clutch accumulator spring (413) for bent coils – located in case (some models).
- Converter clutch blow-off spring (418), spring seat (417) and checkball (420) for damage.
- Left hand axle oil seal (409) for missing garter spring or cut lip on seal.
- Channel plate (401) for:
  - Porosity.
  - Inter-connected fluid passages.
  - Cracks or rough machined surfaces.

Left Hand Axle Oil Seal Replacement

Figure 91

Tool Required:

J 34115 Axle Seal Installer

Remove or Disconnect

- Axle oil seal (409).

Install or Connect

- Tap new seal assembly into place with J 34115.

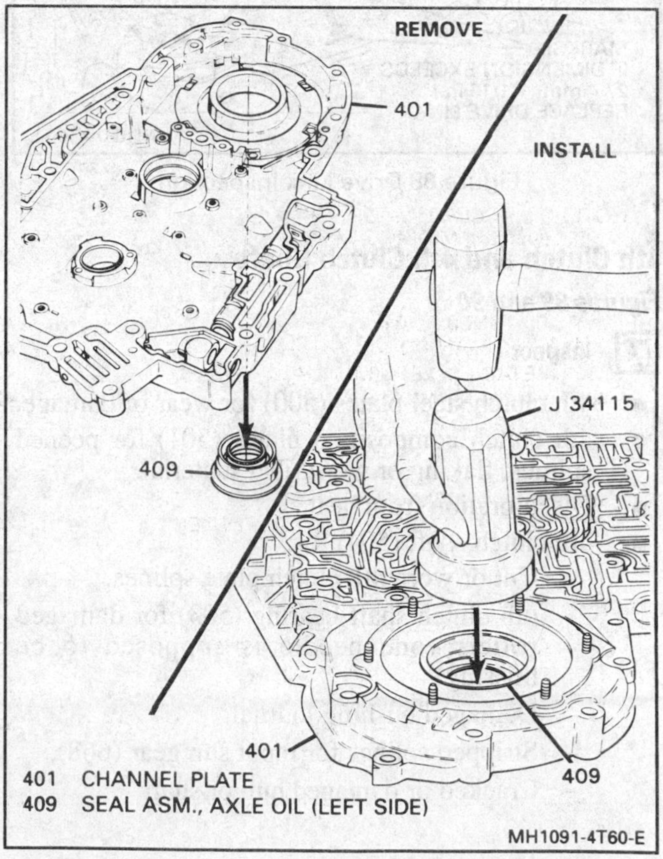
REMOVE
401
INSTALL
J 34115
409
401
409
401 CHANNEL PLATE
409 SEAL ASM., AXLE OIL (LEFT SIDE)
MH1091-4T60-E

Figure 91 Left Hand Axle Oil Seal

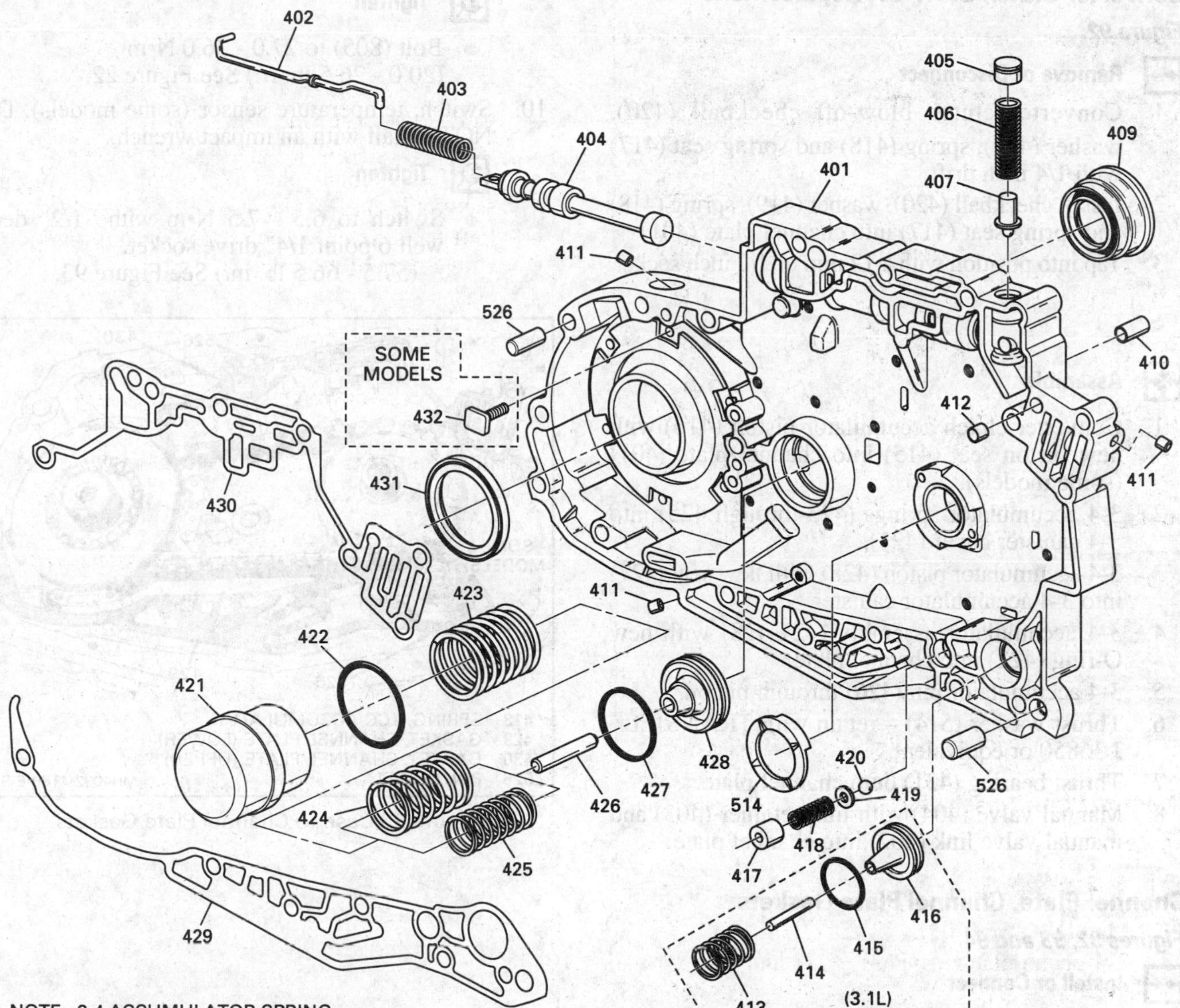

402
403
404
405
406
407
409
401
411
526
SOME MODELS
432
410
412
411
430
431
423
411
422
421
428
420
526
427
514
419
424
426
418
425
417
416
415
429
414
413
(3.1L) 4CMW MODELS ONLY

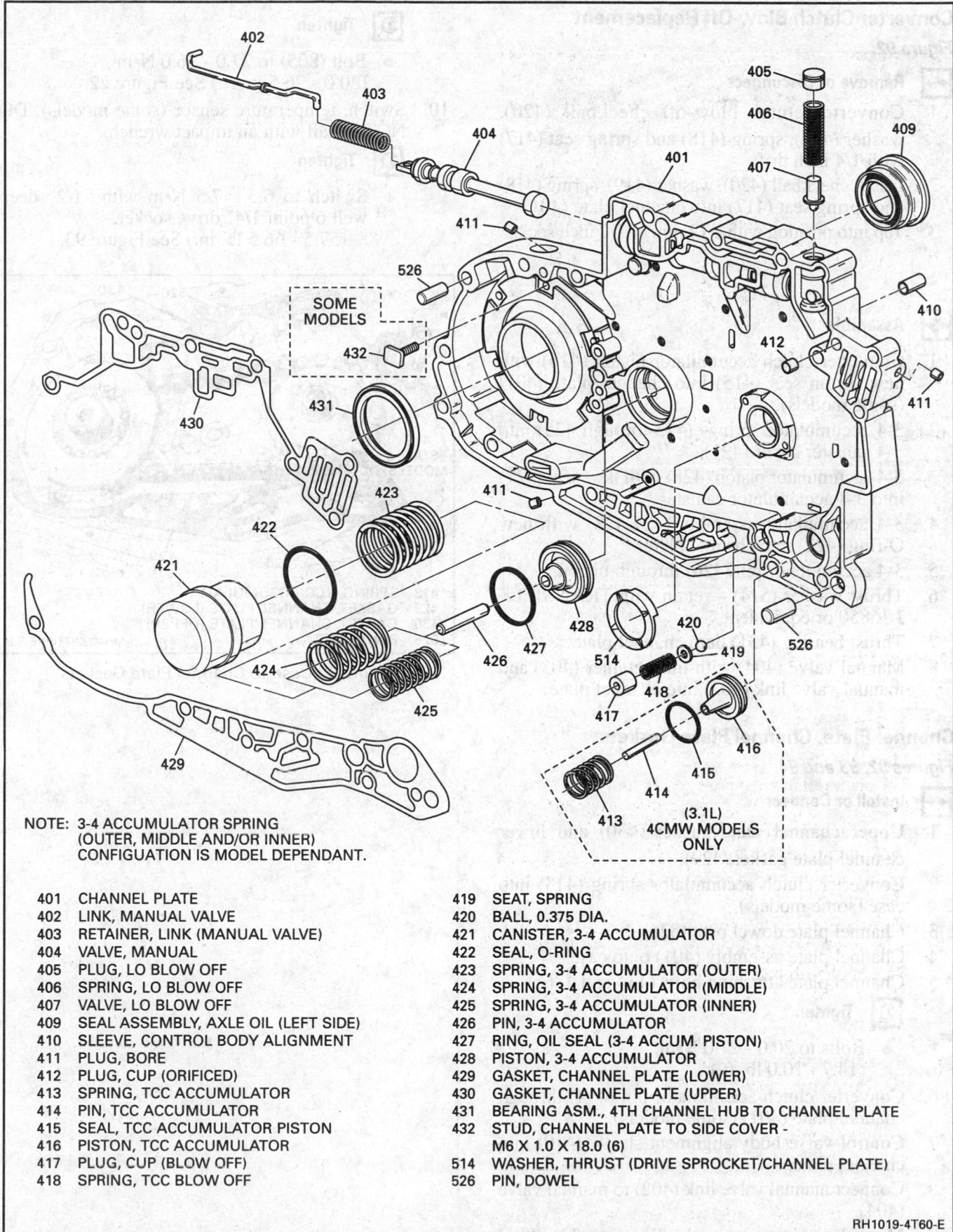

NOTE: 3-4 ACCUMULATOR SPRING (OUTER, MIDDLE AND/OR INNER) CONFIGUATION IS MODEL DEPENDANT.

401 CHANNEL PLATE
402 LINK, MANUAL VALVE
403 RETAINER, LINK (MANUAL VALVE)
404 VALVE, MANUAL
405 PLUG, LO BLOW OFF
406 SPRING, LO BLOW OFF
407 VALVE, LO BLOW OFF
409 SEAL ASSEMBLY, AXLE OIL (LEFT SIDE)
410 SLEEVE, CONTROL BODY ALIGNMENT
411 PLUG, BORE
412 PLUG, CUP (ORIFICED)
413 SPRING, TCC ACCUMULATOR
414 PIN, TCC ACCUMULATOR
415 SEAL, TCC ACCUMULATOR PISTON
416 PISTON, TCC ACCUMULATOR
417 PLUG, CUP (BLOW OFF)
418 SPRING, TCC BLOW OFF
419 SEAT, SPRING
420 BALL, 0.375 DIA.
421 CANISTER, 3-4 ACCUMULATOR
422 SEAL, O-RING
423 SPRING, 3-4 ACCUMULATOR (OUTER)
424 SPRING, 3-4 ACCUMULATOR (MIDDLE)
425 SPRING, 3-4 ACCUMULATOR (INNER)
426 PIN, 3-4 ACCUMULATOR
427 RING, OIL SEAL (3-4 ACCUM. PISTON)
428 PISTON, 3-4 ACCUMULATOR
429 GASKET, CHANNEL PLATE (LOWER)
430 GASKET, CHANNEL PLATE (UPPER)
431 BEARING ASM., 4TH CHANNEL HUB TO CHANNEL PLATE
432 STUD, CHANNEL PLATE TO SIDE COVER - M6 X 1.0 X 18.0 (6)
514 WASHER, THRUST (DRIVE SPROCKET/CHANNEL PLATE)
526 PIN, DOWEL

RH1019-4T60-E

Figure 92 Channel Plate Assembly

Converter Clutch Blow-Off Replacement

Figure 92

Remove or Disconnect

1. Converter clutch blow-off checkball (420), washer (419), spring (418) and spring seat (417) with 1/4 inch drift.
2. Install checkball (420), washer (419), spring (418) and spring seat (417) into channel plate (401).
3. Tap into position with a 12 mm or 1/2 inch socket.

Assemble

1. Converter clutch accumulator piston (416) with new piston seal (415) into channel plate (401) (some models).
2. 3-4 accumulator springs (423 through 425) into 3-4 canister cover (421).
3. 3-4 accumulator piston (428) with new seal (427) into 3-4 accumulator canister.
4. 3-4 accumulator assembly (421-428) with new O-ring (422) into channel plate.
5. 3-4 accumulator pin (426) through piston.
6. Thrust washer (514) – retain with TRANSJEL™ J 36850 or equivalent.
7. Thrust bearing (431) onto channel plate.
8. Manual valve (404) with link retainer (403) and manual valve link (402) into channel plate.

Channel Plate, Channel Plate Gaskets

Figures 92, 93 and 94

Install or Connect

1. Upper channel plate gasket (430) and lower channel plate gasket (429).
2. Converter clutch accumulator spring (413) into case (some models).
3. Channel plate dowel pins (526).
4. Channel plate assembly (401) onto case.
5. Channel plate attaching bolts (434 and 436).

   Tighten

   - Bolts to 20.0 - 27.0 N•m (14.7 - 20.0 lb. ft.)
6. Converter clutch accumulator pin (414) through channel plate (401) (some models).
7. Control valve body alignment sleeve (410) into channel plate.
8. Connect manual valve link (402) to manual valve (404).
9. Manual detent spring and roller assembly (804) and bolt (805).

   Tighten

   - Bolt (805) to 27.0 - 36.0 N•m (20.0 - 26.5 lb. ft.) See Figure 22.
10. Switch, temperature sensor (some models). DO NOT install with an impact wrench.

   Tighten

   - Switch to 6.5 - 7.5 N•m with 1/2" deep well 6 point 1/4" drive socket. (57.5 - 66.5 lb. in.) See Figure 93.

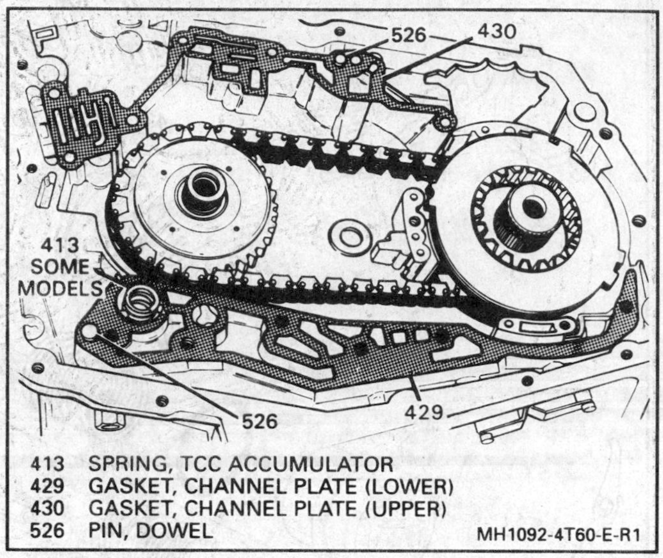
526
430
413
SOME
MODELS
526
429
413 SPRING, TCC ACCUMULATOR
429 GASKET, CHANNEL PLATE (LOWER)
430 GASKET, CHANNEL PLATE (UPPER)
526 PIN, DOWEL
MH1092-4T60-E-R1

Figure 93 Case to Channel Plate Gaskets

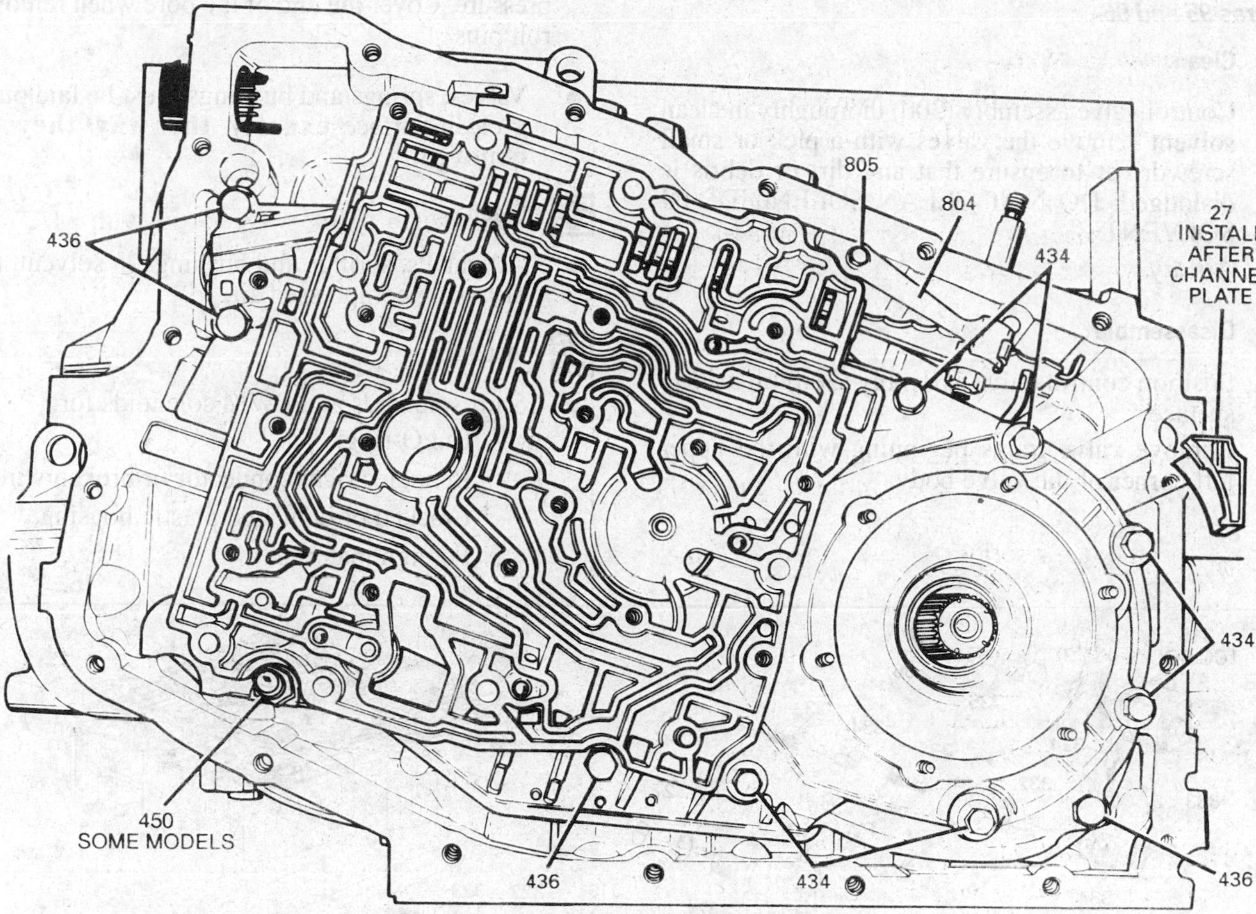
436
805
804
27
INSTALL
AFTER
CHANNEL
PLATE
434
434
450
SOME MODELS
436
434
436

27 WEIR, OIL RESERVOIR
434 BOLT, CHANNEL PLATE TO CASE - M8 X 1.25 X 45.0 (6) 20.0 - 27.0 N•m (14.7 - 20.0 LB. FT.)
436 BOLT, CHANNEL PLATE TO CASE - M8 X 1.25 X 30.0 (4) 20.0 - 27.0 N•m (14.7 - 20.0 LB. FT.)
450 SWITCH, TEMP. TRACTION CONTROL 1/8 - 27 DRYSEAL (1) 6.5 - 7.5 N•m (57.5 - 66.5 LB. IN.)
804 SPRING AND ROLLER ASSEMBLY, MANUAL DETENT
805 BOLT, MANUAL DETENT SPRING TO CHANNEL PLATE - M6 X 1.0 X 16.0 (1) 27.0 - 36.0 N•m (20.0 - 26.5 LB. FT.)

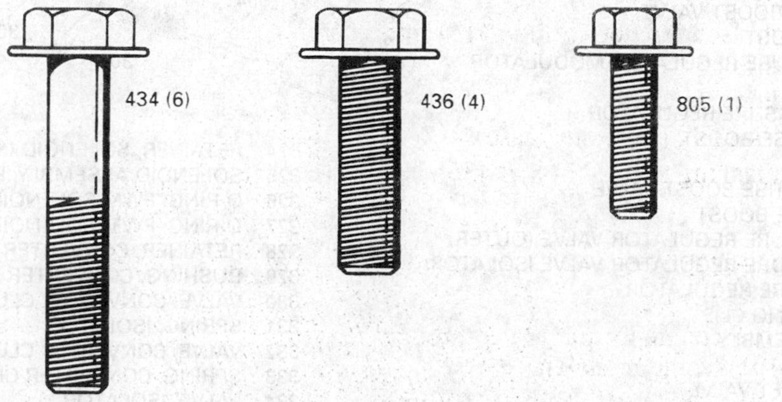
434 (6)
436 (4)
805 (1)

RH1093-4T60-E

Figure 94 Channel Plate Bolt Locations

Control Valve Assembly

Figures 95 and 96

Clean

- Control valve assembly (300) thoroughly in clean solvent – move the valves with a pick or small screwdriver to ensure that any dirt or debris is dislodged. DO NOT CLEAN SOLENOIDS IN SOLVENT.
- Air dry.

Disassemble

- Position control valve assembly (300) on a clean surface.
- Remove valve trains beginning with the upper left corner of the valve body.

IMPORTANT: Some valves are under spring pressure. Cover the end of the bore when removing roll pins.

- Valves, springs and bushings must be laid out on a clean surface **exactly the way they are removed.**

Clean

- All valves, springs and bushings in solvent, then dry using compressed air.

Inspect

- Shift solenoids and PWM solenoids for:
  - Cut O-ring.
  - Bent electrical connector or broken wire.
  - Cracked or damaged plastic housing.
  - Foreign material

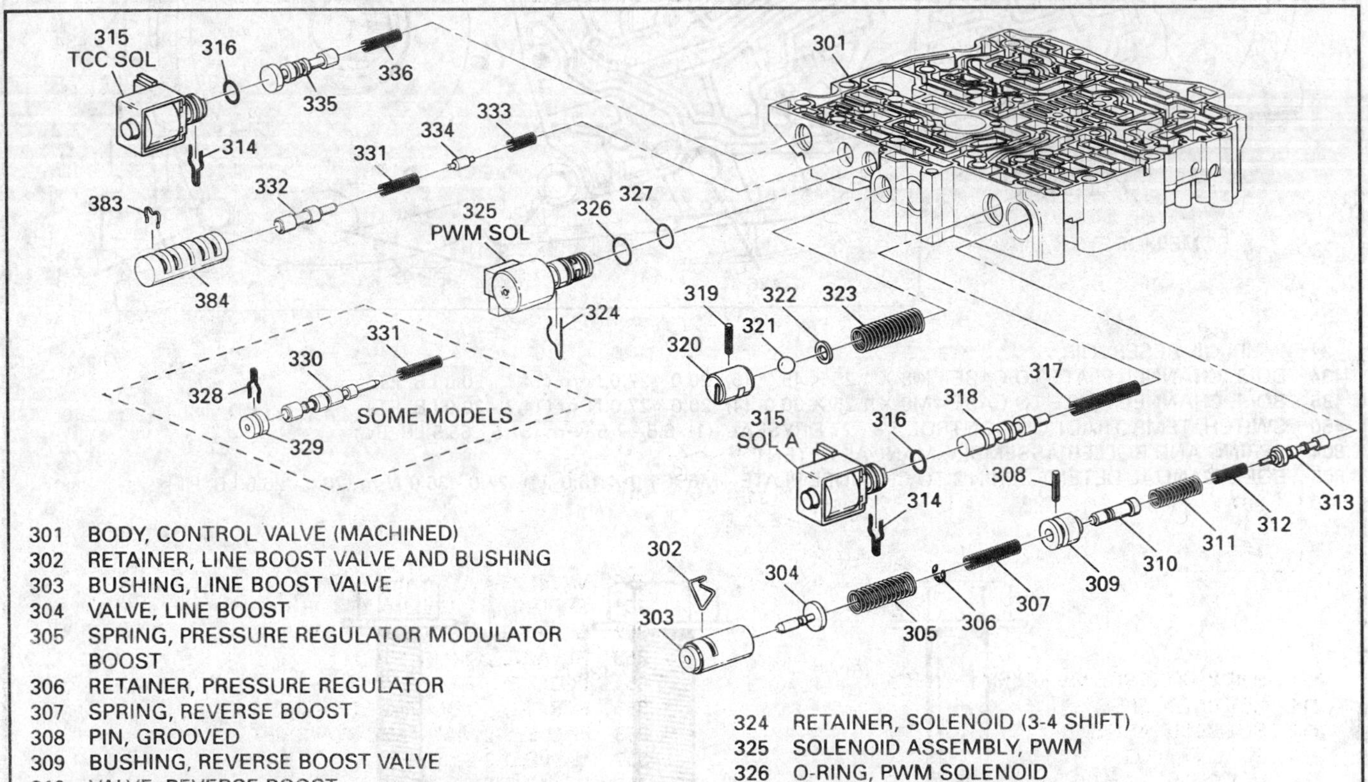
315
TCC SOL
316
336
335
333
334
314
331
332
383
325
PWM SOL
326
327
384
324
301
319
322
323
321
320
331
330
328
SOME MODELS
329
317
318
315
SOL A
316
308
314
313
312
311
310
309
302
304
307
306
305
303

301 BODY, CONTROL VALVE (MACHINED)
302 RETAINER, LINE BOOST VALVE AND BUSHING
303 BUSHING, LINE BOOST VALVE
304 VALVE, LINE BOOST
305 SPRING, PRESSURE REGULATOR MODULATOR BOOST
306 RETAINER, PRESSURE REGULATOR
307 SPRING, REVERSE BOOST
308 PIN, GROOVED
309 BUSHING, REVERSE BOOST VALVE
310 VALVE, REVERSE BOOST
311 SPRING, PRESSURE REGULATOR VALVE (OUTER)
312 SPRING, PRESSURE REGULATOR VALVE ISOLATOR
313 VALVE, PRESSURE REGULATOR
314 RETAINER, SPRING CLIP
315 SOLENOID ASSEMBLY
316 SEAL, O-RING
317 SPRING, 1-2 SHIFT VALVE
318 VALVE, 1-2 SHIFT
319 PIN, COILED SPRING
320 BUSHING, PUMP PRESSURE RELIEF
321 BALL, 0.375 DIA.
322 SEAT, SPRING
323 SPRING, PUMP PRESSURE RELIEF
324 RETAINER, SOLENOID (3-4 SHIFT)
325 SOLENOID ASSEMBLY, PWM
326 O-RING, PWM SOLENOID
327 O-RING, PWM SOLENOID
328 RETAINER, CONVERTER CL. REGULATOR
329 BUSHING, CONVERTER CL. REGULATOR
330 VALVE, CONVERTER CLUTCH REGULATOR
331 SPRING, ISOLATOR
332 VALVE, CONVERTER CLUTCH REGULATOR
333 SPRING, CONVERTER CLUTCH REGULATOR
334 VALVE, ISOLATOR
335 VALVE, CONVERTER CLUTCH
336 SPRING, CONVERTER CLUTCH
383 RETAINER, CONVERTER CLUTCH REGULATOR
384 BUSHING, CONVERTER CLUTCH REGULATOR

RH1094-4T60-E

Figure 95 Control Valve Assembly – A

- All valves and bushings for:
  - Wear.
  - Nicks.
  - Scratches.
- Springs for damage or distorted coils.
- Valve body casting for:
  - Porosity.
  - Interconnected oil passages.
  - Damaged machined surfaces.
  - Damaged pump shaft bearing (368).

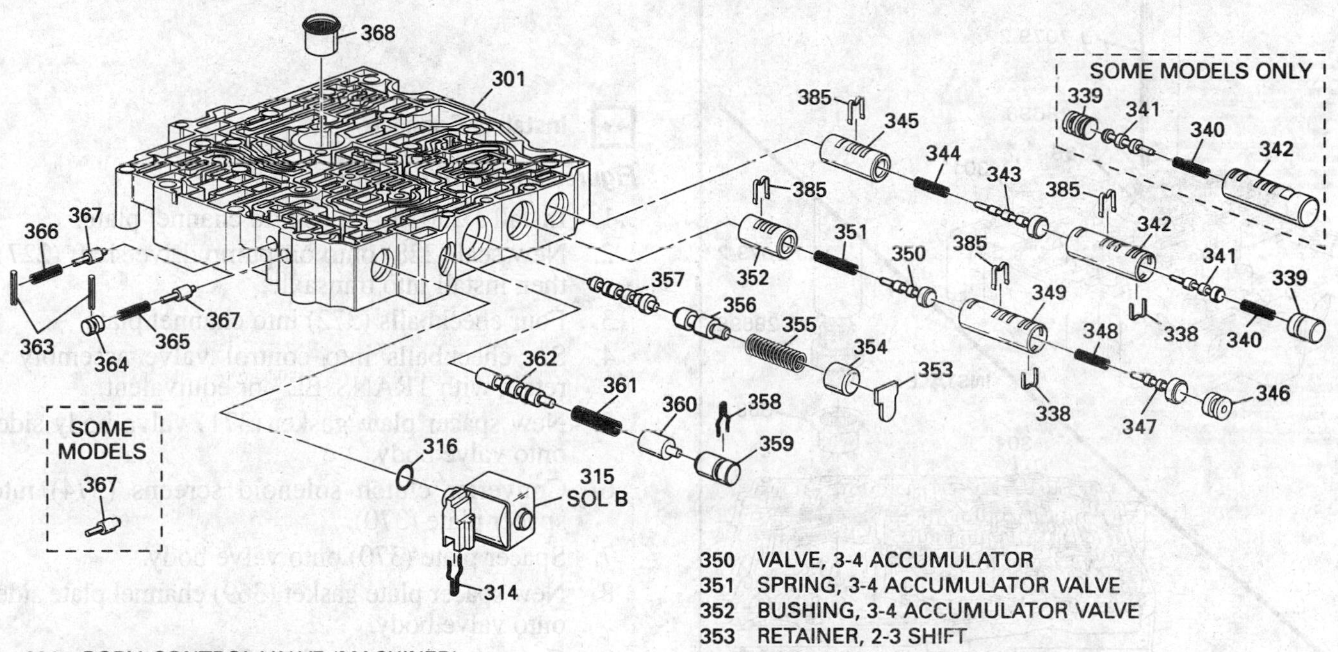
368
301
385
345
344
343
385
SOME MODELS ONLY
339
341
340
342
385
342
341
339
338
340
385
351
350
352
349
348
338
346
347
357
356
355
354
353
362
361
360
358
359
366
367
367
365
363
364
SOME MODELS
367
316
315
SOL B
314

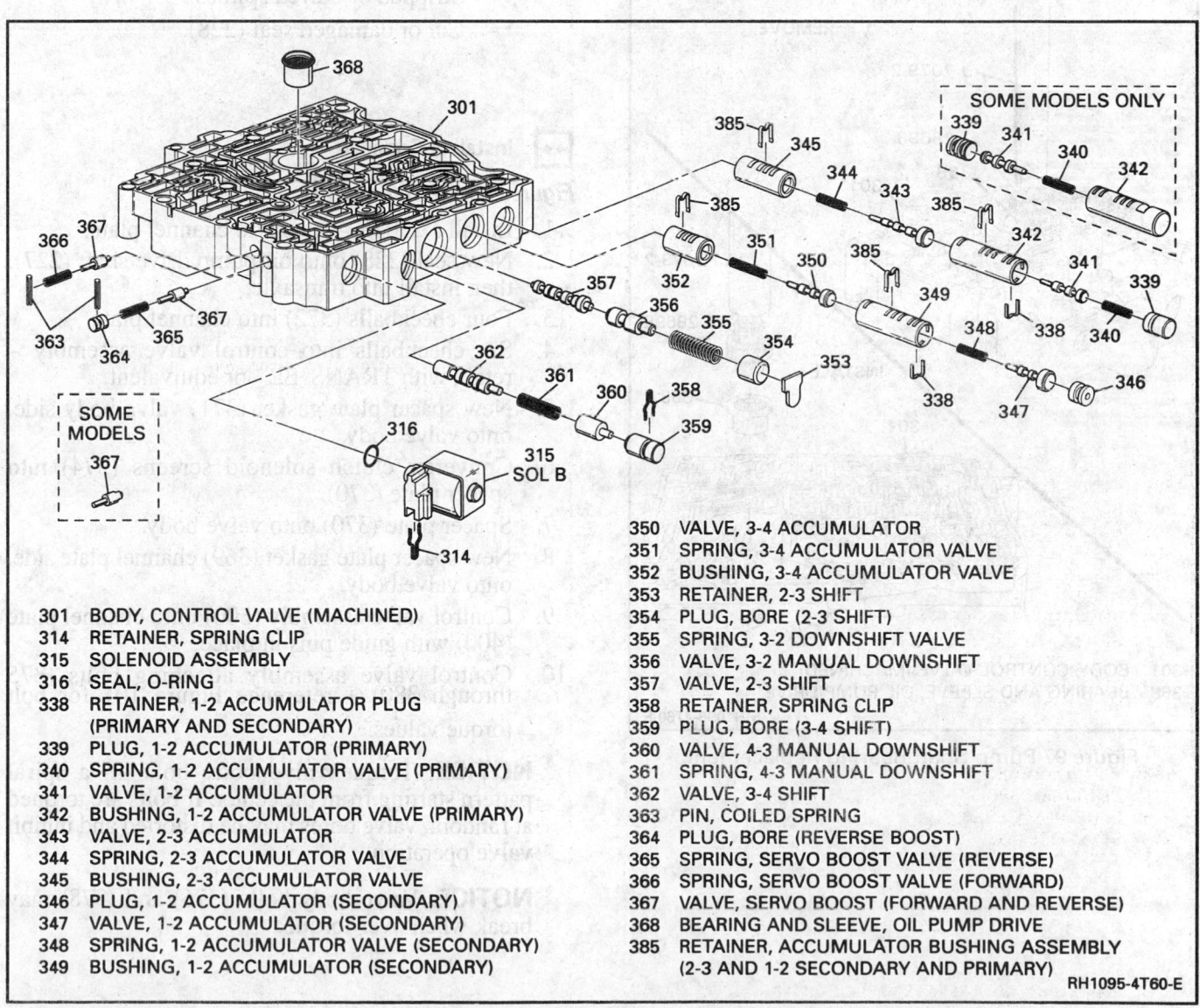

301 BODY, CONTROL VALVE (MACHINED)
314 RETAINER, SPRING CLIP
315 SOLENOID ASSEMBLY
316 SEAL, O-RING
338 RETAINER, 1-2 ACCUMULATOR PLUG (PRIMARY AND SECONDARY)
339 PLUG, 1-2 ACCUMULATOR (PRIMARY)
340 SPRING, 1-2 ACCUMULATOR VALVE (PRIMARY)
341 VALVE, 1-2 ACCUMULATOR
342 BUSHING, 1-2 ACCUMULATOR VALVE (PRIMARY)
343 VALVE, 2-3 ACCUMULATOR
344 SPRING, 2-3 ACCUMULATOR VALVE
345 BUSHING, 2-3 ACCUMULATOR VALVE
346 PLUG, 1-2 ACCUMULATOR (SECONDARY)
347 VALVE, 1-2 ACCUMULATOR (SECONDARY)
348 SPRING, 1-2 ACCUMULATOR VALVE (SECONDARY)
349 BUSHING, 1-2 ACCUMULATOR (SECONDARY)
350 VALVE, 3-4 ACCUMULATOR
351 SPRING, 3-4 ACCUMULATOR VALVE
352 BUSHING, 3-4 ACCUMULATOR VALVE
353 RETAINER, 2-3 SHIFT
354 PLUG, BORE (2-3 SHIFT)
355 SPRING, 3-2 DOWNSHIFT VALVE
356 VALVE, 3-2 MANUAL DOWNSHIFT
357 VALVE, 2-3 SHIFT
358 RETAINER, SPRING CLIP
359 PLUG, BORE (3-4 SHIFT)
360 VALVE, 4-3 MANUAL DOWNSHIFT
361 SPRING, 4-3 MANUAL DOWNSHIFT
362 VALVE, 3-4 SHIFT
363 PIN, COILED SPRING
364 PLUG, BORE (REVERSE BOOST)
365 SPRING, SERVO BOOST VALVE (REVERSE)
366 SPRING, SERVO BOOST VALVE (FORWARD)
367 VALVE, SERVO BOOST (FORWARD AND REVERSE)
368 BEARING AND SLEEVE, OIL PUMP DRIVE
385 RETAINER, ACCUMULATOR BUSHING ASSEMBLY (2-3 AND 1-2 SECONDARY AND PRIMARY)

RH1095-4T60-E

Figure 96 Control Valve Assembly – B

Pump Shaft Bearing Replacement

Figure 97

Remove or Disconnect

- Bearing (368) with J 28698 – push partially out with tool and complete removal with a screwdriver.

Install or Connect

- Tap new bearing into place with J 28698 until fully seated.

Assemble

- Install new o-rings on all solenoids.
- Bushings, springs, valves and shift solenoids **exactly** as shown by noting the position of the valve lands and bushing passages.

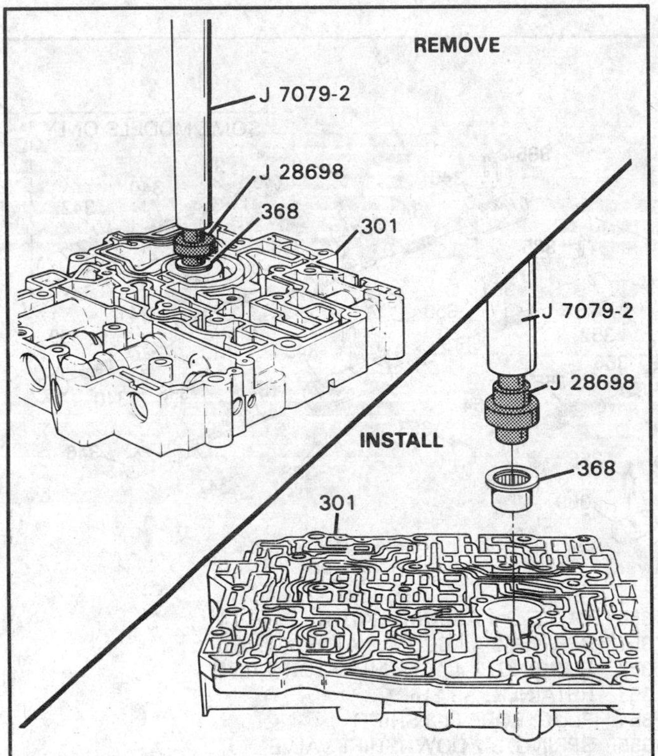
REMOVE
J 7079-2
J 28698
368
301
J 7079-2
J 28698
INSTALL
368
301
301 BODY, CONTROL VALVE (MACHINED)
368 BEARING AND SLEEVE, OIL PUMP DRIVE
MH1096-4T60-E

Figure 97 Pump Shaft Bearing Replacement

Control Valve Assembly Spacer Plate, Spacer Plate Gaskets and Oil Pump Drive Shaft

Figure 100

Tool Required:

J 25025-A Guide Pins

Inspect

- Spacer plate (370) for:
  - Bent or stuck thermal elements.
  - Plugged holes.
  - Peened holes caused by checkballs.
  - Damage from being bent.
- Four solenoid screens (374).
  - Plugged or damaged screen.
- Oil pump drive shaft (227) for:
  - Scored or rough journal surfaces.
  - Stripped or burred splines.
  - Cut or damaged seal (228).

Install or Connect

Figures 98, 99, 100 and 101

1. Install J 25025-A pins into channel plate.
2. New seal (228) onto oil pump drive shaft (227), then install into transaxle.
3. Four checkballs (372) into channel plate.
4. Six checkballs into control valve assembly – retain with TRANSJEL™ or equivalent.
5. New spacer plate gasket (371) valve body side, onto valve body.
6. Converter clutch solenoid screens (374) into spacer plate (370).
7. Spacer plate (370) onto valve body.
8. New spacer plate gasket (369) channel plate side, onto valve body.
9. Control valve assembly (300) onto channel plate (400) with guide pins in place.
10. Control valve assembly attaching bolts (375 through 380) – reference Figure 101 for bolt torque values.

NOTICE: Torque valve body bolts in a spiral pattern starting from the center. If bolts are torqued at random, valve bores may be distorted and inhibit valve operation.

NOTICE: Valve body bolts (376) and (378) may break when over-torqued.

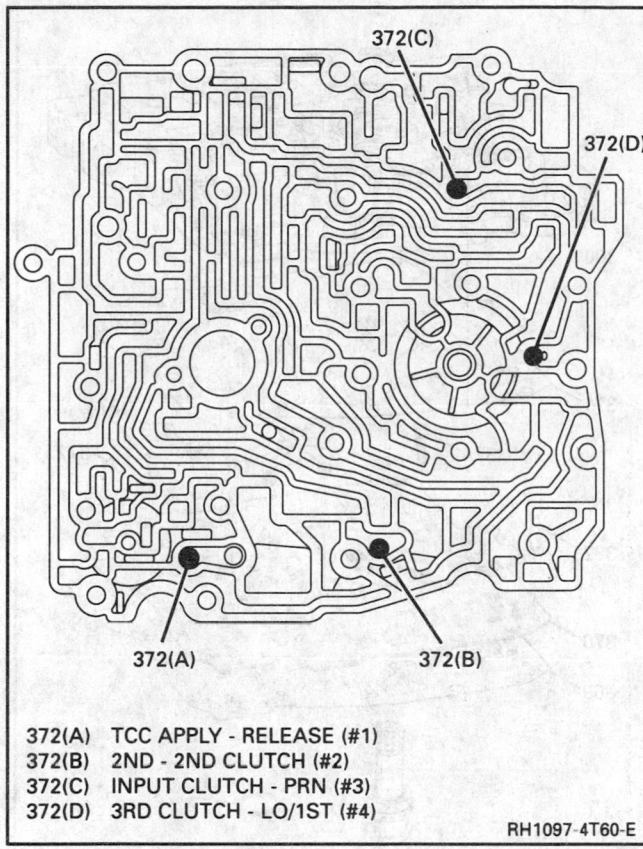

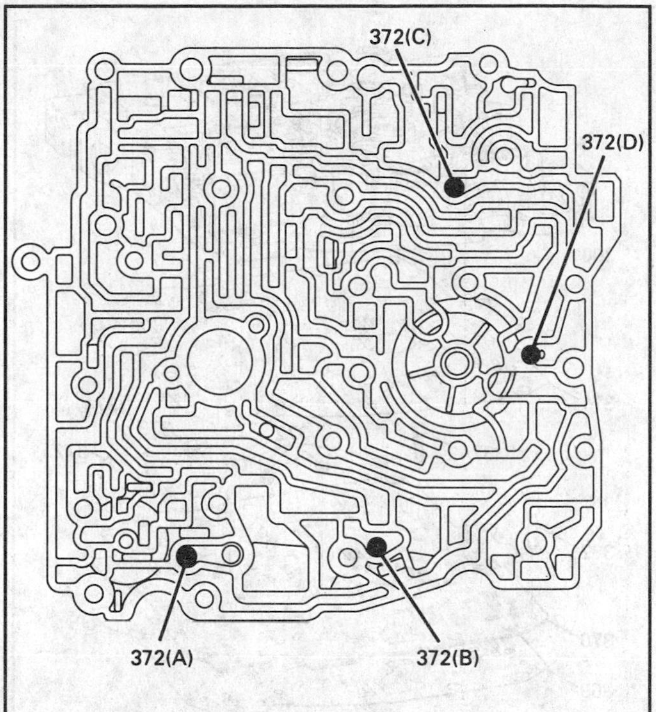
372(C)
372(D)
372(A)
372(B)
372(A) TCC APPLY - RELEASE (#1)
372(B) 2ND - 2ND CLUTCH (#2)
372(C) INPUT CLUTCH - PRN (#3)
372(D) 3RD CLUTCH - LO/1ST (#4)
RH1097-4T60-E

Figure 98 Checkball Locations – Channel Plate

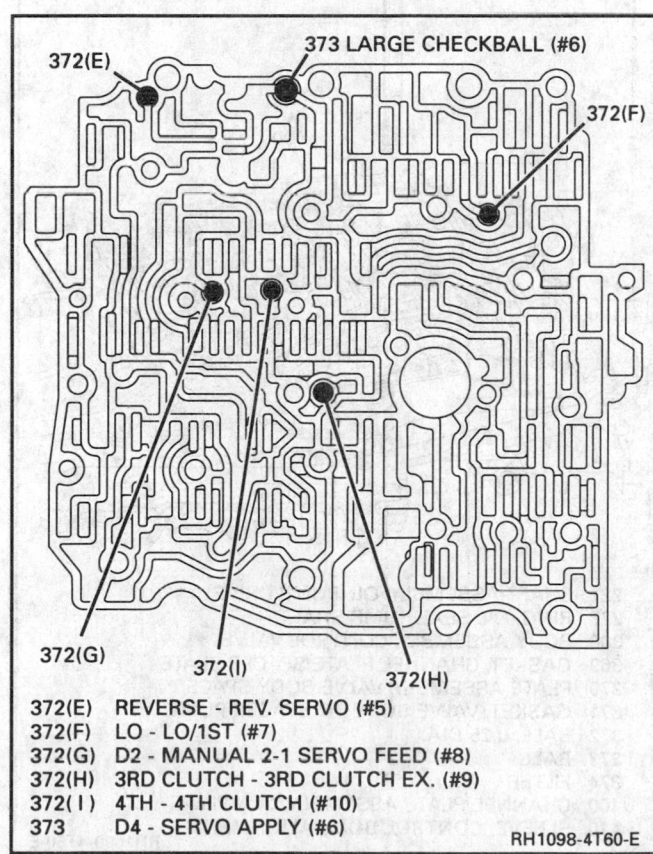

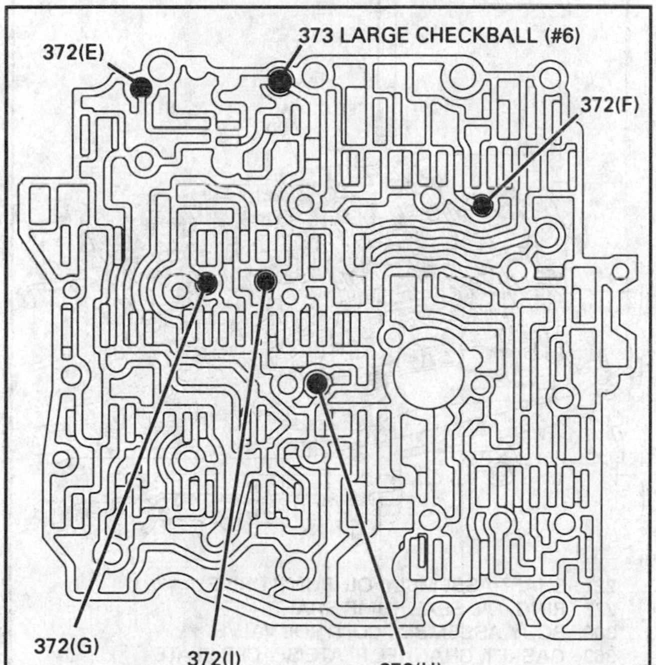
373 LARGE CHECKBALL (#6)
372(E)
372(F)
372(G)
372(I)
372(H)
372(E) REVERSE - REV. SERVO (#5)
372(F) LO - LO/1ST (#7)
372(G) D2 - MANUAL 2-1 SERVO FEED (#8)
372(H) 3RD CLUTCH - 3RD CLUTCH EX. (#9)
372(I) 4TH - 4TH CLUTCH (#10)
373 D4 - SERVO APPLY (#6)
RH1098-4T60-E

Figure 99 Checkball Locations – Control Valve Assembly

Oil Pump Assembly

Figures 102, 103 and 104

Clean

- Oil pump assembly thoroughly with clean solvent.
- Air dry.

Disassemble

NOTICE: The oil pump slide, seal, vanes and rotor are factory selected for size. Do not switch parts with another pump assembly as damage may result.

1. Bolts (205).
2. Pump cover (201) from pump body (202).
3. Vane rings (209) with pump rotor (210).
4. Pump vanes (211), oil seal ring (212) and O-ring seal (213).
5. Outer pump priming spring (222) and inner pump priming spring (223).

CAUTION: Priming springs have high tension against the oil pump slide (214). Cover springs with a clean shop towel during removal to prevent personal injury.

6. Pump slide seal (220) and support slide seal (221).
7. Pivot pin (215).
8. Pressure screen assembly (219).
9. Pressure switch(es) (218) (some models).

Clean

- All components in solvent.
- Air dry.

Inspect

- Pump body (202) for:
  - Porosity.
  - Worn, scored or damaged pump pocket.
  - Interconnected oil passages.
  - Damaged machined surfaces.
- Pressure screen assembly (219) for damage or debris.
- Pressure switch (218) for damage to threads or electrical connector.
- Pump slide (214) for:
  - Worn, scored or gouged surfaces.
- Pump rotor (210) and vanes (211) for cracks, wear or damage.
- Seal (213) for cuts or damage.
- Vane rings (209) for cracks or wear.
- Pump cover (201) for cracks, wear or gouges from pump vanes.

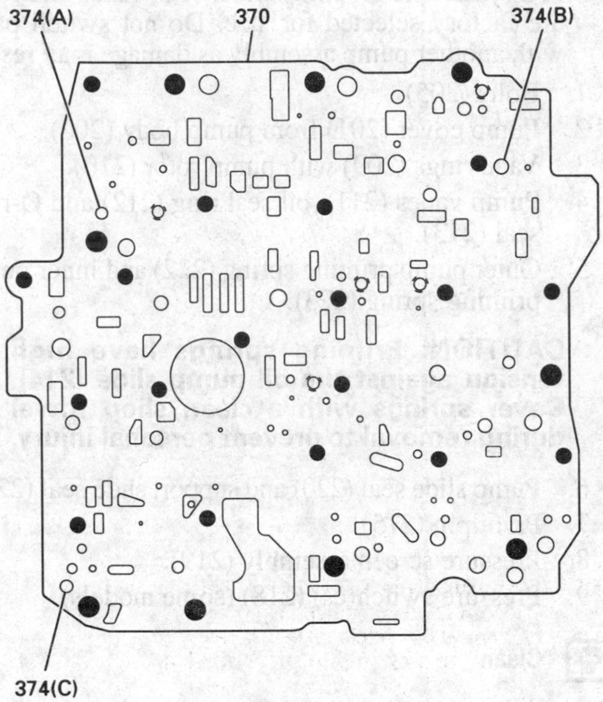
374(A)
370
374(B)
374(C)

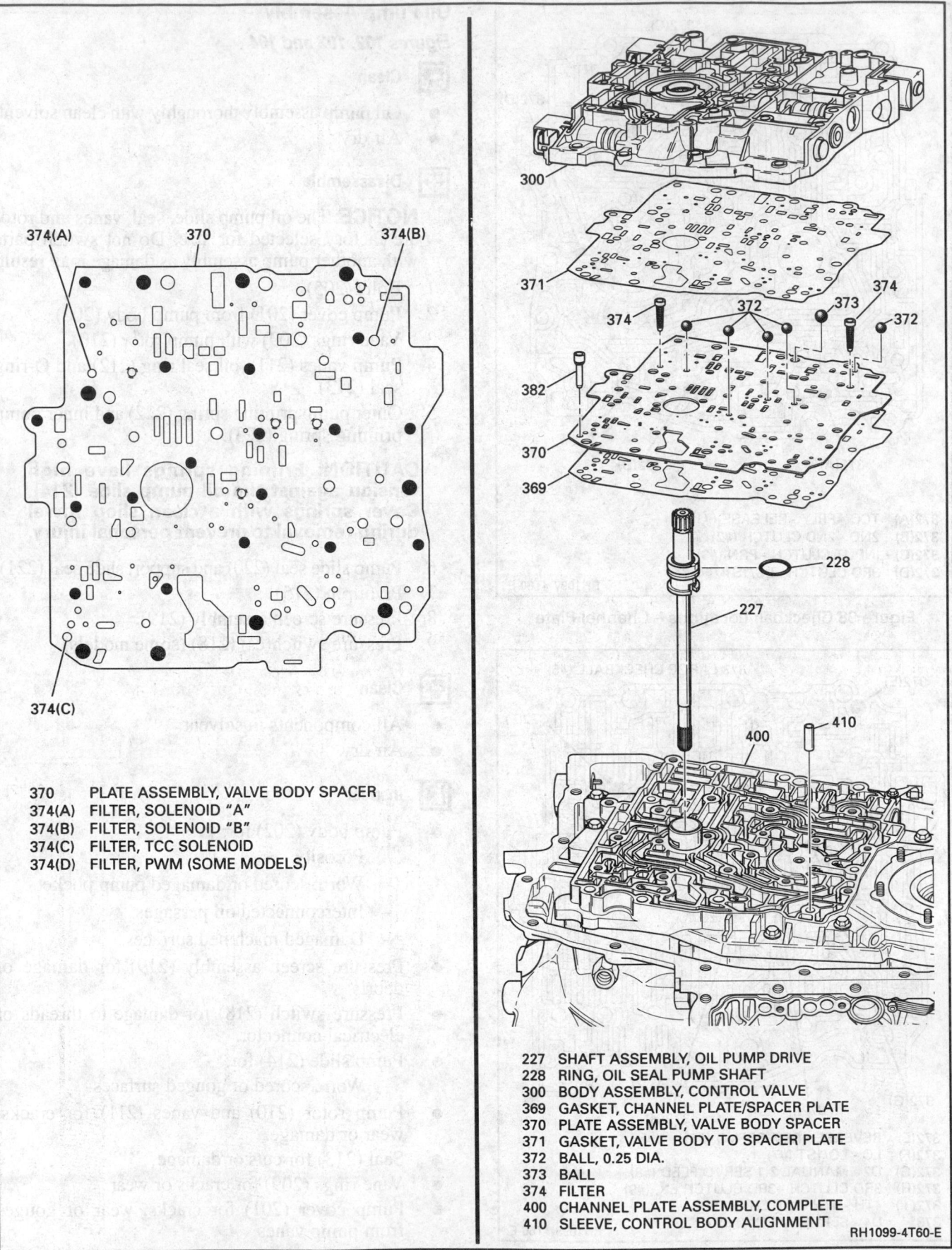

370 PLATE ASSEMBLY, VALVE BODY SPACER
374(A) FILTER, SOLENOID "A"
374(B) FILTER, SOLENOID "B"
374(C) FILTER, TCC SOLENOID
374(D) FILTER, PWM (SOME MODELS)

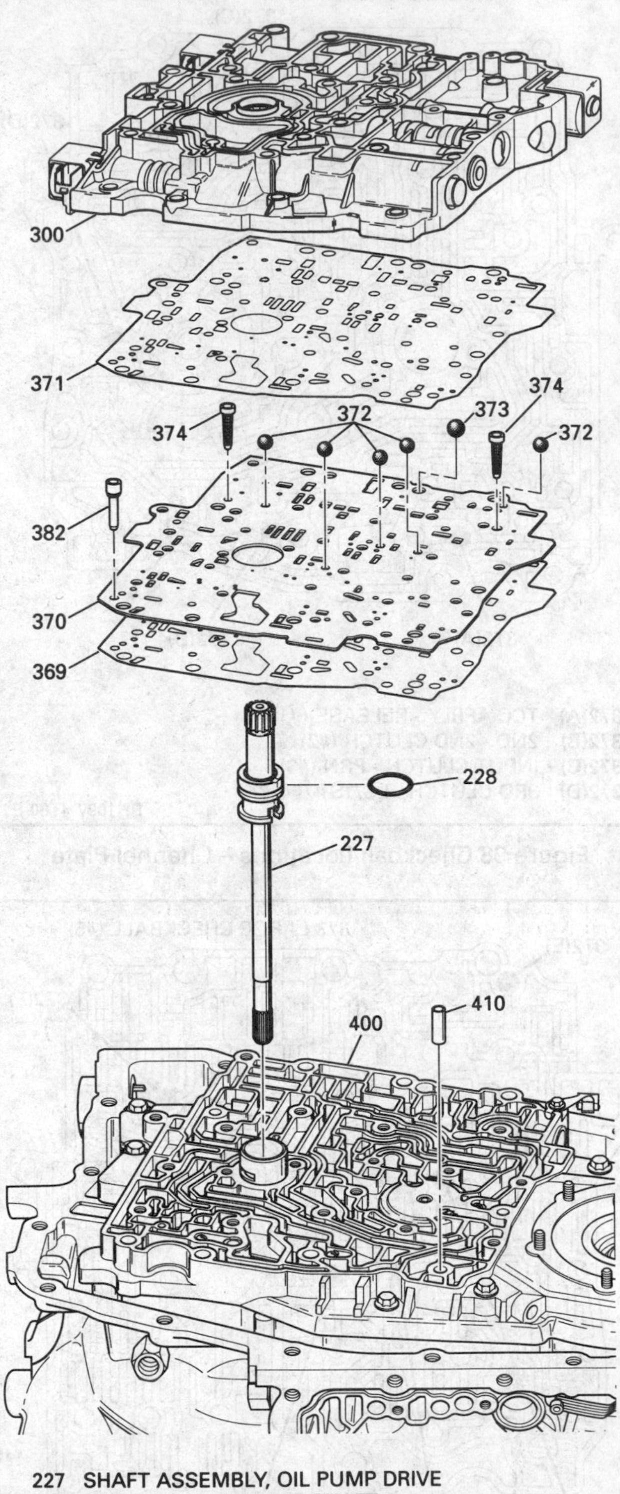
300
371
374
372
373
374
372
382
370
369
228
227
410
400

227 SHAFT ASSEMBLY, OIL PUMP DRIVE
228 RING, OIL SEAL PUMP SHAFT
300 BODY ASSEMBLY, CONTROL VALVE
369 GASKET, CHANNEL PLATE/SPACER PLATE
370 PLATE ASSEMBLY, VALVE BODY SPACER
371 GASKET, VALVE BODY TO SPACER PLATE
372 BALL, 0.25 DIA.
373 BALL
374 FILTER
400 CHANNEL PLATE ASSEMBLY, COMPLETE
410 SLEEVE, CONTROL BODY ALIGNMENT

RH1099-4T60-E

Figure 100 Attaching Pump Shaft, Spacer Plate/Gaskets and Control Valve Assembly

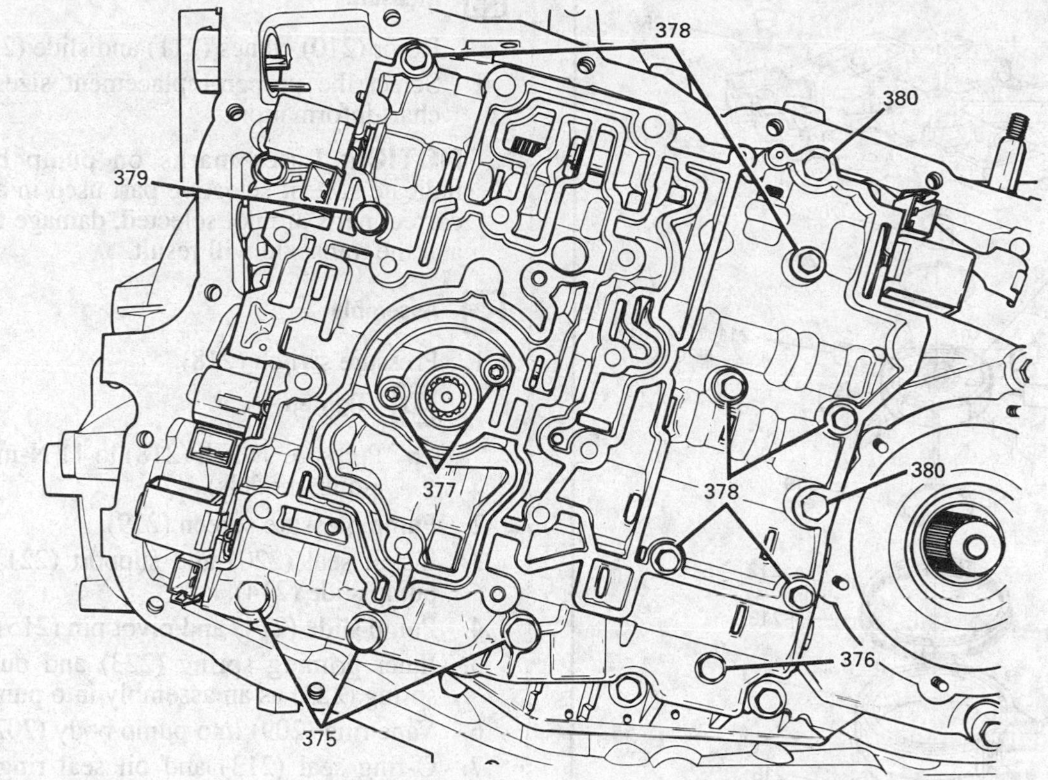
378
380
379
377
378
380
376
375

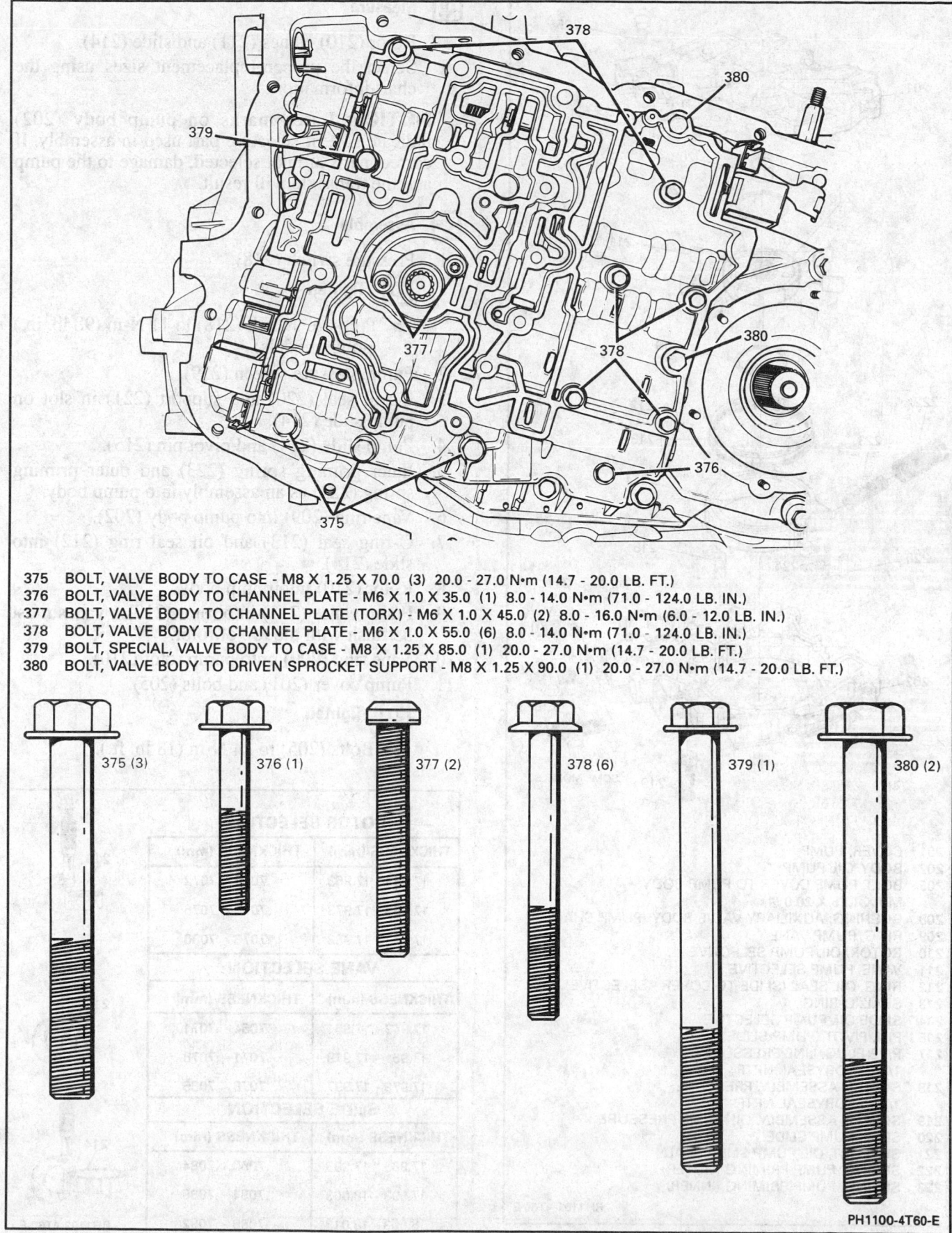

375 BOLT, VALVE BODY TO CASE - M8 X 1.25 X 70.0 (3) 20.0 - 27.0 N•m (14.7 - 20.0 LB. FT.)
376 BOLT, VALVE BODY TO CHANNEL PLATE - M6 X 1.0 X 35.0 (1) 8.0 - 14.0 N•m (71.0 - 124.0 LB. IN.)
377 BOLT, VALVE BODY TO CHANNEL PLATE (TORX) - M6 X 1.0 X 45.0 (2) 8.0 - 16.0 N•m (6.0 - 12.0 LB. IN.)
378 BOLT, VALVE BODY TO CHANNEL PLATE - M6 X 1.0 X 55.0 (6) 8.0 - 14.0 N•m (71.0 - 124.0 LB. IN.)
379 BOLT, SPECIAL, VALVE BODY TO CASE - M8 X 1.25 X 85.0 (1) 20.0 - 27.0 N•m (14.7 - 20.0 LB. FT.)
380 BOLT, VALVE BODY TO DRIVEN SPROCKET SUPPORT - M8 X 1.25 X 90.0 (1) 20.0 - 27.0 N•m (14.7 - 20.0 LB. FT.)

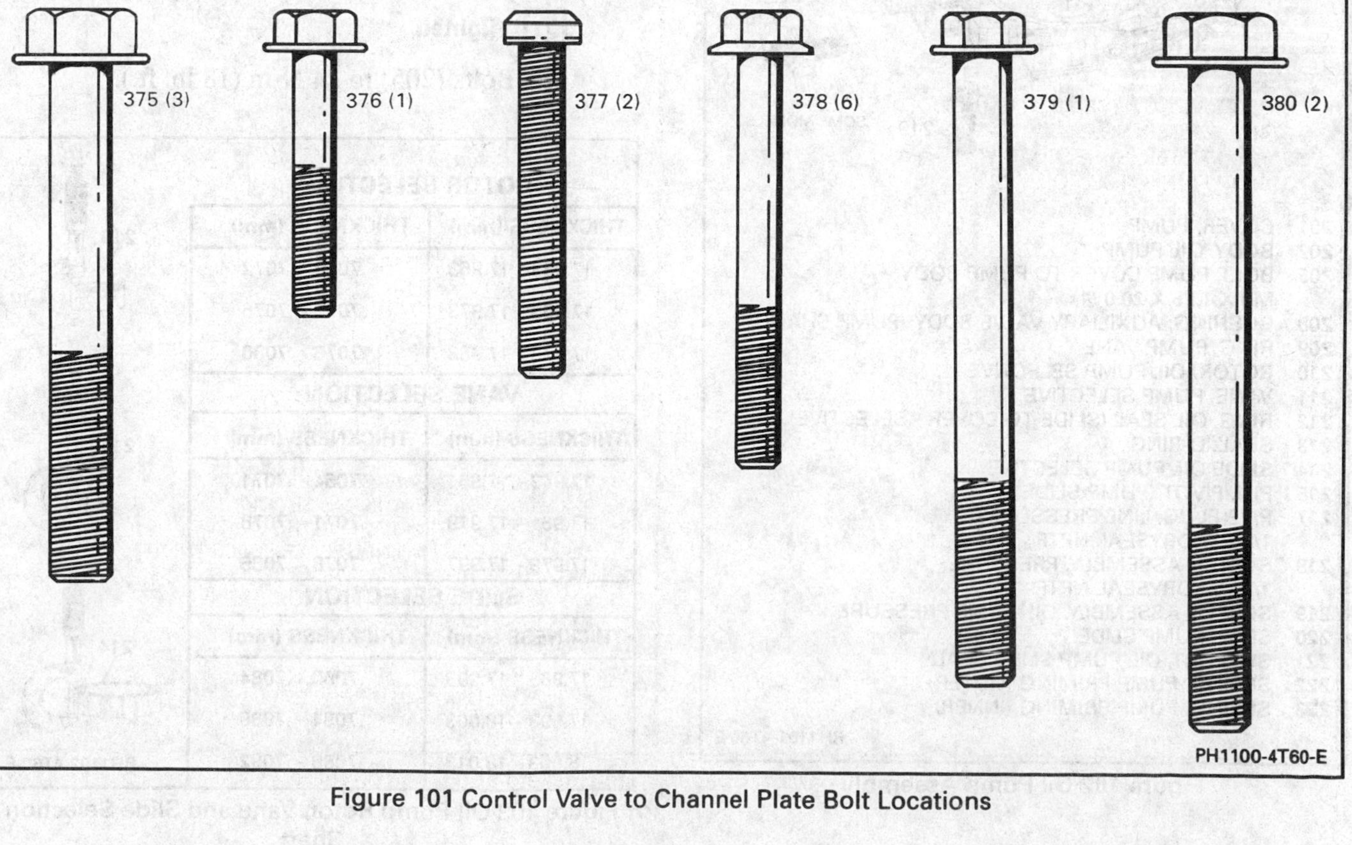
375 (3)
376 (1)
377 (2)
378 (6)
379 (1)
380 (2)
PH1100-4T60-E

Figure 101 Control Valve to Channel Plate Bolt Locations

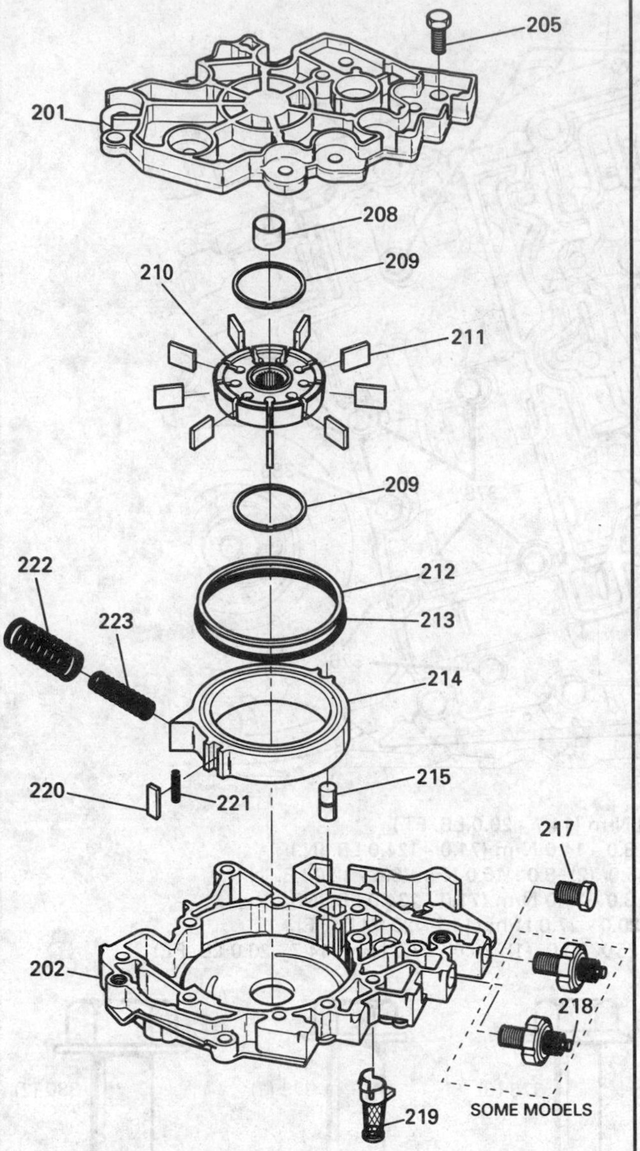
205
201
208
210
209
211
209
222
212
223
213
214
220
221
215
217
202
218
219
SOME MODELS

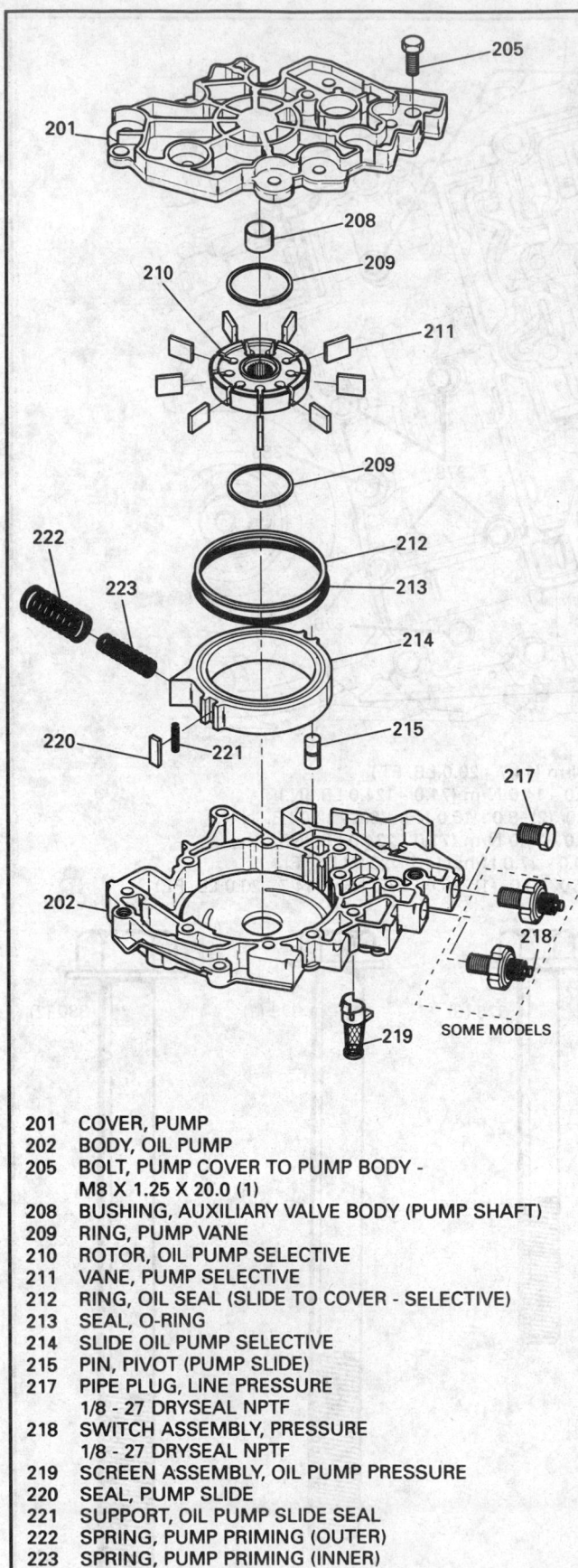

- 201 COVER, PUMP
- 202 BODY, OIL PUMP
- 205 BOLT, PUMP COVER TO PUMP BODY - M8 X 1.25 X 20.0 (1)
- 208 BUSHING, AUXILIARY VALVE BODY (PUMP SHAFT)
- 209 RING, PUMP VANE
- 210 ROTOR, OIL PUMP SELECTIVE
- 211 VANE, PUMP SELECTIVE
- 212 RING, OIL SEAL (SLIDE TO COVER - SELECTIVE)
- 213 SEAL, O-RING
- 214 SLIDE OIL PUMP SELECTIVE
- 215 PIN, PIVOT (PUMP SLIDE)
- 217 PIPE PLUG, LINE PRESSURE 1/8 - 27 DRYSEAL NPTF
- 218 SWITCH ASSEMBLY, PRESSURE 1/8 - 27 DRYSEAL NPTF
- 219 SCREEN ASSEMBLY, OIL PUMP PRESSURE
- 220 SEAL, PUMP SLIDE
- 221 SUPPORT, OIL PUMP SLIDE SEAL
- 222 SPRING, PUMP PRIMING (OUTER)
- 223 SPRING, PUMP PRIMING (INNER)

RH1101-4T60-E

Figure 102 Oil Pump Assembly

Measure

- Rotor (210), vanes (211) and slide (214).
- Select the proper replacement sizes using the chart information.

NOTICE: Laser marks on pump body (202) indicate size of selective part used in assembly. If correct parts are not selected, damage to the pump and the transaxle will result.

Assemble

1. Pressure switch (218).

   Tighten

   - Pressure switch (218) to 11 N•m (98 lb. in.) (some models).
2. Pump pressure screen (219).
3. Install seal (220) and support (221) in slot on pump slide (214).
4. Pump slide (214) and pivot pin (215).
5. Inner priming spring (223) and outer priming spring (222) as an assembly into pump body.
6. Vane ring (209) into pump body (202).
7. O-ring seal (213) and oil seal ring (212) into slide (214).
8. Rotor (210) into pump body.
9. Pump vanes (211) into rotor (210) – vanes must be flush with the top of rotor.
10. Vane ring (209) onto pump rotor (210).
11. Pump cover (201) and bolts (205).

    Tighten

    - Bolts (205) to 24 N•m (18 lb. ft.).

ROTOR SELECTION	
THICKNESS (mm)	THICKNESS (mm)
17.953 - 17.963	.7068 - .7072
17.963 - 17.973	.7072 - .7076
17.973 - 17.983	.7076 - .7080
VANE SELECTION	
THICKNESS (mm)	THICKNESS (mm)
17.943 - 17.961	.7064 - .7071
17.961 - 17.979	.7071 - .7078
17.979 - 17.997	.7078 - .7085
SLIDE SELECTION	
THICKNESS (mm)	THICKNESS (mm)
17.983 - 17.993	.7080 - .7084
17.993 - 18.003	.7084 - .7088
18.003 - 18.013	.7088 - .7092

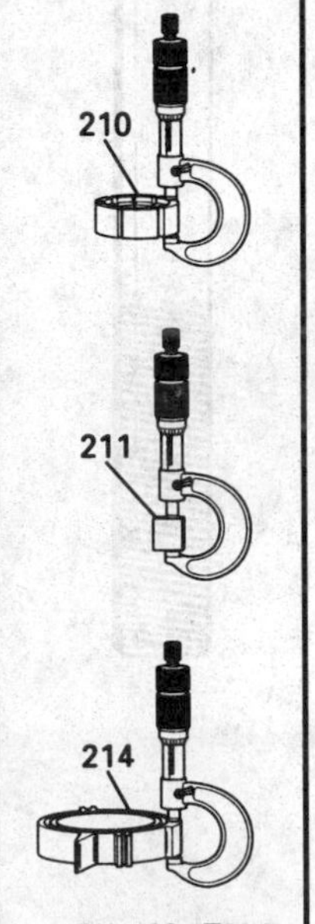
210
211
214

RH1102-4T60-E

Figure 103 Oil Pump Rotor, Vane and Slide Selection Chart

Oil Pump Assembly, Wiring Harness and Case Side Cover Pan Replacement

Figures 104 through 107

Inspect

- Wiring harness (224) for:
  - Cut or pinched wires.
  - Cut wire insulation.
  - Bent or broken electrical connectors.
- Case side cover pan (53) for:
  - Dents to gasket sealing surfaces.
  - Flatness of pan gasket sealing surfaces.

Install or Connect

1. Pump assembly (200) onto control valve assembly (300).
2. Pump to control valve assembly attaching bolts (203-207).
   - See Figure 105 for bolt torque specifications.
3. Wiring harness assembly (224) onto pump assembly (200).
4. Case side cover gasket (54) onto case and inner side cover gasket (55) onto channel plate.
5. Side cover (53) onto case with attaching bolt and conical washer assembly (52). (See figure 107 for strucural side cover bolt locations)

   Tighten

   - Bolts to 11 N•m (98 lb. in.).
6. Conical washers (51) and flanged hex nuts (50) on channel plate studs:

   Tighten

   - Nuts (50) to 8 N•m (71 lb. in.).

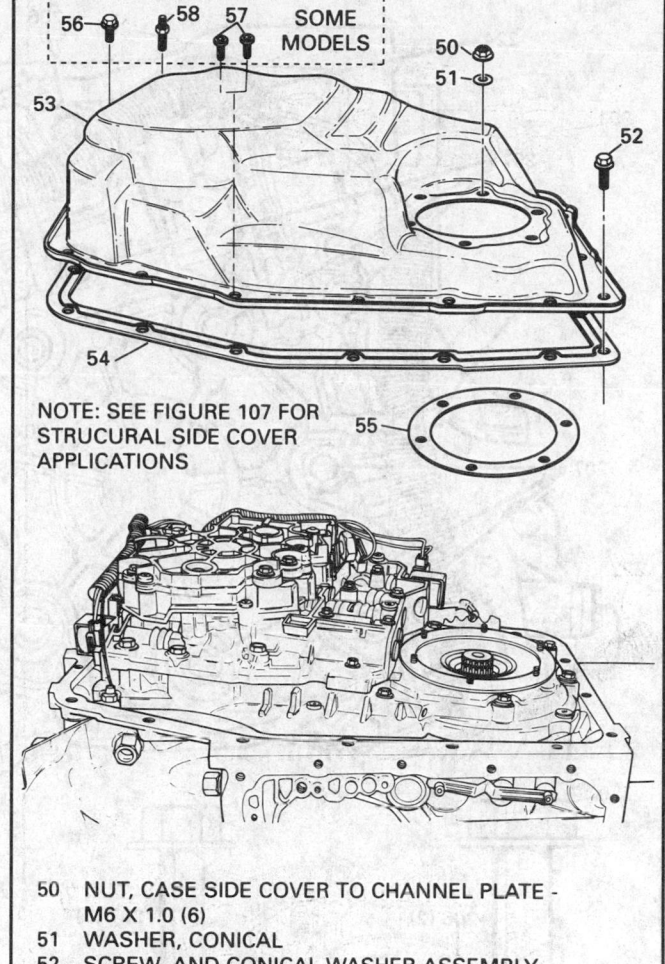

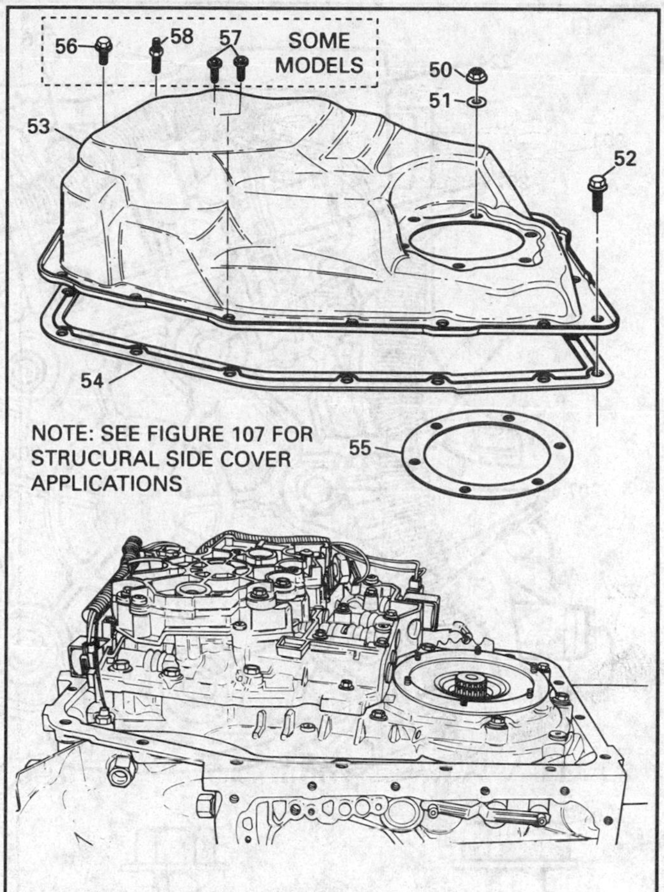
56
58
57
SOME MODELS
50
51
53
52
54
NOTE: SEE FIGURE 107 FOR STRUCURAL SIDE COVER APPLICATIONS
55

50 NUT, CASE SIDE COVER TO CHANNEL PLATE - M6 X 1.0 (6)
51 WASHER, CONICAL
52 SCREW, AND CONICAL WASHER ASSEMBLY - M8 X 1.25 X 21.3 (17)
53 PAN, CASE SIDE COVER
54 GASKET, CASE SIDE COVER
55 GASKET, INNER CASE SIDE COVER

RH1011-4T60-E

Figure 104 Side Cover and Gaskets

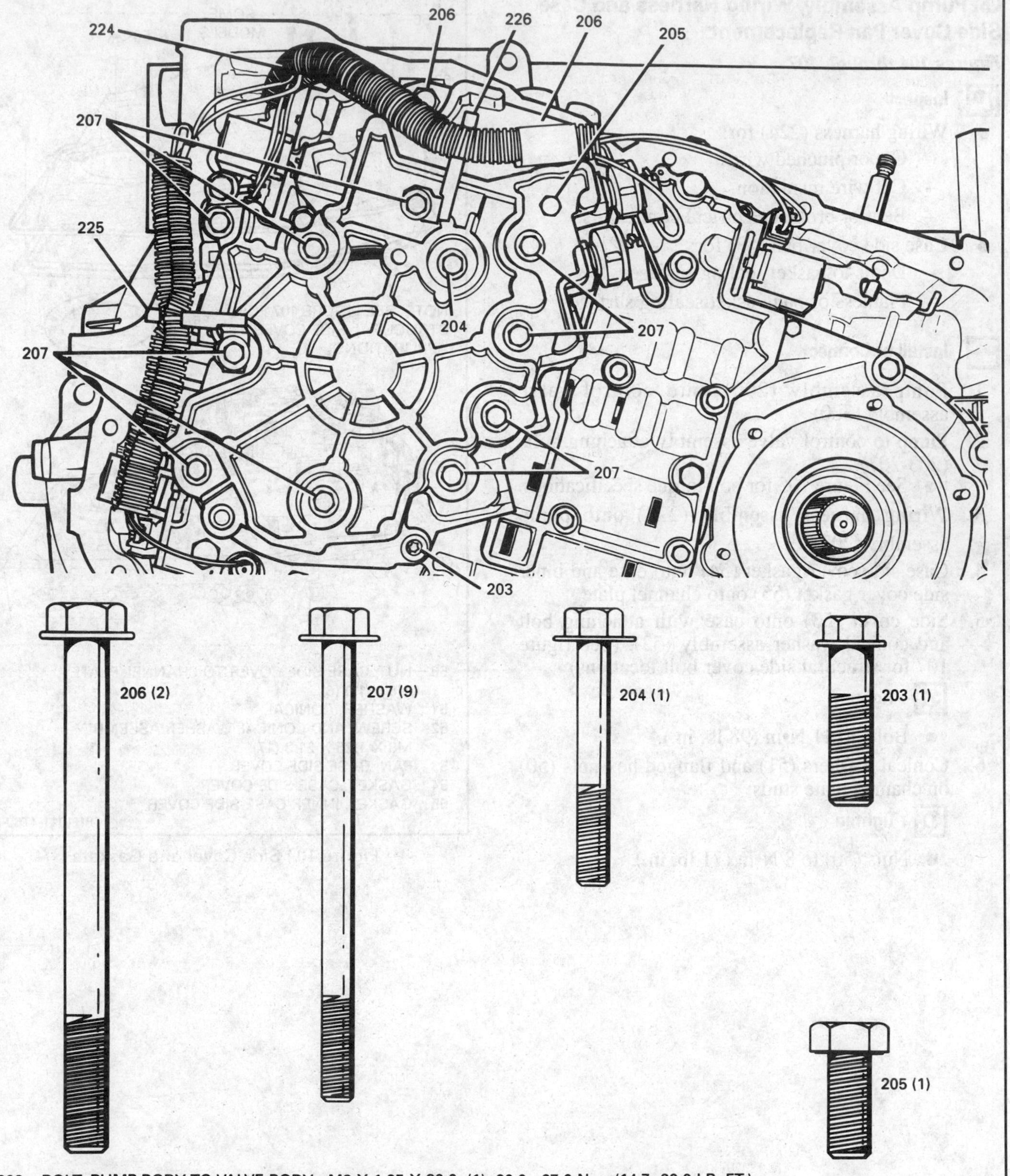
224
206
226
206
205
207
225
204
207
207
207
203
206 (2)
207 (9)
204 (1)
203 (1)
205 (1)

203 BOLT, PUMP BODY TO VALVE BODY - M8 X 1.25 X 30.0 (1) 20.0 - 27.0 N•m (14.7 -20.0 LB. FT.)
204 BOLT, PUMP COVER TO VALVE BODY - M6 X 1.0 X 45.0 (1) 8.0 - 14.0 N•m (71.0 - 124.0 LB. IN.)
205 BOLT, PUMP COVER TO PUMP BODY - M8 X 1.25 X 20.0 (1) 20.0 - 27.0 N•m (14.7 - 20.0 LB. FT.)
206 BOLT, PUMP BODY TO CASE - M8 X 1.25 X 95.0 (2) 20.0 - 27.0 N•m (14.7 - 20.0 LB. FT.)
207 BOLT, PUMP COVER TO CHANNEL PLATE - M6 X 1.0 X 85.0 (10) 8.0 - 14.0 N•m (71.0 - 124.0 LB. IN.)
224 HARNESS ASSEMBLY, WIRING
225 CLIP, CONDUIT
226 CLIP, CONDUIT

RH1103-4T60-E

Figure 105 Oil Pump to Valve Body Bolt Locations

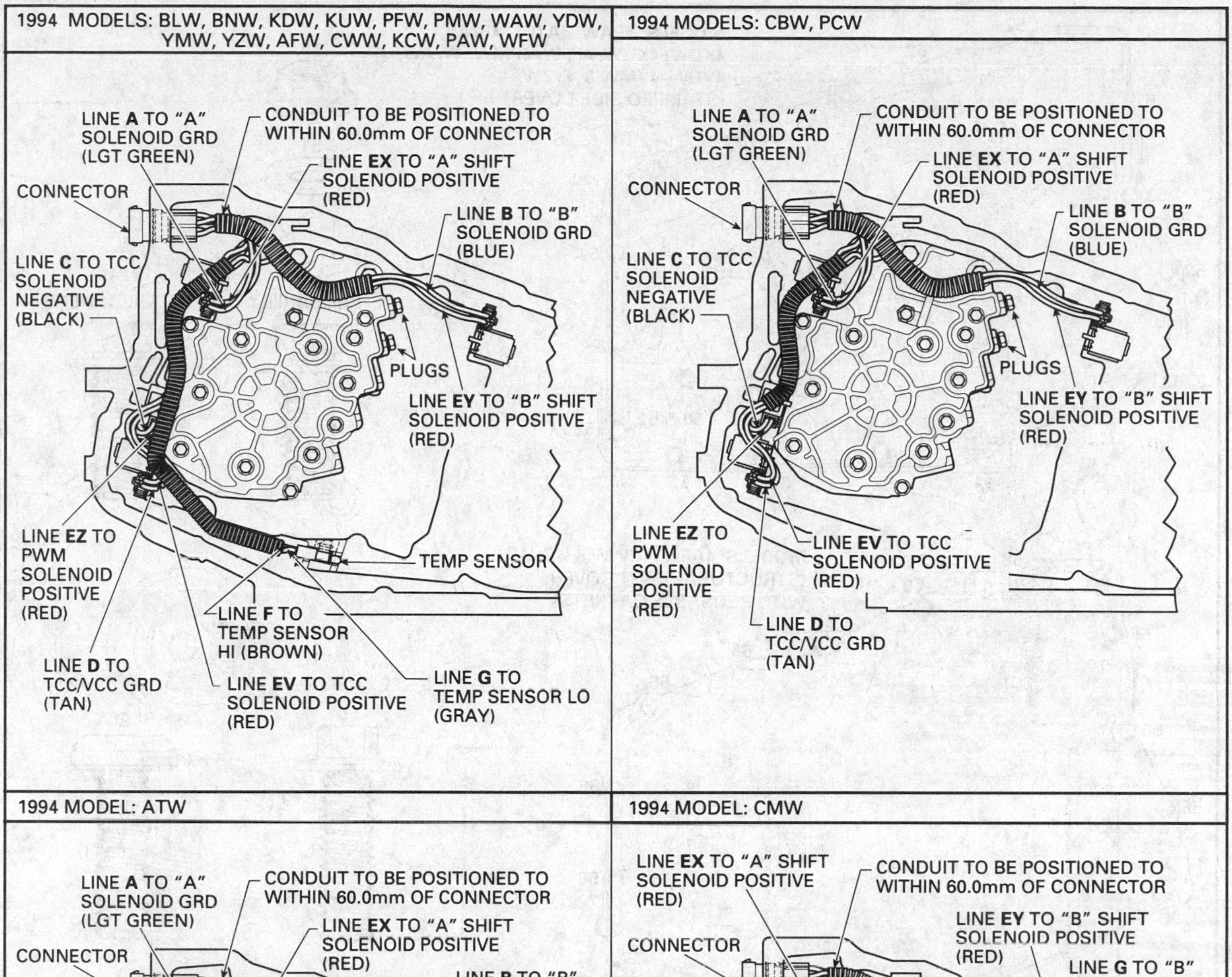
1994 MODELS: BLW, BNW, KDW, KUW, PFW, PMW, WAW, YDW, YMW, YZW, AFW, CWW, KCW, PAW, WFW
LINE A TO "A" SOLENOID GRD (LGT GREEN)
CONDUIT TO BE POSITIONED TO WITHIN 60.0mm OF CONNECTOR
LINE EX TO "A" SHIFT SOLENOID POSITIVE (RED)
CONNECTOR
LINE B TO "B" SOLENOID GRD (BLUE)
LINE C TO TCC SOLENOID NEGATIVE (BLACK)
PLUGS
LINE EY TO "B" SHIFT SOLENOID POSITIVE (RED)
LINE EZ TO PWM SOLENOID POSITIVE (RED)
TEMP SENSOR
LINE F TO TEMP SENSOR HI (BROWN)
LINE D TO TCC/VCC GRD (TAN)
LINE EV TO TCC SOLENOID POSITIVE (RED)
LINE G TO TEMP SENSOR LO (GRAY)
1994 MODELS: CBW, PCW
LINE A TO "A" SOLENOID GRD (LGT GREEN)
CONDUIT TO BE POSITIONED TO WITHIN 60.0mm OF CONNECTOR
LINE EX TO "A" SHIFT SOLENOID POSITIVE (RED)
CONNECTOR
LINE B TO "B" SOLENOID GRD (BLUE)
LINE C TO TCC SOLENOID NEGATIVE (BLACK)
PLUGS
LINE EY TO "B" SHIFT SOLENOID POSITIVE (RED)
LINE EZ TO PWM SOLENOID POSITIVE (RED)
LINE EV TO TCC SOLENOID POSITIVE (RED)
LINE D TO TCC/VCC GRD (TAN)
1994 MODEL: ATW
LINE A TO "A" SOLENOID GRD (LGT GREEN)
CONDUIT TO BE POSITIONED TO WITHIN 60.0mm OF CONNECTOR
LINE EX TO "A" SHIFT SOLENOID POSITIVE (RED)
CONNECTOR
LINE B TO "B" SOLENOID GRD (BLUE)
LINE C TO TCC SOLENOID NEGATIVE (BLACK)
PLUGS
LINE EY TO "B" SHIFT SOLENOID POSITIVE (RED)
LINE G TO TEMP SENSOR LO (GRAY)
LINE EZ TO PWM SOLENOID POSITIVE (RED)
TEMP SENSOR
LINE F TO TEMP SENSOR HI (BROWN)
LINE D TO TCC/VCC GRD (TAN)
LINE EV TO TCC SOLENOID POSITIVE (RED)
1994 MODEL: CMW
LINE EX TO "A" SHIFT SOLENOID POSITIVE (RED)
CONDUIT TO BE POSITIONED TO WITHIN 60.0mm OF CONNECTOR
LINE EY TO "B" SHIFT SOLENOID POSITIVE (RED)
CONNECTOR
LINE G TO "B" SOLENOID GRD (GREEN)
LINE F TO "A" SOLENOID GRD (LT BLUE)
LINE C TO LO DISCRETE SW. (PURPLE)
LINE B TO 4TH CL DISCRETE SW. (DK. BLUE)
4TH CL DISCRETE PRESSURE SW. (N.O.)
LINE D TO TCC SOLENOID NEGATIVE (BLACK)
LINE A TO TCC SOLENOID POSITIVE (GRAY)
LO DISCRETE PRESSURE SW. (N.O.)
SWITCH ASM.
ASSEMBLE TERMINAL WITH WIRE IN THE DOWNWARD POSITION AS SHOWN
RH1104-4T60-E

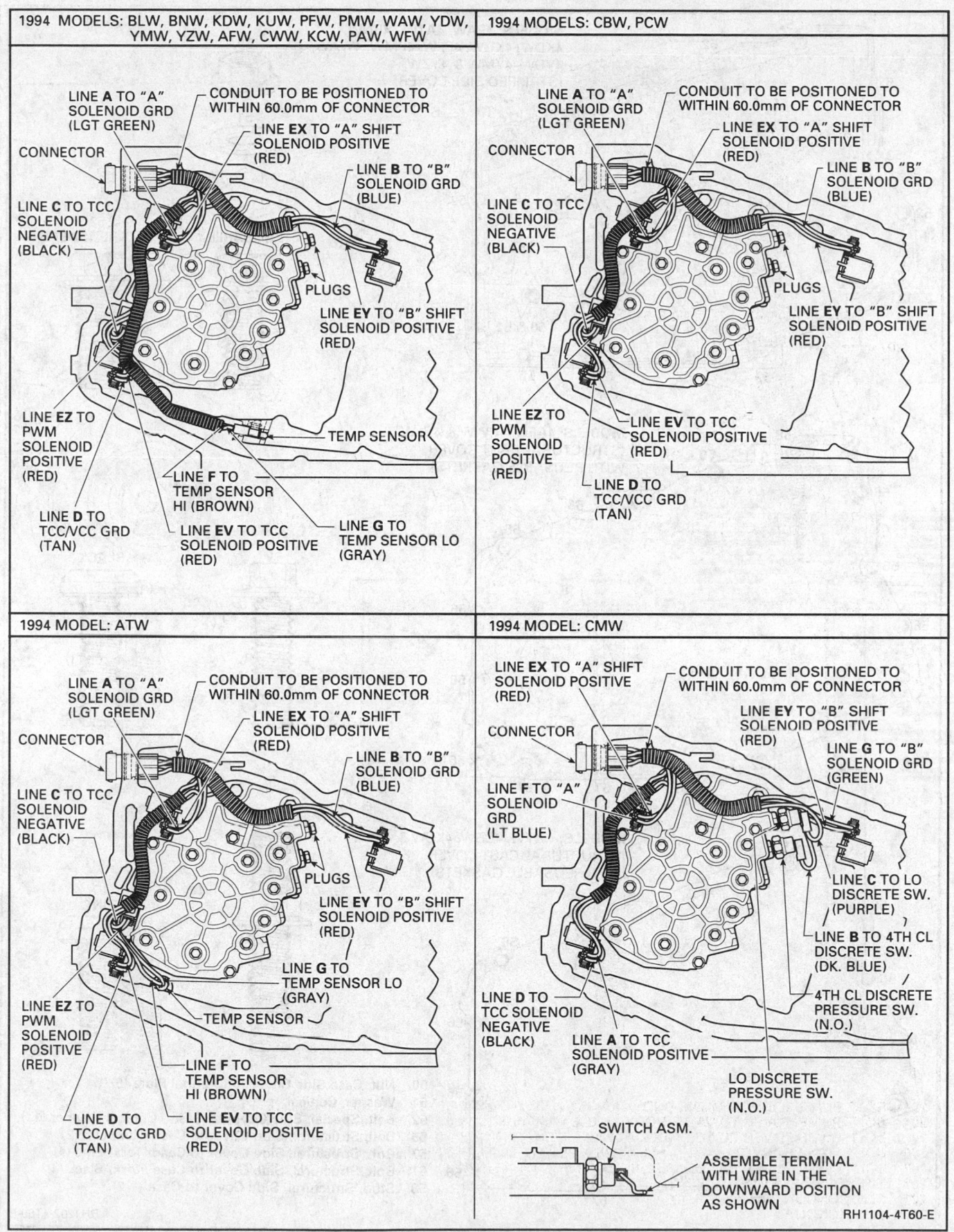

Figure 106 Proper Wiring Harness Connections

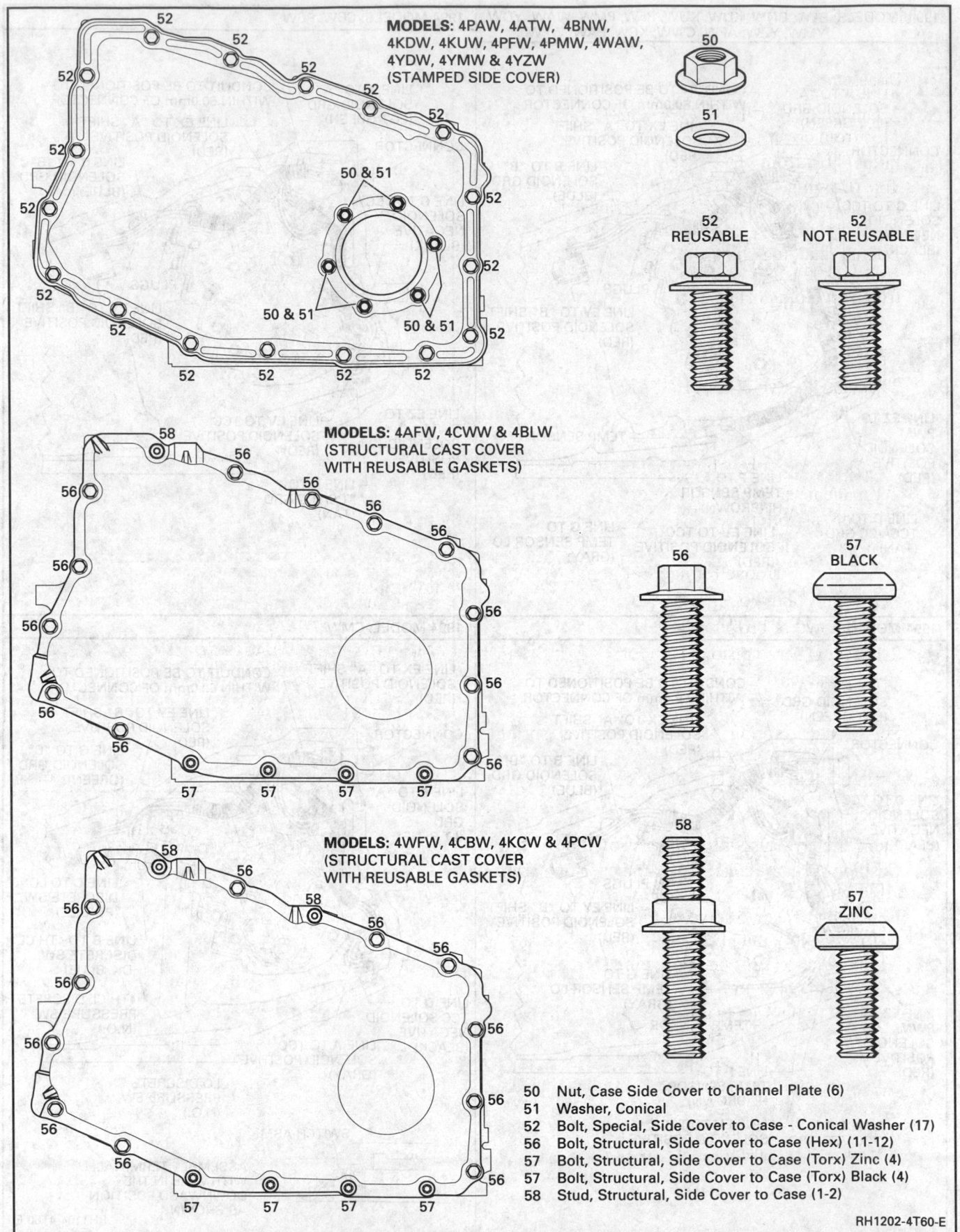

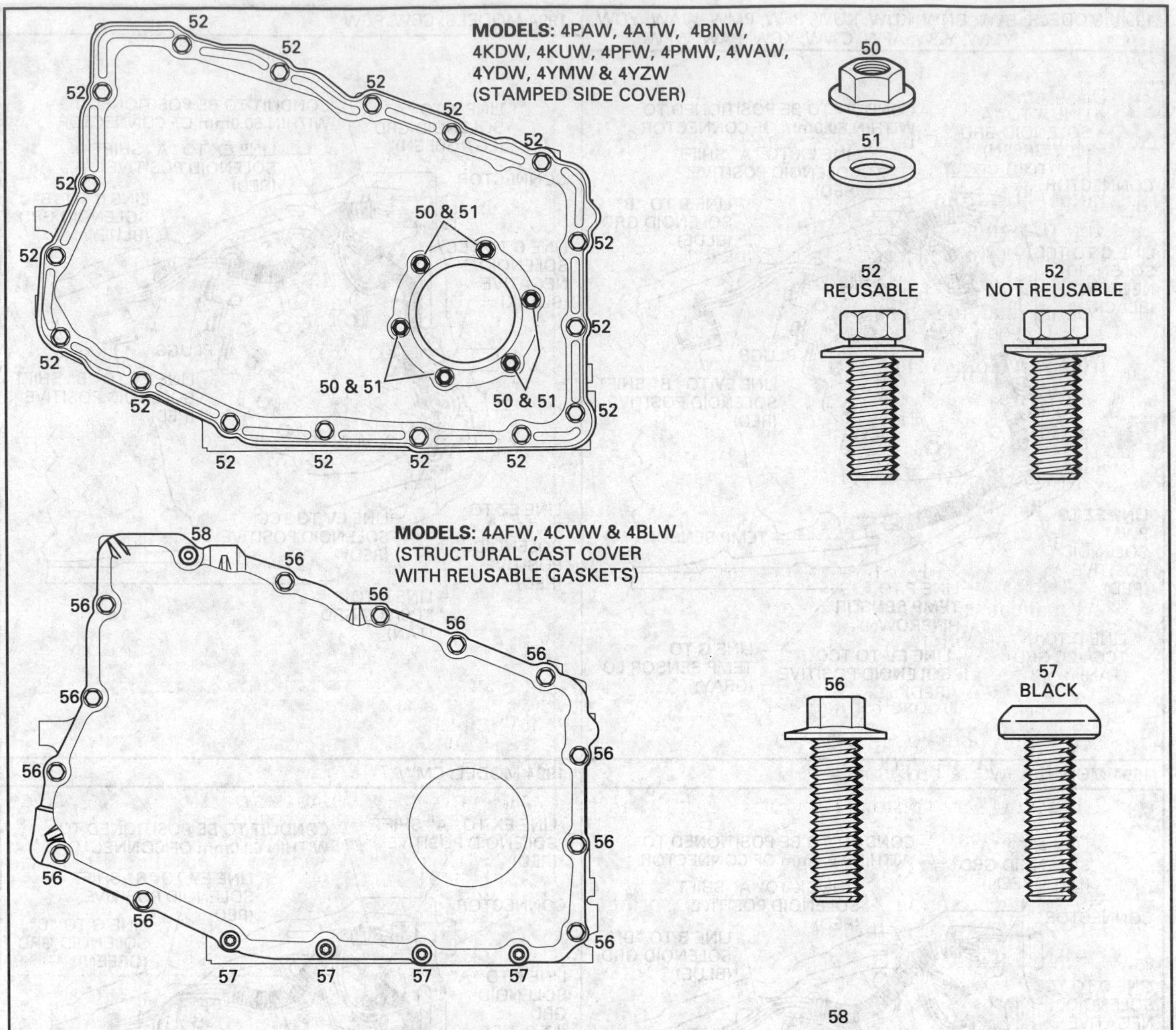
MODELS: 4PAW, 4ATW, 4BNW, 4KDW, 4KUW, 4PFW, 4PMW, 4WAW, 4YDW, 4YMW & 4YZW (STAMPED SIDE COVER)
52
50 & 51
50
51
52 REUSABLE
52 NOT REUSABLE
MODELS: 4AFW, 4CWW & 4BLW (STRUCTURAL CAST COVER WITH REUSABLE GASKETS)
56
57
58
57 BLACK
MODELS: 4WFW, 4CBW, 4KCW & 4PCW (STRUCTURAL CAST COVER WITH REUSABLE GASKETS)
57 ZINC
50 Nut, Case Side Cover to Channel Plate (6)
51 Washer, Conical
52 Bolt, Special, Side Cover to Case - Conical Washer (17)
56 Bolt, Structural, Side Cover to Case (Hex) (11-12)
57 Bolt, Structural, Side Cover to Case (Torx) Zinc (4)
57 Bolt, Structural, Side Cover to Case (Torx) Black (4)
58 Stud, Structural, Side Cover to Case (1-2)
RH1202-4T60-E

Figure 107 Side Cover Conical Washer/Bolt and Bottom Pan Bolt

2-1 Manual Servo Assembly

Figure 108

Disassemble

1. 2-1 manual servo body (114) and O-rings (105, 113) from cover (104).
2. Filter (115) from servo body (114).
3. Top retaining clip (116), 2-1 manual apply pin assembly (108-111), and return spring (112) from servo body (114).
4. Bottom retaining clip (106), piston (108), cushion spring (109), and cushion spring retainer (110) from servo pin (111).

Inspect

- 2-1 manual servo cover (104) for:
  - Cracks in casting.
  - Porosity.
  - Damaged or rough machined surfaces.
- 2-1 manual servo body (114) for:
  - Porosity or cracks.
  - Scored piston bore.
  - Seal ring groove for nicks or burrs.
  - Wear in pin bore.
  - Plugged or broken filter (115).
- 2-1 manual servo piston (108) for:
  - Porosity.
  - Cut or nicked O-ring (107).
- Servo return spring (112) and cushion spring (109) for distorted or broken coils.
- O-ring seal (113) for cuts or nicks.

Assemble

- Lubricate all seals with transmission fluid.

1. Cushion spring retainer (110) and cushion spring (109) on pin (111).
2. New seal (107) onto servo piston (108) and install piston on apply pin (111).
3. Retaining clip (106) on apply pin (111).
4. O-ring seal (113) onto servo body (114).
5. Spring (112) and apply pin assembly (106 through 112) into servo body (114).
6. Retaining clip (116) on apply pin (111).
7. 2-1 servo assembly (106 through 116) into manual servo cover (104).
8. Install filter (115) into body, 2-1 manual servo (114).

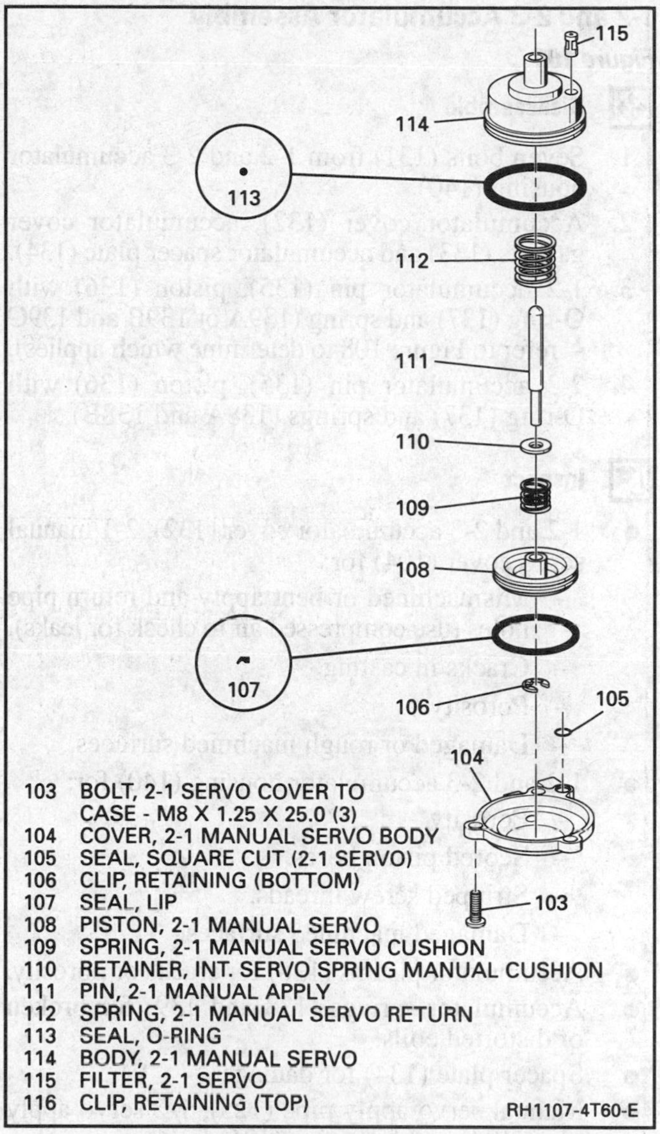

115
114
113
112
111
110
109
108
107
106
105
104
103
103 BOLT, 2-1 SERVO COVER TO CASE - M8 X 1.25 X 25.0 (3)
104 COVER, 2-1 MANUAL SERVO BODY
105 SEAL, SQUARE CUT (2-1 SERVO)
106 CLIP, RETAINING (BOTTOM)
107 SEAL, LIP
108 PISTON, 2-1 MANUAL SERVO
109 SPRING, 2-1 MANUAL SERVO CUSHION
110 RETAINER, INT. SERVO SPRING MANUAL CUSHION
111 PIN, 2-1 MANUAL APPLY
112 SPRING, 2-1 MANUAL SERVO RETURN
113 SEAL, O-RING
114 BODY, 2-1 MANUAL SERVO
115 FILTER, 2-1 SERVO
116 CLIP, RETAINING (TOP)
RH1107-4T60-E

Figure 108 2-1 Manual Servo

1-2 and 2-3 Accumulator Assembly

Figure 109

Disassemble

1. Seven bolts (131) from 1-2 and 2-3 accumulator housing (140).
2. Accumulator cover (132), accumulator cover gaskets (133) and accumulator spacer plate (134).
3. 1-2 accumulator pin (135), piston (136) with O-ring (137) and spring (139A or 139B and 139C – refer to Figure 108 to determine which applies).
4. 2-3 accumulator pin (135), piston (136) with O-ring (137) and springs (138A and 138B).

Inspect

- 1-2 and 2-3 accumulator cover (132), 2-1 manual servo cover (104) for:
  - Mismachined or bent apply and return pipe holes (use compressed air to check for leaks).
  - Cracks in casting.
  - Porosity.
  - Damaged or rough machined surfaces.
- 1-2 and 2-3 accumulator housing (140) for:
  - Porosity.
  - Scored piston bores.
  - Stripped screw threads.
  - Damaged machined surfaces.
- Accumulator pistons (136) for cracks or porosity.
- Accumulator springs (138 and 139) for broken or distorted coils.
- Spacer plate (134) for damage.
- Manual servo apply pipe (125), 1-2 servo apply pipe (124) and lube pipe (126) for:
  - Split tubes or hose (128).
  - Deformed, kinked or restricted tubes.
- Hose clamps (127) and lube pipe retainer clip (129) for cracks or over-expansion.

Assemble

- Lubricate all seals with transmission fluid.

1. New seals (137) onto 1-2 and 2-3 accumulator pistons (136).
2. 1-2 and 2-3 accumulator pins (135) into pistons (136).
3. 1-2 accumulator spring (139A) and 2-3 accumulator springs (138A and 138B) into housing (140).
4. 1-2 accumulator piston and pin assembly (135-139) into housing (140).
5. 2-3 accumulator piston and pin assembly (135 through 138) into housing (140).
6. Accumulator cover gasket (133), spacer plate (134) and cover gasket (133) onto accumulator cover (132).
7. 1-2 and 2-3 accumulator cover (132) onto housing (140).
8. Bolts (131) into accumulator housing (140).

Tighten

- Bolts (131) to 11 N•m (98 lb. in.).

9. Connect the 1-2 and 3-4 accumulator assembly (140) to the forward and manual servo apply pipes (124 and 125) then the lube pipe (126) by pushing the pipes firmly in place – DO NOT USE SEALANT ON PIPES.

2-1 Manual Servo and 1-2 and 2-3 Accumulator Assembly

Figures 109 and 110

Install or Connect

1. O-ring (105) into case.

Important

- If O-ring (105) is mislocated or missing, the transaxle will not have Drive, only reverse gear.

2. Position 2-1 manual servo assembly and 1-2 and 2-3 accumulator assembly into case (3).
3. Lube pipe (130) into final drive internal gear (694) – retain with pipe clip (129).
4. 2-1 manual servo cover bolts (103).

Tighten

- Bolts (103) to 24 N•m (18 lb. ft.).

Important

- The 2-1 manual servo body (114) must be fully seated into cover (104) before installing to the case. The O-ring (113) could be cut if the servo body (114) was cocked in the cover (104).
- Ensure apply pin (111) engages 2-1 manual band.

5. Accumulator housing bolts (131).

Tighten

- Bolts (131) to 11 N•m (98 lb. in.).

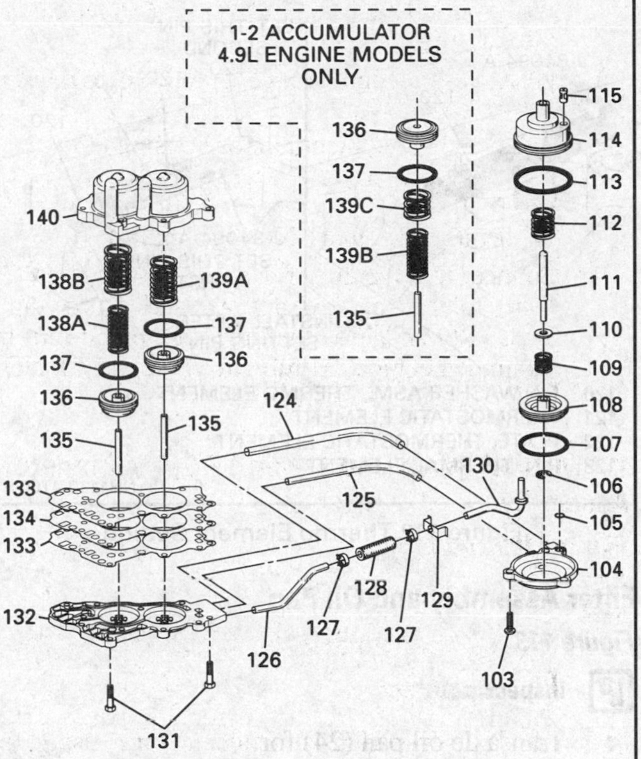
1-2 ACCUMULATOR
4.9L ENGINE MODELS
ONLY
115
136
114
137
113
139C
112
140
139B
111
138B
139A
135
110
138A
137
137
136
109
136
108
124
135
135
107
130
106
133
125
134
105
133
104
128
129
132
127
127
126
103
131

103	BOLT, 2-1 SERVO COVER TO CASE - M8 X 1.25 X 25.0 (3)
104	COVER, 2-1 MANUAL SERVO BODY
105	SEAL, SQUARE CUT (2-1 SERVO)
106	CLIP, RETAINING (BOTTOM)
107	SEAL, LIP
108	PISTON, 2-1 MANUAL SERVO
109	SPRING, 2-1 MANUAL SERVO CUSHION
110	RETAINER, INT. SERVO SPRING MANUAL CUSHION
111	PIN, 2-1 MANUAL APPLY
112	SPRING, 2-1 MANUAL SERVO RETURN
113	SEAL, O-RING
114	BODY, 2-1 MANUAL SERVO
115	FILTER, 2-1 SERVO
116	CLIP, RETAINING (TOP)
124	PIPE, FORWARD SERVO APPLY
125	PIPE, MANUAL SERVO APPLY
126	PIPE, LUBE OIL
127	CLAMP, HOSE
128	HOSE, LUBE OIL
129	RETAINER, LUBE PIPE CLIP
130	PIPE AND WASHER ASSEMBLY
131	BOLT, ACCUMULATOR COVER TO CASE AND ACCUMULATOR HSG. - M6 X 1.0 X 28.0 (1)
132	COVER, ACCUMULATOR
133	GASKET, ACCUMULATOR COVER
134	PLATE, ACCUMULATOR SPACER
135	PIN, 2-3 ACCUMULATOR
136	PISTON, 1-2 AND 2-3 ACCUMULATOR
137	RING, OIL SEAL ACCUMULATOR PISTON
138A	SPRING, 2-3 ACCUMULATOR (INNER)
138B	SPRING, 2-3 ACCUMULATOR (OUTER)
139A	SPRING, 1-2 ACCUMULATOR
139B	SPRING, 1-2 ACCUMULATOR (INNER)
139C	SPRING, 1-2 ACCUMULATOR (OUTER)
140	HOUSING, ACCUMULATOR (MACHINED)

RH1108-4T60-E

Figure 109 Servo and Accumulator Assembly

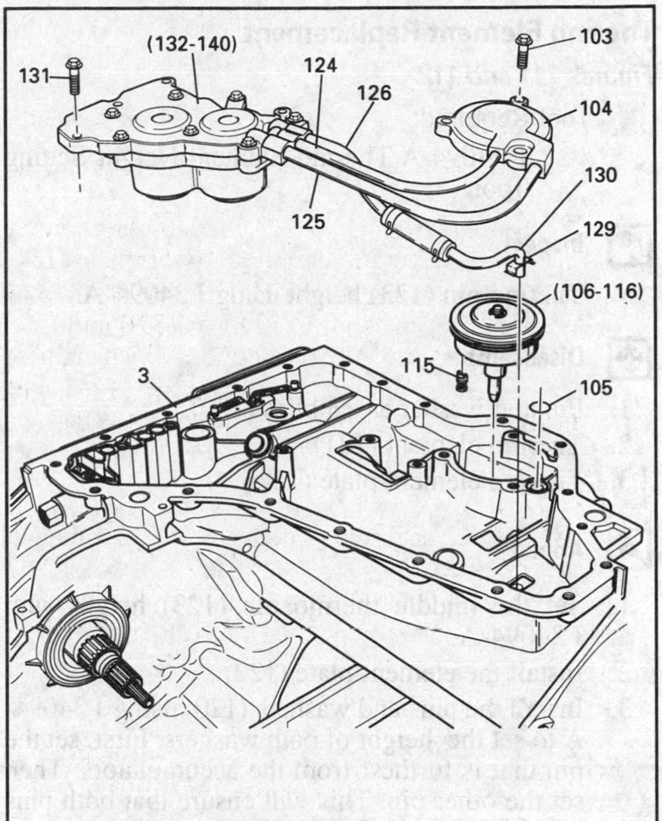
(132-140)
103
131
124
126
104
130
125
129
(106-116)
3
115
105

3	CASE, TRANSMISSION
103	BOLT, 2-1 SERVO COVER TO CASE - M8 X 1.25 X 25.0 (3)
104	COVER, 2-1 MANUAL SERVO BODY
105	SEAL, SQUARE CUT (2-1 SERVO)
106-116	2-1 MANUAL SERVO ASSEMBLY
129	RETAINER, LUBE PIPE CLIP
130	PIPE AND WASHER ASSEMBLY
131	BOLT, ACCUMULATOR COVER TO CASE AND ACCUMULATOR HSG. - M6 X 1.0 X 28.0 (1)
132-140	1-2/2-3 ACCUMULATOR ASSEMBLY

RH1010-4T60-E

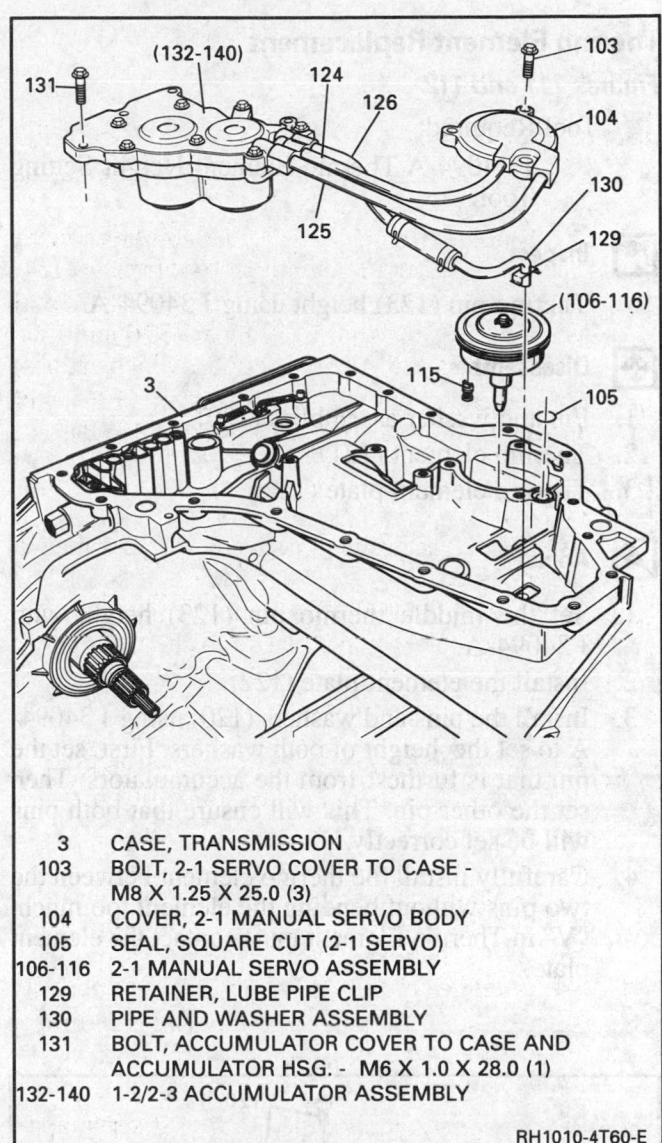

Figure 110 Installing Servo and Accumulator Assembly

Thermo Element Replacement

Figures 111 and 112

Tool Required:

J 34094-A Thermo Element Height Setting Tool

Inspect

- Thermo pin (123) height using J 34094-A.

Disassemble

1. Pin and washer assemblies (120).
2. Thermo element (121).
3. Thermo element plate (122).

Adjust

1. Set the middle thermo pin (123) height with J 34094-A.
2. Install the element plate (122).
3. Install the pins and washers (120) using J 34094-A to set the height of both washers. First, set the pin that is furthest from the accumulators. Then set the other pin. This will ensure that both pins will be set correctly.
4. Carefully install the thermo element between the two pins without bending the element too much. "V" in Thermo Element must contact the element plate.

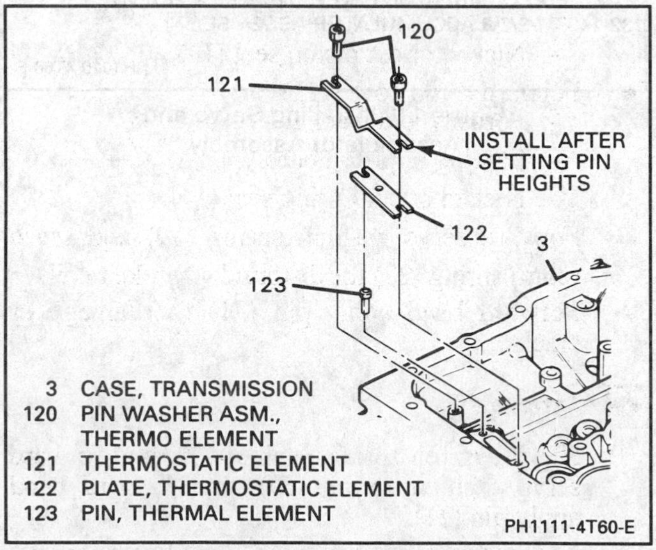
120
121
INSTALL AFTER SETTING PIN HEIGHTS
122
3
123
3 CASE, TRANSMISSION
120 PIN WASHER ASM., THERMO ELEMENT
121 THERMOSTATIC ELEMENT
122 PLATE, THERMOSTATIC ELEMENT
123 PIN, THERMAL ELEMENT
PH1111-4T60-E

Figure 111 Thermo Element

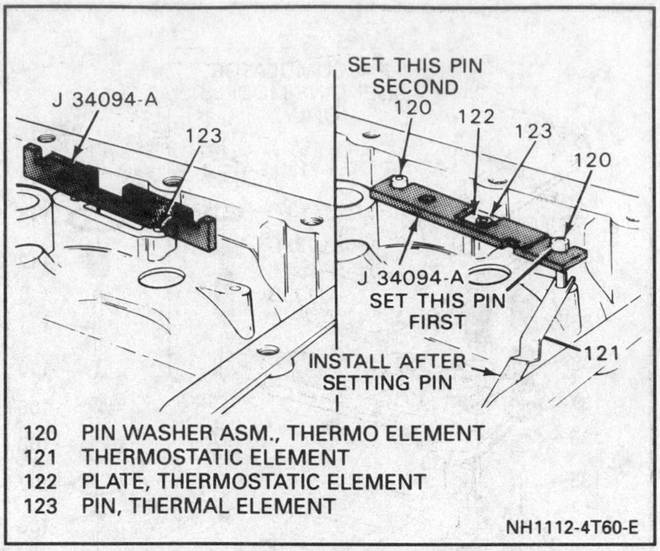
J 34094-A
123
SET THIS PIN SECOND
120
122
123
120
J 34094-A
SET THIS PIN FIRST
INSTALL AFTER SETTING PIN
121
120 PIN WASHER ASM., THERMO ELEMENT
121 THERMOSTATIC ELEMENT
122 PLATE, THERMOSTATIC ELEMENT
123 PIN, THERMAL ELEMENT
NH1112-4T60-E

Figure 112 Thermo Element Setting

Filter Assembly and Oil Pan

Figure 113

Inspect

- Transaxle oil pan (24) for:
  - Dents.
  - Flatness of gasket seal surface.
  - Cracks.

Clean

- Oil pan (24) thoroughly in solvent – air dry.
- Chip collector magnet (26) and position in bottom pan.

Install or Connect

1. New oil filter seal assembly (101) into case – use 18 mm socket to tap in.
2. New oil filter assembly (100) into case.
3. Transaxle oil pan gasket (25) onto case (reusable if ribs are not broken).
4. Transaxle oil pan (24) and black bolts (23).

Tighten

- Bolts (23) to 17 N•m (13 lb. ft.).

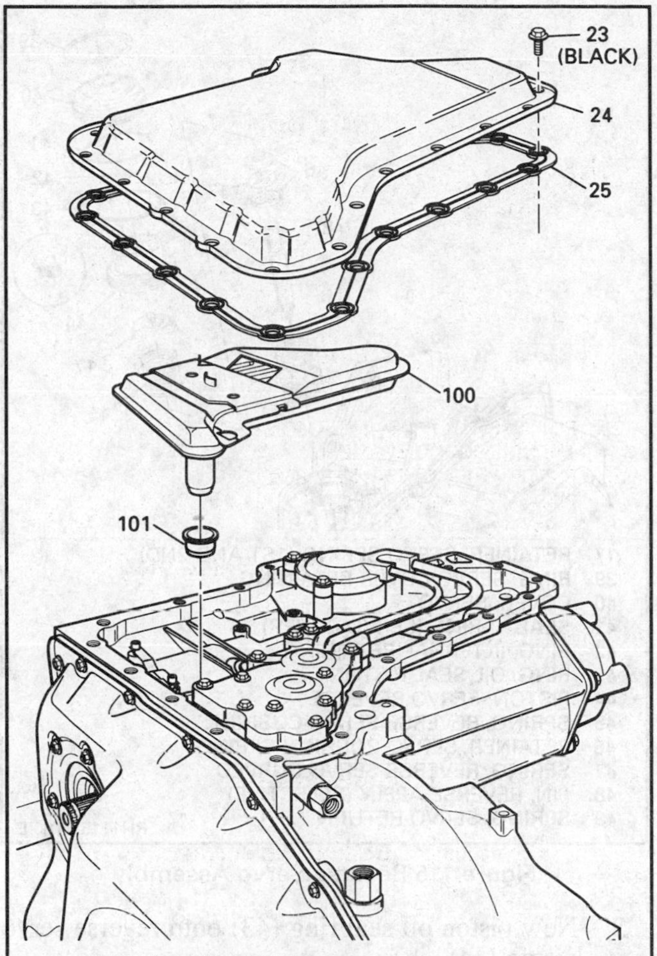
23
(BLACK)
24
25
100
101

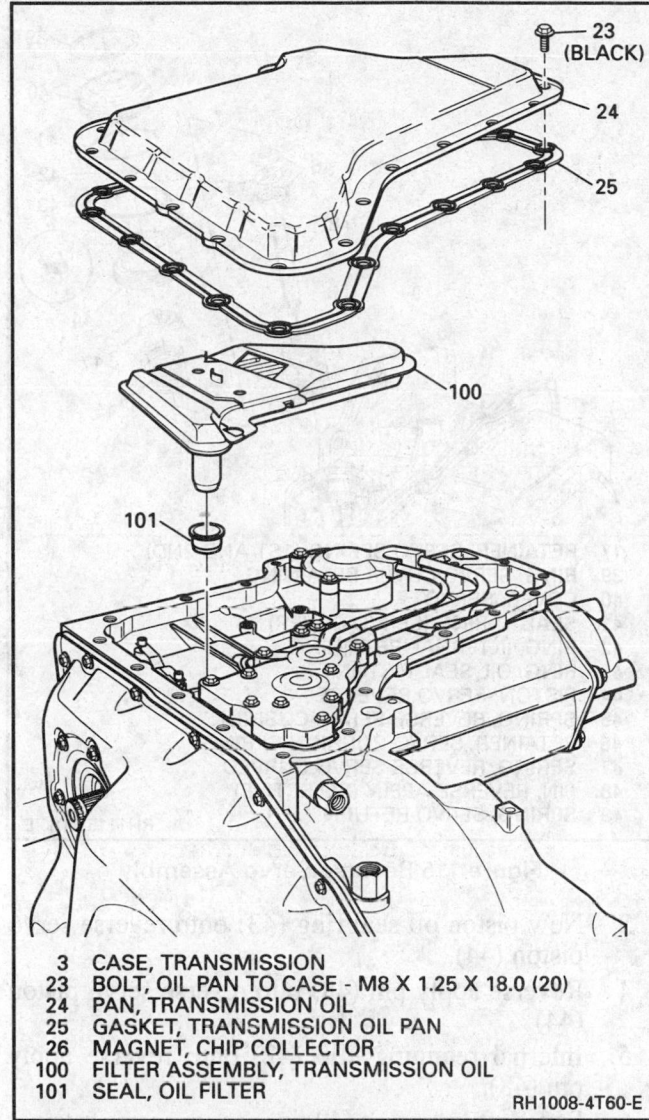

3 CASE, TRANSMISSION
23 BOLT, OIL PAN TO CASE - M8 X 1.25 X 18.0 (20)
24 PAN, TRANSMISSION OIL
25 GASKET, TRANSMISSION OIL PAN
26 MAGNET, CHIP COLLECTOR
100 FILTER ASSEMBLY, TRANSMISSION OIL
101 SEAL, OIL FILTER

RH1008-4T60-E

Figure 113 Oil Pan and Filter Assembly

Forward Servo Assembly

Figure 114

Disassemble

1. Servo return spring (22) from forward servo piston (16).
2. Internal retaining ring (15) from forward band apply pin (21).
3. Band apply pin (21) from forward servo piston (16).
4. Forward servo cushion spring (19) and cushion spring retainer (20) from forward piston (16).
5. Return spring retainer (17) from forward servo piston (16) – do not remove unless broken or damaged.

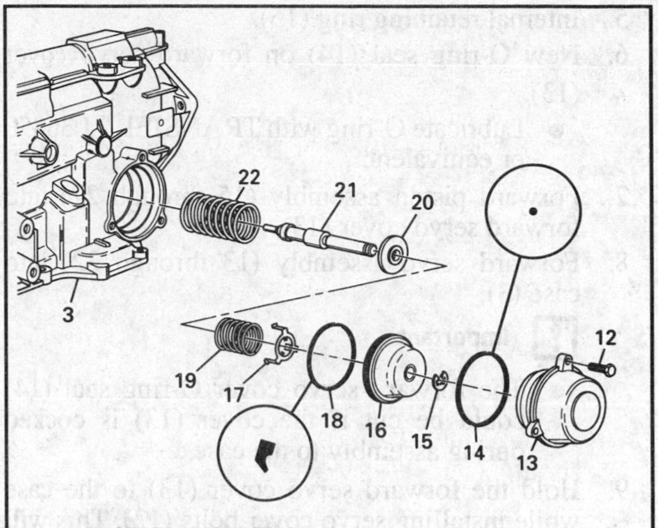
22
21
20
3
12
19
17
18
16
15
14
13

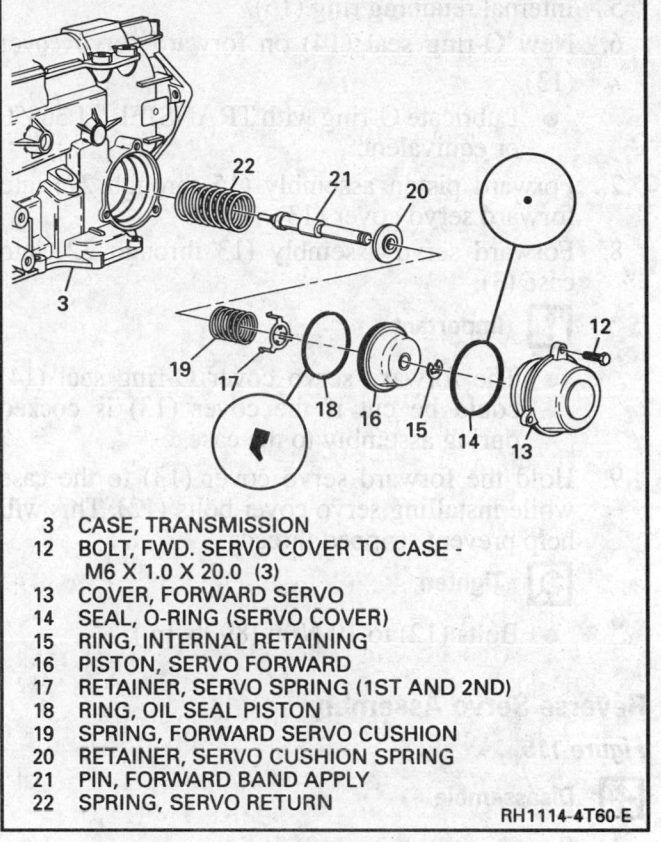

3 CASE, TRANSMISSION
12 BOLT, FWD. SERVO COVER TO CASE - M6 X 1.0 X 20.0 (3)
13 COVER, FORWARD SERVO
14 SEAL, O-RING (SERVO COVER)
15 RING, INTERNAL RETAINING
16 PISTON, SERVO FORWARD
17 RETAINER, SERVO SPRING (1ST AND 2ND)
18 RING, OIL SEAL PISTON
19 SPRING, FORWARD SERVO CUSHION
20 RETAINER, SERVO CUSHION SPRING
21 PIN, FORWARD BAND APPLY
22 SPRING, SERVO RETURN

RH1114-4T60-E

Figure 114 Forward Servo Assembly

Inspect

- Forward servo piston (16) for:
  - Porosity and cracks.
  - Excess wear in pin bore.
  - Nicked or cut piston seal (18).
- Forward servo cover (13) for:
  - Porosity and cracks.
  - Scoring in piston bore.
  - Nicked or cut O-ring seal (14).
- Forward servo cushion spring (19) and servo return spring (22) for distorted or broken coils.
- Forward band apply pin (21) for damage or cracks.

Assemble

1. Servo cushion spring retainer (20) and forward servo cushion spring (19) onto forward band apply pin (21).
2. New piston oil seal ring (18) onto forward servo piston (16).
3. Servo return spring (22) into forward servo piston (16).
4. Forward servo piston (16) and servo spring retainer (17) if removed onto band apply pin (21).

5. Internal retaining ring (15).
6. New O-ring seal (14) on forward servo cover (13).
   - Lubricate O-ring with TRANSJEL™ J 36850 or equivalent.
7. Forward piston assembly (15 through 22) into forward servo cover (13).
8. Forward servo assembly (13 through 22) into case (3).

Important

- The forward servo cover O-ring seal (14) could be cut if the cover (13) is cocked during assembly to the case.

9. Hold the forward servo cover (13) to the case while installing servo cover bolts (12). This will help prevent stripped threads.

Tighten

- Bolts (12) to 10 N•m (89 lb. in.).

Reverse Servo Assembly

Figure 115

Disassemble

1. Servo return spring (49) from reverse servo piston (44).
2. Internal retaining ring (42) from reverse apply pin (48).
3. Reverse servo piston (44) with servo spring retainer (17) and reverse servo cushion spring (45) from apply pin (48).
4. Cushion spring retainers (46) and reverse servo curved spring (47).
5. Return spring retainer (17) from reverse servo piston (44) – do not remove unless broken or damaged.

Inspect

- Reverse servo piston (44) for cracks or porosity.
- Oil seal piston ring (43) for cuts, nicks or wear.
- Reverse servo cushion spring (45) and reverse servo return spring (49) for distorted or broken coils.
- Servo spring retainer (17) for cracks or damage.
- Servo cover (40) for cracks, porosity or burrs in seal groove.

Assemble

1. Servo cushion spring retainer (46) and reverse servo curved spring (47) onto reverse apply pin (48).
2. Reverse servo cushion spring (45) onto reverse apply pin (48).

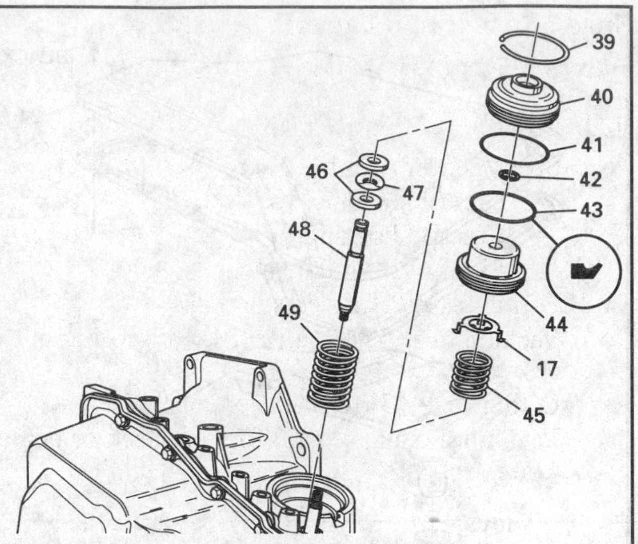
39
40
41
42
43
44
45
46
47
48
49
17

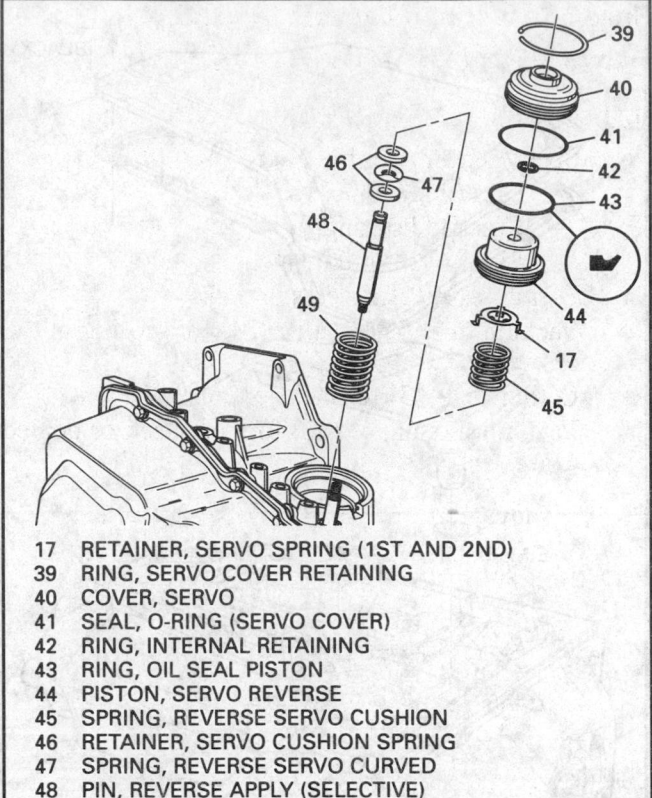

17 RETAINER, SERVO SPRING (1ST AND 2ND)
39 RING, SERVO COVER RETAINING
40 COVER, SERVO
41 SEAL, O-RING (SERVO COVER)
42 RING, INTERNAL RETAINING
43 RING, OIL SEAL PISTON
44 PISTON, SERVO REVERSE
45 SPRING, REVERSE SERVO CUSHION
46 RETAINER, SERVO CUSHION SPRING
47 SPRING, REVERSE SERVO CURVED
48 PIN, REVERSE APPLY (SELECTIVE)
49 SPRING, SERVO RETURN

RH1115-4T60-E

Figure 115 Reverse Servo Assembly

3. New piston oil seal ring (43) onto reverse servo piston (44).
4. Reverse apply pin (48) into reverse servo piston (44).
5. Internal retaining clip (42) onto reverse apply pin (48).
6. Servo return spring (49) into servo spring retainer (17) in piston.

Install or Connect

- Before installing the reverse servo, check that the band is in the proper location by putting a long cross recess screwdriver down the band apply pin hole – push down on the screwdriver, and it must spring back up. If not, the band is mislocated and must be relocated towards the engine with a screwdriver (carefully, so the band apply pin bore in the case does not get damaged).

Important

- If this procedure is not followed, the transaxle will have partial or no reverse gear due to the band apply pin missing the band.

1. New O-ring seal (41) onto servo cover (40).
2. Reverse servo assembly (41 through 49) into case.
3. Servo cover (40) and servo cover retaining ring (39) into case.
   - Lubricate O-ring with TRANSJEL™ J 36850 or equivalent.

Speed Sensor and Vacuum Modulator

Figures 116 and 117

Inspect

- Speed sensor (10) for:
  - Damaged connector.
  - Cracked housing.
  - Signs of rotor damage.
- O-ring seal (11) for cuts or nicks.
- Vacuum modulator valve (34) for scoring, nicks or burrs.
- O-ring seal (33) for nicks or cuts.
- Vacuum modulator (32) for bent neck or dented can.

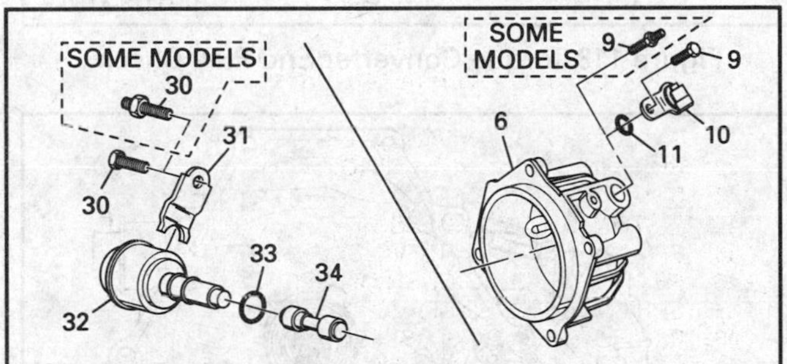

SOME MODELS
SOME MODELS
30
31
30
33
34
32
6
9
9
10
11

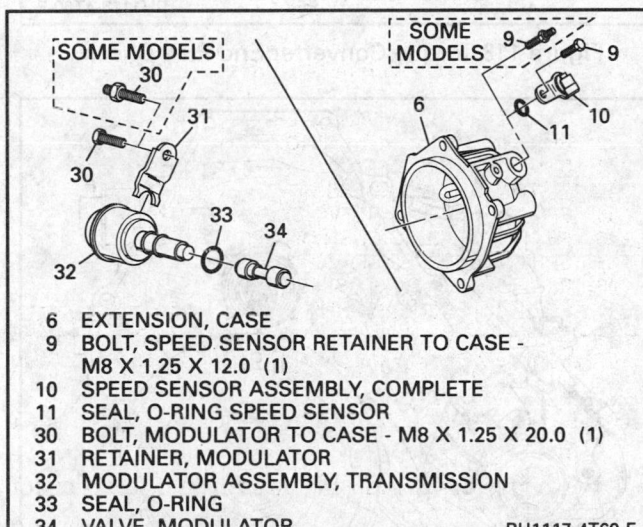

6 EXTENSION, CASE
9 BOLT, SPEED SENSOR RETAINER TO CASE - M8 X 1.25 X 12.0 (1)
10 SPEED SENSOR ASSEMBLY, COMPLETE
11 SEAL, O-RING SPEED SENSOR
30 BOLT, MODULATOR TO CASE - M8 X 1.25 X 20.0 (1)
31 RETAINER, MODULATOR
32 MODULATOR ASSEMBLY, TRANSMISSION
33 SEAL, O-RING
34 VALVE, MODULATOR

RH1117-4T60-E

Figure 116 Speed Sensor and Vacuum Modulator Assembly

Modulator Assembly Functional Check

Figures 116 and 117

Tools Required:

J 23738-A Hand Operated Vacuum Pump

J 36619 Modulator Checking Tool – Non-Turbo Models

Inspect

1. Install J 23738-A and apply 15 kPa (18 in. hg.) vacuum – pressure must hold for 30 seconds.
2. Modulator (32) with J 36619 and a known good modulator of same type.
3. Place gage between the modulators and apply pressure to both.
   - If indicator line moves out of view, the modulator must be replaced.

Install or Connect

1. Modulator valve (34) into case.
2. New O-ring seal (33) onto modulator (32).
3. Modulator assembly (32-33) into case.
4. Modulator retainer (31) and bolt (30).

   Tighten

   - Bolt (30) to 24 N•m (18 lb. ft.)
5. New O-ring seal (11) onto speed sensor assembly (10).
6. Speed sensor assembly (10) and speed sensor bolt (9) into case.

   Tighten

   - Bolt (9) to 11 N•m (98 lb. in.).

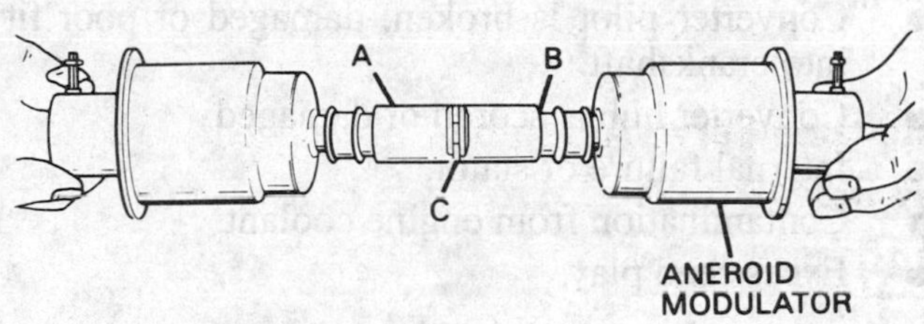

A
B
C
ANEROID MODULATOR

A COMPARISON GAGE J 36619
B OUTER GAGE LINE
C CENTER LINE

PH1116-4T60-E

Figure 117 Modulator Check

Torque Converter Assembly

Figures 118 and 119

Tools Required:

J 8001 Dial Indicator

J 26900-13 Magnetic Base

J 35138 Torque Converter End Play Checking Tool

Inspect

The torque converter assembly (1) must be replaced for any of the following conditions:

- Evidence of overheating (converter will have a blue color).
- Evidence of damage to the pump assembly.
- Metal particles are found after flushing the cooler and cooler lines.
- External leaks in hub weld area.
- Converter pilot is broken, damaged or poor fit into crankshaft.
- Converter hub is scored or damaged.
- Internal failure of stator.
- Contamination from engine coolant.
- Excess end play.

The torque converter should not be replaced if:

- There is no evidence of metal or clutch plate material in the fluid.
  - Drain as much fluid as possible.
  - FLUSHING THE TORQUE CONVERTER IS NOT RECOMMENDED.
- There is damage to bolt hole threads.
  - Correct with thread inserts.

Measure

- Install J 35138 and J 26900-13 with dial indicator gage J 8001
  - end play should be 0.0 to 0.5 mm (0.020 inch).

Install or Connect

1. Torque converter (1) onto transaxle.
2. Converter holding strap J 21366.

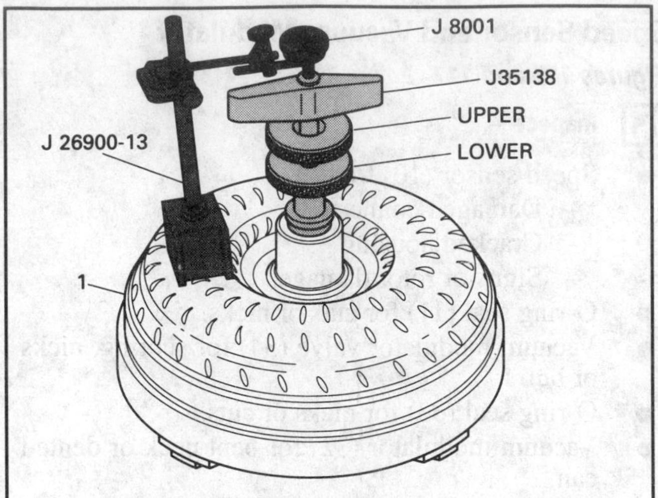
J 8001
J35138
UPPER
LOWER
J 26900-13
1

1 CONVERTER ASSEMBLY, COMPLETE RH1118-4T60-E

Figure 118 Torque Converter End Play Check

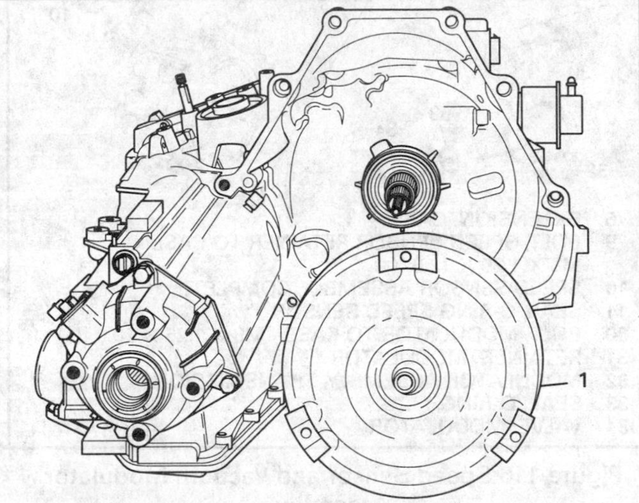
1

1 CONVERTER ASSEMBLY, COMPLETE RH1001-4T60-E

Figure 119 Torque Converter Installation

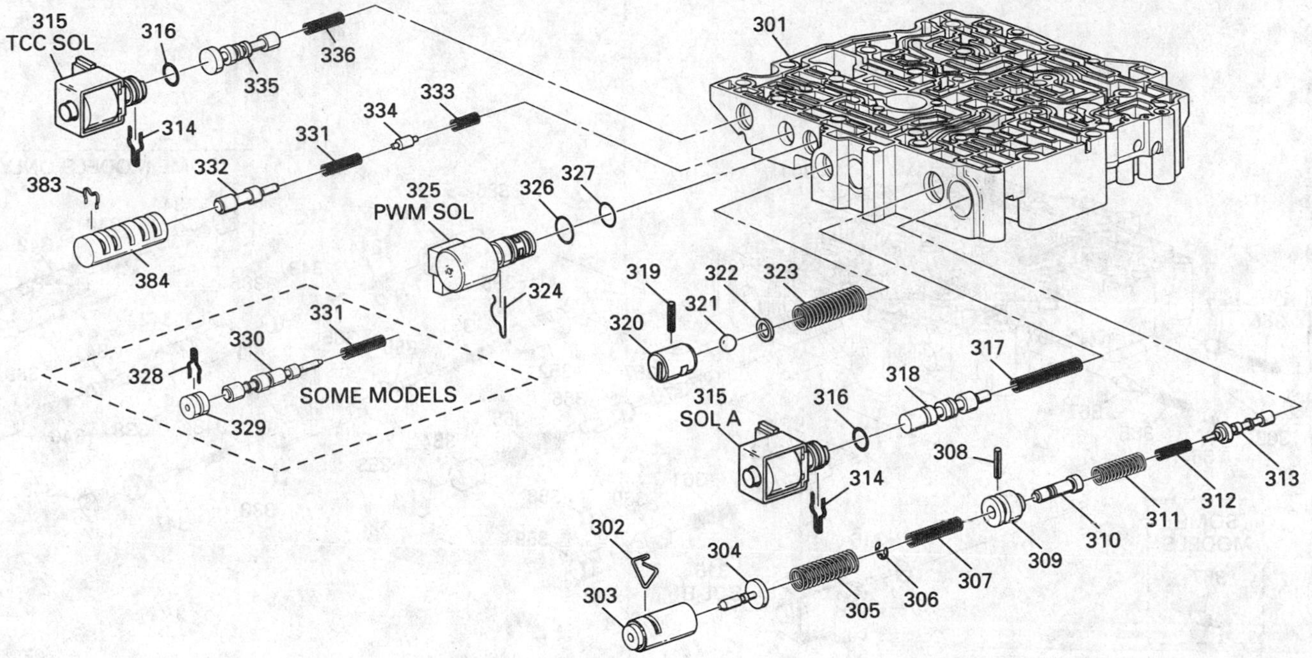
315
TCC SOL
316
336
335
314
334
333
331
332
383
325
PWM SOL
326
327
384
324
331
330
328
SOME MODELS
329
301
319
322
323
321
320
317
318
315
SOL A
316
308
314
313
312
311
310
309
302
304
307
306
305
303

301	BODY, CONTROL VALVE (MACHINED)	320	BUSHING, PUMP PRESSURE RELIEF
302	RETAINER, LINE BOOST VALVE AND BUSHING	321	BALL, 0.375 DIA.
303	BUSHING, LINE BOOST VALVE	322	SEAT, SPRING
304	VALVE, LINE BOOST	323	SPRING, PUMP PRESSURE RELIEF
305	SPRING, PRESSURE REGULATOR MODULATOR BOOST	324	RETAINER, SOLENOID (3-4 SHIFT)
306	RETAINER, PRESSURE REGULATOR	325	SOLENOID ASSEMBLY, PWM
307	SPRING, REVERSE BOOST	326	O-RING, PWM SOLENOID
308	PIN, GROOVED	327	O-RING, PWM SOLENOID
309	BUSHING, REVERSE BOOST VALVE	328	RETAINER, CONVERTER CL. REGULATOR
310	VALVE, REVERSE BOOST	329	BUSHING, CONVERTER CL. REGULATOR
311	SPRING, PRESSURE REGULATOR VALVE (OUTER)	330	VALVE, CONVERTER CLUTCH REGULATOR
312	SPRING, PRESSURE REGULATOR VALVE ISOLATOR	331	SPRING, ISOLATOR
313	VALVE, PRESSURE REGULATOR	332	VALVE, CONVERTER CLUTCH REGULATOR
314	RETAINER, SPRING CLIP	333	SPRING, CONVERTER CLUTCH REGULATOR
315	SOLENOID ASSEMBLY	334	VALVE, ISOLATOR
316	SEAL, O-RING	335	VALVE, CONVERTER CLUTCH
317	SPRING, 1-2 SHIFT VALVE	336	SPRING, CONVERTER CLUTCH
318	VALVE, 1-2 SHIFT	383	RETAINER, CONVERTER CLUTCH REGULATOR
319	PIN, COILED SPRING	384	BUSHING, CONVERTER CLUTCH REGULATOR

RH1094-4T60-E

Figure 120 Control Valve Assembly – A

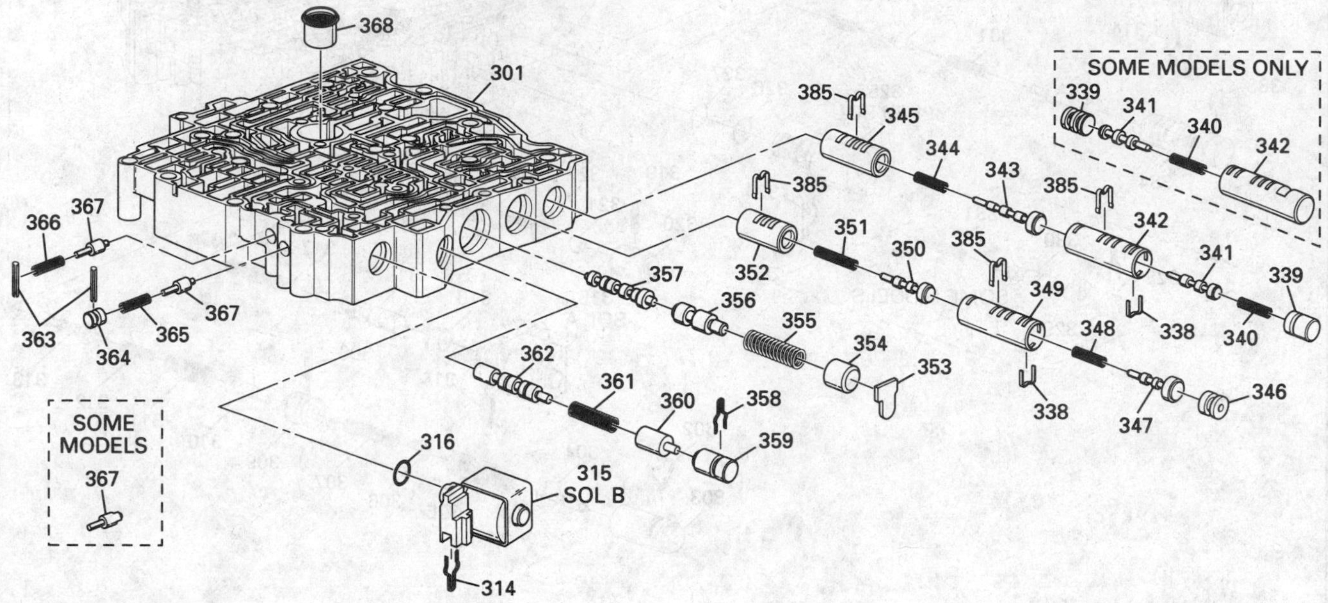
368
301
385
345
344
343
385
342
351
350
385
352
357
356
355
349
348
338
354
353
362
361
360
358
359
316
315
SOL B
314
SOME MODELS ONLY
339
341
340
342
341
339
338
340
346
347
338
366
367
363
364
365
367
SOME MODELS
367

301 BODY, CONTROL VALVE (MACHINED)
314 RETAINER, SPRING CLIP
315 SOLENOID ASSEMBLY
316 SEAL, O-RING
338 RETAINER, 1-2 ACCUMULATOR PLUG (PRIMARY AND SECONDARY)
339 PLUG, 1-2 ACCUMULATOR (PRIMARY)
340 SPRING, 1-2 ACCUMULATOR VALVE (PRIMARY)
341 VALVE, 1-2 ACCUMULATOR
342 BUSHING, 1-2 ACCUMULATOR VALVE (PRIMARY)
343 VALVE, 2-3 ACCUMULATOR
344 SPRING, 2-3 ACCUMULATOR VALVE
345 BUSHING, 2-3 ACCUMULATOR VALVE
346 PLUG, 1-2 ACCUMULATOR (SECONDARY)
347 VALVE, 1-2 ACCUMULATOR (SECONDARY)
348 SPRING, 1-2 ACCUMULATOR VALVE (SECONDARY)
349 BUSHING, 1-2 ACCUMULATOR (SECONDARY)
350 VALVE, 3-4 ACCUMULATOR
351 SPRING, 3-4 ACCUMULATOR VALVE
352 BUSHING, 3-4 ACCUMULATOR VALVE
353 RETAINER, 2-3 SHIFT
354 PLUG, BORE (2-3 SHIFT)
355 SPRING, 3-2 DOWNSHIFT VALVE
356 VALVE, 3-2 MANUAL DOWNSHIFT
357 VALVE, 2-3 SHIFT
358 RETAINER, SPRING CLIP
359 PLUG, BORE (3-4 SHIFT)
360 VALVE, 4-3 MANUAL DOWNSHIFT
361 SPRING, 4-3 MANUAL DOWNSHIFT
362 VALVE, 3-4 SHIFT
363 PIN, COILED SPRING
364 PLUG, BORE (REVERSE BOOST)
365 SPRING, SERVO BOOST VALVE (REVERSE)
366 SPRING, SERVO BOOST VALVE (FORWARD)
367 VALVE, SERVO BOOST (FORWARD AND REVERSE)
368 BEARING AND SLEEVE, OIL PUMP DRIVE
385 RETAINER, ACCUMULATOR BUSHING ASSEMBLY (2-3 AND 1-2 SECONDARY AND PRIMARY)

RH1095-4T60-E

Figure 121 Control Valve Assembly – B

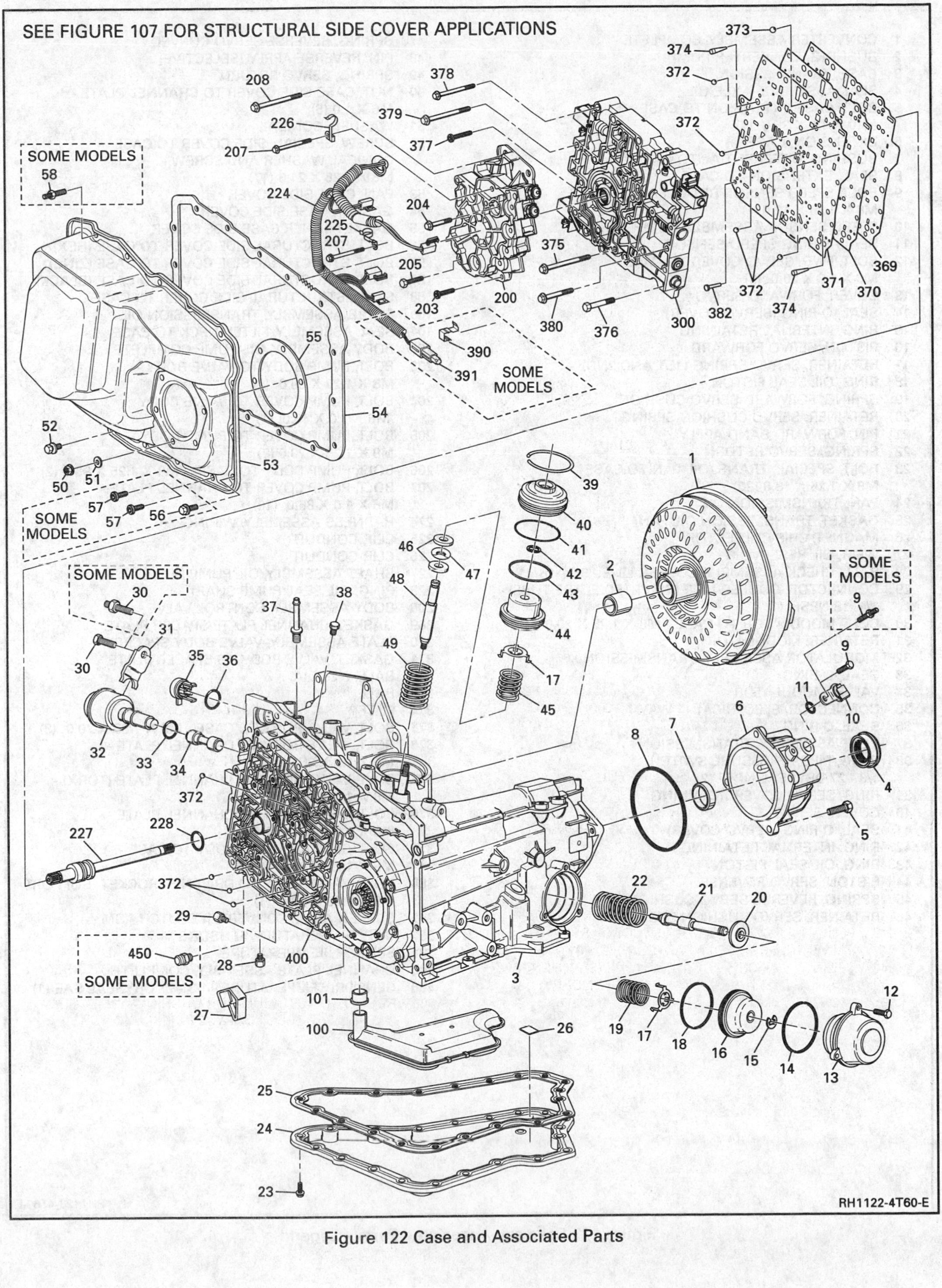
SEE FIGURE 107 FOR STRUCTURAL SIDE COVER APPLICATIONS
SOME MODELS
SOME MODELS
SOME MODELS
SOME MODELS
SOME MODELS
SOME MODELS
373
374
372
372
378
208
379
226
377
207
58
224
204
225
207
205
203
200
375
380
376
300
382
374
372
371
370
369
55
390
391
54
52
53
50
51
57
57
56
39
40
41
42
43
44
17
45
46
47
48
49
1
2
9
9
11
10
30
31
30
38
37
35
36
32
33
34
372
227
228
372
29
450
28
400
27
101
100
26
3
22
21
20
8
7
6
4
5
12
19
17
18
16
15
14
13
25
24
23
RH1122-4T60-E

Figure 122 Case and Associated Parts

1 CONVERTER ASSEMBLY, COMPLETE
2 BUSHING, CONVERTER PUMP
3 CASE, TRANSMISSION
4 SEAL ASSEMBLY, AXLE OIL
5 BOLT, CASE EXTENSION TO CASE - M10 X 1.5 X 35.0 (4)
6 EXTENSION, CASE
7 BUSHING, DIFFERENTIAL TO CASE
8 SEAL, EXTENSION TO CASE
9 BOLT, SPEED SENSOR RETAINER TO CASE - M8 X 1.25 X 12.0 (1)
10 SPEED SENSOR ASSEMBLY, COMPLETE
11 SEAL, O-RING SPEED SENSOR
12 BOLT, FWD. SERVO COVER TO CASE - M6 X 1.0 X 20.0 (3)
13 COVER, FORWARD SERVO
14 SEAL, O-RING (SERVO COVER)
15 RING, INTERNAL RETAINING
16 PISTON, SERVO FORWARD
17 RETAINER, SERVO SPRING (1ST AND 2ND)
18 RING, OIL SEAL PISTON
19 SPRING, FORWARD SERVO CUSHION
20 RETAINER, SERVO CUSHION SPRING
21 PIN, FORWARD BAND APPLY
22 SPRING, SERVO RETURN
23 BOLT, SPECIAL, TRANS. OIL PAN TO CASE - M8 X 1.25 X 18.0 (20)
24 PAN, TRANSMISSION OIL
25 GASKET, TRANSMISSION OIL PAN
26 MAGNET, CHIP COLLECTOR
27 WEIR, OIL RESERVOIR
28 BALL, CHECK ASSEMBLY, COOLER LINE - 3/8 - 18 (1)
29 CONNECTOR, COOLER-LINE (INVERTED FLARE TUBE) - 1/4- 18 NPSF (1)
30 BOLT, MODULATOR TO CASE - M8 X 1.25 X 20.0 (1)
31 RETAINER, MODULATOR
32 MODULATOR ASSEMBLY, TRANSMISSION
33 SEAL, O-RING
34 VALVE, MODULATOR
35 CONNECTOR, ELECTRICAL (7 WAY)
36 SEAL, O-RING
37 VENT ASSEMBLY, TRANSMISSION
38 PLUG, PIPE - PRESSURE SWITCH 1/8 - 27 DRYSEAL NPTF (2)
39 RING, SERVO COVER RETAINING
40 COVER, SERVO
41 SEAL, O-RING (SERVO COVER)
42 RING, INTERNAL RETAINING
43 RING, OIL SEAL PISTON
44 PISTON, SERVO REVERSE
45 SPRING, REVERSE SERVO CUSHION
46 RETAINER, SERVO CUSHION SPRING
47 SPRING, REVERSE SERVO CURVED
48 PIN, REVERSE APPLY (SELECTIVE)
49 SPRING, SERVO RETURN
50 NUT, CASE SIDE COVER TO CHANNEL PLATE - M6 X 1.0 (6)
51 WASHER, CONICAL
52 SCREW, SPECIAL, SIDE COVER TO CASE CONICAL WASHER AND SCREW - M8 X 1.25 X 21.3 (17)
53 PAN, CASE SIDE COVER
54 GASKET, CASE SIDE COVER
55 GASKET, INNER CASE SIDE COVER
56 BOLT, STRUCTURAL SIDE COVER TO CASE (HEX)
57 BOLT, STRUCTURAL SIDE COVER TO CASE (ZINC)
57 BOLT, STRUCTURAL SIDE COVER TO CASE (BLACK)
58 STUD, STRUCTURAL SIDE COVER TO CASE
100 FILTER ASSEMBLY, TRANSMISSION OIL
101 SEAL ASSEMBLY, FILTER NECK TO CASE
200 BODY ASSEMBLY, OIL PUMP COMPLETE
203 BOLT, PUMP BODY TO VALVE BODY - M8 X 1.25 X 30.0 (1)
204 BOLT, PUMP COVER TO VALVE BODY - M6 X 1.0 X 45.0 (1)
205 BOLT, PUMP COVER TO PUMP BODY - M8 X 1.25 X 20.0 (2)
206 BOLT, PUMP BODY TO CASE - M8 X 1.25 X 95.0 (2)
207 BOLT, PUMP COVER TO CHANNEL PLATE - M6 X 1.0 X 85.0 (10)
224 HARNESS ASSEMBLY, WIRING
225 CLIP, CONDUIT
226 CLIP, CONDUIT
227 SHAFT ASSEMBLY, OIL PUMP DRIVE
228 RING, OIL SEAL PUMP SHAFT
300 BODY ASSEMBLY, CONTROL VALVE
369 GASKET, CHANNEL PLATE/SPACER PLATE
370 PLATE ASSEMBLY, VALVE BODY SPACER
371 GASKET, VALVE BODY TO SPACER PLATE
372 BALL, 0.25 DIA.
373 BALL
374 FILTER
375 BOLT, VALVE BODY TO CASE - M8 X 1.25 X 70.0 (3)
376 BOLT, VALVE BODY TO CHANNEL PLATE - M6 X 1.0 X 35.0 (1)
377 BOLT, VALVE BODY TO CHANNEL PLATE (TORX) - M6 X 1.0 X 45.0 (2)
378 BOLT, VALVE BODY TO CHANNEL PLATE - M6 X 1.0 X 55.0 (6)
379 BOLT, SPECIAL, VALVE BODY TO CASE - M8 X 1.25 X 85.0 (1)
380 BOLT, VALVE BODY TO DRIVEN SPROCKET SUPPORT - M8 X 1.25 X 90.0 (1)
382 SCREEN ASM., CONVERTER CLUTCH ASM.
390 CLIP, TEMPERATURE SENSOR
391 SENSOR, TEMPERATURE
400 CHANNEL PLATE ASSEMBLY, COMPLETE
450 SENSOR, TEMPERATURE - 1/8 - 27 DRYSEAL SAE (1)

RH1123-4T60-E

Figure 123 Case and Associated Parts – Legend

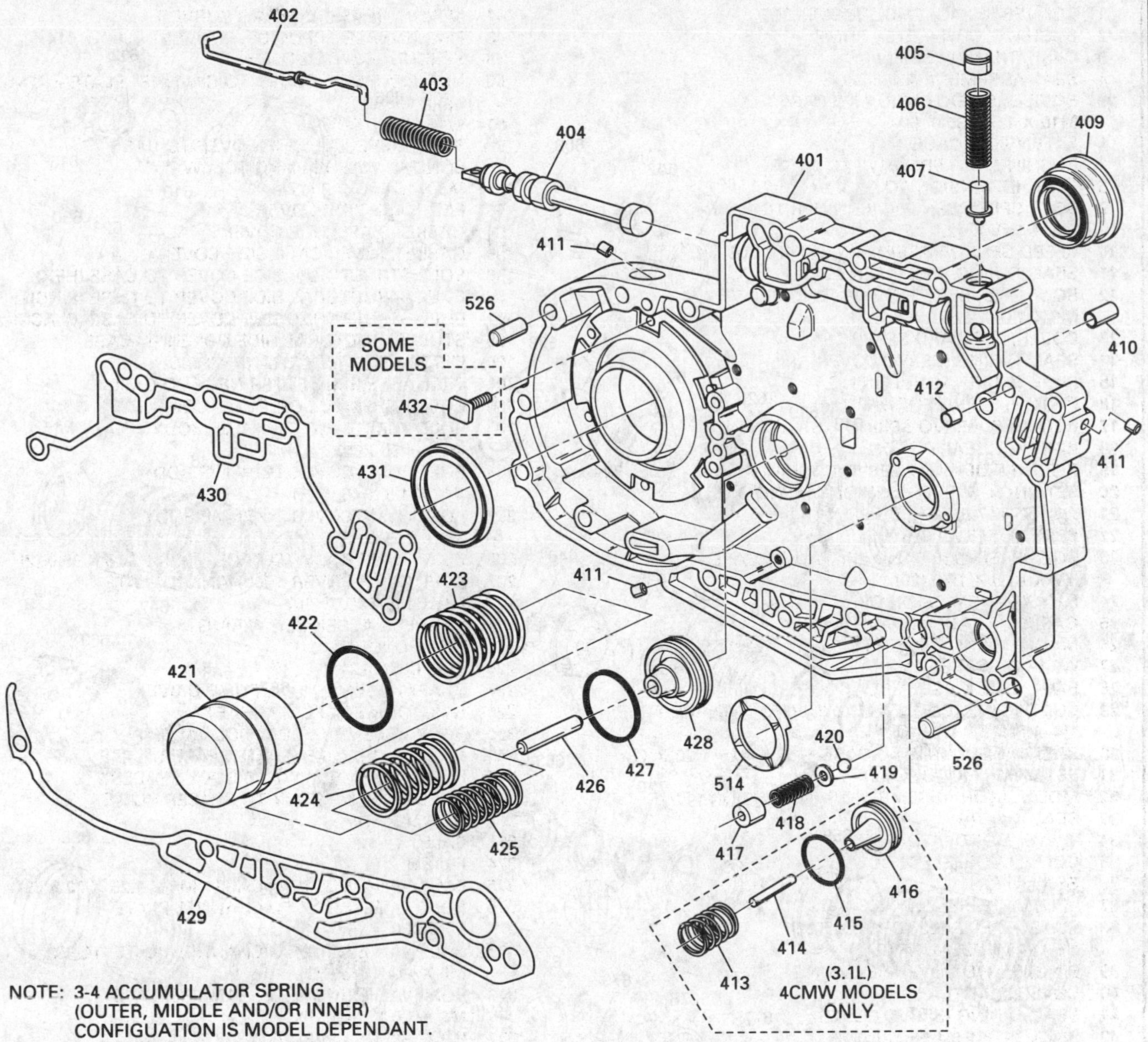
402
403
404
405
406
407
409
401
411
526
SOME MODELS
432
410
412
411
430
431
423
411
422
421
428
427
426
420
419
514
526
424
425
418
417
416
415
414
413
429
(3.1L) 4CMW MODELS ONLY

NOTE: 3-4 ACCUMULATOR SPRING (OUTER, MIDDLE AND/OR INNER) CONFIGUATION IS MODEL DEPENDANT.

401	CHANNEL PLATE
402	LINK, MANUAL VALVE
403	RETAINER, LINK (MANUAL VALVE)
404	VALVE, MANUAL
405	PLUG, LO BLOW OFF
406	SPRING, LO BLOW OFF
407	VALVE, LO BLOW OFF
409	SEAL ASSEMBLY, AXLE OIL (LEFT SIDE)
410	SLEEVE, CONTROL BODY ALIGNMENT
411	PLUG, BORE
412	PLUG, CUP (ORIFICED)
413	SPRING, TCC ACCUMULATOR
414	PIN, TCC ACCUMULATOR
415	SEAL, TCC ACCUMULATOR PISTON
416	PISTON, TCC ACCUMULATOR
417	PLUG, CUP (BLOW OFF)
418	SPRING, TCC BLOW OFF
419	SEAT, SPRING
420	BALL, 0.375 DIA.
421	CANISTER, 3-4 ACCUMULATOR
422	SEAL, O-RING
423	SPRING, 3-4 ACCUMULATOR (OUTER)
424	SPRING, 3-4 ACCUMULATOR (MIDDLE)
425	SPRING, 3-4 ACCUMULATOR (INNER)
426	PIN, 3-4 ACCUMULATOR
427	RING, OIL SEAL (3-4 ACCUM. PISTON)
428	PISTON, 3-4 ACCUMULATOR
429	GASKET, CHANNEL PLATE (LOWER)
430	GASKET, CHANNEL PLATE (UPPER)
431	BEARING ASM., 4TH CHANNEL HUB TO CHANNEL PLATE
432	STUD, CHANNEL PLATE TO SIDE COVER - M6 X 1.0 X 18.0 (6)
514	WASHER, THRUST (DRIVE SPROCKET/CHANNEL PLATE)
526	PIN, DOWEL

RH1019-4T60-E

Figure 124 Channel Plate Assembly – Case Side

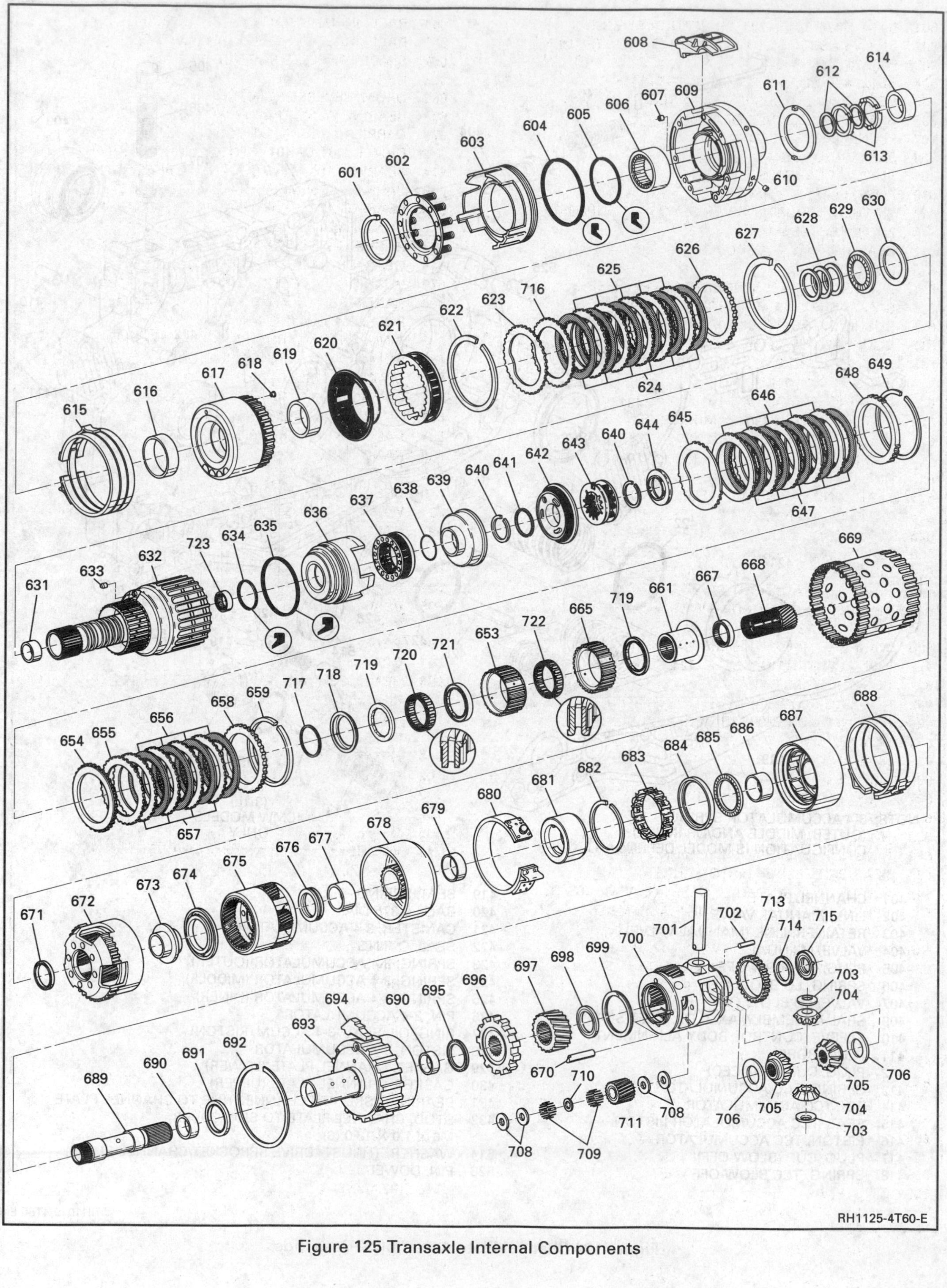
608
614
612
607
609
611
606
605
604
613
603
602
610
601
630
629
628
627
626
625
716
623
622
621
620
618
619
617
616
615
624
649
648
646
645
644
640
643
642
641
640
639
638
637
636
635
634
723
632
633
631
647
669
668
667
719
661
665
722
653
721
720
719
718
717
659
658
656
655
654
657
688
687
686
685
684
683
682
681
680
679
678
677
676
675
674
673
672
671
713
702
714
715
701
700
699
698
697
696
703
704
694
690
695
693
692
691
690
689
670
710
708
711
709
708
705
706
705
704
706
703
RH1125-4T60-E

Figure 125 Transaxle Internal Components

601 RING, SNAP (4TH CLUTCH RETURN SPRING)
602 SPRING ASSEMBLY, 4TH CLUTCH PISTON RETURN
603 PISTON, 4TH CLUTCH
604 SEAL, 4TH CLUTCH PISTON (OUTER)
605 SEAL, 4TH CLUTCH PISTON (INNER)
606 BEARING ASSEMBLY, DRAWN CUP
607 PLUG, CUP ORIFICED
608 SCOOP, CHAIN SCAVENGING
609 SUPPORT DRIVEN SPROCKET
610 PLUG, CUP
611 WASHER, THRUST (DRIVEN SPROCKET SUPPORT/ 2ND CLUTCH DRUM)
612 SEAL, RING FOUR LOBED
613 RING, OIL SEAL
614 BUSHING, DRIVEN SPROCKET SUPPORT
615 BAND ASSEMBLY, REVERSE
616 BUSHING, 75.5 O.D. X 8.0
617 HOUSING, 2ND CLUTCH
618 RETAINER AND BALL ASSEMBLY, CHECK VALVE (FORWARD CLUTCH)
619 BUSHING, 70.0 O.D. X 11.0
620 PISTON, 2ND CLUTCH W/MOLDED SEAL
621 APPLY RING AND RELEASE SPRING ASSEMBLY, 2ND CLUTCH
622 RING, SNAP
623 PLATE, 2ND CLUTCH (WAVED)
624 PLATE ASSEMBLY, 2ND CLUTCH (FIBER)
625 PLATE, 2ND CLUTCH REACTION (STEEL)
626 PLATE, BACKING SUPPORT RING (STEEL)
627 RING, SNAP 2ND CLUTCH (OUTER)
628 RING, OIL SEAL (INPUT SHAFT)
629 BEARING, THRUST (SUPPORT SPROCKET/ THRUST WASHER)
630 WASHER, THRUST (BEARING/ INPUT CLUTCH HUB) SELECTIVE
631 BUSHING, INPUT SHAFT
632 HOUSING SLEEVE AND SHAFT ASM., INPUT
633 RETAINER AND BALL ASM., CHECK VALVE
634 SEAL, INPUT CLUTCH PISTON (INNER)
635 SEAL, INPUT CLUTCH PISTON (OUTER)
636 PISTON, INPUT CLUTCH
637 SPRING AND RETAINER ASM., INPUT
638 SEAL, O-RING
639 HOUSING, 3RD CLUTCH PISTON
640 RING, SNAP (3RD CL. PISTON HSG./INPUT SHAFT)
641 SEAL, 3RD CLUTCH PISTON (INNER)
642 PISTON, SEAL AND BALL CAPSULE ASM., 3RD CL.
643 SPRING RETAINER AND GUIDE ASSEMBLY, 3RD CL.
644 BEARING ASSEMBLY, THRUST
645 PLATE, 3RD CLUTCH (WAVED)
646 PLATE ASSEMBLY, 3RD CLUTCH (SPROCKET SUPPORT/SPLINE O.D.)
647 PLATE ASSEMBLY, 3RD CLUTCH (SPROCKET SUPPORT/SPLINE I.D.)
648 PLATE, BACKING
649 RING, SNAP
653 RACE, 3RD SPRAG CLUTCH (OUTER)
654 PLATE, INPUT CLUTCH APPLY
655 PLATE, INPUT CLUTCH, (WAVED)
656 PLATE ASM., INPUT CLUTCH (FIBER)
657 PLATE, INPUT CLUTCH (1.9 FLAT)
658 PLATE, CLUTCH BACKING (STEEL)
659 RING, SNAP
661 RACE, INPUT SPRAG CLUTCH (INNER)
665 RACE, INPUT SPRAG CLUTCH (OUTER)
667 SPACER, INPUT SUN GEAR
668 GEAR, INPUT SUN
669 DRUM, REVERSE REACTION
671 BEARING ASM., THRUST
672 CARRIER ASM., INPUT COMPLETE
673 DAM, INPUT CARRIER TO REACTION CARRIER
674 BEARING ASM., THRUST (INPUT/REACTION CARRIER)
675 CARRIER ASSEMBLY, REACTION COMPLETE
676 BEARING ASM., THRUST (REACTION CARRIER/ SUN GEAR)
677 BUSHING, REACTION SUN GEAR (LEFT HAND)
678 GEAR, DRUM BUSHING ASM., REACTION SUN
679 BUSHING, REACTION SUN GEAR (RIGHT HAND)
680 BAND ASSEMBLY, 2/1
681 RACE, 1/2 SUPPORT (INNER)
682 RING, SNAP (1/2 ROLLER ASM.)
683 ROLLER ASSEMBLY, 1/2 SUPPORT
684 SPACER, 1/2 SUPPORT
685 BEARING ASM., THRUST ASM./LO RACE
686 BUSHING, 1/2 SUPPORT
687 RACE, 1/2 SUPPORT (OUTER)
688 BAND ASSEMBLY, FORWARD
689 SHAFT, FINAL DRIVE SUN GEAR
690 BUSHING, FINAL DRIVE INTERNAL GEAR
691 WASHER, THRUST (1/2 SUPPORT/INTERNAL GEAR)
692 RING, SNAP (FINAL DRIVE INTERNAL GEAR SPROCKET)
693 GEAR, FINAL DRIVE INTERNAL
694 PAWL AND PIN ASM., PAWL LOCKOUT
695 BEARING ASM., THRUST (INTERNAL GEAR/ PARKING GEAR)
696 GEAR, PARKING
697 GEAR, FINAL DRIVE SUN
698 BEARING ASM., THRUST CARRIER/SUN GEAR
699 RING, SPIRAL PIN RETAINING
700 CARRIER ASSEMBLY, DIFFERENTIAL/ FINAL DRIVE COMP.
701 SHAFT, DIFFERENTIAL PINION
702 PIN, DIFFERENTIAL PINION SHAFT RETAINING
703 WASHER, THRUST (DIFFERENTIAL PINION)
704 GEAR, DIFFERENTIAL PINION
705 GEAR, DIFFERENTIAL SIDE
706 WASHER, THRUST (DIFFERENTIAL SIDE GEAR) BRONZE
708 WASHER, PINION THRUST (STEEL)
709 BEARING, ROLLER NEEDLE
710 SPACER, PINION NEEDLE BEARING
711 PINION, FINAL DRIVE PLANET
712 PIN, PLANET PINION
713 ROTOR, SPEED SENSOR (29 OR 30 T.)
714 WASHER, DIFFERENTIAL CARRIER/CASE (THRUST)
715 BEARING ASM., THRUST (DIFFERENTIAL CARRIER/CASE)
716 PLATE, 2ND CL. APPLY REACTION (TAPERED)
717 RING, SPIRAL LOCK
718 RETAINER, 3RD CLUTCH SPRAG
719 BEARING, END (2)
720 3RD SPRAG ASSEMBLY
721 BEARING, CENTER
722 SPRAG ASSEMBLY, INPUT
723 BEARING, 4TH CLUTCH SHAFT TO INPUT HOUSING

RH1126-4T60-E

Figure 126 Transaxle Internal Components – Legend

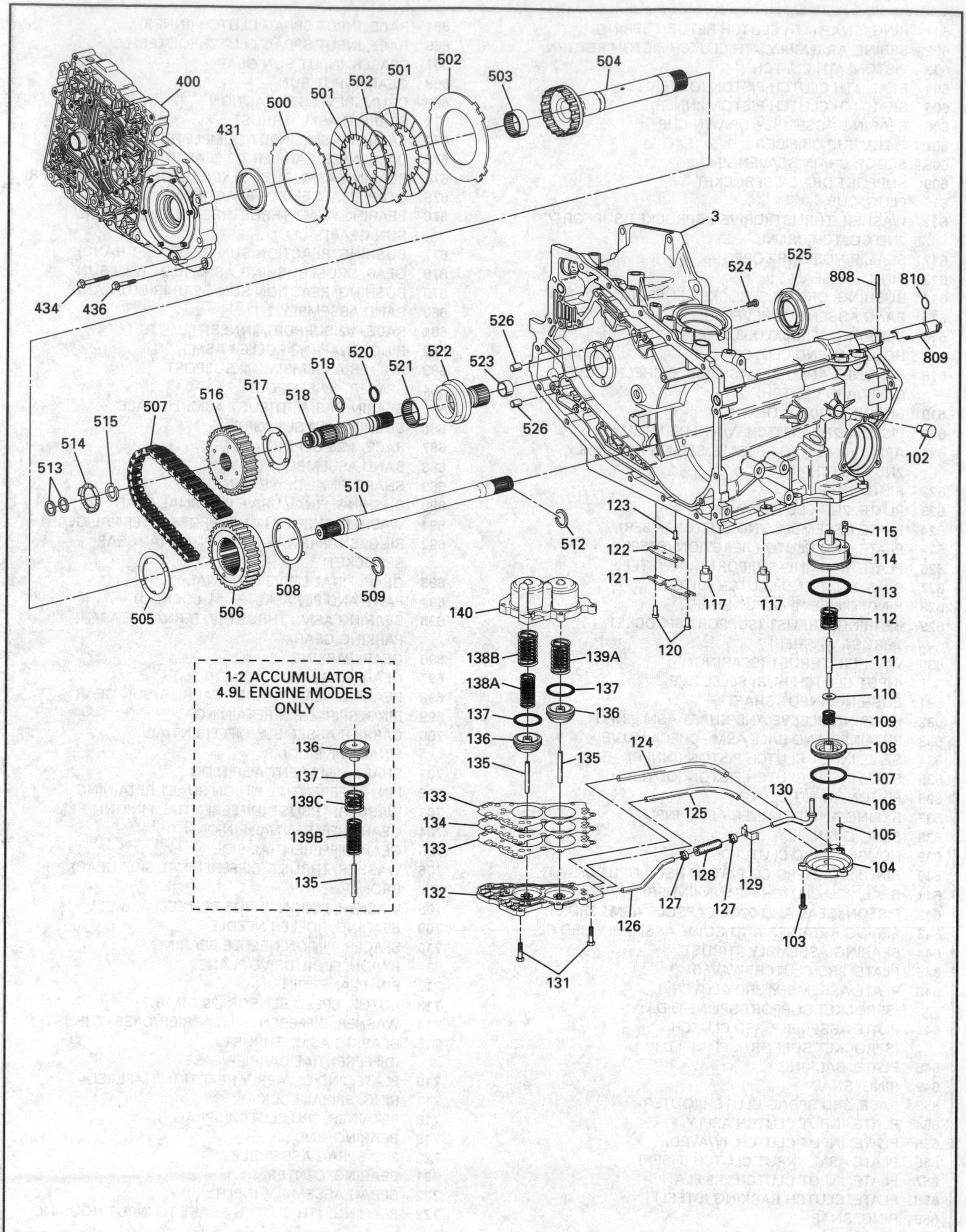
400
500
431
501
502
501
502
503
504
434
436
3
525
524
808
810
809
526
520
522
523
519
521
516
517
518
526
507
515
514
513
510
102
123
512
115
114
122
121
113
117
117
112
120
140
505
506
508
509
138B
139A
1-2 ACCUMULATOR
4.9L ENGINE MODELS
ONLY
138A
137
111
110
137
136
136
109
136
124
108
135
135
137
107
130
106
139C
133
125
134
105
139B
133
128
129
104
135
127
132
127
103
126
131
RH1127-4T60-E

Figure 127 Drive Link Assembly, 4th Clutch, Accumulator Assemblies, and Case Seals

3	CASE, TRANSMISSION
102	PIN, BAND ANCHOR (2-1 MANUAL)
103	BOLT, 2-1 SERVO COVER TO CASE - M8 X 1.25 X 25.0 (3)
104	COVER, 2-1 MANUAL SERVO BODY
105	SEAL, SQUARE CUT (2-1 SERVO)
106	CLIP, RETAINING (BOTTOM)
107	SEAL, LIP
108	PISTON, 2-1 MANUAL SERVO
109	SPRING, 2-1 MANUAL SERVO CUSHION
110	RETAINER, INT. SERVO SPRING MANUAL CUSHION
111	PIN, 2-1 MANUAL APPLY
112	SPRING, 2-1 MANUAL SERVO RETURN
113	SEAL, O-RING
114	BODY, 2-1 MANUAL SERVO
115	FILTER, 2-1 SERVO
116	CLIP, RETAINING (TOP)
117	PIN, BAND ANCHOR FORWARD AND REVERSE
120	PIN WASHER ASM., THERMO ELEMENT
121	THERMOSTATIC ELEMENT
122	PLATE, THERMOSTATIC ELEMENT
123	PIN, THERMAL ELEMENT
124	PIPE, FORWARD SERVO APPLY
125	PIPE, MANUAL SERVO APPLY
126	PIPE, LUBE OIL
127	CLAMP, HOSE
128	HOSE, LUBE OIL
129	RETAINER, LUBE PIPE CLIP
130	PIPE AND WASHER ASSEMBLY
131	BOLT, ACCUMULATOR COVER TO CASE AND ACCUMULATOR HSG. - M6 X 1.0 X 28.0 (1)
132	COVER, ACCUMULATOR
133	GASKET, ACCUMULATOR COVER
134	PLATE, ACCUMULATOR SPACER
135	PIN, 2-3 ACCUMULATOR
136	PISTON, 1-2 AND 2-3 ACCUMULATOR
137	RING, OIL SEAL ACCUMULATOR PISTON
138A	SPRING, 2-3 ACCUMULATOR (INNER)
138B	SPRING, 2-3 ACCUMULATOR (OUTER)
139A	SPRING, 1-2 ACCUMULATOR
139B	SPRING, 1-2 ACCUMULATOR (INNER)
139C	SPRING, 1-2 ACCUMULATOR (OUTER)
140	HOUSING, ACCUMULATOR (MACHINED)
400	CHANNEL PLATE ASM., COMPLETE
431	BEARING ASM., 4TH CHANNEL HUB/ CHANNEL PLATE
434	BOLT, CHANNEL PLATE TO CASE - M8 X 1.25 X 45.0 (6)
436	BOLT, CHANNEL PLATE TO CASE - M8 X 1.25 X 30.0 (4)
500	PLATE, 4TH CLUTCH REACTION
501	PLATE ASM., 4TH CLUTCH
502	PLATE, 4TH CLUTCH APPLY
503	BEARING ASM., 4TH CLUTCH
504	HUB AND SHAFT ASM., 4TH CLUTCH
505	WASHER, THRUST (4TH CL. HUB TO DRIVEN SPROCKET)
506	SPROCKET, DRIVEN
507	LINK ASSEMBLY, DRIVE
508	WASHER, THRUST (DRIVEN AND 2ND CL. DRUM)
509	RING, OUTPUT SHAFT/DRIVE AXLE (SNAP)
510	SHAFT, OUTPUT
512	RING, OUTPUT SHAFT/DIFFER. INBOARD (SNAP)
513	RING, OIL SEAL (TURBINE SHAFT/SLEEVE) (2)
514	WASHER, THRUST (DRIVE SPROCKET/ CHANNEL PLATE)
515	RING, TURBINE SHAFT TO DRIVE SPROCKET (SNAP)
516	SPROCKET, DRIVE
517	WASHER, THRUST (DRIVE SPROCKET/SUPPORT)
518	SHAFT, TURBINE
519	RING, OIL SEAL (TURBINE SHAFT/SUPPORT)
520	SEAL, O RING (TURBINE SHAFT/HUB) GREEN
521	BEARING ASM., DRIVE SUPPORT/SPROCKET (DRAWN CUP)
522	SUPPORT, DRIVE SPROCKET
523	BUSHING, DRIVE SPROCKET SUPPORT
524	BOLT, CASE TO DRIVE SPROCKET SUPPORT - M8 X 1.25 X 23.5 (4)
525	HELIX SEAL ASM., CONVERTER OIL
526	PIN, DOWEL
808	PIN, GUIDE RETAINING
809	GUIDE, ACTUATOR
810	SEAL, O-RING

RH1128-4T60-E

Figure 128 Drive Link Assembly, 4th Clutch, Accumulator Assemblies, and Case Seals – Legend

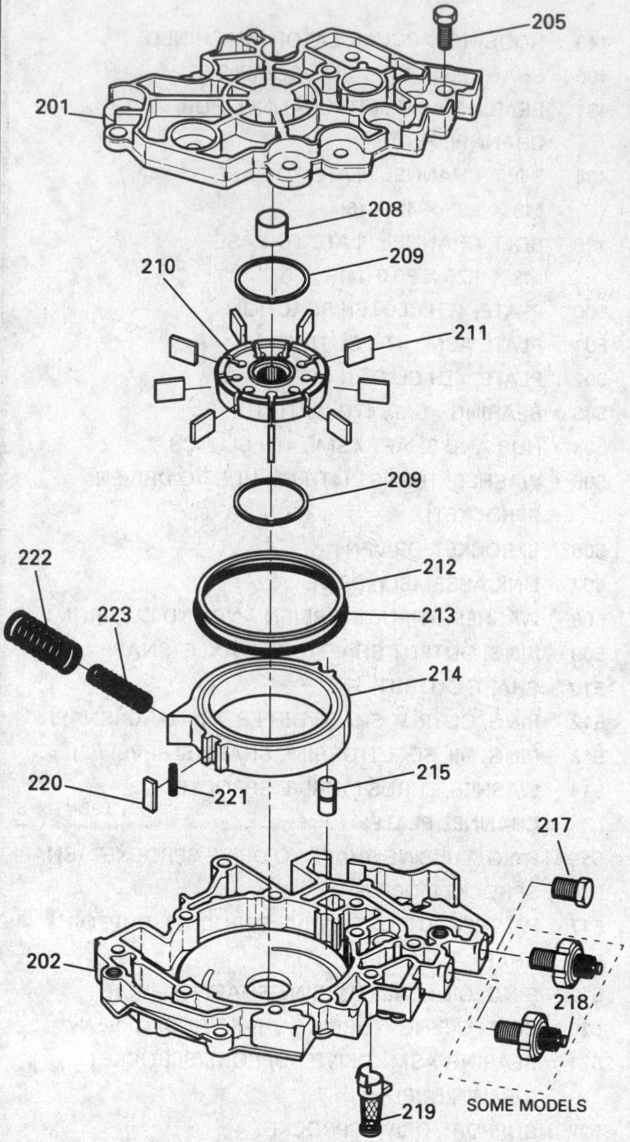
205
201
208
209
210
211
209
222
212
223
213
214
215
220
221
217
202
218
219
SOME MODELS

201 COVER, PUMP
202 BODY, OIL PUMP
205 BOLT, PUMP COVER TO PUMP BODY - M8 X 1.25 X 20.0 (1)
208 BUSHING, AUXILIARY VALVE BODY (PUMP SHAFT)
209 RING, PUMP VANE
210 ROTOR, OIL PUMP SELECTIVE
211 VANE, PUMP SELECTIVE
212 RING, OIL SEAL (SLIDE TO COVER - SELECTIVE)
213 SEAL, O-RING
214 SLIDE OIL PUMP SELECTIVE
215 PIN, PIVOT (PUMP SLIDE)
217 PIPE PLUG, LINE PRESSURE 1/8 - 27 DRYSEAL NPTF
218 SWITCH ASSEMBLY, PRESSURE 1/8 - 27 DRYSEAL NPTF
219 SCREEN ASSEMBLY, OIL PUMP PRESSURE
220 SEAL, PUMP SLIDE
221 SUPPORT, OIL PUMP SLIDE SEAL
222 SPRING, PUMP PRIMING (OUTER)
223 SPRING, PUMP PRIMING (INNER)

RH1101-4T60-E

Figure 129 Oil Pump Assembly

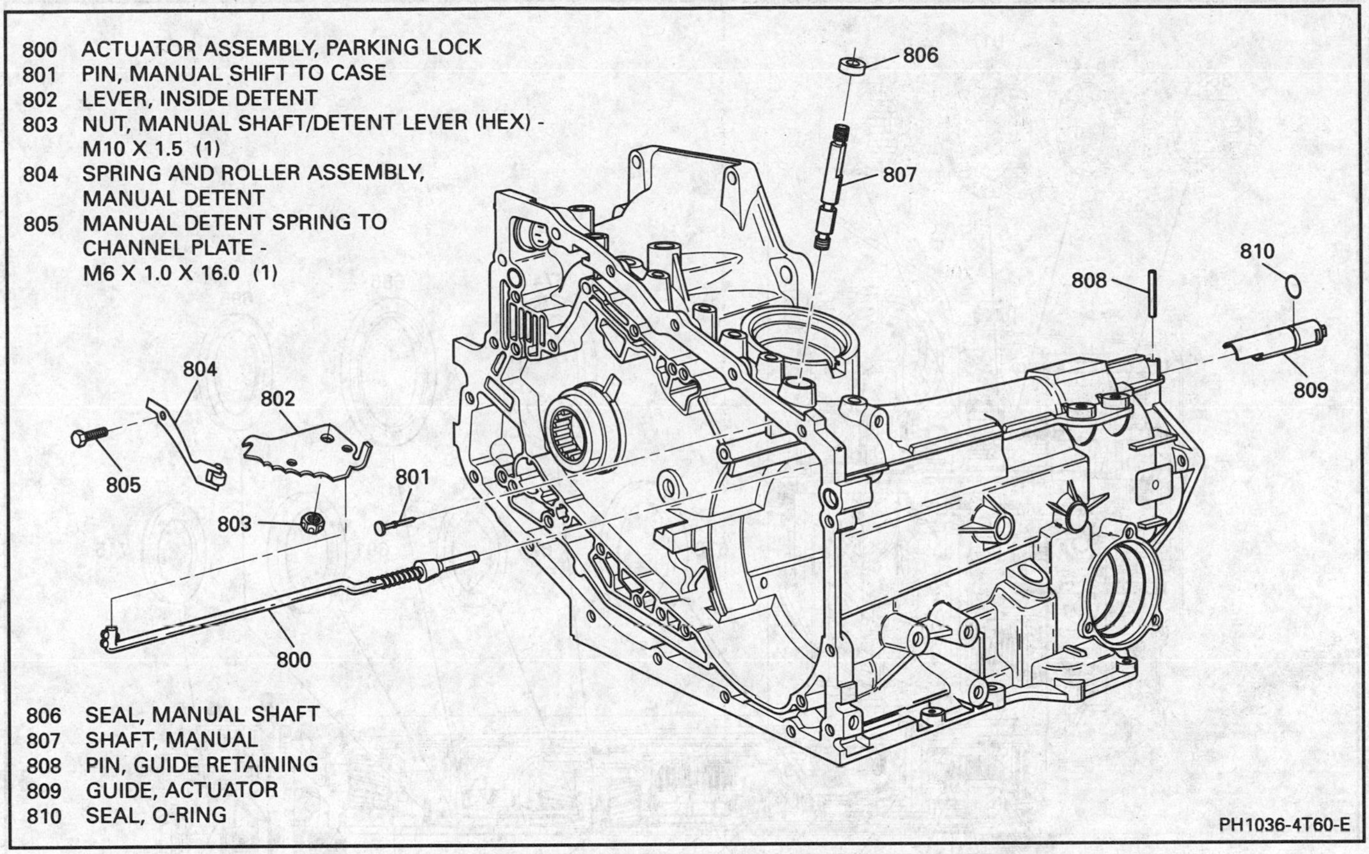
800 ACTUATOR ASSEMBLY, PARKING LOCK
801 PIN, MANUAL SHIFT TO CASE
802 LEVER, INSIDE DETENT
803 NUT, MANUAL SHAFT/DETENT LEVER (HEX) - M10 X 1.5 (1)
804 SPRING AND ROLLER ASSEMBLY, MANUAL DETENT
805 MANUAL DETENT SPRING TO CHANNEL PLATE - M6 X 1.0 X 16.0 (1)
806
807
808
809
810
804
802
805
801
803
800
806 SEAL, MANUAL SHAFT
807 SHAFT, MANUAL
808 PIN, GUIDE RETAINING
809 GUIDE, ACTUATOR
810 SEAL, O-RING
PH1036-4T60-E

Figure 130 Manual Shaft and Park System Components

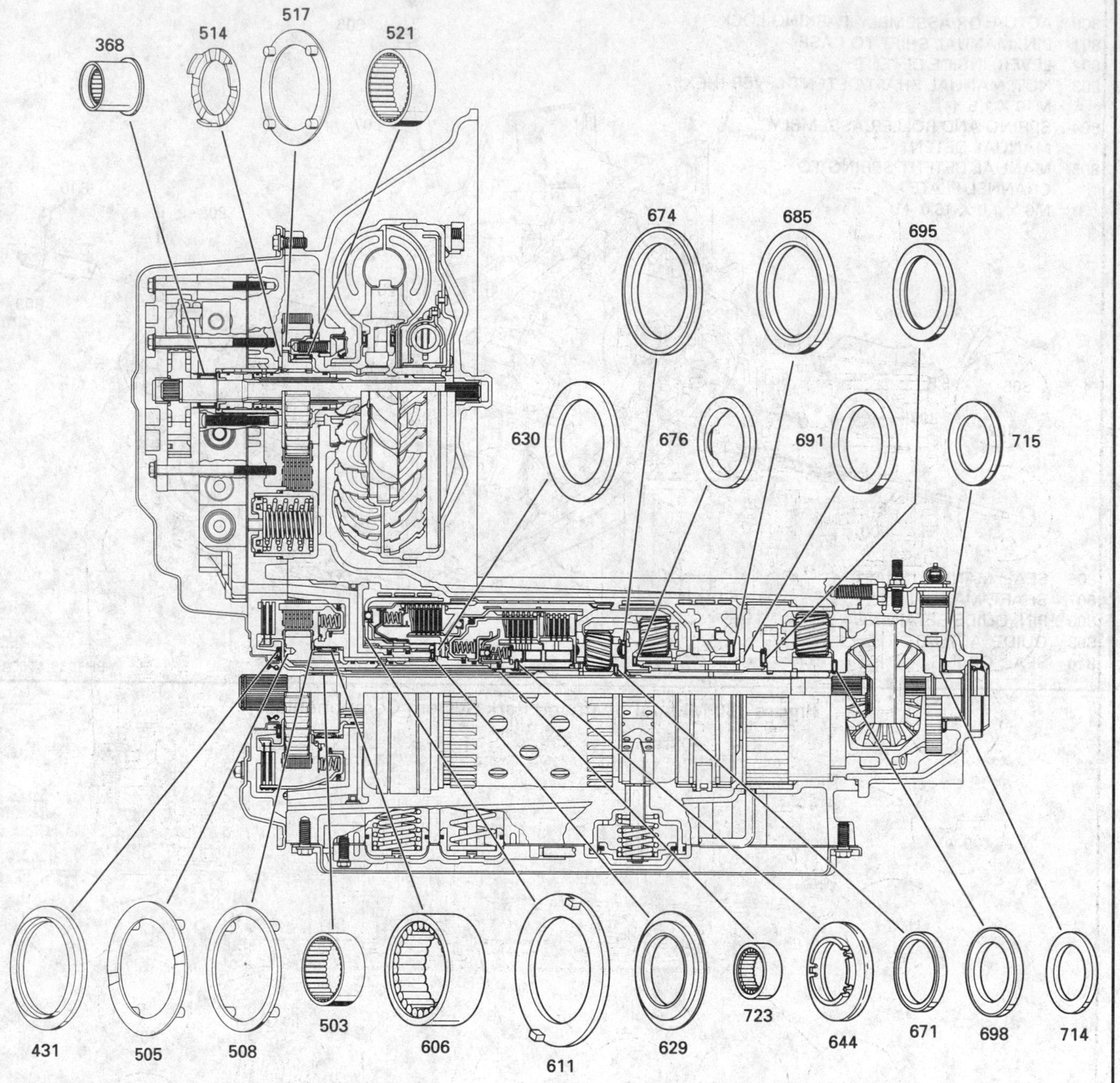
368
514
517
521
674
685
695
630
676
691
715
431
505
508
503
606
611
629
723
644
671
698
714

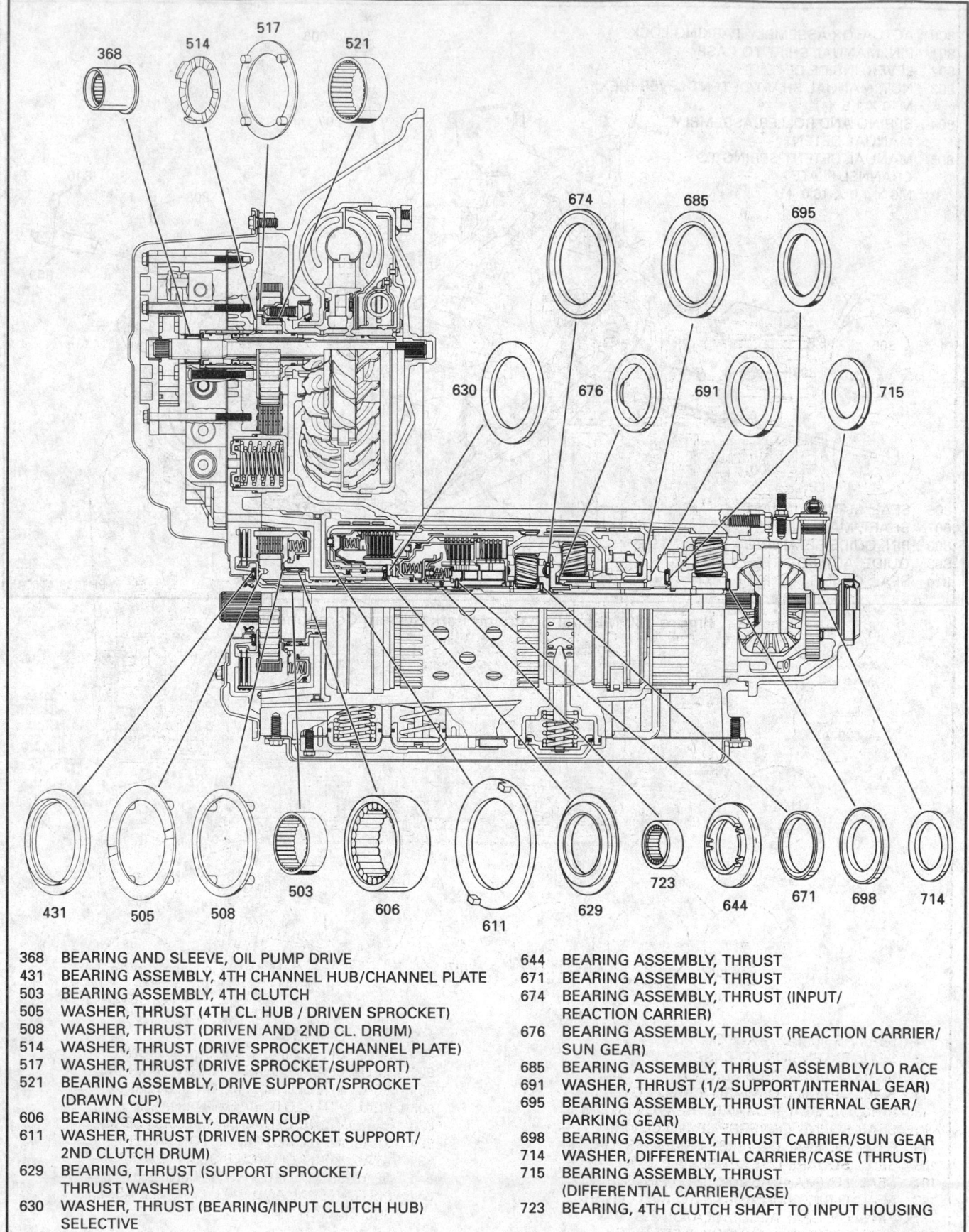

368 BEARING AND SLEEVE, OIL PUMP DRIVE
431 BEARING ASSEMBLY, 4TH CHANNEL HUB/CHANNEL PLATE
503 BEARING ASSEMBLY, 4TH CLUTCH
505 WASHER, THRUST (4TH CL. HUB / DRIVEN SPROCKET)
508 WASHER, THRUST (DRIVEN AND 2ND CL. DRUM)
514 WASHER, THRUST (DRIVE SPROCKET/CHANNEL PLATE)
517 WASHER, THRUST (DRIVE SPROCKET/SUPPORT)
521 BEARING ASSEMBLY, DRIVE SUPPORT/SPROCKET (DRAWN CUP)
606 BEARING ASSEMBLY, DRAWN CUP
611 WASHER, THRUST (DRIVEN SPROCKET SUPPORT/ 2ND CLUTCH DRUM)
629 BEARING, THRUST (SUPPORT SPROCKET/ THRUST WASHER)
630 WASHER, THRUST (BEARING/INPUT CLUTCH HUB) SELECTIVE
644 BEARING ASSEMBLY, THRUST
671 BEARING ASSEMBLY, THRUST
674 BEARING ASSEMBLY, THRUST (INPUT/ REACTION CARRIER)
676 BEARING ASSEMBLY, THRUST (REACTION CARRIER/ SUN GEAR)
685 BEARING ASSEMBLY, THRUST ASSEMBLY/LO RACE
691 WASHER, THRUST (1/2 SUPPORT/INTERNAL GEAR)
695 BEARING ASSEMBLY, THRUST (INTERNAL GEAR/ PARKING GEAR)
698 BEARING ASSEMBLY, THRUST CARRIER/SUN GEAR
714 WASHER, DIFFERENTIAL CARRIER/CASE (THRUST)
715 BEARING ASSEMBLY, THRUST (DIFFERENTIAL CARRIER/CASE)
723 BEARING, 4TH CLUTCH SHAFT TO INPUT HOUSING

RH1131-4T60-E

Figure 131 Thrust Washer and Bearing Locations

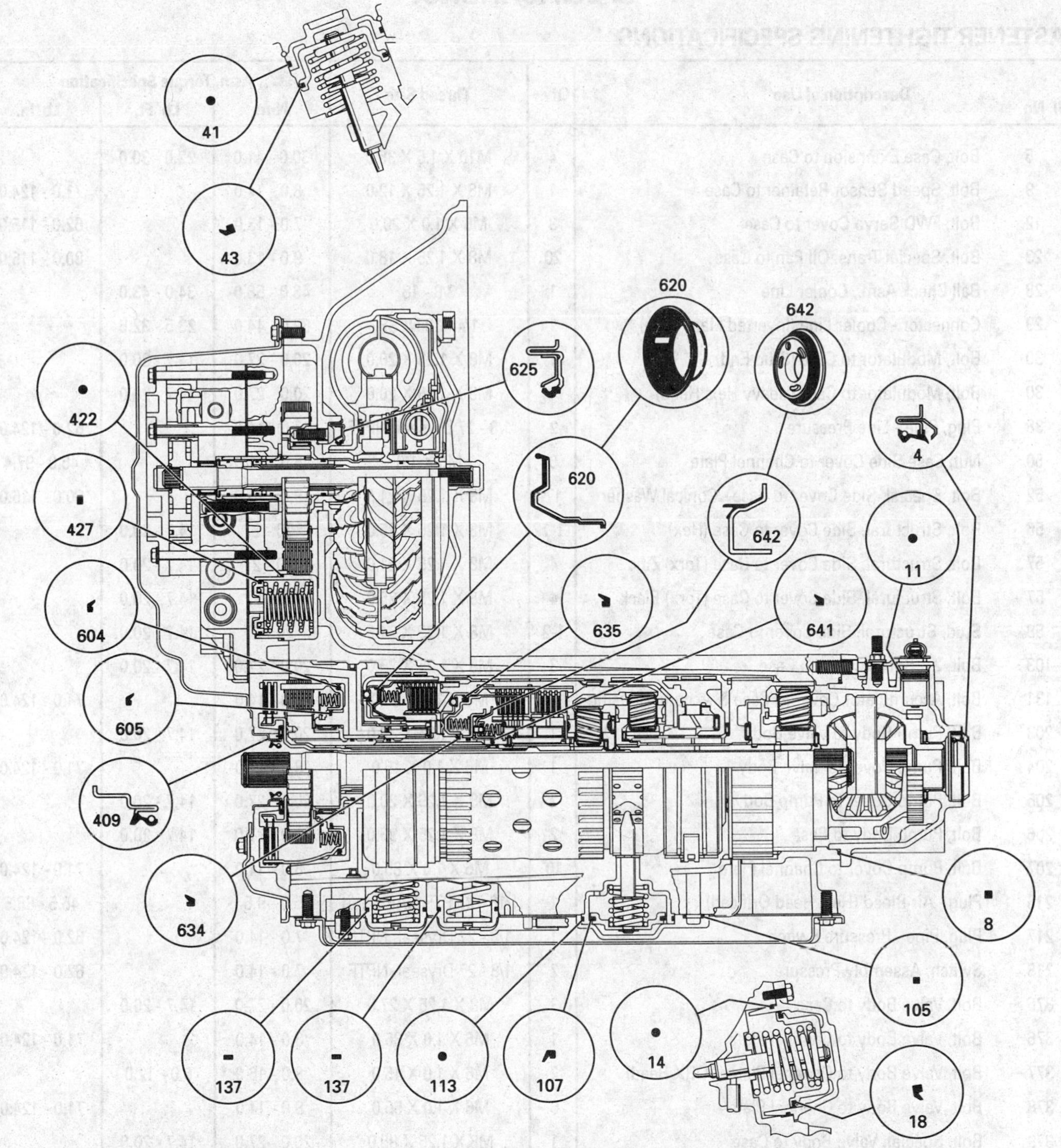
41
43
620
642
625
4
422
620
642
11
427
635
641
604
605
409
634
8
105
14
137
137
113
107
18

4 SEAL ASSEMBLY, AXLE OIL
8 SEAL, EXTENSION TO CASE
11 SEAL, O-RING SPEED SENSOR
14 SEAL, O-RING (FORWARD SERVO COVER)
18 RING, OIL SEAL (FORWARD SERVO PISTON)
41 SEAL, O-RING (REVERSE SERVO COVER)
43 RING, OIL SEAL (REVERSE SERVO PISTON)
105 SEAL, SQUARE CUT (2/1 SERVO)
107 SEAL, LIP (MANUAL 2/1 SERVO PISTON)
113 SEAL, O-RING (MANUAL 2/1 SERVO COVER)
137 RING, OIL SEAL ACCUMULATOR PISTON
409 SEAL ASSEMBLY, AXLE OIL (LEFT SIDE)
422 SEAL, O-RING
427 RING, OIL SEAL (3-4 ACCUM. PISTON)
525 HELIX SEAL ASSEMBLY, CONVERTER OIL
604 SEAL, 4TH CLUTCH PISTON (OUTER)
605 SEAL, 4TH CLUTCH PISTON (INNER)
620 PISTON, 2ND CLUTCH W/MOLDED SEAL
634 SEAL, INPUT CLUTCH PISTON (INNER)
635 SEAL, INPUT CLUTCH PISTON (OUTER)
641 SEAL, 3RD CLUTCH PISTON (INNER)
642 PISTON, SEAL AND BALL CAPSULE ASM., 3RD CLUTCH

RH1132-4T60-E

Figure 132 Lip Seal Locations

SPECIFICATIONS

FASTENER TIGHTENING SPECIFICATIONS

Ill. No.	Description of Use	Qty.	Thread Size	Asm. Torque Specification		
				N·m	Lb. Ft.	Lb. In.
5	Bolt, Case Extension to Case	4	M10 X 1.5 X 35.0	30.0 - 41.0	22.0 - 30.0	
9	Bolt, Speed Sensor Retainer to Case	1	M8 X 1.25 X 12.0	8.0 - 14.0		71.0 - 124.0
12	Bolt, FWD Servo Cover to Case	3	M6 X 1.0 X 20.0	7.0 - 13.0		62.0 - 115.0
23	Bolt, Special Trans. Oil Pan to Case	20	M8 X 1.25 X 18.0	9.0 - 13.0		80.0 - 115.0
28	Ball Check Asm., Cooler Line	1	3/8 - 18	46.0 - 58.0	34.0 - 43.0	
29	Connector - Cooler Line (Inverted Flare Tube)	1	1/4 - 18 NPSF	32.0 - 44.0	23.5 - 32.5	
30	Bolt, Modulator to Case (Stud End)	1	M8 X 1.25 X 20.0	20.0 - 27.0	14.7 - 20.0	
30	Bolt, Modulator to Case (Heavy Hex. Head)	1	M8 X 1.25 X 20.0	20.0 - 27.0	14.7 - 20.0	
38	Plug, Pipe - Line Pressure	2	1/8 - 27 Dryseal, NPTF	7.0 - 14.0		62.0 - 124.0
50	Nut, Case Side Cover to Channel Plate	6	M6 X 1.0	5.0 - 11.0		45.0 - 97.4
52	Bolt, Special, Side Cover to Case - Conical Washer	17	M8 X 1.25 X 21.3	9.0 - 13.0		80.0 - 115.0
56	Bolt, Structural, Side Cover to Case (Hex)	11-12	M8 X 1.25 X 25.0	20 - 27	14.7 - 20.0	
57	Bolt, Structural, Side Cover to Case (Torx) Zinc	4	M8 X 1.25 X 21.0	20 - 27	14.7 - 20.0	
57	Bolt, Structural, Side Cover to Case (Torx) Black	4	M8 X 1.25 X 25.0	20 - 27	14.7 - 20.0	
58	Stud, Structural, Side Cover to Case	1-2	M8 X 1.25 X 24.6	20 - 27	14.7 - 20.0	
103	Bolt, 2-1 Servo Cover to Case	3	M8 X 1.25 X 25.0	20.0 - 27.0	14.7 - 20.0	
131	Bolt, Accumulator Cover to Case & Accum. Housing	11	M6 X 1.0 X 28.0	8.0 - 14.0		71.0 - 124.0
203	Bolt, Pump Body to Valve Body	1	M8 X 1.25 X 30.0	20.0 - 27.0	14.7 - 20.0	
204	Bolt, Pump Cover to Valve Body	1	M6 X 1.0 X 45.0	8.0 - 14.0		71.0 - 124.0
205	Bolt, Pump Cover to Pump Body	2	M8 X 1.25 X 20.0	20.0 - 27.0	14.7 - 20.0	
206	Bolt, Pump Body to Case	2	M8 X 1.25 X 95.0	20.0 - 27.0	14.7 - 20.0	
207	Bolt, Pump Cover to Channel Plate	10	M6 X 1.0 X 85.0	8.0 - 14.0		71.0 - 124.0
216	Plug - Air Bleed (Hex. Head Orificed)	1	1/16 - 27 PTF, SAE Short	5.0 - 9.5		46.5 - 88.5
217	Plug, Pipe - Pressure Switch	1	1/8 - 27 Dryseal, NPTF	7.0 - 14.0		62.0 - 124.0
218	Switch, Assembly Pressure	2	1/8 - 27 Dryseal, NPTF	7.0 - 14.0		62.0 - 124.0
375	Bolt, Valve Body to Case	3	M8 X 1.25 X 27.0	20.0 - 27.0	14.7 - 20.0	
376	Bolt, Valve Body to Channel Plate	1	M6 X 1.0 X 35.0	8.0 - 14.0		71.0 - 124.0
377	Bolt, Valve Body to Channel Plate (TORX Head)	2	M6 X 1.0 X 45.0	8.0 - 16.0	6.0 - 12.0	
378	Bolt, Valve Body to Channel Plate	6	M6 X 1.0 X 55.0	8.0 - 14.0		71.0 - 124.0
379	Bolt, Special, Valve Body to Case	1	M8 X 1.25 X 85.0	20.0 - 27.0	14.7 - 20.0	
380	Bolt, Valve Body to Driven Sprocket Support	1	M8 X 1.25 X 90.0	20.0 - 27.0	14.7 - 20.0	
434	Bolt, Channel Plate to Case	6	M8 X 1.25 X 45.0	20.0 - 27.0	14.7 - 20.0	
436	Bolt, Channel Plate to Case	4	M8 X 1.25 X 30.0	20.0 - 27.0	14.7 - 20.0	
450	Temperature Sensor	1	1/8 - 27 Dryseal, SAE Sh.	6.5 - 7.5		57.5 - 66.5
524	Bolt, Case to Drive Sprocket Support	4	M8 X 1.25 X 23.5	20.0 - 27.0	14.7 - 20.0	
803	Nut, Manual Shaft to Inside Detent Lever	1	M10 X 1.5	27.0 - 36.0	20.0 - 26.5	
805	Bolt, Manual Detent Spring to Channel Plate	1	M6 X 1.0 X 16.0	8.0 - 14.0		71.0 - 124.0

RH1133-4T60-E

SPECIAL TOOLS

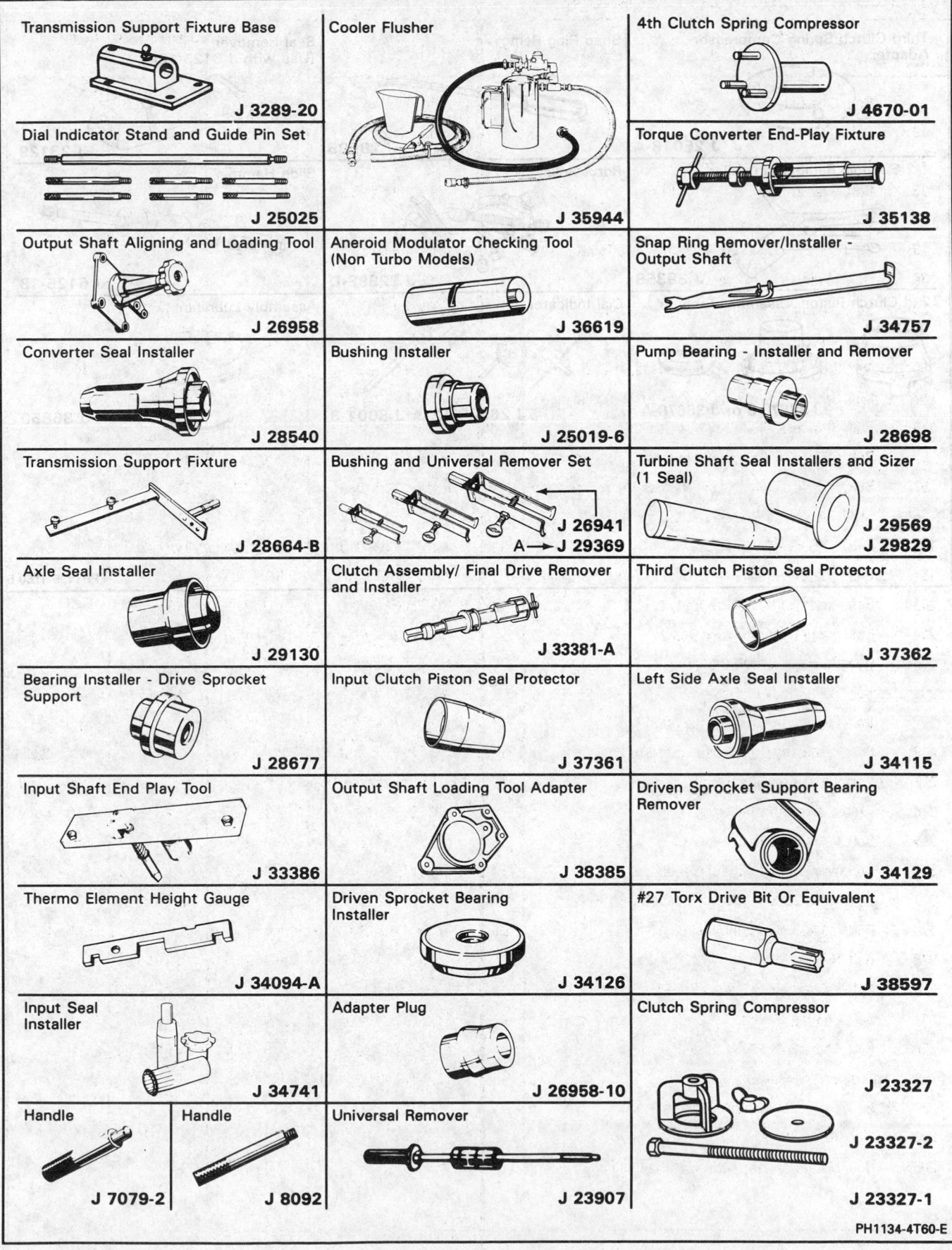

Transmission Support Fixture Base

J 3289-20

Cooler Flusher
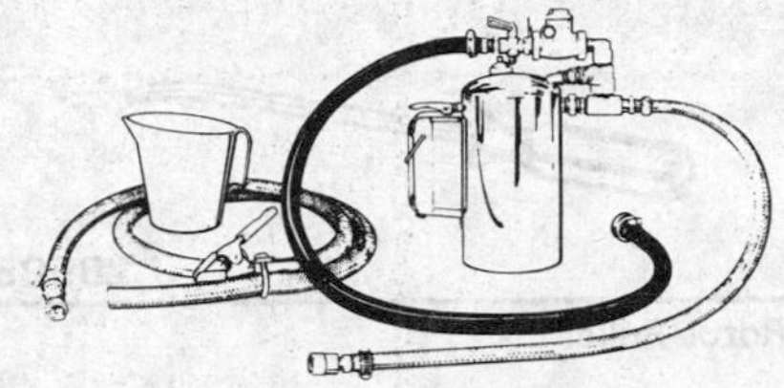
J 35944

4th Clutch Spring Compressor
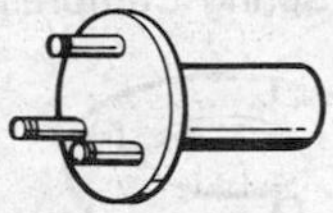
J 4670-01

Dial Indicator Stand and Guide Pin Set
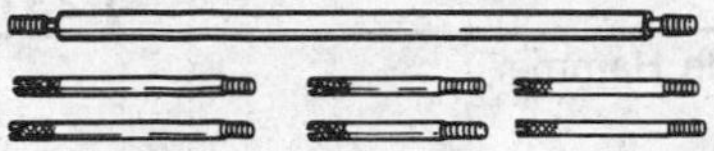
J 25025

Torque Converter End-Play Fixture
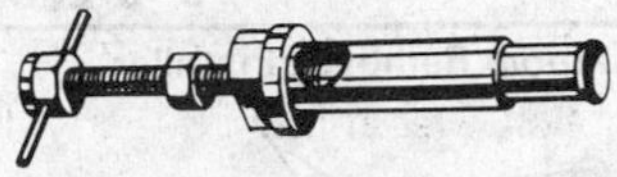
J 35138

Output Shaft Aligning and Loading Tool

J 26958

Aneroid Modulator Checking Tool (Non Turbo Models)

J 36619

Snap Ring Remover/Installer - Output Shaft
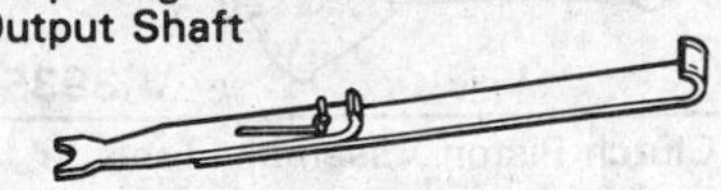
J 34757

Converter Seal Installer
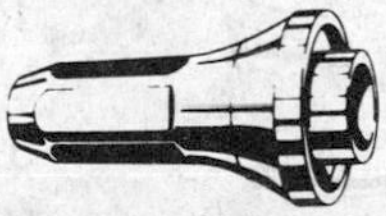
J 28540

Bushing Installer

J 25019-6

Pump Bearing - Installer and Remover
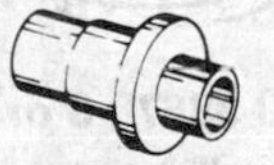
J 28698

Transmission Support Fixture
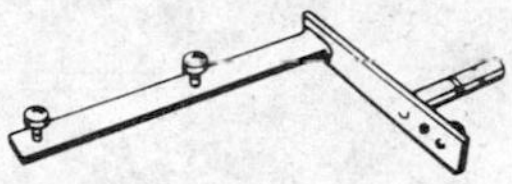
J 28664-B

Bushing and Universal Remover Set
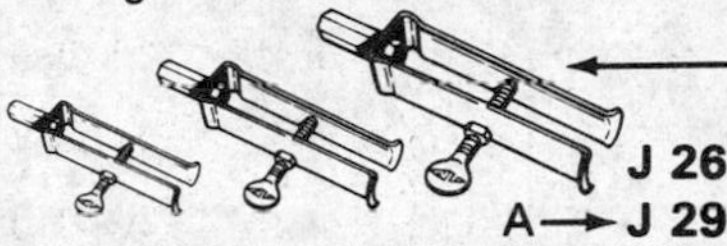
J 26941
A → J 29369

Turbine Shaft Seal Installers and Sizer (1 Seal)
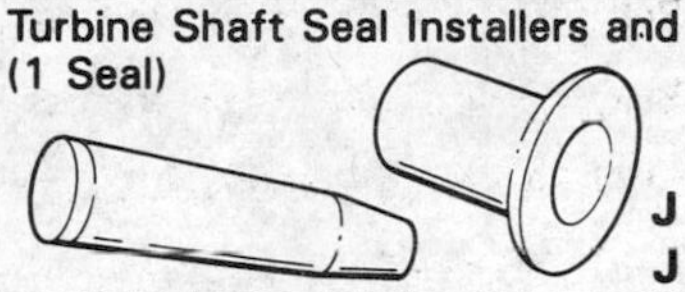
J 29569
J 29829

Axle Seal Installer

J 29130

Clutch Assembly/ Final Drive Remover and Installer
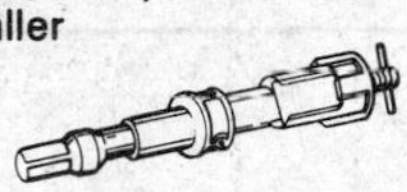
J 33381-A

Third Clutch Piston Seal Protector

J 37362

Bearing Installer - Drive Sprocket Support

J 28677

Input Clutch Piston Seal Protector

J 37361

Left Side Axle Seal Installer

J 34115

Input Shaft End Play Tool

J 33386

Output Shaft Loading Tool Adapter
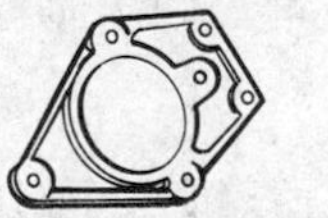
J 38385

Driven Sprocket Support Bearing Remover

J 34129

Thermo Element Height Gauge
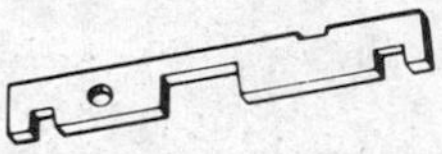
J 34094-A

Driven Sprocket Bearing Installer

J 34126

#27 Torx Drive Bit Or Equivalent
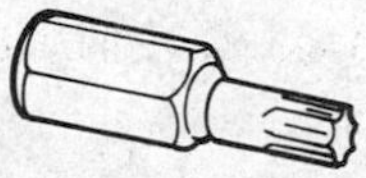
J 38597

Input Seal Installer

J 34741

Adapter Plug
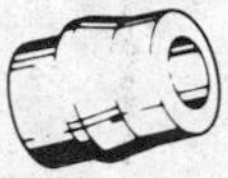
J 26958-10

Clutch Spring Compressor
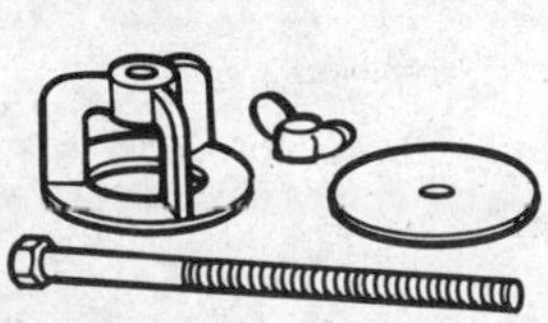
J 23327
J 23327-2
J 23327-1

Handle

J 7079-2

Handle

J 8092

Universal Remover

J 23907

PH1134-4T60-E

SPECIAL TOOLS (CONT.)

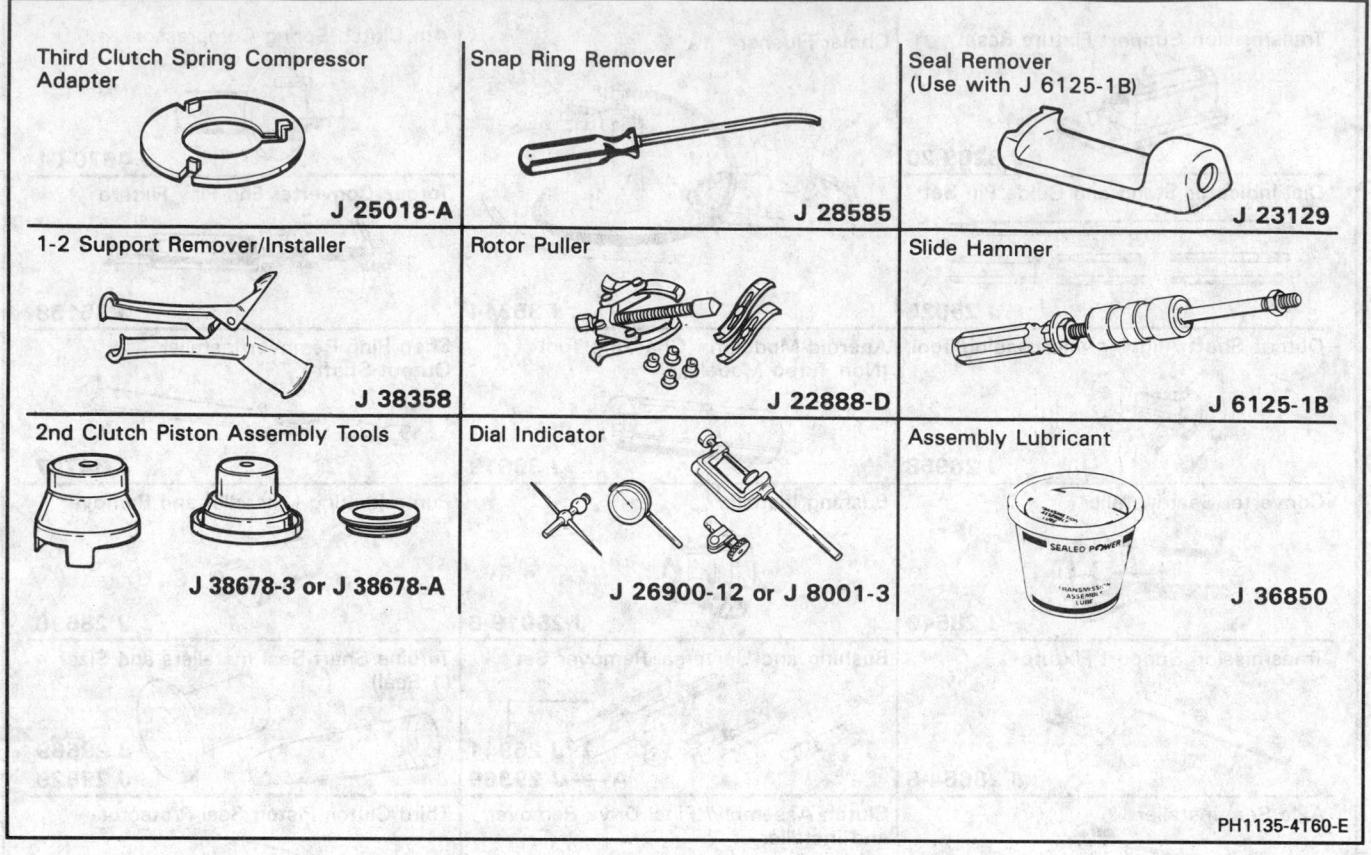

Third Clutch Spring Compressor Adapter

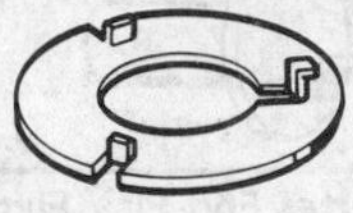

J 25018-A

Snap Ring Remover

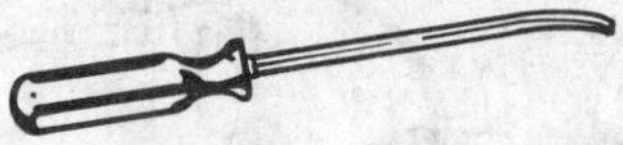

J 28585

Seal Remover (Use with J 6125-1B)

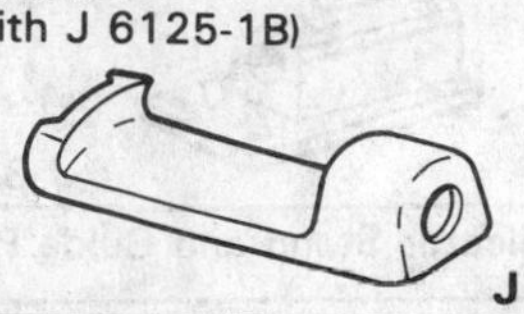

J 23129

1-2 Support Remover/Installer

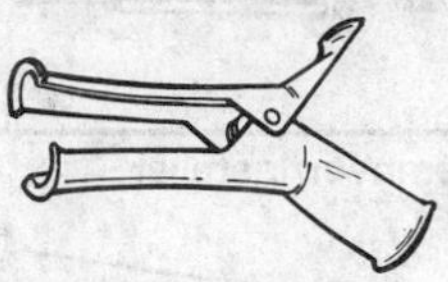

J 38358

Rotor Puller

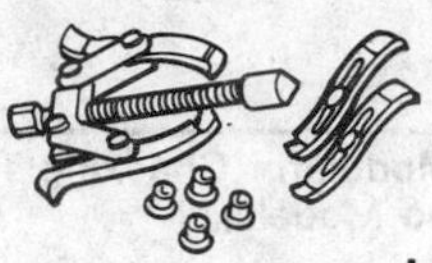

J 22888-D

Slide Hammer

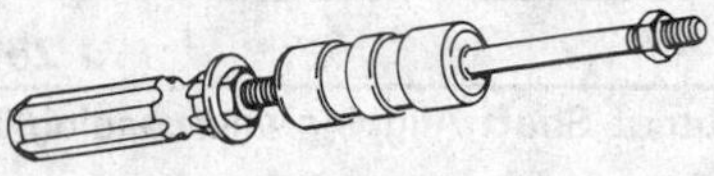

J 6125-1B

2nd Clutch Piston Assembly Tools

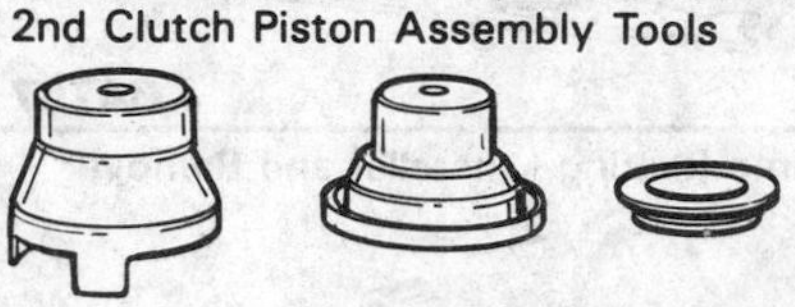

J 38678-3 or J 38678-A

Dial Indicator

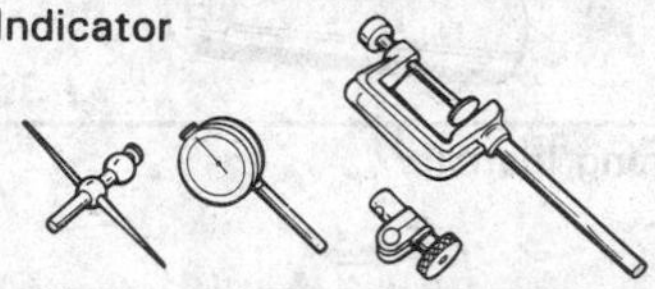

J 26900-12 or J 8001-3

Assembly Lubricant

SEALED POWER
TRANSMISSION ASSEMBLY LUBE

J 36850

PH1135-4T60-E

SECTION 8

CHASSIS AND BODY ELECTRICAL

CONTENTS

SECTION 8A
ELECTRICAL DIAGNOSIS
BUICK REGAL

INDEX

INDEX

INTRODUCTION

DIAGNOSTIC INFORMATION

The Electrical Diagnosis section contains the following types of diagnostic information (the way in which the information is arranged may vary from system to system or vehicle to vehicle):

- Electrical Schematics
- Component Location Lists
- Harness Connector Faces
- Troubleshooting Hints
- System Checks
- System Diagnosis
- Circuit Operation Descriptions
- Harness Routing Views

Using these elements together will make electrical troubleshooting faster and easier. Each element is described below.

The **Circuit Schematic** shows the electrical current paths when a circuit is operating properly. It is essential to understand how a circuit *should* work before trying to diagnose a failure.

The **Component Location List** helps to find where the components of a system can be located. A brief statement of the location is given and also a reference to a drawing that shows the component and its connecting wires. These **Component Location Views** are in SECTION 8A-201.

The **Harness Connector Faces** show the cavity or terminal locations in all the 4 pin or larger connectors shown in the schematic. Together with the wire colors and terminals given in the schematic, they help locate test points. The drawings show the connector faces as seen after the harness connector has been disconnected from a component or mating connector.

The **Troubleshooting Hints** offer short-cuts or checks to help determine the cause of a complaint. They are not intended to be a rigid procedure for solving an electrical situation. Rather, Troubleshooting Hints represent a common-sense approach, based on an understanding of the circuit.

The **System Check** gives a summary of how the system should be operated and what should happen. This is especially important when working on a new system. The System Check will help identify symptoms, lead to diagnosis and confirm normal operation of the system after repair.

The **System Diagnosis** provides a procedure to follow that will locate the condition in a circuit causing a malfunction. If your own knowledge of the system and the Troubleshooting Hints have not produced a quick fix, follow the System Diagnosis. All procedures are based on symptoms to assist in locating the condition as fast as possible.

The **Circuit Operation** describes the components and how the circuit works.

Harness Routing Views are found in SECTION 8A-203. These views show the routing of the major wiring harnesses and the in-line connectors between the major harnesses.

SECTION/PAGE NUMBER

Sections are organized by sub-systems with most containing a circuit schematic and the associated text. This makes the section easy to use, since the page number will stay the same year after year. For example, the Cruise Control schematic will always begin on page 8A-34-0. The other information for Cruise Control follows and is paged 8A-34-1, 8A-34-2, etc.

Some sections may have more than one circuit schematic, such as Power Distribution, Interior Lights and Air Conditioning. The circuit of interest can either be located by using the Index or by a quick look through the related section.

All the engine circuits for a particular engine VIN type are in the same section. This makes that section easy to use, since schematics for other engines are not in your way. The Instrument Panel schematics are organized similarly. If you are working on a vehicle with a Digital Cluster, only the schematics that apply to that vehicle's Digital Cluster will be in the section you use. Information on the Indicators and Gages Clusters will be in other sections.

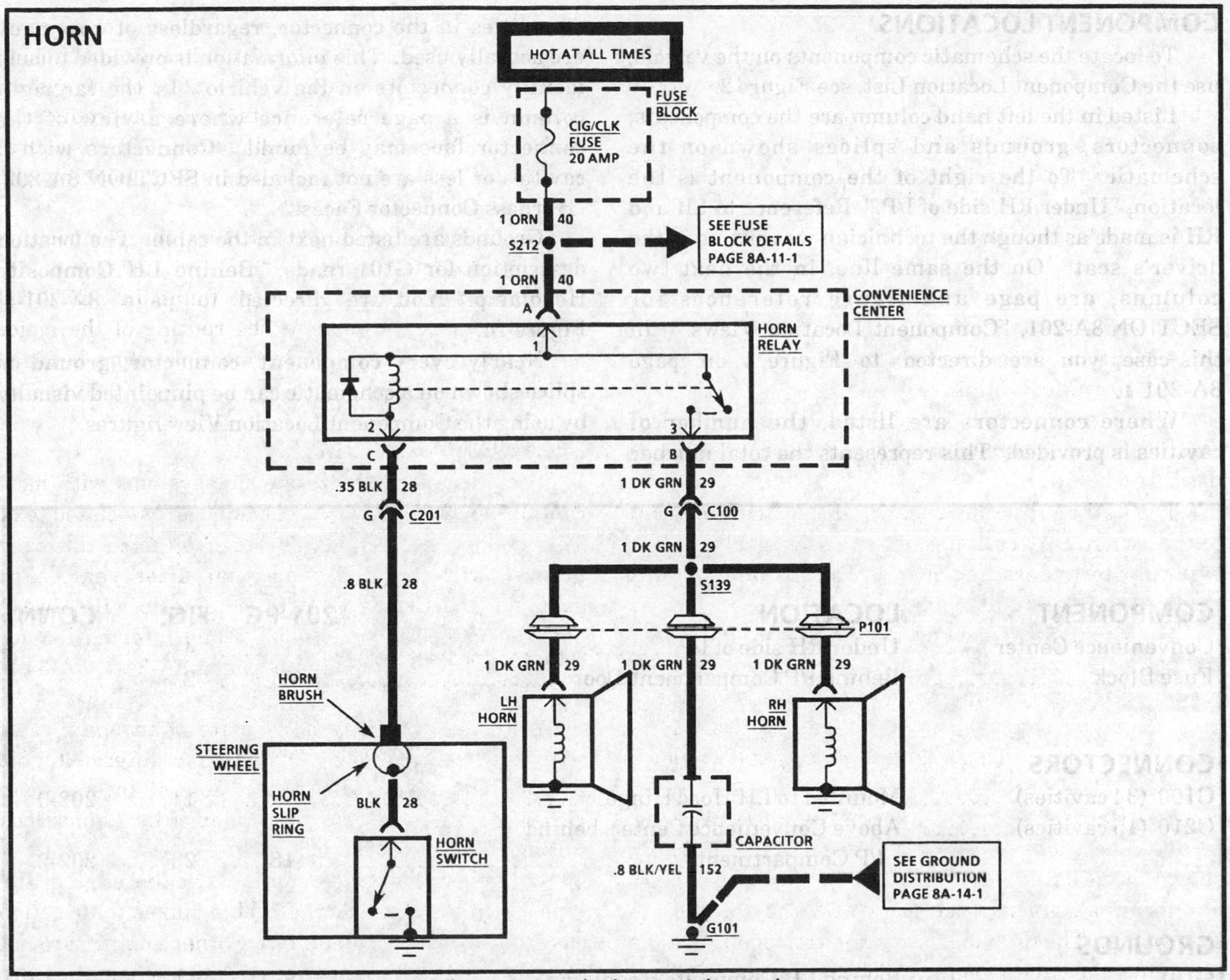
HORN
HOT AT ALL TIMES
FUSE BLOCK
CIG/CLK FUSE 20 AMP
1 ORN 40
S212
SEE FUSE BLOCK DETAILS PAGE 8A-11-1
1 ORN 40
A
CONVENIENCE CENTER
HORN RELAY
1
2
3
C
B
.35 BLK 28
G C201
1 DK GRN 29
G C100
1 DK GRN 29
S139
.8 BLK 28
P101
1 DK GRN 29
1 DK GRN 29
1 DK GRN 29
HORN BRUSH
LH HORN
RH HORN
STEERING WHEEL
HORN SLIP RING
BLK 28
HORN SWITCH
CAPACITOR
.8 BLK/YEL 152
SEE GROUND DISTRIBUTION PAGE 8A-14-1
G101

Figure 1 - Typical Horn Schematic

SCHEMATICS

Schematics break the entire electrical system down into individual circuits. Wiring which is not part of the circuit of interest is referenced to another page, where the circuit is shown complete.

Important:

- It is important to realize that no attempt is made on the schematic to represent components and wiring as they physically appear on the vehicle. For example, a 4-foot length of wire is treated no differently in a schematic from one which is only a few inches long. The number of cavities for each connector is listed in the Component Location List. Similarly, switches and other components are shown as simply as possible, with regard to function only.

When diagnosing a Horn problem, the technician would reference the Horn section. The schematic in Figure 1 is a typical example of what would be found in a Horn section of SECTION 8A, along with the following text.

Voltage is applied to the Horn Relay at all times. When the relay coil is grounded by closing the Horn Switch, the relay contacts close. When the relay contacts are closed, both the LH and RH Horns are energized.

INTRODUCTION

COMPONENT LOCATIONS

To locate the schematic components on the vehicle, use the Component Location List, see Figure 2.

Listed in the left hand column are the components, connectors, grounds and splices shown on the schematic. To the right of the component is the location, "Under RH side of I/P." Reference to LH and RH is made as though the technician was sitting in the driver's seat. On the same line, in the next two columns, are page and figure references for SECTION 8A-201, "Component Location Views." In this case, you are directed to Figure 4 on page 8A-201-1.

Where connectors are listed, the number of cavities is provided. This represents the total number of cavities in the connector, regardless of how many are actually used. This information is provided to help identify connectors on the vehicle. In the far right column is a page reference where a view of the connector face may be found. Connectors with 3 cavities or less are not included in SECTION 8A-202, "Harness Connector Faces."

Grounds are listed next in the table. The location description for G101 reads, "Behind LH Composite Headlamp." You are directed to page 8A-201-8, Figure 14.

Nearly every component, connector, ground or splice shown on a schematic can be pinpointed visually by using the Component Location View figures.

COMPONENT	LOCATION	201-PG	FIG.	CONN
Convenience Center	Under RH side of I/P	1	4	
Fuse Block	Behind I/P Compartment Door	0	2	
CONNECTORS				
C100 (34 cavities)	Mounted to LH Hood Hinge	7	11 ...	202-0
C210 (15 cavities)	Above Convenience Center, behind I/P Compartment	18 ...	23 ...	202-2
GROUNDS				
G101	Behind LH Composite Headlamp	8	14	
SPLICES				
S139	Forward Lamp Wiring Harn, behind RH Composite Headlamp	8	15	
S212	I/P Wiring Harn, behind I/P, above Steering Column	6	8	

Figure 2 - Typical Entries in the Component Location List

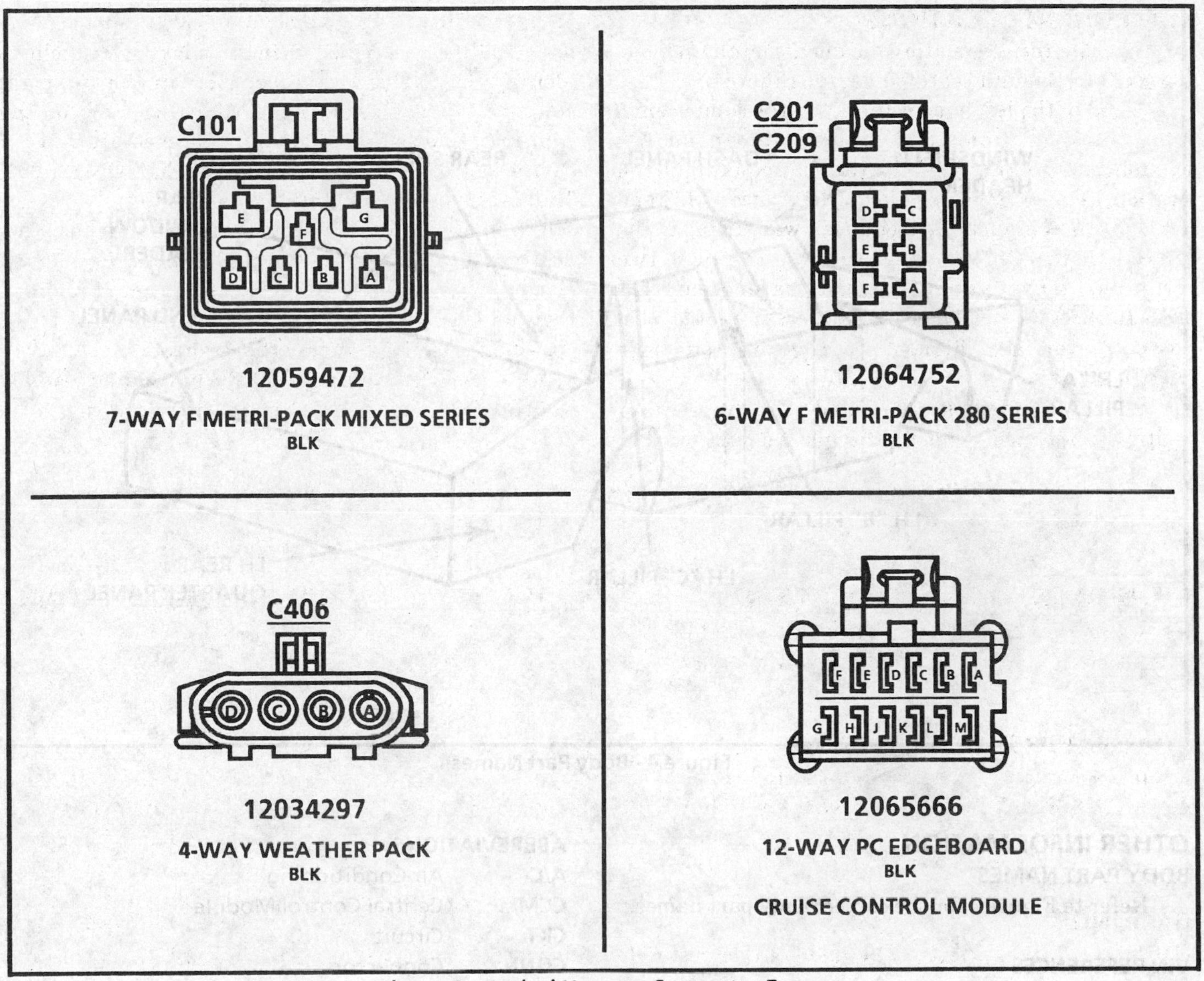

C101
E
F
G
D
C
B
A
12059472
7-WAY F METRI-PACK MIXED SERIES
BLK
C201
C209
D
C
E
B
F
A
12064752
6-WAY F METRI-PACK 280 SERIES
BLK
C406
D
C
B
A
12034297
4-WAY WEATHER PACK
BLK
F
E
D
C
B
A
G
H
J
K
L
M
12065666
12-WAY PC EDGEBOARD
BLK
CRUISE CONTROL MODULE

Figure 3 - Typical Harness Connector Faces

HARNESS CONNECTOR FACES

The connectors, see Figure 3, are labeled with the component they are connected to, or the connector number. In addition the color of the connector is given along with the family/series name.

If you need to backprobe a connector while it is on the component (refer to page 8A-4-3 for probing procedures), the order of the terminals must be mentally reversed. The wire color is a help in this situation. If there is more than one wire of the same color, you may need to locate a test point from its terminal number. A useful trick is to imagine that you are probing a terminal from behind the page you are looking at. Then mentally locate that terminal with respect to the keyway or other reference mark.

INTRODUCTION

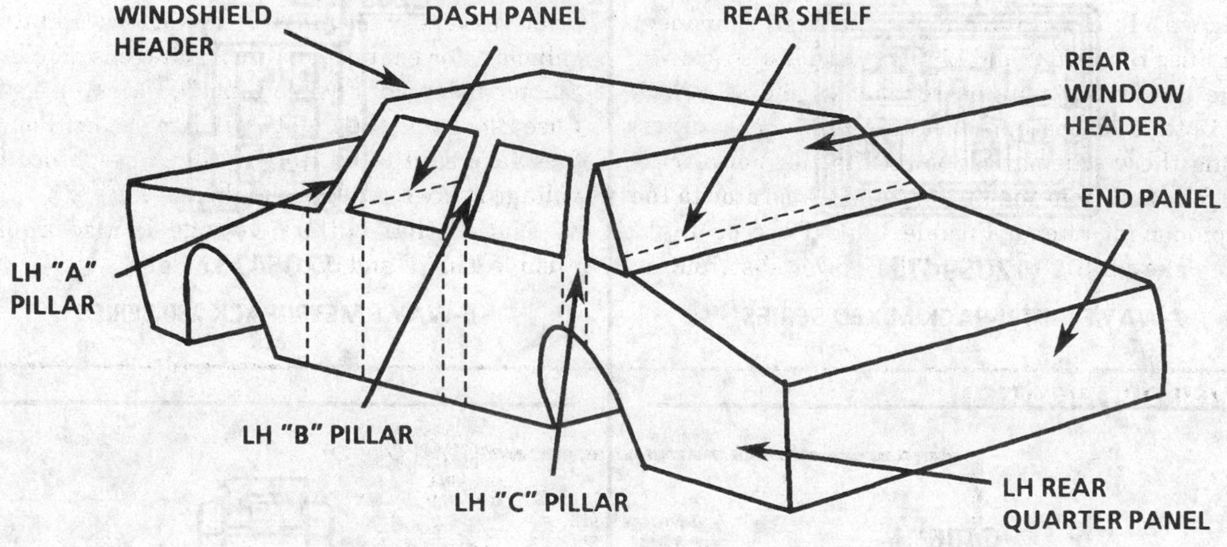
WINDSHIELD
HEADER
DASH PANEL
REAR SHELF
REAR
WINDOW
HEADER
END PANEL
LH "A"
PILLAR
LH "B" PILLAR
LH "C" PILLAR
LH REAR
QUARTER PANEL

Figure 4 - Body Part Names

OTHER INFORMATION

BODY PART NAMES

Refer to Figure 4 for the correct body part names.

VIN REFERENCES

If schematics for more than one variation of an engine type – V6, for example – are shown, then the schematics will be labeled with VIN designation to distinguish the variations.

SERVICE PARTS IDENTIFICATION LABEL

To aid service and parts personnel in identifying options and parts originally installed, a Service Parts Identification Label has been placed in the vehicle. See SECTION 0A for the location of the label and the definition of the option codes.

ABBREVIATIONS

A/C	Air Conditioning
CCM	Central Control Module
CKT	Circuit
CONN	Connector
EBCM	Electronic Brake Control Module
EBTCM	Electronic Brake and Traction Control Module
ECM	Engine Control Module
HARN	Harness
I/P	Instrument Panel
LH	Left Hand
PCM	Powertrain Control Module
RH	Right Hand
TERM	Terminal

For a list of additional abbreviations, refer to SECTION 0A.

POWER DISTRIBUTION

The Power Distribution schematic shows the wiring from the Battery and Generator to the Starter Solenoid, Fuse Block, Ignition Switch and Light Switch. The first component after a Fusible Link is also shown. In certain instances, the first component after a Fuse Block fuse and Light Switch is also shown.

The Power Distribution schematic refers to Fuse Block Details or the appropriate section schematics. By using these schematics, power distribution wiring can be followed from the Battery and Generator to the first component after a Fusible Link, Fuse or Light Switch. The ability to follow the power distribution wiring to the first component in each circuit is extremely helpful in locating short circuits which cause fusible links and fuses to open.

Figure 5 is a sample Power Distribution schematic. It shows how voltage is applied from the positive battery terminal to the various circuits on the vehicle. For example, battery voltage is applied to the Starter Solenoid, Fusible Link D, Fuses 1 and 2 in the Fuse Block and the Light Switch in the LH Pod. These fuses are said to be Hot At All Times, since battery voltage is always applied to them.

Notice that battery voltage is also applied to Fusible Link F and Coolant Fan Relay.

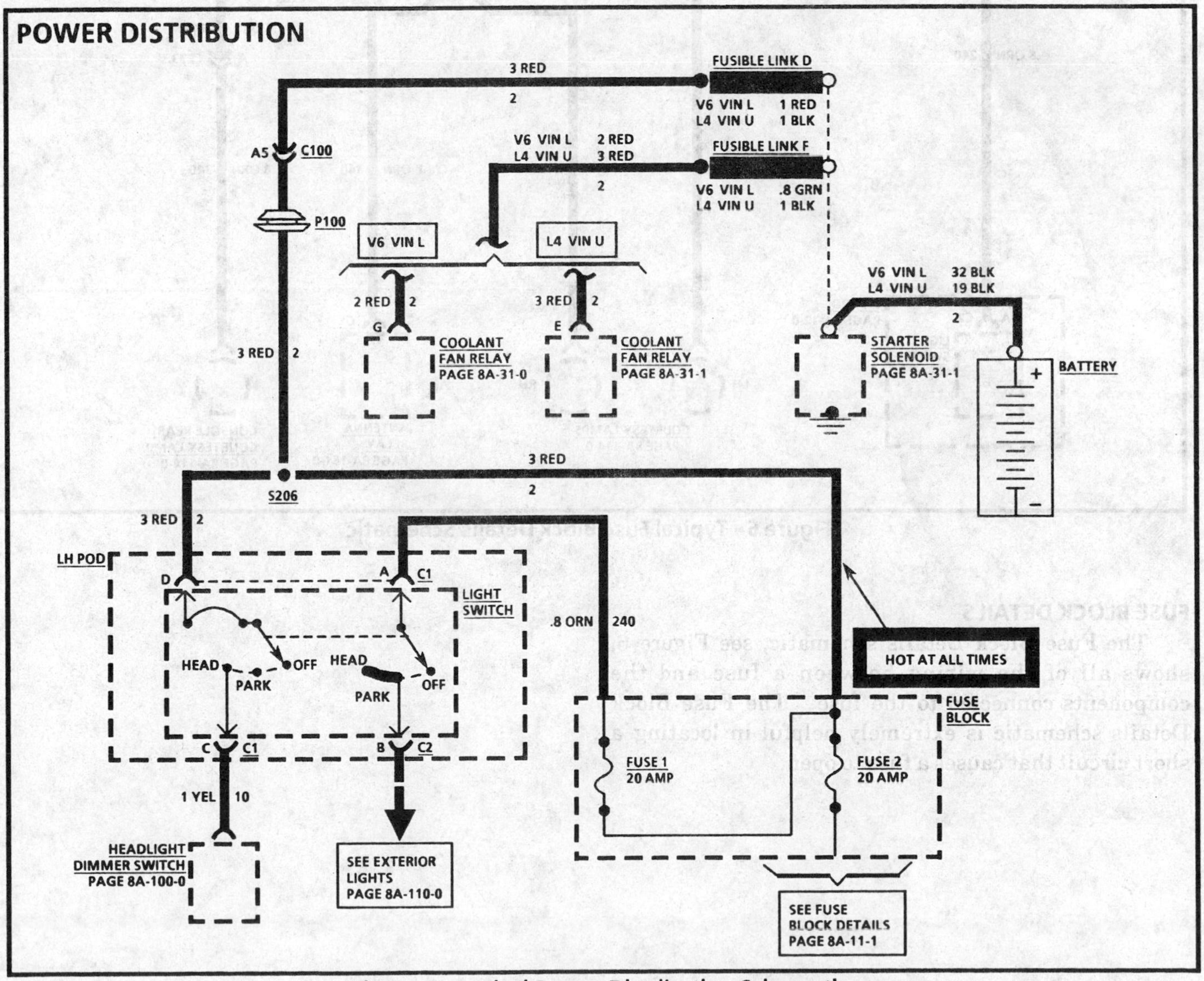
POWER DISTRIBUTION
3 RED
2
FUSIBLE LINK D
V6 VIN L 1 RED
L4 VIN U 1 BLK
V6 VIN L 2 RED
L4 VIN U 3 RED
FUSIBLE LINK F
A5
C100
2
V6 VIN L .8 GRN
L4 VIN U 1 BLK
P100
V6 VIN L
L4 VIN U
V6 VIN L 32 BLK
L4 VIN U 19 BLK
2 RED 2
G
3 RED 2
E
COOLANT
FAN RELAY
PAGE 8A-31-0
COOLANT
FAN RELAY
PAGE 8A-31-1
STARTER
SOLENOID
PAGE 8A-31-1
BATTERY
3 RED 2
3 RED
2
S206
3 RED 2
LH POD
D
A
C1
LIGHT
SWITCH
.8 ORN 240
HEAD
OFF
PARK
HEAD
PARK
OFF
HOT AT ALL TIMES
FUSE
BLOCK
C
C1
B
C2
FUSE 1
20 AMP
FUSE 2
20 AMP
1 YEL 10
HEADLIGHT
DIMMER SWITCH
PAGE 8A-100-0
SEE EXTERIOR
LIGHTS
PAGE 8A-110-0
SEE FUSE
BLOCK DETAILS
PAGE 8A-11-1

Figure 5 - Typical Power Distribution Schematic

INTRODUCTION

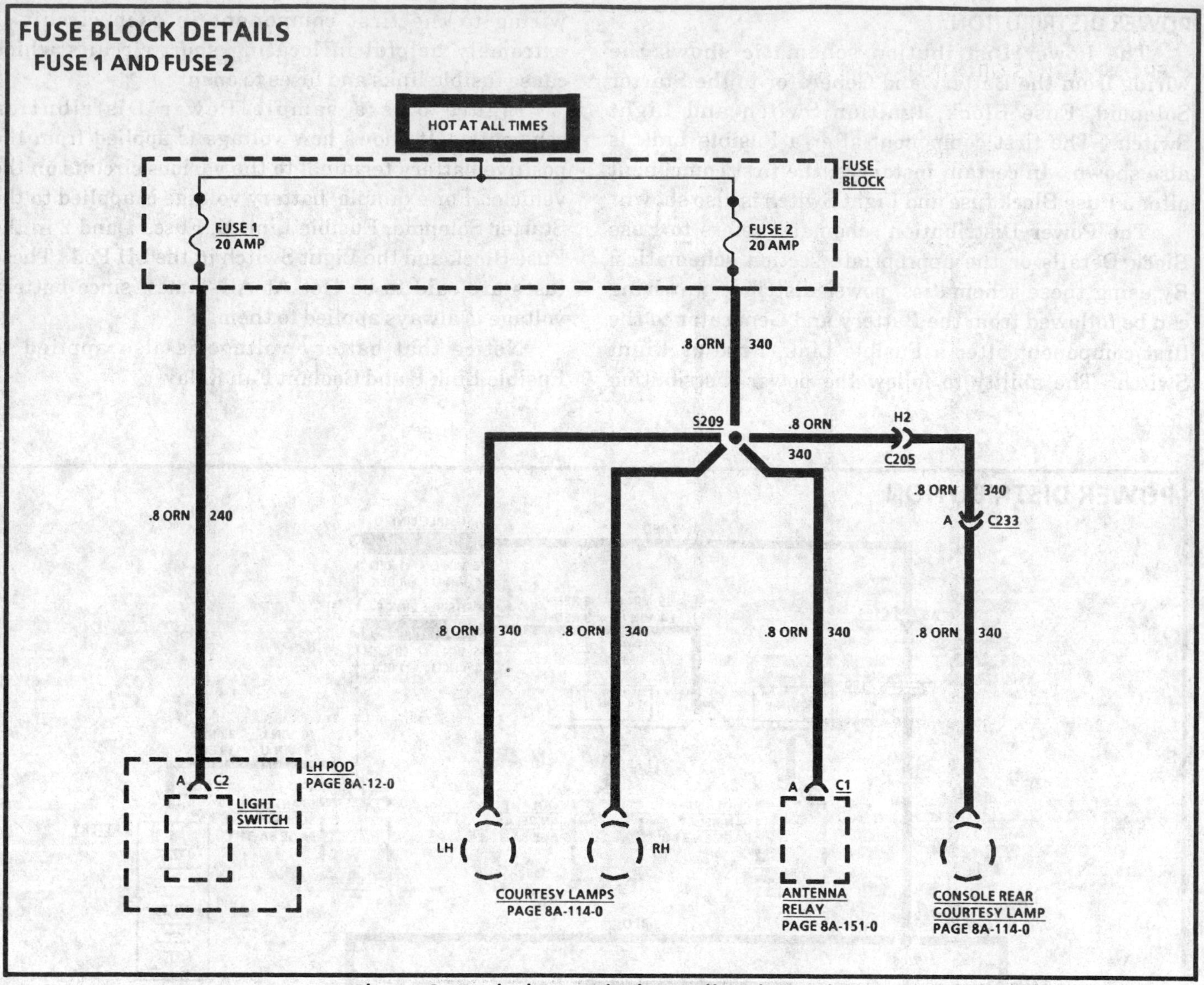
FUSE BLOCK DETAILS
FUSE 1 AND FUSE 2
HOT AT ALL TIMES
FUSE BLOCK
FUSE 1
20 AMP
FUSE 2
20 AMP
.8 ORN 340
S209
.8 ORN
340
H2
C205
.8 ORN 340
A
C233
.8 ORN 240
.8 ORN 340
.8 ORN 340
.8 ORN 340
.8 ORN 340
LH POD
PAGE 8A-12-0
A
C2
LIGHT SWITCH
A
C1
LH
RH
COURTESY LAMPS
PAGE 8A-114-0
ANTENNA RELAY
PAGE 8A-151-0
CONSOLE REAR COURTESY LAMP
PAGE 8A-114-0

Figure 6 - Typical Fuse Block Details Schematic

FUSE BLOCK DETAILS

The Fuse Block Details schematic, see Figure 6, shows all of the wiring between a fuse and the components connected to the fuse. The Fuse Block Details schematic is extremely helpful in locating a short circuit that causes a fuse to open.

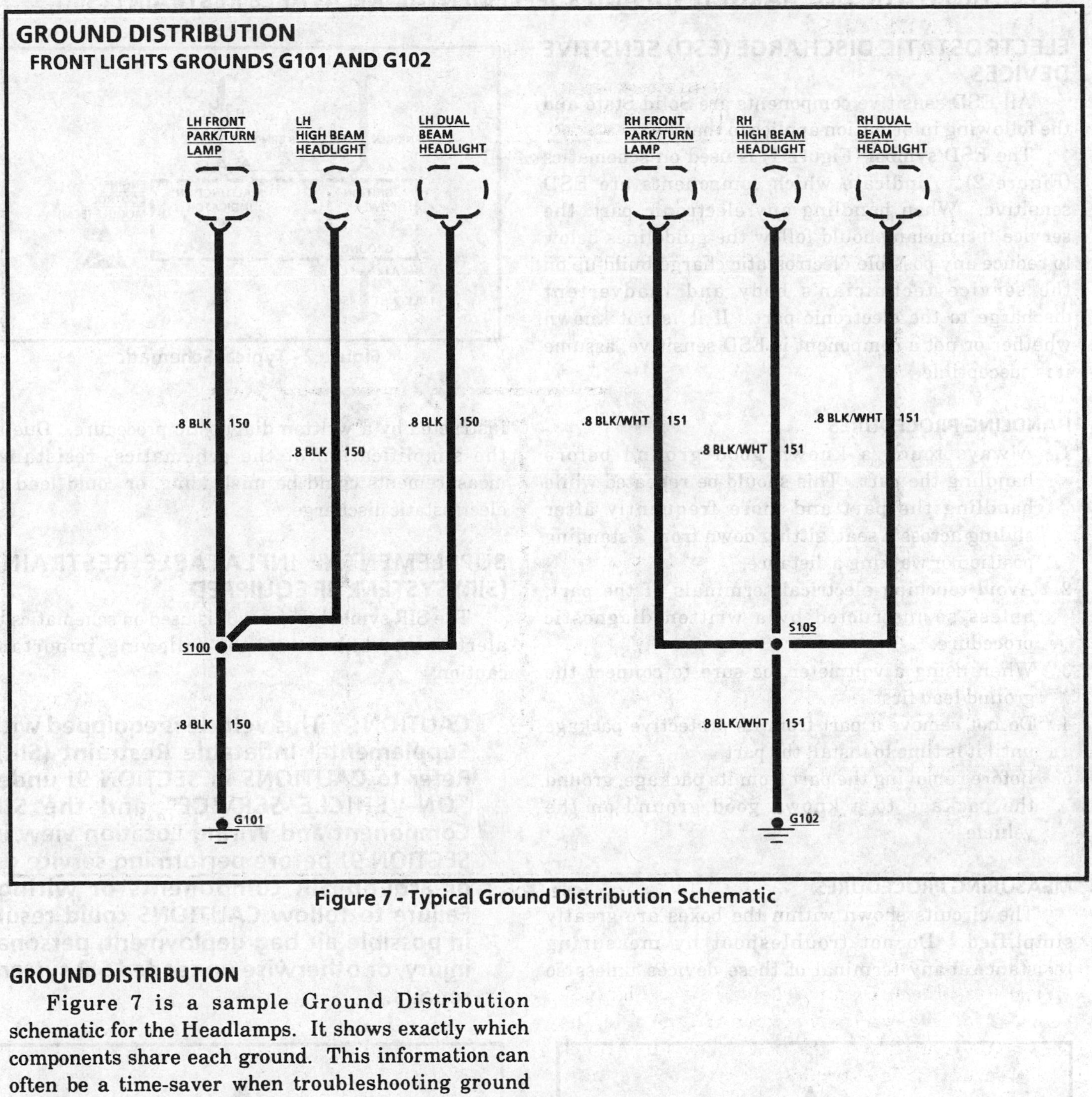
GROUND DISTRIBUTION
FRONT LIGHTS GROUNDS G101 AND G102
LH FRONT PARK/TURN LAMP
LH HIGH BEAM HEADLIGHT
LH DUAL BEAM HEADLIGHT
RH FRONT PARK/TURN LAMP
RH HIGH BEAM HEADLIGHT
RH DUAL BEAM HEADLIGHT
.8 BLK 150
.8 BLK 150
.8 BLK 150
.8 BLK/WHT 151
.8 BLK/WHT 151
.8 BLK/WHT 151
S100
S105
.8 BLK 150
.8 BLK/WHT 151
G101
G102

Figure 7 - Typical Ground Distribution Schematic

GROUND DISTRIBUTION

Figure 7 is a sample Ground Distribution schematic for the Headlamps. It shows exactly which components share each ground. This information can often be a time-saver when troubleshooting ground circuits.

For example, if both Headlamps and the Park/Turn Lamp on one side are out, suspect an open in their common ground wire or the ground connection itself. On the other hand, if one of the lamps work, the ground and the wire up to the splice are good. You have learned this just by inspecting the schematic and knowing the vehicle's symptoms. No actual work on the lighting system was needed.

SYMBOLS

ELECTROSTATIC DISCHARGE (ESD) AND SUPPLEMENTAL INFLATABLE RESTRAINT (SIR)

ELECTROSTATIC DISCHARGE (ESD) SENSITIVE DEVICES

All ESD sensitive components are Solid State and the following information applies to them.

The ESD symbol (Figure 1) is used on schematics (Figure 2) to indicate which components are ESD sensitive. When handling any electronic part, the service technician should follow the guidelines below to reduce any possible electrostatic charge build-up on the service technician's body and inadvertent discharge to the electronic part. If it is not known whether or not a component is ESD sensitive, assume it is susceptible.

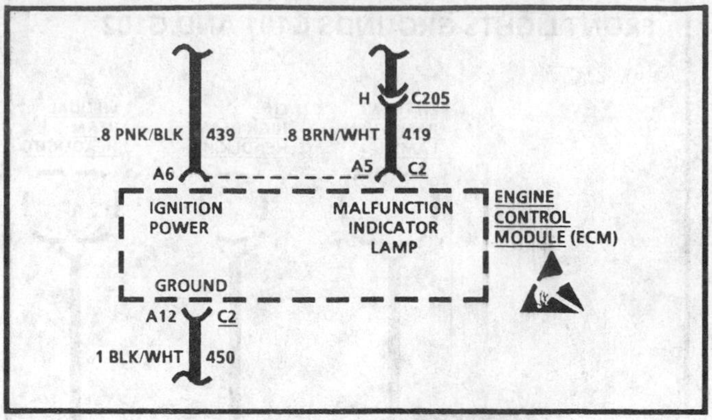

H
C205
.8 PNK/BLK
439
.8 BRN/WHT
419
A6
A5
C2
IGNITION POWER
MALFUNCTION INDICATOR LAMP
ENGINE CONTROL MODULE (ECM)
GROUND
A12
C2
1 BLK/WHT
450

Figure 2 - Typical Schematic

HANDLING PROCEDURES

1. Always touch a known good ground before handling the part. This should be repeated while handling the part and more frequently after sliding across a seat, sitting down from a standing position or walking a distance.
2. Avoid touching electrical terminals of the part, unless so instructed by a written diagnostic procedure.
3. When using a voltmeter, be sure to connect the ground lead first.
4. Do not remove a part from its protective package until it is time to install the part.
5. Before removing the part from its package, ground the package to a known good ground on the vehicle.

MEASURING PROCEDURES

The circuits shown within the boxes are greatly simplified. Do not troubleshoot by measuring resistance at any terminal of these devices unless so instructed by a written diagnostic procedure. Due to the simplification of the schematics, resistance measurements could be misleading, or could lead to electrostatic discharge.

SUPPLEMENTAL INFLATABLE RESTRAINT (SIR) SYSTEM: IF EQUIPPED

The SIR symbol (Figure 3) is used on schematics to alert the technician of the following important caution:

CAUTION: This vehicle is equipped with Supplemental Inflatable Restraint (SIR). Refer to CAUTIONS in SECTION 9J under "ON-VEHICLE SERVICE" and the SIR Component and Wiring Location view in SECTION 9J before performing service on or around SIR components or wiring. Failure to follow CAUTIONS could result in possible air bag deployment, personal injury, or otherwise unneeded SIR system repairs.

Figure 1 - ESD Symbol

Figure 3 - SIR Symbol

SYMBOLS

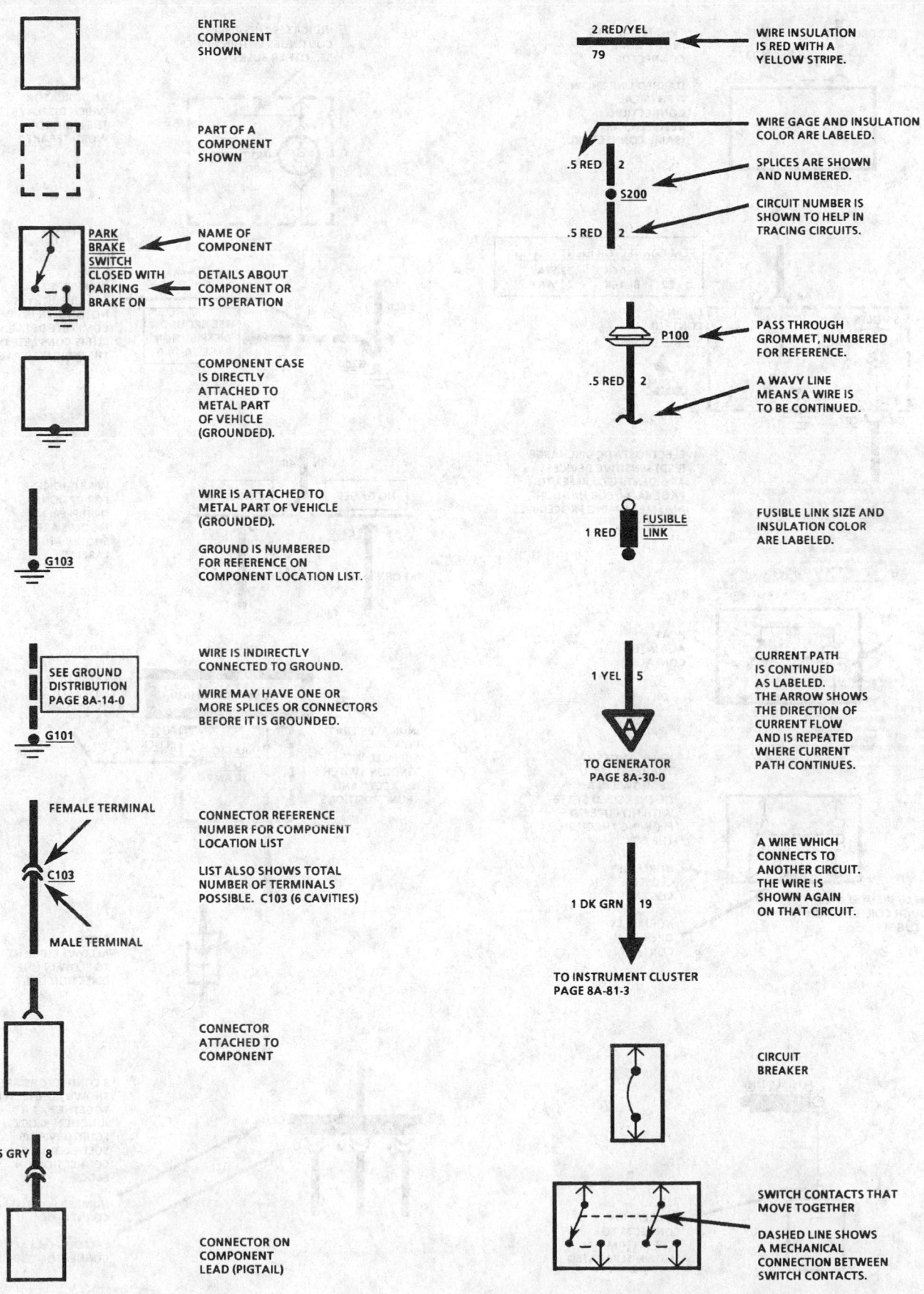

ENTIRE COMPONENT SHOWN

PART OF A COMPONENT SHOWN

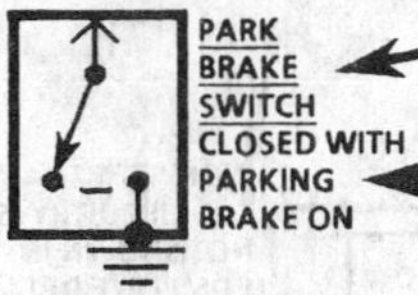
PARK
BRAKE
SWITCH
CLOSED WITH
PARKING
BRAKE ON

NAME OF COMPONENT

DETAILS ABOUT COMPONENT OR ITS OPERATION

COMPONENT CASE IS DIRECTLY ATTACHED TO METAL PART OF VEHICLE (GROUNDED).

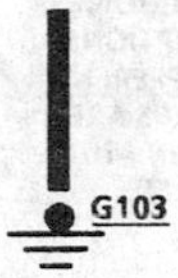
G103

WIRE IS ATTACHED TO METAL PART OF VEHICLE (GROUNDED).

GROUND IS NUMBERED FOR REFERENCE ON COMPONENT LOCATION LIST.

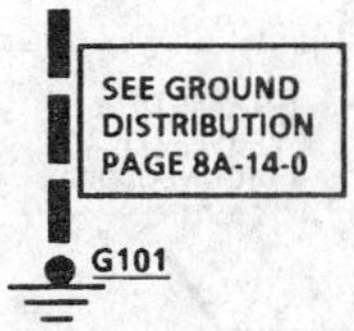
SEE GROUND DISTRIBUTION PAGE 8A-14-0
G101

WIRE IS INDIRECTLY CONNECTED TO GROUND.

WIRE MAY HAVE ONE OR MORE SPLICES OR CONNECTORS BEFORE IT IS GROUNDED.

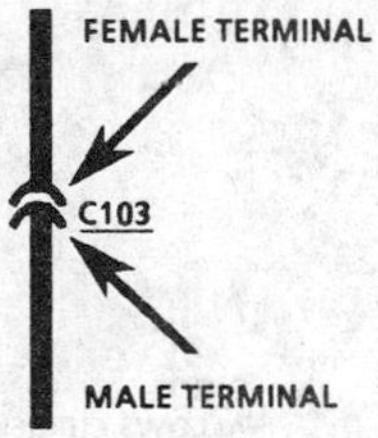
FEMALE TERMINAL
C103
MALE TERMINAL

CONNECTOR REFERENCE NUMBER FOR COMPONENT LOCATION LIST

LIST ALSO SHOWS TOTAL NUMBER OF TERMINALS POSSIBLE. C103 (6 CAVITIES)

CONNECTOR ATTACHED TO COMPONENT

.5 GRY
8

CONNECTOR ON COMPONENT LEAD (PIGTAIL)

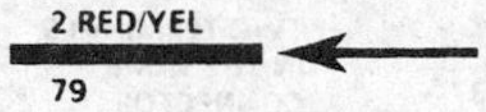
2 RED/YEL
79

WIRE INSULATION IS RED WITH A YELLOW STRIPE.

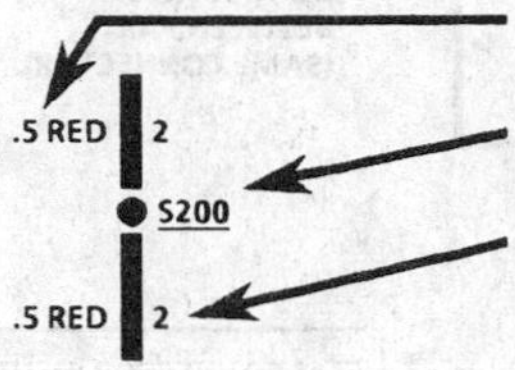
.5 RED
2
S200
.5 RED
2

WIRE GAGE AND INSULATION COLOR ARE LABELED.

SPLICES ARE SHOWN AND NUMBERED.

CIRCUIT NUMBER IS SHOWN TO HELP IN TRACING CIRCUITS.

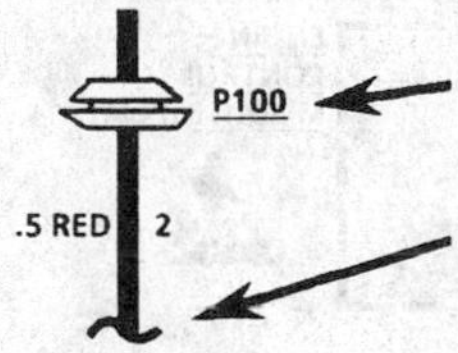
P100
.5 RED
2

PASS THROUGH GROMMET, NUMBERED FOR REFERENCE.

A WAVY LINE MEANS A WIRE IS TO BE CONTINUED.

1 RED
FUSIBLE
LINK

FUSIBLE LINK SIZE AND INSULATION COLOR ARE LABELED.

1 YEL
5
A
TO GENERATOR
PAGE 8A-30-0

CURRENT PATH IS CONTINUED AS LABELED. THE ARROW SHOWS THE DIRECTION OF CURRENT FLOW AND IS REPEATED WHERE CURRENT PATH CONTINUES.

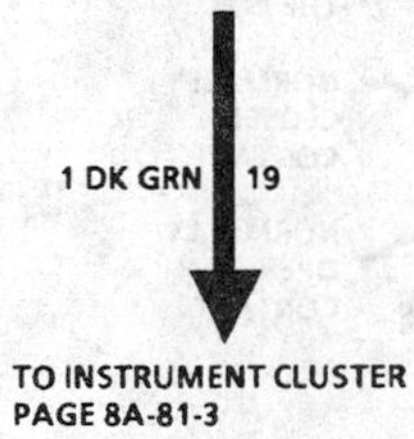
1 DK GRN
19
TO INSTRUMENT CLUSTER
PAGE 8A-81-3

A WIRE WHICH CONNECTS TO ANOTHER CIRCUIT. THE WIRE IS SHOWN AGAIN ON THAT CIRCUIT.

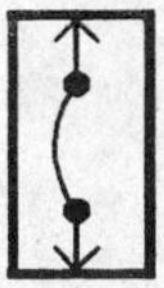

CIRCUIT BREAKER

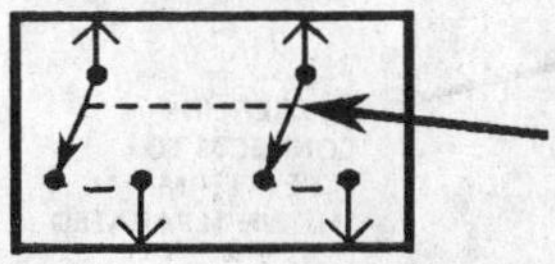

SWITCH CONTACTS THAT MOVE TOGETHER

DASHED LINE SHOWS A MECHANICAL CONNECTION BETWEEN SWITCH CONTACTS.

SYMBOLS

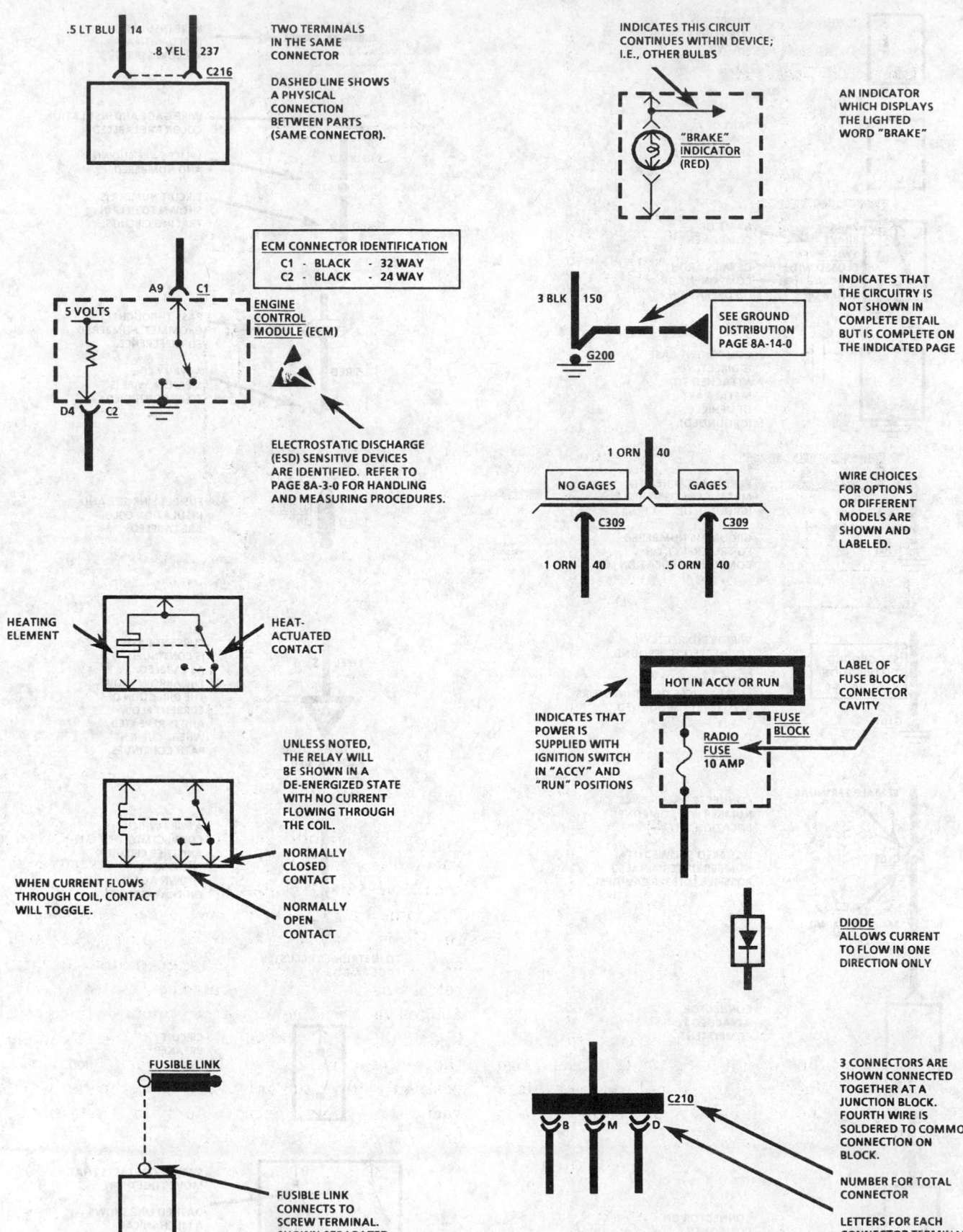

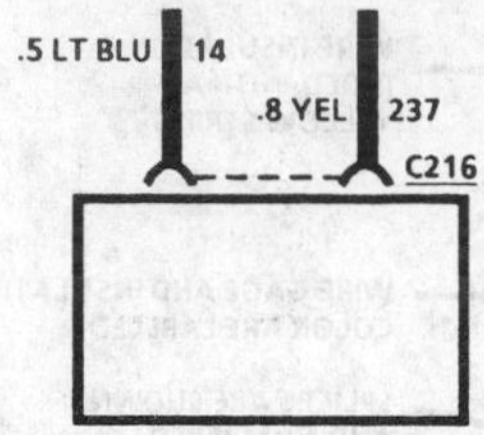
.5 LT BLU 14
.8 YEL 237
C216

TWO TERMINALS IN THE SAME CONNECTOR

DASHED LINE SHOWS A PHYSICAL CONNECTION BETWEEN PARTS (SAME CONNECTOR).

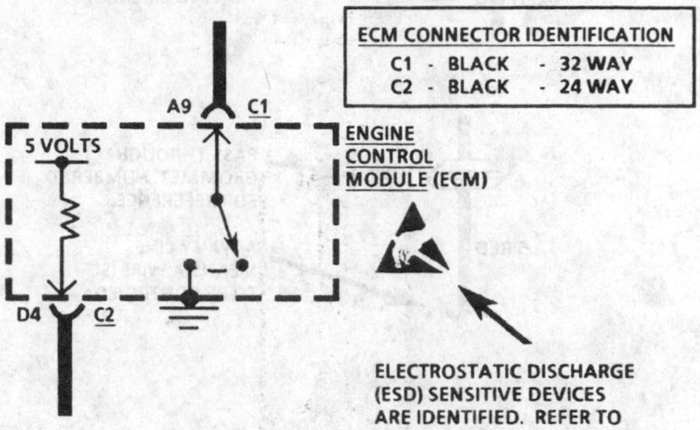
ECM CONNECTOR IDENTIFICATION
C1 - BLACK - 32 WAY
C2 - BLACK - 24 WAY
A9
C1
5 VOLTS
ENGINE CONTROL MODULE (ECM)
D4
C2

ELECTROSTATIC DISCHARGE (ESD) SENSITIVE DEVICES ARE IDENTIFIED. REFER TO PAGE 8A-3-0 FOR HANDLING AND MEASURING PROCEDURES.

INDICATES THIS CIRCUIT CONTINUES WITHIN DEVICE; I.E., OTHER BULBS

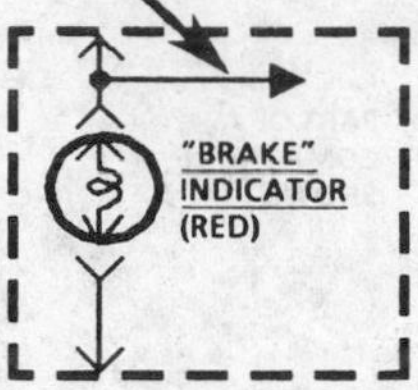
"BRAKE" INDICATOR (RED)

AN INDICATOR WHICH DISPLAYS THE LIGHTED WORD "BRAKE"

3 BLK 150
SEE GROUND DISTRIBUTION PAGE 8A-14-0
G200

INDICATES THAT THE CIRCUITRY IS NOT SHOWN IN COMPLETE DETAIL BUT IS COMPLETE ON THE INDICATED PAGE

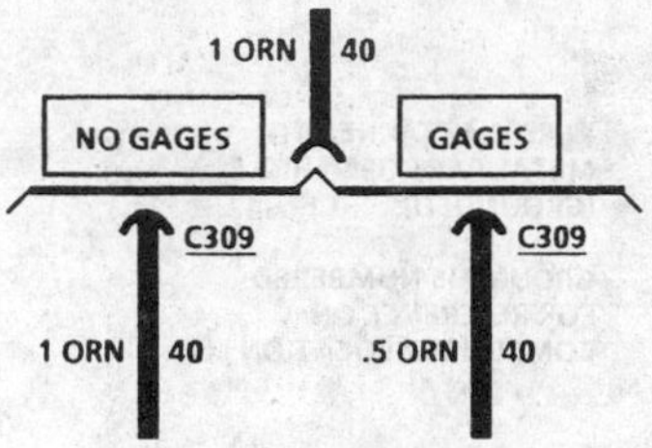
1 ORN 40
NO GAGES
GAGES
C309
C309
1 ORN 40
.5 ORN 40

WIRE CHOICES FOR OPTIONS OR DIFFERENT MODELS ARE SHOWN AND LABELED.

HEATING ELEMENT

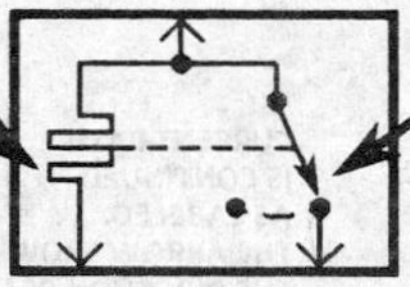

HEAT-ACTUATED CONTACT

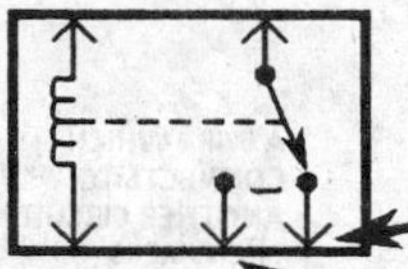

UNLESS NOTED, THE RELAY WILL BE SHOWN IN A DE-ENERGIZED STATE WITH NO CURRENT FLOWING THROUGH THE COIL.

NORMALLY CLOSED CONTACT

WHEN CURRENT FLOWS THROUGH COIL, CONTACT WILL TOGGLE.

NORMALLY OPEN CONTACT

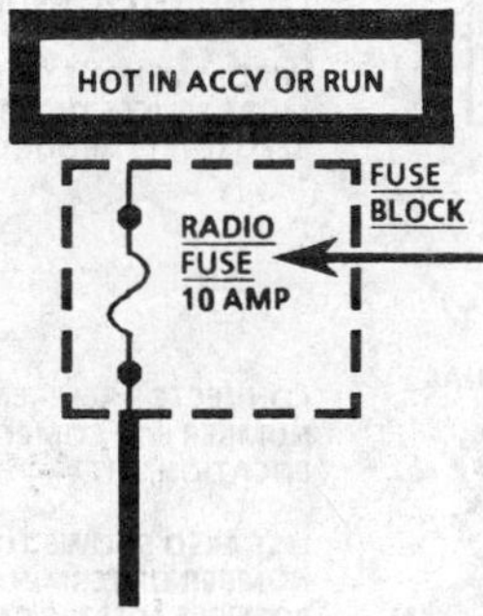
HOT IN ACCY OR RUN
FUSE BLOCK
RADIO FUSE 10 AMP

INDICATES THAT POWER IS SUPPLIED WITH IGNITION SWITCH IN "ACCY" AND "RUN" POSITIONS

LABEL OF FUSE BLOCK CONNECTOR CAVITY

DIODE ALLOWS CURRENT TO FLOW IN ONE DIRECTION ONLY

FUSIBLE LINK

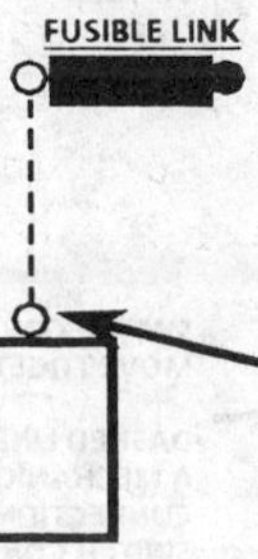

FUSIBLE LINK CONNECTS TO SCREW TERMINAL. SHOWN SEPARATED

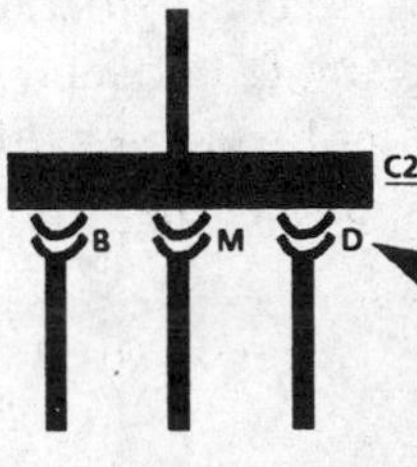
C210
B
M
D

3 CONNECTORS ARE SHOWN CONNECTED TOGETHER AT A JUNCTION BLOCK. FOURTH WIRE IS SOLDERED TO COMMON CONNECTION ON BLOCK.

NUMBER FOR TOTAL CONNECTOR

LETTERS FOR EACH CONNECTOR TERMINAL

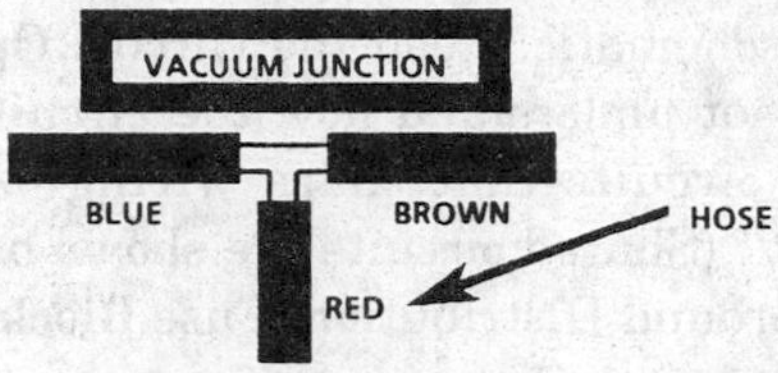
VACUUM JUNCTION
BLUE
BROWN
HOSE COLOR
RED

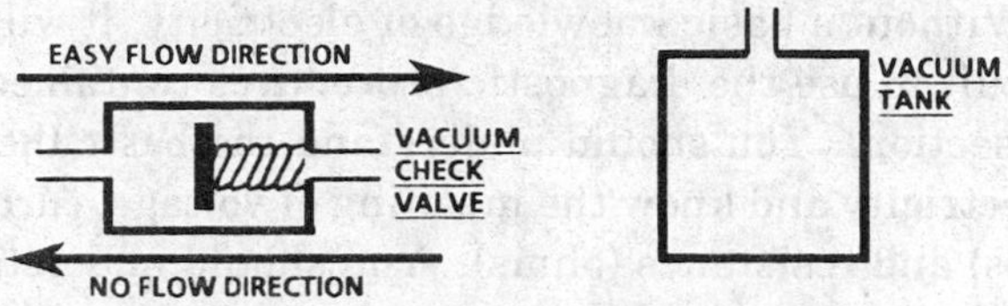
EASY FLOW DIRECTION
VACUUM CHECK VALVE
VACUUM TANK
NO FLOW DIRECTION

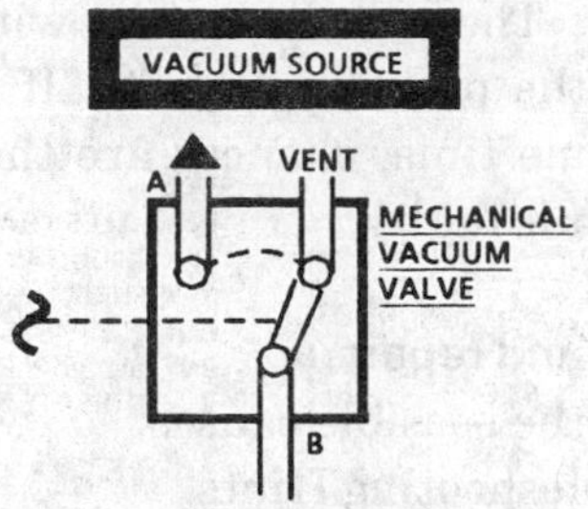
VACUUM SOURCE
A
VENT
MECHANICAL VACUUM VALVE
B

IN THE "AT REST" POSITION SHOWN, THE VALVE DOES THE FOLLOWING:
PORT A IS SEALED.
PORT B IS VENTED TO THE ATMOSPHERE.

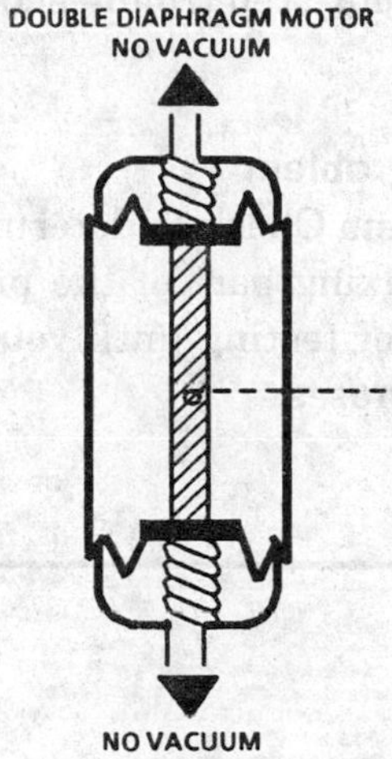
DOUBLE DIAPHRAGM MOTOR
NO VACUUM
NO VACUUM

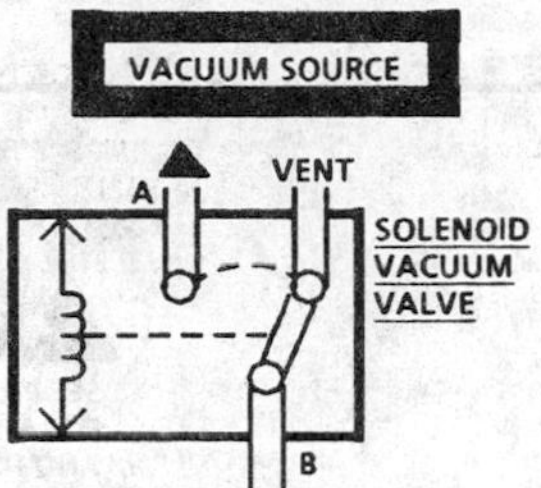
VACUUM SOURCE
A
VENT
SOLENOID VACUUM VALVE
B

WHEN THE VALVE IS MOVED TO THE "OPERATED" POSITION, VACUUM FROM PORT A IS CONNECTED TO PORT B.

THE SOLENOID VACUUM VALVE USES THE SOLENOID TO MOVE THE VALVE.

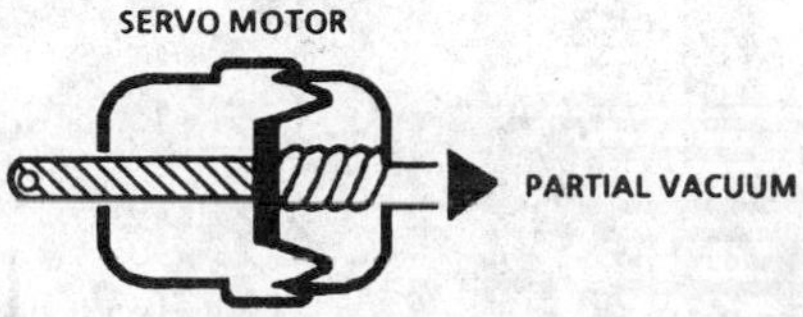
SERVO MOTOR
PARTIAL VACUUM

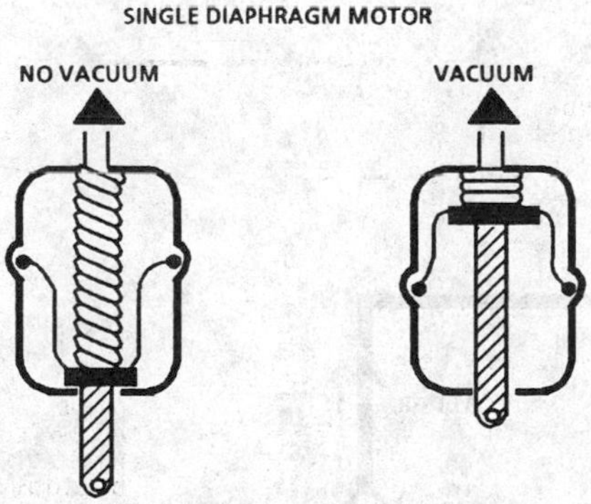
SINGLE DIAPHRAGM MOTOR
NO VACUUM
VACUUM

Vacuum Motors operate like electrical solenoids, mechanically pushing or pulling a shaft between two fixed positions. When vacuum is applied, the shaft is pulled in. When no vacuum is applied, the shaft is pushed all the way out by a spring.

Double Diaphragm Motors can be operated by vacuum in two directions. When there is no vacuum, the motor is in the center "at rest" position.

Some Vacuum Motors such as the Servo Motor in the Cruise Control can position the actuating arm at any position between fully extended and fully retracted. The servo is operated by a control valve that applies varying amounts of vacuum to the motor. The higher the vacuum level, the greater the retraction of the motor arm. Servo Motors work like the two position motors; the only difference is in the way the vacuum is applied. Servo Motors are generally larger and provide a calibrated control.

TROUBLESHOOTING PROCEDURES

BASIC KNOWLEDGE REQUIRED

Without a basic knowledge of electricity, it will be difficult to use the diagnostic procedures contained in this section. You should understand the basic theory of electricity and know the meaning of voltage, current (amps) and resistance (ohms). You should understand what happens in a circuit with an open or a shorted wire. You should be able to read and understand a wiring diagram.

The following four-step troubleshooting procedure is recommended:

Step 1: Check the Problem

Perform a System Check to determine a symptom. Don't waste time fixing part of the problem! Do not begin disassembly or testing until you have narrowed down the possible causes.

Step 2: Read the Electrical Schematic

Study the schematic. Read the Circuit Operation text if you do not understand how the circuit should work. Check circuits that share wiring with the problem circuit. (Shared circuits are shown on Power Distribution, Ground Distribution, Fuse Block Details and Light Switch Details pages.) Try to operate the shared circuits. If the shared circuits work, then the shared wiring is OK. The cause must be within the wiring used only by the problem circuit. If several circuits fail at the same time, chances are the power (fuse) or ground circuit is faulty.

Step 3: Find the fault and repair

- Narrow down the possible causes.
- Use the Troubleshooting Hints.
- Make the necessary measurements or checks as given in the System Diagnosis.

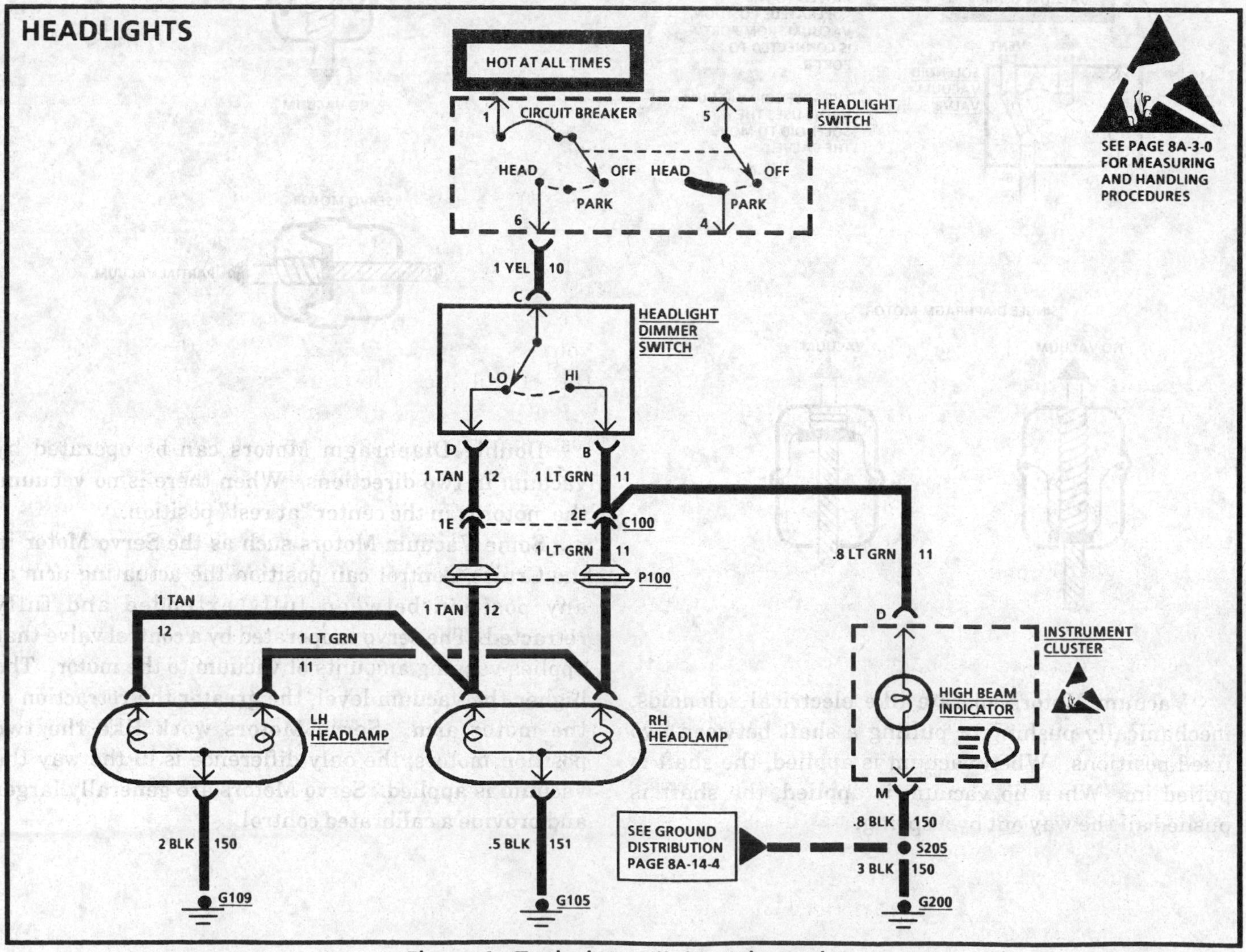
HEADLIGHTS
HOT AT ALL TIMES
CIRCUIT BREAKER
HEADLIGHT SWITCH
1
5
HEAD
OFF
HEAD
OFF
PARK
PARK
6
4
SEE PAGE 8A-3-0 FOR MEASURING AND HANDLING PROCEDURES
1 YEL 10
C
HEADLIGHT DIMMER SWITCH
LO
HI
D
B
1 TAN 12
1 LT GRN 11
1E
2E
C100
1 LT GRN 11
P100
.8 LT GRN 11
1 TAN
12
1 TAN 12
1 LT GRN
11
D
INSTRUMENT CLUSTER
HIGH BEAM INDICATOR
LH HEADLAMP
RH HEADLAMP
M
.8 BLK 150
SEE GROUND DISTRIBUTION PAGE 8A-14-4
S205
3 BLK 150
2 BLK 150
.5 BLK 151
G109
G105
G200

Figure 1 - Typical Headlights Schematic

- Before replacing a component, check power, signal and ground wires at the component harness connector. If the checks and connections are OK, the most probable cause is component failure.

Step 4: Test the Repair

Repeat the System Check to verify the fault has been corrected and that no other faults were induced during the repair.

Example:

A customer brings in a vehicle and says that the HI beams do not work.

Step 1: Perform a System Check on the Headlight Circuit. You may discover that both LO beams operate. In "HI," you may notice that the HI Beam Indicator comes on, but neither HI beam operates.

Step 2: Read the Headlights Electrical Schematic, see Figure 1. This is the step that will save time and labor. Remember, it is essential to understand how a circuit should work, before trying to figure out why it doesn't.

After you understand how the circuit should operate, read the schematic again, this time keeping in mind what you have learned by operating the circuit.

Since both LO beams work, you know that the Headlight Switch, the YEL wire, the LO contacts of the Headlight Dimmer Switch, terminal "1E" of C100, the TAN wires and grounds G105 and G109 are all good.

Furthermore, since you saw that the HI Beam Indicator came on when the Headlight Dimmer Switch was moved to "HI," you know that the HI contacts of the Headlight Dimmer Switch and the LT GRN wire between the Headlight Dimmer Switch and C100 are good.

At this point, you could test for voltage at the RH Headlamp with the Headlight Dimmer Switch in "HI." However, it is extremely unlikely that the HI beam filaments have burned out in both headlamps, or that both headlamps connections are bad. The cause must be a bad connection at C100, or a break in the LT GRN wire between C100 and the RH Headlamp.

You have quickly narrowed the possible causes down to one specific area, and have *done* absolutely *no* work on the vehicle itself.

Step 3: Find the fault and repair it. Using the Component Location List and the corresponding figure, you can quickly find C100 and the LT GRN wire, locate the exact trouble point and make the repair.

Step 4: Check the repair by performing a System Check on the Headlights Circuit. This, of course, means making sure that both HI beams, both LO beams and the HI Beam Indicator are all working.

Now suppose that the symptoms were different. You may have operated the Headlamps and found that the LO beams were working, but neither the HI beams nor the HI Beam Indicator were working. Looking at the schematic, you might conclude that it is unlikely that both HI beam filaments and the HI Beam Indicator have all burned out at once. The cause is probably the Headlight Dimmer Switch or its connector.

TROUBLESHOOTING TOOLS

Electrical troubleshooting requires the use of common electrical test equipment.

TEST LIGHT/DIGITAL VOLTMETER

Use a test light to check for voltage. A Test Light (J 34142-B) is made up of a 12 volt light bulb with a pair of leads attached. After grounding one lead, touch the other lead to various points along the circuit where voltage should be present. When the bulb goes on, there is voltage at the point being tested.

A DVM can be used instead of a test light. While a test light shows whether or not voltage is present, a DVM indicates how much voltage is present.

An increasing number of circuits include solid state control modules. One example is the Engine Control Module (ECM). Voltages in these circuits should be tested only with a 10-megohm or higher impedance DVM or multimeter (J 39200). Unless directed to within the diagnostics, never use a test light on circuits that contain solid state components, since damage to these components may result.

TROUBLESHOOTING PROCEDURES

When testing for voltage or continuity at the connection, it is not necessary to separate the two halves of the connector. Unless testing a Weather Pack® connector, always probe the connector from the back. Always check both sides of the connector. An accumulation of dirt and corrosion between contact surfaces is sometimes a cause of electrical problems. A terminal contact checking procedure can be found on page 8A-4-6.

CONNECTOR TEST ADAPTERS

Connector Test Adapter Kit (J 35616-A) is available for making tests and measurements at separated connectors. This kit contains an assortment of probes which mate with many of the types of terminals you will see. Avoid using paper clips and other substitutes since they can damage terminals and cause incorrect measurements.

SELF-POWERED TEST LIGHT

A self-powered test light (J 21008-A) can be used to check for continuity. This tool is made up of a light bulb, Battery and two leads. If the leads are touched together, the bulb will go on.

A self-powered test light is used only on an unpowered circuit. First remove the fuse which feeds the circuit you're working on. Select two specific points along the circuit through which there should be continuity. Connect one lead of the self-powered test light to each point. If there is continuity, the test light circuit will be completed and the bulb will go on.

Never use a self-powered test light on circuits that contain solid state components, since damage to these components may result.

OHMMETER

An ohmmeter can be used instead of a self-powered test light. The ohmmeter shows how much resistance there is between two points along a circuit. Low resistance means good continuity.

Circuits which include any solid state control modules, such as the Engine Control Module (ECM), should be tested only with a 10-megohm or higher impedance digital multimeter (J 39200).

When measuring resistance with a DVM, the vehicle Battery should be disconnected. This will prevent incorrect readings. DVMs apply such a small voltage to measure resistance that the presence of voltages can upset a resistance reading.

Diodes and solid state components in a circuit can cause an ohmmeter to give a false reading. To find out if a component is affecting a measurement, take a reading once, reverse the leads and take a second reading. If the readings differ, the solid state component is affecting the measurement.

FUSED JUMPER WIRE

A fused jumper (J 36169) is available with small clamp connectors providing adaptation to most connectors without damage. This fused jumper wire is supplied with a 20 amp fuse which may not be suitable for some circuits. Do not use a fuse with a higher rating than the fuse that protects the circuit being tested.

NOTICE: A fused jumper may not protect solid state components from being damaged.

SHORT FINDER

Short Finders (J 8681-A) are available to locate hidden shorts to ground. The short finder creates a pulsing magnetic field in the shorted circuit and shows you the location of the short through body trim or sheet metal.

FUSE TESTER

A simple tester (J 34764) can detect a blown fuse. To check a fuse, the tester is applied directly to the fuse in the Fuse Block. Two probes contact the fuse, either into the slots of a flat fuse or to the metal ends of a glass fuse. With power on, a red LED in the tester lights if the fuse is open. The handle of the tester is a tool for removing either type of fuse.

TROUBLESHOOTING TESTS

Always check for aftermarket accessories (non OEM) as the first step in diagnosing electrical problems. If the vehicle is so equipped, disconnect the system to verify that these add-on accessories are not the cause of the problems.

Some possible causes of vehicle problems related to aftermarket accessories include:

1. Power feeds connected to points other than the Battery.
2. Antenna location.
3. Transceiver wiring located too close to vehicle electronic modules or wiring.
4. Poor shielding or poor connectors on antenna feedline.

Refer to 1990/1991 model year bulletin entitled, "Installation Guidelines for Aftermarket Accessories" for specific information.

PROBING

After probing, when reconnecting connectors or replacing terminals, always be sure to reinstall Connector Position Assurance (CPA) and Terminal Position Assurance (TPA).

Frontprobe

When frontprobing of connectors is required, always use a mating terminal adapter from Connector Test Adapter Kit (J 35616-A). The use of proper adaptors will ensure that proper terminal contact integrity is maintained. For a terminal contact checking procedure, refer to page 8A-4-6.

Backprobe

Only backprobe connector terminals when specifically called for in diagnostic procedures. Since backprobing can be a source of damage to connector terminals, extra care must be taken to avoid deforming the terminal, either by forcing the test probe too far into the cavity or by using too large a test probe.

After backprobing any connector, always check for terminal damage. If terminal damage is suspected, check for proper terminal contact, refer to "Checking Terminal Contact," page 8A-4-6.

TESTING FOR VOLTAGE (Figure 2)

1. Connect one lead of a test light to a known good ground. When using a DVM, be sure the voltmeter's negative lead is connected to ground.
2. Connect the other lead of the test light or voltmeter to a selected test point (connector or terminal).
3. If the test light illuminates, there is voltage present. When using a DVM, note the voltage reading.

TESTING FOR CONTINUITY (Figure 3)

1. Remove the fuse to the circuit involved.
2. Connect one lead of a self-powered test light or ohmmeter to one end of the part of the circuit you wish to test.
3. Connect the other lead to the other end of the circuit.
4. If the self-powered test light glows, there is continuity. When using an ohmmeter, low or no resistance means good continuity.

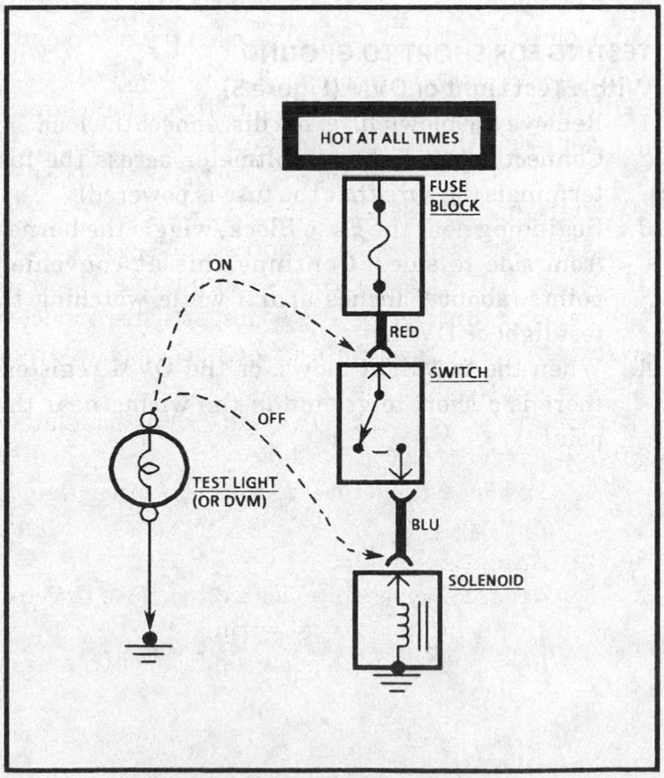
HOT AT ALL TIMES
FUSE BLOCK
ON
RED
SWITCH
OFF
TEST LIGHT (OR DVM)
BLU
SOLENOID

Figure 2 - Voltage Check

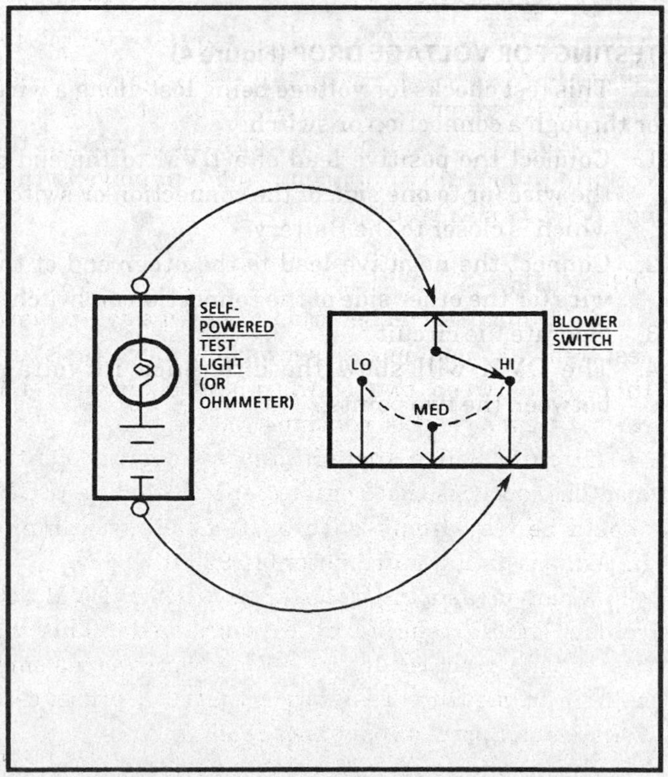
SELF-POWERED TEST LIGHT (OR OHMMETER)
BLOWER SWITCH
LO
HI
MED

Figure 3 - Continuity Check through a Switch

TROUBLESHOOTING PROCEDURES

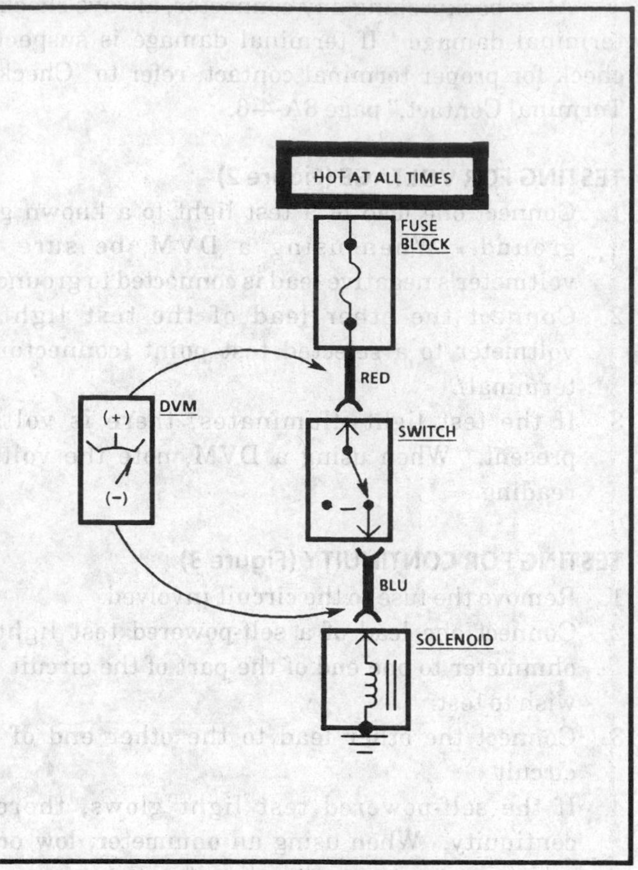
HOT AT ALL TIMES
FUSE BLOCK
RED
DVM
(+)
(−)
SWITCH
BLU
SOLENOID

Figure 4 - Voltage Drop Test

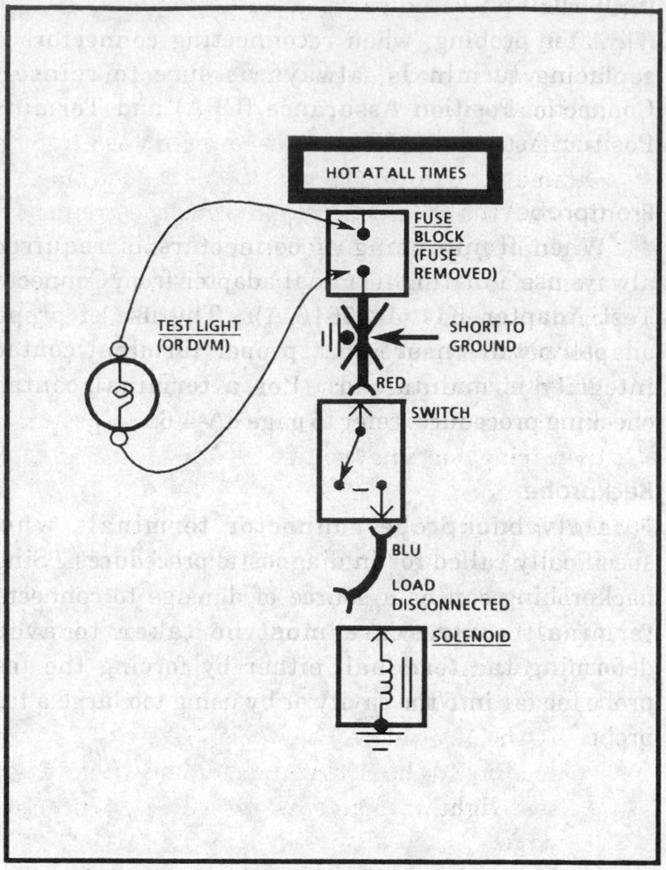
HOT AT ALL TIMES
FUSE BLOCK (FUSE REMOVED)
TEST LIGHT (OR DVM)
SHORT TO GROUND
RED
SWITCH
BLU
LOAD DISCONNECTED
SOLENOID

Figure 5 - Testing for Short with Test Light or DVM

TESTING FOR VOLTAGE DROP (Figure 4)

This test checks for voltage being lost along a wire, or through a connection or switch.

1. Connect the positive lead of a DVM to the end of the wire (or to one side of the connection or switch) which is closer to the Battery.
2. Connect the negative lead to the other end of the wire (or the other side of the connection or switch).
3. Operate the circuit.
4. The DVM will show the difference in voltage between the two points.

TESTING FOR SHORT TO GROUND With a Test Light or DVM (Figure 5)

1. Remove the blown fuse and disconnect the load.
2. Connect a test light or voltmeter across the fuse terminals (be sure that the fuse is powered).
3. Beginning near the Fuse Block, wiggle the harness from side to side. Continue this at convenient points (about 6 inches apart) while watching the test light or DVM.
4. When the test light glows, or the DVM registers, there is a short to ground in the wiring near that point.

With a Self-Powered Test Light or Ohmmeter (Figure 6)

1. Remove the blown fuse and disconnect the Battery and load.
2. Connect one lead of a self-powered test light or ohmmeter to the fuse terminal on the load side.
3. Connect the other lead to a known good ground.
4. Beginning near the Fuse Block, wiggle the harness from side to side. Continue this at convenient points (about 6 inches apart) while watching the self-powered test light or ohmmeter.
5. When the self-powered test light glows, or the ohmmeter registers, there is a short to ground in the wiring near that point.

Fuses Powering Several Loads

1. Find the schematic in "Fuse Block Details," page 8A-11-0 for the fuse that has blown.
2. Open the first connector or switch leading from the fuse to each load.
3. Replace the fuse.
   - If the fuse blows, the short is in the wiring leading to the first connector or switch. Use a test light or meter as described on previous page.
   - If fuse does not blow, refer to next step.
4. Close each connector or switch until the fuse blows in order to find which circuit has the short. Connect test lamp or meter at the connector to the suspect circuit (disconnected) rather than at the fuse terminals.

JUMP STARTING PROCEDURE

Refer to SECTION 6D-1 for jump starting procedure.

INTERMITTENTS AND POOR CONNECTIONS

Most intermittents are caused by faulty electrical connections or wiring, although occasionally a sticking relay or solenoid can be a problem. Some items to check are:

- Poor mating of connector halves, or terminals not fully seated in the connector body (backed out).
- Dirt or corrosion on the terminals. The terminals must be clean and free of any foreign material which could impede proper terminal contact.

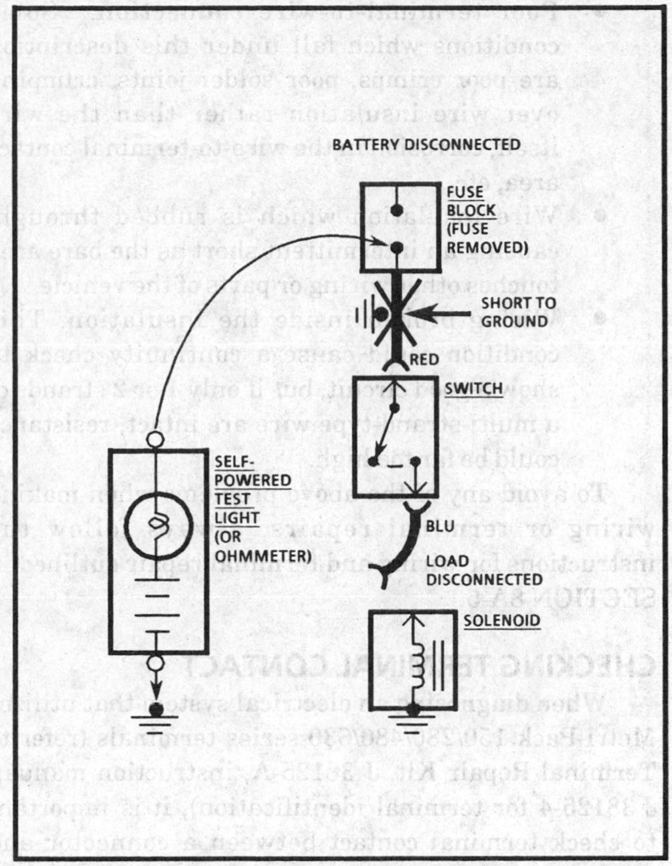
BATTERY DISCONNECTED
FUSE BLOCK (FUSE REMOVED)
SHORT TO GROUND
RED
SWITCH
SELF-POWERED TEST LIGHT (OR OHMMETER)
BLU
LOAD DISCONNECTED
SOLENOID

Figure 6 - Testing for Short with Self-Powered Test Light or Ohmmeter

- Damaged connector body, exposing the terminals to moisture and dirt, as well as not maintaining proper terminal orientation with the component or mating connector.
- Improperly formed or damaged terminals. All connector terminals in problem circuits should be checked carefully to ensure good contact tension. Use a corresponding mating terminal to check for proper tension. Refer to "Checking Terminal Contact" in this section for the specific procedure.
- The J 35616-A Connector Test Adapter Kit must be used whenever a diagnostic procedure requests checking or probing a terminal. Using the adapter will ensure that no damage to the terminal will occur, as well as giving an idea of whether contact tension is sufficient. If contact tension seems incorrect, refer to "Checking Terminal Contact" in this section for specifics.

TROUBLESHOOTING PROCEDURES

- Poor terminal-to-wire connection. Some conditions which fall under this description are poor crimps, poor solder joints, crimping over wire insulation rather than the wire itself, corrosion in the wire-to-terminal contact area, etc.
- Wire insulation which is rubbed through, causing an intermittent short as the bare area touches other wiring or parts of the vehicle.
- Wiring broken inside the insulation. This condition could cause a continuity check to show a good circuit, but if only 1 or 2 strands of a multi-strand-type wire are intact, resistance could be far too high.

To avoid any of the above problems when making wiring or terminal repairs, always follow the instructions for wiring and terminal repair outlined in SECTION 8A-5.

CHECKING TERMINAL CONTACT

When diagnosing an electrical system that utilizes Metri-Pack 150/280/480/630 series terminals (refer to Terminal Repair Kit, J 38125-A, instruction manual, J 38125-4 for terminal identification), it is important to check terminal contact between a connector and component, or between in-line connectors, before replacing a suspect component.

Frequently, a diagnostic chart leads to a step that reads: "Check for poor connection." Mating terminals must be inspected to assure good terminal contact. A poor connection between the male and female terminal at a connector may be the result of contamination or deformation.

Contamination is caused by the connector halves being improperly connected, a missing or damaged connector seal, or damage to the connector itself, exposing the terminals to moisture and dirt. Contamination, usually in underhood or underbody connectors, leads to terminal corrosion, causing an open circuit or intermittently open circuit.

Deformation is caused by probing the mating side of a connector terminal without the proper adapter, improperly joining the connector halves or repeatedly separating and joining the connector halves. Deformation, usually to the female terminal contact tang, can result in poor terminal contact, see figure 7, causing an open or intermittently open circuit.

Follow the procedure below to check terminal contact.

1. Separate the connector halves. Refer to Terminal Repair Kit, J 38125-A, instruction manual, J 38125-4.
2. Inspect the connector halves for contamination. Contamination will result in a white or green build-up within the connector body or between terminals, causing high terminal resistance, intermittent contact or an open circuit. An underhood or underbody connector that shows signs of contamination should be replaced in its entirety: terminals, seals and connector body.
3. Using an equivalent male terminal from the Terminal Repair Kit, J 38125-A, check the retention force of the female terminal in question by inserting and removing the male terminal to the female terminal in the connector body. Good terminal contact will require a certain amount of force to separate the terminals.
4. Using an equivalent female terminal from the Terminal Repair Kit, J 38125-A, compare the retention force of this terminal to the female terminal in question by joining and separating the male terminal to the good female terminal, and then joining and separating the male terminal to the female terminal in question. If the retention force is significantly different between the two female terminals, replace the female terminal in question, refer to Terminal Repair Kit, J 38125-A.

If a visual (physical) check does not reveal the cause of the problem, the vehicle may be able to be driven with a DVM connected to the suspected circuit. An abnormal voltage reading when the problem occurs indicates the problem may be in that circuit.

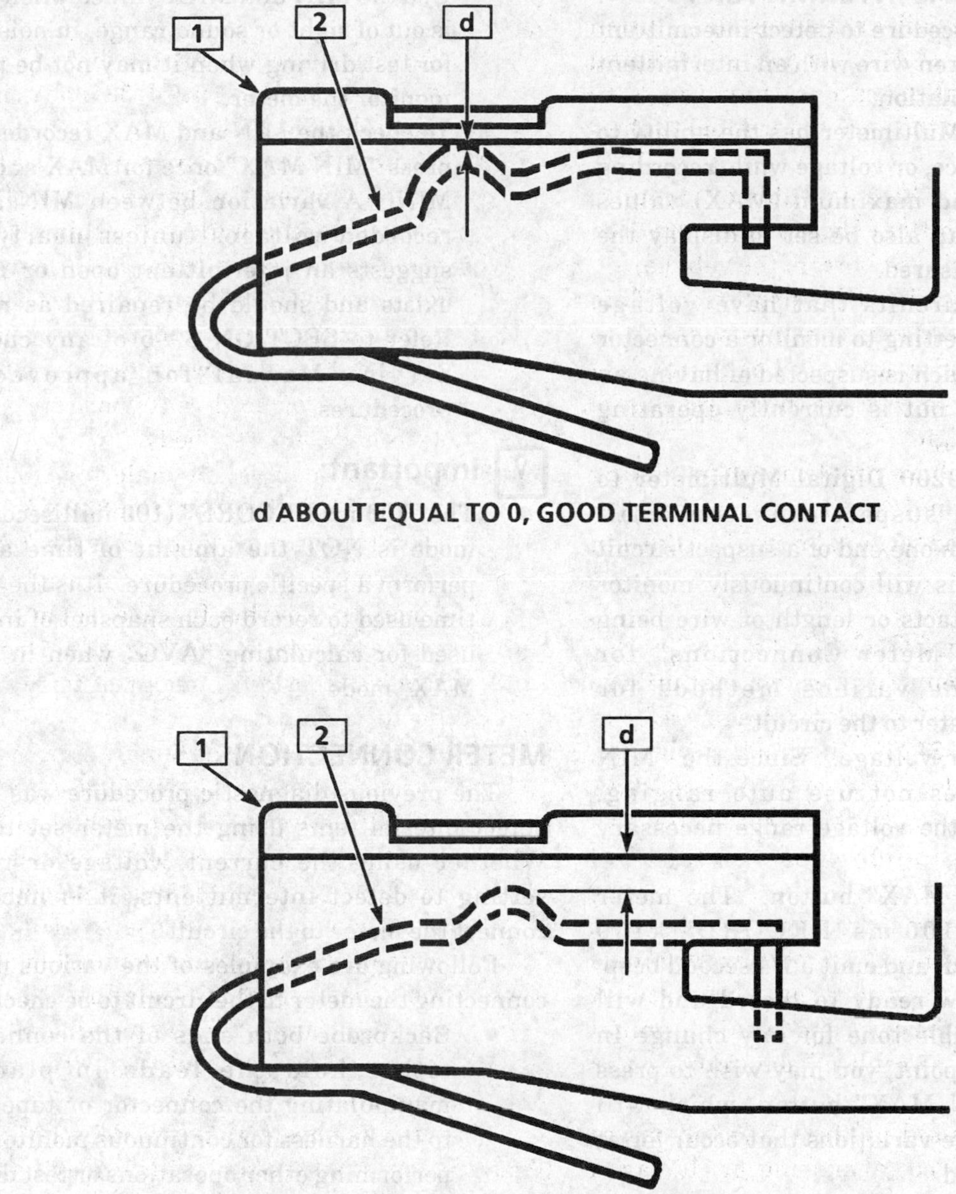
1
2
d
d ABOUT EQUAL TO 0, GOOD TERMINAL CONTACT
1
2
d
d MUCH GREATER THAN 0, POOR TERMINAL CONTACT

1 TYPICAL METRI-PACK 150/280/480/630 SERIES FEMALE TERMINAL (150 SERIES PUSH-TO-SEAT SHOWN)

2 CONTACT TANG

d AMOUNT OF DEFORMATION

Figure 7 - Deformation of a Typical Metri-Pack 150/280/480/630 Series Female Terminal

TROUBLESHOOTING PROCEDURES

DETECTING ELECTRICAL INTERMITTENTS

Use the following procedure to detect intermittent terminal contact or a broken wire with an intermittent connection inside the insulation.

The J 39200 Digital Multimeter has the ability to monitor current, resistance, or voltage while recording the minimum (MIN) and maximum (MAX) values measured. The meter can also be set to display the average (AVG) value measured.

When diagnosing circuits that have voltage applied, use the voltage setting to monitor a connector (or length of a circuit) which is suspected of having an intermittent connection but is currently operating normally.

1. Connect the J 39200 Digital Multimeter to both sides of a suspect connector (still connected) or from one end of a suspect circuit to the other. This will continuously monitor the terminal contacts or length of wire being checked. See "Meter Connections" for examples of the various methods for connecting the meter to the circuit.
2. Set the meter for voltage. Since the "MIN MAX" mode does not use auto ranging, manually select the voltage range necessary before proceeding.
3. Press the "MIN MAX" button. The meter should read "100 ms RECORD" (100 millisecond record) and emit a 1/4 second beep. The meter is now ready to record and will generate an audible tone for any change in voltage. At this point, you may wish to press the "PEAK MIN MAX" button, which will record any voltage variations that occur for at least 1 millisecond.
4. Try to simulate the condition that is potentially causing an intermittent connection, either by wiggling connections or wiring, test driving or performing other operations. If an open or resistance is created, a voltage will be present and the meter will emit a tone for as long as the open or resistance exists. Any change in voltage will cause the meter to emit a tone for no less than 1/4 second. (Listening for a tone while manipulating wiring is very helpful for narrowing in on an intermittent connection.)

   Use the MIN and MAX values when the meter is out of sight or sound range, in noisy areas or for test driving when it may not be possible to monitor the meter.

   To check the MIN and MAX recorded voltages press "MIN MAX" once for MAX and twice for MIN. A variation between MIN and MAX recorded voltages (unless nearly 0 volts) suggests an intermittent open or resistance exists and should be repaired as necessary. Refer to SECTION 8A-5 of any current GM Service Manual for approved repair procedures.

Important:

- The "100 ms RECORD" (100 millisecond record) mode is NOT the amount of time allowed to perform a specific procedure. It is the amount of time used to record each snapshot of information used for calculating "AVG" when in the "MIN MAX" mode.

METER CONNECTIONS

The previous diagnostic procedure was written to detect intermittents using the meter set to voltage. Whether using the current, voltage or resistance setting to detect intermittents, it is necessary to connect the meter to the circuit.

Following are examples of the various methods of connecting the meter to the circuit to be checked:

- Backprobe both ends of the connector and either hold the leads in place while manipulating the connector or tape the leads to the harness for continuous monitoring while performing other operations or test driving. (Do not backprobe "Weather Pack" type connectors.)
- Disconnect the harness at both ends of the suspect circuit where it connects either to a component or to other harnesses.
- Use Connector Test Adapter Kit J 35616-A to connect the meter to the circuit.
- If the system being diagnosed has a specified pinout or breakout box, it may be used to simplify connecting the meter to the circuit or for checking multiple circuits quickly.

ADDITIONAL INFORMATION

NOTICE: Turn off power to the test circuit before attempting in-circuit resistance measurements to prevent false readings or damage to the meter. Do not use the meter to measure resistance through a solid state module.

Continuity tests that work well for detecting intermittent shorts to ground can be performed by setting the meter to ohms then pressing the "PEAK MIN MAX" button. An audible tone will be heard whenever the meter detects continuity for at least 1 millisecond.

The J 39200 Instruction Manual is a good source of information and should be read thoroughly upon receipt of the meter as well as kept on hand for reference during new procedures.

REPAIR PROCEDURES

ELECTRICAL REPAIRS

This section provides instruction in the following repairs:

- Circuit Protection
- Typical Electrical Repairs
- Splicing Copper Wire
- Splicing Twisted/Shielded Cable
- Repairing Connectors (Except Weather Pack®)
- Repairing Weather Pack® (Environmental) Connectors
- Terminal Repair

After any electrical repair is made, always test the circuit afterwards by operating the devices in the circuit. This confirms not only that the repair is correct, but also, that it was the cause of the complaint.

CIRCUIT PROTECTION

The purpose of circuit protection is to protect the wiring assembly during normal and overload conditions. An overload is defined as a current requirement that is higher than normal. This overload could be caused by a short circuit or system malfunction. The short circuit could be the result of a pinched or cut wire or an internal device short circuit, such as an electronic module failure.

The circuit protection device is only applied to protect the wiring assembly, and not the electrical load at the end of the assembly. For example, if an electronic component short circuits, the circuit protection device will assure a minimal amount of damage to the wiring assembly. However, it will not necessarily prevent damage to the component.

CIRCUIT PROTECTION DEVICES

There are three basic types of circuit protection devices: Circuit Breaker, Fuse and Fusible Link.

CIRCUIT BREAKERS

A circuit breaker is a protective device designed to open the circuit when a current load is in excess of rated breaker capacity. If there is a short or other type of overload condition in the circuit, the excessive current will open the circuit between the circuit breaker terminals. There are two basic types of circuit breakers used in GM vehicles: cycling and non-cycling.

CYCLING CIRCUIT BREAKER

The cycling breaker will open due to heat generated when excessive current passes through it for a period of time. Once the circuit breaker cools, it will close again after a few seconds. If the cause of the high current is still present it will open again. It will continue to cycle open and closed until the condition causing the high current is removed.

NON-CYCLING CIRCUIT BREAKER

There are two types of non-cycling circuit breakers. One type is mechanical and is nearly the same as a cycling breaker. The difference is a small heater wire within the non-cycling circuit breaker. This wire provides enough heat to keep the bimetallic element open until the current source is removed.

The other type is solid state, called out in this section as Electronic Circuit Breaker (ECB). This device has a Positive Temperature Coefficient. It increases its resistance greatly when excessive current passes through it. The excessive current heats the ECB. As it heats, its resistance increases, therefore having a Positive Temperature Coefficient. Eventually the resistance gets so high that the circuit is effectively open. The ECB will not reset until the circuit is opened, removing voltage from its terminals. Once voltage is removed, the circuit breaker will re-close within a second or two.

FUSES

The most common method of automotive wiring circuit protection is the fuse (Figure 1). A fuse is a device that, by the melting of its element, opens an electrical circuit when the current exceeds a given level for a sufficient time. The action is non-reversible and the fuse must be replaced each time a circuit is overloaded or after a malfunction is repaired.

Fuses are color coded. The standardized color identification and ratings are shown in Figure 2. For service replacement, non-color coded fuses of the same respective current rating can be used.

Examine a suspect fuse for a break in the element. If the element is broken or melted, replace the fuse with one of equal current rating.

There are additional specific circuits with in-line fuses. These fuses are located within the individual wiring harness and will appear to be an open circuit if blown.

AUTOFUSE

The Autofuse, normally referred to simply as "Fuse," is the most common circuit protection device in today's vehicle. The Autofuse is most often used to protect the wiring assembly between the Fuse Block and the system components.

MAXIFUSE

The Maxifuse was designed to replace the fusible link and Pacific Fuse Elements. The Maxifuse is designed to protect cables, normally between the Battery and Fuse Block, from both direct short circuits and resistive short circuits.

Compared to a fusible link or a Pacific Fuse Element, the Maxifuse performs much more like an Autofuse, although the average opening time is slightly longer. This is because the Maxifuse was designed to be a slower blowing fuse, with less chance of nuisance blows.

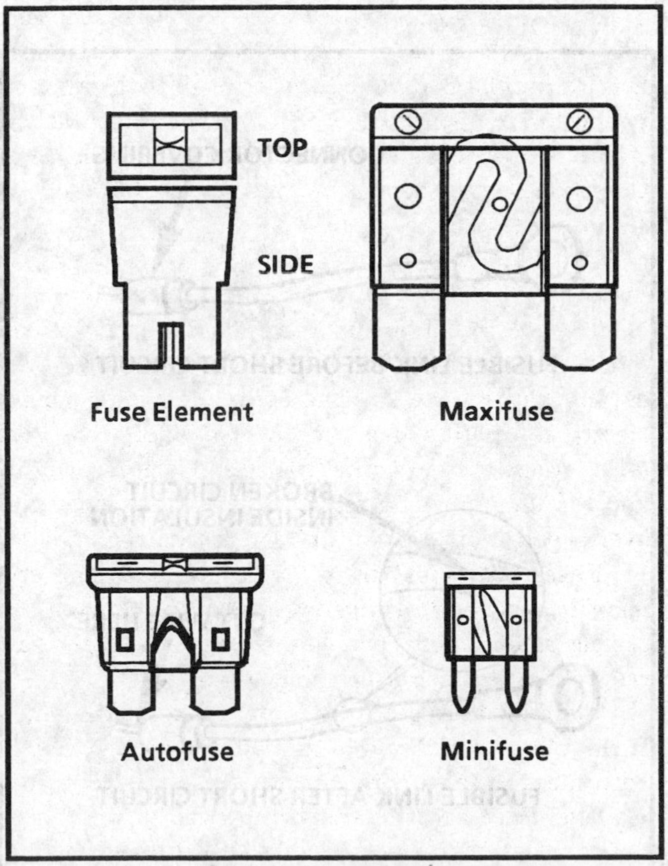
TOP
SIDE
Fuse Element
Maxifuse
Autofuse
Minifuse

Figure 1 - Fuse Devices

AUTOFUSE

CURRENT RATING	COLOR
3	VIOLET
5	TAN
7.5	BROWN
10	RED
15	BLUE
20	YELLOW
25	NATURAL
30	GREEN

MAXIFUSE

CURRENT RATING	COLOR
20	YELLOW
30	GREEN
40	AMBER
50	RED
60	BLUE
70	BROWN
80	NATURAL

MINIFUSE

CURRENT RATING	COLOR
5	TAN
7.5	BROWN
10	RED
15	BLUE
20	YELLOW
25	WHITE
30	GREEN

PACIFIC FUSE ELEMENT

CURRENT RATING	COLOR
30	PINK
40	GREEN
50	RED
60	YELLOW

Figure 2 - Fuse Rating and Color

REPAIR PROCEDURES

MINIFUSE

The Minifuse is a smaller version of the Autofuse and has a similar performance. As with the Autofuse, the Minifuse is usually used to protect the wiring assembly between a Fuse Block and system components. Since the Minifuse is a smaller device, it allows for more system specific fusing to be accomplished within the same amount of space as Autofuses.

PACIFIC FUSE ELEMENT/MAXIFUSE

The Pacific Fuse Element and Maxifuse were developed to be a replacement for the fusible link. Like a fusible link, the fuses are designed to protect wiring from a direct short to ground. These elements are easier to service and inspect than a fusible link and will eventually replace fusible links in all future vehicle applications.

FUSIBLE LINKS

In addition to circuit breakers and fuses, some circuits use fusible links to protect the wiring. Like fuses, fusible links are "one-time" protection devices that will melt and create an open circuit (see Figure 3).

Not all fusible link open circuits can be detected by observation. Always inspect that there is battery voltage past the fusible link to verify continuity.

Fusible links are used instead of a fuse in wiring circuits that are not normally fused, such as the ignition circuit. For AWG sizes, each fusible link is four wire gage sizes smaller than the wire it is designed to protect. For example: to protect a 10 gage wire use a 14 gage link or for metric, to protect a 5 mm^2 wire use a 2 mm^2 link (see Figure 6). Links are marked on the insulation with wire-gage size because the heavy insulation makes the link appear to be a heavier gage than it actually is. The same wire size fusible link must be used when replacing a blown fusible link.

Fusible links are available with three types of insulation: Hypalon®, Silicone/GXL (SIL/GXL) and Expanded Duty. All future vehicles that use fusible links will utilize the Expanded Duty type of fusible link. When servicing fusible links, all fusible links can be replaced with the Expanded Duty type. SIL/GXI fusible links can be used to replace either SIL/GXI or Hypalon® fusible links. Hypalon® fusible links can only be used to replace Hypalon® fusible links.

Determining characteristics of the types of fusible links:

- Hypalon® (limited use): only available in .35 mm^2 or smaller and its insulation is one color all the way through.
- SIL/GXL (widely used): available in all sizes and has a white inner core under the outer color of insulation.
- Expanded Duty: available in all sizes, has an insulation that is one color all the way through and has three dots following the writing on the insulation.

Service fusible links are available in many lengths. Choose the shortest length that is suitable. If the fusible link is to be cut from a spool, it should be cut 150-225 mm (approx 6-9 in.) long. NEVER make a fusible link longer than 225 mm (approx 9 in.).

CAUTION: Fusible links cut longer than 225 mm (approx 9 in.) will not provide sufficient overload protection.

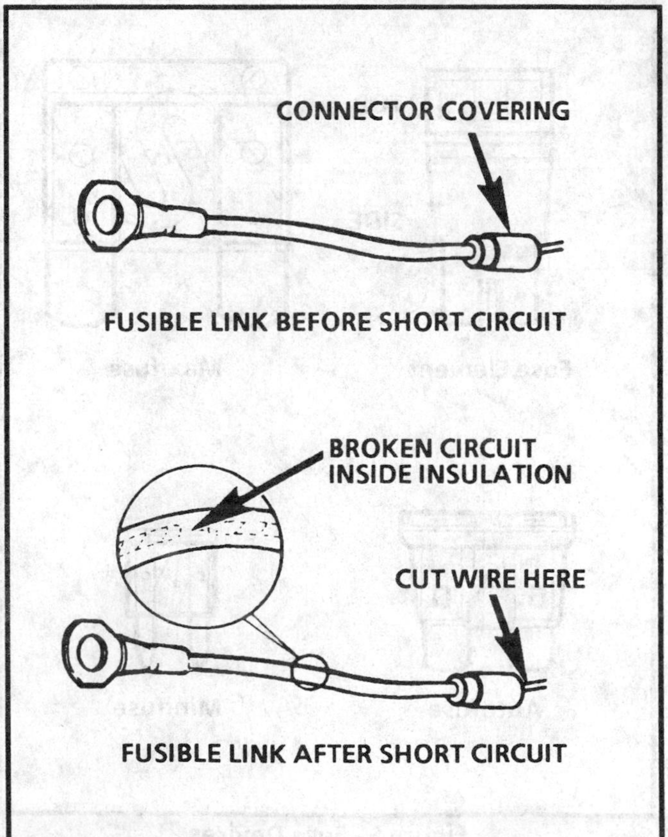
CONNECTOR COVERING
FUSIBLE LINK BEFORE SHORT CIRCUIT
BROKEN CIRCUIT
INSIDE INSULATION
CUT WIRE HERE
FUSIBLE LINK AFTER SHORT CIRCUIT

Figure 3 - Good and Damaged Fusible Links

To replace a damaged fusible link (Figure 4), cut it off beyond the splice. Replace with a repair link. When connecting the repair link, strip wire and use staking-type pliers to crimp the splice securely in two places. For more details on splicing procedures, see "Splicing Copper Wire." Use Crimp and Seal splices whenever possible. When using Splice Clips, refer to page 8A-5-3; when using Crimp and Seal splice sleeves, refer to page 8A-5-6.

To replace a damaged fusible link which feeds two harness wires, cut them both off beyond the splice. Use two repair links, one spliced to each harness wire (see Figure 5).

TYPICAL ELECTRICAL REPAIRS

An open circuit is an incomplete circuit. Power cannot reach the load or reach ground. If a circuit is open, active components do not energize. A short circuit is an unwanted connection between one part of the circuit and either ground or another part of the circuit. A short circuit causes a fuse to blow or a circuit breaker to open.

SHORT CIRCUITS CAUSED BY DAMAGED WIRE INSULATION

- Locate the damaged wire.
- Find and correct the cause of the wire insulation damage.
- For minor damage, tape over the wire. If damage is more extensive, replace the faulty segment of the wire (Refer to the splicing instructions for copper or shielded cable for the correct splicing procedure).

SPLICING COPPER WIRE USING SPLICE CLIPS

Splice Clips are included in the J 38125-A Terminal Repair Kit. The Splice Clip is a general purpose wire repair device. It may not be acceptable for applications having special requirements such as moisture sealing. Refer to the appropriate Service Manual Section to determine if there are any special requirements.

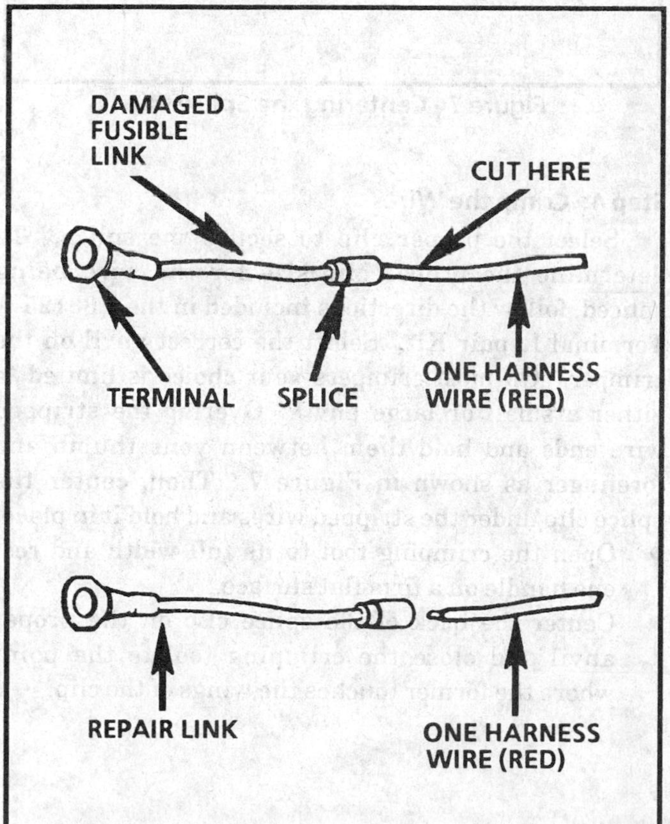
DAMAGED
FUSIBLE
LINK
CUT HERE
TERMINAL
SPLICE
ONE HARNESS
WIRE (RED)
REPAIR LINK
ONE HARNESS
WIRE (RED)

Figure 4 - Single Wire Feed Fusible Link

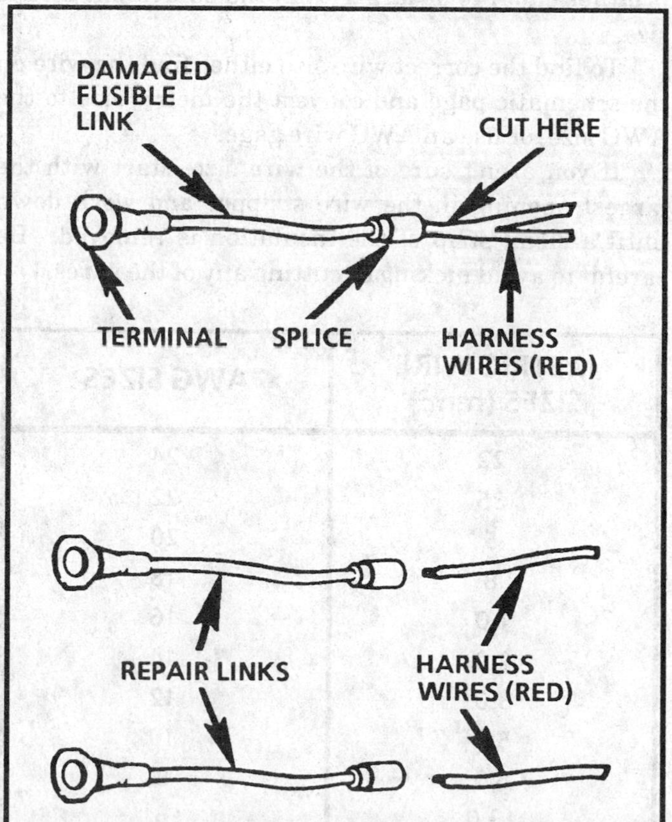
DAMAGED
FUSIBLE
LINK
CUT HERE
TERMINAL
SPLICE
HARNESS
WIRES (RED)
REPAIR LINKS
HARNESS
WIRES (RED)

Figure 5 - Double Wire Feed Fusible Link

REPAIR PROCEDURES

Step 1: Open the Harness

If the harness is taped, remove the tape. To avoid wire insulation damage, use a sewing "seam ripper" to cut open the harness (available from sewing supply stores). If the harness has a black plastic conduit, simply pull out the desired wire.

Step 2: Cut the Wire

Begin by cutting as little wire off the harness as possible. You may need the extra length of the wire later if you decide to cut more wire off to change the location of a splice. You may have to adjust splice locations to make certain that each splice is at least 40 mm (1½") away from other splices, harness branches or connectors.

Step 3: Strip the Insulation

When replacing a wire, use a wire of the same size as the original wire or larger. The schematics list wire size in metric units. The following table (Figure 6) shows the commercial (AWG) wire sizes that can be used to replace each metric wire size. Each AWG size is either equal to or larger than the equivalent metric size.

To find the correct wire size either find the wire on the schematic page and convert the metric size to the AWG size, or use an AWG wire gage.

If you aren't sure of the wire size, start with the largest opening in the wire stripper and work down until a clean strip of the insulation is removed. Be careful to avoid nicking or cutting any of the wires.

METRIC WIRE SIZES (mm^2)	AWG SIZES
.22	24
.35	22
.5	20
.8	18
1.0	16
2.0	14
3.0	12
5.0	10
8.0	8
13.0	6
19.0	4
32.0	2

Figure 6 - Wire Size Conversion Table

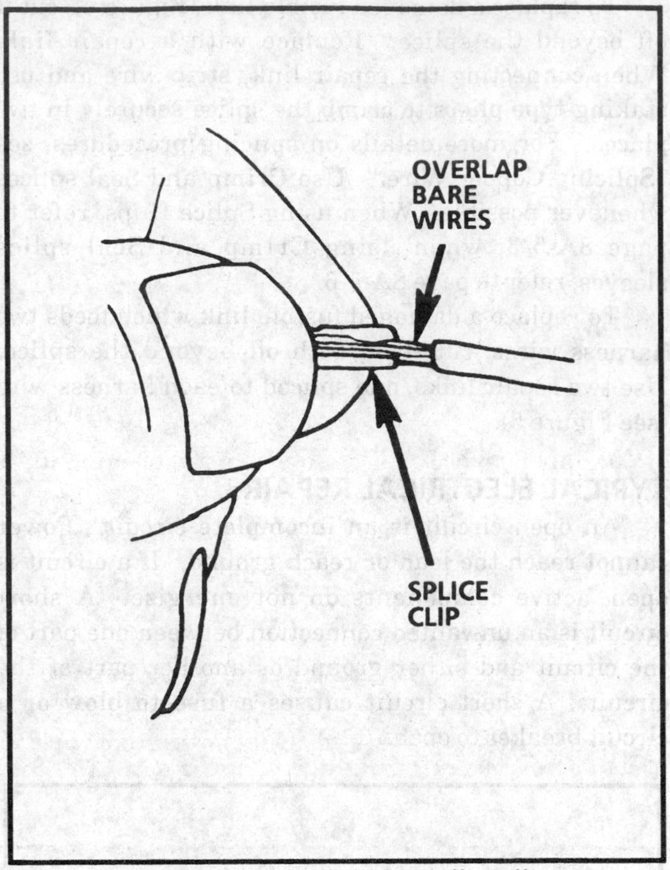
OVERLAP BARE WIRES
SPLICE CLIP

Figure 7 - Centering the Splice Clip

Step 4: Crimp the Wires

Select the proper clip to secure the splice. To determine the proper clip size for the wire being spliced, follow the directions included in the J 38125-A Terminal Repair Kit. Select the correct anvil on the crimper. On most crimpers your choice is limited to either a small or large anvil. Overlap the stripped wire ends and hold them between your thumb and forefinger as shown in Figure 7. Then, center the splice clip under the stripped wires and hold it in place.

- Open the crimping tool to its full width and rest one handle on a firm flat surface.
- Center the back of the splice clip on the proper anvil and close the crimping tool to the point where the former touches the wings of the clip.

- Make sure that the clip and wires are still in the correct position. Then, apply steady pressure until the crimping tool closes (see Figure 8).
- Before crimping the ends of the clip, be sure that:
  - The wires extend beyond the clip in each direction.
  - No strands of wire are cut loose, and
  - No insulation is caught under the clip.

Crimp the splice again, once on each end. Do not let the crimping tool extend beyond the edge of the clip or you may damage or nick the wires (Figure 9).

Step 5: Solder

Apply 60/40 rosin core solder to the opening in the back of the clip (see Figure 10). Follow the manufacturer's instruction for the solder equipment you are using.

Step 6: Tape the Splice

Center and roll the splicing tape. The tape should cover the entire splice. Roll on enough tape to duplicate the thickness of the insulation on the existing wires. Do not flag the tape. Flagged tape may not provide enough insulation, and the flagged ends will tangle with the other wires in the harness (see Figure 11).

If the wire does not belong in a conduit or other harness covering, tape the wire again. Use a winding motion to cover the first piece of tape (Figure 12).

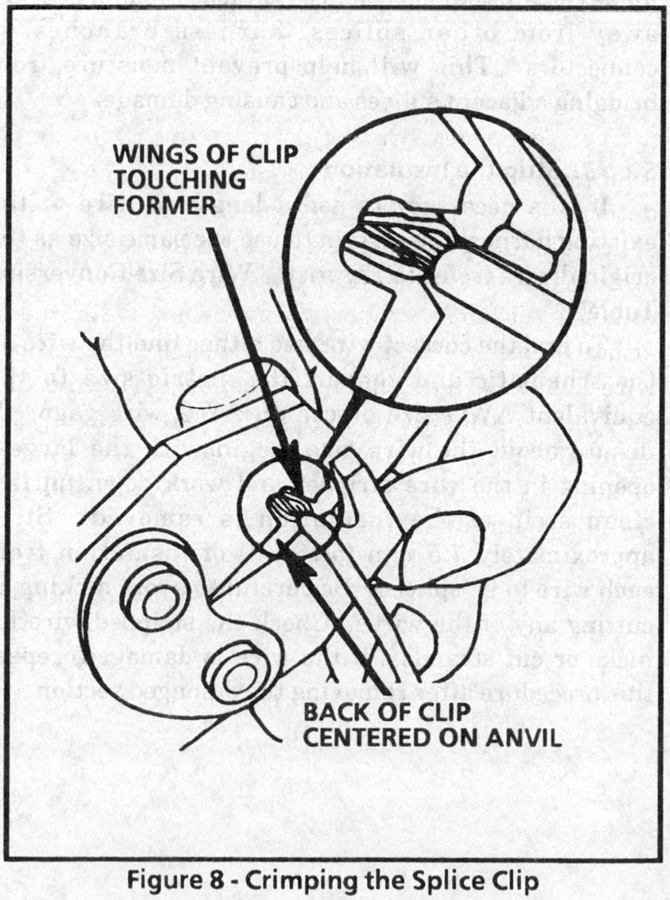
WINGS OF CLIP
TOUCHING
FORMER
BACK OF CLIP
CENTERED ON ANVIL

Figure 8 - Crimping the Splice Clip

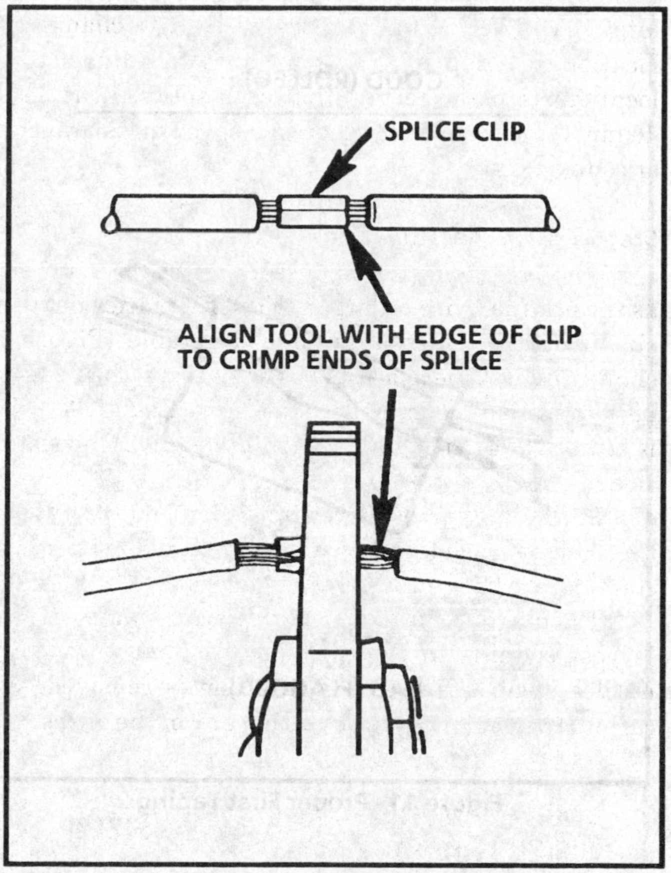
SPLICE CLIP
ALIGN TOOL WITH EDGE OF CLIP
TO CRIMP ENDS OF SPLICE

Figure 9 - Completing the Crimp

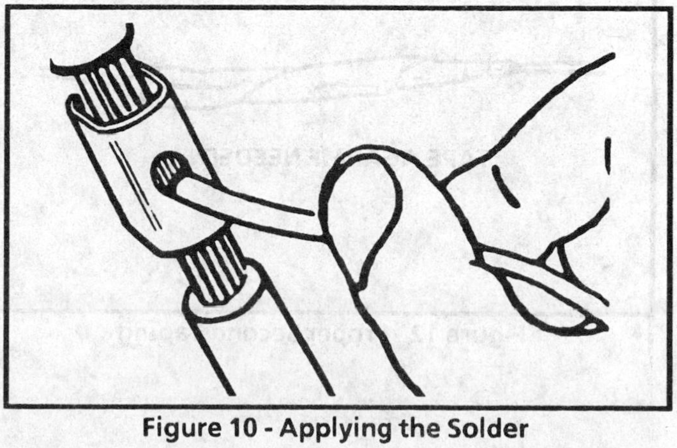

Figure 10 - Applying the Solder

REPAIR PROCEDURES

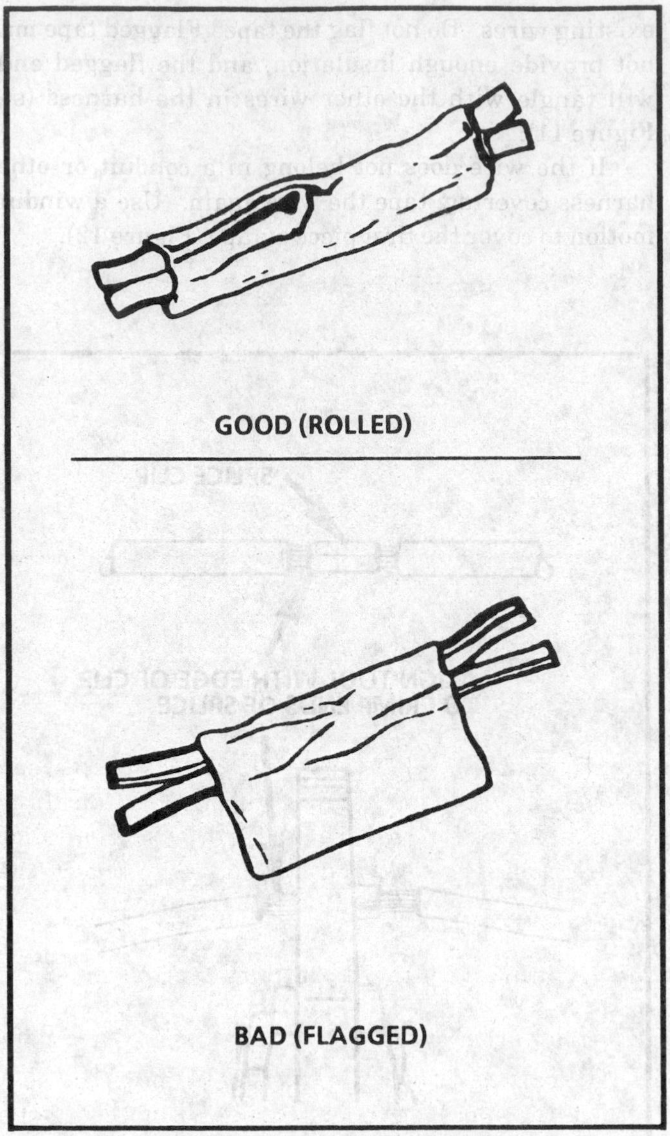
GOOD (ROLLED)
BAD (FLAGGED)

Figure 11 - Proper First Taping

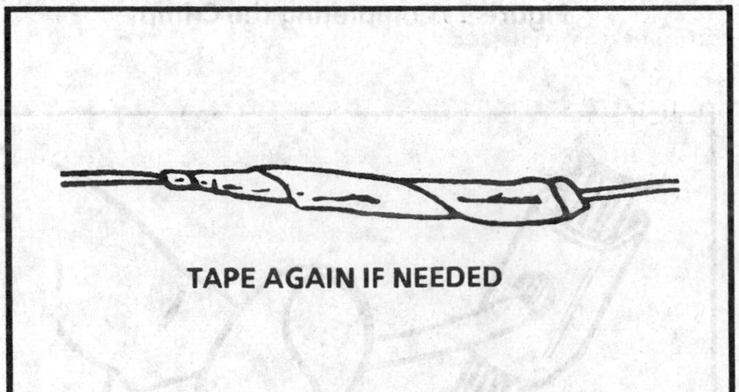
TAPE AGAIN IF NEEDED

Figure 12 - Proper Second Taping

SPLICING COPPER WIRE USING CRIMP AND SEAL SPLICE SLEEVES

Crimp and Seal splice sleeves may be used on all types of insulation except tefzel and coaxial to form a one to one splice. They are to be used where there are special requirements such as moisture sealing. Refer to the appropriate section of the Service Manual to determine if the Crimp and Seal is necessary. Crimp and Seal splice sleeves are included in the J 38125-A Terminal Repair Kit.

Step 1: Open the Harness

If the harness is taped, remove the tape. To avoid wire insulation damage, use a sewing "seam ripper" to cut open the harness (available from sewing supply stores). The Crimp and Seal splice sleeves may be used on all types of insulation except tefzel and coaxial and may only be used to form a one to one splice.

Step 2: Cut the Wire

Begin by cutting as little wire off the harness as possible. You may need the extra length of wire later if you decide to cut more wire to change the location of a splice. You may have to adjust splice locations to make certain that each splice is at least 40 mm (1.5 in.) away from other splices, harness branches or connectors. This will help prevent moisture from bridging adjacent splices and causing damage.

Step 3: Strip the Insulation

If it is necessary to add a length of wire to the existing harness, be certain to use the same size as the original wire (refer to Figure 6, "Wire Size Conversion Table").

To find the correct wire size either find the wire on the schematic and convert the metric size to the equivalent AWG size or use an AWG wire gage. If unsure about the wire size, begin with the largest opening in the wire stripper and work down until a clean strip of the insulation is removed. Strip approximately 7.5 mm (5/16 in.) of insulation from each wire to be spliced. Be careful to avoid nicking or cutting any of the wires. Check the stripped wire for nicks or cut strands. If the wire is damaged, repeat this procedure after removing the damaged section.

Step 4: Select and Position the Splice Sleeve

Select the proper splice sleeve according to wire size. The splice sleeves and tool nests are color coded (see following chart).

CRIMP AND SEAL SPLICE SLEEVE CHART

Color splice sleeve	Crimp tool nest color	Wire gage AWG / (metric)
Salmon (yellowish-pink)	Red	20, 18/ (0.5, 0.8)
Blue	Blue	16, 14/ (1.0, 2.0)
Yellow	Yellow	12, 10/ (3.0, 5.0)

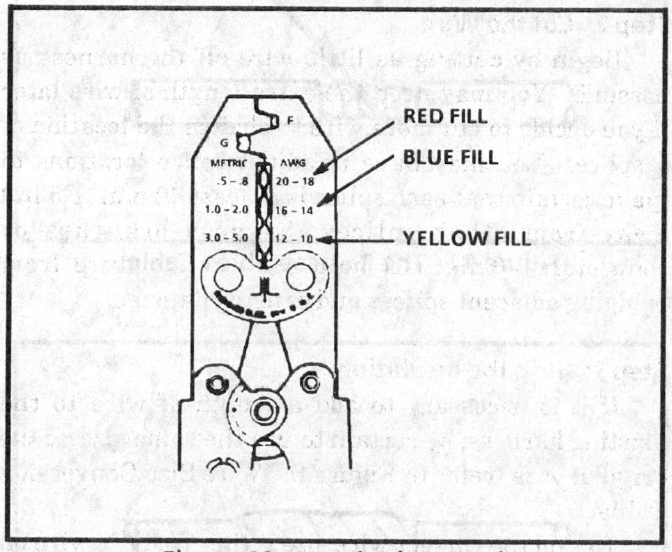
RED FILL
BLUE FILL
YELLOW FILL
F
G
METRIC
AWG
.5 - .8
20 - 18
1.0 - 2.0
16 - 14
3.0 - 5.0
12 - 10

Figure 13 - Hand Crimp Tool

Using the J 38125-8 splice crimp tool (Figure 13), position the splice sleeve in the proper color nest of the hand crimp tool. Place the splice sleeve in the nest so that the crimp falls midway between the end of the barrel and the stop.

The sleeve has a stop in the middle of the barrel to prevent the wire from going further (Figure 14). Close the hand crimper handles slightly to hold the splice sleeve firmly in the proper nest.

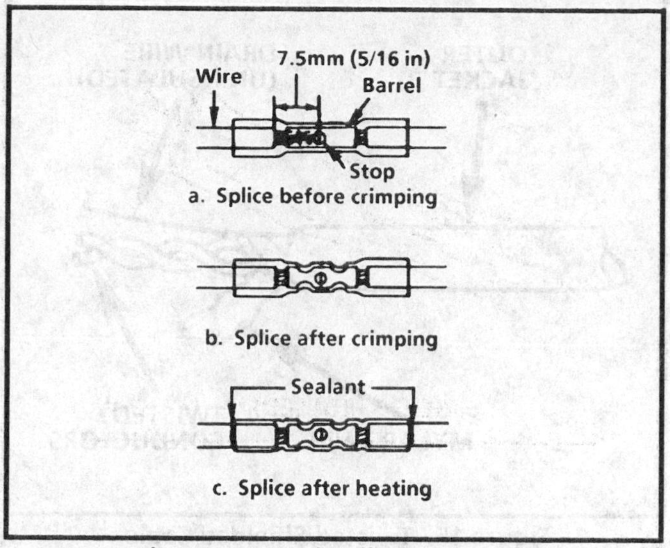
7.5mm (5/16 in)
Wire
Barrel
Stop
a. Splice before crimping
b. Splice after crimping
Sealant
c. Splice after heating

Figure 14 - Seal Splice Sequence

Step 5: Insert Wires into Splice Sleeve and Crimp

Insert the wire into the splice sleeve until it hits the barrel stop and close the handles of the J 38125-8 crimper tightly until the crimper handles open when released. The crimper handles will not open until the proper amount of pressure is applied to the splice sleeve. Repeat steps 4 and 5 for opposite end of the splice.

Step 6: Shrink the Insulation around the Splice

Using the Ultratorch J 38125-5 (follow instructions that accompany Ultratorch), apply heat where the barrel is crimped. Gradually move the heat barrel to the open end of the tubing, shrinking the tubing completely as the heat is moved along the insulation. A small amount of sealant will come out of the end of the tubing when sufficient shrinking is achieved (Figure 14).

SPLICING TWISTED/SHIELDED CABLE

Twisted/shielded cable is sometimes used to protect wiring from electrical noise (stray signals). For example, two-conductor cable of this construction is used between the ECM and the distributor. See Figure 15 for a breakdown of twisted/shielded cable construction.

REPAIR PROCEDURES

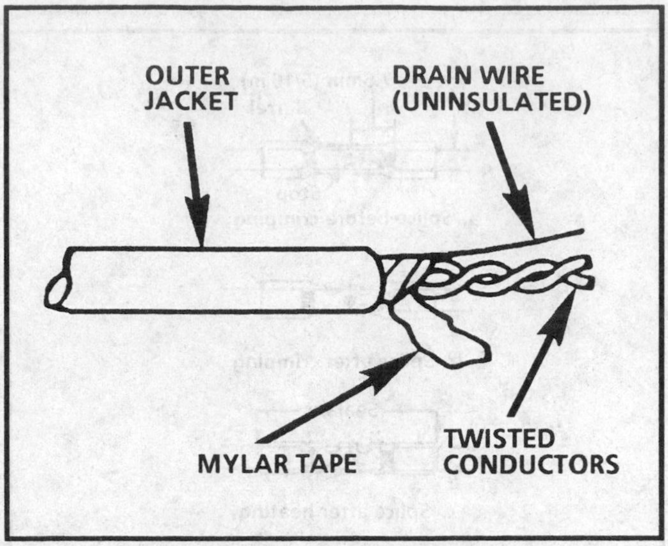
OUTER
JACKET
DRAIN WIRE
(UNINSULATED)
MYLAR TAPE
TWISTED
CONDUCTORS

Figure 15 - Twisted/Shielded Cable

Step 1: Remove Outer Jacket

Remove the outer jacket and discard it. Be careful to avoid cutting into the drain wire or the mylar tape.

Step 2: Unwrap the Tape

Unwrap the aluminum/mylar tape, but do not remove it. The tape will be used to rewrap the twisted conductors after the splices have been made.

Step 3: Prepare the Splice

Untwist the conductors. Then, prepare the splice by following the splicing instructions for copper wire presented earlier. Remember to stagger splices to avoid shorts (Figure 16).

Step 4: Re-assemble the Cable

After you have spliced and taped each wire, rewrap the conductors with the mylar tape. Be careful to avoid wrapping the drain wire in the tape.

Next, splice the drain wire following the splicing instructions for copper wire. Then, wrap the drain wire around the conductors and mylar tape (Figure 17).

Step 5: Tape the Cable

Tape over the entire cable using a winding motion (see Figure 18). This tape will replace the section of the jacket you removed to make the repair.

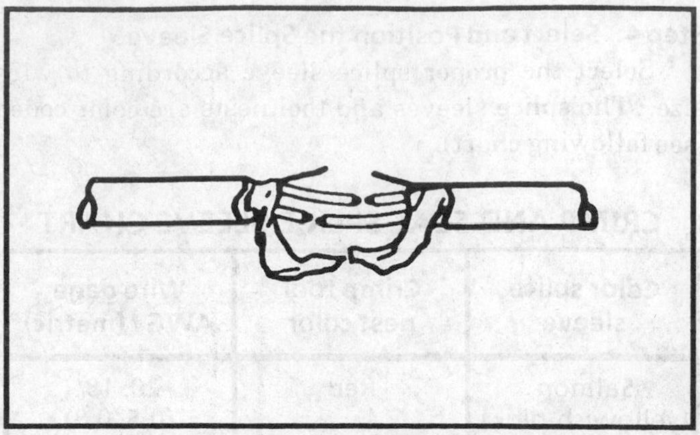

Figure 16 - The Untwisted Conductors

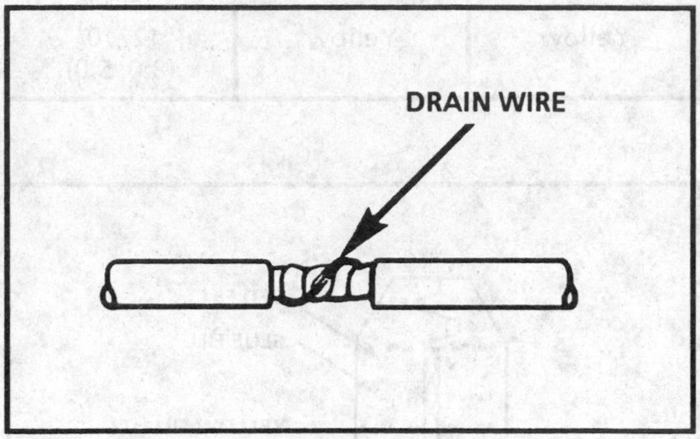
DRAIN WIRE

Figure 17 - The Re-assembled Cable

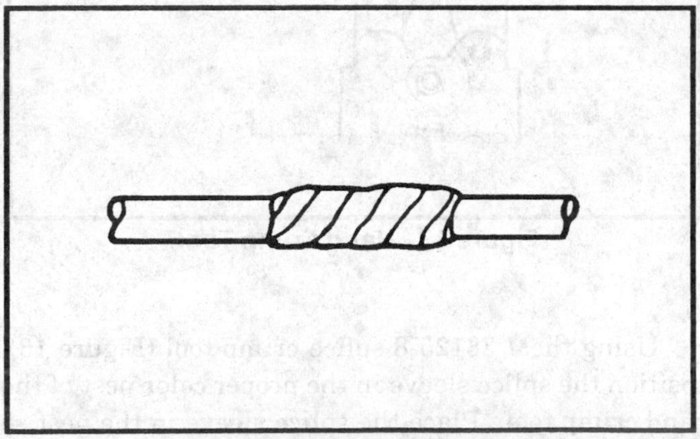

Figure 18 - Proper Taping

REPAIRING CONNECTORS

- The following general repair procedures can be used to repair most types of connectors. The repair procedures are divided into three general groups: Push-to-Seat and Pull-to-Seat and Weather Pack®.
- See "Harness Connector Faces," page 8A-202-0 to determine which type of connector is to be serviced.
- Use the proper Pick(s) or Tool(s) that apply to the terminal.
- The Terminal Repair Kit (J 38125-A) contains further information.

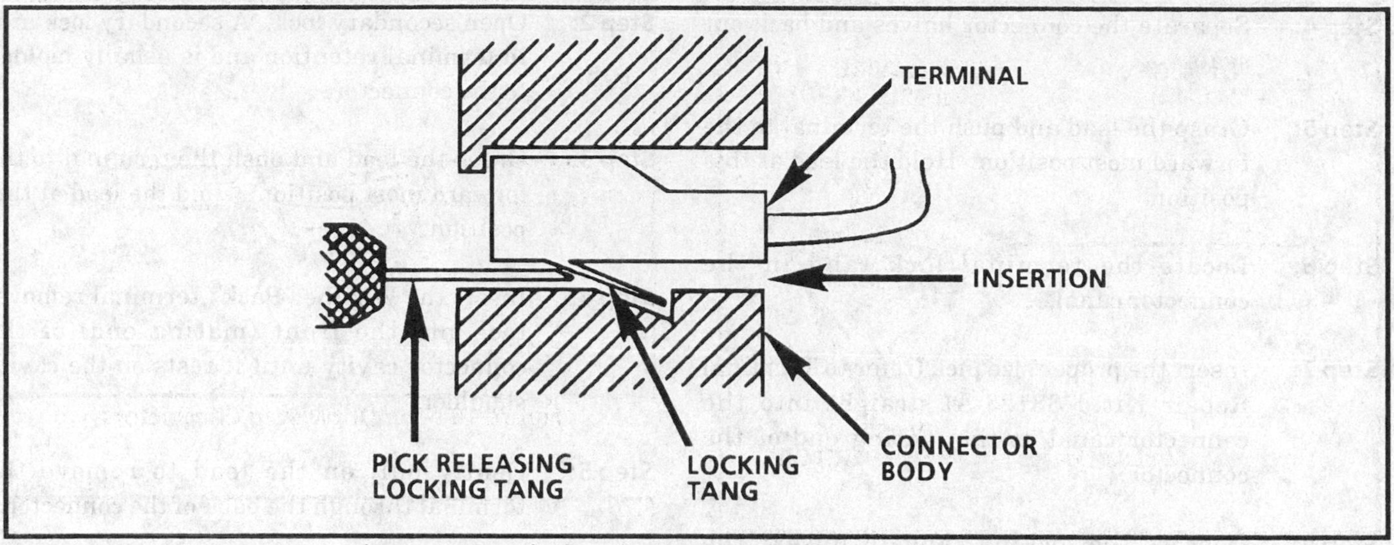
TERMINAL
INSERTION
PICK RELEASING
LOCKING TANG
LOCKING
TANG
CONNECTOR
BODY

Figure 19 - Typical Push-to-Seat Connector and Terminal

PUSH-TO-SEAT AND PULL-TO-SEAT

Follow the steps below to repair Push-to-Seat (Figure 19) or Pull-to-Seat (Figure 20) connectors. The steps are illustrated with typical connectors. Your connector may differ, but the repair steps are similar. Some connectors do not require all the steps shown. Skip those that don't apply.

Step 1: Remove any CPA (Connector Position Assurance) Locks. CPAs are designed to retain connectors when mated.

Step 2: Remove any TPA (Terminal Position Assurance) Locks. TPAs are designed to keep the terminal from backing out of the connector.

NOTICE: The TPA must be removed prior to terminal removal and must be replaced when the terminal is repaired and reseated.

Step 3: Open any secondary locks. A secondary lock aids in terminal retention and is usually molded to the connector.

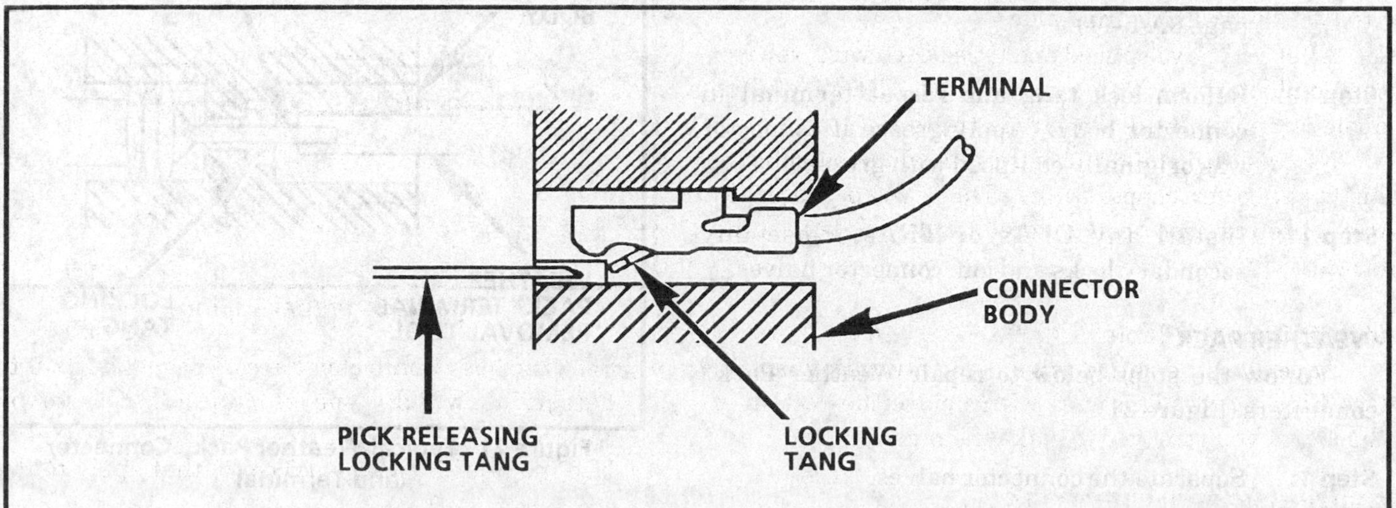
TERMINAL
CONNECTOR
BODY
PICK RELEASING
LOCKING TANG
LOCKING
TANG

Figure 20 - Typical Pull-to-Seat Connector and Terminal

REPAIR PROCEDURES

Step 4: Separate the connector halves and back out seals.

Step 5: Grasp the lead and push the terminal to the forward most position. Hold the lead at this position.

Step 6: Locate the terminal lock tang in the connector canal.

Step 7: Insert the proper size pick (refer to Terminal Repair Kit J 38125-A) straight into the connector canal at the mating end of the connector.

Step 8: Depress the locking tang to unseat the terminal.

Push-to-Seat – Gently pull on the lead to remove the terminal through the back of the connector.

Pull-to-Seat – Gently push on the lead to remove the terminal through the front of the connector.

NOTICE: Never use force to remove a terminal from a connector.

Step 9: Inspect terminal and connector for damage. Repair as necessary (see "Terminal Repair," page 8A-5-11).

Step 10: Reform lock tang and reseat terminal in connector body. Apply grease if connector was originally equipped with grease.

Step 11: Install any CPAs or TPAs, close any secondary locks and join connector halves.

WEATHER PACK®

Follow the steps below to repair Weather Pack® connectors (Figure 21).

Step 1: Separate the connector halves.

Step 2: Open secondary lock. A secondary lock aids in terminal retention and is usually molded to the connector.

Step 3: Grasp the lead and push the terminal to the forward most position. Hold the lead at this position.

Step 4: Insert the Weather Pack® terminal removal tool into the front (mating end) of the connector cavity until it rests on the cavity shoulder.

Step 5: Gently pull on the lead to remove the terminal through the back of the connector.

NOTICE: Never use force to remove a terminal from a connector.

Step 6: Inspect the terminal and connector for damage. Repair as necessary (see "Terminal Repair," on the following page).

Step 7: Reform the lock tang and reseat terminal in connector body.

Step 8: Close secondary locks and join connector halves.

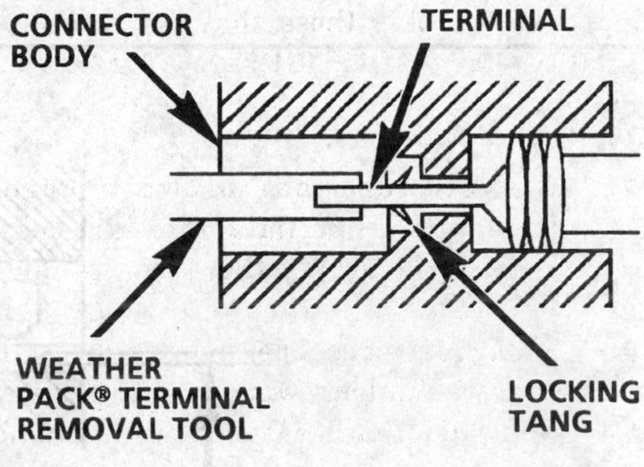
CONNECTOR BODY
TERMINAL
WEATHER PACK® TERMINAL REMOVAL TOOL
LOCKING TANG

Figure 21 - Typical Weather Pack® Connector and Terminal

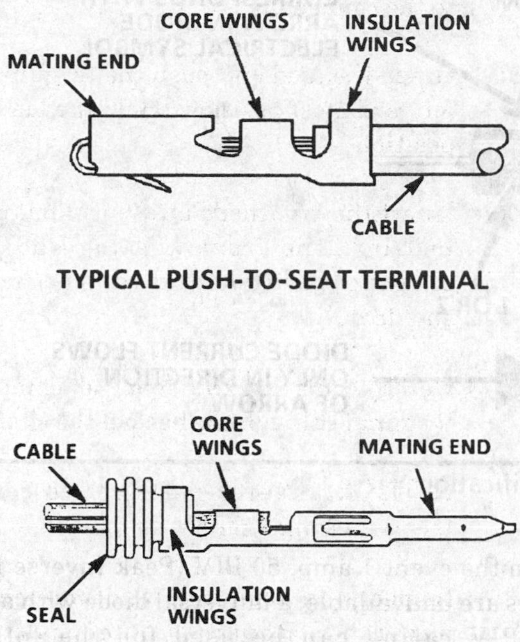
CORE WINGS
INSULATION WINGS
MATING END
CABLE
TYPICAL PUSH-TO-SEAT TERMINAL
CORE WINGS
CABLE
MATING END
INSULATION WINGS
SEAL
TYPICAL WEATHER PACK® TERMINAL

Figure 22 - Terminal Repair

TERMINAL REPAIR

The following repair procedures can be used to repair Push-to-Seat, Pull-to-Seat or Weather Pack® terminals (Figure 22). Some terminals do not require all steps shown. Skip those that don't apply. The Terminal Repair Kit (J 38125-A) contains further information.

Step 1: Cut off terminal between core and insulation crimp (minimize wire loss) and remove seal for Weather Pack® terminals.

Step 2: Apply correct seal per gauge size of wire and slide back along wire to enable insulation removal (Weather Pack® terminals only).

Step 3: Remove insulation.

Step 4: Align seal with end of cable insulation (Weather Pack® terminals only).

Step 5: Position strip (and seal for Weather Pack®) in terminal.

Step 6: Hand crimp core wings.

Step 7: Hand crimp insulation wings (non-Weather Pack®). Hand crimp insulation wings around seal and cable (Weather Pack®).

Step 8: Solder all hand crimped terminals.

DIODE REPLACEMENT

Many vehicle electrical systems use a diode to isolate circuits and protect the components from voltage spikes. When installing a new diode, use the following procedure:

Step 1: Open the Harness

If the diode is taped to the harness, remove all of the tape.

Step 2: Remove Inoperative Diode

Paying attention to current flow direction, remove inoperative diode from the harness with a suitable soldering tool. If the diode is located next to a connector terminal, remove the terminal(s) from the connector to prevent damage from the soldering tool.

Step 3: Strip the Insulation

Carefully strip away a section of insulation next to the old soldered portion of the wire(s). Do not remove any more than is needed to attach the new diode.

Step 4: Install New Diode

Check current flow direction of the new diode, being sure to install the diode with correct bias. Reference the appropriate service manual wiring schematic to obtain the correct diode installation position. Reference Figure 23 for replacement diode symbols and current flow explanations. Attach the new diode to the wire(s) using 60/40 rosin core solder. Use a heat sink (aluminum alligator clip) attached across the diode wire ends to protect the diode from excess heat. Follow the manufacturer's instructions for the soldering equipment you are using.

REPAIR PROCEDURES

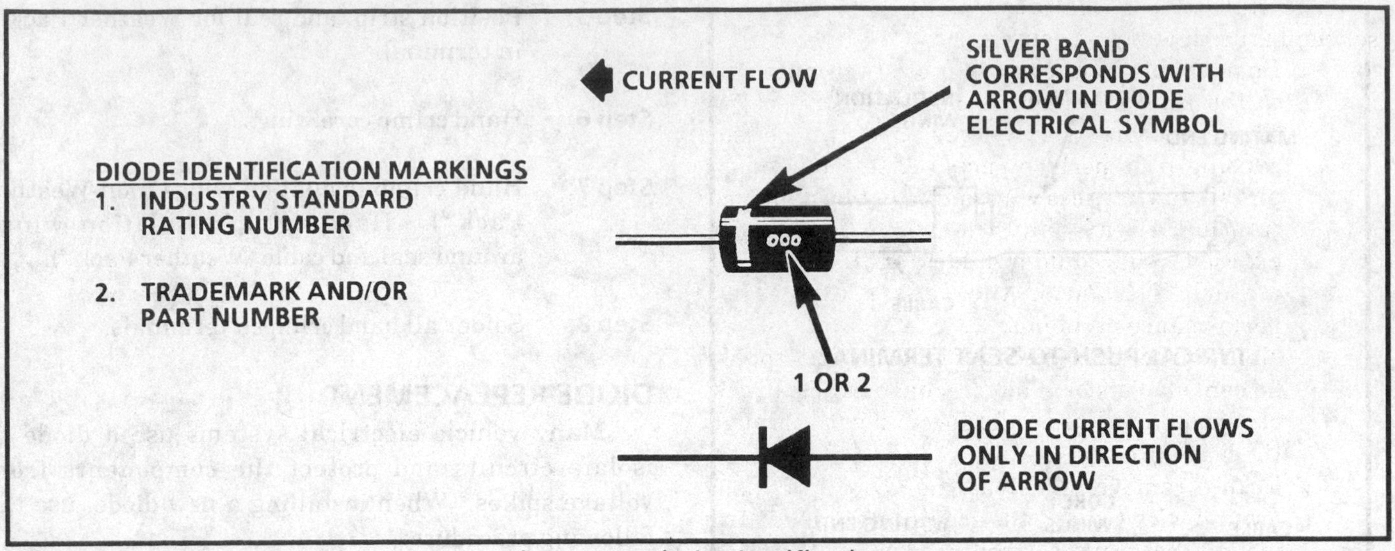
CURRENT FLOW
SILVER BAND CORRESPONDS WITH ARROW IN DIODE ELECTRICAL SYMBOL
DIODE IDENTIFICATION MARKINGS
1. INDUSTRY STANDARD RATING NUMBER
2. TRADEMARK AND/OR PART NUMBER
000
1 OR 2
DIODE CURRENT FLOWS ONLY IN DIRECTION OF ARROW

Figure 23 - Diode Identification

Step 5: Install Terminal(s)

Install terminal(s) into the connector body if previously removed in step 2.

Step 6: Tape Diode to Harness

Tape the diode to the harness or connector using electrical tape. To prevent shorts to ground and water intrusion, completely cover all exposed wire and diode attachment points.

ACCEPTABLE DIODE REPLACEMENTS

Diode Brand	Rating Number	RATING	P/N
GMSPO	1N4004	1 amp, 400 PIV	12112421
GMSPO	1N5404	3 amp, 400 PIV	12112422
GMSPO	1N4001	1 amp, 50 PIV	16020519
GMSPO	1N4005	1 amp, 600 PIV	16011840
GMSPO	1N4004	1 amp, 400 PIV	16039386

In the event 1 amp, 50 PIV (Peak Inverse Rating) diodes are unavailable, a universal diode with a 1 amp, 400 PIV rating can be used for the following applications:

- A/C Compressor Clutch
- ABS/4WAL (the ABS Diode on the Delco Moraine is hidden inside of an electrical connector under the carpet at the right panel)
- Wiper
- Charging System (hidden in wire harness)
- Parking Brake (vehicle with ABS)
- Relays
- Solenoids
- Diesel Glow Plug Circuit

HEATED OXYGEN SENSOR (O2S) REPAIR

If the Heated Oxygen Sensor pigtail wiring, connector or terminal is damaged, the entire Oxygen Sensor Assembly must be replaced. Do not attempt to repair the wiring, connector or terminals. In order for the sensor to function properly, it must have provided to it a clean air reference. This clean air reference is obtained by way of the Oxygen Sensor signal and heater wires. Any attempt to repair the wires, connectors or terminals could result in the obstruction of the air reference and degraded Oxygen Sensor performance.

The following guidelines should be used when servicing the Heated Oxygen Sensor:

- Do not apply contact cleaner or other materials to the sensor or vehicle harness connectors. These materials may get into the sensor causing poor performance. Also, the sensor pigtail and harness wires must not be damaged in such a way that the wires inside are exposed. This could provide a path for foreign materials to enter the sensor and cause performance problems.
- Neither the sensor or vehicle lead wires should be bent sharply or kinked. Sharp bends, kinks, etc., could block the reference air path through the lead wire.
- Do not remove or defeat the Oxygen Sensor ground wire (where applicable). Vehicles that utilize the ground wired sensor may rely on this ground as the only ground contact to the sensor. Removal of the ground wire will also cause poor engine performance.
- To prevent damage due to water intrusion, be sure that the peripheral seal remains intact on the vehicle harness connector.

The Engine Harness may be repaired using Packard's Crimp and Splice Seals Terminal Repair Kit J 38125-A. Under no circumstances should repairs be soldered since this could result in the air reference being obstructed.

REPAIR PROCEDURES

SPECIAL TOOLS

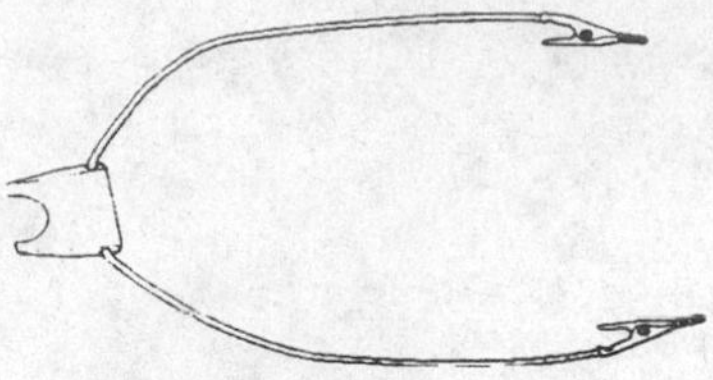

J 36169
Jumper Wire

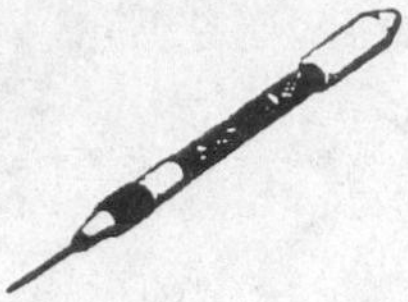

J 35689-A
Micro-Pack Connector Terminal Remover

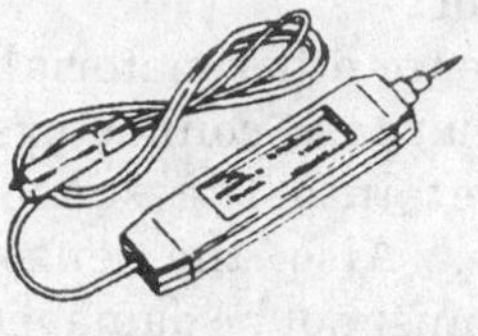

J 34636
Solenoid, Relay and Circuit Tester

J 35616-A
Connector Test Adapter Kit

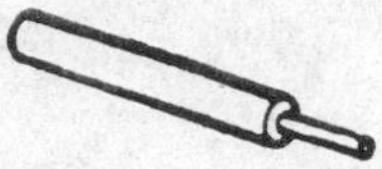

J 28742-A
Weather Pack II Terminal Remover

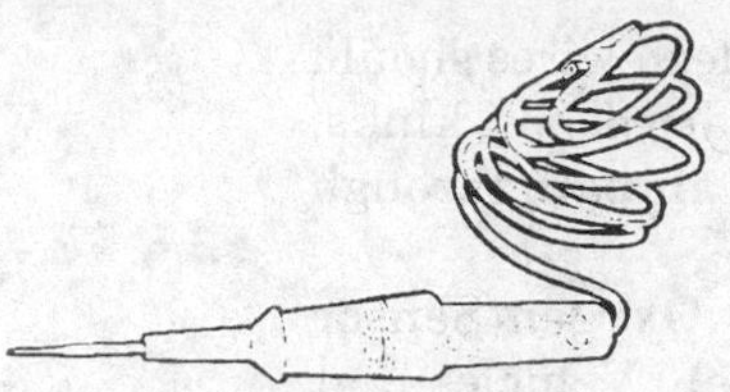

J 34142-B
Unpowered Test Light

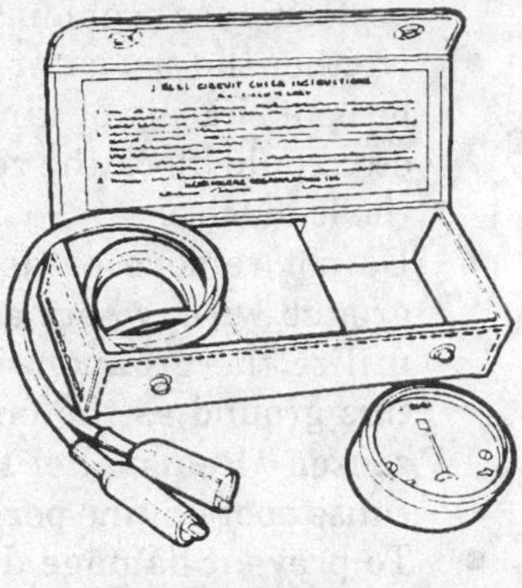

J 8681-A
Universal Short Checker

J 22727
Electrical Terminal Remover

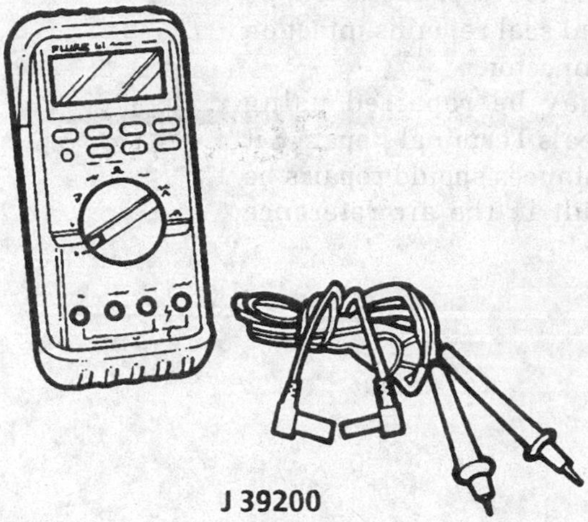

J 39200
Digital Multimeter

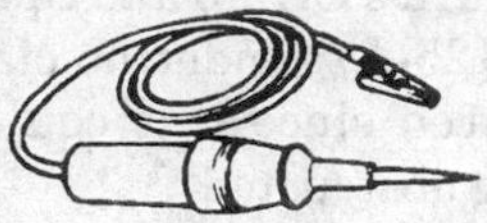

J 21008-A
Self-Powered Test Light

J 33095
Terminal Remover: Micro-Pack, Com-Pack III and ECM Edgeboard Connectors

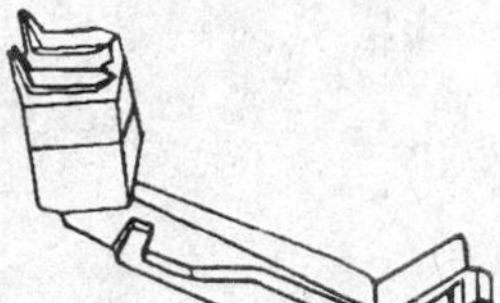

J 34764
Autofuse Tester

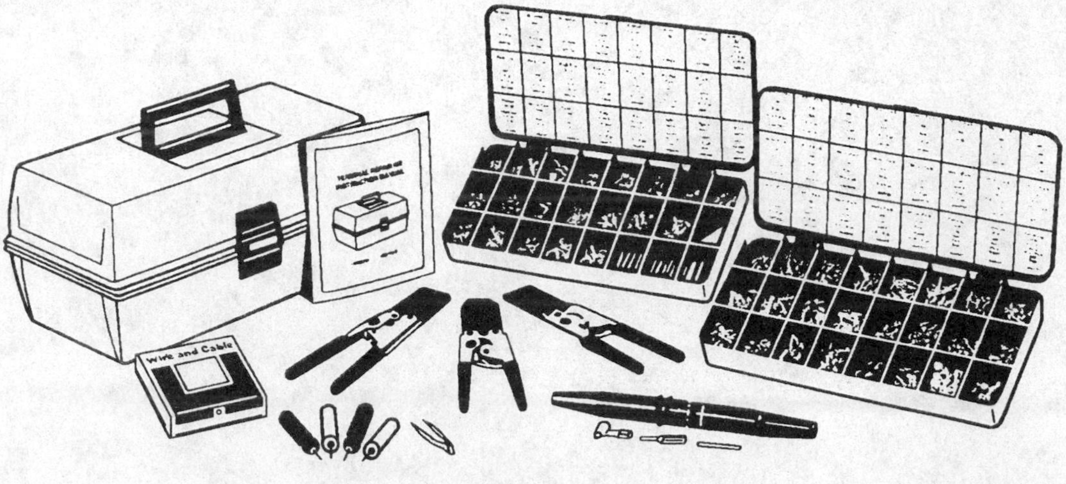
Wire and Cable

J 38125-A
Terminal Repair Kit

BLANK

POWER DISTRIBUTION

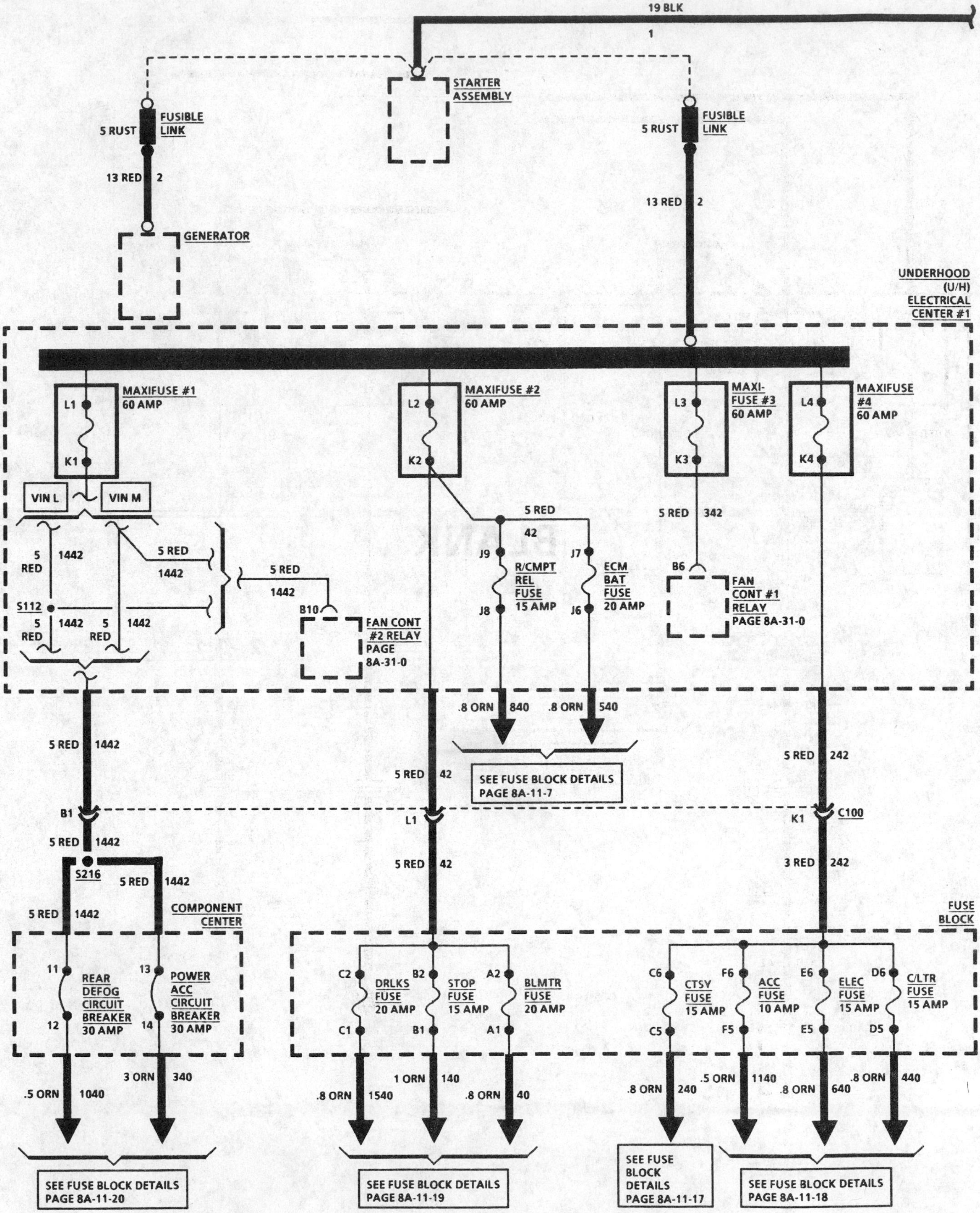
19 BLK
1
STARTER ASSEMBLY
5 RUST
FUSIBLE LINK
13 RED 2
GENERATOR
5 RUST
FUSIBLE LINK
13 RED 2
UNDERHOOD (U/H) ELECTRICAL CENTER #1
L1
K1
MAXIFUSE #1 60 AMP
L2
K2
MAXIFUSE #2 60 AMP
L3
K3
MAXI-FUSE #3 60 AMP
L4
K4
MAXIFUSE #4 60 AMP
VIN L
VIN M
5 RED 1442
5 RED 1442
5 RED 1442
S112
5 RED 1442
5 RED 1442
B10
FAN CONT #2 RELAY PAGE 8A-31-0
5 RED 42
J9
J8
R/CMPT REL FUSE 15 AMP
J7
J6
ECM BAT FUSE 20 AMP
5 RED 342
B6
FAN CONT #1 RELAY PAGE 8A-31-0
.8 ORN 840
.8 ORN 540
SEE FUSE BLOCK DETAILS PAGE 8A-11-7
5 RED 1442
5 RED 42
5 RED 242
B1
L1
K1
C100
5 RED 1442
5 RED 42
3 RED 242
S216
5 RED 1442
5 RED 1442
COMPONENT CENTER
11
12
REAR DEFOG CIRCUIT BREAKER 30 AMP
13
14
POWER ACC CIRCUIT BREAKER 30 AMP
FUSE BLOCK
C2
C1
DRLKS FUSE 20 AMP
B2
B1
STOP FUSE 15 AMP
A2
A1
BLMTR FUSE 20 AMP
C6
C5
CTSY FUSE 15 AMP
F6
F5
ACC FUSE 10 AMP
E6
E5
ELEC FUSE 15 AMP
D6
D5
C/LTR FUSE 15 AMP
.5 ORN 1040
3 ORN 340
.8 ORN 1540
1 ORN 140
.8 ORN 40
.8 ORN 240
.5 ORN 1140
.8 ORN 640
.8 ORN 440
SEE FUSE BLOCK DETAILS PAGE 8A-11-20
SEE FUSE BLOCK DETAILS PAGE 8A-11-19
SEE FUSE BLOCK DETAILS PAGE 8A-11-17
SEE FUSE BLOCK DETAILS PAGE 8A-11-18

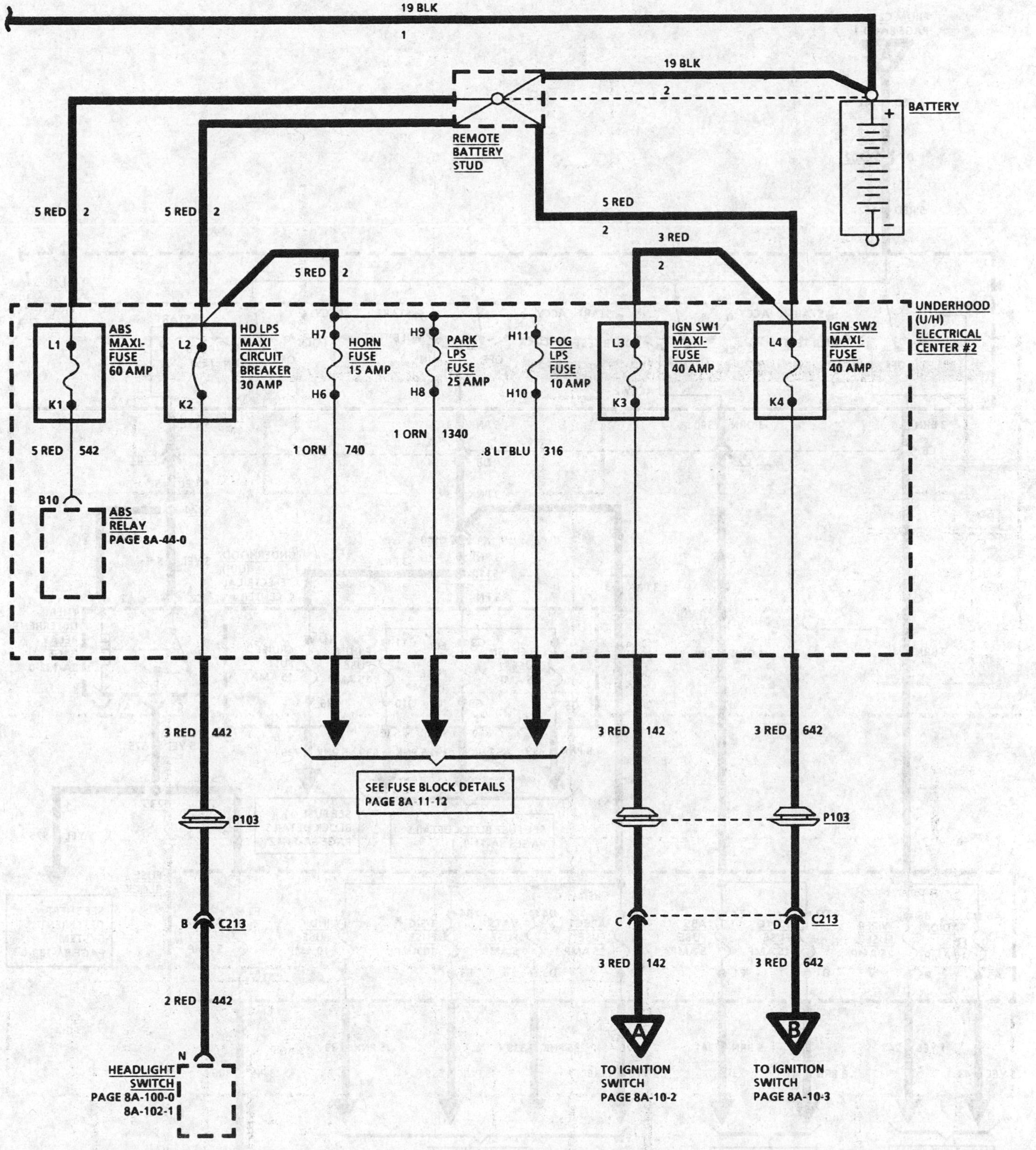

19 BLK
1
19 BLK
2
BATTERY
REMOTE BATTERY STUD
5 RED 2
5 RED 2
5 RED
2
3 RED
2
5 RED 2
UNDERHOOD (U/H) ELECTRICAL CENTER #2
L1
K1
ABS MAXI-FUSE 60 AMP
L2
K2
HD LPS MAXI CIRCUIT BREAKER 30 AMP
H7
H6
HORN FUSE 15 AMP
H9
H8
PARK LPS FUSE 25 AMP
H11
H10
FOG LPS FUSE 10 AMP
L3
K3
IGN SW1 MAXI-FUSE 40 AMP
L4
K4
IGN SW2 MAXI-FUSE 40 AMP
5 RED 542
1 ORN 740
1 ORN 1340
.8 LT BLU 316
B10
ABS RELAY PAGE 8A-44-0
3 RED 442
SEE FUSE BLOCK DETAILS PAGE 8A-11-12
3 RED 142
3 RED 642
P103
P103
B
C213
C
D
C213
2 RED 442
3 RED 142
3 RED 642
N
HEADLIGHT SWITCH PAGE 8A-100-0 8A-102-1
A
B
TO IGNITION SWITCH PAGE 8A-10-2
TO IGNITION SWITCH PAGE 8A-10-3

POWER DISTRIBUTION

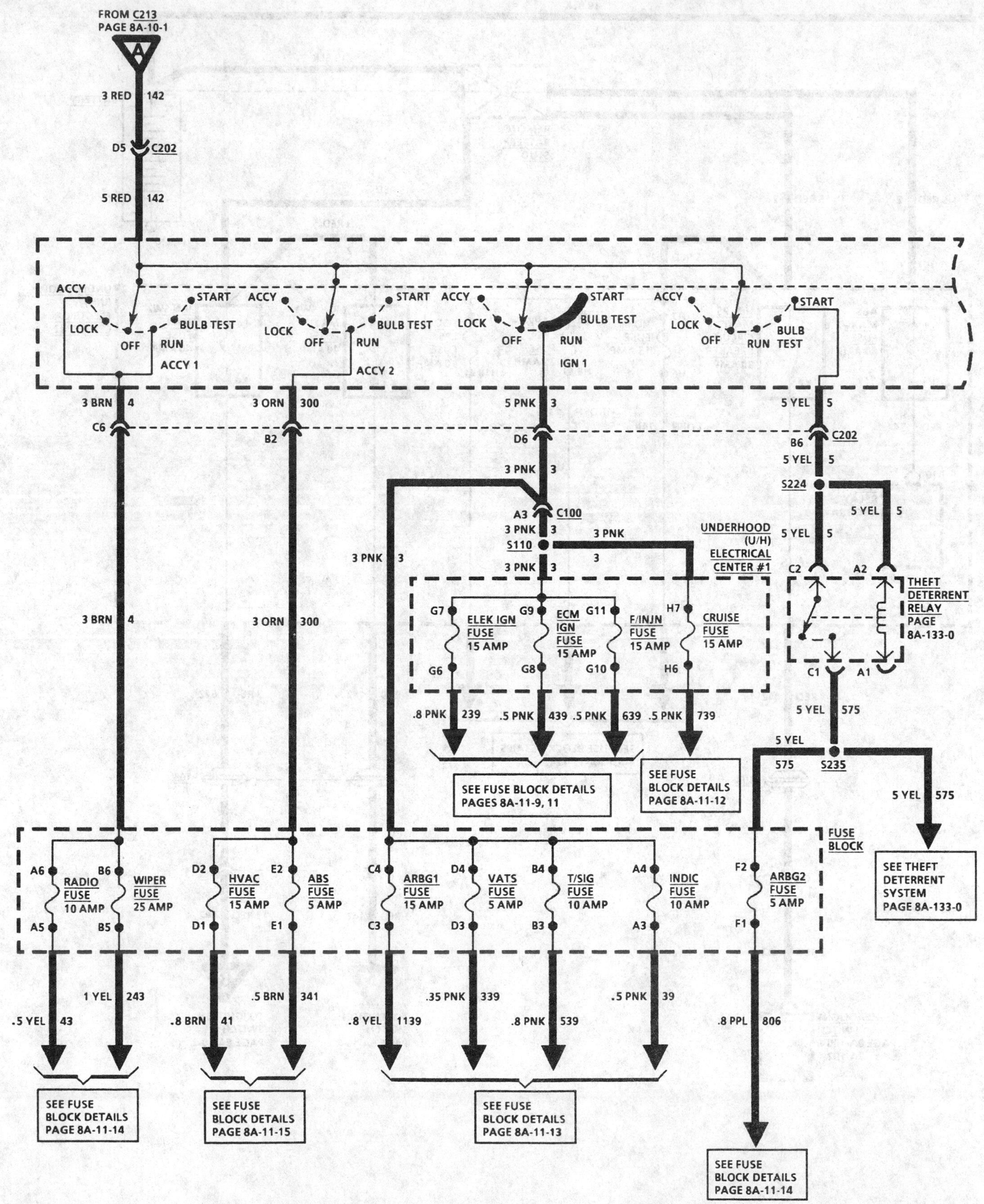
FROM C213
PAGE 8A-10-1
A
3 RED 142
D5 C202
5 RED 142
ACCY
LOCK
OFF
RUN
START
BULB TEST
ACCY 1
ACCY 2
IGN 1
BULB
TEST
3 BRN 4
C6
3 ORN 300
B2
5 PNK 3
D6
3 PNK 3
A3 C100
S110
3 PNK
3
5 YEL 5
B6 C202
S224
UNDERHOOD
(U/H)
ELECTRICAL
CENTER #1
C2
A2
THEFT
DETERRENT
RELAY
PAGE
8A-133-0
C1
A1
G7
ELEK IGN
FUSE
15 AMP
G6
G9
ECM
IGN
FUSE
15 AMP
G8
G11
F/INJN
FUSE
15 AMP
G10
H7
CRUISE
FUSE
15 AMP
H6
.8 PNK 239
.5 PNK 439
.5 PNK 639
.5 PNK 739
5 YEL 575
S235
SEE FUSE BLOCK DETAILS
PAGES 8A-11-9, 11
SEE FUSE
BLOCK DETAILS
PAGE 8A-11-12
FUSE
BLOCK
SEE THEFT
DETERRENT
SYSTEM
PAGE 8A-133-0
A6
RADIO
FUSE
10 AMP
A5
B6
WIPER
FUSE
25 AMP
B5
D2
HVAC
FUSE
15 AMP
D1
E2
ABS
FUSE
5 AMP
E1
C4
ARBG1
FUSE
15 AMP
C3
D4
VATS
FUSE
5 AMP
D3
B4
T/SIG
FUSE
10 AMP
B3
A4
INDIC
FUSE
10 AMP
A3
F2
ARBG2
FUSE
5 AMP
F1
1 YEL 243
.5 YEL 43
.5 BRN 341
.8 BRN 41
.35 PNK 339
.8 YEL 1139
.8 PNK 539
.5 PNK 39
.8 PPL 806
SEE FUSE
BLOCK DETAILS
PAGE 8A-11-14
SEE FUSE
BLOCK DETAILS
PAGE 8A-11-15
SEE FUSE
BLOCK DETAILS
PAGE 8A-11-13
SEE FUSE
BLOCK DETAILS
PAGE 8A-11-14

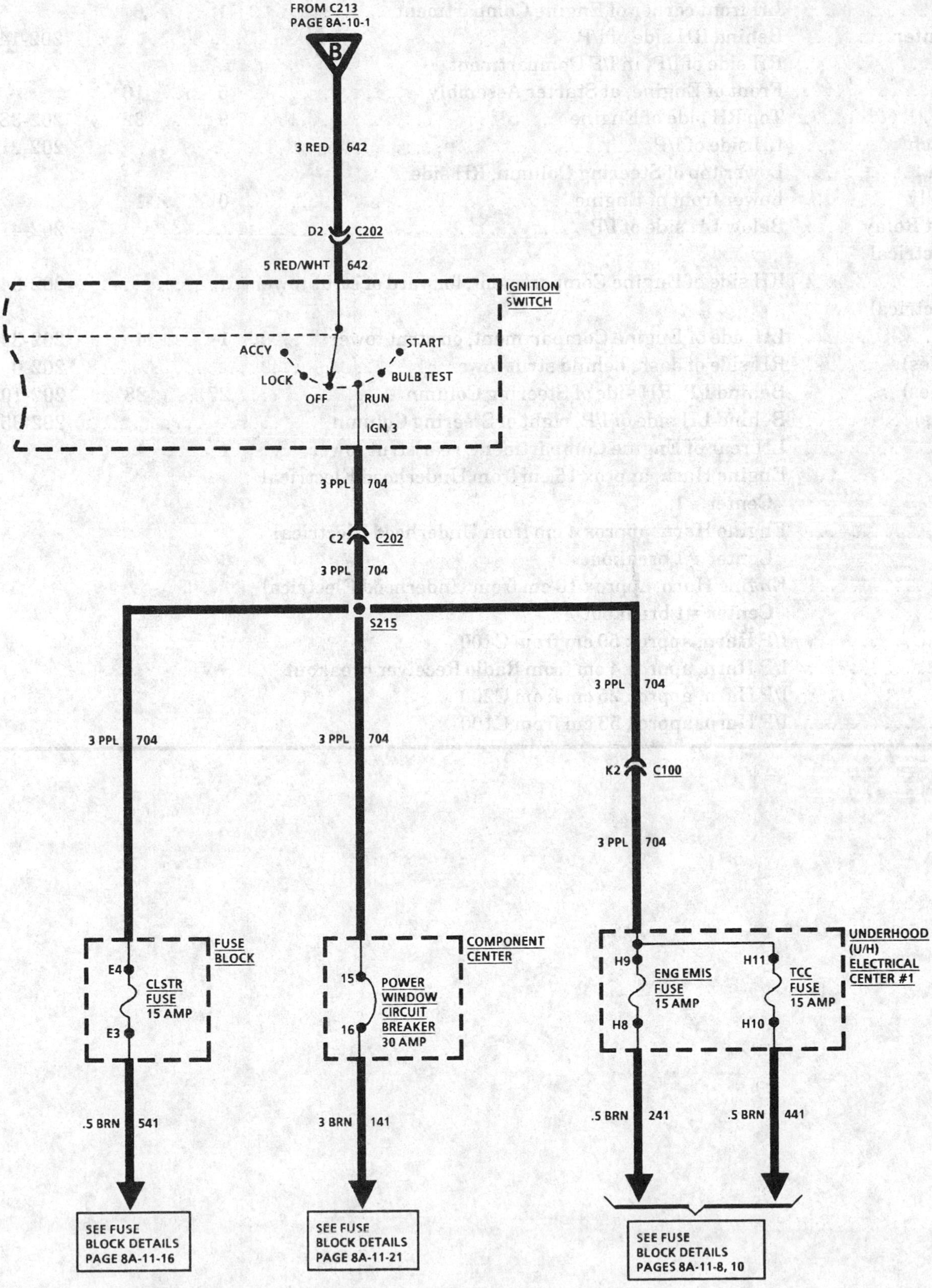
FROM C213
PAGE 8A-10-1
B
3 RED 642
D2 C202
5 RED/WHT 642
IGNITION
SWITCH
ACCY
START
LOCK
BULB TEST
OFF
RUN
IGN 3
3 PPL 704
C2 C202
3 PPL 704
S215
3 PPL 704
3 PPL 704
3 PPL 704
3 PPL 704
K2 C100
3 PPL 704
FUSE
BLOCK
E4
CLSTR
FUSE
15 AMP
E3
COMPONENT
CENTER
15
POWER
WINDOW
CIRCUIT
BREAKER
30 AMP
16
UNDERHOOD
(U/H)
ELECTRICAL
CENTER #1
H9
ENG EMIS
FUSE
15 AMP
H8
H11
TCC
FUSE
15 AMP
H10
.5 BRN 541
3 BRN 141
.5 BRN 241
.5 BRN 441
SEE FUSE
BLOCK DETAILS
PAGE 8A-11-16
SEE FUSE
BLOCK DETAILS
PAGE 8A-11-21
SEE FUSE
BLOCK DETAILS
PAGES 8A-11-8, 10

POWER DISTRIBUTION

COMPONENT	LOCATION	201-PG	FIG.	CONN
Battery	LH front corner of Engine Compartment	1	6	
Component Center	Behind RH side of I/P			202-14
Fuse Block	RH side of I/P, in I/P Compartment			
Fusible Link	Front of Engine, at Starter Assembly	5	16	
Generator	Top RH side of Engine	9	32	202-38
Headlight Switch	LH side of I/P			202-21
Ignition Switch	Lower top of Steering Column, RH side			
Starter Assembly	Lower front of Engine	0	1	
Theft Deterrent Relay	Below LH side of I/P			202-41
Underhood Electrical Center #1	RH side of Engine Compartment, forward of strut tower			202-34
Underhood Electrical Center #2	LH side of Engine Compartment, on strut tower	1	4	202-34
C100 (36 cavities)	RH side of dash, behind strut tower			202-0
C202 (48 cavities)	Behind I/P, RH side of Steering Column	27	88	202-10
C213 (4 cavities)	Behind LH side of I/P, right of Steering Column			202-35
P103	LH rear of Engine Compartment, rear strut tower	1	4	
S110 (VIN L)	Engine Harn, approx 16 cm from Underhood Electrical Center #1			
S110 (VIN M)	Engine Harn, approx 4 cm from Underhood Electrical Center #1 breakout			
S112 (VIN M)	Engine Harn, approx 10 cm from Underhood Electrical Center #1 breakout			
S215	I/P Harn, approx 59 cm from C100			
S216	I/P Harn, approx 4 cm from Radio Receiver breakout			
S224	I/P Harn, approx 25 cm from C200			
S235	I/P Harn, approx 53 cm from C100			

BLANK

FUSE BLOCK DETAILS
UNDERHOOD ELECTRICAL CENTER #1

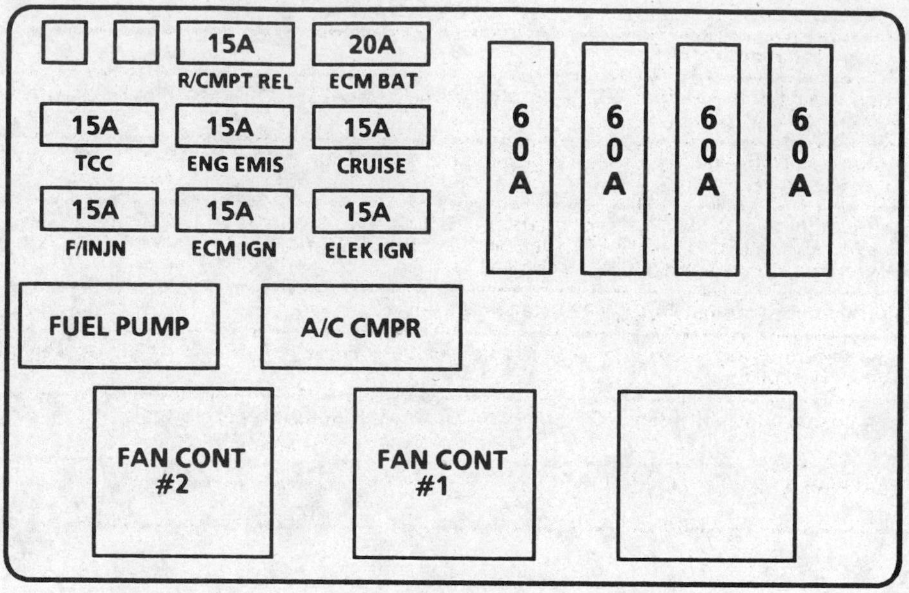
15A
R/CMPT REL
20A
ECM BAT
15A
TCC
15A
ENG EMIS
15A
CRUISE
15A
F/INJN
15A
ECM IGN
15A
ELEK IGN
60A
60A
60A
60A
FUEL PUMP
A/C CMPR
FAN CONT #2
FAN CONT #1

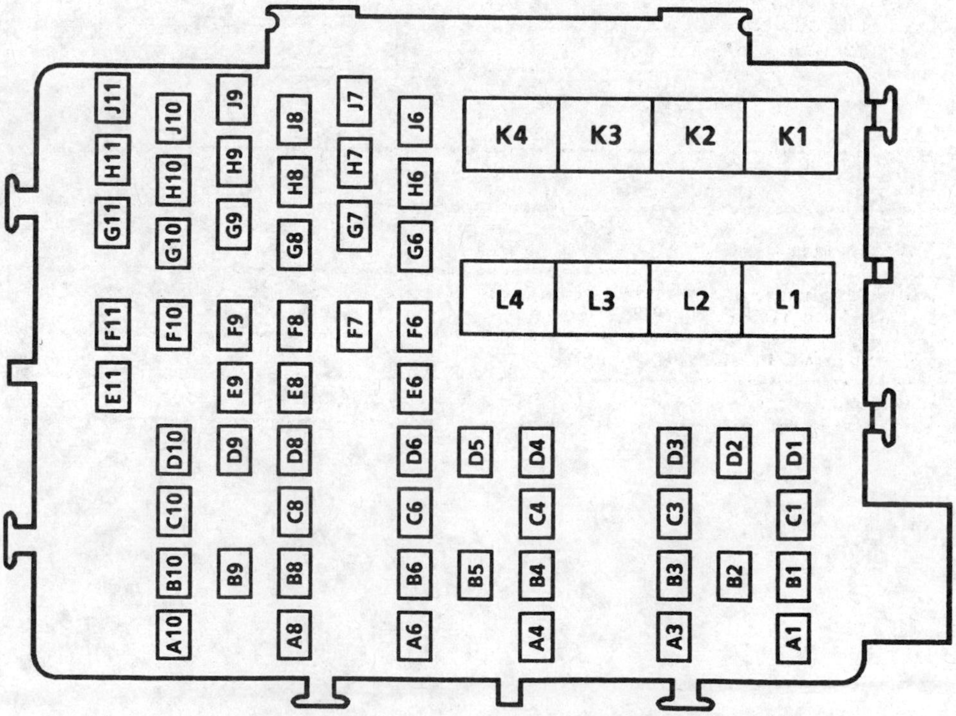
J11
J10
J9
J8
J7
J6
H11
H10
H9
H8
H7
H6
G11
G10
G9
G8
G7
G6
K4
K3
K2
K1
L4
L3
L2
L1
F11
F10
F9
F8
F7
F6
E11
E9
E8
E6
D10
D9
D8
D6
D5
D4
D3
D2
D1
C10
C8
C6
C4
C3
C1
B10
B9
B8
B6
B5
B4
B3
B2
B1
A10
A8
A6
A4
A3
A1

UNDERHOOD (U/H) ELECTRICAL CENTER #1

MINIFUSE	DESCRIPTION	PAGE
R/CMPT REL	Transaxle Range Switch	8A-11-7
ECM BAT	Powertrain Control Module (PCM), Fuel Pump/Oil Pressure Switch, Fuel Pump Relay, FAN CONT #1 Relay	8A-11-7
TCC	Automatic Transaxle, Transaxle Range Switch (w/VIN M only)	8A-11-8, 8A-11-10
ENG EMIS	Generator, Digital Exhaust Recirculation (DEGR) Valve, Evaporative Emissions (EVAP) Canister Purge Valve Solenoid, Heated Oxygen Sensor, FAN CONT #2 Relay, A/C CMPR Relay (VIN M only), Powertrain Control Module (VIN L only)	8A-11-8, 8A-11-10
CRUISE	Cruise Control Module, A/C CMPR Relay (VIN L only)	8A-11-12
F/INJN	Fuel Injectors, High Resolution 24X Crankshaft Position Sensor (VIN M only), Camshaft Position Sensor (VIN M only)	8A-11-9, 8A-11-11
ECM IGN	Powertrain Control Module (PCM), Mass Air Flow (MAF) Sensor (VIN L only)	8A-11-9, 8A-11-11
ELEK IGN	Electronic Ignition (EI) Control Module	8A-11-9, 8A-11-11

RELAY	DESCRIPTION	PAGE
FUEL PUMP	Fuel Pump Relay	8A-20-2, 8A-21-2
A/C CMPR	A/C Compressor Relay	8A-64-1
FAN CONT #1	Primary Cooling Fan	8A-31-0
FAN CONT #2	Secondary Cooling Fan	8A-31-0

MAXIFUSE	DESCRIPTION	PAGE
1	60 amp power to FAN CONT #2 Relay, Component Center: REAR DEFOG Circuit Breaker, POWER ACC Circuit Breaker	8A-10-0
2	60 amp power to Underhood Electrical Center #1: R/CMPT REL Fuse, ECM BAT Fuse, I/P Fuse Block: BLMTR Fuse, STOP Fuse, DRLKS Fuse	8A-10-0
3	60 amp power to FAN CONT #1 Relay	8A-10-0
4	60 amp power to I/P Fuse Block: CTSY Fuse, C/LTR Fuse, ELEC Fuse, ACC Fuse	8A-10-0

FUSE BLOCK DETAILS
UNDERHOOD ELECTRICAL CENTER #2

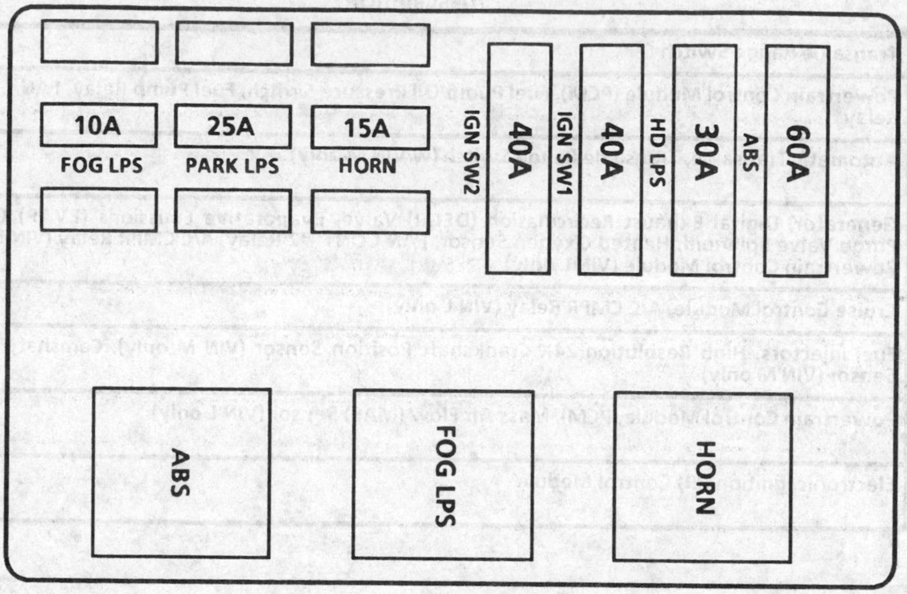
10A
FOG LPS
25A
PARK LPS
15A
HORN
IGN SW2
40A
IGN SW1
40A
HD LPS
30A
ABS
60A
ABS
FOG LPS
HORN

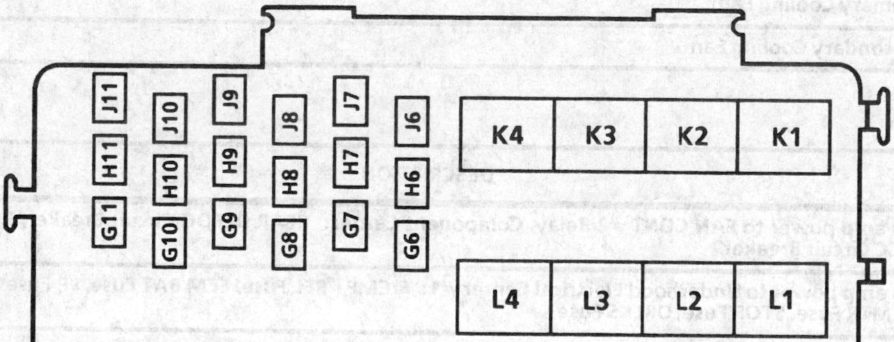
J11
H11
G11
J10
H10
G10
J9
H9
G9
J8
H8
G8
J7
H7
G7
J6
H6
G6
K4
K3
K2
K1
L4
L3
L2
L1
D10
C10
B10
A10
D9
B9
D8
C8
B8
A8
D6
C6
B6
A6
D5
B5
D4
C4
B4
A4
D3
C3
B3
A3
D2
B2
D1
C1
B1
A1

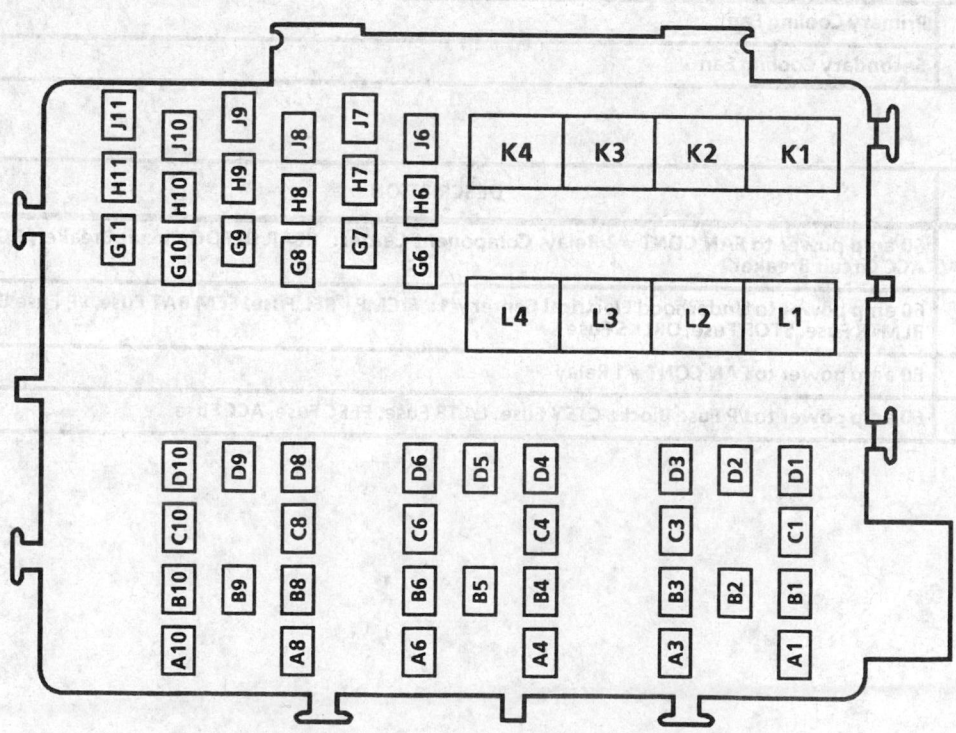

UNDERHOOD (U/H) ELECTRICAL CENTER #2

MINIFUSE	DESCRIPTION	PAGE
FOG LPS	FOG LPS Relay	8A-11-12
PARK LPS	Headlight Switch	8A-11-12
HORN	HORN Relay, Underhood Light	8A-11-12

RELAY	DESCRIPTION	PAGE
ABS	Anti Lock Brake System Relay	8A-44-0
FOG LPS	Fog Lamp Relay	8A-100-0, 8A-102-1
HORN	Horn Relay	8A-40-0

MAXIFUSE	DESCRIPTION	PAGE
ABS	60 amp power to ABS Relay	8A-10-1
HD LPS	30 amp circuit breaker to Headlight Switch	8A-10-1
IGN SW1	40 amp power to I/P Fuse Block: RADIO Fuse, WIPER Fuse, HVAC Fuse, ABS Fuse, INDIC Fuse, T/SIG Fuse, ARBG1 Fuse, VATS Fuse, Underhood Electrical Center #1: CRUISE Fuse, F/INJN Fuse, ECM IGN Fuse, ELEK IGN Fuse, Theft Deterrent Relay	8A-10-1
IGN SW2	40 amp power to Underhood Electrical Center #1: TCC Fuse, ENG EMIS Fuse, I/P Fuse Block: CLSTR Fuse, Component Center: Power Window Circuit Breaker	8A-10-1

FUSE BLOCK DETAILS

INSTRUMENT PANEL (I/P) FUSE BLOCK

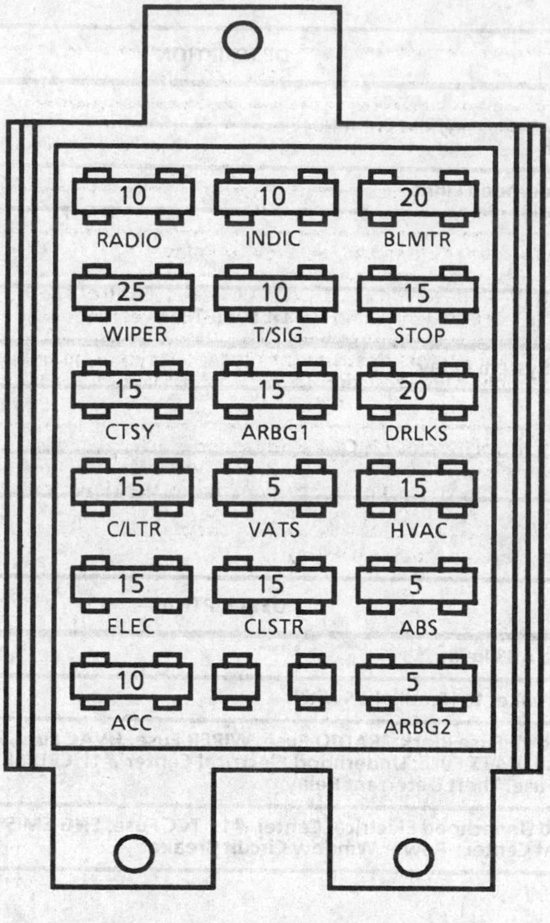
10
RADIO
10
INDIC
20
BLMTR
25
WIPER
10
T/SIG
15
STOP
15
CTSY
15
ARBG1
20
DRLKS
15
C/LTR
5
VATS
15
HVAC
15
ELEC
15
CLSTR
5
ABS
10
ACC
5
ARBG2

INSTRUMENT PANEL (I/P) FUSE BLOCK

AUTOFUSE	DESCRIPTION	PAGE
RADIO	Radio Receiver, Steering Wheel Radio Switches, Radio Control Interface Module	8A-11-14
INDIC	Headlight Switch, Diagnostic Energy Reserve Module (DERM), ABS Lamp Driver Module, Daytime Running Lamps Module (w/DRL), TCC/Brake Switch, Cruise Control Cut-Out Switch, Instrument Cluster, Component Center: Chime Module, Rear Defogger Timer Relay	8A-11-13
BLMTR	Component Center: A/C HI Blower Relay	8A-11-19
WIPER	Wiper/Washer Switch	8A-11-14
T/SIG	Turn Signal Flasher	8A-11-13
STOP	Component Center: Hazard Flasher, TCC/Brake Switch	8A-11-19
CTSY	Vanity Mirror Lights, I/P Compartment Light, I/P Courtesy Lights, Trunk Courtesy Light, I/S Lighted Mirror, Rear Courtesy Lights, Dome/Reading Light, Cigar Lighter, Door Courtesy Lights, Dome Light	8A-11-17
ARBG1	Diagnostic Energy Reserve Module (DERM), Arming Sensor	8A-11-13

(CONTINUED ON NEXT PAGE)

(CONTINUED FROM PREVIOUS PAGE)

AUTOFUSE	DESCRIPTION	PAGE
DR LKS	Power Door Lock Relay, Keyless Entry Receiver	8A-11-19
C/LTR	Console Cigar Lighter	8A-11-18
VATS	Theft Deterrent Module	8A-11-13
HVAC	Solenoid Box, Component Center: A/C LO Blower Relay	8A-11-15
ELEC	Component Center: Chime Module, Electronic Brake Control Module (EBCM),Theft Deterrent Module, Radio, Passive Restraint Timer Relay, Low Oil Level Module	8A-11-18
CLSTR	Air Temperature Valve Motors, Instrument Cluster, Daytime Running Lights Module (w/DRL), HVAC Control Assembly, Multi-Function Lever, Heated Oxygen Sensor #2, Passenger Temperature Control	8A-11-16
ABS	Electronic Brake Control Module (EBCM), Underhood Electrical Center #2, ABS Relay	8A-11-15
ACC	Antenna Relay, Outside Mirror Control Switch, Front Window/Door Lock Switches, Front Door Handle Switches	8A-11-18
ARBG2	Diagnostic Energy Reserve Module (DERM)	8A-11-14

FUSE BLOCK DETAILS
COMPONENT CENTER

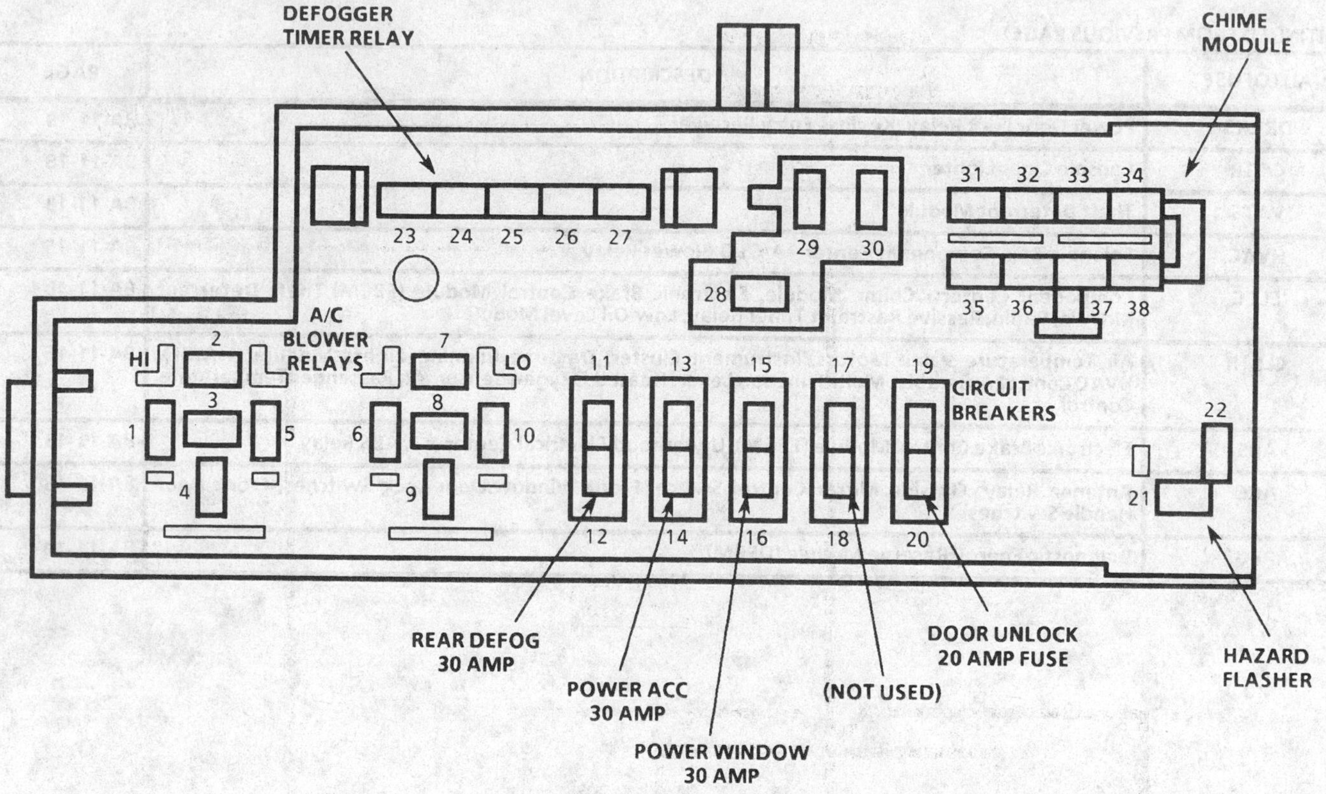
DEFOGGER TIMER RELAY
CHIME MODULE
23 24 25 26 27
29 30
31 32 33 34
35 36 37 38
28
A/C BLOWER RELAYS
HI
LO
1 2 3 4 5 6 7 8 9 10
11 13 15 17 19
12 14 16 18 20
CIRCUIT BREAKERS
21 22
REAR DEFOG 30 AMP
POWER ACC 30 AMP
POWER WINDOW 30 AMP
(NOT USED)
DOOR UNLOCK 20 AMP FUSE
HAZARD FLASHER

COMPONENT CENTER

AUTOFUSE	DESCRIPTION	PAGE
DOOR UNLOCK	Door Lock Relay	8A-11-21

CIRCUIT BREAKER	DESCRIPTION	PAGE
REAR DEFOG	Component Center: Rear Defogger Timer Relay	8A-11-20
POWER ACC	LH Power Seat Switch, RH Power Seat Switch	8A-11-20
POWER WINDOW	LH Master Switch Assembly, RH Switch Assembly, Sunroof Switch	8A-11-21

RELAY	DESCRIPTION	PAGE
A	A/C HI Blower Relay	8A-63-1
B	A/C LO Blower Relay	8A-63-0

FUSE BLOCK DETAILS
ECM BAT AND R/CMPT REL FUSES

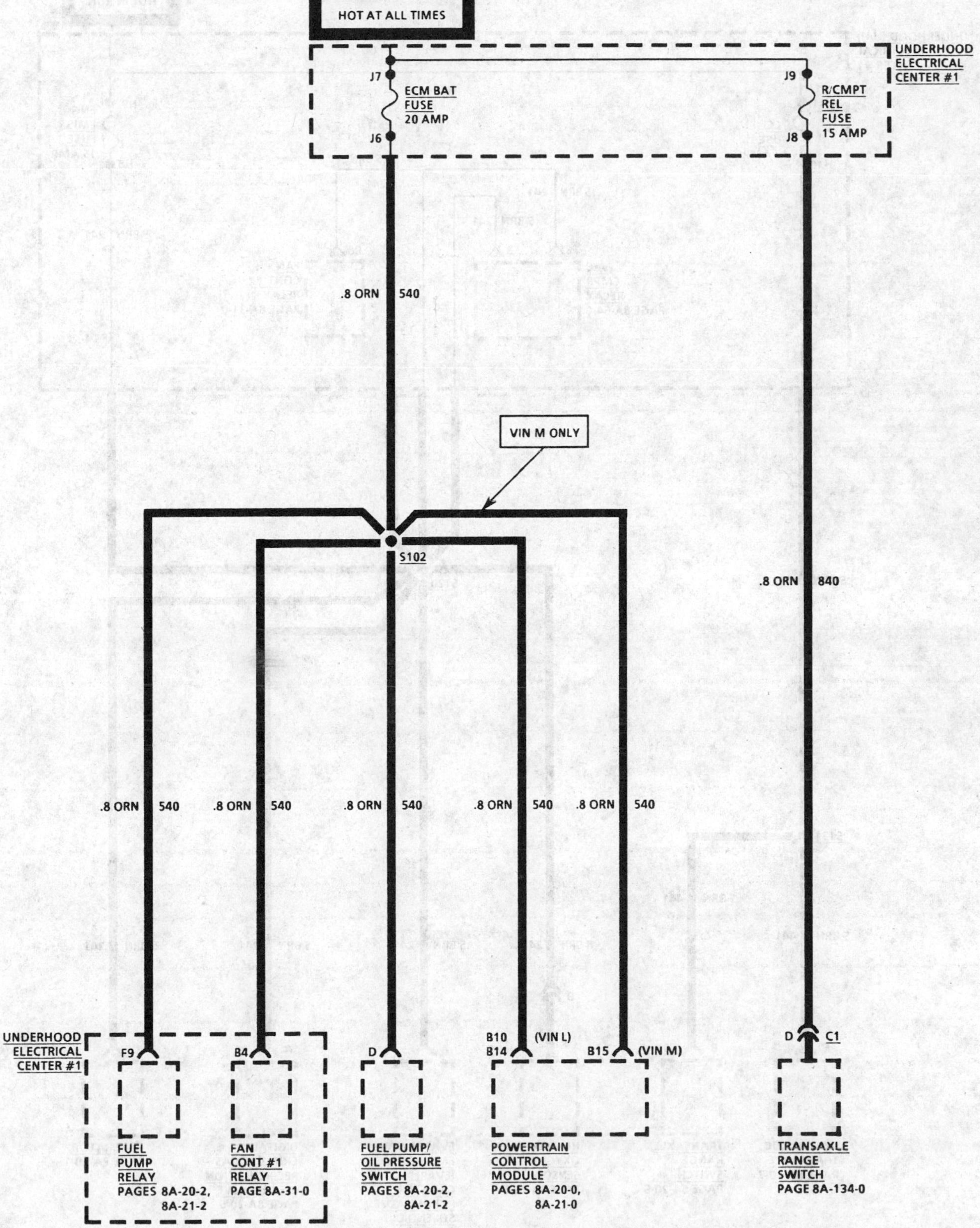

HOT AT ALL TIMES
UNDERHOOD ELECTRICAL CENTER #1
J7
ECM BAT FUSE 20 AMP
J6
J9
R/CMPT REL FUSE 15 AMP
J8
.8 ORN 540
VIN M ONLY
S102
.8 ORN 840
.8 ORN 540
.8 ORN 540
.8 ORN 540
.8 ORN 540
.8 ORN 540
UNDERHOOD ELECTRICAL CENTER #1
F9
B4
D
B10 B14 (VIN L)
B15 (VIN M)
D C1
FUEL PUMP RELAY PAGES 8A-20-2, 8A-21-2
FAN CONT #1 RELAY PAGE 8A-31-0
FUEL PUMP/ OIL PRESSURE SWITCH PAGES 8A-20-2, 8A-21-2
POWERTRAIN CONTROL MODULE PAGES 8A-20-0, 8A-21-0
TRANSAXLE RANGE SWITCH PAGE 8A-134-0

FUSE BLOCK DETAILS
TCC AND ENG EMIS FUSES
VIN M

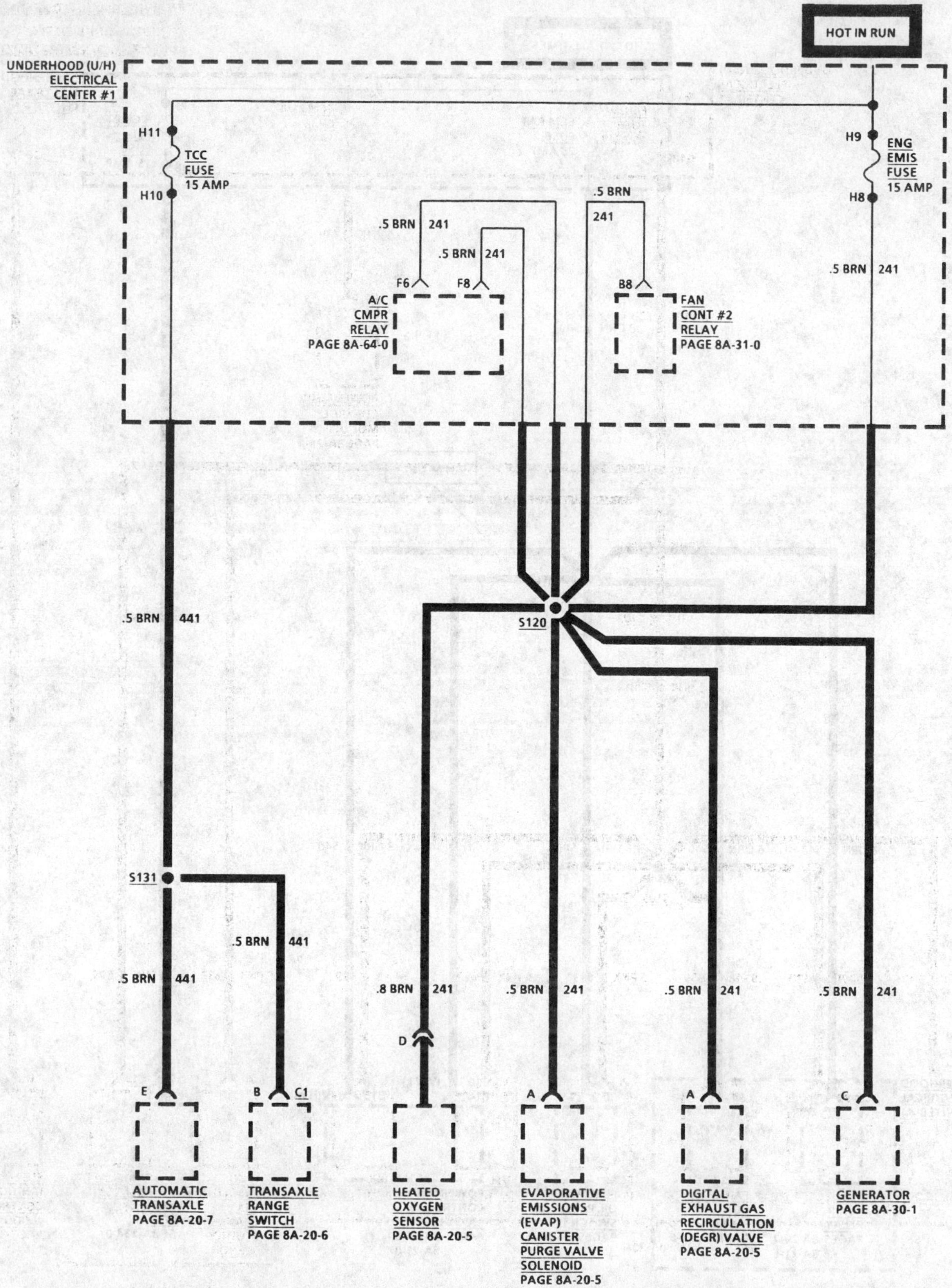
HOT IN RUN
UNDERHOOD (U/H) ELECTRICAL CENTER #1
H11
TCC FUSE 15 AMP
H10
H9
ENG EMIS FUSE 15 AMP
H8
.5 BRN 241
.5 BRN 241
.5 BRN
241
.5 BRN 241
F6
F8
B8
A/C CMPR RELAY PAGE 8A-64-0
FAN CONT #2 RELAY PAGE 8A-31-0
.5 BRN 441
S120
S131
.5 BRN 441
.5 BRN 441
.8 BRN 241
.5 BRN 241
.5 BRN 241
.5 BRN 241
D
E
B
C1
A
A
C
AUTOMATIC TRANSAXLE PAGE 8A-20-7
TRANSAXLE RANGE SWITCH PAGE 8A-20-6
HEATED OXYGEN SENSOR PAGE 8A-20-5
EVAPORATIVE EMISSIONS (EVAP) CANISTER PURGE VALVE SOLENOID PAGE 8A-20-5
DIGITAL EXHAUST GAS RECIRCULATION (DEGR) VALVE PAGE 8A-20-5
GENERATOR PAGE 8A-30-1

FUSE BLOCK DETAILS
F/INJN, ECM IGN AND ELEK IGN FUSES
VIN M

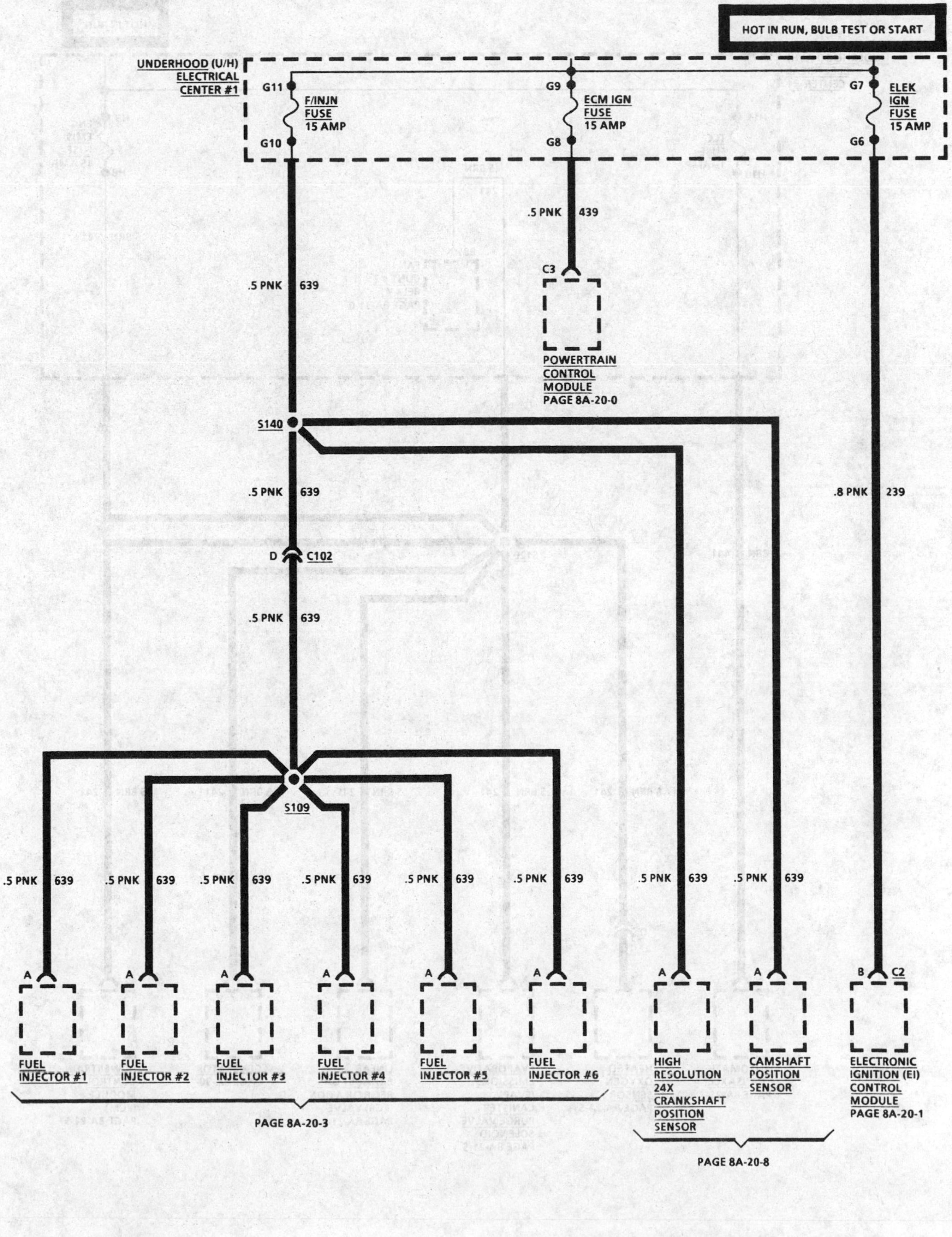
HOT IN RUN, BULB TEST OR START
UNDERHOOD (U/H) ELECTRICAL CENTER #1
G11
F/INJN FUSE 15 AMP
G10
G9
ECM IGN FUSE 15 AMP
G8
G7
ELEK IGN FUSE 15 AMP
G6
.5 PNK 439
C3
POWERTRAIN CONTROL MODULE
PAGE 8A-20-0
.5 PNK 639
S140
.5 PNK 639
.8 PNK 239
D C102
.5 PNK 639
S109
.5 PNK 639
A
FUEL INJECTOR #1
FUEL INJECTOR #2
FUEL INJECTOR #3
FUEL INJECTOR #4
FUEL INJECTOR #5
FUEL INJECTOR #6
HIGH RESOLUTION 24X CRANKSHAFT POSITION SENSOR
CAMSHAFT POSITION SENSOR
B C2
ELECTRONIC IGNITION (EI) CONTROL MODULE
PAGE 8A-20-1
PAGE 8A-20-3
PAGE 8A-20-8

FUSE BLOCK DETAILS
TCC AND ENG EMIS FUSES
VIN L

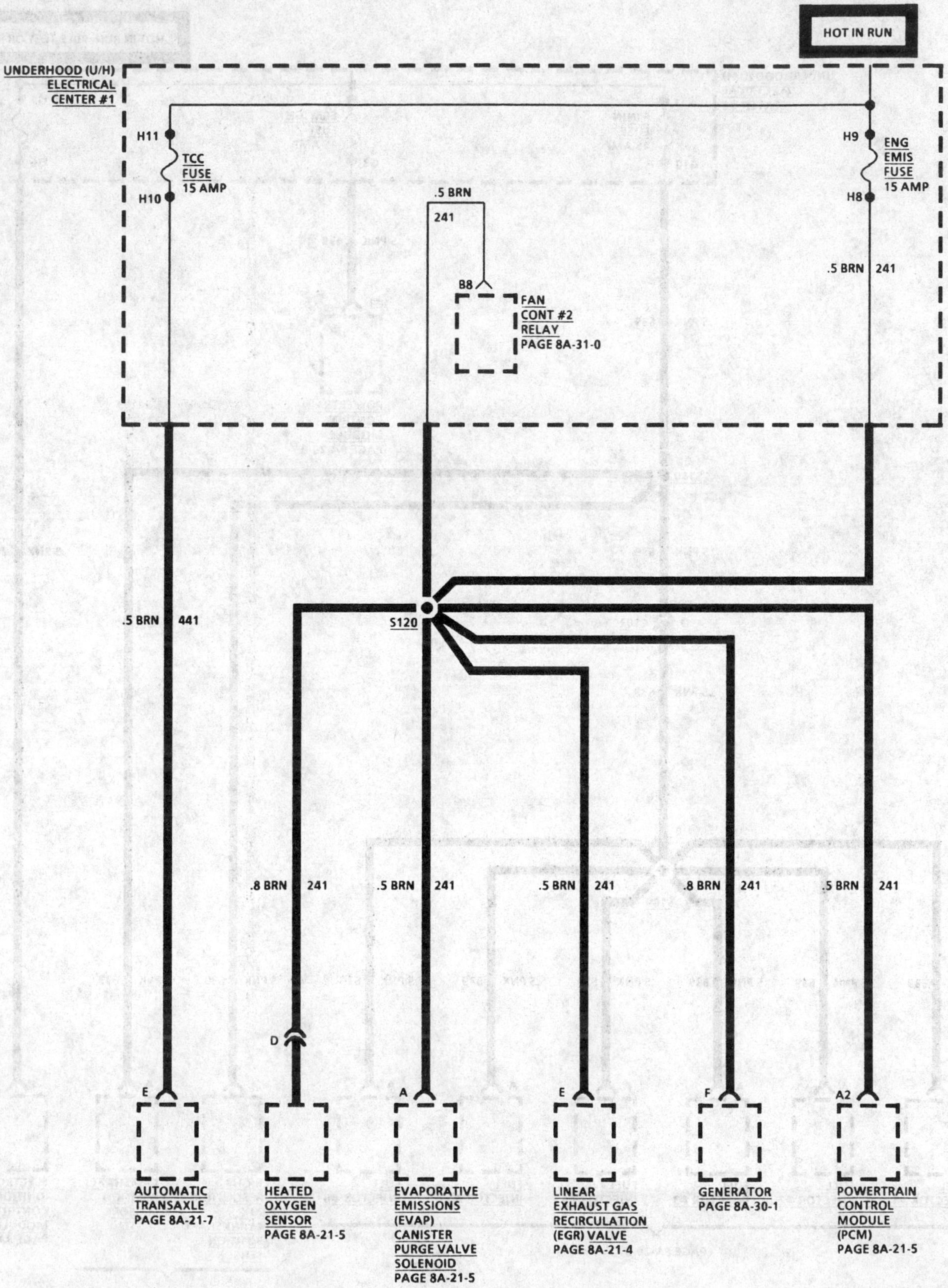
HOT IN RUN
UNDERHOOD (U/H) ELECTRICAL CENTER #1
H11
TCC FUSE 15 AMP
H10
H9
ENG EMIS FUSE 15 AMP
H8
.5 BRN
241
B8
FAN CONT #2 RELAY PAGE 8A-31-0
.5 BRN 241
.5 BRN 441
S120
.8 BRN 241
.5 BRN 241
.5 BRN 241
.8 BRN 241
.5 BRN 241
D
E
A
E
F
A2
AUTOMATIC TRANSAXLE PAGE 8A-21-7
HEATED OXYGEN SENSOR PAGE 8A-21-5
EVAPORATIVE EMISSIONS (EVAP) CANISTER PURGE VALVE SOLENOID PAGE 8A-21-5
LINEAR EXHAUST GAS RECIRCULATION (EGR) VALVE PAGE 8A-21-4
GENERATOR PAGE 8A-30-1
POWERTRAIN CONTROL MODULE (PCM) PAGE 8A-21-5

FUSE BLOCK DETAILS
F/INJN, ECM IGN AND ELEK IGN FUSES
VIN L

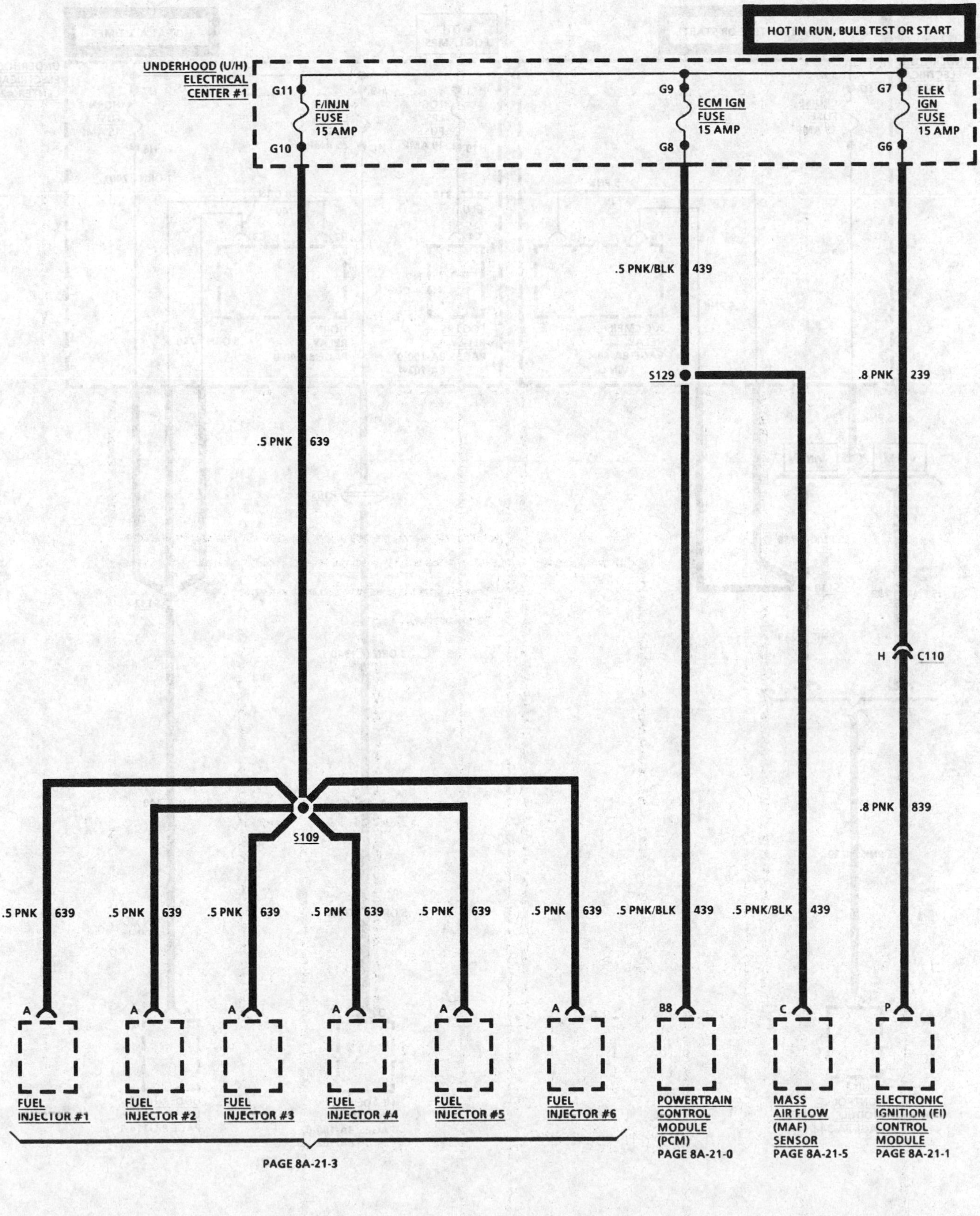

HOT IN RUN, BULB TEST OR START
UNDERHOOD (U/H) ELECTRICAL CENTER #1
G11
F/INJN FUSE 15 AMP
G10
G9
ECM IGN FUSE 15 AMP
G8
G7
ELEK IGN FUSE 15 AMP
G6
.5 PNK/BLK 439
S129
.8 PNK 239
.5 PNK 639
H C110
.8 PNK 839
S109
.5 PNK 639
.5 PNK 639
.5 PNK 639
.5 PNK 639
.5 PNK 639
.5 PNK 639
.5 PNK/BLK 439
.5 PNK/BLK 439
A
A
A
A
A
A
B8
C
P
FUEL INJECTOR #1
FUEL INJECTOR #2
FUEL INJECTOR #3
FUEL INJECTOR #4
FUEL INJECTOR #5
FUEL INJECTOR #6
POWERTRAIN CONTROL MODULE (PCM)
PAGE 8A-21-0
MASS AIR FLOW (MAF) SENSOR
PAGE 8A-21-5
ELECTRONIC IGNITION (EI) CONTROL MODULE
PAGE 8A-21-1
PAGE 8A-21-3

FUSE BLOCK DETAILS
CRUISE, FOG LPS, PARK LPS AND HORN FUSES

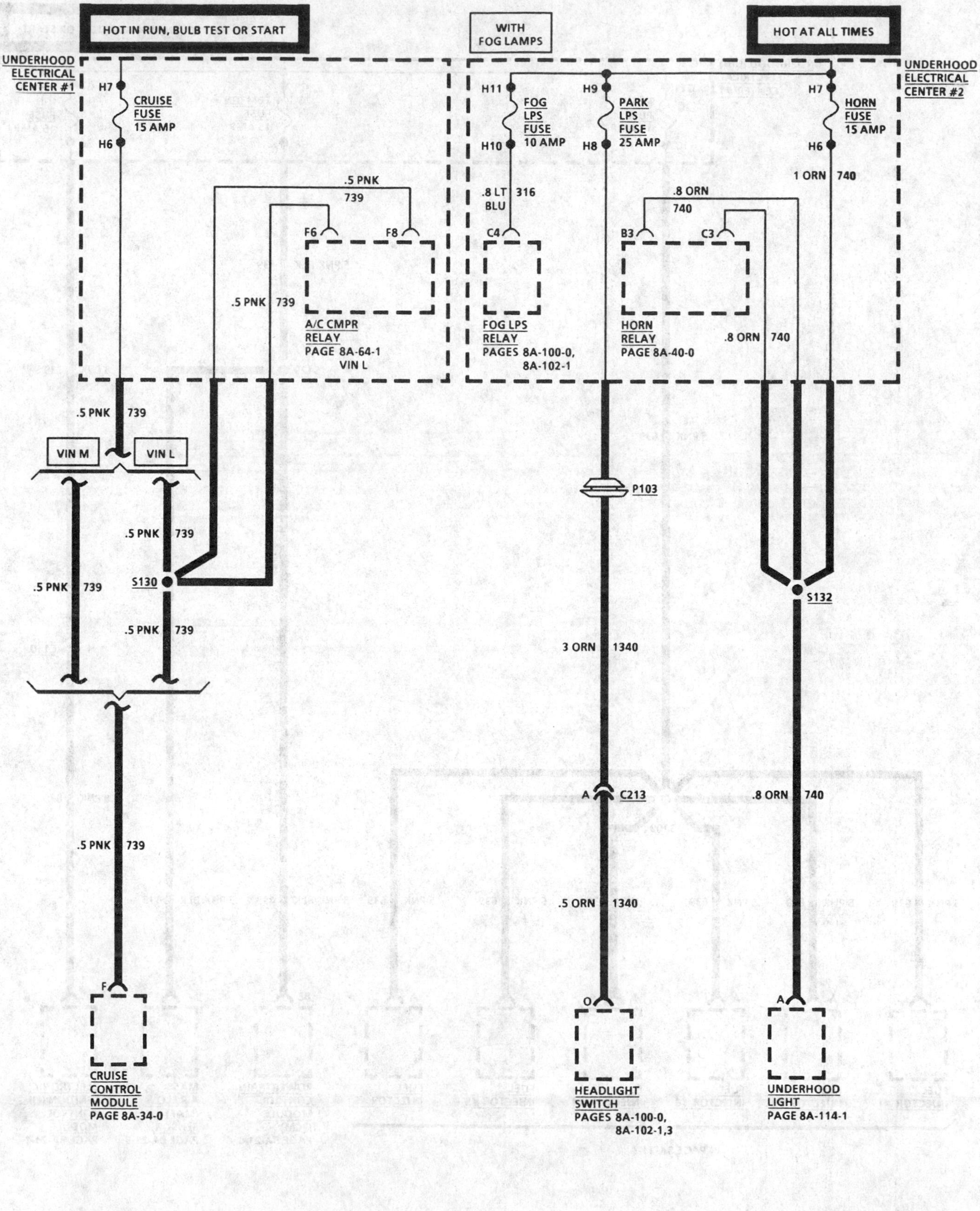
HOT IN RUN, BULB TEST OR START
WITH FOG LAMPS
HOT AT ALL TIMES
UNDERHOOD ELECTRICAL CENTER #1
H7
CRUISE FUSE 15 AMP
H6
.5 PNK 739
F6
F8
A/C CMPR RELAY
PAGE 8A-64-1
VIN L
VIN M
VIN L
S130
CRUISE CONTROL MODULE
PAGE 8A-34-0
F
H11
FOG LPS FUSE 10 AMP
H10
.8 LT BLU 316
C4
FOG LPS RELAY
PAGES 8A-100-0, 8A-102-1
H9
PARK LPS FUSE 25 AMP
H8
P103
3 ORN 1340
A
C213
.5 ORN 1340
O
HEADLIGHT SWITCH
PAGES 8A-100-0, 8A-102-1,3
UNDERHOOD ELECTRICAL CENTER #2
H7
HORN FUSE 15 AMP
H6
1 ORN 740
.8 ORN 740
B3
C3
HORN RELAY
PAGE 8A-40-0
S132
A
UNDERHOOD LIGHT
PAGE 8A-114-1

FUSE BLOCK DETAILS
VATS, T/SIG, INDIC AND ARBG1 FUSES

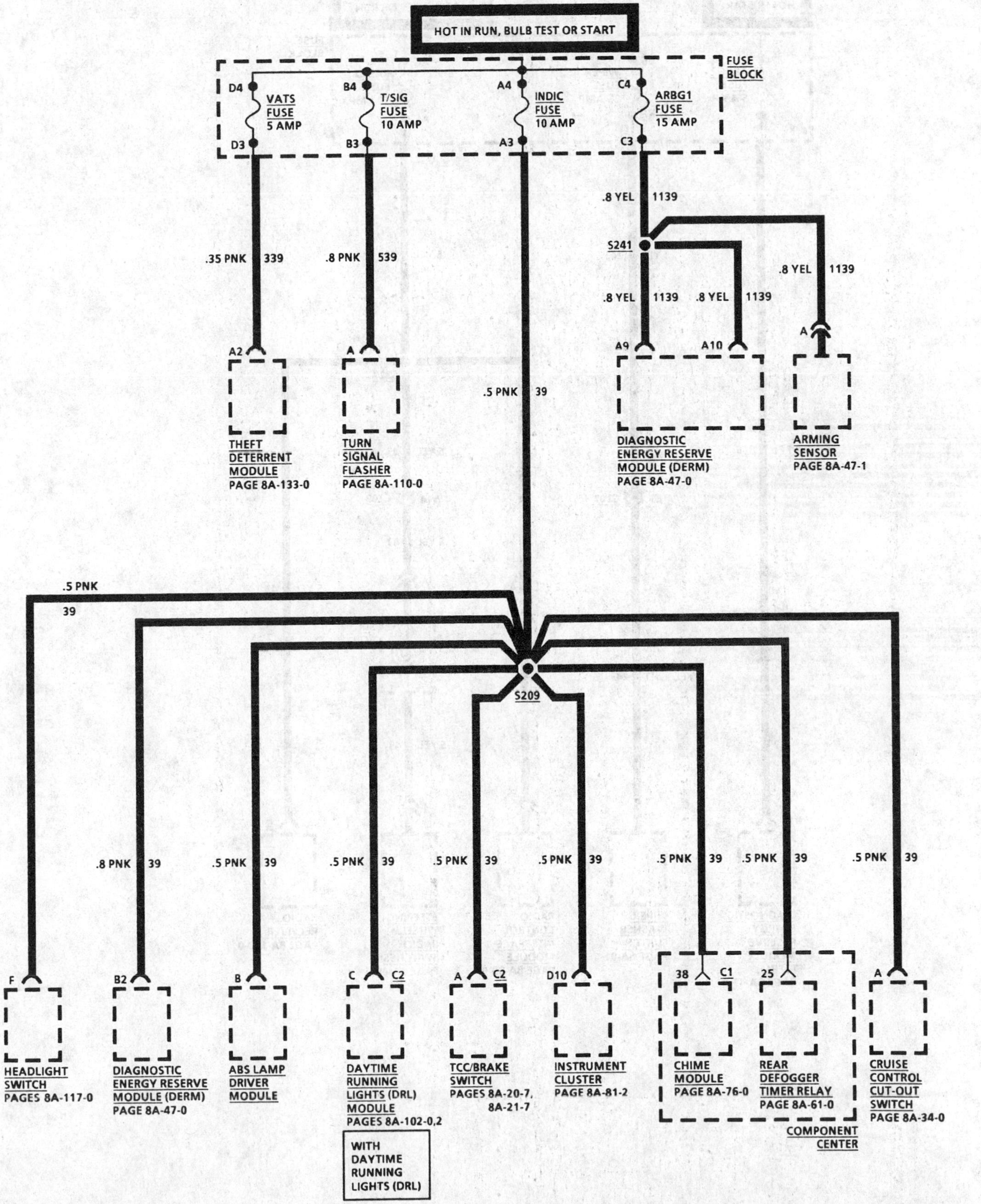
HOT IN RUN, BULB TEST OR START
FUSE BLOCK
D4
VATS FUSE 5 AMP
D3
B4
T/SIG FUSE 10 AMP
B3
A4
INDIC FUSE 10 AMP
A3
C4
ARBG1 FUSE 15 AMP
C3
.8 YEL 1139
S241
.35 PNK 339
.8 PNK 539
.8 YEL 1139
.8 YEL 1139
.8 YEL 1139
A2
A
THEFT DETERRENT MODULE PAGE 8A-133-0
TURN SIGNAL FLASHER PAGE 8A-110-0
.5 PNK 39
A9
A10
DIAGNOSTIC ENERGY RESERVE MODULE (DERM) PAGE 8A-47-0
A
ARMING SENSOR PAGE 8A-47-1
.5 PNK
39
S209
.8 PNK 39
.5 PNK 39
.5 PNK 39
.5 PNK 39
.5 PNK 39
.5 PNK 39
.5 PNK 39
.5 PNK 39
F
HEADLIGHT SWITCH PAGES 8A-117-0
B2
DIAGNOSTIC ENERGY RESERVE MODULE (DERM) PAGE 8A-47-0
B
ABS LAMP DRIVER MODULE
C C2
DAYTIME RUNNING LIGHTS (DRL) MODULE PAGES 8A-102-0,2
WITH DAYTIME RUNNING LIGHTS (DRL)
A C2
TCC/BRAKE SWITCH PAGES 8A-20-7, 8A-21-7
D10
INSTRUMENT CLUSTER PAGE 8A-81-2
38 C1
CHIME MODULE PAGE 8A-76-0
25
REAR DEFOGGER TIMER RELAY PAGE 8A-61-0
COMPONENT CENTER
A
CRUISE CONTROL CUT-OUT SWITCH PAGE 8A-34-0

FUSE BLOCK DETAILS
ARBG2, WIPER AND RADIO FUSES

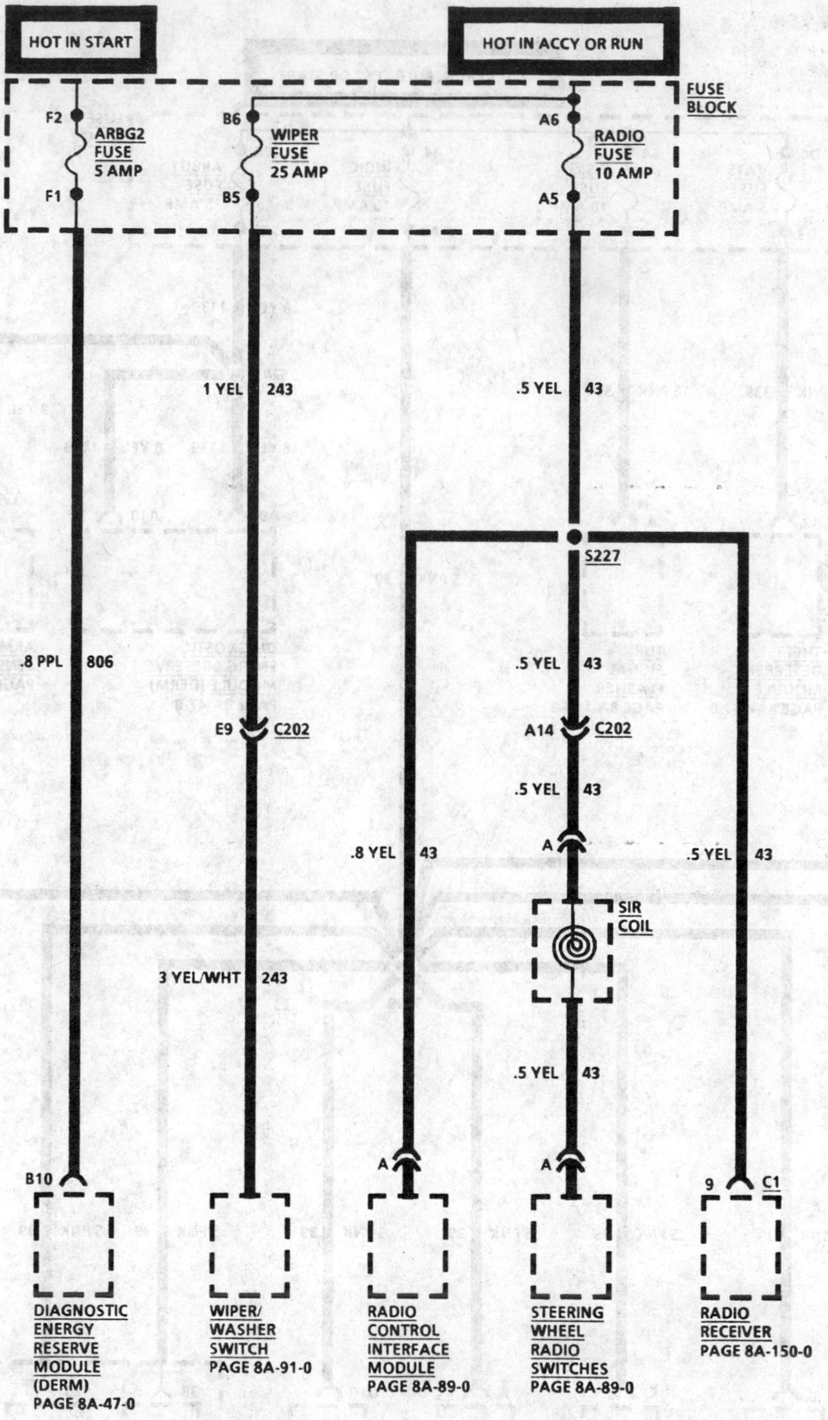

HOT IN START
HOT IN ACCY OR RUN
FUSE BLOCK
F2
ARBG2 FUSE 5 AMP
F1
B6
WIPER FUSE 25 AMP
B5
A6
RADIO FUSE 10 AMP
A5
1 YEL 243
.5 YEL 43
S227
.8 PPL 806
.5 YEL 43
E9
C202
A14
C202
.5 YEL 43
.8 YEL 43
A
.5 YEL 43
SIR COIL
3 YEL/WHT 243
.5 YEL 43
B10
A
A
9
C1
DIAGNOSTIC ENERGY RESERVE MODULE (DERM) PAGE 8A-47-0
WIPER/ WASHER SWITCH PAGE 8A-91-0
RADIO CONTROL INTERFACE MODULE PAGE 8A-89-0
STEERING WHEEL RADIO SWITCHES PAGE 8A-89-0
RADIO RECEIVER PAGE 8A-150-0

FUSE BLOCK DETAILS
HVAC AND ABS FUSES

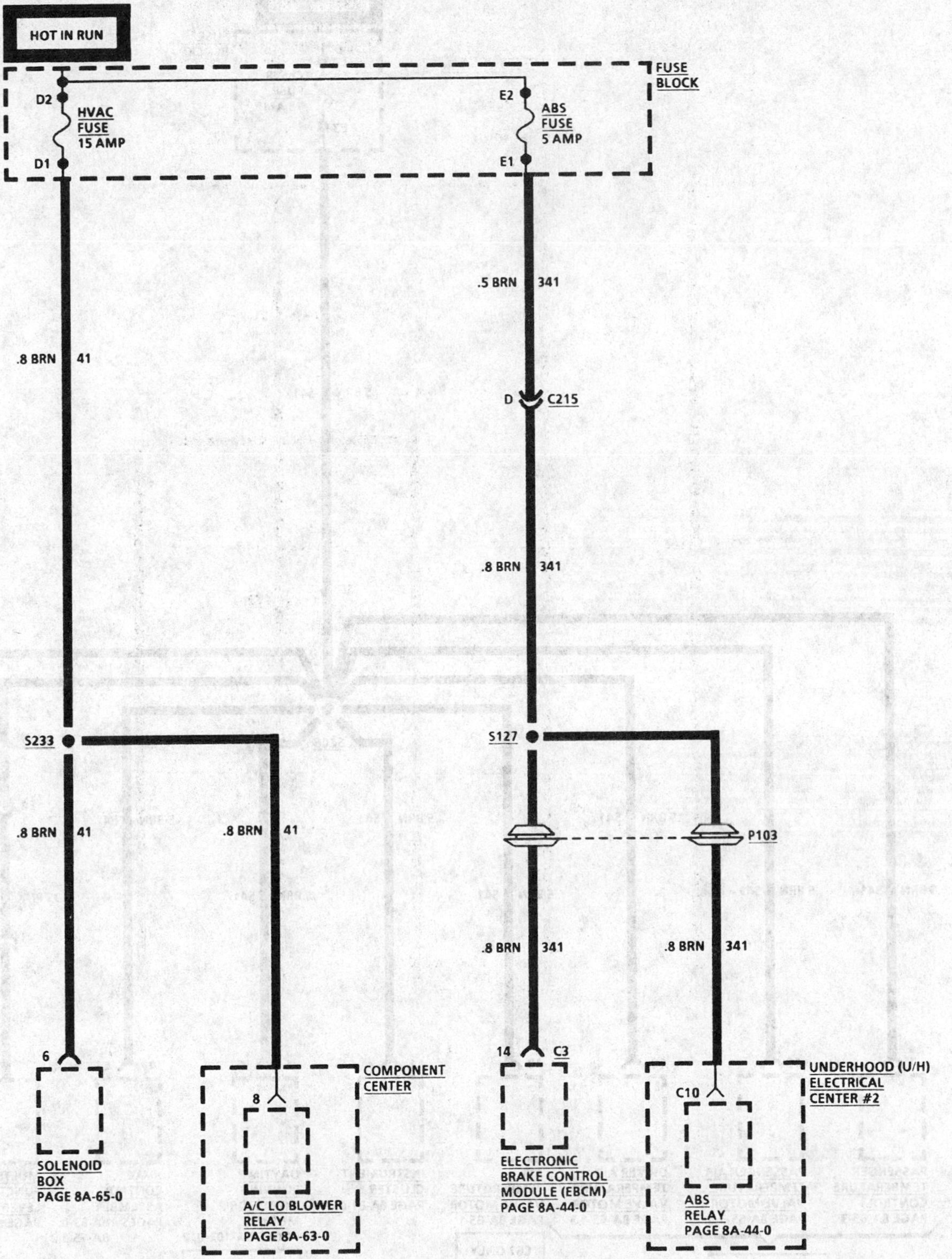
HOT IN RUN
FUSE BLOCK
D2
HVAC FUSE 15 AMP
D1
E2
ABS FUSE 5 AMP
E1
.5 BRN 341
.8 BRN 41
D C215
.8 BRN 341
S233
S127
.8 BRN 41
.8 BRN 41
P103
.8 BRN 341
.8 BRN 341
6
COMPONENT CENTER
8
14 C3
C10
UNDERHOOD (U/H) ELECTRICAL CENTER #2
SOLENOID BOX PAGE 8A-65-0
A/C LO BLOWER RELAY PAGE 8A-63-0
ELECTRONIC BRAKE CONTROL MODULE (EBCM) PAGE 8A-44-0
ABS RELAY PAGE 8A-44-0

FUSE BLOCK DETAILS
CLSTR FUSE

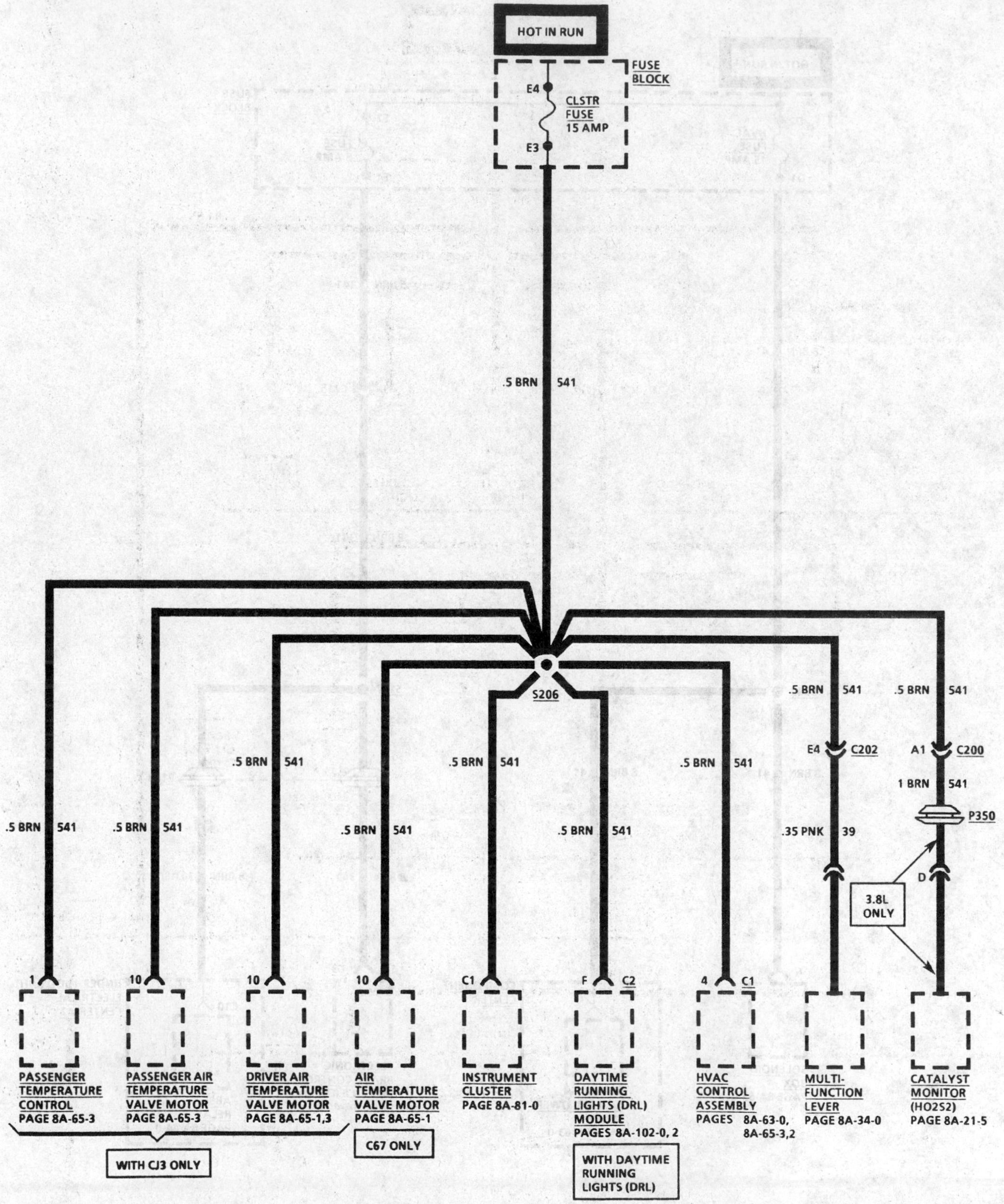

HOT IN RUN
FUSE BLOCK
E4
CLSTR FUSE 15 AMP
E3
.5 BRN 541
S206
.5 BRN 541
E4 C202
.35 PNK 39
A1 C200
1 BRN 541
P350
D
3.8L ONLY
1
10
10
10
C1
F C2
4 C1
PASSENGER TEMPERATURE CONTROL PAGE 8A-65-3
PASSENGER AIR TEMPERATURE VALVE MOTOR PAGE 8A-65-3
DRIVER AIR TEMPERATURE VALVE MOTOR PAGE 8A-65-1,3
AIR TEMPERATURE VALVE MOTOR PAGE 8A-65-1
INSTRUMENT CLUSTER PAGE 8A-81-0
DAYTIME RUNNING LIGHTS (DRL) MODULE PAGES 8A-102-0, 2
HVAC CONTROL ASSEMBLY PAGES 8A-63-0, 8A-65-3,2
MULTI-FUNCTION LEVER PAGE 8A-34-0
CATALYST MONITOR (HO2S2) PAGE 8A-21-5
WITH CJ3 ONLY
C67 ONLY
WITH DAYTIME RUNNING LIGHTS (DRL)

FUSE BLOCK DETAILS
CTSY FUSE

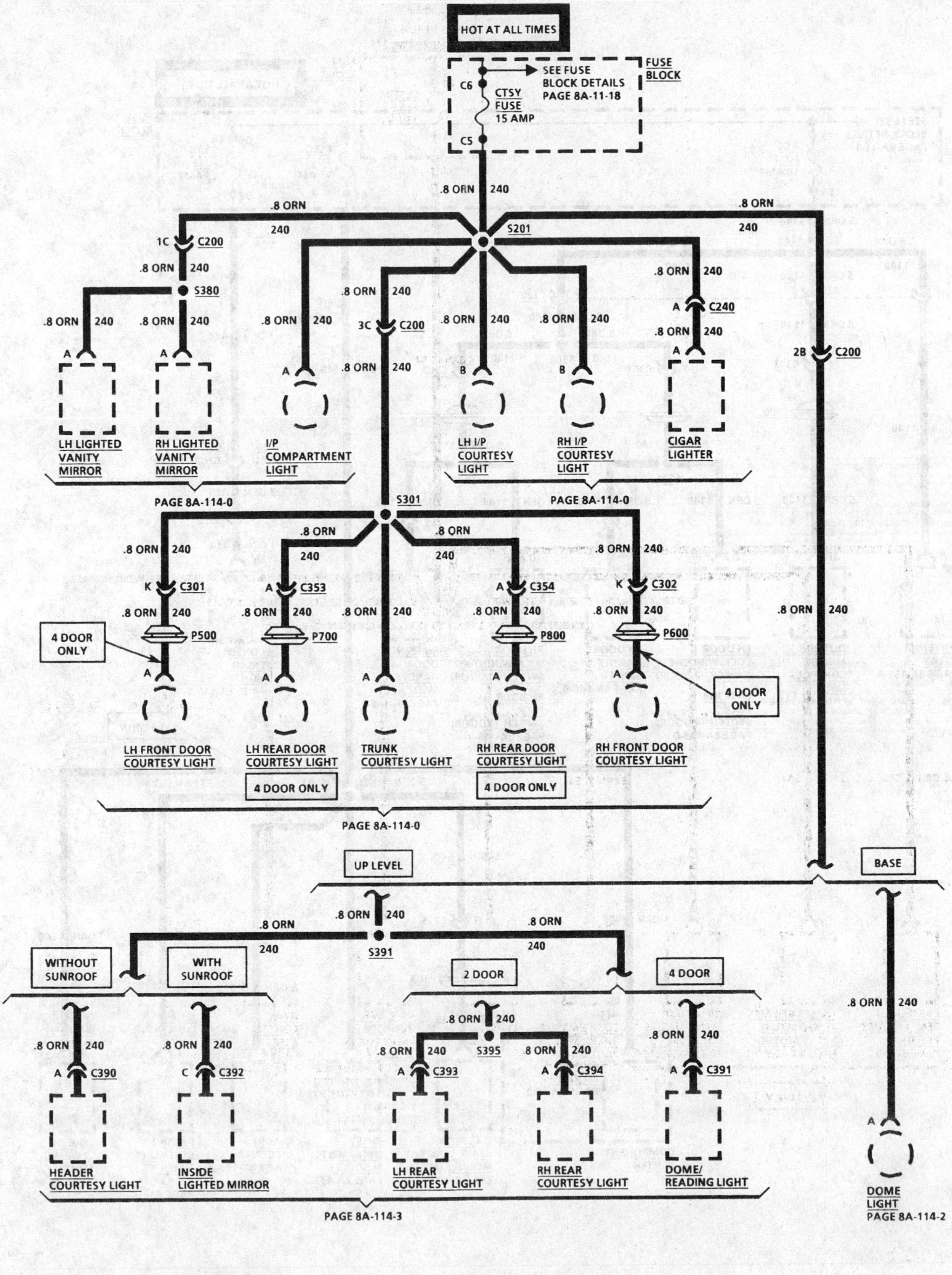

HOT AT ALL TIMES
FUSE BLOCK
SEE FUSE BLOCK DETAILS PAGE 8A-11-18
C6
CTSY FUSE 15 AMP
C5
.8 ORN 240
S201
1C C200
S380
LH LIGHTED VANITY MIRROR
RH LIGHTED VANITY MIRROR
I/P COMPARTMENT LIGHT
3C C200
LH I/P COURTESY LIGHT
RH I/P COURTESY LIGHT
A C240
CIGAR LIGHTER
2B C200
PAGE 8A-114-0
S301
K C301
A C353
A C354
K C302
P500
P700
P800
P600
4 DOOR ONLY
LH FRONT DOOR COURTESY LIGHT
LH REAR DOOR COURTESY LIGHT
TRUNK COURTESY LIGHT
RH REAR DOOR COURTESY LIGHT
RH FRONT DOOR COURTESY LIGHT
UP LEVEL
BASE
S391
WITHOUT SUNROOF
WITH SUNROOF
2 DOOR
4 DOOR
S395
A C390
C C392
A C393
A C394
A C391
HEADER COURTESY LIGHT
INSIDE LIGHTED MIRROR
LH REAR COURTESY LIGHT
RH REAR COURTESY LIGHT
DOME/ READING LIGHT
PAGE 8A-114-3
DOME LIGHT
PAGE 8A-114-2

FUSE BLOCK DETAILS
ACC, ELEC AND C/LTR FUSES

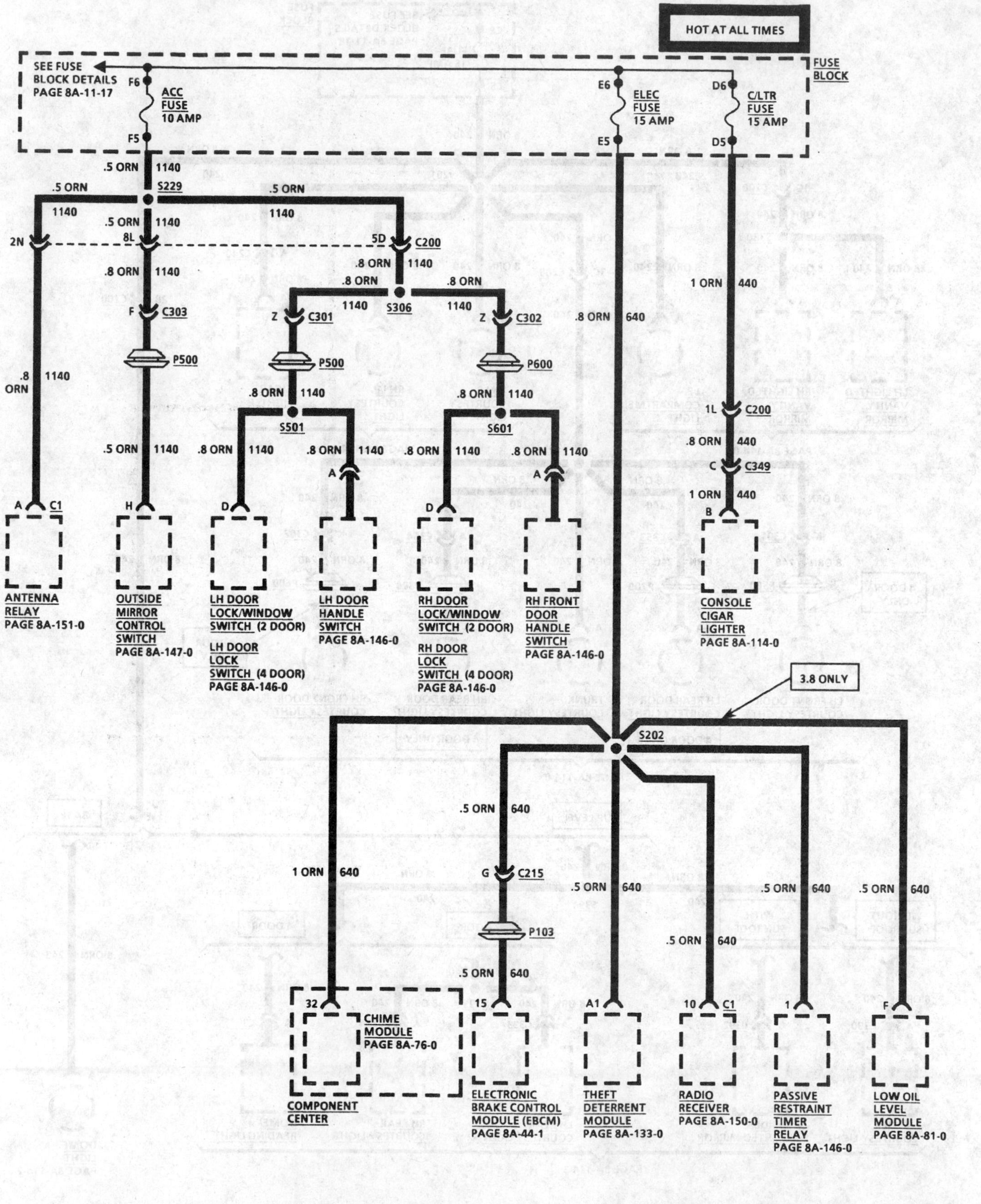
HOT AT ALL TIMES
SEE FUSE BLOCK DETAILS PAGE 8A-11-17
FUSE BLOCK
F6
ACC FUSE 10 AMP
F5
E6
ELEC FUSE 15 AMP
E5
D6
C/LTR FUSE 15 AMP
D5
.5 ORN 1140
S229
.5 ORN 1140
.5 ORN 1140
.5 ORN 1140
2N
8L
5D
C200
.8 ORN 1140
.8 ORN 1140
.8 ORN 1140
.8 ORN 1140
F C303
S306
Z C301
Z C302
P500
P500
P600
.8 ORN 1140
.8 ORN 1140
.8 ORN 1140
S501
S601
.5 ORN 1140
.8 ORN 1140
.8 ORN 1140
.8 ORN 1140
.8 ORN 1140
.8 ORN 640
1 ORN 440
1L C200
.8 ORN 440
C C349
1 ORN 440
A C1
H
D
A
D
A
B
ANTENNA RELAY PAGE 8A-151-0
OUTSIDE MIRROR CONTROL SWITCH PAGE 8A-147-0
LH DOOR LOCK/WINDOW SWITCH (2 DOOR)
LH DOOR LOCK SWITCH (4 DOOR) PAGE 8A-146-0
LH DOOR HANDLE SWITCH PAGE 8A-146-0
RH DOOR LOCK/WINDOW SWITCH (2 DOOR)
RH DOOR LOCK SWITCH (4 DOOR) PAGE 8A-146-0
RH FRONT DOOR HANDLE SWITCH PAGE 8A-146-0
CONSOLE CIGAR LIGHTER PAGE 8A-114-0
3.8 ONLY
S202
.5 ORN 640
G C215
P103
.5 ORN 640
1 ORN 640
.5 ORN 640
.5 ORN 640
.5 ORN 640
.5 ORN 640
.5 ORN 640
32
15
A1
10 C1
1
F
CHIME MODULE PAGE 8A-76-0
COMPONENT CENTER
ELECTRONIC BRAKE CONTROL MODULE (EBCM) PAGE 8A-44-1
THEFT DETERRENT MODULE PAGE 8A-133-0
RADIO RECEIVER PAGE 8A-150-0
PASSIVE RESTRAINT TIMER RELAY PAGE 8A-146-0
LOW OIL LEVEL MODULE PAGE 8A-81-0

FUSE BLOCK DETAILS
DRLKS, BLMTR AND STOP FUSES

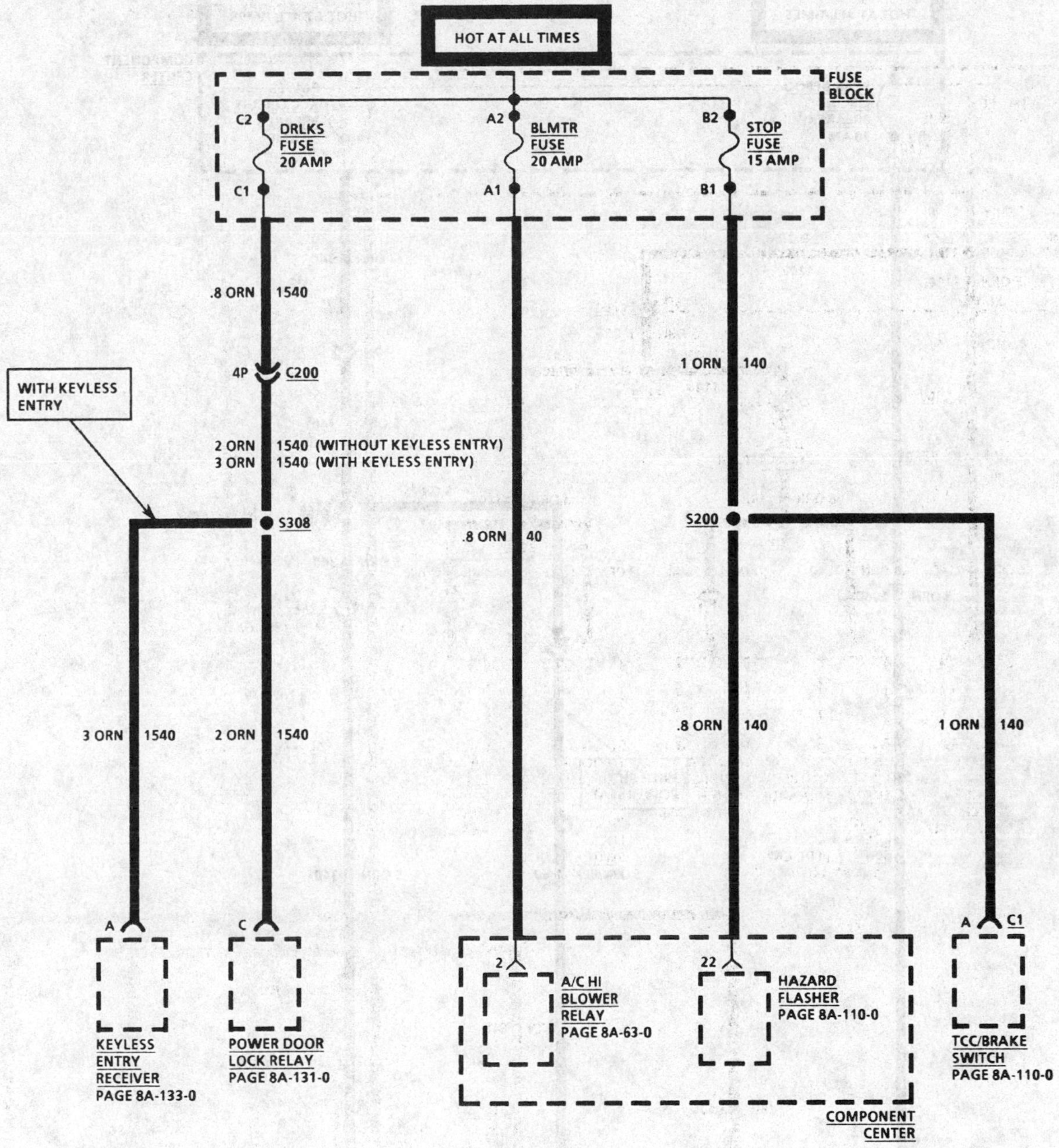

HOT AT ALL TIMES
FUSE BLOCK
C2
DRLKS FUSE 20 AMP
C1
A2
BLMTR FUSE 20 AMP
A1
B2
STOP FUSE 15 AMP
B1
.8 ORN 1540
4P C200
WITH KEYLESS ENTRY
2 ORN 1540 (WITHOUT KEYLESS ENTRY)
3 ORN 1540 (WITH KEYLESS ENTRY)
S308
.8 ORN 40
1 ORN 140
S200
3 ORN 1540
2 ORN 1540
.8 ORN 140
1 ORN 140
A
C
2
22
A C1
KEYLESS ENTRY RECEIVER PAGE 8A-133-0
POWER DOOR LOCK RELAY PAGE 8A-131-0
A/C HI BLOWER RELAY PAGE 8A-63-0
HAZARD FLASHER PAGE 8A-110-0
TCC/BRAKE SWITCH PAGE 8A-110-0
COMPONENT CENTER

FUSE BLOCK DETAILS
REAR DEFOG AND POWER ACC CIRCUIT BREAKERS

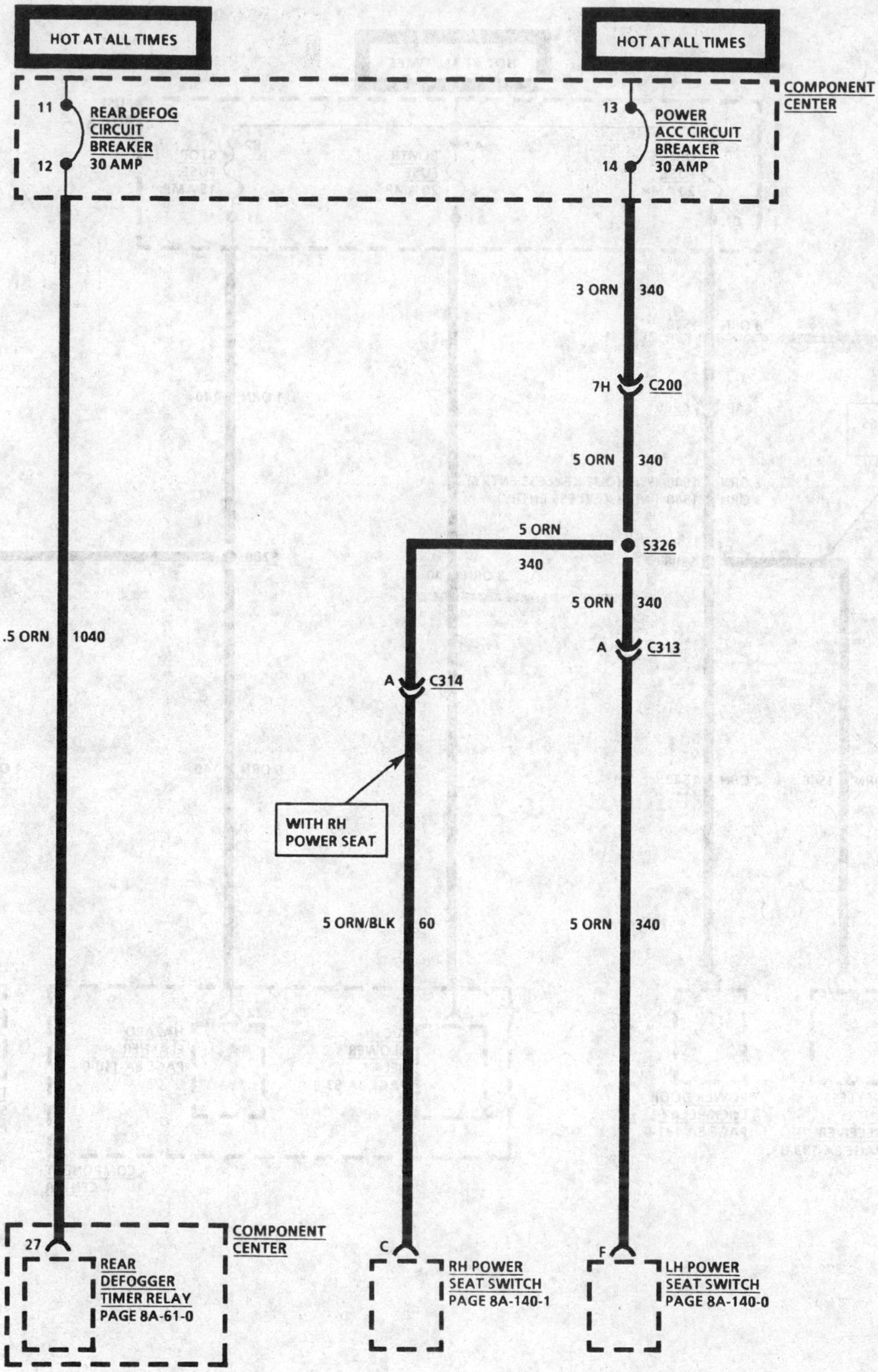

HOT AT ALL TIMES
HOT AT ALL TIMES
COMPONENT CENTER
11
REAR DEFOG CIRCUIT BREAKER 30 AMP
12
13
POWER ACC CIRCUIT BREAKER 30 AMP
14
3 ORN 340
7H C200
5 ORN 340
5 ORN
S326
340
5 ORN 340
A C313
.5 ORN 1040
A C314
WITH RH POWER SEAT
5 ORN/BLK 60
5 ORN 340
27
COMPONENT CENTER
REAR DEFOGGER TIMER RELAY PAGE 8A-61-0
C
RH POWER SEAT SWITCH PAGE 8A-140-1
F
LH POWER SEAT SWITCH PAGE 8A-140-0

FUSE BLOCK DETAILS

POWER WINDOW CIRCUIT BREAKER AND DOOR UNLOCK FUSE

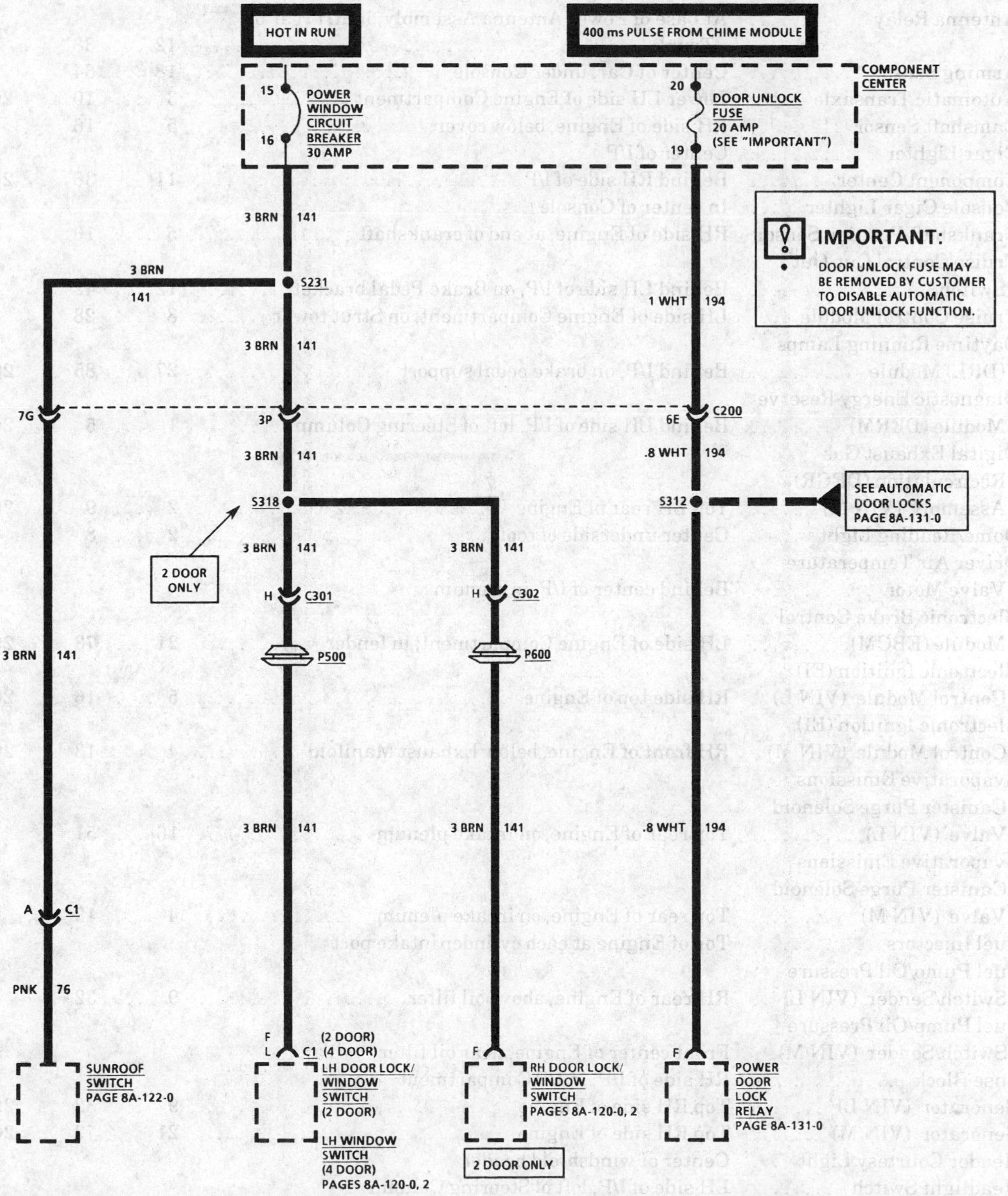
HOT IN RUN
400 ms PULSE FROM CHIME MODULE
COMPONENT CENTER
15
POWER WINDOW CIRCUIT BREAKER 30 AMP
16
20
DOOR UNLOCK FUSE 20 AMP (SEE "IMPORTANT")
19
IMPORTANT:
DOOR UNLOCK FUSE MAY BE REMOVED BY CUSTOMER TO DISABLE AUTOMATIC DOOR UNLOCK FUNCTION.
3 BRN 141
S231
1 WHT 194
7G
3P
6E
C200
.8 WHT 194
S318
S312
SEE AUTOMATIC DOOR LOCKS PAGE 8A-131-0
2 DOOR ONLY
H C301
H C302
P500
P600
A C1
PNK 76
F
L
C1
(2 DOOR)
(4 DOOR)
SUNROOF SWITCH PAGE 8A-122-0
LH DOOR LOCK/ WINDOW SWITCH (2 DOOR)
LH WINDOW SWITCH (4 DOOR) PAGES 8A-120-0, 2
RH DOOR LOCK/ WINDOW SWITCH PAGES 8A-120-0, 2
2 DOOR ONLY
POWER DOOR LOCK RELAY PAGE 8A-131-0

FUSE BLOCK DETAILS

COMPONENT	LOCATION	201-PG	FIG.	CONN
ABS Lamp Driver Module	Behind I/P, right of Steering Column			202-38
Antenna Relay	At base of Power Antenna Assembly, in RH rear of Trunk	12	38	
Arming Sensor	Center of Car, under Console	18	64	
Automatic Transaxle	Lower LH side of Engine Compartment	3	10	202-36
Camshaft Sensor	RH side of Engine, below cover	5	16	
Cigar Lighter	Center of I/P			
Component Center	Behind RH side of I/P	11	36	202-14
Console Cigar Lighter	In center of Console			
Crankshaft Position Sensor	RH side of Engine, at end of crankshaft	5	16	
Cruise Control Cut-Out Switch	Behind LH side of I/P, on Brake Pedal bracket	12	42	
Cruise Control Module	LH side of Engine Compartment, on Strut tower	8	28	
Daytime Running Lamps (DRL) Module	Behind I/P, on brake pedal support	27	85	202-37
Diagnostic Energy Reserve Module (DERM)	Behind LH side of I/P, left of Steering Column	1	5	202-18
Digital Exhaust Gas Recirculation (DEGR) Assembly (VIN M)	Top LH rear of Engine	2	9	202-37
Dome/Reading Light	Center underside of roof	2	8	
Driver Air Temperature Valve Motor	Behind center of I/P, in plenum			
Electronic Brake Control Module (EBCM)	LH side of Engine Compartment, in fender	21	73	202-19
Electronic Ignition (EI) Control Module (VIN L)	RH side top of Engine	5	16	202-20
Electronic Ignition (EI) Control Module (VIN M)	RH front of Engine, below Exhaust Manifold	4	13	202-37
Evaporative Emissions Canister Purge Solenoid Valve (VIN L)	Top rear of Engine, on intake plenum	16	51	
Evaporative Emissions Canister Purge Solenoid Valve (VIN M)	Top rear of Engine, on intake plenum	4	13	
Fuel Injectors	Top of Engine at each cylinder intake port			
Fuel Pump/Oil Pressure Switch/Sender (VIN L)	RH rear of Engine, above oil filter	9	32	
Fuel Pump/Oil Pressure Switch/Sender (VIN M)	Front center of Engine, near oil filter			
Fuse Block	RH side of I/P, in I/P Compartment			
Generator (VIN L)	Top RH side of Engine	9	32	202-38
Generator (VIN M)	Top RH side of Engine	21	72	202-38
Header Courtesy Light	Center of windshield header			
Headlight Switch	LH side of I/P, left of Steering Column			
Heated Oxygen Sensor #2	In Exhaust system, behind Catalytic Converter	28	89	202-38
Heated Oxygen Sensor (VIN L)	Rear of Engine, in Exhaust Manifold	9	32	202-38

COMPONENT	LOCATION	201-PG	FIG.	CONN
Heated Oxygen Sensor (VIN M)	Rear of Engine, in Exhaust Manifold	4	13	202-38
High Resolution 24X Crankshaft Sensor	RH side of Engine, at end of crankshaft	27	86	
HVAC Control Assembly	Center of I/P	23	78	202-22
Inside Lighted Mirror	Center of windshield header			
Instrument Cluster	RH side of I/P	16	52	
I/P Compartment Light	RH side of I/P, in I/P Compartment			
Keyless Entry Receiver	RH side of rear shelf	15	49	202-38
LH Door Handle Switch	Center of LH door			
LH I/P Courtesy Light	Under I/P, at LH shroud			
LH Power Seat Switch	On LH side of LH front seat			202-25
LH Rear Door Courtesy Light	In rear of door			
LH Vanity Mirror Light	LH side of windshield Header in Sunshade	12	40	
LH Window/Door Lock Switch (2 door)	In center of LH front door panel	17	57	202-23
LH Window/Door Lock Switch (4 door)	In center of LH front door panel	17	57	202-39
Linear Exhaust Gas Recirculation (EGR) Assembly (VIN L)	Top LH rear of Engine	3	11	202-39
Low Oil Level Module (VIN L)	Behind LH side of I/P	11	37	
Mass Air Flow Sensor	Top LH side of Engine	24	80	
Multi-Function Lever	Top LH side of Steering Column	12	43	
Outside Mirror Control Switch	Center of LH front door	17	58	202-39
Passenger Air Temperature Valve Motor	Behind I/P, in RH side of plenum	11	36	
Passenger Temperature Control	Center of I/P	28	90	202-40
Passive Restraint Timer Relay	Behind RH side of I/P			202-40
Power Door Lock Relay	RH shroud, above center access hole			202-40
Powertrain Control Module (PCM) (VIN L)	RH side of Engine Compartment, forward of strut tower	19	68	202-29
Powertrain Control Module (PCM) (VIN M)	RH side of Engine Compartment, forward of strut tower	19	69	202-26
Radio Control Interface Module	Behind LH side of I/P, on top of DERM bracket			202-40
Radio Receiver	Center of I/P	16	53	202-32
RH Door Handle Switch	Center of LH door			
RH Door Window Switch	In center of right front door panel	17	57	202-24
RH Front Door Lock Switch	Middle rear of RH front door	16	53	
RH I/P Courtesy Light	Under I/P, at RH shroud			
RH Power Seat Switch	On RH side of RH front seat			202-25

(CONTINUED ON NEXT PAGE)

FUSE BLOCK DETAILS

(CONTINUED FROM PREVIOUS PAGE)

COMPONENT	LOCATION	201-PG	FIG.	CONN
RH Rear Door Courtesy Light	In rear of door			
RH Vanity Mirror Light	RH side of windshield header in sun shade	12	40	
Solenoid Box	Behind I/P, RH side of plenum	11	36	
Steering Wheel Radio Switches	Center front of Steering Wheel			
Sunroof Switch	Center of windshield header	12	39	
TCC/Brake Switch	Behind I/P, on brake pedal support	12	42	202-41
Theft Deterrent Module	Behind LH side of I/P, above Brake Pedal Bracket			202-33
Transaxle Range Switch	Left of Engine, on Transaxle	3	10	202-41
Trunk Courtesy Light	Center of Luggage Compartment Lid			
Turn Signal Flasher	Behind I/P, right of Steering Column			
Underhood Electrical Center #1	RH side of Engine Compartment, forward of strut tower			202-33
Underhood Electrical #2 Center	LH side of Engine Compartment, on strut tower	1	4	202-33
Underhood Light	On underside of Engine Hood	10	34	
Wiper/Washer Switch	Top of Steering Column	12	43	
C110 (8 cavities)	Top RH side of Engine	16	51	202-35
C200 (102 cavities)	Behind RH side of I/P, near shroud	22	74	202-3
C202 (48 cavities)	Behind I/P, RH side of Steering Column	27	88	202-9
C213 (4 cavities)	Behind I/P, RH side of Steering Column			202-35
C215 (10 cavities)	Behind LH side of I/P, left of Steering Column			202-11
C301 (23 cavities)	Below I/P, at LH shroud	6	20	202-12
C302 (23 cavities)	Below I/P, at RH shroud	6	20	202-13
C303 (6 cavities)	Below I/P, at RH shroud	6	20	202-35
C313 (2 cavities)	Under LH front seat	15	50	
C314 (2 cavities)	Under RH front seat			
C353 (4 cavities)	In LH "B" pillar			202-35
C354 (4 cavities)	In RH "B" pillar			202-35
P103	LH rear of Engine Compartment, near strut tower	1	4	
P350	Under front seat, LH side	28	89	
P500	In LH front door jamb	6	20	
P600	In RH front door jamb	23	77	
P700	In LH rear door jamb	17	57	
P800	In RH rear door jamb	17	57	
S102	Engine Harn, approx 4 cm from Underhood Electrical Center #1 breakout			
S109 (VIN L)	Engine Harn, approx 12 cm from Injector #1 breakout			
S109 (VIN M)	Engine Jumper Harn, approx 8 cm from Fuel Injector #1			
S120	Engine Harn, approx 7 cm from Underhood Electrical Center #1 breakout			
S120 (VIN L)	Engine Harn, approx 12 cm from Underhood Electrical Center #1 breakout			
S127	Wiper Harn, approx 14 cm from P103			
S129	Engine Harn, approx 5 cm from C100 breakout			

COMPONENT	LOCATION	201-PG	FIG.	CONN
S130	Engine Harn, approx 4 cm from Underhood Electrical Center #1 breakout			
S131	Engine Harn, approx 4 cm from C100 breakout			
S132	Wiper Harn, approx 10 cm from Washer Pump breakout			
S140	Engine Jumper Harn, approx 10 cm from Camshaft Sensor breakout			
S200	I/P Harn, approx 4 cm from Radio breakout			
S201	I/P Harn, approx 3 cm from RH Front Speaker breakout			
S202	I/P Harn, approx 51 cm from Instrument Cluster breakout			
S206	I/P Harn, approx 9 cm from Fuse Block breakout			
S209	I/P Harn, approx 15 cm from Fuse Block breakout			
S227	I/P Harn, approx 3 cm from Fuse Block breakout			
S231	I/P Harn, approx 3 cm from RH Front Speaker breakout			
S233	I/P Harn, approx 22 cm from Fuse Block			
S241	SIR Harn, approx 7 cm from C200 breakout			
S308	Cross Car Harn, approx 19 cm from RH front Seat Belt breakout			
S312	Cross Car Harn, approx 22 cm from RH front Seat Belt breakout			
S318	Cross Car Harn, approx 32 cm from RH front Seat Belt breakout			
S380	Vanity Mirror Harn, approx 4 cm from vanity mirrors breakout			
S501	Left front door Harn, approx 10 cm from Door Locks Switch breakout			
S601	Right front door Harn, approx 10 cm from Door Locks Switch breakout			

GROUND DISTRIBUTION
G101 AND G102

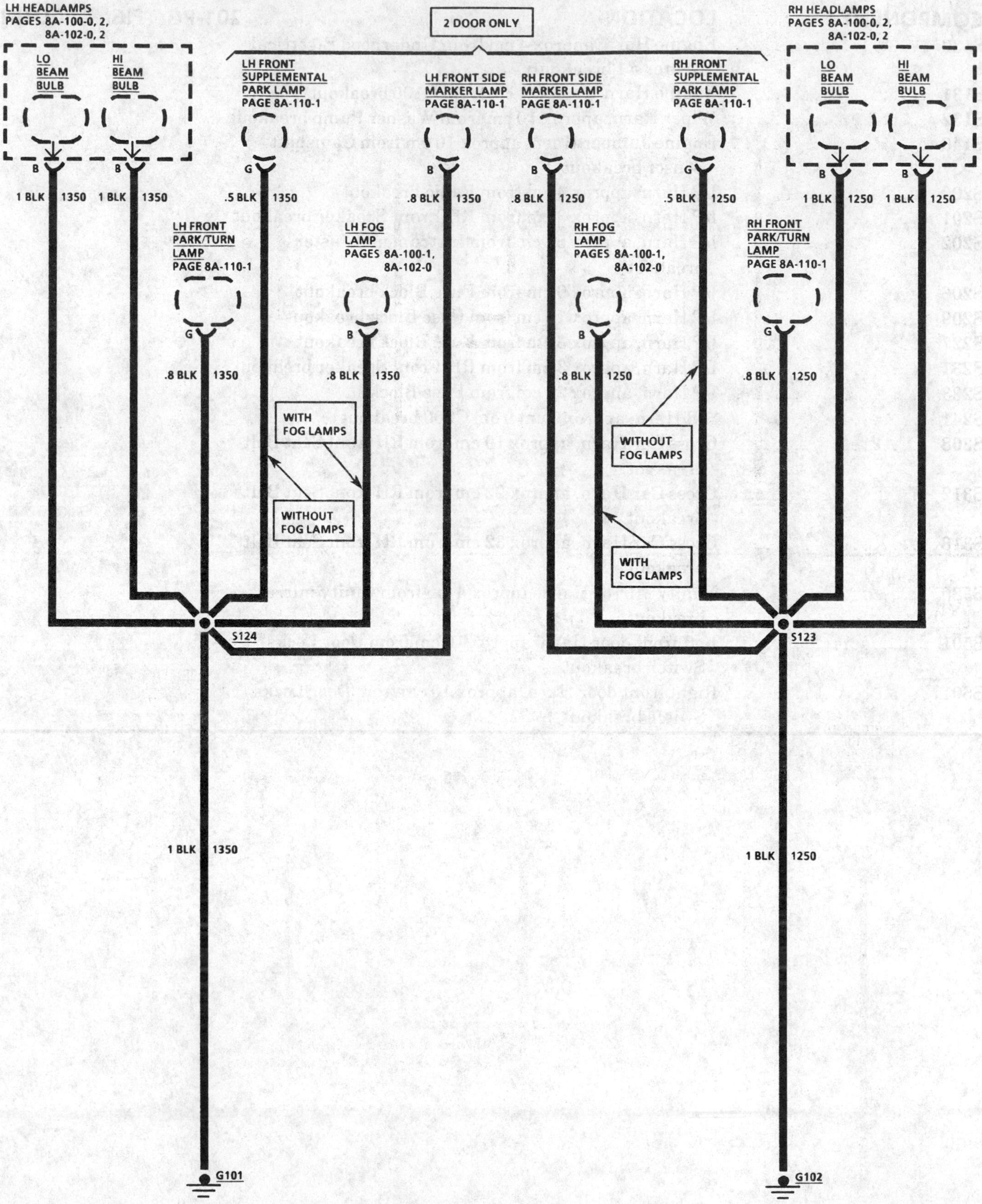

LH HEADLAMPS
PAGES 8A-100-0, 2, 8A-102-0, 2
LO BEAM BULB
HI BEAM BULB
2 DOOR ONLY
LH FRONT SUPPLEMENTAL PARK LAMP PAGE 8A-110-1
LH FRONT SIDE MARKER LAMP PAGE 8A-110-1
RH FRONT SIDE MARKER LAMP PAGE 8A-110-1
RH FRONT SUPPLEMENTAL PARK LAMP PAGE 8A-110-1
RH HEADLAMPS
PAGES 8A-100-0, 2, 8A-102-0, 2
LO BEAM BULB
HI BEAM BULB
B
G
1 BLK 1350
.5 BLK 1350
.8 BLK 1350
.8 BLK 1250
.5 BLK 1250
1 BLK 1250
LH FRONT PARK/TURN LAMP PAGE 8A-110-1
LH FOG LAMP PAGES 8A-100-1, 8A-102-0
RH FOG LAMP PAGES 8A-100-1, 8A-102-0
RH FRONT PARK/TURN LAMP PAGE 8A-110-1
.8 BLK 1350
.8 BLK 1250
WITH FOG LAMPS
WITHOUT FOG LAMPS
S124
S123
G101
G102

GROUND DISTRIBUTION
G111 AND G113

VIN M

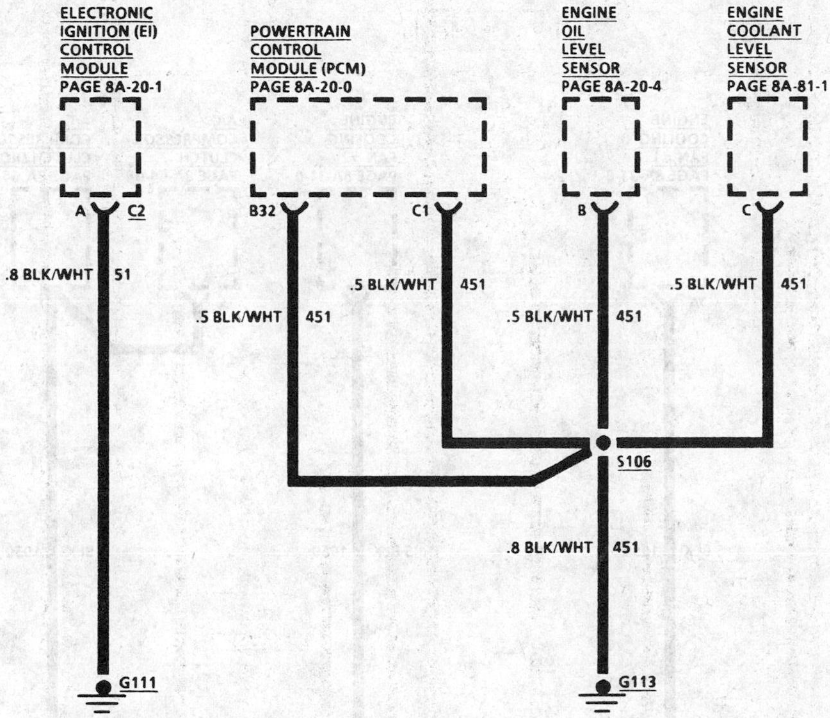
ELECTRONIC IGNITION (EI) CONTROL MODULE PAGE 8A-20-1
POWERTRAIN CONTROL MODULE (PCM) PAGE 8A-20-0
ENGINE OIL LEVEL SENSOR PAGE 8A-20-4
ENGINE COOLANT LEVEL SENSOR PAGE 8A-81-1
A
C2
B32
C1
B
C
.8 BLK/WHT 51
.5 BLK/WHT 451
.5 BLK/WHT 451
.5 BLK/WHT 451
.5 BLK/WHT 451
S106
.8 BLK/WHT 451
G111
G113

VIN L

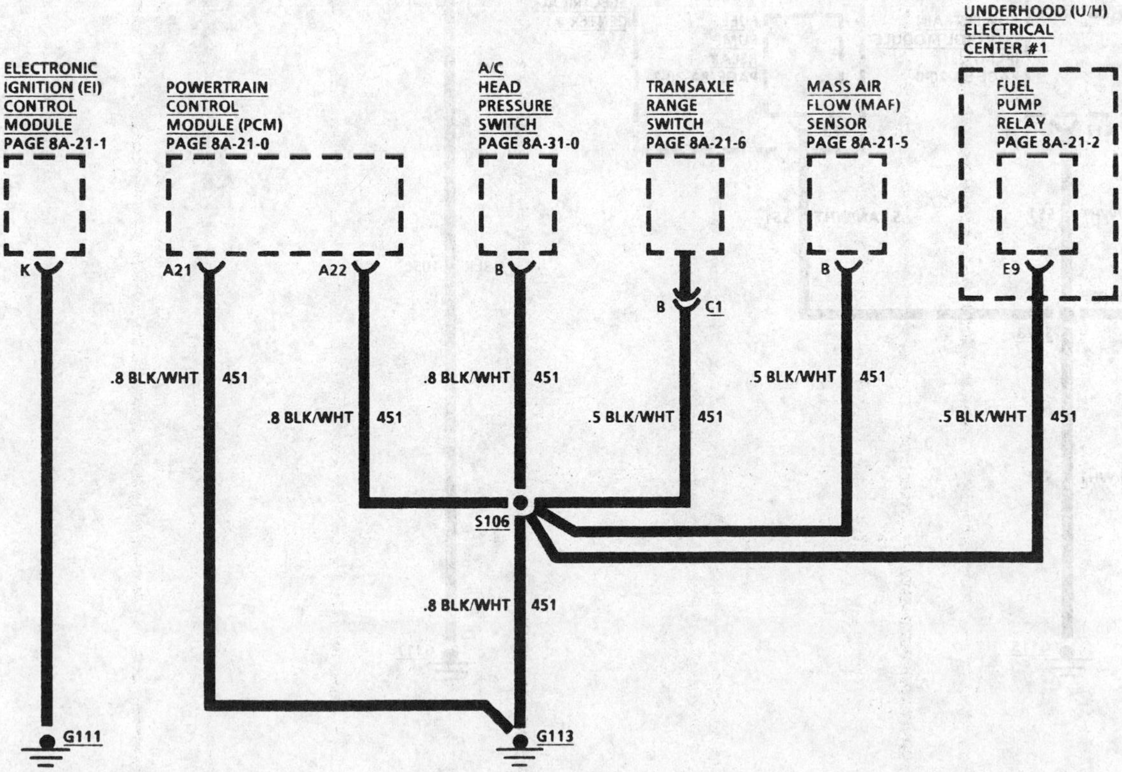
UNDERHOOD (U/H) ELECTRICAL CENTER #1
ELECTRONIC IGNITION (EI) CONTROL MODULE PAGE 8A-21-1
POWERTRAIN CONTROL MODULE (PCM) PAGE 8A-21-0
A/C HEAD PRESSURE SWITCH PAGE 8A-31-0
TRANSAXLE RANGE SWITCH PAGE 8A-21-6
MASS AIR FLOW (MAF) SENSOR PAGE 8A-21-5
FUEL PUMP RELAY PAGE 8A-21-2
K
A21
A22
B
B
C1
B
E9
.8 BLK/WHT 451
.8 BLK/WHT 451
.8 BLK/WHT 451
.5 BLK/WHT 451
.5 BLK/WHT 451
.5 BLK/WHT 451
S106
.8 BLK/WHT 451
G111
G113

GROUND DISTRIBUTION
G115 AND G117
VIN M

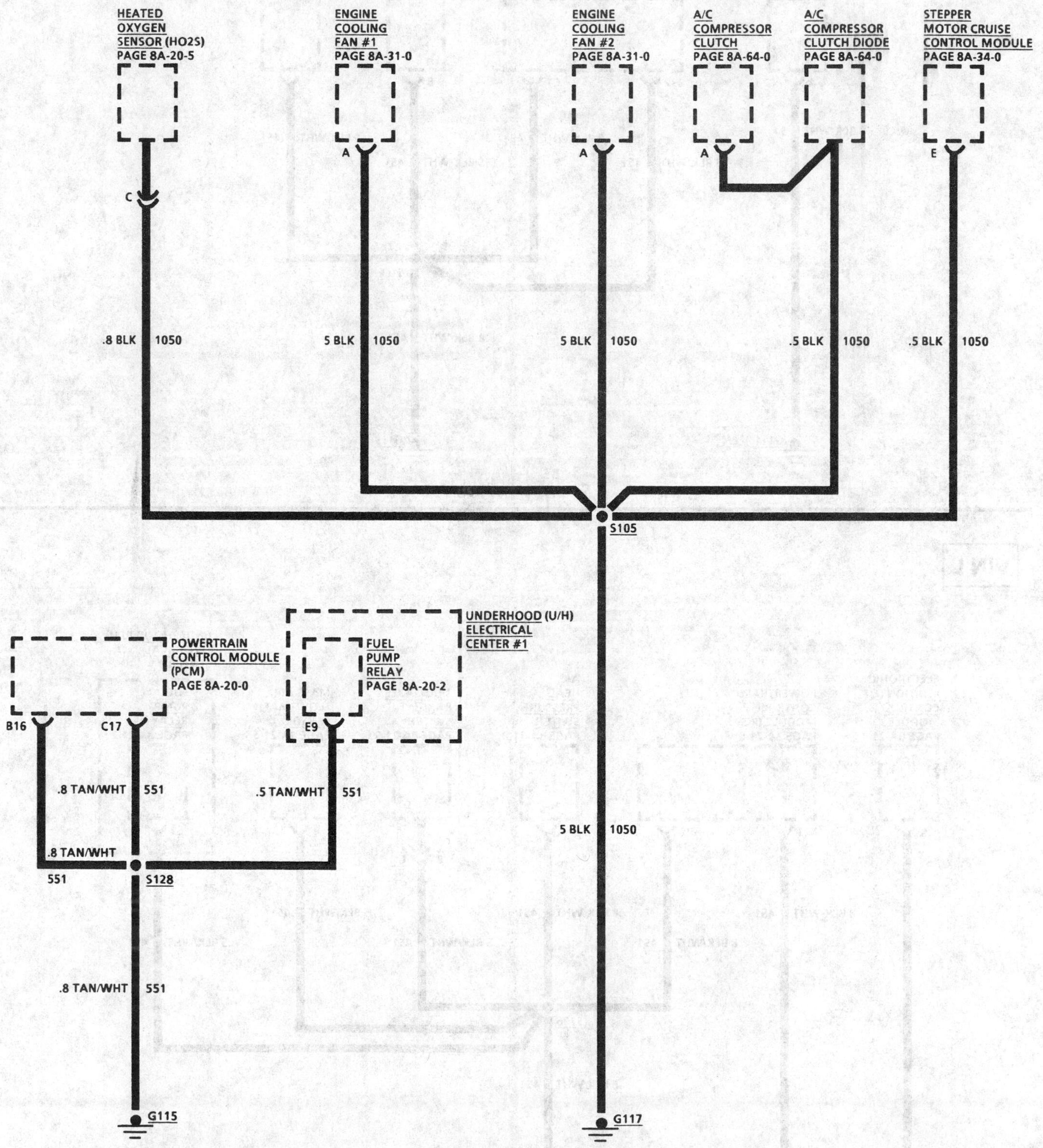
HEATED OXYGEN SENSOR (HO2S) PAGE 8A-20-5
ENGINE COOLING FAN #1 PAGE 8A-31-0
ENGINE COOLING FAN #2 PAGE 8A-31-0
A/C COMPRESSOR CLUTCH PAGE 8A-64-0
A/C COMPRESSOR CLUTCH DIODE PAGE 8A-64-0
STEPPER MOTOR CRUISE CONTROL MODULE PAGE 8A-34-0
C
A
A
A
E
.8 BLK 1050
5 BLK 1050
5 BLK 1050
.5 BLK 1050
.5 BLK 1050
S105
UNDERHOOD (U/H) ELECTRICAL CENTER #1
POWERTRAIN CONTROL MODULE (PCM) PAGE 8A-20-0
FUEL PUMP RELAY PAGE 8A-20-2
B16
C17
E9
.8 TAN/WHT 551
.5 TAN/WHT 551
5 BLK 1050
.8 TAN/WHT
551
S128
.8 TAN/WHT 551
G115
G117

GROUND DISTRIBUTION
G115 AND G117
VIN L

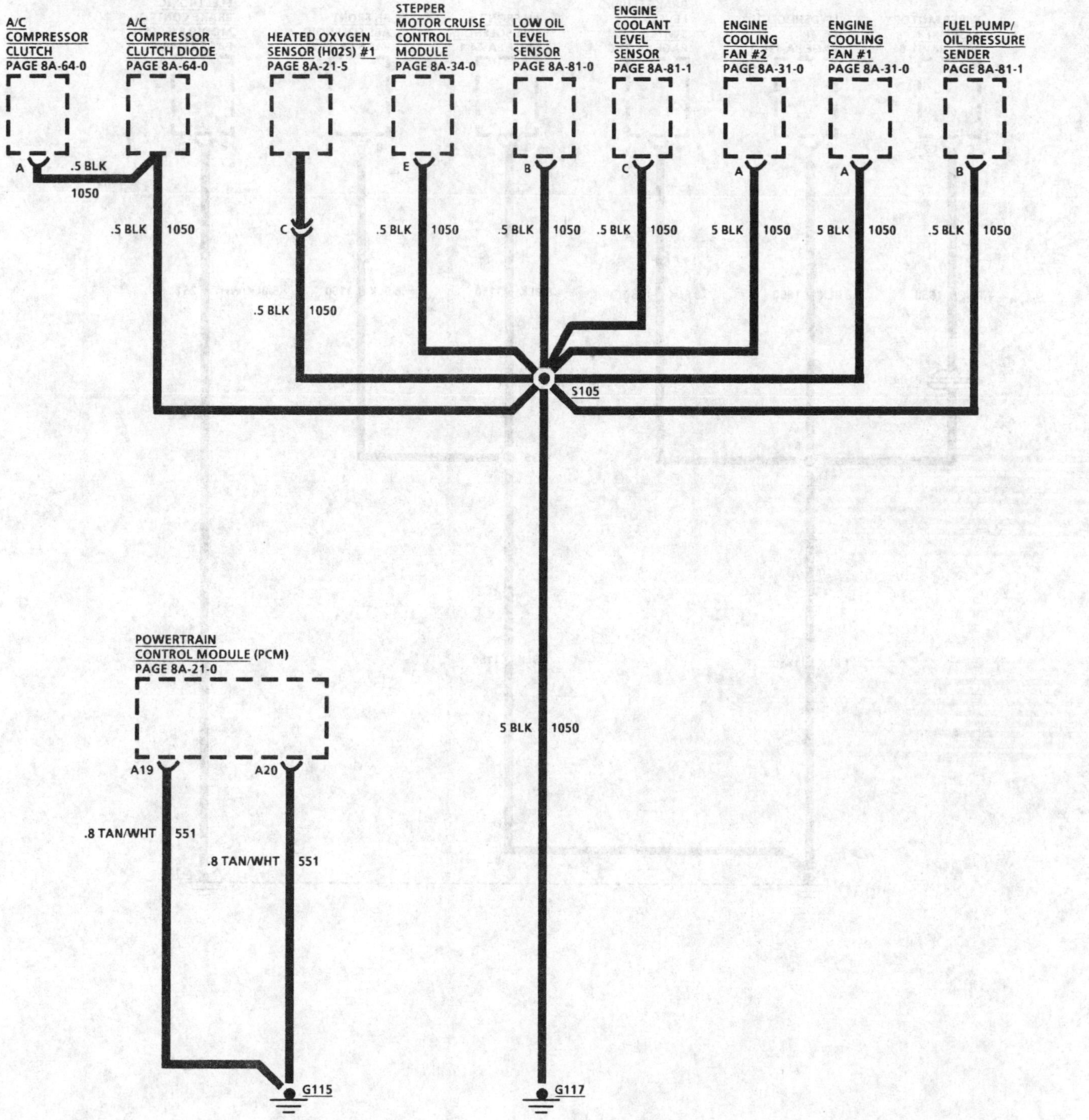

A/C COMPRESSOR CLUTCH
PAGE 8A-64-0
A/C COMPRESSOR CLUTCH DIODE
PAGE 8A-64-0
HEATED OXYGEN SENSOR (H02S) #1
PAGE 8A-21-5
STEPPER MOTOR CRUISE CONTROL MODULE
PAGE 8A-34-0
LOW OIL LEVEL SENSOR
PAGE 8A-81-0
ENGINE COOLANT LEVEL SENSOR
PAGE 8A-81-1
ENGINE COOLING FAN #2
PAGE 8A-31-0
ENGINE COOLING FAN #1
PAGE 8A-31-0
FUEL PUMP/ OIL PRESSURE SENDER
PAGE 8A-81-1
A
.5 BLK
1050
.5 BLK 1050
C
.5 BLK 1050
E
.5 BLK 1050
B
.5 BLK 1050
C
.5 BLK 1050
A
5 BLK 1050
A
5 BLK 1050
B
.5 BLK 1050
S105
POWERTRAIN CONTROL MODULE (PCM)
PAGE 8A-21-0
A19
A20
.8 TAN/WHT 551
.8 TAN/WHT 551
5 BLK 1050
G115
G117

GROUND DISTRIBUTION
G119

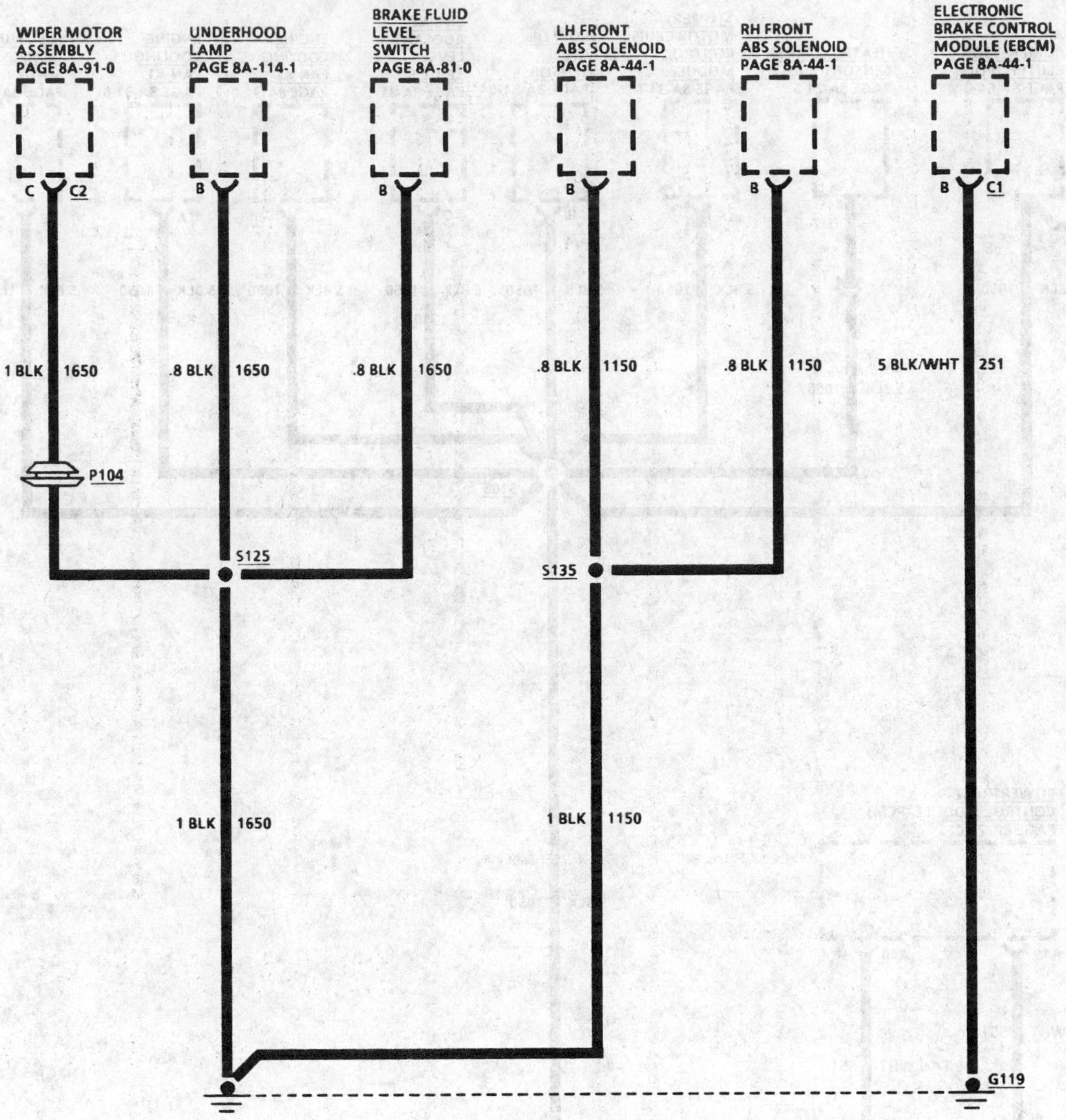
WIPER MOTOR ASSEMBLY PAGE 8A-91-0
UNDERHOOD LAMP PAGE 8A-114-1
BRAKE FLUID LEVEL SWITCH PAGE 8A-81-0
LH FRONT ABS SOLENOID PAGE 8A-44-1
RH FRONT ABS SOLENOID PAGE 8A-44-1
ELECTRONIC BRAKE CONTROL MODULE (EBCM) PAGE 8A-44-1
C
C2
B
B
B
B
B
C1
1 BLK 1650
.8 BLK 1650
.8 BLK 1650
.8 BLK 1150
.8 BLK 1150
5 BLK/WHT 251
P104
S125
S135
1 BLK 1650
1 BLK 1150
G119

GROUND DISTRIBUTION
G201

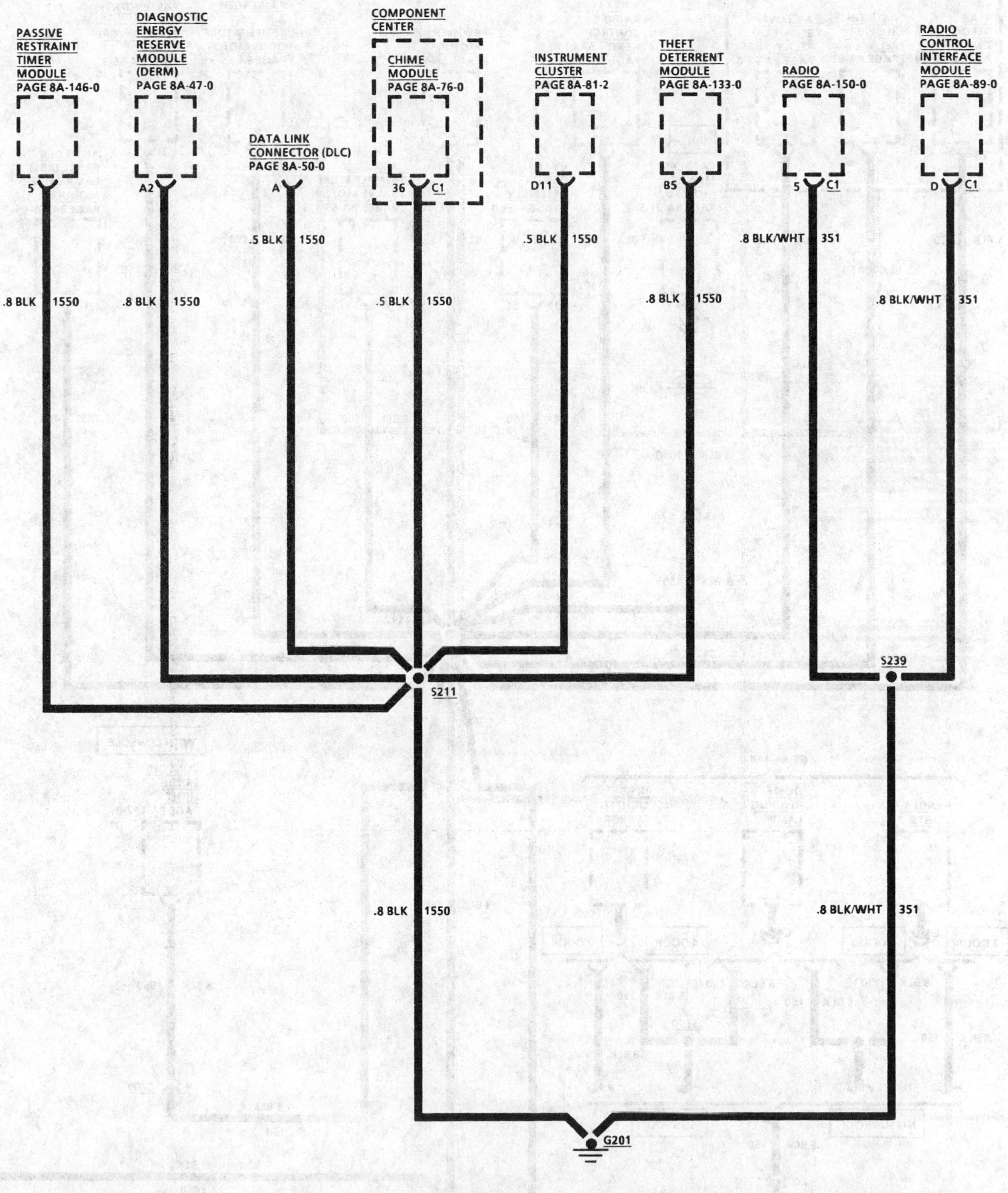
PASSIVE RESTRAINT TIMER MODULE
PAGE 8A-146-0
5
.8 BLK 1550
DIAGNOSTIC ENERGY RESERVE MODULE (DERM)
PAGE 8A-47-0
A2
.8 BLK 1550
DATA LINK CONNECTOR (DLC)
PAGE 8A-50-0
A
.5 BLK 1550
COMPONENT CENTER
CHIME MODULE
PAGE 8A-76-0
36 C1
.5 BLK 1550
INSTRUMENT CLUSTER
PAGE 8A-81-2
D11
.5 BLK 1550
THEFT DETERRENT MODULE
PAGE 8A-133-0
B5
.8 BLK 1550
RADIO
PAGE 8A-150-0
5 C1
.8 BLK/WHT 351
RADIO CONTROL INTERFACE MODULE
PAGE 8A-89-0
D C1
.8 BLK/WHT 351
S211
S239
.8 BLK 1550
.8 BLK/WHT 351
G201

GROUND DISTRIBUTION
G203

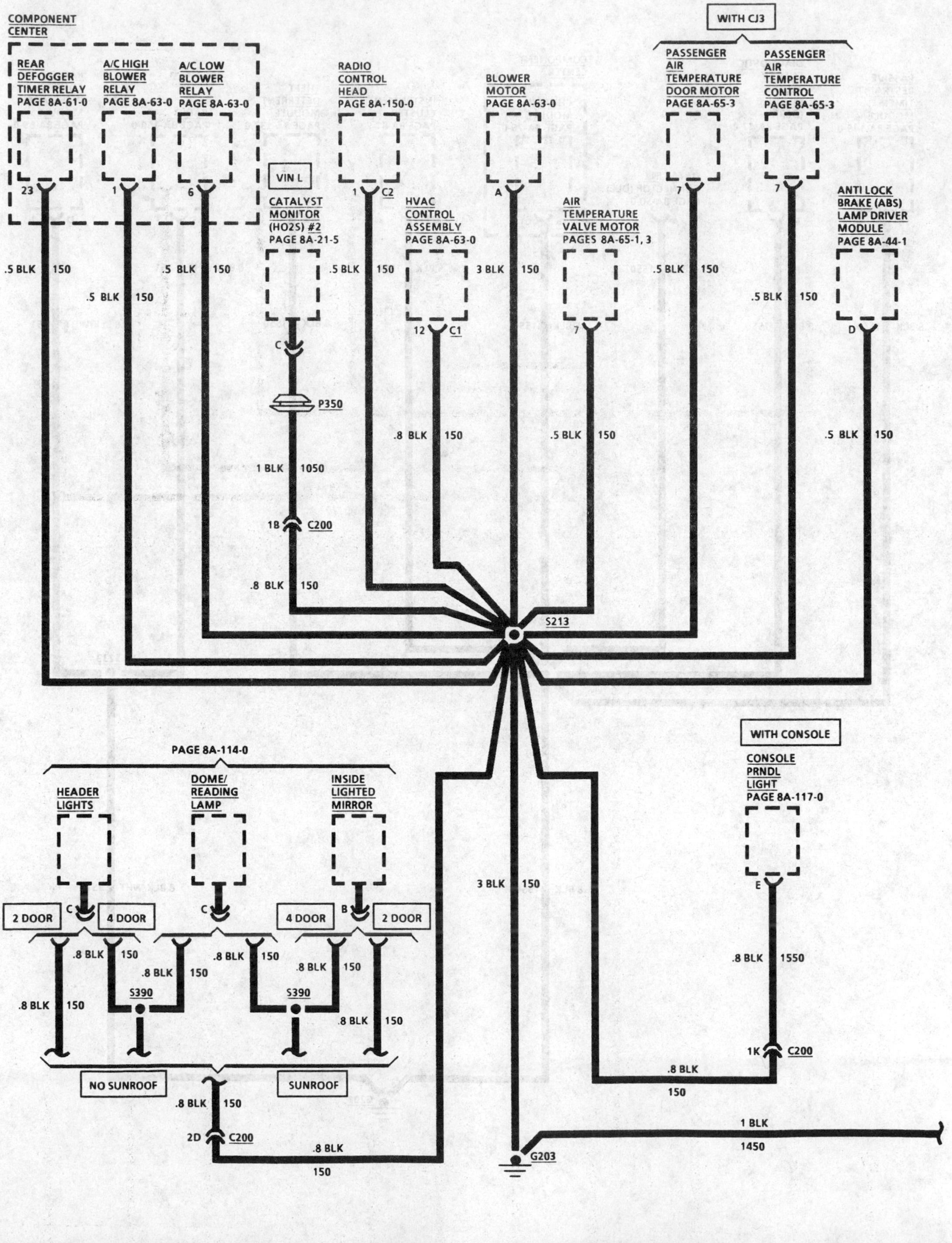
COMPONENT CENTER
REAR DEFOGGER TIMER RELAY PAGE 8A-61-0
A/C HIGH BLOWER RELAY PAGE 8A-63-0
A/C LOW BLOWER RELAY PAGE 8A-63-0
RADIO CONTROL HEAD PAGE 8A-150-0
BLOWER MOTOR PAGE 8A-63-0
WITH CJ3
PASSENGER AIR TEMPERATURE DOOR MOTOR PAGE 8A-65-3
PASSENGER AIR TEMPERATURE CONTROL PAGE 8A-65-3
23
1
6
VIN L
1 C2
A
7
7
CATALYST MONITOR (HO2S) #2 PAGE 8A-21-5
HVAC CONTROL ASSEMBLY PAGE 8A-63-0
AIR TEMPERATURE VALVE MOTOR PAGES 8A-65-1, 3
ANTI LOCK BRAKE (ABS) LAMP DRIVER MODULE PAGE 8A-44-1
.5 BLK 150
.5 BLK 150
.5 BLK 150
.5 BLK 150
3 BLK 150
.5 BLK 150
.5 BLK 150
12 C1
7
D
C
P350
.8 BLK 150
.5 BLK 150
.5 BLK 150
1 BLK 1050
1B C200
.8 BLK 150
S213
PAGE 8A-114-0
HEADER LIGHTS
DOME/ READING LAMP
INSIDE LIGHTED MIRROR
WITH CONSOLE
CONSOLE PRNDL LIGHT PAGE 8A-117-0
3 BLK 150
C
C
B
E
2 DOOR
4 DOOR
4 DOOR
2 DOOR
.8 BLK 150
.8 BLK 150
.8 BLK 150
.8 BLK 150
.8 BLK 1550
S390
S390
.8 BLK 150
.8 BLK 150
1K C200
.8 BLK
150
NO SUNROOF
SUNROOF
.8 BLK 150
2D C200
.8 BLK
150
1 BLK
1450
G203

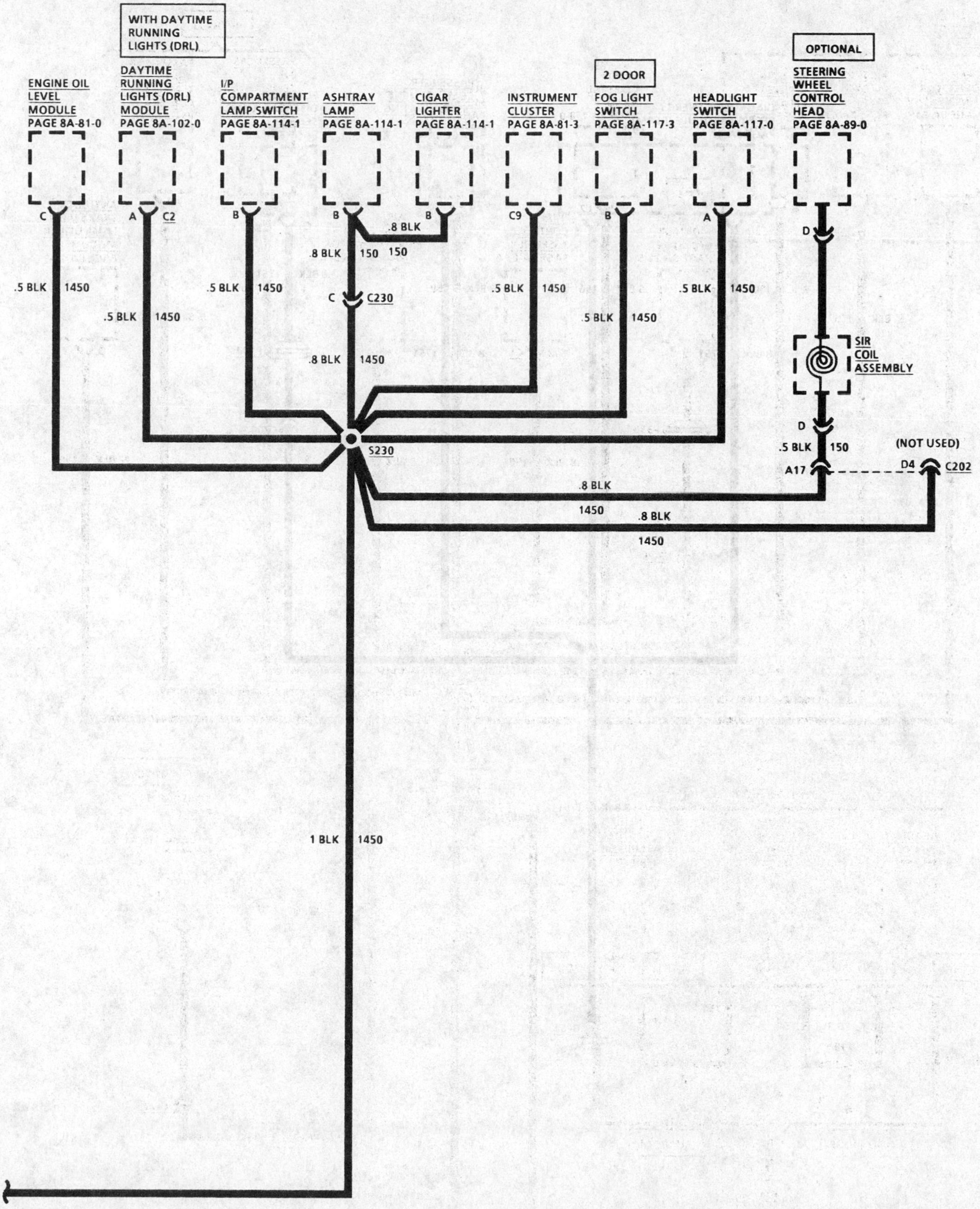

WITH DAYTIME RUNNING LIGHTS (DRL)
ENGINE OIL LEVEL MODULE PAGE 8A-81-0
DAYTIME RUNNING LIGHTS (DRL) MODULE PAGE 8A-102-0
I/P COMPARTMENT LAMP SWITCH PAGE 8A-114-1
ASHTRAY LAMP PAGE 8A-114-1
CIGAR LIGHTER PAGE 8A-114-1
INSTRUMENT CLUSTER PAGE 8A-81-3
2 DOOR
FOG LIGHT SWITCH PAGE 8A-117-3
HEADLIGHT SWITCH PAGE 8A-117-0
OPTIONAL
STEERING WHEEL CONTROL HEAD PAGE 8A-89-0
C
A
C2
B
B
B
C9
B
A
D
.8 BLK
.8 BLK 150
150
C
C230
.5 BLK 1450
.5 BLK 1450
.5 BLK 1450
.5 BLK 1450
.5 BLK 1450
.5 BLK 1450
.8 BLK 1450
SIR COIL ASSEMBLY
D
.5 BLK 150
(NOT USED)
A17
D4
C202
S230
.8 BLK
1450
.8 BLK
1450
1 BLK 1450

GROUND DISTRIBUTION
G251

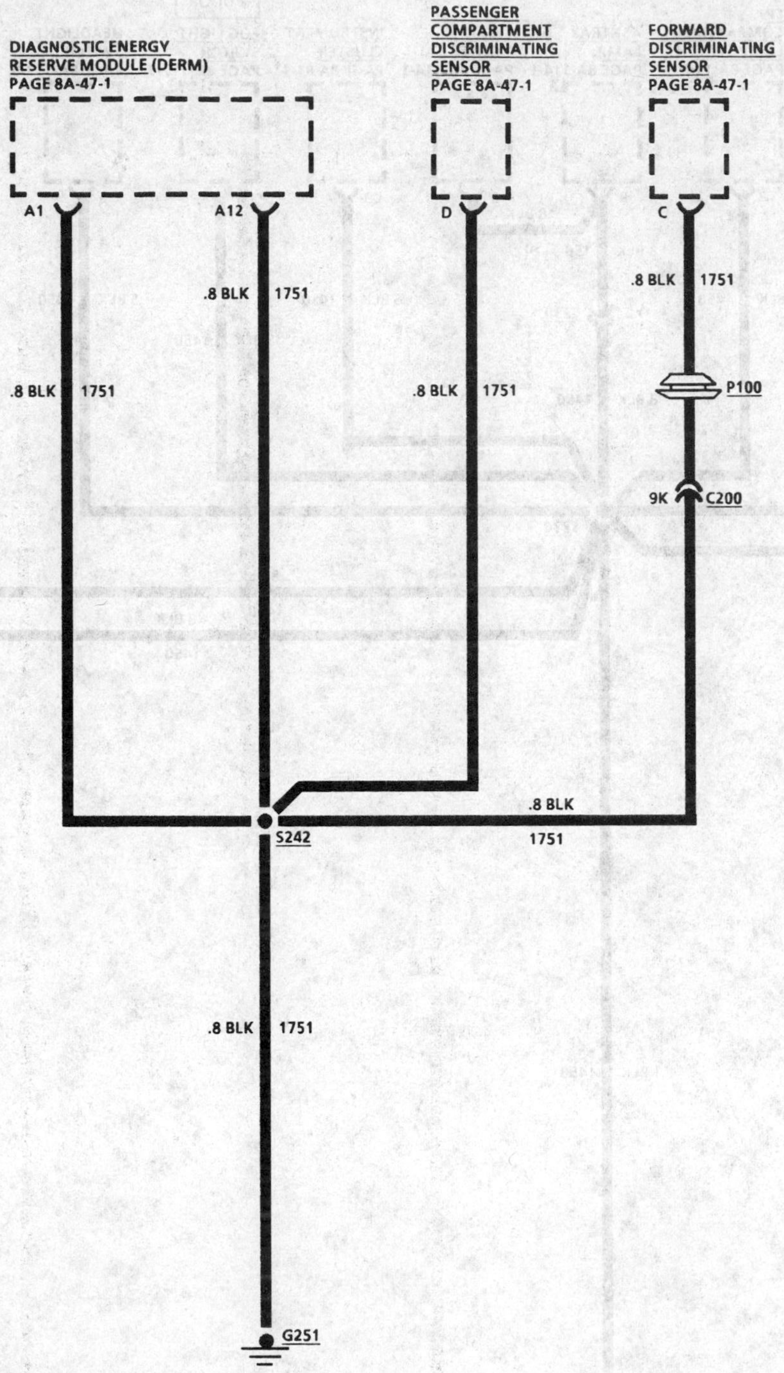

DIAGNOSTIC ENERGY RESERVE MODULE (DERM)
PAGE 8A-47-1
PASSENGER COMPARTMENT DISCRIMINATING SENSOR
PAGE 8A-47-1
FORWARD DISCRIMINATING SENSOR
PAGE 8A-47-1
A1
A12
D
C
.8 BLK 1751
.8 BLK 1751
.8 BLK 1751
.8 BLK 1751
P100
9K C200
.8 BLK
1751
S242
.8 BLK 1751
G251

GROUND DISTRIBUTION
G301, G311, G313, AND G349

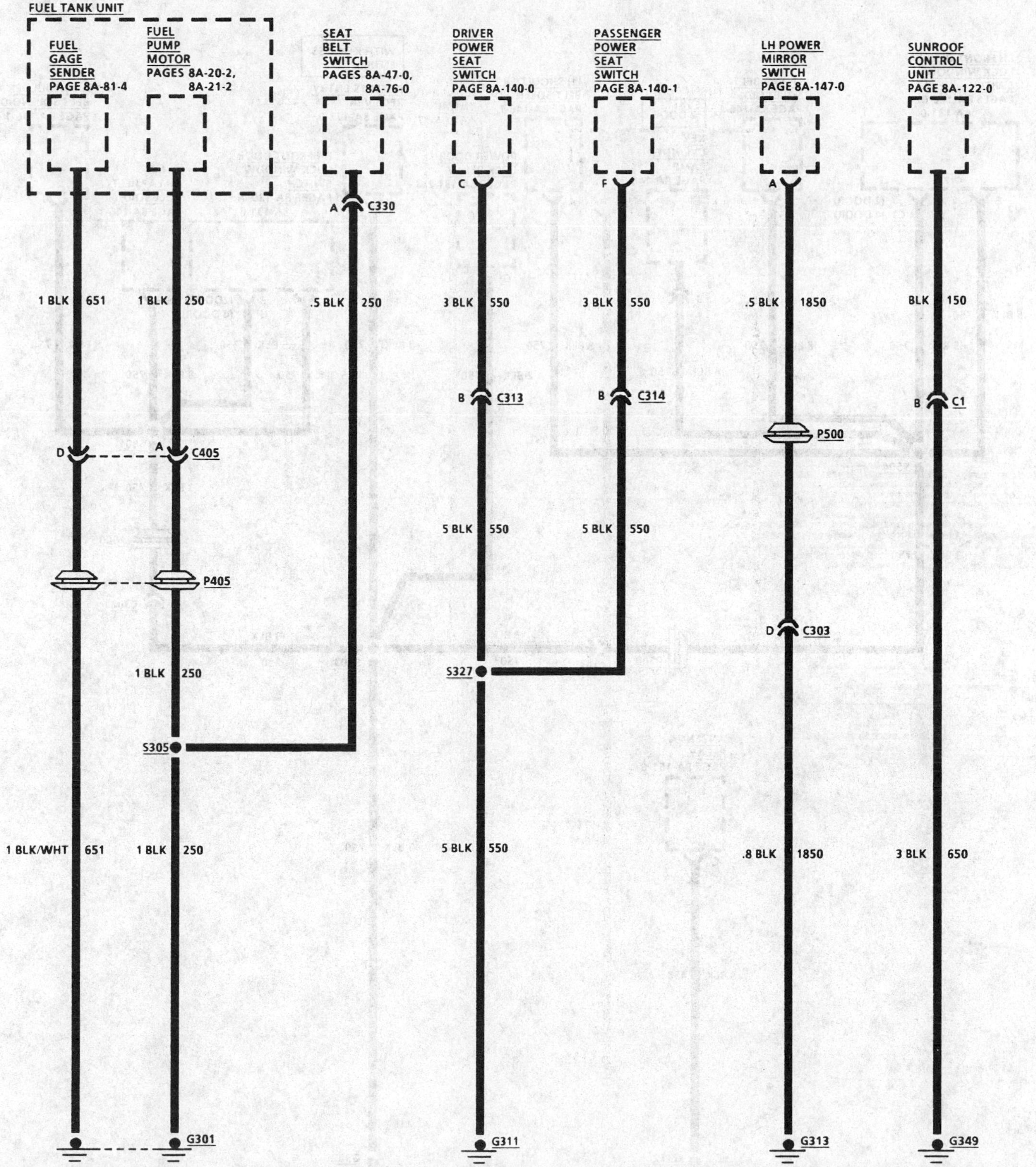
FUEL TANK UNIT
FUEL GAGE SENDER PAGE 8A-81-4
FUEL PUMP MOTOR PAGES 8A-20-2, 8A-21-2
SEAT BELT SWITCH PAGES 8A-47-0, 8A-76-0
DRIVER POWER SEAT SWITCH PAGE 8A-140-0
PASSENGER POWER SEAT SWITCH PAGE 8A-140-1
LH POWER MIRROR SWITCH PAGE 8A-147-0
SUNROOF CONTROL UNIT PAGE 8A-122-0
A C330
C
F
A
1 BLK 651
1 BLK 250
.5 BLK 250
3 BLK 550
3 BLK 550
.5 BLK 1850
BLK 150
B C313
B C314
B C1
P500
D
A C405
5 BLK 550
5 BLK 550
P405
D C303
1 BLK 250
S327
S305
1 BLK/WHT 651
1 BLK 250
5 BLK 550
.8 BLK 1850
3 BLK 650
G301
G311
G313
G349

GROUND DISTRIBUTION
G302 AND 312

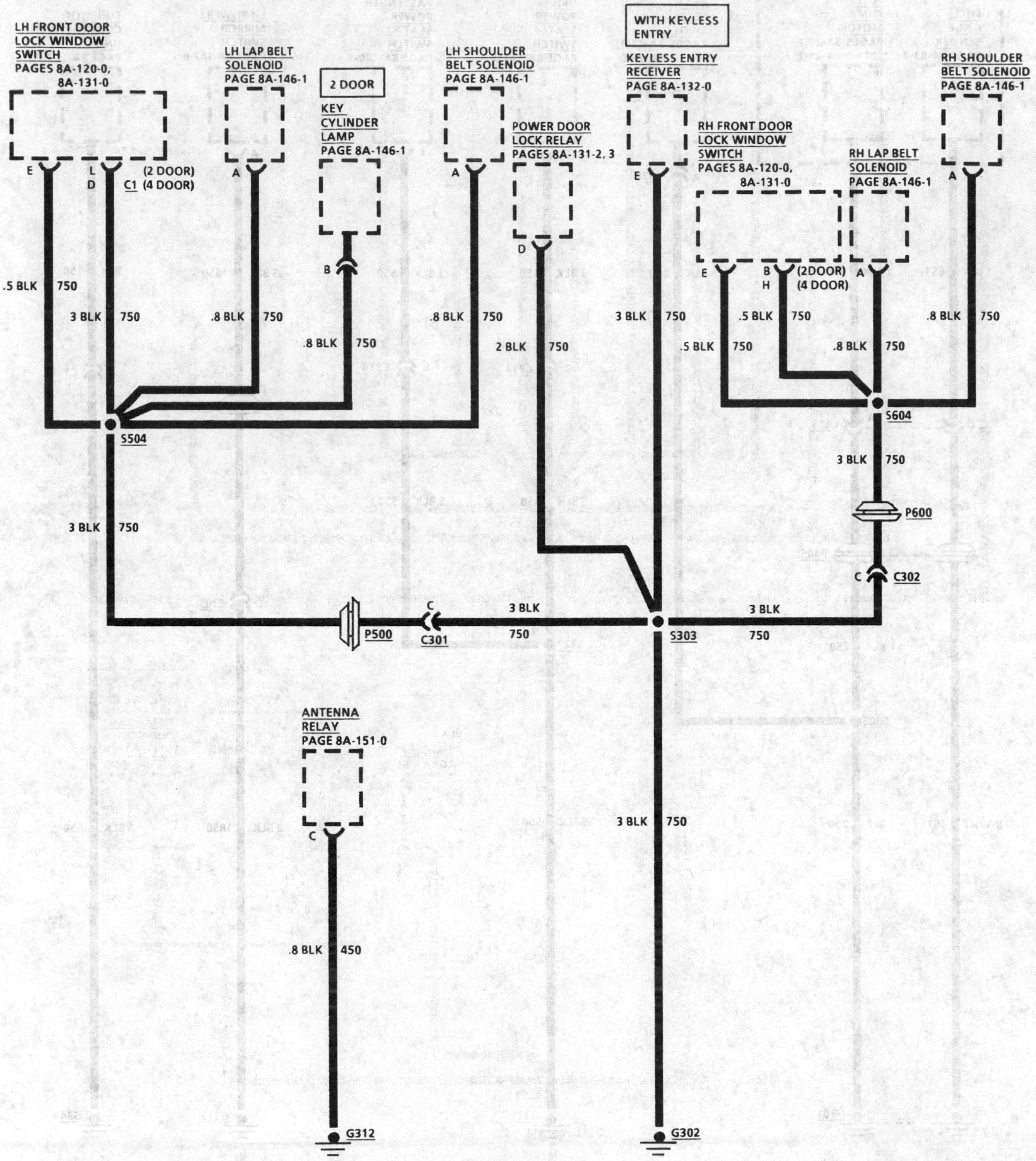

LH FRONT DOOR LOCK WINDOW SWITCH
PAGES 8A-120-0, 8A-131-0
E
L (2 DOOR)
D C1 (4 DOOR)
LH LAP BELT SOLENOID
PAGE 8A-146-1
A
2 DOOR
KEY CYLINDER LAMP
PAGE 8A-146-1
B
LH SHOULDER BELT SOLENOID
PAGE 8A-146-1
A
POWER DOOR LOCK RELAY
PAGES 8A-131-2, 3
D
WITH KEYLESS ENTRY
KEYLESS ENTRY RECEIVER
PAGE 8A-132-0
E
RH FRONT DOOR LOCK WINDOW SWITCH
PAGES 8A-120-0, 8A-131-0
E
B (2DOOR)
H (4 DOOR)
RH LAP BELT SOLENOID
PAGE 8A-146-1
A
RH SHOULDER BELT SOLENOID
PAGE 8A-146-1
A
.5 BLK 750
3 BLK 750
.8 BLK 750
.8 BLK 750
.8 BLK 750
2 BLK 750
3 BLK 750
.5 BLK 750
.5 BLK 750
.8 BLK 750
.8 BLK 750
S504
S604
3 BLK 750
P600
C C302
3 BLK 750
P500
C C301
3 BLK 750
S303
3 BLK 750
ANTENNA RELAY
PAGE 8A-151-0
C
3 BLK 750
.8 BLK 450
G312
G302

GROUND DISTRIBUTION
G302 (4 DOOR)

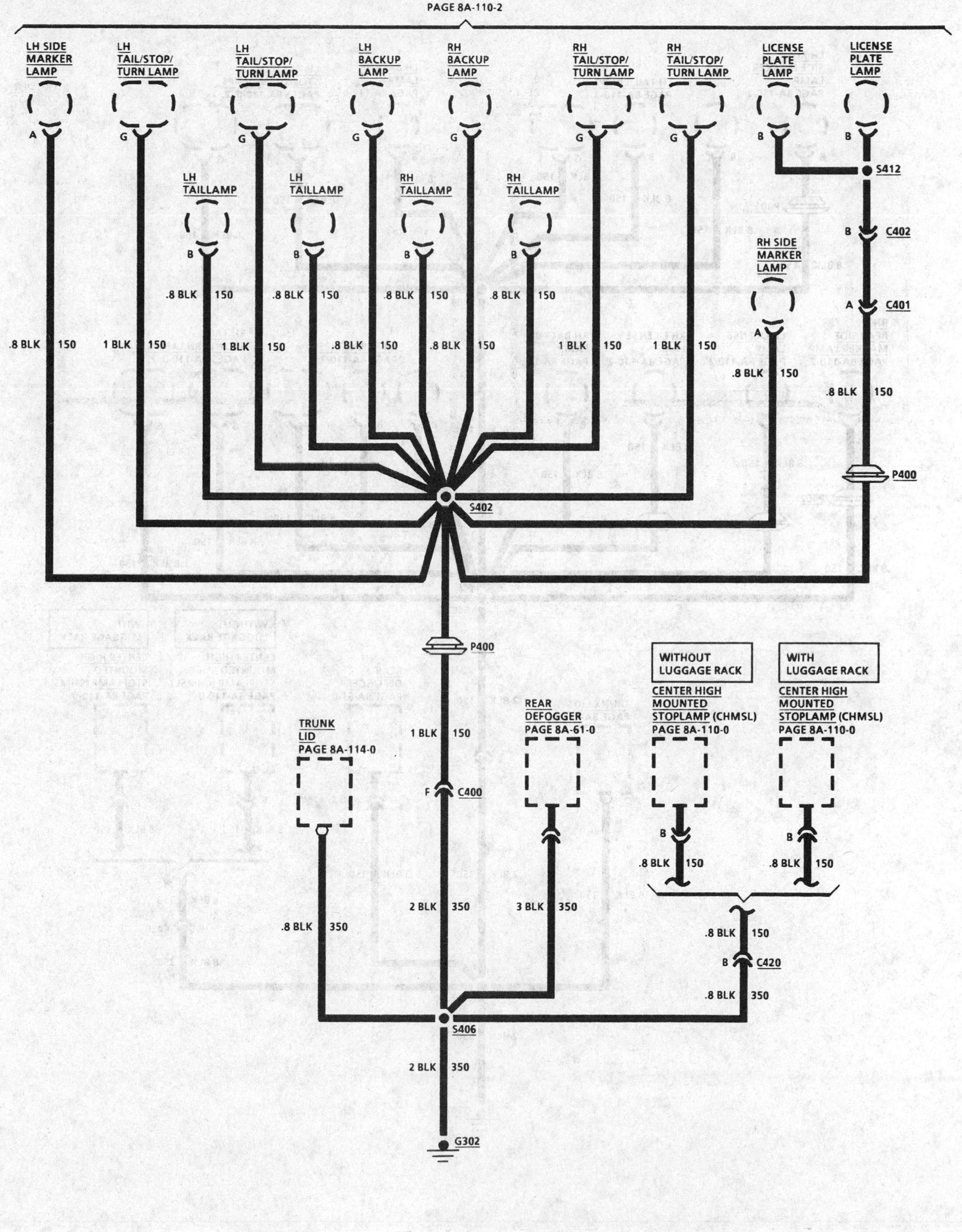

PAGE 8A-110-2
LH SIDE MARKER LAMP
LH TAIL/STOP/ TURN LAMP
LH TAIL/STOP/ TURN LAMP
LH BACKUP LAMP
RH BACKUP LAMP
RH TAIL/STOP/ TURN LAMP
RH TAIL/STOP/ TURN LAMP
LICENSE PLATE LAMP
LICENSE PLATE LAMP
A
G
G
G
G
G
G
B
B
S412
LH TAILLAMP
LH TAILLAMP
RH TAILLAMP
RH TAILLAMP
B
B
B
B
C402
RH SIDE MARKER LAMP
.8 BLK 150
.8 BLK 150
.8 BLK 150
.8 BLK 150
A
C401
.8 BLK 150
1 BLK 150
1 BLK 150
.8 BLK 150
.8 BLK 150
1 BLK 150
1 BLK 150
A
.8 BLK 150
.8 BLK 150
P400
S402
P400
WITHOUT LUGGAGE RACK
WITH LUGGAGE RACK
CENTER HIGH MOUNTED STOPLAMP (CHMSL) PAGE 8A-110-0
CENTER HIGH MOUNTED STOPLAMP (CHMSL) PAGE 8A-110-0
REAR DEFOGGER PAGE 8A-61-0
TRUNK LID PAGE 8A-114-0
1 BLK 150
F
C400
B
B
.8 BLK 150
.8 BLK 150
2 BLK 350
3 BLK 350
.8 BLK 350
.8 BLK 150
B
C420
.8 BLK 350
S406
2 BLK 350
G302

GROUND DISTRIBUTION
G302 (2 DOOR)

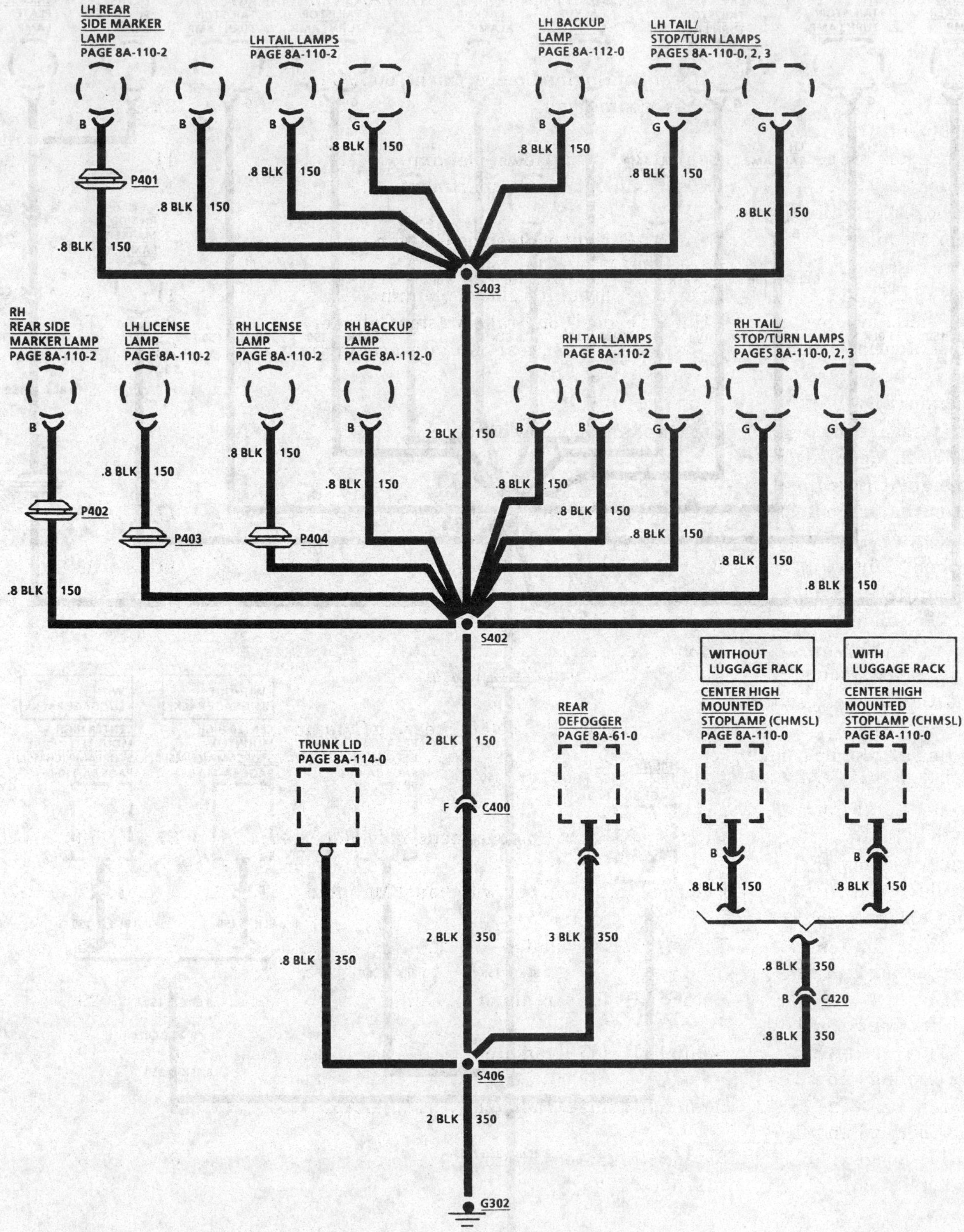

LH REAR SIDE MARKER LAMP PAGE 8A-110-2
LH TAIL LAMPS PAGE 8A-110-2
LH BACKUP LAMP PAGE 8A-112-0
LH TAIL/ STOP/TURN LAMPS PAGES 8A-110-0, 2, 3
B
G
P401
.8 BLK 150
S403
RH REAR SIDE MARKER LAMP PAGE 8A-110-2
LH LICENSE LAMP PAGE 8A-110-2
RH LICENSE LAMP PAGE 8A-110-2
RH BACKUP LAMP PAGE 8A-112-0
RH TAIL LAMPS PAGE 8A-110-2
RH TAIL/ STOP/TURN LAMPS PAGES 8A-110-0, 2, 3
2 BLK 150
P402
P403
P404
S402
WITHOUT LUGGAGE RACK
WITH LUGGAGE RACK
CENTER HIGH MOUNTED STOPLAMP (CHMSL) PAGE 8A-110-0
TRUNK LID PAGE 8A-114-0
REAR DEFOGGER PAGE 8A-61-0
F
C400
2 BLK 350
3 BLK 350
.8 BLK 350
C420
S406
G302

GROUND DISTRIBUTION

COMPONENT	LOCATION	201-PG	FIG.	CONN
A/C Compressor Clutch	RH front of Engine, on A/C Compressor	7	21	
A/C Compressor Clutch Diode	In Engine Harn, approx 17 cm from A/C Compressor Clutch			
A/C Head Pressure Switch	LH front of Engine Compartment, on A/C line near accumulator	26	83	
Air Temperature Valve Motor	Behind I/P, in RH side of plenum	11	36	202-36
Antenna Relay	RH side of Luggage Compartment	12	38	
Antilock Brake (ABS) Lamp Driver Module	Behind I/P, right of Steering Column			202-38
Ashtray Lamp	Center of I/P, in Ashtray			
Blower Motor	Behind I/P, lower RH side of plenum	11	36	
Brake Fluid Level Switch	LH front of dash, on Brake Master Cylinder	2	7	
Catalyst Monitor (H02S) #2	In Exhaust system, rear of catalyst convertor	28	89	
Center High Mounted Stoplamp (CHMSL) (With Luggage Rack)	Center of rear window header			
Center High Mounted Stop Light (CHMSL) (Without Luggage Rack)	Center of rear shelf	17	60	
Cigar Lighter	Center of I/P, below Radio			
Component Center	Behind RH side of I/P	11	36	202-14
Console PRNDL Light	In center console			
Data Link Connector (DLC)	On bottom of I/P, right of Steering Column			202-17
Daytime Running Lights (DRL) Module	Behind I/P, on brake pedal support			202-37
Diagnostic Energy Reserve Module (DERM)	Behind LH side of I/P, left of Steering Column	1	5	202-18
Dome/Reading Lamp	Center of roof	2	8	
Driver Power Seat Switch	On LH side of LH front seat			202-25
Electronic Brake Control Module (EBCM)	LH side of Engine Compartment, in fender	21	73	202-19
Electronic Ignition (EI) Control Module	RH front of Engine, below Exhaust Manifold	5	17	202-20
Engine Coolant Level Sensor	Top RH rear of radiator	8	25	
Engine Cooling Fan #1 (VIN L)	Behind LH side of radiator	8	29	
Engine Cooling Fan #1 (VIN T)	Behind LH side of radiator	6	19	
Engine Cooling Fan #2 (VIN L)	Behind RH side of radiator	8	29	
Engine Cooling Fan #2 (VIN T)	Behind RH side of radiator	6	19	
Fog Lamp Switch	LH side of I/P			

(CONTINUED ON NEXT PAGE)

GROUND DISTRIBUTION

(CONTINUED FROM PREVIOUS PAGE)

COMPONENT	LOCATION	201-PG	FIG.	CONN
Forward Discriminating Sensor	On center radiator support	14	47	
Fuel Pump/Oil Pressure Sender (VIN L)	RH rear of Engine, above oil filter			202-39
Fuel Tank Unit	Below rear of vehicle, top of fuel tank	10	35	
Header Lights	Front underside of roof			
Headlight Switch	LH side of I/P, left of Steering Column			202-21
Heated Oxygen Sensor	Rear of Engine, in Exhaust Manifold			202-38
High Blower Relay	Component Center			
HVAC Control Assembly	Center of I/P	15	49	202-22
Inside Lighted Mirror	Center of windshield header	16	54	
Instrument Cluster	LH side of I/P	16	52	
I/P Compartment Lamp Switch	RH side of I/P, in I/P Compartment			
Keyless Entry Receiver	RH side of rear shelf	22	76	202-38
LH Backup Lamp	LH rear of vehicle	18	66	
LH Headlamp	LH front of vehicle	10	33	
LH Fog Lamp	LH front of vehicle	10	33	
LH Front ABS Solenoid	LH rear of Engine Compartment			
LH Front Door Lock/ Window Switch	In center of LH front door panel	6	20	202-23
LH Front Park/Turn Lamp	LH front of vehicle	10	33	
LH Front Side Marker	LH side front of vehicle			
LH Front Supplemental Park Lamp	LH front of vehicle			
LH Lap Belt Solenoid	In rear of LH front door	6	20	
LH Power Mirror Switch	In center of LH front door panel	17	58	202-39
LH Rear Side Marker Lamp	LH rear of vehicle	18	66	
LH Shoulder Belt Solenoid	In rear of LH front door	6	20	
LH Tail Lamps	Rear of vehicle, LH side	18	66	
LH Tail/Stop/Turn Lamps	LH rear of vehicle	19	67	
License Lamps	Center rear of vehicle	19	67	
Low Blower Relay	Component Center			
Low Oil Level Sensor	Center of Oil Pan			
Mass Air Flow (MAF) Sensor	Top LH side of Engine	24	80	
Passenger Air Temperature Control	Center of I/P, below HVAC Control Assembly	9	30	202-40
Passenger Air Temperature Valve Motor	Behind I/P, in RH side of plenum	28	90	202-39
Passenger Compartment Discriminating Sensor	Behind LH side of I/P, on RH side of mag bracket			
Passenger Power Seat Switch	RH side of RH front seat			202-25
Passive Restraint Timer Module	Behind RH side of I/P			202-40
Power Door Lock Relay	RH shroud, above center access hole	13	44	202-40

COMPONENT	LOCATION	201-PG	FIG.	CONN
Powertrain Control Module (PCM) (VIN L)	RH side of Engine Compartment , forward of strut tower	19	68	202-29
Powertrain Control Module (PCM) (VIN M)	RH side of Engine Compartment, forward of strut tower	19	69	202-26
Radio Control Head	Center of I/P	26	84	202-40
Radio Control Interface Module	Behind I/P, on Steering Column			
Radio Receiver	Behind RH side of I/P	16	53	202-32
Rear Defogger	In rear window	4	14	
Rear Defogger Timer Relay	Component Center			
RH Backup Lamp	Rear of vehicle, RH side	19	67	
RH Fog Lamp	RH front of vehicle	10	33	
RH Front ABS Solenoid	LH rear of Engine Compartment			
RH Front Door Lock/ Window Switch	In center of LH front door panel	6	20	202-24
RH Front Park/Turn Lamps	RH front of vehicle	10	33	
RH Front Side Marker	RH side front of vehicle	10	33	
RH Front Supplemental Park Lamp	RH front of vehicle			
RH Headlamp	RH front of vehicle	10	33	
RH Lap Belt Solenoid	In rear of RH front door	6	20	
RH Rear Side Marker Lamps	RH rear of vehicle	18	66	
RH Shoulder Belt Solenoid	In rear of RH front door	6	20	
RH Tail Lamps	Rear of vehicle, RH side			
RH Tail/Stop/Turn Lamps	RH rear of vehicle	18	67	
Seat Belt Switch	In LH front seat belt buckle	18	62	
Steering Wheel Control Head	Center front of Steering Wheel			
Stepper Motor Cruise Control Module	LH side of Engine Compartment, on strut tower	8	28	202-16
Sunroof Control Unit	Center of windshield header	13	45	
Theft Deterrent Module	Behind RH side of I/P			202-34
Transaxle Range Switch	Left of Engine, on Transaxle	3	10	202-41
Underhood Electrical (U/H) Center #1	RH side of Engine Compartment, forward of strut tower			202-34
Underhood Lamp	On underside of Engine hood	10	34	
Wiper Motor Assembly	LH front of dash	2	7	202-42
C200 (106 cavities)	Behind RH side of I/P, near shroud	2	8	202-3
C202 (48 cavities)	Behind I/P, RH side of Steering Column	14	48	202-9
C230 (3 cavities)	Behind Radio in I/P	15	49	
C301 (23 cavities)	Below I/P, at LH shroud	6	20	202-12
C302 (23 cavities)	Below I/P, at LH shroud	6	20	202-13
C303 (6 cavities)	Below I/P, at LH shroud	6	20	202-35
C313 (2 cavities)	Under LH front seat			

(CONTINUED ON NEXT PAGE)

GROUND DISTRIBUTION

(CONTINUED FROM PREVIOUS PAGE)

COMPONENT	LOCATION	201-PG	FIG.	CONN
C314	Under RH front seat			
C400 (6 cavities)	RH rear of Trunk, above RH Tail Light Assembly	17	60	202-35
C401 (2 cavities)	Rear of vehicle center	20	71	
C405 (6 cavities)	Center rear of vehicle, near front of fuel tank	17	61	202-36
C420 (2 cavities)	In Trunk, at RH wheelhouse	17	60	
G101	LH front of Engine Compartment, on radiator support	1	6	
G102	RH front of Engine Compartment, on radiator support			
G111 (VIN L)	Behind Electronic Ignition (E/I) Control Module	0	3	
G111 (VIN M)	Lower LH front of Engine, on Transaxle stud	0	1	
G113 (VIN L)	Behind Electronic Ignition (E/I) Control Module	0	3	
G113 (VIN M)	Lower LH front of Engine, on Transaxle stud	0	1	
G115 (VIN L)	Behind Electronic Ignition (E/I) Control Module	0	3	
G115 (VIN M)	Lower LH front of Engine, on Transaxle stud	0	1	
G117	Lower LH front of Engine, on Transaxle stud	0	1	
G119	On LH strut tower	1	4	
G201	Behind LH side of I/P on mag bracket	14	48	
G203	Behind LH side of I/P on mag bracket	14	48	
G251	Behind LH side of I/P on mag bracket	14	48	
G301	Under LH front seat	15	50	
G302	Under RH front seat	15	50	
G311	Under LH front seat			
G312	Under RH front seat			
G313	Under LH front seat			
G349	Center of windshield header, near rearview mirror	13	45	
P104	Center rear of Engine Compartment	2	7	
P400	RH rear of Trunk	2	9	
P401	LH rear, Rear Compartment			
P402	RH rear, Rear Compartment			
P403	Behind center of rear bumper			
P404	Behind center of rear bumper			
P405	Rear underside of vehicle above fuel tank			
P500	In left front door jamb			
P600	In right front door jamb	23	77	
S105 (VIN L)	Engine Harn, approx 5 cm from Engine Cooling Fan #1 breakout			
S105 (VIN M)	Engine Harn, approx 5 cm from Engine Cooling Fan #1 breakout			
S106 (VIN L)	Engine Harn, approx 19 cm from PCM breakout			
S106 (VIN M)	Engine Harn, approx 4 cm from Engine Cooling Fan #2 breakout			
S123	Forward Lights Harn, approx 8 cm from RH Headlamp breakout	10	33	
S124	Forward Lights Harn, approx 8 cm from LH Headlamp breakout			
S125	Wiper Harn, approx 4 cm from Actuator Motor			
S128 (VIN M)	Engine Harn, approx 12 cm from Engine Cooling Fan #2 breakout			

COMPONENT	LOCATION	201-PG	FIG.	CONN
S135	Forward Lights Harn, approx 5 cm from Actuator Motor Assembly breakout			
S211	I/P Harn, approx 9 cm from Radio Control Head breakout			
S213	I/P Harn, approx 8 cm from HVAC Control Switch breakout			
S230	I/P Harn, approx 27 cm from Radio Control Head breakout			
S239	I/P Harn, approx 8 cm from HVAC Control Assembly breakout	15	49	
S242	SIR Jumper Harn, approx 26 cm from DERM Connector			
S303	Cross Car Harn, approx 38 cm from Driver Seat Belt Switch breakout	13	44	
S305	Cross Car Harn, approx 5 cm from G302 breakout	17	61	
S385	Console Harn, approx 8 cm from Ashtray Lamp breakout			
S390	Roof Harn, approx 18 cm from Dome Lamp breakout			
S327	Body Harn, approx 50 cm from G311 breakout			
S402	Rear Body Harn, approx 10 cm from RH Backup Lamp breakout			
S403	Rear Body Harn, approx 5 cm from LH Backup Lamp breakout			
S406	Cross Car Harn, approx 9 cm from RH Rear Speaker breakout			
S412	License Lamp Harn, approx 20 cm from C402			
S504	LH Front Door Harn, approx 4 cm from Door Lock Switch breakout			
S604	RH Front Door Harn, approx 4 cm from Door Lock Switch breakout			

SEQUENTIAL FUEL INJECTION: 3.1L VIN M
POWER, GROUND, DLC AND MALFUNCTION INDICATOR LAMP (MIL)

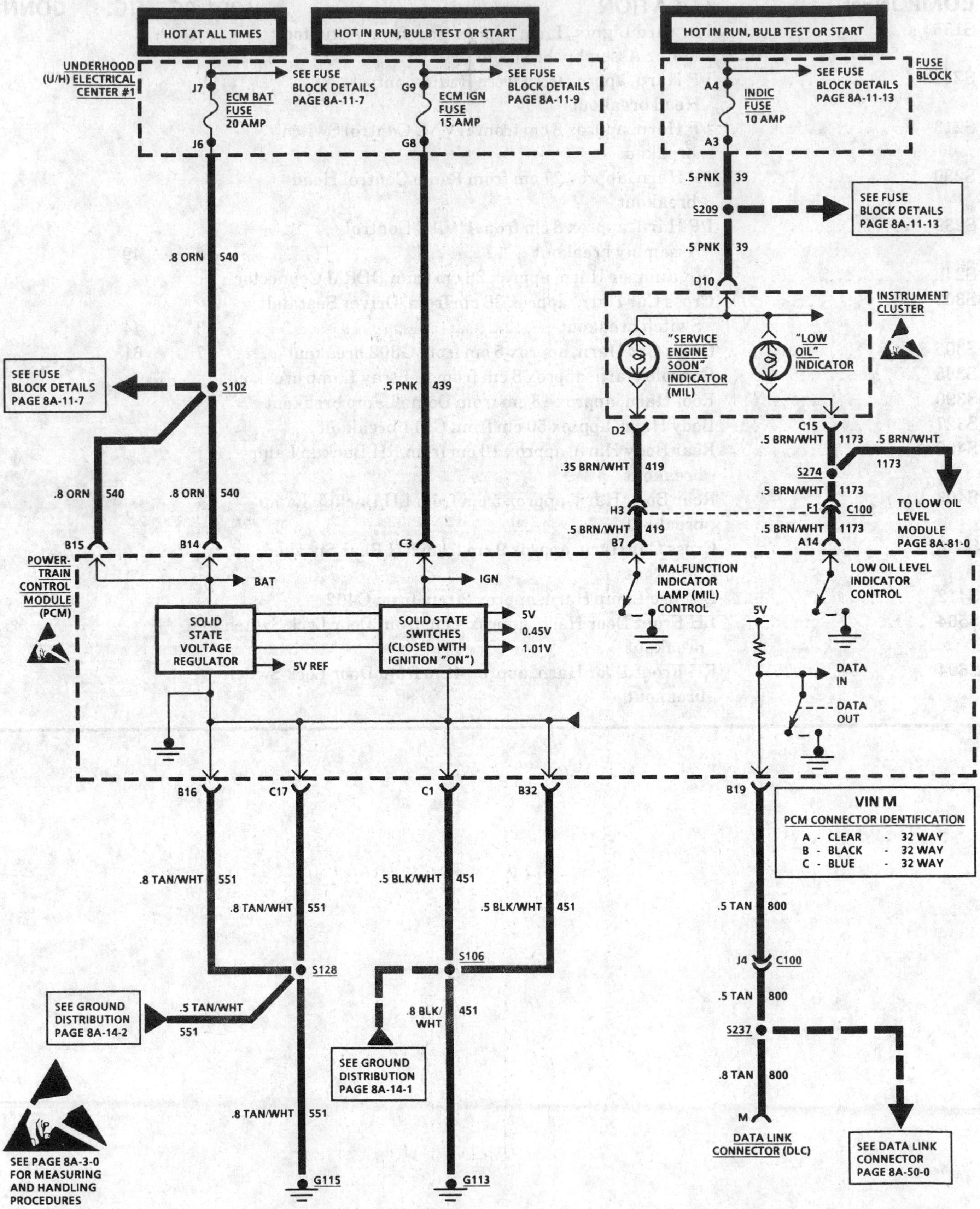
HOT AT ALL TIMES
HOT IN RUN, BULB TEST OR START
HOT IN RUN, BULB TEST OR START
UNDERHOOD (U/H) ELECTRICAL CENTER #1
J7
ECM BAT FUSE 20 AMP
J6
SEE FUSE BLOCK DETAILS PAGE 8A-11-7
G9
ECM IGN FUSE 15 AMP
G8
SEE FUSE BLOCK DETAILS PAGE 8A-11-9
A4
INDIC FUSE 10 AMP
A3
SEE FUSE BLOCK DETAILS PAGE 8A-11-13
FUSE BLOCK
.5 PNK 39
S209
SEE FUSE BLOCK DETAILS PAGE 8A-11-13
.5 PNK 39
D10
INSTRUMENT CLUSTER
"SERVICE ENGINE SOON" INDICATOR (MIL)
"LOW OIL" INDICATOR
.8 ORN 540
SEE FUSE BLOCK DETAILS PAGE 8A-11-7
S102
.5 PNK 439
D2
C15
.5 BRN/WHT 1173
.5 BRN/WHT 1173
.35 BRN/WHT 419
S274
.8 ORN 540
.8 ORN 540
.5 BRN/WHT 1173
H3
F1
C100
TO LOW OIL LEVEL MODULE PAGE 8A-81-0
.5 BRN/WHT 419
.5 BRN/WHT 1173
B15
B14
C3
B7
A14
POWER-TRAIN CONTROL MODULE (PCM)
BAT
IGN
MALFUNCTION INDICATOR LAMP (MIL) CONTROL
LOW OIL LEVEL INDICATOR CONTROL
SOLID STATE VOLTAGE REGULATOR
SOLID STATE SWITCHES (CLOSED WITH IGNITION "ON")
5V
0.45V
1.01V
5V REF
5V
DATA IN
DATA OUT
B16
C17
C1
B32
B19
VIN M
PCM CONNECTOR IDENTIFICATION
A - CLEAR - 32 WAY
B - BLACK - 32 WAY
C - BLUE - 32 WAY
.8 TAN/WHT 551
.5 BLK/WHT 451
.8 TAN/WHT 551
.5 BLK/WHT 451
.5 TAN 800
S106
S128
J4
C100
SEE GROUND DISTRIBUTION PAGE 8A-14-2
.5 TAN/WHT 551
.8 BLK/WHT 451
.5 TAN 800
S237
SEE GROUND DISTRIBUTION PAGE 8A-14-1
.8 TAN 800
.8 TAN/WHT 551
M
DATA LINK CONNECTOR (DLC)
SEE DATA LINK CONNECTOR PAGE 8A-50-0
SEE PAGE 8A-3-0 FOR MEASURING AND HANDLING PROCEDURES
G115
G113

SEQUENTIAL FUEL INJECTION: 3.1L VIN M
ELECTRONIC IGNITION (EI) SYSTEM

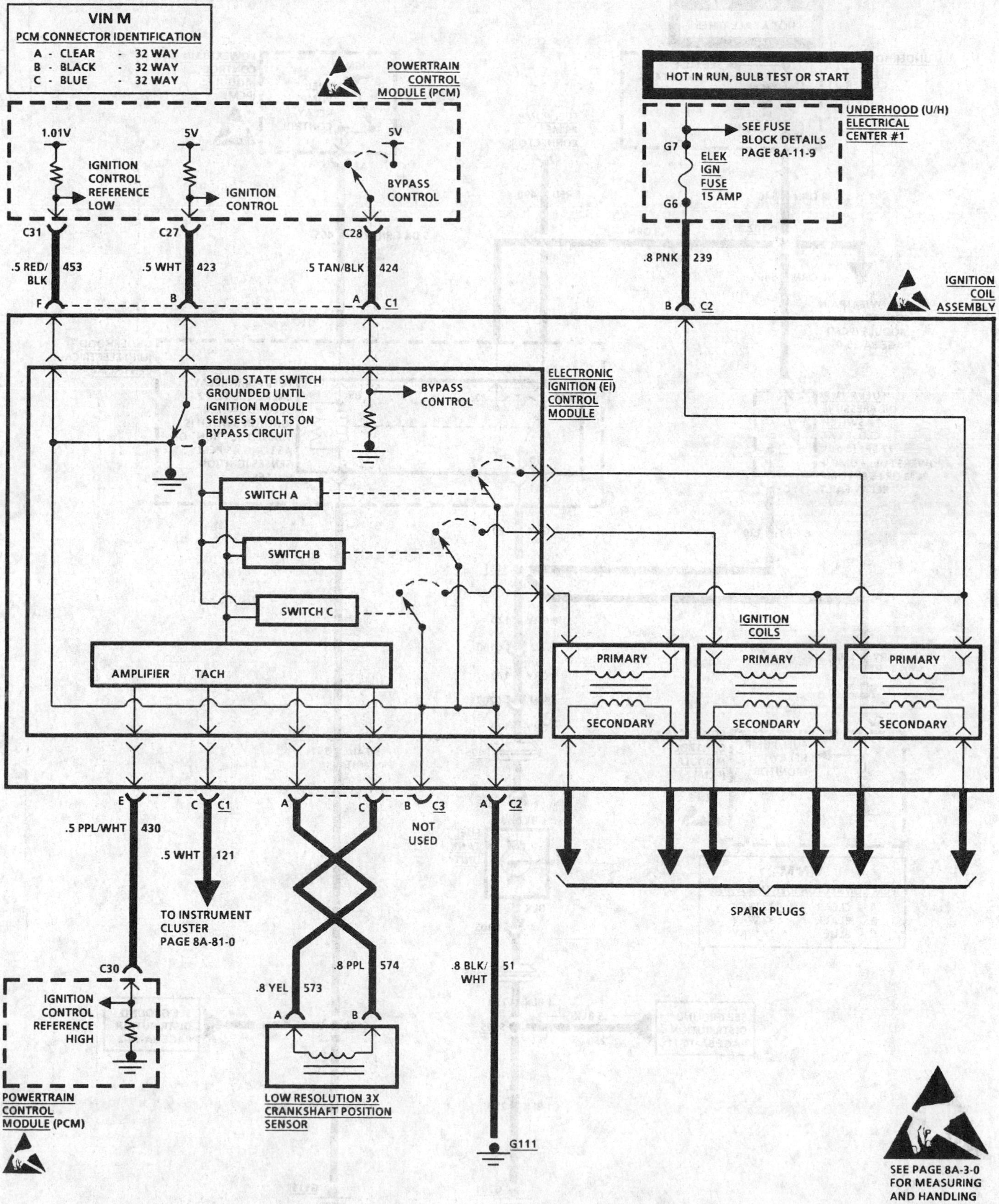
VIN M
PCM CONNECTOR IDENTIFICATION
A - CLEAR - 32 WAY
B - BLACK - 32 WAY
C - BLUE - 32 WAY
POWERTRAIN CONTROL MODULE (PCM)
1.01V
IGNITION CONTROL REFERENCE LOW
5V
IGNITION CONTROL
5V
BYPASS CONTROL
C31
C27
C28
.5 RED/BLK 453
.5 WHT 423
.5 TAN/BLK 424
F
B
A
C1
HOT IN RUN, BULB TEST OR START
UNDERHOOD (U/H) ELECTRICAL CENTER #1
SEE FUSE BLOCK DETAILS PAGE 8A-11-9
G7
ELEK IGN FUSE 15 AMP
G6
.8 PNK 239
B
C2
IGNITION COIL ASSEMBLY
SOLID STATE SWITCH GROUNDED UNTIL IGNITION MODULE SENSES 5 VOLTS ON BYPASS CIRCUIT
BYPASS CONTROL
ELECTRONIC IGNITION (EI) CONTROL MODULE
SWITCH A
SWITCH B
SWITCH C
AMPLIFIER
TACH
IGNITION COILS
PRIMARY
SECONDARY
PRIMARY
SECONDARY
PRIMARY
SECONDARY
E
C
C1
A
C
B
C3
A
C2
.5 PPL/WHT 430
.5 WHT 121
NOT USED
TO INSTRUMENT CLUSTER PAGE 8A-81-0
SPARK PLUGS
C30
IGNITION CONTROL REFERENCE HIGH
POWERTRAIN CONTROL MODULE (PCM)
.8 PPL 574
.8 YEL 573
A
B
LOW RESOLUTION 3X CRANKSHAFT POSITION SENSOR
.8 BLK/WHT 51
G111
SEE PAGE 8A-3-0 FOR MEASURING AND HANDLING PROCEDURES

SEQUENTIAL FUEL INJECTION: 3.1L VIN M
FUEL INJECTOR AND FUEL CONTROL

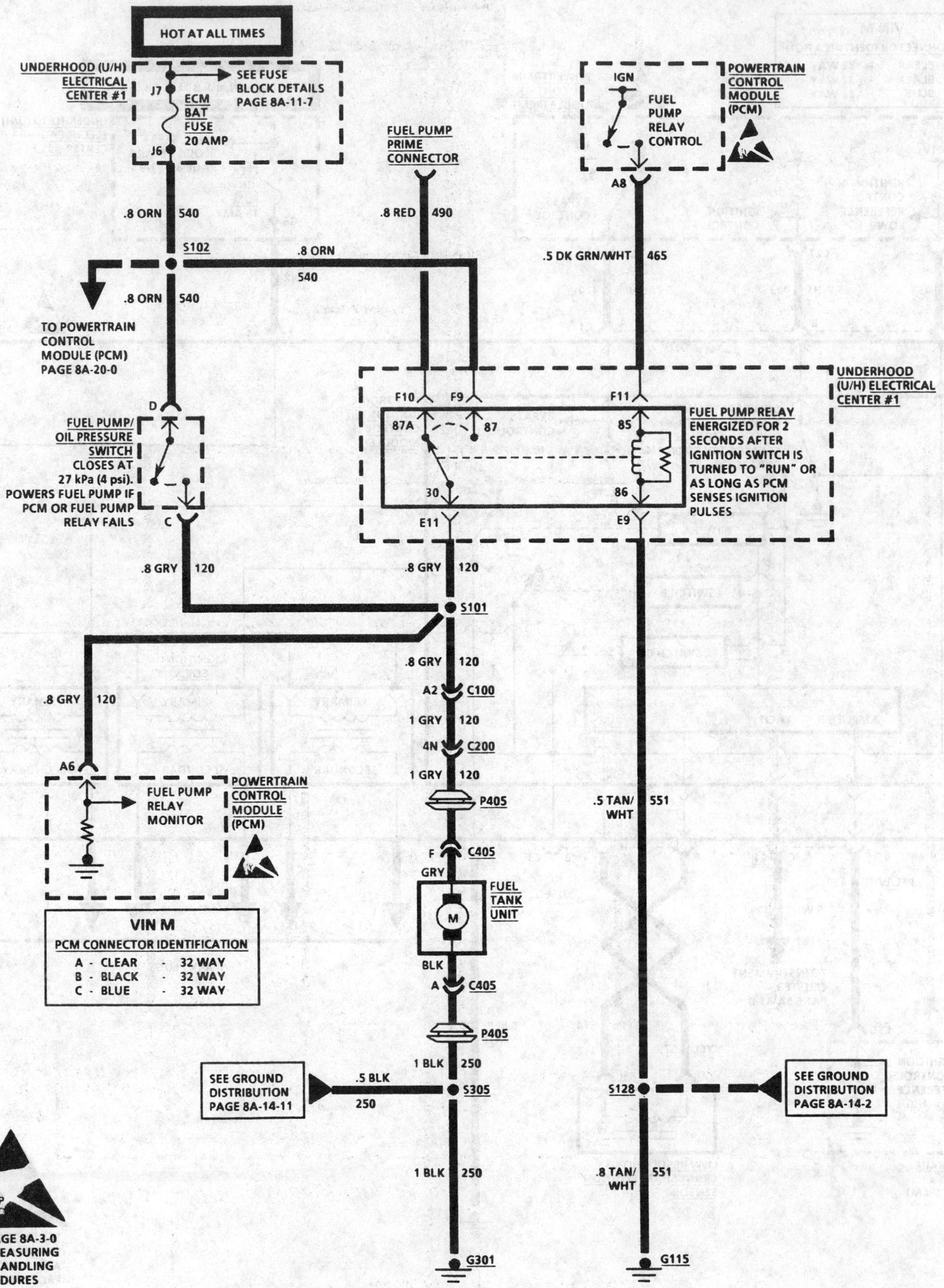
HOT AT ALL TIMES
UNDERHOOD (U/H) ELECTRICAL CENTER #1
J7
ECM BAT FUSE 20 AMP
SEE FUSE BLOCK DETAILS PAGE 8A-11-7
J6
.8 ORN 540
S102
.8 ORN
540
.8 ORN 540
TO POWERTRAIN CONTROL MODULE (PCM) PAGE 8A-20-0
FUEL PUMP PRIME CONNECTOR
.8 RED 490
POWERTRAIN CONTROL MODULE (PCM)
IGN
FUEL PUMP RELAY CONTROL
A8
.5 DK GRN/WHT 465
UNDERHOOD (U/H) ELECTRICAL CENTER #1
F10
F9
F11
87A
87
85
30
86
E11
E9
FUEL PUMP RELAY ENERGIZED FOR 2 SECONDS AFTER IGNITION SWITCH IS TURNED TO "RUN" OR AS LONG AS PCM SENSES IGNITION PULSES
D
FUEL PUMP/ OIL PRESSURE SWITCH CLOSES AT 27 kPa (4 psi). POWERS FUEL PUMP IF PCM OR FUEL PUMP RELAY FAILS
C
.8 GRY 120
.8 GRY 120
S101
.8 GRY 120
.8 GRY 120
A2
C100
1 GRY 120
4N
C200
1 GRY 120
P405
A6
FUEL PUMP RELAY MONITOR
POWERTRAIN CONTROL MODULE (PCM)
.5 TAN/ WHT 551
F
C405
GRY
FUEL TANK UNIT
M
BLK
A
C405
P405
1 BLK 250
SEE GROUND DISTRIBUTION PAGE 8A-14-11
.5 BLK
250
S305
S128
SEE GROUND DISTRIBUTION PAGE 8A-14-2
1 BLK 250
.8 TAN/ WHT 551
G301
G115

VIN M		
PCM CONNECTOR IDENTIFICATION		
A - CLEAR	-	32 WAY
B - BLACK	-	32 WAY
C - BLUE	-	32 WAY

SEE PAGE 8A-3-0 FOR MEASURING AND HANDLING PROCEDURES

SEQUENTIAL FUEL INJECTION: 3.1L VIN M
FUEL INJECTORS

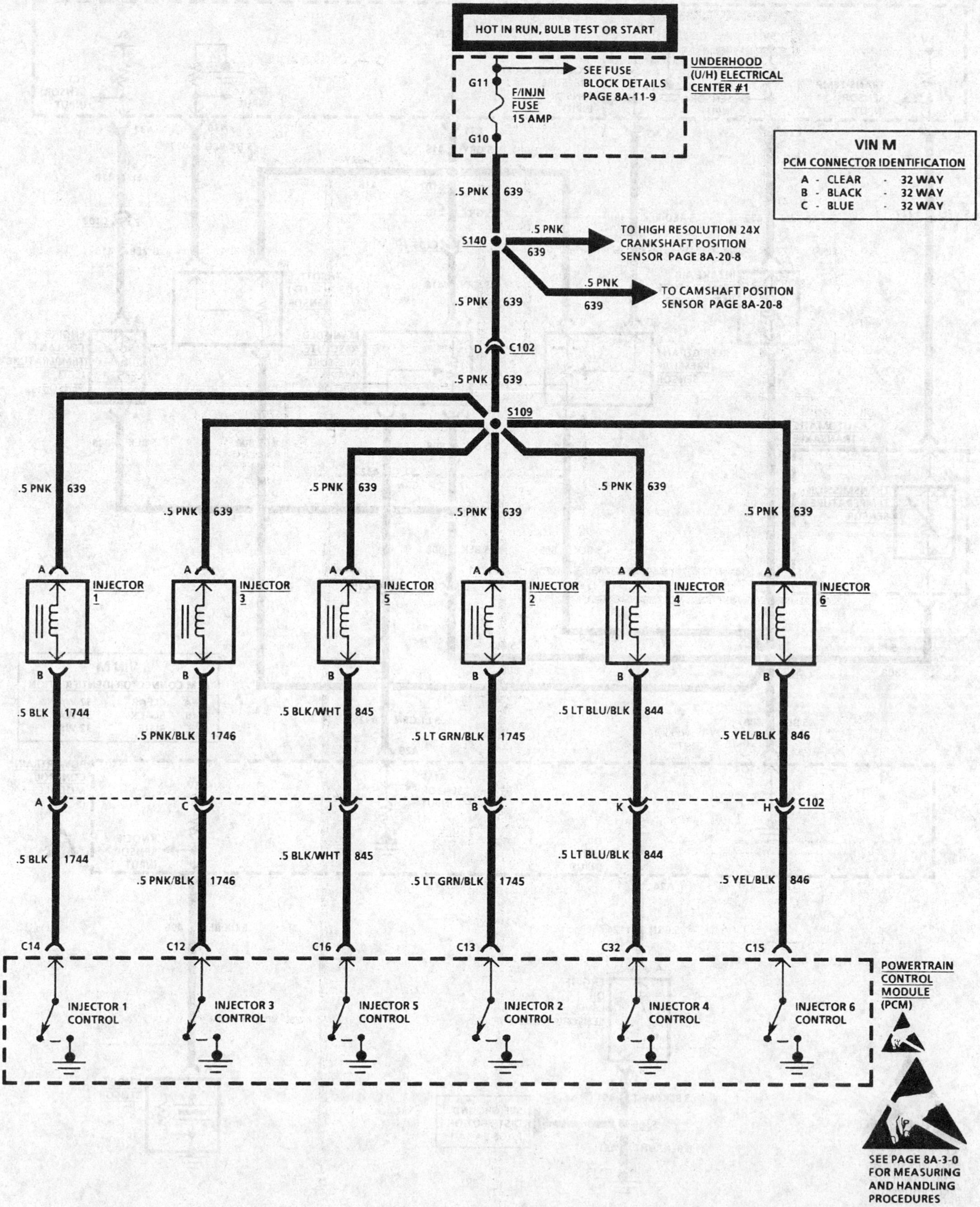

HOT IN RUN, BULB TEST OR START
G11
SEE FUSE BLOCK DETAILS PAGE 8A-11-9
F/INJN FUSE 15 AMP
G10
UNDERHOOD (U/H) ELECTRICAL CENTER #1
VIN M
PCM CONNECTOR IDENTIFICATION
A - CLEAR - 32 WAY
B - BLACK - 32 WAY
C - BLUE - 32 WAY
.5 PNK 639
S140
TO HIGH RESOLUTION 24X CRANKSHAFT POSITION SENSOR PAGE 8A-20-8
TO CAMSHAFT POSITION SENSOR PAGE 8A-20-8
D C102
S109
INJECTOR 1
INJECTOR 3
INJECTOR 5
INJECTOR 2
INJECTOR 4
INJECTOR 6
A
B
.5 BLK 1744
.5 PNK/BLK 1746
.5 BLK/WHT 845
.5 LT GRN/BLK 1745
.5 LT BLU/BLK 844
.5 YEL/BLK 846
A C J B K H C102
C14 C12 C16 C13 C32 C15
INJECTOR 1 CONTROL
INJECTOR 3 CONTROL
INJECTOR 5 CONTROL
INJECTOR 2 CONTROL
INJECTOR 4 CONTROL
INJECTOR 6 CONTROL
POWERTRAIN CONTROL MODULE (PCM)
SEE PAGE 8A-3-0 FOR MEASURING AND HANDLING PROCEDURES

SEQUENTIAL FUEL INJECTION: 3.1L VIN M
ENGINE DATA SENSORS

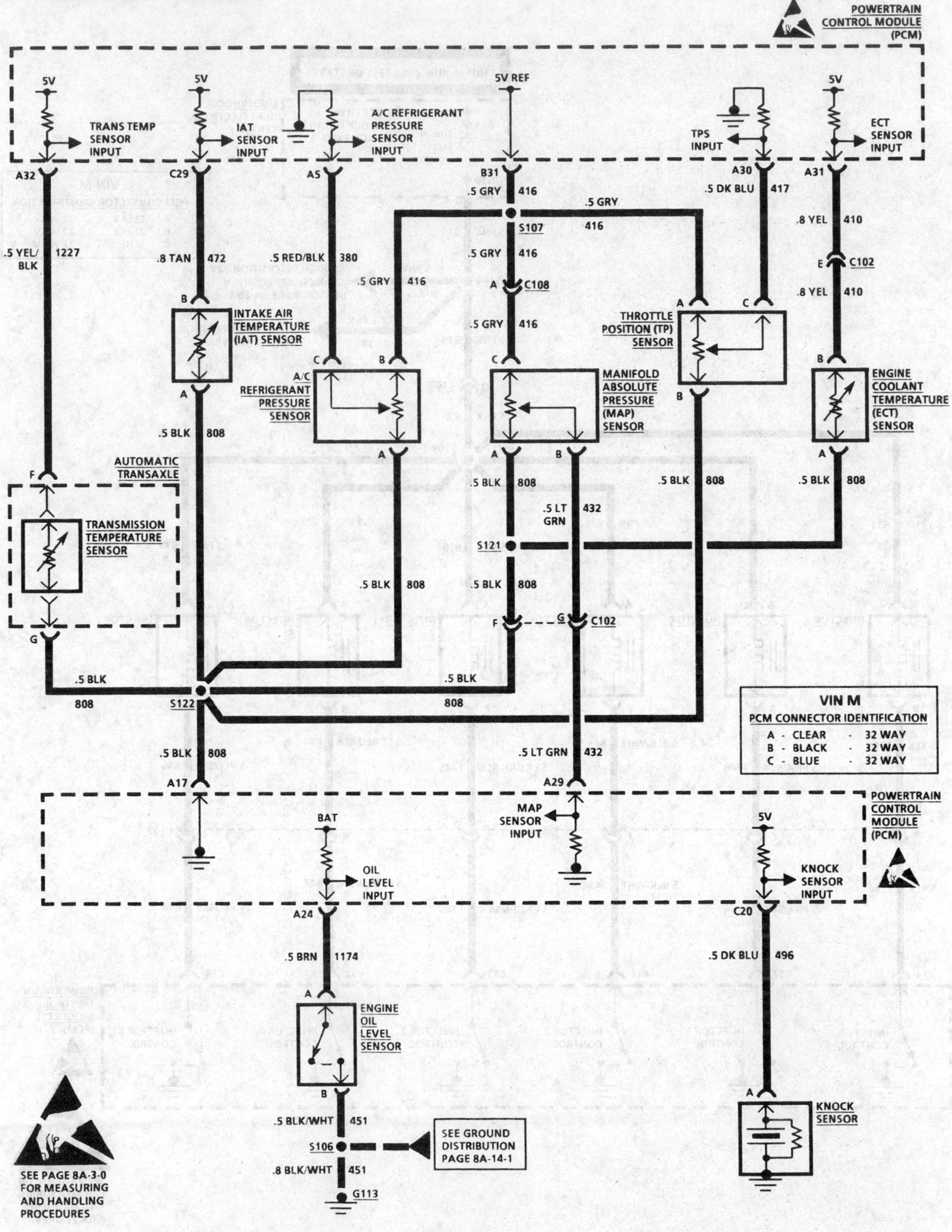

POWERTRAIN CONTROL MODULE (PCM)
5V
TRANS TEMP SENSOR INPUT
5V
IAT SENSOR INPUT
A/C REFRIGERANT PRESSURE SENSOR INPUT
5V REF
TPS INPUT
5V
ECT SENSOR INPUT
A32
C29
A5
B31
A30
A31
.5 GRY 416
.5 GRY 416
S107
.5 DK BLU 417
.8 YEL 410
C102
.8 YEL 410
.5 YEL/BLK 1227
.8 TAN 472
.5 RED/BLK 380
.5 GRY 416
C108
.5 GRY 416
.5 GRY 416
INTAKE AIR TEMPERATURE (IAT) SENSOR
THROTTLE POSITION (TP) SENSOR
A/C REFRIGERANT PRESSURE SENSOR
MANIFOLD ABSOLUTE PRESSURE (MAP) SENSOR
ENGINE COOLANT TEMPERATURE (ECT) SENSOR
.5 BLK 808
AUTOMATIC TRANSAXLE
TRANSMISSION TEMPERATURE SENSOR
.5 BLK 808
.5 LT GRN 432
.5 BLK 808
.5 BLK 808
S121
.5 BLK 808
.5 BLK 808
C102
.5 BLK 808
.5 BLK 808
S122
.5 BLK 808
.5 LT GRN 432
A17
A29
VIN M
PCM CONNECTOR IDENTIFICATION
A - CLEAR - 32 WAY
B - BLACK - 32 WAY
C - BLUE - 32 WAY
POWERTRAIN CONTROL MODULE (PCM)
BAT
MAP SENSOR INPUT
5V
OIL LEVEL INPUT
KNOCK SENSOR INPUT
A24
C20
.5 BRN 1174
.5 DK BLU 496
ENGINE OIL LEVEL SENSOR
KNOCK SENSOR
.5 BLK/WHT 451
S106
SEE GROUND DISTRIBUTION PAGE 8A-14-1
.8 BLK/WHT 451
G113
SEE PAGE 8A-3-0 FOR MEASURING AND HANDLING PROCEDURES

SEQUENTIAL FUEL INJECTION: 3.1L VIN M
DIGITAL EXHAUST GAS RECIRCULATION

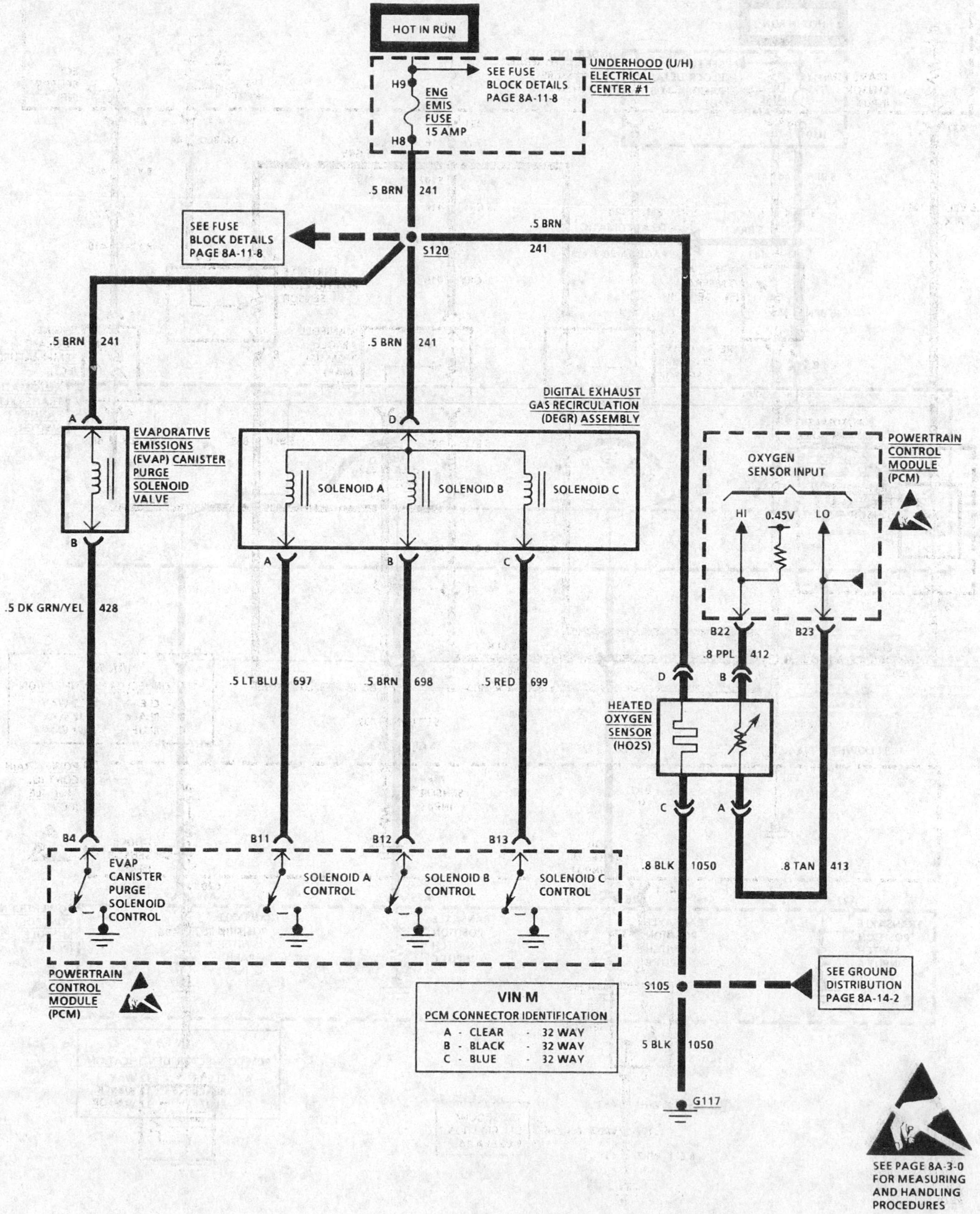
HOT IN RUN
UNDERHOOD (U/H) ELECTRICAL CENTER #1
H9
ENG EMIS FUSE 15 AMP
H8
SEE FUSE BLOCK DETAILS PAGE 8A-11-8
.5 BRN 241
SEE FUSE BLOCK DETAILS PAGE 8A-11-8
S120
.5 BRN
241
.5 BRN 241
.5 BRN 241
A
EVAPORATIVE EMISSIONS (EVAP) CANISTER PURGE SOLENOID VALVE
B
DIGITAL EXHAUST GAS RECIRCULATION (DEGR) ASSEMBLY
D
SOLENOID A
SOLENOID B
SOLENOID C
A
B
C
POWERTRAIN CONTROL MODULE (PCM)
OXYGEN SENSOR INPUT
HI
0.45V
LO
B22
B23
.8 PPL 412
.5 DK GRN/YEL 428
.5 LT BLU 697
.5 BRN 698
.5 RED 699
D
B
HEATED OXYGEN SENSOR (HO2S)
C
A
B4
B11
B12
B13
EVAP CANISTER PURGE SOLENOID CONTROL
SOLENOID A CONTROL
SOLENOID B CONTROL
SOLENOID C CONTROL
.8 BLK 1050
.8 TAN 413
POWERTRAIN CONTROL MODULE (PCM)
S105
SEE GROUND DISTRIBUTION PAGE 8A-14-2
5 BLK 1050
G117

VIN M

PCM CONNECTOR IDENTIFICATION

A -	CLEAR	- 32 WAY
B -	BLACK	- 32 WAY
C -	BLUE	- 32 WAY

SEE PAGE 8A-3-0 FOR MEASURING AND HANDLING PROCEDURES

SEQUENTIAL FUEL INJECTION: 3.1L VIN M
4 SPEED AUTOMATIC TRANSAXLE

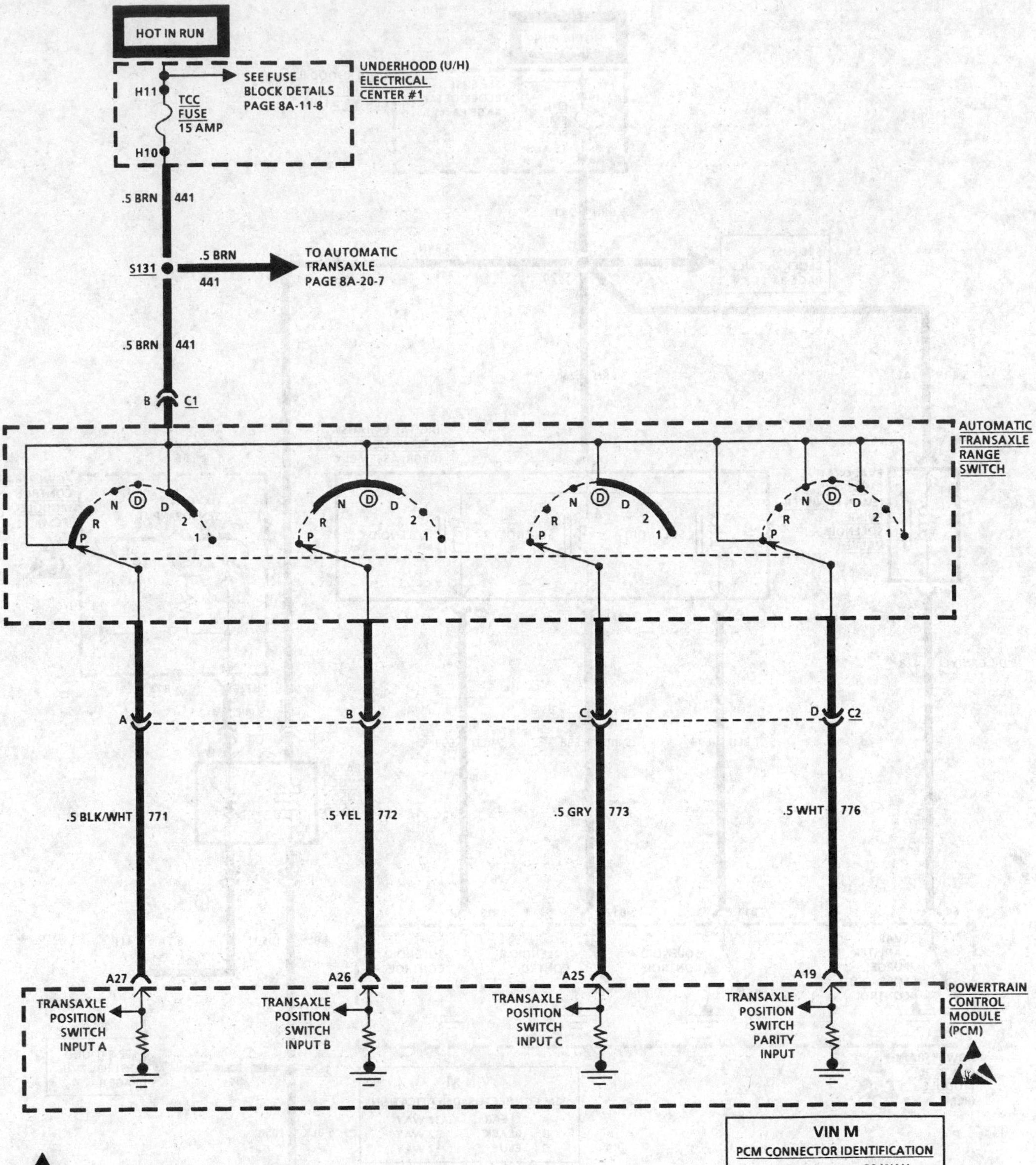
HOT IN RUN
SEE FUSE BLOCK DETAILS PAGE 8A-11-8
UNDERHOOD (U/H) ELECTRICAL CENTER #1
H11
TCC FUSE 15 AMP
H10
.5 BRN 441
S131
.5 BRN
441
TO AUTOMATIC TRANSAXLE PAGE 8A-20-7
.5 BRN 441
B C1
AUTOMATIC TRANSAXLE RANGE SWITCH
P R N D D 2 1
A B C D C2
.5 BLK/WHT 771
.5 YEL 772
.5 GRY 773
.5 WHT 776
A27
A26
A25
A19
TRANSAXLE POSITION SWITCH INPUT A
TRANSAXLE POSITION SWITCH INPUT B
TRANSAXLE POSITION SWITCH INPUT C
TRANSAXLE POSITION SWITCH PARITY INPUT
POWERTRAIN CONTROL MODULE (PCM)

VIN M		
PCM CONNECTOR IDENTIFICATION		
A - CLEAR	-	32 WAY
B - BLACK	-	32 WAY
C - BLUE	-	32 WAY

SEE PAGE 8A-3-0 FOR MEASURING AND HANDLING PROCEDURES

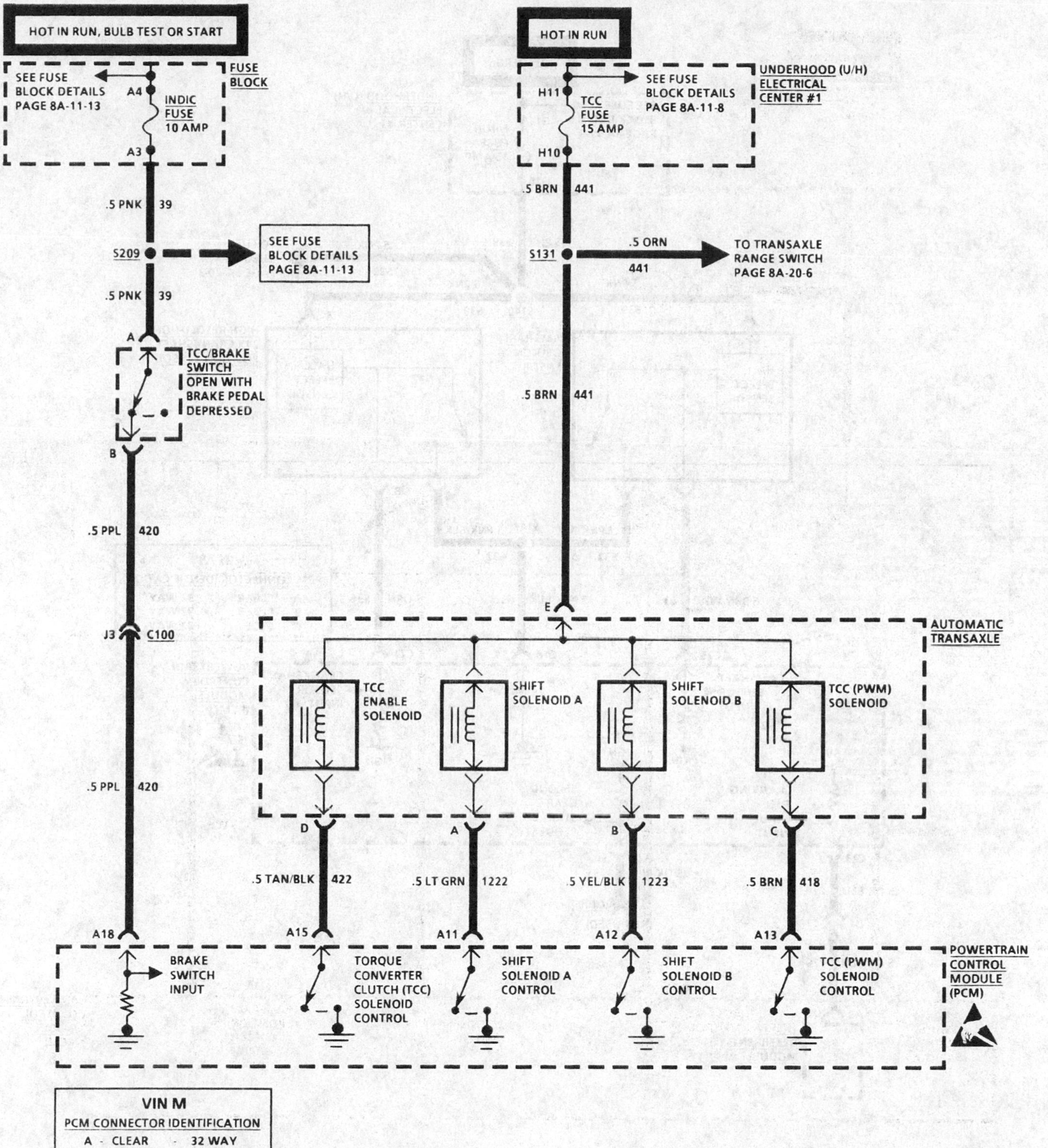
HOT IN RUN, BULB TEST OR START
SEE FUSE BLOCK DETAILS PAGE 8A-11-13
A4
INDIC FUSE 10 AMP
A3
FUSE BLOCK
.5 PNK 39
S209
SEE FUSE BLOCK DETAILS PAGE 8A-11-13
.5 PNK 39
A
TCC/BRAKE SWITCH OPEN WITH BRAKE PEDAL DEPRESSED
B
.5 PPL 420
J3
C100
.5 PPL 420
HOT IN RUN
H11
TCC FUSE 15 AMP
H10
SEE FUSE BLOCK DETAILS PAGE 8A-11-8
UNDERHOOD (U/H) ELECTRICAL CENTER #1
.5 BRN 441
S131
.5 ORN
441
TO TRANSAXLE RANGE SWITCH PAGE 8A-20-6
.5 BRN 441
E
AUTOMATIC TRANSAXLE
TCC ENABLE SOLENOID
SHIFT SOLENOID A
SHIFT SOLENOID B
TCC (PWM) SOLENOID
D
A
B
C
.5 TAN/BLK 422
.5 LT GRN 1222
.5 YEL/BLK 1223
.5 BRN 418
A18
A15
A11
A12
A13
BRAKE SWITCH INPUT
TORQUE CONVERTER CLUTCH (TCC) SOLENOID CONTROL
SHIFT SOLENOID A CONTROL
SHIFT SOLENOID B CONTROL
TCC (PWM) SOLENOID CONTROL
POWERTRAIN CONTROL MODULE (PCM)

VIN M

PCM CONNECTOR IDENTIFICATION

A	-	CLEAR	-	32 WAY
B	-	BLACK	-	32 WAY
C	-	BLUE	-	32 WAY

SEE PAGE 8A-3-0 FOR MEASURING AND HANDLING PROCEDURES

SEQUENTIAL FUEL INJECTION: 3.1L VIN M

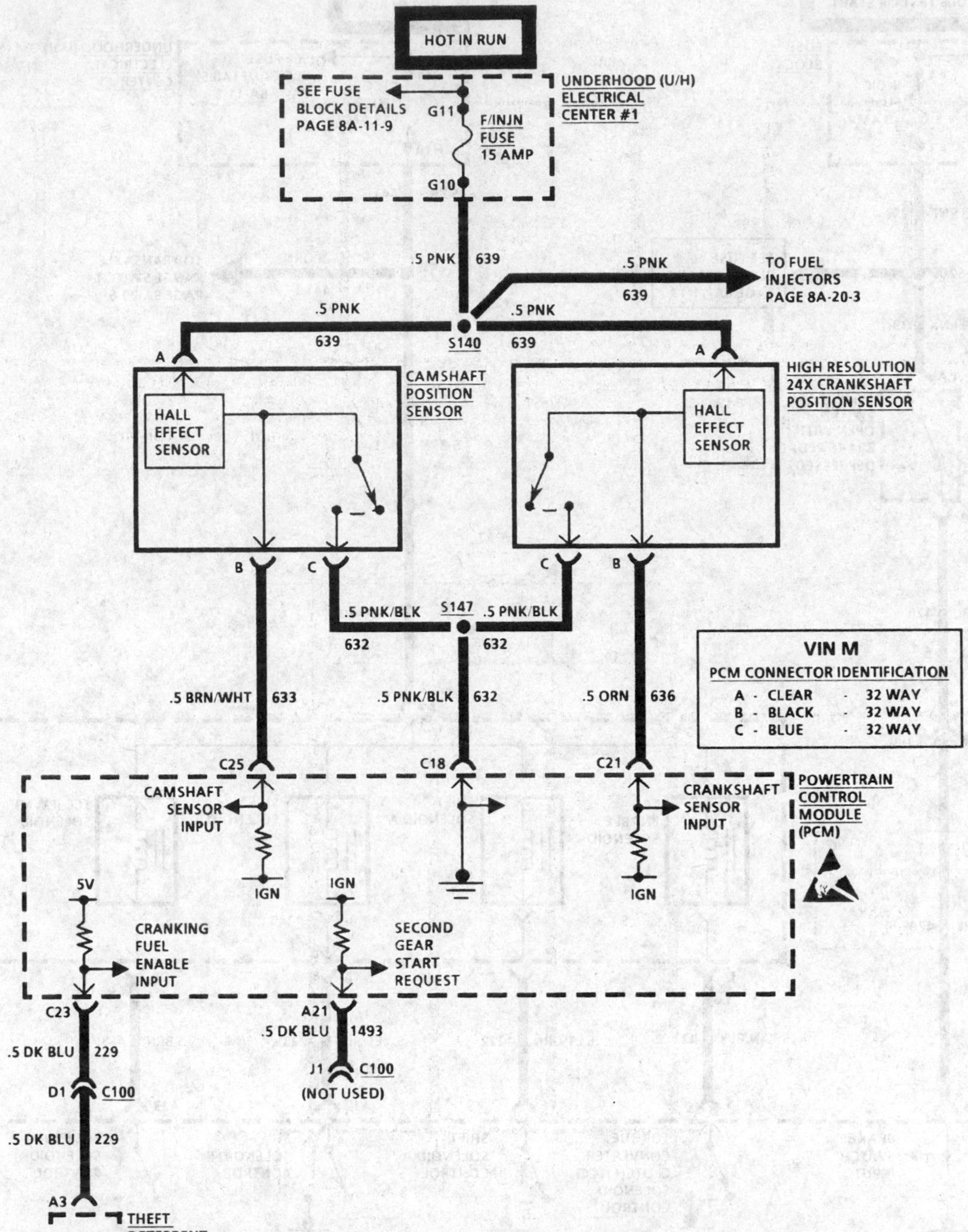

HOT IN RUN
SEE FUSE BLOCK DETAILS PAGE 8A-11-9
UNDERHOOD (U/H) ELECTRICAL CENTER #1
G11
F/INJN FUSE 15 AMP
G10
.5 PNK 639
.5 PNK 639
TO FUEL INJECTORS PAGE 8A-20-3
.5 PNK 639
S140
.5 PNK 639
A
CAMSHAFT POSITION SENSOR
HALL EFFECT SENSOR
HIGH RESOLUTION 24X CRANKSHAFT POSITION SENSOR
HALL EFFECT SENSOR
B
C
C
B
.5 PNK/BLK 632
S147
.5 PNK/BLK 632
.5 BRN/WHT 633
.5 PNK/BLK 632
.5 ORN 636
C25
C18
C21
CAMSHAFT SENSOR INPUT
CRANKSHAFT SENSOR INPUT
POWERTRAIN CONTROL MODULE (PCM)
IGN
IGN
IGN
5V
CRANKING FUEL ENABLE INPUT
SECOND GEAR START REQUEST
C23
A21
.5 DK BLU 229
.5 DK BLU 1493
D1 C100
J1 C100 (NOT USED)
.5 DK BLU 229
A3
THEFT DETERRENT MODULE

VIN M

PCM CONNECTOR IDENTIFICATION

A -	CLEAR	-	32 WAY
B -	BLACK	-	32 WAY
C -	BLUE	-	32 WAY

SEE PAGE 8A-3-0 FOR MEASURING AND HANDLING PROCEDURES

SEQUENTIAL FUEL INJECTION: 3.1L VIN M
IDLE AIR CONTROL

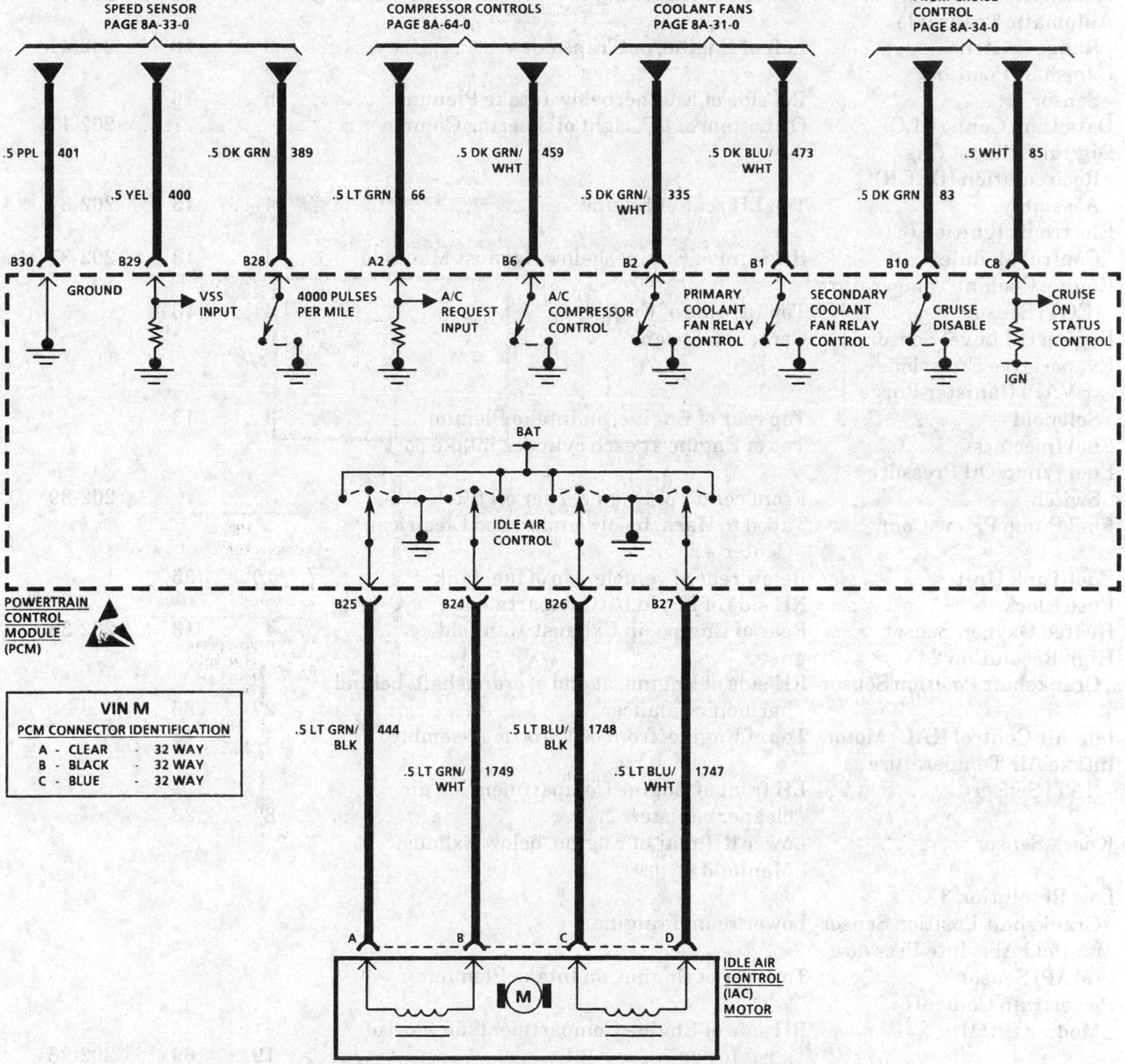
FROM VEHICLE SPEED SENSOR PAGE 8A-33-0
FROM HVAC COMPRESSOR CONTROLS PAGE 8A-64-0
FROM COOLANT FANS PAGE 8A-31-0
FROM CRUISE CONTROL PAGE 8A-34-0
.5 PPL 401
.5 YEL 400
.5 DK GRN 389
.5 LT GRN 66
.5 DK GRN/WHT 459
.5 DK GRN/WHT 335
.5 DK BLU/WHT 473
.5 DK GRN 83
.5 WHT 85
B30
B29
B28
A2
B6
B2
B1
B10
C8
GROUND
VSS INPUT
4000 PULSES PER MILE
A/C REQUEST INPUT
A/C COMPRESSOR CONTROL
PRIMARY COOLANT FAN RELAY CONTROL
SECONDARY COOLANT FAN RELAY CONTROL
CRUISE DISABLE
CRUISE ON STATUS CONTROL
IGN
BAT
IDLE AIR CONTROL
POWERTRAIN CONTROL MODULE (PCM)
B25
B24
B26
B27
.5 LT GRN/BLK 444
.5 LT GRN/WHT 1749
.5 LT BLU/BLK 1748
.5 LT BLU/WHT 1747
A
B
C
D
M
IDLE AIR CONTROL (IAC) MOTOR

VIN M		
PCM CONNECTOR IDENTIFICATION		
A - CLEAR	-	32 WAY
B - BLACK	-	32 WAY
C - BLUE	-	32 WAY

SEE PAGE 8A-3-0 FOR MEASURING AND HANDLING PROCEDURES

SEQUENTIAL FUEL INJECTION: 3.1L VIN M

COMPONENT	LOCATION	201-PG	FIG.	CONN
A/C Refrigerant Pressure Sensor	LH front of Engine Compartment, on A/C line	7	21	
Automatic Transaxle	Lower LH side of Engine Compartment	3	10	202-35
Automatic Transaxle Range Switch	Left of Engine, on Transaxle	3	10	202-41
Camshaft Position Sensor	RH side of Engine, below Intake Plenum	5	16	
Data Link Conn (DLC)	On bottom of I/P, right of Steering Column			202-17
Digital Exhaust Gas Recirculation (DEGR) Assembly	Top LH rear of Engine	4	13	202-37
Electronic Ignition (EI) Control Module	RH front of Engine, below Exhaust Manifold	4	13	202-37
Engine Coolant Temperature (ECT) Sensor	Top LH side of Engine	4	13	
Engine Oil Level Sensor	Center of oil pan			
Evaporative Emissions (EVAP) Canister Purge Solenoid	Top rear of Engine, on Intake Plenum	4	13	
Fuel Injectors	Top of Engine at each cylinder intake port			
Fuel Pump/Oil Pressure Switch	Front center of Engine, near oil filter			202-39
Fuel Pump Prime Conn	Taped to Harn, below Underhood Electrical Center #2			
Fuel Tank Unit	Below rear of vehicle, top of fuel tank	10	35	
Fuse Block	RH side of I/P, in I/P Compartment			
Heated Oxygen Sensor	Rear of Engine, in Exhaust Manifold	4	13	202-38
High Resolution 24X Crankshaft Position Sensor	RH side of Engine, at end of crankshaft, behind harmonic balancer	27	86	
Idle Air Control (IAC) Motor	Top of Engine, front of Throttle Assembly	4	13	
Intake Air Temperature (IAT) Sensor	LH front of Engine Compartment, on air cleaner canister	8	28	
Knock Sensor	Lower RH rear of Engine, below Exhaust Manifold			
Low Resolution 3X Crankshaft Position Sensor	Lower rear of Engine			
Manifold Absolute Pressure (MAP) Sensor	Top rear of Engine, on Intake Plenum			
Powertrain Control Module (PCM)	RH side of Engine Compartment, forward of strut tower	19	69	202-26
TCC/Brake Switch	Behind I/P, on brake pedal support	12	42	202-41
Theft Deterrent Module	Below LH side of I/P, left of Steering Column			202-34
Throttle Position (TP) Sensor	Top of Engine, on Throttle Assembly	4	13	

COMPONENT	LOCATION	201-PG	FIG.	CONN
Underhood Electrical Center #1	RH side Engine Compartment, forward of strut tower			202-34
C100 (36 cavities)	RH side of dash, behind strut tower			202-0
C102 (10 cavities)	RH rear of Engine Compartment, near Generator	21	72	202-2
C108 (1 cavity)	RH rear of Engine Compartment, near Generator	21	72	
C200 (102 cavities)	Behind RH side of I/P, near shroud	2	8	202-3
C405 (6 cavities)	Center rear of vehicle, near front of fuel tank	10	35	202-38
G111	Lower LH front of Engine, on Transaxle stud	0	1	
G113	Lower LH front of Engine, on Transaxle stud	0	1	
G115	Lower LH front of Engine, on Transaxle stud	0	1	
G117	Lower LH front of Engine, on Transaxle stud	0	1	
G301	Under LH front seat	15	50	
P405	Center front of Luggage Compartment, in floor			
S101	Engine Harn, approx 8 cm from Camshaft Position Sensor breakout			
S102	Engine Harn, approx 4 cm from Underhood Electrical Center #1 breakout			
S105	Engine Harn, approx 4 cm from Engine Cooling Fan #2 Breakout			
S106	Engine Harn, approx 21 cm from Engine Cooling Fan #2 breakout			
S107	Engine Harn, approx 8 cm from Powertrain Control Module (PCM) breakout			
S109	Engine Jumper Harn, approx 24 cm from C102			
S120	Engine Harn, approx 6 cm from Fuel Injector Harn breakout			
S121	Engine Jumper Harn, approx 6 cm from Fuel Injectors breakout			
S122	Engine Harn, approx 28 cm from Engine Cooling Fan #2 breakout			
S128	Engine Harn, approx 12 cm from Engine Cooling Fan #2 breakout			
S131	Engine Harn, approx 4 cm from Fusible Link breakout			
S140	Engine Harn, approx 8 cm from Camshaft Position Sensor breakout			
S147	Engine Harn, approx 4 cm from Camshaft Position Sensor breakout			
S209	I/P Harn, approx 16 cm from Fuse Block breakout			
S237	I/P Harn, approx 14 cm from Headlight Switch breakout	15	49	
S274	I/P Harn, approx 22 cm from Radio Control head breakout			
S305	Cross Car Harn, approx 5 cm from G302 breakout	17	61	

SEQUENTIAL FUEL INJECTION: 3.8L VIN L
POWER, GROUND, DLC AND MALFUNCTION INDICATOR LAMP (MIL)

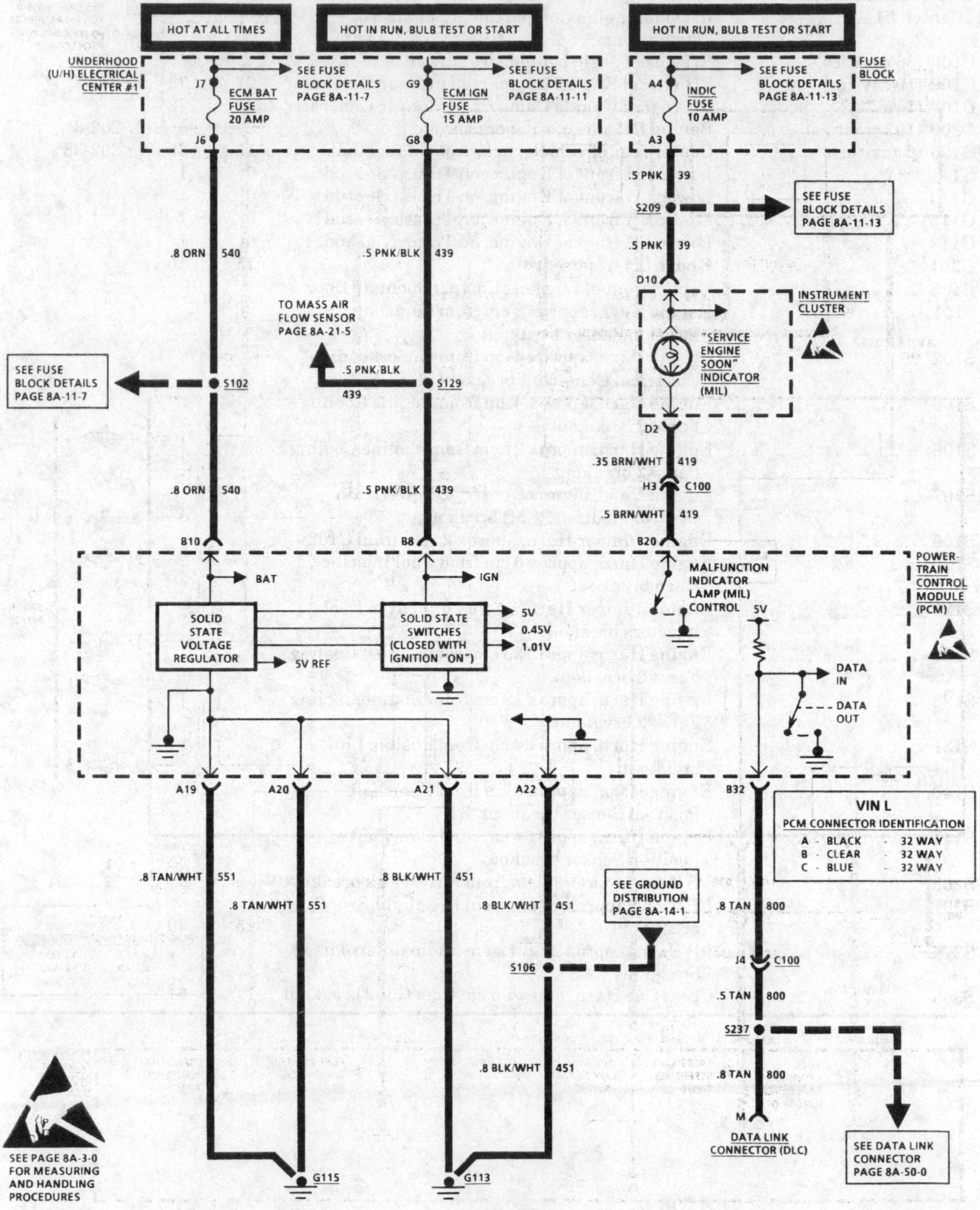

HOT AT ALL TIMES
HOT IN RUN, BULB TEST OR START
HOT IN RUN, BULB TEST OR START
UNDERHOOD (U/H) ELECTRICAL CENTER #1
J7
ECM BAT FUSE 20 AMP
J6
SEE FUSE BLOCK DETAILS PAGE 8A-11-7
G9
ECM IGN FUSE 15 AMP
G8
SEE FUSE BLOCK DETAILS PAGE 8A-11-11
A4
INDIC FUSE 10 AMP
A3
SEE FUSE BLOCK DETAILS PAGE 8A-11-13
FUSE BLOCK
.5 PNK 39
S209
SEE FUSE BLOCK DETAILS PAGE 8A-11-13
.5 PNK 39
D10
INSTRUMENT CLUSTER
"SERVICE ENGINE SOON" INDICATOR (MIL)
D2
.8 ORN 540
.5 PNK/BLK 439
TO MASS AIR FLOW SENSOR PAGE 8A-21-5
SEE FUSE BLOCK DETAILS PAGE 8A-11-7
S102
.5 PNK/BLK
439
S129
.35 BRN/WHT 419
H3 C100
.5 BRN/WHT 419
.8 ORN 540
.5 PNK/BLK 439
B10
B8
B20
BAT
IGN
MALFUNCTION INDICATOR LAMP (MIL) CONTROL
POWER-TRAIN CONTROL MODULE (PCM)
SOLID STATE VOLTAGE REGULATOR
5V REF
SOLID STATE SWITCHES (CLOSED WITH IGNITION "ON")
5V
0.45V
1.01V
5V
DATA IN
DATA OUT
A19
A20
A21
A22
B32
VIN L
PCM CONNECTOR IDENTIFICATION
A - BLACK - 32 WAY
B - CLEAR - 32 WAY
C - BLUE - 32 WAY
.8 TAN/WHT 551
.8 BLK/WHT 451
.8 TAN/WHT 551
.8 BLK/WHT 451
SEE GROUND DISTRIBUTION PAGE 8A-14-1
.8 TAN 800
S106
J4 C100
.5 TAN 800
S237
.8 BLK/WHT 451
.8 TAN 800
M
DATA LINK CONNECTOR (DLC)
SEE DATA LINK CONNECTOR PAGE 8A-50-0
G115
G113
SEE PAGE 8A-3-0 FOR MEASURING AND HANDLING PROCEDURES

SEQUENTIAL FUEL INJECTION: 3.8L VIN L
ELECTRONIC IGNITION (EI) MODULE

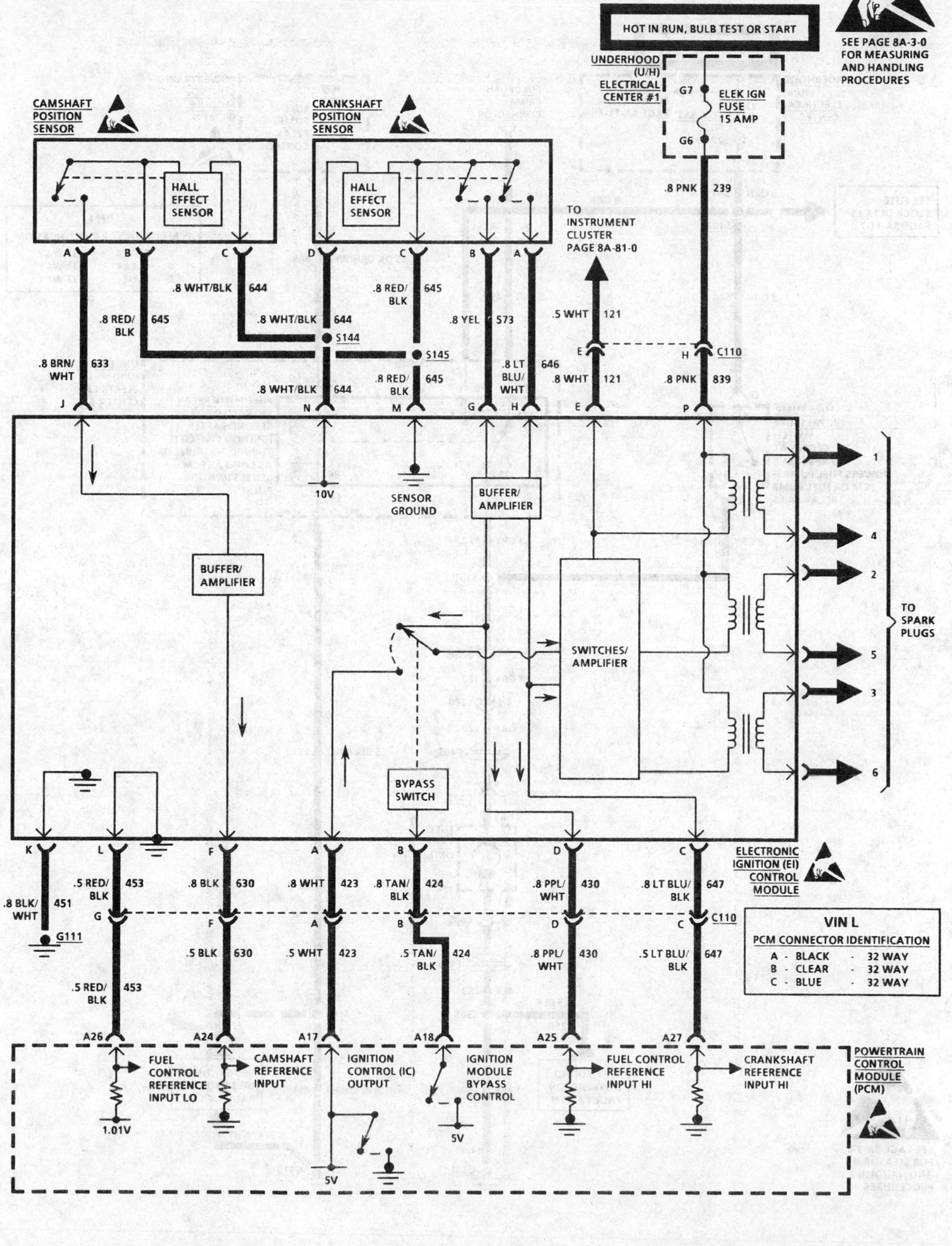

HOT IN RUN, BULB TEST OR START
SEE PAGE 8A-3-0 FOR MEASURING AND HANDLING PROCEDURES
UNDERHOOD (U/H) ELECTRICAL CENTER #1
G7
ELEK IGN FUSE 15 AMP
G6
.8 PNK 239
CAMSHAFT POSITION SENSOR
HALL EFFECT SENSOR
CRANKSHAFT POSITION SENSOR
HALL EFFECT SENSOR
TO INSTRUMENT CLUSTER PAGE 8A-81-0
.8 WHT/BLK 644
.8 RED/BLK 645
.8 RED/BLK 645
.8 WHT/BLK 644
.8 YEL 573
.5 WHT 121
S144
S145
.8 BRN/WHT 633
.8 WHT/BLK 644
.8 RED/BLK 645
.8 LT BLU/WHT 646
.8 WHT 121
C110
.8 PNK 839
10V
SENSOR GROUND
BUFFER/AMPLIFIER
BUFFER/AMPLIFIER
SWITCHES/AMPLIFIER
BYPASS SWITCH
TO SPARK PLUGS
ELECTRONIC IGNITION (EI) CONTROL MODULE
.8 BLK/WHT 451
G111
.5 RED/BLK 453
.8 BLK 630
.8 WHT 423
.8 TAN/BLK 424
.8 PPL/WHT 430
.8 LT BLU/BLK 647
C110
.5 BLK 630
.5 WHT 423
.5 TAN/BLK 424
.8 PPL/WHT 430
.5 LT BLU/BLK 647
.5 RED/BLK 453
A26
A24
A17
A18
A25
A27
FUEL CONTROL REFERENCE INPUT LO
1.01V
CAMSHAFT REFERENCE INPUT
IGNITION CONTROL (IC) OUTPUT
5V
IGNITION MODULE BYPASS CONTROL
5V
FUEL CONTROL REFERENCE INPUT HI
CRANKSHAFT REFERENCE INPUT HI
POWERTRAIN CONTROL MODULE (PCM)

VIN L

PCM CONNECTOR IDENTIFICATION

A	BLACK	-	32 WAY
B	CLEAR	-	32 WAY
C	BLUE	-	32 WAY

SEQUENTIAL FUEL INJECTION: 3.8L VIN L
FUEL CONTROL

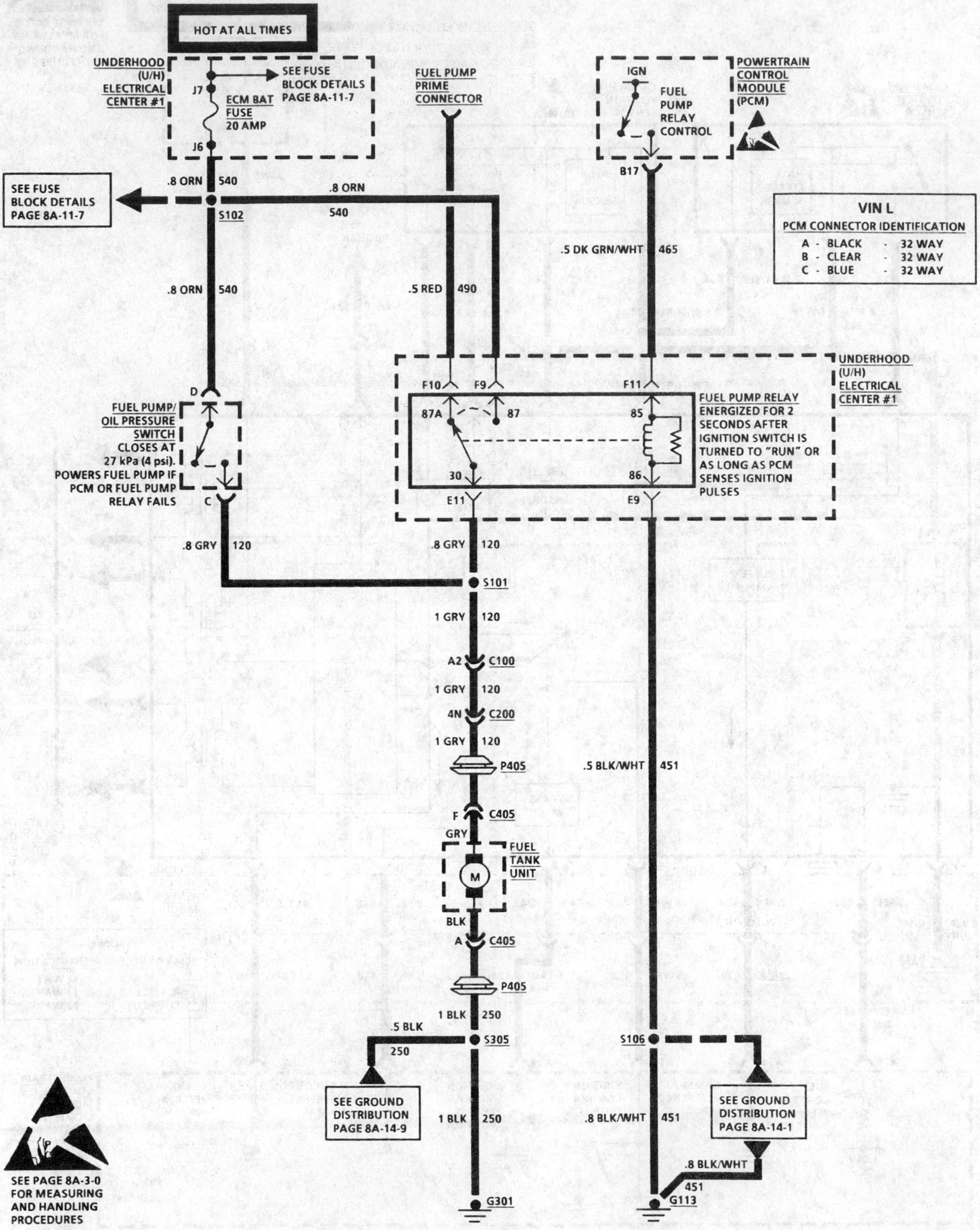

HOT AT ALL TIMES
UNDERHOOD (U/H) ELECTRICAL CENTER #1
J7
ECM BAT FUSE 20 AMP
J6
SEE FUSE BLOCK DETAILS PAGE 8A-11-7
FUEL PUMP PRIME CONNECTOR
IGN
FUEL PUMP RELAY CONTROL
POWERTRAIN CONTROL MODULE (PCM)
B17
.8 ORN 540
SEE FUSE BLOCK DETAILS PAGE 8A-11-7
S102
.8 ORN
540
VIN L
PCM CONNECTOR IDENTIFICATION
A - BLACK - 32 WAY
B - CLEAR - 32 WAY
C - BLUE - 32 WAY
.5 DK GRN/WHT 465
.8 ORN 540
.5 RED 490
UNDERHOOD (U/H) ELECTRICAL CENTER #1
D
F10
F9
F11
FUEL PUMP/ OIL PRESSURE SWITCH CLOSES AT 27 kPa (4 psi). POWERS FUEL PUMP IF PCM OR FUEL PUMP RELAY FAILS
87A
87
85
FUEL PUMP RELAY ENERGIZED FOR 2 SECONDS AFTER IGNITION SWITCH IS TURNED TO "RUN" OR AS LONG AS PCM SENSES IGNITION PULSES
30
86
C
E11
E9
.8 GRY 120
.8 GRY 120
S101
1 GRY 120
A2 C100
1 GRY 120
4N C200
1 GRY 120
P405
.5 BLK/WHT 451
F C405
GRY
FUEL TANK UNIT
M
BLK
A C405
P405
1 BLK 250
.5 BLK
250
S305
S106
SEE GROUND DISTRIBUTION PAGE 8A-14-9
1 BLK 250
.8 BLK/WHT 451
SEE GROUND DISTRIBUTION PAGE 8A-14-1
.8 BLK/WHT
451
G301
G113
SEE PAGE 8A-3-0 FOR MEASURING AND HANDLING PROCEDURES

SEQUENTIAL FUEL INJECTION: 3.8L VIN L
FUEL INJECTORS

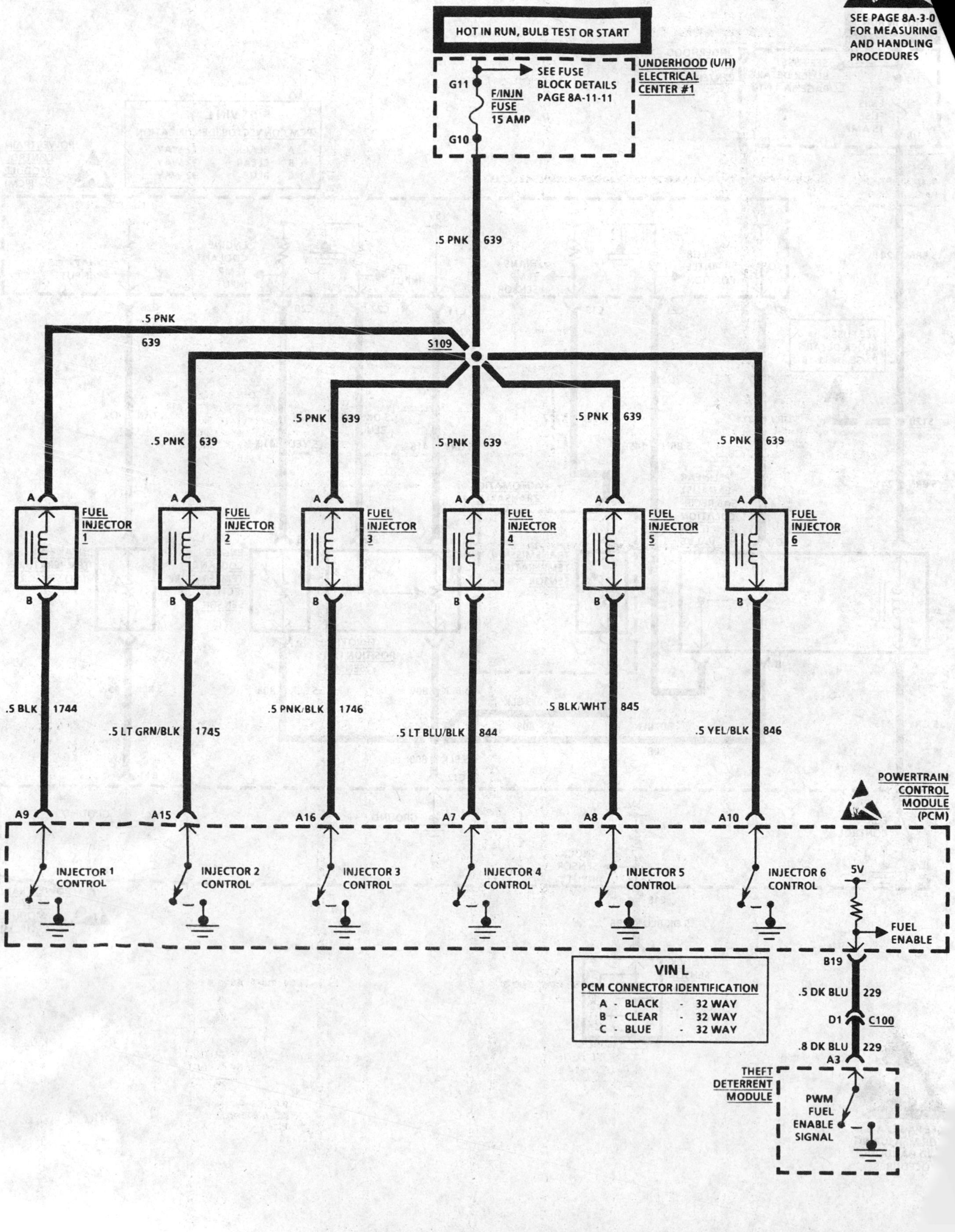
SEE PAGE 8A-3-0 FOR MEASURING AND HANDLING PROCEDURES
HOT IN RUN, BULB TEST OR START
UNDERHOOD (U/H) ELECTRICAL CENTER #1
G11
SEE FUSE BLOCK DETAILS PAGE 8A-11-11
F/INJN FUSE 15 AMP
G10
.5 PNK 639
S109
FUEL INJECTOR 1
FUEL INJECTOR 2
FUEL INJECTOR 3
FUEL INJECTOR 4
FUEL INJECTOR 5
FUEL INJECTOR 6
A
B
.5 BLK 1744
.5 LT GRN/BLK 1745
.5 PNK/BLK 1746
.5 LT BLU/BLK 844
.5 BLK/WHT 845
.5 YEL/BLK 846
A9
A15
A16
A7
A8
A10
POWERTRAIN CONTROL MODULE (PCM)
INJECTOR 1 CONTROL
INJECTOR 2 CONTROL
INJECTOR 3 CONTROL
INJECTOR 4 CONTROL
INJECTOR 5 CONTROL
INJECTOR 6 CONTROL
5V
FUEL ENABLE
B19
.5 DK BLU 229
D1
C100
.8 DK BLU 229
A3
THEFT DETERRENT MODULE
PWM FUEL ENABLE SIGNAL

VIN L		
PCM CONNECTOR IDENTIFICATION		
A - BLACK	-	32 WAY
B - CLEAR	-	32 WAY
C - BLUE	-	32 WAY

21-3

FUEL INJECTION: 3.8L VIN L
A SENSORS

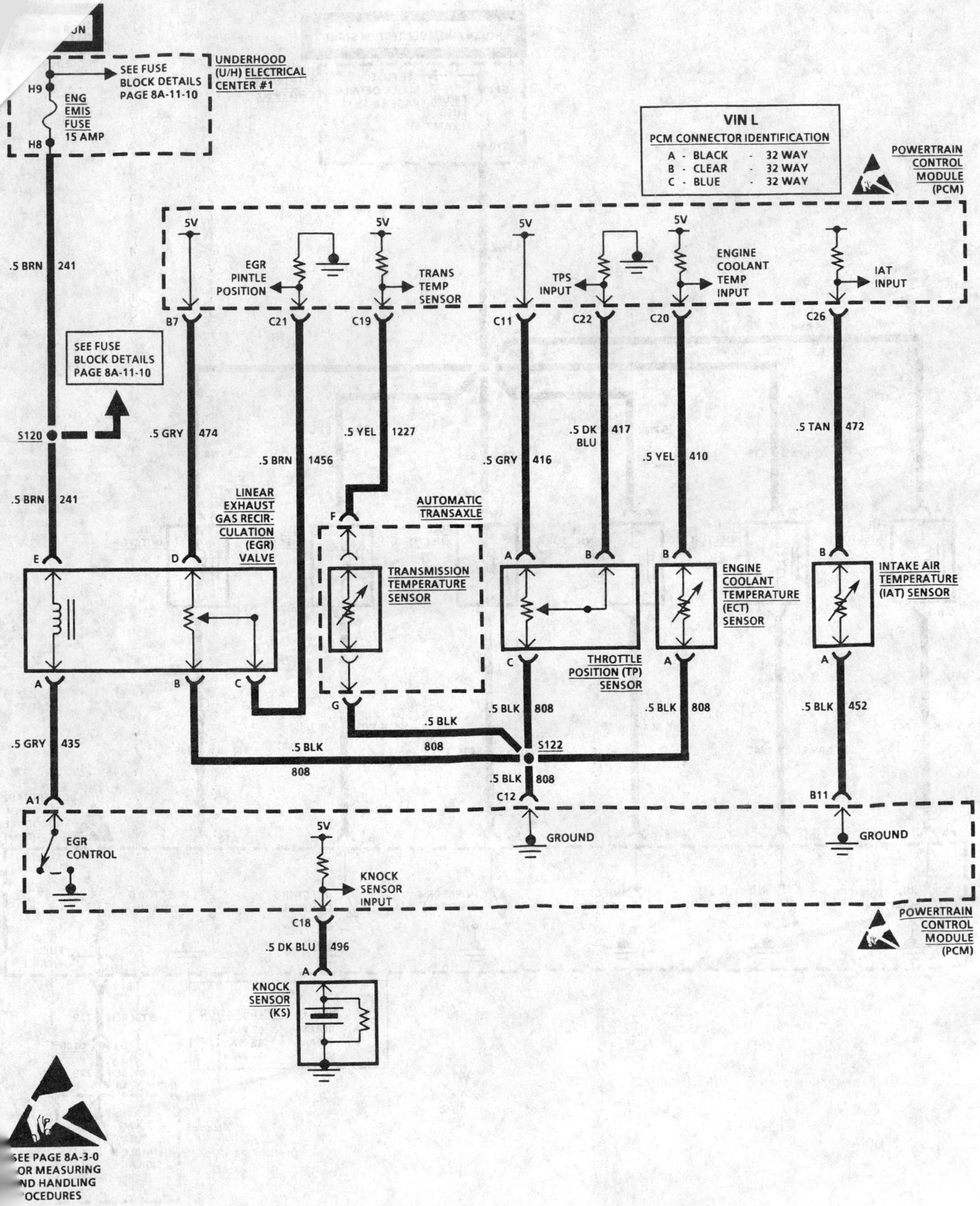
RUN
SEE FUSE BLOCK DETAILS PAGE 8A-11-10
UNDERHOOD (U/H) ELECTRICAL CENTER #1
H9
ENG EMIS FUSE 15 AMP
H8
VIN L
PCM CONNECTOR IDENTIFICATION
A - BLACK - 32 WAY
B - CLEAR - 32 WAY
C - BLUE - 32 WAY
POWERTRAIN CONTROL MODULE (PCM)
5V
EGR PINTLE POSITION
TRANS TEMP SENSOR
TPS INPUT
ENGINE COOLANT TEMP INPUT
IAT INPUT
.5 BRN 241
B7
C21
C19
C11
C22
C20
C26
SEE FUSE BLOCK DETAILS PAGE 8A-11-10
S120
.5 GRY 474
.5 YEL 1227
.5 DK BLU 417
.5 TAN 472
.5 BRN 1456
.5 GRY 416
.5 YEL 410
LINEAR EXHAUST GAS RECIRCULATION (EGR) VALVE
AUTOMATIC TRANSAXLE
TRANSMISSION TEMPERATURE SENSOR
ENGINE COOLANT TEMPERATURE (ECT) SENSOR
INTAKE AIR TEMPERATURE (IAT) SENSOR
THROTTLE POSITION (TP) SENSOR
.5 GRY 435
.5 BLK 808
.5 BLK 452
S122
C12
B11
A1
EGR CONTROL
GROUND
KNOCK SENSOR INPUT
C18
.5 DK BLU 496
KNOCK SENSOR (KS)
SEE PAGE 8A-3-0 OR MEASURING ND HANDLING OCEDURES

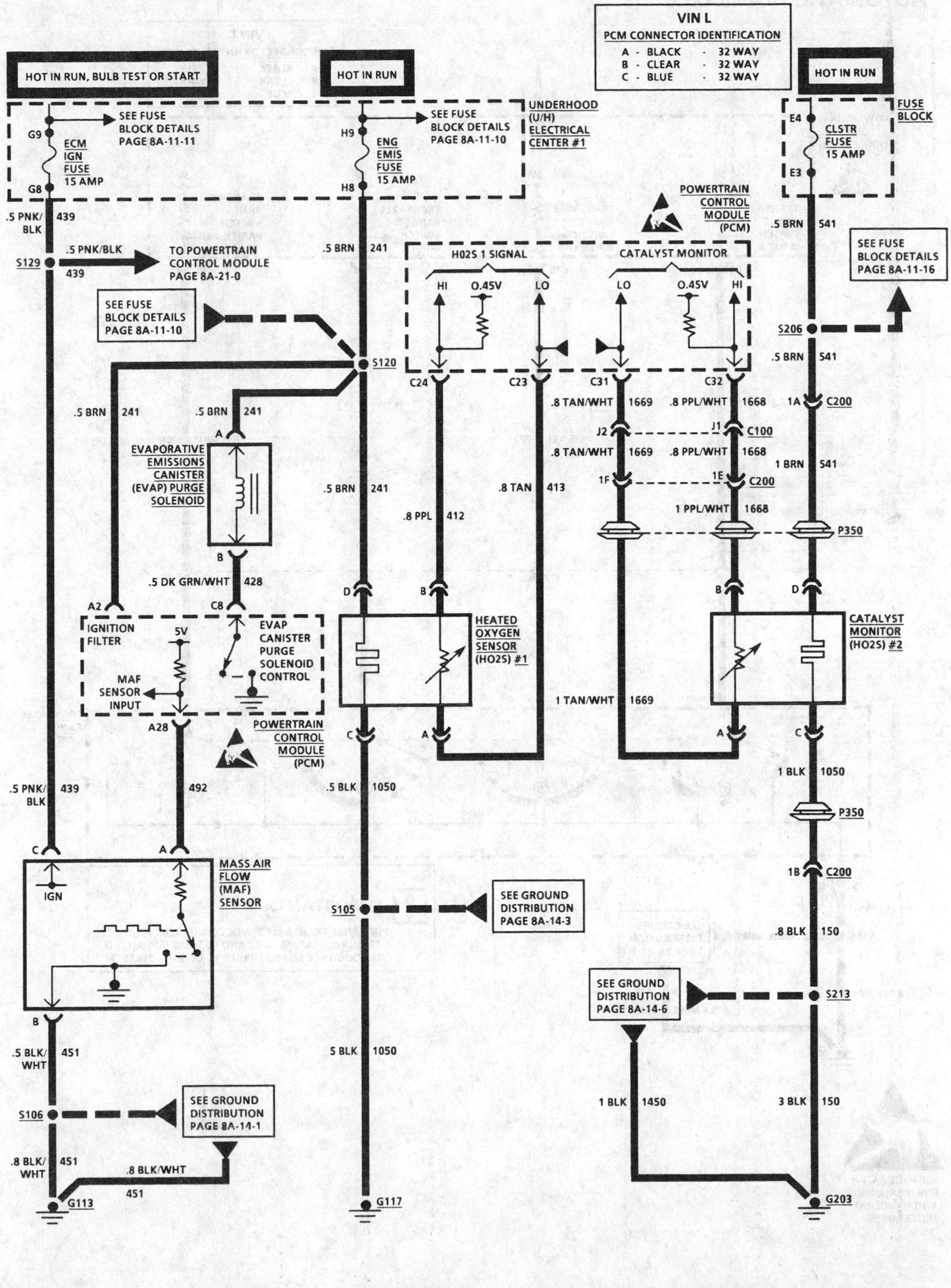
VIN L
PCM CONNECTOR IDENTIFICATION
A - BLACK - 32 WAY
B - CLEAR - 32 WAY
C - BLUE - 32 WAY
HOT IN RUN, BULB TEST OR START
HOT IN RUN
HOT IN RUN
SEE FUSE BLOCK DETAILS PAGE 8A-11-11
ECM IGN FUSE 15 AMP
G9
G8
H9
H8
ENG EMIS FUSE 15 AMP
SEE FUSE BLOCK DETAILS PAGE 8A-11-10
UNDERHOOD (U/H) ELECTRICAL CENTER #1
FUSE BLOCK
E4
E3
CLSTR FUSE 15 AMP
POWERTRAIN CONTROL MODULE (PCM)
.5 PNK/BLK 439
.5 PNK/BLK
S129
439
TO POWERTRAIN CONTROL MODULE PAGE 8A-21-0
.5 BRN 241
H02S 1 SIGNAL
CATALYST MONITOR
HI
0.45V
LO
LO
0.45V
HI
.5 BRN 541
SEE FUSE BLOCK DETAILS PAGE 8A-11-16
SEE FUSE BLOCK DETAILS PAGE 8A-11-10
S206
S120
.5 BRN 541
C24
C23
C31
C32
.8 TAN/WHT 1669
.8 PPL/WHT 1668
1A
C200
.5 BRN 241
.5 BRN 241
J2
J1
C100
A
.8 TAN/WHT 1669
.8 PPL/WHT 1668
EVAPORATIVE EMISSIONS CANISTER (EVAP) PURGE SOLENOID
1 BRN 541
1F
1E
C200
.5 BRN 241
.8 TAN 413
1 PPL/WHT 1668
.8 PPL 412
P350
B
.5 DK GRN/WHT 428
D
B
B
D
A2
C8
IGNITION FILTER
5V
EVAP CANISTER PURGE SOLENOID CONTROL
MAF SENSOR INPUT
HEATED OXYGEN SENSOR (HO2S) #1
CATALYST MONITOR (HO2S) #2
1 TAN/WHT 1669
A28
POWERTRAIN CONTROL MODULE (PCM)
C
A
A
C
1 BLK 1050
.5 PNK/BLK 439
492
.5 BLK 1050
P350
C
A
1B
C200
MASS AIR FLOW (MAF) SENSOR
IGN
S105
SEE GROUND DISTRIBUTION PAGE 8A-14-3
.8 BLK 150
SEE GROUND DISTRIBUTION PAGE 8A-14-6
S213
B
.5 BLK/WHT 451
5 BLK 1050
S106
SEE GROUND DISTRIBUTION PAGE 8A-14-1
1 BLK 1450
3 BLK 150
.8 BLK/WHT 451
.8 BLK/WHT
451
G113
G117
G203

SEQUENTIAL FUEL INJECTION: 3.8L VIN L
AUTOMATIC TRANSAXLE

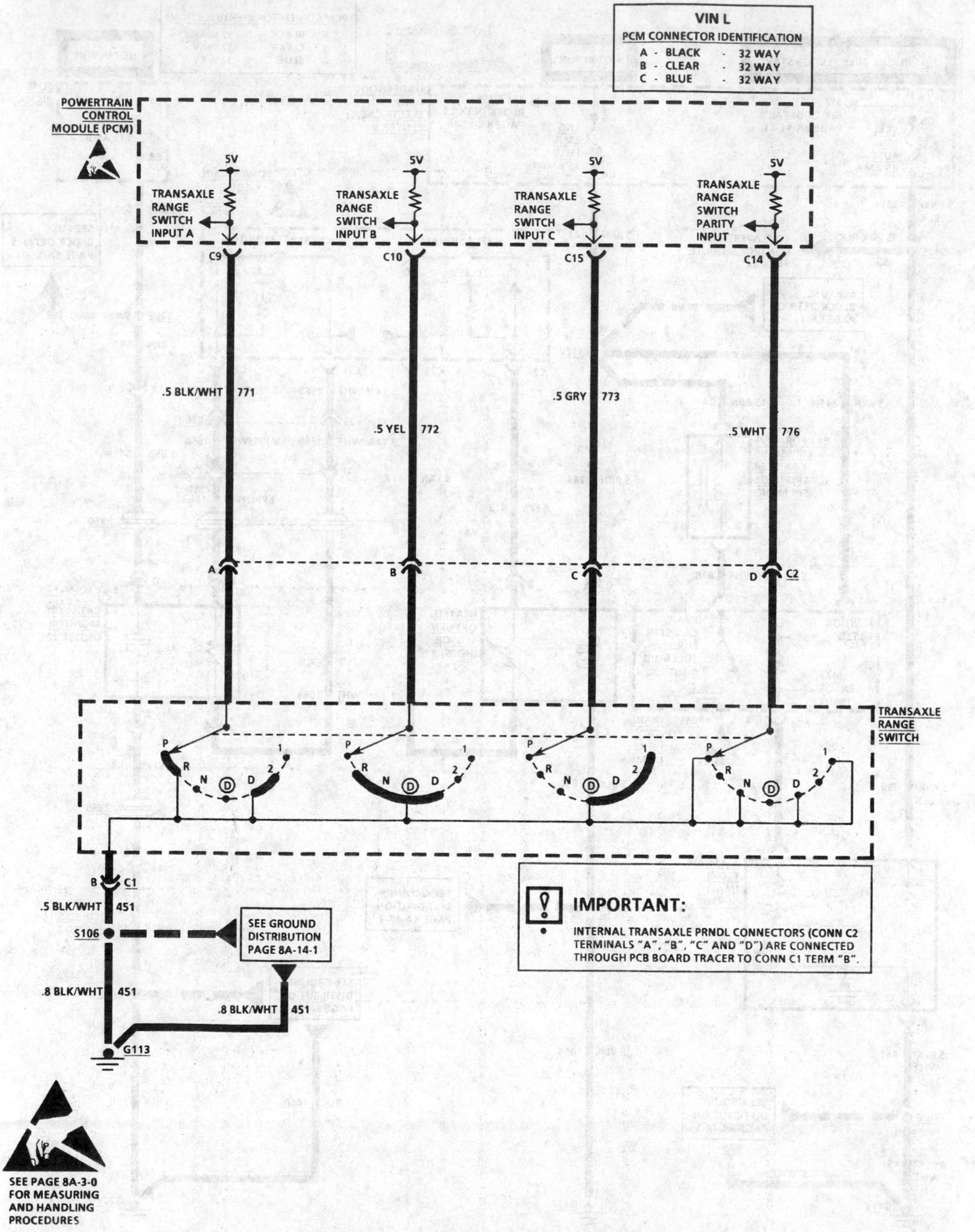
VIN L
PCM CONNECTOR IDENTIFICATION
A - BLACK - 32 WAY
B - CLEAR - 32 WAY
C - BLUE - 32 WAY
POWERTRAIN CONTROL MODULE (PCM)
5V
TRANSAXLE RANGE SWITCH INPUT A
TRANSAXLE RANGE SWITCH INPUT B
TRANSAXLE RANGE SWITCH INPUT C
TRANSAXLE RANGE SWITCH PARITY INPUT
C9
C10
C15
C14
.5 BLK/WHT 771
.5 YEL 772
.5 GRY 773
.5 WHT 776
A
B
C
D
C2
TRANSAXLE RANGE SWITCH
P R N D D 2 1
B C1
.5 BLK/WHT 451
S106
SEE GROUND DISTRIBUTION PAGE 8A-14-1
.8 BLK/WHT 451
.8 BLK/WHT 451
G113
IMPORTANT:
INTERNAL TRANSAXLE PRNDL CONNECTORS (CONN C2 TERMINALS "A", "B", "C" AND "D") ARE CONNECTED THROUGH PCB BOARD TRACER TO CONN C1 TERM "B".
SEE PAGE 8A-3-0 FOR MEASURING AND HANDLING PROCEDURES

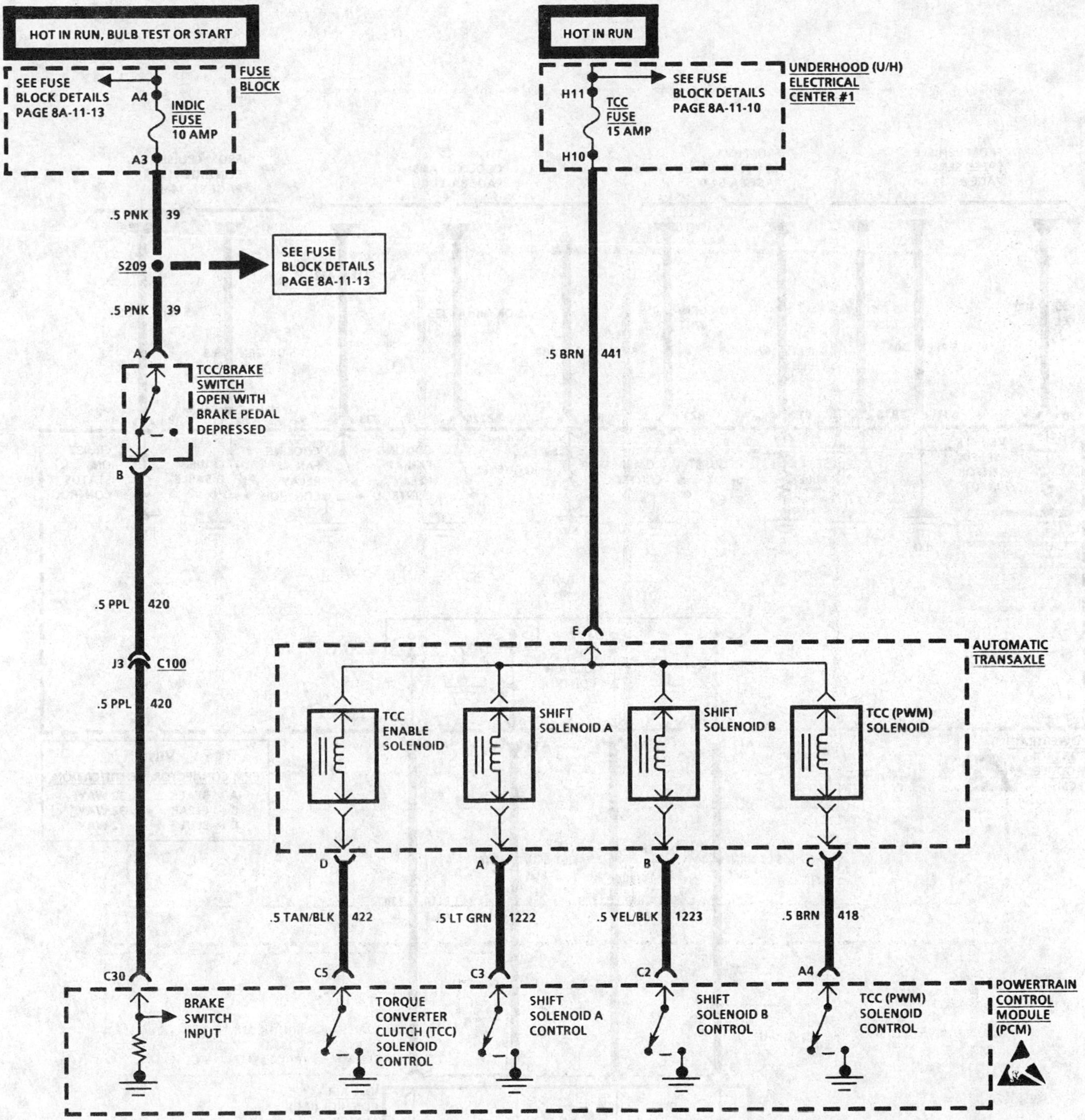

HOT IN RUN, BULB TEST OR START
SEE FUSE BLOCK DETAILS PAGE 8A-11-13
FUSE BLOCK
A4
INDIC FUSE 10 AMP
A3
.5 PNK 39
S209
SEE FUSE BLOCK DETAILS PAGE 8A-11-13
.5 PNK 39
A
TCC/BRAKE SWITCH
OPEN WITH BRAKE PEDAL DEPRESSED
B
.5 PPL 420
J3
C100
.5 PPL 420
C30
BRAKE SWITCH INPUT
HOT IN RUN
UNDERHOOD (U/H) ELECTRICAL CENTER #1
SEE FUSE BLOCK DETAILS PAGE 8A-11-10
H11
TCC FUSE 15 AMP
H10
.5 BRN 441
E
AUTOMATIC TRANSAXLE
TCC ENABLE SOLENOID
SHIFT SOLENOID A
SHIFT SOLENOID B
TCC (PWM) SOLENOID
D
A
B
C
.5 TAN/BLK 422
.5 LT GRN 1222
.5 YEL/BLK 1223
.5 BRN 418
C5
C3
C2
A4
TORQUE CONVERTER CLUTCH (TCC) SOLENOID CONTROL
SHIFT SOLENOID A CONTROL
SHIFT SOLENOID B CONTROL
TCC (PWM) SOLENOID CONTROL
POWERTRAIN CONTROL MODULE (PCM)

VIN L

PCM CONNECTOR IDENTIFICATION

A -	BLACK	- 32 WAY
B -	CLEAR	- 32 WAY
C -	BLUE	- 32 WAY

SEE PAGE 8A-3-0 FOR MEASURING AND HANDLING PROCEDURES

SEQUENTIAL FUEL INJECTION: 3.8L VIN L

IDLE AIR CONTROL

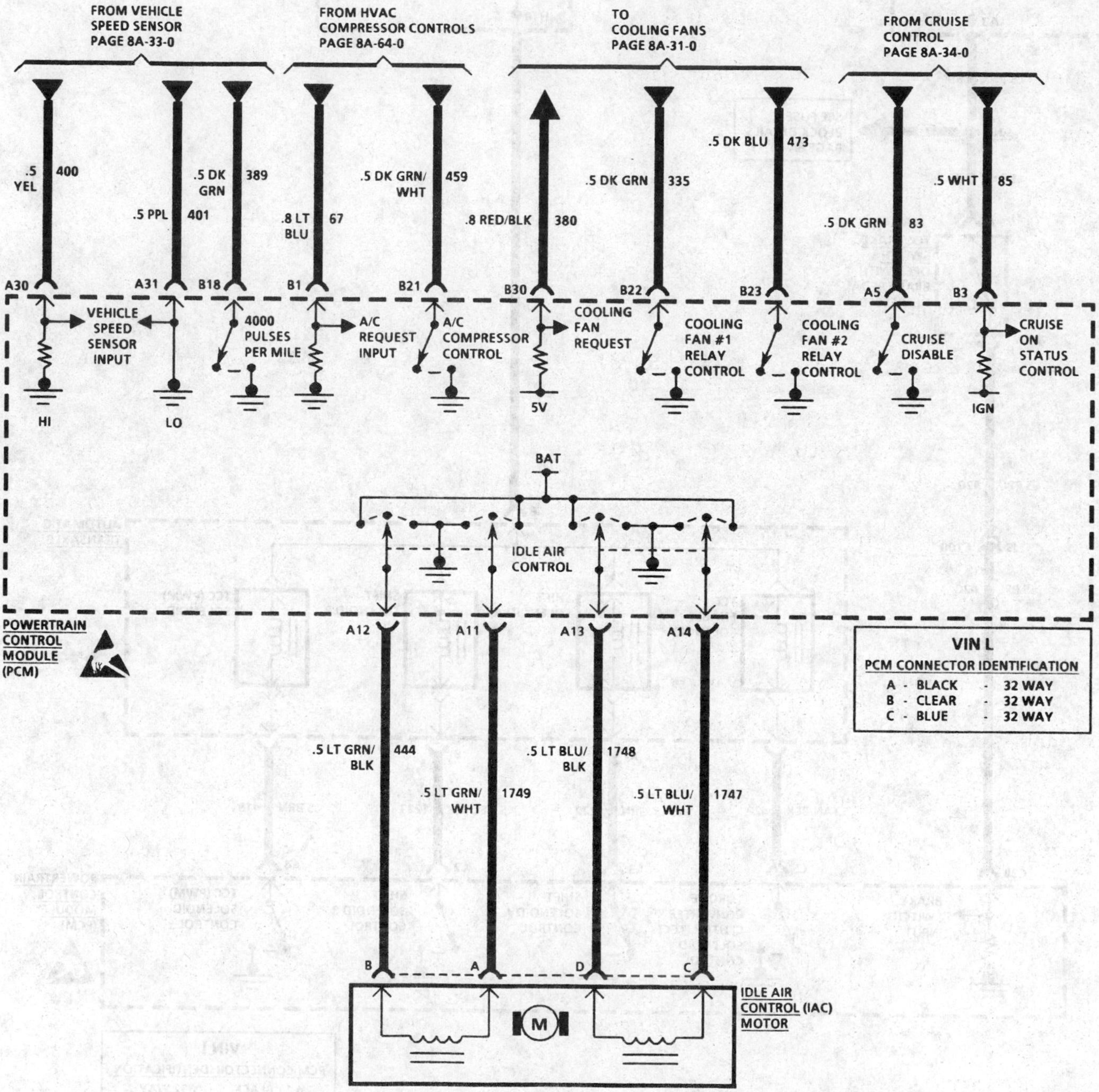
FROM VEHICLE SPEED SENSOR PAGE 8A-33-0
FROM HVAC COMPRESSOR CONTROLS PAGE 8A-64-0
TO COOLING FANS PAGE 8A-31-0
FROM CRUISE CONTROL PAGE 8A-34-0
.5 YEL 400
.5 PPL 401
.5 DK GRN 389
.8 LT BLU 67
.5 DK GRN/WHT 459
.8 RED/BLK 380
.5 DK GRN 335
.5 DK BLU 473
.5 DK GRN 83
.5 WHT 85
A30
A31
B18
B1
B21
B30
B22
B23
A5
B3
VEHICLE SPEED SENSOR INPUT
HI
LO
4000 PULSES PER MILE
A/C REQUEST INPUT
A/C COMPRESSOR CONTROL
COOLING FAN REQUEST
5V
COOLING FAN #1 RELAY CONTROL
COOLING FAN #2 RELAY CONTROL
CRUISE DISABLE
CRUISE ON STATUS CONTROL
IGN
BAT
IDLE AIR CONTROL
POWERTRAIN CONTROL MODULE (PCM)
A12
A11
A13
A14
.5 LT GRN/BLK 444
.5 LT GRN/WHT 1749
.5 LT BLU/BLK 1748
.5 LT BLU/WHT 1747
B
A
D
C
M
IDLE AIR CONTROL (IAC) MOTOR

VIN L

PCM CONNECTOR IDENTIFICATION

A -	BLACK	- 32 WAY
B -	CLEAR	- 32 WAY
C -	BLUE	- 32 WAY

SEE PAGE 8A-3-0 FOR MEASURING AND HANDLING PROCEDURES

SEQUENTIAL FUEL INJECTION: 3.8L VIN L

COMPONENT	LOCATION	201-PG	FIG.	CONN
Automatic Transaxle	LH side of Engine Compartment	3	10	
Camshaft Position Sensor	RH side of Engine, below cover	5	16	
Catalyst Monitor (HO2S #2)	In Exhaust System, behind Catalytic Converter	28	89	
Crankshaft Position Sensor	Lower RH side of Engine	5	16	
Data Link Conn (DLC)	Below I/P, left of Steering Column			202-17
Electronic Ignition (EI) Control Module	Top RH front of Engine	5	16	202-36,37
Engine Coolant Temperature (ECT) Sensor	Top LH side of Engine	7	24	
Evaporative Emission (EVAP) Canister Purge Solenoid	Top center of Engine, on Intake Plenum	16	51	
Fuel Injectors	Part of Sequential Fuel Injection Unit	7	24	
Fuel Pump/Oil Pressure Sender/Switch	Front of Engine, next to Oil Filter	9	32	202-39
Fuel Pump Prime Conn	Engine Wiring Harn, below Underhood Electrical Center #2	1	4	
Fuel Tank Unit	Mounted in Fuel Tank	10	35	
Fuse Block	RH side of I/P, in I/P Compartment			
Heated Oxygen Sensor (HO2S)	Rear of Engine, mounted to Exhaust Manifold	9	32	202-38
Idle Air Control (IAC) Motor	Top LH side of Engine	24	80	202-38
Instrument Cluster	LH side of I/P			
Intake Air Temperature (IAT) Sensor	LH front of Engine Compartment, on Air Cleaner Canister			
Knock Sensor	Rear RH side of Engine	11	37	
Linear Exhaust Gas Recirculation (EGR) Assembly	Upper RH side of Engine	2	9	202-39
Mass Air Flow (MAF) Sensor	Top LH side of Engine	24	80	
Powertrain Control Module (PCM)	RH side of Engine Compartment, forward of strut tower	19	68	202-29
TCC/Brake Switch	Mounted to brake pedal support	12	42	202-41
Theft Deterrent Module	Behind RH side of I/P	27	88	
Throttle Position (TP) Sensor	Mounted to Sequential Fuel Injection Unit	2	9	
Transaxle Range Switch	Rear LH side of Engine Compartment, mounted to top of Transaxle	3	10	202-41
Underhood (U/H) Electrical Center #1	RH side of Engine Compartment, forward of strut tower			202-34
C100 (36 cavities)	RH side of dash, behind strut tower			202-0
C110 (8 cavities)	Top RH side of Engine	5	16	202-35
C200 (102 cavities)	Behind RH side of I/P, near shroud	13	44	202-3

(CONTINUED ON NEXT PAGE)

SEQUENTIAL FUEL INJECTION: 3.8L VIN L

(CONTINUED FROM PREVIOUS PAGE)

COMPONENT	LOCATION	201-PG	FIG.	CONN
C405 (6 cavities)	Center rear of vehicle, near fuel tank	10	35	202-36
G111	RH side of Engine, below Electronic Ignition Control Module	0	3	
G113	RH side of Engine, below Electronic Ignition Control Module	0	3	
G115	RH side of Engine, below Electronic Ignition Control Module	0	3	
G117	Front of Engine, on Transaxle stud	11	37	
G203	Behind LH side of I/P, on Steering Column support			
G301	Below LH front seat	15	50	
P350	Between LH and RH front seats on floor	28	89	
P405	Center front of Trunk, in floor			
S101	Engine Harn, approx 4 cm from C100 breakout			
S102	Engine Harn, approx 12 cm from Underhood (U/H) Electrical Center #1			
S105	Engine Harn, approx 20 cm from Underhood (U/H) Electrical Center #1			
S106	Engine Harn, approx 10 cm from PCM breakout			
S109	Engine Harn, approx 4 cm from Electronic Ignition (EI) Module breakout	7	27	
S120	Engine Harn, approx 4 cm from PCM breakout			
S122	Engine Harn, approx 4 cm from Electronic Ignition (EI) Module breakout			
S129	Engine Harn, approx 5 cm from C400 breakout			
S144	Engine Jumper Harn, approx 8 cm from Crankshaft Sensor breakout			
S145	Engine Jumper Harn, approx 6 cm from Crankshaft Sensor breakout			
S206	I/P Harn, approx 10 cm from Fuse Block breakout	15	49	
S209	I/P Harn, approx 19 cm from Fuse Block breakout			
S213	I/P Harn, approx 8 cm from HVAC Control Switch breakout			
S237	I/P Harn, approx 14 cm from Headlight Switch breakout	15	49	
S305	Cross Car Harn, approx 6 cm from G302 breakout	17	61	

BLANK

STARTER AND CHARGING SYSTEM

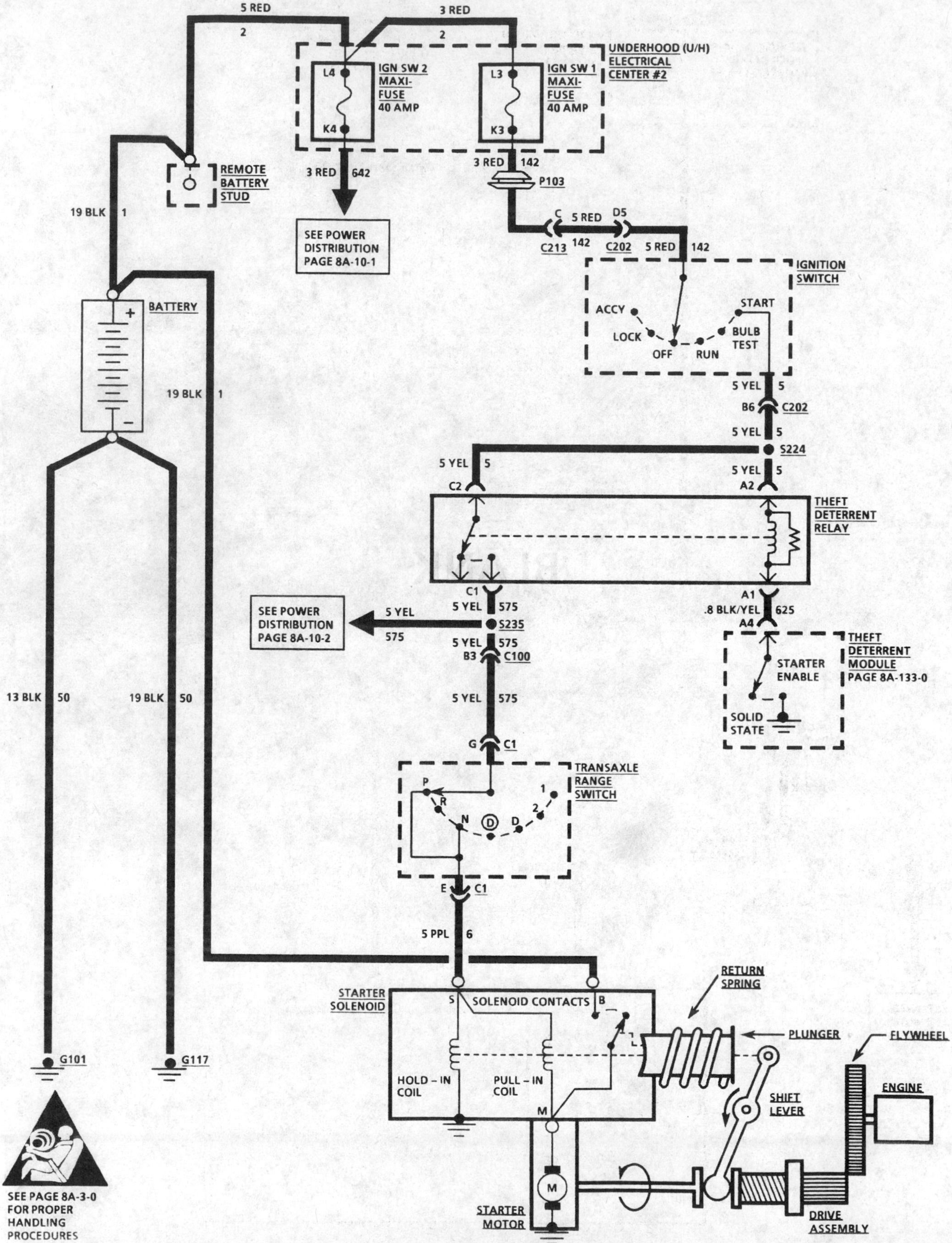
5 RED
2
3 RED
2
UNDERHOOD (U/H) ELECTRICAL CENTER #2
L4
IGN SW 2 MAXI-FUSE 40 AMP
K4
L3
IGN SW 1 MAXI-FUSE 40 AMP
K3
REMOTE BATTERY STUD
3 RED 642
SEE POWER DISTRIBUTION PAGE 8A-10-1
3 RED 142
P103
19 BLK 1
C 5 RED D5
C213 142
C202 5 RED 142
IGNITION SWITCH
ACCY
LOCK
OFF
RUN
START
BULB TEST
BATTERY
19 BLK 1
5 YEL 5
B6 C202
5 YEL 5
S224
5 YEL 5
5 YEL 5
C2
A2
THEFT DETERRENT RELAY
C1
A1
5 YEL 575
.8 BLK/YEL 625
A4
SEE POWER DISTRIBUTION PAGE 8A-10-2
5 YEL
575
S235
5 YEL 575
B3 C100
THEFT DETERRENT MODULE PAGE 8A-133-0
STARTER ENABLE
SOLID STATE
13 BLK 50
19 BLK 50
5 YEL 575
G C1
TRANSAXLE RANGE SWITCH
P
R
N
D
1
2
E C1
5 PPL 6
STARTER SOLENOID
S
SOLENOID CONTACTS
B
RETURN SPRING
PLUNGER
FLYWHEEL
G101
G117
HOLD - IN COIL
PULL - IN COIL
M
SHIFT LEVER
ENGINE
STARTER MOTOR
DRIVE ASSEMBLY

SEE PAGE 8A-3-0 FOR PROPER HANDLING PROCEDURES

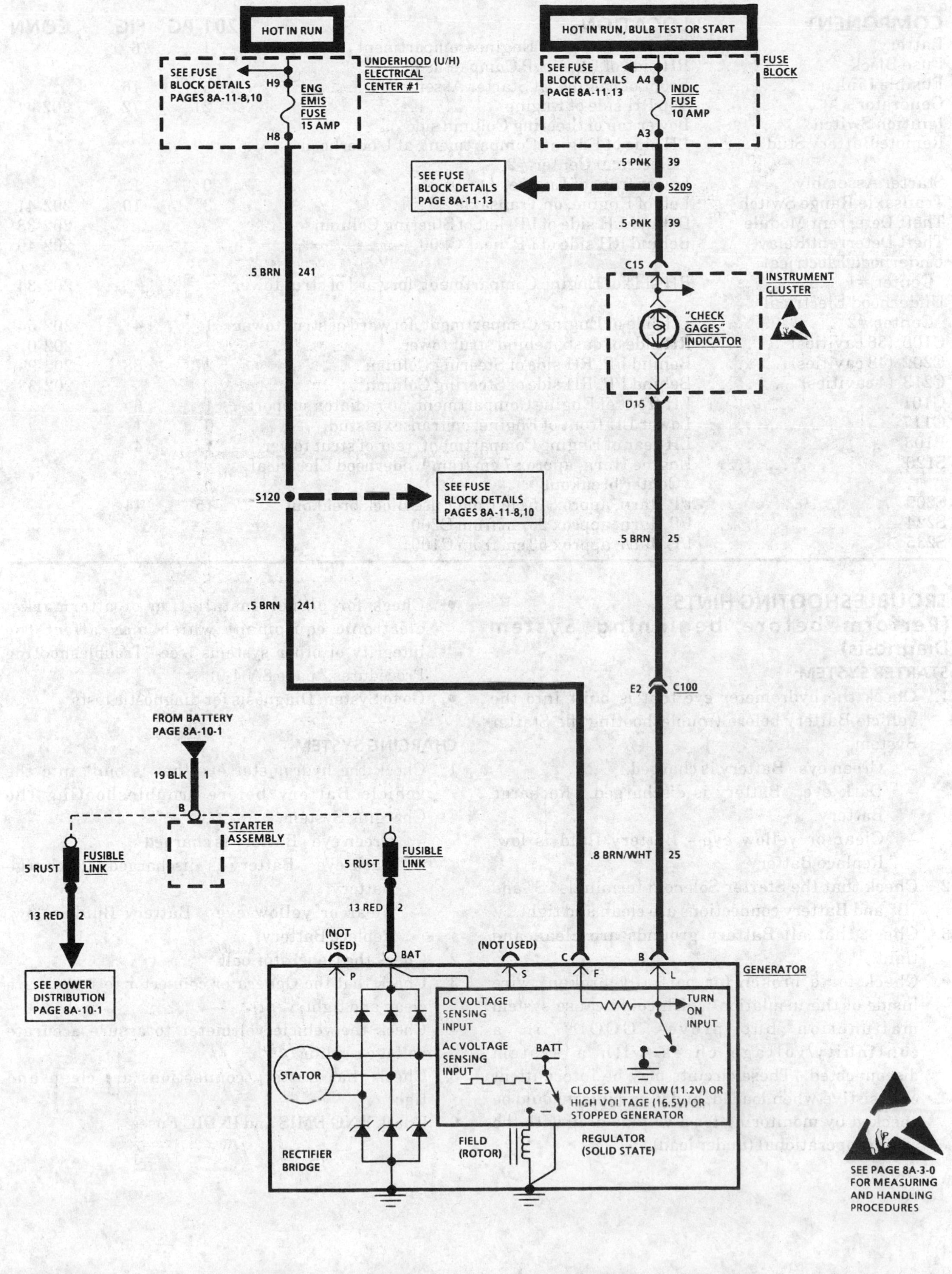
HOT IN RUN
SEE FUSE BLOCK DETAILS PAGES 8A-11-8,10
H9
ENG EMIS FUSE 15 AMP
H8
UNDERHOOD (U/H) ELECTRICAL CENTER #1
HOT IN RUN, BULB TEST OR START
SEE FUSE BLOCK DETAILS PAGE 8A-11-13
A4
INDIC FUSE 10 AMP
A3
FUSE BLOCK
.5 PNK 39
SEE FUSE BLOCK DETAILS PAGE 8A-11-13
S209
.5 PNK 39
.5 BRN 241
C15
INSTRUMENT CLUSTER
"CHECK GAGES" INDICATOR
D15
S120
SEE FUSE BLOCK DETAILS PAGES 8A-11-8,10
.5 BRN 25
.5 BRN 241
E2
C100
FROM BATTERY PAGE 8A-10-1
19 BLK 1
B
STARTER ASSEMBLY
5 RUST
FUSIBLE LINK
5 RUST
FUSIBLE LINK
.8 BRN/WHT 25
13 RED 2
13 RED 2
SEE POWER DISTRIBUTION PAGE 8A-10-1
(NOT USED)
BAT
(NOT USED)
C
B
P
S
F
L
GENERATOR
DC VOLTAGE SENSING INPUT
AC VOLTAGE SENSING INPUT
TURN ON INPUT
BATT
STATOR
CLOSES WITH LOW (11.2V) OR HIGH VOLTAGE (16.5V) OR STOPPED GENERATOR
FIELD (ROTOR)
REGULATOR (SOLID STATE)
RECTIFIER BRIDGE
SEE PAGE 8A-3-0 FOR MEASURING AND HANDLING PROCEDURES

STARTER AND CHARGING SYSTEM

COMPONENT	LOCATION	201-PG	FIG.	CONN
Battery	LH front corner of Engine Compartment	1	6	
Fuse Block	RH side of I/P, in I/P Compartment			
Fusible Link	Front of Engine, at Starter Assembly	5	16	
Generator	Top RH side of Engine	21	72	202-41
Ignition Switch	Lower top of Steering Column side			
Remote Battery Stud	LH side of Engine Compartment, at Underhood Electrical Center #2			
Starter Assembly	Lower front of Engine	0	1	
Transaxle Range Switch	Left of Engine, on Transaxle	3	10	202-41
Theft Deterrent Module	Behind LH side of I/P, left of Steering Column			202-38
Theft Deterrent Relay	Behind RH side of I/P, near C200			202-40
Underhood Electrical Center #1	RH side of Engine Compartment, forward of strut tower			202-34
Underhood Electrical Center #2	LH side of Engine Compartment, forward of strut tower	1	4	202-54
C100 (36 cavities)	RH side of dash, behind strut tower			202-0
C202 (48 cavities)	Behind I/P, RH side of Steering Column	27	88	202-9
C213 (4 cavities)	Behind I/P, RH side of Steering Column			202-33
G101	LH front of Engine Compartment, on radiator support	1	6	
G117	Lower LH front of Engine, on transaxle stud	0	1	
P103	LH rear of Engine Compartment, rear of strut tower	1	4	
S120	Engine Harn, approx 7 cm from Underhood Electrical Center breakout			
S209	I/P Harn, approx 15 cm from Fuse Block breakout	15	44	
S224	I/P Harn, approx 25 cm from C200			
S235	I/P Harn, approx 53 cm from C100			

TROUBLESHOOTING HINTS (Perform before beginning System Diagnosis)

STARTER SYSTEM

1. Check the hydrometer eye that is built into the vehicle Battery before troubleshooting the Starter System.
   - Green eye - Battery is charged.
   - Dark eye - Battery is discharged. Recharge Battery.
   - Clear or yellow eye - Battery fluid is low. Replace Battery.
2. Check that the Starter Solenoid terminals "S" and "B" and Battery connections are clean and tight.
3. Check that all Battery grounds are clean and tight.

- Check for a broken (or partially broken) wire inside of the insulation which could cause system malfunction but prove "GOOD" in a continuity/voltage check with a system disconnected. These circuits may be intermittent or resistive when loaded, and if possible, should be checked by monitoring for a voltage drop with the system operational (under load).
- Check for proper installation of aftermarket electronic equipment which may affect the integrity of other systems (see "Troubleshooting Procedures," page 8A-4-0).
- Go to System Diagnosis for diagnostic tests.

CHARGING SYSTEM

1. Check the hydrometer eye that is built into the vehicle Battery before troubleshooting the Charging System.
   - Green eye - Battery is charged.
   - Dark eye - Battery is discharged. Recharge Battery.
   - Clear or yellow eye - Battery fluid is low. Replace Battery.
2. Check the Generator belt.
3. Check that the Generator connector terminals are clean and tight.
4. Check the vehicle voltmeter to assure accurate voltage reading.
5. Check that Battery connections are clean and tight.
6. Check ENG EMIS and INDIC Fuses.

- Check for a broken (or partially broken) wire inside of the insulation which could cause system malfunction but prove "GOOD" in a continuity/voltage check with a system disconnected. These circuits may be intermittent or resistive when loaded, and if possible, should be checked by monitoring for a voltage drop with the system operational (under load).
- Check for proper installation of aftermarket electronic equipment which may affect the integrity of other systems (see "Troubleshooting Procedures," page 8A-4-0).
- Go to System Diagnosis for diagnostic tests.

SYSTEM DIAGNOSIS

Important:

- If the Starter and Charging System continues to malfunction after the following diagnostic procedures are performed, refer to SECTION 6E.

SYMPTOM TABLE

SYMPTOM	PROCEDURE	PAGE NUMBER
Engine does not crank, Starter Solenoid does not click.	Chart #1	8A-30-3
Starter Solenoid clicks, Engine does not crank.	Chart #2	8A-30-4
Engine cranks/cranks slowly but does not start.	Refer to SECTION 6E3.	
Battery is undercharged or overcharged.	Chart #3	8A-30-4
"CHECK GAGES" Indicator on at all times.	Chart #4	8A-30-5
"CHECK GAGES" Indicator inoperative.	Chart #5	8A-30-5

CHART #1

ENGINE DOES NOT CRANK, STARTER SOLENOID DOES NOT CLICK

IMPORTANT:

- TO AVOID MISDIAGNOSIS, REFER TO THEFT DETERRENT: PASSKEY®II PAGE 8A-133-0.
- BATTERY MUST BE IN A CHARGED STATE TO AVOID MISDIAGNOSIS.

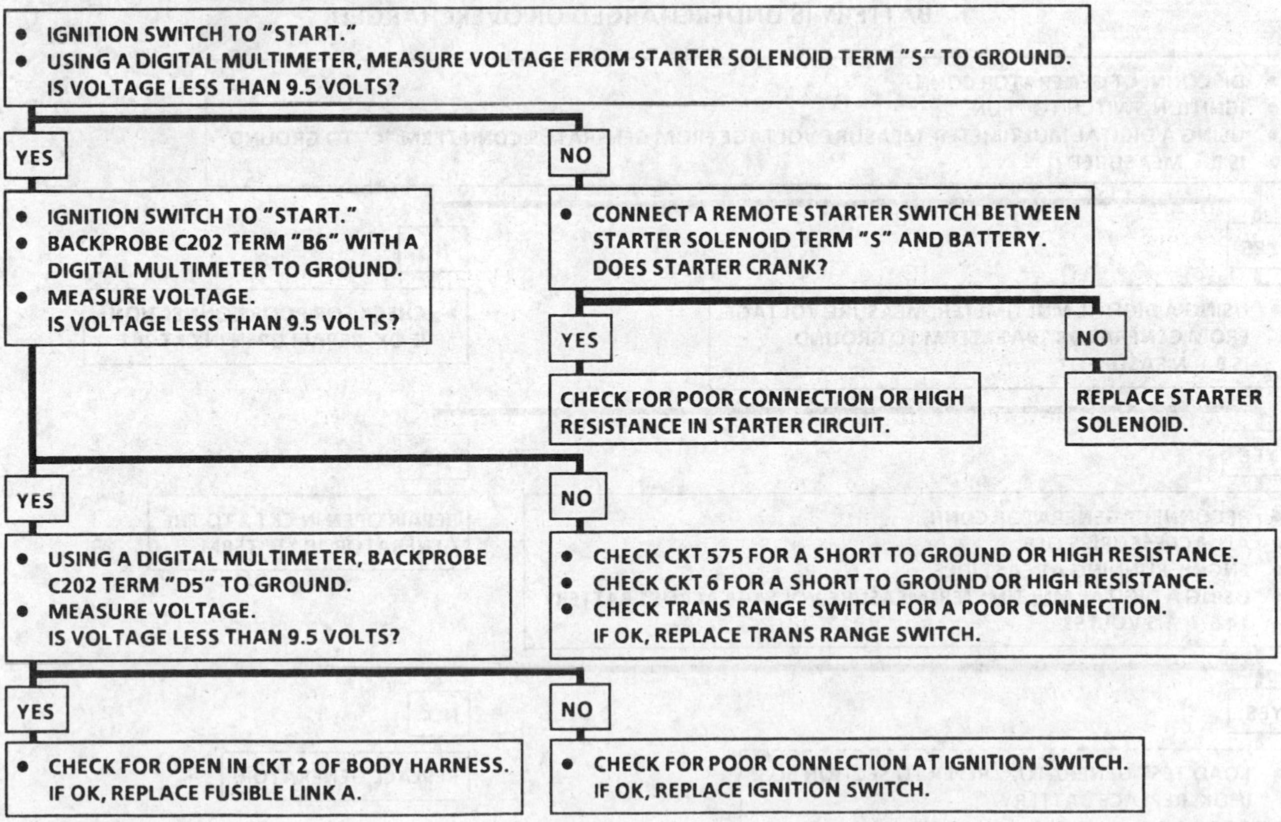
• IGNITION SWITCH TO "START."
• USING A DIGITAL MULTIMETER, MEASURE VOLTAGE FROM STARTER SOLENOID TERM "S" TO GROUND. IS VOLTAGE LESS THAN 9.5 VOLTS?
YES
NO
• IGNITION SWITCH TO "START." • BACKPROBE C202 TERM "B6" WITH A DIGITAL MULTIMETER TO GROUND. • MEASURE VOLTAGE. IS VOLTAGE LESS THAN 9.5 VOLTS?
• CONNECT A REMOTE STARTER SWITCH BETWEEN STARTER SOLENOID TERM "S" AND BATTERY. DOES STARTER CRANK?
YES
NO
CHECK FOR POOR CONNECTION OR HIGH RESISTANCE IN STARTER CIRCUIT.
REPLACE STARTER SOLENOID.
YES
NO
• USING A DIGITAL MULTIMETER, BACKPROBE C202 TERM "D5" TO GROUND. • MEASURE VOLTAGE. IS VOLTAGE LESS THAN 9.5 VOLTS?
• CHECK CKT 575 FOR A SHORT TO GROUND OR HIGH RESISTANCE. • CHECK CKT 6 FOR A SHORT TO GROUND OR HIGH RESISTANCE. • CHECK TRANS RANGE SWITCH FOR A POOR CONNECTION. IF OK, REPLACE TRANS RANGE SWITCH.
YES
NO
• CHECK FOR OPEN IN CKT 2 OF BODY HARNESS. IF OK, REPLACE FUSIBLE LINK A.
• CHECK FOR POOR CONNECTION AT IGNITION SWITCH. IF OK, REPLACE IGNITION SWITCH.

STARTER AND CHARGING SYSTEM

CHART #2
STARTER SOLENOID CLICKS, ENGINE DOES NOT CRANK

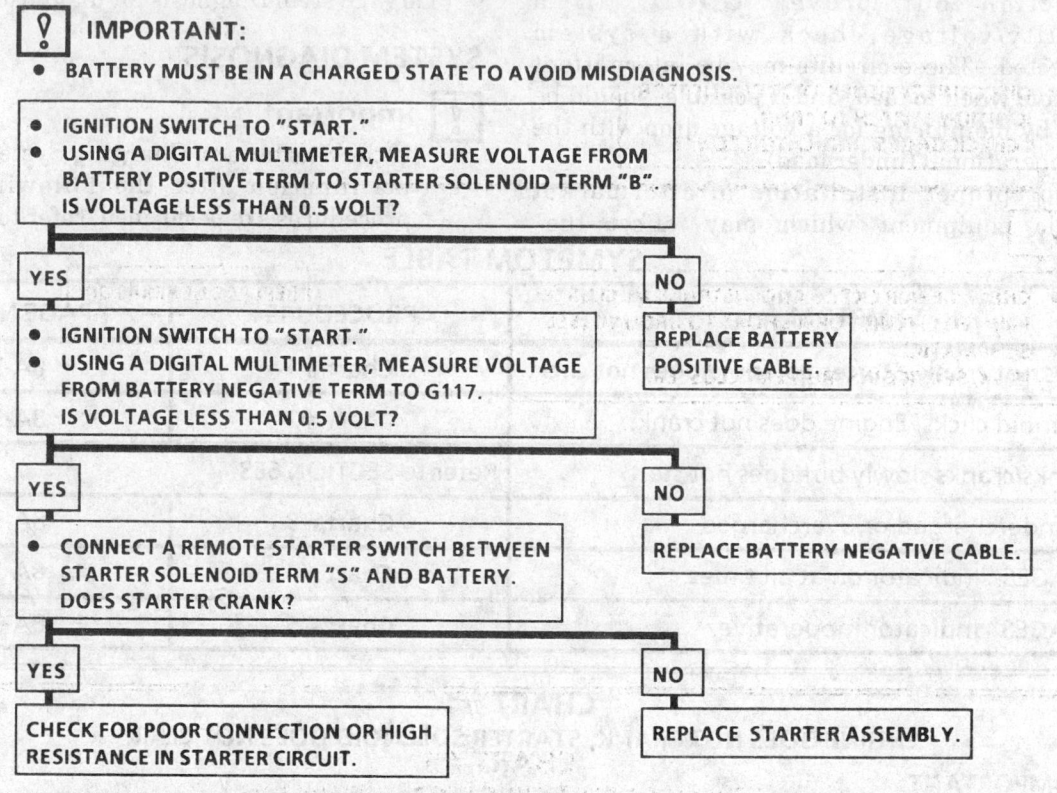

IMPORTANT:
- BATTERY MUST BE IN A CHARGED STATE TO AVOID MISDIAGNOSIS.

- IGNITION SWITCH TO "START."
- USING A DIGITAL MULTIMETER, MEASURE VOLTAGE FROM BATTERY POSITIVE TERM TO STARTER SOLENOID TERM "B". IS VOLTAGE LESS THAN 0.5 VOLT?

NO: REPLACE BATTERY POSITIVE CABLE.

YES:
- IGNITION SWITCH TO "START."
- USING A DIGITAL MULTIMETER, MEASURE VOLTAGE FROM BATTERY NEGATIVE TERM TO G117. IS VOLTAGE LESS THAN 0.5 VOLT?

NO: REPLACE BATTERY NEGATIVE CABLE.

YES:
- CONNECT A REMOTE STARTER SWITCH BETWEEN STARTER SOLENOID TERM "S" AND BATTERY. DOES STARTER CRANK?

YES: CHECK FOR POOR CONNECTION OR HIGH RESISTANCE IN STARTER CIRCUIT.

NO: REPLACE STARTER ASSEMBLY.

CHART #3
BATTERY IS UNDERCHARGED OR OVERCHARGED

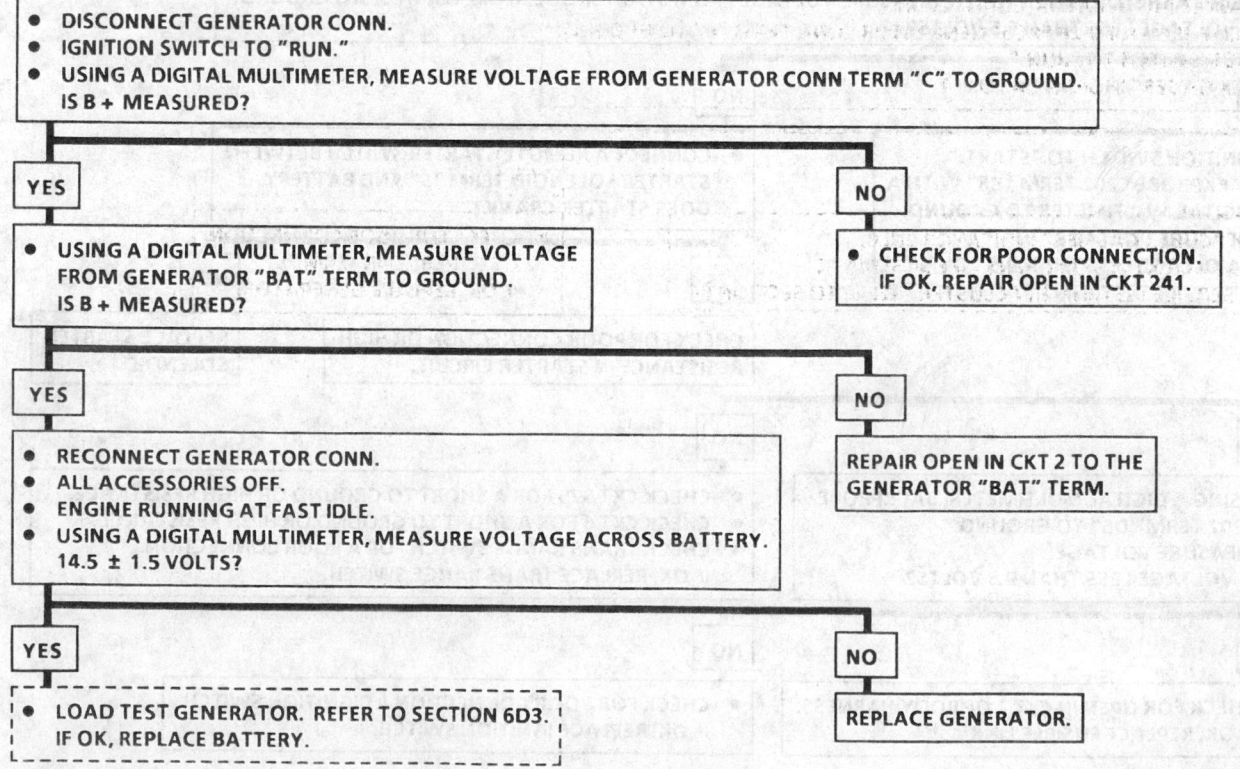

- DISCONNECT GENERATOR CONN.
- IGNITION SWITCH TO "RUN."
- USING A DIGITAL MULTIMETER, MEASURE VOLTAGE FROM GENERATOR CONN TERM "C" TO GROUND. IS B + MEASURED?

NO:
- CHECK FOR POOR CONNECTION. IF OK, REPAIR OPEN IN CKT 241.

YES:
- USING A DIGITAL MULTIMETER, MEASURE VOLTAGE FROM GENERATOR "BAT" TERM TO GROUND. IS B + MEASURED?

NO: REPAIR OPEN IN CKT 2 TO THE GENERATOR "BAT" TERM.

YES:
- RECONNECT GENERATOR CONN.
- ALL ACCESSORIES OFF.
- ENGINE RUNNING AT FAST IDLE.
- USING A DIGITAL MULTIMETER, MEASURE VOLTAGE ACROSS BATTERY. 14.5 ± 1.5 VOLTS?

YES:
- LOAD TEST GENERATOR. REFER TO SECTION 6D3. IF OK, REPLACE BATTERY.

NO: REPLACE GENERATOR.

CHART #4
"CHACK GAGES" INDICATOR ON AT ALL TIMES

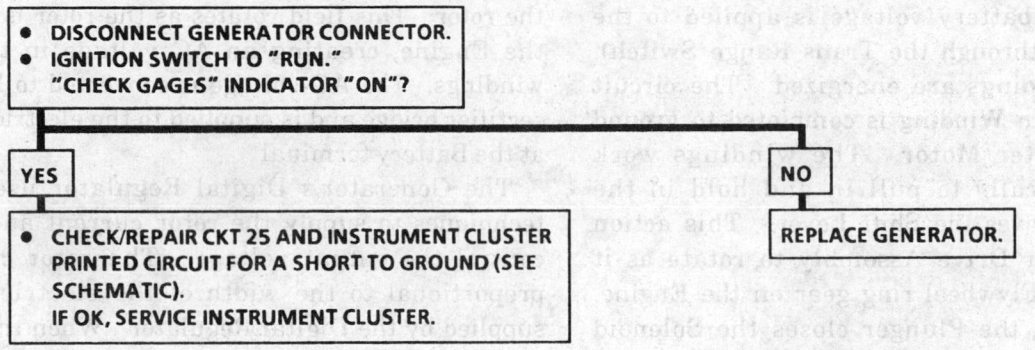

- DISCONNECT GENERATOR CONNECTOR.
- IGNITION SWITCH TO "RUN."
  "CHECK GAGES" INDICATOR "ON"?

YES

- CHECK/REPAIR CKT 25 AND INSTRUMENT CLUSTER PRINTED CIRCUIT FOR A SHORT TO GROUND (SEE SCHEMATIC).
  IF OK, SERVICE INSTRUMENT CLUSTER.

NO

REPLACE GENERATOR.

CHART #5
"CHECK GAGES" INDICATOR INOPERATIVE

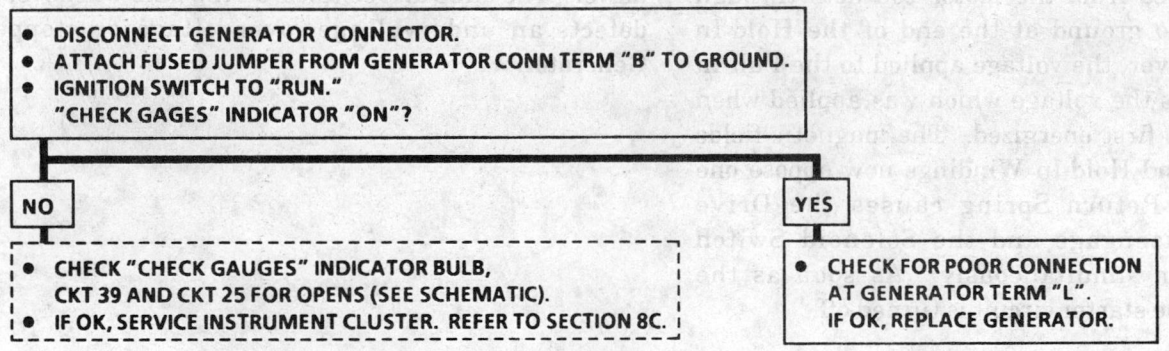

- DISCONNECT GENERATOR CONNECTOR.
- ATTACH FUSED JUMPER FROM GENERATOR CONN TERM "B" TO GROUND.
- IGNITION SWITCH TO "RUN."
  "CHECK GAGES" INDICATOR "ON"?

NO

- CHECK "CHECK GAUGES" INDICATOR BULB, CKT 39 AND CKT 25 FOR OPENS (SEE SCHEMATIC).
- IF OK, SERVICE INSTRUMENT CLUSTER. REFER TO SECTION 8C.

YES

- CHECK FOR POOR CONNECTION AT GENERATOR TERM "L".
  IF OK, REPLACE GENERATOR.

STARTER AND CHARGING SYSTEM

CIRCUIT OPERATION

STARTER

When the Ignition Switch is moved to the "START" position (and the Theft Deterrent Module recognizes the "Key Code"), battery voltage is applied to the Starter Solenoid (through the Trans Range Switch). Both solenoid windings are energized. The circuit through the Pull-In Winding is completed to ground through the Starter Motor. The windings work together magnetically to pull in and hold in the Plunger, which moves the Shift Lever. This action causes the Starter Drive Assembly to rotate as it engages with the Flywheel ring gear on the Engine. At the same time, the Plunger closes the Solenoid Switch contacts in the Starter Solenoid. Full Battery voltage is applied directly to the Starter Motor, which cranks the Engine.

When the Solenoid Switch contacts close, voltage is no longer applied through the Pull-In Winding, as battery voltage is applied to both ends of the windings. The Hold-In Winding remains energized, and its magnetic field is strong enough to hold the Plunger, Shift Lever, Drive Assembly and Solenoid Switch contacts in place to continue cranking the Engine.

When the Ignition Switch is released from the "START" position, battery voltage is removed from the CKT 6 wire and the junction of the two windings. Voltage is applied from the motor contacts through both windings to ground at the end of the Hold-In Winding. However, the voltage applied to the Pull-In Winding opposes the voltage which was applied when the winding was first energized. The magnetic fields of the Pull-In and Hold-In Windings now oppose one another. The Return Spring causes the Drive Assembly to disengage and the Solenoid Switch contacts to open simultaneously. As soon as the contacts open, the starter circuit is turned off.

CHARGING

The Generator provides voltage to operate the vehicle's electrical system and to charge its Battery. A magnetic field is created when current flows through the rotor. This field rotates as the rotor is driven by the Engine, creating an AC voltage in the stator windings. The AC voltage is converted to DC by the rectifier bridge and is supplied to the electrical system at the Battery terminal.

The Generator's Digital Regulator uses digital techniques to supply the rotor current and thereby control the output voltage. The rotor current is proportional to the width of the electrical pulses supplied by the Digital Regulator. When the Ignition Switch is placed in "RUN," voltage is supplied to terminals "L" and "F" turning on the Digital Regulator. Narrow width pulses are supplied to the digital rotor, creating a weak magnetic field. When the Engine is started, the Digital Regulator senses Generator rotation by detecting AC voltage at the Stator through an internal wire. Once the Engine is running, the Digital Regulator varies the field current by controlling the pulse width. This regulates the Generator output voltage for proper Battery charging and electrical system operation.

The Digital Regulator controls the "CHECK GAUGES" Indicator bulb with a solid state lamp driver. The lamp driver turns on the bulb whenever it detects an undervoltage, overvoltage or stopped Generator.

BLANK

COOLING FANS

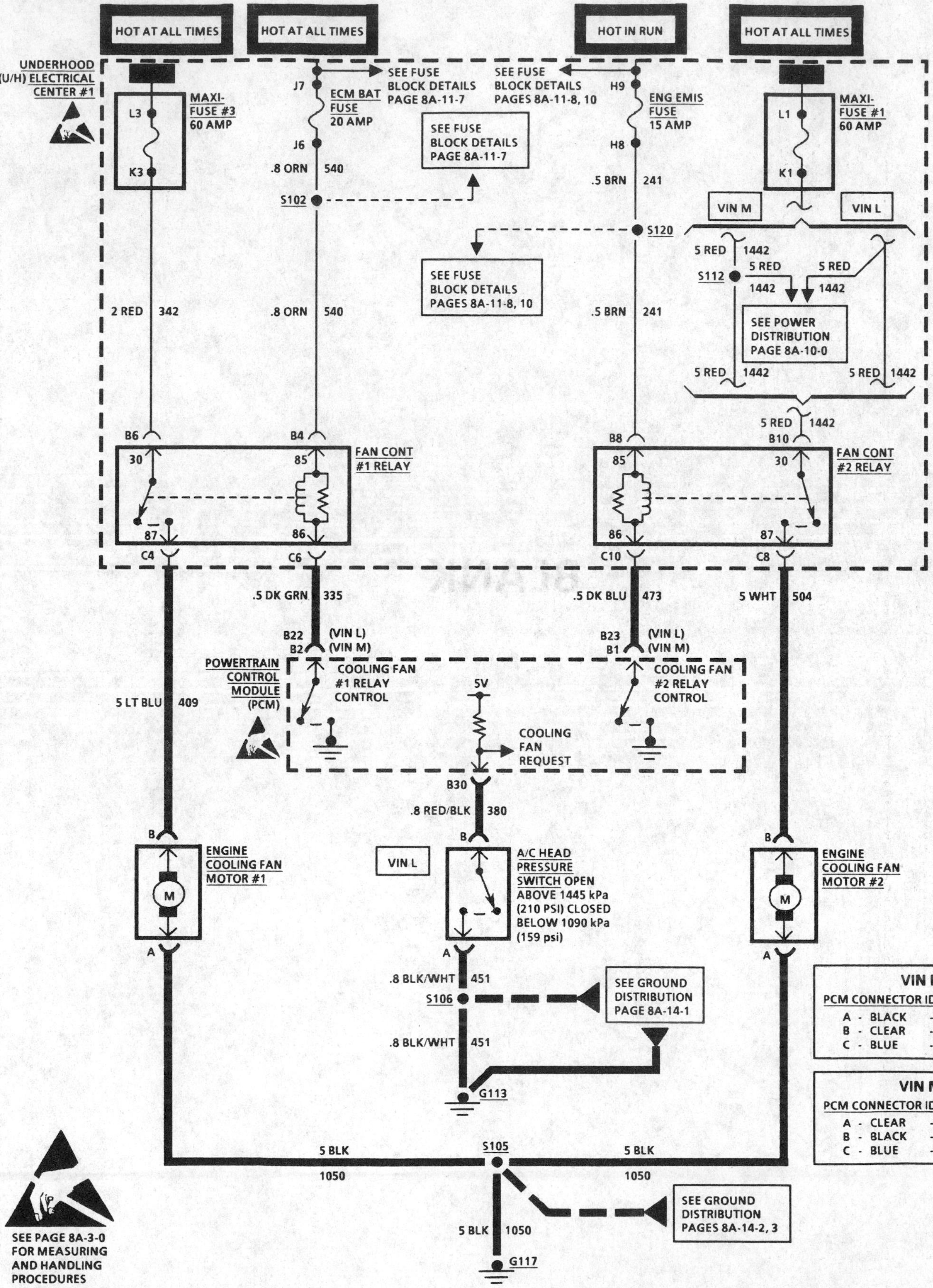
HOT AT ALL TIMES
HOT AT ALL TIMES
HOT IN RUN
HOT AT ALL TIMES
UNDERHOOD (U/H) ELECTRICAL CENTER #1
MAXI-FUSE #3 60 AMP
L3
K3
J7
ECM BAT FUSE 20 AMP
J6
SEE FUSE BLOCK DETAILS PAGE 8A-11-7
SEE FUSE BLOCK DETAILS PAGES 8A-11-8, 10
H9
ENG EMIS FUSE 15 AMP
H8
MAXI-FUSE #1 60 AMP
L1
K1
SEE FUSE BLOCK DETAILS PAGE 8A-11-7
.8 ORN 540
S102
.5 BRN 241
VIN M
VIN L
S120
5 RED 1442
S112
SEE FUSE BLOCK DETAILS PAGES 8A-11-8, 10
SEE POWER DISTRIBUTION PAGE 8A-10-0
2 RED 342
.8 ORN 540
.5 BRN 241
B6
B4
B8
B10
FAN CONT #1 RELAY
FAN CONT #2 RELAY
30
85
86
87
C4
C6
C10
C8
.5 DK GRN 335
.5 DK BLU 473
5 WHT 504
B22 (VIN L)
B2 (VIN M)
B23 (VIN L)
B1 (VIN M)
POWERTRAIN CONTROL MODULE (PCM)
COOLING FAN #1 RELAY CONTROL
5V
COOLING FAN REQUEST
COOLING FAN #2 RELAY CONTROL
5 LT BLU 409
B30
.8 RED/BLK 380
ENGINE COOLING FAN MOTOR #1
VIN L
A/C HEAD PRESSURE SWITCH OPEN ABOVE 1445 kPa (210 PSI) CLOSED BELOW 1090 kPa (159 psi)
ENGINE COOLING FAN MOTOR #2
M
B
A
.8 BLK/WHT 451
S106
SEE GROUND DISTRIBUTION PAGE 8A-14-1
G113
5 BLK 1050
S105
SEE GROUND DISTRIBUTION PAGES 8A-14-2, 3
G117
SEE PAGE 8A-3-0 FOR MEASURING AND HANDLING PROCEDURES

VIN L

PCM CONNECTOR IDENTIFICATION

A -	BLACK	- 32 WAY
B -	CLEAR	- 32 WAY
C -	BLUE	- 32 WAY

VIN M

PCM CONNECTOR IDENTIFICATION

A -	CLEAR	- 32 WAY
B -	BLACK	- 32 WAY
C -	BLUE	- 32 WAY

COMPONENT	LOCATION	201-PG	FIG.	CONN
A/C Head Pressure Switch	LH front of Engine Compartment, on A/C Line near accumulator	26	83	
Engine Cooling Fan Motor #1	Behind LH side of Radiator	6	19	
Engine Cooling Fan Motor #2	Behind RH side of Radiator	6	19	
Powertrain Control Module (PCM) (VIN L)	RH side of Engine Compartment, forward of strut tower	19	68	202-29
Powertrain Control Module (PCM) (VIN M)	RH side of Engine Compartment, forward of strut tower	19	69	202-26
Underhood Electrical Center #1	RH side of Engine Compartment, forward of strut tower	19	68	202-47
G113 (VIN L)	Behind Electronic Ignition (EI) Control Module	0	3	
G117	Lower LH front of Engine, on Transaxle stud	0	1	
S102 (VIN M)	Engine Harn, approx 4 cm from Underhood Electrical Center #1 breakout			
S102 (VIN L)	Engine Harn, approx 12 cm from Underhood Electrical Center #1 breakout			
S105	Engine Harn, approx 5 cm from Engine Cooling Fan #1 breakout			
S106 (VIN L)	Engine Harn, approx 19 cm from PCM breakout			
S112 (VIN M)	Engine Harn, approx 10 cm from Underhood Electrical Center #1 breakout			
S120 (VIN L)	Engine Harn, approx 9 cm from Underhood Electrical Center #1 breakout			
S120 (VIN M)	Engine Harn, approx 7 cm from Underhood Electrical Center #1 breakout			

SYSTEM DIAGNOSIS

- Refer to SECTION 6E3-C12 .

VEHICLE SPEED SENSOR

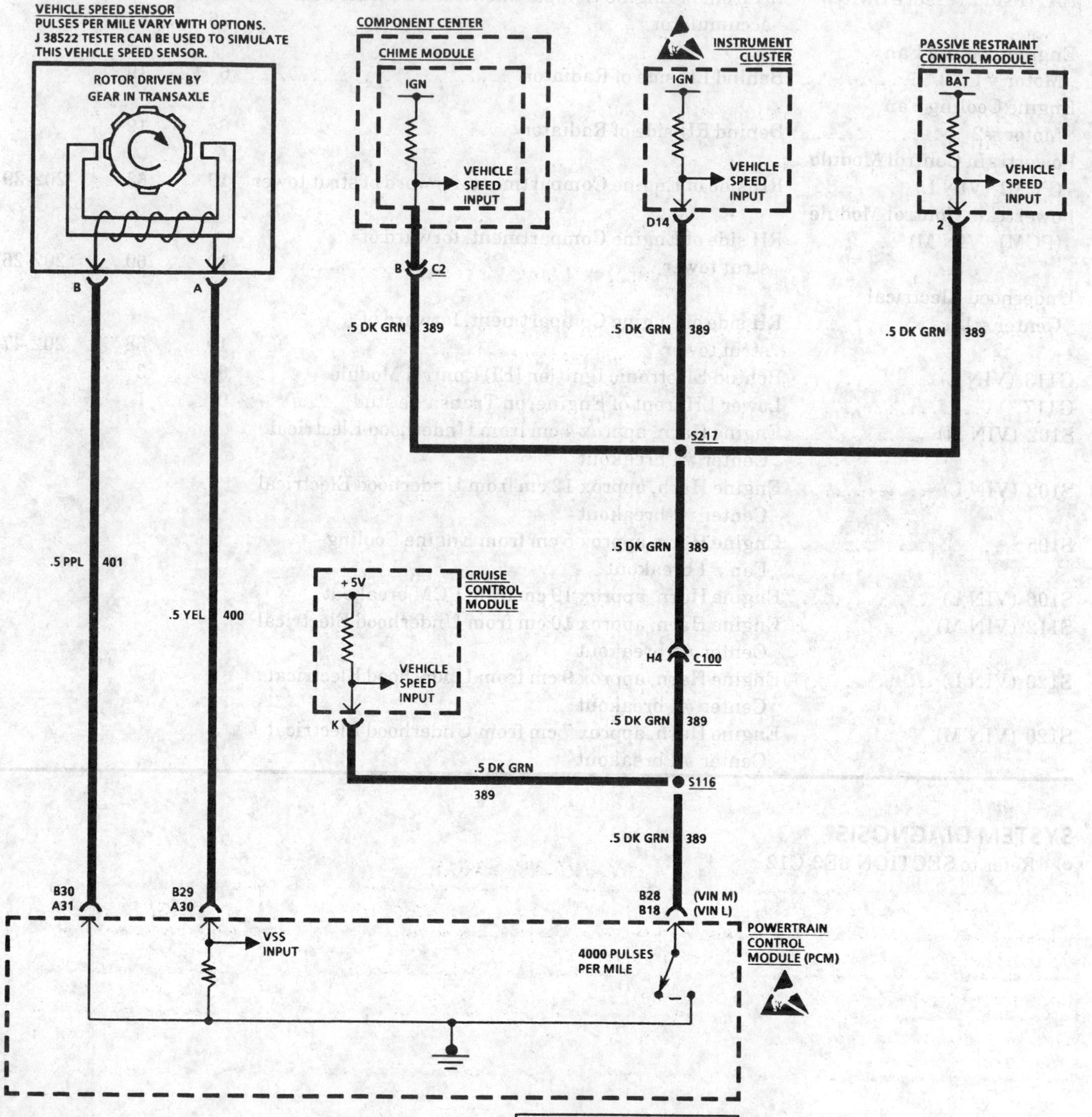
VEHICLE SPEED SENSOR
PULSES PER MILE VARY WITH OPTIONS.
J 38522 TESTER CAN BE USED TO SIMULATE
THIS VEHICLE SPEED SENSOR.
ROTOR DRIVEN BY
GEAR IN TRANSAXLE
B
A
COMPONENT CENTER
CHIME MODULE
IGN
VEHICLE
SPEED
INPUT
B
C2
INSTRUMENT
CLUSTER
IGN
VEHICLE
SPEED
INPUT
D14
PASSIVE RESTRAINT
CONTROL MODULE
BAT
VEHICLE
SPEED
INPUT
2
.5 DK GRN 389
.5 DK GRN 389
.5 DK GRN 389
S217
.5 DK GRN 389
.5 PPL 401
.5 YEL 400
+5V
CRUISE
CONTROL
MODULE
VEHICLE
SPEED
INPUT
K
H4
C100
.5 DK GRN 389
.5 DK GRN
389
S116
.5 DK GRN 389
B30
A31
B29
A30
B28 (VIN M)
B18 (VIN L)
VSS
INPUT
4000 PULSES
PER MILE
POWERTRAIN
CONTROL
MODULE (PCM)

PCM CONNECTOR IDENTIFICATION

A - CLEAR	-	32 WAY
B - BLACK	-	32 WAY
C - BLUE	-	32 WAY

SEE PAGE 8A-3-0 FOR MEASURING AND HANDLING PROCEDURES

COMPONENT	LOCATION	201-PG	FIG.	CONN
Chime Module	Component Center			
Component Center	Behind RH side of I/P	11	36	202-14
Cruise Control Module	LH rear of Engine Compartment, near strut tower	8	28	202-16
Passive Restraint Control Module	Behind RH side of I/P			202-40
Powertrain Control Module (PCM) (VIN L)	RH side of Engine Compartment, forward of strut tower	19	68	202-28
Powertrain Control Module (PCM) (VIN M)	RH side of Engine Compartment, forward of strut tower	19	69	202-31
Vehicle Speed Sensor (VIN L)	RH rear of Engine, on Transaxle	9	32	
Vehicle Speed Sensor (VIN M)	RH rear of Engine, on Transaxle			
C100 (36 cavities)	RH side of dash, behind strut tower	8	29	202-0
S116	Engine Harn, approx 5 cm from PCM breakout			
S217	I/P Harn, approx 58 cm from C100			

TROUBLESHOOTING HINTS
(Perform before beginning System Diagnosis)

- Check for a broken (or partially broken) wire inside of the insulation which could cause system malfunction but prove "GOOD" in a continuity/voltage check with a system disconnected. These circuits may be intermittent or resistive when loaded, and if possible, should be checked by monitoring for a voltage drop with the system operational (under load).
- Check for proper installation of aftermarket electronic equipment which may affect the integrity of other systems (see "Troubleshooting Procedures," page 8A-4-0).
- If any PCM codes are set, see SECTION 6E.
- Refer to System Diagnosis.

SYSTEM DIAGNOSIS

- Refer to the Symptom Table for the appropriate diagnostic procedures.

SYMPTOM TABLE

SYMPTOM	PROCEDURE	PAGE NUMBER
Speedometer is inaccurate (J 38522 unavailable).	Chart #1	8A-33-2
Speedometer is inaccurate (J 38522 available).	Chart #2	8A-33-2
One or more of the speed signal dependent features do not operate properly.	Chart #3	8A-33-3

VEHICLE SPEED SENSOR

CHART #1

SPEEDOMETER IS INACCURATE (J 38522 UNAVAILABLE)

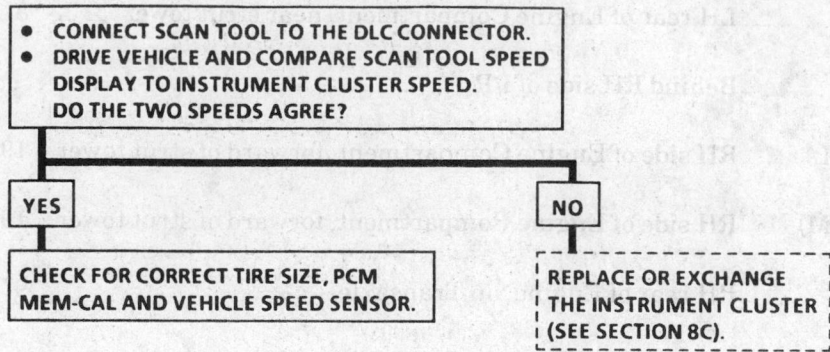

- CONNECT SCAN TOOL TO THE DLC CONNECTOR.
- DRIVE VEHICLE AND COMPARE SCAN TOOL SPEED DISPLAY TO INSTRUMENT CLUSTER SPEED.
  DO THE TWO SPEEDS AGREE?

YES

CHECK FOR CORRECT TIRE SIZE, PCM MEM-CAL AND VEHICLE SPEED SENSOR.

NO

REPLACE OR EXCHANGE THE INSTRUMENT CLUSTER (SEE SECTION 8C).

CHART #2

SPEEDOMETER IS INACCURATE (J 38522 AVAILABLE)

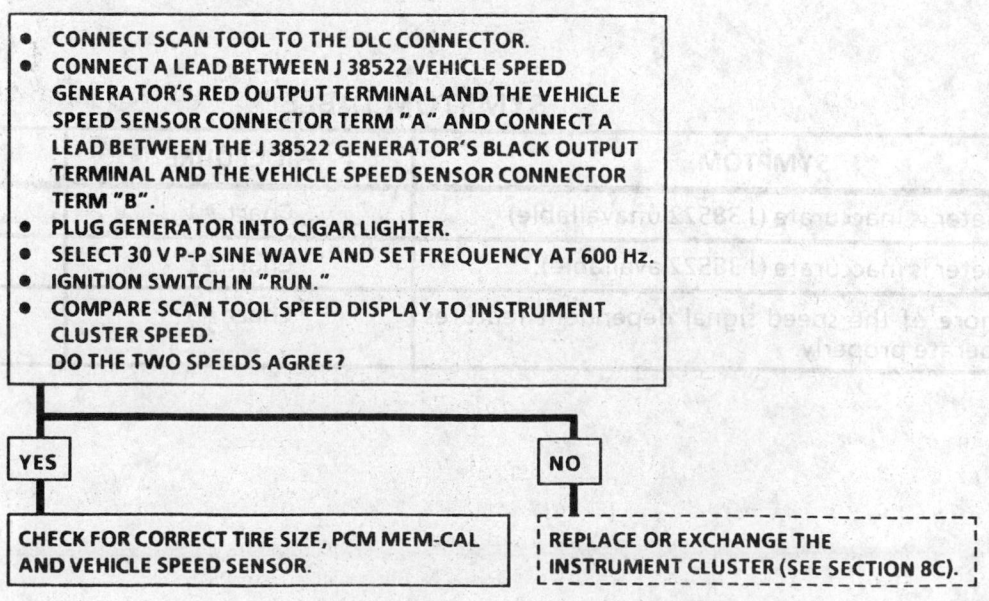

- CONNECT SCAN TOOL TO THE DLC CONNECTOR.
- CONNECT A LEAD BETWEEN J 38522 VEHICLE SPEED GENERATOR'S RED OUTPUT TERMINAL AND THE VEHICLE SPEED SENSOR CONNECTOR TERM "A" AND CONNECT A LEAD BETWEEN THE J 38522 GENERATOR'S BLACK OUTPUT TERMINAL AND THE VEHICLE SPEED SENSOR CONNECTOR TERM "B".
- PLUG GENERATOR INTO CIGAR LIGHTER.
- SELECT 30 V P-P SINE WAVE AND SET FREQUENCY AT 600 Hz.
- IGNITION SWITCH IN "RUN."
- COMPARE SCAN TOOL SPEED DISPLAY TO INSTRUMENT CLUSTER SPEED.
  DO THE TWO SPEEDS AGREE?

YES

CHECK FOR CORRECT TIRE SIZE, PCM MEM-CAL AND VEHICLE SPEED SENSOR.

NO

REPLACE OR EXCHANGE THE INSTRUMENT CLUSTER (SEE SECTION 8C).

CHART #3
ONE OR MORE OF THE SPEED RELATED FEATURES DO NOT OPERATE PROPERLY

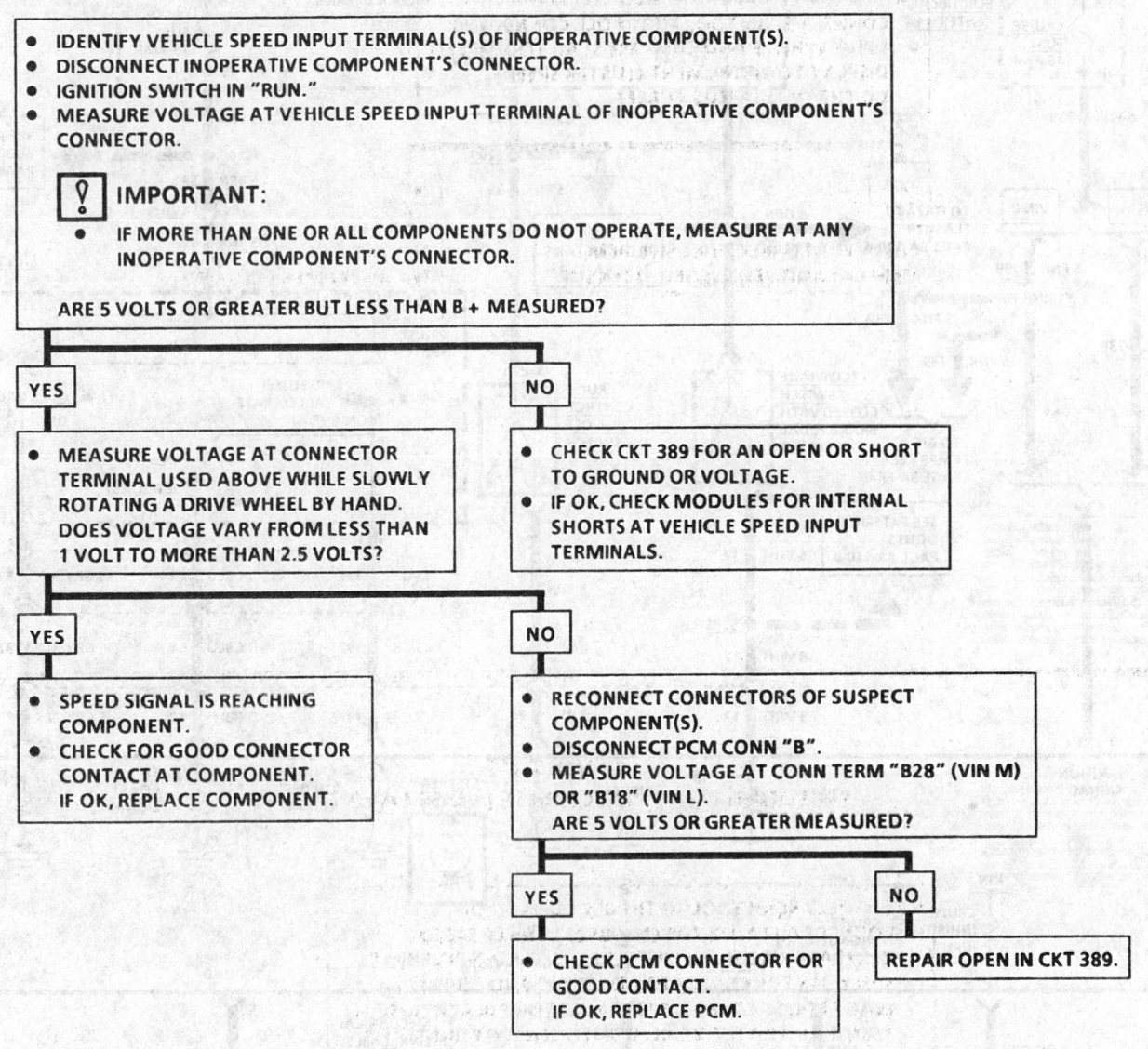

- IDENTIFY VEHICLE SPEED INPUT TERMINAL(S) OF INOPERATIVE COMPONENT(S).
- DISCONNECT INOPERATIVE COMPONENT'S CONNECTOR.
- IGNITION SWITCH IN "RUN."
- MEASURE VOLTAGE AT VEHICLE SPEED INPUT TERMINAL OF INOPERATIVE COMPONENT'S CONNECTOR.

IMPORTANT:
- IF MORE THAN ONE OR ALL COMPONENTS DO NOT OPERATE, MEASURE AT ANY INOPERATIVE COMPONENT'S CONNECTOR.

ARE 5 VOLTS OR GREATER BUT LESS THAN B + MEASURED?

YES

- MEASURE VOLTAGE AT CONNECTOR TERMINAL USED ABOVE WHILE SLOWLY ROTATING A DRIVE WHEEL BY HAND. DOES VOLTAGE VARY FROM LESS THAN 1 VOLT TO MORE THAN 2.5 VOLTS?

YES

- SPEED SIGNAL IS REACHING COMPONENT.
- CHECK FOR GOOD CONNECTOR CONTACT AT COMPONENT. IF OK, REPLACE COMPONENT.

NO

- RECONNECT CONNECTORS OF SUSPECT COMPONENT(S).
- DISCONNECT PCM CONN "B".
- MEASURE VOLTAGE AT CONN TERM "B28" (VIN M) OR "B18" (VIN L). ARE 5 VOLTS OR GREATER MEASURED?

YES

- CHECK PCM CONNECTOR FOR GOOD CONTACT. IF OK, REPLACE PCM.

NO

REPAIR OPEN IN CKT 389.

NO

- CHECK CKT 389 FOR AN OPEN OR SHORT TO GROUND OR VOLTAGE.
- IF OK, CHECK MODULES FOR INTERNAL SHORTS AT VEHICLE SPEED INPUT TERMINALS.

CIRCUIT OPERATION

The Vehicle Speed Sensor is a gear-driven Permanent Magnet Generator housed in the vehicle's Transaxle. This sensor generates a sine wave output with a frequency proportional to vehicle speed. The PCM converts this signal to an output that is switched to ground at a frequency of 4000 pulses per mile at the CKT 389 output. This output is pulled up to 5 volts or greater by the components that use this speed signal as an input.

CRUISE CONTROL

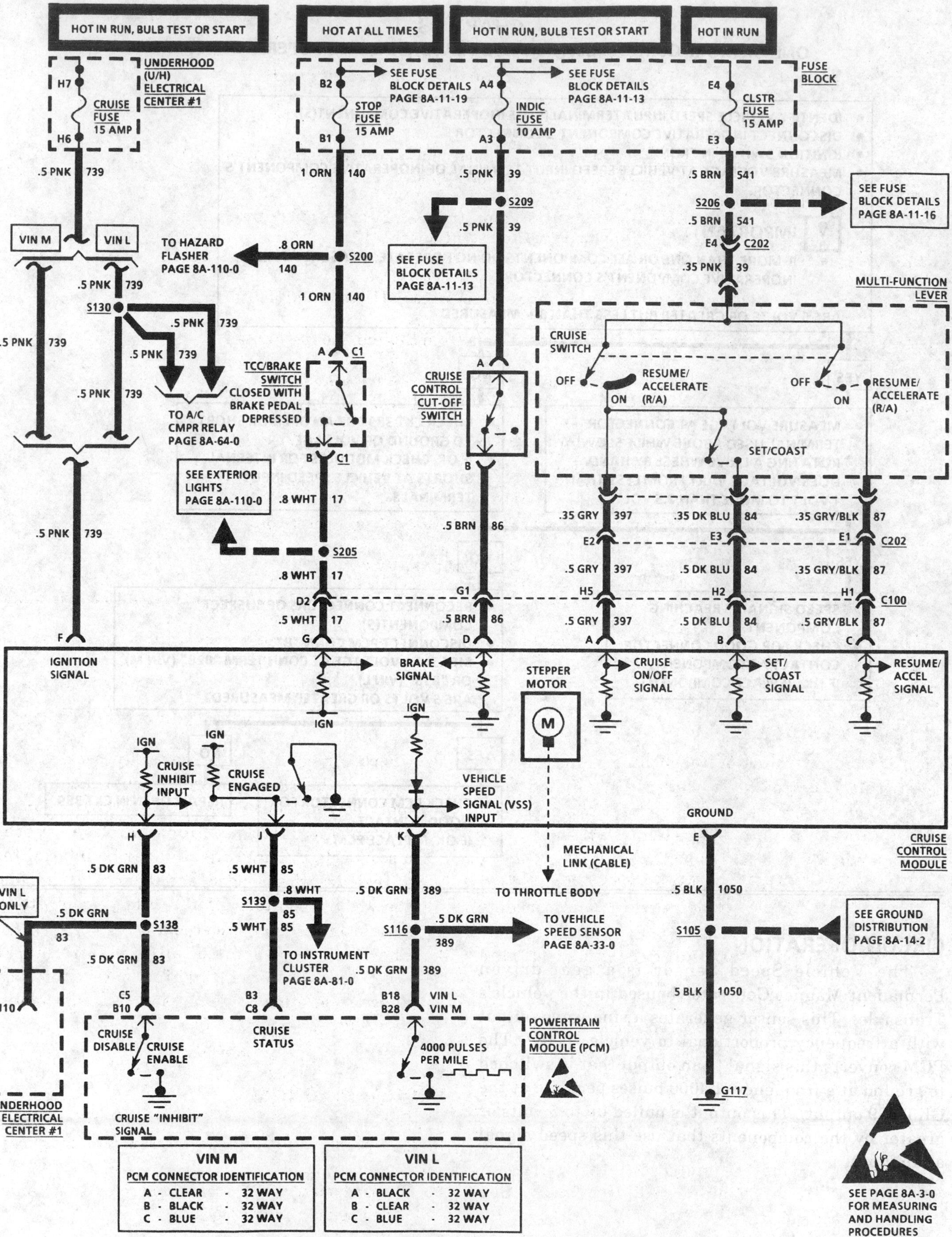
HOT IN RUN, BULB TEST OR START
HOT AT ALL TIMES
HOT IN RUN, BULB TEST OR START
HOT IN RUN
UNDERHOOD (U/H) ELECTRICAL CENTER #1
H7
CRUISE FUSE 15 AMP
H6
B2
SEE FUSE BLOCK DETAILS PAGE 8A-11-19
STOP FUSE 15 AMP
B1
A4
SEE FUSE BLOCK DETAILS PAGE 8A-11-13
INDIC FUSE 10 AMP
A3
FUSE BLOCK
E4
CLSTR FUSE 15 AMP
E3
.5 PNK 739
1 ORN 140
.5 PNK 39
.5 BRN 541
S209
.5 PNK 39
S206
SEE FUSE BLOCK DETAILS PAGE 8A-11-16
.5 BRN 541
E4 C202
.35 PNK 39
VIN M
VIN L
TO HAZARD FLASHER PAGE 8A-110-0
.8 ORN 140
S200
SEE FUSE BLOCK DETAILS PAGE 8A-11-13
1 ORN 140
.5 PNK 739
S130
.5 PNK 739
.5 PNK 739
.5 PNK 739
.5 PNK 739
TO A/C CMPR RELAY PAGE 8A-64-0
MULTI-FUNCTION LEVER
CRUISE SWITCH
OFF
RESUME/ ACCELERATE (R/A)
ON
OFF
RESUME/ ACCELERATE (R/A)
ON
SET/COAST
A C1
TCC/BRAKE SWITCH
CLOSED WITH BRAKE PEDAL DEPRESSED
A
CRUISE CONTROL CUT-OFF SWITCH
B C1
B
SEE EXTERIOR LIGHTS PAGE 8A-110-0
.8 WHT 17
.5 BRN 86
S205
.8 WHT 17
.35 GRY 397
.35 DK BLU 84
.35 GRY/BLK 87
E2
E3
E1 C202
.5 GRY 397
.5 DK BLU 84
.35 GRY/BLK 87
D2
G1
H5
H2
H1 C100
.5 PNK 739
.5 WHT 17
.5 BRN 86
.5 GRY 397
.5 DK BLU 84
.5 GRY/BLK 87
F
G
D
A
B
C
IGNITION SIGNAL
BRAKE SIGNAL
IGN
STEPPER MOTOR
M
CRUISE ON/OFF SIGNAL
SET/ COAST SIGNAL
RESUME/ ACCEL SIGNAL
IGN
IGN
IGN
CRUISE INHIBIT INPUT
CRUISE ENGAGED
VEHICLE SPEED SIGNAL (VSS) INPUT
GROUND
H
J
K
E
CRUISE CONTROL MODULE
MECHANICAL LINK (CABLE)
.5 DK GRN 83
.5 WHT 85
.8 WHT
.5 DK GRN 389
TO THROTTLE BODY
.5 BLK 1050
VIN L ONLY
S139
85
.5 DK GRN
S138
.5 WHT 85
S116
.5 DK GRN
TO VEHICLE SPEED SENSOR PAGE 8A-33-0
389
83
S105
SEE GROUND DISTRIBUTION PAGE 8A-14-2
.5 DK GRN 83
TO INSTRUMENT CLUSTER PAGE 8A-81-0
.5 DK GRN 389
.5 BLK 1050
J10
C5 B10
B3 C8
B18 B28
VIN L VIN M
CRUISE DISABLE
CRUISE ENABLE
CRUISE STATUS
4000 PULSES PER MILE
POWERTRAIN CONTROL MODULE (PCM)
G117
UNDERHOOD ELECTRICAL CENTER #1
CRUISE "INHIBIT" SIGNAL

VIN M

PCM CONNECTOR IDENTIFICATION

A	CLEAR	-	32 WAY
B	BLACK	-	32 WAY
C	BLUE	-	32 WAY

VIN L

PCM CONNECTOR IDENTIFICATION

A	BLACK	-	32 WAY
B	CLEAR	-	32 WAY
C	BLUE	-	32 WAY

SEE PAGE 8A-3-0 FOR MEASURING AND HANDLING PROCEDURES

COMPONENT	LOCATION	201-PG	FIG.	CONN
Cruise Control Cut-off Switch	Behind I/P, on brake pedal support	12	42	
Cruise Control Module	LH side of Engine Compartment, near strut tower	8	28	202-16
Fuse Block	RH side of I/P, in I/P Compartment			
Multi-Function Lever	LH side of Steering Column	12	43	
Powertrain Control Module (PCM)	RH side of Engine Compartment, forward of strut tower	19	68, 69	202-26
TCC Brake Switch	Behind I/P, on brake pedal support	12	42	202-41
Underhood (U/H) Electrical Center #1	RH side of Engine Compartment, forward of strut tower			202-34
C100 (36 cavities)	RH side of dash, behind strut tower			202-0
C202 (48 cavities)	Behind I/P, RH side of Steering Column	14	48	202-9
G117	LH front of Engine, on Transaxle stud	0	1	
S105 (VIN L)	Engine Harn, approx 20 cm from U/H Electrical Center #1 breakout			
S105 (VIN M)	Engine Harn, approx 5 cm from Engine Cooling Fan #1 breakout			
S116	Engine Harn, approx 5 cm from PCM breakout			
S130	Engine Harn, approx 4 cm from U/H Electrical Center #1 breakout			
S138	Engine Harn, approx 8 cm from U/H Electrical Center #1 breakout			
S139	Engine Harn, approx 12 cm from U/H Electrical Center #1 breakout			
S200	I/P Harn, approx 4 cm from Radio Receiver breakout			
S205	I/P Harn, approx 4 cm from G201 breakout			
S206	I/P Harn, approx 10 cm from Fuse Block breakout			
S209	I/P Harn, approx 16 cm from Fuse Block breakout			

TROUBLESHOOTING HINTS (Perform before beginning System Diagnosis)

Important:

- The Powertrain Control Module will "Inhibit" Cruise Control when there is a malfunction in any of the Cruise Control Inhibit Criteria. The PCM will "Inhibit" Cruise Control when:
  - When VSS is less than 25 mph.
  - When "PARK," "REVERSE," "NEUTRAL," or "1st GEAR" is indicated by the Transaxle Range Switch.
  - When an over/under battery voltage condition exists.
  - With low Engine RPM.
  - With high Engine RPM (fuel cut-off).

1. Check all cruise control inhibit criteria.
2. Check for Diagnostic Trouble Codes (DTCs). Refer to SECTION 6E.
3. Check that Cruise Control Module Linkage is connected and moving freely.
4. Check Cruise Cable Adjustment. See SECTION 9B.
5. Check Brake Switch for proper adjustment/alignment.

- Make sure that Center High Mounted Stoplamp is working. If inoperative, Cruise Module will be disabled.
- Check for a broken (or partially broken) wire inside of the insulation which could cause system malfunction but prove "GOOD" in a continuity/voltage check with a system disconnected. These circuits may be intermittent or resistive when loaded, and if possible, should be checked by monitoring for a voltage drop with the system operational (under load).
- Check for proper installation of aftermarket electronic equipment which may affect the integrity of other systems (see "Troubleshooting Procedures," page 8A-4-0).
- Refer to System Diagnosis.

SYSTEM DIAGNOSIS

- Perform the System Check and refer to the Symptom Table for the appropriate diagnostic procedure(s).
- If speedometer is inoperative, refer to "Vehicle Speed Sensor," page 8A-33-2.

CRUISE CONTROL

SYSTEM CHECK

ACTION	NORMAL RESULTS
[1] • Drive vehicle above 25 mph. • Cruise Switch to "ON." • Depress Set/Coast Switch once and release. • Remove foot from accelerator pedal.	Vehicle maintains set speed.
[2] • Depress and hold R/A Switch until vehicle speed increases by 4 to 5 mph. • Release R/A Switch.	Vehicle accelerates and maintains a new higher set speed.
[3] • Depress and hold Set/Coast Switch until vehicle speed decreases by 4 to 5 mph. • Release Set/Coast Switch.	Vehicle decelerates and maintains a new lower set speed, if speed is above 25 mph.
[4] • Depress brake pedal slightly.	Cruise Control disengages. Memory unchanged.
[5] • Depress R/A Switch once and release.	Vehicle accelerates to and maintains previous set speed.
[6] • Depress R/A Switch once (tap up) and release (less than 3/4 of a second).	Vehicle speed increases by 1 mph and maintains new set speed.
[7] • Depress Set/Coast Switch once (tap down) and release (less than 3/8 of a second).	Vehicle speed decreases by 1 mph and maintains new set speed.
[8] • Depress Set/Coast and R/A Switches simultaneously.	Cruise Control disengages with memory unchanged.
[9] • Depress R/A Switch once and release.	Vehicle accelerates to and maintains previous set speed.
[10] • Cruise Switch to "OFF."	Cruise Control disengages. Set speed memory is erased.

ADDITIONAL SYSTEM CHECK

The following procedure may be used as a System Check to verify operation of the Cruise Control System after repairs.

- (VIN L) Ground CKT 83 at Underhood (U/H) Electrical Center #1 at terminal "J10".
- (VIN M) With a Tech 1 scan tool, command SMCC to "Allow" Cruise.
- Set Park Brake.
- Start Engine.
- Move Cruise Switch to "OFF."
- Move Cruise Switch to "ON" and wait at least 3 seconds before doing next step.
- Push Set/Coast Switch in and hold.
- Hold Cruise Slider Switch in "R/A" position.
- Fully depress and hold brake pedal.
- After 10 seconds, release brake pedal while still holding R/A and Set Switches.
- Engine RPM should increase momentarily then return to normal.
- Clear any Diagnostic Trouble Codes (DTC).

SYMPTOM TABLE

SYMPTOM	PROCEDURE	PAGE NUMBER
Cruise Control is inoperative.	Chart #1	8A-34-3
Cruise Control will not resume, accelerate, tap-up or tap-down.	Chart #2	8A-34-6
"CRUISE" Indicator inoperative.	Chart #3	8A-34-6
"CRUISE" Indicator on at all times.	Chart #4	8A-34-7

CHART #1

CRUISE CONTROL IS INOPERATIVE

IMPORTANT:

TO AVOID MISDIAGNOSIS;

- CHECK FOR PROPER OPERATION OF BRAKE AND CHMSL LIGHTS.
- CHECK THROTTLE LINKAGE FOR MECHANICAL BINDING WHICH COULD CAUSE SYSTEM MALFUNCTION.
- CHECK FOR STORED DIAGNOSTIC TROUBLE CODES (DTC) (REFER TO SECTION 6E).

THE PCM WILL "INHIBIT" CRUISE CONTROL:

- WHEN VSS IS LESS THAN 25 mph.
- WHEN "PARK," "REVERSE," "NEUTRAL," OR "1st GEAR" IS INDICATED BY THE TRANSAXLE RANGE SWITCH.
- WHEN AN OVER/UNDER BATTERY VOLTAGE CONDITION EXISTS.
- WITH LOW ENGINE rpm.
- WITH HIGH ENGINE rpm (FUEL CUT-OFF).

REFER TO SECTION 6E FOR CRUISE CONTROL INHIBIT CRITERIA DIAGNOSIS.

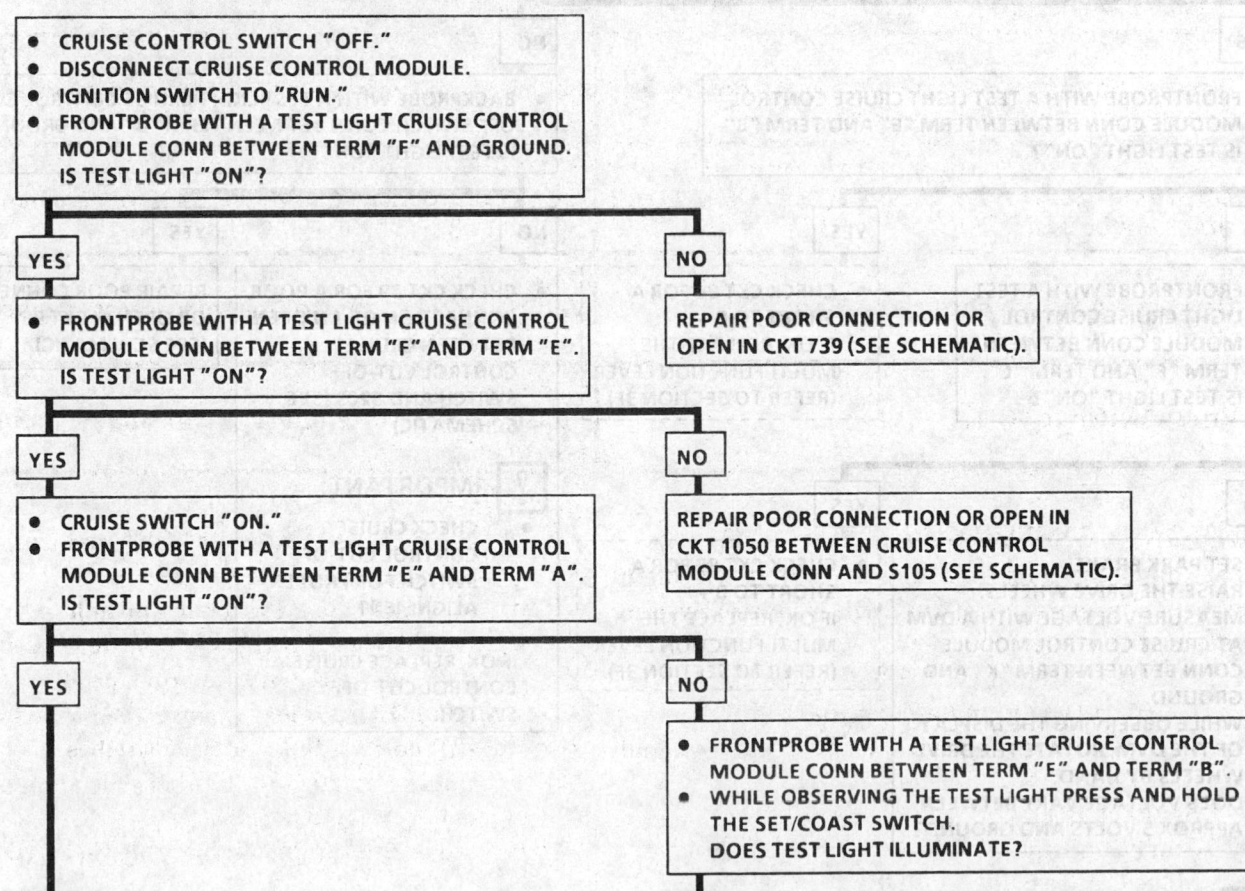

- CRUISE CONTROL SWITCH "OFF."
- DISCONNECT CRUISE CONTROL MODULE.
- IGNITION SWITCH TO "RUN."
- FRONTPROBE WITH A TEST LIGHT CRUISE CONTROL MODULE CONN BETWEEN TERM "F" AND GROUND.

IS TEST LIGHT "ON"?

NO → REPAIR POOR CONNECTION OR OPEN IN CKT 739 (SEE SCHEMATIC).

YES →

- FRONTPROBE WITH A TEST LIGHT CRUISE CONTROL MODULE CONN BETWEEN TERM "F" AND TERM "E".

IS TEST LIGHT "ON"?

NO → REPAIR POOR CONNECTION OR OPEN IN CKT 1050 BETWEEN CRUISE CONTROL MODULE CONN AND S105 (SEE SCHEMATIC).

YES →

- CRUISE SWITCH "ON."
- FRONTPROBE WITH A TEST LIGHT CRUISE CONTROL MODULE CONN BETWEEN TERM "E" AND TERM "A".

IS TEST LIGHT "ON"?

YES → A (CONTINUED ON NEXT PAGE)

NO →

- FRONTPROBE WITH A TEST LIGHT CRUISE CONTROL MODULE CONN BETWEEN TERM "E" AND TERM "B".
- WHILE OBSERVING THE TEST LIGHT PRESS AND HOLD THE SET/COAST SWITCH.

DOES TEST LIGHT ILLUMINATE?

→ B (CONTINUED ON PAGE 5)

CRUISE CONTROL

CHART #1 (continued)
CRUISE CONTROL IS INOPERATIVE

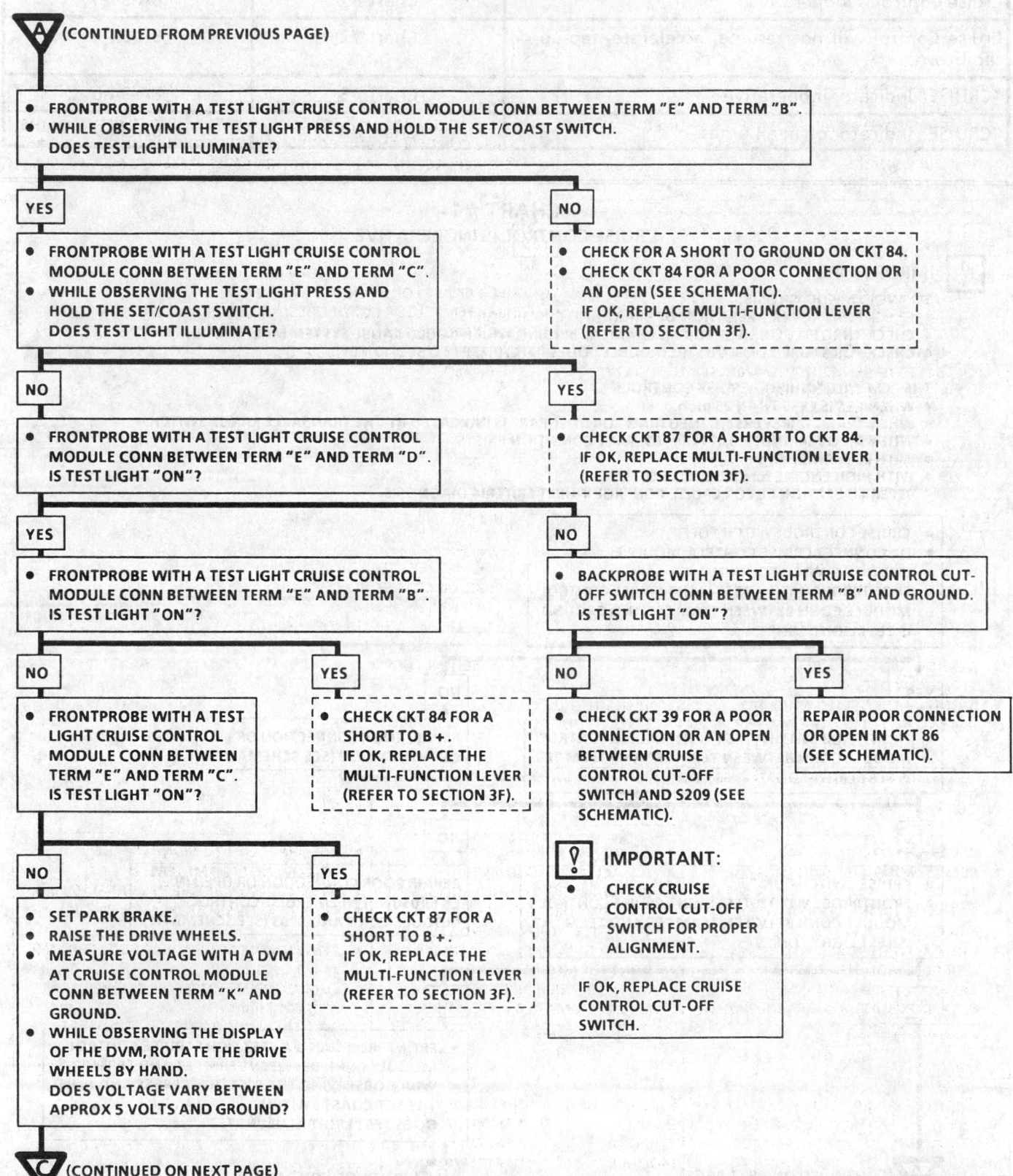

A (CONTINUED FROM PREVIOUS PAGE)

- FRONTPROBE WITH A TEST LIGHT CRUISE CONTROL MODULE CONN BETWEEN TERM "E" AND TERM "B".
- WHILE OBSERVING THE TEST LIGHT PRESS AND HOLD THE SET/COAST SWITCH.
  DOES TEST LIGHT ILLUMINATE?

YES

- FRONTPROBE WITH A TEST LIGHT CRUISE CONTROL MODULE CONN BETWEEN TERM "E" AND TERM "C".
- WHILE OBSERVING THE TEST LIGHT PRESS AND HOLD THE SET/COAST SWITCH.
  DOES TEST LIGHT ILLUMINATE?

NO

- CHECK FOR A SHORT TO GROUND ON CKT 84.
- CHECK CKT 84 FOR A POOR CONNECTION OR AN OPEN (SEE SCHEMATIC).
  IF OK, REPLACE MULTI-FUNCTION LEVER (REFER TO SECTION 3F).

NO

- FRONTPROBE WITH A TEST LIGHT CRUISE CONTROL MODULE CONN BETWEEN TERM "E" AND TERM "D".
  IS TEST LIGHT "ON"?

YES

- CHECK CKT 87 FOR A SHORT TO CKT 84.
  IF OK, REPLACE MULTI-FUNCTION LEVER (REFER TO SECTION 3F).

YES

- FRONTPROBE WITH A TEST LIGHT CRUISE CONTROL MODULE CONN BETWEEN TERM "E" AND TERM "B".
  IS TEST LIGHT "ON"?

NO

- BACKPROBE WITH A TEST LIGHT CRUISE CONTROL CUT-OFF SWITCH CONN BETWEEN TERM "B" AND GROUND.
  IS TEST LIGHT "ON"?

NO

- FRONTPROBE WITH A TEST LIGHT CRUISE CONTROL MODULE CONN BETWEEN TERM "E" AND TERM "C".
  IS TEST LIGHT "ON"?

YES

- CHECK CKT 84 FOR A SHORT TO B+.
  IF OK, REPLACE THE MULTI-FUNCTION LEVER (REFER TO SECTION 3F).

NO

- CHECK CKT 39 FOR A POOR CONNECTION OR AN OPEN BETWEEN CRUISE CONTROL CUT-OFF SWITCH AND S209 (SEE SCHEMATIC).

IMPORTANT:

- CHECK CRUISE CONTROL CUT-OFF SWITCH FOR PROPER ALIGNMENT.

IF OK, REPLACE CRUISE CONTROL CUT-OFF SWITCH.

YES

REPAIR POOR CONNECTION OR OPEN IN CKT 86 (SEE SCHEMATIC).

NO

- SET PARK BRAKE.
- RAISE THE DRIVE WHEELS.
- MEASURE VOLTAGE WITH A DVM AT CRUISE CONTROL MODULE CONN BETWEEN TERM "K" AND GROUND.
- WHILE OBSERVING THE DISPLAY OF THE DVM, ROTATE THE DRIVE WHEELS BY HAND.
  DOES VOLTAGE VARY BETWEEN APPROX 5 VOLTS AND GROUND?

YES

- CHECK CKT 87 FOR A SHORT TO B+.
  IF OK, REPLACE THE MULTI-FUNCTION LEVER (REFER TO SECTION 3F).

C (CONTINUED ON NEXT PAGE)

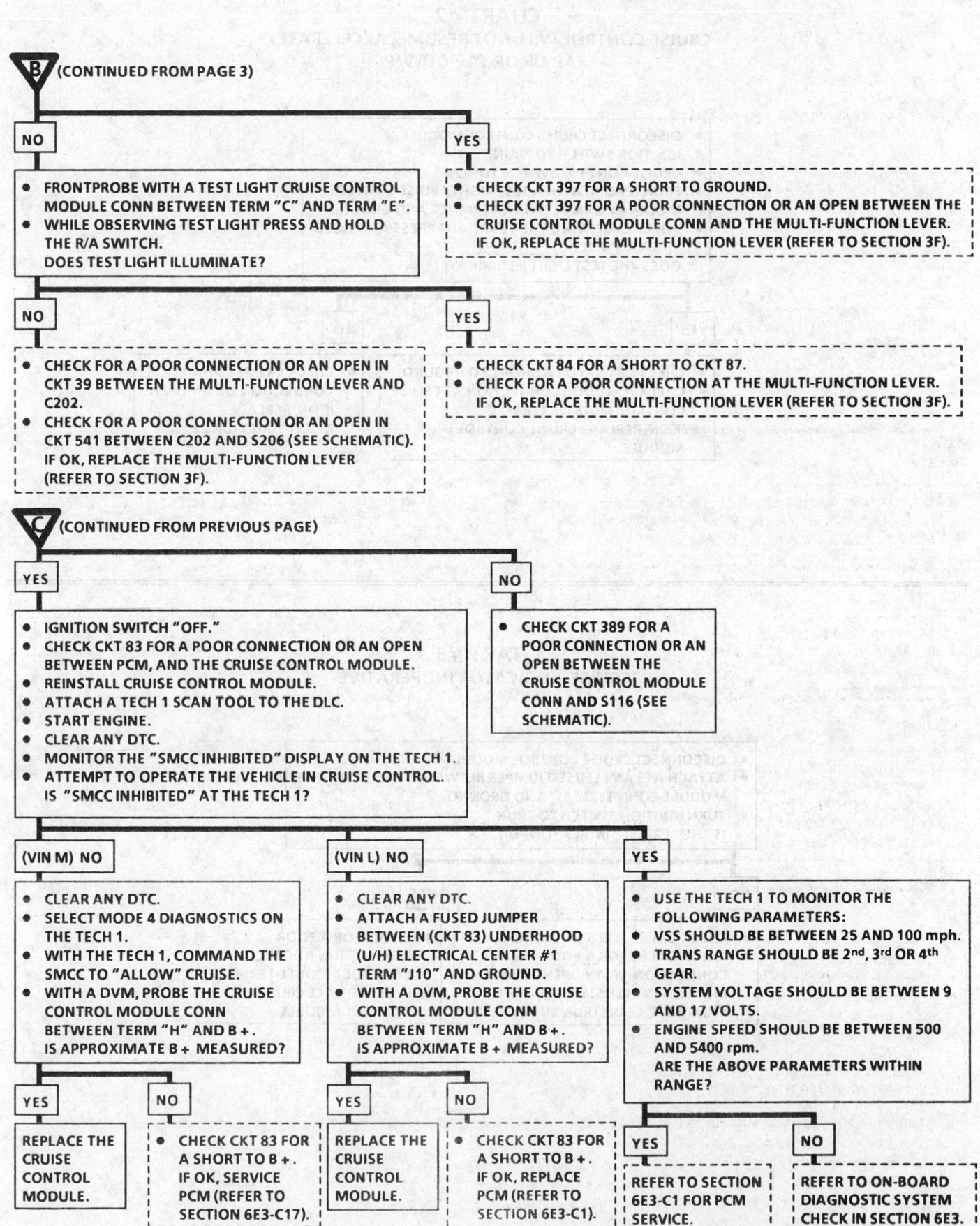

B (CONTINUED FROM PAGE 3)

NO

- FRONTPROBE WITH A TEST LIGHT CRUISE CONTROL MODULE CONN BETWEEN TERM "C" AND TERM "E".
- WHILE OBSERVING TEST LIGHT PRESS AND HOLD THE R/A SWITCH.

DOES TEST LIGHT ILLUMINATE?

NO

- CHECK FOR A POOR CONNECTION OR AN OPEN IN CKT 39 BETWEEN THE MULTI-FUNCTION LEVER AND C202.
- CHECK FOR A POOR CONNECTION OR AN OPEN IN CKT 541 BETWEEN C202 AND S206 (SEE SCHEMATIC).

IF OK, REPLACE THE MULTI-FUNCTION LEVER (REFER TO SECTION 3F).

YES

- CHECK CKT 84 FOR A SHORT TO CKT 87.
- CHECK FOR A POOR CONNECTION AT THE MULTI-FUNCTION LEVER.

IF OK, REPLACE THE MULTI-FUNCTION LEVER (REFER TO SECTION 3F).

YES

- CHECK CKT 397 FOR A SHORT TO GROUND.
- CHECK CKT 397 FOR A POOR CONNECTION OR AN OPEN BETWEEN THE CRUISE CONTROL MODULE CONN AND THE MULTI-FUNCTION LEVER.

IF OK, REPLACE THE MULTI-FUNCTION LEVER (REFER TO SECTION 3F).

C (CONTINUED FROM PREVIOUS PAGE)

YES

- IGNITION SWITCH "OFF."
- CHECK CKT 83 FOR A POOR CONNECTION OR AN OPEN BETWEEN PCM, AND THE CRUISE CONTROL MODULE.
- REINSTALL CRUISE CONTROL MODULE.
- ATTACH A TECH 1 SCAN TOOL TO THE DLC.
- START ENGINE.
- CLEAR ANY DTC.
- MONITOR THE "SMCC INHIBITED" DISPLAY ON THE TECH 1.
- ATTEMPT TO OPERATE THE VEHICLE IN CRUISE CONTROL.

IS "SMCC INHIBITED" AT THE TECH 1?

(VIN M) NO

- CLEAR ANY DTC.
- SELECT MODE 4 DIAGNOSTICS ON THE TECH 1.
- WITH THE TECH 1, COMMAND THE SMCC TO "ALLOW" CRUISE.
- WITH A DVM, PROBE THE CRUISE CONTROL MODULE CONN BETWEEN TERM "H" AND B+.

IS APPROXIMATE B+ MEASURED?

YES

REPLACE THE CRUISE CONTROL MODULE.

NO

- CHECK CKT 83 FOR A SHORT TO B+.

IF OK, SERVICE PCM (REFER TO SECTION 6E3-C17).

(VIN L) NO

- CLEAR ANY DTC.
- ATTACH A FUSED JUMPER BETWEEN (CKT 83) UNDERHOOD (U/H) ELECTRICAL CENTER #1 TERM "J10" AND GROUND.
- WITH A DVM, PROBE THE CRUISE CONTROL MODULE CONN BETWEEN TERM "H" AND B+.

IS APPROXIMATE B+ MEASURED?

YES

REPLACE THE CRUISE CONTROL MODULE.

NO

- CHECK CKT 83 FOR A SHORT TO B+.

IF OK, REPLACE PCM (REFER TO SECTION 6E3-C1).

YES

- USE THE TECH 1 TO MONITOR THE FOLLOWING PARAMETERS:
- VSS SHOULD BE BETWEEN 25 AND 100 mph.
- TRANS RANGE SHOULD BE 2nd, 3rd OR 4th GEAR.
- SYSTEM VOLTAGE SHOULD BE BETWEEN 9 AND 17 VOLTS.
- ENGINE SPEED SHOULD BE BETWEEN 500 AND 5400 rpm.

ARE THE ABOVE PARAMETERS WITHIN RANGE?

YES

REFER TO SECTION 6E3-C1 FOR PCM SERVICE.

NO

REFER TO ON-BOARD DIAGNOSTIC SYSTEM CHECK IN SECTION 6E3.

NO

- CHECK CKT 389 FOR A POOR CONNECTION OR AN OPEN BETWEEN THE CRUISE CONTROL MODULE CONN AND S116 (SEE SCHEMATIC).

CRUISE CONTROL

CHART #2
CRUISE CONTROL WILL NOT RESUME, ACCELERATE, TAP-UP OR TAP-DOWN

- DISCONNECT CRUISE CONTROL MODULE.
- IGNITION SWITCH TO "RUN."
- CRUISE CONTROL SWITCH TO "ON."
- FRONTPROBE WITH A TEST LIGHT CRUISE CONTROL MODULE CONN BETWEEN TERM "C" AND GROUND.
- WHILE OBSERVING THE TEST LIGHT PRESS AND HOLD THE R/A SWITCH.

DOES THE TEST LIGHT ILLUMINATE?

YES

- CHECK CKT 87 FOR A SHORT TO GROUND.
- CHECK FOR POOR CONNECTION AT CRUISE CONTROL MODULE TERM "C".

IF OK, REPLACE CRUISE CONTROL MODULE.

NO

- CHECK CKT 87 FOR A POOR CONNECTION OR AN OPEN.

IF OK, REPLACE MULTI-FUNCTION LEVER.

CHART #3
"CRUISE" INDICATOR INOPERATIVE

- DISCONNECT CRUISE CONTROL MODULE CONNECTOR.
- ATTACH A (3 AMP) FUSED JUMPER BETWEEN CRUISE CONTROL MODULE CONN TERM "J" AND GROUND.
- TURN IGNITION SWITCH TO "RUN."

IS THE "CRUISE" INDICATOR "ON"?

NO

- CHECK CKT 85 FOR A SHORT TO B +.
- CHECK CKT 85 FOR A POOR CONNECTION OR AN OPEN BETWEEN INSTRUMENT CLUSTER AND S139.

IF OK, SERVICE INSTRUMENT CLUSTER.

YES

- CHECK FOR A POOR CONNECTION AT CRUISE CONTROL MODULE TERM "J".

IF OK, REPLACE CRUISE CONTROL MODULE.

CHART #4
"CRUISE" INDICATOR ON AT ALL TIMES

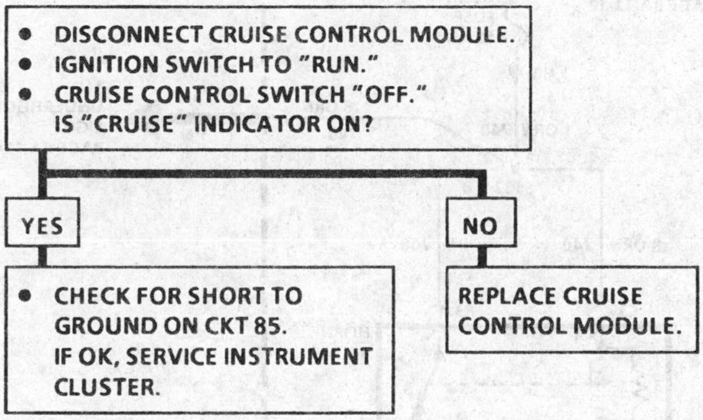
• DISCONNECT CRUISE CONTROL MODULE.
• IGNITION SWITCH TO "RUN."
• CRUISE CONTROL SWITCH "OFF."
IS "CRUISE" INDICATOR ON?
YES
NO
• CHECK FOR SHORT TO GROUND ON CKT 85.
IF OK, SERVICE INSTRUMENT CLUSTER.
REPLACE CRUISE CONTROL MODULE.

CIRCUIT OPERATION

The Stepper Motor Cruise Control (SMCC) is a speed control system which maintains a desired vehicle speed under normal driving conditions. The system has the capability to CRUISE, COAST, RESUME SPEED, ACCELERATE, TAP-UP AND TAP-DOWN.

An Electronic Controller and Electric Motor are contained in the Cruise Control Module. The Controller monitors vehicle speed and operates the Electric Motor. In response to the Controller, the motor moves a connecting strap that is attached to the Cruise Control Cable. The Cable moves the Throttle Linkage to vary throttle position in order to maintain the desired cruise speed. The Cruise Control Module contains a low speed limit which will prevent system engagement below a minimum speed, approximately 25 mph. The module is controlled by mode control switches located on the Multi-Function Lever. Cruise Control is in "Standby Disabled" mode until all conditions inconsistent with Cruise Control operation are cleared.

With the Ignition Switch in "RUN," battery voltage is applied to terminal "F" of the Cruise Control Module. When the Slider Switch is moved to the "ON" position, battery voltage is applied to terminal "A" of the Cruise Control Module Connector. If the brake pedal is not depressed, battery voltage is present at module terminal "D". If the brake pedal is depressed, battery voltage is present at module terminal "G". Terminal "G" must see current flow [through the Center High Mounted Stop Lamp (CHMSL) bulbs] for cruise to operate (disable) properly. When the Slider Switch is moved to the "R/A" position, battery voltage is applied to terminal "C" of the module. With the Set Switch depressed, battery voltage is present at module terminal "B". Cruise Control Module Connector terminal "K" is the speed signal terminal. In operation, voltage will oscillate between a high of 4 to 5 volts and a low of near ground. Ground is at module terminal "E". Terminal "J" is used to signal the Powertrain Control Module (PCM) when Cruise Control is "engaged" and illuminate the "Cruise" Indicator on the Instrument Cluster. The PCM will then determine the correct shift pattern for the transmission. Terminal "H" is used by the PCM to "Inhibit" Cruise Control when conditions not consistent with cruise operation are present. These are Cruise Control Inhibit Criteria.

The PCM will "Inhibit" Cruise Control:

- When VSS is less than 25 mph.
- When "PARK," "REVERSE," "NEUTRAL," or "1st GEAR" is indicated by the Transaxle Range Switch.
- When an over/under battery voltage condition exists.
- With low Engine RPM.
- With high Engine RPM (fuel cut-off).

HORNS

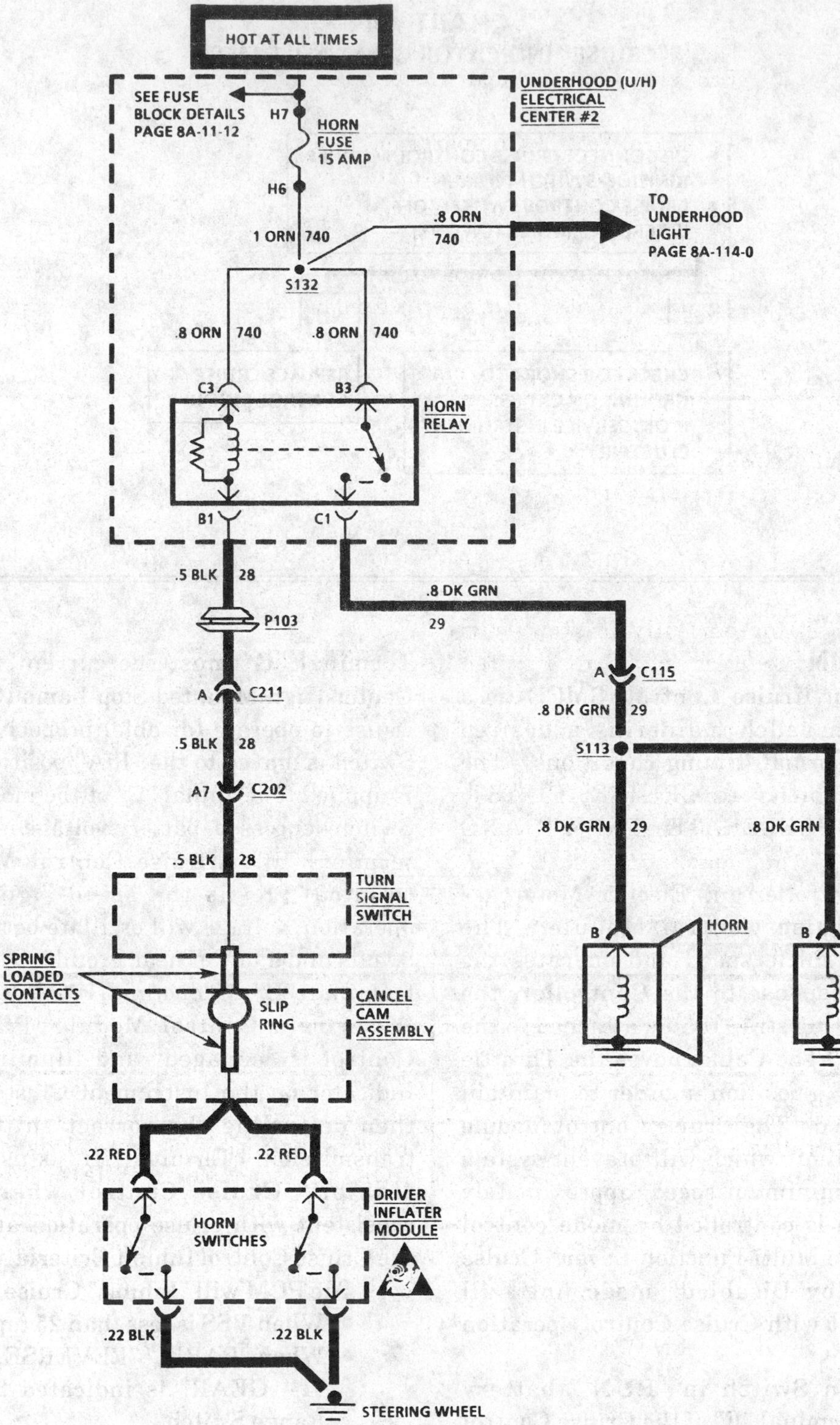
HOT AT ALL TIMES
SEE FUSE BLOCK DETAILS PAGE 8A-11-12
H7
HORN FUSE 15 AMP
H6
UNDERHOOD (U/H) ELECTRICAL CENTER #2
1 ORN 740
.8 ORN 740
TO UNDERHOOD LIGHT PAGE 8A-114-0
S132
.8 ORN 740
.8 ORN 740
C3
B3
HORN RELAY
B1
C1
.5 BLK 28
.8 DK GRN 29
P103
A C211
A C115
.8 DK GRN 29
.5 BLK 28
S113
A7 C202
.8 DK GRN 29
.8 DK GRN 29
.5 BLK 28
TURN SIGNAL SWITCH
B HORN
B HORN
SPRING LOADED CONTACTS
SLIP RING
CANCEL CAM ASSEMBLY
.22 RED
.22 RED
DRIVER INFLATER MODULE
HORN SWITCHES
.22 BLK
.22 BLK
STEERING WHEEL

SEE PAGE 8A-3-0 FOR PROPER HANDLING PROCEDURES

CAUTION: This vehicle is equipped with Supplemental Inflatable Restraint (SIR). Refer to CAUTIONS in Section 9J under "ON-VEHICLE SERVICE" and the SIR Component and Wiring Location view in Section 9J before performing service on or around SIR components or wiring. Failure to follow CAUTIONS could result in possible air bag deployment, personal injury, or otherwise unneeded SIR system repairs.

COMPONENT	LOCATION	201-PG	FIG.	CONN
Driver Inflater Module	Center of Steering Wheel, behind Horn pad	27	88	
Horns	Front of Engine Compartment, on Radiator Support	11	33	
Underhood (U/H) Electrical Center #2	LH side of Engine Compartment, on strut tower	1	4	202-34
C115 (3 cavities)	LH side of Engine Compartment, on strut tower	27	87	
C202 (48 cavities)	Behind I/P, RH side of Steering Column	2	8	202-9
C211 (8 cavities)	Below LH side of I/P, RH side of Steering Column			
P103	LH rear of Engine Compartment, near strut tower	1	4	
S113	Forward Lights Harn, approx 5 cm from Horns breakout			
S132	Wiper Harn, approx 10 cm from Washer Pump breakout			

TROUBLESHOOTING HINTS (Perform before beginning System Diagnosis)

1. Check for open in the Horn Fuse. Check for poor ground at Horns.

- Check for a broken (or partially broken) wire inside of the insulation which could cause system malfunction but prove "GOOD" in a continuity/voltage check with a system disconnected. These circuits may be intermittent or resistive when loaded, and if possible, should be checked by monitoring for a voltage drop with the system operational (under load).
- Check for proper installation of aftermarket electronic equipment which may affect the integrity of other systems (see "Troubleshooting Procedures," page 8A-4-0).
- Refer to System Diagnosis.

SYSTEM DIAGNOSIS

- Perform the System Check and refer to the Symptom Table for the appropriate diagnostic procedures.

SYMPTOM TABLE

SYMPTOM	PROCEDURE	PAGE NUMBER
Horns inoperative.	Chart #1	8A-40-2
One Horn inoperative.	Chart #2	8A-40-3
Horns "ON" at all times.	Chart #3	8A-40-3
One Horn switch inoperative.	Check for poor connections at Driver Inflator Module. If OK, replace Driver Inflator Module. Refer to SECTION 9J.	

HORNS

CHART #1
HORNS INOPERATIVE

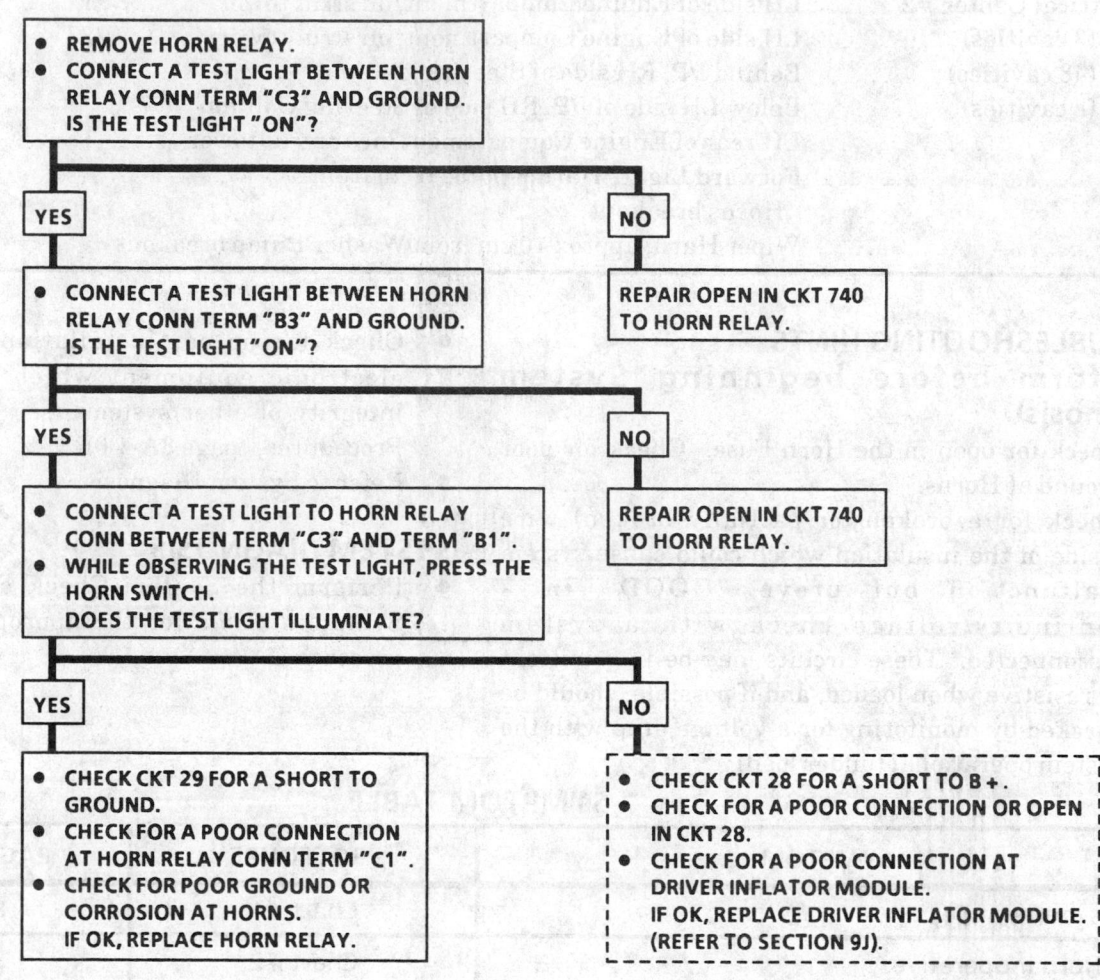

- REMOVE HORN RELAY.
- CONNECT A TEST LIGHT BETWEEN HORN RELAY CONN TERM "C3" AND GROUND.
IS THE TEST LIGHT "ON"?

NO

REPAIR OPEN IN CKT 740 TO HORN RELAY.

YES

- CONNECT A TEST LIGHT BETWEEN HORN RELAY CONN TERM "B3" AND GROUND.
IS THE TEST LIGHT "ON"?

NO

REPAIR OPEN IN CKT 740 TO HORN RELAY.

YES

- CONNECT A TEST LIGHT TO HORN RELAY CONN BETWEEN TERM "C3" AND TERM "B1".
- WHILE OBSERVING THE TEST LIGHT, PRESS THE HORN SWITCH.
DOES THE TEST LIGHT ILLUMINATE?

YES

- CHECK CKT 29 FOR A SHORT TO GROUND.
- CHECK FOR A POOR CONNECTION AT HORN RELAY CONN TERM "C1".
- CHECK FOR POOR GROUND OR CORROSION AT HORNS.
IF OK, REPLACE HORN RELAY.

NO

- CHECK CKT 28 FOR A SHORT TO B +.
- CHECK FOR A POOR CONNECTION OR OPEN IN CKT 28.
- CHECK FOR A POOR CONNECTION AT DRIVER INFLATOR MODULE.
IF OK, REPLACE DRIVER INFLATOR MODULE. (REFER TO SECTION 9J).

CHART #2
ONE HORN INOPERATIVE

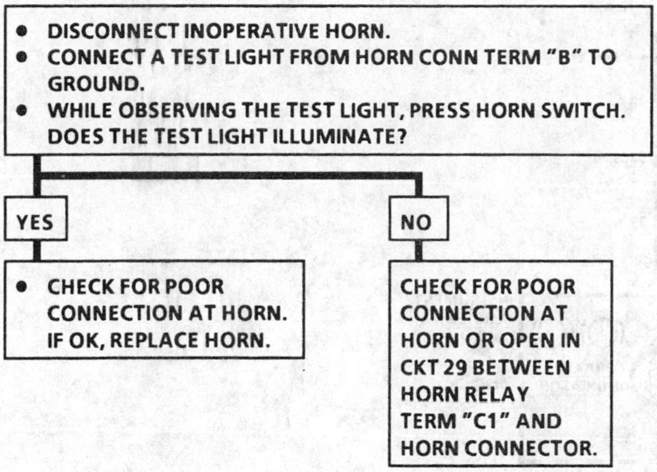
• DISCONNECT INOPERATIVE HORN.
• CONNECT A TEST LIGHT FROM HORN CONN TERM "B" TO GROUND.
• WHILE OBSERVING THE TEST LIGHT, PRESS HORN SWITCH. DOES THE TEST LIGHT ILLUMINATE?
YES
NO
• CHECK FOR POOR CONNECTION AT HORN. IF OK, REPLACE HORN.
CHECK FOR POOR CONNECTION AT HORN OR OPEN IN CKT 29 BETWEEN HORN RELAY TERM "C1" AND HORN CONNECTOR.

CHART #3
HORNS "ON" AT ALL TIMES

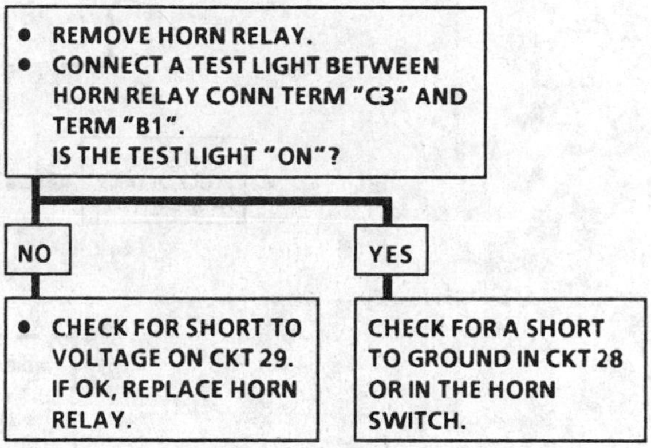
• REMOVE HORN RELAY.
• CONNECT A TEST LIGHT BETWEEN HORN RELAY CONN TERM "C3" AND TERM "B1". IS THE TEST LIGHT "ON"?
NO
YES
• CHECK FOR SHORT TO VOLTAGE ON CKT 29. IF OK, REPLACE HORN RELAY.
CHECK FOR A SHORT TO GROUND IN CKT 28 OR IN THE HORN SWITCH.

CIRCUIT OPERATION

Battery voltage is applied at all times to the Horn Relay at terminals "1" and "3". When the Horn Switch is closed to ground, the Horn Relay is energized. Battery voltage is applied to the horns through the closed contacts of the Horn Relay to sound the horns.

BRAKE WARNING SYSTEM

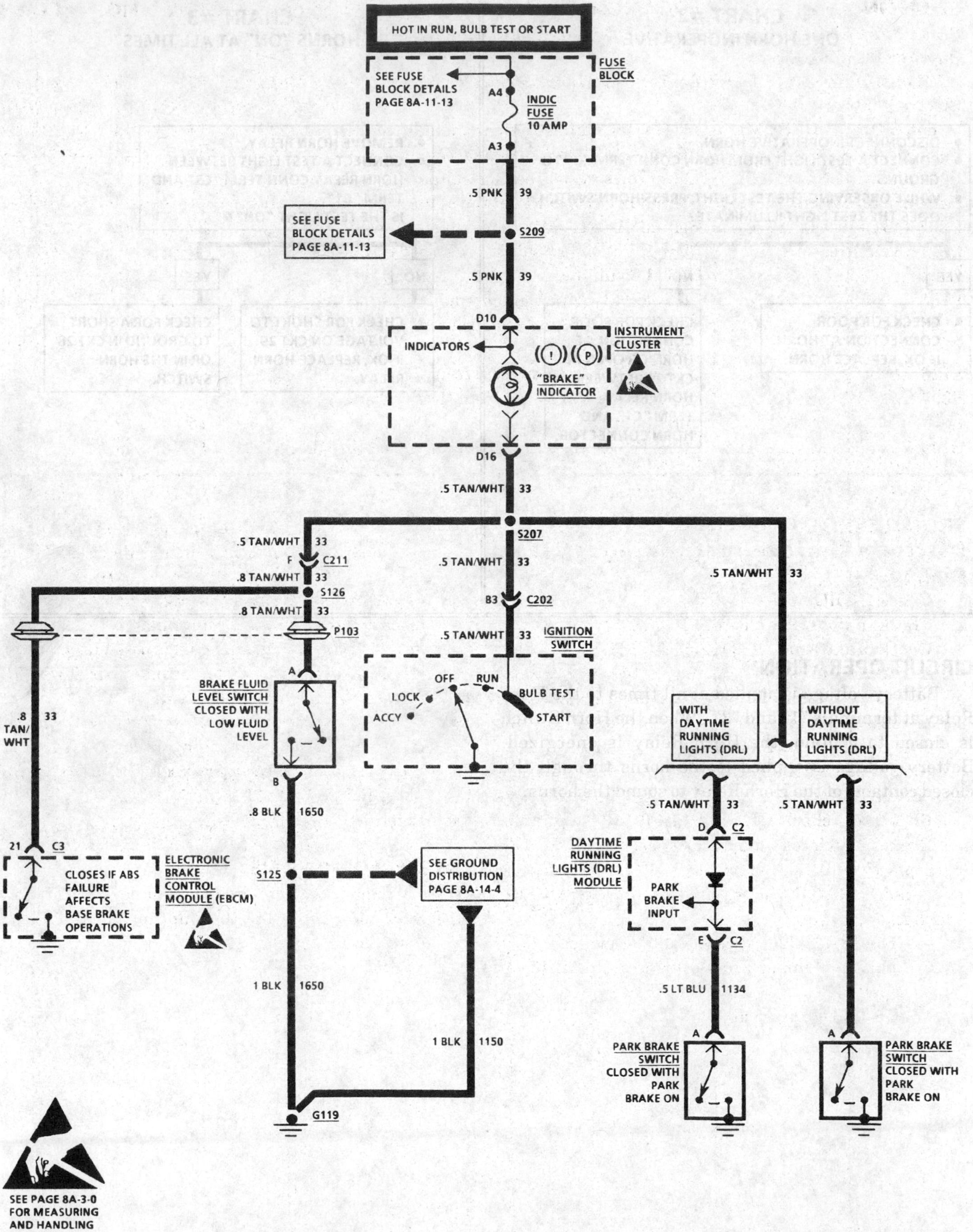
HOT IN RUN, BULB TEST OR START
SEE FUSE BLOCK DETAILS PAGE 8A-11-13
FUSE BLOCK
A4
INDIC FUSE 10 AMP
A3
.5 PNK 39
SEE FUSE BLOCK DETAILS PAGE 8A-11-13
S209
.5 PNK 39
D10
INDICATORS
INSTRUMENT CLUSTER
"BRAKE" INDICATOR
D16
.5 TAN/WHT 33
S207
.5 TAN/WHT 33
F C211
.8 TAN/WHT 33
S126
.8 TAN/WHT 33
P103
.5 TAN/WHT 33
B3 C202
.5 TAN/WHT 33
IGNITION SWITCH
OFF RUN
LOCK
BULB TEST
ACCY
START
.5 TAN/WHT 33
WITH DAYTIME RUNNING LIGHTS (DRL)
WITHOUT DAYTIME RUNNING LIGHTS (DRL)
A
BRAKE FLUID LEVEL SWITCH CLOSED WITH LOW FLUID LEVEL
B
.8 33 TAN/WHT
.8 BLK 1650
21 C3
CLOSES IF ABS FAILURE AFFECTS BASE BRAKE OPERATIONS
ELECTRONIC BRAKE CONTROL MODULE (EBCM)
S125
SEE GROUND DISTRIBUTION PAGE 8A-14-4
.5 TAN/WHT 33
.5 TAN/WHT 33
D C2
DAYTIME RUNNING LIGHTS (DRL) MODULE
PARK BRAKE INPUT
E C2
1 BLK 1650
.5 LT BLU 1134
1 BLK 1150
A
A
PARK BRAKE SWITCH CLOSED WITH PARK BRAKE ON
PARK BRAKE SWITCH CLOSED WITH PARK BRAKE ON
G119
SEE PAGE 8A-3-0 FOR MEASURING AND HANDLING PROCEDURES

COMPONENT	LOCATION	201-PG	FIG.	CONN
Brake Fluid Level Switch	LH front of dash, on brake master cylinder	2	7	
Daytime Running Lights (DRL) Module	Behind I/P, on brake pedal support	27	85	202-37
Electronic Brake Control Module (EBCM)	LH side of Engine Compartment, in fender	21	73	202-19
Fuse Block	RH side of I/P, in I/P Compartment			
Ignition Switch	Lower top side of Steering Column			
Park Brake Switch	Behind LH side of I/P, at top of Park Brake Assembly			
C202 (48 cavities)	Behind I/P, RH side of Steering Column	27	88	202-9
C211 (8 cavities)	Behind I/P, on RH side of brake pedal support			202-35
G119	On LH strut tower	1	4	
P103	LH rear of Engine Compartment, near strut tower	1	4	
S125	Wiper Harn, approx 4 cm from Actuator Motor breakout			
S126	Wiper Harn, approx 17 cm from P103			
S207	I/P Harn, approx 12 cm from HVAC Control breakout	15	49	
S209	I/P Harn, approx 19 cm from Fuse Block breakout	15	49	

TROUBLESHOOTING HINTS (Perform before beginning System Diagnosis)

1. Check INDIC Fuse.
2. Check that G119 is clean and tight.
3. Check brake fluid. If low, refer to SECTION 5.
4. If brake fluid is low and the "BRAKE" Indicator does not light, check the Brake Fluid Level Switch.
5. If "BRAKE" Indicator is lit, check for trouble codes. Refer to SECTION 5E.
6. If equipped with Daytime Running Lights, and the "BRAKE" Indicator does not light with the Park Brake set, check CKT 33, CKT 1134 and Park Brake Switch for an open or short to B+. If OK, replace the DRL Module.
7. If the "BRAKE" Indicator does not light at all, check:
   - The "BRAKE" Indicator bulb for an open.
   - The Instrument Cluster printed circuit for an open.
   - CKT 33 for an open.

- Check for a broken (or partially broken) wire inside of the insulation which could cause system malfunction but prove "GOOD" in a continuity/voltage check with a system disconnected. These circuits may be intermittent or resistive when loaded, and if possible, should be checked by monitoring for a voltage drop with the system operational (under load).
- Check for proper installation of aftermarket electronic equipment which may affect the integrity of other systems (see "Troubleshooting Procedures," page 8A-4-0).
- Refer to System Diagnosis.

SYSTEM DIAGNOSIS

- Perform the System Check and refer to the Symptom Table for the appropriate diagnostic procedures.

BRAKE WARNING SYSTEM

SYSTEM CHECK

ACTION	NORMAL RESULTS
[1] • Release Park Brake. • Turn Ignition Switch to "BULB TEST" (just past the "RUN" position). • Turn Ignition Switch to "OFF."	"BRAKE" Indicator remains "ON" only when Ignition Switch is in "BULB TEST" or "START."
[2] • Ignition Switch in "RUN." • Set Park Brake. • Release Park Brake.	"BRAKE" Indicator remains "ON" only when Park Brake is set.

SYMPTOM TABLE

SYMPTOM	PROCEDURE	PAGE NUMBER
"BRAKE" Indicator inoperative.	Chart #1	8A-41-2
Ignition Switch will not activate the "BRAKE" Indicator.	Chart #2	8A-41-3
Park Brake will not activate the "BRAKE" Indicator.	Chart #3	8A-41-3
"BRAKE" Indicator remains "ON" when Ignition Switch is in "RUN" and Park Brake is released.	Chart #4	8A-41-3
Park Brake will not activate the "BRAKE" Indicator [vehicles equipped with Daytime Running Lights (DRL)].	Chart #5	8A-41-4
"BRAKE" Indicator remains "ON" when Ignition Switch is in "RUN" and Park Brake is released [vehicles equipped with Daytime Running Lights (DRL)].	Chart #6	8A-41-5

CHART #1
"BRAKE" INDICATOR INOPERATIVE

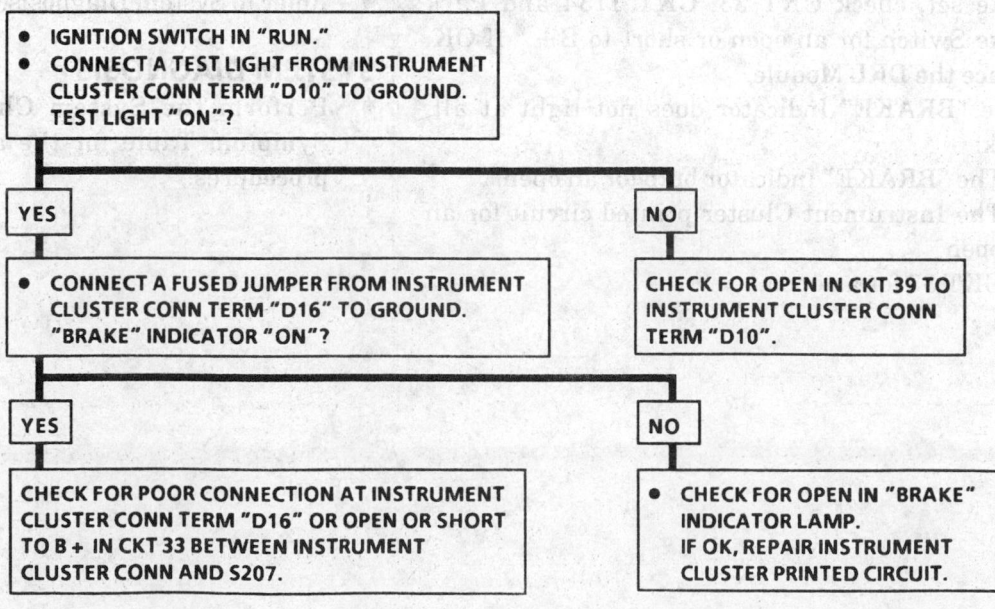

- IGNITION SWITCH IN "RUN."
- CONNECT A TEST LIGHT FROM INSTRUMENT CLUSTER CONN TERM "D10" TO GROUND. TEST LIGHT "ON"?

YES

- CONNECT A FUSED JUMPER FROM INSTRUMENT CLUSTER CONN TERM "D16" TO GROUND. "BRAKE" INDICATOR "ON"?

YES

CHECK FOR POOR CONNECTION AT INSTRUMENT CLUSTER CONN TERM "D16" OR OPEN OR SHORT TO B+ IN CKT 33 BETWEEN INSTRUMENT CLUSTER CONN AND S207.

NO

- CHECK FOR OPEN IN "BRAKE" INDICATOR LAMP. IF OK, REPAIR INSTRUMENT CLUSTER PRINTED CIRCUIT.

NO

CHECK FOR OPEN IN CKT 39 TO INSTRUMENT CLUSTER CONN TERM "D10".

CHART #2
IGNITION SWITCH WILL NOT ACTIVATE THE "BRAKE" INDICATOR

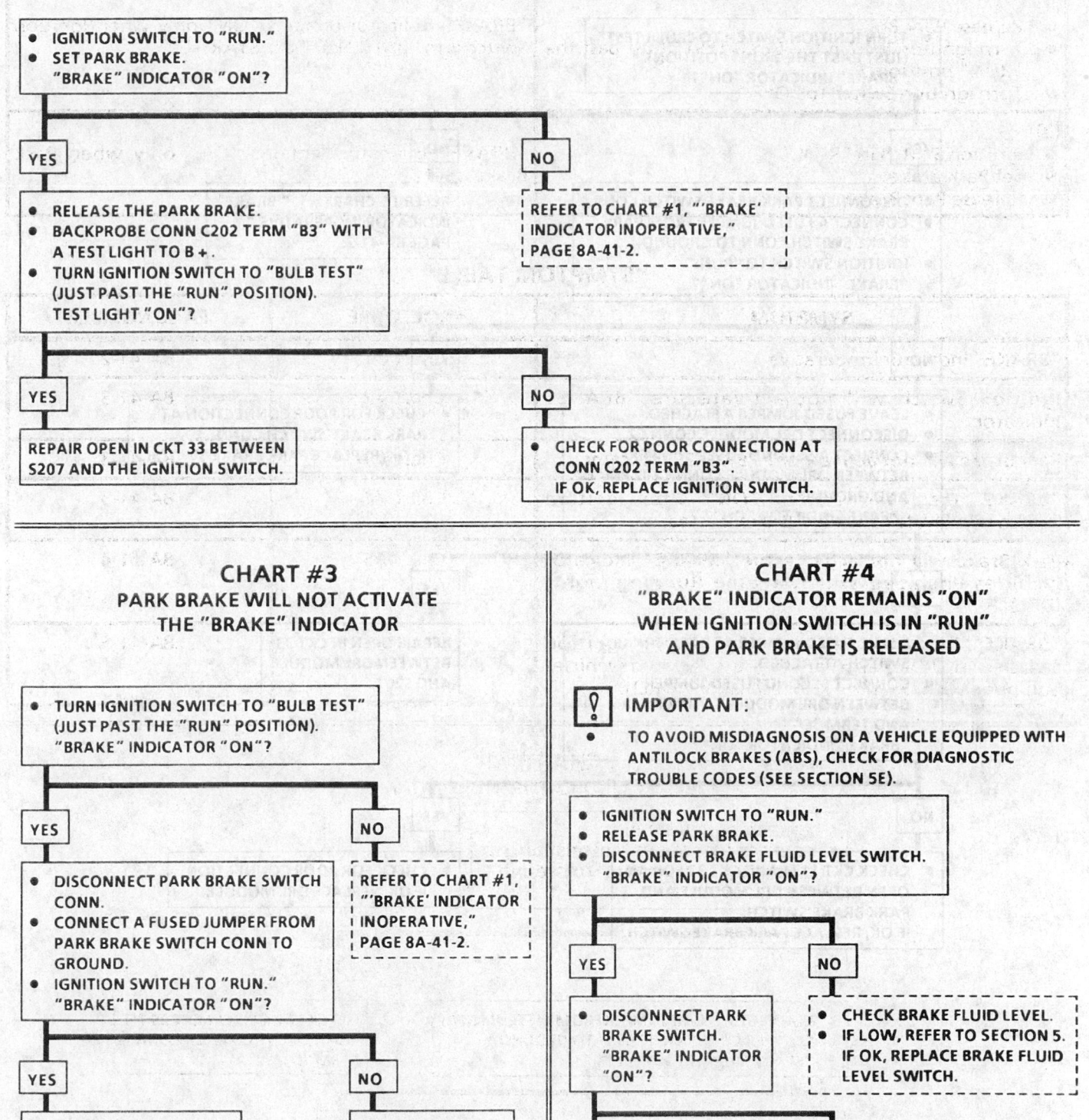

- IGNITION SWITCH TO "RUN."
- SET PARK BRAKE.
  "BRAKE" INDICATOR "ON"?

YES

- RELEASE THE PARK BRAKE.
- BACKPROBE CONN C202 TERM "B3" WITH A TEST LIGHT TO B +.
- TURN IGNITION SWITCH TO "BULB TEST" (JUST PAST THE "RUN" POSITION).
  TEST LIGHT "ON"?

YES

REPAIR OPEN IN CKT 33 BETWEEN S207 AND THE IGNITION SWITCH.

NO

- CHECK FOR POOR CONNECTION AT CONN C202 TERM "B3".
  IF OK, REPLACE IGNITION SWITCH.

NO

REFER TO CHART #1, "'BRAKE' INDICATOR INOPERATIVE," PAGE 8A-41-2.

CHART #3
PARK BRAKE WILL NOT ACTIVATE THE "BRAKE" INDICATOR

- TURN IGNITION SWITCH TO "BULB TEST" (JUST PAST THE "RUN" POSITION).
  "BRAKE" INDICATOR "ON"?

YES

- DISCONNECT PARK BRAKE SWITCH CONN.
- CONNECT A FUSED JUMPER FROM PARK BRAKE SWITCH CONN TO GROUND.
- IGNITION SWITCH TO "RUN."
  "BRAKE" INDICATOR "ON"?

YES

- CHECK FOR POOR CONNECTION AT PARK BRAKE SWITCH CONN.
  IF OK, REPLACE PARK BRAKE SWITCH.

NO

REPAIR OPEN IN CKT 33 BETWEEN PARK BRAKE SWITCH AND S207.

NO

REFER TO CHART #1, "'BRAKE' INDICATOR INOPERATIVE," PAGE 8A-41-2.

CHART #4
"BRAKE" INDICATOR REMAINS "ON" WHEN IGNITION SWITCH IS IN "RUN" AND PARK BRAKE IS RELEASED

IMPORTANT:

- TO AVOID MISDIAGNOSIS ON A VEHICLE EQUIPPED WITH ANTILOCK BRAKES (ABS), CHECK FOR DIAGNOSTIC TROUBLE CODES (SEE SECTION 5E).

- IGNITION SWITCH TO "RUN."
- RELEASE PARK BRAKE.
- DISCONNECT BRAKE FLUID LEVEL SWITCH.
  "BRAKE" INDICATOR "ON"?

YES

- DISCONNECT PARK BRAKE SWITCH.
  "BRAKE" INDICATOR "ON"?

NO

REPLACE PARK BRAKE SWITCH.

YES

REPAIR SHORT TO GROUND IN CKT 33.

NO

- CHECK BRAKE FLUID LEVEL.
- IF LOW, REFER TO SECTION 5.
  IF OK, REPLACE BRAKE FLUID LEVEL SWITCH.

BRAKE WARNING SYSTEM

CHART #5

PARK BRAKE WILL NOT ACTIVATE THE "BRAKE" INDICATOR [VEHICLES EQUIPPED WITH DAYTIME RUNNING LIGHTS (DRL)]

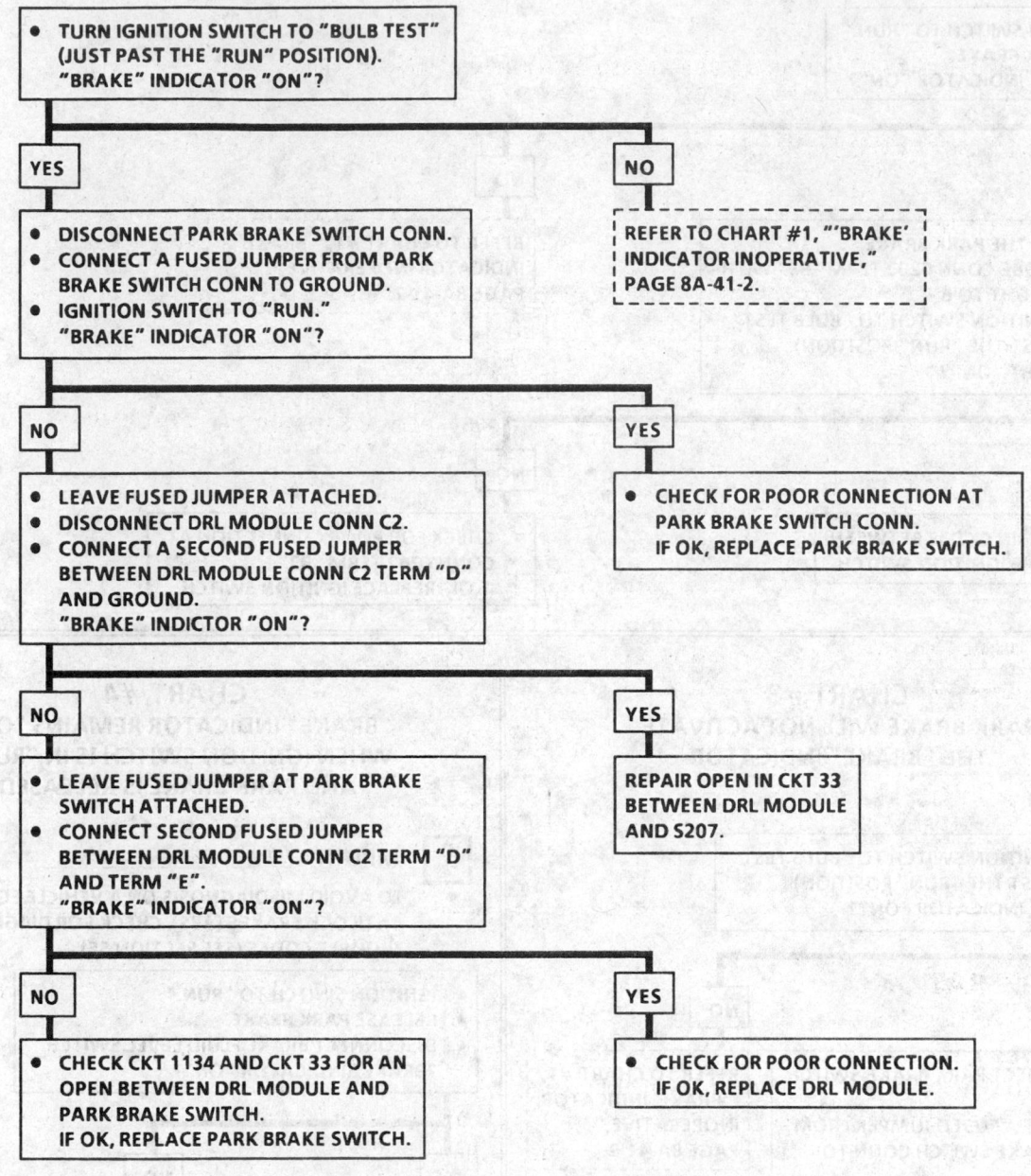

- TURN IGNITION SWITCH TO "BULB TEST" (JUST PAST THE "RUN" POSITION). "BRAKE" INDICATOR "ON"?

YES

- DISCONNECT PARK BRAKE SWITCH CONN.
- CONNECT A FUSED JUMPER FROM PARK BRAKE SWITCH CONN TO GROUND.
- IGNITION SWITCH TO "RUN." "BRAKE" INDICATOR "ON"?

NO

REFER TO CHART #1, "'BRAKE' INDICATOR INOPERATIVE," PAGE 8A-41-2.

(After "IGNITION SWITCH TO 'RUN.'")

NO

- LEAVE FUSED JUMPER ATTACHED.
- DISCONNECT DRL MODULE CONN C2.
- CONNECT A SECOND FUSED JUMPER BETWEEN DRL MODULE CONN C2 TERM "D" AND GROUND. "BRAKE" INDICTOR "ON"?

YES

- CHECK FOR POOR CONNECTION AT PARK BRAKE SWITCH CONN. IF OK, REPLACE PARK BRAKE SWITCH.

(After "DISCONNECT DRL MODULE CONN C2.")

NO

- LEAVE FUSED JUMPER AT PARK BRAKE SWITCH ATTACHED.
- CONNECT SECOND FUSED JUMPER BETWEEN DRL MODULE CONN C2 TERM "D" AND TERM "E". "BRAKE" INDICATOR "ON"?

YES

REPAIR OPEN IN CKT 33 BETWEEN DRL MODULE AND S207.

(After "CONNECT SECOND FUSED JUMPER … AND TERM 'E'.")

NO

- CHECK CKT 1134 AND CKT 33 FOR AN OPEN BETWEEN DRL MODULE AND PARK BRAKE SWITCH. IF OK, REPLACE PARK BRAKE SWITCH.

YES

- CHECK FOR POOR CONNECTION. IF OK, REPLACE DRL MODULE.

CHART 6
"BRAKE" INDICATOR REMAINS "ON" WHEN IGNITION SWITCH IS IN "RUN" AND PARK BRAKE IS RELEASED [VEHICLES EQUIPPED WITH DAYTIME RUNNING LIGHTS (DRL)]

IMPORTANT:

- TO AVOID MISDIAGNOSIS ON A VEHICLE EQUIPPED WITH ANTILOCK BRAKES (ABS), CHECK FOR DIAGNOSTIC TROUBLE CODES (SEE SECTION 5E).

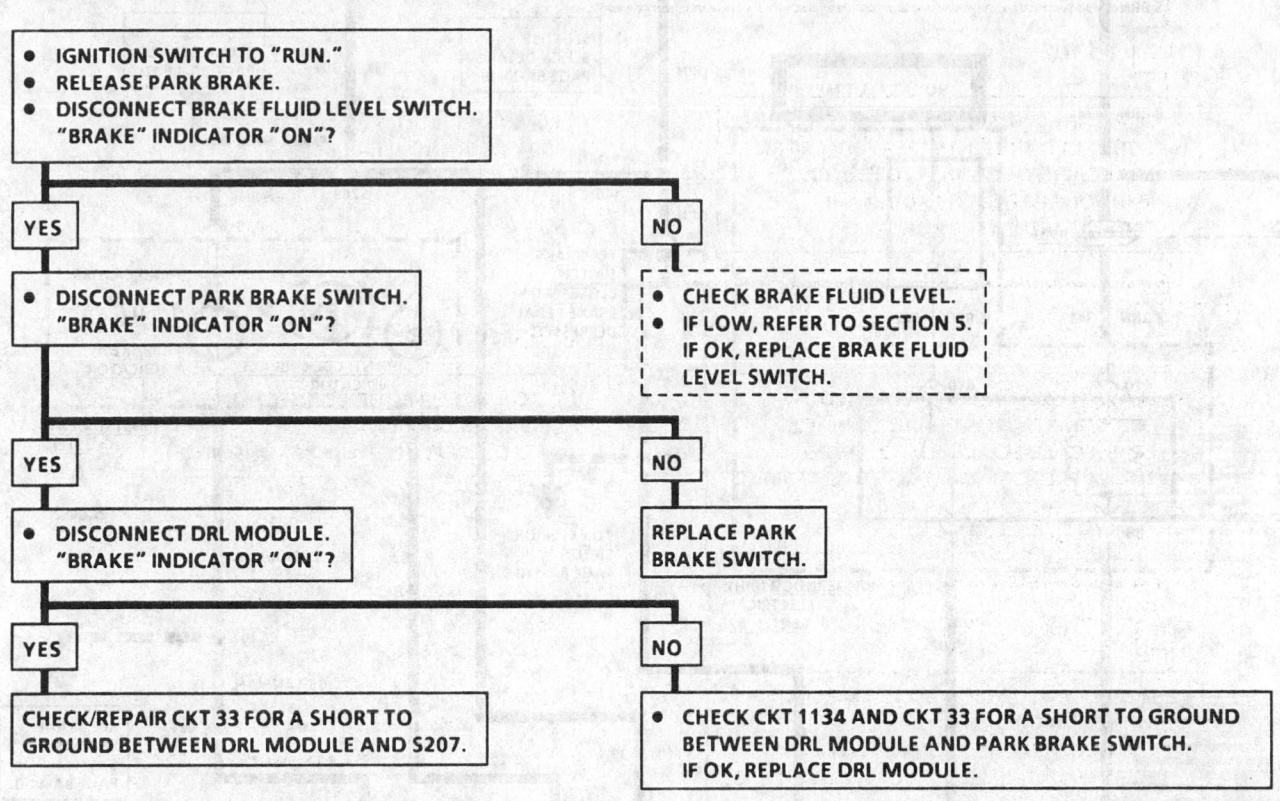

- IGNITION SWITCH TO "RUN."
- RELEASE PARK BRAKE.
- DISCONNECT BRAKE FLUID LEVEL SWITCH.

"BRAKE" INDICATOR "ON"?

YES

- DISCONNECT PARK BRAKE SWITCH.

"BRAKE" INDICATOR "ON"?

YES

- DISCONNECT DRL MODULE.

"BRAKE" INDICATOR "ON"?

YES

CHECK/REPAIR CKT 33 FOR A SHORT TO GROUND BETWEEN DRL MODULE AND S207.

NO

- CHECK CKT 1134 AND CKT 33 FOR A SHORT TO GROUND BETWEEN DRL MODULE AND PARK BRAKE SWITCH. IF OK, REPLACE DRL MODULE.

NO

REPLACE PARK BRAKE SWITCH.

NO

- CHECK BRAKE FLUID LEVEL.
- IF LOW, REFER TO SECTION 5. IF OK, REPLACE BRAKE FLUID LEVEL SWITCH.

CIRCUIT OPERATION

Battery voltage is applied to the "BRAKE" Indicator when the Ignition Switch is in "RUN," "BULB TEST" or "START." Four switches are connected to the "BRAKE" Indicator. When any of these switches close, ground is provided and the indicator lights.

The Ignition Switch provides a ground when it is in the "BULB TEST" and "START" positions.

The Park Brake Switch provides a ground when the Park Brake is applied.

The Brake Fluid Level Switch closes to light the "BRAKE" Indicator with low brake fluid in one of the two hydraulic brake fluid reservoirs. This could be caused by a leak in one of the brake lines. The switch can be reset to "OPEN" by refilling the reservoir; however, this can only be accomplished after the faulty system is repaired. The Electronic Brake Control Module (EBCM) closes to light the "BRAKE" Indicator and sets a diagnostic trouble code when an Antilock Brake failure will affect base brake operation.

ANTILOCK BRAKES

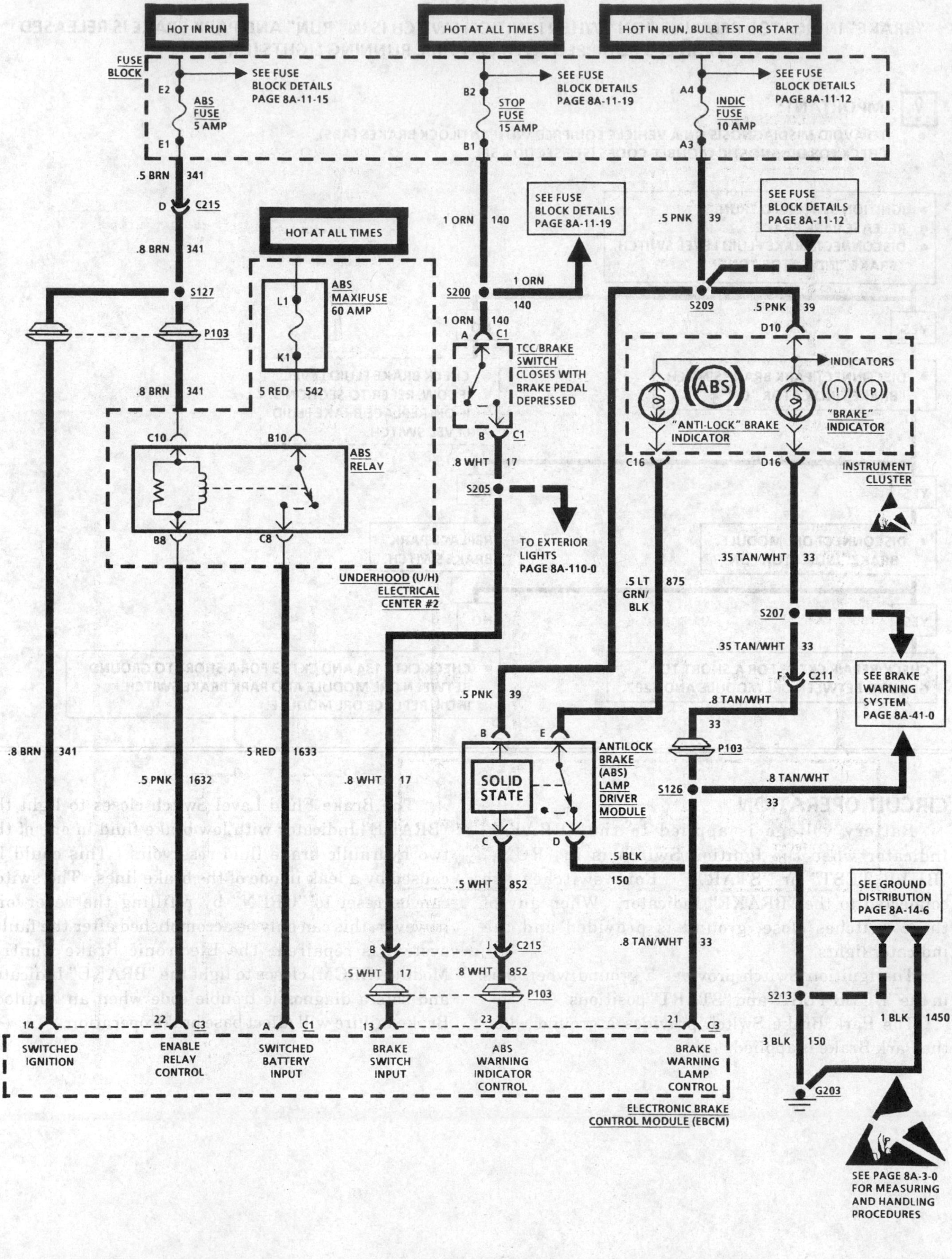

HOT IN RUN
HOT AT ALL TIMES
HOT IN RUN, BULB TEST OR START
FUSE BLOCK
E2
ABS FUSE 5 AMP
E1
SEE FUSE BLOCK DETAILS PAGE 8A-11-15
B2
STOP FUSE 15 AMP
B1
SEE FUSE BLOCK DETAILS PAGE 8A-11-19
A4
INDIC FUSE 10 AMP
A3
SEE FUSE BLOCK DETAILS PAGE 8A-11-12
.5 BRN 341
D C215
.8 BRN 341
HOT AT ALL TIMES
ABS MAXIFUSE 60 AMP
L1
K1
S127
P103
.8 BRN 341
5 RED 542
C10
B10
ABS RELAY
B8
C8
UNDERHOOD (U/H) ELECTRICAL CENTER #2
1 ORN 140
SEE FUSE BLOCK DETAILS PAGE 8A-11-19
1 ORN
S200
140
1 ORN 140
A C1
TCC/BRAKE SWITCH CLOSES WITH BRAKE PEDAL DEPRESSED
B C1
.8 WHT 17
S205
TO EXTERIOR LIGHTS PAGE 8A-110-0
.5 PNK 39
SEE FUSE BLOCK DETAILS PAGE 8A-11-12
S209
.5 PNK 39
D10
INDICATORS
ABS
"ANTI-LOCK" BRAKE INDICATOR
"BRAKE" INDICATOR
C16
D16
INSTRUMENT CLUSTER
.35 TAN/WHT 33
.5 LT GRN/BLK 875
S207
.35 TAN/WHT 33
F C211
.8 TAN/WHT
SEE BRAKE WARNING SYSTEM PAGE 8A-41-0
33
P103
.8 TAN/WHT
S126
33
.5 PNK 39
B
E
ANTILOCK BRAKE (ABS) LAMP DRIVER MODULE
SOLID STATE
C
D
.5 BLK
150
.8 BRN 341
.5 PNK 1632
5 RED 1633
.8 WHT 17
.5 WHT 852
.8 TAN/WHT 33
SEE GROUND DISTRIBUTION PAGE 8A-14-6
J C215
B
.5 WHT 17
.8 WHT 852
P103
S213
1 BLK 1450
3 BLK 150
G203
14
22 C3
A C1
13
23
21 C3
SWITCHED IGNITION
ENABLE RELAY CONTROL
SWITCHED BATTERY INPUT
BRAKE SWITCH INPUT
ABS WARNING INDICATOR CONTROL
BRAKE WARNING LAMP CONTROL
ELECTRONIC BRAKE CONTROL MODULE (EBCM)
SEE PAGE 8A-3-0 FOR MEASURING AND HANDLING PROCEDURES

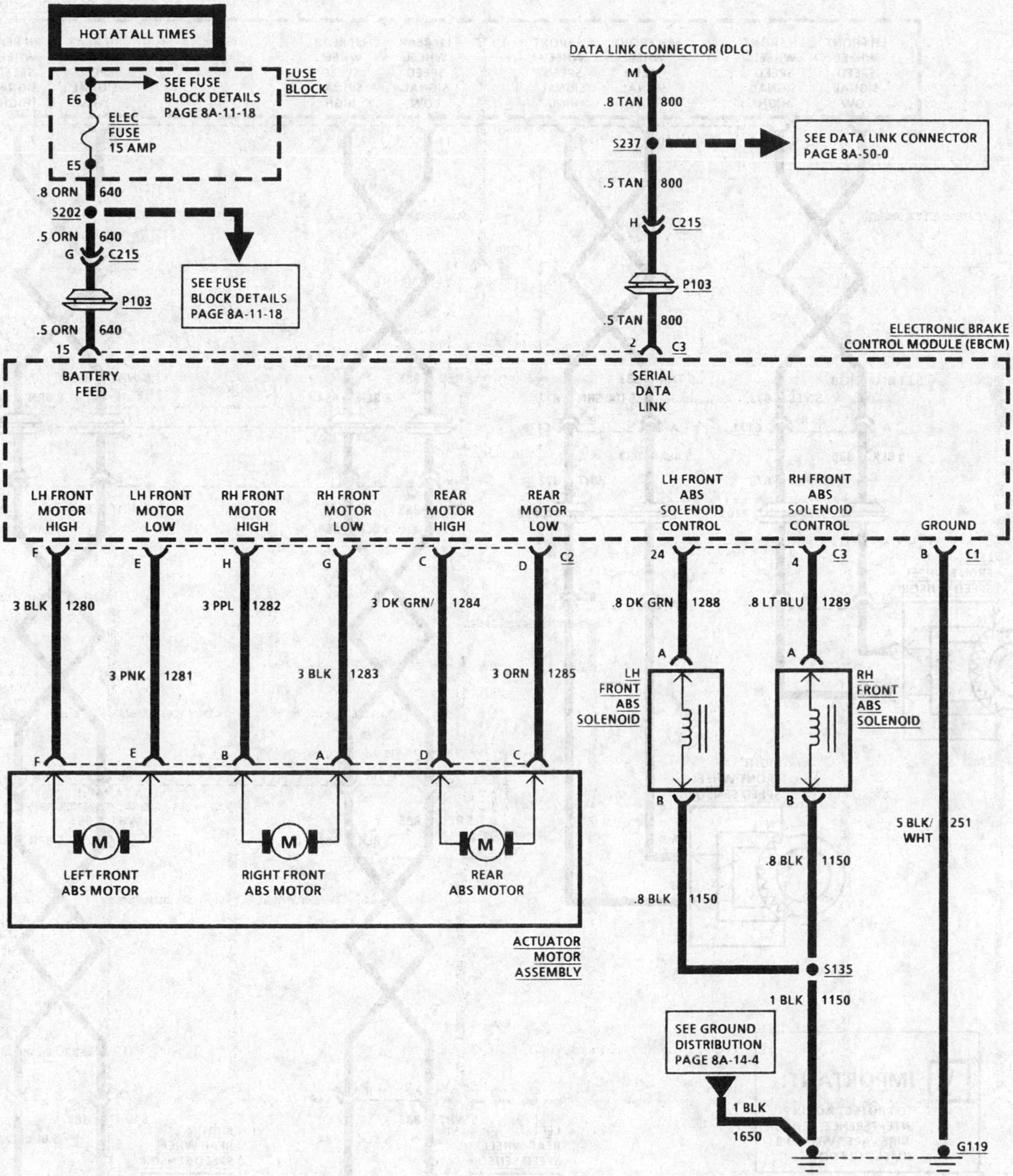
HOT AT ALL TIMES
FUSE BLOCK
E6
SEE FUSE BLOCK DETAILS PAGE 8A-11-18
ELEC FUSE 15 AMP
E5
.8 ORN 640
S202
.5 ORN 640
G C215
SEE FUSE BLOCK DETAILS PAGE 8A-11-18
P103
.5 ORN 640
15
BATTERY FEED
DATA LINK CONNECTOR (DLC)
M
.8 TAN 800
S237
SEE DATA LINK CONNECTOR PAGE 8A-50-0
.5 TAN 800
H C215
P103
.5 TAN 800
2 C3
SERIAL DATA LINK
ELECTRONIC BRAKE CONTROL MODULE (EBCM)
LH FRONT MOTOR HIGH
LH FRONT MOTOR LOW
RH FRONT MOTOR HIGH
RH FRONT MOTOR LOW
REAR MOTOR HIGH
REAR MOTOR LOW
LH FRONT ABS SOLENOID CONTROL
RH FRONT ABS SOLENOID CONTROL
GROUND
F E H G C D C2
24 4 C3
B C1
3 BLK 1280
3 PNK 1281
3 PPL 1282
3 BLK 1283
3 DK GRN/ 1284
3 ORN 1285
.8 DK GRN 1288
.8 LT BLU 1289
A
LH FRONT ABS SOLENOID
RH FRONT ABS SOLENOID
B
F E B A D C
M
LEFT FRONT ABS MOTOR
RIGHT FRONT ABS MOTOR
REAR ABS MOTOR
ACTUATOR MOTOR ASSEMBLY
5 BLK/ WHT 251
.8 BLK 1150
.8 BLK 1150
S135
1 BLK 1150
SEE GROUND DISTRIBUTION PAGE 8A-14-4
1 BLK
1650
G119

ANTILOCK BRAKES

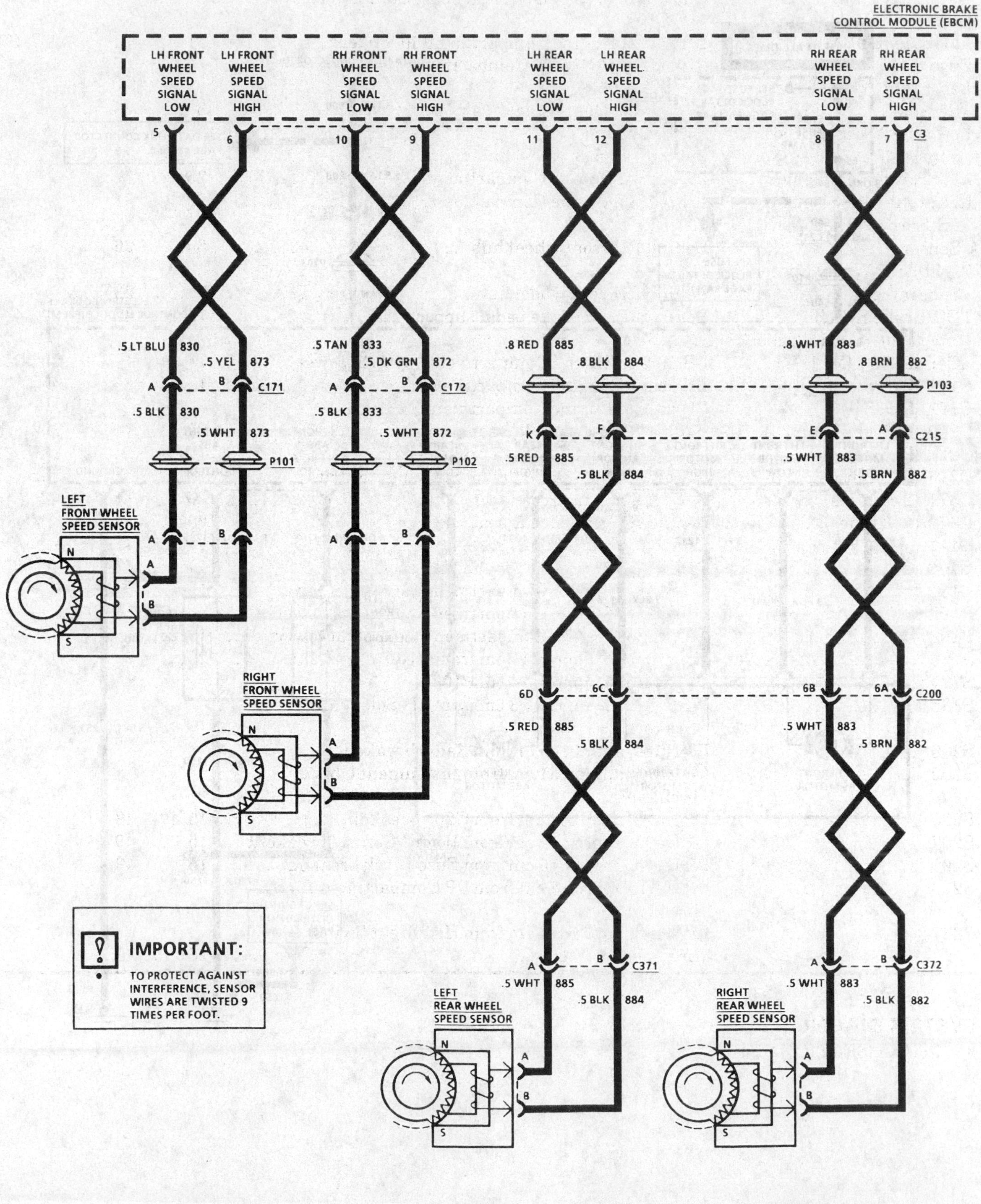
ELECTRONIC BRAKE CONTROL MODULE (EBCM)
LH FRONT WHEEL SPEED SIGNAL LOW
LH FRONT WHEEL SPEED SIGNAL HIGH
RH FRONT WHEEL SPEED SIGNAL LOW
RH FRONT WHEEL SPEED SIGNAL HIGH
LH REAR WHEEL SPEED SIGNAL LOW
LH REAR WHEEL SPEED SIGNAL HIGH
RH REAR WHEEL SPEED SIGNAL LOW
RH REAR WHEEL SPEED SIGNAL HIGH
5
6
10
9
11
12
8
7
C3
.5 LT BLU 830
.5 YEL 873
.5 TAN 833
.5 DK GRN 872
.8 RED 885
.8 BLK 884
.8 WHT 883
.8 BRN 882
C171
C172
P103
.5 BLK 830
.5 WHT 873
.5 BLK 833
.5 WHT 872
C215
P101
P102
.5 RED 885
.5 BLK 884
.5 WHT 883
.5 BRN 882
LEFT FRONT WHEEL SPEED SENSOR
RIGHT FRONT WHEEL SPEED SENSOR
6D
6C
6B
6A
C200
.5 RED 885
.5 BLK 884
.5 WHT 883
.5 BRN 882
C371
C372
.5 WHT 885
.5 BLK 884
.5 WHT 883
.5 BLK 882
LEFT REAR WHEEL SPEED SENSOR
RIGHT REAR WHEEL SPEED SENSOR
IMPORTANT:
TO PROTECT AGAINST INTERFERENCE, SENSOR WIRES ARE TWISTED 9 TIMES PER FOOT.

COMPONENT	LOCATION	201-PG	FIG.	CONN
Actuator Motor Assembly	LH rear of Engine Compartment	23	77	202-36
Antilock Brake (ABS) Lamp Driver Module	Behind I/P, right of Steering Column			202-38
Data Link Conn (DLC)	On bottom of I/P, right of Steering Column			202-17
Electronic Brake Control Module (EBCM)	LH side of Engine Compartment, in fender	21	73	202-19
Fuse Block	RH side of I/P, in I/P Compartment			
Left Front Wheel Speed Sensor	Behind LH front wheel hub	8	26	
Left Rear Wheel Speed Sensor	Behind LH rear wheel hub	7	23	
LH Front ABS Solenoid	LH rear of Engine Compartment	25	81	
RH Front ABS Solenoid	LH rear of Engine Compartment	25	81	
Right Front Wheel Speed Sensor	Behind RH front wheel hub	8	26	
Right Rear Wheel Speed Sensor	Behind RH rear wheel hub	7	23	
TCC/Brake Switch	Behind I/P, on brake pedal support	12	42	202-41
Underhood (U/H) Electrical Center #2	LH side of Engine Compartment, on strut tower	1	4	202-34
C171 (2 cavities)	LH rear of Engine Compartment	1	4	
C172 (2 cavities)	RH rear of Engine Compartment			
C200 (102 cavities)	Behind RH side of I/P, near shroud	22	74	202-3
C211 (8 cavities)	Behind I/P, on RH side of brake pedal support			202-35
C215 (10 cavities)	Behind LH side of I/P, left of Steering Column			202-11
C371 (2 cavities)	Behind LH side of rear seat	20	71	
C372 (2 cavities)	Behind RH side of rear seat	20	70	
G119	LH strut tower	1	4	
G203	Behind LH side of I/P, on mag bracket	14	48	
P101	LH rear of Engine Compartment, near strut tower	1	4	
P102	RH rear of Engine Compartment, near strut tower			
P103	LH rear of Engine Compartment, near strut tower	1	4	
S126	Wiper Harn, approx 17 cm from P103	2	7	
S127	Wiper Harn, approx 14 cm P103			
S135	Wiper Harn, approx 53 cm from LH Solenoid Brake Valve			
S200	I/P Harn, approx 4 cm from Radio breakout			
S202	I/P Harn, approx 51 cm from Instrument Cluster breakout			
S205	I/P Harn, approx 4 cm from G201 breakout	15	49	
S207	I/P Harn, approx 12 cm from HVAC Control breakout	15	49	
S209	I/P Harn, approx 15 cm from Fuse Block breakout	15	49	
S213	I/P Harn, approx 7 cm from I/P Compartment Light breakout			
S237	I/P Harn, approx 14 cm from Headlight Switch breakout	15	49	

SYSTEM DIAGNOSIS

- Refer to SECTION 5E.

SUPPLEMENTAL INFLATABLE RESTRAINT (SIR)

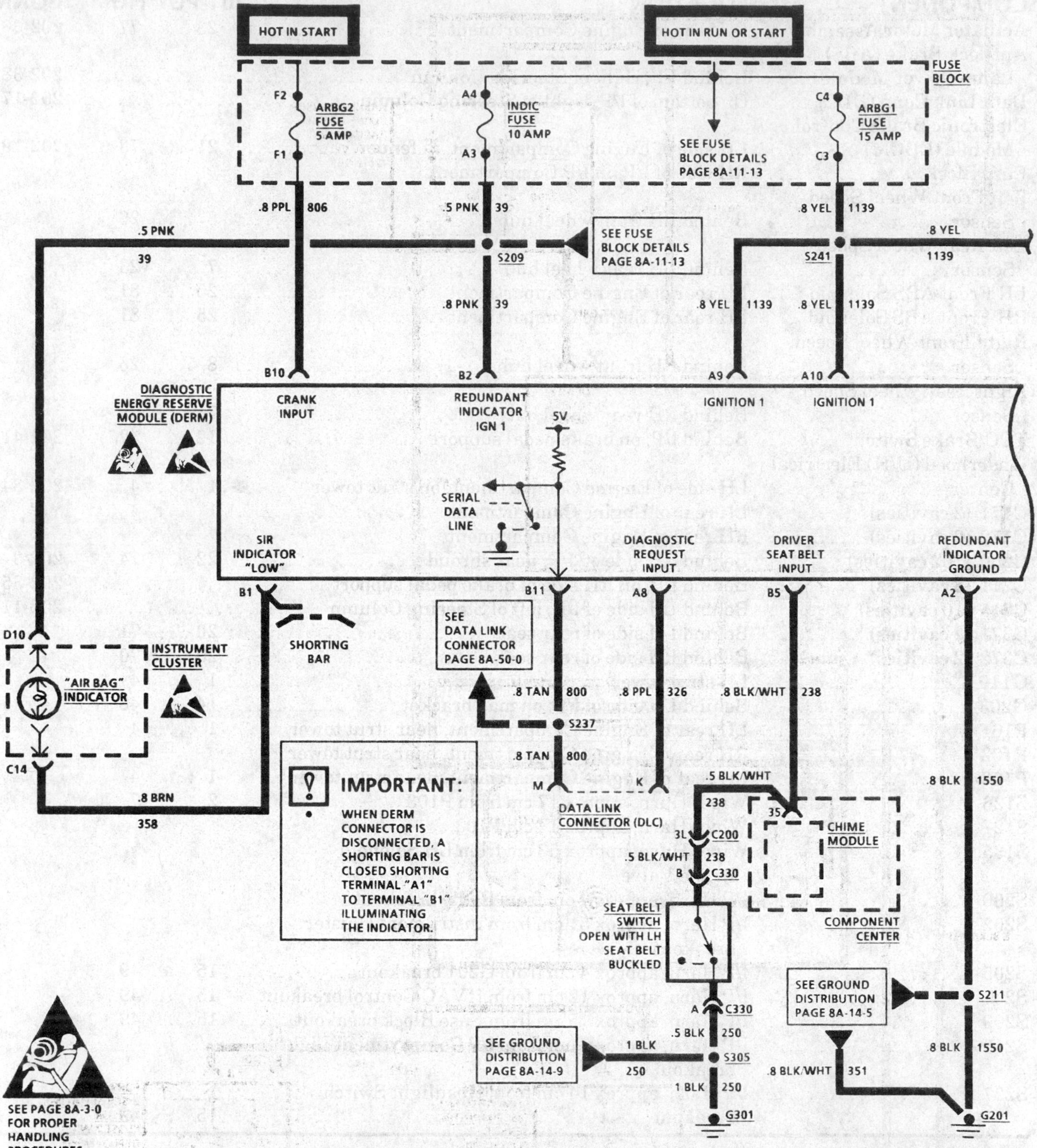
HOT IN START
HOT IN RUN OR START
FUSE BLOCK
F2
ARBG2 FUSE 5 AMP
F1
A4
INDIC FUSE 10 AMP
A3
SEE FUSE BLOCK DETAILS PAGE 8A-11-13
C4
ARBG1 FUSE 15 AMP
C3
.8 PPL 806
.5 PNK 39
.8 YEL 1139
.5 PNK
39
S209
SEE FUSE BLOCK DETAILS PAGE 8A-11-13
S241
.8 YEL
1139
.8 PNK 39
.8 YEL 1139
.8 YEL 1139
B10
B2
A9
A10
DIAGNOSTIC ENERGY RESERVE MODULE (DERM)
CRANK INPUT
REDUNDANT INDICATOR IGN 1
5V
IGNITION 1
IGNITION 1
SERIAL DATA LINE
SIR INDICATOR "LOW"
DIAGNOSTIC REQUEST INPUT
DRIVER SEAT BELT INPUT
REDUNDANT INDICATOR GROUND
B1
B11
A8
B5
A2
D10
INSTRUMENT CLUSTER
"AIR BAG" INDICATOR
C14
SHORTING BAR
SEE DATA LINK CONNECTOR PAGE 8A-50-0
.8 TAN 800
.8 PPL 326
.8 BLK/WHT 238
S237
.8 TAN 800
M
K
DATA LINK CONNECTOR (DLC)
.5 BLK/WHT
238
35
CHIME MODULE
3L
C200
.5 BLK/WHT 238
B
C330
.8 BLK 1550
.8 BRN
358
IMPORTANT:
WHEN DERM CONNECTOR IS DISCONNECTED, A SHORTING BAR IS CLOSED SHORTING TERMINAL "A1" TO TERMINAL "B1" ILLUMINATING THE INDICATOR.
SEAT BELT SWITCH OPEN WITH LH SEAT BELT BUCKLED
COMPONENT CENTER
SEE GROUND DISTRIBUTION PAGE 8A-14-5
S211
A
C330
.5 BLK 250
SEE GROUND DISTRIBUTION PAGE 8A-14-9
1 BLK
250
S305
1 BLK 250
.8 BLK/WHT 351
.8 BLK 1550
G301
G201

SEE PAGE 8A-3-0 FOR PROPER HANDLING PROCEDURES

SEE PAGE 8A-3-0 FOR MEASURING AND HANDLING PROCEDURES

CAUTION: This vehicle is equipped with Supplemental Inflatable Restraint (SIR). Refer to CAUTIONS in Section 9J under "ON-VEHICLE SERVICE" and the SIR Component and Wiring Location view in Section 9J before performing service on or around SIR components or wiring. Failure to follow CAUTIONS could result in possible air bag deployment, personal injury, or otherwise unneeded SIR system repairs.

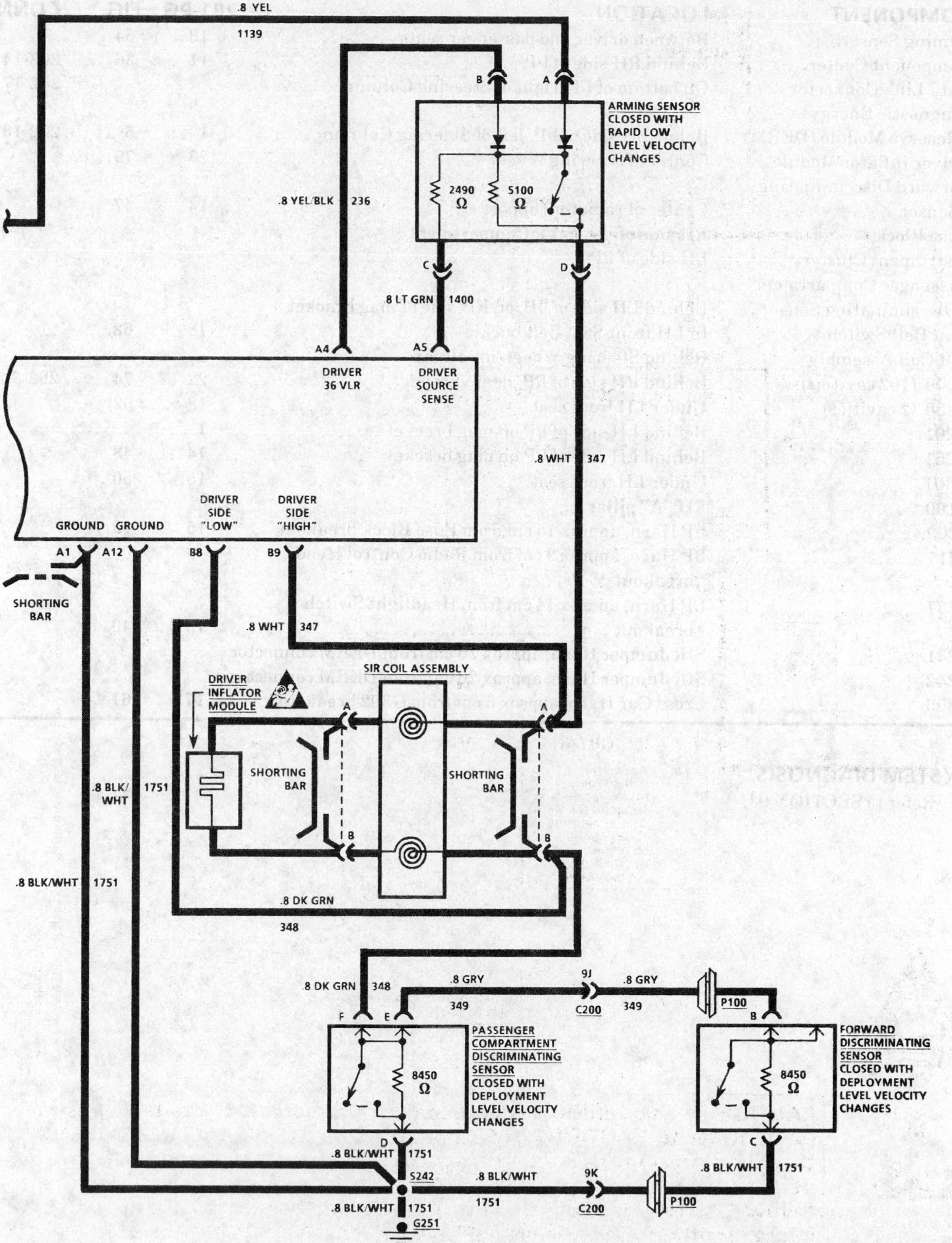

.8 YEL
1139
B
A
ARMING SENSOR
CLOSED WITH
RAPID LOW
LEVEL VELOCITY
CHANGES
2490 Ω
5100 Ω
.8 YEL/BLK 236
C
D
8 LT GRN 1400
A4
A5
DRIVER
36 VLR
DRIVER
SOURCE
SENSE
.8 WHT 347
DRIVER
SIDE
"LOW"
DRIVER
SIDE
"HIGH"
GROUND
GROUND
A1
A12
B8
B9
SHORTING
BAR
.8 WHT 347
SIR COIL ASSEMBLY
DRIVER
INFLATOR
MODULE
A
A
SHORTING
BAR
SHORTING
BAR
B
B
.8 BLK/
WHT 1751
.8 BLK/WHT 1751
.8 DK GRN
348
8 DK GRN 348
.8 GRY
349
9J
C200
.8 GRY
349
P100
F
E
B
PASSENGER
COMPARTMENT
DISCRIMINATING
SENSOR
CLOSED WITH
DEPLOYMENT
LEVEL VELOCITY
CHANGES
8450 Ω
FORWARD
DISCRIMINATING
SENSOR
CLOSED WITH
DEPLOYMENT
LEVEL VELOCITY
CHANGES
8450 Ω
D
C
.8 BLK/WHT 1751
S242
.8 BLK/WHT
1751
9K
C200
P100
.8 BLK/WHT 1751
.8 BLK/WHT 1751
G251

SUPPLEMENTAL INFLATABLE RESTRAINT (SIR)

COMPONENT	LOCATION	201-PG	FIG.	CONN
Arming Sensor	Between driver and passenger seats	18	64	
Component Center	Behind RH side of I/P	11	36	202-14
Data Link Connector	On bottom of I/P, right of Steering Column			202-17
Diagnostic Energy Reserve Module (DERM)	Below LH side of I/P, left of Steering Column	1	5	202-18
Driver Inflator Module	Center of Steering Wheel	23	79	
Forward Discriminating Sensor	Center of radiator support	14	47	
Fuse Block	RH side of I/P, in I/P Compartment			
Instrument Cluster	LH side of I/P			
Passenger Compartment Discriminating Sensor	Behind LH side of I/P, on RH side of mag bracket			
Seat Belt Switch	In LH front Seat Belt buckle	18	62	
SIR Coil Assembly	Behind Steering Wheel, in column			
C200 (102 cavities)	Behind RH side of I/P, near shroud	22	74	202-3
C330 (2 cavities)	Under LH front seat	18	62	
G201	Behind LH side of I/P on mag bracket	1	4	
G251	Behind LH side of I/P on mag bracket	14	48	
G301	Under LH front seat	15	50	
P100	RH "A" pillar			
S209	I/P Harn, approx 15 cm from Fuse Block breakout	15	19	
S211	I/P Harn, approx 9 cm from Radio Control Head breakout			
S237	I/P Harn, approx 14 cm from Headlight Switch breakout	15	49	
S241	SIR Jumper Harn, approx 26 cm from DERM connector			
S242	SIR Jumper Harn, approx 26 cm from DERM connector			
S305	Cross Car Harn, approx 5 cm from G302 breakout	17	61	

SYSTEM DIAGNOSIS

- Refer to SECTION 9J.

BLANK

DATA LINK CONNECTOR (DLC) PIN ASSIGNMENT

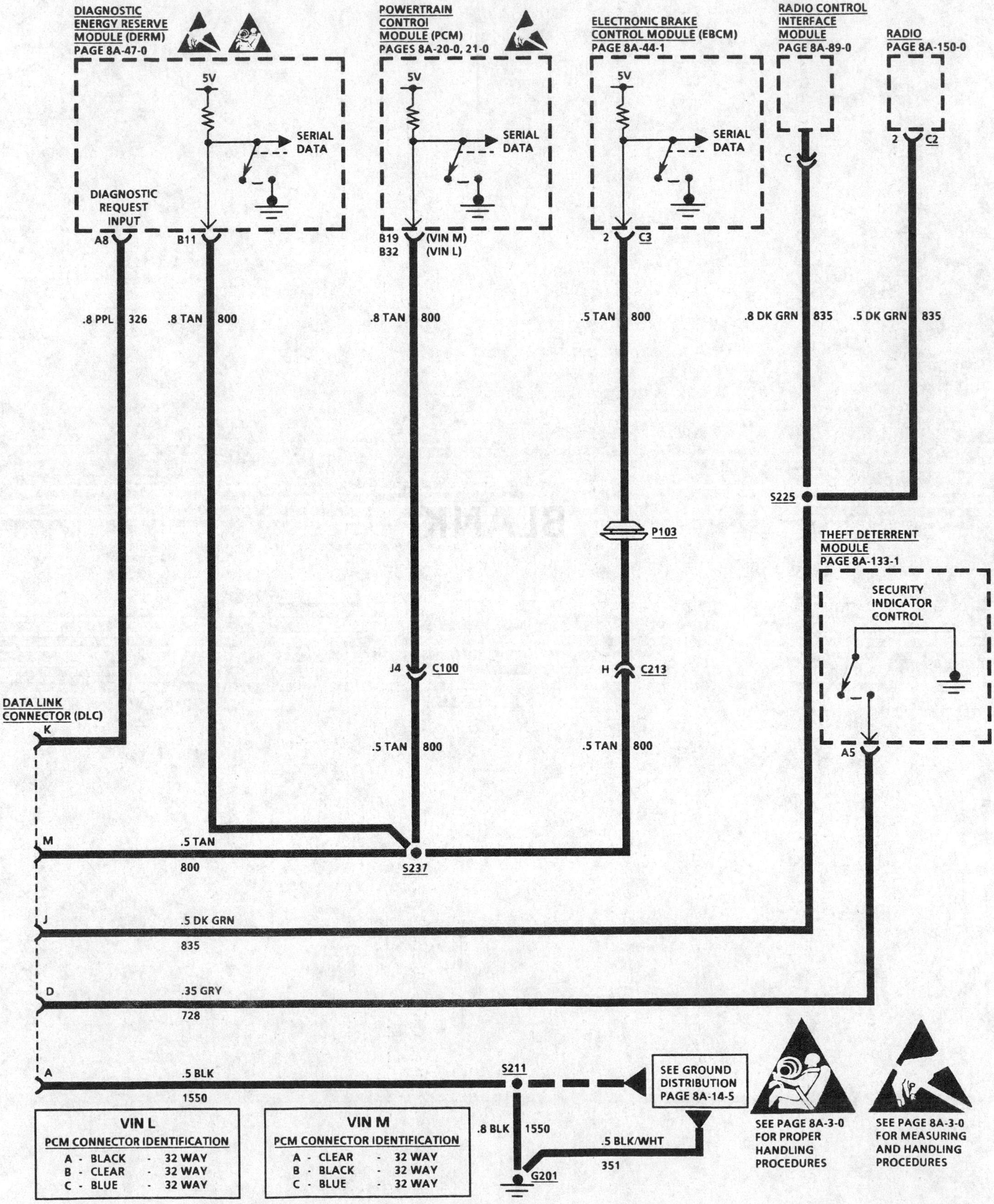
DIAGNOSTIC ENERGY RESERVE MODULE (DERM)
PAGE 8A-47-0
5V
SERIAL DATA
DIAGNOSTIC REQUEST INPUT
A8
B11
POWERTRAIN CONTROL MODULE (PCM)
PAGES 8A-20-0, 21-0
5V
SERIAL DATA
B19 (VIN M)
B32 (VIN L)
ELECTRONIC BRAKE CONTROL MODULE (EBCM)
PAGE 8A-44-1
5V
SERIAL DATA
2 C3
RADIO CONTROL INTERFACE MODULE
PAGE 8A-89-0
C
RADIO
PAGE 8A-150-0
2 C2
.8 PPL 326
.8 TAN 800
.8 TAN 800
.5 TAN 800
.8 DK GRN 835
.5 DK GRN 835
S225
P103
THEFT DETERRENT MODULE
PAGE 8A-133-1
SECURITY INDICATOR CONTROL
J4 C100
H C213
A5
DATA LINK CONNECTOR (DLC)
K
.5 TAN 800
.5 TAN 800
M
.5 TAN
800
S237
J
.5 DK GRN
835
D
.35 GRY
728
A
.5 BLK
1550
S211
SEE GROUND DISTRIBUTION PAGE 8A-14-5
.8 BLK 1550
.5 BLK/WHT
351
G201
SEE PAGE 8A-3-0 FOR PROPER HANDLING PROCEDURES
SEE PAGE 8A-3-0 FOR MEASURING AND HANDLING PROCEDURES

VIN L
PCM CONNECTOR IDENTIFICATION

A -	BLACK	-	32 WAY
B -	CLEAR	-	32 WAY
C -	BLUE	-	32 WAY

VIN M
PCM CONNECTOR IDENTIFICATION

A -	CLEAR	-	32 WAY
B -	BLACK	-	32 WAY
C -	BLUE	-	32 WAY

COMPONENT	LOCATION	201-PG	FIG.	CONN
Data Link Conn (DLC)	On bottom of I/P, right of Steering Column			202-17
Diagnostic Energy Reserve Module (DERM)	Behind LH side of I/P, left of Steering Column	1	5	202-18
Electronic Brake Control Module (EBCM)	LH side of Engine Compartment, in fender	21	73	202-19
Radio Control Interface Module	Behind LH side of I/P, left of Steering Column			202-40
Powertrain Control Module (PCM)	RH side of Engine Compartment, forward of strut tower	19	68	202-26, 29
Radio Receiver	RH side of I/P	16	53	202-32
C100 (36 cavities)	RH side of dash behind strut tower			202-0
C215 (10 cavities)	Behind LH side of I/P, left of Steering Column			202-11
G201	Behind I/P, on RH side of mag bracket	14	48	
P103	LH rear of Engine Compartment, near strut tower	1	4	
S211	I/P Harn, approx 9 cm from Radio Control Head breakout			
S225	I/P Harn, approx 25 cm from Radio Control Head			
S237	I/P Harn, approx 14 cm from Headlight Switch breakout			

TROUBLESHOOTING HINTS

PCM DATA LINE

1. If all components are not accessible with a scan tool, check for an open in CKT 800 between DLC terminal "M" and S237.
2. If a single component is not accessible with a scan tool, check for an open in CKT 800 between S237 and the component. If the wire is OK, refer to SECTION 6E for Powertrain Control Module diagnosis, SECTION 5E-1 for ABS diagnosis and to SECTION 9J for Supplemental Inflatable Restraint diagnosis.

ENTERTAINMENT AND COMFORT (E & C) DATA LINE

1. If all components are not accessible with a scan tool, check for an open in CKT 835 between DLC terminal "J" and S225.
2. If a single component is not accessible with a scan tool, check for an open in CKT 835 between S225 and the component. If the wire is OK, refer to page 8A-89-0 for Redundant Steering Controls diagnosis.

SYMPTOM TABLE

SYMPTOM	PROCEDURE	PAGE NUMBER
Scan tool will not communicate.	Chart #1	8A-50-2

CHART #1
SCAN TOOL WILL NOT COMMUNICATE

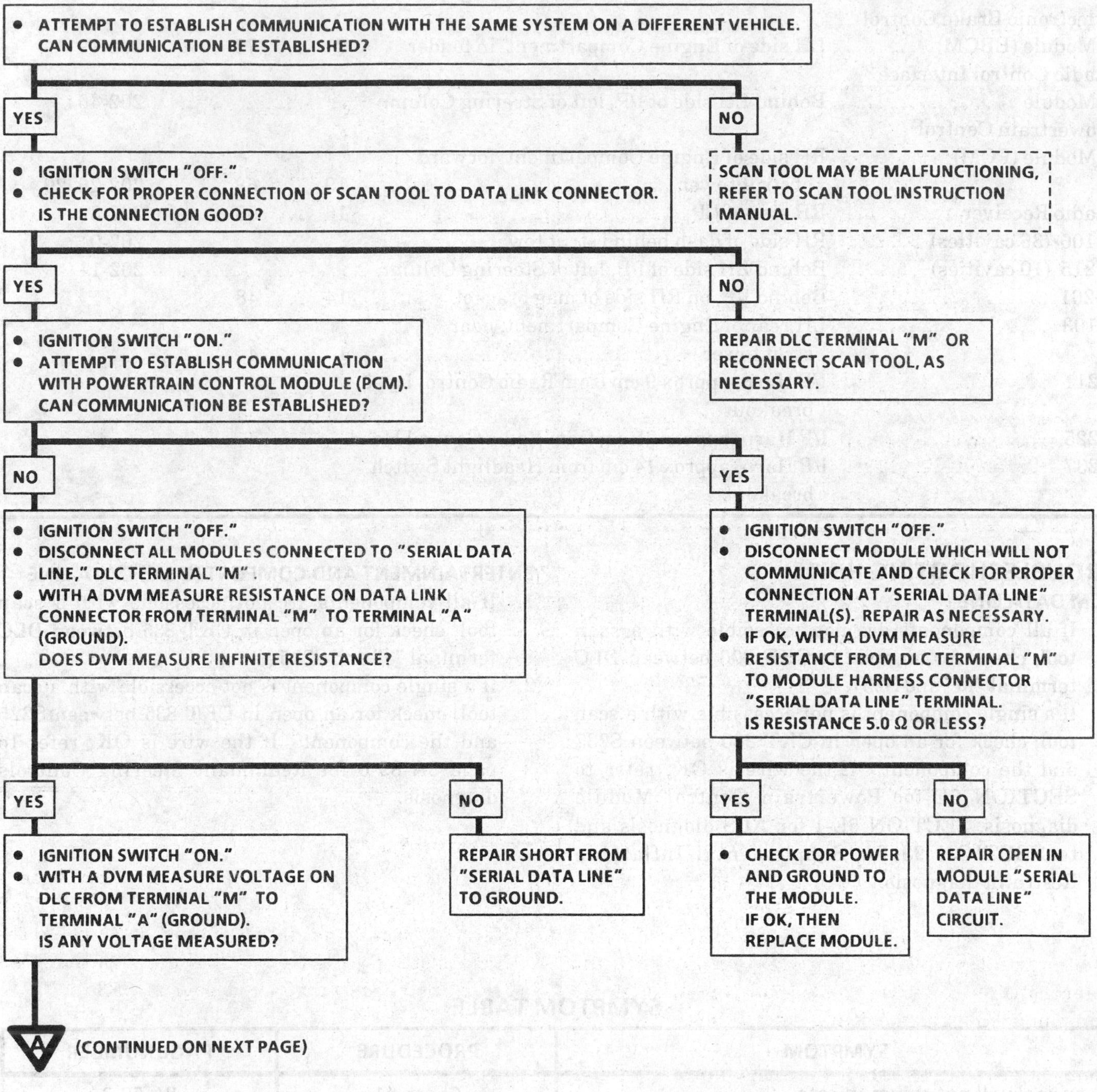
• ATTEMPT TO ESTABLISH COMMUNICATION WITH THE SAME SYSTEM ON A DIFFERENT VEHICLE. CAN COMMUNICATION BE ESTABLISHED?
YES
NO
• IGNITION SWITCH "OFF."
• CHECK FOR PROPER CONNECTION OF SCAN TOOL TO DATA LINK CONNECTOR. IS THE CONNECTION GOOD?
SCAN TOOL MAY BE MALFUNCTIONING, REFER TO SCAN TOOL INSTRUCTION MANUAL.
YES
NO
• IGNITION SWITCH "ON."
• ATTEMPT TO ESTABLISH COMMUNICATION WITH POWERTRAIN CONTROL MODULE (PCM). CAN COMMUNICATION BE ESTABLISHED?
REPAIR DLC TERMINAL "M" OR RECONNECT SCAN TOOL, AS NECESSARY.
NO
YES
• IGNITION SWITCH "OFF."
• DISCONNECT ALL MODULES CONNECTED TO "SERIAL DATA LINE," DLC TERMINAL "M".
• WITH A DVM MEASURE RESISTANCE ON DATA LINK CONNECTOR FROM TERMINAL "M" TO TERMINAL "A" (GROUND). DOES DVM MEASURE INFINITE RESISTANCE?
• IGNITION SWITCH "OFF."
• DISCONNECT MODULE WHICH WILL NOT COMMUNICATE AND CHECK FOR PROPER CONNECTION AT "SERIAL DATA LINE" TERMINAL(S). REPAIR AS NECESSARY.
• IF OK, WITH A DVM MEASURE RESISTANCE FROM DLC TERMINAL "M" TO MODULE HARNESS CONNECTOR "SERIAL DATA LINE" TERMINAL. IS RESISTANCE 5.0 Ω OR LESS?
YES
NO
YES
NO
• IGNITION SWITCH "ON."
• WITH A DVM MEASURE VOLTAGE ON DLC FROM TERMINAL "M" TO TERMINAL "A" (GROUND). IS ANY VOLTAGE MEASURED?
REPAIR SHORT FROM "SERIAL DATA LINE" TO GROUND.
• CHECK FOR POWER AND GROUND TO THE MODULE. IF OK, THEN REPLACE MODULE.
REPAIR OPEN IN MODULE "SERIAL DATA LINE" CIRCUIT.
A

(CONTINUED ON NEXT PAGE)

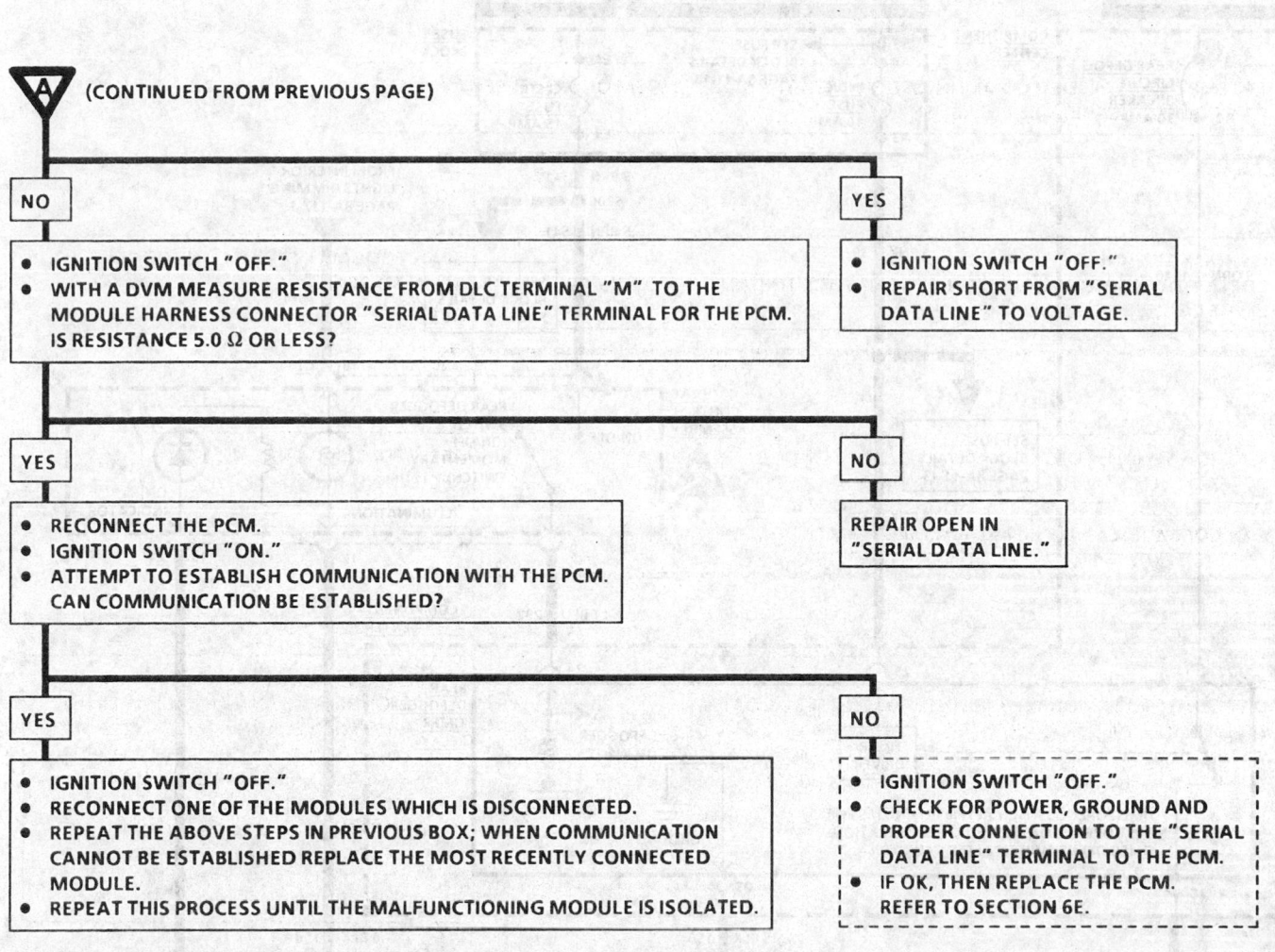

A (CONTINUED FROM PREVIOUS PAGE)

NO

- IGNITION SWITCH "OFF."
- WITH A DVM MEASURE RESISTANCE FROM DLC TERMINAL "M" TO THE MODULE HARNESS CONNECTOR "SERIAL DATA LINE" TERMINAL FOR THE PCM. IS RESISTANCE 5.0 Ω OR LESS?

YES

- IGNITION SWITCH "OFF."
- REPAIR SHORT FROM "SERIAL DATA LINE" TO VOLTAGE.

YES

- RECONNECT THE PCM.
- IGNITION SWITCH "ON."
- ATTEMPT TO ESTABLISH COMMUNICATION WITH THE PCM. CAN COMMUNICATION BE ESTABLISHED?

NO

REPAIR OPEN IN "SERIAL DATA LINE."

YES

- IGNITION SWITCH "OFF."
- RECONNECT ONE OF THE MODULES WHICH IS DISCONNECTED.
- REPEAT THE ABOVE STEPS IN PREVIOUS BOX; WHEN COMMUNICATION CANNOT BE ESTABLISHED REPLACE THE MOST RECENTLY CONNECTED MODULE.
- REPEAT THIS PROCESS UNTIL THE MALFUNCTIONING MODULE IS ISOLATED.

NO

- IGNITION SWITCH "OFF."
- CHECK FOR POWER, GROUND AND PROPER CONNECTION TO THE "SERIAL DATA LINE" TERMINAL TO THE PCM.
- IF OK, THEN REPLACE THE PCM. REFER TO SECTION 6E.

CIRCUIT OPERATION

There are two data lines that can be accessed with a scan tool. The 800 circuit data line is the PCM Data Line. It allows the Powertrain Control Module, Diagnostic Energy Reserve Module (DERM) and Electronic Brake Control Module (EBCM) to communicate by transmitting data through CKT 800. The 835 circuit data line is the Entertainment and Comfort (E & C Bus) Data Line. It allows the Radio and Radio Control Interface Module to communicate via CKT 835.

A scan tool can be connected to the DLC; this allows the scan tool to communicate with both the PCM Data Line and E & C Data Lines. System operations can then be monitored for diagnostic purposes.

SECURITY INDICATOR

The Theft Deterrent Module will produce a switched ground signal when a fault in the Theft Deterrent System is detected and also when the vehicle is being started as a bulb check. For diagnosis refer to Theft Deterrent System page 8A-133-0.

REAR DEFOGGER

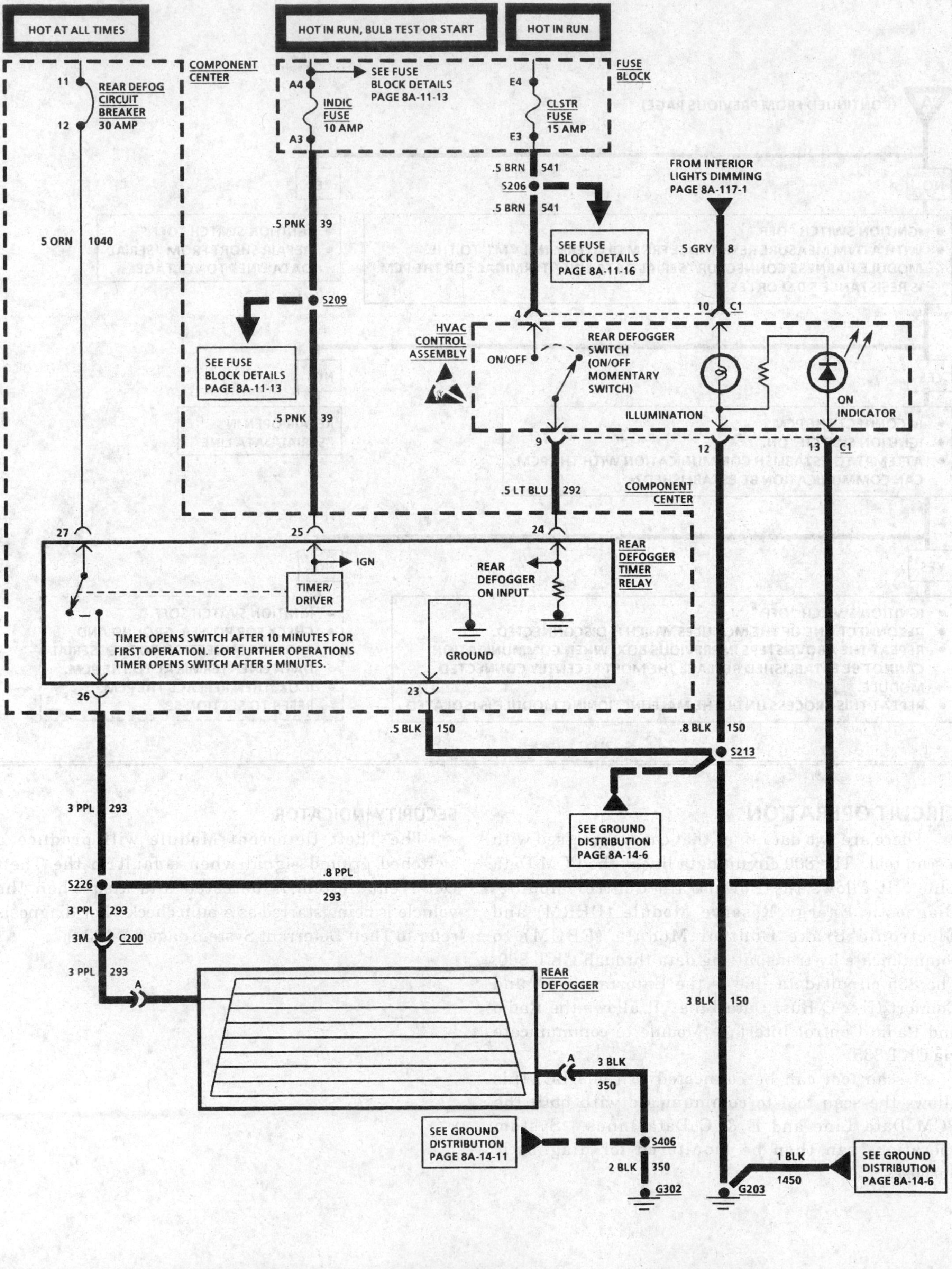

HOT AT ALL TIMES
HOT IN RUN, BULB TEST OR START
HOT IN RUN
COMPONENT CENTER
FUSE BLOCK
11
REAR DEFOG CIRCUIT BREAKER 30 AMP
12
A4
SEE FUSE BLOCK DETAILS PAGE 8A-11-13
INDIC FUSE 10 AMP
A3
E4
CLSTR FUSE 15 AMP
E3
.5 BRN 541
S206
.5 BRN 541
FROM INTERIOR LIGHTS DIMMING PAGE 8A-117-1
.5 PNK 39
5 ORN 1040
SEE FUSE BLOCK DETAILS PAGE 8A-11-16
.5 GRY 8
S209
4
10 C1
HVAC CONTROL ASSEMBLY
ON/OFF
REAR DEFOGGER SWITCH (ON/OFF MOMENTARY SWITCH)
SEE FUSE BLOCK DETAILS PAGE 8A-11-13
ILLUMINATION
ON INDICATOR
.5 PNK 39
9
12
13 C1
.5 LT BLU 292
COMPONENT CENTER
27
25
24
IGN
REAR DEFOGGER TIMER RELAY
REAR DEFOGGER ON INPUT
TIMER/ DRIVER
GROUND
TIMER OPENS SWITCH AFTER 10 MINUTES FOR FIRST OPERATION. FOR FURTHER OPERATIONS TIMER OPENS SWITCH AFTER 5 MINUTES.
26
23
.5 BLK 150
.8 BLK 150
S213
3 PPL 293
SEE GROUND DISTRIBUTION PAGE 8A-14-6
S226
.8 PPL 293
3 PPL 293
3M C200
3 PPL 293
A
REAR DEFOGGER
3 BLK 150
A
3 BLK 350
SEE GROUND DISTRIBUTION PAGE 8A-14-11
S406
2 BLK 350
G302
G203
1 BLK 1450
SEE GROUND DISTRIBUTION PAGE 8A-14-6

COMPONENT	LOCATION	201-PG	FIG.	CONN
Component Center	Behind RH side of I/P	11	36	202-14
Fuse Block	RH side of I/P, in I/P Compartment			
HVAC Control Assembly	Center of I/P	15	49	202-22
Rear Defogger	In rear window			
C200 (102 cavities)	Behind RH side of I/P, near shroud	22	76	202-3
G203	Behind I/P, on RH side of mag bracket	14	43	
G302	Under LH front seat			
S206	I/P Harn, approx 10 cm from Fuse Block breakout			
S209	I/P Harn, approx 16 cm from Fuse Block breakout			
S213	I/P Harn, approx 8 cm from HVAC Control breakout			
S226	I/P Harn, approx 8 cm from RH Front Speaker breakout			

TROUBLESHOOTING HINTS (Perform before beginning System Diagnosis)

1. Check INDIC Fuse, CLSTR Fuse, and REAR DEFOG Circuit Breaker.
2. If REAR DEFOG Circuit Breaker is open, check CKT 1040 for a short to ground.
3. Check Rear Defogger Grid for opens, refer to SECTION 10-2.
4. Check that G203 and G302 are clean and tight.

- Check for a broken (or partially broken) wire inside of the insulation which could cause system malfunction but prove "GOOD" in a continuity/voltage check with a system disconnected. These circuits may be intermittent or resistive when loaded, and if possible, should be checked by monitoring for a voltage drop with the system operational (under load).
- Check for proper installation of aftermarket electronic equipment which may affect the integrity of other systems (see "Troubleshooting Procedures," page 8A-4-0).
- Refer to System Diagnosis.

SYSTEM DIAGNOSIS

- Perform the System Check and refer to the Symptom Table for the appropriate diagnostic procedures.

REAR DEFOGGER

SYSTEM CHECK

ACTION	NORMAL RESULTS
[1] ● Engine running. ● Press Rear Defogger Switch once and release.	Switch returns to "REST" position. Rear Defogger Indicator is "ON" and Rear Defogger Grid becomes warm. Indicator and Rear Defogger Grid turn "OFF" in approximately 10 minutes.
[2] ● Press Rear Defogger Switch once and release.	Switch returns to "REST" position. Indicator and Rear Defogger Grid remain "ON" for 5 minutes and then turn "OFF."
[3] ● Press Rear Defogger Switch once and release. ● Press Rear Defogger Switch a second time and release.	Indicator and Rear Defogger Grid remain "ON" until the Rear Defogger Switch is pressed a second time.

SYMPTOM TABLE

SYMPTOM	PROCEDURE	PAGE NUMBER
Rear Defogger Grid and Indicator inoperative.	Chart #1	8A-61-3
Rear Defogger Grid inoperative but Indicator operates normally.	Chart #2	8A-61-4
Indicator inoperative but Rear Defogger Grid operates normally.	Check for poor connection at HVAC Control Assembly Connector C1 terminal "13" or open in CKT 293 between S226 and HVAC Control Assembly. If OK, replace HVAC Control Assembly.	
Rear Defogger Grid and Indicator operative, but will not cycle "ON/OFF" for 10 minutes or 5 minutes.	Replace Rear Defogger Timer Relay.	
Rear Defogger Switch does not return to "REST" position.	Replace HVAC Control Assembly.	
Rear Defogger Switch Illumination inoperative.	Refer to "Interior Lights Dimming," page 8A-117-0.	

CHART #1

REAR DEFOGGER GRID AND INDICATOR INOPERATIVE

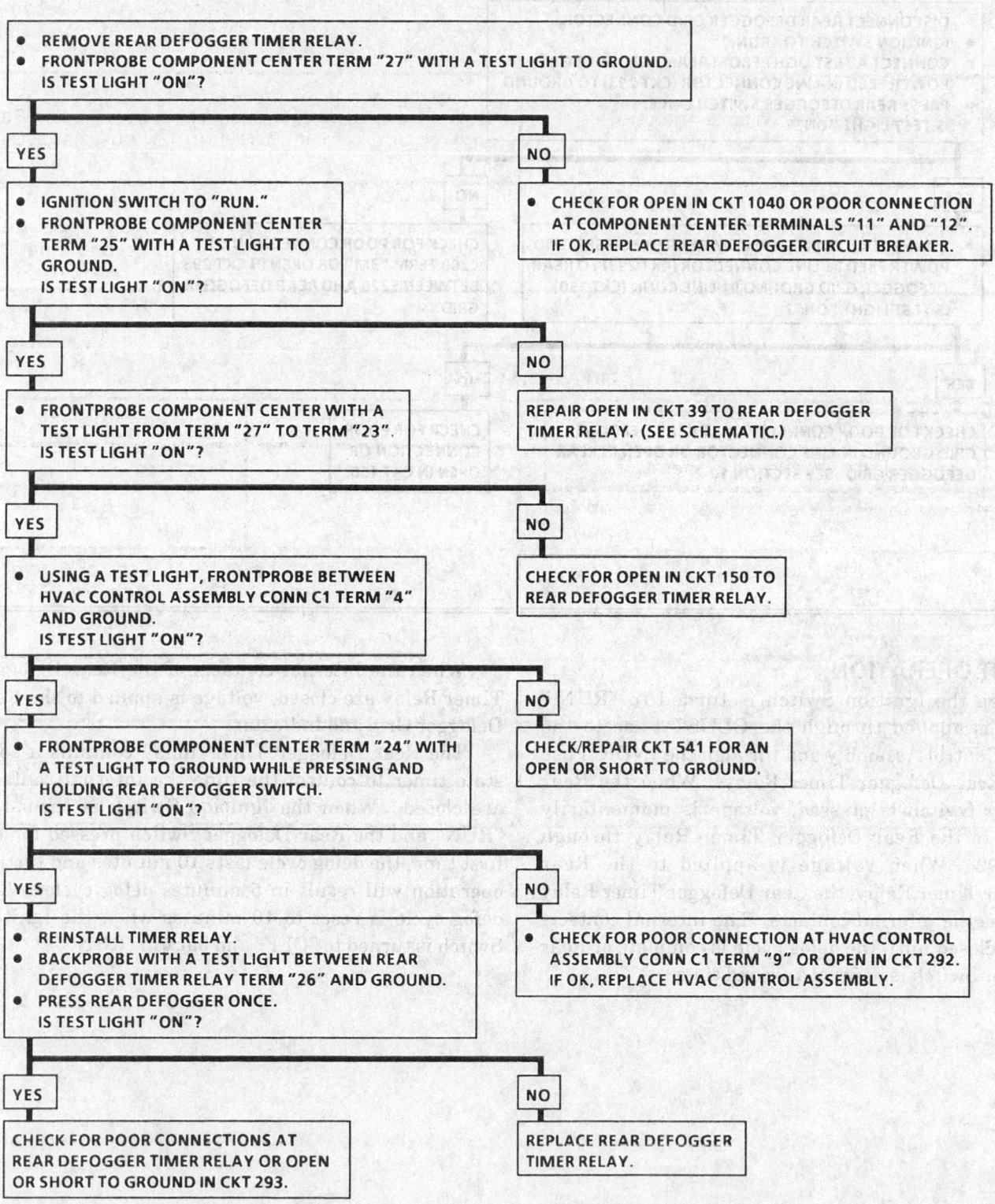

- REMOVE REAR DEFOGGER TIMER RELAY.
- FRONTPROBE COMPONENT CENTER TERM "27" WITH A TEST LIGHT TO GROUND.

IS TEST LIGHT "ON"?

YES

- IGNITION SWITCH TO "RUN."
- FRONTPROBE COMPONENT CENTER TERM "25" WITH A TEST LIGHT TO GROUND.

IS TEST LIGHT "ON"?

NO

- CHECK FOR OPEN IN CKT 1040 OR POOR CONNECTION AT COMPONENT CENTER TERMINALS "11" AND "12". IF OK, REPLACE REAR DEFOGGER CIRCUIT BREAKER.

YES

- FRONTPROBE COMPONENT CENTER WITH A TEST LIGHT FROM TERM "27" TO TERM "23".

IS TEST LIGHT "ON"?

NO

REPAIR OPEN IN CKT 39 TO REAR DEFOGGER TIMER RELAY. (SEE SCHEMATIC.)

YES

- USING A TEST LIGHT, FRONTPROBE BETWEEN HVAC CONTROL ASSEMBLY CONN C1 TERM "4" AND GROUND.

IS TEST LIGHT "ON"?

NO

CHECK FOR OPEN IN CKT 150 TO REAR DEFOGGER TIMER RELAY.

YES

- FRONTPROBE COMPONENT CENTER TERM "24" WITH A TEST LIGHT TO GROUND WHILE PRESSING AND HOLDING REAR DEFOGGER SWITCH.

IS TEST LIGHT "ON"?

NO

CHECK/REPAIR CKT 541 FOR AN OPEN OR SHORT TO GROUND.

YES

- REINSTALL TIMER RELAY.
- BACKPROBE WITH A TEST LIGHT BETWEEN REAR DEFOGGER TIMER RELAY TERM "26" AND GROUND.
- PRESS REAR DEFOGGER ONCE.

IS TEST LIGHT "ON"?

NO

- CHECK FOR POOR CONNECTION AT HVAC CONTROL ASSEMBLY CONN C1 TERM "9" OR OPEN IN CKT 292. IF OK, REPLACE HVAC CONTROL ASSEMBLY.

YES

CHECK FOR POOR CONNECTIONS AT REAR DEFOGGER TIMER RELAY OR OPEN OR SHORT TO GROUND IN CKT 293.

NO

REPLACE REAR DEFOGGER TIMER RELAY.

REAR DEFOGGER

CHART #2

REAR DEFOGGER GRID INOPERATIVE BUT INDICATOR OPERATES NORMALLY

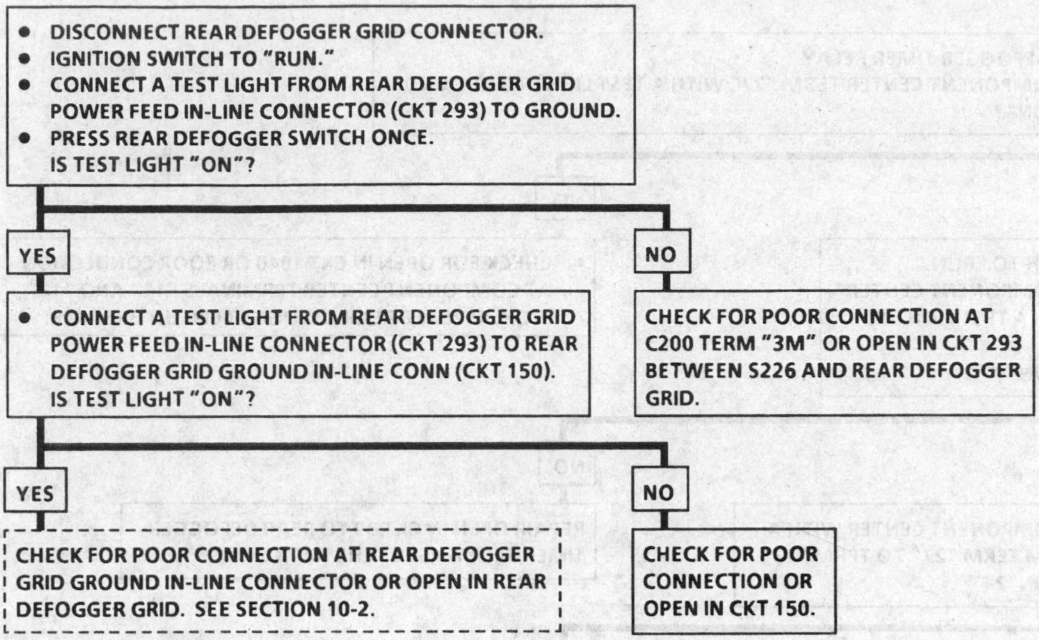
• DISCONNECT REAR DEFOGGER GRID CONNECTOR.
• IGNITION SWITCH TO "RUN."
• CONNECT A TEST LIGHT FROM REAR DEFOGGER GRID POWER FEED IN-LINE CONNECTOR (CKT 293) TO GROUND.
• PRESS REAR DEFOGGER SWITCH ONCE.
IS TEST LIGHT "ON"?
YES
NO
• CONNECT A TEST LIGHT FROM REAR DEFOGGER GRID POWER FEED IN-LINE CONNECTOR (CKT 293) TO REAR DEFOGGER GRID GROUND IN-LINE CONN (CKT 150).
IS TEST LIGHT "ON"?
CHECK FOR POOR CONNECTION AT C200 TERM "3M" OR OPEN IN CKT 293 BETWEEN S226 AND REAR DEFOGGER GRID.
YES
NO
CHECK FOR POOR CONNECTION AT REAR DEFOGGER GRID GROUND IN-LINE CONNECTOR OR OPEN IN REAR DEFOGGER GRID. SEE SECTION 10-2.
CHECK FOR POOR CONNECTION OR OPEN IN CKT 150.

CIRCUIT OPERATION

When the Ignition Switch is turned to "RUN," voltage is applied through the CLUST Fuse to the HVAC Control Assembly and through the INDIC Fuse to the Rear Defogger Timer Relay. When the Rear Defogger Switch is pressed, voltage is momentarily applied to the Rear Defogger Timer Relay through CKT 292. When voltage is applied to the Rear Defogger Timer Relay, the Rear Defogger Timer Relay will close the internal contacts. The internal contacts remain closed until the defog cycle is complete or Rear Defogger Switch is pressed a second time.

When the internal contacts of the Rear Defogger Timer Relay are closed, voltage is applied to the Rear Defogger Grid and Indicator.

The Rear Defogger Timer Relay contains a solid state timer to control the time the internal contacts are closed. When the Ignition Switch is turned to "RUN" and the Rear Defogger Switch pressed for the first time, the defog cycle lasts 10 minutes and further operation will result in 5 minutes defog cycles. The defog cycle is reset to 10 minutes when the Ignition Switch is turned to "OFF" and back to "RUN."

BLANK

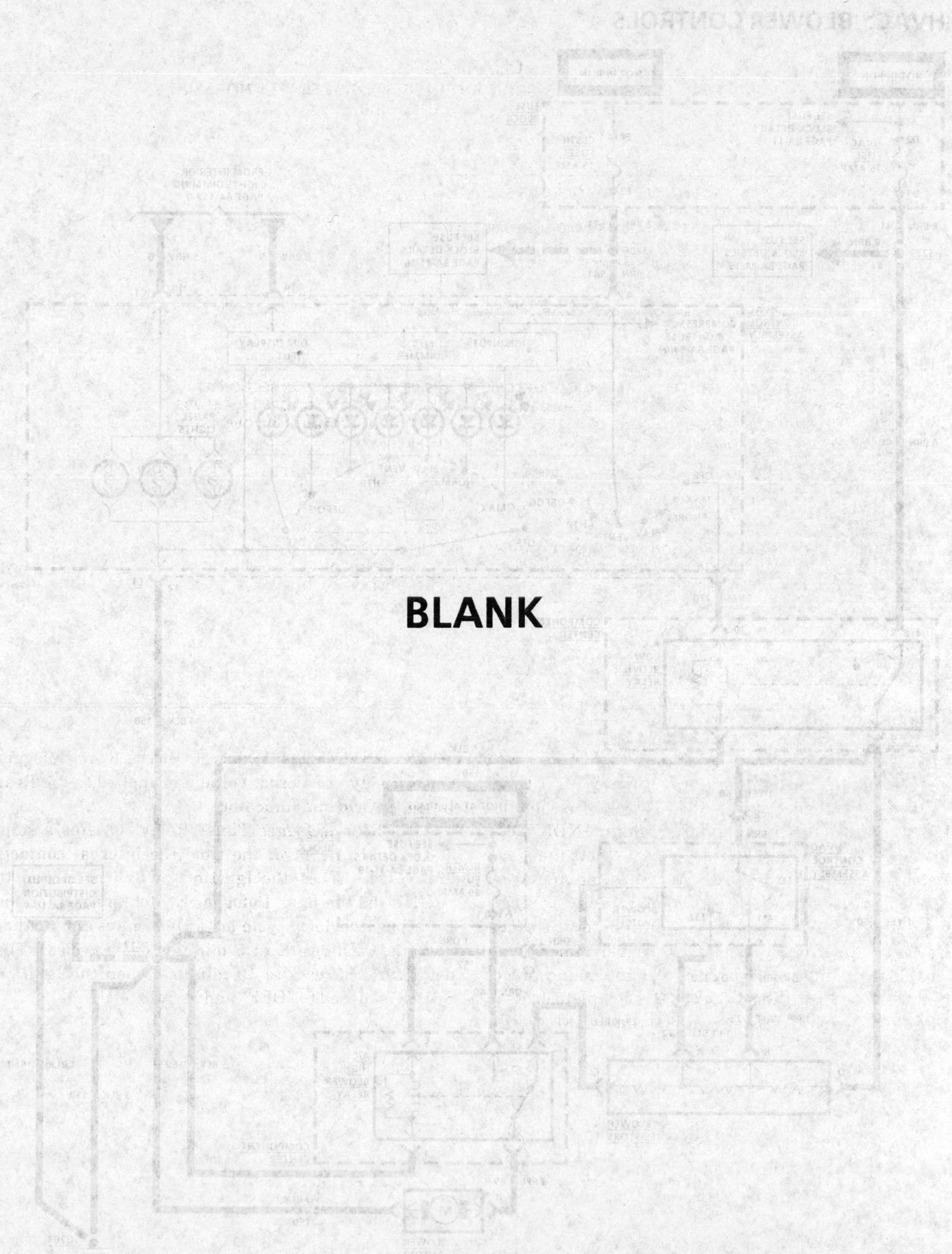

HVAC: BLOWER CONTROLS

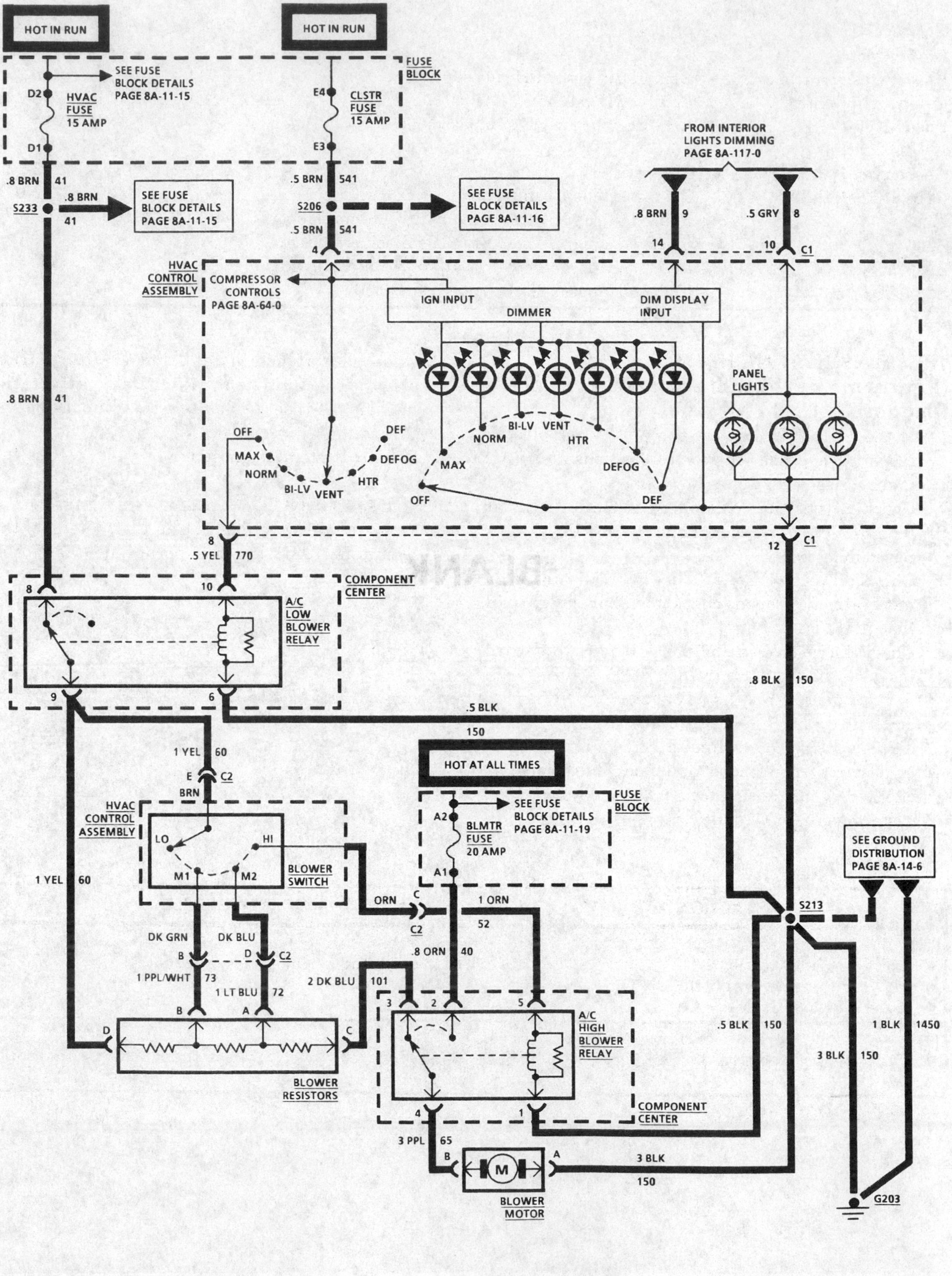
HOT IN RUN
HOT IN RUN
SEE FUSE BLOCK DETAILS PAGE 8A-11-15
D2
HVAC FUSE 15 AMP
D1
E4
CLSTR FUSE 15 AMP
E3
FUSE BLOCK
.8 BRN 41
S233
.8 BRN 41
SEE FUSE BLOCK DETAILS PAGE 8A-11-15
.5 BRN 541
S206
.5 BRN 541
SEE FUSE BLOCK DETAILS PAGE 8A-11-16
FROM INTERIOR LIGHTS DIMMING PAGE 8A-117-0
.8 BRN 9
.5 GRY 8
14
10
C1
4
HVAC CONTROL ASSEMBLY
COMPRESSOR CONTROLS PAGE 8A-64-0
IGN INPUT
DIMMER
DIM DISPLAY INPUT
PANEL LIGHTS
.8 BRN 41
OFF
MAX
NORM
BI-LV
VENT
HTR
DEFOG
DEF
NORM
BI-LV
VENT
HTR
MAX
DEFOG
OFF
DEF
8
.5 YEL 770
12
C1
8
10
COMPONENT CENTER
A/C LOW BLOWER RELAY
9
6
.8 BLK 150
.5 BLK 150
1 YEL 60
E
C2
BRN
HOT AT ALL TIMES
HVAC CONTROL ASSEMBLY
LO
HI
M1
M2
BLOWER SWITCH
SEE FUSE BLOCK DETAILS PAGE 8A-11-19
FUSE BLOCK
A2
BLMTR FUSE 20 AMP
A1
SEE GROUND DISTRIBUTION PAGE 8A-14-6
1 YEL 60
ORN
C
C2
1 ORN 52
S213
DK GRN
DK BLU
B
D
C2
1 PPL/WHT 73
1 LT BLU 72
.8 ORN 40
2 DK BLU 101
B
A
3
2
5
D
C
BLOWER RESISTORS
A/C HIGH BLOWER RELAY
COMPONENT CENTER
.5 BLK 150
3 BLK 150
1 BLK 1450
4
1
3 PPL 65
B
A
M
3 BLK 150
BLOWER MOTOR
G203

COMPONENT	LOCATION	201-PG	FIG.	CONN
Blower Motor	Behind I/P, lower RH side of plenum	11	36	
Blower Resistors	Behind I/P, lower RH side of plenum	11	36	202-36
Component Center	Behind RH side of I/P	11	36	202-14
Fuse Block	RH side of I/P, in I/P Compartment			
HVAC Control Assembly	Center of I/P	23	78	202-22
C100 (36 cavities)	RH side of dash, behind strut tower			202-0
G203	Behind I/P, on RH side of Steering Column Support	14	48	
S206	I/P Harn, approx 9 cm from Fuse Block breakout			
S213	I/P Harn, approx 8 cm from HVAC Control breakout			
S233	I/P Harn, approx 22 cm from Fuse Block			

TROUBLESHOOTING HINTS (Perform before beginning System Diagnosis)

1. If the HVAC Control Assembly is completely inoperative, check for poor connections at HVAC Control Assembly Connector C1.
2. Check for missing or damaged connector seals at the Blower Motor Resistor and Blower Motor High Speed Relay.
3. Check HVAC Fuse if the Blower Motor is inoperative. If open, check for short to ground though CKT 41.

- Check for a broken (or partially broken) wire inside of the insulation which could cause system malfunction but prove "GOOD" in a continuity/voltage check with a system disconnected. These circuits may be intermittent or resistive when loaded, and if possible, should be checked by monitoring for a voltage drop with the system operational (under load).
- Check for proper installation of aftermarket electronic equipment which may affect the integrity of other systems (see "Troubleshooting Procedures," page 8A-4-0).
- Refer to System Diagnosis.

SYSTEM DIAGNOSIS

- Perform the System Check and refer to the Symptom Table for the appropriate diagnostic procedure(s).

SYSTEM CHECK

ACTION	NORMAL RESULTS
[1] • Ignition Switch to "RUN." • HVAC Control Assembly to "UPPER." • Blower Switch to "LO."	Blower Motor is "ON" at low speed.
[2] • Cycle Blower Switch from "LO" to "HI" and back to "LO."	Blower Motor cycles from low speed to high and back to low.

HVAC: BLOWER CONTROLS

SYMPTOM TABLE

SYMPTOM	PROCEDURE	PAGE NUMBER
Blower Motor inoperative or will not operate at low speed.	Chart #1	8A-63-2
Blower Motor goes to high speed as soon as HVAC Control Assembly is activated.	Chart #2	8A-63-4
Blower Motor will operate at low, but not at medium speeds.	Chart #3	8A-63-4
Blower Motor will operate at low and medium speeds, but not at high speed.	Chart #4	8A-63-5
Blower on "HIGH" at all times.	• Check CKT 52 for short to B+. • Check CKT 65 for short to B+. If OK, replace High Blower Relay.	

CHART #1

BLOWER MOTOR INOPERATIVE OR WILL NOT OPERATE AT LOW SPEED

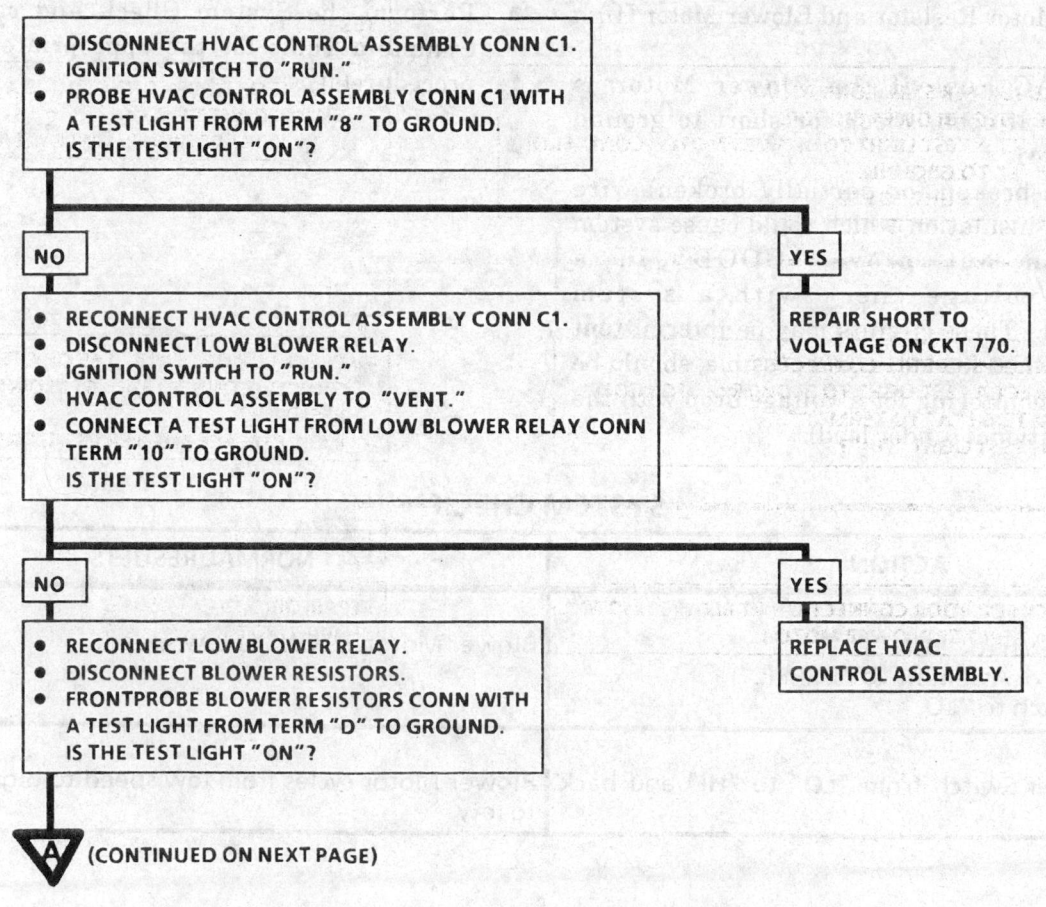

- DISCONNECT HVAC CONTROL ASSEMBLY CONN C1.
- IGNITION SWITCH TO "RUN."
- PROBE HVAC CONTROL ASSEMBLY CONN C1 WITH A TEST LIGHT FROM TERM "8" TO GROUND.

IS THE TEST LIGHT "ON"?

YES: REPAIR SHORT TO VOLTAGE ON CKT 770.

NO:

- RECONNECT HVAC CONTROL ASSEMBLY CONN C1.
- DISCONNECT LOW BLOWER RELAY.
- IGNITION SWITCH TO "RUN."
- HVAC CONTROL ASSEMBLY TO "VENT."
- CONNECT A TEST LIGHT FROM LOW BLOWER RELAY CONN TERM "10" TO GROUND.

IS THE TEST LIGHT "ON"?

YES: REPLACE HVAC CONTROL ASSEMBLY.

NO:

- RECONNECT LOW BLOWER RELAY.
- DISCONNECT BLOWER RESISTORS.
- FRONTPROBE BLOWER RESISTORS CONN WITH A TEST LIGHT FROM TERM "D" TO GROUND.

IS THE TEST LIGHT "ON"?

A (CONTINUED ON NEXT PAGE)

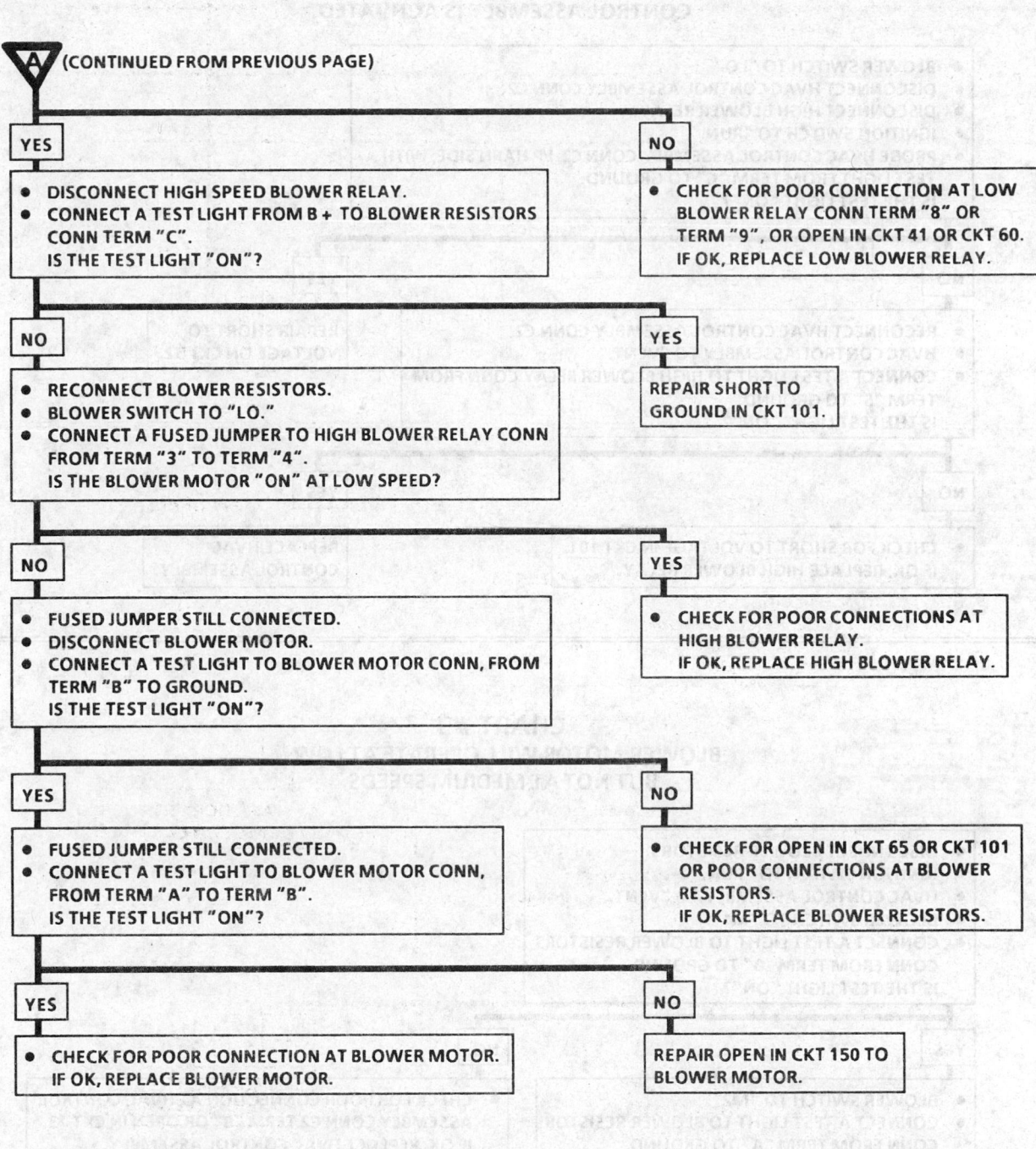

A (CONTINUED FROM PREVIOUS PAGE)

YES

- DISCONNECT HIGH SPEED BLOWER RELAY.
- CONNECT A TEST LIGHT FROM B + TO BLOWER RESISTORS CONN TERM "C".
  IS THE TEST LIGHT "ON"?

NO

- CHECK FOR POOR CONNECTION AT LOW BLOWER RELAY CONN TERM "8" OR TERM "9", OR OPEN IN CKT 41 OR CKT 60.
  IF OK, REPLACE LOW BLOWER RELAY.

(Test light "ON"?)

NO

- RECONNECT BLOWER RESISTORS.
- BLOWER SWITCH TO "LO."
- CONNECT A FUSED JUMPER TO HIGH BLOWER RELAY CONN FROM TERM "3" TO TERM "4".
  IS THE BLOWER MOTOR "ON" AT LOW SPEED?

YES

REPAIR SHORT TO GROUND IN CKT 101.

(Blower motor "ON" at low speed?)

NO

- FUSED JUMPER STILL CONNECTED.
- DISCONNECT BLOWER MOTOR.
- CONNECT A TEST LIGHT TO BLOWER MOTOR CONN, FROM TERM "B" TO GROUND.
  IS THE TEST LIGHT "ON"?

YES

- CHECK FOR POOR CONNECTIONS AT HIGH BLOWER RELAY.
  IF OK, REPLACE HIGH BLOWER RELAY.

(Test light "ON"?)

YES

- FUSED JUMPER STILL CONNECTED.
- CONNECT A TEST LIGHT TO BLOWER MOTOR CONN, FROM TERM "A" TO TERM "B".
  IS THE TEST LIGHT "ON"?

NO

- CHECK FOR OPEN IN CKT 65 OR CKT 101 OR POOR CONNECTIONS AT BLOWER RESISTORS.
  IF OK, REPLACE BLOWER RESISTORS.

(Test light "ON"?)

YES

- CHECK FOR POOR CONNECTION AT BLOWER MOTOR.
  IF OK, REPLACE BLOWER MOTOR.

NO

REPAIR OPEN IN CKT 150 TO BLOWER MOTOR.

HVAC: BLOWER CONTROLS

CHART #2

BLOWER MOTOR GOES TO HIGH SPEED AS SOON AS HVAC CONTROL ASSEMBLY IS ACTIVATED

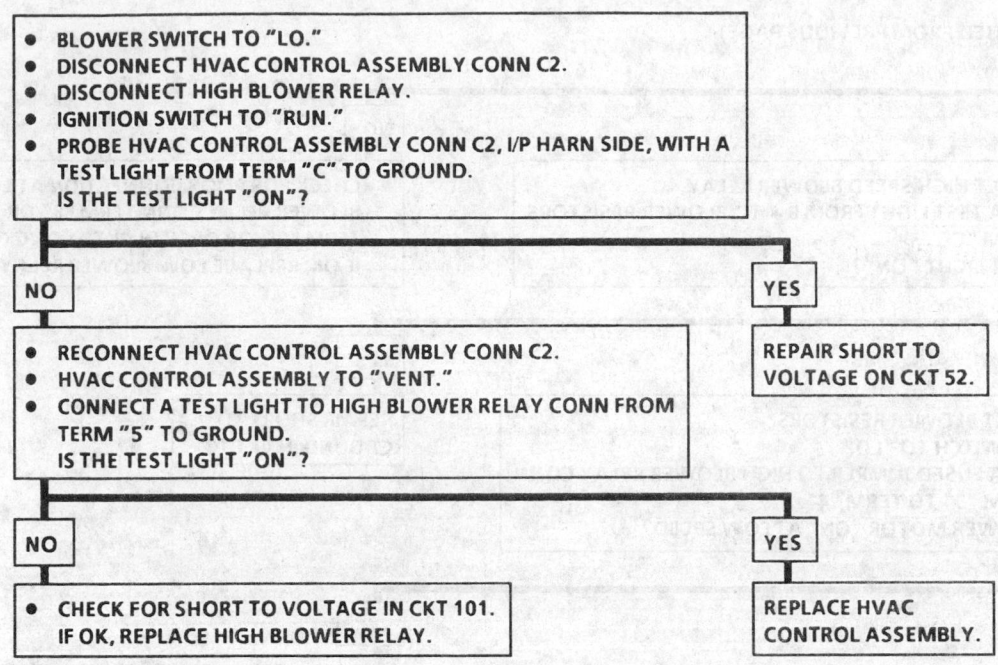

- BLOWER SWITCH TO "LO."
- DISCONNECT HVAC CONTROL ASSEMBLY CONN C2.
- DISCONNECT HIGH BLOWER RELAY.
- IGNITION SWITCH TO "RUN."
- PROBE HVAC CONTROL ASSEMBLY CONN C2, I/P HARN SIDE, WITH A TEST LIGHT FROM TERM "C" TO GROUND.
  IS THE TEST LIGHT "ON"?

NO

- RECONNECT HVAC CONTROL ASSEMBLY CONN C2.
- HVAC CONTROL ASSEMBLY TO "VENT."
- CONNECT A TEST LIGHT TO HIGH BLOWER RELAY CONN FROM TERM "5" TO GROUND.
  IS THE TEST LIGHT "ON"?

  NO

  - CHECK FOR SHORT TO VOLTAGE IN CKT 101.
    IF OK, REPLACE HIGH BLOWER RELAY.

  YES

  REPLACE HVAC CONTROL ASSEMBLY.

YES

REPAIR SHORT TO VOLTAGE ON CKT 52.

CHART #3

BLOWER MOTOR WILL OPERATE AT LOW, BUT NOT AT MEDIUM SPEEDS

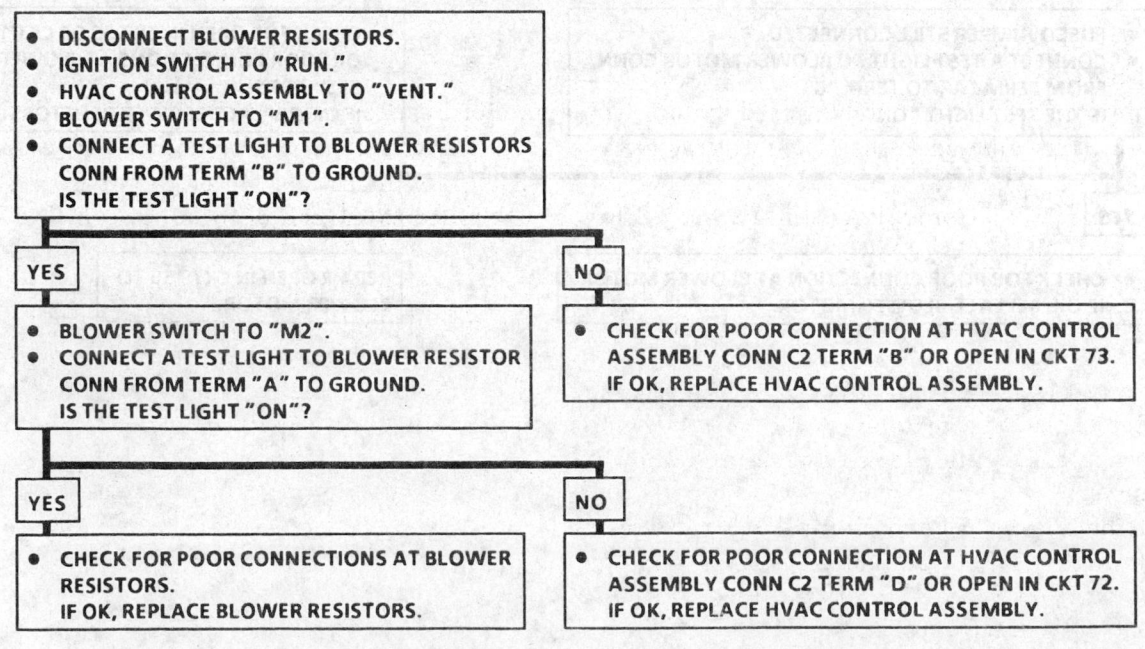

- DISCONNECT BLOWER RESISTORS.
- IGNITION SWITCH TO "RUN."
- HVAC CONTROL ASSEMBLY TO "VENT."
- BLOWER SWITCH TO "M1".
- CONNECT A TEST LIGHT TO BLOWER RESISTORS CONN FROM TERM "B" TO GROUND.
  IS THE TEST LIGHT "ON"?

YES

- BLOWER SWITCH TO "M2".
- CONNECT A TEST LIGHT TO BLOWER RESISTOR CONN FROM TERM "A" TO GROUND.
  IS THE TEST LIGHT "ON"?

  YES

  - CHECK FOR POOR CONNECTIONS AT BLOWER RESISTORS.
    IF OK, REPLACE BLOWER RESISTORS.

  NO

  - CHECK FOR POOR CONNECTION AT HVAC CONTROL ASSEMBLY CONN C2 TERM "D" OR OPEN IN CKT 72.
    IF OK, REPLACE HVAC CONTROL ASSEMBLY.

NO

- CHECK FOR POOR CONNECTION AT HVAC CONTROL ASSEMBLY CONN C2 TERM "B" OR OPEN IN CKT 73.
  IF OK, REPLACE HVAC CONTROL ASSEMBLY.

CHART #4

BLOWER MOTOR WILL OPERATE AT LOW AND MEDIUM SPEEDS, BUT NOT AT HIGH SPEED

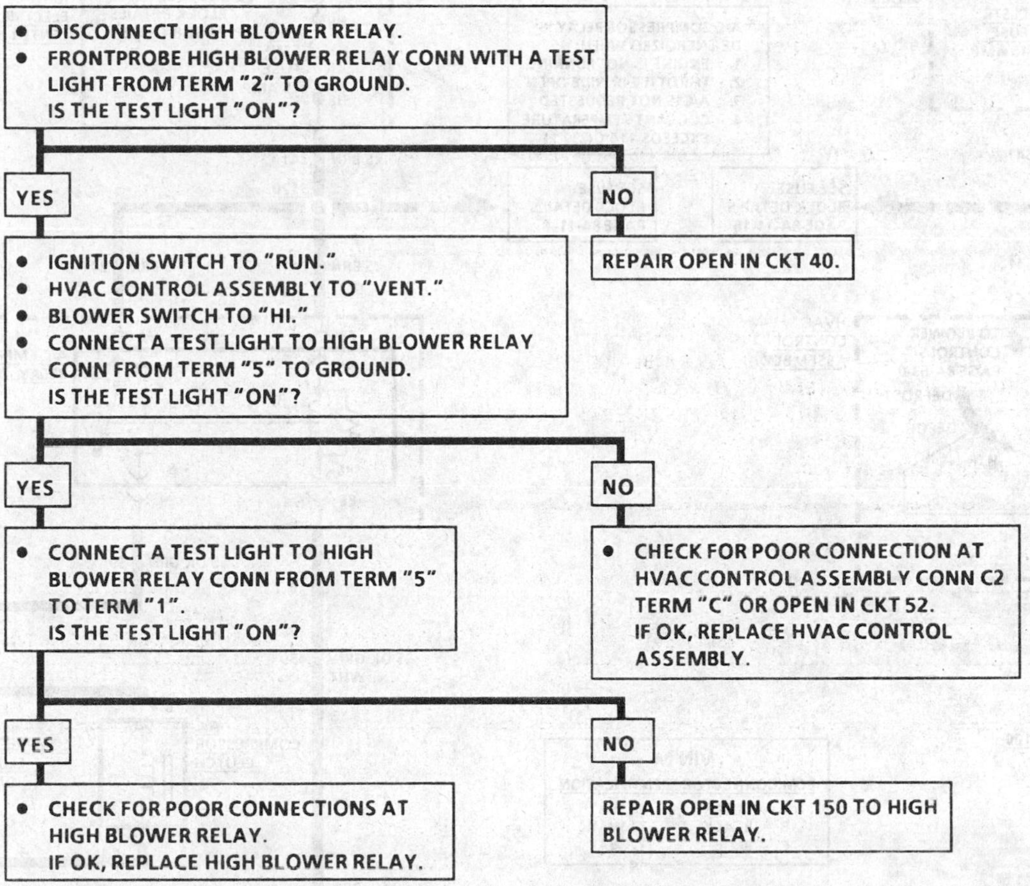
• DISCONNECT HIGH BLOWER RELAY.
• FRONTPROBE HIGH BLOWER RELAY CONN WITH A TEST LIGHT FROM TERM "2" TO GROUND. IS THE TEST LIGHT "ON"?
YES
NO
REPAIR OPEN IN CKT 40.
• IGNITION SWITCH TO "RUN."
• HVAC CONTROL ASSEMBLY TO "VENT."
• BLOWER SWITCH TO "HI."
• CONNECT A TEST LIGHT TO HIGH BLOWER RELAY CONN FROM TERM "5" TO GROUND. IS THE TEST LIGHT "ON"?
YES
NO
• CONNECT A TEST LIGHT TO HIGH BLOWER RELAY CONN FROM TERM "5" TO TERM "1". IS THE TEST LIGHT "ON"?
• CHECK FOR POOR CONNECTION AT HVAC CONTROL ASSEMBLY CONN C2 TERM "C" OR OPEN IN CKT 52. IF OK, REPLACE HVAC CONTROL ASSEMBLY.
YES
NO
• CHECK FOR POOR CONNECTIONS AT HIGH BLOWER RELAY. IF OK, REPLACE HIGH BLOWER RELAY.
REPAIR OPEN IN CKT 150 TO HIGH BLOWER RELAY.

CIRCUIT OPERATION

BLOWER MOTOR

The Blower Motor is a variable speed motor. The higher the voltage applied to the motor, the faster the speed.

With the HVAC Control Assembly in "OFF," voltage is applied to the Blower Motor Low Speed Relay coil. The relay is energized and voltage to the Blower Switch is removed. No voltage is supplied to the Blower Motor.

When any other mode except "OFF" is selected, the Blower Motor Low Speed Relay is de-energized and voltage is applied to the Blower Switch and Blower Motor Resistor.

When the Blower Switch is in "LO," voltage is applied through the Blower Motor Resistor and the Blower Motor High Speed Relay to the Blower Motor. The Blower Motor runs at low speed.

As the Blower Switch is moved through positions "M1" and "M2", the switch bypasses part of the Blower Motor Resistor, allowing more voltage to be applied to the Blower Motor, which will increase its speed.

When the Blower Motor Switch is in "HI," voltage is applied to the coil of the Blower Motor High Speed Relay. The Blower Motor High Speed Relay is energized removing the Blower Motor Resistor from the circuit. Battery voltage is then applied directly to the Blower Motor though the Blower Motor High Speed Relay contacts. The motor runs at maximum speed.

HVAC COMPRESSOR CONTROLS
VIN M

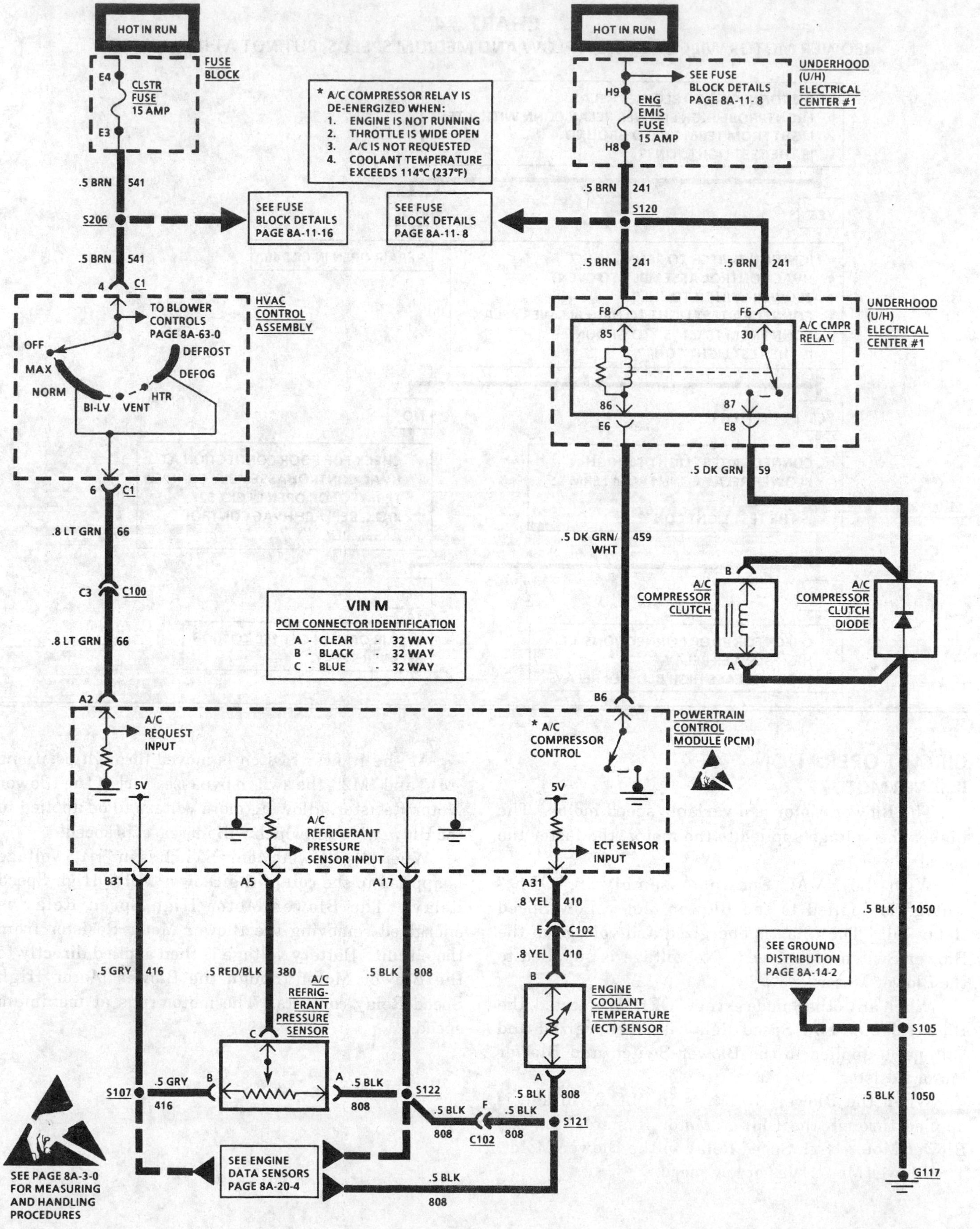
HOT IN RUN
FUSE BLOCK
E4
CLSTR FUSE 15 AMP
E3
.5 BRN 541
S206
SEE FUSE BLOCK DETAILS PAGE 8A-11-16
.5 BRN 541
4 C1
TO BLOWER CONTROLS PAGE 8A-63-0
HVAC CONTROL ASSEMBLY
OFF
MAX
NORM
BI-LV
VENT
HTR
DEFOG
DEFROST
6 C1
.8 LT GRN 66
C3 C100
.8 LT GRN 66
* A/C COMPRESSOR RELAY IS DE-ENERGIZED WHEN:
1. ENGINE IS NOT RUNNING
2. THROTTLE IS WIDE OPEN
3. A/C IS NOT REQUESTED
4. COOLANT TEMPERATURE EXCEEDS 114°C (237°F)
VIN M
PCM CONNECTOR IDENTIFICATION
A - CLEAR - 32 WAY
B - BLACK - 32 WAY
C - BLUE - 32 WAY
HOT IN RUN
SEE FUSE BLOCK DETAILS PAGE 8A-11-8
UNDERHOOD (U/H) ELECTRICAL CENTER #1
H9
ENG EMIS FUSE 15 AMP
H8
.5 BRN 241
S120
SEE FUSE BLOCK DETAILS PAGE 8A-11-8
.5 BRN 241
.5 BRN 241
F8
F6
85
30
A/C CMPR RELAY
UNDERHOOD (U/H) ELECTRICAL CENTER #1
86
87
E6
E8
.5 DK GRN 59
.5 DK GRN/WHT 459
B
A/C COMPRESSOR CLUTCH
A/C COMPRESSOR CLUTCH DIODE
A
A2
B6
A/C REQUEST INPUT
5V
* A/C COMPRESSOR CONTROL
POWERTRAIN CONTROL MODULE (PCM)
A/C REFRIGERANT PRESSURE SENSOR INPUT
5V
ECT SENSOR INPUT
B31
A5
A17
A31
.8 YEL 410
E C102
.8 YEL 410
B
ENGINE COOLANT TEMPERATURE (ECT) SENSOR
A
.5 GRY 416
.5 RED/BLK 380
.5 BLK 808
A/C REFRIG-ERANT PRESSURE SENSOR
C
S107
.5 GRY 416
B
A
.5 BLK 808
S122
.5 BLK 808
F C102
.5 BLK 808
.5 BLK 808
S121
SEE ENGINE DATA SENSORS PAGE 8A-20-4
.5 BLK 808
.5 BLK 1050
SEE GROUND DISTRIBUTION PAGE 8A-14-2
S105
.5 BLK 1050
G117
SEE PAGE 8A-3-0 FOR MEASURING AND HANDLING PROCEDURES

HVAC COMPRESSOR CONTROLS

VIN L

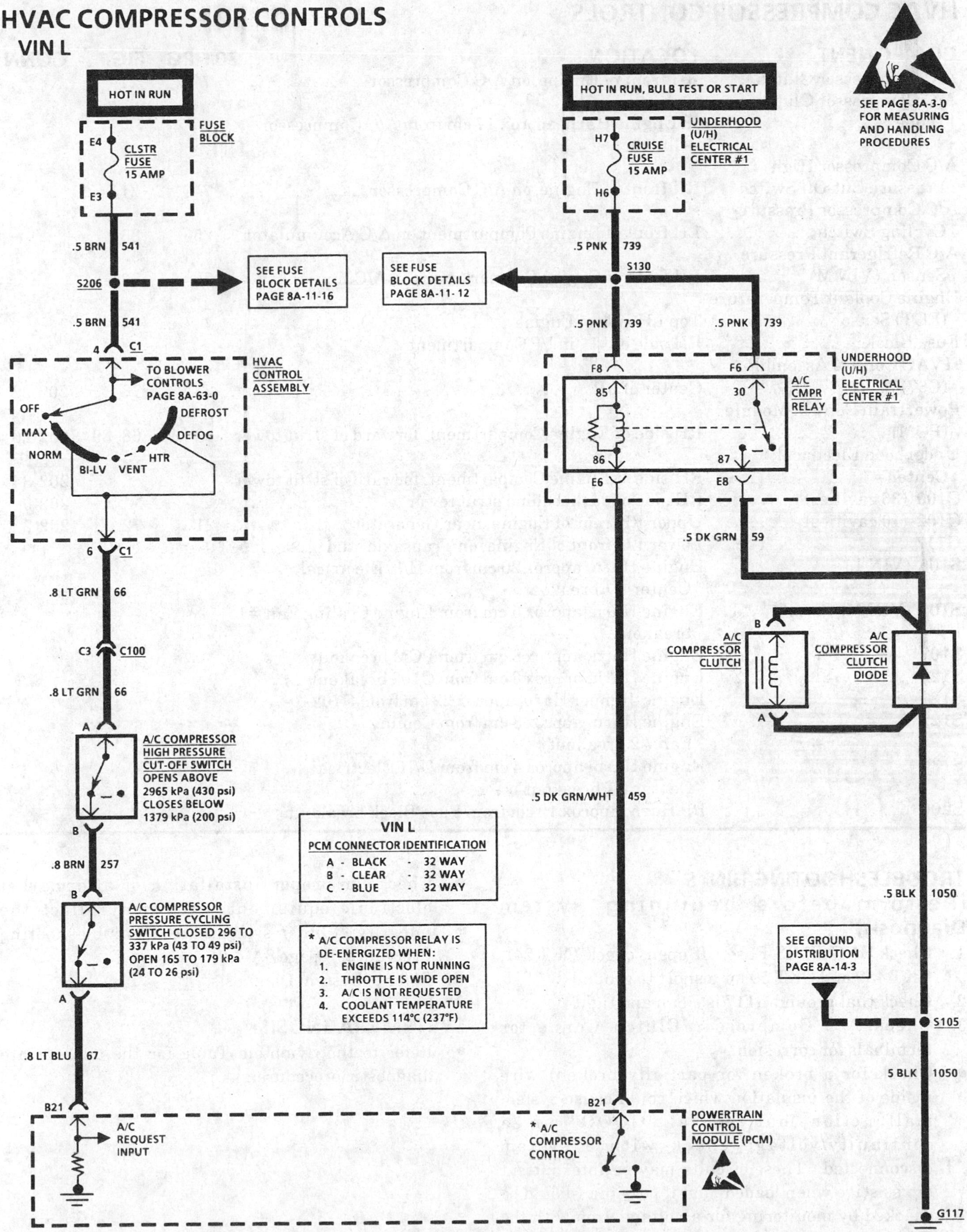
HOT IN RUN
FUSE BLOCK
E4
CLSTR FUSE 15 AMP
E3
.5 BRN 541
S206
SEE FUSE BLOCK DETAILS PAGE 8A-11-16
.5 BRN 541
4 C1
TO BLOWER CONTROLS PAGE 8A-63-0
HVAC CONTROL ASSEMBLY
OFF
MAX
NORM
BI-LV
VENT
HTR
DEFOG
DEFROST
6 C1
.8 LT GRN 66
C3 C100
.8 LT GRN 66
A
A/C COMPRESSOR HIGH PRESSURE CUT-OFF SWITCH OPENS ABOVE 2965 kPa (430 psi) CLOSES BELOW 1379 kPa (200 psi)
B
.8 BRN 257
B
A/C COMPRESSOR PRESSURE CYCLING SWITCH CLOSED 296 TO 337 kPa (43 TO 49 psi) OPEN 165 TO 179 kPa (24 TO 26 psi)
A
.8 LT BLU 67
B21
A/C REQUEST INPUT
HOT IN RUN, BULB TEST OR START
UNDERHOOD (U/H) ELECTRICAL CENTER #1
H7
CRUISE FUSE 15 AMP
H6
.5 PNK 739
S130
SEE FUSE BLOCK DETAILS PAGE 8A-11- 12
.5 PNK 739
.5 PNK 739
F8
F6
85
30
A/C CMPR RELAY
86
87
E6
E8
UNDERHOOD (U/H) ELECTRICAL CENTER #1
.5 DK GRN 59
B
A/C COMPRESSOR CLUTCH
A
A/C COMPRESSOR CLUTCH DIODE
.5 DK GRN/WHT 459
VIN L
PCM CONNECTOR IDENTIFICATION
A - BLACK - 32 WAY
B - CLEAR - 32 WAY
C - BLUE - 32 WAY
* A/C COMPRESSOR RELAY IS DE-ENERGIZED WHEN:
1. ENGINE IS NOT RUNNING
2. THROTTLE IS WIDE OPEN
3. A/C IS NOT REQUESTED
4. COOLANT TEMPERATURE EXCEEDS 114°C (237°F)
.5 BLK 1050
SEE GROUND DISTRIBUTION PAGE 8A-14-3
S105
.5 BLK 1050
B21
* A/C COMPRESSOR CONTROL
POWERTRAIN CONTROL MODULE (PCM)
G117
SEE PAGE 8A-3-0 FOR MEASURING AND HANDLING PROCEDURES

HVAC COMPRESSOR CONTROLS

COMPONENT	LOCATION	201-PG	FIG.	CONN
A/C Compressor Clutch	RH front of Engine, on A/C Compressor	7	21	
A/C Compressor Clutch Diode	In Engine Harn, approx 17 cm from A/C Compressor Clutch			
A/C Compressor High Pressure Cut-Off Switch	RH front of Engine, on A/C Compressor	7	21	
A/C Compressor Pressure Cycling Switch	LH front of Engine Compartment on A/C Accumulator	25	83	
A/C Refrigerant Pressure Sensor (VIN M)	LH front of Engine Compartment, on A/C line	25	83	
Engine Coolant Temperature (ECT) Sensor	Top LH side of Engine	7	24	
Fuse Block	RH side of I/P, in I/P Compartment			
HVAC Control Assembly (C67)	Center of I/P	23	78	202-22
Powertrain Control Module (PCM)	RH side of Engine Compartment, forward of strut tower	19	68, 69	202-26
Underhood Electrical Center #1	RH side of Engine Compartment, forward of strut tower			202-34
C100 (36 cavities)	RH side of dash, behind strut tower			202-0
C102 (10 cavities)	Upper RH rear of Engine, near Generator	21	72	202-2
G117	Lower LH front of Engine, on Transaxle stud	0	1	
S105 (VIN L)	Engine Harn, approx 20 cm from U/H Electrical Center #1 breakout			
S105 (VIN M)	Engine Harn, approx 5 cm from Engine Cooling Fan #1 breakout			
S107	Engine Harn, approx 8 cm from PCM breakout			
S120	Engine Harn, approx 6 cm from C102 breakout			
S121	Engine Jumper Harn, approx 22 cm from C102			
S122	Engine Harn, approx 8 cm from Cooling Fan #2 breakout			
S130	Engine Harn, approx 4 cm from U/H Electrical Center #1 breakout			
S206	I/P Harn, approx 10 cm from Fuse Block breakout			

TROUBLESHOOTING HINTS (Perform before beginning System Diagnosis)

1. Check ENG EMIS Fuse. If open, check CKT 241, CKT 459 and CKT 59 for a short to ground.
2. Check that ground G117 is clean and tight.
3. Check A/C Compressor Clutch Connector terminals for corrosion.

- Check for a broken (or partially broken) wire inside of the insulation which could cause system malfunction but prove "GOOD" in a continuity/voltage check with a system disconnected. These circuits may be intermittent or resistive when loaded, and if possible, should be checked by monitoring for a voltage drop with the system operational (under load).
- Check for proper installation of aftermarket electronic equipment which may affect the integrity of other systems (see "Troubleshooting Procedures," page 8A-4-0).
- Refer to System Diagnosis.

SYSTEM DIAGNOSIS

- Refer to the Symptom Table for the appropriate diagnostic procedure(s).

SYMPTOM TABLE

SYMPTOM	PROCEDURE	PAGE NUMBER
A/C Compressor Clutch never engages.	Chart #1	8A-64-3
A/C Compressor Clutch always engaged.	Chart #2	8A-64-5
A/C Compressor Clutch engages with HVAC Control Assembly in "VENT" or "HTR."	Replace HVAC Control Assembly.	
Engine stalls or idles roughly when the A/C Compressor is engaged.	See SECTION 6E.	

CHART #1
A/C COMPRESSOR CLUTCH NEVER ENGAGES

IMPORTANT:

- TO AVOID MISDIAGNOSIS:
  1. CHECK FOR A/C DIAGNOSTIC TROUBLE CODES (DTC). REFER TO SECTION 6E.
  2. CHECK THAT THE A/C REFRIGERANT SYSTEM IS IN PROPER MECHANICAL CONDITION (NO LEAKS, CORRECT REFRIGERANT LEVEL, ETC.) BEFORE PROCEEDING. REFER TO "HEATING AND AIR CONDITIONING" (SECTION 1B).

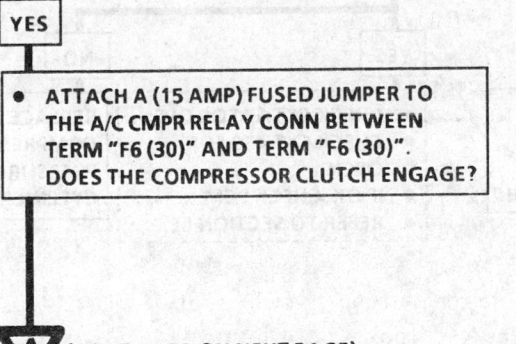

- REMOVE A/C CMPR RELAY.
- IGNITION SWITCH TO "RUN."
- PROBE WITH A TEST LIGHT A/C CMPR RELAY CONN BETWEEN TERM "F6 (30)" AND GROUND.
- PROBE BETWEEN TERM "F8 (85)" AND GROUND.

DOES THE TEST LIGHT ILLUMINATE IN BOTH CASES?

YES

- ATTACH A (15 AMP) FUSED JUMPER TO THE A/C CMPR RELAY CONN BETWEEN TERM "F6 (30)" AND TERM "F6 (30)".

DOES THE COMPRESSOR CLUTCH ENGAGE?

NO

- (VIN M) REPAIR OPEN IN CKT 241 FROM S120 TO RELAY.
- (VIN L) REPAIR OPEN IN CKT 739 FROM S130 TO RELAY.

A (CONTINUED ON NEXT PAGE)

HVAC COMPRESSOR CONTROLS

CHART #1 (continued)
A/C COMPRESSOR CLUTCH NEVER ENGAGES

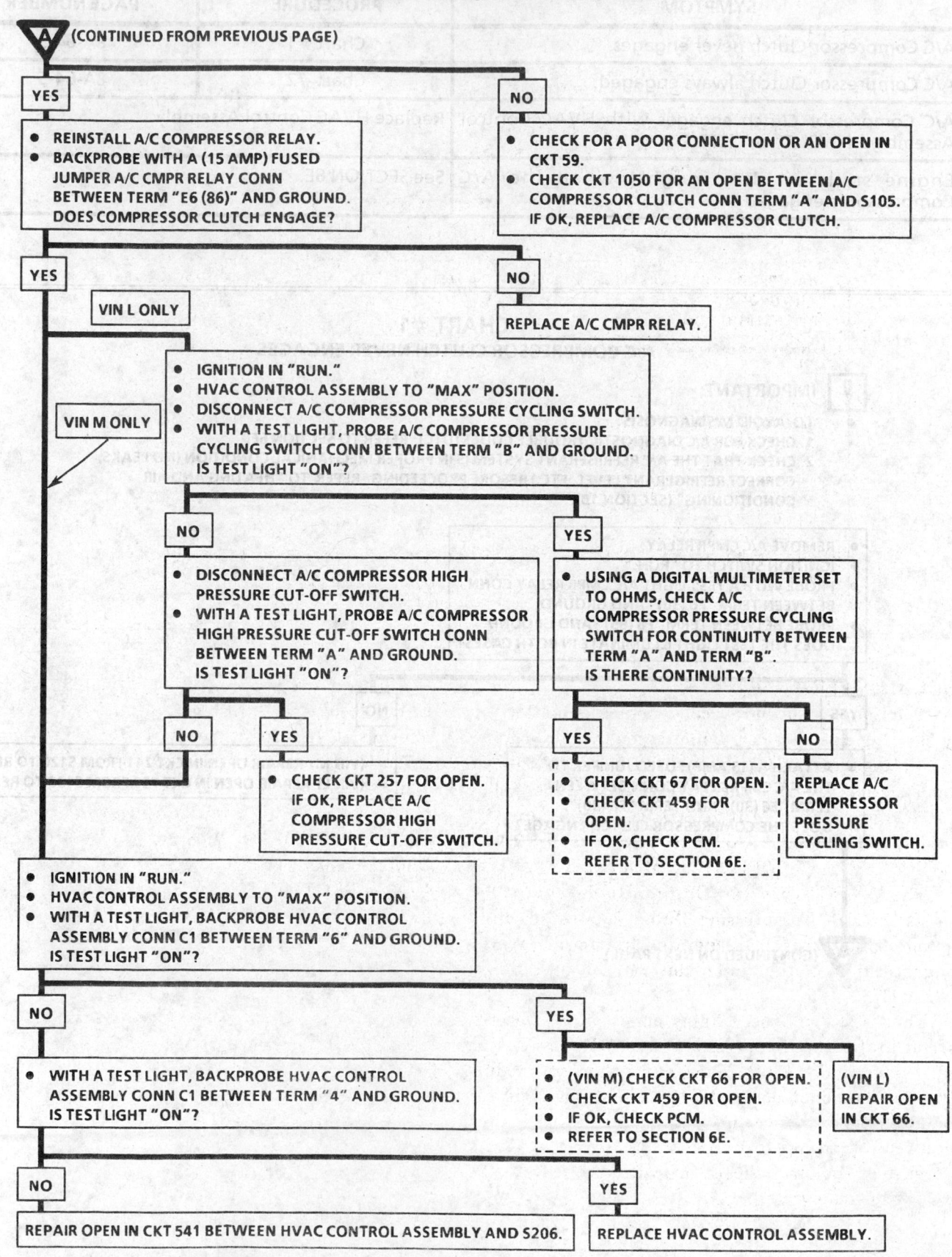

A (CONTINUED FROM PREVIOUS PAGE)

YES
- REINSTALL A/C COMPRESSOR RELAY.
- BACKPROBE WITH A (15 AMP) FUSED JUMPER A/C CMPR RELAY CONN BETWEEN TERM "E6 (86)" AND GROUND. DOES COMPRESSOR CLUTCH ENGAGE?

NO
- CHECK FOR A POOR CONNECTION OR AN OPEN IN CKT 59.
- CHECK CKT 1050 FOR AN OPEN BETWEEN A/C COMPRESSOR CLUTCH CONN TERM "A" AND S105. IF OK, REPLACE A/C COMPRESSOR CLUTCH.

YES

VIN L ONLY
- IGNITION IN "RUN."
- HVAC CONTROL ASSEMBLY TO "MAX" POSITION.
- DISCONNECT A/C COMPRESSOR PRESSURE CYCLING SWITCH.
- WITH A TEST LIGHT, PROBE A/C COMPRESSOR PRESSURE CYCLING SWITCH CONN BETWEEN TERM "B" AND GROUND. IS TEST LIGHT "ON"?

VIN M ONLY

NO

REPLACE A/C CMPR RELAY.

NO
- DISCONNECT A/C COMPRESSOR HIGH PRESSURE CUT-OFF SWITCH.
- WITH A TEST LIGHT, PROBE A/C COMPRESSOR HIGH PRESSURE CUT-OFF SWITCH CONN BETWEEN TERM "A" AND GROUND. IS TEST LIGHT "ON"?

YES
- USING A DIGITAL MULTIMETER SET TO OHMS, CHECK A/C COMPRESSOR PRESSURE CYCLING SWITCH FOR CONTINUITY BETWEEN TERM "A" AND TERM "B". IS THERE CONTINUITY?

NO

YES
- CHECK CKT 257 FOR OPEN. IF OK, REPLACE A/C COMPRESSOR HIGH PRESSURE CUT-OFF SWITCH.

YES
- CHECK CKT 67 FOR OPEN.
- CHECK CKT 459 FOR OPEN.
- IF OK, CHECK PCM.
- REFER TO SECTION 6E.

NO

REPLACE A/C COMPRESSOR PRESSURE CYCLING SWITCH.

- IGNITION IN "RUN."
- HVAC CONTROL ASSEMBLY TO "MAX" POSITION.
- WITH A TEST LIGHT, BACKPROBE HVAC CONTROL ASSEMBLY CONN C1 BETWEEN TERM "6" AND GROUND. IS TEST LIGHT "ON"?

NO
- WITH A TEST LIGHT, BACKPROBE HVAC CONTROL ASSEMBLY CONN C1 BETWEEN TERM "4" AND GROUND. IS TEST LIGHT "ON"?

YES
- (VIN M) CHECK CKT 66 FOR OPEN.
- CHECK CKT 459 FOR OPEN.
- IF OK, CHECK PCM.
- REFER TO SECTION 6E.

(VIN L) REPAIR OPEN IN CKT 66.

NO

REPAIR OPEN IN CKT 541 BETWEEN HVAC CONTROL ASSEMBLY AND S206.

YES

REPLACE HVAC CONTROL ASSEMBLY.

CHART #2
A/C COMPRESSOR CLUTCH ALWAYS ENGAGED

IMPORTANT:

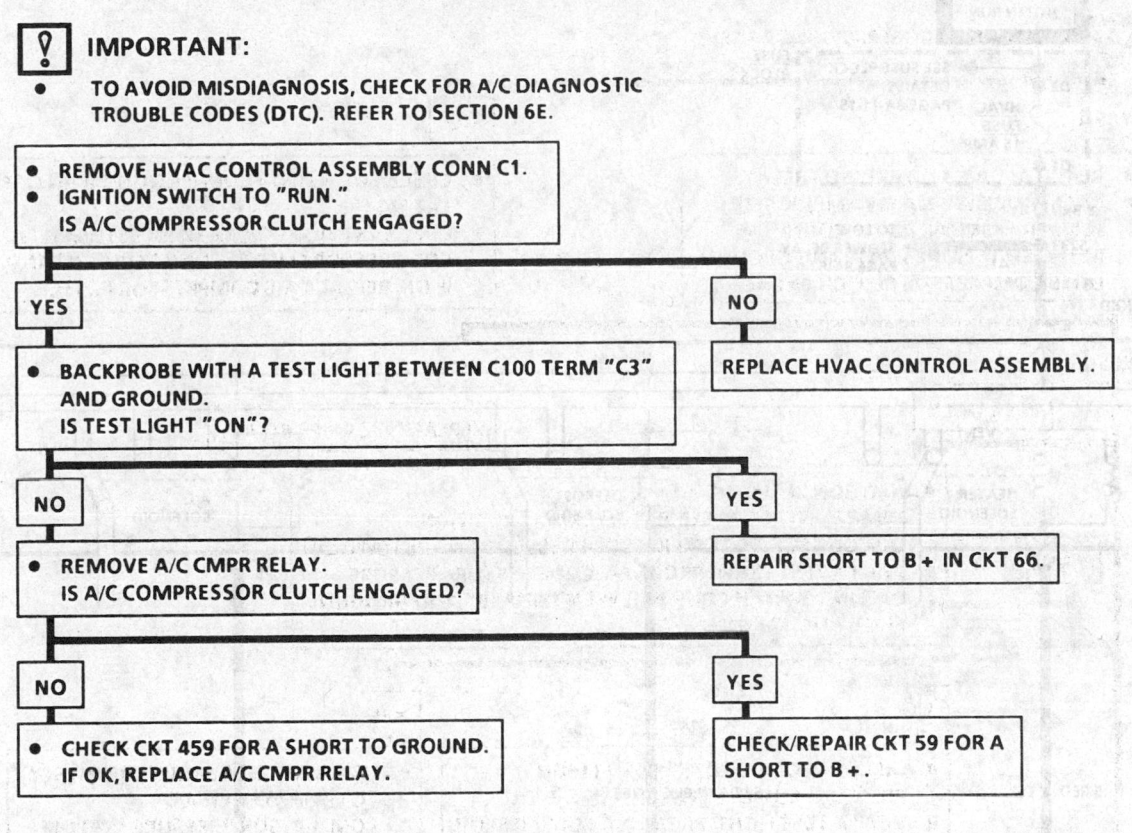

- TO AVOID MISDIAGNOSIS, CHECK FOR A/C DIAGNOSTIC TROUBLE CODES (DTC). REFER TO SECTION 6E.

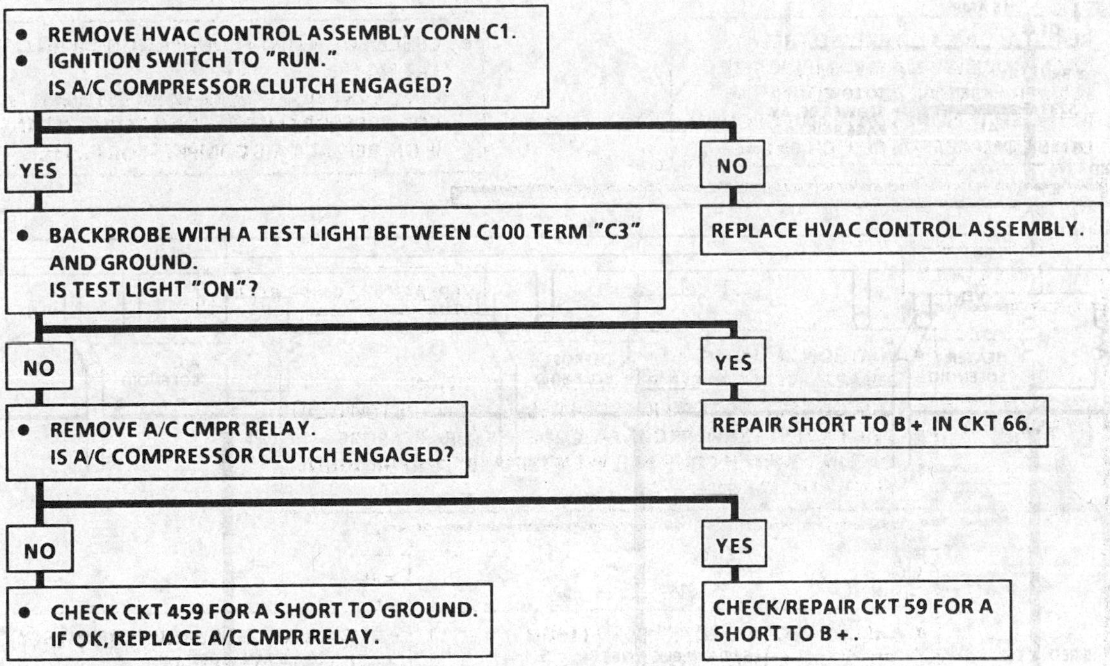
• REMOVE HVAC CONTROL ASSEMBLY CONN C1.
• IGNITION SWITCH TO "RUN."
IS A/C COMPRESSOR CLUTCH ENGAGED?
YES
NO
REPLACE HVAC CONTROL ASSEMBLY.
• BACKPROBE WITH A TEST LIGHT BETWEEN C100 TERM "C3" AND GROUND.
IS TEST LIGHT "ON"?
NO
YES
REPAIR SHORT TO B + IN CKT 66.
• REMOVE A/C CMPR RELAY.
IS A/C COMPRESSOR CLUTCH ENGAGED?
NO
YES
• CHECK CKT 459 FOR A SHORT TO GROUND.
IF OK, REPLACE A/C CMPR RELAY.
CHECK/REPAIR CKT 59 FOR A SHORT TO B +.

CIRCUIT OPERATION

The Compressor for air conditioning is belt driven by the Engine. The A/C Compressor Clutch engages and disengages the Compressor to remove the air conditioning load from the Engine when needed. The A/C Compressor Control Clutch engages the Compressor when the A/C mode selector is in "MAX", "NORM", "BI-LV", "DEFOG" or "DEFROST."

The A/C Compressor Clutch Diode connected across the A/C Compressor Clutch suppresses high voltage spikes that are generated by the collapsing magnetic field of the clutch coil when the clutch is turned off.

The A/C Compressor Relay opens and closes the circuit to the A/C Compressor Clutch. The coil of the relay is grounded by the Powertrain Control Module (PCM). This enables the PCM to disengage the air conditioning to reduce the load on the Engine when required. Wide open throttle, high power steering pressure or coolant temperature will also prevent the A/C system from engaging.

The PCM receives an air conditioning "ON" signal, which is battery voltage from the HVAC Control Assembly. It signals the PCM that A/C Compressor operation is required. The PCM also monitors a signal voltage from the A/C Refrigerant Pressure Sensor. If either a low or high refrigerant pressure condition occurs, the PCM will prevent the A/C Compressor Clutch from engaging.

See SECTION 6E for complete PCM operating details.

HVAC: AIR DELIVERY AND TEMPERATURE CONTROL

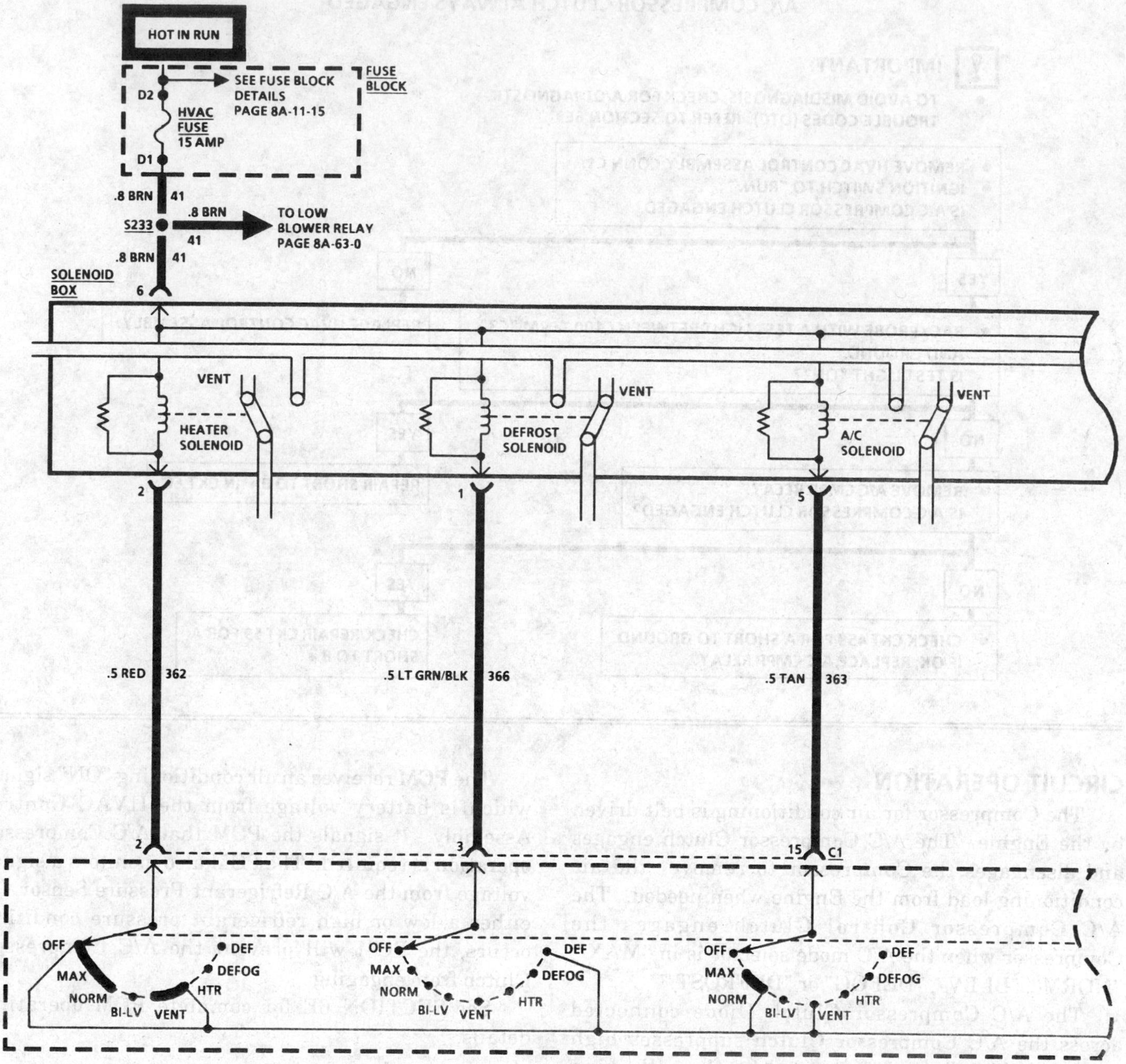

HOT IN RUN
SEE FUSE BLOCK DETAILS PAGE 8A-11-15
FUSE BLOCK
D2
HVAC FUSE 15 AMP
D1
.8 BRN 41
S233
.8 BRN 41
TO LOW BLOWER RELAY PAGE 8A-63-0
.8 BRN 41
SOLENOID BOX
6
VENT
HEATER SOLENOID
VENT
DEFROST SOLENOID
VENT
A/C SOLENOID
2
1
5
.5 RED 362
.5 LT GRN/BLK 366
.5 TAN 363
2
3
15 C1
OFF
DEF
DEFOG
MAX
NORM
HTR
BI-LV
VENT
OFF
DEF
MAX
DEFOG
NORM
HTR
BI-LV
VENT
OFF
DEF
MAX
DEFOG
NORM
HTR
BI-LV
VENT

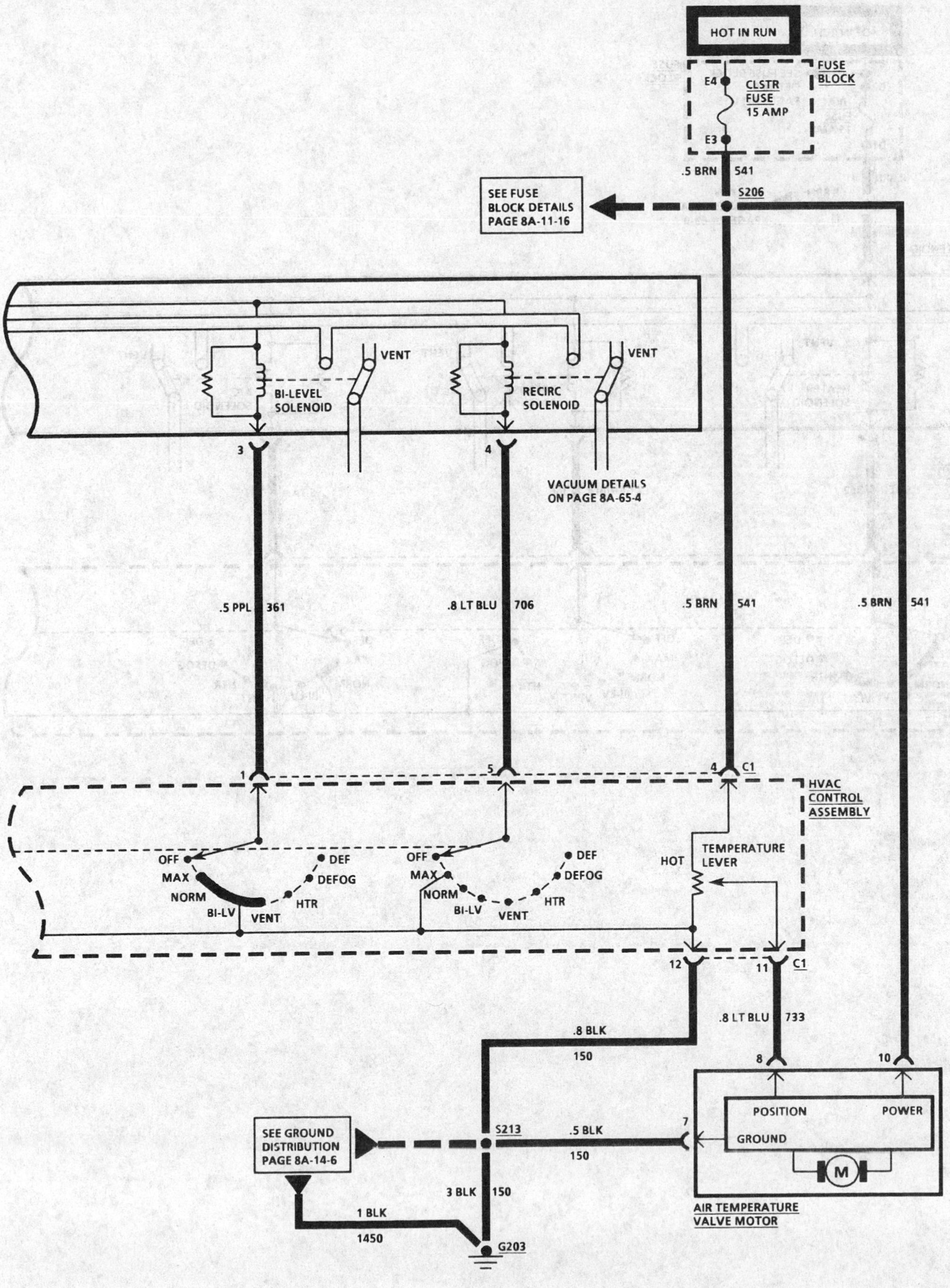
HOT IN RUN
FUSE BLOCK
E4
CLSTR FUSE 15 AMP
E3
.5 BRN 541
S206
SEE FUSE BLOCK DETAILS PAGE 8A-11-16
VENT
BI-LEVEL SOLENOID
VENT
RECIRC SOLENOID
3
4
VACUUM DETAILS ON PAGE 8A-65-4
.5 PPL 361
.8 LT BLU 706
.5 BRN 541
.5 BRN 541
1
5
4 C1
HVAC CONTROL ASSEMBLY
OFF
MAX
NORM
BI-LV
VENT
HTR
DEFOG
DEF
OFF
MAX
NORM
BI-LV
VENT
HTR
DEFOG
DEF
HOT
TEMPERATURE LEVER
12
11 C1
.8 LT BLU 733
.8 BLK
150
8
10
POSITION
POWER
GROUND
M
7
SEE GROUND DISTRIBUTION PAGE 8A-14-6
S213
.5 BLK
150
3 BLK 150
1 BLK
1450
G203
AIR TEMPERATURE VALVE MOTOR

HVAC: AIR DELIVERY AND TEMPERATURE CONTROL (C67)
WITH PASSENGER TEMPERATURE CONTROL

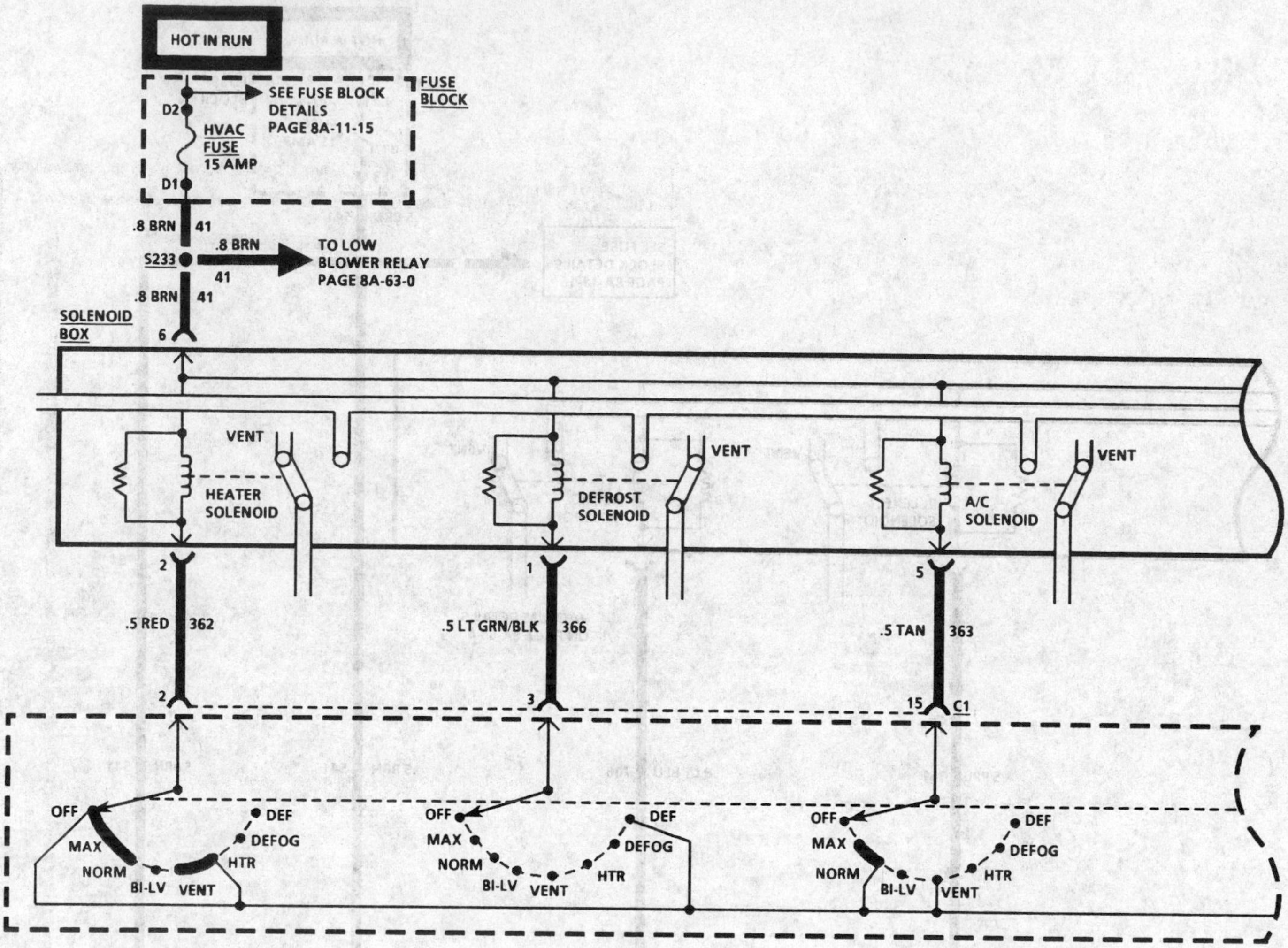

HOT IN RUN
FUSE BLOCK
D2
SEE FUSE BLOCK DETAILS PAGE 8A-11-15
HVAC FUSE 15 AMP
D1
.8 BRN 41
S233
.8 BRN 41
TO LOW BLOWER RELAY PAGE 8A-63-0
.8 BRN 41
SOLENOID BOX
6
VENT
HEATER SOLENOID
VENT
DEFROST SOLENOID
VENT
A/C SOLENOID
2
.5 RED 362
2
1
.5 LT GRN/BLK 366
3
5
.5 TAN 363
15 C1
OFF
MAX
NORM
BI-LV
VENT
HTR
DEFOG
DEF
OFF
MAX
NORM
BI-LV
VENT
HTR
DEFOG
DEF
OFF
MAX
NORM
BI-LV
VENT
HTR
DEFOG
DEF

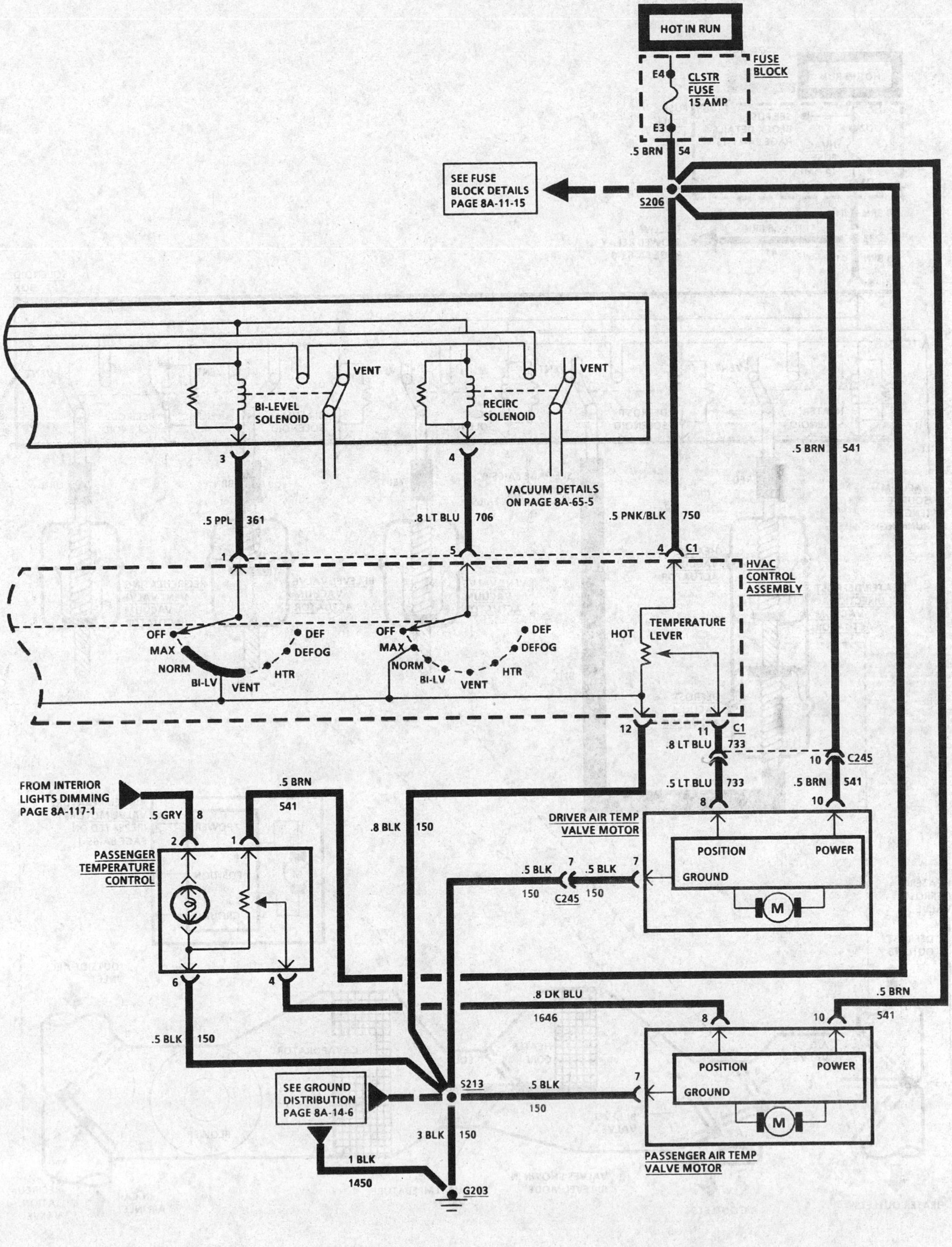
HOT IN RUN
FUSE BLOCK
E4
CLSTR FUSE 15 AMP
E3
.5 BRN 54
SEE FUSE BLOCK DETAILS PAGE 8A-11-15
S206
VENT
BI-LEVEL SOLENOID
VENT
RECIRC SOLENOID
VACUUM DETAILS ON PAGE 8A-65-5
.5 BRN 541
.5 PPL 361
.8 LT BLU 706
.5 PNK/BLK 750
C1
HVAC CONTROL ASSEMBLY
OFF
MAX
NORM
BI-LV
VENT
HTR
DEFOG
DEF
HOT
TEMPERATURE LEVER
12
11
C1
.8 LT BLU 733
C245
.5 LT BLU 733
.5 BRN 541
FROM INTERIOR LIGHTS DIMMING PAGE 8A-117-1
.5 GRY 8
.5 BRN 541
.8 BLK 150
DRIVER AIR TEMP VALVE MOTOR
POSITION
POWER
GROUND
PASSENGER TEMPERATURE CONTROL
.5 BLK 150
.5 BLK 150
C245
.8 DK BLU 1646
.5 BRN 541
.5 BLK 150
SEE GROUND DISTRIBUTION PAGE 8A-14-6
S213
.5 BLK 150
3 BLK 150
1 BLK 1450
G203
PASSENGER AIR TEMP VALVE MOTOR

HVAC: AIR DELIVERY AND TEMPERATURE CONTROL (C67)

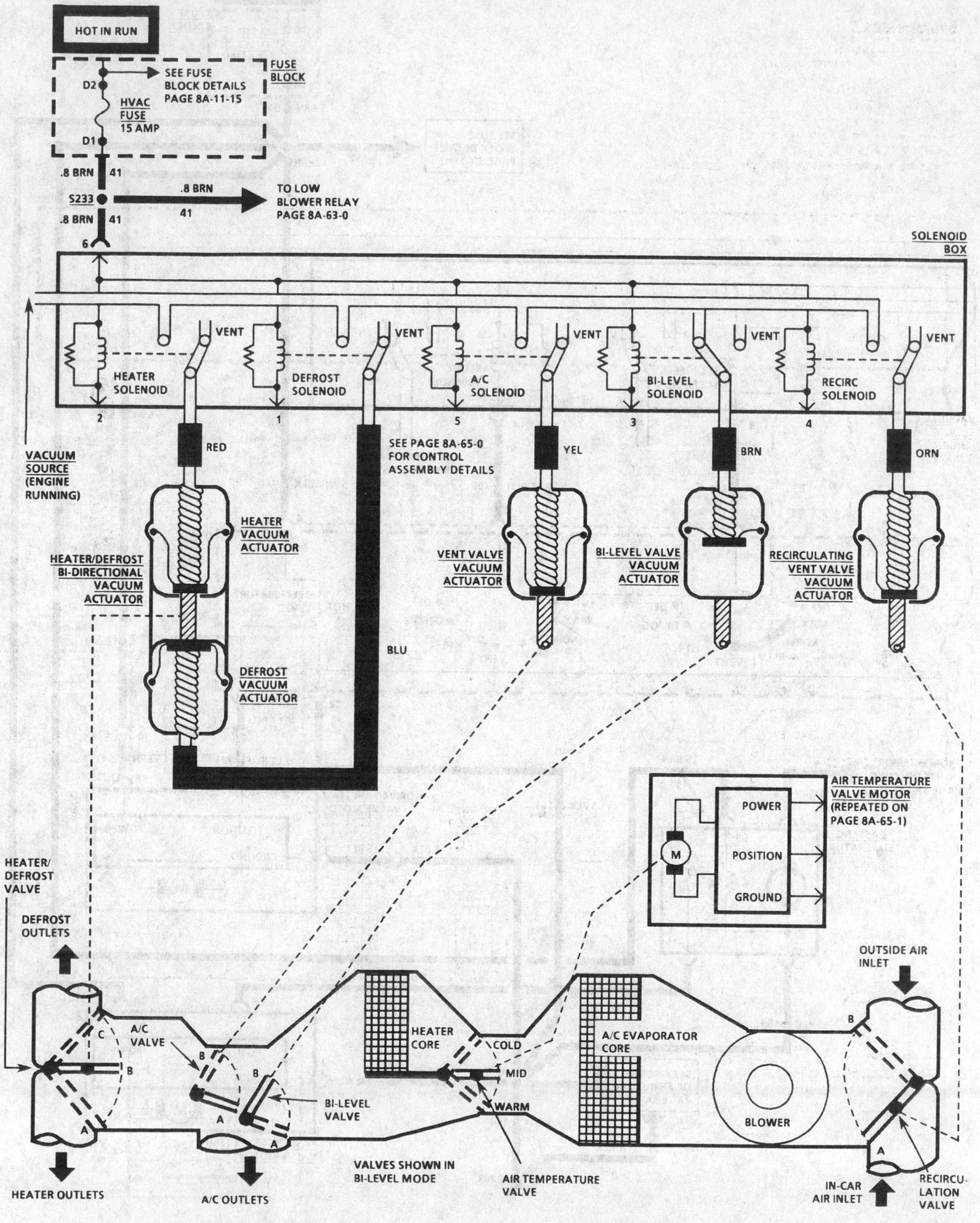
HOT IN RUN
FUSE BLOCK
D2
SEE FUSE BLOCK DETAILS PAGE 8A-11-15
HVAC FUSE 15 AMP
D1
.8 BRN 41
S233
.8 BRN
41
TO LOW BLOWER RELAY PAGE 8A-63-0
.8 BRN 41
6
SOLENOID BOX
VENT
VENT
VENT
VENT
VENT
HEATER SOLENOID
DEFROST SOLENOID
A/C SOLENOID
BI-LEVEL SOLENOID
RECIRC SOLENOID
2
1
5
3
4
RED
SEE PAGE 8A-65-0 FOR CONTROL ASSEMBLY DETAILS
YEL
BRN
ORN
VACUUM SOURCE (ENGINE RUNNING)
HEATER VACUUM ACTUATOR
HEATER/DEFROST BI-DIRECTIONAL VACUUM ACTUATOR
VENT VALVE VACUUM ACTUATOR
BI-LEVEL VALVE VACUUM ACTUATOR
RECIRCULATING VENT VALVE VACUUM ACTUATOR
BLU
DEFROST VACUUM ACTUATOR
AIR TEMPERATURE VALVE MOTOR (REPEATED ON PAGE 8A-65-1)
POWER
M
POSITION
GROUND
HEATER/ DEFROST VALVE
DEFROST OUTLETS
OUTSIDE AIR INLET
C
A/C VALVE
B
B
B
A
A
A
BI-LEVEL VALVE
HEATER CORE
COLD
MID
WARM
A/C EVAPORATOR CORE
BLOWER
B
A
HEATER OUTLETS
A/C OUTLETS
VALVES SHOWN IN BI-LEVEL MODE
AIR TEMPERATURE VALVE
IN-CAR AIR INLET
RECIRCULATION VALVE

HVAC: AIR DELIVERY AND TEMPERATURE CONTROL (C67)
WITH PASSENGER TEMPERATURE CONTROL

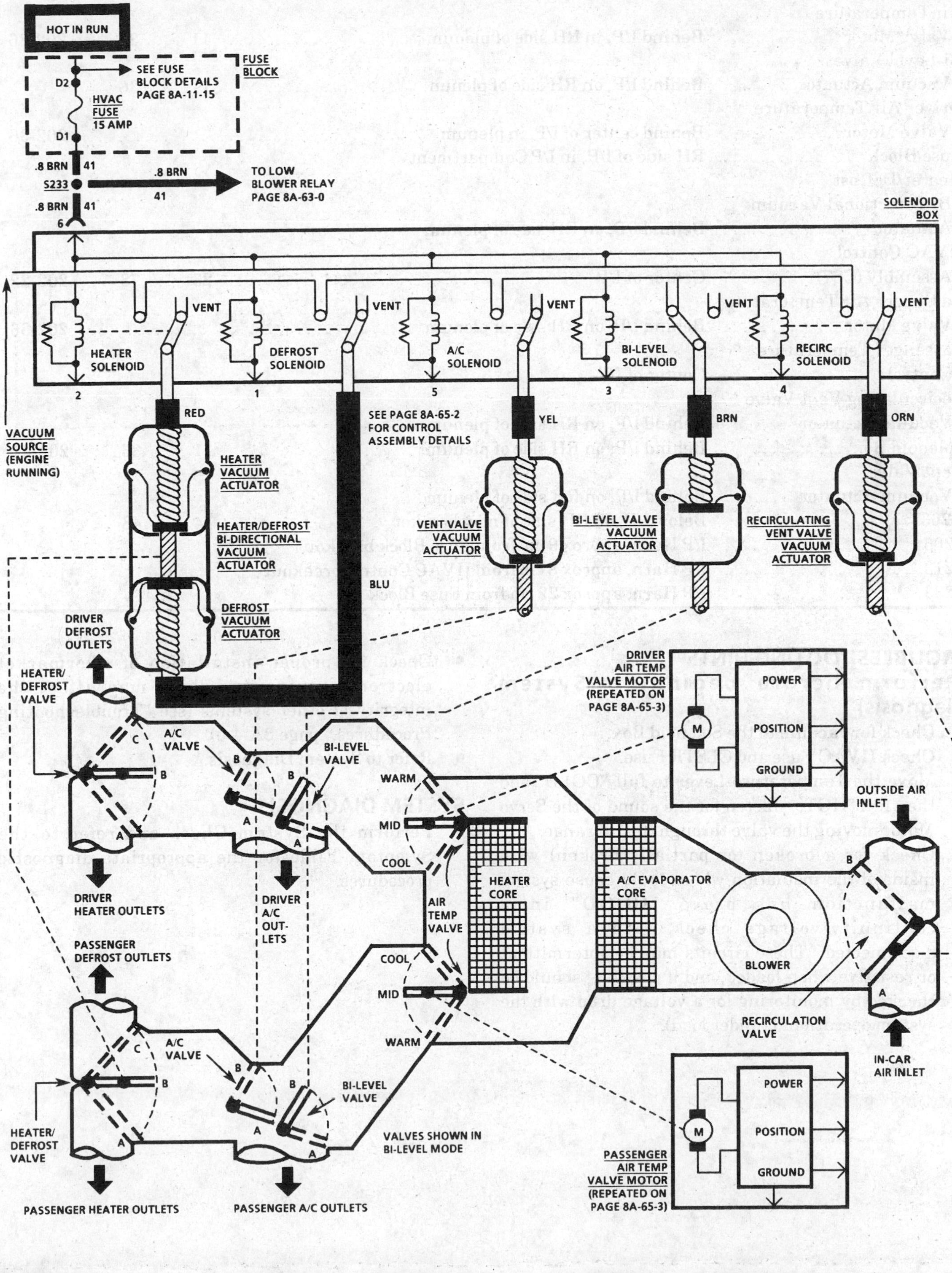
HOT IN RUN
FUSE BLOCK
SEE FUSE BLOCK DETAILS PAGE 8A-11-15
D2
HVAC FUSE 15 AMP
D1
.8 BRN 41
S233
.8 BRN
41
TO LOW BLOWER RELAY PAGE 8A-63-0
.8 BRN 41
6
SOLENOID BOX
VENT
HEATER SOLENOID
DEFROST SOLENOID
A/C SOLENOID
BI-LEVEL SOLENOID
RECIRC SOLENOID
2
1
5
3
4
RED
YEL
BRN
ORN
VACUUM SOURCE (ENGINE RUNNING)
SEE PAGE 8A-65-2 FOR CONTROL ASSEMBLY DETAILS
HEATER VACUUM ACTUATOR
HEATER/DEFROST BI-DIRECTIONAL VACUUM ACTUATOR
DEFROST VACUUM ACTUATOR
VENT VALVE VACUUM ACTUATOR
BI-LEVEL VALVE VACUUM ACTUATOR
RECIRCULATING VENT VALVE VACUUM ACTUATOR
BLU
DRIVER DEFROST OUTLETS
HEATER/ DEFROST VALVE
A/C VALVE
BI-LEVEL VALVE
WARM
MID
COOL
DRIVER HEATER OUTLETS
DRIVER A/C OUT-LETS
HEATER CORE
A/C EVAPORATOR CORE
AIR TEMP VALVE
DRIVER AIR TEMP VALVE MOTOR (REPEATED ON PAGE 8A-65-3)
POWER
POSITION
GROUND
M
OUTSIDE AIR INLET
BLOWER
RECIRCULATION VALVE
IN-CAR AIR INLET
PASSENGER DEFROST OUTLETS
HEATER/ DEFROST VALVE
VALVES SHOWN IN BI-LEVEL MODE
PASSENGER AIR TEMP VALVE MOTOR (REPEATED ON PAGE 8A-65-3)
PASSENGER HEATER OUTLETS
PASSENGER A/C OUTLETS
A
B
C

HVAC: AIR DELIVERY AND TEMPERATURE CONTROL (C67)

COMPONENT	LOCATION	201-PG	FIG.	CONN
Air Temperature Valve Motor	Behind I/P, in RH side of plenum	11	36	202-36
Bi-Level Valve Vacuum Actuator	Behind I/P, on RH side of plenun	11	36	
Driver Air Temperature Valve Motor	Behind center of I/P, in plenum			202-36
Fuse Block	RH side of I/P, in I/P Compartment			
Heater/Defrost Bi-Directional Vacuum Actuator	Behind I/P, on RH side of plenum			
HVAC Control Assembly (C67)	Center of I/P	23	78	202-22
Passenger Air Temperature Valve Motor	Behind I/P, on RH side of plenum			202-36
Passenger Temperature Control	Center of I/P			
Recirculating Vent Valve Vacuum Actuator	Behind I/P, on RH side of plenum			
Solenoid Box	Behind I/P, on RH side of plenum	11	36	202-41
Vent Valve Vacuum Actuator	Behind I/P, on RH side of plenum			
G203	Below I/P, on RH side of mag bracket	14	48	
S206	I/P Harn, approx 9 cm from Fuse Block breakout			
S213	I/P Harn, approx 8 cm from HVAC Control breakout			
S233	I/P Harn, approx 22 cm from Fuse Block			

TROUBLESHOOTING HINTS (Perform before beginning System Diagnosis)

1. Check for vacuum to the Solenoid Box.
2. Check HVAC Fuse and CLSTR Fuse.
3. Move the Temperature Lever to full "COLD" and then full "HOT." Listen for the sound of the Servo Motor moving the valve through its full range.

- Check for a broken (or partially broken) wire inside of the insulation which could cause system malfunction but prove "GOOD" in a continuity/voltage check with a system disconnected. These circuits may be intermittent or resistive when loaded, and if possible, should be checked by monitoring for a voltage drop with the system operational (under load).
- Check for proper installation of aftermarket electronic equipment which may affect the integrity of other systems (see "Troubleshooting Procedures," page 8A-4-0).
- Refer to System Diagnosis.

SYSTEM DIAGNOSIS

- Perform the System Check and refer to the Symptom Table for the appropriate diagnostic procedures.

SYSTEM CHECK

ACTION	NORMAL RESULTS
[1] ● Start Engine to build adequate vacuum supply. ● HVAC Control Assembly to "NORM." ● Blower Switch to medium speed.	Air flow from panel outlets, slight air flow from floor outlets.
[2] ● HVAC Control Assembly to "BI-LV".	Air flow from panel and floor outlets.
[3] ● HVAC Control Assembly to "VENT."	Air flow from panel outlets.
[4] ● HVAC Control Assembly to "HTR."	Air flow from heater outlets, slight air flow from defrost outlets.
[5] ● HVAC Control Assembly to "DEFOG."	Air flow from floor and defrost outlets.
[6] ● HVAC Control Assembly to "DEF".	Air flow from defrost outlets, slight air flow from floor outlets.
[7] ● HVAC Control Assembly to "VENT." ● Blower Switch to "LO." ● Temperature Lever to "HOT."	Sound of the Air Temperature Valve Motor rotating Air Temperature Valve and warm air flow from outlets.
[8] ● Temperature Lever to "COLD."	Sound of the Air Temperature Valve Motor rotating Air Temperature Valve and cool air flow from outlets.

SYMPTOM TABLE

SYMPTOM	PROCEDURE	PAGE NUMBER
Temperature Lever does not cause air flow at outlets to get warmer or colder.	Chart #1	8A-65-8
Air flow from outlets is incorrect.	Chart #2	8A-65-9

HVAC: AIR DELIVERY AND TEMPERATURE CONTROL (C67)

CHART #1

TEMPERATURE LEVER DOES NOT CAUSE AIR FLOW AT OUTLETS TO GET WARMER OR COLDER

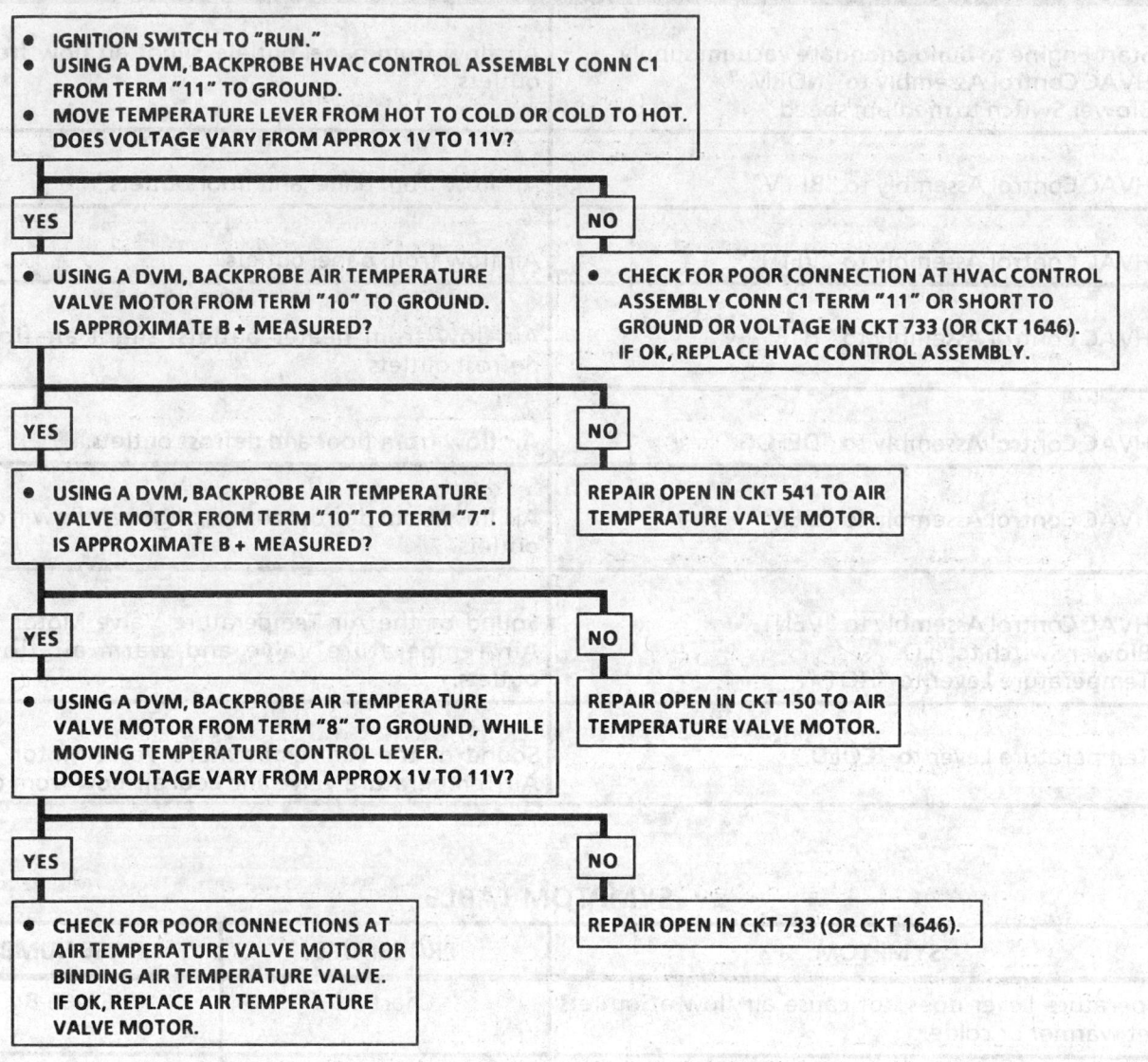

- IGNITION SWITCH TO "RUN."
- USING A DVM, BACKPROBE HVAC CONTROL ASSEMBLY CONN C1 FROM TERM "11" TO GROUND.
- MOVE TEMPERATURE LEVER FROM HOT TO COLD OR COLD TO HOT. DOES VOLTAGE VARY FROM APPROX 1V TO 11V?

NO:

- CHECK FOR POOR CONNECTION AT HVAC CONTROL ASSEMBLY CONN C1 TERM "11" OR SHORT TO GROUND OR VOLTAGE IN CKT 733 (OR CKT 1646). IF OK, REPLACE HVAC CONTROL ASSEMBLY.

YES:

- USING A DVM, BACKPROBE AIR TEMPERATURE VALVE MOTOR FROM TERM "10" TO GROUND. IS APPROXIMATE B + MEASURED?

NO:

REPAIR OPEN IN CKT 541 TO AIR TEMPERATURE VALVE MOTOR.

YES:

- USING A DVM, BACKPROBE AIR TEMPERATURE VALVE MOTOR FROM TERM "10" TO TERM "7". IS APPROXIMATE B + MEASURED?

NO:

REPAIR OPEN IN CKT 150 TO AIR TEMPERATURE VALVE MOTOR.

YES:

- USING A DVM, BACKPROBE AIR TEMPERATURE VALVE MOTOR FROM TERM "8" TO GROUND, WHILE MOVING TEMPERATURE CONTROL LEVER. DOES VOLTAGE VARY FROM APPROX 1V TO 11V?

NO:

REPAIR OPEN IN CKT 733 (OR CKT 1646).

YES:

- CHECK FOR POOR CONNECTIONS AT AIR TEMPERATURE VALVE MOTOR OR BINDING AIR TEMPERATURE VALVE. IF OK, REPLACE AIR TEMPERATURE VALVE MOTOR.

CHART #2
AIR FLOW FROM OUTLETS IS INCORRECT

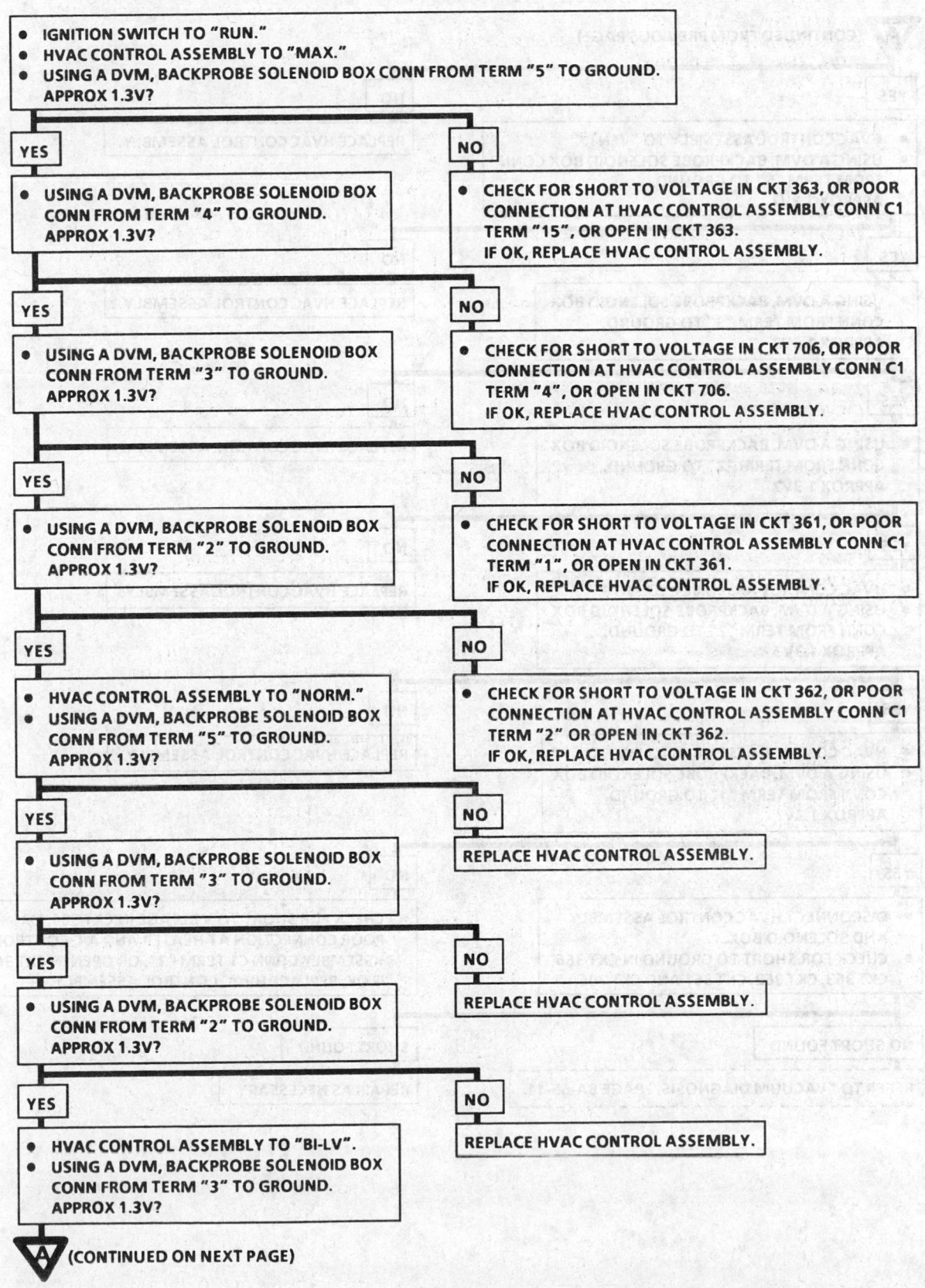

- IGNITION SWITCH TO "RUN."
- HVAC CONTROL ASSEMBLY TO "MAX."
- USING A DVM, BACKPROBE SOLENOID BOX CONN FROM TERM "5" TO GROUND. APPROX 1.3V?

NO:
- CHECK FOR SHORT TO VOLTAGE IN CKT 363, OR POOR CONNECTION AT HVAC CONTROL ASSEMBLY CONN C1 TERM "15", OR OPEN IN CKT 363. IF OK, REPLACE HVAC CONTROL ASSEMBLY.

YES:
- USING A DVM, BACKPROBE SOLENOID BOX CONN FROM TERM "4" TO GROUND. APPROX 1.3V?

NO:
- CHECK FOR SHORT TO VOLTAGE IN CKT 706, OR POOR CONNECTION AT HVAC CONTROL ASSEMBLY CONN C1 TERM "4", OR OPEN IN CKT 706. IF OK, REPLACE HVAC CONTROL ASSEMBLY.

YES:
- USING A DVM, BACKPROBE SOLENOID BOX CONN FROM TERM "3" TO GROUND. APPROX 1.3V?

NO:
- CHECK FOR SHORT TO VOLTAGE IN CKT 361, OR POOR CONNECTION AT HVAC CONTROL ASSEMBLY CONN C1 TERM "1", OR OPEN IN CKT 361. IF OK, REPLACE HVAC CONTROL ASSEMBLY.

YES:
- USING A DVM, BACKPROBE SOLENOID BOX CONN FROM TERM "2" TO GROUND. APPROX 1.3V?

NO:
- CHECK FOR SHORT TO VOLTAGE IN CKT 362, OR POOR CONNECTION AT HVAC CONTROL ASSEMBLY CONN C1 TERM "2" OR OPEN IN CKT 362. IF OK, REPLACE HVAC CONTROL ASSEMBLY.

YES:
- HVAC CONTROL ASSEMBLY TO "NORM."
- USING A DVM, BACKPROBE SOLENOID BOX CONN FROM TERM "5" TO GROUND. APPROX 1.3V?

NO: REPLACE HVAC CONTROL ASSEMBLY.

YES:
- USING A DVM, BACKPROBE SOLENOID BOX CONN FROM TERM "3" TO GROUND. APPROX 1.3V?

NO: REPLACE HVAC CONTROL ASSEMBLY.

YES:
- USING A DVM, BACKPROBE SOLENOID BOX CONN FROM TERM "2" TO GROUND. APPROX 1.3V?

NO: REPLACE HVAC CONTROL ASSEMBLY.

YES:
- HVAC CONTROL ASSEMBLY TO "BI-LV".
- USING A DVM, BACKPROBE SOLENOID BOX CONN FROM TERM "3" TO GROUND. APPROX 1.3V?

A (CONTINUED ON NEXT PAGE)

HVAC: AIR DELIVERY AND TEMPERATURE CONTROL (C67)

CHART #2 (continued)

AIR FLOW FROM OUTLETS IS INCORRECT

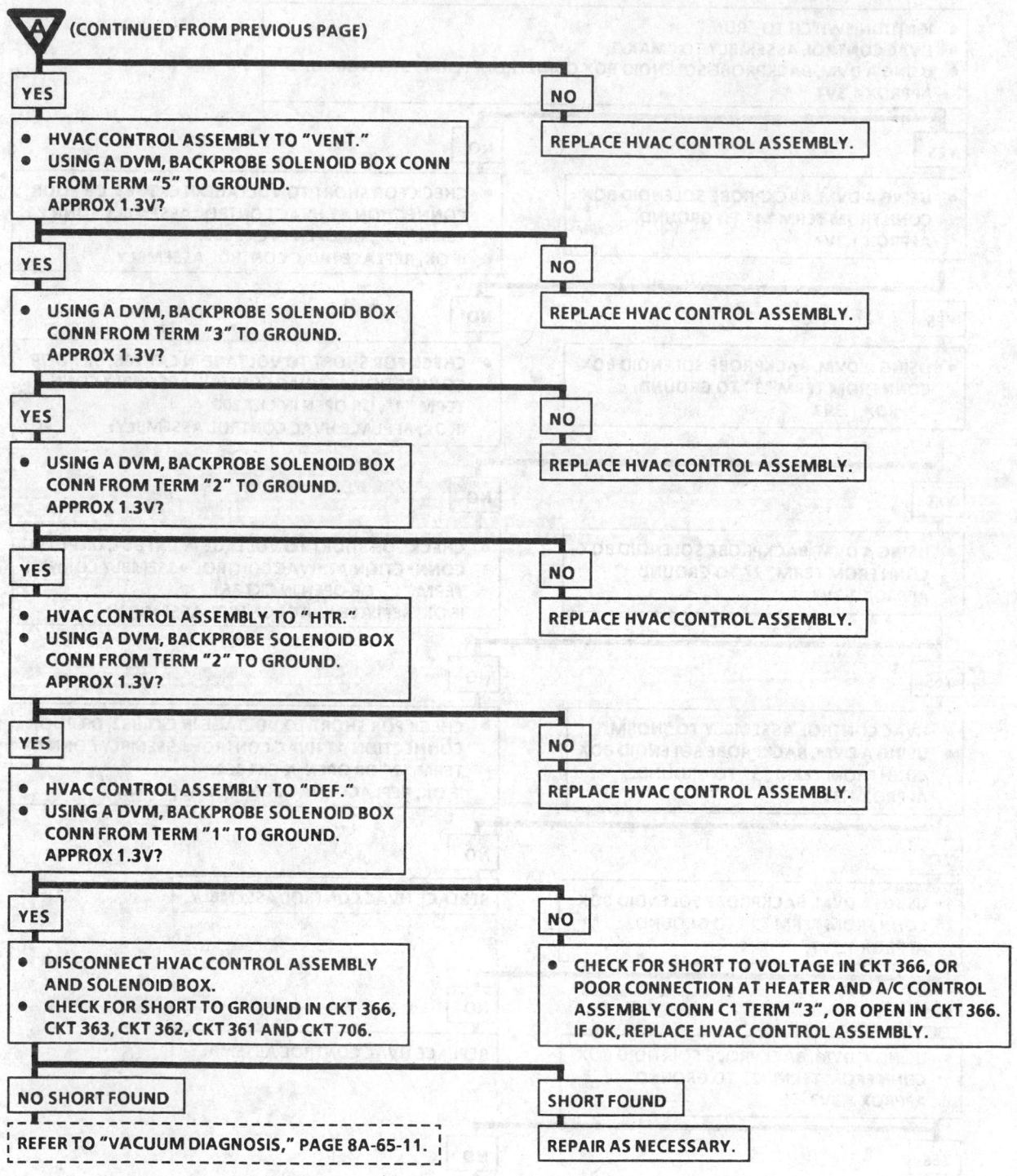

A (CONTINUED FROM PREVIOUS PAGE)

YES

- HVAC CONTROL ASSEMBLY TO "VENT."
- USING A DVM, BACKPROBE SOLENOID BOX CONN FROM TERM "5" TO GROUND. APPROX 1.3V?

NO

REPLACE HVAC CONTROL ASSEMBLY.

YES

- USING A DVM, BACKPROBE SOLENOID BOX CONN FROM TERM "3" TO GROUND. APPROX 1.3V?

NO

REPLACE HVAC CONTROL ASSEMBLY.

YES

- USING A DVM, BACKPROBE SOLENOID BOX CONN FROM TERM "2" TO GROUND. APPROX 1.3V?

NO

REPLACE HVAC CONTROL ASSEMBLY.

YES

- HVAC CONTROL ASSEMBLY TO "HTR."
- USING A DVM, BACKPROBE SOLENOID BOX CONN FROM TERM "2" TO GROUND. APPROX 1.3V?

NO

REPLACE HVAC CONTROL ASSEMBLY.

YES

- HVAC CONTROL ASSEMBLY TO "DEF."
- USING A DVM, BACKPROBE SOLENOID BOX CONN FROM TERM "1" TO GROUND. APPROX 1.3V?

NO

REPLACE HVAC CONTROL ASSEMBLY.

YES

- DISCONNECT HVAC CONTROL ASSEMBLY AND SOLENOID BOX.
- CHECK FOR SHORT TO GROUND IN CKT 366, CKT 363, CKT 362, CKT 361 AND CKT 706.

NO

- CHECK FOR SHORT TO VOLTAGE IN CKT 366, OR POOR CONNECTION AT HEATER AND A/C CONTROL ASSEMBLY CONN C1 TERM "3", OR OPEN IN CKT 366. IF OK, REPLACE HVAC CONTROL ASSEMBLY.

NO SHORT FOUND

REFER TO "VACUUM DIAGNOSIS," PAGE 8A-65-11.

SHORT FOUND

REPAIR AS NECESSARY.

VACUUM DIAGNOSIS

Important:

- To avoid misdiagnosis, complete Chart #2, "Air Flow From Outlets is Incorrect," before beginning Vacuum Diagnosis.

1. Check vacuum supply to Solenoid Box (black vacuum hose) while Engine is running.
   - Vacuum should be approximately 60 kPa (18 psi) with Engine running.
   - Vacuum should remain at approximately 60 kPa (18 psi) when Engine is turned "OFF."
2. Test each vacuum actuator by disconnecting the vacuum hose and applying vacuum directly to the actuator. Repair or replace as necessary.
3. Reconnect all vacuum and electrical connections. Run Engine and cycle through the operating modes of the HVAC Control Assembly while observing the vacuum actuators.
   - Check for vacuum to the vacuum actuators by noting vacuum actuator position. When vacuum is applied, the actuator will retract, refer to Air Delivery Vacuum Distribution Table.
   - If a vacuum actuator retracts when it should not, replace the HVAC Control Assembly.
   - If a vacuum actuator does not retract when it should, check for vacuum leaks, collapsed vacuum hoses or binding valves. If OK, replace the Solenoid Box.

AIR DELIVERY VACUUM DISTRIBUTION

VAC HOSE COLOR – SOLENOID	RED – HEATER SOLENOID	YEL – A/C SOLENOID	BRN – BI-LEVEL SOLENOID	BLU – DEFROST SOLENOID	ORN – RECIRC SOLENOID
HEATER AND A/C CONTROL ASSEMBLY	HEATER/DEFROST BI-DIRECTIONAL VACUUM ACTUATOR	VENT VALVE VACUUM ACTUATOR	BI-LEVEL VALVE VACUUM ACTUATOR	HEATER/DEFROST BI-DIRECTIONAL VACUUM ACTUATOR	RECIRCULATING VENT VALVE VACUUM ACTUATOR
"OFF"	VAC	No VAC	No VAC	No VAC	No VAC
"MAX"	VAC	VAC	VAC	No VAC	VAC
"NORM"	VAC	VAC	VAC	No VAC	No VAC
"BI-LV"	No VAC	No VAC	VAC	No VAC	No VAC
"UPPER"	VAC	VAC	VAC	No VAC	No VAC
"LOWER"	VAC	No VAC	No VAC	No VAC	No VAC
"DEFOG"	No VAC	No VAC	No VAC	No VAC	No VAC
"DEF"	No VAC	No VAC	No VAC	VAC	No VAC

VAC = VACUUM

HVAC: AIR DELIVERY AND TEMPERATURE CONTROL (C67)

CIRCUIT OPERATION

HVAC CONTROL ASSEMBLY

With the Ignition Switch in "RUN," voltage is applied through the CLSTR Fuse and CKT 541 to the HVAC Control Assembly. The voltage from CKT 733 is varied from Battery to approximately 1.5 volts by the Temperature Control Potentiometer. The Control Assembly provides ground paths for the Solenoid Box through CKT 150 and the control switches.

SOLENOID BOX

The Solenoid Box contains the solenoid valves that control the Vacuum Actuators. There is one solenoid for each Vacuum Actuator. When the solenoids are de-energized, the valves vent the Vacuum Actuators, allowing the Vacuum Actuator to return to the vent position determined by a spring. Voltage is supplied to the solenoids through CKT 41 and the HVAC Fuse, which is powered in "RUN."

RECIRCULATION VALVE

The Recirculation Valve closed the outside air inlet so that air from the inside of the vehicle is recirculated through the A/C system for maximum cooling. The outside air inlet is closed when vacuum is applied to the actuator. When the Recirculation Valve Vacuum Actuator is vented, the spring returns the Recirculation Valve to position A, which allows outside air to be drawn into the vehicle.

AIR TEMPERATURE VALVE

The Air Temperature Valve determines how much air flows through the Heater core, which determines the temperature of the air to the outlets. It is moved by the Air Temperature Valve Motor. The position of the valve is determine by the voltage level of the temperature control output from the HVAC Control Assembly. The Air Temperature Valve is powered with the Ignition Switch in "RUN." Voltage is applied through the CLSTR Fuse and CKT 541.

With the CJ3 System there are two Temperature Controls and Valve Motors. This allows individual adjustment of air being supplied to the driver and passenger. Back control operates in a manner similar to the one described.

A/C VALVE

The A/C Valve determines whether air flow will be directed to the A/C Outlets or the Heater/Defrost Outlets. With no vacuum applied to the actuator, the valve is in position A, which directs air to the Heater/Defrost Outlet.

BI-LEVEL VALVE

The Bi-Level Valve is a small valve which allows partial air flow to the A/C Outlets when the A/C Valve is in position A. The Bi-Level Valve is opened when vacuum is applied to the Bi-Level Vacuum Actuator.

HEATER/DEFROST VALVE

The Heater/Defrost Valve can assume three positions and is operated by a Bi-Directional Vacuum Actuator which can move the valve to either of two positions. If no vacuum is applied to either Vacuum Actuator, the valve is in midposition. Air flow with the valve in the midposition (B) will be delivered to both the Defrost Outlets at the windshield and the Heater Outlets at floor level. When the Heater Vacuum Actuator is operated, the valve moves to position (C), forcing all air flow to the Heater Outlets. When the Defrost Vacuum Actuator is operated, the valve is moved to position (A) which will force air flow to the Defrost Outlets.

BLANK

AUDIBLE WARNINGS

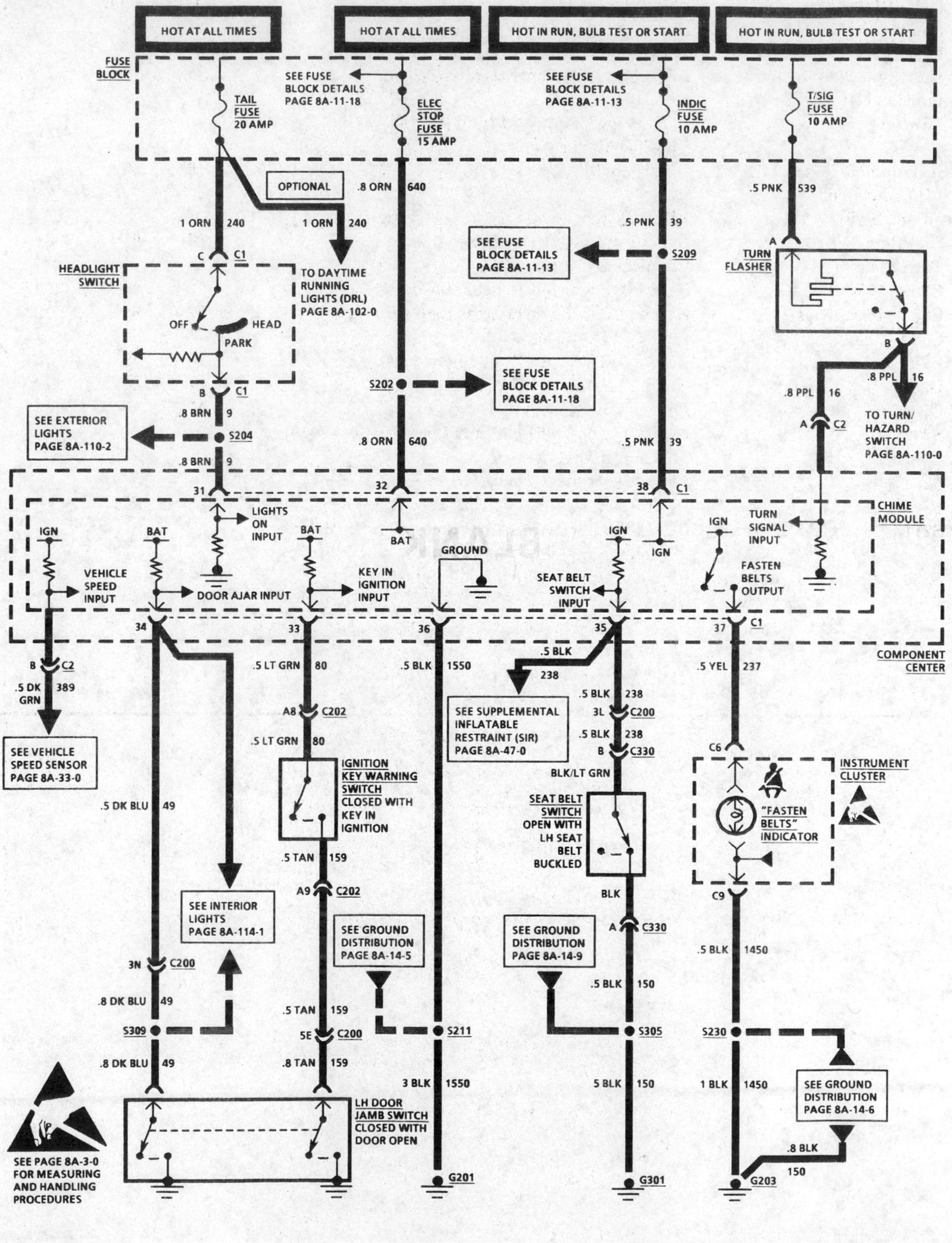
HOT AT ALL TIMES
HOT AT ALL TIMES
HOT IN RUN, BULB TEST OR START
HOT IN RUN, BULB TEST OR START
FUSE BLOCK
TAIL FUSE 20 AMP
SEE FUSE BLOCK DETAILS PAGE 8A-11-18
ELEC STOP FUSE 15 AMP
SEE FUSE BLOCK DETAILS PAGE 8A-11-13
INDIC FUSE 10 AMP
T/SIG FUSE 10 AMP
OPTIONAL
.8 ORN 640
.5 PNK 539
1 ORN 240
1 ORN 240
.5 PNK 39
SEE FUSE BLOCK DETAILS PAGE 8A-11-13
S209
TURN FLASHER
HEADLIGHT SWITCH
TO DAYTIME RUNNING LIGHTS (DRL) PAGE 8A-102-0
OFF
HEAD
PARK
S202
SEE FUSE BLOCK DETAILS PAGE 8A-11-18
.8 PPL 16
.8 PPL 16
.8 BRN 9
SEE EXTERIOR LIGHTS PAGE 8A-110-2
S204
.8 ORN 640
.5 PNK 39
TO TURN/ HAZARD SWITCH PAGE 8A-110-0
.8 BRN 9
CHIME MODULE
LIGHTS ON INPUT
BAT
IGN
TURN SIGNAL INPUT
IGN
BAT
BAT
IGN
GROUND
VEHICLE SPEED INPUT
DOOR AJAR INPUT
KEY IN IGNITION INPUT
SEAT BELT SWITCH INPUT
FASTEN BELTS OUTPUT
COMPONENT CENTER
.5 DK GRN 389
.5 LT GRN 80
.5 BLK 1550
.5 BLK 238
.5 YEL 237
SEE VEHICLE SPEED SENSOR PAGE 8A-33-0
SEE SUPPLEMENTAL INFLATABLE RESTRAINT (SIR) PAGE 8A-47-0
.5 BLK 238
.5 BLK 238
BLK/LT GRN
IGNITION KEY WARNING SWITCH CLOSED WITH KEY IN IGNITION
INSTRUMENT CLUSTER
"FASTEN BELTS" INDICATOR
.5 DK BLU 49
SEAT BELT SWITCH OPEN WITH LH SEAT BELT BUCKLED
.5 TAN 159
BLK
SEE INTERIOR LIGHTS PAGE 8A-114-1
SEE GROUND DISTRIBUTION PAGE 8A-14-5
SEE GROUND DISTRIBUTION PAGE 8A-14-9
.5 BLK 1450
.5 BLK 150
.8 DK BLU 49
.5 TAN 159
S309
S211
S305
S230
.8 DK BLU 49
.8 TAN 159
3 BLK 1550
5 BLK 150
1 BLK 1450
SEE GROUND DISTRIBUTION PAGE 8A-14-6
LH DOOR JAMB SWITCH CLOSED WITH DOOR OPEN
.8 BLK 150
SEE PAGE 8A-3-0 FOR MEASURING AND HANDLING PROCEDURES
G201
G301
G203

COMPONENT	LOCATION	201-PG	FIG.	CONN
Component Center	Behind RH side of I/P	11	36	202-17
Fuse Block	RH side of I/P, in I/P Compartment			
Headlight Switch	LH side of I/P, left of Steering Column			
Ignition Key Warning Switch	In Steering Column, at Ignition Key Lock Cylinder			
Instrument Cluster	LH side of I/P	16	52	
LH Front Door Jamb Switch	LH "A" pillar			
Seat Belt Switch	In LH front Seat Belt buckle	18	62	
Turn Flasher	Component Center			
C200 (106 cavities)	Behind RH side of I/P, near shroud	22	74	202-3
C202 (48 cavities)	Behind I/P, RH side of Steering Column	27	88	202-9
C330 (2 cavities)	Under LH front seat			
G201	Behind LH side of I/P on Mag bracket	14	48	
G203	Behind LH side of I/P on Mag bracket	14	48	
G301	Below LH front seat	15	50	
S202	I/P Harn, approx 51 cm from Instrument Cluster breakout			
S204	I/P Harn, approx 27 cm from C200			
S209	I/P Harn, approx 15 cm from Fuse Block breakout	15	49	
S211	I/P Harn, approx 9 cm from Radio Control Head breakout			
S230	I/P Harn, approx 27 cm from Radio Control Head breakout			
S305	Cross Car Harn, approx 5 cm from G302 breakout	17	61	
S309	Cross Car Harn, approx 13 cm from Driver Seat Belt Switch			

AUDIBLE WARNINGS

TROUBLESHOOTING HINTS (Perform before beginning System Diagnosis)

1. Check INDIC, ELEC, TAIL and T/SIG Fuses.
2. Check that grounds G201, G203 and G301 are clean and tight.

- Check for a broken (or partially broken) wire inside of the insulation which could cause system malfunction but prove "GOOD" in a continuity/voltage check with a system disconnected. These circuits may be intermittent or resistive when loaded, and if possible, should be checked by monitoring for a voltage drop with the system operational (under load).
- Check for proper installation of aftermarket electronic equipment which may affect the integrity of other systems (see "Troubleshooting Procedures," page 8A-4-0).
- Refer to System Diagnosis.

SYSTEM DIAGNOSIS

- Perform the System Check and refer to the Symptom Table for the appropriate diagnostic procedure(s).

SYSTEM CHECK

ACTION	NORMAL RESULTS
[1] LIGHTS "ON" WARNING • Remove Ignition Key from Ignition Switch. • Headlamp Switch to "HEAD." • Headlamp Switch to "OFF."	Lights "ON" Warning (approximately one pulse per half second) sounds as long as the Headlamps are "ON."
[2] IGNITION KEY WARNING • Ignition Key in Ignition Switch. • Ignition Switch to "OFF." • Open LH front door. • Close LH front door.	Ignition Key Warning (approximately one pulse per second) sounds when the key is in the Ignition Switch and the LH front door is open.
[3] IGNITION KEY WARNING • Driver's seat belt latched. • Ignition Switch to "RUN." • Open LH front door. • Close LH front door.	No chime sounds.
[4] SEAT BELT WARNING • Ignition Switch to "OFF." • Close LH front door. • Driver's seat belt unlatched. • Ignition Switch to "RUN."	Seat Belt Warning sounds for 4 to 8 seconds and the "FASTEN BELTS" Indicator is "ON."
[5] SEAT BELT WARNING • Close LH front door. • Latch driver's seat belt. • Ignition Switch to "OFF" and back to "RUN."	Seat Belt Warning does not sound. "FASTEN BELTS" Indicator remains "OFF."

SYMPTOM TABLE

SYMPTOM	PROCEDURE	PAGE NUMBER
All warning chimes inoperative.	Chart #1	8A-76-3
Ignition Key Warning inoperative.	Chart #2	8A-76-4
Seat Belt Warning inoperative.	Chart #3	8A-76-4
"FASTEN BELTS" Indicator "ON" continuously with Driver's Seat Belt latched.	Chart #4	8A-76-5
"FASTEN BELTS" Indicator inoperative.	Chart #5	8A-76-5
Lights "ON" Warning inoperative.	Check for poor connection at Component Center Conn C1 terminal "31" or open or short to ground in CKT 9 to the Chime Module. If OK, replace Chime Module.	
Lights "ON" Warning sounds continuously with Ignition Switch in "RUN."	Check for poor connection at Component Center Conn C1 terminal "38" or open or short to ground in CKT 39 to the Chime Module. If OK, replace Chime Module.	
Ignition Key Warning sounds when LH front door is open and key is not in Ignition Switch.	Check for short to ground in CKT 80. If OK, replace Ignition Key Warning Switch.	
Ignition Key Warning continues to sound when LH front door is closed and Ignition Switch is in "RUN."	Check for poor connection at Component Center Conn C1 terminal "38" or open in CKT 39 to the Chime Module.	
Seat Belt Warning sounds continuously.	Replace Chime Module.	
Turn Signal Chime inoperative.	Check for poor connection at Chime Module Connector C2 terminal "A" or open in CKT 16. If OK, check "Vehicle Speed Signal," Section 8A-33.	
Turn Signal Chime sounds continuously.	Replace Chime Module.	

CHART #1
ALL WARNING CHIMES INOPERATIVE

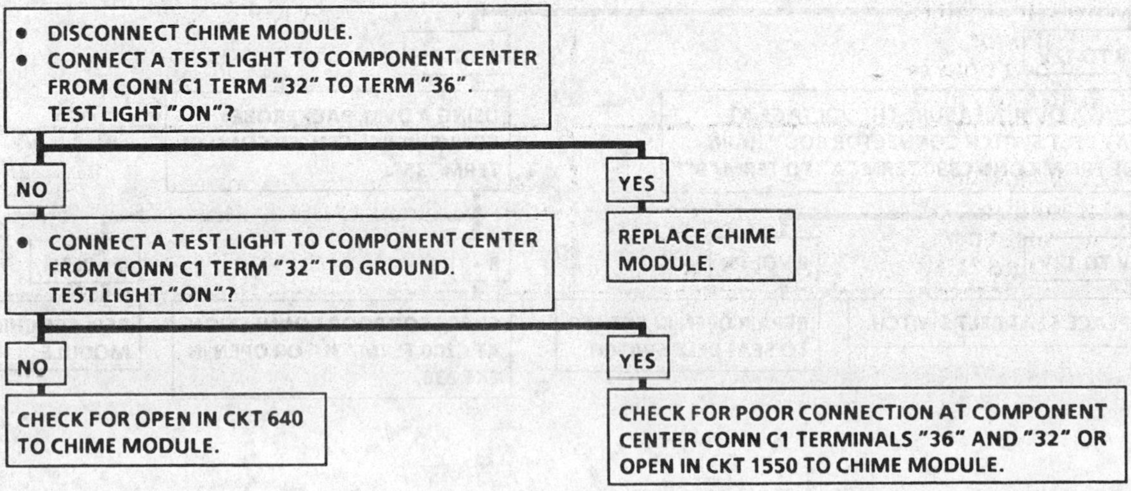

• DISCONNECT CHIME MODULE.
• CONNECT A TEST LIGHT TO COMPONENT CENTER FROM CONN C1 TERM "32" TO TERM "36". TEST LIGHT "ON"?
NO
YES
REPLACE CHIME MODULE.
• CONNECT A TEST LIGHT TO COMPONENT CENTER FROM CONN C1 TERM "32" TO GROUND. TEST LIGHT "ON"?
NO
YES
CHECK FOR OPEN IN CKT 640 TO CHIME MODULE.
CHECK FOR POOR CONNECTION AT COMPONENT CENTER CONN C1 TERMINALS "36" AND "32" OR OPEN IN CKT 1550 TO CHIME MODULE.

AUDIBLE WARNINGS

CHART #2
IGNITION KEY WARNING INOPERATIVE

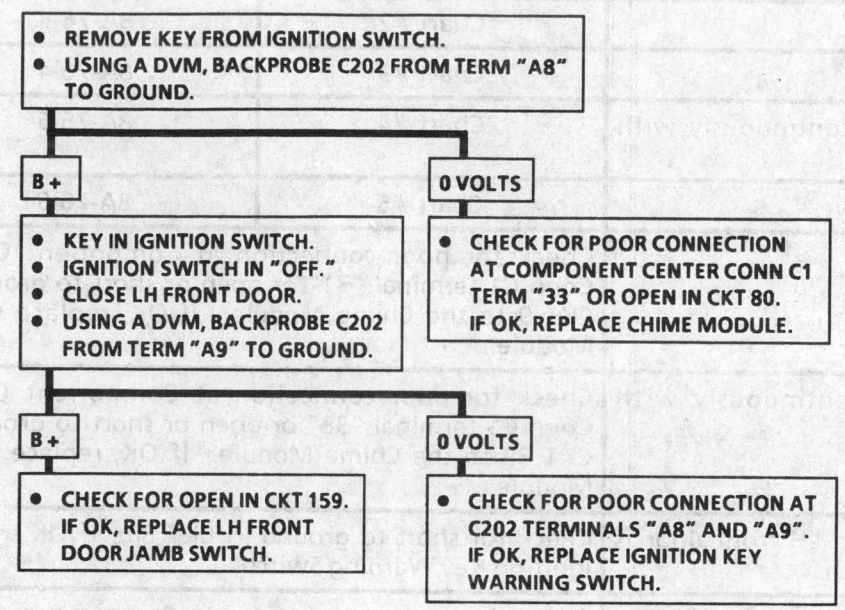

- REMOVE KEY FROM IGNITION SWITCH.
- USING A DVM, BACKPROBE C202 FROM TERM "A8" TO GROUND.

B +

- KEY IN IGNITION SWITCH.
- IGNITION SWITCH IN "OFF."
- CLOSE LH FRONT DOOR.
- USING A DVM, BACKPROBE C202 FROM TERM "A9" TO GROUND.

  B +

  - CHECK FOR OPEN IN CKT 159. IF OK, REPLACE LH FRONT DOOR JAMB SWITCH.

  0 VOLTS

  - CHECK FOR POOR CONNECTION AT C202 TERMINALS "A8" AND "A9". IF OK, REPLACE IGNITION KEY WARNING SWITCH.

0 VOLTS

- CHECK FOR POOR CONNECTION AT COMPONENT CENTER CONN C1 TERM "33" OR OPEN IN CKT 80. IF OK, REPLACE CHIME MODULE.

CHART #3
SEAT BELT WARNING INOPERATIVE

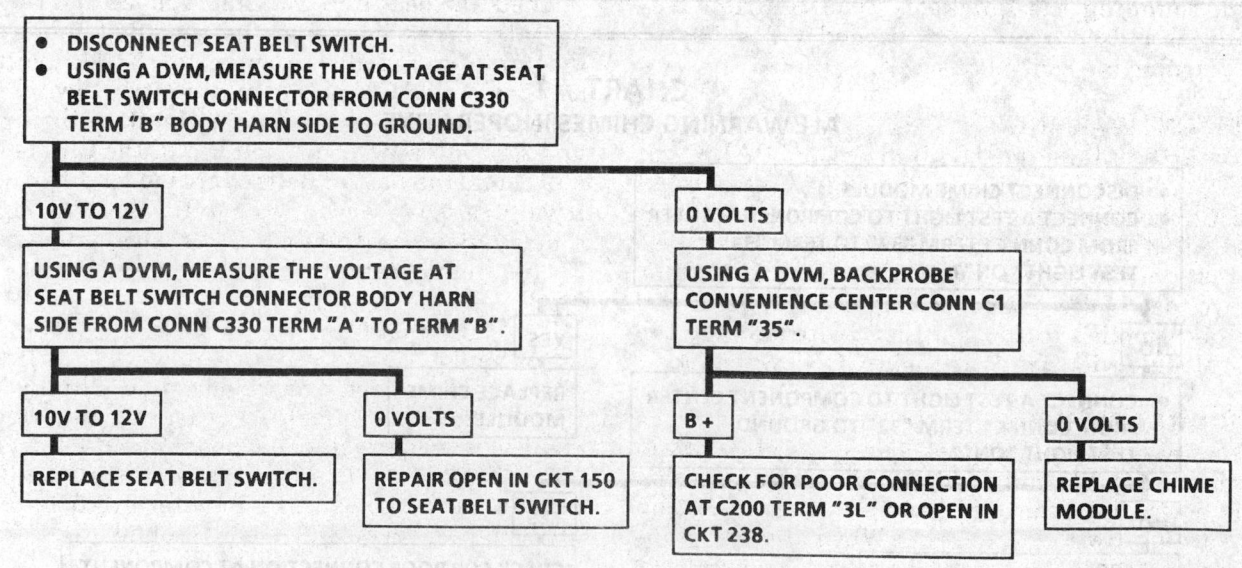

- DISCONNECT SEAT BELT SWITCH.
- USING A DVM, MEASURE THE VOLTAGE AT SEAT BELT SWITCH CONNECTOR FROM CONN C330 TERM "B" BODY HARN SIDE TO GROUND.

10V TO 12V

USING A DVM, MEASURE THE VOLTAGE AT SEAT BELT SWITCH CONNECTOR BODY HARN SIDE FROM CONN C330 TERM "A" TO TERM "B".

- **10V TO 12V** — REPLACE SEAT BELT SWITCH.
- **0 VOLTS** — REPAIR OPEN IN CKT 150 TO SEAT BELT SWITCH.

0 VOLTS

USING A DVM, BACKPROBE CONVENIENCE CENTER CONN C1 TERM "35".

- **B +** — CHECK FOR POOR CONNECTION AT C200 TERM "3L" OR OPEN IN CKT 238.
- **0 VOLTS** — REPLACE CHIME MODULE.

CHART #4
"FASTEN BELTS" INDICATOR "ON" CONTINUOUSLY WITH DRIVER'S SEAT BELT LATCHED

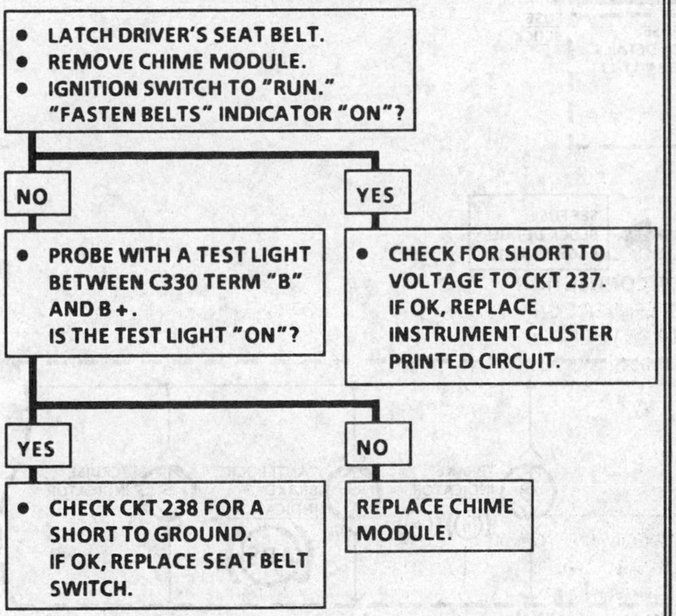
• LATCH DRIVER'S SEAT BELT.
• REMOVE CHIME MODULE.
• IGNITION SWITCH TO "RUN."
"FASTEN BELTS" INDICATOR "ON"?
NO
YES
• PROBE WITH A TEST LIGHT BETWEEN C330 TERM "B" AND B+.
IS THE TEST LIGHT "ON"?
• CHECK FOR SHORT TO VOLTAGE TO CKT 237.
IF OK, REPLACE INSTRUMENT CLUSTER PRINTED CIRCUIT.
YES
NO
• CHECK CKT 238 FOR A SHORT TO GROUND.
IF OK, REPLACE SEAT BELT SWITCH.
REPLACE CHIME MODULE.

CHART #5
"FASTEN BELTS" INDICATOR INOPERATIVE

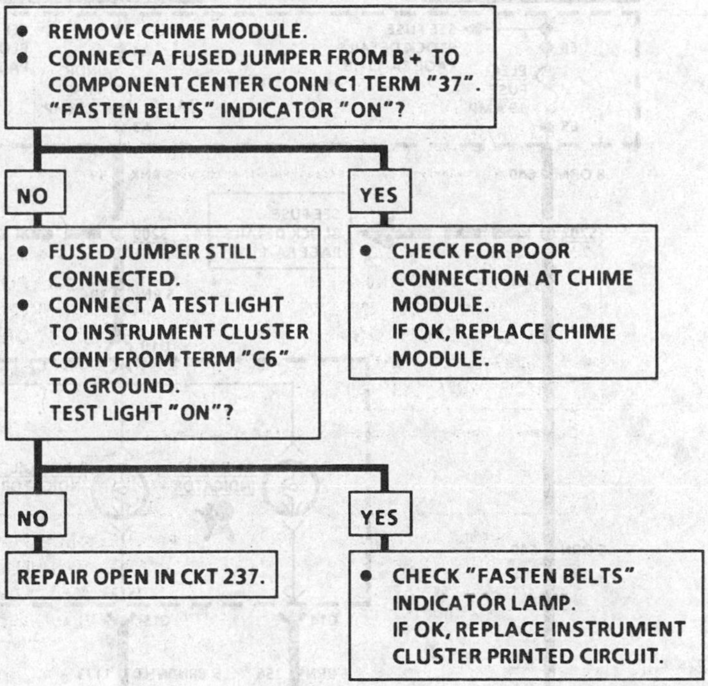
• REMOVE CHIME MODULE.
• CONNECT A FUSED JUMPER FROM B+ TO COMPONENT CENTER CONN C1 TERM "37".
"FASTEN BELTS" INDICATOR "ON"?
NO
YES
• FUSED JUMPER STILL CONNECTED.
• CONNECT A TEST LIGHT TO INSTRUMENT CLUSTER CONN FROM TERM "C6" TO GROUND.
TEST LIGHT "ON"?
• CHECK FOR POOR CONNECTION AT CHIME MODULE.
IF OK, REPLACE CHIME MODULE.
NO
YES
REPAIR OPEN IN CKT 237.
• CHECK "FASTEN BELTS" INDICATOR LAMP.
IF OK, REPLACE INSTRUMENT CLUSTER PRINTED CIRCUIT.

CIRCUIT OPERATION

The Chime Module generates audible warnings for four conditions: Lights "ON" Warning, Ignition Key Warning, Fasten Belts Warning and Turn Signal Warning. The Lights "ON" Warning and Turn Signal Warning are pulsed approximately once every one half second, sounding the quickest. The Ignition Key Warning is pulsed once every second. The Fasten Belts Warning is a continuous tone.

LIGHTS "ON" WARNING

When the Headlight Switch is in "PARK" or "HEAD," voltage is applied to the Lights "ON" Input of the Chime Module. When the Ignition Switch is turned out of the "RUN" position, voltage is removed from the Ignition Switch Input of the Chime Module. When voltage is present at the Lights "ON" Input and no voltage applied to the Ignition Switch Input, the Chime Module will sound the Lights "ON" Warning.

IGNITION KEY WARNING

The Chime Module applies voltage at all times to the Ignition Key Warning Switch. When the Ignition Key is placed into the Ignition Switch, the Ignition Key Warning Switch is closed. When the LH front door is open, the LH Front Door Jamb Switch closes the circuit to ground. The Chime Module senses a voltage drop at the Ignition Key Input and will sound the Ignition Key Warning.

FASTEN BELTS WARNING

The Chime Module applies voltage to the Seat Belt Switch at all times. The Chime Module senses a voltage drop at the Seat Belt Input through the closed contacts of the Seat Belt Switch when the driver's seat belt is unlatched. When the driver's seat belt is latched, the Seat Belt Switch is opened and the Chime Module senses voltage at the Seat Belt Input. When the Ignition Switch is turned to "RUN," voltage is applied to the Chime Module Ignition Switch Input. When voltage is present at the Ignition Switch Input and zero volt at the Seat Belt Input, the Chime Module will sound the Fasten Belts Warning for 4 to 8 seconds. If voltage is present at the Ignition Switch Input and the Seat Belt Input, the Chime Module will disable the Fasten Belts Warning.

TURN SIGNAL CHIME

When a turn signal is operated, voltage is alternately applied and removed to Chime Module Connector C2, terminal "A". The module begins to monitor vehicle distance at connector C2, terminal "B". If the Turn Signal is still flashing after the vehicle has traveled 0.8 kilometers (0.5 miles), the Turn Signal Warning chime will sound.

INSTRUMENT CLUSTER: GAGES

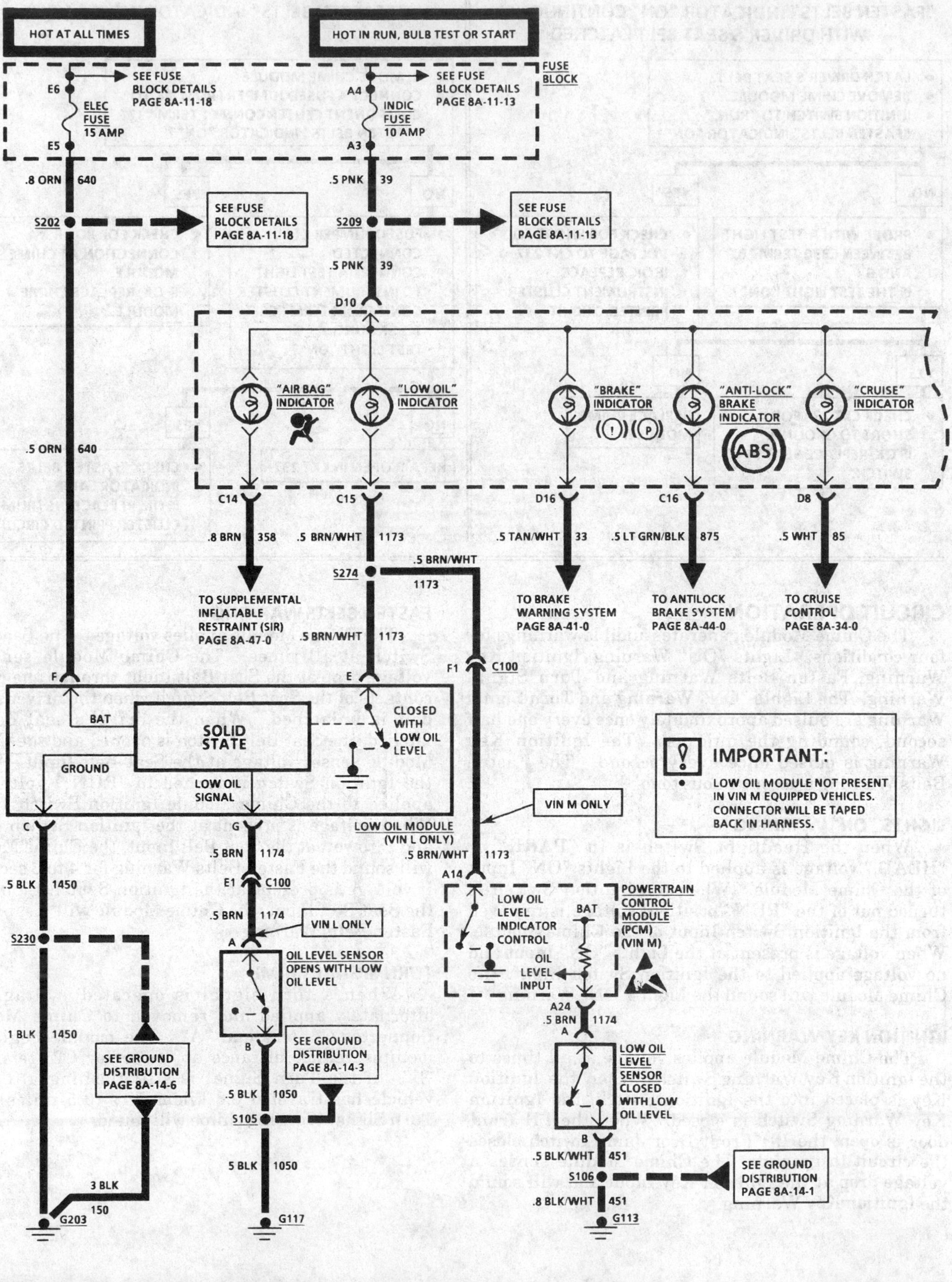

HOT AT ALL TIMES
HOT IN RUN, BULB TEST OR START
FUSE BLOCK
E6
SEE FUSE BLOCK DETAILS PAGE 8A-11-18
ELEC FUSE 15 AMP
E5
A4
SEE FUSE BLOCK DETAILS PAGE 8A-11-13
INDIC FUSE 10 AMP
A3
.8 ORN 640
.5 PNK 39
S202
SEE FUSE BLOCK DETAILS PAGE 8A-11-18
S209
SEE FUSE BLOCK DETAILS PAGE 8A-11-13
.5 PNK 39
D10
"AIR BAG" INDICATOR
"LOW OIL" INDICATOR
"BRAKE" INDICATOR
"ANTI-LOCK" BRAKE INDICATOR
ABS
"CRUISE" INDICATOR
.5 ORN 640
C14
C15
D16
C16
D8
.8 BRN 358
.5 BRN/WHT 1173
.5 TAN/WHT 33
.5 LT GRN/BLK 875
.5 WHT 85
.5 BRN/WHT
S274
1173
TO SUPPLEMENTAL INFLATABLE RESTRAINT (SIR) PAGE 8A-47-0
TO BRAKE WARNING SYSTEM PAGE 8A-41-0
TO ANTILOCK BRAKE SYSTEM PAGE 8A-44-0
TO CRUISE CONTROL PAGE 8A-34-0
.5 BRN/WHT 1173
F1 C100
F
E
BAT
SOLID STATE
GROUND
CLOSED WITH LOW OIL LEVEL
LOW OIL SIGNAL
LOW OIL MODULE (VIN L ONLY)
VIN M ONLY
IMPORTANT:
LOW OIL MODULE NOT PRESENT IN VIN M EQUIPPED VEHICLES. CONNECTOR WILL BE TAPED BACK IN HARNESS.
C
G
.5 BRN 1174
.5 BRN/WHT 1173
.5 BLK 1450
E1 C100
A14
.5 BRN 1174
VIN L ONLY
LOW OIL LEVEL INDICATOR CONTROL
BAT
POWERTRAIN CONTROL MODULE (PCM) (VIN M)
OIL LEVEL INPUT
S230
A
OIL LEVEL SENSOR OPENS WITH LOW OIL LEVEL
A24
.5 BRN 1174
A
1 BLK 1450
SEE GROUND DISTRIBUTION PAGE 8A-14-6
B
SEE GROUND DISTRIBUTION PAGE 8A-14-3
LOW OIL LEVEL SENSOR CLOSED WITH LOW OIL LEVEL
.5 BLK 1050
S105
B
.5 BLK/WHT 451
S106
SEE GROUND DISTRIBUTION PAGE 8A-14-1
5 BLK 1050
3 BLK
150
.8 BLK/WHT 451
G203
G117
G113

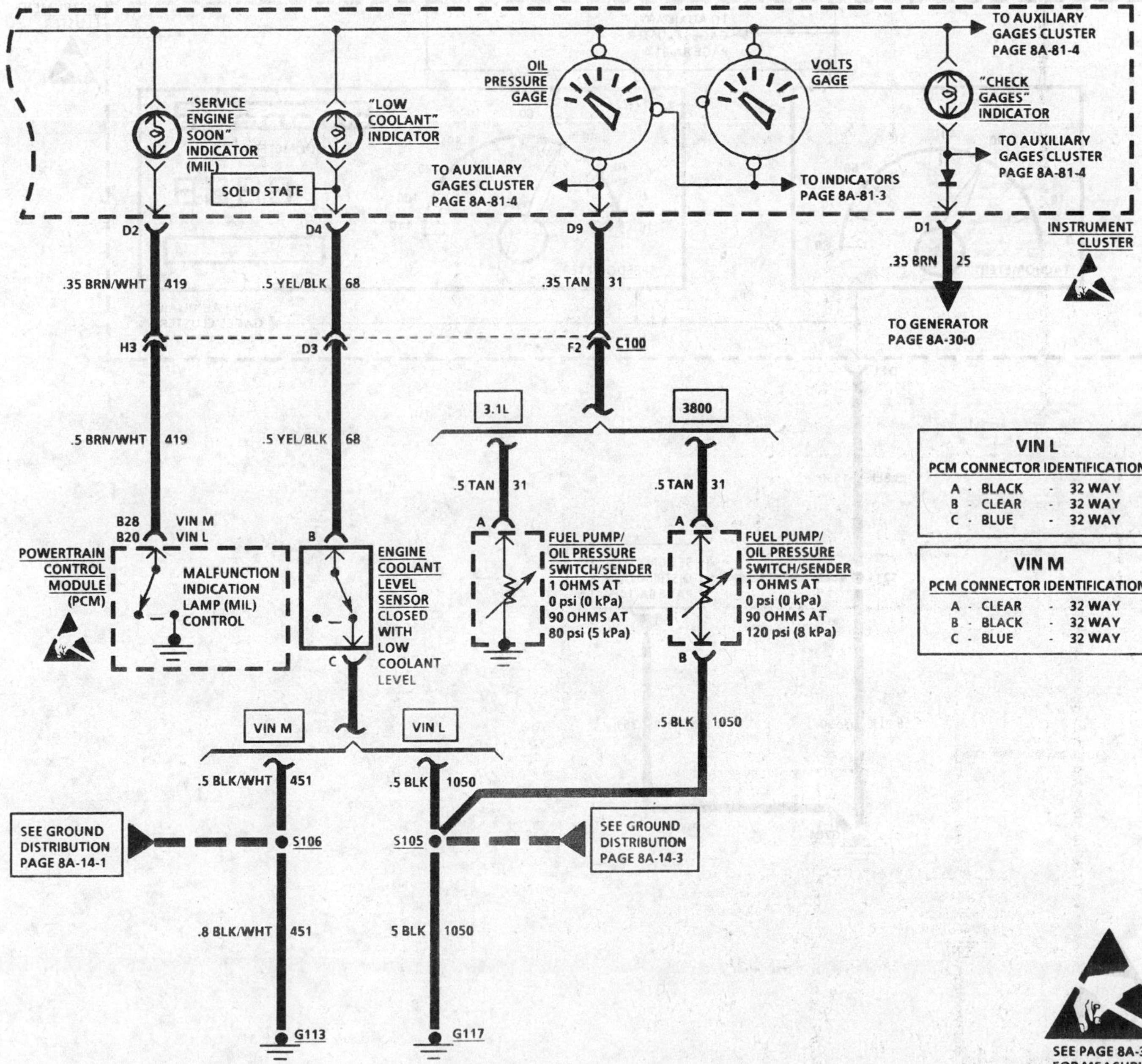
TO AUXILIARY GAGES CLUSTER PAGE 8A-81-4
OIL PRESSURE GAGE
VOLTS GAGE
"SERVICE ENGINE SOON" INDICATOR (MIL)
"LOW COOLANT" INDICATOR
"CHECK GAGES" INDICATOR
TO AUXILIARY GAGES CLUSTER PAGE 8A-81-4
SOLID STATE
TO AUXILIARY GAGES CLUSTER PAGE 8A-81-4
TO INDICATORS PAGE 8A-81-3
D2
D4
D9
D1
INSTRUMENT CLUSTER
.35 BRN/WHT 419
.5 YEL/BLK 68
.35 TAN 31
.35 BRN 25
TO GENERATOR PAGE 8A-30-0
H3
D3
F2
C100
3.1L
3800
.5 BRN/WHT 419
.5 YEL/BLK 68
.5 TAN 31
.5 TAN 31
B28 VIN M
B20 VIN L
B
A
A
POWERTRAIN CONTROL MODULE (PCM)
MALFUNCTION INDICATION LAMP (MIL) CONTROL
ENGINE COOLANT LEVEL SENSOR CLOSED WITH LOW COOLANT LEVEL
FUEL PUMP/ OIL PRESSURE SWITCH/SENDER 1 OHMS AT 0 psi (0 kPa) 90 OHMS AT 80 psi (5 kPa)
FUEL PUMP/ OIL PRESSURE SWITCH/SENDER 1 OHMS AT 0 psi (0 kPa) 90 OHMS AT 120 psi (8 kPa)
C
B
.5 BLK 1050
VIN M
VIN L
.5 BLK/WHT 451
.5 BLK 1050
SEE GROUND DISTRIBUTION PAGE 8A-14-1
S106
S105
SEE GROUND DISTRIBUTION PAGE 8A-14-3
.8 BLK/WHT 451
5 BLK 1050
G113
G117

VIN L

PCM CONNECTOR IDENTIFICATION

A	BLACK	32 WAY
B	CLEAR	32 WAY
C	BLUE	32 WAY

VIN M

PCM CONNECTOR IDENTIFICATION

A	CLEAR	32 WAY
B	BLACK	32 WAY
C	BLUE	32 WAY

SEE PAGE 8A-3-0 FOR MEASURING AND HANDLING PROCEDURES

INSTRUMENT CLUSTER: GAGES

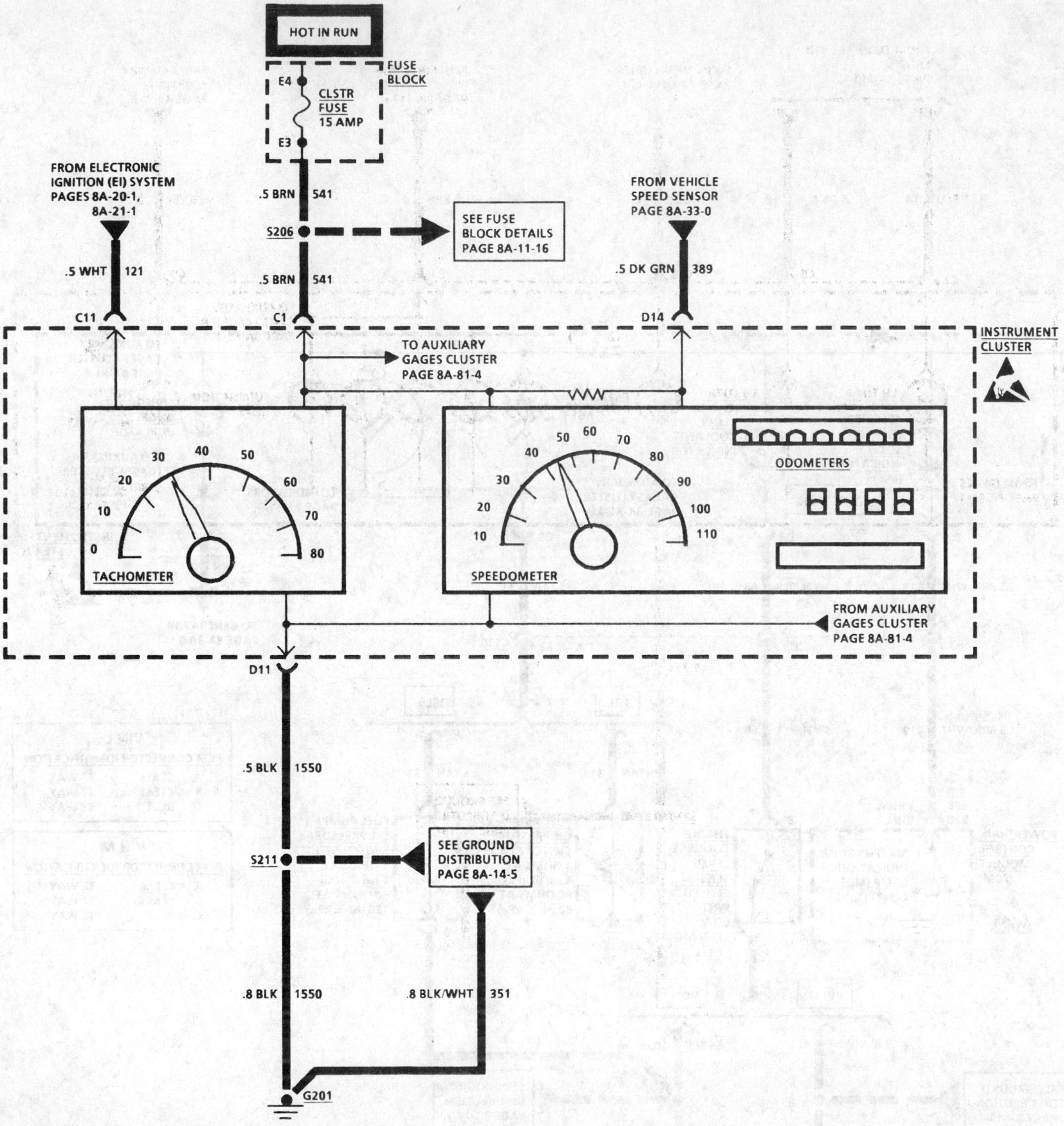
HOT IN RUN
FUSE BLOCK
E4
CLSTR FUSE 15 AMP
E3
FROM ELECTRONIC IGNITION (EI) SYSTEM PAGES 8A-20-1, 8A-21-1
.5 BRN 541
S206
SEE FUSE BLOCK DETAILS PAGE 8A-11-16
FROM VEHICLE SPEED SENSOR PAGE 8A-33-0
.5 WHT 121
.5 BRN 541
.5 DK GRN 389
C11
C1
D14
TO AUXILIARY GAGES CLUSTER PAGE 8A-81-4
INSTRUMENT CLUSTER
ODOMETERS
TACHOMETER
SPEEDOMETER
FROM AUXILIARY GAGES CLUSTER PAGE 8A-81-4
D11
.5 BLK 1550
S211
SEE GROUND DISTRIBUTION PAGE 8A-14-5
.8 BLK 1550
.8 BLK/WHT 351
G201

SEE PAGE 8A-3-0 FOR MEASURING AND HANDLING PROCEDURES

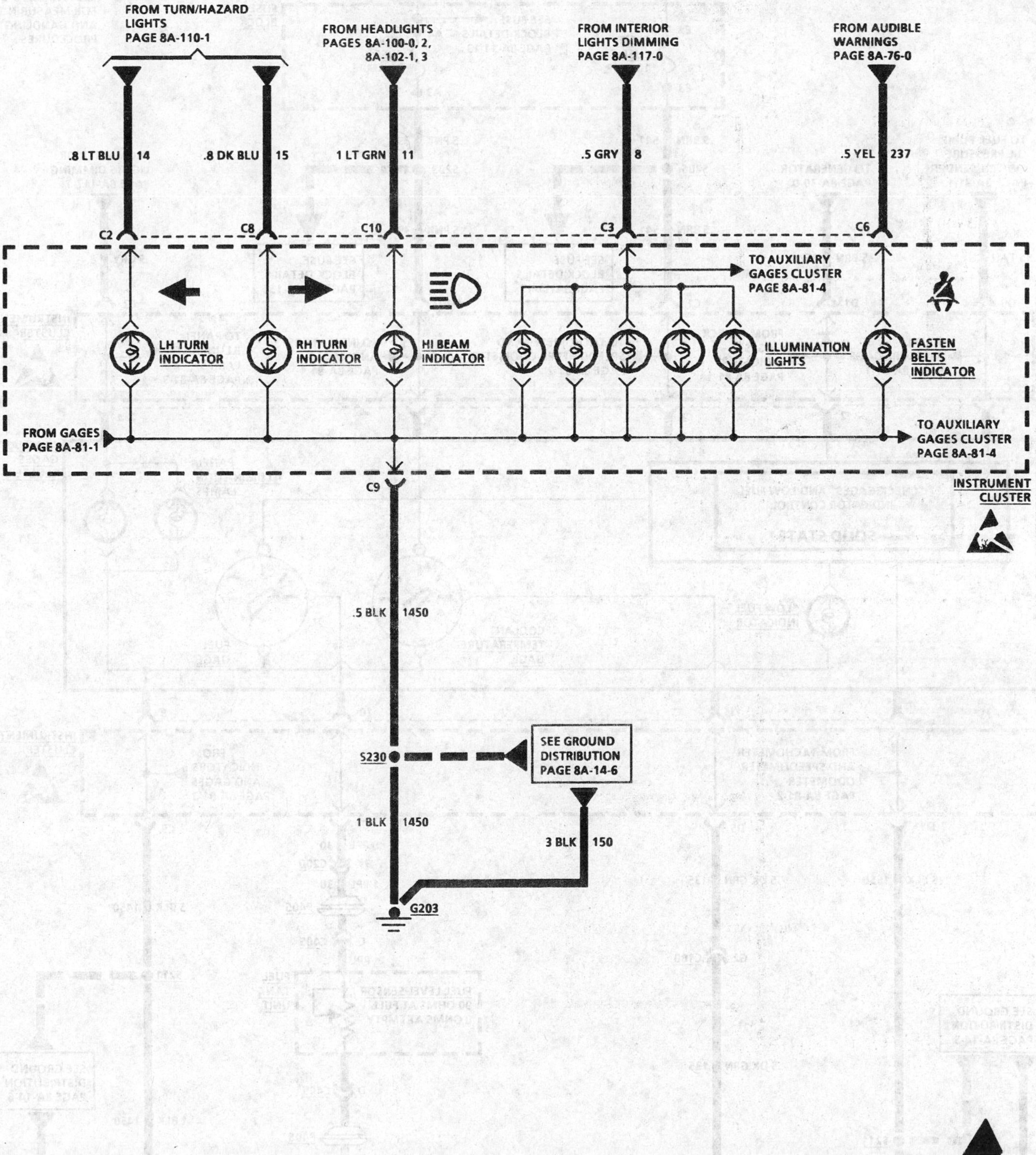
FROM TURN/HAZARD LIGHTS PAGE 8A-110-1
FROM HEADLIGHTS PAGES 8A-100-0, 2, 8A-102-1, 3
FROM INTERIOR LIGHTS DIMMING PAGE 8A-117-0
FROM AUDIBLE WARNINGS PAGE 8A-76-0
.8 LT BLU 14
.8 DK BLU 15
1 LT GRN 11
.5 GRY 8
.5 YEL 237
C2
C8
C10
C3
C6
TO AUXILIARY GAGES CLUSTER PAGE 8A-81-4
LH TURN INDICATOR
RH TURN INDICATOR
HI BEAM INDICATOR
ILLUMINATION LIGHTS
FASTEN BELTS INDICATOR
FROM GAGES PAGE 8A-81-1
TO AUXILIARY GAGES CLUSTER PAGE 8A-81-4
C9
INSTRUMENT CLUSTER
.5 BLK 1450
S230
SEE GROUND DISTRIBUTION PAGE 8A-14-6
1 BLK 1450
3 BLK 150
G203

SEE PAGE 8A-3-0 FOR MEASURING AND HANDLING PROCEDURES

INSTRUMENT CLUSTER: GAGES
AUXILIARY GAGES CLUSTER

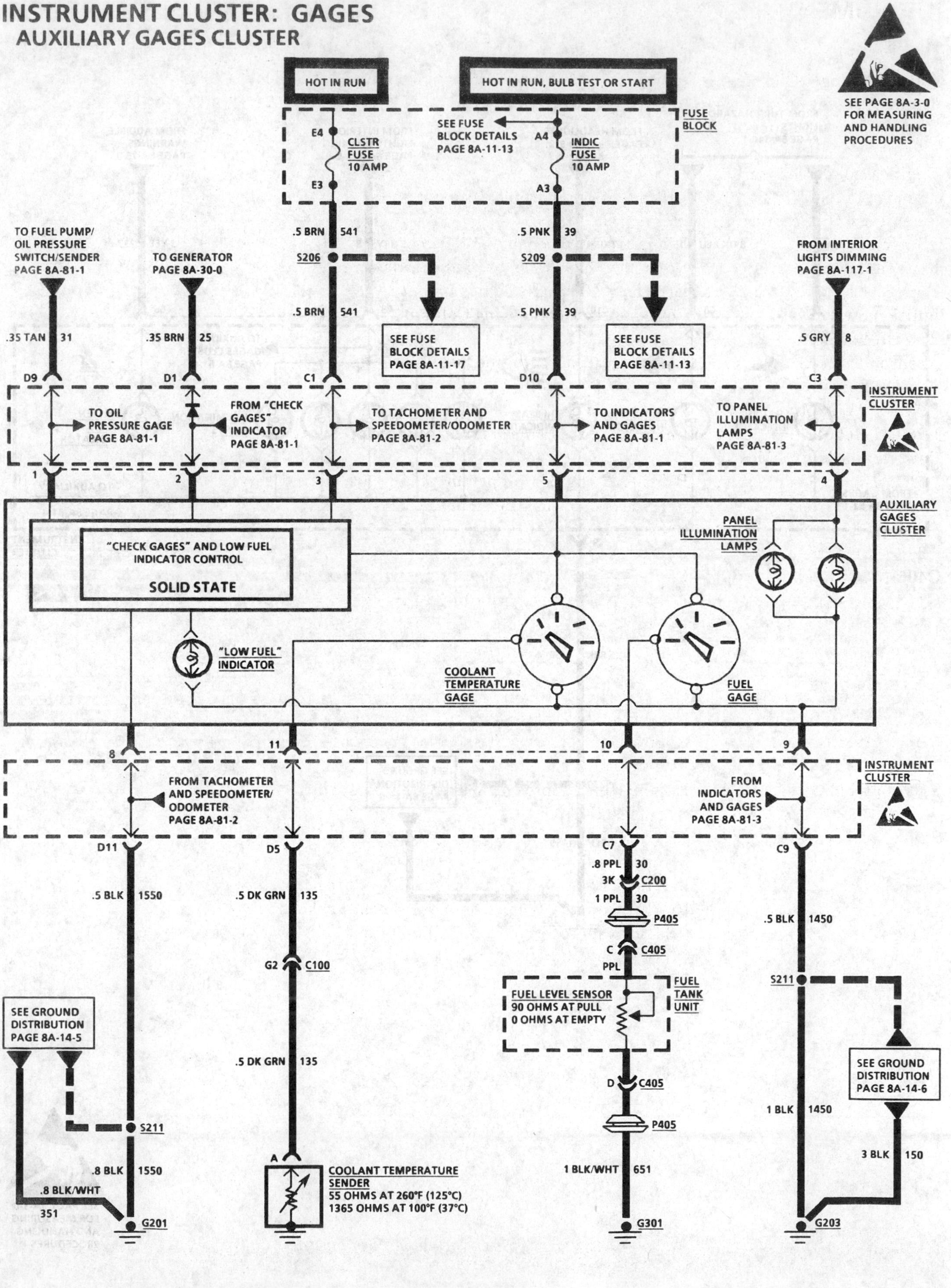

HOT IN RUN
HOT IN RUN, BULB TEST OR START
SEE PAGE 8A-3-0 FOR MEASURING AND HANDLING PROCEDURES
FUSE BLOCK
E4
CLSTR FUSE 10 AMP
E3
SEE FUSE BLOCK DETAILS PAGE 8A-11-13
A4
INDIC FUSE 10 AMP
A3
TO FUEL PUMP/ OIL PRESSURE SWITCH/SENDER PAGE 8A-81-1
TO GENERATOR PAGE 8A-30-0
.5 BRN 541
S206
.5 PNK 39
S209
FROM INTERIOR LIGHTS DIMMING PAGE 8A-117-1
.35 TAN 31
.35 BRN 25
SEE FUSE BLOCK DETAILS PAGE 8A-11-17
SEE FUSE BLOCK DETAILS PAGE 8A-11-13
.5 GRY 8
D9
D1
C1
D10
C3
INSTRUMENT CLUSTER
TO OIL PRESSURE GAGE PAGE 8A-81-1
FROM "CHECK GAGES" INDICATOR PAGE 8A-81-1
TO TACHOMETER AND SPEEDOMETER/ODOMETER PAGE 8A-81-2
TO INDICATORS AND GAGES PAGE 8A-81-1
TO PANEL ILLUMINATION LAMPS PAGE 8A-81-3
1
2
3
5
4
AUXILIARY GAGES CLUSTER
PANEL ILLUMINATION LAMPS
"CHECK GAGES" AND LOW FUEL INDICATOR CONTROL
SOLID STATE
"LOW FUEL" INDICATOR
COOLANT TEMPERATURE GAGE
FUEL GAGE
8
11
10
9
FROM TACHOMETER AND SPEEDOMETER/ ODOMETER PAGE 8A-81-2
FROM INDICATORS AND GAGES PAGE 8A-81-3
D11
D5
C7
C9
.5 BLK 1550
.5 DK GRN 135
.8 PPL 30
3K
C200
1 PPL 30
P405
C
C405
PPL
.5 BLK 1450
G2
C100
S211
FUEL LEVEL SENSOR 90 OHMS AT PULL 0 OHMS AT EMPTY
FUEL TANK UNIT
SEE GROUND DISTRIBUTION PAGE 8A-14-5
.5 DK GRN 135
D
C405
P405
SEE GROUND DISTRIBUTION PAGE 8A-14-6
1 BLK 1450
S211
3 BLK 150
A
.8 BLK 1550
.8 BLK/WHT
351
COOLANT TEMPERATURE SENDER
55 OHMS AT 260°F (125°C)
1365 OHMS AT 100°F (37°C)
1 BLK/WHT 651
G201
G301
G203

INSTRUMENT CLUSTER: GAGES

COMPONENT	LOCATION	201-PG	FIG.	CONN
Auxiliary Gages Cluster	LH side of I/P, next to Instrument Cluster			
Engine Coolant Level Sensor	Top RH rear of radiator	8	25	
Engine Coolant Temperature Sender (VIN L)	Top LH side of Engine	7	24	
Engine Coolant Temperature Sender (VIN M)	LH rear of Engine, below coolant outlet	4	13	
Fuel Pump/Oil Pressure Switch/Sender	RH rear of Engine, above oil filter	9	32	202-39
Fuel Tank Unit	Below rear of vehicle, top of fuel tank	10	35	
Fuse Block	RH side of I/P, in I/P Compartment			
Ignition Switch	Lower top side of Steering Column			
Low Oil Level Sensor (VIN L)	Lower LH front of Engine, below Starter Motor			
Low Oil Level Sensor (VIN M)	Center of oil pan			
Low Oil Module	Below I/P, on LH side of brake pedal support			
Powertrain Control Module (PCM)	RH side of Engine Compartment, forward of strut tower	19	68	202-26
C100 (36 cavities)	RH side of dash, behind strut tower			202-0
C200 (102 cavities)	Behind RH side of I/P, near shroud	22	74	202-3
C202 (48 cavities)	Behind I/P, RH side of Steering Column	14	48	202-10
C405 (6 cavities)	Center rear of vehicle, near fuel tank	10	35	202-36
G113 (VIN M)	Lower LH front of Engine, on Transaxle stud	0	1	
G117 (VIN L)	Lower LH front of Engine, on Transaxle stud	26	82	
G201	Behind I/P, on RH side of mag bracket			
G203	Behind I/P, on RH side of mag bracket			
G301	Under LH front seat	15	50	
P405	Center front of Trunk, in floor			
S105 (VIN L)	Engine Harn, approx 20 cm from Underhood Electrical Center #1 breakout			
S106 (VIN M)	Engine Harn, approx 4 cm from Engine Cooling Fan #2 breakout			
S202	I/P Harn, approx 13 cm from Radio Control Head breakout			
S206	I/P Harn, approx 10 cm from Fuse Block breakout			
S209	I/P Harn, approx 16 cm from Fuse Block breakout			
S211	I/P Harn, approx 9 cm from Radio Control Head breakout			
S213	I/P Harn, approx 8 cm from HVAC Control Head breakout			
S230	I/P Harn, approx 27 cm from Radio Control head breakout			
S274	I/P Harn, approx 22 cm from Radio Control Head breakout			

INSTRUMENT CLUSTER: GAGES

INSTRUMENT CLUSTER REARVIEW

Instrument Cluster

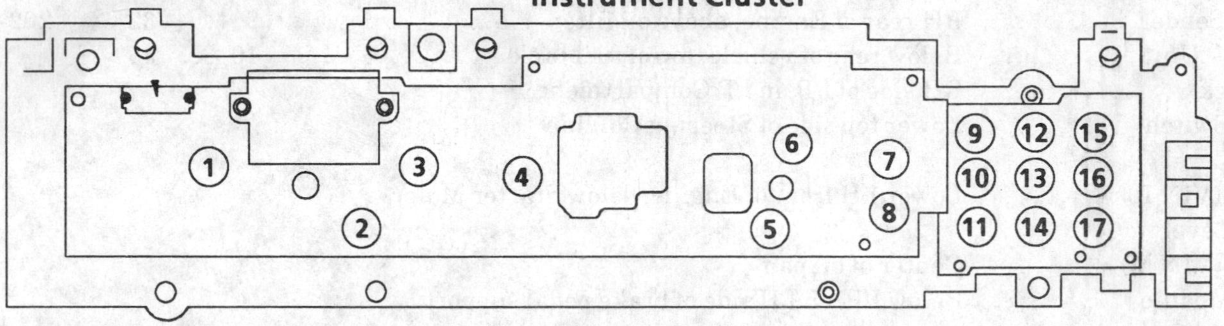
1
2
3
4
5
6
7
8
9
10
11
12
13
14
15
16
17

INSTRUMENT CLUSTER BULB LOCATIONS

1 Illumination
2 Illumination
3 RH Turn Indicator
4 Illumination
5 Illumination
6 HI Beam Indicator
7 LH Turn Indicator
8 Illumination
9 AIR BAG Indicator
10 Fasten Belts Indicator
11 LOW OIL Indicator
12 CHECK GAGES Indicator
13 CRUISE Indicator
14 ANTI-LOCK Indicator
15 BRAKE Indicator
16 LOW COOLANT Indicator
17 SERVICE ENGINE SOON Indicator

Auxiliary Gages Cluster

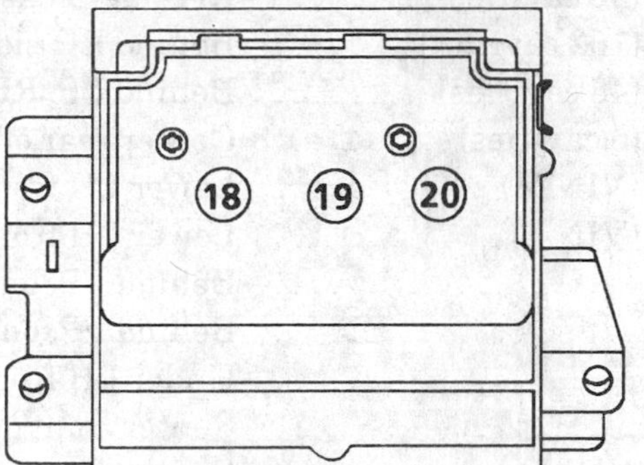
18
19
20

BULB LOCATIONS

18 Illumination
19 LOW FUEL Indicator
20 Illumination

INSTRUMENT CLUSTER: GAGES

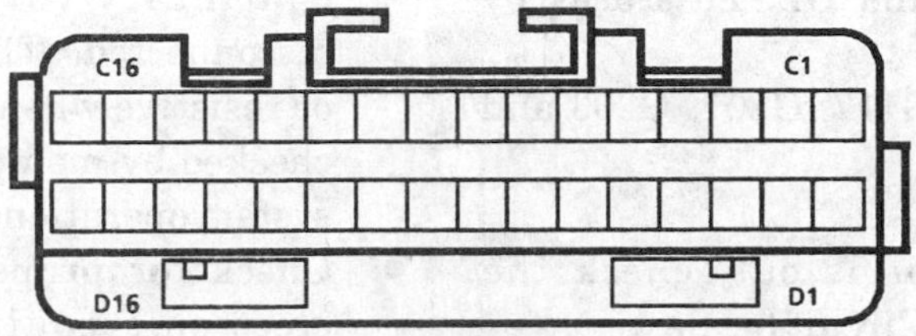
C16
C1
D16
D1

12045575

32-WAY F MICRO-PACK 100 SERIES
BLK

INSTRUMENT CLUSTER CONNECTOR

**CAVITIES NOT LISTED ARE NOT USED

CAVITY	WIRE COLOR	CKT	DESCRIPTION	PAGE
C1	BRN	541	IGNITION FEED	8A-11-15
C2	LT BLU	14	LH TURN INDICATOR	8A-110-1
C3	GRY	8	PANEL ILLUMINATION LAMPS	8A-117-0
C6	YEL	237	"FASTEN BELTS" INDICATOR	8A-76-0
C7	PPL	30	FUEL LEVEL INPUT	8A-81-4
C8	DK BLU	15	RH TURN INDICATOR	8A-110-1
C9	BLK	1450	GROUND	8A-14-6
C10	LT GRN	11	HI BEAM INDICATOR	8A-100-0, 2 8A-102-1, 3
C11	WHT	121	TACHOMETER INPUT	8A-20-1 8A-21-1
C14	BRN	358	"AIR BAG" INDICATOR	8A-47-0
C15	BRN/WHT	1173	"LOW OIL" INDICATOR	8A-81-0
C16	LT GRN/BLK	875	"ANTI-LOCK" BRAKE INDICATOR	8A-44-0

CAVITY	WIRE COLOR	CKT	DESCRIPTION	PAGE
D1	BRN	25	"CHECK GAGES" INDICATOR GENERATOR INPUT	8A-30-0
D2	BRN/WHT	419	"SERVICE ENGINE SOON" INDICATOR	8A-20-0 8A-21-0
D4	YEL/BLK	68	"LOW COOLANT" INDICATOR	8A-81-1
D5	DK GRN	135	COOLANT TEMPERATURE INPUT	8A-81-4
D8	WHT	85	"CRUISE" INDICATOR	8A-34-0
D9	TAN	31	OIL PRESSURE GAGE INPUT	8A-81-1
D10	PNK	39	INDICATORS IGNITION FEED	8A-11-13
D11	BLK	1550	GROUND	8A-14-5
D14	DK GRN	389	VEHICLE SPEED INPUT	8A-33-0
D16	TAN/WHT	33	"BRAKE" INDICATOR	8A-41-0

INSTRUMENT CLUSTER: GAGES

TROUBLESHOOTING HINTS (Perform before beginning System Diagnosis)

1. Check the INDIC, ELEC, and CLSTR Fuses by visual inspection.
2. Check that grounds G113, G117, G201, G203 and G301 are clean and tight.
3. Check the indicator bulbs.
4. If more than one indicator is out, check the Instrument Cluster Printed Circuit for flaws.
5. If the Auxiliary Gages Cluster does not function, check for poor connection at the Auxiliary Gages Cluster.

- For Instrument Cluster removal and replacement procedures, refer to SECTION 8C.
- Check for a broken (or partially broken) wire inside of the insulation which could cause system malfunction but prove "GOOD" in a continuity/voltage check with a system disconnected. These circuits may be intermittent or resistive when loaded, and if possible, should be checked by monitoring for a voltage drop with the system operational (under load).
- Check for proper installation of aftermarket electronic equipment which may affect the integrity of other systems (see "Troubleshooting Procedures," page 8A-4-0).
- Refer to System Diagnosis.

SYSTEM DIAGNOSIS

- Perform the System Check and refer to the Symptom Table for the appropriate diagnostic procedure(s).

SYSTEM CHECK

ACTION	NORMAL RESULTS
[1] • Turn Ignition Switch to "RUN."	"SERVICE ENGINE SOON" Indicator is "ON." Fasten Belts Indicator will come "ON" until the driver's seat belt is buckled. "LOW COOLANT" Indicator is "ON." "ANTI-LOCK" Indicator is "ON" for 3 to 5 seconds. (if equipped with Antilock Brakes). Fuel Gage shows current fuel level. "LOW OIL" Indicator is "ON" for 2 seconds. Volts Gage shows battery voltage. "CHECK GAGES" Indicator is "ON." Oil Pressure Gage show 0 psi. Coolant Temperature Gage shows coolant temperature. "AIR BAG" Indicator flashes 7 times.
[2] • With Ignition Switch in "RUN," first operate the RH Turn Signal then the LH Turn Signal.	RH and LH Turn Indicators flash.
[3] • With Ignition Switch in "RUN," turn the HI Beam Headlights "ON."	HI Beam Indicator is "ON."
[4] • With Ignition Switch in "RUN," apply the Park Brake.	"BRAKE" Indicator is "ON."
[5] • With Ignition Switch in "RUN," turn the Head or Park Lights "ON" and adjust the dimmer control.	Instrument Cluster and Speedometer Display illumination varies with dimmer control.
[6] • Turn Ignition Switch to "BULB TEST."	"BRAKE" Indicator is "ON." Coolant Temperature Gage moves through full scale.

SYMPTOM TABLE

SYMPTOM	PROCEDURE	PAGE NUMBER
"LOW OIL" Indicator "ON," oil level OK (VIN L).	Chart #1	8A-81-10
"LOW OIL" Indicator inoperative, oil level low (VIN L).	Chart #2	8A-81-11
Fuel Gage inoperative or inaccurate.	Chart #3	8A-81-12
"BRAKE" Indicator is inoperative or remains "ON" when Park Brake is released.	Refer to "Brake Warning System," page 8A-41-0.	
Fasten Belts Indicator does not work properly.	Refer to "Audible Warnings," page 8A-76-0.	
HI Beam Indicator does not work properly.	Refer to "Headlights," page 8A-100-0 or 8A-102-0.	
Turn Indicators do not work properly.	Refer to "Exterior Lights," page 8A-110-0.	
"CRUISE" Indicator does not work properly.	Refer to "Cruise Control," page 8A-34-0.	
Cluster illumination inoperative.	Refer to "Interior Lights Dimming," page 8A-117-0.	
"SERVICE ENGINE SOON" Indicator remains illuminated or flashes.	Refer to SECTION 6E.	
"ANTI-LOCK" Indicator is inoperative or does not work properly (if equipped with Antilock Brakes).	Refer to SECTION 5E1.	
Tachometer inoperative or inaccurate.	Check CKT 121 for an open or short to ground. If OK, repair Tachometer.	
Speedometer and/or Odometers inoperative or inaccurate.	Refer to "Vehicle Speed Sensor," page 8A-33-0.	
"CHECK GAGES" Indicator is inoperative or does not function properly.	Check Instrument Cluster Printed Circuit for an open or short. Check for poor connection at Auxiliary Gages Cluster Connector. If OK, replace Auxiliary Gages Cluster.	
"LOW FUEL" Indicator is inoperative or does not function properly.	Check Auxiliary Gages Cluster Printed Circuit for an open or short. If OK, replace Auxiliary Gages Cluster.	
Oil Pressure Gage and Volts Gage are inaccurate.	Check for a poor connection or high resistance in CKT 1450 (see schematic). If OK, service Instrument Cluster.	
Fuel Gage and Coolant Temperature Gage are inaccurate.	Connect a jumper wire from a good chassis ground to Auxiliary Gages Cluster Connector terminal "9". If gages are still inaccurate, service Auxiliary Gages Cluster. If gages operate properly, repair Cluster.	
Volts Gage inoperative or inaccurate.	Check for open or short in Instrument Cluster Printed Circuit. If OK, service Instrument Cluster.	
Coolant Temperature Gage inoperative or inaccurate.	Chart #4	8A-81-14
Oil Pressure Gage inoperative or inaccurate.	Chart #5	8A-81-14
"LOW COOLANT" Indicator "ON," coolant level OK.	Chart #6	8A-81-15
"LOW COOLANT" Indicator "OFF," coolant level low.	Chart #7	8A-81-15

(CONTINUED ON NEXT PAGE)

INSTRUMENT CLUSTER: GAGES

(CONTINUED FROM PREVIOUS PAGE)

SYMPTOM TABLE

SYMPTOM	PROCEDURE	PAGE NUMBER
"LOW OIL" Indicator "ON," oil level OK (VIN M).	Chart #8	8A-81-15
"LOW OIL" Indicator inoperative, oil level low (VIN M).	Chart #9	8A-81-15
"AIR BAG" Indicator inoperative, remains illuminated or flashes continuously.	Refer to SECTION 9J.	

CHART #1
"LOW OIL" INDICATOR "ON," OIL LEVEL OK (VIN L)

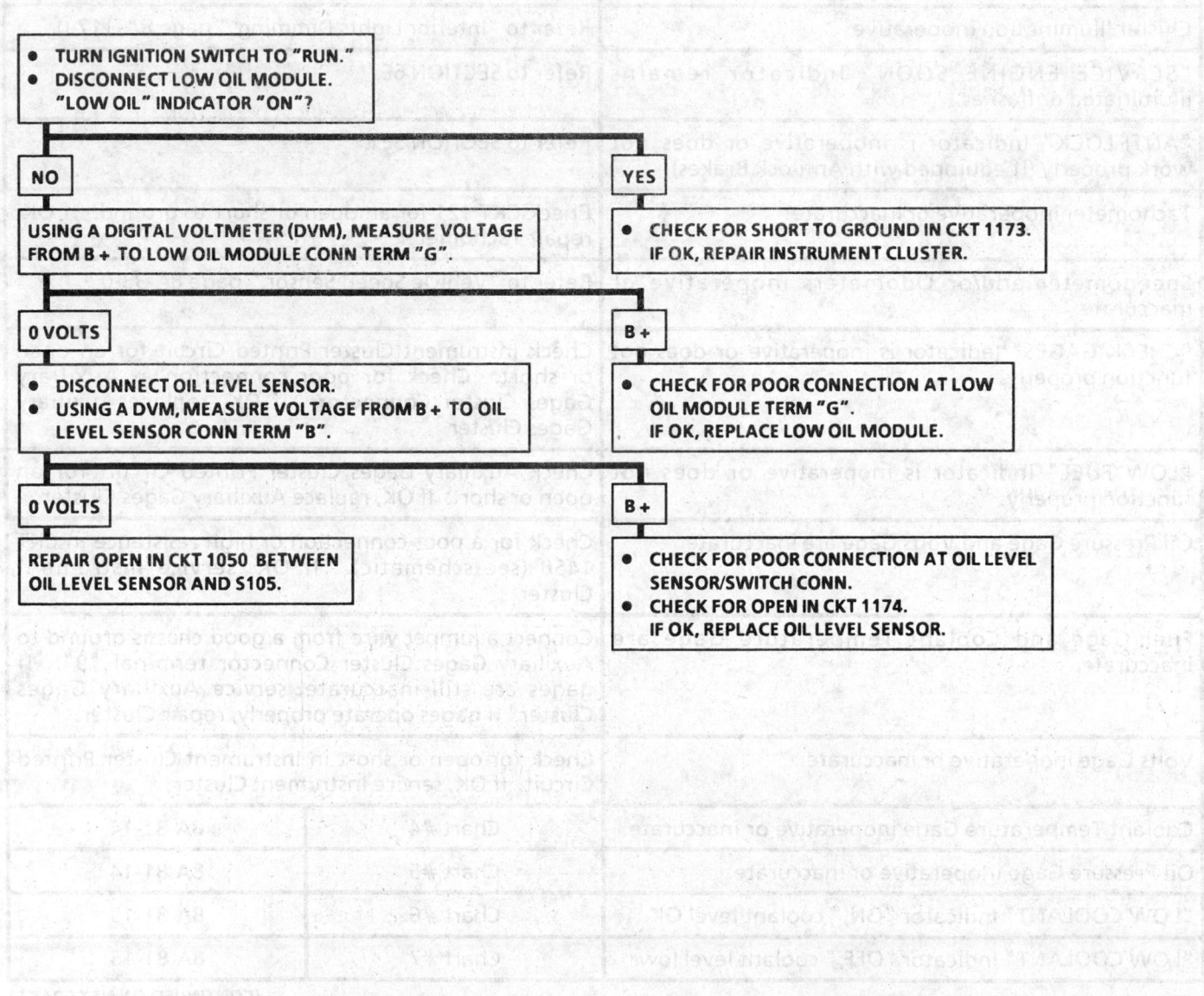

- TURN IGNITION SWITCH TO "RUN."
- DISCONNECT LOW OIL MODULE.
  "LOW OIL" INDICATOR "ON"?

NO

USING A DIGITAL VOLTMETER (DVM), MEASURE VOLTAGE FROM B + TO LOW OIL MODULE CONN TERM "G".

0 VOLTS

- DISCONNECT OIL LEVEL SENSOR.
- USING A DVM, MEASURE VOLTAGE FROM B + TO OIL LEVEL SENSOR CONN TERM "B".

0 VOLTS

REPAIR OPEN IN CKT 1050 BETWEEN OIL LEVEL SENSOR AND S105.

B +

- CHECK FOR POOR CONNECTION AT OIL LEVEL SENSOR/SWITCH CONN.
- CHECK FOR OPEN IN CKT 1174.
  IF OK, REPLACE OIL LEVEL SENSOR.

B +

- CHECK FOR POOR CONNECTION AT LOW OIL MODULE TERM "G".
  IF OK, REPLACE LOW OIL MODULE.

YES

- CHECK FOR SHORT TO GROUND IN CKT 1173.
  IF OK, REPAIR INSTRUMENT CLUSTER.

CHART #2
"LOW OIL" INDICATOR INOPERATIVE, OIL LEVEL LOW (VIN L)

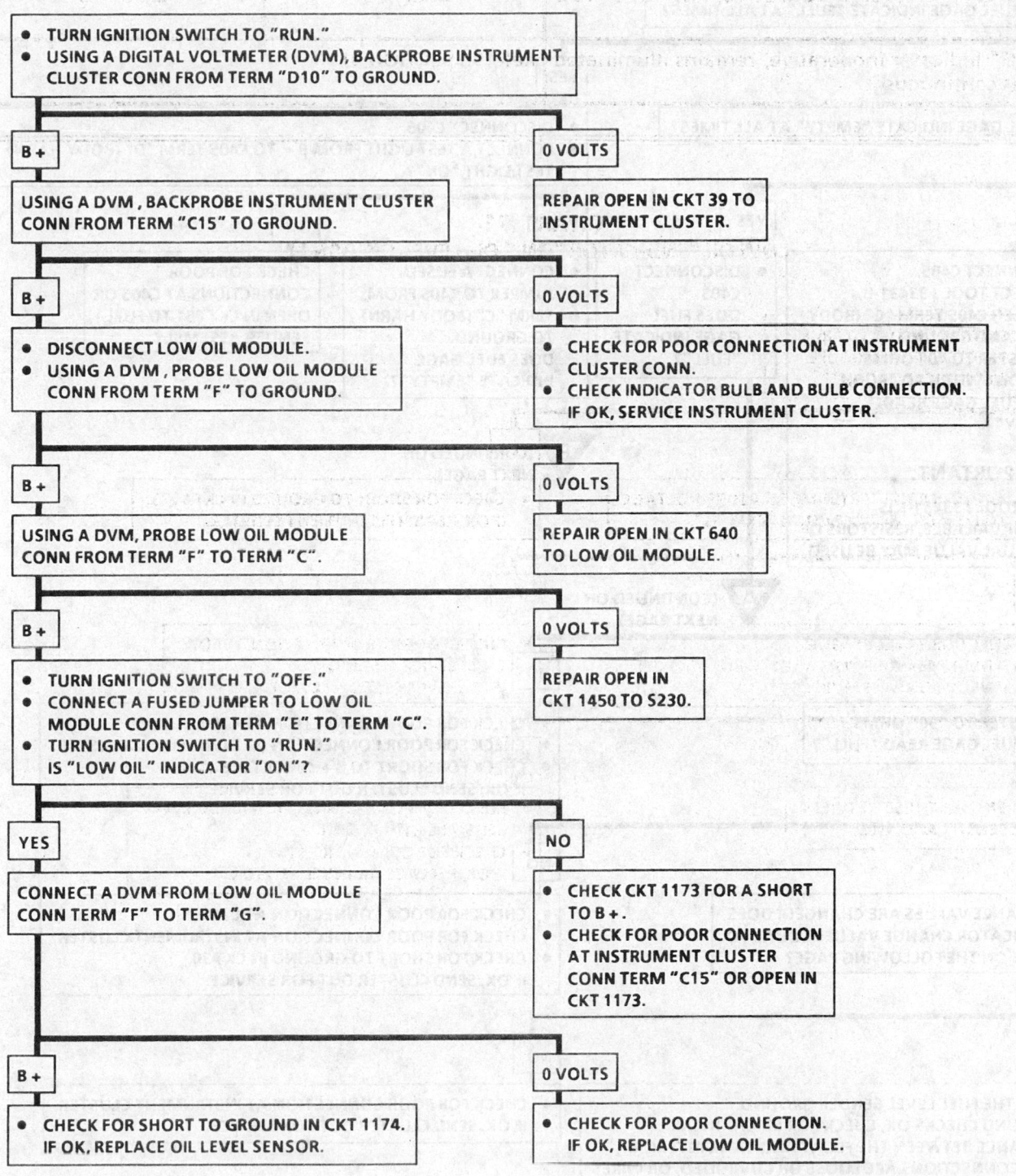

- TURN IGNITION SWITCH TO "RUN."
- USING A DIGITAL VOLTMETER (DVM), BACKPROBE INSTRUMENT CLUSTER CONN FROM TERM "D10" TO GROUND.

B + → USING A DVM , BACKPROBE INSTRUMENT CLUSTER CONN FROM TERM "C15" TO GROUND.

0 VOLTS → REPAIR OPEN IN CKT 39 TO INSTRUMENT CLUSTER.

(From "C15" test:)

B + →
- DISCONNECT LOW OIL MODULE.
- USING A DVM , PROBE LOW OIL MODULE CONN FROM TERM "F" TO GROUND.

0 VOLTS →
- CHECK FOR POOR CONNECTION AT INSTRUMENT CLUSTER CONN.
- CHECK INDICATOR BULB AND BULB CONNECTION. IF OK, SERVICE INSTRUMENT CLUSTER.

(From term "F" to ground test:)

B + → USING A DVM, PROBE LOW OIL MODULE CONN FROM TERM "F" TO TERM "C".

0 VOLTS → REPAIR OPEN IN CKT 640 TO LOW OIL MODULE.

(From term "F" to term "C" test:)

B + →
- TURN IGNITION SWITCH TO "OFF."
- CONNECT A FUSED JUMPER TO LOW OIL MODULE CONN FROM TERM "E" TO TERM "C".
- TURN IGNITION SWITCH TO "RUN." IS "LOW OIL" INDICATOR "ON"?

0 VOLTS → REPAIR OPEN IN CKT 1450 TO S230.

(From "LOW OIL" indicator test:)

YES → CONNECT A DVM FROM LOW OIL MODULE CONN TERM "F" TO TERM "G".

NO →
- CHECK CKT 1173 FOR A SHORT TO B +.
- CHECK FOR POOR CONNECTION AT INSTRUMENT CLUSTER CONN TERM "C15" OR OPEN IN CKT 1173.

(From term "F" to term "G" test:)

B + →
- CHECK FOR SHORT TO GROUND IN CKT 1174. IF OK, REPLACE OIL LEVEL SENSOR.

0 VOLTS →
- CHECK FOR POOR CONNECTION. IF OK, REPLACE LOW OIL MODULE.

INSTRUMENT CLUSTER: GAGES

CHART #3
FUEL GAGE INOPERATIVE OR INACCURATE

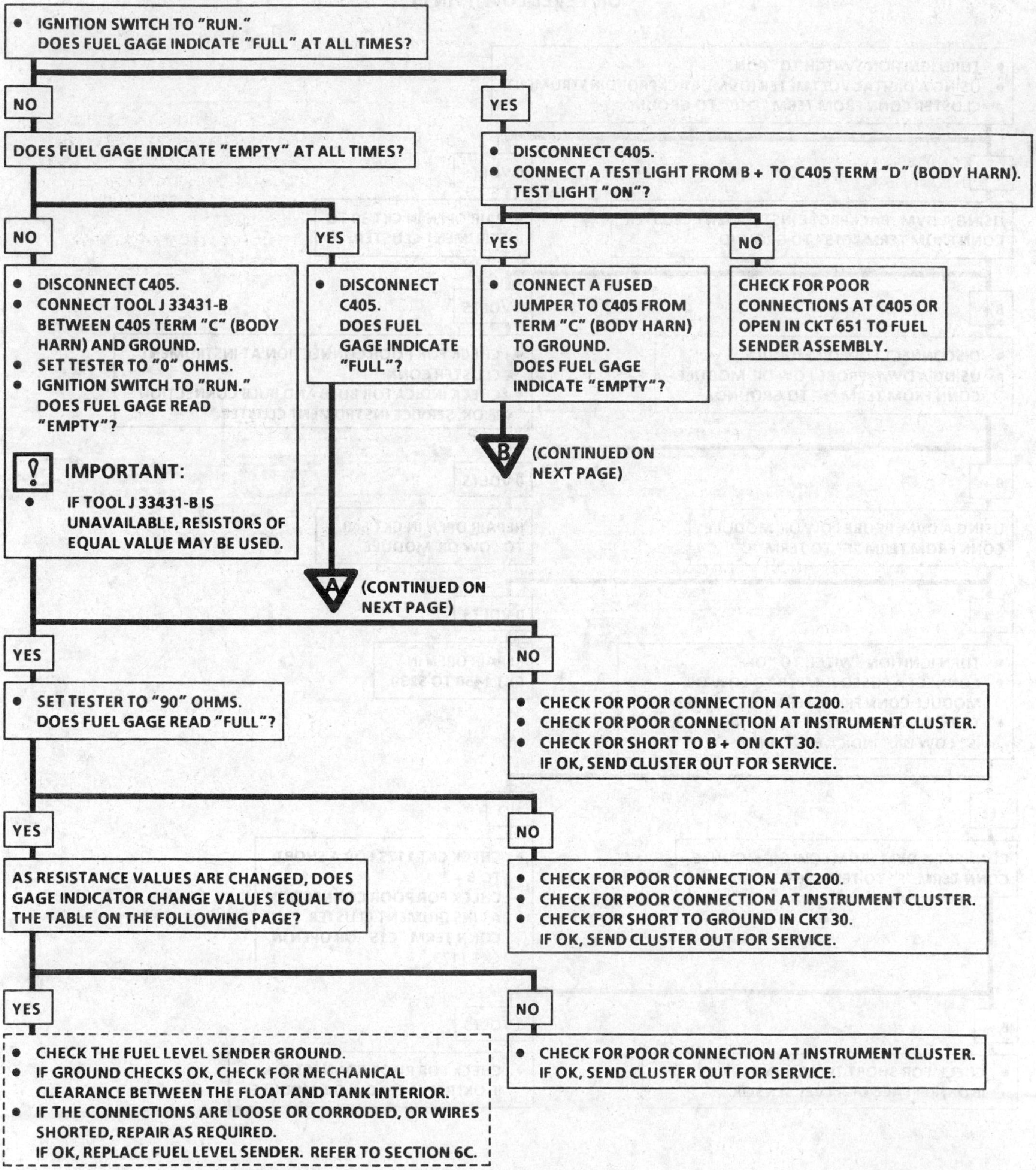

• IGNITION SWITCH TO "RUN." DOES FUEL GAGE INDICATE "FULL" AT ALL TIMES?
NO
YES
DOES FUEL GAGE INDICATE "EMPTY" AT ALL TIMES?
• DISCONNECT C405.
• CONNECT A TEST LIGHT FROM B + TO C405 TERM "D" (BODY HARN). TEST LIGHT "ON"?
NO
YES
YES
NO
• DISCONNECT C405.
• CONNECT TOOL J 33431-B BETWEEN C405 TERM "C" (BODY HARN) AND GROUND.
• SET TESTER TO "0" OHMS.
• IGNITION SWITCH TO "RUN." DOES FUEL GAGE READ "EMPTY"?
IMPORTANT:
• IF TOOL J 33431-B IS UNAVAILABLE, RESISTORS OF EQUAL VALUE MAY BE USED.
• DISCONNECT C405. DOES FUEL GAGE INDICATE "FULL"?
• CONNECT A FUSED JUMPER TO C405 FROM TERM "C" (BODY HARN) TO GROUND. DOES FUEL GAGE INDICATE "EMPTY"?
CHECK FOR POOR CONNECTIONS AT C405 OR OPEN IN CKT 651 TO FUEL SENDER ASSEMBLY.
B (CONTINUED ON NEXT PAGE)
A (CONTINUED ON NEXT PAGE)
YES
NO
• SET TESTER TO "90" OHMS. DOES FUEL GAGE READ "FULL"?
• CHECK FOR POOR CONNECTION AT C200.
• CHECK FOR POOR CONNECTION AT INSTRUMENT CLUSTER.
• CHECK FOR SHORT TO B + ON CKT 30. IF OK, SEND CLUSTER OUT FOR SERVICE.
YES
NO
AS RESISTANCE VALUES ARE CHANGED, DOES GAGE INDICATOR CHANGE VALUES EQUAL TO THE TABLE ON THE FOLLOWING PAGE?
• CHECK FOR POOR CONNECTION AT C200.
• CHECK FOR POOR CONNECTION AT INSTRUMENT CLUSTER.
• CHECK FOR SHORT TO GROUND IN CKT 30. IF OK, SEND CLUSTER OUT FOR SERVICE.
YES
NO
• CHECK THE FUEL LEVEL SENDER GROUND.
• IF GROUND CHECKS OK, CHECK FOR MECHANICAL CLEARANCE BETWEEN THE FLOAT AND TANK INTERIOR.
• IF THE CONNECTIONS ARE LOOSE OR CORRODED, OR WIRES SHORTED, REPAIR AS REQUIRED. IF OK, REPLACE FUEL LEVEL SENDER. REFER TO SECTION 6C.
• CHECK FOR POOR CONNECTION AT INSTRUMENT CLUSTER. IF OK, SEND CLUSTER OUT FOR SERVICE.

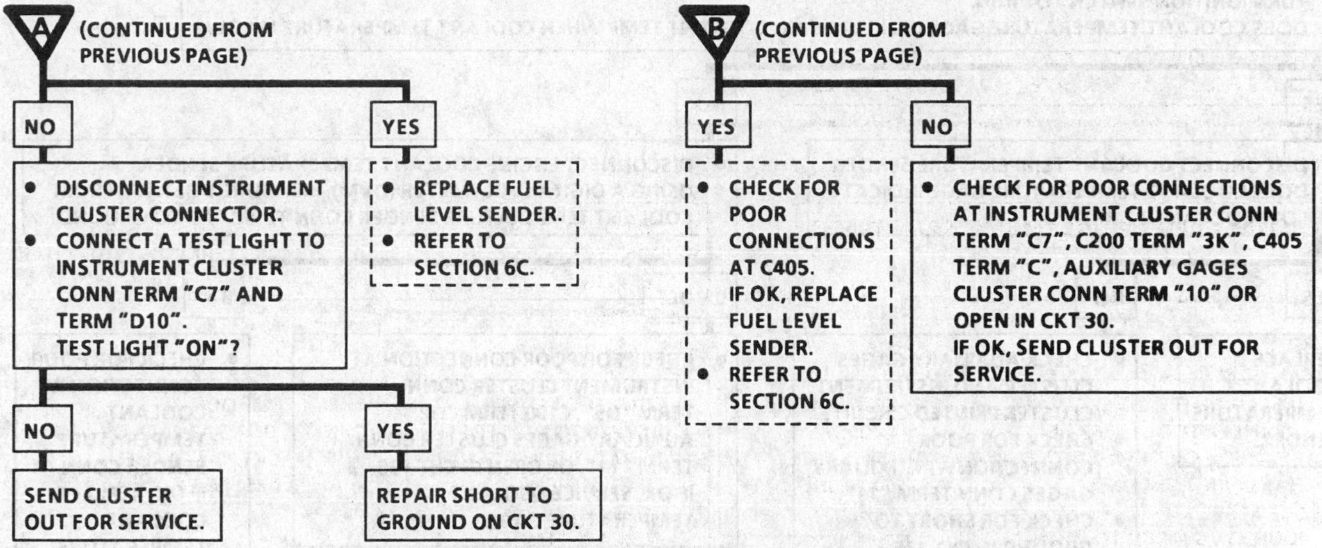
A
(CONTINUED FROM PREVIOUS PAGE)
NO
YES
• DISCONNECT INSTRUMENT CLUSTER CONNECTOR.
• CONNECT A TEST LIGHT TO INSTRUMENT CLUSTER CONN TERM "C7" AND TERM "D10".
TEST LIGHT "ON"?
• REPLACE FUEL LEVEL SENDER.
• REFER TO SECTION 6C.
NO
YES
SEND CLUSTER OUT FOR SERVICE.
REPAIR SHORT TO GROUND ON CKT 30.
B
(CONTINUED FROM PREVIOUS PAGE)
YES
NO
• CHECK FOR POOR CONNECTIONS AT C405.
IF OK, REPLACE FUEL LEVEL SENDER.
• REFER TO SECTION 6C.
• CHECK FOR POOR CONNECTIONS AT INSTRUMENT CLUSTER CONN TERM "C7", C200 TERM "3K", C405 TERM "C", AUXILIARY GAGES CLUSTER CONN TERM "10" OR OPEN IN CKT 30.
IF OK, SEND CLUSTER OUT FOR SERVICE.

SENDER RESISTANCE	APPROXIMATE FUEL LEVEL
88 Ω	FULL
60 Ω	3/4
50 Ω	1/2
26 Ω	1/4
1.0 Ω	EMPTY

INSTRUMENT CLUSTER: GAGES

CHART #4
COOLANT TEMPERATURE GAGE INOPERATIVE OR INACCURATE

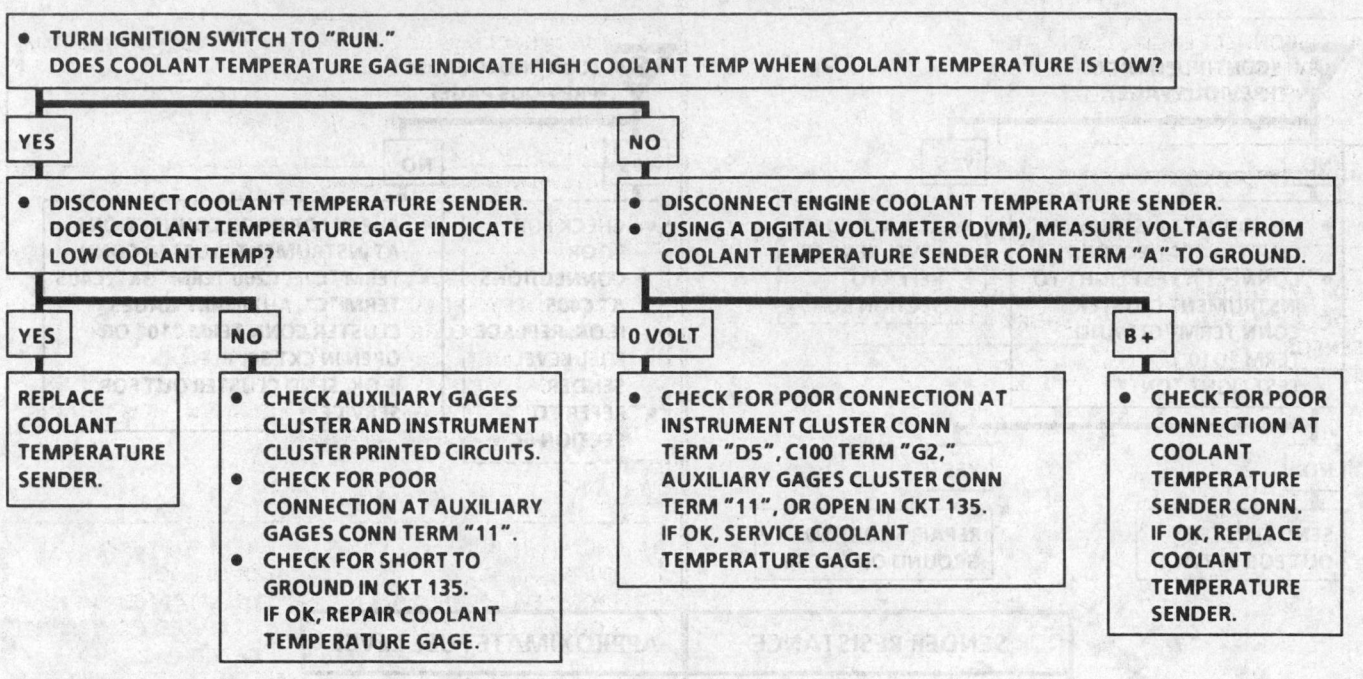

- TURN IGNITION SWITCH TO "RUN."
  DOES COOLANT TEMPERATURE GAGE INDICATE HIGH COOLANT TEMP WHEN COOLANT TEMPERATURE IS LOW?

YES

- DISCONNECT COOLANT TEMPERATURE SENDER.
  DOES COOLANT TEMPERATURE GAGE INDICATE LOW COOLANT TEMP?

  YES

  REPLACE COOLANT TEMPERATURE SENDER.

  NO

  - CHECK AUXILIARY GAGES CLUSTER AND INSTRUMENT CLUSTER PRINTED CIRCUITS.
  - CHECK FOR POOR CONNECTION AT AUXILIARY GAGES CONN TERM "11".
  - CHECK FOR SHORT TO GROUND IN CKT 135.
    IF OK, REPAIR COOLANT TEMPERATURE GAGE.

NO

- DISCONNECT ENGINE COOLANT TEMPERATURE SENDER.
- USING A DIGITAL VOLTMETER (DVM), MEASURE VOLTAGE FROM COOLANT TEMPERATURE SENDER CONN TERM "A" TO GROUND.

  0 VOLT

  - CHECK FOR POOR CONNECTION AT INSTRUMENT CLUSTER CONN TERM "D5", C100 TERM "G2," AUXILIARY GAGES CLUSTER CONN TERM "11", OR OPEN IN CKT 135.
    IF OK, SERVICE COOLANT TEMPERATURE GAGE.

  B +

  - CHECK FOR POOR CONNECTION AT COOLANT TEMPERATURE SENDER CONN.
    IF OK, REPLACE COOLANT TEMPERATURE SENDER.

CHART #5
OIL PRESSURE GAGE INOPERATIVE OR INACCURATE

- TURN IGNITION SWITCH TO "RUN," WITH ENGINE "OFF."
  DOES OIL PRESSURE GAGE INDICATE LOW OR NO PRESSURE?

NO

DOES OIL PRESSURE GAGE INDICATE HIGH OIL PRESSURE?

  NO

  - TURN IGNITION SWITCH TO "OFF."
  - DISCONNECT INSTRUMENT CLUSTER.
  - USING A DIGITAL VOLTMETER (DVM), MEASURE RESISTANCE AT INSTRUMENT CLUSTER CONN FROM TERM "D9" TO GROUND.
    IS RESISTANCE APPROX 1 Ω?

    NO

    REPLACE FUEL PUMP/OIL PRESSURE SWITCH/SENDER.

    YES

    SERVICE OIL PRESSURE GAGE.

  YES

  USING A DIGITAL VOLTMETER (DVM), MEASURE VOLTAGE FROM FUEL PUMP/OIL PRESSURE SWITCH/SENDER CONN TERM "A" TO GROUND.

    0 VOLTS

    - CHECK FOR POOR CONNECTION AT INSTRUMENT CLUSTER CONN TERM "D9", C100 TERM "F2", OR OPEN IN CKT 31 BETWEEN FUEL PUMP/OIL PRESSURE SWITCH/SENDER AND INSTRUMENT CLUSTER.
    - CHECK FOR OPEN IN CKT 1050 (VIN L ONLY).
      IF OK, SERVICE OIL PRESSURE GAGE.

    B +

    - CHECK FOR POOR CONNECTION AT FUEL PUMP/OIL PRESSURE SWITCH/SENDER CONN.
      IF OK, REPLACE FUEL PUMP/OIL PRESSURE SWITCH/SENDER.

YES

- DISCONNECT FUEL PUMP/OIL PRESSURE SWITCH/SENDER
  DOES OIL PRESSURE GAGE INDICATE HIGH OIL PRESSURE?

  NO

  - CHECK FOR SHORT TO GROUND IN CKT 31.
    IF OK, SERVICE OIL PRESSURE GAGE.

  YES

  REPLACE FUEL PUMP/OIL PRESSURE SWITCH/SENDER.

CHART #6
"LOW COOLANT" INDICATOR "ON," COOLANT LEVEL OK

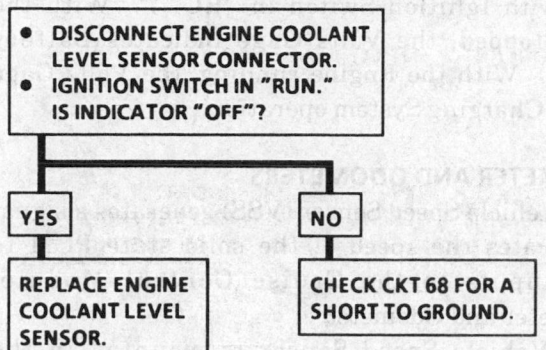

- DISCONNECT ENGINE COOLANT LEVEL SENSOR CONNECTOR.
- IGNITION SWITCH IN "RUN." IS INDICATOR "OFF"?

YES
- REPLACE ENGINE COOLANT LEVEL SENSOR.

NO
- CHECK CKT 68 FOR A SHORT TO GROUND.

CHART #7
"LOW COOLANT" INDICATOR "OFF," COOLANT LEVEL LOW

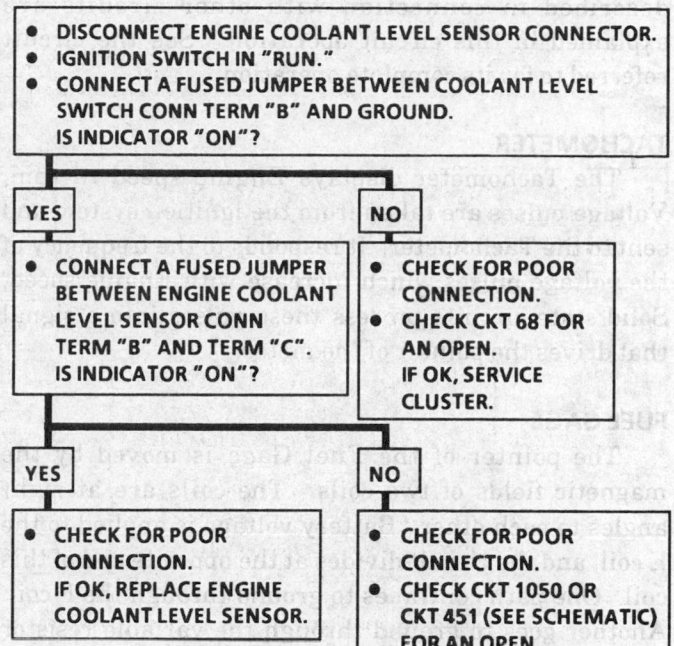

- DISCONNECT ENGINE COOLANT LEVEL SENSOR CONNECTOR.
- IGNITION SWITCH IN "RUN."
- CONNECT A FUSED JUMPER BETWEEN COOLANT LEVEL SWITCH CONN TERM "B" AND GROUND. IS INDICATOR "ON"?

YES
- CONNECT A FUSED JUMPER BETWEEN ENGINE COOLANT LEVEL SENSOR CONN TERM "B" AND TERM "C". IS INDICATOR "ON"?
  - **YES**
    - CHECK FOR POOR CONNECTION. IF OK, REPLACE ENGINE COOLANT LEVEL SENSOR.
  - **NO**
    - CHECK FOR POOR CONNECTION.
    - CHECK CKT 1050 OR CKT 451 (SEE SCHEMATIC) FOR AN OPEN.

NO
- CHECK FOR POOR CONNECTION.
- CHECK CKT 68 FOR AN OPEN. IF OK, SERVICE CLUSTER.

CHART #8
"LOW OIL" INDICATOR "ON," OIL LEVEL OK (VIN M)

IMPORTANT:
- TO AVOID MISDIAGNOSIS, CHECK FOR STORED DIAGNOSTIC TROUBLE CODES (DTCs). REFER TO SECTION 6E.

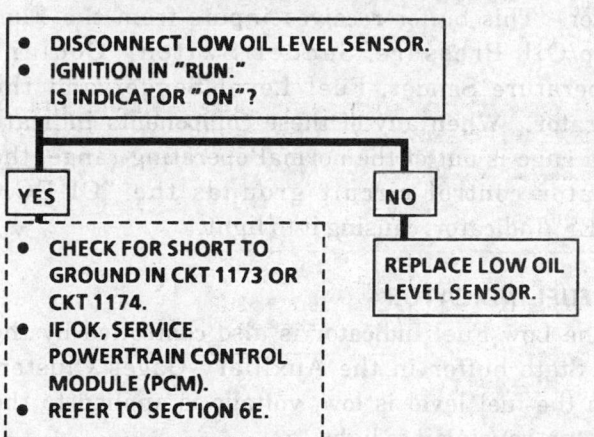

- DISCONNECT LOW OIL LEVEL SENSOR.
- IGNITION IN "RUN." IS INDICATOR "ON"?

YES
- CHECK FOR SHORT TO GROUND IN CKT 1173 OR CKT 1174.
- IF OK, SERVICE POWERTRAIN CONTROL MODULE (PCM).
- REFER TO SECTION 6E.

NO
- REPLACE LOW OIL LEVEL SENSOR.

CHART #9
"LOW OIL" INDICATOR INOPERATIVE, OIL LEVEL LOW (VIN M)

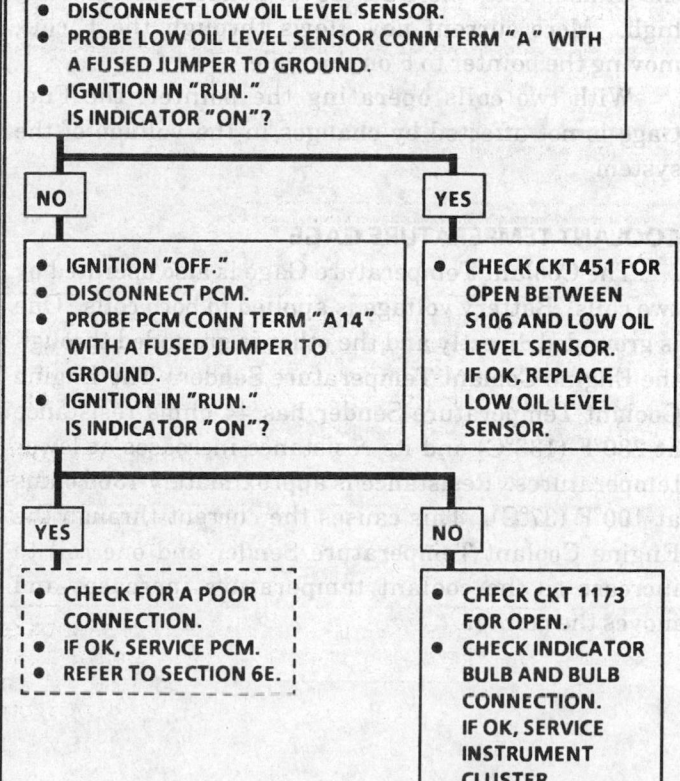

- DISCONNECT LOW OIL LEVEL SENSOR.
- PROBE LOW OIL LEVEL SENSOR CONN TERM "A" WITH A FUSED JUMPER TO GROUND.
- IGNITION IN "RUN." IS INDICATOR "ON"?

NO
- IGNITION "OFF."
- DISCONNECT PCM.
- PROBE PCM CONN TERM "A14" WITH A FUSED JUMPER TO GROUND.
- IGNITION IN "RUN." IS INDICATOR "ON"?
  - **YES**
    - CHECK FOR A POOR CONNECTION.
    - IF OK, SERVICE PCM.
    - REFER TO SECTION 6E.
  - **NO**
    - CHECK CKT 1173 FOR OPEN.
    - CHECK INDICATOR BULB AND BULB CONNECTION. IF OK, SERVICE INSTRUMENT CLUSTER.

YES
- CHECK CKT 451 FOR OPEN BETWEEN S106 AND LOW OIL LEVEL SENSOR. IF OK, REPLACE LOW OIL LEVEL SENSOR.

INSTRUMENT CLUSTER: GAGES

CIRCUIT OPERATION

Only those indicators and gages that are not described in connection with other circuits are explained in this circuit operation. See the circuit referred to for its complete operation.

TACHOMETER

The Tachometer displays Engine speed in rpm. Voltage pulses are taken from the ignition system and sent to the Tachometer. It responds to the frequency of the voltage pulses which increase with Engine speed. Solid state circuits process these pulses into a signal that drives the pointer of the meter.

FUEL GAGE

The pointer of the Fuel Gage is moved by the magnetic fields of two coils. The coils are at right angles to each other. Battery voltage is applied to the E coil, and the circuit divides at the opposite end of this coil. One path continues to ground through the F coil. Another goes to ground through the variable resistor of the Fuel Level Sender.

When the tank is low, the resistance of the Fuel Level Sender is low. A large flow of current passes through the E coil and the Fuel Level Sender resistor. This pulls the pointer towards E on the scale. When the tank is full, the Fuel Level Sender resistance is high. More current now flows through the F coil, moving the pointer to F on the scale.

With two coils operating the pointer, the Fuel Gage is not affected by changes in the voltage of the system.

COOLANT TEMPERATURE GAGE

The Coolant Temperature Gage is also operated by two coils. Battery voltage is applied to both coils. One is grounded directly and the other is grounded through the Engine Coolant Temperature Sender. The Engine Coolant Temperature Sender has 44 ohms resistance at 280°F (138°C) and its resistance increases at lower temperatures. Resistance is approximately 1365 ohms at 100°F (37°C). This causes the current through the Engine Coolant Temperature Sender and one coil to increase as the coolant temperature increases and moves the pointer.

VOLTS GAGE

The Volts Gage measures the electrical system's voltage with Ignition Switch in "RUN." With the Engine stopped, the Volts Gage indicates Battery condition. With the Engine running, the Volts Gage indicates Charging System operation.

SPEEDOMETER AND ODOMETERS

The Vehicle Speed Sensor (VSS) generates a signal that indicates the speed of the solid state PCM to supply inputs to the Cruise Control Module, Speedometer and Odometer.

The Vehicle Speed Sensor is mounted in the Transaxle. A magnet rotates near a coil, producing voltage pulses in the coil. The frequency of the AC voltage coming from this coil depends on the vehicle speed. The VSS sends pulses to the PCM at the rate of 40,000 pulses per mile.

The PCM takes the voltage pulses from the sensor and uses them to close a solid state output switch. The output terminal is switched to ground at a rate that is proportional to the speed of the vehicle. The Speedometer and Odometers are switched at 4,000 pulses per mile.

"CHECK GAGES" INDICATOR

The "CHECK GAGES" Indicator is controlled by a Solid State buffer located in the Auxiliary Gages Cluster. This buffer receives inputs from the Fuel Pump/Oil Pressure Sender/Switch, Coolant Temperature Sender, Fuel Level Sender and the Generator. When any of these components indicate that a gage is out of the normal operating range, the indicator control circuit grounds the "CHECK GAGES" Indicator, causing it to light.

LOW FUEL INDICATOR

The Low Fuel Indicator is also controlled by the Solid State buffer in the Auxiliary Gages Cluster. When the fuel level is low, voltage is applied to the indicator, causing it to light.

"LOW COOLANT" INDICATOR

The "LOW COOLANT" Indicator receives battery voltage with the Ignition Switch in "RUN," "BULB TEST" or "START." The indicator is grounded by the Engine Coolant Level Switch with the coolant level in the Coolant Reservoir below a minimum recommended level.

OIL PRESSURE GAGE

The Engine oil pressure is displayed by the Oil Pressure Gage. The pointer of the gage is moved by two coils, and its operation is similar to that of the Fuel Gage.

The Fuel Pump/Oil Pressure Switch/Sender is connected to the junction of the two coils. It has low resistance when the oil pressure is low, and 90 ohms resistance when the oil pressure is high. This changing resistance changes the current flow through the coils to move the pointer between 0 and 80 psi.

"LOW OIL" INDICATOR (VIN L)

The "LOW OIL" Indicator is controlled by the Low Oil Module. The Low Oil Module uses two timers to determine whether it should sample oil level at power-up. The power-down timer must show more than 32 minutes if the last Ignition cycle was less than 12 minutes. If the last Ignition cycle was longer than 12 minutes, then the power-down timer must show at least three minutes before oil level is sampled.

"LOW OIL" INDICATOR (VIN M)

The "LOW OIL" Indicator is controlled by logic set up in the Powertrain Control Module (PCM). The PCM will sample the oil level once per ignition cycle at power-up only if criteria has been met indicating that the oil has had sufficient time to drain into the oil pan from the last power-down. Three minutes must elapse since power-down if Engine coolant temperature is greater than 75°C at power-down for the PCM to sample oil level. If the Engine coolant temperature is less than 75°C at power-down, the PCM looks for at least an 11°C drop in Engine coolant temperature before sampling oil level at power-up.

STEERING WHEEL CONTROLS

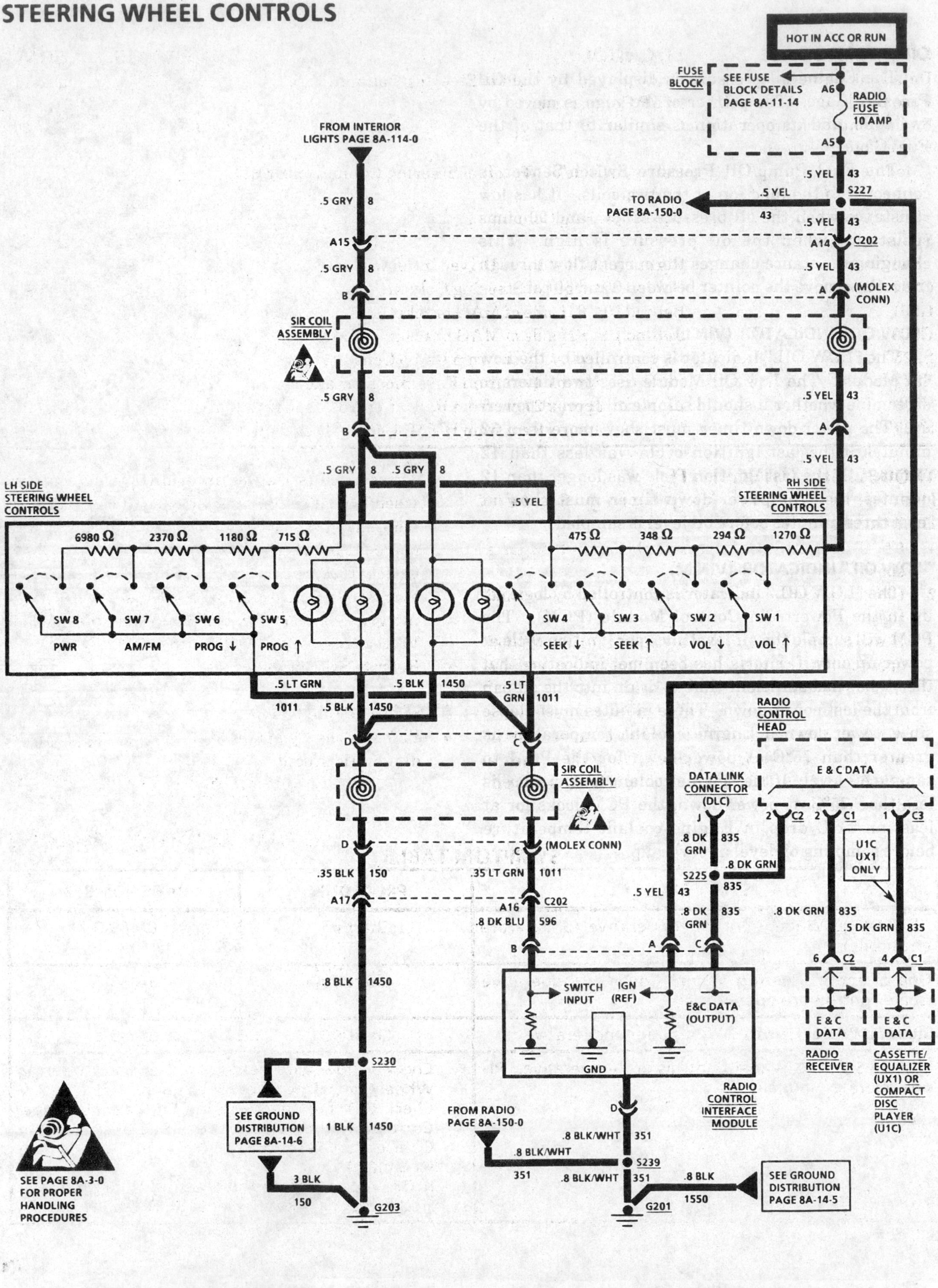
HOT IN ACC OR RUN
FUSE BLOCK
SEE FUSE BLOCK DETAILS PAGE 8A-11-14
A6
RADIO FUSE 10 AMP
A5
FROM INTERIOR LIGHTS PAGE 8A-114-0
.5 YEL 43
.5 YEL
S227
TO RADIO PAGE 8A-150-0
43
.5 GRY 8
A15
A14
C202
(MOLEX CONN)
SIR COIL ASSEMBLY
LH SIDE STEERING WHEEL CONTROLS
RH SIDE STEERING WHEEL CONTROLS
6980 Ω
2370 Ω
1180 Ω
715 Ω
475 Ω
348 Ω
294 Ω
1270 Ω
SW 8
SW 7
SW 6
SW 5
SW 4
SW 3
SW 2
SW 1
PWR
AM/FM
PROG ↓
PROG ↑
SEEK ↓
SEEK ↑
VOL ↓
VOL ↑
.5 LT GRN 1011
.5 BLK 1450
RADIO CONTROL HEAD
E & C DATA
DATA LINK CONNECTOR (DLC)
.8 DK GRN 835
S225
U1C UX1 ONLY
.5 DK GRN 835
.35 BLK 150
.35 LT GRN 1011
A17
A16
.8 DK BLU 596
.8 BLK 1450
SWITCH INPUT
IGN (REF)
E&C DATA (OUTPUT)
GND
RADIO RECEIVER
CASSETTE/ EQUALIZER (UX1) OR COMPACT DISC PLAYER (U1C)
RADIO CONTROL INTERFACE MODULE
S230
SEE GROUND DISTRIBUTION PAGE 8A-14-6
1 BLK 1450
3 BLK 150
G203
FROM RADIO PAGE 8A-150-0
.8 BLK/WHT 351
S239
.8 BLK 1550
G201
SEE GROUND DISTRIBUTION PAGE 8A-14-5
SEE PAGE 8A-3-0 FOR PROPER HANDLING PROCEDURES

COMPONENT	LOCATION	201-PG	FIG.	CONN
Data Link Conn (DLC)	On bottom of I/P, right of Steering Column			202-17
Fuse Block	In I/P Compartment			
Radio Control Head	Center of I/P	26	84	202-40
Radio Control Interface Module	Below LH side of I/P, left of Steering Column on DERM bracket			
SIR Coil Assembly	Top of Steering Column			
Steering Wheel Control Switches	Right and Left sides of Driver Inflator Module			
C202 (48 cavities)	Behind I/P, right of Steering Column	14	48	202-9
G201	Behind I/P, RH side of MAG bracket	14	48	
G203	Behind I/P, RH side of MAG bracket	14	48	
S225	I/P Harn, approx 25 cm from Radio Control Head			
S227	I/P Harn, approx 4 cm from Fuse Block breakout			
S230	I/P Harn, approx 27 cm from Radio Control Head breakout			
S239	I/P Harn, approx 8 cm from HVAC Control breakout			

TROUBLESHOOTING HINTS (Perform before beginning System Diagnosis)

1. Check RADIO Fuse. If open, check CKT 43 for a short to ground.
2. Check that grounds G201 and G203 are clean and tight.
3. If switches on one side of the Steering Wheel operate but the other side is inoperative, replace Steering Wheel Control Switches.

- Check for a broken (or partially broken) wire inside of the insulation which could cause system malfunction but prove "GOOD" in a continuity/voltage check with a system disconnected. These circuits may be intermittent or resistive when loaded, and if possible, should be checked by monitoring for a voltage drop with the system operational (under load).
- Check for proper installation of aftermarket electronic equipment which may affect the integrity of other systems (see "Troubleshooting Procedures," page 8A-4-0).
- Refer to System Diagnosis.

SYSTEM DIAGNOSIS

- Refer to the Symptom Table for the appropriate diagnostic procedure(s).

SYMPTOM TABLE

SYMPTOM	PROCEDURE	PAGE NUMBER
All Steering Wheel Controls inoperative (or operate erratically).	Chart #1	8A-89-2
One or more Steering Wheel Controls inoperative (some controls are operational).	Chart #2	8A-89-5
Steering Wheel Controls illumination inoperative.	Chart #3	8A-89-6
LH Side Steering Wheel Controls are inoperative. RH side operates normally.	• Check yellow wire between LH and RH Steering Wheel Control Switches for an open. • Check CKT 1101 between the LH Steering Wheel Control Switches and the SIR Coil Assembly Connector Terminal "C" for an open (see schematic). If OK, repair/replace the Steering Wheel Control Switches as necessary (refer to SECTION 3F).	

STEERING WHEEL CONTROLS

CHART #1

ALL STEERING WHEEL RADIO CONTROLS INOPERATIVE (OR OPERATE ERRATICALLY)

ARE ALL RADIO FUNCTIONS OPERATING NORMALLY AT RADIO?

NO → A (CONTINUED ON NEXT PAGE)

YES

- DISCONNECT RADIO CONTROL INTERFACE CONN.
- IGNITION "ON."
- RADIO "ON."
- MEASURE VOLTAGE BETWEEN RADIO CONTROL INTERFACE CONN TERM "B" AND GROUND WHILE OPERATING EACH STEERING WHEEL CONTROL BUTTON.
- COMPARE EACH VOLTAGE WITH THE "STEERING WHEEL CONTROLS RESISTANCE/VOLTAGE CHART" ON PAGE 8A-89-5.

ARE THE VOLTAGES WITHIN RANGE?

YES → B (CONTINUED ON PAGE 4)

NO

- IGNITION SWITCH "OFF."
- DISABLE THE SUPPLEMENTAL INFLATABLE RESTRAINT (SIR) SYSTEM AND REMOVE AND DISCONNECT INFLATOR MODULE FROM STEERING WHEEL (REFER TO SECTION 9JB, THEN RETURN TO THIS CHART).
- DISCONNECT STEERING WHEEL CONTROL SWITCHES CONN.
- MEASURE RESISTANCE BETWEEN STEERING WHEEL SWITCHES CONN TERM "A" AND TERM "C" WHILE OPERATING EACH STEERING WHEEL CONTROL BUTTON.
- COMPARE EACH RESISTANCE WITH THE "STEERING WHEEL CONTROLS RESISTANCE/VOLTAGE CHART" ON PAGE 8A-89-5.

ARE THE MEASURED RESISTANCES APPROXIMATELY EQUAL TO THE VALUES IN THE CHART?

NO

- REPLACE STEERING WHEEL CONTROL SWITCHES.
- REFER TO SECTION 3F.

YES

- CHECK CKT 43 FOR OPEN BETWEEN SIR COIL ASSEMBLY CONN TERM "A" AND S227.
- CHECK CKT 1011 FOR OPEN OR HIGH RESISTANCE BETWEEN SIR COIL ASSEMBLY CONN TERM "C" AND RADIO INTERFACE MODULE CONN TERM "B".

ARE CIRCUITS GOOD?

YES

- CHECK CKT 596 FOR AN OPEN OR SHORT.
- CHECK FOR POOR CONNECTION.

IF OK, REPLACE RADIO CONTROL INTERFACE MODULE.

NO

- REPAIR CKT 43 OR CKT 1011 OR REPLACE SIR COIL ASSEMBLY AS NECESSARY.
- REFER TO SECTION 9J FOR SIR SERVICE.

SEE PAGE 8A-3-0 FOR PROPER HANDLING PROCEDURES

CAUTION: This vehicle is equipped with Supplemental Inflatable Restraint (SIR). Refer to CAUTIONS in Section 9J under "ON-VEHICLE SERVICE" and the SIR Component and Wiring Location view in Section 9J before performing service on or around SIR components or wiring. Failure to follow CAUTIONS could result in possible air bag deployment, personal injury, or otherwise unneeded SIR system repairs.

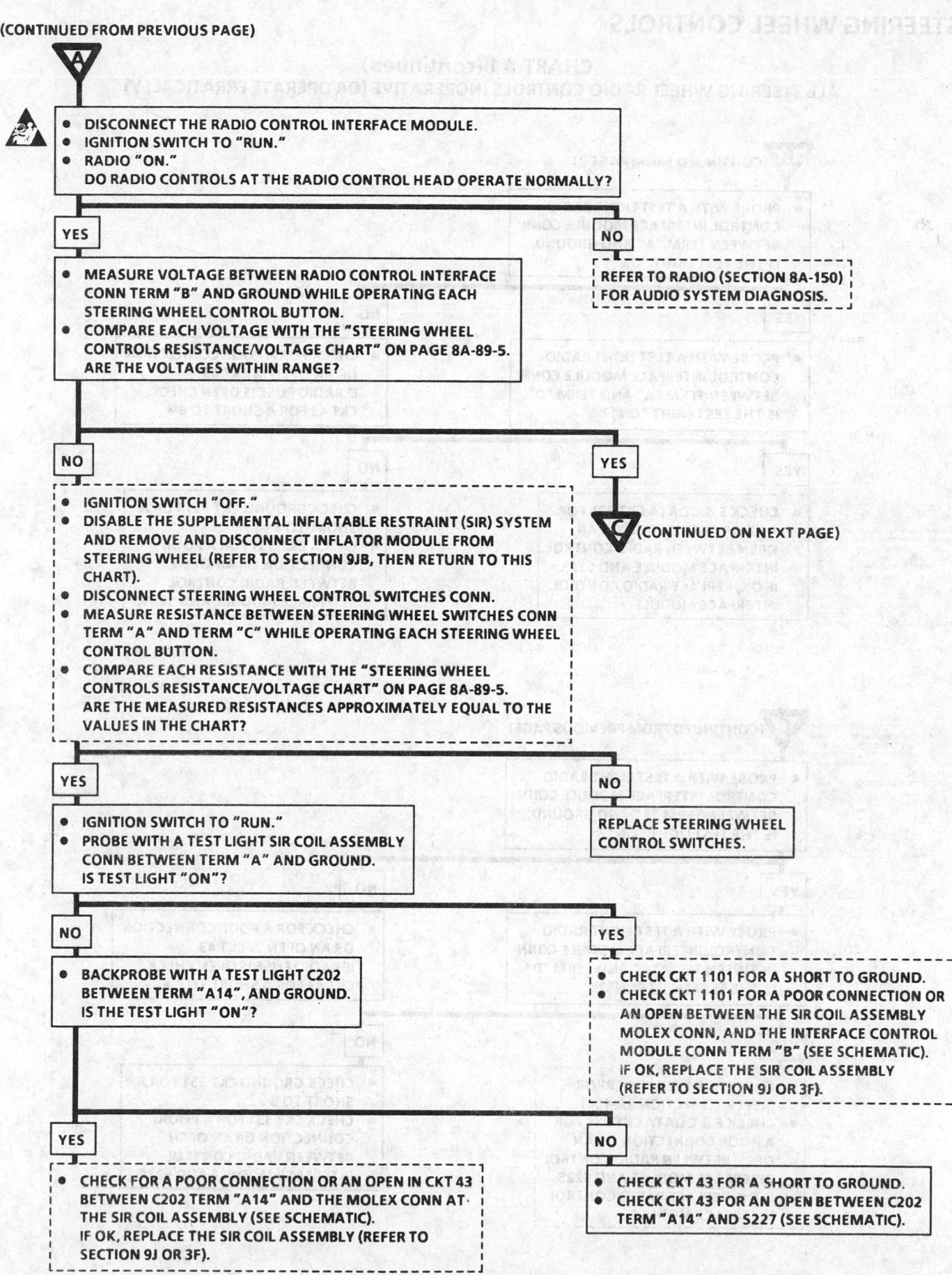

(CONTINUED FROM PREVIOUS PAGE)

A

- DISCONNECT THE RADIO CONTROL INTERFACE MODULE.
- IGNITION SWITCH TO "RUN."
- RADIO "ON."

DO RADIO CONTROLS AT THE RADIO CONTROL HEAD OPERATE NORMALLY?

NO

- REFER TO RADIO (SECTION 8A-150) FOR AUDIO SYSTEM DIAGNOSIS.

YES

- MEASURE VOLTAGE BETWEEN RADIO CONTROL INTERFACE CONN TERM "B" AND GROUND WHILE OPERATING EACH STEERING WHEEL CONTROL BUTTON.
- COMPARE EACH VOLTAGE WITH THE "STEERING WHEEL CONTROLS RESISTANCE/VOLTAGE CHART" ON PAGE 8A-89-5.

ARE THE VOLTAGES WITHIN RANGE?

YES

C (CONTINUED ON NEXT PAGE)

NO

- IGNITION SWITCH "OFF."
- DISABLE THE SUPPLEMENTAL INFLATABLE RESTRAINT (SIR) SYSTEM AND REMOVE AND DISCONNECT INFLATOR MODULE FROM STEERING WHEEL (REFER TO SECTION 9JB, THEN RETURN TO THIS CHART).
- DISCONNECT STEERING WHEEL CONTROL SWITCHES CONN.
- MEASURE RESISTANCE BETWEEN STEERING WHEEL SWITCHES CONN TERM "A" AND TERM "C" WHILE OPERATING EACH STEERING WHEEL CONTROL BUTTON.
- COMPARE EACH RESISTANCE WITH THE "STEERING WHEEL CONTROLS RESISTANCE/VOLTAGE CHART" ON PAGE 8A-89-5.

ARE THE MEASURED RESISTANCES APPROXIMATELY EQUAL TO THE VALUES IN THE CHART?

NO

- REPLACE STEERING WHEEL CONTROL SWITCHES.

YES

- IGNITION SWITCH TO "RUN."
- PROBE WITH A TEST LIGHT SIR COIL ASSEMBLY CONN BETWEEN TERM "A" AND GROUND.

IS TEST LIGHT "ON"?

YES

- CHECK CKT 1101 FOR A SHORT TO GROUND.
- CHECK CKT 1101 FOR A POOR CONNECTION OR AN OPEN BETWEEN THE SIR COIL ASSEMBLY MOLEX CONN, AND THE INTERFACE CONTROL MODULE CONN TERM "B" (SEE SCHEMATIC).

  IF OK, REPLACE THE SIR COIL ASSEMBLY (REFER TO SECTION 9J OR 3F).

NO

- BACKPROBE WITH A TEST LIGHT C202 BETWEEN TERM "A14", AND GROUND.

IS THE TEST LIGHT "ON"?

YES

- CHECK FOR A POOR CONNECTION OR AN OPEN IN CKT 43 BETWEEN C202 TERM "A14" AND THE MOLEX CONN AT THE SIR COIL ASSEMBLY (SEE SCHEMATIC).

  IF OK, REPLACE THE SIR COIL ASSEMBLY (REFER TO SECTION 9J OR 3F).

NO

- CHECK CKT 43 FOR A SHORT TO GROUND.
- CHECK CKT 43 FOR AN OPEN BETWEEN C202 TERM "A14" AND S227 (SEE SCHEMATIC).

STEERING WHEEL CONTROLS

CHART #1 (continued)

ALL STEERING WHEEL RADIO CONTROLS INOPERATIVE (OR OPERATE ERRATICALLY)

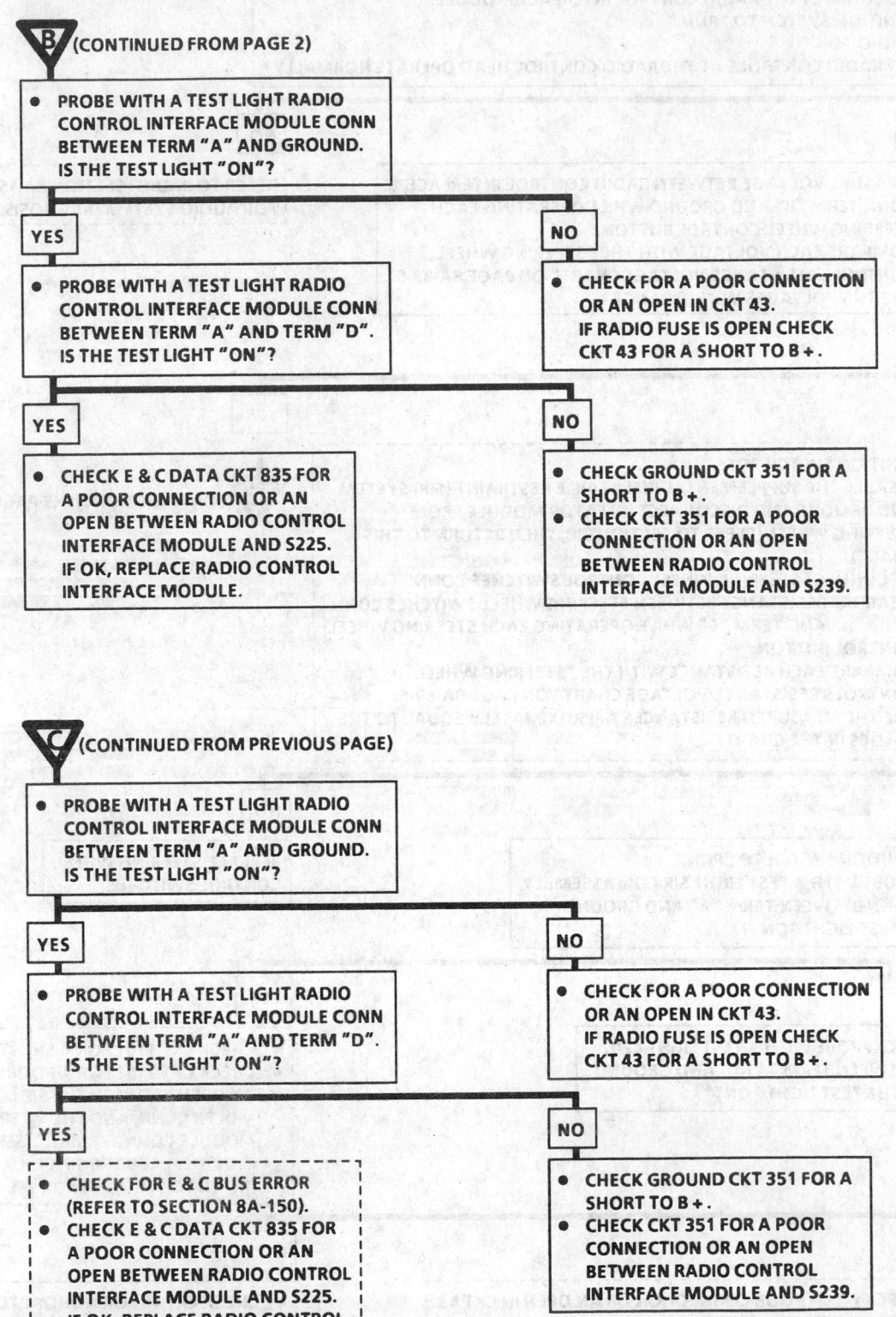

B (CONTINUED FROM PAGE 2)

- PROBE WITH A TEST LIGHT RADIO CONTROL INTERFACE MODULE CONN BETWEEN TERM "A" AND GROUND. IS THE TEST LIGHT "ON"?

YES

- PROBE WITH A TEST LIGHT RADIO CONTROL INTERFACE MODULE CONN BETWEEN TERM "A" AND TERM "D". IS THE TEST LIGHT "ON"?

YES

- CHECK E & C DATA CKT 835 FOR A POOR CONNECTION OR AN OPEN BETWEEN RADIO CONTROL INTERFACE MODULE AND S225. IF OK, REPLACE RADIO CONTROL INTERFACE MODULE.

NO

- CHECK GROUND CKT 351 FOR A SHORT TO B+.
- CHECK CKT 351 FOR A POOR CONNECTION OR AN OPEN BETWEEN RADIO CONTROL INTERFACE MODULE AND S239.

NO

- CHECK FOR A POOR CONNECTION OR AN OPEN IN CKT 43. IF RADIO FUSE IS OPEN CHECK CKT 43 FOR A SHORT TO B+.

C (CONTINUED FROM PREVIOUS PAGE)

- PROBE WITH A TEST LIGHT RADIO CONTROL INTERFACE MODULE CONN BETWEEN TERM "A" AND GROUND. IS THE TEST LIGHT "ON"?

YES

- PROBE WITH A TEST LIGHT RADIO CONTROL INTERFACE MODULE CONN BETWEEN TERM "A" AND TERM "D". IS THE TEST LIGHT "ON"?

YES

- CHECK FOR E & C BUS ERROR (REFER TO SECTION 8A-150).
- CHECK E & C DATA CKT 835 FOR A POOR CONNECTION OR AN OPEN BETWEEN RADIO CONTROL INTERFACE MODULE AND S225. IF OK, REPLACE RADIO CONTROL INTERFACE MODULE.

NO

- CHECK GROUND CKT 351 FOR A SHORT TO B+.
- CHECK CKT 351 FOR A POOR CONNECTION OR AN OPEN BETWEEN RADIO CONTROL INTERFACE MODULE AND S239.

NO

- CHECK FOR A POOR CONNECTION OR AN OPEN IN CKT 43. IF RADIO FUSE IS OPEN CHECK CKT 43 FOR A SHORT TO B+.

STEERING WHEEL CONTROLS

CHART #2
ONE OR MORE STEERING WHEEL CONTROLS INOPERATIVE (SOME CONTROLS ARE OPERATIONAL)

IMPORTANT:

- ASSUME ALL FUNCTIONS OPERATE NORMALLY AT RADIO. IF THEY DO NOT OPERATE NORMALLY, REFER TO SECTION 8A-150.

- IGNITION "ON."
- RADIO "ON."
- BACKPROBE FROM CONN C202 TERM "A16" TO GROUND USING A DVM.
- MEASURE AND NOTE THE VOLTAGE WHILE PRESSING EACH OF THE STEERING WHEEL RADIO CONTROL BUTTONS.
- COMPARE THE VOLTAGES TO THE CHART BELOW. ARE THE VOLTAGES WITHIN RANGE?

YES

- CHECK FOR POOR CONNECTION. IF OK, REPLACE RADIO CONTROL INTERFACE MODULE.

NO

- REPLACE STEERING WHEEL CONTROL SWITCHES.
- REFER TO SECTION 9J FOR SIR DISABLE PROCEDURE.

STEERING WHEEL CONTROLS RESISTANCE/VOLTAGE CHART

STEERING WHEEL CONTROL SWITCH	APPROXIMATE RESISTANCE BETWEEN STEERING WHEEL CONTROL SWITCHES CONN TERM "A" AND TERM "C" IN OHMS.	VOLTAGE/MEASURED FROM RADIO CONTROL INTERFACE MODULE CONN TERM "B" TO GROUND. (IGNITION "ON" AND BATTERY FULLY CHARGED.) VOLTAGE RANGE IN VOLTS	
		LOW	HIGH
VOL (UP)	1270	4.29	4.75
VOL (DOWN)	1564	3.61	4.12
SEEK (UP)	1912	3.07	3.51
SEEK (DOWN)	2387	2.50	2.98
PROG (UP)	3102	1.97	2.41
PROG (DOWN)	4282	1.42	1.88
AM/FM	6652	.874	1.33
PWR	13632	.285	.779

STEERING WHEEL CONTROLS

CHART #3
STEERING WHEEL CONTROLS ILLUMINATION IS INOPERATIVE

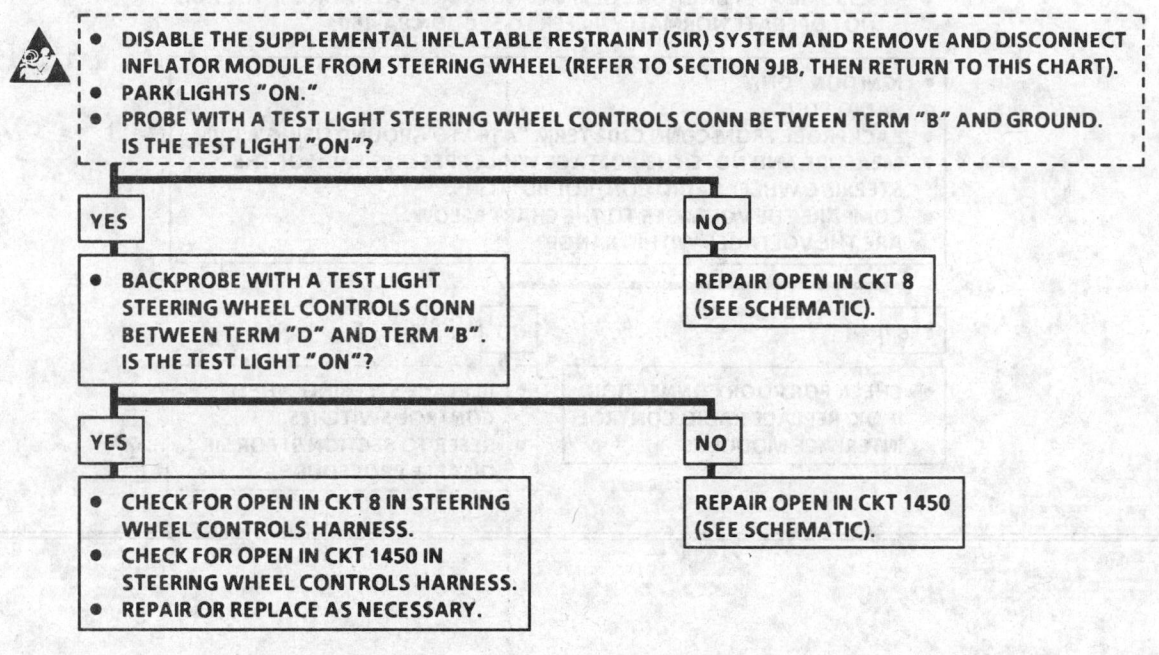

- DISABLE THE SUPPLEMENTAL INFLATABLE RESTRAINT (SIR) SYSTEM AND REMOVE AND DISCONNECT INFLATOR MODULE FROM STEERING WHEEL (REFER TO SECTION 9JB, THEN RETURN TO THIS CHART).
- PARK LIGHTS "ON."
- PROBE WITH A TEST LIGHT STEERING WHEEL CONTROLS CONN BETWEEN TERM "B" AND GROUND. IS THE TEST LIGHT "ON"?

YES

- BACKPROBE WITH A TEST LIGHT STEERING WHEEL CONTROLS CONN BETWEEN TERM "D" AND TERM "B". IS THE TEST LIGHT "ON"?

YES

- CHECK FOR OPEN IN CKT 8 IN STEERING WHEEL CONTROLS HARNESS.
- CHECK FOR OPEN IN CKT 1450 IN STEERING WHEEL CONTROLS HARNESS.
- REPAIR OR REPLACE AS NECESSARY.

NO

REPAIR OPEN IN CKT 1450 (SEE SCHEMATIC).

NO

REPAIR OPEN IN CKT 8 (SEE SCHEMATIC).

CIRCUIT OPERATION

The Steering Wheel Controls consist of several components. They include the following:

- Steering Wheel Radio Control Switches
- SIR Coil Assembly
- Radio Control Interface Module

STEERING WHEEL RADIO SWITCHES

The Steering Wheel Control Switches control Radio power, volume and station frequency tuning. These switches are actually a ladder network consisting of the switches and a series of resistors. The ladder network is arranged so that each switch has a different resistance. This allows a different voltage output to the Radio Control Interface Module for each switch pressed.

The Steering Wheel Control (SWC) Switches use incandescent backlighting. The illumination signal CKT 8 is a Pulse Width Modulated (PWM) signal from the Headlight Switch. The bulbs are serviceable.

SIR COIL ASSEMBLY

The SIR Coil Assembly contains four wires used by the Steering Wheel Controls. This allows voltages to be sent from the Steering Wheel Switches to the Interface Module while the Steering Wheel is being turned.

RADIO CONTROL INTERFACE MODULE

The Radio Control Interface Module receives different voltages from the Steering Wheel Control Switches and transforms these voltages into messages to be output to the Entertainment and Comfort (E & C) Data Line (CKT 835). The E & C Data Line (CKT 835) is used for communication of Radio commands and information such as clock, volume control, station frequency tuning and display.

BLANK

WIPER/WASHER: PULSE (CD4)

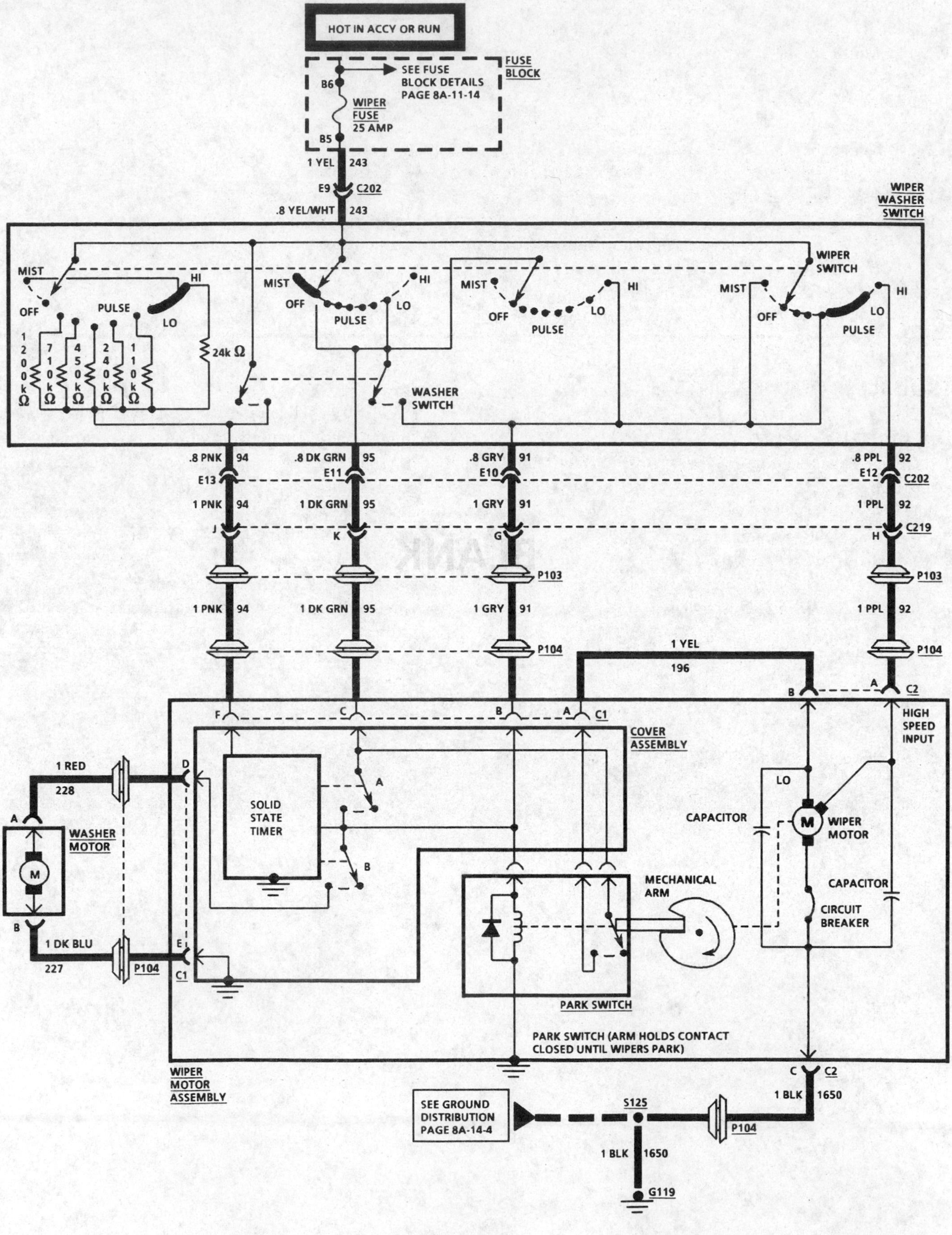
HOT IN ACCY OR RUN
FUSE BLOCK
SEE FUSE BLOCK DETAILS PAGE 8A-11-14
B6
WIPER FUSE 25 AMP
B5
1 YEL 243
E9 C202
.8 YEL/WHT 243
WIPER WASHER SWITCH
WIPER SWITCH
MIST
OFF
PULSE
LO
HI
1200 kΩ
710 kΩ
450 kΩ
240 kΩ
110 kΩ
24k Ω
WASHER SWITCH
.8 PNK 94
.8 DK GRN 95
.8 GRY 91
.8 PPL 92
E13
E11
E10
E12
C202
1 PNK 94
1 DK GRN 95
1 GRY 91
1 PPL 92
J
K
G
H
C219
P103
P104
1 YEL
196
A
B
C2
F
C
C1
HIGH SPEED INPUT
COVER ASSEMBLY
1 RED
228
D
SOLID STATE TIMER
WASHER MOTOR
M
LO
CAPACITOR
WIPER MOTOR
CAPACITOR
CIRCUIT BREAKER
MECHANICAL ARM
1 DK BLU
227
E
PARK SWITCH
PARK SWITCH (ARM HOLDS CONTACT CLOSED UNTIL WIPERS PARK)
WIPER MOTOR ASSEMBLY
1 BLK 1650
SEE GROUND DISTRIBUTION PAGE 8A-14-4
S125
G119

COMPONENT	LOCATION	201-PG	FIG.	CONN
Fuse Block	RH side of I/P, below RH front door opening	21	73	
Washer Motor	LH side of Engine Compartment, in Washer Fluid Reservoir	1	4	
Wiper Motor Assembly	LH front of dash	2	7	202-42
Wiper/Washer Switch	Top of Steering Column	12	43	
C202 (48 cavities)	Behind I/P, RH side of Steering Column	14	48	202-9
C219 (23 cavities)	Behind I/P, on RH side of brake pedal support			
G119	LH front frame rail	1	4	
P103	LH rear of Engine Compartment, near strut tower	2	7	
P104	LH rear of Engine Compartment, near Wiper Motor Assembly	2	7	
S125	Wiper Harn, approx 4 cm from ABS Actuator Motor breakout			

TROUBLESHOOTING HINTS
(Perform before beginning System Diagnosis)

1. Check Fuse 29. If open, check CKT 243 for short to ground.
2. If Washer does not operate, check that:
   - Washer Reservoir is filled.
   - Hoses are correctly attached.
   - Hoses are not cut, kinked or pinched.
   - Nozzles are not clogged.
   - Connector seal at Washer Motor is not damaged or missing.
3. If Washer does not operate and Wipers run in "HI" only (low speed inoperative), check CKT 91 for open.
4. Check for binding or broken Wiper Arm Linkage.
5. Check for missing or damaged connector seal at Windshield Wiper Motor Module.

- Check for a broken (or partially broken) wire inside of the insulation which could cause system malfunction but prove "GOOD" in a continuity/voltage check with a system disconnected. These circuits may be intermittent or resistive when loaded, and if possible, should be checked by monitoring for a voltage drop with the system operational (under load).
- Check for proper installation of aftermarket electronic equipment which may affect the integrity of other systems (see "Troubleshooting Procedures," page 8A-4-0).
- Refer to System Diagnosis.

SYSTEM DIAGNOSIS

- Perform the System Check and refer to the Symptom Table for the appropriate diagnostic procedures.

WIPER/WASHER: PULSE (CD4)

SYSTEM CHECK

ACTION	NORMAL RESULTS
[1] • Ignition Switch to "RUN." • Hold Washer Switch "ON" for 1 to 2 seconds.	Wipers operate at "LO" speed. Washer sprays windshield as long as the Washer Switch is held in "ON" position. After releasing the switch, Washer stops and Wipers return to park after approx 6 seconds.
[2] • Wiper Switch to "DELAY" (pulse mode).	Wipers make one complete sweep then pause for 0 to 25 seconds before making the next sweep. The pause time is adjusted by turning the Wiper Switch through the delay range.
[3] • Wiper Switch in "DELAY." • Hold Washer Switch "ON" for 1 to 2 seconds.	Washer sprays windshield as long as Washer Switch is held on. Wipers run at low speed while spraying and continue until Washer Switch is released. Wipers then return to pulse operation.
[4] • Wiper Switch to "LO."	Wipers run continuously at low speed.
[5] • Wiper Switch to "HI."	Wipers run continuously at faster speed.
[6] • Wiper Switch to "OFF."	Wipers return to park position at low speed then stop.
[7] • Wiper Switch to "MIST," then release.	Wipers make one complete sweep then return to park position.

SYMPTOM TABLE

SYMPTOM	PROCEDURE	PAGE NUMBER
Wipers do not operate in any mode.	Chart #1	8A-91-3
Wipers run at high speed only (low speed inoperative).	Chart #2	8A-91-4
Wipers run at low speed only (high speed inoperative).	Chart #3	8A-91-4
Wipers run intermittently in low or high speed.	Chart #4	8A-91-5
Wipers will not turn off.	Chart #5	8A-91-6
Pulse delay operates incorrectly or not at all.	Chart #6	8A-91-7
Washer will not operate.	Chart #7	8A-91-8
Washer will not shut off.	Chart #8	8A-91-8
Wipers cycle in and out of park position after wipers are shut off.	Replace Park Switch. If trouble is not corrected, replace Wiper Motor Assembly.	

CHART #1
WIPERS DO NOT OPERATE IN ANY MODE

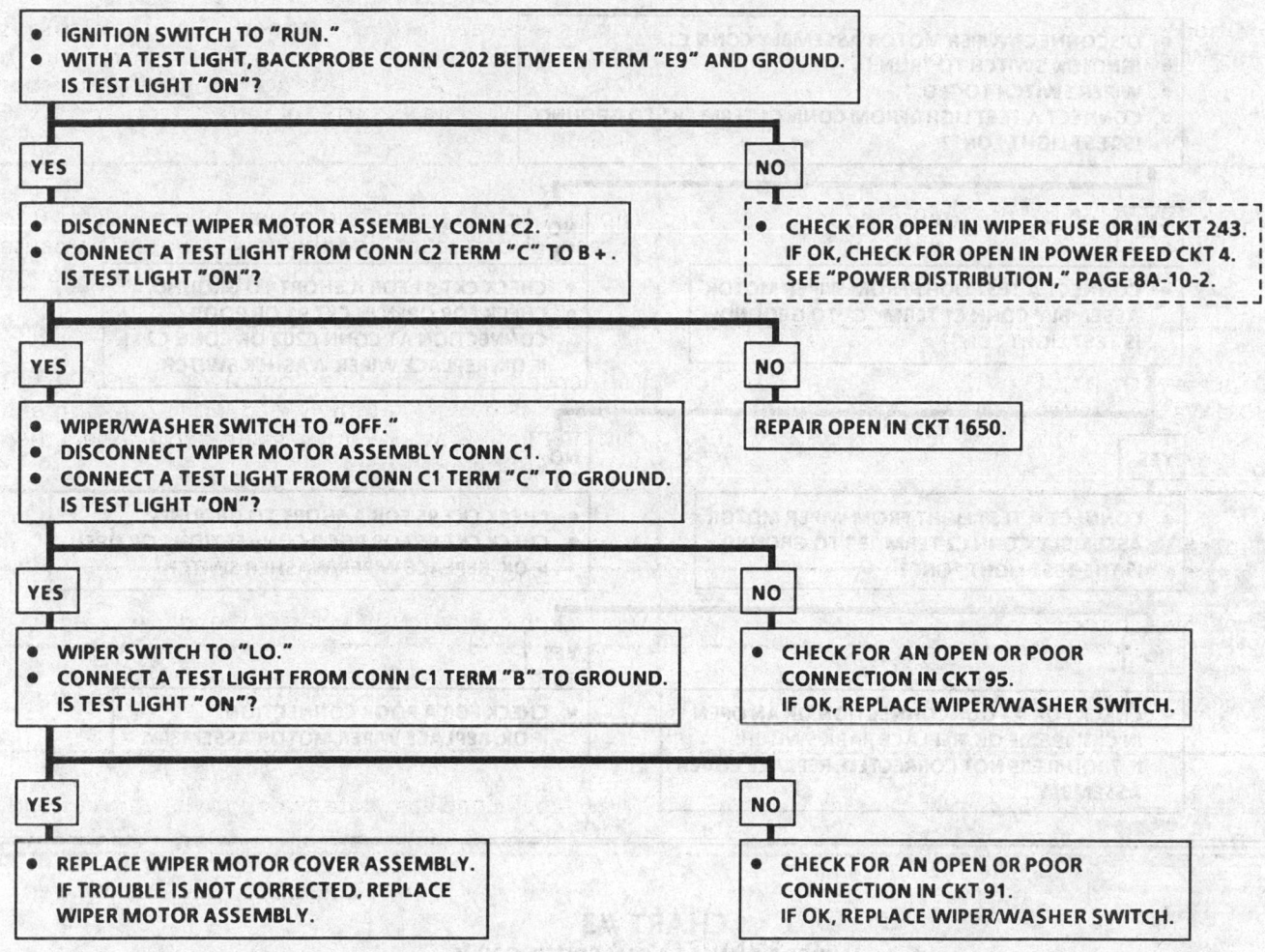

- IGNITION SWITCH TO "RUN."
- WITH A TEST LIGHT, BACKPROBE CONN C202 BETWEEN TERM "E9" AND GROUND.

IS TEST LIGHT "ON"?

YES:

- DISCONNECT WIPER MOTOR ASSEMBLY CONN C2.
- CONNECT A TEST LIGHT FROM CONN C2 TERM "C" TO B+.

IS TEST LIGHT "ON"?

NO:

- CHECK FOR OPEN IN WIPER FUSE OR IN CKT 243. IF OK, CHECK FOR OPEN IN POWER FEED CKT 4. SEE "POWER DISTRIBUTION," PAGE 8A-10-2.

(From "IS TEST LIGHT 'ON'?" at CONN C2 TERM "C")

YES:

- WIPER/WASHER SWITCH TO "OFF."
- DISCONNECT WIPER MOTOR ASSEMBLY CONN C1.
- CONNECT A TEST LIGHT FROM CONN C1 TERM "C" TO GROUND.

IS TEST LIGHT "ON"?

NO:

REPAIR OPEN IN CKT 1650.

(From "IS TEST LIGHT 'ON'?" at CONN C1 TERM "C")

YES:

- WIPER SWITCH TO "LO."
- CONNECT A TEST LIGHT FROM CONN C1 TERM "B" TO GROUND.

IS TEST LIGHT "ON"?

NO:

- CHECK FOR AN OPEN OR POOR CONNECTION IN CKT 95. IF OK, REPLACE WIPER/WASHER SWITCH.

(From "IS TEST LIGHT 'ON'?" at CONN C1 TERM "B")

YES:

- REPLACE WIPER MOTOR COVER ASSEMBLY. IF TROUBLE IS NOT CORRECTED, REPLACE WIPER MOTOR ASSEMBLY.

NO:

- CHECK FOR AN OPEN OR POOR CONNECTION IN CKT 91. IF OK, REPLACE WIPER/WASHER SWITCH.

WIPER/WASHER: PULSE (CD4)

CHART #2

WIPERS RUN AT HIGH SPEED ONLY
(LOW SPEED INOPERATIVE)

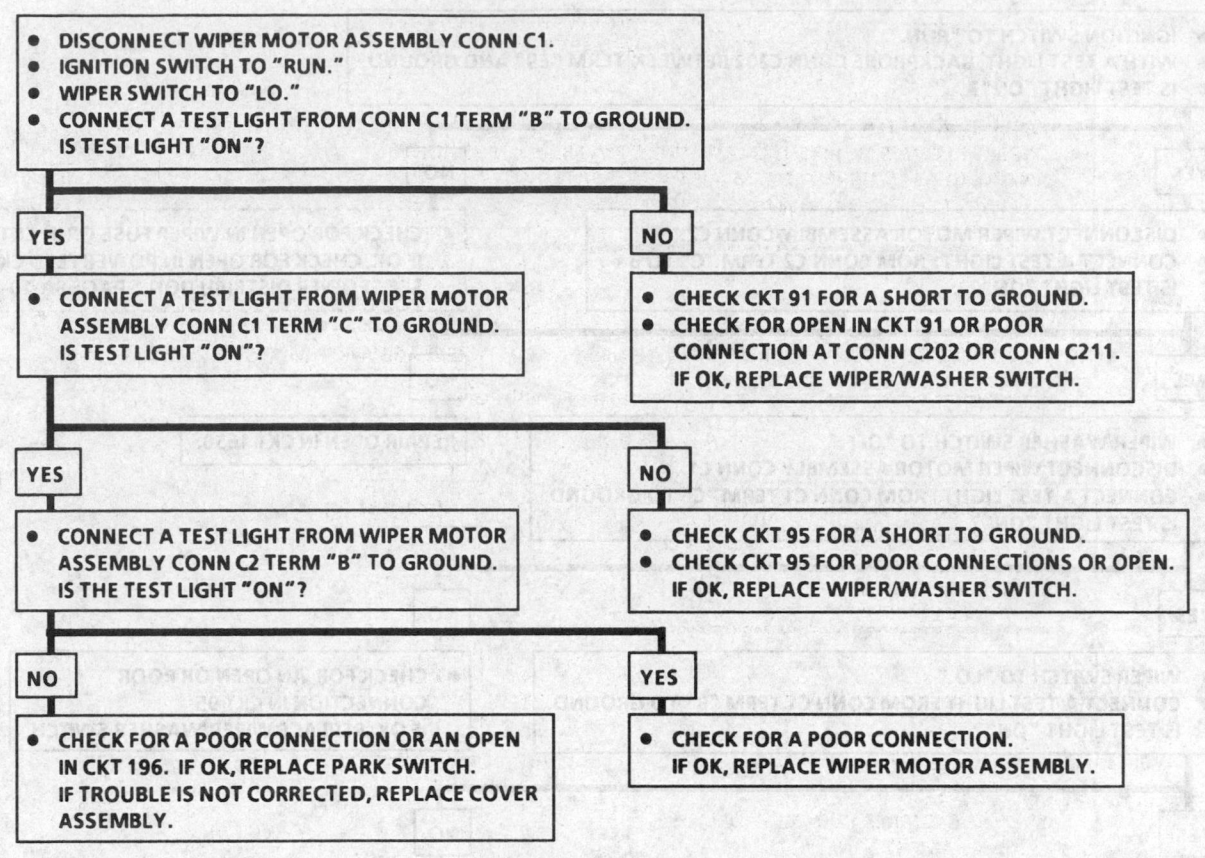

- DISCONNECT WIPER MOTOR ASSEMBLY CONN C1.
- IGNITION SWITCH TO "RUN."
- WIPER SWITCH TO "LO."
- CONNECT A TEST LIGHT FROM CONN C1 TERM "B" TO GROUND.

IS TEST LIGHT "ON"?

YES

- CONNECT A TEST LIGHT FROM WIPER MOTOR ASSEMBLY CONN C1 TERM "C" TO GROUND.

  IS TEST LIGHT "ON"?

  YES

  - CONNECT A TEST LIGHT FROM WIPER MOTOR ASSEMBLY CONN C2 TERM "B" TO GROUND.

    IS THE TEST LIGHT "ON"?

    NO

    - CHECK FOR A POOR CONNECTION OR AN OPEN IN CKT 196. IF OK, REPLACE PARK SWITCH. IF TROUBLE IS NOT CORRECTED, REPLACE COVER ASSEMBLY.

    YES

    - CHECK FOR A POOR CONNECTION. IF OK, REPLACE WIPER MOTOR ASSEMBLY.

  NO

  - CHECK CKT 95 FOR A SHORT TO GROUND.
  - CHECK CKT 95 FOR POOR CONNECTIONS OR OPEN. IF OK, REPLACE WIPER/WASHER SWITCH.

NO

- CHECK CKT 91 FOR A SHORT TO GROUND.
- CHECK FOR OPEN IN CKT 91 OR POOR CONNECTION AT CONN C202 OR CONN C211. IF OK, REPLACE WIPER/WASHER SWITCH.

CHART #3

WIPERS RUN AT LOW SPEED ONLY
(HIGH SPEED INOPERATIVE)

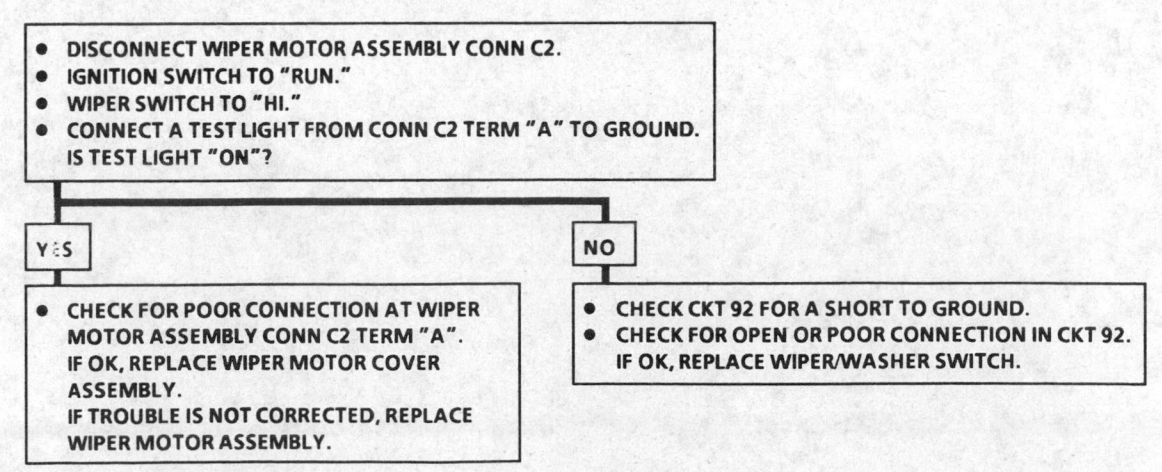

- DISCONNECT WIPER MOTOR ASSEMBLY CONN C2.
- IGNITION SWITCH TO "RUN."
- WIPER SWITCH TO "HI."
- CONNECT A TEST LIGHT FROM CONN C2 TERM "A" TO GROUND.

IS TEST LIGHT "ON"?

YES

- CHECK FOR POOR CONNECTION AT WIPER MOTOR ASSEMBLY CONN C2 TERM "A". IF OK, REPLACE WIPER MOTOR COVER ASSEMBLY. IF TROUBLE IS NOT CORRECTED, REPLACE WIPER MOTOR ASSEMBLY.

NO

- CHECK CKT 92 FOR A SHORT TO GROUND.
- CHECK FOR OPEN OR POOR CONNECTION IN CKT 92. IF OK, REPLACE WIPER/WASHER SWITCH.

CHART #4

WIPERS RUN INTERMITTENTLY IN LOW OR HIGH SPEED

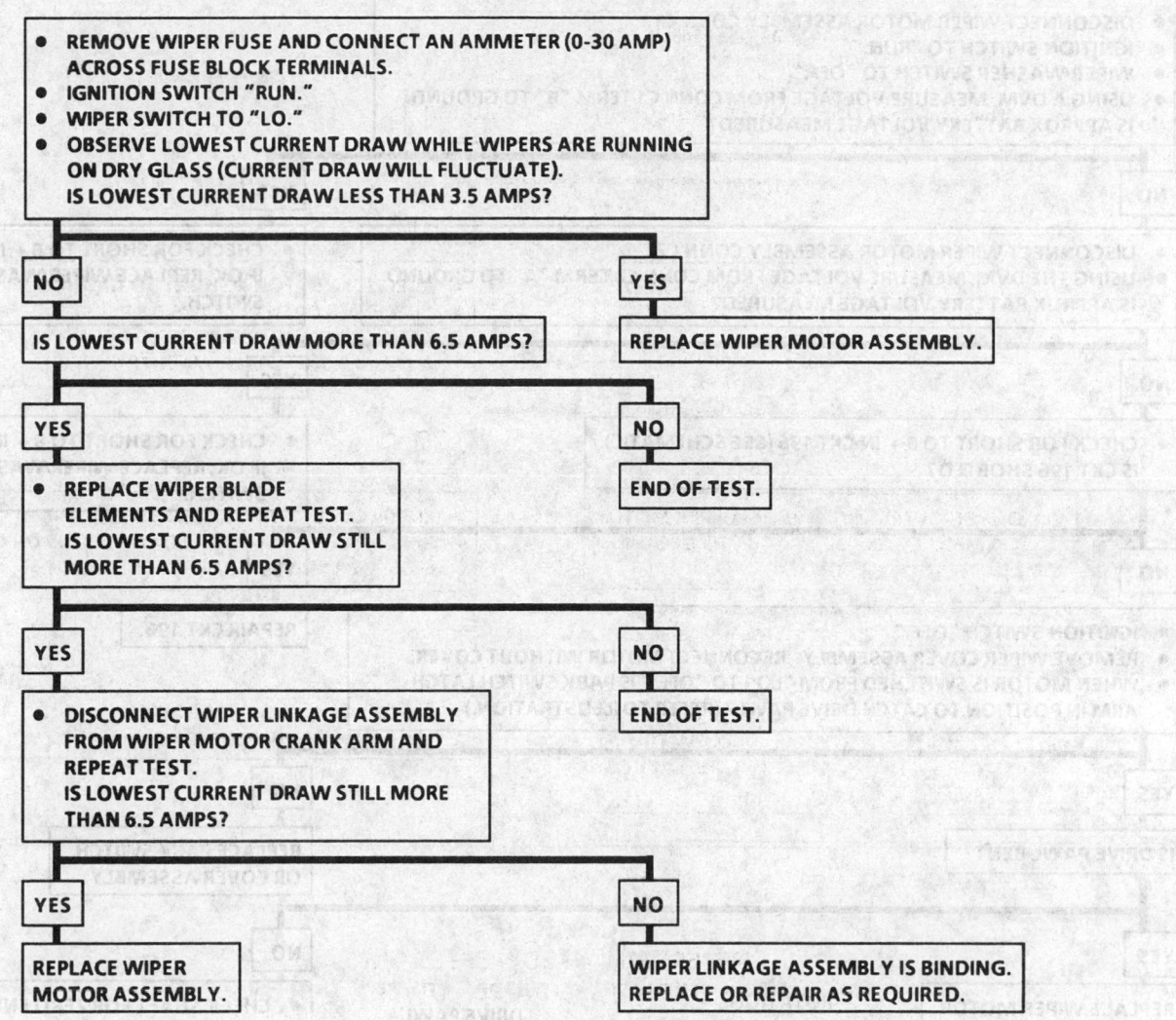

- REMOVE WIPER FUSE AND CONNECT AN AMMETER (0-30 AMP) ACROSS FUSE BLOCK TERMINALS.
- IGNITION SWITCH "RUN."
- WIPER SWITCH TO "LO."
- OBSERVE LOWEST CURRENT DRAW WHILE WIPERS ARE RUNNING ON DRY GLASS (CURRENT DRAW WILL FLUCTUATE).
  IS LOWEST CURRENT DRAW LESS THAN 3.5 AMPS?

NO

IS LOWEST CURRENT DRAW MORE THAN 6.5 AMPS?

YES

REPLACE WIPER MOTOR ASSEMBLY.

(From "IS LOWEST CURRENT DRAW MORE THAN 6.5 AMPS?")

YES

- REPLACE WIPER BLADE ELEMENTS AND REPEAT TEST.
  IS LOWEST CURRENT DRAW STILL MORE THAN 6.5 AMPS?

NO

END OF TEST.

(From "IS LOWEST CURRENT DRAW STILL MORE THAN 6.5 AMPS?")

YES

- DISCONNECT WIPER LINKAGE ASSEMBLY FROM WIPER MOTOR CRANK ARM AND REPEAT TEST.
  IS LOWEST CURRENT DRAW STILL MORE THAN 6.5 AMPS?

NO

END OF TEST.

(From "DISCONNECT WIPER LINKAGE ASSEMBLY ...")

YES

REPLACE WIPER MOTOR ASSEMBLY.

NO

WIPER LINKAGE ASSEMBLY IS BINDING. REPLACE OR REPAIR AS REQUIRED.

WIPER/WASHER: PULSE (CD4)

CHART #5
WIPERS WILL NOT TURN OFF

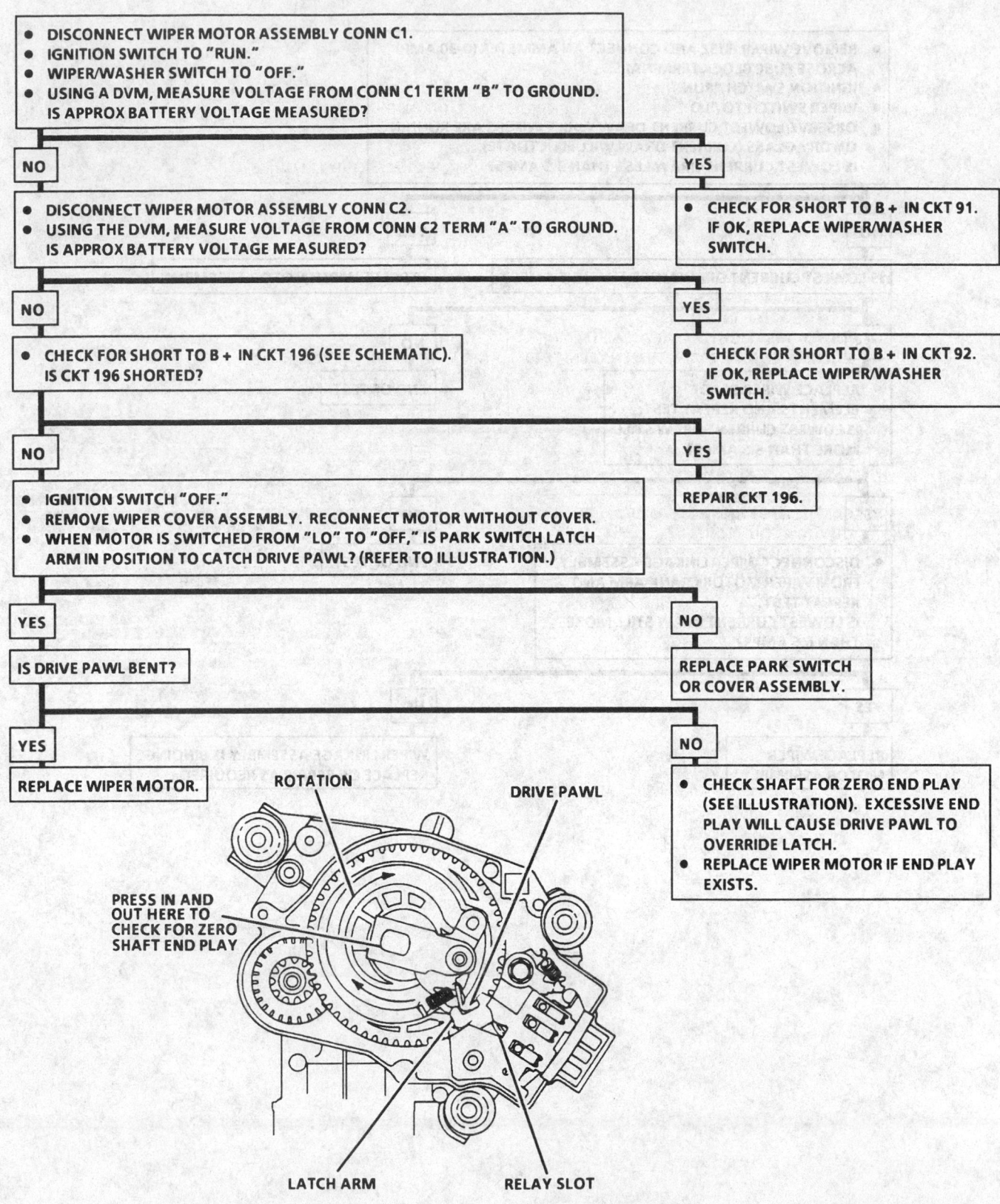

- DISCONNECT WIPER MOTOR ASSEMBLY CONN C1.
- IGNITION SWITCH TO "RUN."
- WIPER/WASHER SWITCH TO "OFF."
- USING A DVM, MEASURE VOLTAGE FROM CONN C1 TERM "B" TO GROUND.

IS APPROX BATTERY VOLTAGE MEASURED?

YES

- CHECK FOR SHORT TO B + IN CKT 91. IF OK, REPLACE WIPER/WASHER SWITCH.

NO

- DISCONNECT WIPER MOTOR ASSEMBLY CONN C2.
- USING THE DVM, MEASURE VOLTAGE FROM CONN C2 TERM "A" TO GROUND.

IS APPROX BATTERY VOLTAGE MEASURED?

YES

- CHECK FOR SHORT TO B + IN CKT 92. IF OK, REPLACE WIPER/WASHER SWITCH.

NO

- CHECK FOR SHORT TO B + IN CKT 196 (SEE SCHEMATIC).

IS CKT 196 SHORTED?

YES

REPAIR CKT 196.

NO

- IGNITION SWITCH "OFF."
- REMOVE WIPER COVER ASSEMBLY. RECONNECT MOTOR WITHOUT COVER.
- WHEN MOTOR IS SWITCHED FROM "LO" TO "OFF," IS PARK SWITCH LATCH ARM IN POSITION TO CATCH DRIVE PAWL? (REFER TO ILLUSTRATION.)

NO

REPLACE PARK SWITCH OR COVER ASSEMBLY.

YES

IS DRIVE PAWL BENT?

YES

REPLACE WIPER MOTOR.

NO

- CHECK SHAFT FOR ZERO END PLAY (SEE ILLUSTRATION). EXCESSIVE END PLAY WILL CAUSE DRIVE PAWL TO OVERRIDE LATCH.
- REPLACE WIPER MOTOR IF END PLAY EXISTS.

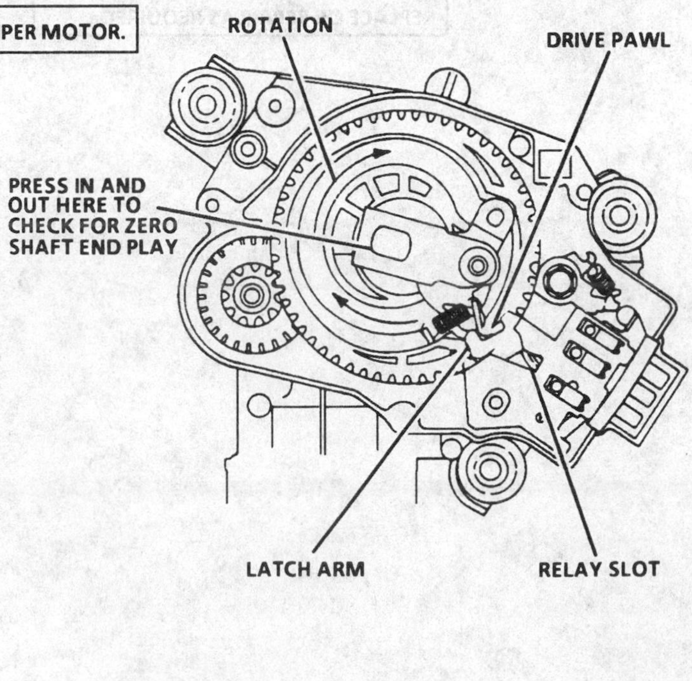
ROTATION
DRIVE PAWL
PRESS IN AND OUT HERE TO CHECK FOR ZERO SHAFT END PLAY
LATCH ARM
RELAY SLOT

CHART #6

PULSE DELAY OPERATES INCORRECTLY OR NOT AT ALL

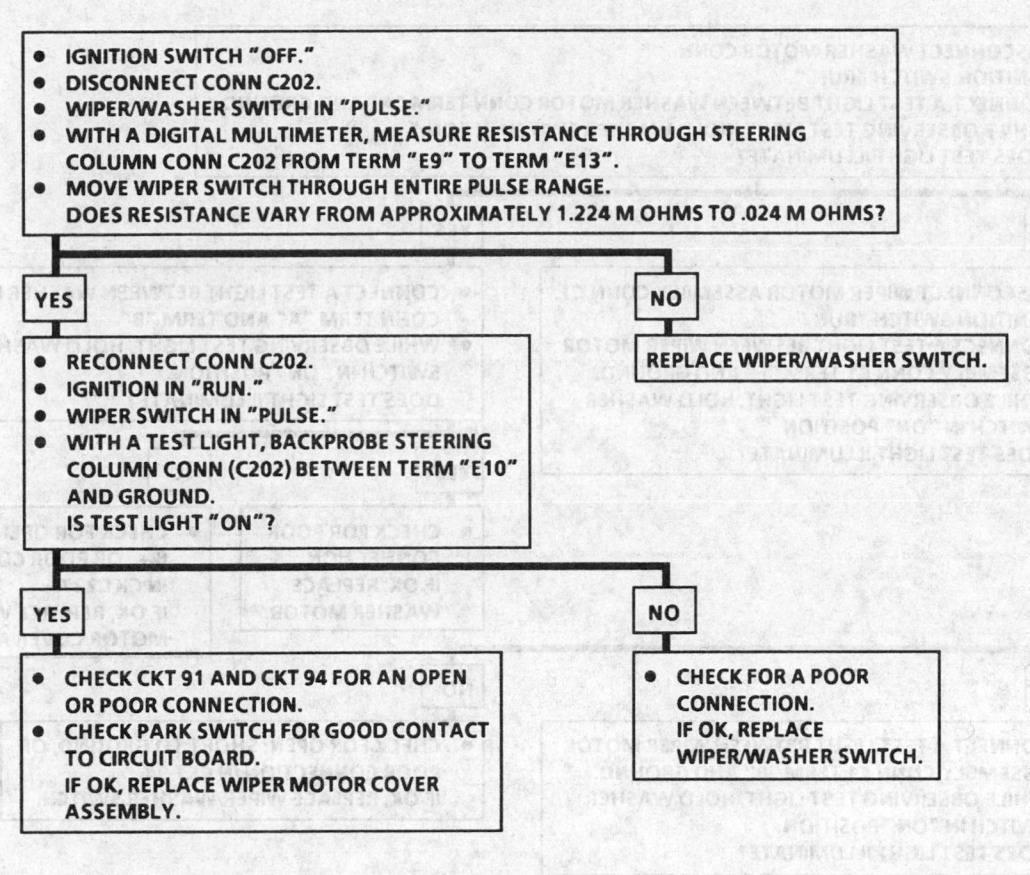

- IGNITION SWITCH "OFF."
- DISCONNECT CONN C202.
- WIPER/WASHER SWITCH IN "PULSE."
- WITH A DIGITAL MULTIMETER, MEASURE RESISTANCE THROUGH STEERING COLUMN CONN C202 FROM TERM "E9" TO TERM "E13".
- MOVE WIPER SWITCH THROUGH ENTIRE PULSE RANGE.

DOES RESISTANCE VARY FROM APPROXIMATELY 1.224 M OHMS TO .024 M OHMS?

YES

- RECONNECT CONN C202.
- IGNITION IN "RUN."
- WIPER SWITCH IN "PULSE."
- WITH A TEST LIGHT, BACKPROBE STEERING COLUMN CONN (C202) BETWEEN TERM "E10" AND GROUND.

IS TEST LIGHT "ON"?

YES

- CHECK CKT 91 AND CKT 94 FOR AN OPEN OR POOR CONNECTION.
- CHECK PARK SWITCH FOR GOOD CONTACT TO CIRCUIT BOARD.

IF OK, REPLACE WIPER MOTOR COVER ASSEMBLY.

NO

- CHECK FOR A POOR CONNECTION.

IF OK, REPLACE WIPER/WASHER SWITCH.

NO

REPLACE WIPER/WASHER SWITCH.

WIPER/WASHER: PULSE (CD4)

CHART #7
WASHER WILL NOT OPERATE

- DISCONNECT WASHER MOTOR CONN.
- IGNITION SWITCH "RUN."
- CONNECT A TEST LIGHT BETWEEN WASHER MOTOR CONN TERM "A" AND GROUND.
- WHILE OBSERVING TEST LIGHT, HOLD WASHER SWITCH IN "ON."
  DOES TEST LIGHT ILLUMINATE?

NO

- DISCONNECT WIPER MOTOR ASSEMBLY CONN C1.
- IGNITION SWITCH "RUN."
- CONNECT A TEST LIGHT BETWEEN WIPER MOTOR ASSEMBLY CONN C1 TERM "F" AND GROUND.
- WHILE OBSERVING TEST LIGHT, HOLD WASHER SWITCH IN "ON" POSITION.
  DOES TEST LIGHT ILLUMINATE?

YES

- CONNECT A TEST LIGHT BETWEEN WIPER MOTOR ASSEMBLY CONN C1 TERM "B" AND GROUND.
- WHILE OBSERVING TEST LIGHT, HOLD WASHER SWITCH IN "ON" POSITION.
  DOES TEST LIGHT ILLUMINATE?

YES

- CHECK FOR OPEN, SHORT TO GROUND, OR POOR CONNECTION IN CKT 228.
  IF OK, REPLACE WIPER MOTOR COVER ASSEMBLY.

NO

- CHECK FOR OPEN, SHORT TO GROUND, OR POOR CONNECTION IN CKT 91.
  IF OK, REPLACE WIPER/WASHER SWITCH.

NO

- CHECK FOR OPEN, SHORT TO GROUND, OR POOR CONNECTION IN CKT 94.
  IF OK, REPLACE WIPER/WASHER SWITCH.

YES

- CONNECT A TEST LIGHT BETWEEN WASHER MOTOR CONN TERM "A" AND TERM "B".
- WHILE OBSERVING TEST LIGHT, HOLD WASHER SWITCH IN "ON" POSITION.
  DOES TEST LIGHT ILLUMINATE?

YES

- CHECK FOR POOR CONNECTION.
  IF OK, REPLACE WASHER MOTOR.

NO

- CHECK FOR OPEN, SHORT TO B +, OR POOR CONNECTION IN CKT 227.
  IF OK, REPLACE WIPER MOTOR COVER ASSEMBLY.

CHART #8
WASHER WILL NOT SHUT OFF

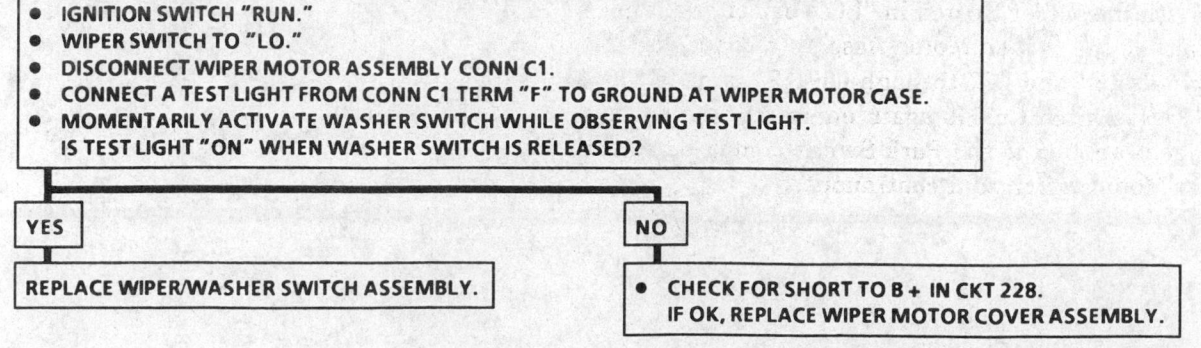

- IGNITION SWITCH "RUN."
- WIPER SWITCH TO "LO."
- DISCONNECT WIPER MOTOR ASSEMBLY CONN C1.
- CONNECT A TEST LIGHT FROM CONN C1 TERM "F" TO GROUND AT WIPER MOTOR CASE.
- MOMENTARILY ACTIVATE WASHER SWITCH WHILE OBSERVING TEST LIGHT.
  IS TEST LIGHT "ON" WHEN WASHER SWITCH IS RELEASED?

YES

REPLACE WIPER/WASHER SWITCH ASSEMBLY.

NO

- CHECK FOR SHORT TO B + IN CKT 228.
  IF OK, REPLACE WIPER MOTOR COVER ASSEMBLY.

CIRCUIT OPERATION

In addition to the features of a conventional (non-pulse) wiper system (low and high speed), the pulse-type Windshield Wiper/Washer System includes an operating mode in which the Wipers make single strokes with an adjustable time interval between strokes. The time interval is controlled by a Solid State Timer in the Wiper Motor Assembly. The duration of the delay interval is determined by the delay resistors in the Wiper Switch Assembly.

The Wiper Motor is protected by a Circuit Breaker. If the Wipers are blocked (by snow or ice for example) the Circuit Breaker will open the circuit. The Circuit Breaker resets automatically when it cools.

DELAY (PULSE) OPERATION

With the Wiper/Washer Switch in "PULSE," battery voltage is applied to the Wiper Motor Assembly at terminal "B" of connector C1 through CKT 91. Voltage is also applied to terminal "F" through CKT 94, and the pulse delay resistors in the Wiper Switch Assembly. The battery voltage at terminal "B" energizes the Park Switch Coil,which closes its contacts. In response to the voltage at terminal "F," the Solid State Timer momentarily closes contact A on the Cover Assembly which applies battery voltage at terminal "B" to the contacts of the Park Switch, starting the Wiper Motor.

A mechanical arm (end of sweep input) operates contacts on the Cover Assembly, which causes contact A to open when the Wipers have completed their sweep. Since the Park Switch Coil remains energized, the Wipers do not park but remain just above the "PARK" position until the Cover Assembly closes contact A again to start another sweep.

The length of delay time between sweeps is controlled by the delay resistors. The delay is adjustable from 0 to 25 seconds.

LOW SPEED

With the Wiper Switch in "LO," battery voltage is applied at the Wiper Motor Assembly connector C1, terminals "B" and "C" through CKT 91 and CKT 95. The Park Switch Coil is again energized and battery voltage is applied to the Park Switch contacts and the Wiper Motor, which runs continuously.

HIGH SPEED

With the Wiper Switch in the "HI" position, battery voltage is applied directly to the Wiper Motor, at terminal "A" of connector C2, without passing through the Park Switch contacts. Terminal "A" is connected to a separate Wiper Motor brush for high speed operation. The Park Switch coil remains energized in the "HI" position because of the voltage that is present at the low speed Wiper Motor brush when voltage is applied to the high speed brush. The current path from the low speed brush to the Park Switch coil is completed through the Wiper/Washer Switch. An open in this circuit will cause the wipers to cycle in and out of Park in "HI" and possible prevent "LO" speed operation.

When turned off from "HI," the wipers complete the last sweep at low speed and park. To do this, the Wiper Motor receives voltage in the "OFF" position of the Wiper Switch, which is applied through CKT 95 to terminal "C" of connector C1. The Park Switch is de-energized when the Wiper Switch is moved to "OFF," but the contacts remain closed until the wipers reach the "PARK" position.

WASHER

When the Washer Switch is held "ON," battery voltage is applied to the Cover Assembly through CKT 94 and CKT 91. The Park Switch is energized by the battery voltage at terminal "B" of connector C1. The Cover Assembly turns on the Washer and Wiper Motors by closing contacts A and B. The Cover Assembly turns the Wiper Motor off approximately six seconds after it interrupts power to the Washer Motor. If the Wipers had been in "PULSE," "LO" or "HI," they would return to that operation after the wash cycle.

MIST

When the control is moved to "MIST" and released, the wipers make one sweep at low speed and return to "PARK." The circuit operation is the same as that of "LO."

HEADLIGHTS
WITH FOG LIGHTS

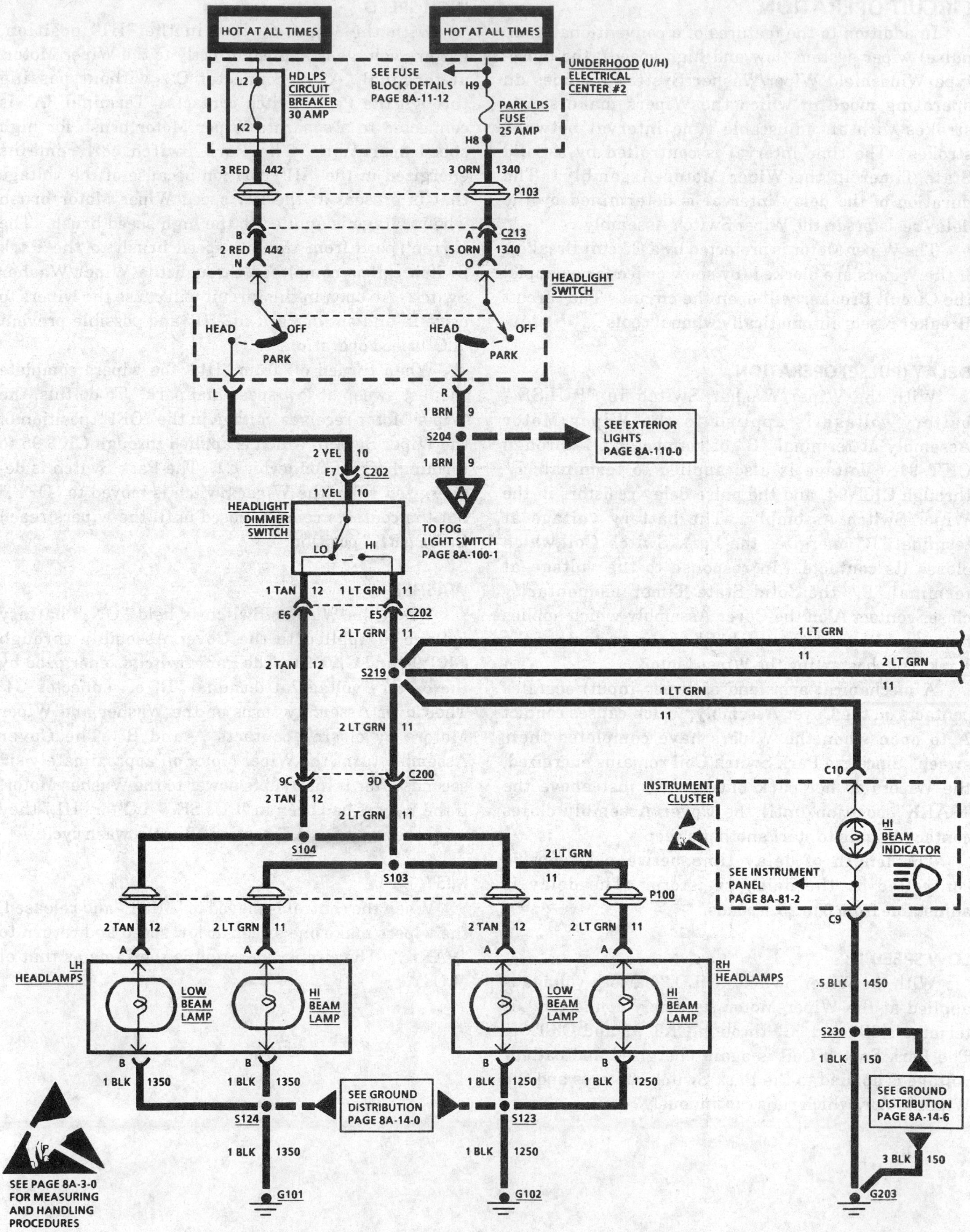
HOT AT ALL TIMES
HOT AT ALL TIMES
L2
K2
HD LPS
CIRCUIT
BREAKER
30 AMP
SEE FUSE
BLOCK DETAILS
PAGE 8A-11-12
H9
H8
PARK LPS
FUSE
25 AMP
UNDERHOOD (U/H)
ELECTRICAL
CENTER #2
3 RED 442
3 ORN 1340
P103
B
A
C213
2 RED 442
.5 ORN 1340
N
O
HEADLIGHT
SWITCH
HEAD
OFF
PARK
HEAD
OFF
PARK
L
R
1 BRN 9
S204
SEE EXTERIOR
LIGHTS
PAGE 8A-110-0
2 YEL 10
E7
C202
1 BRN 9
1 YEL 10
A
HEADLIGHT
DIMMER
SWITCH
LO
HI
TO FOG
LIGHT SWITCH
PAGE 8A-100-1
1 TAN 12
1 LT GRN 11
E6
E5
C202
2 LT GRN 11
1 LT GRN
11
2 TAN 12
S219
2 LT GRN
11
1 LT GRN
11
2 LT GRN 11
9C
9D
C200
C10
2 TAN 12
2 LT GRN 11
INSTRUMENT
CLUSTER
HI
BEAM
INDICATOR
S104
2 LT GRN
11
SEE INSTRUMENT
PANEL
PAGE 8A-81-2
S103
P100
C9
2 TAN 12
2 LT GRN 11
2 TAN 12
2 LT GRN 11
A
A
A
A
LH
HEADLAMPS
LOW
BEAM
LAMP
HI
BEAM
LAMP
LOW
BEAM
LAMP
HI
BEAM
LAMP
RH
HEADLAMPS
.5 BLK 1450
B
B
B
B
S230
1 BLK 150
1 BLK 1350
1 BLK 1350
1 BLK 1250
1 BLK 1250
SEE GROUND
DISTRIBUTION
PAGE 8A-14-0
S124
S123
SEE GROUND
DISTRIBUTION
PAGE 8A-14-6
1 BLK 1350
1 BLK 1250
3 BLK 150
G101
G102
G203
SEE PAGE 8A-3-0
FOR MEASURING
AND HANDLING
PROCEDURES

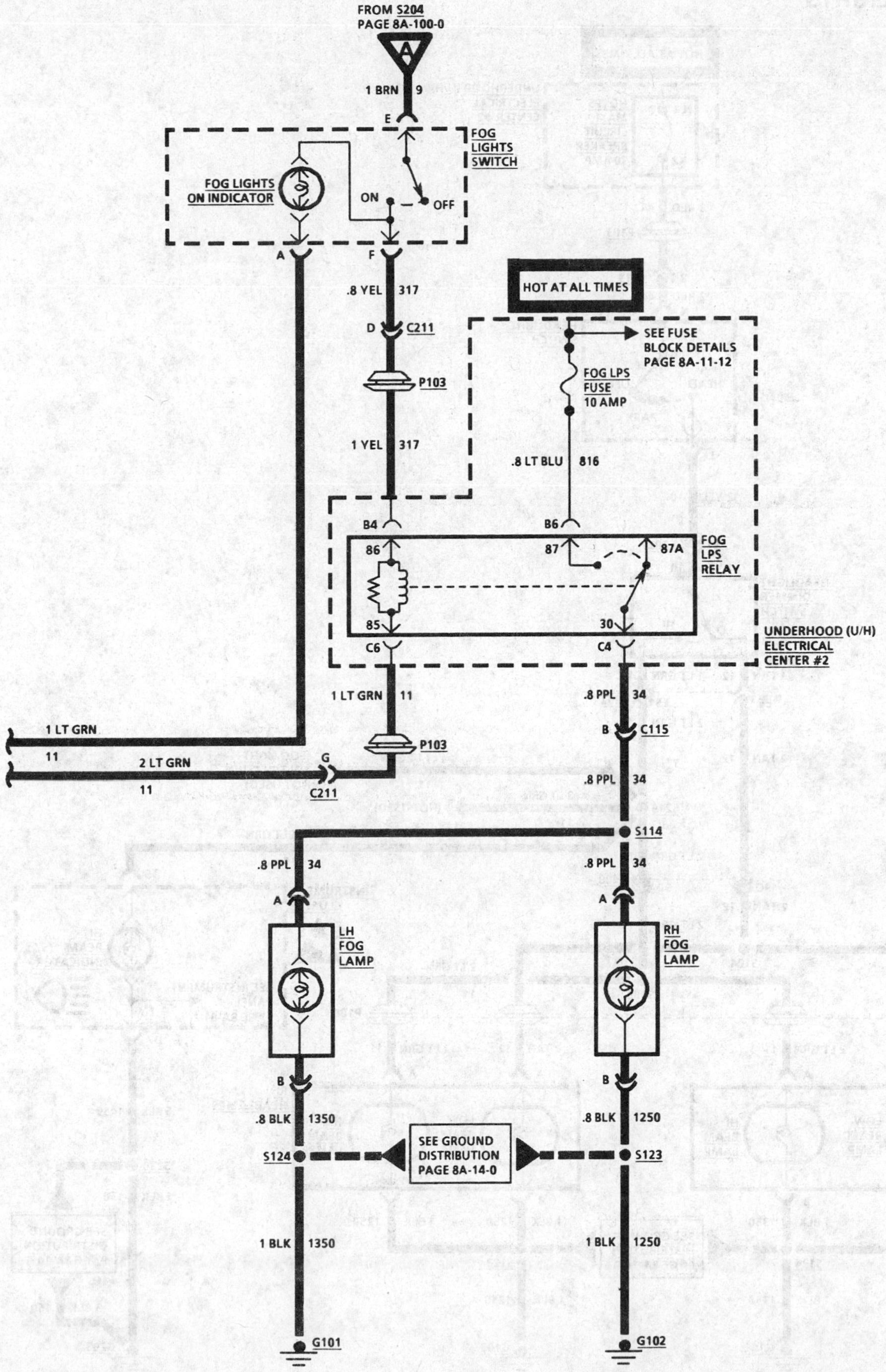
FROM S204
PAGE 8A-100-0
1 BRN 9
E
FOG
LIGHTS
SWITCH
FOG LIGHTS
ON INDICATOR
ON
OFF
A
F
.8 YEL 317
D C211
P103
1 YEL 317
HOT AT ALL TIMES
SEE FUSE
BLOCK DETAILS
PAGE 8A-11-12
FOG LPS
FUSE
10 AMP
.8 LT BLU 816
B4
B6
86
87
87A
FOG
LPS
RELAY
85
30
C6
C4
UNDERHOOD (U/H)
ELECTRICAL
CENTER #2
1 LT GRN 11
.8 PPL 34
B C115
1 LT GRN
11
2 LT GRN
11
G
C211
P103
.8 PPL 34
S114
.8 PPL 34
.8 PPL 34
A
A
LH
FOG
LAMP
RH
FOG
LAMP
B
B
.8 BLK 1350
.8 BLK 1250
S124
SEE GROUND
DISTRIBUTION
PAGE 8A-14-0
S123
1 BLK 1350
1 BLK 1250
G101
G102

HEADLIGHTS
WITHOUT FOG LIGHTS

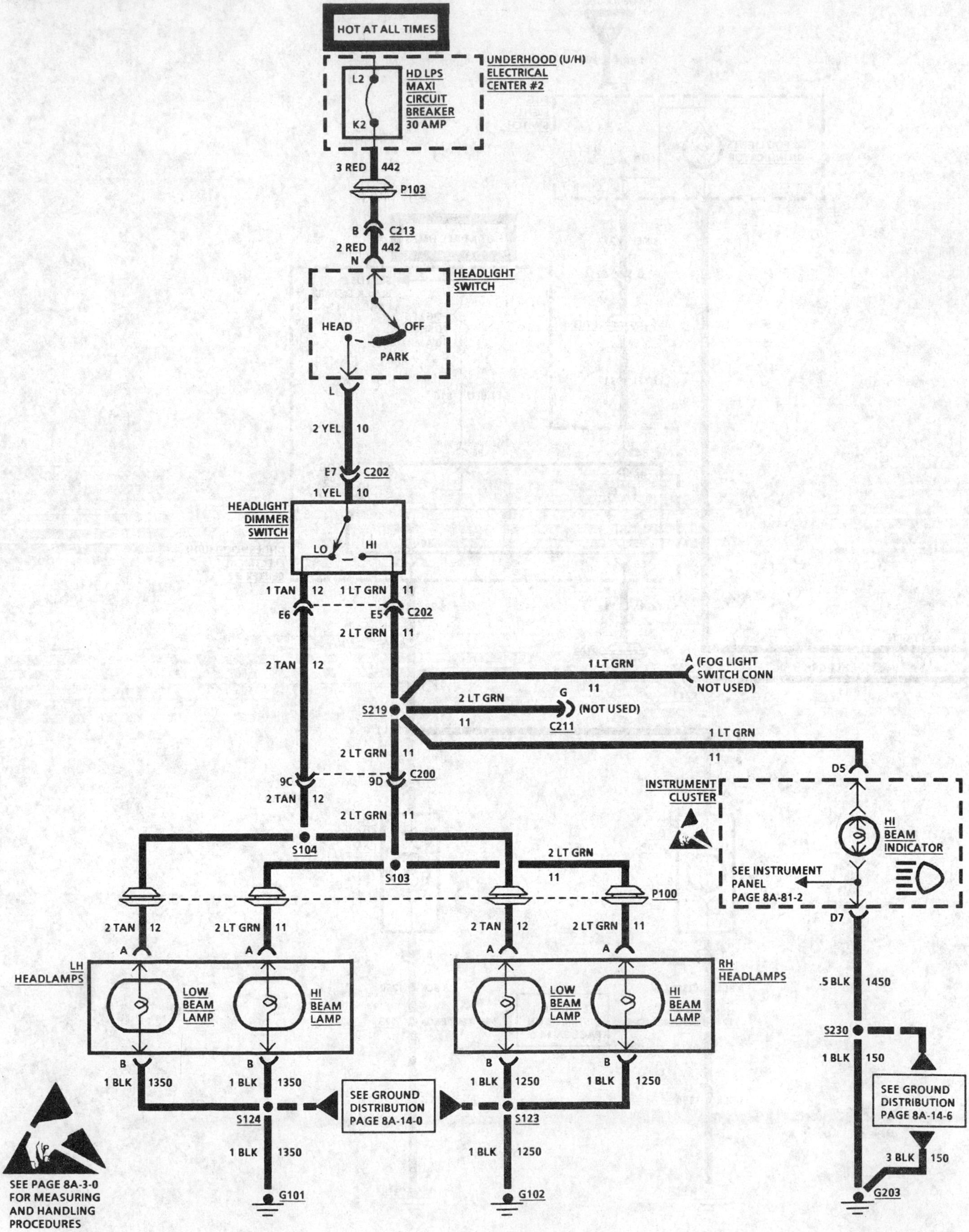

HOT AT ALL TIMES
UNDERHOOD (U/H) ELECTRICAL CENTER #2
L2
K2
HD LPS MAXI CIRCUIT BREAKER 30 AMP
3 RED 442
P103
B C213
2 RED 442
N
HEADLIGHT SWITCH
HEAD
OFF
PARK
L
2 YEL 10
E7 C202
1 YEL 10
HEADLIGHT DIMMER SWITCH
LO
HI
1 TAN 12
1 LT GRN 11
E6
E5 C202
2 LT GRN 11
2 TAN 12
1 LT GRN 11
A (FOG LIGHT SWITCH CONN NOT USED)
2 LT GRN 11
G (NOT USED)
C211
S219
1 LT GRN 11
2 LT GRN 11
9C
9D C200
2 TAN 12
2 LT GRN 11
D5
INSTRUMENT CLUSTER
HI BEAM INDICATOR
SEE INSTRUMENT PANEL PAGE 8A-81-2
D7
S104
S103
2 LT GRN 11
P100
2 TAN 12
2 LT GRN 11
2 TAN 12
2 LT GRN 11
A
LH HEADLAMPS
LOW BEAM LAMP
HI BEAM LAMP
RH HEADLAMPS
LOW BEAM LAMP
HI BEAM LAMP
B
1 BLK 1350
1 BLK 1350
1 BLK 1250
1 BLK 1250
.5 BLK 1450
S230
1 BLK 150
SEE GROUND DISTRIBUTION PAGE 8A-14-0
S124
S123
SEE GROUND DISTRIBUTION PAGE 8A-14-6
1 BLK 1350
1 BLK 1250
3 BLK 150
G101
G102
G203
SEE PAGE 8A-3-0 FOR MEASURING AND HANDLING PROCEDURES

HEADLIGHTS

COMPONENT	LOCATION	201-PG	FIG.	CONN
Fog Light Switch	LH side of I/P			
Headlight Dimmer Switch	On LH side of Steering Column	12	43	
Headlight Switch	LH side of I/P, left of Steering Column			202-21
Instrument Cluster	LH side of I/P	16	52	
LH Composite Headlight Assembly	LH front of vehicle	10	33	
LH Fog Lamp	LH front of vehicle	10	33	
RH Composite Headlight Assembly	RH front of vehicle	10	33	
RH Fog Lamp	RH front of vehicle	10	33	
Underhood Electrical Center #2	LH side of Engine Compartment, on strut tower	1	4	202-34
C115 (3 cavities)	LH side of Engine Compartment, near strut tower	27	87	
C200 (102 cavities)	Behind RH side of I/P, near shroud	22	74	202-3
C202 (48 cavities)	Behind I/P, RH side of Steering Column	14	48	202-9
C211 (8 cavities)	Behind I/P, RH side of Steering Column			
C213 (4 cavities)	Behind I/P, RH side of Steering Column			
G101	LH front of Engine Compartment, on radiator support	1	6	
G102	RH front of Engine Compartment, on radiator support			
G203	Behind LH side of I/P, on Mag bracket	14	48	
P100	RH rear of Engine Compartment, near strut tower	23	77	
P103	LH rear of Engine Compartment, near strut tower	2	7	
S103	Forward Light Harn, approx 17 cm from C200			
S104	Forward Light Harn, approx 13 cm from C200			
S114	Forward Light Harn, approx 10 cm from LH Headlight breakout			
S123	Forward Light Harn, approx 8 cm from RH Headlight breakout			
S124	Forward Light Harn, approx 8 cm from LH Headlight breakout			
S204	I/P Harn, approx 27 cm from C200 breakout			
S219	I/P Harn, approx 14 cm from Fuse Block breakout			
S230	I/P Harn, approx 27 cm from Radio Control Head breakout			

HEADLIGHTS

TROUBLESHOOTING HINTS
(Perform before beginning System Diagnosis)

CAUTION: Halogen bulbs contain a gas under pressure. Handling a bulb improperly could cause it to shatter into flying glass fragments. To help avoid personal injury:

- **Turn "OFF" the Light Switch and allow bulb to cool before changing bulbs. Leave the Switch "OFF" until bulb change is complete.**
- **Always wear eye protection when changing a halogen bulb.**
- **Handle the bulb only by its base. Avoid touching the glass.**
- **Do not drop or scratch the bulb. Keep moisture away.**
- **Place the used bulb in the new bulb's carton and dispose of it properly. Keep halogen bulbs out of reach of children.**

1. Check LOW Beam Lamps and HI Beam Lamps for damage to the filament or bulb.
2. If a LOW Beam Lamp or HI Beam Lamp has been found damaged and an unusually high amount of moisture is noticeable in the Headlamp Capsule, check the Vent Tube and Drain Tube for restriction. Small amounts of moisture are normally found in the Headlamp Capsule, however, excessive moisture can damage the lamps.
3. Check the LH and RH Headlamp Capsule connectors to be sure the connector seal is not damaged or missing.
4. If one Headlight does not work, check the lamp, connections and wires to the Headlight.
5. If HI Beams do not light, but the HI Beam Indicator lights, check CKT 11 for an open (see schematic).
6. If the Headlights do not turn "OFF," check CKT 10 for a short to Battery. If OK, replace the Headlight Switch.
7. If the Fog Lamps do not operate, check the FOG LPS Fuse.

- Check for a broken (or partially broken) wire inside of the insulation which could cause system malfunction but prove "GOOD" in a continuity/voltage check with a system disconnected. These circuits may be intermittent or resistive when loaded, and if possible, should be checked by monitoring for a voltage drop with the system operational (under load).
- Check for proper installation of aftermarket electronic equipment which may affect the integrity of other systems (see "Troubleshooting Procedures," page 8A-4-0).
- Refer to System Diagnosis.

SYSTEM DIAGNOSIS

- Perform the System Check and refer to the Symptom Table for the appropriate diagnostic procedure(s).

SYSTEM CHECK

ACTION	NORMAL RESULTS
[1] ● Headlight Switch to "HEAD."	LOW Beam Headlights only are "ON."
[2] ● Headlight Dimmer Switch to "HI."	LOW Beam Headlights are "OFF." HI Beam Headlights are "ON." HI Beam Indicator is "ON."
[3] ● Headlight Dimmer Switch to "LO."	HI Beam Headlights are "OFF." HI Beam Indicator is "OFF." LOW Beam Headlights are "ON."

SYMPTOM TABLE

SYMPTOM	PROCEDURE	PAGE NUMBER
LOW Beam and HI Beam Headlights are inoperative.	Chart #1	8A-100-6
LOW Beam Headlights inoperative, HI Beam Headlights operate normally.	Chart #2	8A-100-6
HI Beam Headlights inoperative, LOW Beam Headlights operate normally.	Chart #3	8A-100-7
HI Beam Indicator inoperative, HI Beam Headlights operate normally.	Chart #4	8A-100-7
One LOW Beam or one HI Beam Headlamp inoperative.	Chart #5	8A-100-7
HI Beam Headlights and LOW Beam Headlights "ON" at the same time (4 Door).	Check for short to B+ on CKT 12 or CKT 11. If OK, replace Headlight Dimmer Switch.	
Fog Lights are inoperative.	Chart #6	8A-100-8
Fog Lights always "ON."	Chart #7	8A-100-9
Fog Lights Indicator is inoperative.	Check for open in CKT 11 or indicator bulb. If OK, replace Fog Light Switch.	

HEADLIGHTS

CHART #1
LOW BEAM AND HI BEAM HEADLIGHTS ARE INOPERATIVE

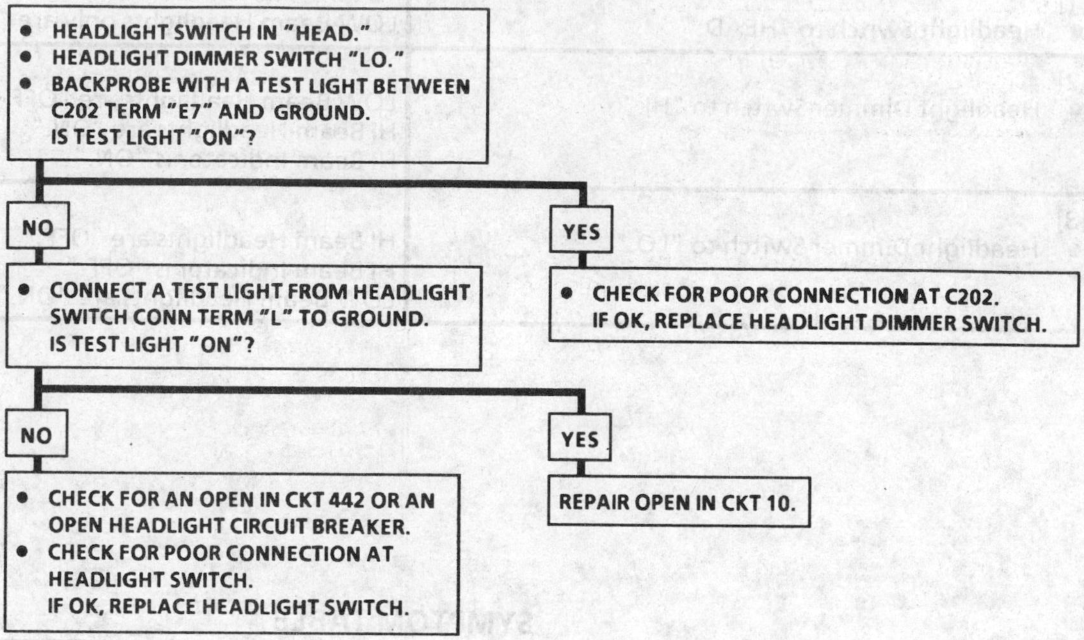

• HEADLIGHT SWITCH IN "HEAD."
• HEADLIGHT DIMMER SWITCH "LO."
• BACKPROBE WITH A TEST LIGHT BETWEEN C202 TERM "E7" AND GROUND.
IS TEST LIGHT "ON"?
NO
YES
• CONNECT A TEST LIGHT FROM HEADLIGHT SWITCH CONN TERM "L" TO GROUND.
IS TEST LIGHT "ON"?
• CHECK FOR POOR CONNECTION AT C202.
IF OK, REPLACE HEADLIGHT DIMMER SWITCH.
NO
YES
• CHECK FOR AN OPEN IN CKT 442 OR AN OPEN HEADLIGHT CIRCUIT BREAKER.
• CHECK FOR POOR CONNECTION AT HEADLIGHT SWITCH.
IF OK, REPLACE HEADLIGHT SWITCH.
REPAIR OPEN IN CKT 10.

CHART #2
LOW BEAM HEADLIGHTS INOPERATIVE, HI BEAM HEADLIGHTS OPERATE NORMALLY

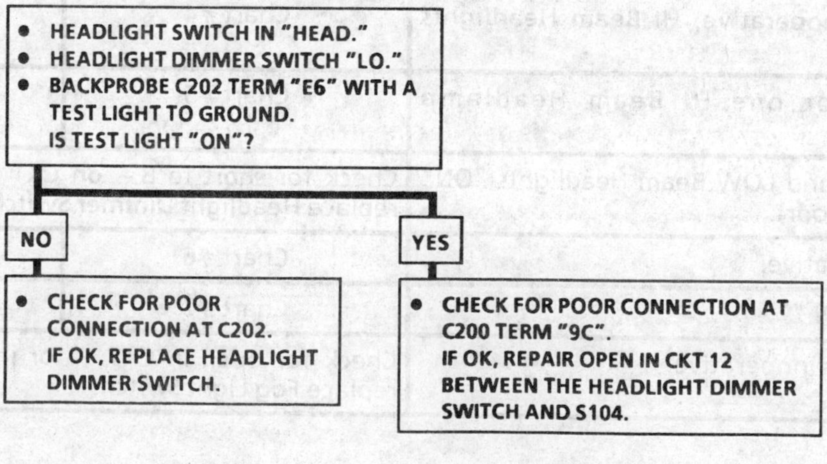

• HEADLIGHT SWITCH IN "HEAD."
• HEADLIGHT DIMMER SWITCH "LO."
• BACKPROBE C202 TERM "E6" WITH A TEST LIGHT TO GROUND.
IS TEST LIGHT "ON"?
NO
YES
• CHECK FOR POOR CONNECTION AT C202.
IF OK, REPLACE HEADLIGHT DIMMER SWITCH.
• CHECK FOR POOR CONNECTION AT C200 TERM "9C".
IF OK, REPAIR OPEN IN CKT 12 BETWEEN THE HEADLIGHT DIMMER SWITCH AND S104.

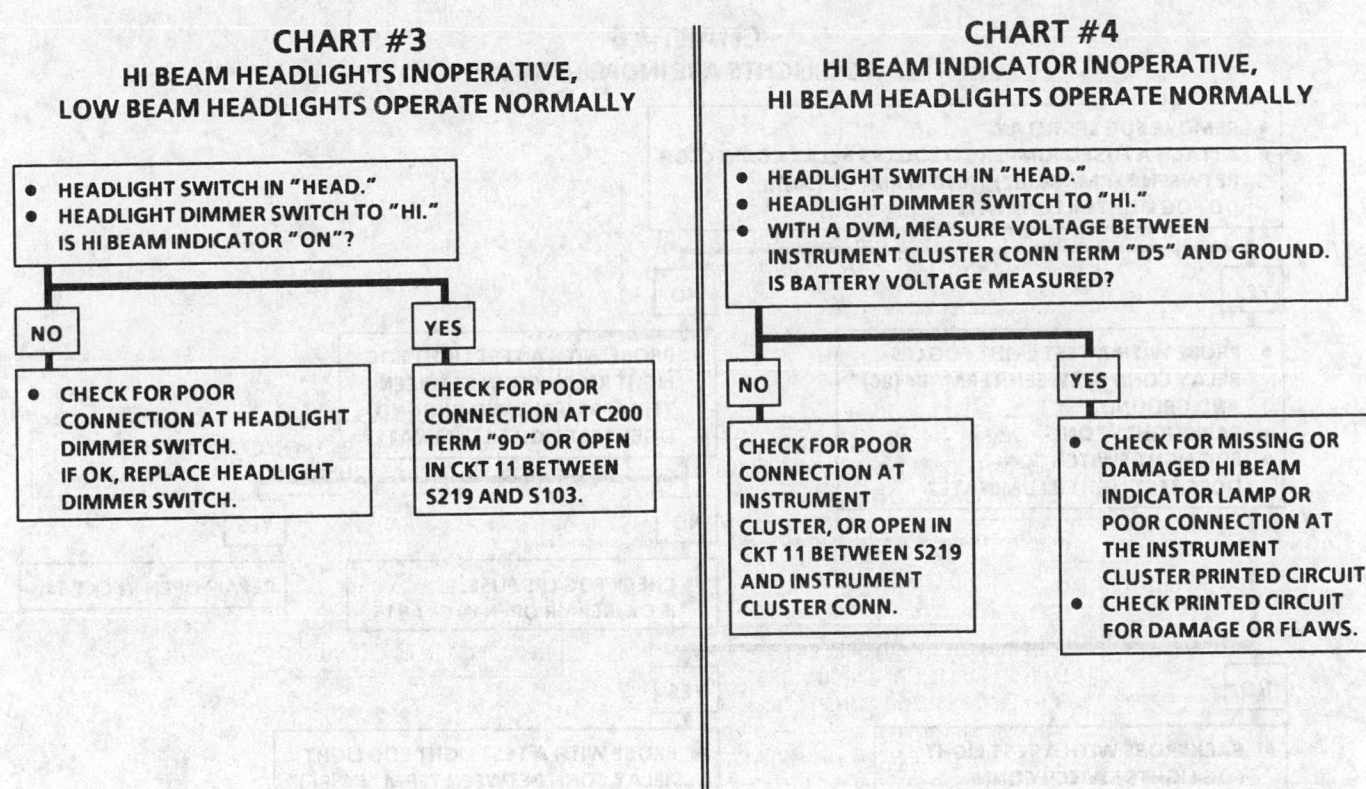

CHART #3
HI BEAM HEADLIGHTS INOPERATIVE, LOW BEAM HEADLIGHTS OPERATE NORMALLY

- HEADLIGHT SWITCH IN "HEAD."
- HEADLIGHT DIMMER SWITCH TO "HI." IS HI BEAM INDICATOR "ON"?

NO

- CHECK FOR POOR CONNECTION AT HEADLIGHT DIMMER SWITCH. IF OK, REPLACE HEADLIGHT DIMMER SWITCH.

YES

CHECK FOR POOR CONNECTION AT C200 TERM "9D" OR OPEN IN CKT 11 BETWEEN S219 AND S103.

CHART #4
HI BEAM INDICATOR INOPERATIVE, HI BEAM HEADLIGHTS OPERATE NORMALLY

- HEADLIGHT SWITCH IN "HEAD."
- HEADLIGHT DIMMER SWITCH TO "HI."
- WITH A DVM, MEASURE VOLTAGE BETWEEN INSTRUMENT CLUSTER CONN TERM "D5" AND GROUND. IS BATTERY VOLTAGE MEASURED?

NO

CHECK FOR POOR CONNECTION AT INSTRUMENT CLUSTER, OR OPEN IN CKT 11 BETWEEN S219 AND INSTRUMENT CLUSTER CONN.

YES

- CHECK FOR MISSING OR DAMAGED HI BEAM INDICATOR LAMP OR POOR CONNECTION AT THE INSTRUMENT CLUSTER PRINTED CIRCUIT.
- CHECK PRINTED CIRCUIT FOR DAMAGE OR FLAWS.

CHART #5
ONE LO BEAM OR ONE HI BEAM HEADLAMP INOPERATIVE

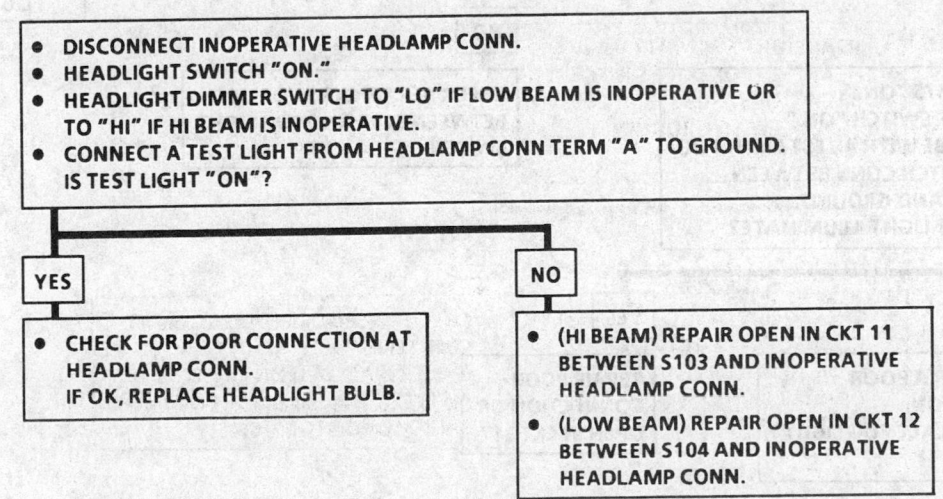

- DISCONNECT INOPERATIVE HEADLAMP CONN.
- HEADLIGHT SWITCH "ON."
- HEADLIGHT DIMMER SWITCH TO "LO" IF LOW BEAM IS INOPERATIVE OR TO "HI" IF HI BEAM IS INOPERATIVE.
- CONNECT A TEST LIGHT FROM HEADLAMP CONN TERM "A" TO GROUND. IS TEST LIGHT "ON"?

YES

- CHECK FOR POOR CONNECTION AT HEADLAMP CONN. IF OK, REPLACE HEADLIGHT BULB.

NO

- (HI BEAM) REPAIR OPEN IN CKT 11 BETWEEN S103 AND INOPERATIVE HEADLAMP CONN.
- (LOW BEAM) REPAIR OPEN IN CKT 12 BETWEEN S104 AND INOPERATIVE HEADLAMP CONN.

HEADLIGHTS

CHART #6
FOG LIGHTS ARE INOPERATIVE

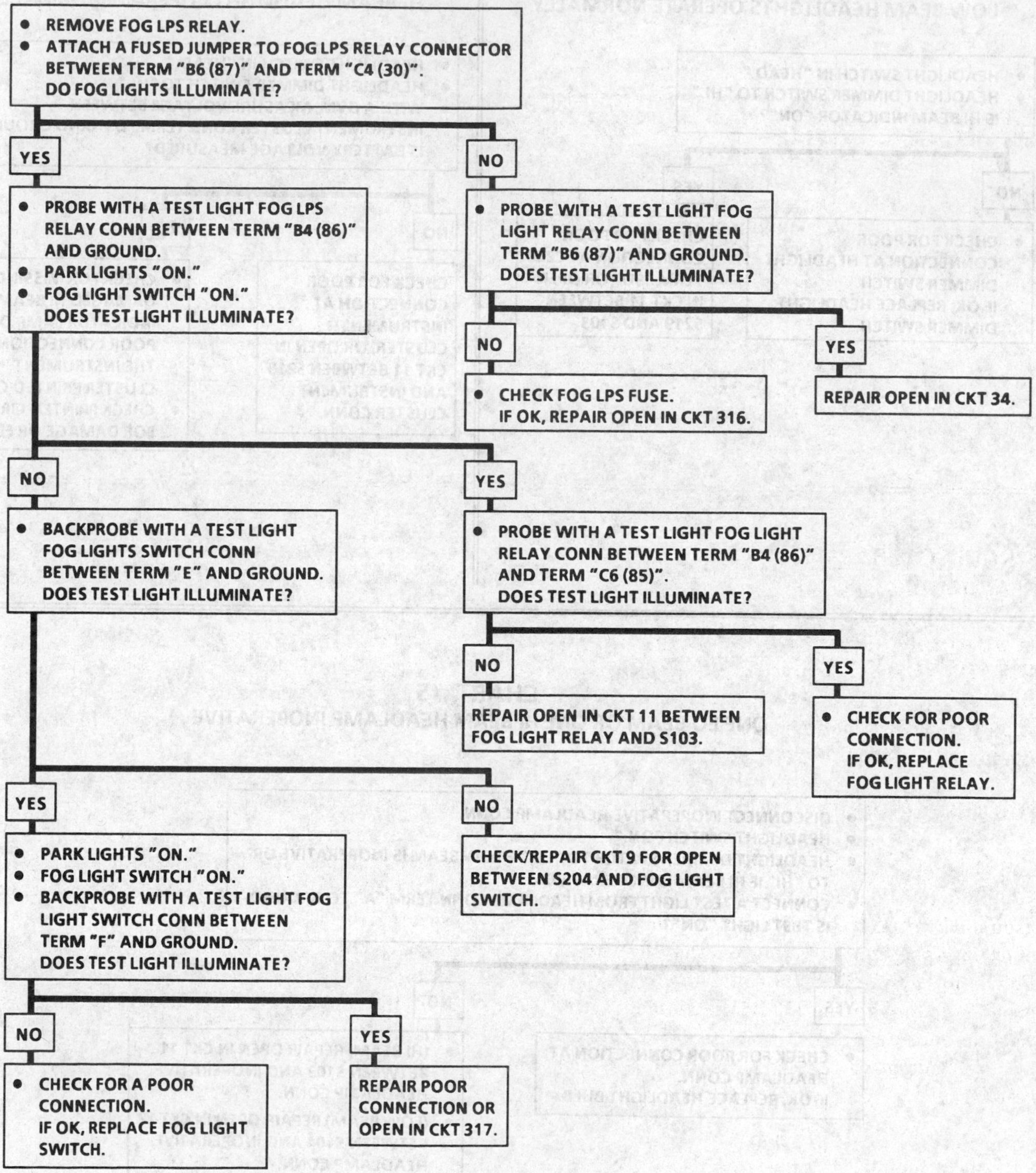

• REMOVE FOG LPS RELAY.
• ATTACH A FUSED JUMPER TO FOG LPS RELAY CONNECTOR BETWEEN TERM "B6 (87)" AND TERM "C4 (30)". DO FOG LIGHTS ILLUMINATE?
YES
NO
• PROBE WITH A TEST LIGHT FOG LPS RELAY CONN BETWEEN TERM "B4 (86)" AND GROUND.
• PARK LIGHTS "ON."
• FOG LIGHT SWITCH "ON." DOES TEST LIGHT ILLUMINATE?
• PROBE WITH A TEST LIGHT FOG LIGHT RELAY CONN BETWEEN TERM "B6 (87)" AND GROUND. DOES TEST LIGHT ILLUMINATE?
NO
YES
• CHECK FOG LPS FUSE. IF OK, REPAIR OPEN IN CKT 316.
REPAIR OPEN IN CKT 34.
NO
YES
• BACKPROBE WITH A TEST LIGHT FOG LIGHTS SWITCH CONN BETWEEN TERM "E" AND GROUND. DOES TEST LIGHT ILLUMINATE?
• PROBE WITH A TEST LIGHT FOG LIGHT RELAY CONN BETWEEN TERM "B4 (86)" AND TERM "C6 (85)". DOES TEST LIGHT ILLUMINATE?
NO
YES
REPAIR OPEN IN CKT 11 BETWEEN FOG LIGHT RELAY AND S103.
• CHECK FOR POOR CONNECTION. IF OK, REPLACE FOG LIGHT RELAY.
YES
NO
• PARK LIGHTS "ON."
• FOG LIGHT SWITCH "ON."
• BACKPROBE WITH A TEST LIGHT FOG LIGHT SWITCH CONN BETWEEN TERM "F" AND GROUND. DOES TEST LIGHT ILLUMINATE?
CHECK/REPAIR CKT 9 FOR OPEN BETWEEN S204 AND FOG LIGHT SWITCH.
NO
YES
• CHECK FOR A POOR CONNECTION. IF OK, REPLACE FOG LIGHT SWITCH.
REPAIR POOR CONNECTION OR OPEN IN CKT 317.

CHART #7
FOG LIGHTS ALWAYS "ON"

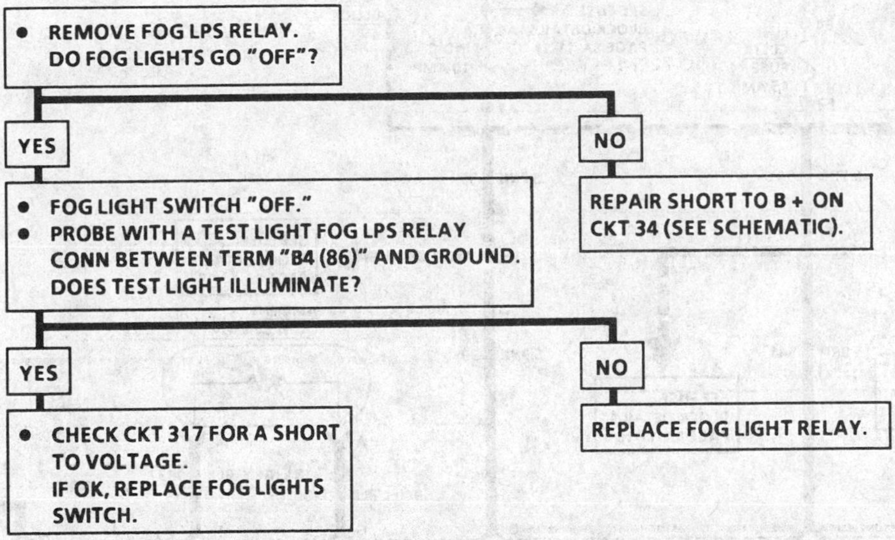
• REMOVE FOG LPS RELAY. DO FOG LIGHTS GO "OFF"?
YES
NO
REPAIR SHORT TO B + ON CKT 34 (SEE SCHEMATIC).
• FOG LIGHT SWITCH "OFF."
• PROBE WITH A TEST LIGHT FOG LPS RELAY CONN BETWEEN TERM "B4 (86)" AND GROUND. DOES TEST LIGHT ILLUMINATE?
YES
NO
REPLACE FOG LIGHT RELAY.
• CHECK CKT 317 FOR A SHORT TO VOLTAGE. IF OK, REPLACE FOG LIGHTS SWITCH.

CIRCUIT OPERATION

HEADLIGHTS

Battery voltage is applied to the Headlight Switch at all times. When the Headlight Switch is in "HEAD," voltage is applied directly to the Headlight Dimmer Switch. When the Headlight Dimmer Switch is placed in "HI," battery voltage is applied to the HI Beam Lights and HI Beam Indicator.

FOG LIGHTS (2 DOOR)

With the Headlight Switch in "PARK" or "HEAD" and the Fog Light Switch "ON," battery voltage is supplied to the Fog LPS Relay coil. The coil is grounded through the HI beam filaments. The relay energizes and applies voltage to the Fog Lamps. The Fog Lamps glow. Since the coil of the Fog LPS Relay is grounded through the HI Beam filaments, the relay will de-energized any time the HI Beams are on because voltage is applied to both sides of the relay coil.

FOG LIGHTS (4 DOOR)

With the Headlights Switch in "PARK" or "HEAD" and the Fog Light Switch "OFF," a reduced voltage is applied to the Fog Lamps through the resistance wire and the Fog LPS Relay. The Fog Lamps glow at reduced brilliance. With the Headlight Switch in "PARK" or "HEAD" and the Fog Light Switch "ON," battery voltage is applied to the Fog LPS Relay coil. The coil is grounded through the HI Beam filaments. The relay energizes, bypassing the resistance wire, and applies battery voltage directly to the Fog Lamps. The Fog Lamps glow at full brilliance. Since the coil of the Fog LPS Relay is grounded through the HI Beam filaments, the relay will de-energize any time the HI Beams are on because battery voltage is applied to both sides of the relay coil. With the relay de-energized, the Fog Lamps will again glow at reduced brilliance.

HEADLIGHTS: DAYTIME RUNNING LIGHTS (DRL)
WITH FOG LIGHTS

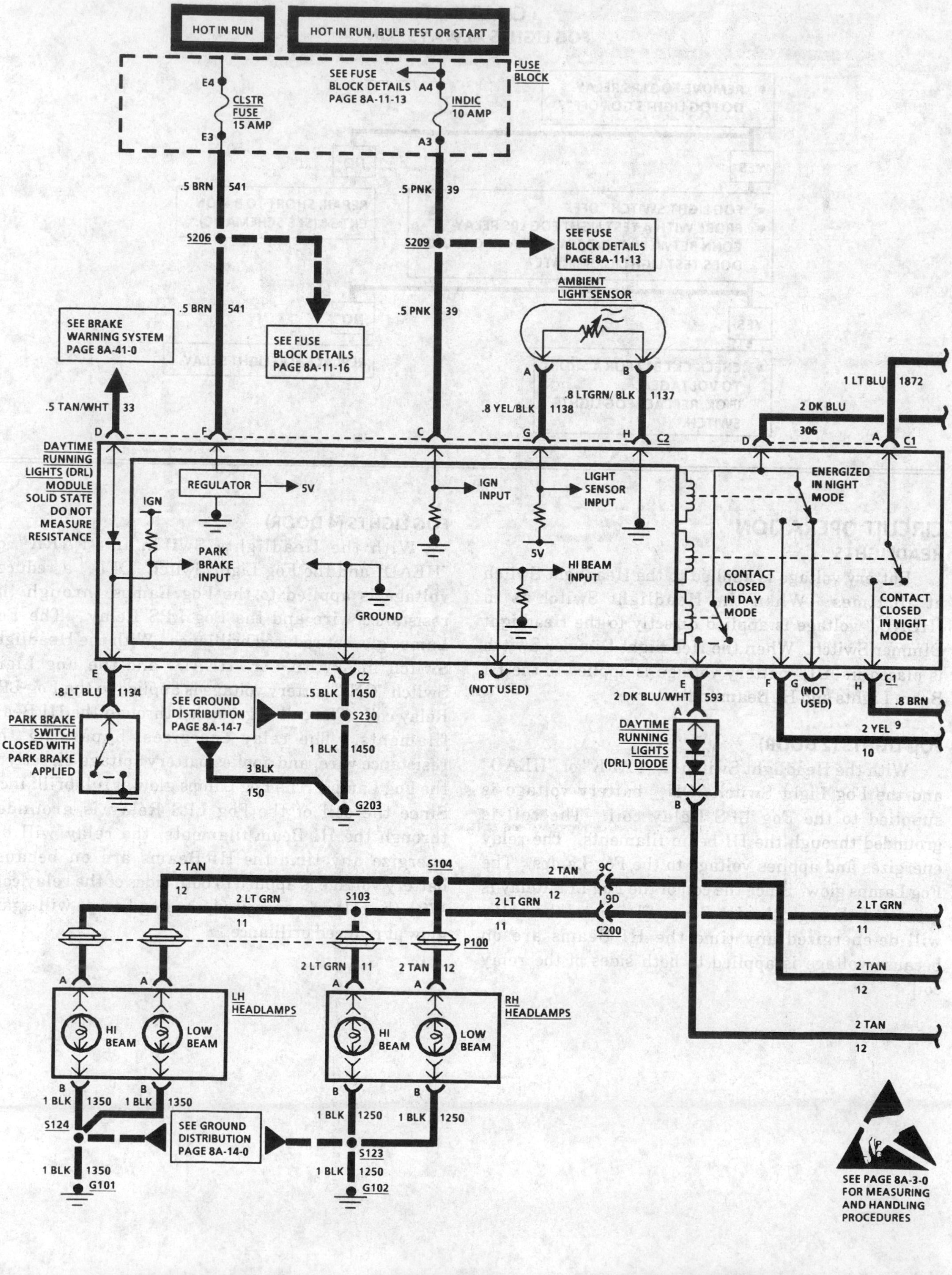

HOT IN RUN
HOT IN RUN, BULB TEST OR START
FUSE BLOCK
E4
CLSTR FUSE 15 AMP
E3
SEE FUSE BLOCK DETAILS PAGE 8A-11-13
A4
INDIC 10 AMP
A3
.5 BRN 541
.5 PNK 39
S206
S209
SEE FUSE BLOCK DETAILS PAGE 8A-11-13
AMBIENT LIGHT SENSOR
.5 BRN 541
.5 PNK 39
SEE BRAKE WARNING SYSTEM PAGE 8A-41-0
SEE FUSE BLOCK DETAILS PAGE 8A-11-16
A
B
.8 LTGRN/ BLK 1137
.8 YEL/BLK 1138
.5 TAN/WHT 33
1 LT BLU 1872
2 DK BLU
306
D
F
C
G
H
C2
D
A
C1
DAYTIME RUNNING LIGHTS (DRL) MODULE
SOLID STATE DO NOT MEASURE RESISTANCE
REGULATOR
5V
IGN
IGN INPUT
LIGHT SENSOR INPUT
5V
ENERGIZED IN NIGHT MODE
PARK BRAKE INPUT
GROUND
HI BEAM INPUT
CONTACT CLOSED IN DAY MODE
CONTACT CLOSED IN NIGHT MODE
E
A
C2
B
(NOT USED)
E
F
G
(NOT USED)
H
C1
.8 LT BLU 1134
.5 BLK 1450
SEE GROUND DISTRIBUTION PAGE 8A-14-7
S230
2 DK BLU/WHT 593
.8 BRN
2 YEL 9
10
PARK BRAKE SWITCH
CLOSED WITH PARK BRAKE APPLIED
1 BLK 1450
3 BLK
150
G203
DAYTIME RUNNING LIGHTS (DRL) DIODE
A
B
2 TAN
S104
12
2 TAN
9C
12
2 LT GRN
S103
2 LT GRN
9D
11
11
C200
2 LT GRN
11
P100
2 LT GRN 11
2 TAN 12
2 TAN
12
A
A
A
A
LH HEADLAMPS
RH HEADLAMPS
HI BEAM
LOW BEAM
HI BEAM
LOW BEAM
2 TAN
12
B
B
B
B
1 BLK 1350
1 BLK 1350
1 BLK 1250
1 BLK 1250
S124
SEE GROUND DISTRIBUTION PAGE 8A-14-0
S123
1 BLK 1350
G101
1 BLK 1250
G102
SEE PAGE 8A-3-0 FOR MEASURING AND HANDLING PROCEDURES

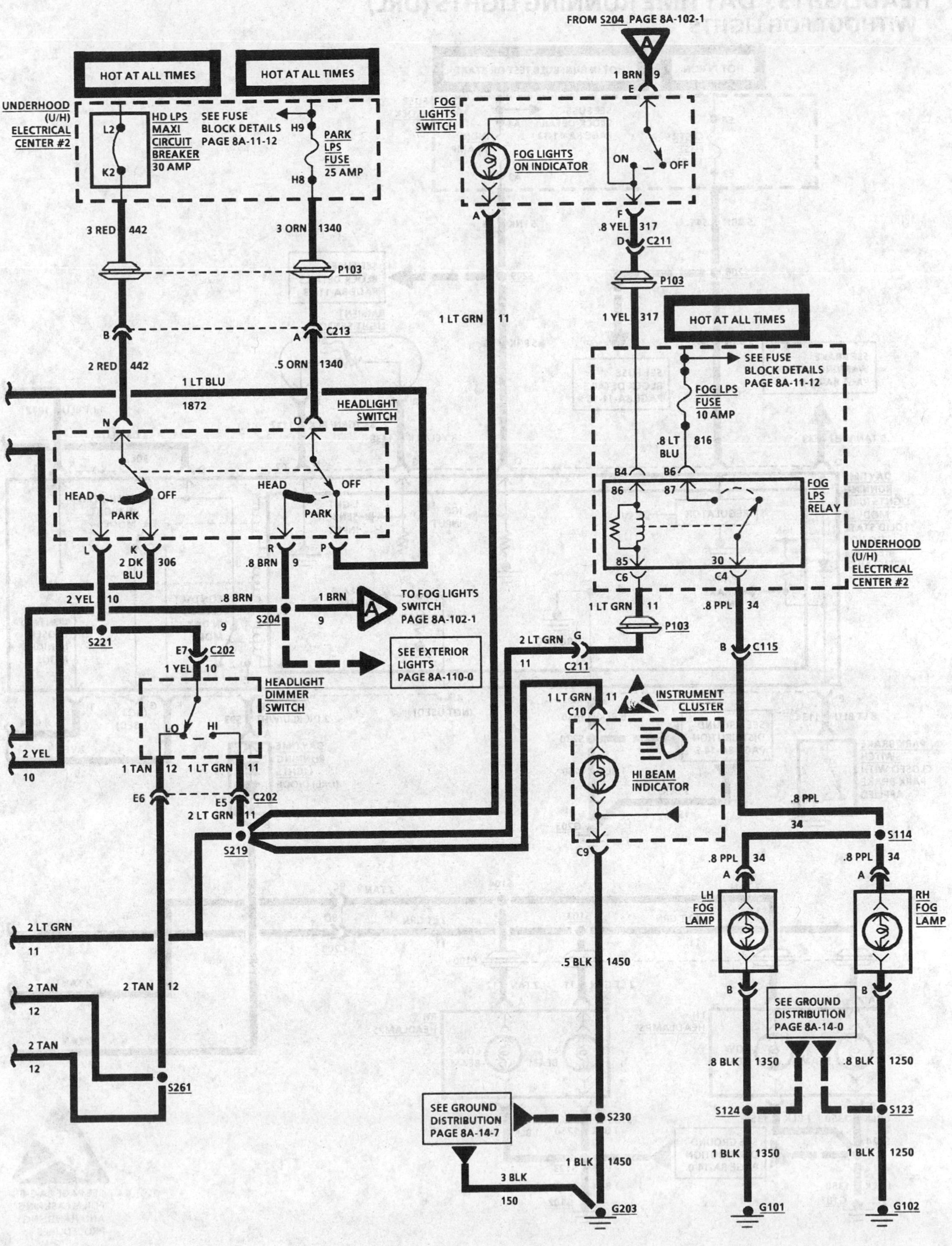

FROM S204 PAGE 8A-102-1
A
HOT AT ALL TIMES
HOT AT ALL TIMES
UNDERHOOD (U/H) ELECTRICAL CENTER #2
L2
K2
HD LPS MAXI CIRCUIT BREAKER 30 AMP
SEE FUSE BLOCK DETAILS PAGE 8A-11-12
H9
H8
PARK LPS FUSE 25 AMP
3 RED 442
3 ORN 1340
P103
B
A
C213
2 RED 442
.5 ORN 1340
1 LT BLU
1872
HEADLIGHT SWITCH
N
O
HEAD
OFF
PARK
HEAD
OFF
PARK
L
K
R
P
2 DK BLU 306
.8 BRN 9
2 YEL 10
.8 BRN
1 BRN
S204
9
TO FOG LIGHTS SWITCH PAGE 8A-102-1
SEE EXTERIOR LIGHTS PAGE 8A-110-0
S221
9
E7
C202
1 YEL 10
HEADLIGHT DIMMER SWITCH
LO
HI
2 YEL
10
1 TAN 12
1 LT GRN 11
E6
E5
C202
2 LT GRN 11
S219
2 LT GRN
11
2 TAN
12
2 TAN 12
2 TAN
12
S261
1 BRN 9
E
FOG LIGHTS SWITCH
FOG LIGHTS ON INDICATOR
ON
OFF
A
F
.8 YEL 317
D
C211
P103
1 LT GRN 11
1 YEL 317
HOT AT ALL TIMES
SEE FUSE BLOCK DETAILS PAGE 8A-11-12
FOG LPS FUSE 10 AMP
.8 LT BLU 816
B4
B6
86
87
FOG LPS RELAY
85
30
C6
C4
UNDERHOOD (U/H) ELECTRICAL CENTER #2
1 LT GRN 11
.8 PPL 34
P103
2 LT GRN
G
11
C211
B
C115
1 LT GRN 11
C10
INSTRUMENT CLUSTER
HI BEAM INDICATOR
C9
.8 PPL
34
S114
.8 PPL 34
.8 PPL 34
A
A
LH FOG LAMP
RH FOG LAMP
.5 BLK 1450
B
B
SEE GROUND DISTRIBUTION PAGE 8A-14-0
.8 BLK 1350
.8 BLK 1250
S124
S123
SEE GROUND DISTRIBUTION PAGE 8A-14-7
S230
1 BLK 1450
1 BLK 1350
1 BLK 1250
3 BLK
150
G203
G101
G102

HEADLIGHTS: DAYTIME RUNNING LIGHTS (DRL)
WITHOUT FOG LIGHTS

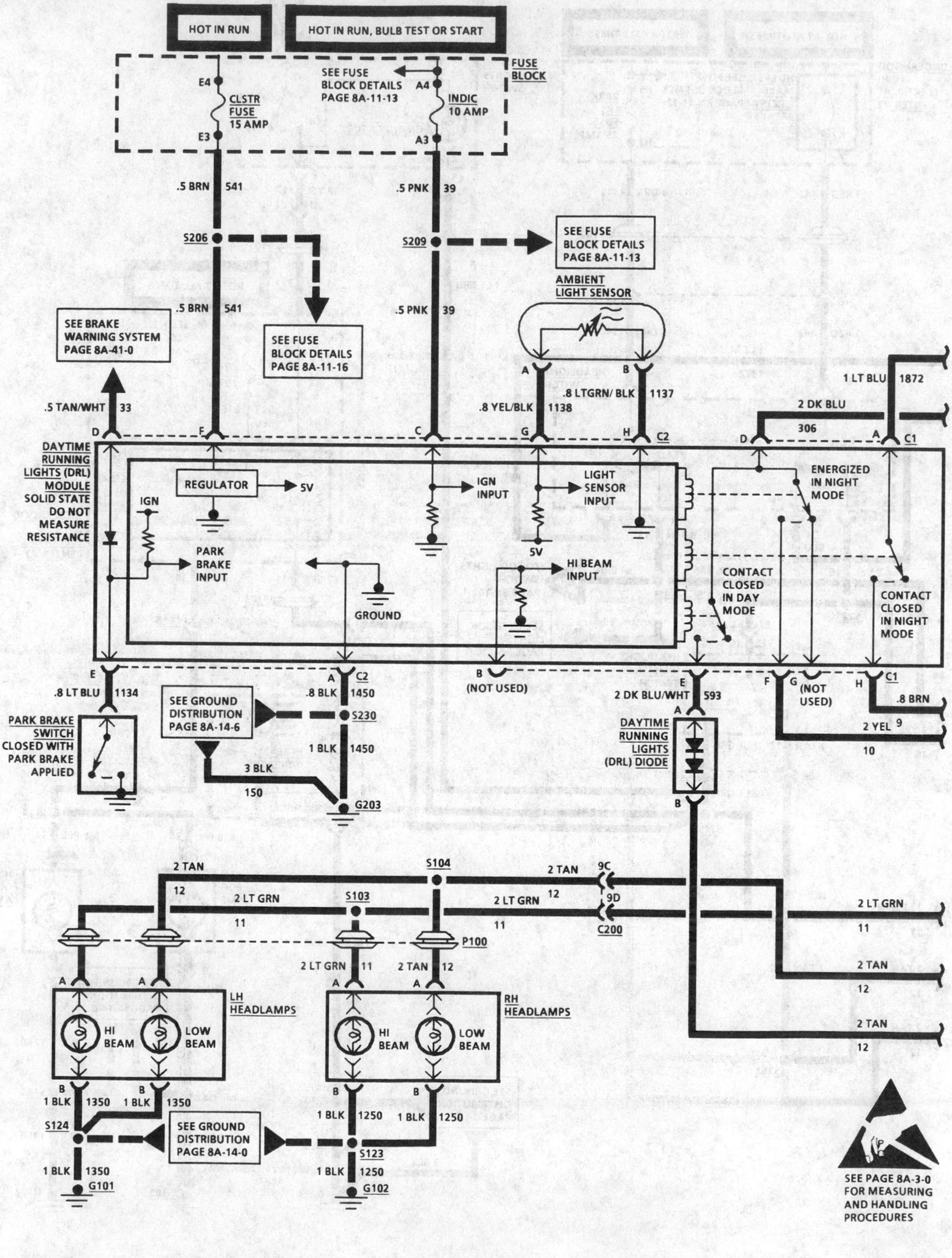

HOT IN RUN
HOT IN RUN, BULB TEST OR START
FUSE BLOCK
SEE FUSE BLOCK DETAILS PAGE 8A-11-13
CLSTR FUSE 15 AMP
INDIC 10 AMP
.5 BRN 541
.5 PNK 39
S206
S209
SEE FUSE BLOCK DETAILS PAGE 8A-11-13
SEE FUSE BLOCK DETAILS PAGE 8A-11-16
AMBIENT LIGHT SENSOR
SEE BRAKE WARNING SYSTEM PAGE 8A-41-0
.5 TAN/WHT 33
.8 YEL/BLK 1138
.8 LTGRN/ BLK 1137
1 LT BLU 1872
2 DK BLU 306
DAYTIME RUNNING LIGHTS (DRL) MODULE SOLID STATE DO NOT MEASURE RESISTANCE
REGULATOR
5V
IGN
IGN INPUT
LIGHT SENSOR INPUT
ENERGIZED IN NIGHT MODE
PARK BRAKE INPUT
HI BEAM INPUT
GROUND
CONTACT CLOSED IN DAY MODE
CONTACT CLOSED IN NIGHT MODE
(NOT USED)
.8 LT BLU 1134
.8 BLK 1450
2 DK BLU/WHT 593
.8 BRN
2 YEL 9
10
PARK BRAKE SWITCH CLOSED WITH PARK BRAKE APPLIED
SEE GROUND DISTRIBUTION PAGE 8A-14-6
S230
1 BLK 1450
3 BLK 150
G203
DAYTIME RUNNING LIGHTS (DRL) DIODE
2 TAN 12
S104
S103
2 LT GRN 11
C200
P100
2 LT GRN 11
2 TAN 12
LH HEADLAMPS
RH HEADLAMPS
HI BEAM
LOW BEAM
1 BLK 1350
1 BLK 1250
S124
S123
SEE GROUND DISTRIBUTION PAGE 8A-14-0
G101
G102
SEE PAGE 8A-3-0 FOR MEASURING AND HANDLING PROCEDURES

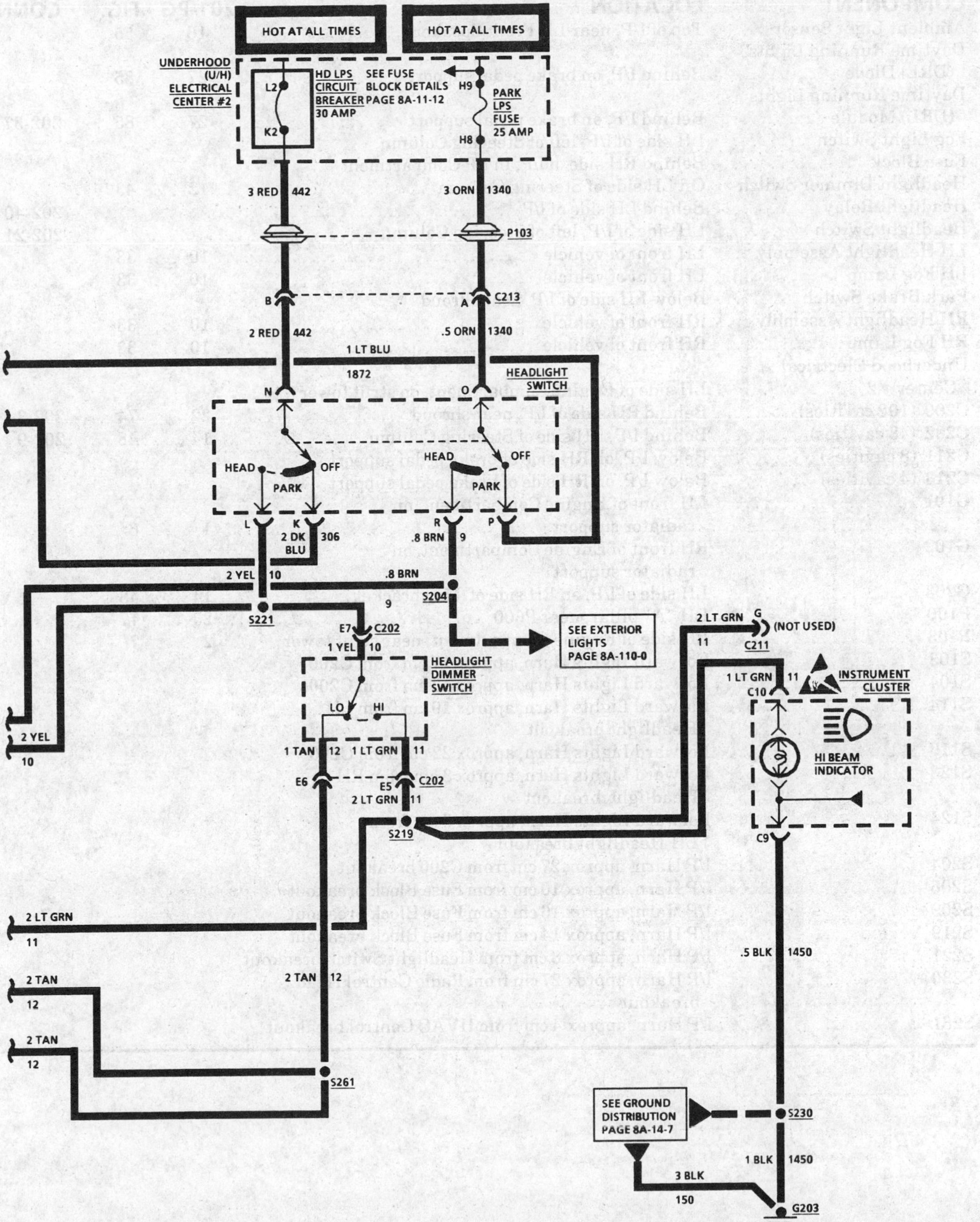
HOT AT ALL TIMES
HOT AT ALL TIMES
UNDERHOOD (U/H) ELECTRICAL CENTER #2
L2
K2
HD LPS CIRCUIT BREAKER 30 AMP
SEE FUSE BLOCK DETAILS PAGE 8A-11-12
H9
PARK LPS FUSE 25 AMP
H8
3 RED 442
3 ORN 1340
P103
B
A
C213
2 RED 442
.5 ORN 1340
1 LT BLU
1872
HEADLIGHT SWITCH
N
O
HEAD
OFF
PARK
HEAD
OFF
PARK
L
K
R
P
2 DK BLU
306
.8 BRN
9
2 YEL
10
.8 BRN
S204
9
S221
E7
C202
1 YEL
10
SEE EXTERIOR LIGHTS PAGE 8A-110-0
2 LT GRN
11
G
(NOT USED)
C211
HEADLIGHT DIMMER SWITCH
LO
HI
1 TAN
12
1 LT GRN
11
E6
E5
C202
2 LT GRN
11
S219
2 YEL
10
1 LT GRN
11
C10
INSTRUMENT CLUSTER
HI BEAM INDICATOR
C9
2 LT GRN
11
.5 BLK
1450
2 TAN
12
2 TAN
12
2 TAN
12
S261
SEE GROUND DISTRIBUTION PAGE 8A-14-7
S230
1 BLK
1450
3 BLK
150
G203

HEADLIGHTS: DAYTIME RUNNING LIGHTS (DRL)

COMPONENT	LOCATION	201-PG	FIG.	CONN
Ambient Light Sensor	Top of I/P, near LH Front Speaker	16	55	
Daytime Running Lights (DRL) Diode	Behind I/P, on brake pedal support	27	85	
Daytime Running Lights (DRL) Module	Behind I/P, on brake pedal support	27	85	202-37
Fog Light Switch	LH side of I/P, left of Steering Column			
Fuse Block	Behind RH side of I/P, in I/P Compartment			
Headlight Dimmer Switch	On LH side of Steering Column	12	43	
Headlight Relay	Behind LH side of I/P			202-40
Headlight Switch	LH side of I/P, left of Steering Column			202-21
LH Headlight Assembly	LH front of vehicle	10	33	
LH Fog Lamp	LH front of vehicle	10	33	
Park Brake Switch	Below LH side of I/P, near shroud			
RH Headlight Assembly	RH front of vehicle	10	33	
RH Fog Lamp	RH front of vehicle	10	33	
Underhood Electrical Center #2	LH side of Engine Compartment, on strut tower			
C200 (102 cavities)	Behind RH side of I/P, near shroud	22	74	202-3
C202 (48 cavities)	Behind I/P, RH side of Steering Column	14	48	202-9
C211 (8 cavities)	Below I/P, on RH side of brake pedal support			
C213 (4 cavities)	Below I/P, on RH side of brake pedal support			
G101	LH front of Engine Compartment, on radiator support	1	6	
G102	RH front of Engine Compartment, on radiator support			
G203	LH side of I/P, on RH side of Mag bracket	14	48	
P100	RH "A" pillar, near P600	23	77	
P103	LH side of Engine Compartment, near strut tower	2	7	
S103	Forward Lights Harn, approx 17 cm from C200			
S104	Forward Lights Harn, approx 13 cm from C200			
S114	Forward Lights Harn, approx 10 cm from LH Headlight breakout			
S119	Forward Lights Harn, approx 22 cm from C200			
S123	Forward Lights Harn, approx 8 cm from RH Headlight breakout			
S124	Forward Lights Harn, approx 8 cm from LH Headlight breakout			
S204	I/P Harn, approx 27 cm from C200 breakout			
S206	I/P Harn, approx 10 cm from Fuse Block breakout			
S209	I/P Harn, approx 16 cm from Fuse Block breakout			
S219	I/P Harn, approx 14 cm from Fuse Block breakout			
S221	I/P Harn, approx 8 cm from Headlight Switch breakout			
S230	I/P Harn, approx 27 cm from Radio Control Head breakout			
S261	I/P Harn, approx 4 cm from HVAC Control breakout			

TROUBLESHOOTING HINTS
(Perform before beginning System Diagnosis)

CAUTION: Halogen bulbs contain a gas under pressure. Handling a bulb improperly could cause it to shatter into flying glass fragments. To help avoid personal injury:

- **Turn "OFF" the Light Switch and allow bulb to cool before changing bulbs. Leave the Switch "OFF" until bulb change is complete.**
- **Always wear eye protection when changing a halogen bulb.**
- **Handle the bulb only by its base. Avoid touching the glass.**
- **Do not drop or scratch the bulb. Keep moisture away.**
- **Place the used bulb in the new bulb's carton and dispose of it properly. Keep halogen bulbs out of reach of children.**

1. Check LOW Beam Lamps and HI Beam Lamps for damage to the filament or bulb.
2. If a LOW Beam Lamp or HI Beam Lamp has been found damaged and an unusually high amount of moisture is noticeable in the Headlamp Capsule, check the Vent Tube and Drain Tube for restriction. Small amounts of moisture are normally found in the Headlamp Capsule, however, excessive moisture can damage the lamps.
3. Check the LH and RH Headlamp Capsule connectors to be sure the connector seal is not damaged or missing.
4. If one Headlight does not work, check the lamp, connections and wires to the Headlight.
5. If HI Beams do not light, but the HI Beam Indicator lights, check CKT 11 for an open (see schematic).
6. If the Headlights do not turn "OFF," check CKT 10 for a short to Battery. If OK, replace the Headlight Switch.
7. If the Fog Lamps do not operate, check the Fog Lamp Relay Fuse.
8. If the "BRAKE" Indicator is lit with the Ignition Switch in "RUN" and the Park Brake released, see "Brake Warning System," page 8A-41-0 or SECTION 5E1 for diagnosis.
9. If the Night Mode of the Daytime Running Lights (DRL) Module is activated in bright light, check that the Photoresistor is not obstructed (by dirt or lint, for example).
10. If one Fog Lamp does not light, check the bulb, connections, and wires to the Fog Lamp.

- Check for a broken (or partially broken) wire inside of the insulation which could cause system malfunction but prove "GOOD" in a continuity/voltage check with a system disconnected. These circuits may be intermittent or resistive when loaded, and if possible, should be checked by monitoring for a voltage drop with the system operational (under load).
- Check for proper installation of aftermarket electronic equipment which may affect the integrity of other systems (see "Troubleshooting Procedures," page 8A-4-0).
- Refer to System Diagnosis.

SYSTEM DIAGNOSIS

- Perform the System Check and refer to the Symptom Table for the appropriate diagnostic procedures.

HEADLIGHTS: DAYTIME RUNNING LIGHTS (DRL)

HEADLIGHTS: SYSTEM CHECK

ACTION	NORMAL RESULTS
[1] ● Headlight Switch to "HEAD."	LOW Beam Headlights only are "ON."
[2] ● Headlight Dimmer Switch to "HI."	LOW Beam Headlights are "OFF." (Low Beams are "ON" while HI Beams are "ON" with 2 Door.) HI Beam Headlights are "ON." HI Beam Indicator is "ON."
[3] ● Headlight Dimmer Switch to "LO."	HI Beam Headlights are "OFF." HI Beam Indicator is "OFF." LOW Beam Headlights are "ON."
[4] ● Headlight Switch to "OFF."	HI and LOW Beam Headlights and HI Beam Indicator are "OFF."

DAYTIME RUNNING LIGHTS (DRL): SYSTEM CHECK

ACTION	NORMAL RESULTS
[1] ● Headlight Switch to "OFF." ● Set Park Brake. ● Apply a bright light to the Photocell Light Sensor. ● Ignition Switch to "RUN."	Tail and License Lamps "OFF." Front and Park Lamps "OFF." Headlights "OFF."
[2] ● Remove light from Photocell Light Sensor. ● Cover Photocell Light Sensor. ● Release Park Brake.	Tail, License and Front Park Lamps "ON." LO Beam Headlights "ON" at full intensity.
[3] ● Apply a bright light to the Photocell Light Sensor.	Tail, License and Front Park Lamps "OFF." LO Beam Headlights "ON" at reduced intensity.
[4] ● Cover Photocell Light Sensor. ● Headlight Dimmer Switch to "HI."	Tail, License and Front Park Lamps "ON." LO Beam Headlights "OFF." HI Beam Headlights and Indicator "ON."
[5] ● Headlight Dimmer Switch to "LO." ● Apply Park Brake.	Tail, License and Front Park Lamps "ON." LO Beam Headlights "ON."
[6] ● Ignition Switch to "OFF."	Tail, License, Front Park Lamps and Headlights "OFF."

HEADLIGHTS: SYMPTOM TABLE

SYMPTOM	PROCEDURE	PAGE NUMBER
Low Beam and HI Beam Headlights are inoperative.	Chart #1	8A-102-8
Low Beam Headlights inoperative, HI Beam Headlights operate normally.	Chart #2	8A-102-9
HI Beam Headlights inoperative, Low Beam Headlights operate normally.	Chart #3	8A-102-9
HI Beam Indicator inoperative, HI Beam Headlights operate normally.	Chart #4	8A-102-9
One Low Beam or one HI Beam Headlamp inoperative.	Chart #5	8A-102-10
HI Beam Headlights and Low Beam Headlights "ON" at the same time. (4 Door only)	Check for short to B + on CKT 12 or CKT 11. If OK, replace Headlight Dimmer Switch. (4 Door only)	
Fog Lights are inoperative.	Chart #6	8A-102-10
Fog Lights always "ON."	Chart #7	8A-102-11
Fog Light Indicator is inoperative.	Replace Fog Light Switch.	

DAYTIME RUNNING LIGHTS (DRL): SYMPTOM TABLE

SYMPTOM	PROCEDURE	PAGE NUMBER
Park Lights remain "ON" with daylight conditions and Headlight Switch "OFF."	Chart #8	8A-102-12
Park Lights do not turn "ON" with low light conditions and Headlight Switch "OFF."	Chart #9	8A-102-12
Low Beam Headlights remain "OFF" with daylight or low light conditions.	Chart #10	8A-102-13
Low Beam Headlights remain "OFF" with daylight conditions but switch to full intensity with low light conditions.	Chart #11	8A-102-14
Low Beam Headlights "ON" at full intensity with daylight conditions and Headlight Switch "OFF."	Chart #12	8A-102-14
Low Beam Headlights do not switch from reduced intensity to full intensity with low light conditions.	Chart #13	8A-102-15
HI Beam Headlights "ON" with Headlight Switch "OFF."	Check for short to voltage in CKT 11. If OK, replace Dimmer Switch.	

(CONTINUED ON NEXT PAGE)

HEADLIGHTS: DAYTIME RUNNING LIGHTS (DRL)

(CONTINUED FROM PREVIOUS PAGE)

DAYTIME RUNNING LIGHTS (DRL): SYMPTOM TABLE

SYMPTOM	PROCEDURE	PAGE NUMBER
DRL System (Park, Tail and Low Beam Headlights) completely inoperative, Headlight Switch operates normally.	Check for open in CKT 541 or CKT 1450 to DRL Module or poor connection at DRL Module Connector C1 terminal "A" and terminal "F". If OK, replace DRL Module.	
Low Beam Headlights switch "ON" when the Park Brake is set and the Ignition Switch is turned to "RUN."	Replace DRL Module.	
Low Beam Headlights switch "OFF" when the Ignition Switch is in "RUN" and the Park Brake is applied.	Replace DRL Module.	

CHART #1

LOW BEAM AND HI BEAM HEADLIGHTS ARE INOPERATIVE (FROM HEADLIGHT SWITCH)

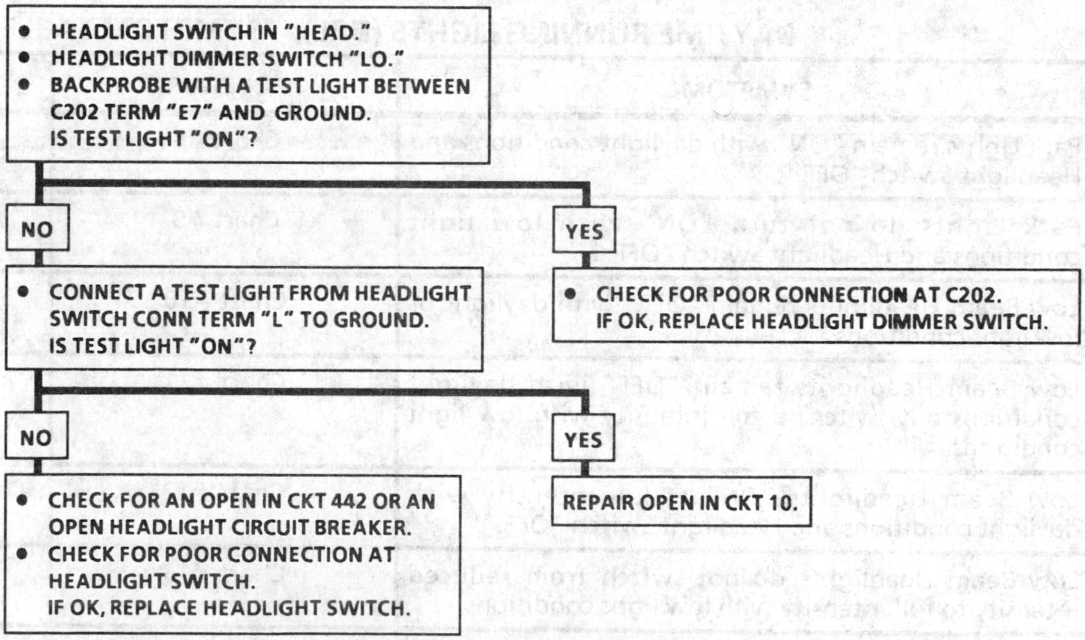
• HEADLIGHT SWITCH IN "HEAD."
• HEADLIGHT DIMMER SWITCH "LO."
• BACKPROBE WITH A TEST LIGHT BETWEEN C202 TERM "E7" AND GROUND. IS TEST LIGHT "ON"?
NO
YES
• CONNECT A TEST LIGHT FROM HEADLIGHT SWITCH CONN TERM "L" TO GROUND. IS TEST LIGHT "ON"?
• CHECK FOR POOR CONNECTION AT C202. IF OK, REPLACE HEADLIGHT DIMMER SWITCH.
NO
YES
• CHECK FOR AN OPEN IN CKT 442 OR AN OPEN HEADLIGHT CIRCUIT BREAKER.
• CHECK FOR POOR CONNECTION AT HEADLIGHT SWITCH. IF OK, REPLACE HEADLIGHT SWITCH.
REPAIR OPEN IN CKT 10.

CHART #2
LOW BEAM HEADLIGHTS INOPERATIVE, HI BEAM HEADLIGHTS OPERATE NORMALLY (FROM HEADLIGHT SWITCH)

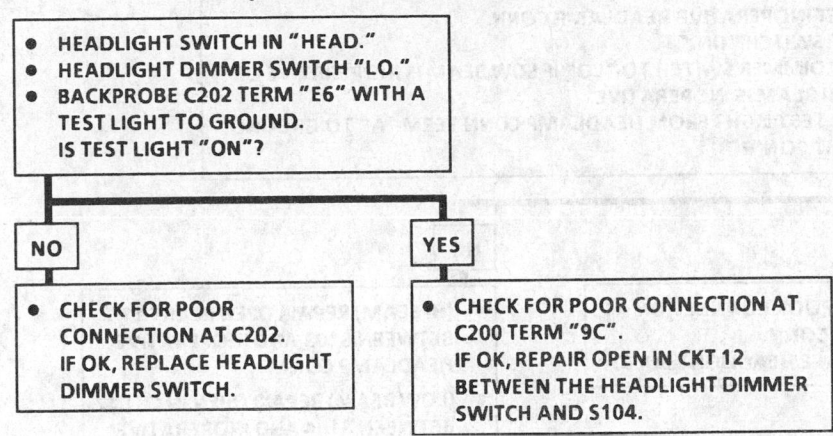

- HEADLIGHT SWITCH IN "HEAD."
- HEADLIGHT DIMMER SWITCH "LO."
- BACKPROBE C202 TERM "E6" WITH A TEST LIGHT TO GROUND.
  IS TEST LIGHT "ON"?

NO

- CHECK FOR POOR CONNECTION AT C202.
  IF OK, REPLACE HEADLIGHT DIMMER SWITCH.

YES

- CHECK FOR POOR CONNECTION AT C200 TERM "9C".
  IF OK, REPAIR OPEN IN CKT 12 BETWEEN THE HEADLIGHT DIMMER SWITCH AND S104.

CHART #3
HI BEAM HEADLIGHTS INOPERATIVE, LOW BEAM HEADLIGHTS OPERATE NORMALLY

- HEADLIGHT SWITCH IN "HEAD."
- HEADLIGHT DIMMER SWITCH TO "HI."
  IS HI BEAM INDICATOR "ON"?

NO

- CHECK FOR POOR CONNECTION AT HEADLIGHT DIMMER SWITCH.
  IF OK, REPLACE HEADLIGHT DIMMER SWITCH.

YES

CHECK FOR POOR CONNECTION AT C200 TERM "9D" OR OPEN IN CKT 11 BETWEEN S219 AND S103.

CHART #4
HI BEAM INDICATOR INOPERATIVE, HI BEAM HEADLIGHTS OPERATE NORMALLY

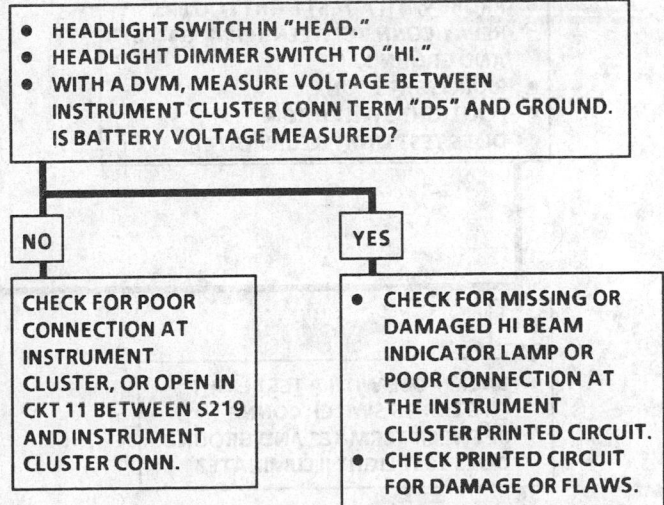

- HEADLIGHT SWITCH IN "HEAD."
- HEADLIGHT DIMMER SWITCH TO "HI."
- WITH A DVM, MEASURE VOLTAGE BETWEEN INSTRUMENT CLUSTER CONN TERM "D5" AND GROUND.
  IS BATTERY VOLTAGE MEASURED?

NO

CHECK FOR POOR CONNECTION AT INSTRUMENT CLUSTER, OR OPEN IN CKT 11 BETWEEN S219 AND INSTRUMENT CLUSTER CONN.

YES

- CHECK FOR MISSING OR DAMAGED HI BEAM INDICATOR LAMP OR POOR CONNECTION AT THE INSTRUMENT CLUSTER PRINTED CIRCUIT.
- CHECK PRINTED CIRCUIT FOR DAMAGE OR FLAWS.

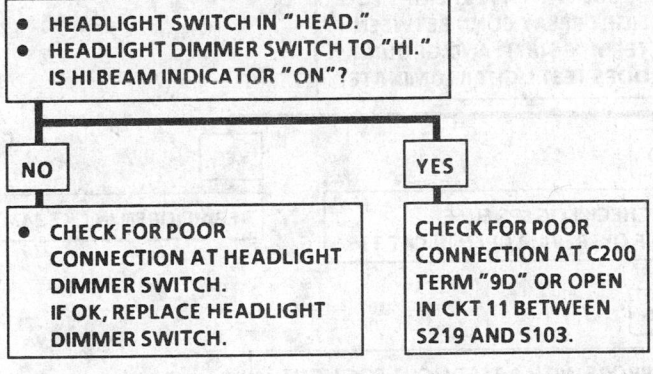

HEADLIGHTS: DAYTIME RUNNING LIGHTS (DRL)

CHART #5
ONE LO BEAM OR ONE HI BEAM HEADLAMP INOPERATIVE

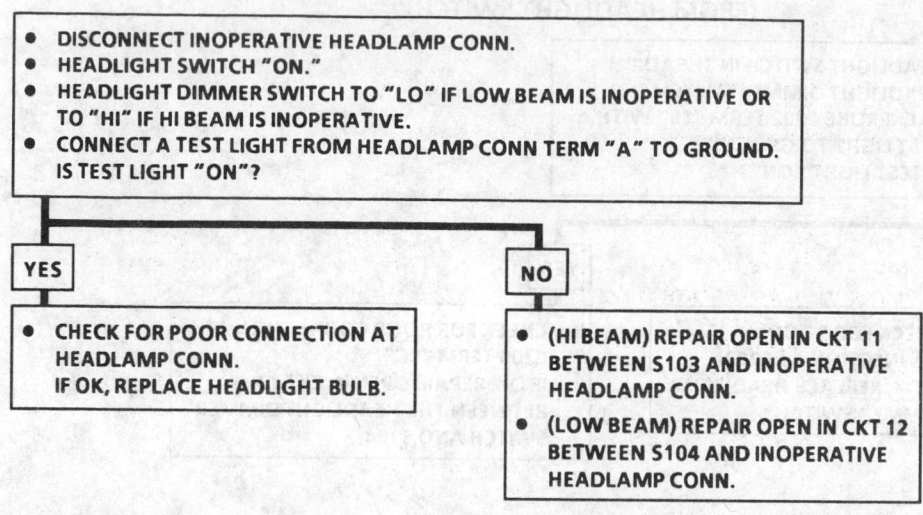

- DISCONNECT INOPERATIVE HEADLAMP CONN.
- HEADLIGHT SWITCH "ON."
- HEADLIGHT DIMMER SWITCH TO "LO" IF LOW BEAM IS INOPERATIVE OR TO "HI" IF HI BEAM IS INOPERATIVE.
- CONNECT A TEST LIGHT FROM HEADLAMP CONN TERM "A" TO GROUND.
  IS TEST LIGHT "ON"?

YES

- CHECK FOR POOR CONNECTION AT HEADLAMP CONN.
  IF OK, REPLACE HEADLIGHT BULB.

NO

- (HI BEAM) REPAIR OPEN IN CKT 11 BETWEEN S103 AND INOPERATIVE HEADLAMP CONN.
- (LOW BEAM) REPAIR OPEN IN CKT 12 BETWEEN S104 AND INOPERATIVE HEADLAMP CONN.

CHART #6
FOG LIGHTS ARE INOPERATIVE

- REMOVE FOG LPS RELAY.
- ATTACH A FUSED JUMPER TO FOG LPS RELAY CONNECTOR BETWEEN TERM "B6 (87)" AND TERM "C4 (30)".
  DO FOG LIGHTS ILLUMINATE?

YES

- PROBE WITH A TEST LIGHT FOG LPS RELAY CONN BETWEEN TERM "B4 (86)" AND GROUND.
- PARK LIGHTS "ON."
- FOG LIGHT SWITCH "ON."
  DOES TEST LIGHT ILLUMINATE?

  NO

  - BACKPROBE WITH A TEST LIGHT FOG LIGHTS SWITCH CONN BETWEEN TERM "E" AND GROUND.
    DOES TEST LIGHT ILLUMINATE?

    A

    (CONTINUED ON NEXT PAGE)

  YES

  - PROBE WITH A TEST LIGHT FOG LIGHT RELAY CONN BETWEEN TERM "B4 (86)" AND TERM "C6 (85)".
    DOES TEST LIGHT ILLUMINATE?

    NO

    REPAIR OPEN IN CKT 11 BETWEEN FOG LIGHT RELAY AND S103.

    YES

    - CHECK FOR POOR CONNECTION.
      IF OK, REPLACE FOG LIGHT RELAY.

NO

- PROBE WITH A TEST LIGHT FOG LIGHT RELAY CONN BETWEEN TERM "B6 (87)" AND GROUND.
  DOES TEST LIGHT ILLUMINATE?

  NO

  - CHECK FOG LPS FUSE.
    IF OK, REPAIR OPEN IN CKT 316.

  YES

  REPAIR OPEN IN CKT 34.

CHART #6 (continued)
FOG LIGHTS ARE INOPERATIVE

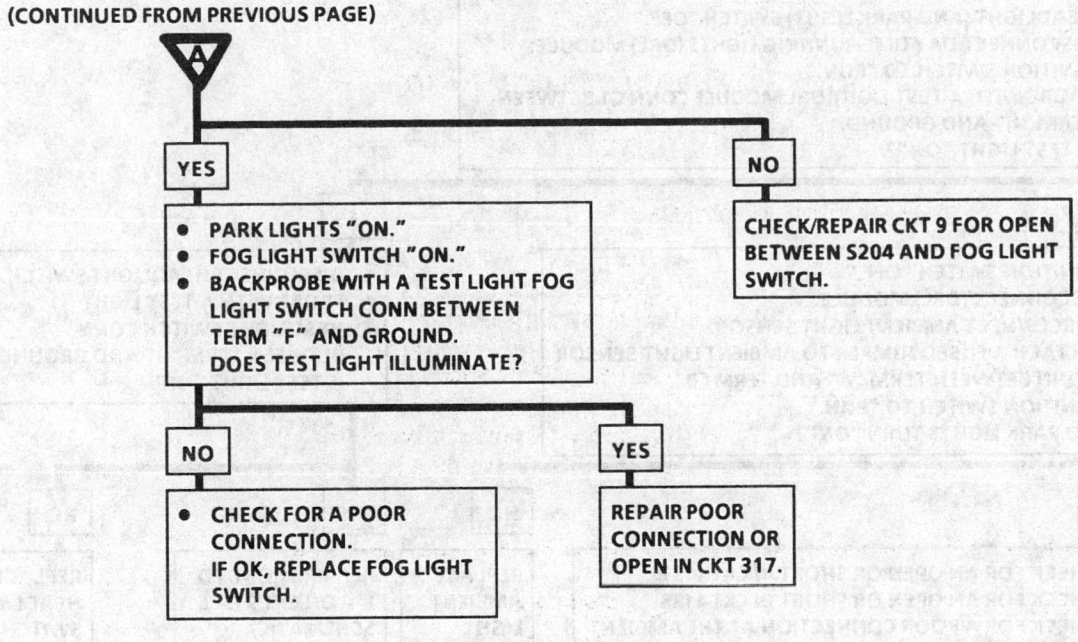

(CONTINUED FROM PREVIOUS PAGE)

A

YES

- PARK LIGHTS "ON."
- FOG LIGHT SWITCH "ON."
- BACKPROBE WITH A TEST LIGHT FOG LIGHT SWITCH CONN BETWEEN TERM "F" AND GROUND.
  DOES TEST LIGHT ILLUMINATE?

NO

- CHECK FOR A POOR CONNECTION.
  IF OK, REPLACE FOG LIGHT SWITCH.

YES

REPAIR POOR CONNECTION OR OPEN IN CKT 317.

NO

CHECK/REPAIR CKT 9 FOR OPEN BETWEEN S204 AND FOG LIGHT SWITCH.

CHART #7
FOG LIGHTS ALWAYS "ON"

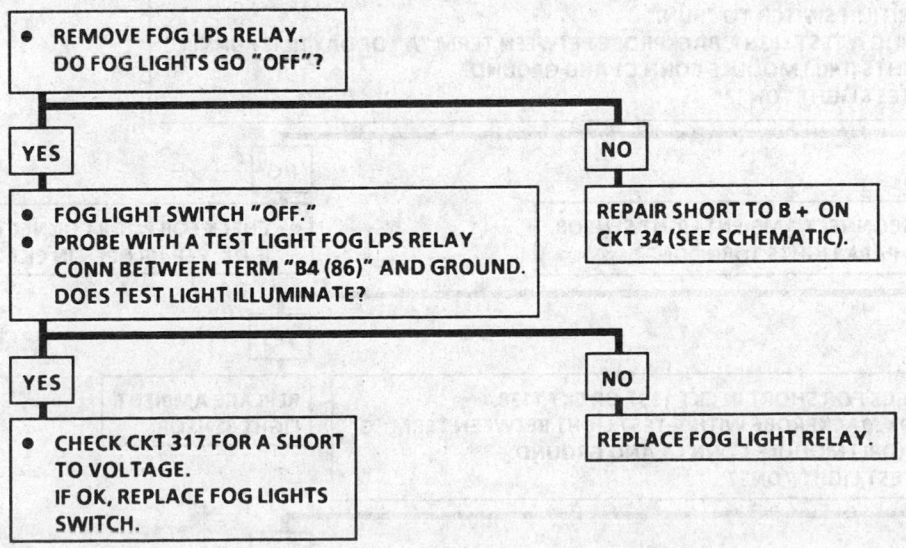

- REMOVE FOG LPS RELAY.
  DO FOG LIGHTS GO "OFF"?

YES

- FOG LIGHT SWITCH "OFF."
- PROBE WITH A TEST LIGHT FOG LPS RELAY CONN BETWEEN TERM "B4 (86)" AND GROUND.
  DOES TEST LIGHT ILLUMINATE?

YES

- CHECK CKT 317 FOR A SHORT TO VOLTAGE.
  IF OK, REPLACE FOG LIGHTS SWITCH.

NO

REPLACE FOG LIGHT RELAY.

NO

REPAIR SHORT TO B + ON CKT 34 (SEE SCHEMATIC).

HEADLIGHTS: DAYTIME RUNNING LIGHTS (DRL)

CHART #8

PARK LIGHTS REMAIN "ON" WITH DAYLIGHT CONDITIONS AND HEADLIGHT SWITCH "OFF" (HEADLIGHTS OPERATE NORMALLY)

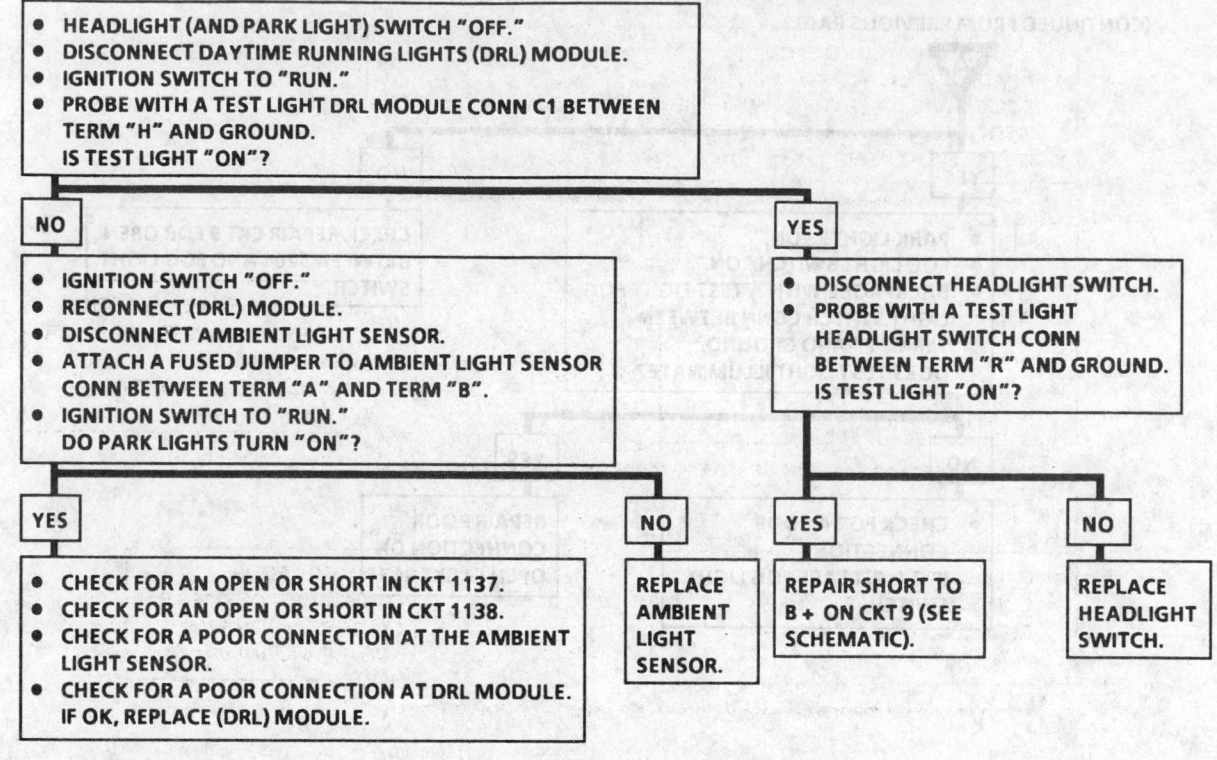

- HEADLIGHT (AND PARK LIGHT) SWITCH "OFF."
- DISCONNECT DAYTIME RUNNING LIGHTS (DRL) MODULE.
- IGNITION SWITCH TO "RUN."
- PROBE WITH A TEST LIGHT DRL MODULE CONN C1 BETWEEN TERM "H" AND GROUND.
  IS TEST LIGHT "ON"?

NO

- IGNITION SWITCH "OFF."
- RECONNECT (DRL) MODULE.
- DISCONNECT AMBIENT LIGHT SENSOR.
- ATTACH A FUSED JUMPER TO AMBIENT LIGHT SENSOR CONN BETWEEN TERM "A" AND TERM "B".
- IGNITION SWITCH TO "RUN."
  DO PARK LIGHTS TURN "ON"?

YES

- CHECK FOR AN OPEN OR SHORT IN CKT 1137.
- CHECK FOR AN OPEN OR SHORT IN CKT 1138.
- CHECK FOR A POOR CONNECTION AT THE AMBIENT LIGHT SENSOR.
- CHECK FOR A POOR CONNECTION AT DRL MODULE.
  IF OK, REPLACE (DRL) MODULE.

NO

REPLACE AMBIENT LIGHT SENSOR.

YES

- DISCONNECT HEADLIGHT SWITCH.
- PROBE WITH A TEST LIGHT HEADLIGHT SWITCH CONN BETWEEN TERM "R" AND GROUND.
  IS TEST LIGHT "ON"?

YES

REPAIR SHORT TO B + ON CKT 9 (SEE SCHEMATIC).

NO

REPLACE HEADLIGHT SWITCH.

CHART #9

PARK LIGHTS DO NOT TURN "ON" WITH LOW LIGHT CONDITIONS AND HEADLIGHT SWITCH "OFF"

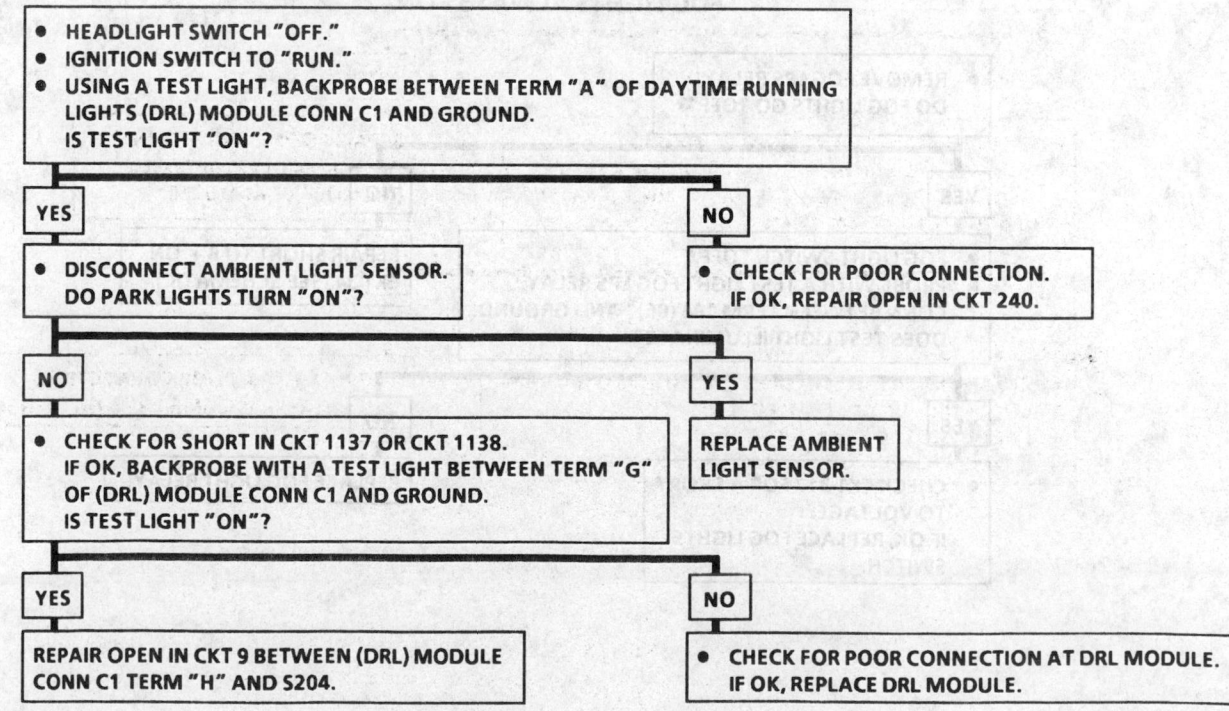

- HEADLIGHT SWITCH "OFF."
- IGNITION SWITCH TO "RUN."
- USING A TEST LIGHT, BACKPROBE BETWEEN TERM "A" OF DAYTIME RUNNING LIGHTS (DRL) MODULE CONN C1 AND GROUND.
  IS TEST LIGHT "ON"?

YES

- DISCONNECT AMBIENT LIGHT SENSOR.
  DO PARK LIGHTS TURN "ON"?

NO

- CHECK FOR SHORT IN CKT 1137 OR CKT 1138.
  IF OK, BACKPROBE WITH A TEST LIGHT BETWEEN TERM "G" OF (DRL) MODULE CONN C1 AND GROUND.
  IS TEST LIGHT "ON"?

YES

REPAIR OPEN IN CKT 9 BETWEEN (DRL) MODULE CONN C1 TERM "H" AND S204.

NO

- CHECK FOR POOR CONNECTION AT DRL MODULE.
  IF OK, REPLACE DRL MODULE.

YES

REPLACE AMBIENT LIGHT SENSOR.

NO

- CHECK FOR POOR CONNECTION.
  IF OK, REPAIR OPEN IN CKT 240.

CHART #10

LOW BEAM HEADLIGHTS REMAIN "OFF" WITH DAYLIGHT OR LOW LIGHT CONDITIONS (AND HEADLIGHT SWITCH "OFF")

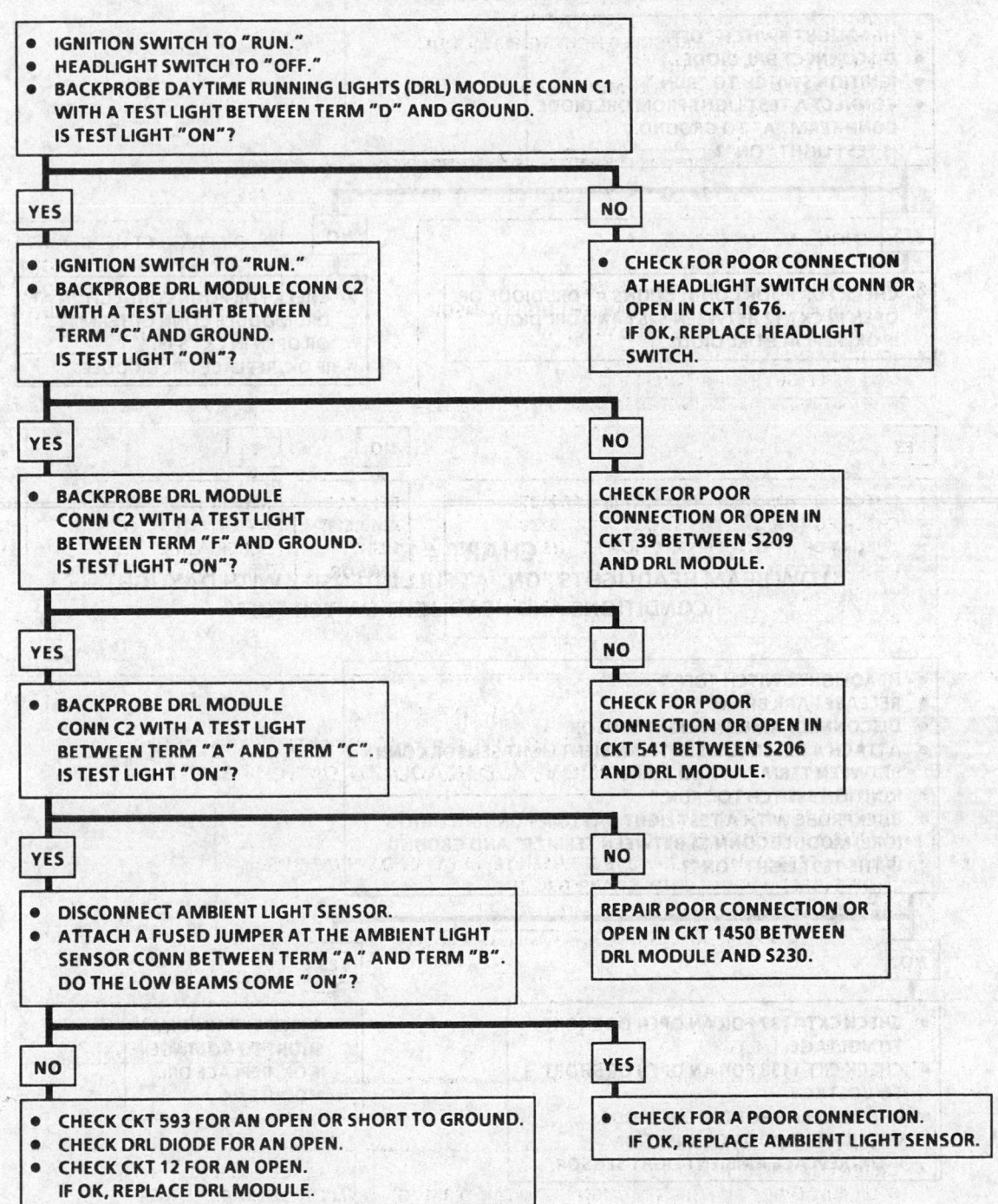

- IGNITION SWITCH TO "RUN."
- HEADLIGHT SWITCH TO "OFF."
- BACKPROBE DAYTIME RUNNING LIGHTS (DRL) MODULE CONN C1 WITH A TEST LIGHT BETWEEN TERM "D" AND GROUND.

IS TEST LIGHT "ON"?

NO

- CHECK FOR POOR CONNECTION AT HEADLIGHT SWITCH CONN OR OPEN IN CKT 1676.

IF OK, REPLACE HEADLIGHT SWITCH.

YES

- IGNITION SWITCH TO "RUN."
- BACKPROBE DRL MODULE CONN C2 WITH A TEST LIGHT BETWEEN TERM "C" AND GROUND.

IS TEST LIGHT "ON"?

NO

CHECK FOR POOR CONNECTION OR OPEN IN CKT 39 BETWEEN S209 AND DRL MODULE.

YES

- BACKPROBE DRL MODULE CONN C2 WITH A TEST LIGHT BETWEEN TERM "F" AND GROUND.

IS TEST LIGHT "ON"?

NO

CHECK FOR POOR CONNECTION OR OPEN IN CKT 541 BETWEEN S206 AND DRL MODULE.

YES

- BACKPROBE DRL MODULE CONN C2 WITH A TEST LIGHT BETWEEN TERM "A" AND TERM "C".

IS TEST LIGHT "ON"?

NO

REPAIR POOR CONNECTION OR OPEN IN CKT 1450 BETWEEN DRL MODULE AND S230.

YES

- DISCONNECT AMBIENT LIGHT SENSOR.
- ATTACH A FUSED JUMPER AT THE AMBIENT LIGHT SENSOR CONN BETWEEN TERM "A" AND TERM "B".

DO THE LOW BEAMS COME "ON"?

NO

- CHECK CKT 593 FOR AN OPEN OR SHORT TO GROUND.
- CHECK DRL DIODE FOR AN OPEN.
- CHECK CKT 12 FOR AN OPEN.

IF OK, REPLACE DRL MODULE.

YES

- CHECK FOR A POOR CONNECTION.

IF OK, REPLACE AMBIENT LIGHT SENSOR.

HEADLIGHTS: DAYTIME RUNNING LIGHTS (DRL)

CHART #11

LOW BEAM HEADLIGHTS REMAIN "OFF" WITH DAYLIGHT CONDITIONS BUT SWITCH TO FULL INTENSITY WITH LOW LIGHT CONDITIONS

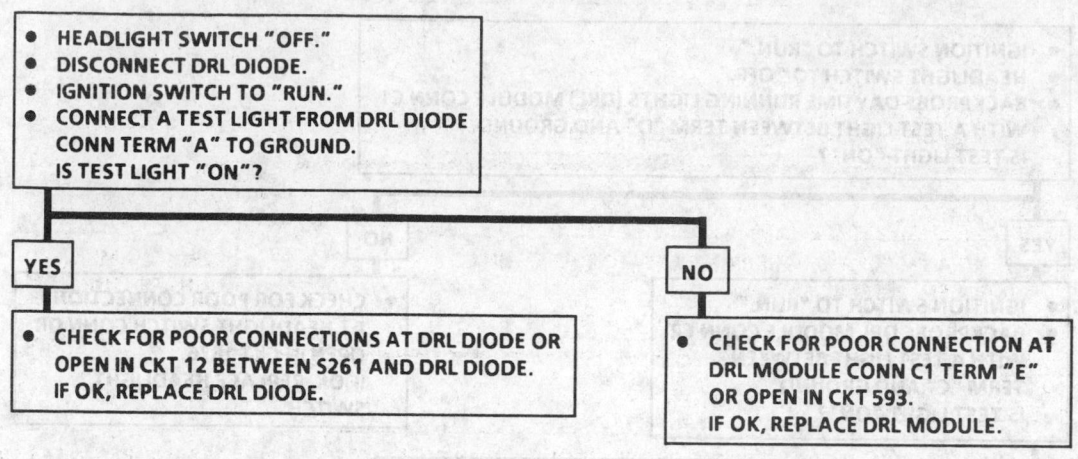

- HEADLIGHT SWITCH "OFF."
- DISCONNECT DRL DIODE.
- IGNITION SWITCH TO "RUN."
- CONNECT A TEST LIGHT FROM DRL DIODE CONN TERM "A" TO GROUND.

IS TEST LIGHT "ON"?

YES

- CHECK FOR POOR CONNECTIONS AT DRL DIODE OR OPEN IN CKT 12 BETWEEN S261 AND DRL DIODE.

IF OK, REPLACE DRL DIODE.

NO

- CHECK FOR POOR CONNECTION AT DRL MODULE CONN C1 TERM "E" OR OPEN IN CKT 593.

IF OK, REPLACE DRL MODULE.

CHART #12

LOW BEAM HEADLIGHTS "ON" AT FULL INTENSITY WITH DAYLIGHT CONDITIONS AND HEADLIGHT SWITCH "OFF"

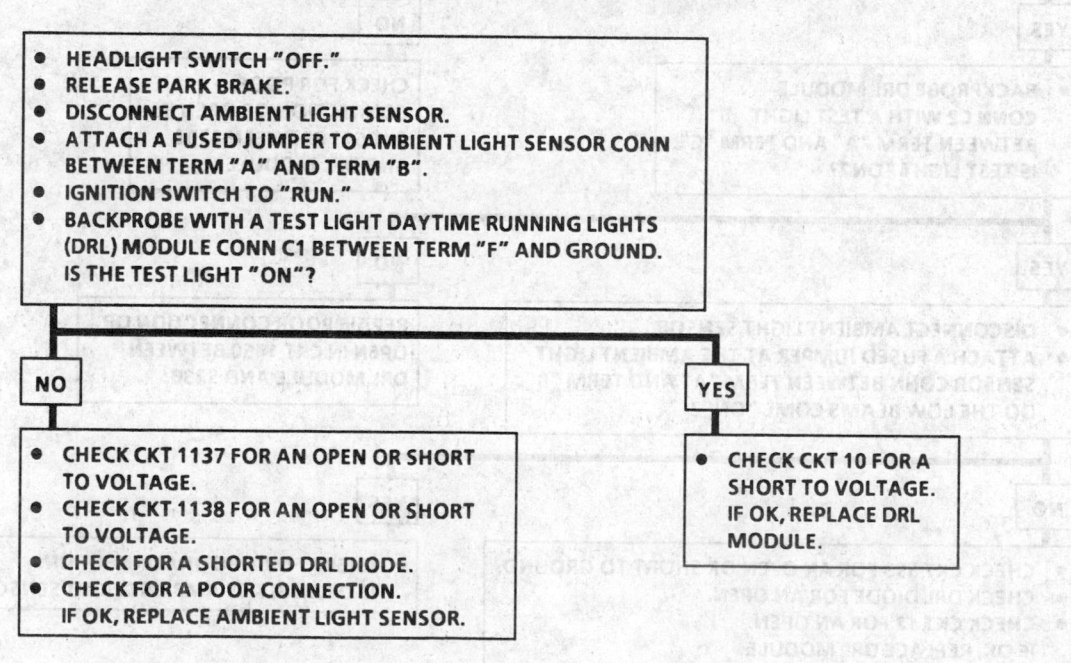

- HEADLIGHT SWITCH "OFF."
- RELEASE PARK BRAKE.
- DISCONNECT AMBIENT LIGHT SENSOR.
- ATTACH A FUSED JUMPER TO AMBIENT LIGHT SENSOR CONN BETWEEN TERM "A" AND TERM "B".
- IGNITION SWITCH TO "RUN."
- BACKPROBE WITH A TEST LIGHT DAYTIME RUNNING LIGHTS (DRL) MODULE CONN C1 BETWEEN TERM "F" AND GROUND.

IS THE TEST LIGHT "ON"?

NO

- CHECK CKT 1137 FOR AN OPEN OR SHORT TO VOLTAGE.
- CHECK CKT 1138 FOR AN OPEN OR SHORT TO VOLTAGE.
- CHECK FOR A SHORTED DRL DIODE.
- CHECK FOR A POOR CONNECTION.

IF OK, REPLACE AMBIENT LIGHT SENSOR.

YES

- CHECK CKT 10 FOR A SHORT TO VOLTAGE.

IF OK, REPLACE DRL MODULE.

CHART #13

LOW BEAM HEADLIGHTS DO NOT SWITCH FROM REDUCED INTENSITY TO FULL INTENSITY WITH LOW LIGHT CONDITIONS

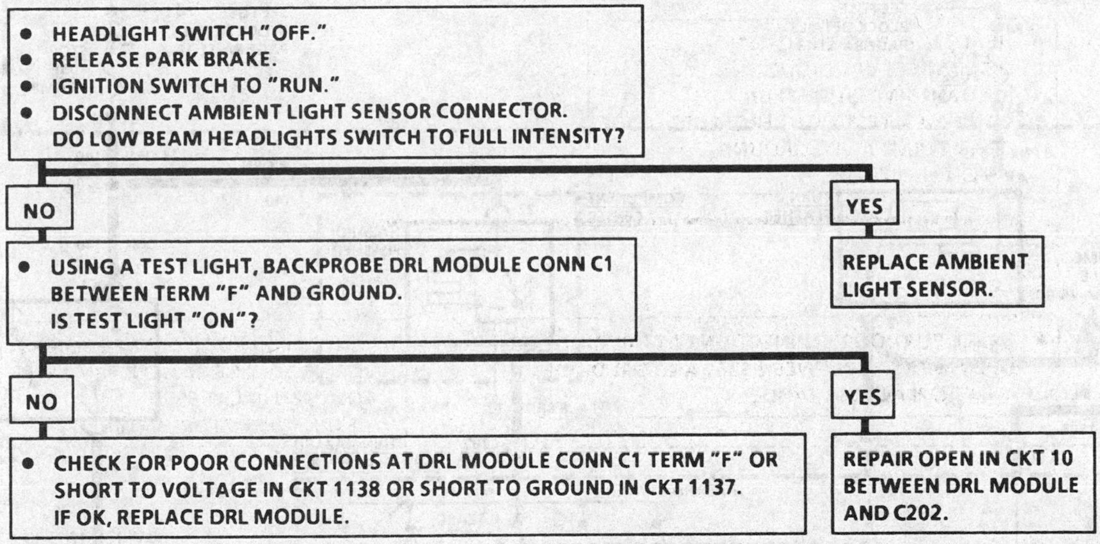
• HEADLIGHT SWITCH "OFF."
• RELEASE PARK BRAKE.
• IGNITION SWITCH TO "RUN."
• DISCONNECT AMBIENT LIGHT SENSOR CONNECTOR.
DO LOW BEAM HEADLIGHTS SWITCH TO FULL INTENSITY?
NO
YES
• USING A TEST LIGHT, BACKPROBE DRL MODULE CONN C1 BETWEEN TERM "F" AND GROUND.
IS TEST LIGHT "ON"?
REPLACE AMBIENT LIGHT SENSOR.
NO
YES
• CHECK FOR POOR CONNECTIONS AT DRL MODULE CONN C1 TERM "F" OR SHORT TO VOLTAGE IN CKT 1138 OR SHORT TO GROUND IN CKT 1137.
IF OK, REPLACE DRL MODULE.
REPAIR OPEN IN CKT 10 BETWEEN DRL MODULE AND C202.

CIRCUIT OPERATION

The Daytime Running Lights (DRL) Module is designed to automatically operate Exterior Lights depending on outside light conditions. The DRL Module operates in two modes. In the Day Mode, the LOW Beam Headlights are lit at reduced brilliance. In the Night Mode, the LOW Beam Headlights are lit at full brilliance and the Front Marker, Park and Tail Lights are lit.

When the DRL Module is in the Day Mode, the Day Mode contacts close, applying voltage to the DRL Diode and the LOW Beam Headlights. The DRL Diode reduces the voltage applied to the Headlights, thus reducing the brilliance of the Headlights.

When the Ambient Light Sensor senses darkness, the DRL Module operates in the Night Mode. The Night Mode contacts close, applying voltage to the Headlights and other Exterior Lights through the same circuit path as when the Headlight Switch is in "HEAD."

If the Engine should stall with the DRL Module in the Night Mode, the DRL Module will turn off the Headlights and leave the Marker, Park and Tail Lights lit while the Engine is being cranked. The Headlight Switch operates as usual.

AMBIENT LIGHT SENSOR

The Ambient Sensor is a light sensitive variable resistor. Its resistance decreases as outside light intensity increases. The DRL Module measures the voltage drop across the Ambient Light Sensor and determines whether it should operate in the Day Mode or Night Mode.

PARK BRAKE INPUT

If the Park Brake is applied before the Ignition Switch is turned to "RUN," the DRL Module will not operate any Headlights or Exterior Lights. This allows the operator to start the vehicle and keep the Headlights off, as long as the Park Brake is applied. When the Park Brake is released with the Ignition Switch in "RUN," the DRL Module will activate the Headlights.

This feature will only function when the Park Brake is applied before the Ignition Switch is turned to "RUN." If the Park Brake is applied after the Ignition Switch is turned to "RUN," the Headlights will not turn off.

FOG LAMPS

When the Light Switch is in "PARK" or "HEAD" or when the DRL Module is operating in the Night Mode, voltage is applied to the Fog Lamp Switch. When the Fog Lamp Switch is turned "ON," voltage is applied to the "FOG LPS" Relay. With the Headlight Dimmer Switch in "LO," ground is provided for the "FOG LPS" Relay through the HI Beam filaments and the Fog Lamps turn "ON." When the Headlight Dimmer Switch is moved to "HI," battery voltage is at both sides of the "FOG LPS" Relay coil and the Fog Lamps go "OFF."

EXTERIOR LIGHTS

TURN/STOP/HAZARD/CENTER HIGH MOUNTED STOP

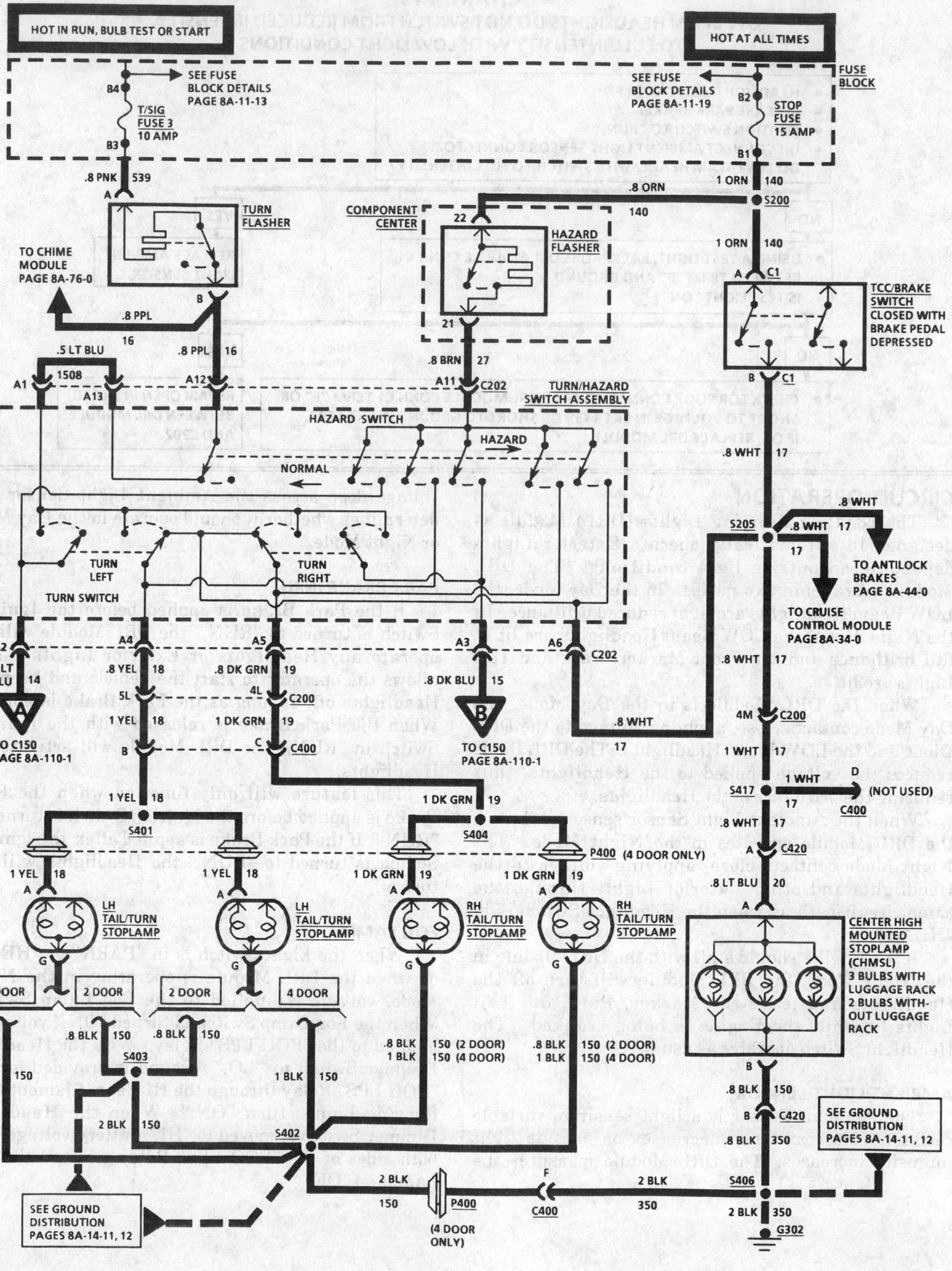
HOT IN RUN, BULB TEST OR START
HOT AT ALL TIMES
FUSE BLOCK
SEE FUSE BLOCK DETAILS PAGE 8A-11-13
B4
T/SIG FUSE 3 10 AMP
B3
SEE FUSE BLOCK DETAILS PAGE 8A-11-19
B2
STOP FUSE 15 AMP
B1
.8 PNK 539
A
TURN FLASHER
B
TO CHIME MODULE PAGE 8A-76-0
.8 PPL
16
.8 PPL 16
.5 LT BLU
A1 1508
A12
A13
COMPONENT CENTER
22
HAZARD FLASHER
21
.8 ORN
140
1 ORN 140
S200
1 ORN 140
A C1
TCC/BRAKE SWITCH CLOSED WITH BRAKE PEDAL DEPRESSED
B C1
.8 BRN 27
A11 C202
TURN/HAZARD SWITCH ASSEMBLY
HAZARD SWITCH
HAZARD
NORMAL
TURN LEFT
TURN RIGHT
TURN SWITCH
.8 WHT 17
.8 WHT
S205
.8 WHT 17
17
TO ANTILOCK BRAKES PAGE 8A-44-0
TO CRUISE CONTROL MODULE PAGE 8A-34-0
A2
A4
A5
A3
A6
C202
.8 LT BLU 14
.8 YEL 18
.8 DK GRN 19
.8 DK BLU 15
.8 WHT 17
5L
4L
C200
1 YEL 18
1 DK GRN 19
A
B
TO C150 PAGE 8A-110-1
TO C150 PAGE 8A-110-1
B
C
C400
4M C200
.8 WHT
17
1 WHT 17
1 WHT
D
S417
17
(NOT USED)
C400
.8 WHT 17
A C420
1 YEL 18
1 DK GRN 19
S401
S404
P400 (4 DOOR ONLY)
1 YEL 18
1 YEL 18
1 DK GRN 19
1 DK GRN 19
.8 LT BLU 20
A
A
A
A
A
LH TAIL/TURN STOPLAMP
LH TAIL/TURN STOPLAMP
RH TAIL/TURN STOPLAMP
RH TAIL/TURN STOPLAMP
CENTER HIGH MOUNTED STOPLAMP (CHMSL) 3 BULBS WITH LUGGAGE RACK 2 BULBS WITHOUT LUGGAGE RACK
G
G
G
B
4 DOOR
2 DOOR
2 DOOR
4 DOOR
.8 BLK 150
.8 BLK 150
S403
.8 BLK 1 BLK
150 (2 DOOR) 150 (4 DOOR)
.8 BLK 1 BLK
150 (2 DOOR) 150 (4 DOOR)
1 BLK 150
1 BLK 150
2 BLK 150
S402
.8 BLK 150
B C420
.8 BLK 350
SEE GROUND DISTRIBUTION PAGES 8A-14-11, 12
2 BLK
150
P400
(4 DOOR ONLY)
F
C400
2 BLK
350
S406
2 BLK 350
G302
SEE GROUND DISTRIBUTION PAGES 8A-14-11, 12

EXTERIOR LIGHTS
FRONT MARKER/HAZARD/PARK/TURN/LICENSE

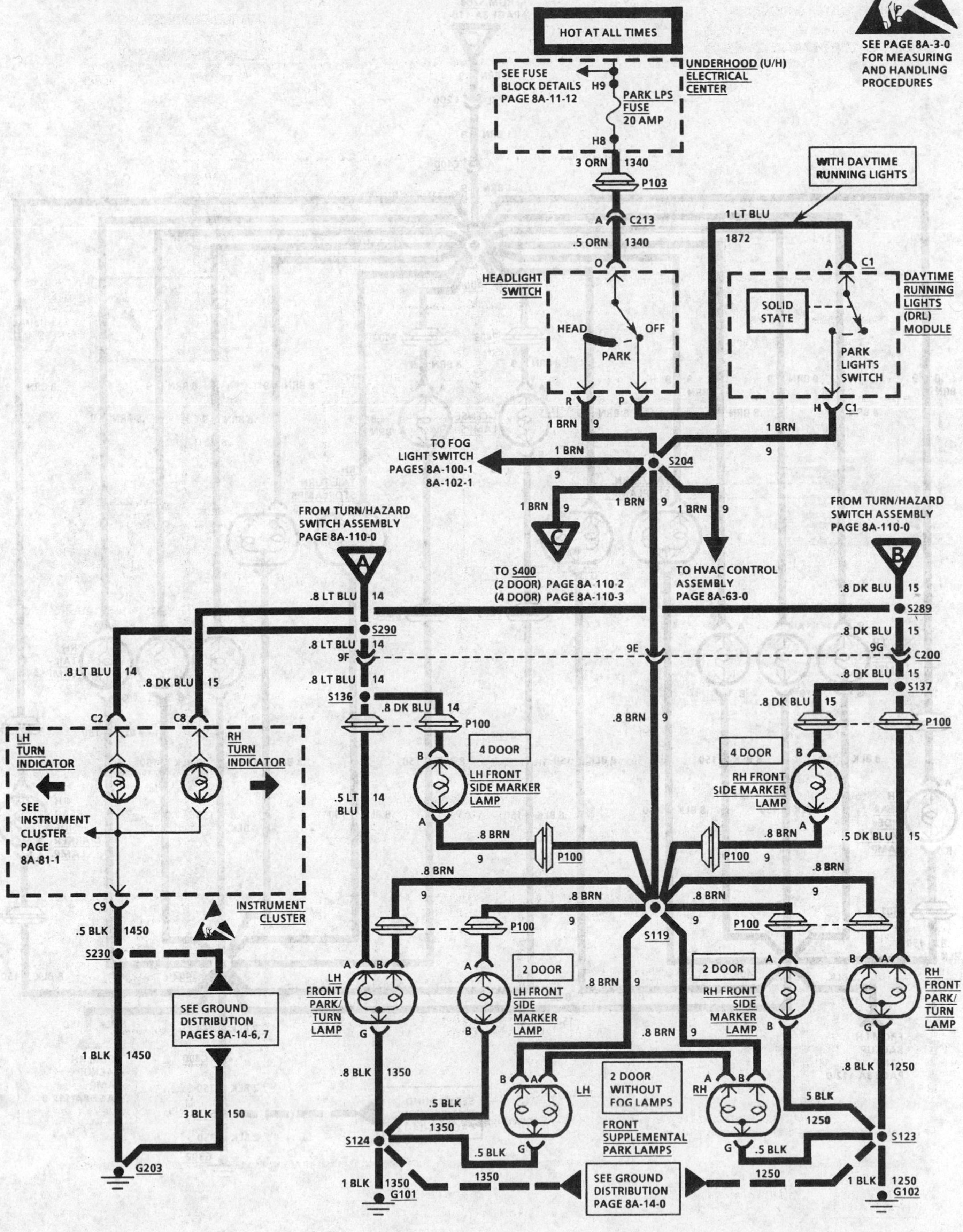

SEE PAGE 8A-3-0 FOR MEASURING AND HANDLING PROCEDURES
HOT AT ALL TIMES
SEE FUSE BLOCK DETAILS PAGE 8A-11-12
H9
PARK LPS FUSE 20 AMP
H8
UNDERHOOD (U/H) ELECTRICAL CENTER
3 ORN 1340
P103
A C213
.5 ORN 1340
O
HEADLIGHT SWITCH
HEAD
OFF
PARK
R
P
WITH DAYTIME RUNNING LIGHTS
1 LT BLU
1872
A C1
SOLID STATE
DAYTIME RUNNING LIGHTS (DRL) MODULE
PARK LIGHTS SWITCH
H C1
1 BRN 9
1 BRN
9
TO FOG LIGHT SWITCH PAGES 8A-100-1 8A-102-1
1 BRN
S204
9
1 BRN 9
1 BRN 9
1 BRN 9
C
TO S400 (2 DOOR) PAGE 8A 110-2 (4 DOOR) PAGE 8A-110-3
TO HVAC CONTROL ASSEMBLY PAGE 8A-63-0
FROM TURN/HAZARD SWITCH ASSEMBLY PAGE 8A-110-0
A
.8 LT BLU 14
FROM TURN/HAZARD SWITCH ASSEMBLY PAGE 8A-110-0
B
.8 DK BLU 15
S289
S290
.8 LT BLU 14
9F
9E
9G
C200
.8 DK BLU 15
.8 LT BLU 14
.8 DK BLU 15
.8 LT BLU 14
.8 DK BLU 15
S137
S136
.8 DK BLU 14
P100
.8 BRN 9
.8 DK BLU 15
P100
C2
C8
LH TURN INDICATOR
RH TURN INDICATOR
SEE INSTRUMENT CLUSTER PAGE 8A-81-1
C9
INSTRUMENT CLUSTER
4 DOOR
LH FRONT SIDE MARKER LAMP
4 DOOR
RH FRONT SIDE MARKER LAMP
B
A
.5 LT BLU 14
.8 BRN
9
P100
P100 9
.8 BRN
.5 DK BLU 15
.8 BRN
9
.8 BRN
.8 BRN
9
.8 BRN
9
S119
P100
P100
.5 BLK 1450
S230
SEE GROUND DISTRIBUTION PAGES 8A-14-6, 7
2 DOOR
2 DOOR
LH FRONT PARK/TURN LAMP
LH FRONT SIDE MARKER LAMP
.8 BRN 9
RH FRONT SIDE MARKER LAMP
RH FRONT PARK/TURN LAMP
G
.8 BRN 9
1 BLK 1450
.8 BLK 1350
.8 BLK 1250
2 DOOR WITHOUT FOG LAMPS
LH
RH
FRONT SUPPLEMENTAL PARK LAMPS
3 BLK 150
.5 BLK
1350
5 BLK
1250
S124
.5 BLK
.5 BLK
S123
G203
1 BLK 1350
1350
SEE GROUND DISTRIBUTION PAGE 8A-14-0
1250
1 BLK 1250
G101
G102

EXTERIOR LIGHTS
REAR LAMPS (2 DOOR)

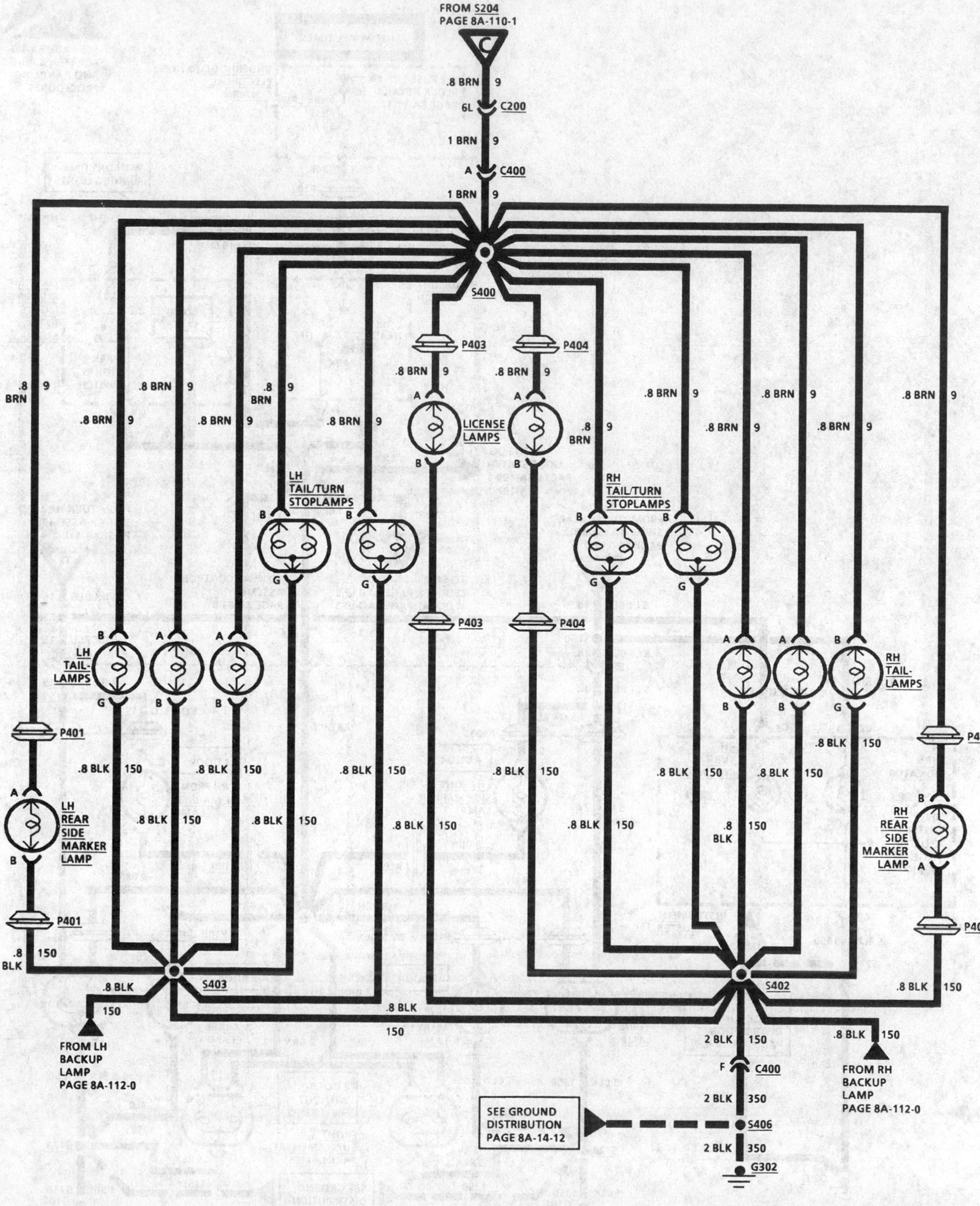

FROM S204
PAGE 8A-110-1
C
.8 BRN 9
6L C200
1 BRN 9
A C400
1 BRN 9
S400
P403
P404
.8 BRN 9
A
LICENSE LAMPS
B
.8 BRN 9
LH TAIL/TURN STOPLAMPS
RH TAIL/TURN STOPLAMPS
B
G
P403
P404
LH TAIL-LAMPS
RH TAIL-LAMPS
P401
P402
.8 BLK 150
LH REAR SIDE MARKER LAMP
RH REAR SIDE MARKER LAMP
S403
S402
FROM LH BACKUP LAMP PAGE 8A-112-0
FROM RH BACKUP LAMP PAGE 8A-112-0
2 BLK 150
F C400
2 BLK 350
SEE GROUND DISTRIBUTION PAGE 8A-14-12
S406
2 BLK 350
G302

EXTERIOR LIGHTS
REAR LAMPS (4 DOOR)

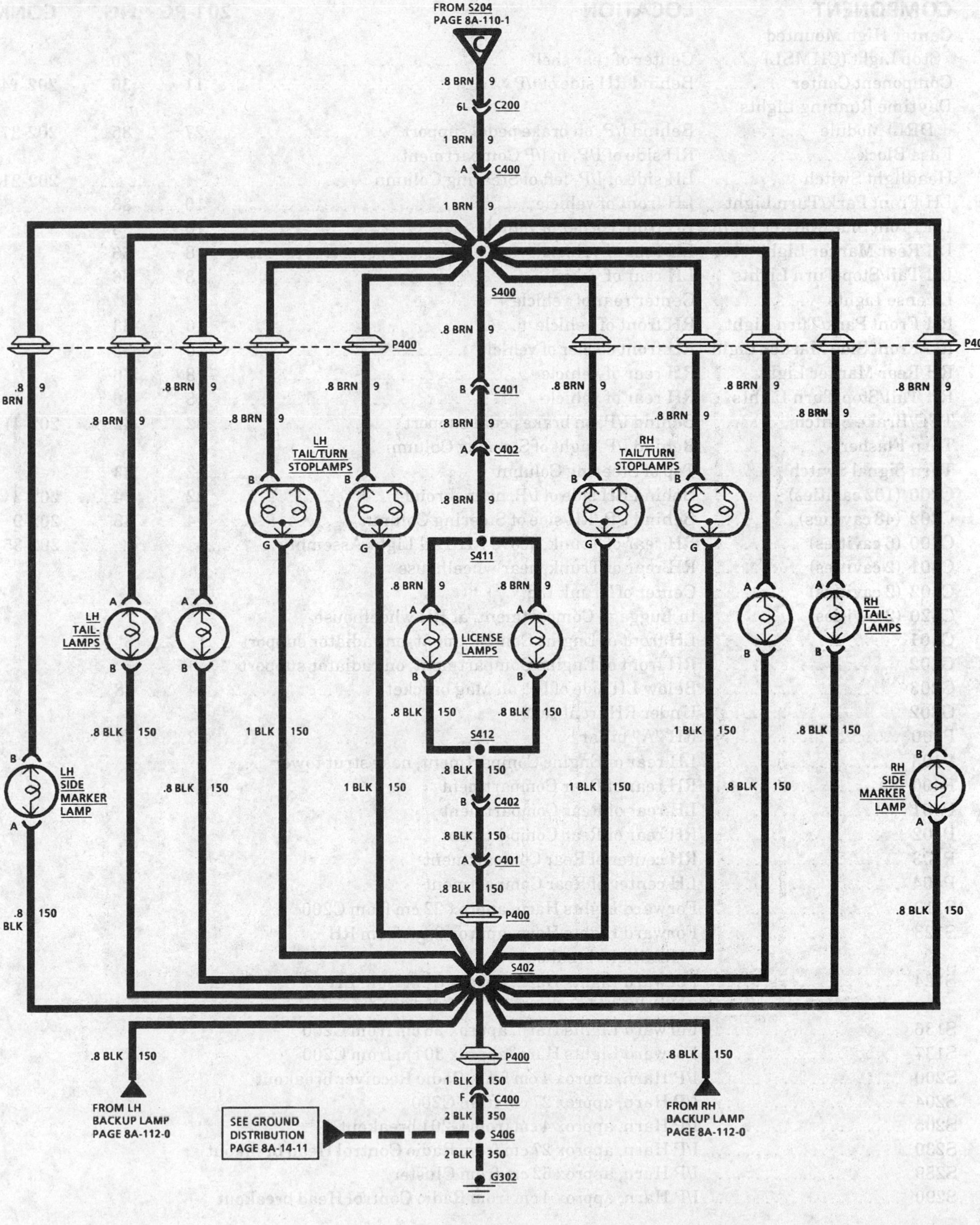
FROM S204
PAGE 8A-110-1
C
.8 BRN 9
6L C200
1 BRN 9
A C400
1 BRN 9
S400
.8 BRN 9
P400
.8 BRN 9
B C401
.8 BRN 9
A C402
LH
TAIL/TURN
STOPLAMPS
RH
TAIL/TURN
STOPLAMPS
.8 BRN 9
S411
LH
TAIL-
LAMPS
LICENSE
LAMPS
RH
TAIL-
LAMPS
.8 BLK 150
S412
LH
SIDE
MARKER
LAMP
RH
SIDE
MARKER
LAMP
1 BLK 150
B C402
A C401
P400
S402
.8 BLK 150
FROM LH
BACKUP LAMP
PAGE 8A-112-0
FROM RH
BACKUP LAMP
PAGE 8A-112-0
1 BLK 150
F C400
2 BLK 350
S406
SEE GROUND
DISTRIBUTION
PAGE 8A-14-11
G302

EXTERIOR LIGHTS

COMPONENT	LOCATION	201-PG	FIG.	CONN
Center High Mounted Stop Light (CHMSL)	Center of rear shelf	17	60	
Component Center	Behind RH side of I/P	11	36	202-14
Daytime Running Lights (DRL) Module	Behind I/P, on brake pedal support	27	85	202-37
Fuse Block	RH side of I/P, in I/P Compartment			
Headlight Switch	LH side of I/P, left of Steering Column			202-21
LH Front Park/Turn Light	LH front of vehicle	10	33	
LH Front Side Marker Light	LH front corner of vehicle	10	33	
LH Rear Marker Light	LH rear of vehicle	18	66	
LH Tail/Stop-Turn Lights	LH rear of vehicle	18	66	
License Lights	Center rear of vehicle			
RH Front Park/Turn Light	RH front of vehicle	10	33	
RH Front Side Marker Light	RH front corner of vehicle	10	33	
RH Rear Marker Light	RH rear of vehicle	18	66	
RH Tail/Stop-Turn Lights	RH rear of vehicle	18	66	
TCC/Brake Switch	Behind I/P, on brake pedal support	12	42	202-41
Turn Flasher	Behind I/P, right of Steering Column			
Turn Signal Switch	Top of Steering Column	12	43	
C200 (102 cavities)	Behind RH side of I/P, near shroud	22	74	202-3
C202 (48 cavities)	Behind I/P, RH side of Steering Column	14	48	202-9
C400 (6 cavities)	RH rear of Trunk, above RH Tail Light Assembly			202-35
C401 (2 cavities)	RH rear of Trunk, near wheelhouse			
C402 (2 cavities)	Center of Trunk Lid			
C420 (2 cavities)	In Luggage Compartment, at RH wheelhouse			
G101	LH front of Engine Compartment, on radiator support	1	6	
G102	RH front of Engine Compartment, on radiator support			
G203	Below LH side of I/P, on Mag bracket	14	48	
G302	Under RH front seat			
P100	RH "A" pillar	23	77	
P103	LH rear of Engine Compartment, near strut tower	2	7	
P400	RH rear of Rear Compartment			
P401	LH rear of Rear Compartment			
P402	RH rear of Rear Compartment			
P403	RH center of Rear Compartment			
P404	LH center of Rear Compartment			
S119	Forward Lights Harn, approx 22 cm from C200			
S123	Forward Lights Harn, approx 8 cm from RH Headlight breakout			
S124	Forward Lights Harn, approx 8 cm from LH Headlight breakout			
S136	Forward Lights Harn, approx 26 cm from C200			
S137	Forward Lights Harn, approx 30 cm from C200			
S200	I/P Harn, approx 4 cm from Radio Receiver breakout			
S204	I/P Harn, approx 27 cm from C200			
S205	I/P Harn, approx 4 cm from G201 breakout			
S230	I/P Harn, approx 27 cm from Radio Control Head breakout			
S289	I/P Harn, approx 52 cm from Cluster			
S290	I/P Harn, approx 4 cm from Radio Control Head breakout			

COMPONENT	LOCATION	201-PG	FIG.	CONN
S400 (2 Door)	Rear Body Harn, approx 27 cm from License Light breakout			
S400 (4 Door)	Rear Body Harn, approx 55 cm from C400			
S401 (2 Door)	Rear Body Harn, approx 5 cm from RH Tail/Stop/ Turn Lights breakout			
S401 (4 Door)	Rear Body Harn, approx 40 cm from C400			
S402 (2 Door)	Rear Body Harn, approx 32 cm from License Light breakout			
S402 (4 Door)	Rear Body Harn, approx 5 cm from breakout to C400			
S403	Rear Body Harn, approx 5 cm from LH Tail Light breakout			
S404 (2 Door)	Rear Body Harn, approx 5 cm from LH Tail Light breakout			
S404 (4 Door)	Rear Body Harn, approx 29 cm from P400			
S406	Cross Car Harn, approx 9 cm from RH Rear Speaker breakout			
S411	License Light Harn, approx 19 cm from C402			
S412	License Light Harn, approx 19 cm from C402			
S417	Cross Car Harn, approx 20 cm from C405 breakout			

TROUBLESHOOTING HINTS (Perform before beginning System Diagnosis)

1. If the Turn Lights do not work, check TURN Fuse.
2. If the Hazard Lights do not work, check STOP Fuse.
3. If one of the Turn Indicators goes on when the Park Lights are turned "ON," check the Front Park/Turn Light on that side for open or poor connection.
4. If Turn Lights stay on (do not flash) in both Turn Left and Turn Right, replace the Turn Flasher.
5. For any of the following symptoms replace the Turn/Hazard Switch Assembly:
   - Turn Signal Switch will not turn "ON"/"OFF."
   - All Turn/Hazard/Stop Lights do not work and C202 is firmly mated.
   - Some Turn Lights work and all Hazard Lights work.
   - Some Hazard Lights work and all Turn Lights work.
   - Hazard Lights do not turn "OFF."
6. If Hazard Lights stay on (do not flash) with Hazard Switch "ON," but Stop Lights operate normally, replace the Hazard Flasher.
7. If Stop Lights do not turn "OFF," adjust/replace the Brake Switch (refer to SECTION 5).
8. If a Turn Indicator does not light but the Turn Signal works, check the bulb, connection and wiring to the Indicator.
9. If only one light does not operate, check the Lamp, Socket and related wiring for opens or corrosion (see schematic).
10. If one Front Park and/or Marker Light does not light, check that its ground is clean and tight.
11. If none of the Park/Tail Lights work, check PARK LPS Fuse.
12. If Park Lights do not turn "OFF," check Headlight Switch. If OK, repair CKT 9 for a short to B+.
13. If one rear light is inoperative, check for open in CKT 150 between S402 or S403 and lamp socket. Check for open in CKT 9 between S400 and inoperative lamp.

- Check for a broken (or partially broken) wire inside of the insulation which could cause system malfunction but prove "GOOD" in a continuity/voltage check with a system disconnected. These circuits may be intermittent or resistive when loaded, and if possible, should be checked by monitoring for a voltage drop with the system operational (under load).
- Check for proper installation of aftermarket electronic equipment which may affect the integrity of other systems (see "Troubleshooting Procedures," page 8A-4-0).
- Refer to System Diagnosis.

SYSTEM DIAGNOSIS

- Perform the System Check and refer to the Symptom Table for the appropriate diagnostic procedures.

EXTERIOR LIGHTS

SYSTEM CHECK

ACTION	NORMAL RESULTS
[1] ● Headlight Switch to "PARK."	All Exterior Lights are "ON" (except Headlights).
[2] ● Hazard Switch to "ON."	Front and Rear Turn Lights flash continuously from minimum intensity to maximum intensity. Front Marker Lights flash continuously from "OFF" to "ON."
[3] ● Headlight Switch still set in "PARK" position. ● Hazard Switch "ON." ● Depress brake pedal.	Front and Rear Turn Lights stay "ON" at maximum intensity, and Front Marker Lights stay "OFF" as long as brake pedal is depressed.
[4] ● Headlight Switch "OFF." ● Brake pedal released. ● Hazard Lights still "ON."	Front and Rear Turn Lights flash continuously from "OFF" to low intensity.
[5] ● Operate LH or RH Turn Switch.	Turn Lights flash continuously "ON" and "OFF."

SYMPTOM TABLE

SYMPTOM	PROCEDURE	PAGE NUMBER
Turn Lights inoperative, Hazard Lights operate normally.	Chart #1	8A-110-7
Hazard Lights inoperative, Turn Signals and Stop Lights operate normally.	Chart #2	8A-110-7
Park and Tail Lights inoperative.	Chart #3	8A-110-8
Stop Lights inoperative.	Chart #4	8A-110-8
RH and/or LH Turn/Stop Lights inoperative, Front Turn Lights operate normally.	Chart #5	8A-110-9
Front Park Lights inoperative, Tail Lights and Turn Signals operate normally.	Chart #6	8A-110-9
Turn Indicator and Front Turn Lamp on one side do not work.	Chart #7	8A-110-9
All Rear Marker, License and Tail Lights inoperative, Front Park Lights operate normally.	Chart #8	8A-110-10
Center High Mounted Stop Light inoperative.	Chart #9	8A-110-10
Center High Mounted Stop Light "ON" at all times.	Check for short to B + on CKT 20. If OK, replace Brake Switch.	

CHART #1
TURN LIGHTS INOPERATIVE, HAZARD LIGHTS OPERATE NORMALLY

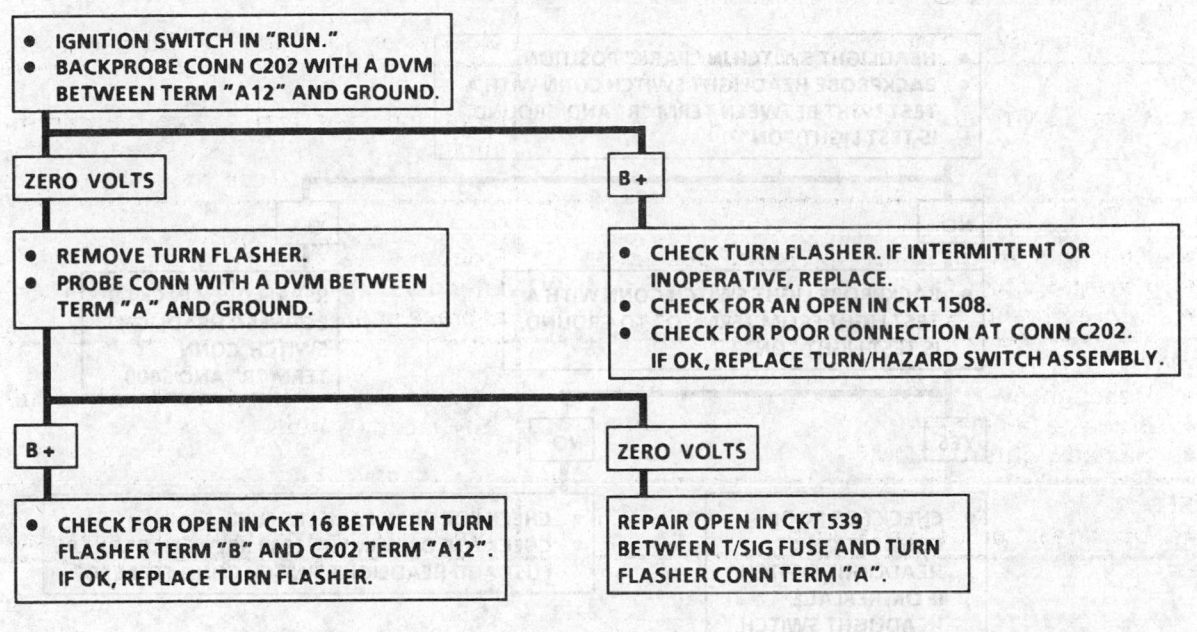

- IGNITION SWITCH IN "RUN."
- BACKPROBE CONN C202 WITH A DVM BETWEEN TERM "A12" AND GROUND.

ZERO VOLTS

- REMOVE TURN FLASHER.
- PROBE CONN WITH A DVM BETWEEN TERM "A" AND GROUND.

B+

- CHECK FOR OPEN IN CKT 16 BETWEEN TURN FLASHER TERM "B" AND C202 TERM "A12". IF OK, REPLACE TURN FLASHER.

ZERO VOLTS

REPAIR OPEN IN CKT 539 BETWEEN T/SIG FUSE AND TURN FLASHER CONN TERM "A".

B+

- CHECK TURN FLASHER. IF INTERMITTENT OR INOPERATIVE, REPLACE.
- CHECK FOR AN OPEN IN CKT 1508.
- CHECK FOR POOR CONNECTION AT CONN C202. IF OK, REPLACE TURN/HAZARD SWITCH ASSEMBLY.

CHART #2
HAZARD LIGHTS INOPERATIVE, TURN SIGNALS AND STOP LIGHTS OPERATE NORMALLY

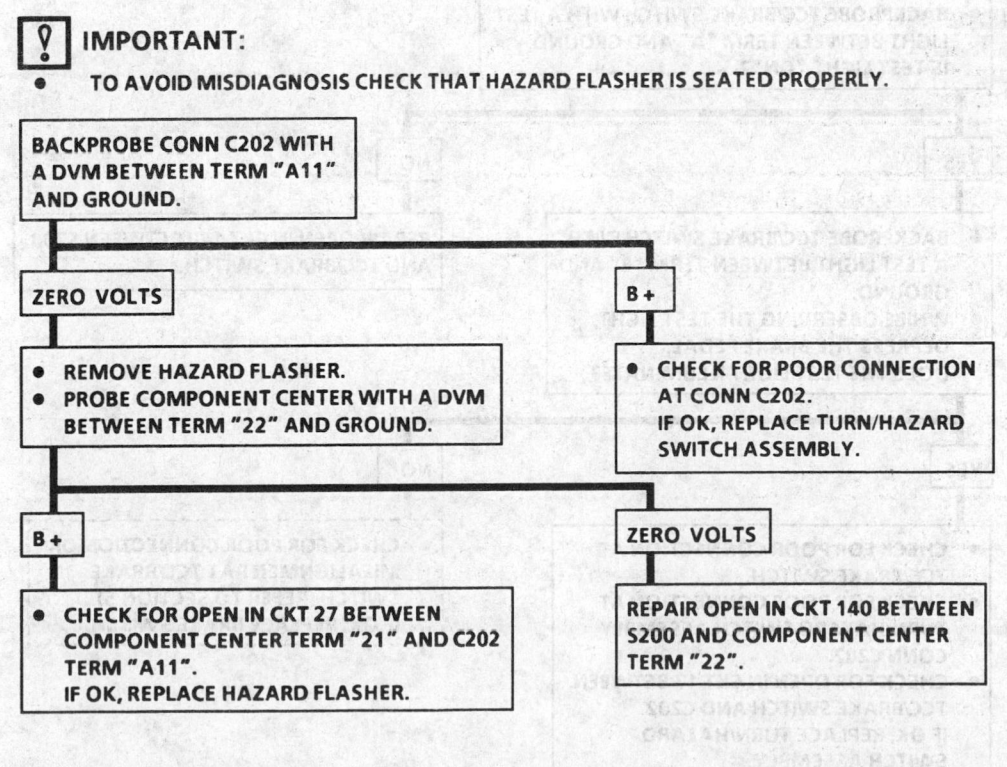

IMPORTANT:

- TO AVOID MISDIAGNOSIS CHECK THAT HAZARD FLASHER IS SEATED PROPERLY.

BACKPROBE CONN C202 WITH A DVM BETWEEN TERM "A11" AND GROUND.

ZERO VOLTS

- REMOVE HAZARD FLASHER.
- PROBE COMPONENT CENTER WITH A DVM BETWEEN TERM "22" AND GROUND.

B+

- CHECK FOR OPEN IN CKT 27 BETWEEN COMPONENT CENTER TERM "21" AND C202 TERM "A11". IF OK, REPLACE HAZARD FLASHER.

ZERO VOLTS

REPAIR OPEN IN CKT 140 BETWEEN S200 AND COMPONENT CENTER TERM "22".

B+

- CHECK FOR POOR CONNECTION AT CONN C202. IF OK, REPLACE TURN/HAZARD SWITCH ASSEMBLY.

EXTERIOR LIGHTS

CHART #3
PARK AND TAIL LIGHTS INOPERATIVE

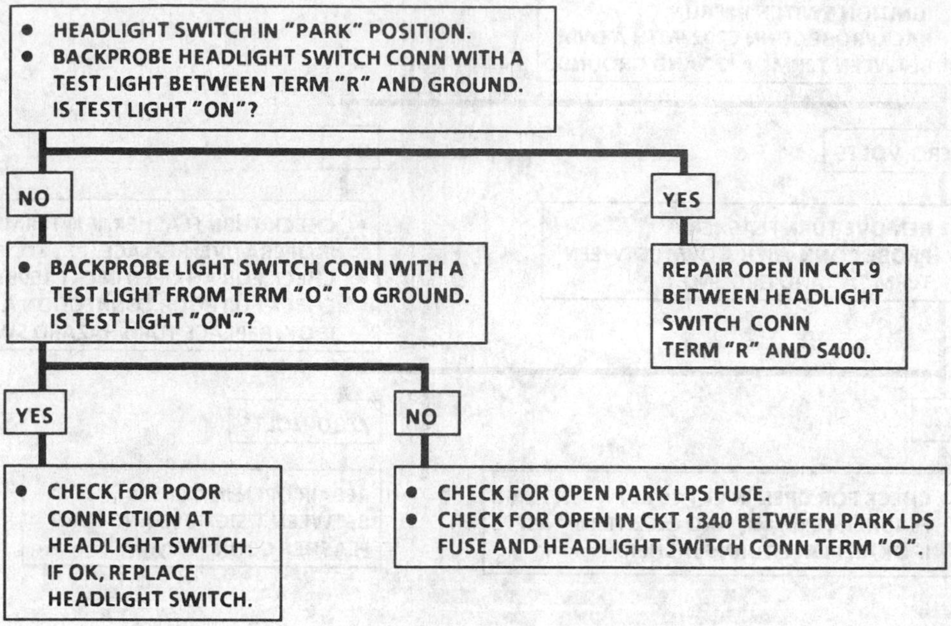

• HEADLIGHT SWITCH IN "PARK" POSITION.
• BACKPROBE HEADLIGHT SWITCH CONN WITH A TEST LIGHT BETWEEN TERM "R" AND GROUND. IS TEST LIGHT "ON"?
NO
YES
• BACKPROBE LIGHT SWITCH CONN WITH A TEST LIGHT FROM TERM "O" TO GROUND. IS TEST LIGHT "ON"?
REPAIR OPEN IN CKT 9 BETWEEN HEADLIGHT SWITCH CONN TERM "R" AND S400.
YES
NO
• CHECK FOR POOR CONNECTION AT HEADLIGHT SWITCH. IF OK, REPLACE HEADLIGHT SWITCH.
• CHECK FOR OPEN PARK LPS FUSE.
• CHECK FOR OPEN IN CKT 1340 BETWEEN PARK LPS FUSE AND HEADLIGHT SWITCH CONN TERM "O".

CHART #4
STOP LIGHTS INOPERATIVE

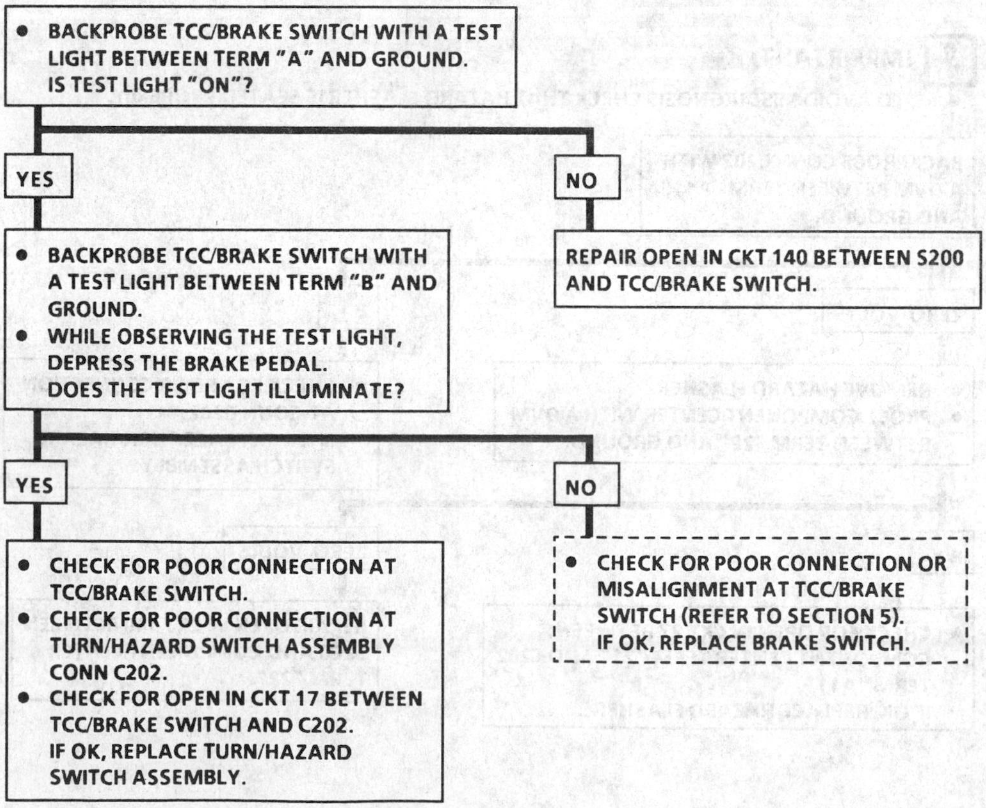

• BACKPROBE TCC/BRAKE SWITCH WITH A TEST LIGHT BETWEEN TERM "A" AND GROUND. IS TEST LIGHT "ON"?
YES
NO
• BACKPROBE TCC/BRAKE SWITCH WITH A TEST LIGHT BETWEEN TERM "B" AND GROUND.
• WHILE OBSERVING THE TEST LIGHT, DEPRESS THE BRAKE PEDAL. DOES THE TEST LIGHT ILLUMINATE?
REPAIR OPEN IN CKT 140 BETWEEN S200 AND TCC/BRAKE SWITCH.
YES
NO
• CHECK FOR POOR CONNECTION AT TCC/BRAKE SWITCH.
• CHECK FOR POOR CONNECTION AT TURN/HAZARD SWITCH ASSEMBLY CONN C202.
• CHECK FOR OPEN IN CKT 17 BETWEEN TCC/BRAKE SWITCH AND C202. IF OK, REPLACE TURN/HAZARD SWITCH ASSEMBLY.
• CHECK FOR POOR CONNECTION OR MISALIGNMENT AT TCC/BRAKE SWITCH (REFER TO SECTION 5). IF OK, REPLACE BRAKE SWITCH.

CHART #5
RH AND/OR LH TURN /STOP LIGHTS INOPERATIVE, FRONT TURN LIGHTS OPERATE NORMALLY

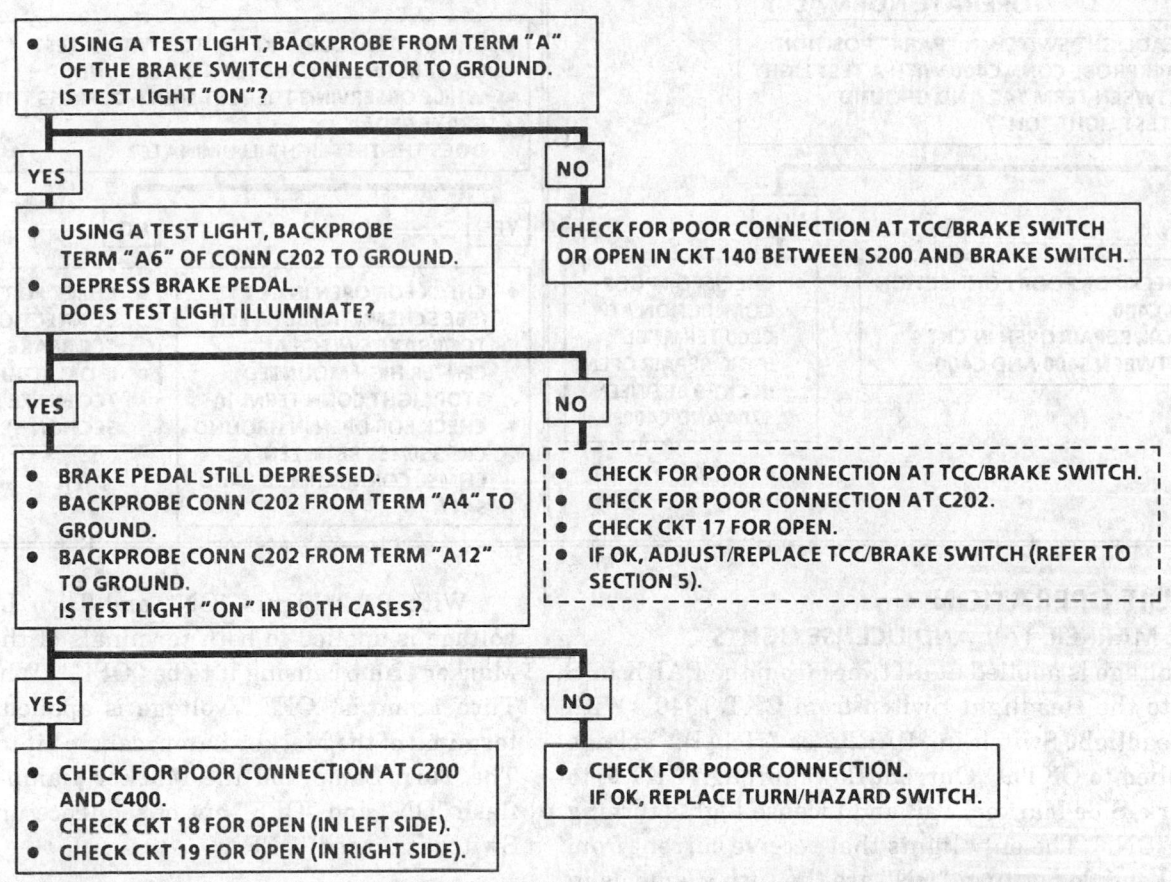

- USING A TEST LIGHT, BACKPROBE FROM TERM "A" OF THE BRAKE SWITCH CONNECTOR TO GROUND. IS TEST LIGHT "ON"?

NO
- CHECK FOR POOR CONNECTION AT TCC/BRAKE SWITCH OR OPEN IN CKT 140 BETWEEN S200 AND BRAKE SWITCH.

YES
- USING A TEST LIGHT, BACKPROBE TERM "A6" OF CONN C202 TO GROUND.
- DEPRESS BRAKE PEDAL. DOES TEST LIGHT ILLUMINATE?

NO
- CHECK FOR POOR CONNECTION AT TCC/BRAKE SWITCH.
- CHECK FOR POOR CONNECTION AT C202.
- CHECK CKT 17 FOR OPEN.
- IF OK, ADJUST/REPLACE TCC/BRAKE SWITCH (REFER TO SECTION 5).

YES
- BRAKE PEDAL STILL DEPRESSED.
- BACKPROBE CONN C202 FROM TERM "A4" TO GROUND.
- BACKPROBE CONN C202 FROM TERM "A12" TO GROUND. IS TEST LIGHT "ON" IN BOTH CASES?

YES
- CHECK FOR POOR CONNECTION AT C200 AND C400.
- CHECK CKT 18 FOR OPEN (IN LEFT SIDE).
- CHECK CKT 19 FOR OPEN (IN RIGHT SIDE).

NO
- CHECK FOR POOR CONNECTION. IF OK, REPLACE TURN/HAZARD SWITCH.

CHART #6
FRONT PARK LIGHTS INOPERATIVE, TAIL LIGHTS AND TURN SIGNALS OPERATE NORMALLY

- DISCONNECT CONN C200 ROW 9.
- HEADLIGHT SWITCH IN "PARK" POSITION.
- PROBE WITH A TEST LIGHT BETWEEN C200 TERM "9E" (BODY HARNESS SIDE) AND GROUND. IS TEST LIGHT "ON"?

YES

CHECK FOR POOR CONNECTION AT C200 TERM "9E," OR OPEN IN CKT 9 BETWEEN S119 AND C200 TERM "9E".

NO
- CHECK FOR POOR CONNECTION AT C200 TERM "9E". IF OK, REPAIR OPEN IN CKT 9 BETWEEN HEADLIGHT SWITCH AND C200.

CHART #7
TURN INDICATOR AND FRONT TURN LAMP ON ONE SIDE INOPERATIVE

- IGNITION IN "RUN."
- TURN SIGNAL "ON" FOR INOPERATIVE SIDE.
- USING A DVM, BACKPROBE FROM TERM "A2" OF CONN C202 TO GROUND FOR LH INOPERATIVE. BACKPROBE FROM TERM "A3" FOR RH INOPERATIVE.

B +

CHECK FOR POOR CONNECTION AT CONN C202 OR OPEN IN CKT 14 (LH SIDE INOPERATIVE) BETWEEN C202 TERM "A2" AND C200 TERM "9E", OR OPEN IN CKT 15 (RH SIDE INOPERATIVE) BETWEEN C202 TERM "A3" AND C200 TERM "9G".

ZERO VOLTS
- CHECK FOR POOR CONNECTION AT CONN C202. IF OK, REPLACE TURN/HAZARD SWITCH.

EXTERIOR LIGHTS

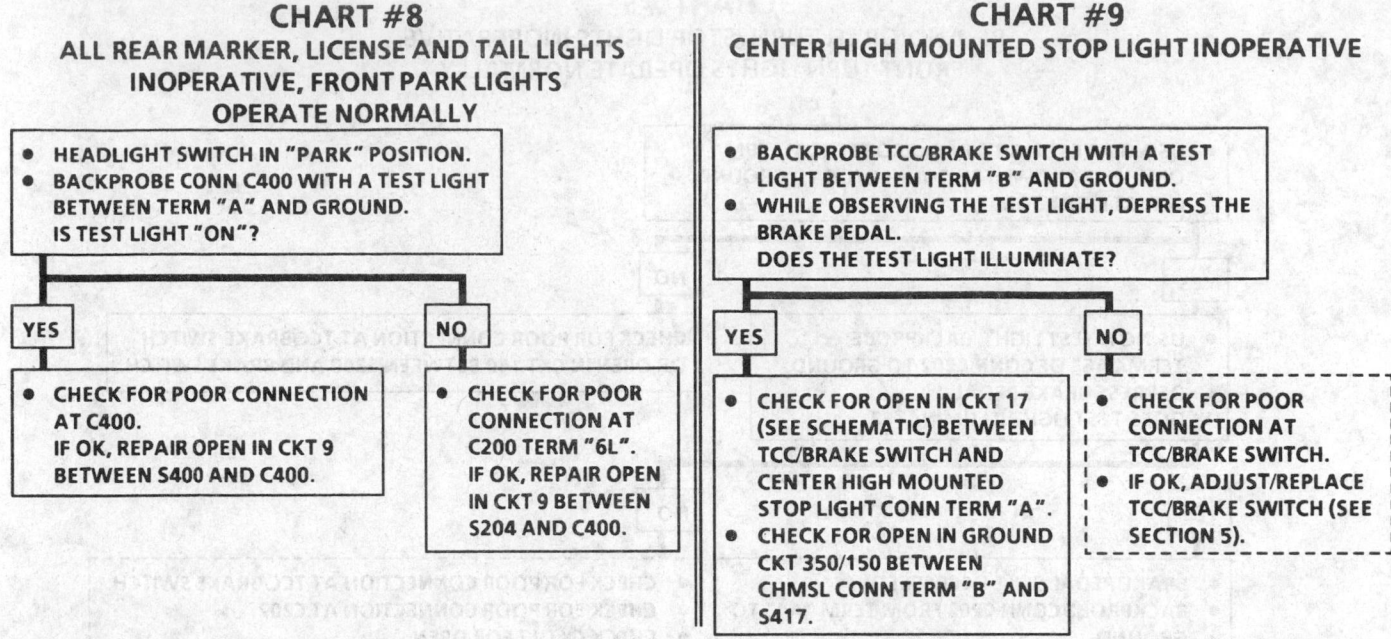

CHART #8
ALL REAR MARKER, LICENSE AND TAIL LIGHTS INOPERATIVE, FRONT PARK LIGHTS OPERATE NORMALLY

- HEADLIGHT SWITCH IN "PARK" POSITION.
- BACKPROBE CONN C400 WITH A TEST LIGHT BETWEEN TERM "A" AND GROUND.
  IS TEST LIGHT "ON"?

YES
- CHECK FOR POOR CONNECTION AT C400.
  IF OK, REPAIR OPEN IN CKT 9 BETWEEN S400 AND C400.

NO
- CHECK FOR POOR CONNECTION AT C200 TERM "6L".
  IF OK, REPAIR OPEN IN CKT 9 BETWEEN S204 AND C400.

CHART #9
CENTER HIGH MOUNTED STOP LIGHT INOPERATIVE

- BACKPROBE TCC/BRAKE SWITCH WITH A TEST LIGHT BETWEEN TERM "B" AND GROUND.
- WHILE OBSERVING THE TEST LIGHT, DEPRESS THE BRAKE PEDAL.
  DOES THE TEST LIGHT ILLUMINATE?

YES
- CHECK FOR OPEN IN CKT 17 (SEE SCHEMATIC) BETWEEN TCC/BRAKE SWITCH AND CENTER HIGH MOUNTED STOP LIGHT CONN TERM "A".
- CHECK FOR OPEN IN GROUND CKT 350/150 BETWEEN CHMSL CONN TERM "B" AND S417.

NO
- CHECK FOR POOR CONNECTION AT TCC/BRAKE SWITCH.
- IF OK, ADJUST/REPLACE TCC/BRAKE SWITCH (SEE SECTION 5).

CIRCUIT OPERATION

PARK, MARKER, TAIL AND LICENSE LIGHTS

Voltage is applied at all times from the PARK LPS Fuse to the Headlight Switch from CKT 1340. With the Headlight Switch in "PARK" or "HEAD," voltage is applied to CKT 9. Current flows through CKT 9, to all Park, Side Marker, Tail and License Lights turning them "ON." The only lights that receive current from CKT 9 and do not turn "ON" are the turn filaments in the Park/Turn Lights. They do not turn "ON" because the voltage drop across the Front Side Marker Lights is much greater than that across the Turn Light Filaments.

TURN LIGHTS

With the Ignition Switch in "RUN," "BULB TEST" or "START," voltage is applied from the T/SIG Fuse and the Turn Flasher to the normally closed pole of the Hazard Switch in the Turn/Hazard Switch Assembly.

With the Turn Switch in the Turn Left position, voltage is applied from the Turn Switch to CKT 14 at terminal "A2" of connector C202 and to CKT 18 at terminal "A4" of C202. LH Front Turn, Rear Turn and Indicator Lights flash "ON" and "OFF" as current flow heats the timing element in the Turn Flasher, and it continuously opens and closes the circuit (for RH Turn Lights, CKT 15 terminal "A3" of C202 and CKT 19 terminal "A5" of C202).

With Park Lights "ON" and Turn Lights "ON," voltage is applied to both terminals of the Front Side Marker Lamp causing it to be "OFF." When the Front Turn Lamp is "OFF," voltage is applied to only one terminal of the Marker Lamp, causing it to flash "ON." The Turn Lamp and the Marker Lamp continue to flash "ON" and "OFF" out of sequence until the Turn Switch is turned "OFF."

HAZARD LIGHTS

Voltage is applied at all times from the STOP Fuse and the Hazard Flasher to the normally open poles of the Hazard Switch in the Turn/Hazard Switch Assembly. With the Hazard Switch in "HAZARD," voltage is applied to the Turn/Stop Lights. All of the Turn/Stop Lights and both Turn Indicators flash "ON" and "OFF."

STOP LIGHTS

Voltage is applied at all times from the STOP Fuse to the Brake Switch. When the brake pedal is depressed, voltage is applied from the TCC/Brake Switch and Turn/Hazard Switch to CKT 17 turning "ON" the LH and RH Tail/Turn/Stop Lights.

When the brake pedal is depressed, voltage is also applied from the Brake Switch to CKT 17 and the Center High Mounted Stop Light, turning "ON" the Center High Mounted Stop Light. The Center High Mounted Stop Light is not affected by the Turn/Hazard Switch Assembly.

BLANK

BACKUP LIGHTS

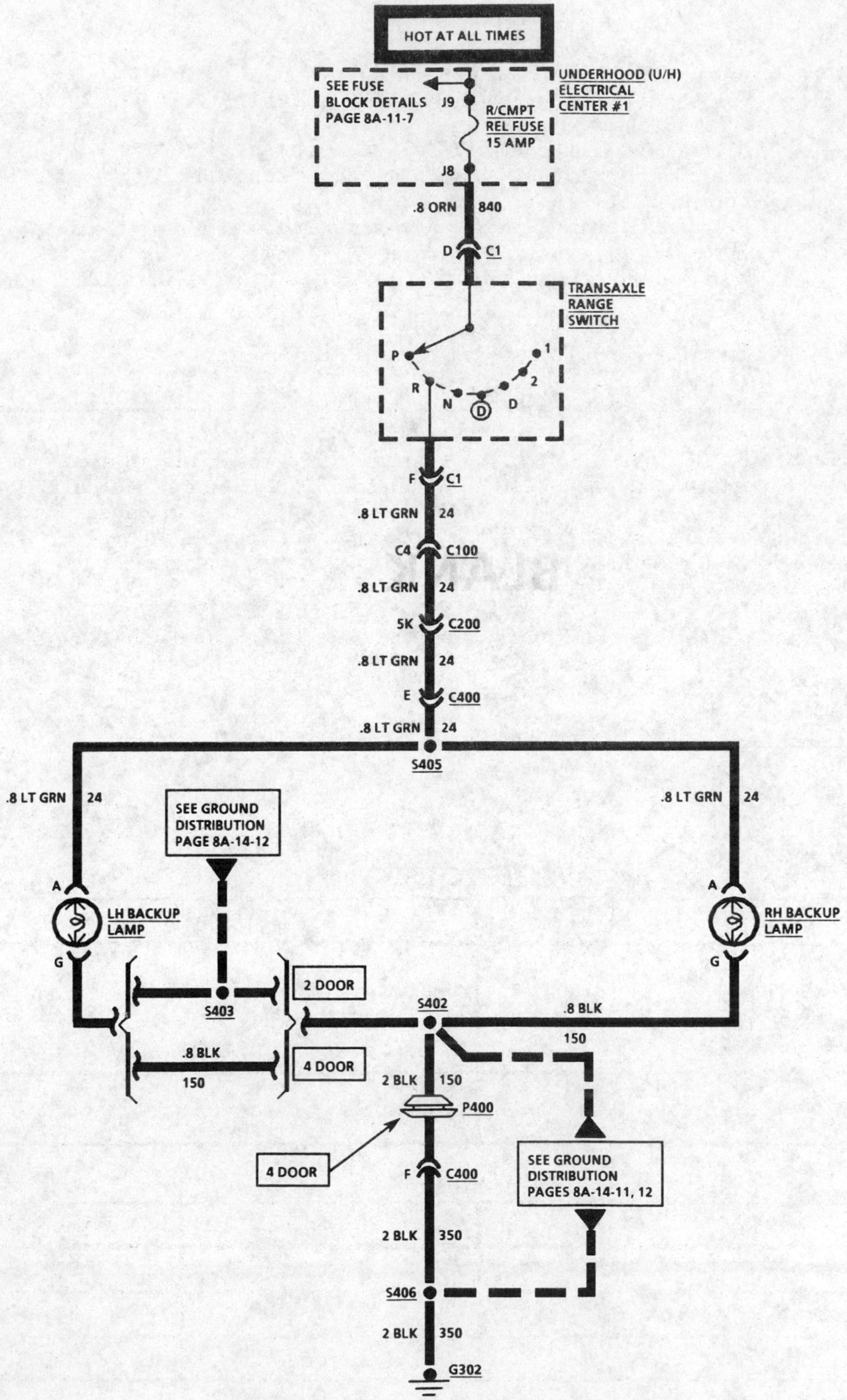
HOT AT ALL TIMES
SEE FUSE BLOCK DETAILS PAGE 8A-11-7
J9
R/CMPT REL FUSE 15 AMP
UNDERHOOD (U/H) ELECTRICAL CENTER #1
J8
.8 ORN 840
D C1
TRANSAXLE RANGE SWITCH
P
R
N
D
D
2
1
F C1
.8 LT GRN 24
C4 C100
.8 LT GRN 24
5K C200
.8 LT GRN 24
E C400
.8 LT GRN 24
S405
.8 LT GRN 24
SEE GROUND DISTRIBUTION PAGE 8A-14-12
.8 LT GRN 24
A
LH BACKUP LAMP
G
A
RH BACKUP LAMP
G
S403
2 DOOR
S402
.8 BLK 150
.8 BLK 150
4 DOOR
2 BLK 150
P400
4 DOOR
F C400
SEE GROUND DISTRIBUTION PAGES 8A-14-11, 12
2 BLK 350
S406
2 BLK 350
G302

COMPONENT	LOCATION	201-PG	FIG.	CONN
LH Backup Lights	LH rear of vehicle	18	66	
RH Backup Lights	RH rear of vehicle	18	66	
Transaxle Range Switch	Left of Engine, on Transaxle	3	10	202-41
Underhood (U/H) Electrical Center #1	Engine Compartment, front of RH strut tower			202-34
C100 (36 cavities)	RH side of dash, behind strut tower			202-0
C200 (106 cavities)	Behind RH side of I/P, near shroud			202-3
C400 (6 cavities)	RH rear of Trunk, near wheelhouse	17	60	202-35
G302	Under RH front seat	15	50	
P400	RH rear corner of Trunk	18	66	
S402	Rear Body Harn, approx 10 cm from RH Backup Lamp breakout			
S403	Rear Body Harn, approx 5 cm from LH Backup Lamp breakout			
S405 (2 Door)	Rear Body Harn, approx 10 cm from RH Backup Lamp breakout			
S405 (4 Door)	Rear Body Harn, approx 19 cm from P400			
S406	Cross Car Harn, approx 9 cm from RH Rear Speaker breakout			

TROUBLESHOOTING HINTS (Perform before beginning System Diagnosis)

1. Check R/CMPT REL Fuse by visual inspection.
2. Check the Backup Lights for damage to the filament or corrosion between the bulb and the lamp socket.

- Check for a broken (or partially broken) wire inside of the insulation which could cause system malfunction but prove "GOOD" in a continuity/voltage check with a system disconnected. These circuits may be intermittent or resistive when loaded, and if possible, should be checked by monitoring for a voltage drop with the system operational (under load).
- Check for proper installation of aftermarket electronic equipment which may affect the integrity of other systems (see "Troubleshooting Procedures," page 8A-4-0).
- Refer to System Diagnosis.

SYSTEM DIAGNOSIS

- Perform the System Check and refer to the Symptom Table for the appropriate diagnostic procedure(s).

SYSTEM CHECK

ACTION	NORMAL RESULTS
[1] ● Set Park Brake. ● Ignition Switch to "RUN." ● Gear Selector Lever to "REVERSE."	All Backup Lights turn "ON."
[2] ● Gear Selector Lever to "PARK" or "NEUTRAL."	All Backup Lights turn "OFF."

SYMPTOM TABLE

SYMPTOM	PROCEDURE	PAGE NUMBER
All Backup Lights inoperative.	Chart #1	8A-112-2
One Backup Light inoperative.	Chart #2	8A-112-3
Backup Lights "ON" at all times.	Chart #3	8A-112-3

BACKUP LIGHTS

CHART #1
ALL BACKUP LIGHTS INOPERATIVE

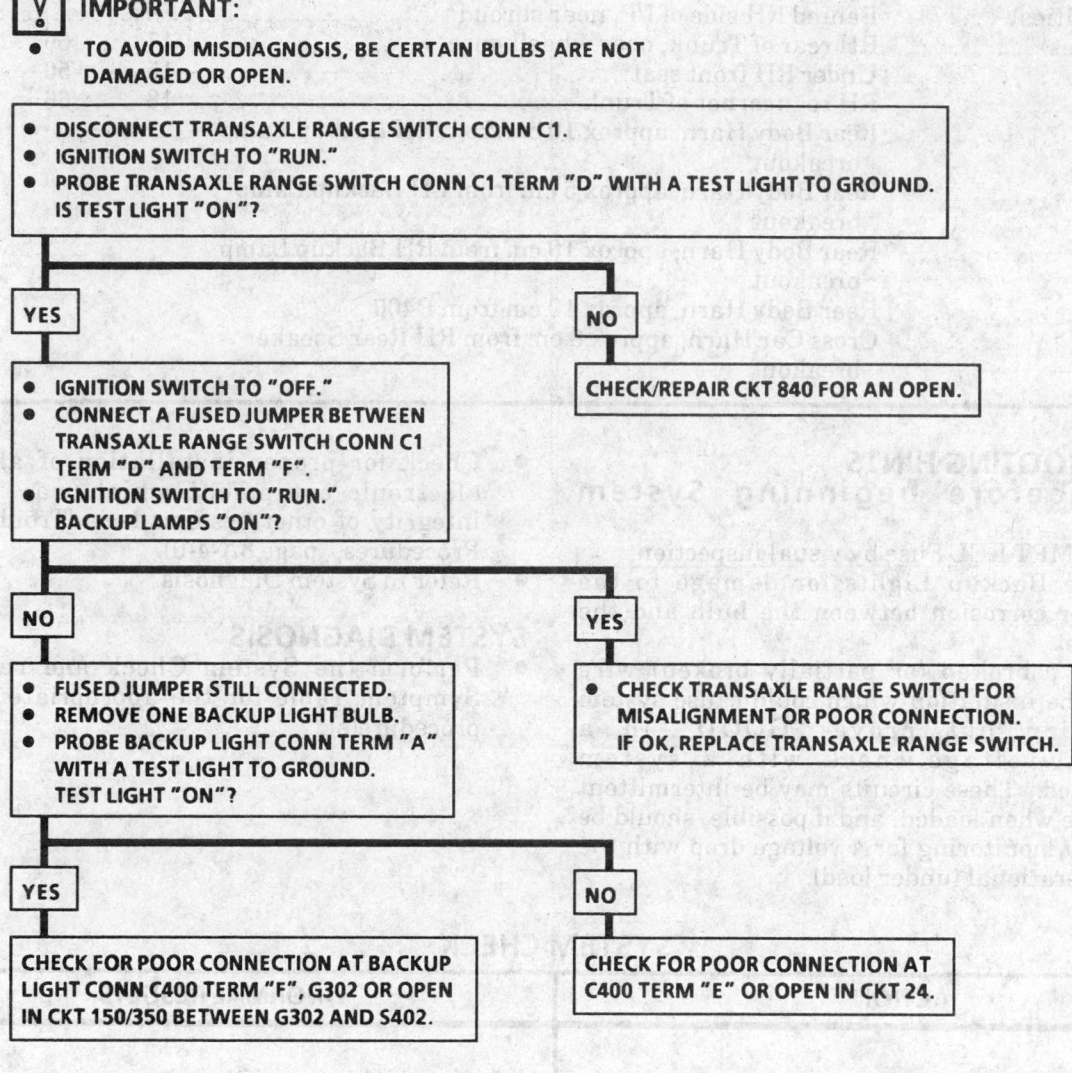

IMPORTANT:
- TO AVOID MISDIAGNOSIS, BE CERTAIN BULBS ARE NOT DAMAGED OR OPEN.

- DISCONNECT TRANSAXLE RANGE SWITCH CONN C1.
- IGNITION SWITCH TO "RUN."
- PROBE TRANSAXLE RANGE SWITCH CONN C1 TERM "D" WITH A TEST LIGHT TO GROUND.
  IS TEST LIGHT "ON"?

YES
- IGNITION SWITCH TO "OFF."
- CONNECT A FUSED JUMPER BETWEEN TRANSAXLE RANGE SWITCH CONN C1 TERM "D" AND TERM "F".
- IGNITION SWITCH TO "RUN."
  BACKUP LAMPS "ON"?

NO
CHECK/REPAIR CKT 840 FOR AN OPEN.

(Backup lamps "ON"?)

NO
- FUSED JUMPER STILL CONNECTED.
- REMOVE ONE BACKUP LIGHT BULB.
- PROBE BACKUP LIGHT CONN TERM "A" WITH A TEST LIGHT TO GROUND.
  TEST LIGHT "ON"?

YES
- CHECK TRANSAXLE RANGE SWITCH FOR MISALIGNMENT OR POOR CONNECTION.
  IF OK, REPLACE TRANSAXLE RANGE SWITCH.

(Test light "ON"?)

YES
CHECK FOR POOR CONNECTION AT BACKUP LIGHT CONN C400 TERM "F", G302 OR OPEN IN CKT 150/350 BETWEEN G302 AND S402.

NO
CHECK FOR POOR CONNECTION AT C400 TERM "E" OR OPEN IN CKT 24.

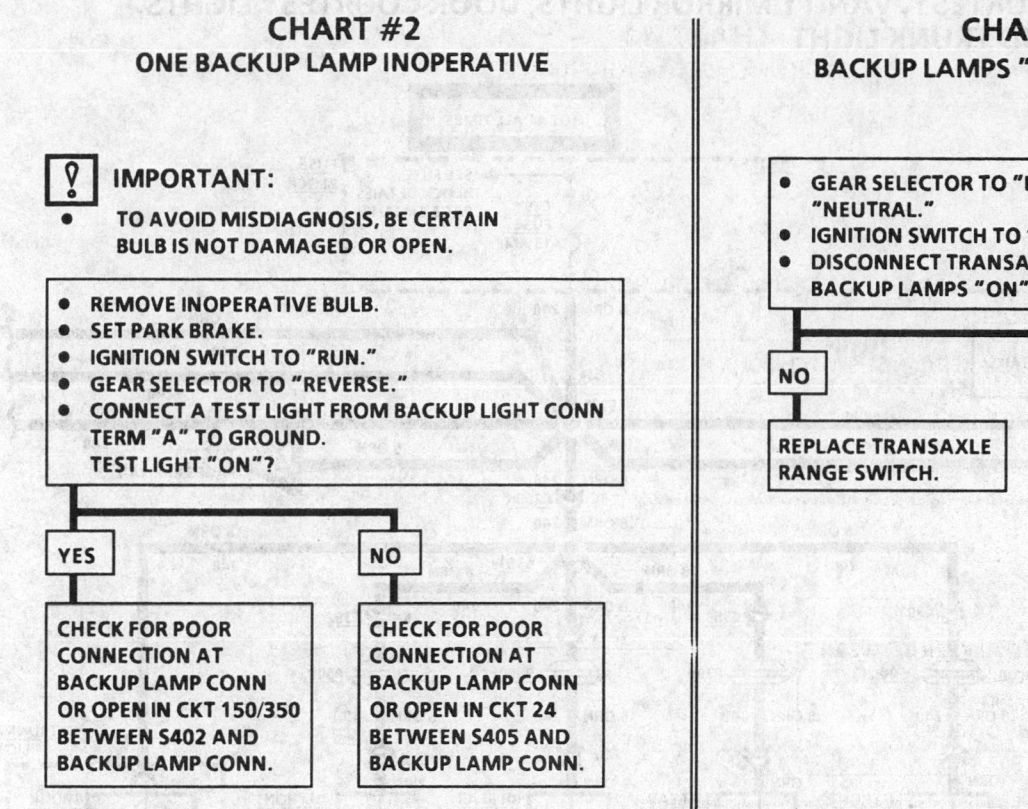

CHART #2
ONE BACKUP LAMP INOPERATIVE

IMPORTANT:
- TO AVOID MISDIAGNOSIS, BE CERTAIN BULB IS NOT DAMAGED OR OPEN.

- REMOVE INOPERATIVE BULB.
- SET PARK BRAKE.
- IGNITION SWITCH TO "RUN."
- GEAR SELECTOR TO "REVERSE."
- CONNECT A TEST LIGHT FROM BACKUP LIGHT CONN TERM "A" TO GROUND.
  TEST LIGHT "ON"?

YES: CHECK FOR POOR CONNECTION AT BACKUP LAMP CONN OR OPEN IN CKT 150/350 BETWEEN S402 AND BACKUP LAMP CONN.

NO: CHECK FOR POOR CONNECTION AT BACKUP LAMP CONN OR OPEN IN CKT 24 BETWEEN S405 AND BACKUP LAMP CONN.

CHART #3
BACKUP LAMPS "ON" AT ALL TIMES

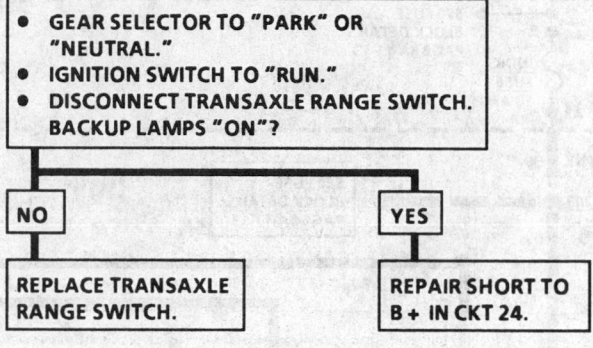

- GEAR SELECTOR TO "PARK" OR "NEUTRAL."
- IGNITION SWITCH TO "RUN."
- DISCONNECT TRANSAXLE RANGE SWITCH.
  BACKUP LAMPS "ON"?

NO: REPLACE TRANSAXLE RANGE SWITCH.

YES: REPAIR SHORT TO B + IN CKT 24.

CIRCUIT OPERATION

Voltage is applied at all times through the R/CMPT REL Fuse to the Transaxle Range Switch. Whenever the gear selector lever is shifted to "REVERSE," the Switch closes and voltage is applied to the Backup Lights.

INTERIOR LIGHTS

CIGAR LIGHTER, I/P COURTESY, VANITY MIRROR LIGHTS, DOOR COURTESY LIGHTS, I/P COMPARTMENT AND TRUNK LIGHT

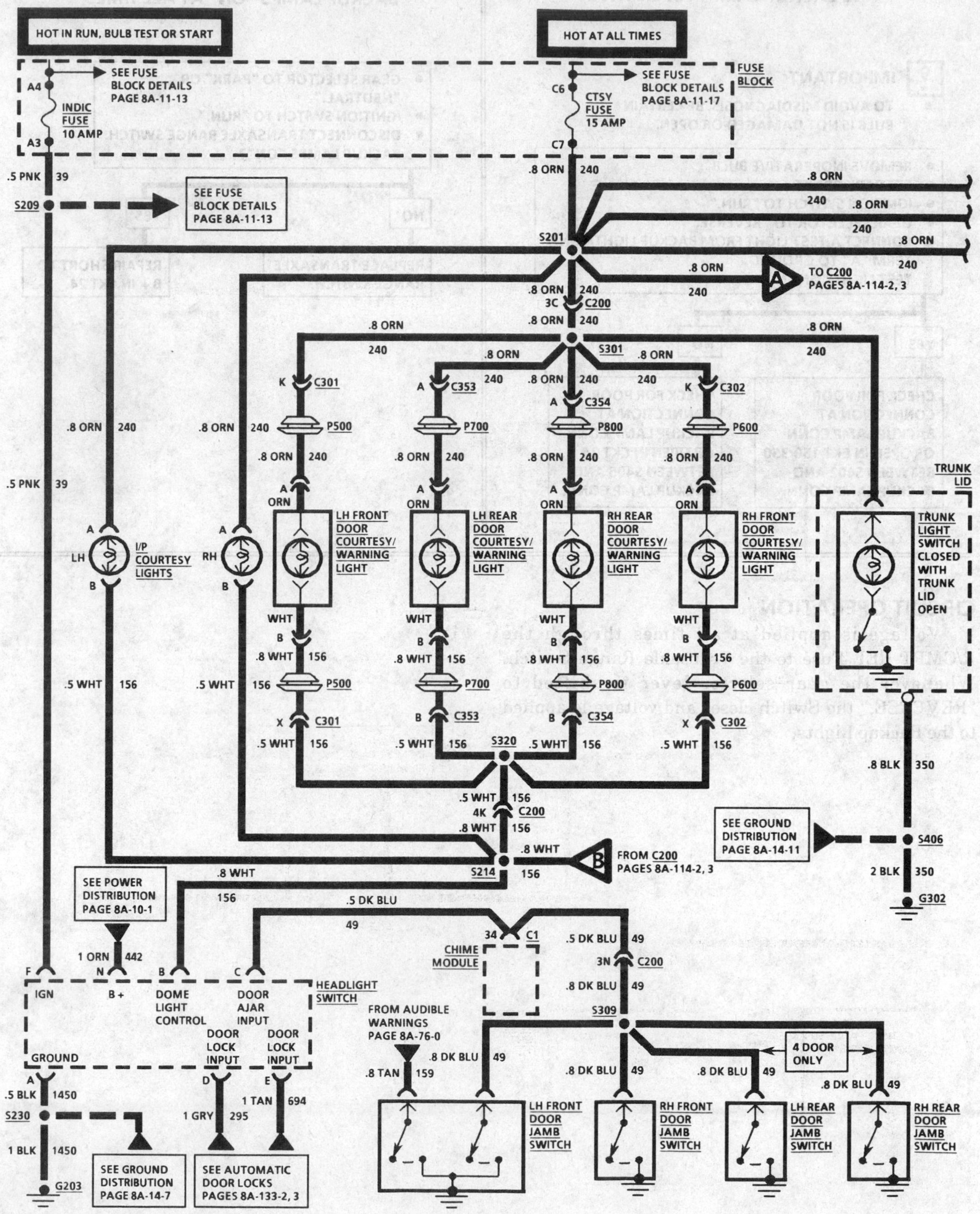

HOT IN RUN, BULB TEST OR START
HOT AT ALL TIMES
SEE FUSE BLOCK DETAILS PAGE 8A-11-13
A4
INDIC FUSE 10 AMP
A3
SEE FUSE BLOCK DETAILS PAGE 8A-11-17
C6
CTSY FUSE 15 AMP
C7
FUSE BLOCK
.5 PNK 39
S209
SEE FUSE BLOCK DETAILS PAGE 8A-11-13
.8 ORN 240
S201
TO C200 PAGES 8A-114-2, 3
3C C200
S301
K C301
A C353
A C354
K C302
P500
P700
P800
P600
ORN
LH FRONT DOOR COURTESY/ WARNING LIGHT
LH REAR DOOR COURTESY/ WARNING LIGHT
RH REAR DOOR COURTESY/ WARNING LIGHT
RH FRONT DOOR COURTESY/ WARNING LIGHT
TRUNK LID
TRUNK LIGHT SWITCH CLOSED WITH TRUNK LID OPEN
LH
RH
I/P COURTESY LIGHTS
WHT
.8 WHT 156
.5 WHT 156
X C301
B C353
B C354
X C302
S320
4K C200
.8 BLK 350
SEE GROUND DISTRIBUTION PAGE 8A-14-11
S406
2 BLK 350
G302
S214
FROM C200 PAGES 8A-114-2, 3
SEE POWER DISTRIBUTION PAGE 8A-10-1
1 ORN 442
.5 DK BLU 49
34 C1
CHIME MODULE
3N C200
S309
4 DOOR ONLY
HEADLIGHT SWITCH
IGN
B +
DOME LIGHT CONTROL
DOOR AJAR INPUT
DOOR LOCK INPUT
GROUND
FROM AUDIBLE WARNINGS PAGE 8A-76-0
.8 DK BLU 49
.8 TAN 159
.5 BLK 1450
S230
1 BLK 1450
G203
1 GRY 295
1 TAN 694
SEE GROUND DISTRIBUTION PAGE 8A-14-7
SEE AUTOMATIC DOOR LOCKS PAGES 8A-133-2, 3
LH FRONT DOOR JAMB SWITCH
RH FRONT DOOR JAMB SWITCH
LH REAR DOOR JAMB SWITCH
RH REAR DOOR JAMB SWITCH

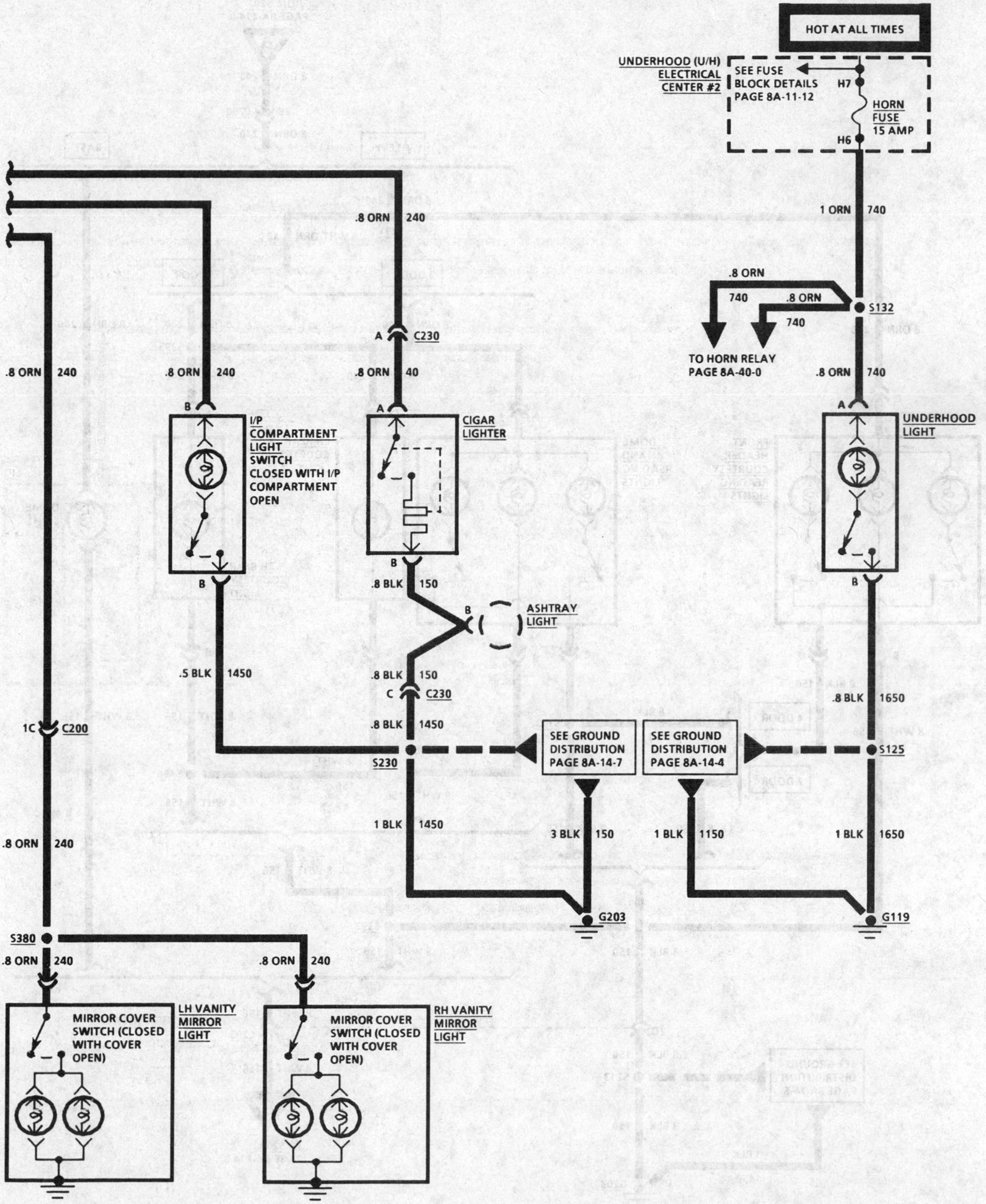

HOT AT ALL TIMES
UNDERHOOD (U/H) ELECTRICAL CENTER #2
SEE FUSE BLOCK DETAILS PAGE 8A-11-12
H7
HORN FUSE 15 AMP
H6
1 ORN 740
.8 ORN 740
.8 ORN 740
740
S132
TO HORN RELAY PAGE 8A-40-0
.8 ORN 740
A
UNDERHOOD LIGHT
B
.8 BLK 1650
S125
1 BLK 1650
G119
.8 ORN 240
A C230
.8 ORN 40
A
CIGAR LIGHTER
B
.8 BLK 150
B
ASHTRAY LIGHT
.8 BLK 150
C C230
.8 BLK 1450
S230
1 BLK 1450
SEE GROUND DISTRIBUTION PAGE 8A-14-7
SEE GROUND DISTRIBUTION PAGE 8A-14-4
3 BLK 150
1 BLK 1150
G203
.8 ORN 240
B
I/P COMPARTMENT LIGHT SWITCH CLOSED WITH I/P COMPARTMENT OPEN
B
.5 BLK 1450
.8 ORN 240
1C C200
.8 ORN 240
S380
.8 ORN 240
.8 ORN 240
MIRROR COVER SWITCH (CLOSED WITH COVER OPEN)
LH VANITY MIRROR LIGHT
MIRROR COVER SWITCH (CLOSED WITH COVER OPEN)
RH VANITY MIRROR LIGHT

INTERIOR LIGHTS
DOME/READING LIGHT, REAR COURTESY LIGHTS AND FRONT HEADER COURTESY/READING LIGHTS (WITHOUT SUNROOF)

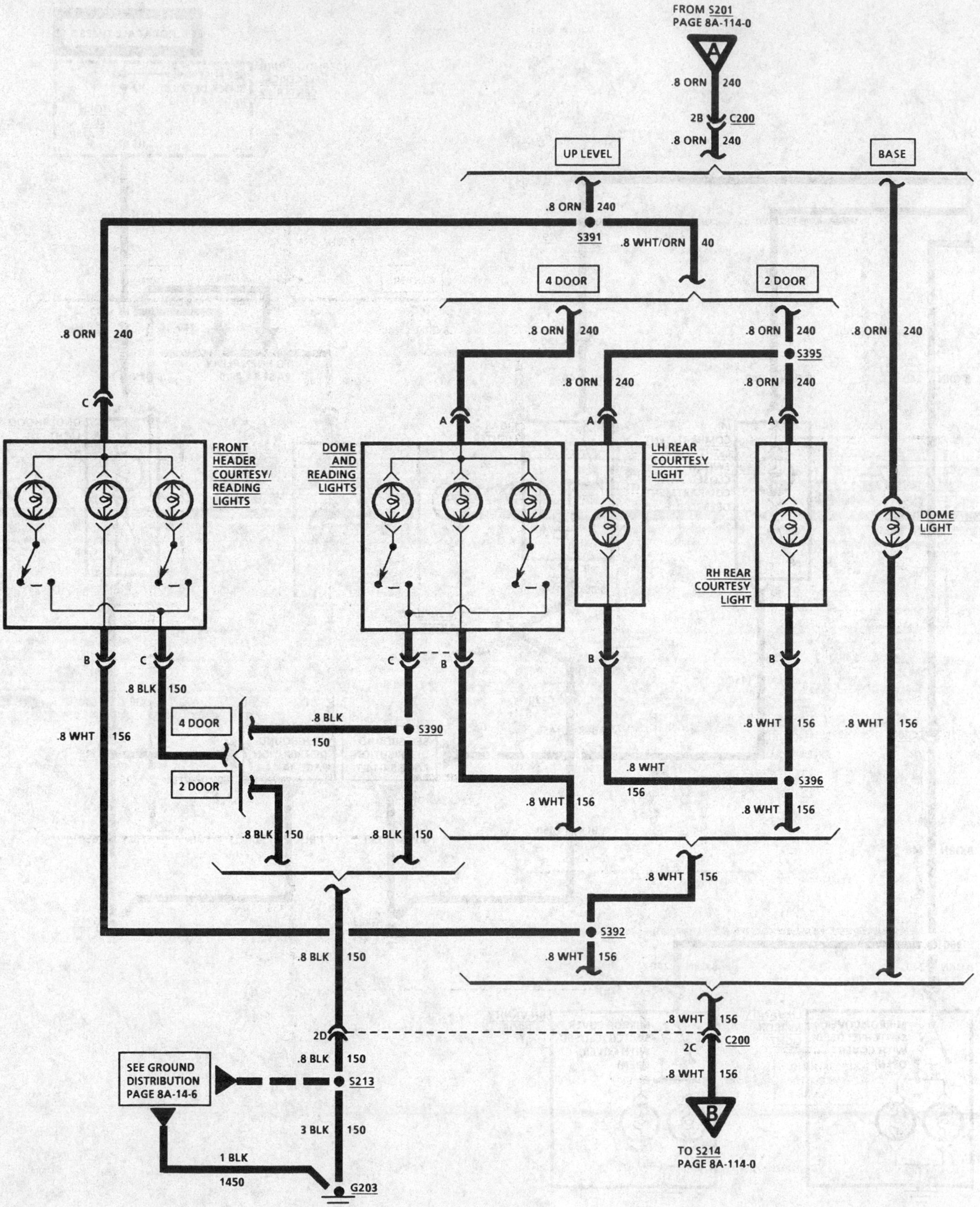

FROM S201
PAGE 8A-114-0
A
.8 ORN 240
2B C200
.8 ORN 240
UP LEVEL
BASE
.8 ORN 240
S391
.8 WHT/ORN 40
4 DOOR
2 DOOR
.8 ORN 240
S395
FRONT HEADER COURTESY/ READING LIGHTS
DOME AND READING LIGHTS
LH REAR COURTESY LIGHT
RH REAR COURTESY LIGHT
DOME LIGHT
.8 BLK 150
.8 WHT 156
4 DOOR
2 DOOR
S390
.8 WHT
S396
S392
2D
2C
C200
SEE GROUND DISTRIBUTION PAGE 8A-14-6
S213
3 BLK 150
1 BLK
1450
G203
B
TO S214
PAGE 8A-114-0

INTERIOR LIGHTS

DOME/READING LIGHT, REAR COURTESY LIGHTS AND INSIDE LIGHTED MIRROR (WITH SUNROOF)

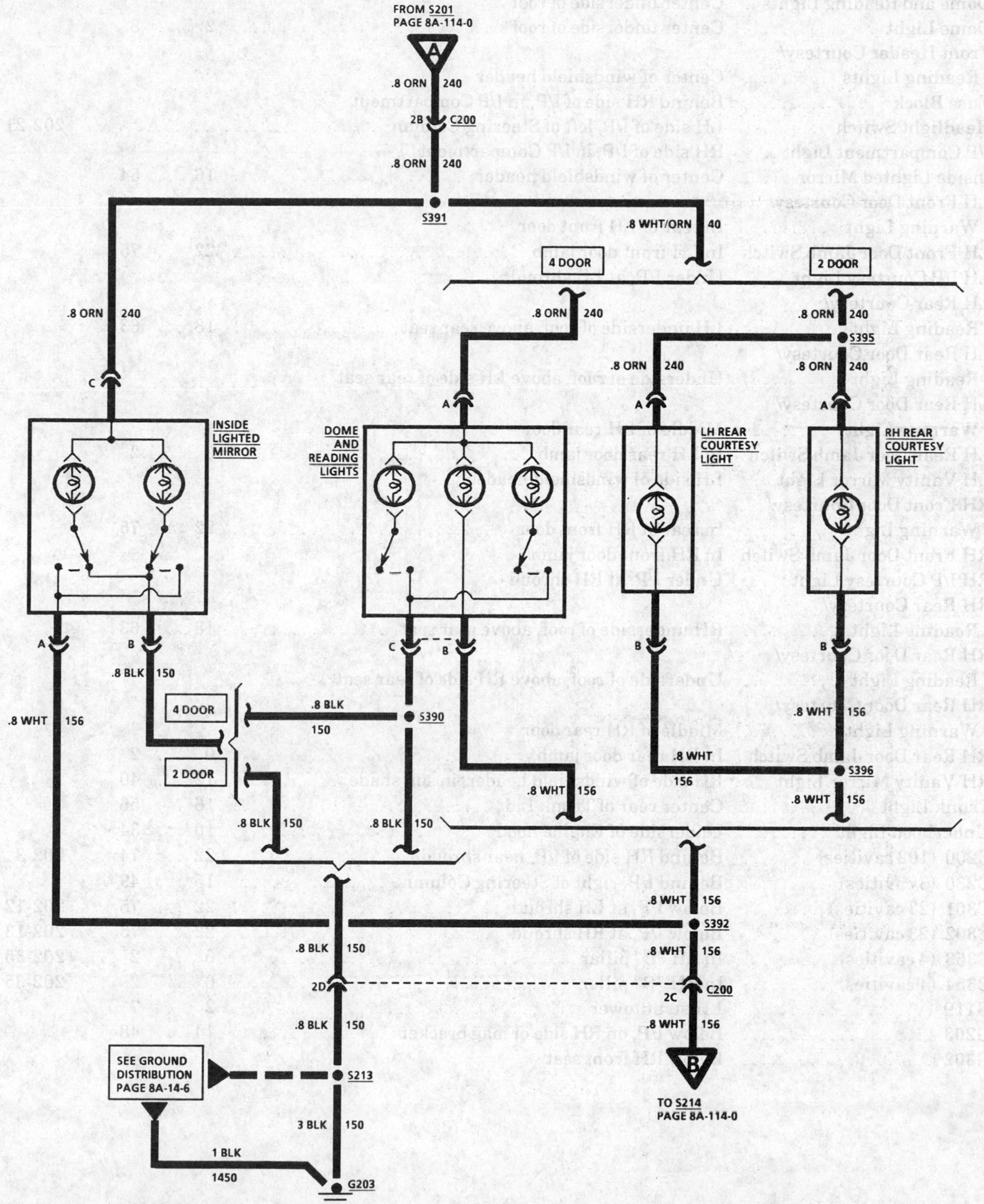
FROM S201
PAGE 8A-114-0
A
.8 ORN 240
2B C200
.8 ORN 240
S391
.8 WHT/ORN 40
4 DOOR
2 DOOR
.8 ORN 240
.8 ORN 240
.8 ORN 240
S395
.8 ORN 240
.8 ORN 240
.8 ORN 240
C
A
A
A
INSIDE
LIGHTED
MIRROR
DOME
AND
READING
LIGHTS
LH REAR
COURTESY
LIGHT
RH REAR
COURTESY
LIGHT
A
B
C
B
B
B
.8 BLK 150
4 DOOR
.8 BLK
150
S390
.8 WHT 156
2 DOOR
.8 WHT 156
.8 WHT
156
S396
.8 WHT 156
.8 WHT 156
.8 BLK 150
.8 BLK 150
.8 WHT 156
S392
.8 BLK 150
.8 WHT 156
2D
2C C200
.8 BLK 150
.8 WHT 156
SEE GROUND
DISTRIBUTION
PAGE 8A-14-6
S213
B
TO S214
PAGE 8A-114-0
3 BLK 150
1 BLK
1450
G203

INTERIOR LIGHTS

COMPONENT	LOCATION	201-PG	FIG.	CONN
Chime Module	Component Center			
Dome and Reading Lights	Center underside of roof			
Dome Light	Center underside of roof	2	8	
Front Header Courtesy/ Reading Lights	Center of windshield header			
Fuse Block	Behind RH side of I/P, in I/P Compartment			
Headlight Switch	LH side of I/P, left of Steering Column			202-21
I/P Compartment Light	RH side of I/P, in I/P Compartment			
Inside Lighted Mirror	Center of windshield header	16	54	
LH Front Door Courtesy/ Warning Light	In rear of LH front door			
LH Front Door Jamb Switch	In LH front door jamb	22	75	
LH I/P Courtesy Light	Under I/P, at LH shroud			
LH Rear Courtesy/ Reading Light	LH underside of roof, above rear seat	18	63	
LH Rear Door Courtesy/ Reading Light	Underside of roof, above LH side of rear seat			
LH Rear Door Courtesy/ Warning Light	Middle of LH rear door			
LH Rear Door Jamb Switch	In LH rear door jamb	0	2	
LH Vanity Mirror Light	LH side of windshield header			
RH Front Door Courtesy/ Warning Light	In rear of RH front door	22	75	
RH Front Door Jamb Switch	In RH front door jamb			
RH I/P Courtesy Light	Under I/P, at RH shroud			
RH Rear Courtesy/ Reading Light	RH underside of roof, above rear seat	18	63	
RH Rear Door Courtesy/ Reading Light	Underside of roof, above RH side of rear seat			
RH Rear Door Courtesy/ Warning Light	Middle of RH rear door			
RH Rear Door Jamb Switch	In RH rear door jamb	0	2	
RH Vanity Mirror Light	RH side of windshield header, in sun shade	12	40	
Trunk Light	Center rear of Trunk Lid	16	56	
Underhood Light	Underside of Engine hood	10	34	
C200 (102 cavities)	Behind RH side of I/P, near shroud	22	74	202-3
C230 (3 cavities)	Behind I/P, right of Steering Column	15	49	
C301 (23 cavities)	Below I/P, at LH shroud	22	75	202-12
C302 (23 cavities)	Below I/P, at RH shroud	22	75	202-13
C353 (4 cavities)	In LH "B" pillar	0	2	202-35
C354 (4 cavities)	In RH "B" pillar	0	2	202-35
G119	LH strut tower	2	7	
G203	Below I/P, on RH side of mag bracket	14	48	
G302	Below RH front seat			

COMPONENT	LOCATION	201-PG	FIG.	CONN
P500	In LH front door jamb	6	20	
P600	In RH front door jamb	6	20	
P700	In LH rear door jamb	17	57	
P800	In RH rear door jamb	17	57	
S125	Wiper Harn, approx 4 cm from ABS Actuator Motor			
S132	Wiper Harn, approx 10 cm from Washer Pump breakout			
S201	I/P Harn, approx 3 cm from RH Front Speaker breakout			
S209	I/P Harn, approx 15 cm from Fuse Block breakout			
S214	I/P Harn, approx 10 cm from RH Front Speaker breakout			
S230	I/P Harn, approx 27 cm from Radio Control Head breakout			
S301	Cross Car Harn, approx 18 cm from G302 breakout			
S309	Cross Car Harn, approx 13 cm from Driver Seat Belt Switch breakout			
S320	Cross Car Harn, approx 34 cm from G302 breakout			
S375	Console Harn, approx 5 cm from Accessory Power Outlet breakout			
S380	Vanity Mirror Harn, approx 4 cm from Vanity Mirror breakout			
S390 (with Sunroof)	Roof Harn, approx 4 cm from RH Rear Courtesy/ Reading Light breakout			
S390 (without Sunroof)	Roof Harn, approx 17 cm from Dome Light breakout			
S391 (with Sunroof)	Roof Harn, approx 22 cm from C200			
S391 (without Sunroof)	Roof Harn, approx 4 cm from Dome Light breakout			
S392 (with Sunroof)	Roof Harn, approx 26 cm from C200			
S392 (without Sunroof)	Roof Harn, approx 10 cm from Dome Light breakout			
S395	Roof Harn, approx 12 cm from RH Rear Courtesy/ Reading Light breakout			
S396	Roof Harn, approx 8 cm from RH Rear Courtesy/ Reading Light breakout			
S406	Cross Car Harn, approx 9 cm from RH Rear Speaker breakout			

TROUBLESHOOTING HINTS (Perform before beginning System Diagnosis)

1. Check CTSY Fuse. If CTSY Fuse is open, check for a short to ground in CKT 240.
2. Check that grounds, G119, G203, G302 are clean and tight.

- Check for a broken (or partially broken) wire inside of the insulation which could cause system malfunction but prove "GOOD" in a continuity/voltage check with a system disconnected. These circuits may be intermittent or resistive when loaded, and if possible, should be checked by monitoring for a voltage drop with the system operational (under load).
- Check for proper installation of aftermarket electronic equipment which may affect the integrity of other systems (see "Troubleshooting Procedures," page 8A-4-0).
- Refer to System Diagnosis.

SYSTEM DIAGNOSIS

- Do the test listed, or make the necessary repairs, for your symptom in the Symptom Table.

INTERIOR LIGHTS

SYMPTOM TABLE

SYMPTOM	FOR DIAGNOSIS
All Courtesy Lamps are inoperative with Door Jamb Switches and Headlight Switch.	Check CKT 240 (between Fuse Block and S201) for an open. Check CKT 156 (between Headlight Switch and S214) for an open. If OK, replace Headlight Switch.
All Courtesy Lamps are inoperative with one or more Door Jamb Switches.	Check CKT 49 (between S309 and Door Jamb Switches) for an open. Also check the Door Jamb Switch for a clean and tight ground connection. If OK, replace defective Door Jamb Switch.
All Courtesy Lamps are inoperative with Headlight Switch only.	Replace Headlight Switch.
Sustained illumination is not defeated by Ignition "ON."	Check CKT 39 for open between Headlight Switch and S209. If OK, replace Headlight Switch.
Any or all of the Courtesy Lamps are on at all times.	Perform Light Short Test on page 8A-114-7.
One or both I/P Courtesy Lamps are inoperative.	Check bulb(s), CKT 240 (between S201 and Lamps) and CKT 156 (between Lamps and S214) for an open.
Some or all Door Courtesy/Warning Lights are inoperative.	Check bulb(s), CKT 240 [between S201 and Light(s)] and CKT 156 (between Light and S320) for an open. If OK, replace Door Courtesy/Warning Light(s).
One or both Rear Courtesy/Reading Lamps are inoperative with Lamp Switches.	Check CKT 150 (between Lamps and S390) for an open. If OK, replace Rear Courtesy/Reading Lamp(s).
Inside Lighted Mirror Lamps, Front Header Courtesy/Reading Lights or Dome/Reading Lights are inoperative with Door Jamb Switches or Headlight Switch.	Check bulbs, CKT 240 (between S201 and Lamps) and CKT 156 (between Lamps and S214) for an open. If OK, replace inoperative component.
Inside Lighted Mirror Lamps, Front Header Courtesy/Reading Lights or Dome/Reading Lights are inoperative with Lamp Switches.	Check CKT 150 (between Lamps and S213) for an open. If OK, replace inoperative component.
Underhood Light is inoperative.	Check bulb, CKT 740 (between S132 and Light) and CKT 1650 (between Light and S125) for an open. If OK, replace Underhood Light.
One or both Vanity Mirror Lights are inoperative.	Check bulbs and CKT 240 (between S201 and Lamps) for an open. Also check Vanity Mirrors for a clean and tight ground connection. If OK, replace Vanity Mirror(s).
I/P Compartment Light is inoperative.	Check bulb, CKT 240 (between S201 and Light) and CKT 150 (between Light and S213) for an open. If OK, replace I/P Compartment Light.
Cigar Lighter is inoperative.	Check for corrosion or heating element damage. Also check CKT 240 (between S201 and Lighter) and CKT 150/1450 (between Lighter and S230) for an open. If OK, replace Cigar Lighter.

LIGHT SHORT TEST

With all the doors closed and the Headlight Switch turned off, disconnect the Door Jamb Switches and the Headlight Switch one at a time.

- If the lights go out when a particular switch is disconnected, replace that switch.
- If the lights remain lit with all switches disconnected, repair short to ground in CKT 156.

CIRCUIT OPERATION

DOOR COURTESY/WARNING, INSIDE LIGHTED MIRROR, I/P COURTESY, REAR COURTESY/READING AND DOME LAMPS

Voltage is applied through the CTSY Fuse at all times to the Door Courtesy/Warning Lights, Inside Lighted Mirror Lamps, I/P Courtesy Lamps, Rear Courtesy/Reading Lamps and to the Dome Lamps. The Door Courtesy/Warning Lighted Mirror, I/P Courtesy, Rear Courtesy/Reading Lamps and the Dome Lamps will light whenever a door is opened or whenever the Headlight Switch is turned to "CTSY". The Inside Lighted Mirror Lamps and the Rear Courtesy/Reading Lamps also have a separate switch in the circuit. When turned to "ON," this switch allows for individual operation of these Lamps.

The Headlight Switch controls the sustained illumination feature for the Courtesy Lights. After all the doors are closed, the Headlight Switch will keep the Courtesy Lights on for approximately sixteen seconds, gradually dimming the lights until they are off. Energizing the Power Door "UNLOCK," with either the key fob or the Door Lock Switch, will also trigger the sustained illumination feature. If the Ignition Switch is turned "ON," the sustained illumination will be defeated, overriding the Power Door "UNLOCK" input. The Remote Door "LOCK" input from the Keyless Entry Receiver will also defeat the sustained illumination feature.

LH AND RH VANITY MIRROR

Voltage is applied through the CTSY Fuse at all times to the LH and RH Vanity Mirror Lamps. The LH and RH Vanity Mirror Lamps will light whenever the Visor is pulled down and the cover is opened.

CIGAR LIGHTER AND I/P COMPARTMENT LAMP

Voltage is applied through the CTSY Fuse at all times to the Cigar Lighter and I/P Compartment Lamp. The Cigar Lighter has a heating element that, when pushed in, completes the circuit and begins to heat. When the element is sufficiently heated, the Cigar Lighter opens the circuit. The I/P Compartment Lamp will light whenever the I/P Compartment is opened.

UNDERHOOD LIGHT

Voltage is applied through the HORN Fuse at all times to the Underhood Light. The Underhood Light uses a Mercury Switch that closes when the hood is opened.

INTERIOR LIGHTS DIMMING

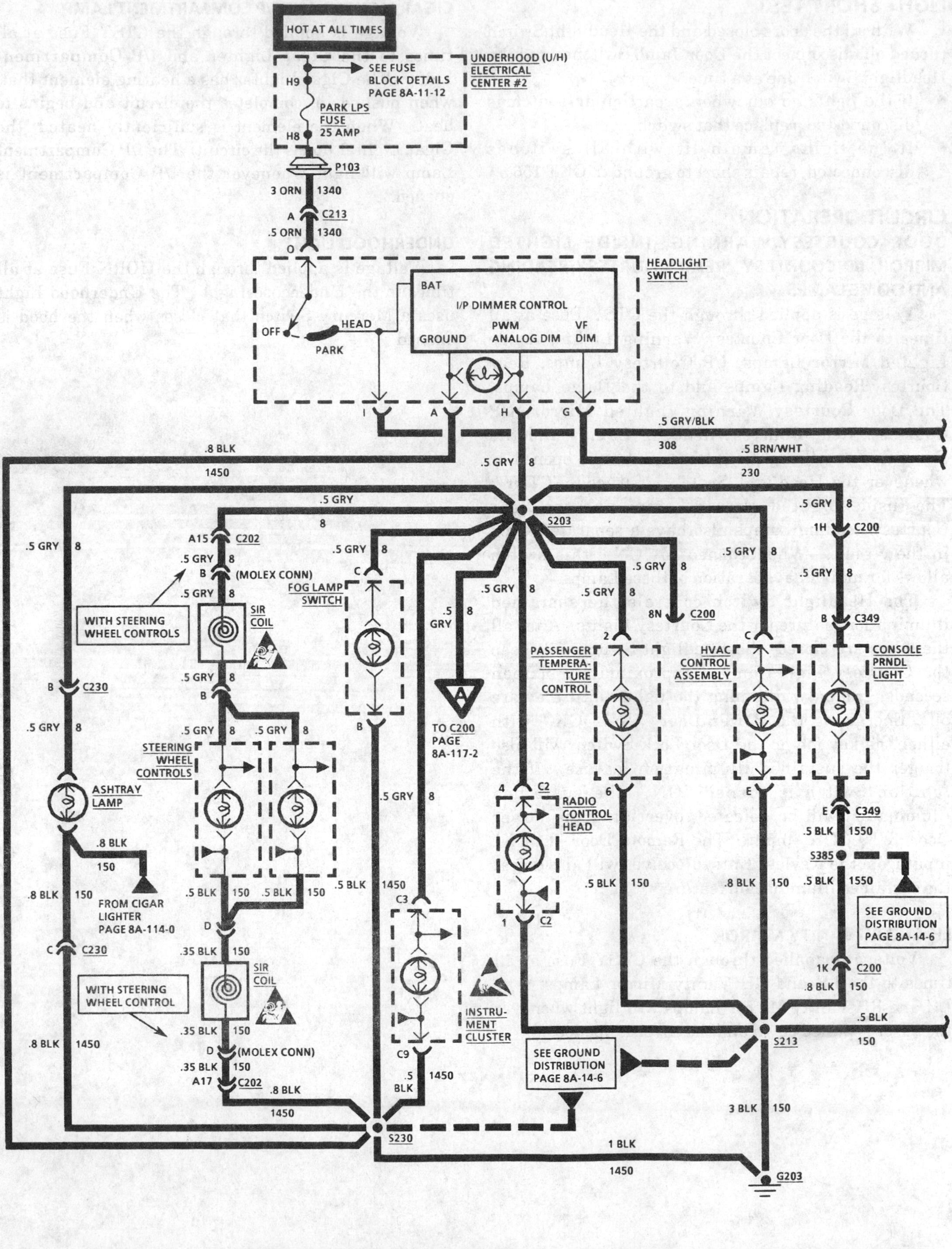
HOT AT ALL TIMES
UNDERHOOD (U/H) ELECTRICAL CENTER #2
SEE FUSE BLOCK DETAILS PAGE 8A-11-12
H9
PARK LPS FUSE 25 AMP
H8
P103
3 ORN 1340
A C213
.5 ORN 1340
O
HEADLIGHT SWITCH
BAT
I/P DIMMER CONTROL
OFF
HEAD
PARK
GROUND
PWM ANALOG DIM
VF DIM
I A H G
.5 GRY/BLK
308
.5 BRN/WHT
230
.8 BLK
1450
.5 GRY 8
.5 GRY
8
S203
.5 GRY 8
1H C200
A15 C202
.5 GRY 8
B (MOLEX CONN)
.5 GRY 8
SIR COIL
WITH STEERING WHEEL CONTROLS
.5 GRY 8
C
FOG LAMP SWITCH
.5 GRY 8
.5 8 GRY
.5 GRY 8
.5 GRY 8
8N C200
.5 GRY 8
.5 GRY 8
B C349
B C230
.5 GRY 8
B
.5 GRY 8
.5 GRY 8
STEERING WHEEL CONTROLS
A
TO C200 PAGE 8A-117-2
B
2
PASSENGER TEMPERATURE CONTROL
C
HVAC CONTROL ASSEMBLY
CONSOLE PRNDL LIGHT
ASHTRAY LAMP
.5 GRY 8
4 C2
RADIO CONTROL HEAD
6
E
E C349
.5 BLK 1550
S385
.5 BLK 1550
.8 BLK
150
FROM CIGAR LIGHTER PAGE 8A-114-0
.8 BLK 150
.5 BLK 150
.5 BLK 150
.5 BLK 1450
C3
1 C2
.5 BLK 150
.8 BLK 150
SEE GROUND DISTRIBUTION PAGE 8A-14-6
D
C C230
.35 BLK 150
SIR COIL
WITH STEERING WHEEL CONTROL
INSTRUMENT CLUSTER
1K C200
.8 BLK 150
.5 BLK
150
.35 BLK 150
.8 BLK 1450
D (MOLEX CONN)
.35 BLK 150
A17 C202
C9
.5 BLK 1450
.8 BLK
1450
SEE GROUND DISTRIBUTION PAGE 8A-14-6
S213
3 BLK 150
S230
1 BLK
1450
G203

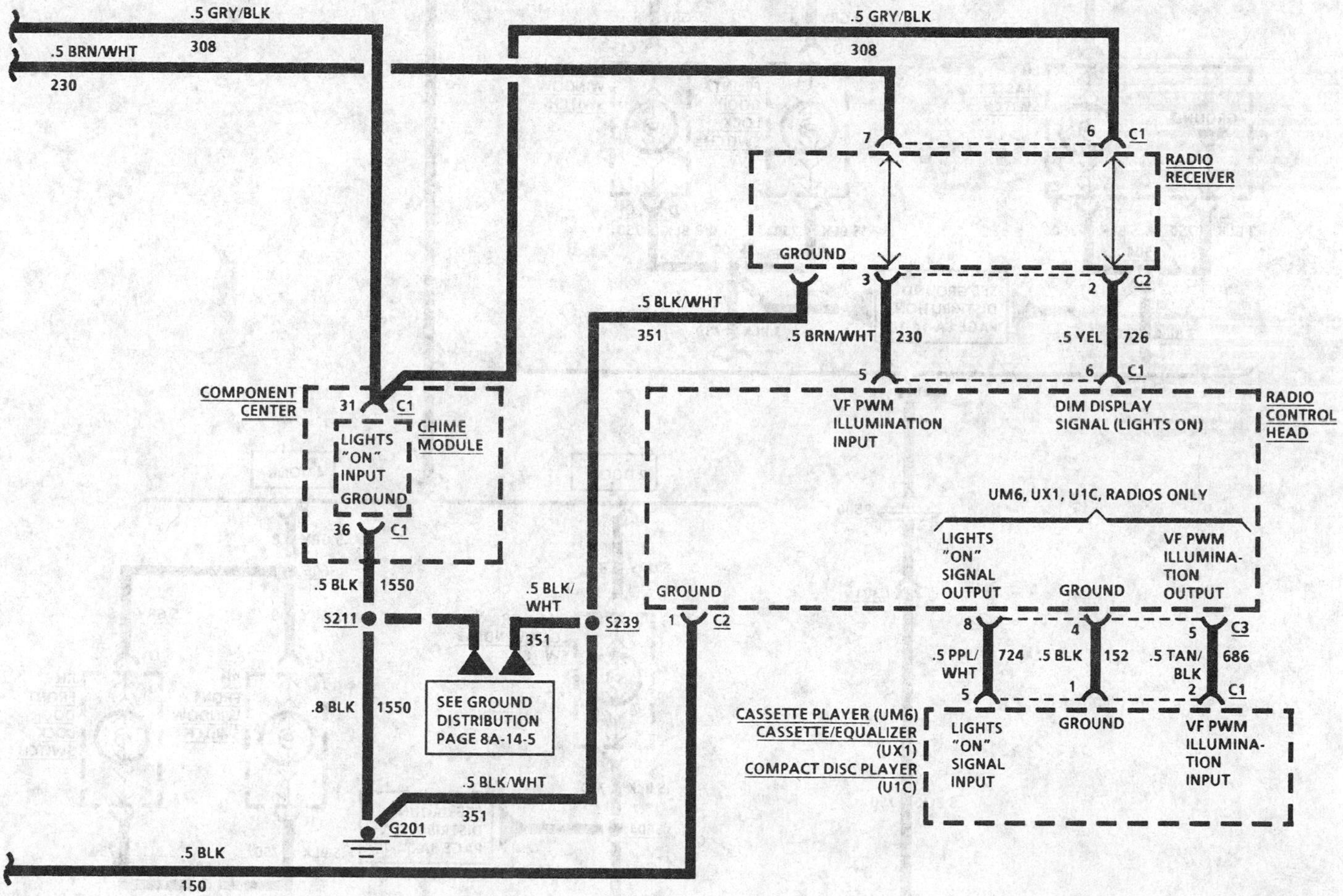
.5 GRY/BLK
308
.5 BRN/WHT
230
.5 GRY/BLK
308
7
6
C1
RADIO
RECEIVER
GROUND
3
2
C2
.5 BLK/WHT
351
.5 BRN/WHT
230
.5 YEL
726
5
6
C1
RADIO
CONTROL
HEAD
COMPONENT
CENTER
31
C1
CHIME
MODULE
LIGHTS
"ON"
INPUT
GROUND
36
C1
VF PWM
ILLUMINATION
INPUT
DIM DISPLAY
SIGNAL (LIGHTS ON)
UM6, UX1, U1C, RADIOS ONLY
LIGHTS
"ON"
SIGNAL
OUTPUT
GROUND
VF PWM
ILLUMINA-
TION
OUTPUT
.5 BLK
1550
.5 BLK/
WHT
GROUND
S211
351
S239
1
C2
8
4
5
C3
.5 PPL/
WHT
724
.5 BLK
152
.5 TAN/
BLK
686
5
1
2
C1
SEE GROUND
DISTRIBUTION
PAGE 8A-14-5
.8 BLK
1550
CASSETTE PLAYER (UM6)
CASSETTE/EQUALIZER
(UX1)
COMPACT DISC PLAYER
(U1C)
LIGHTS
"ON"
SIGNAL
INPUT
GROUND
VF PWM
ILLUMINA-
TION
INPUT
.5 BLK/WHT
351
G201
.5 BLK
150

SEE PAGE 8A-3-0
FOR PROPER
HANDLING
PROCEDURES

SEE PAGE 8A-3-0
FOR MEASURING
AND HANDLING
PROCEDURES

INTERIOR LIGHTS DIMMING

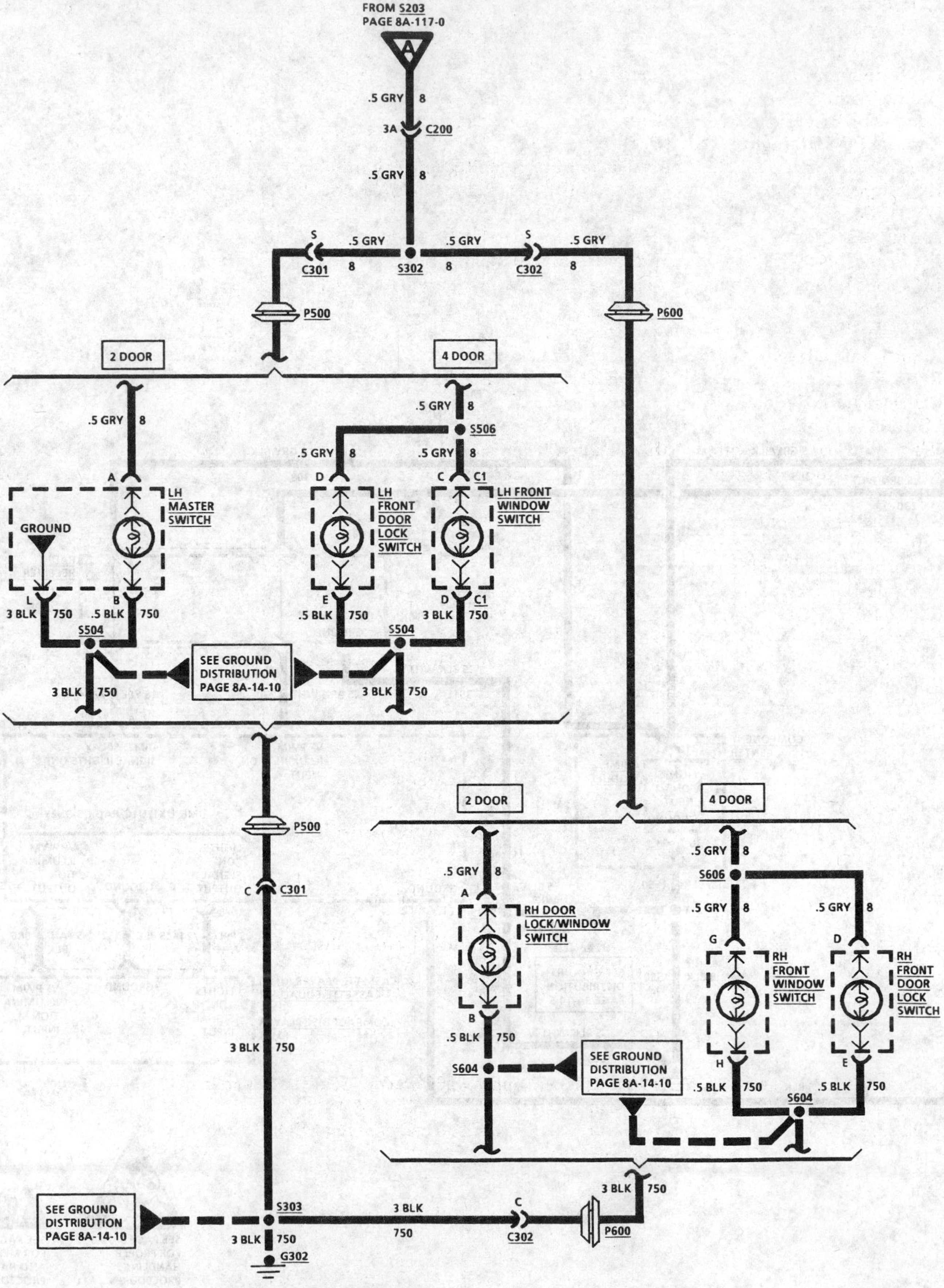

FROM S203
PAGE 8A-117-0
A
.5 GRY 8
3A C200
.5 GRY 8
S C301
.5 GRY 8
S302
.5 GRY 8
S C302
.5 GRY 8
P500
P600
2 DOOR
4 DOOR
.5 GRY 8
S506
A
LH MASTER SWITCH
GROUND
L
B
3 BLK 750
.5 BLK 750
S504
D
C C1
LH FRONT DOOR LOCK SWITCH
LH FRONT WINDOW SWITCH
E
D C1
.5 BLK 750
3 BLK 750
SEE GROUND DISTRIBUTION PAGE 8A-14-10
3 BLK 750
P500
C C301
3 BLK 750
2 DOOR
4 DOOR
.5 GRY 8
A
RH DOOR LOCK/WINDOW SWITCH
B
.5 BLK 750
S604
SEE GROUND DISTRIBUTION PAGE 8A-14-10
S606
G
D
RH FRONT WINDOW SWITCH
RH FRONT DOOR LOCK SWITCH
H
E
.5 BLK 750
S604
3 BLK 750
SEE GROUND DISTRIBUTION PAGE 8A-14-10
S303
3 BLK 750
C C302
P600
3 BLK 750
G302

COMPONENT	LOCATION	201-PG	FIG.	CONN
Ashtray Light	Center of I/P, in ashtray			
Cassette Player	Center of I/P	26	84	202-37
Cassette/Equalizer	Center of I/P	26	84	202-37
Chime Module	Component Center			
Compact Disc Player	Center of I/P	26	84	202-37
Console PRNDL Light	In center console			
Fog Lamp Switch	LH side of I/P, left of Steering Column			
Headlight Switch	LH side of I/P, left of Steering Column			202-21
HVAC Control Assembly	Center of I/P	15	49	202-22
Instrument Cluster	LH side of I/P	16	52	
LH Front Door Lock Switch	Middle of LH front door			202-39
LH Front Window Switch	Middle of LH front door panel			202-23, 39
Passenger Temperature Control	Center of I/P			202-40
Radio Control Head	Center of I/P	26	84	202-40
Radio Receiver	Behind RH side of I/P			202-32
RH Door Lock/Window Switch (2 Door)	Middle of RH door			202-24
RH Front Door Lock Switch	Middle of RH front door			202-38
RH Front Window Switch	Middle of RH front door			202-39
SIR Coil	In Steering Column, behind Steering Wheel			
Steering Wheel Control Head	Center of Steering Wheel			
Underhood Electrical Center #2	LH side of Engine Compartment, forward of strut tower			
C200 (102 cavities)	Behind RH side of I/P, near shroud	22	24	202-3
C202 (48 cavities)	Behind I/P, RH side of Steering Column	14	48	202-9
C213 (4 cavities)	Behind I/P, on RH side of brake pedal support			202-35
C349 (6 cavities)	Below center console			202-35
C301 (23 cavities)	Below I/P, at LH shroud	6	20	202-12
C302 (23 cavities)	Below I/P, at LH shroud	6	20	202-13
G201	Behind I/P, on RH side of Mag bracket	14	48	
G203	Behind I/P, on RH side of Mag bracket	14	48	
G302	Under LH front seat			
P103	RH rear of Engine Compartment, in bulkhead	2	7	
P500	In LH front door jamb	6	20	
P600	In RH front door jamb	6	20	
S203	I/P Harn, approx 4 cm from HVAC Control Assembly breakout			
S213	I/P Harn, approx 8 cm from HVAC Control Assembly breakout			
S230	I/P Harn, approx 27 cm from Radio Control Head breakout			
S239	I/P Harn, approx 8 cm from HVAC Control Assembly breakout			
S302	Cross Car Harn, approx 26 cm from Seat Belt Switch breakout			
S303	Cross Car Harn, approx 38 cm from Seat Belt Switch breakout			
S385	Console Harn, approx 4 cm from Ashtray Lamp breakout			

INTERIOR LIGHTS DIMMING

(CONTINUED FROM PREVIOUS PAGE)

COMPONENT	LOCATION	201-PG	FIG.	CONN
S504	LH Front Door Harn, approx 4 cm from LH Front Door Lock Switch breakout			
S604	RH Front Door Harn, approx 4 cm from LH Front Door Lock Switch breakout			
S506	LH Front Door Harn, approx 2 cm from LH Front Door Speaker breakout			
S606	RH Front Door Harn, approx 2 cm from RH Front Door Speaker breakout			

TROUBLESHOOTING HINTS (Perform before beginning System Diagnosis)

1. Make sure Park Lights turn "ON" and "OFF" normally before proceeding with diagnostic, refer to "Exterior Lights," page 8A-110-0 for Park Lamp diagnosis.
2. If none of the Interior Lights illuminate, check PARK LPS Fuse.
3. If Interior Lights stay "ON" all the time, but Park Lights operate normally, repair short to B+ in CKT 8.
4. If one Interior Lamp does not operate, check the GRY and BLK wires to suspect Interior Lamp for opens, bent terminals, etc. If OK, replace Interior Lamp bulb (see schematic).

- Check for a broken (or partially broken) wire inside of the insulation which could cause system malfunction but prove "GOOD" in a continuity/voltage check with a system disconnected. These circuits may be intermittent or resistive when loaded, and if possible, should be checked by monitoring for a voltage drop with the system operational (under load).
- Check for proper installation of aftermarket electronic equipment which may affect the integrity of other systems (see "Troubleshooting Procedures," page 8A-4-0).
- Refer to System Diagnosis.

SYSTEM DIAGNOSIS

- Refer to the Symptom Table for the appropriate diagnostic procedure(s).

SYMPTOM TABLE

SYMPTOM	PROCEDURE	PAGE NUMBER
None of the Interior Lights will illuminate.	Chart #1	8A-117-5
Interior Lights Dimmer Switch will not change the brightness of the Interior Lights.	Check for short to voltage on CKT 8. If OK, replace Headlight Switch.	
Brightness of Interior Lights changes erratically when Dimmer Switch is turned.	Check for poor connections at Headlight Switch.	
Instrument Cluster and/or Radio do not dim with the Park Lights "ON."	Check for an open in CKT 230. If OK, refer to "Electronic Instrument Cluster," page 8A-80-0 and/or "Radio," page 8A-150-0.	
Dimming override of the Park Lights "ON" input is inoperative.	Chart #2	8A-117-5
Radio (and/or Cluster) display does not dim with Park Lights "ON" and dome Light Switch "OFF."	Chart #3	8A-117-6

(CONTINUED ON NEXT PAGE)

(CONTINUED FROM PREVIOUS PAGE)

SYMPTOM TABLE

SYMPTOM	PROCEDURE	PAGE NUMBER
Radio (and/or Cluster) display does not change to High Brightness when Park Lights are turned "OFF."	Chart #4	8A-117-6
Radio (and/or Cluster) display does not dim with adjustment of the I/P Dimmer Switch and Park Lights "OFF."	Check CKT 230 for a poor connection or an open (see schematic). If OK, replace Headlight Switch.	
Delayed Illumination feature is inoperative.	Refer to "Interior Lights," page 8A-114-0 for CKT 156 diagnosis.	

CHART #1

NONE OF THE INTERIOR LIGHTS WILL ILLUMINATE

- HEADLIGHT SWITCH IN "PARK."
- BACKPROBE WITH A TEST LIGHT AT THE HEADLIGHT SWITCH BETWEEN CONN TERM "G" AND GROUND. TEST LIGHT "ON"?

YES

- INTERIOR LIGHTS DIMMER SWITCH TO "MAX."
- BACKPROBE HEADLIGHT SWITCH BETWEEN CONN TERM "H" AND GROUND. TEST LIGHT "ON"?

  YES

  - CHECK FOR POOR CONNECTION AT HEADLIGHT SWITCH CONNECTOR. IF OK, REPAIR OPEN IN CKT 8 BETWEEN S203 AND HEADLIGHT SWITCH CONN TERM "H".

  NO

  - CHECK FOR POOR CONNECTION AT HEADLIGHT SWITCH CONNECTOR. IF OK, REPLACE HEADLIGHT SWITCH.

NO

- CHECK PARK LPS FUSE FOR OPEN.
- CHECK FOR OPEN IN CKT 1340 BETWEEN PARK LPS FUSE AND HEADLIGHT SWITCH.

CHART #2

DIMMING OVERRIDE OF PARK LIGHTS "ON" INPUT IS INOPERATIVE

- LIGHT SWITCH IN "PARK."
- DIMMER SWITCH IN "OFF," "LO" OR "HI."
- BACKPROBE LIGHT SWITCH WITH A TEST LIGHT BETWEEN TERM "I" AND GROUND. IS TEST LIGHT "ON"?

YES

- DIMMER SWITCH IN "PARADE" OR "DOME."
- TEST LIGHT CONNECTED AS ABOVE. IS TEST LIGHT "ON"?

  YES

  - CHECK FOR A SHORT TO B + ON CKT 308. IF OK, REPLACE THE LIGHT SWITCH.

  NO

  - CHECK FOR OPEN IN CKT 726 BETWEEN THE LIGHT SWITCH AND S224.
  - IF OK, REFER TO "INSTRUMENT CLUSTER," PAGE 8A-81-0 AND/OR "RADIO," PAGE 8A-150-0.

NO

- CHECK FOR A POOR CONNECTION AT THE LIGHT SWITCH. IF OK, REPLACE THE LIGHT SWITCH.

INTERIOR LIGHTS DIMMING

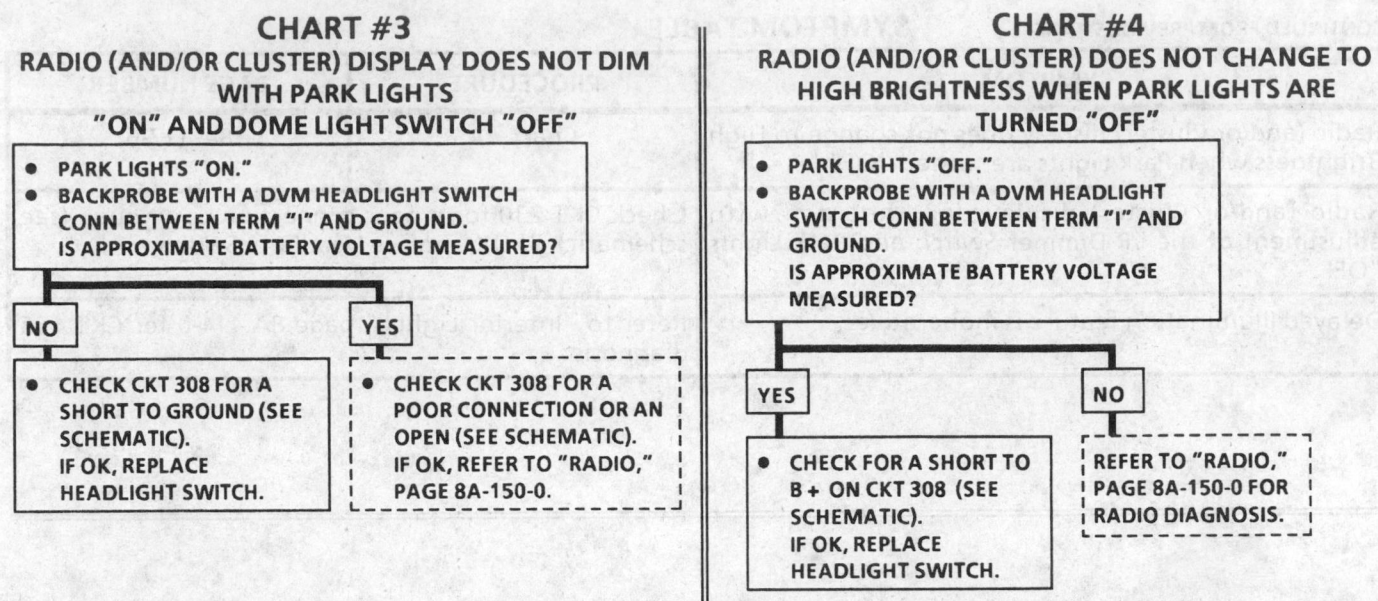

CHART #3

RADIO (AND/OR CLUSTER) DISPLAY DOES NOT DIM WITH PARK LIGHTS "ON" AND DOME LIGHT SWITCH "OFF"

- PARK LIGHTS "ON."
- BACKPROBE WITH A DVM HEADLIGHT SWITCH CONN BETWEEN TERM "I" AND GROUND. IS APPROXIMATE BATTERY VOLTAGE MEASURED?

NO

- CHECK CKT 308 FOR A SHORT TO GROUND (SEE SCHEMATIC). IF OK, REPLACE HEADLIGHT SWITCH.

YES

- CHECK CKT 308 FOR A POOR CONNECTION OR AN OPEN (SEE SCHEMATIC). IF OK, REFER TO "RADIO," PAGE 8A-150-0.

CHART #4

RADIO (AND/OR CLUSTER) DOES NOT CHANGE TO HIGH BRIGHTNESS WHEN PARK LIGHTS ARE TURNED "OFF"

- PARK LIGHTS "OFF."
- BACKPROBE WITH A DVM HEADLIGHT SWITCH CONN BETWEEN TERM "I" AND GROUND. IS APPROXIMATE BATTERY VOLTAGE MEASURED?

YES

- CHECK FOR A SHORT TO B + ON CKT 308 (SEE SCHEMATIC). IF OK, REPLACE HEADLIGHT SWITCH.

NO

REFER TO "RADIO," PAGE 8A-150-0 FOR RADIO DIAGNOSIS.

CIRCUIT OPERATION

The I/P Dimmer Switch controls the brightness of the incandescent lamps and Vacuum Fluorescent (VF) displays. The incandescent lamps are located in various components (see schematics) and the VF displays are located in the Radio and Instrument Cluster.

INCANDESCENT DIMMING

The brightness of the incandescent lamps is determined by a variable voltage signal produced by the Light Switch.

VACUUM FLUORESCENT (VF) DIMMING

The brightness of the Vacuum Fluorescent (VF) Displays is controlled by two signals: the VF Dim Displays Signal and (CKT 308) and the VF Dimming Signal (CKT 230). With the Park Lights "ON" (VF Dim displays CKT 308) the VF display of the Radio and the Instrument Cluster will dim for nighttime viewing. When the VF Dim Displays Signal is not present (Park Lights "OFF"), the VF displays are at high brightness for daytime viewing. When the Park Lights are "ON," the Headlight Switch provides a Pulse Width Modulated (PWM) signal (VF Dimming Signal CKT 230) which controls the brightness of the VF displays when the I/P Dimmer Switch is adjusted.

PARADE MODE

If the I/P Dimmer Switch is moved to "PARADE" or "DOME" (with Park Lights "ON") the VF displays will be at high brightness for daytime viewing.

DELAYED ILLUMINATION

The Interior Lights will come "ON" for approximately 30 seconds when the last door is closed (Dome Light "OFF") or when the Dome Light Switch is moved to off (all doors closed). This feature is a product of the Headlight Switch.

BLANK

POWER WINDOWS
4 DOOR

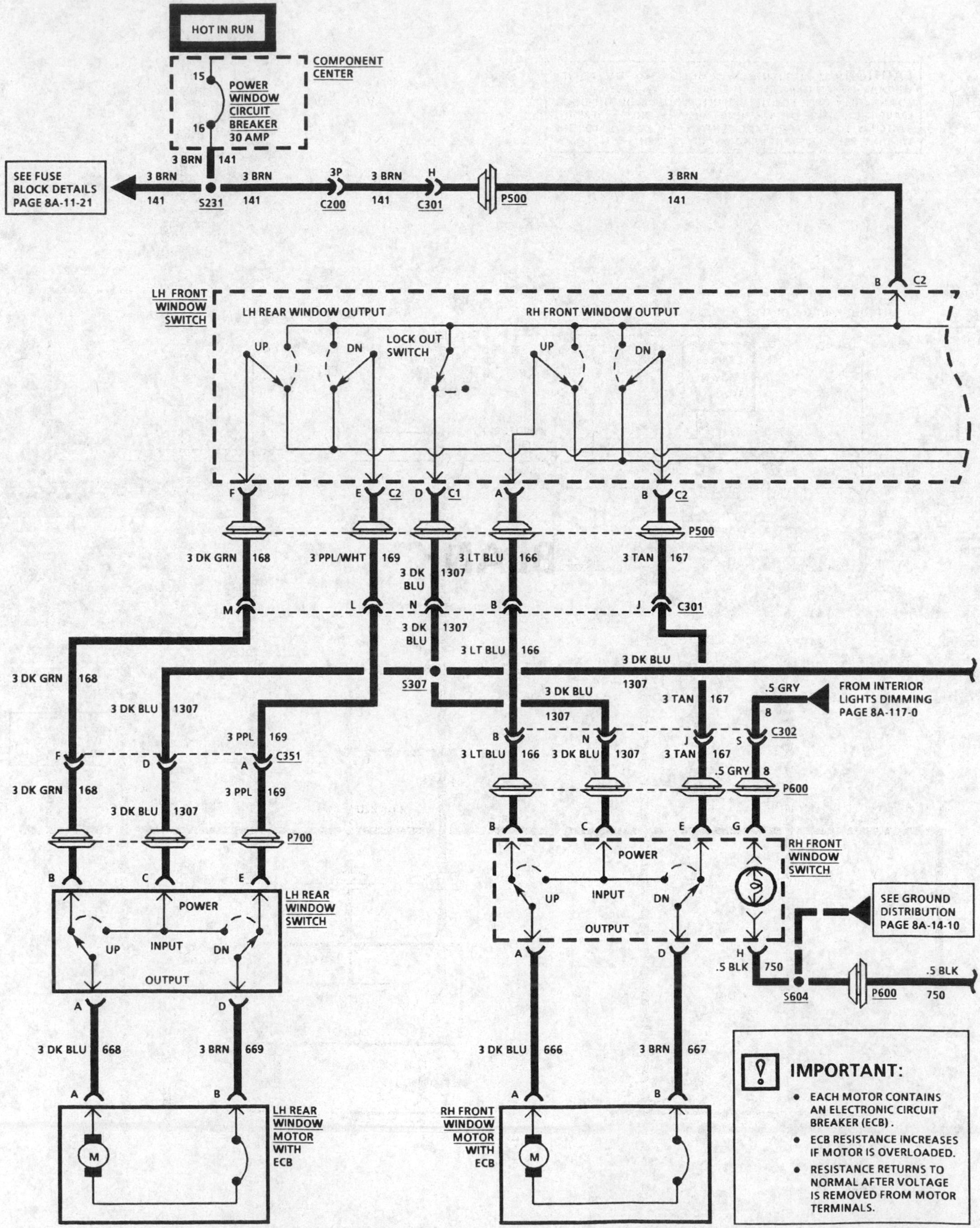

HOT IN RUN
COMPONENT CENTER
POWER WINDOW CIRCUIT BREAKER 30 AMP
15
16
3 BRN 141
SEE FUSE BLOCK DETAILS PAGE 8A-11-21
S231
C200
C301
P500
3P
H
B C2
LH FRONT WINDOW SWITCH
LH REAR WINDOW OUTPUT
RH FRONT WINDOW OUTPUT
UP
DN
LOCK OUT SWITCH
F
E C2
D C1
A
B C2
3 DK GRN 168
3 PPL/WHT 169
3 DK BLU 1307
3 LT BLU 166
3 TAN 167
M
L
N
B
J
C301
S307
3 DK BLU 1307
3 PPL 169
C351
P700
.5 GRY
8
FROM INTERIOR LIGHTS DIMMING PAGE 8A-117-0
C302
S
P600
LH REAR WINDOW SWITCH
POWER
INPUT
OUTPUT
RH FRONT WINDOW SWITCH
SEE GROUND DISTRIBUTION PAGE 8A-14-10
.5 BLK 750
S604
3 DK BLU 668
3 BRN 669
3 DK BLU 666
3 BRN 667
LH REAR WINDOW MOTOR WITH ECB
RH FRONT WINDOW MOTOR WITH ECB
M

IMPORTANT:

- EACH MOTOR CONTAINS AN ELECTRONIC CIRCUIT BREAKER (ECB).
- ECB RESISTANCE INCREASES IF MOTOR IS OVERLOADED.
- RESISTANCE RETURNS TO NORMAL AFTER VOLTAGE IS REMOVED FROM MOTOR TERMINALS.

CAUTION: A MOMENTARY ACTUATION OF THE POWER WINDOW SWITCH CAN CAUSE THE WINDOW TO MOVE DIRECTLY TO THE FULLY OPEN POSITION. WHEN WORKING ON THE DOOR, LEAVE THE IGNITION OFF WHENEVER POSSIBLE. NOTE WHERE THE SWITCH IS, SO YOU WON'T ACCIDENTALLY HIT IT. TO STOP THE WINDOW, PRESS LH FRONT WINDOW "UP" SWITCH.

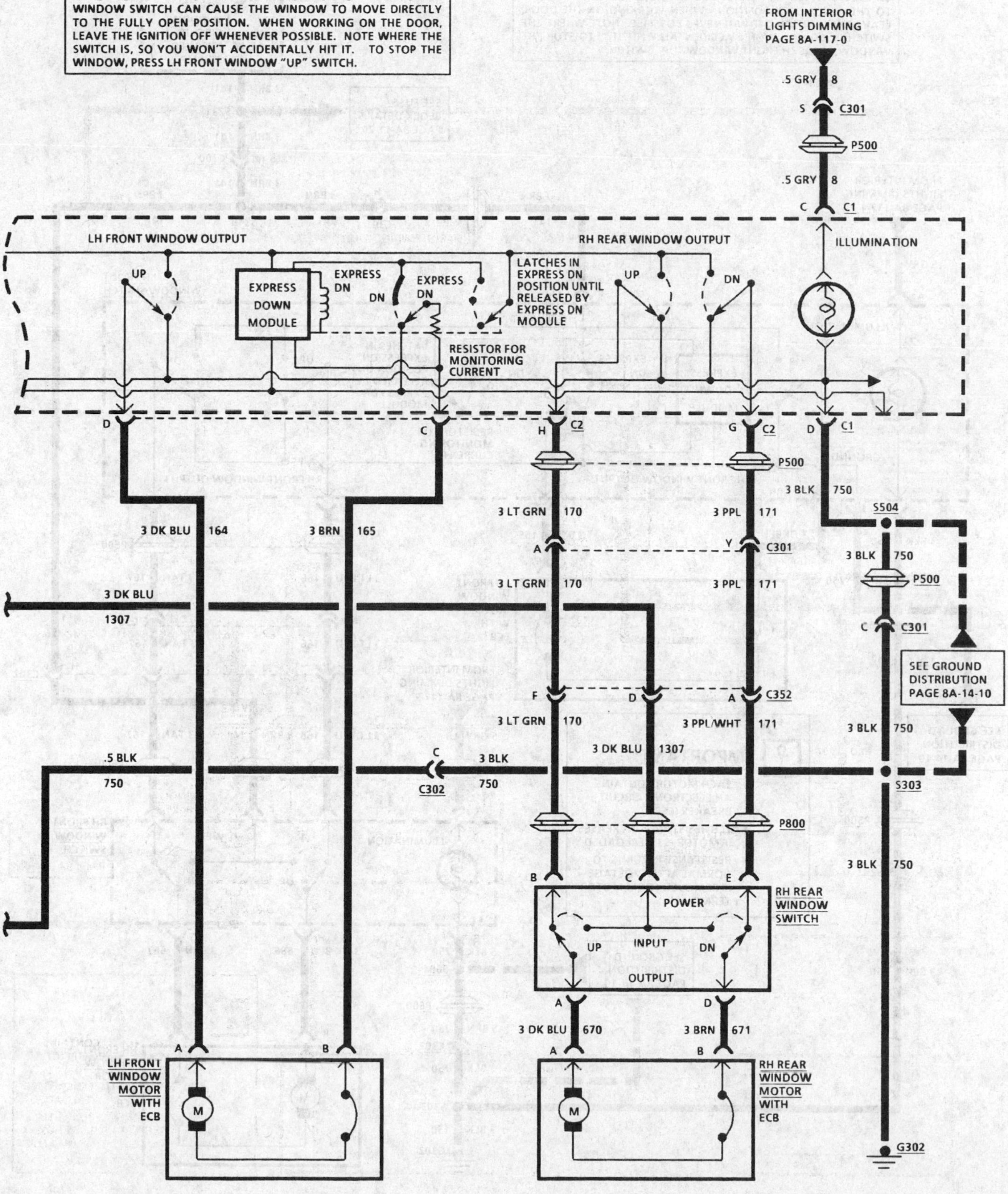
FROM INTERIOR
LIGHTS DIMMING
PAGE 8A-117-0
.5 GRY 8
S C301
P500
.5 GRY 8
C C1
LH FRONT WINDOW OUTPUT
RH REAR WINDOW OUTPUT
ILLUMINATION
UP
EXPRESS
DOWN
MODULE
EXPRESS
DN
DN
EXPRESS
DN
LATCHES IN
EXPRESS DN
POSITION UNTIL
RELEASED BY
EXPRESS DN
MODULE
UP
DN
RESISTOR FOR
MONITORING
CURRENT
D
C
H C2
G C2
D C1
P500
3 BLK 750
S504
3 DK BLU 164
3 BRN 165
3 LT GRN 170
3 PPL 171
A
Y C301
3 BLK 750
P500
3 LT GRN 170
3 PPL 171
3 DK BLU
1307
C C301
SEE GROUND
DISTRIBUTION
PAGE 8A-14-10
F
D
A C352
3 LT GRN 170
3 PPL/WHT 171
3 BLK 750
3 DK BLU 1307
.5 BLK
750
C
C302
3 BLK
750
S303
P800
3 BLK 750
B
C
E
POWER
RH REAR
WINDOW
SWITCH
UP
INPUT
DN
OUTPUT
A
D
3 DK BLU 670
3 BRN 671
A
B
LH FRONT
WINDOW
MOTOR
WITH
ECB
M
A
B
RH REAR
WINDOW
MOTOR
WITH
ECB
M
G302

POWER WINDOWS
2 DOOR

CAUTION: A MOMENTARY ACTUATION OF THE POWER WINDOW SWITCH CAN CAUSE THE WINDOW TO MOVE DIRECTLY TO THE FULLY OPEN POSITION. WHEN WORKING ON THE DOOR, LEAVE THE IGNITION OFF WHENEVER POSSIBLE. NOTE WHERE THE SWITCH IS, SO YOU WON'T ACCIDENTALLY HIT IT. TO STOP THE WINDOW, PRESS LH FRONT WINDOW "UP" SWITCH.

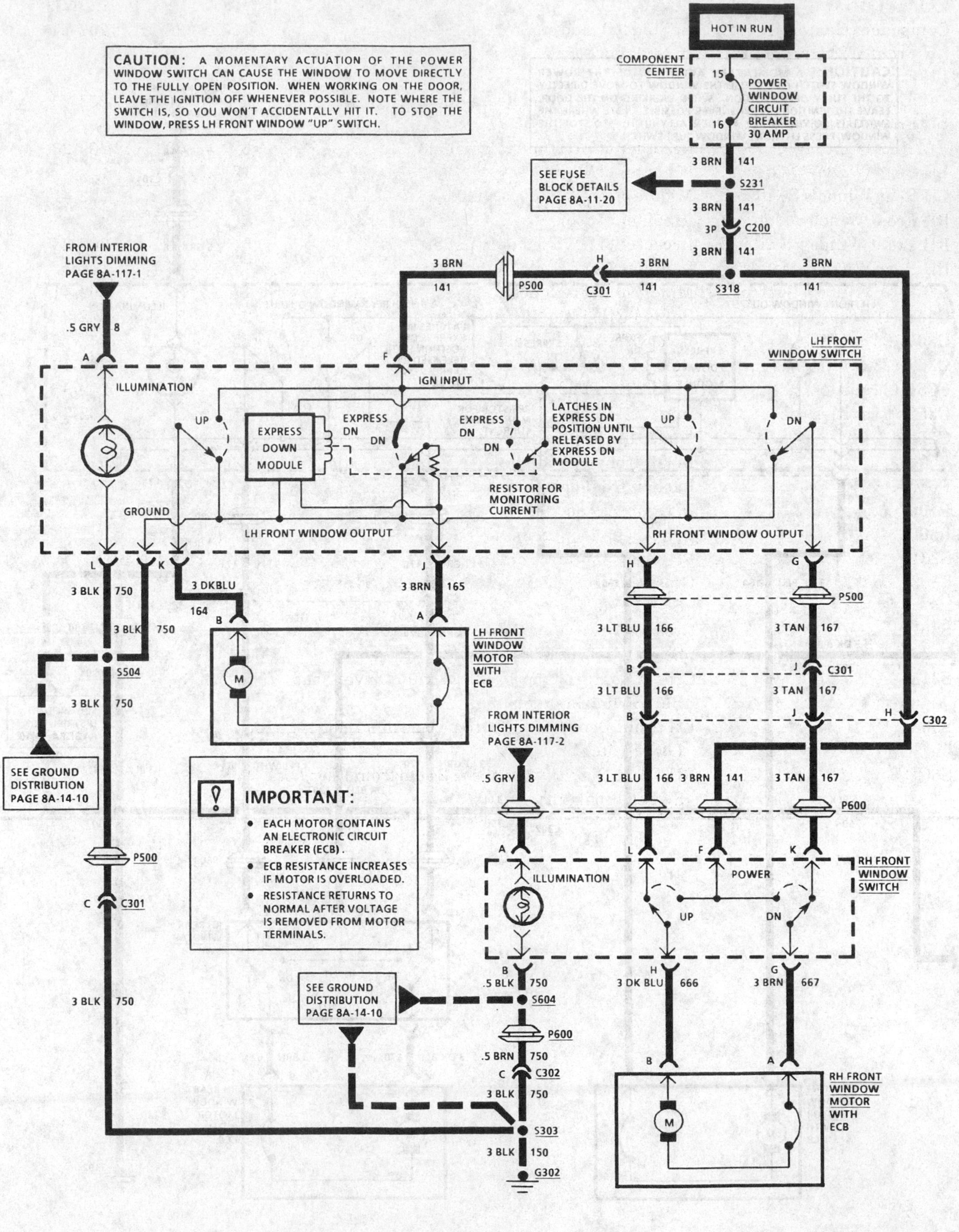

HOT IN RUN
COMPONENT CENTER
15
16
POWER WINDOW CIRCUIT BREAKER 30 AMP
3 BRN 141
S231
SEE FUSE BLOCK DETAILS PAGE 8A-11-20
3 BRN 141
3P C200
3 BRN 141
3 BRN 141
P500
H C301
3 BRN 141
S318
3 BRN 141
FROM INTERIOR LIGHTS DIMMING PAGE 8A-117-1
.5 GRY 8
A
F
LH FRONT WINDOW SWITCH
ILLUMINATION
IGN INPUT
UP
EXPRESS DOWN MODULE
EXPRESS DN
DN
EXPRESS DN
DN
LATCHES IN EXPRESS DN POSITION UNTIL RELEASED BY EXPRESS DN MODULE
UP
DN
RESISTOR FOR MONITORING CURRENT
GROUND
LH FRONT WINDOW OUTPUT
RH FRONT WINDOW OUTPUT
L K J H G
3 BLK 750
3 DKBLU 164
3 BRN 165
B A
3 BLK 750
S504
3 BLK 750
SEE GROUND DISTRIBUTION PAGE 8A-14-10
LH FRONT WINDOW MOTOR WITH ECB
M
P500
3 LT BLU 166
3 TAN 167
B J C301
3 LT BLU 166
3 TAN 167
B J H C302
FROM INTERIOR LIGHTS DIMMING PAGE 8A-117-2
.5 GRY 8
3 LT BLU 166
3 BRN 141
3 TAN 167
P600
IMPORTANT:
• EACH MOTOR CONTAINS AN ELECTRONIC CIRCUIT BREAKER (ECB).
• ECB RESISTANCE INCREASES IF MOTOR IS OVERLOADED.
• RESISTANCE RETURNS TO NORMAL AFTER VOLTAGE IS REMOVED FROM MOTOR TERMINALS.
P500
C C301
A L F K
RH FRONT WINDOW SWITCH
ILLUMINATION
POWER
UP
DN
B H G
.5 BLK 750
3 DK BLU 666
3 BRN 667
SEE GROUND DISTRIBUTION PAGE 8A-14-10
S604
3 BLK 750
P600
.5 BRN 750
C C302
3 BLK 750
B A
RH FRONT WINDOW MOTOR WITH ECB
M
S303
3 BLK 150
G302

POWER WINDOWS

COMPONENT	LOCATION	201-PG	FIG.	CONN
Component Center	Behind RH side of I/P	11	36	202-14
LH Front Window Motor	In center of door	6	20	
LH Front Window Switch (2 Door)	In center of LH front door panel	6	20	202-23
LH Front Window Switch (4 Door)	In center of LH front door panel	6	20	202-23
LH Rear Window Motor	In center of door	17	57	
LH Rear Window Switch	Middle of LH rear door panel	17	57	202-41
RH Front Window Motor	In center of door	6	20	
RH Front Window Switch	In center of RH front door panel	6	20	202-24
RH Rear Window Motor	In center of door	17	57	
RH Rear Window Switch	Middle of RH rear door panel	17	57	202-41
C200 (106 cavities)	Behind RH side of I/P, near shroud	2	8	202-3
C301 (23 cavities)	Below I/P, at LH shroud	22	75	202-12
C302 (23 cavities)	Below I/P, at RH shroud	22	75	202-13
C351 (6 cavities)	In LH "B" pillar	17	57	202-35
C352 (6 cavities)	In RH "B" pillar	17	57	202-35
G302	Under LH front seat			
P500	In left front door jamb	6	20	
P600	In right front door jamb	6	20	
P700	In right rear door jamb	17	57	
P800	In left rear door jamb	17	57	
S231	I/P Harn, approx 23 cm from C200			
S303	Cross Car Harn, approx 38 cm from Driver Front Seat Belt Switch	13	44	
S307	Cross Car Harn, approx 33 cm from Driver Front Seat Belt Switch			
S318	Cross Car Harn, approx 32 cm from Driver Seat Belt Switch breakout			
S504	LH Front Door Harn, approx 4 cm from Door Lock Switch breakout			
S604	RH Front Door Harn, approx 24 cm from Door Lock Switch breakout			

POWER WINDOWS

TROUBLESHOOTING HINTS (Perform before beginning System Diagnosis)

1. If windows only operate from the LH Front Window Switch, check for approximately B+ at LH Front Window Switch Connector C2 terminal "B" (4 Door), terminal "F" (2 Door).
2. Check that Ground G302 is clean and tight.
3. If all power windows do not operate, check POWER WINDOW Circuit Breaker.
4. Before performing any diagnostics, make sure the Lockout Switch is in the "OFF" position (4 Door or Convertible).

- Check for a broken (or partially broken) wire inside of the insulation which could cause system malfunction but prove "GOOD" in a continuity/voltage check with a system disconnected. These circuits may be intermittent or resistive when loaded, and if possible, should be checked by monitoring for a voltage drop with the system operational (under load).
- Check for proper installation of aftermarket electronic equipment which may affect the integrity of other systems (see "Troubleshooting Procedures," page 8A-4-0).
- Refer to System Diagnosis.

SYSTEM DIAGNOSIS

- Perform the System Check and refer to the Symptom Table for the appropriate diagnostic procedures.

SYSTEM CHECK

ACTION	NORMAL RESULTS
[1] • Operate each window "UP" and "DOWN" from the LH Front Window Switch.	Each window operates quietly and smoothly, without sticking.
[2] • Operate each window from its individual switch.	Each window operates quietly and smoothly, without sticking.
[3] • Momentarily press LH Front Window Switch "DOWN" past the first defeat.	Window continues to fully down position.
[4] (4 Door) • Lockout Switch in the "LOCK" position.	Windows operate from the LH Front Window Switch and not from their individual switches.
[5] (4 Door) • Lockout Switch in the "OFF" position.	Windows operate normally from all the switches.

SYMPTOM TABLE

SYMPTOM	PROCEDURE	PAGE NUMBER
All Power Windows inoperative.	Chart #1	8A-120-7
LH Front Window inoperative; all others operate normally.	Chart #2	8A-120-8
RH Front, LH Rear, or RH Rear Window is inoperative from the LH Front Window Switch, with normal operation from the individual Window Switch.	Chart #3	8A-120-9
RH Front, LH Rear, or RH Rear Window is inoperative from the individual Window Switch but operates normally from the LH Front Window Switch.	Chart #4	8A-120-9
One window (other than the LH Front) is inoperative from both the LH Front Window Switch and the individual Window Switch; all other windows operate normally.	Chart #5	8A-120-10
Lockout function (4 Door) does not work but windows operate normally otherwise.	Chart #6	8A-120-11
Only the Express Down feature does not operate.	Replace the LH Front Window Switch.	
Courtesy Lamps on LH Front Window Switch and/or RH Front Window Switch do not illuminate when the Park Lights or Headlights are "ON."	See Interior Lights Dimming.	8A-117-0

CHART #1
ALL POWER WINDOWS INOPERATIVE

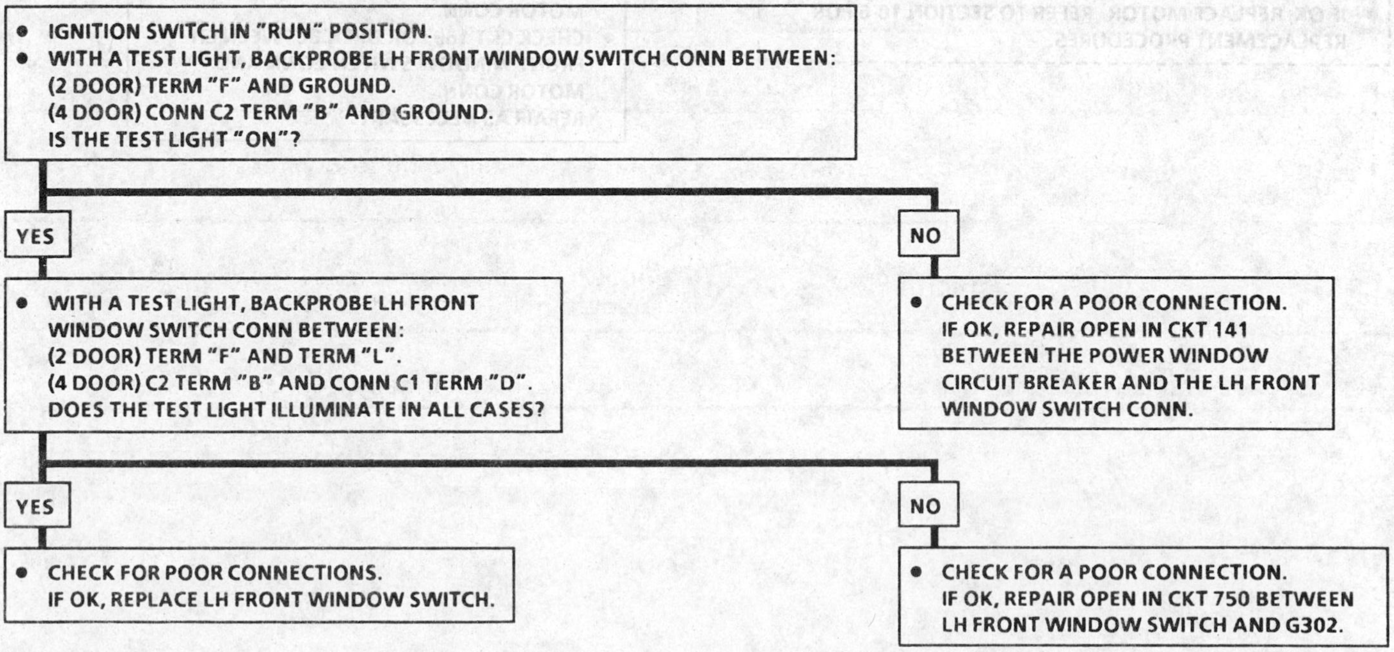
• IGNITION SWITCH IN "RUN" POSITION.
• WITH A TEST LIGHT, BACKPROBE LH FRONT WINDOW SWITCH CONN BETWEEN:
(2 DOOR) TERM "F" AND GROUND.
(4 DOOR) CONN C2 TERM "B" AND GROUND.
IS THE TEST LIGHT "ON"?
YES
NO
• WITH A TEST LIGHT, BACKPROBE LH FRONT WINDOW SWITCH CONN BETWEEN:
(2 DOOR) TERM "F" AND TERM "L".
(4 DOOR) C2 TERM "B" AND CONN C1 TERM "D".
DOES THE TEST LIGHT ILLUMINATE IN ALL CASES?
• CHECK FOR A POOR CONNECTION.
IF OK, REPAIR OPEN IN CKT 141 BETWEEN THE POWER WINDOW CIRCUIT BREAKER AND THE LH FRONT WINDOW SWITCH CONN.
YES
NO
• CHECK FOR POOR CONNECTIONS.
IF OK, REPLACE LH FRONT WINDOW SWITCH.
• CHECK FOR A POOR CONNECTION.
IF OK, REPAIR OPEN IN CKT 750 BETWEEN LH FRONT WINDOW SWITCH AND G302.

POWER WINDOWS

CHART #2

LH FRONT WINDOW INOPERATIVE; ALL OTHERS OPERATE NORMALLY

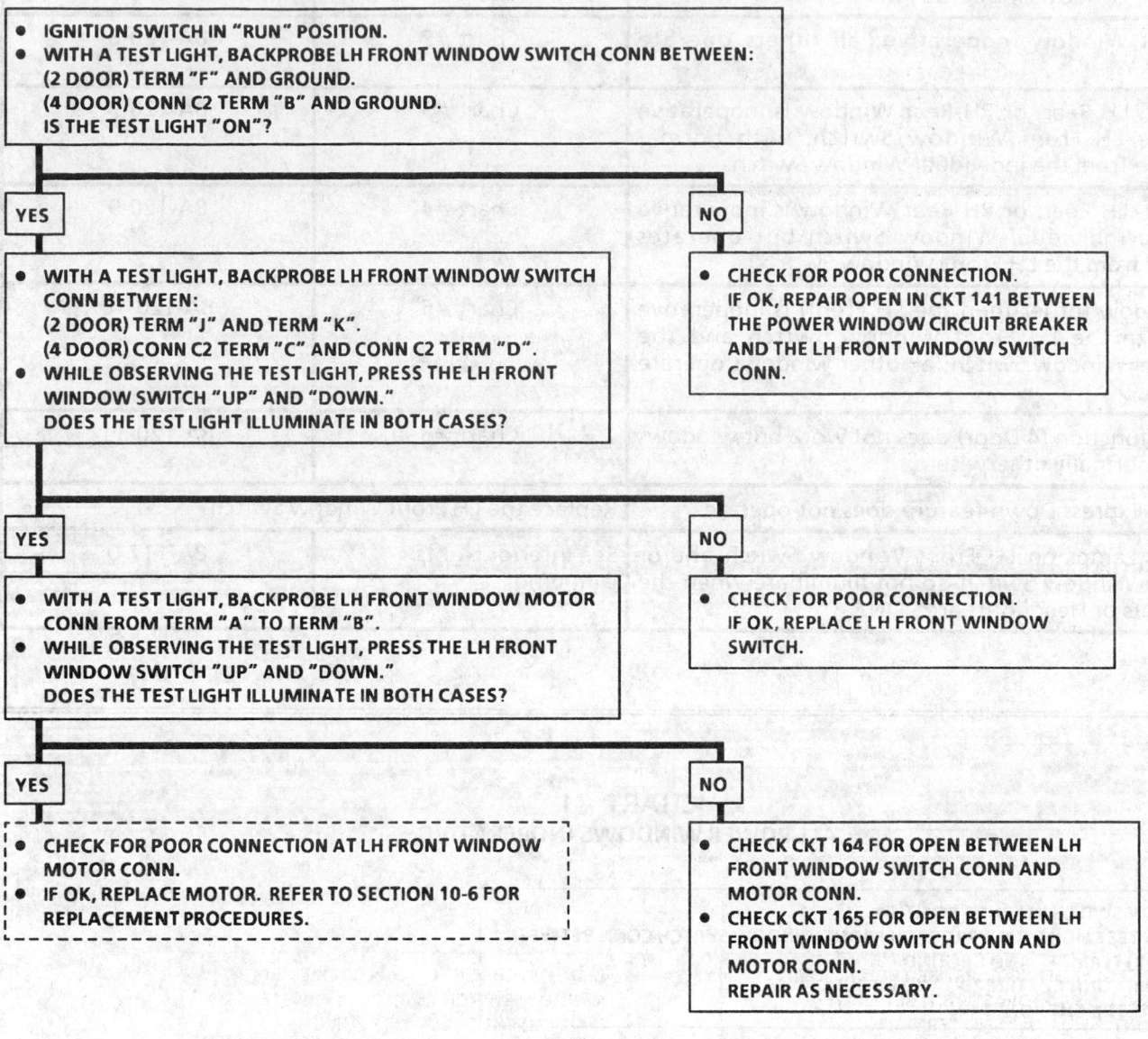

- IGNITION SWITCH IN "RUN" POSITION.
- WITH A TEST LIGHT, BACKPROBE LH FRONT WINDOW SWITCH CONN BETWEEN:
  (2 DOOR) TERM "F" AND GROUND.
  (4 DOOR) CONN C2 TERM "B" AND GROUND.
  IS THE TEST LIGHT "ON"?

YES

- WITH A TEST LIGHT, BACKPROBE LH FRONT WINDOW SWITCH CONN BETWEEN:
  (2 DOOR) TERM "J" AND TERM "K".
  (4 DOOR) CONN C2 TERM "C" AND CONN C2 TERM "D".
- WHILE OBSERVING THE TEST LIGHT, PRESS THE LH FRONT WINDOW SWITCH "UP" AND "DOWN."
  DOES THE TEST LIGHT ILLUMINATE IN BOTH CASES?

NO

- CHECK FOR POOR CONNECTION.
  IF OK, REPAIR OPEN IN CKT 141 BETWEEN THE POWER WINDOW CIRCUIT BREAKER AND THE LH FRONT WINDOW SWITCH CONN.

YES

- WITH A TEST LIGHT, BACKPROBE LH FRONT WINDOW MOTOR CONN FROM TERM "A" TO TERM "B".
- WHILE OBSERVING THE TEST LIGHT, PRESS THE LH FRONT WINDOW SWITCH "UP" AND "DOWN."
  DOES THE TEST LIGHT ILLUMINATE IN BOTH CASES?

NO

- CHECK FOR POOR CONNECTION.
  IF OK, REPLACE LH FRONT WINDOW SWITCH.

YES

- CHECK FOR POOR CONNECTION AT LH FRONT WINDOW MOTOR CONN.
- IF OK, REPLACE MOTOR. REFER TO SECTION 10-6 FOR REPLACEMENT PROCEDURES.

NO

- CHECK CKT 164 FOR OPEN BETWEEN LH FRONT WINDOW SWITCH CONN AND MOTOR CONN.
- CHECK CKT 165 FOR OPEN BETWEEN LH FRONT WINDOW SWITCH CONN AND MOTOR CONN.
  REPAIR AS NECESSARY.

CHART #3
RH FRONT, LH REAR, OR RH REAR WINDOW IS INOPERATIVE FROM THE LH FRONT WINDOW SWITCH, WITH NORMAL OPERATION FROM THE INDIVIDUAL WINDOW SWITCH

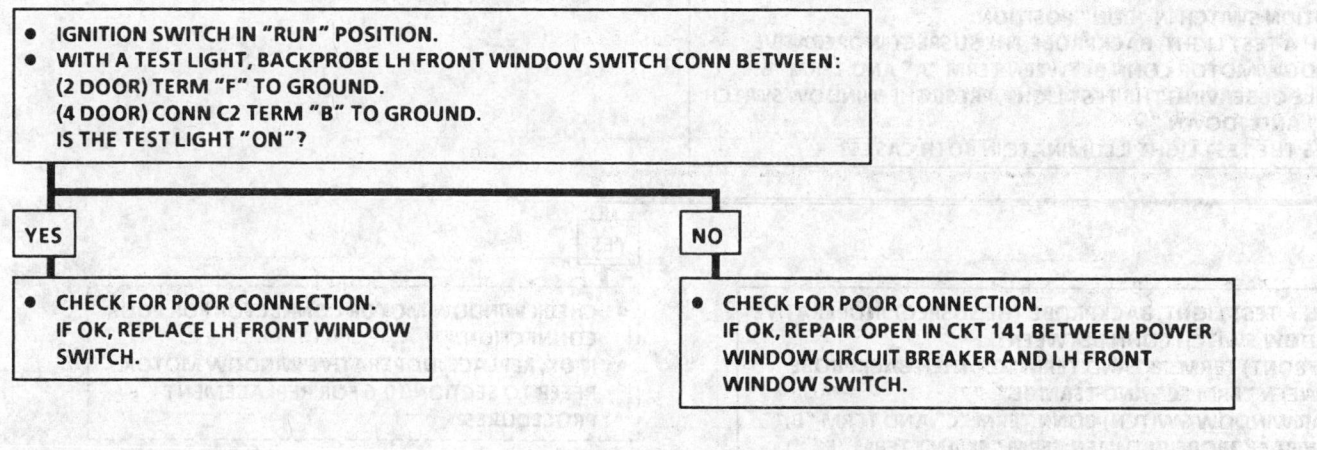

- IGNITION SWITCH IN "RUN" POSITION.
- WITH A TEST LIGHT, BACKPROBE LH FRONT WINDOW SWITCH CONN BETWEEN:
  (2 DOOR) TERM "F" TO GROUND.
  (4 DOOR) CONN C2 TERM "B" TO GROUND.
  IS THE TEST LIGHT "ON"?

YES

- CHECK FOR POOR CONNECTION.
  IF OK, REPLACE LH FRONT WINDOW SWITCH.

NO

- CHECK FOR POOR CONNECTION.
  IF OK, REPAIR OPEN IN CKT 141 BETWEEN POWER WINDOW CIRCUIT BREAKER AND LH FRONT WINDOW SWITCH.

CHART #4
RH FRONT, LH REAR, OR RH REAR WINDOW IS INOPERATIVE FROM INDIVIDUAL WINDOW SWITCH BUT OPERATES NORMALLY FROM LH FRONT WINDOW SWITCH

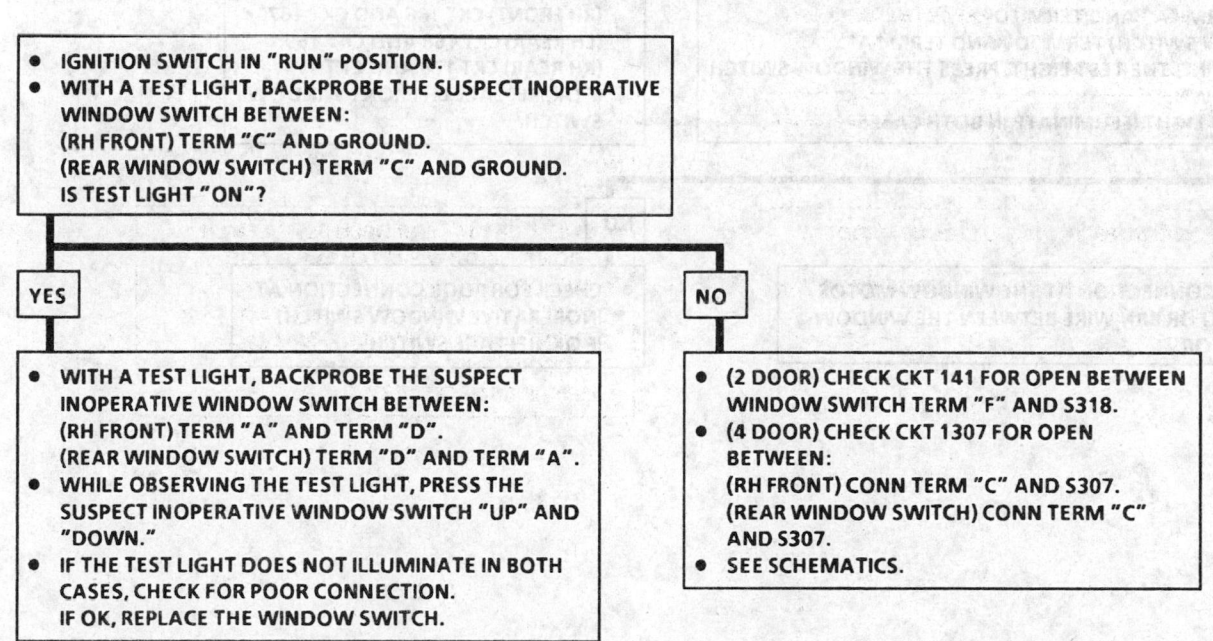

- IGNITION SWITCH IN "RUN" POSITION.
- WITH A TEST LIGHT, BACKPROBE THE SUSPECT INOPERATIVE WINDOW SWITCH BETWEEN:
  (RH FRONT) TERM "C" AND GROUND.
  (REAR WINDOW SWITCH) TERM "C" AND GROUND.
  IS TEST LIGHT "ON"?

YES

- WITH A TEST LIGHT, BACKPROBE THE SUSPECT INOPERATIVE WINDOW SWITCH BETWEEN:
  (RH FRONT) TERM "A" AND TERM "D".
  (REAR WINDOW SWITCH) TERM "D" AND TERM "A".
- WHILE OBSERVING THE TEST LIGHT, PRESS THE SUSPECT INOPERATIVE WINDOW SWITCH "UP" AND "DOWN."
- IF THE TEST LIGHT DOES NOT ILLUMINATE IN BOTH CASES, CHECK FOR POOR CONNECTION.
  IF OK, REPLACE THE WINDOW SWITCH.

NO

- (2 DOOR) CHECK CKT 141 FOR OPEN BETWEEN WINDOW SWITCH TERM "F" AND S318.
- (4 DOOR) CHECK CKT 1307 FOR OPEN BETWEEN:
  (RH FRONT) CONN TERM "C" AND S307.
  (REAR WINDOW SWITCH) CONN TERM "C" AND S307.
- SEE SCHEMATICS.

POWER WINDOWS

CHART #5

ONE WINDOW (OTHER THAN LH FRONT) IS INOPERATIVE FROM BOTH THE LH FRONT WINDOW SWITCH AND THE INDIVIDUAL WINDOW SWITCH; ALL OTHER WINDOWS OPERATE NORMALLY

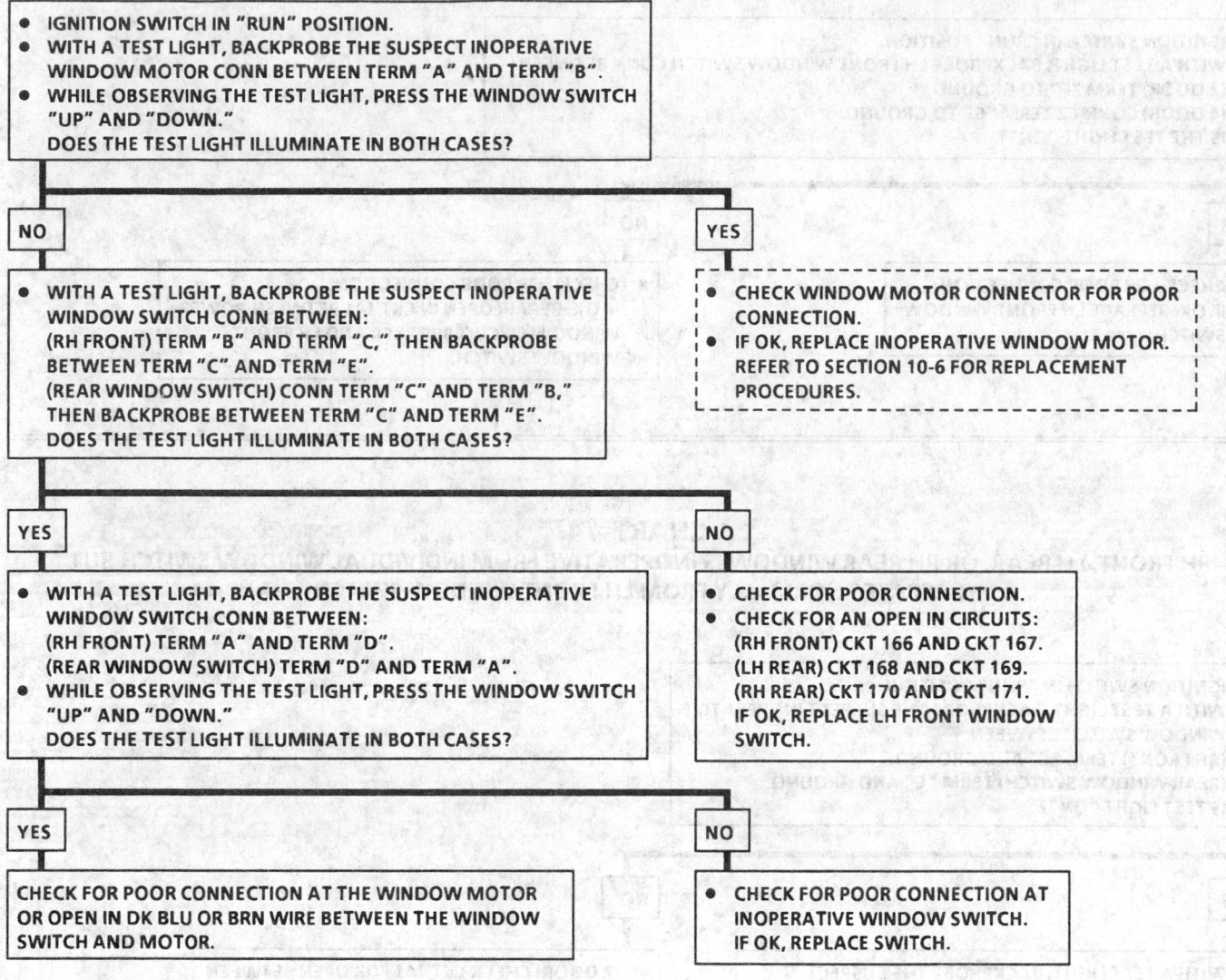

- IGNITION SWITCH IN "RUN" POSITION.
- WITH A TEST LIGHT, BACKPROBE THE SUSPECT INOPERATIVE WINDOW MOTOR CONN BETWEEN TERM "A" AND TERM "B".
- WHILE OBSERVING THE TEST LIGHT, PRESS THE WINDOW SWITCH "UP" AND "DOWN."

DOES THE TEST LIGHT ILLUMINATE IN BOTH CASES?

NO

- WITH A TEST LIGHT, BACKPROBE THE SUSPECT INOPERATIVE WINDOW SWITCH CONN BETWEEN:
  (RH FRONT) TERM "B" AND TERM "C," THEN BACKPROBE BETWEEN TERM "C" AND TERM "E".
  (REAR WINDOW SWITCH) CONN TERM "C" AND TERM "B," THEN BACKPROBE BETWEEN TERM "C" AND TERM "E".

DOES THE TEST LIGHT ILLUMINATE IN BOTH CASES?

YES

- CHECK WINDOW MOTOR CONNECTOR FOR POOR CONNECTION.
- IF OK, REPLACE INOPERATIVE WINDOW MOTOR. REFER TO SECTION 10-6 FOR REPLACEMENT PROCEDURES.

(From "DOES THE TEST LIGHT ILLUMINATE IN BOTH CASES?" under NO above:)

YES

- WITH A TEST LIGHT, BACKPROBE THE SUSPECT INOPERATIVE WINDOW SWITCH CONN BETWEEN:
  (RH FRONT) TERM "A" AND TERM "D".
  (REAR WINDOW SWITCH) TERM "D" AND TERM "A".
- WHILE OBSERVING THE TEST LIGHT, PRESS THE WINDOW SWITCH "UP" AND "DOWN."

DOES THE TEST LIGHT ILLUMINATE IN BOTH CASES?

NO

- CHECK FOR POOR CONNECTION.
- CHECK FOR AN OPEN IN CIRCUITS:
  (RH FRONT) CKT 166 AND CKT 167.
  (LH REAR) CKT 168 AND CKT 169.
  (RH REAR) CKT 170 AND CKT 171.
  IF OK, REPLACE LH FRONT WINDOW SWITCH.

(From the third test:)

YES

CHECK FOR POOR CONNECTION AT THE WINDOW MOTOR OR OPEN IN DK BLU OR BRN WIRE BETWEEN THE WINDOW SWITCH AND MOTOR.

NO

- CHECK FOR POOR CONNECTION AT INOPERATIVE WINDOW SWITCH.
  IF OK, REPLACE SWITCH.

CHART #6
LOCKOUT FUNCTION (4 DOOR) DOES NOT WORK BUT WINDOWS OPERATE NORMALLY OTHERWISE

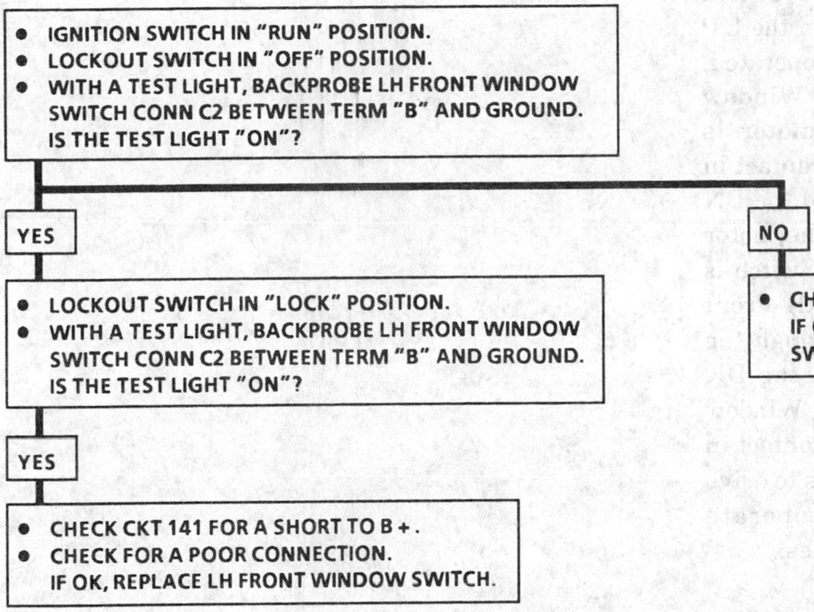
• IGNITION SWITCH IN "RUN" POSITION.
• LOCKOUT SWITCH IN "OFF" POSITION.
• WITH A TEST LIGHT, BACKPROBE LH FRONT WINDOW SWITCH CONN C2 BETWEEN TERM "B" AND GROUND. IS THE TEST LIGHT "ON"?
YES
NO
• CHECK FOR POOR CONNECTION. IF OK, REPLACE LH FRONT WINDOW SWITCH.
• LOCKOUT SWITCH IN "LOCK" POSITION.
• WITH A TEST LIGHT, BACKPROBE LH FRONT WINDOW SWITCH CONN C2 BETWEEN TERM "B" AND GROUND. IS THE TEST LIGHT "ON"?
YES
• CHECK CKT 141 FOR A SHORT TO B+.
• CHECK FOR A POOR CONNECTION. IF OK, REPLACE LH FRONT WINDOW SWITCH.

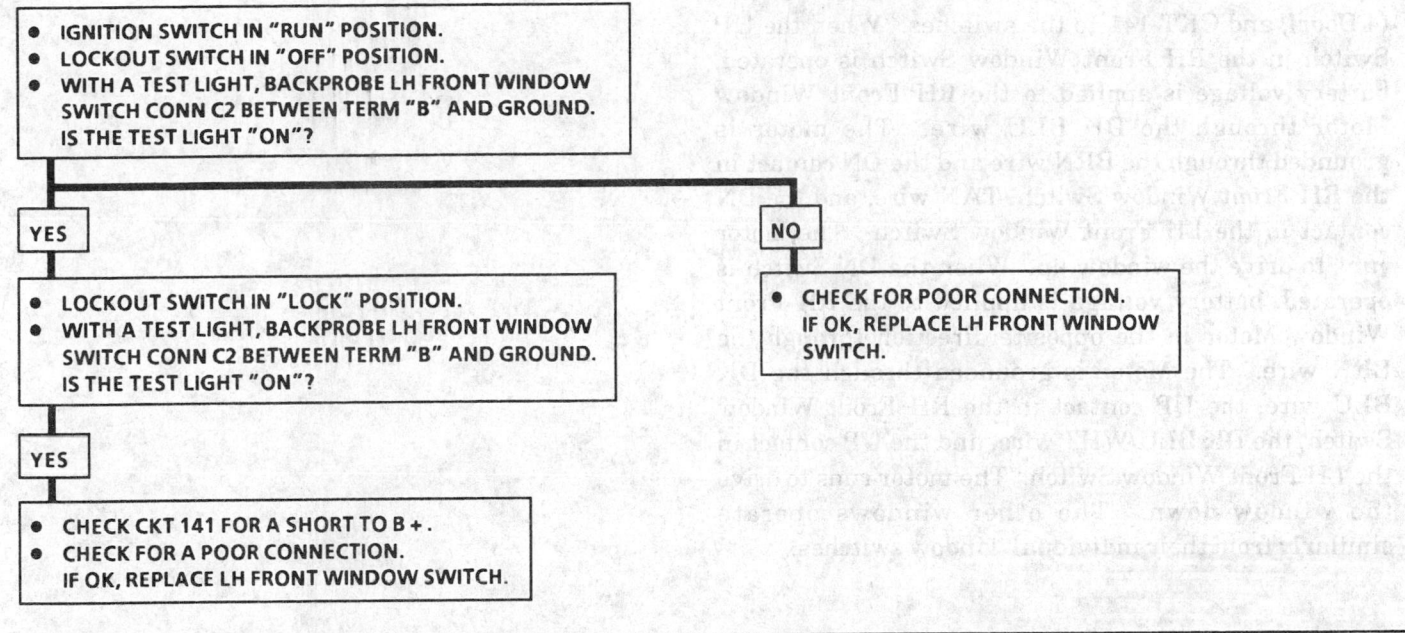

CIRCUIT OPERATION

A Permanent Magnet (PM) Motor operates each of the power windows. Each motor raises or lowers the glass when voltage is supplied to it. The direction the motor turns depends on the polarity of the supply voltage. The switches control the supply voltage polarity.

The LH Front Window Switch is the source of voltage and ground for the other window switches.

Each motor is protected by a built-in circuit breaker. If a window switch is held too long with the window obstructed or after the window is fully up or down, the circuit breaker opens the circuit. The circuit breaker resets only after voltage is removed from the motor.

LH FRONT WINDOW SWITCH ASSEMBLY OPERATION

When the Ignition Switch is in "RUN," battery voltage is applied to the LH Front Window Switch through the Power Window Circuit Breaker and CKT 141. When any of the UP Switches in the LH Front Window Switch are operated, battery voltage is applied to the Window Motor. The Window Motor is grounded through the DN contact in the LH Front Window Switch. The motor runs to drive the window up. When any of the DN Switches in the LH Front Window Switch are operated battery voltage is applied to the Window Motor in the opposite direction. The Window Motor is grounded through the UP contact in the LH Front Window Switch. The motor runs to drive the window down.

If the LH Front DN Switch in the LH Front Window Switch is momentarily pressed down past the first detent, the window will travel to the fully down position.

4 DOOR

The LH Front Window Switch contains a Lockout Switch which will remove battery voltage from the other window switches. This will not allow the operation of the windows from their individual switches. The windows can still be operated as normal from the LH Front Window Switch.

POWER WINDOWS

WINDOW SWITCH OPERATION

When the Ignition Switch is in "RUN," battery voltage is applied to the window switches through the circuit breaker (2 Door), the LH Front Window Switch (4 Door), and CKT 141 to the switches. When the UP Switch in the RH Front Window Switch is operated, battery voltage is applied to the RH Front Window Motor through the DK BLU wire. The motor is grounded through the BRN wire and the DN contact in the RH Front Window Switch, TAN wire, and the DN contact in the LH Front Window Switch. The motor runs to drive the window up. When the DN Switch is operated, battery voltage is applied to the RH Front Window Motor in the opposite direction through the BRN wire. The Motor is grounded through the DK BLU wire, the UP contact in the RH Front Window Switch, the DK BLU/WHT wire, and the UP contact in the LH Front Window Switch. The motor runs to drive the window down. The other windows operate similarly from their individual window switches.

BLANK

SUNROOF

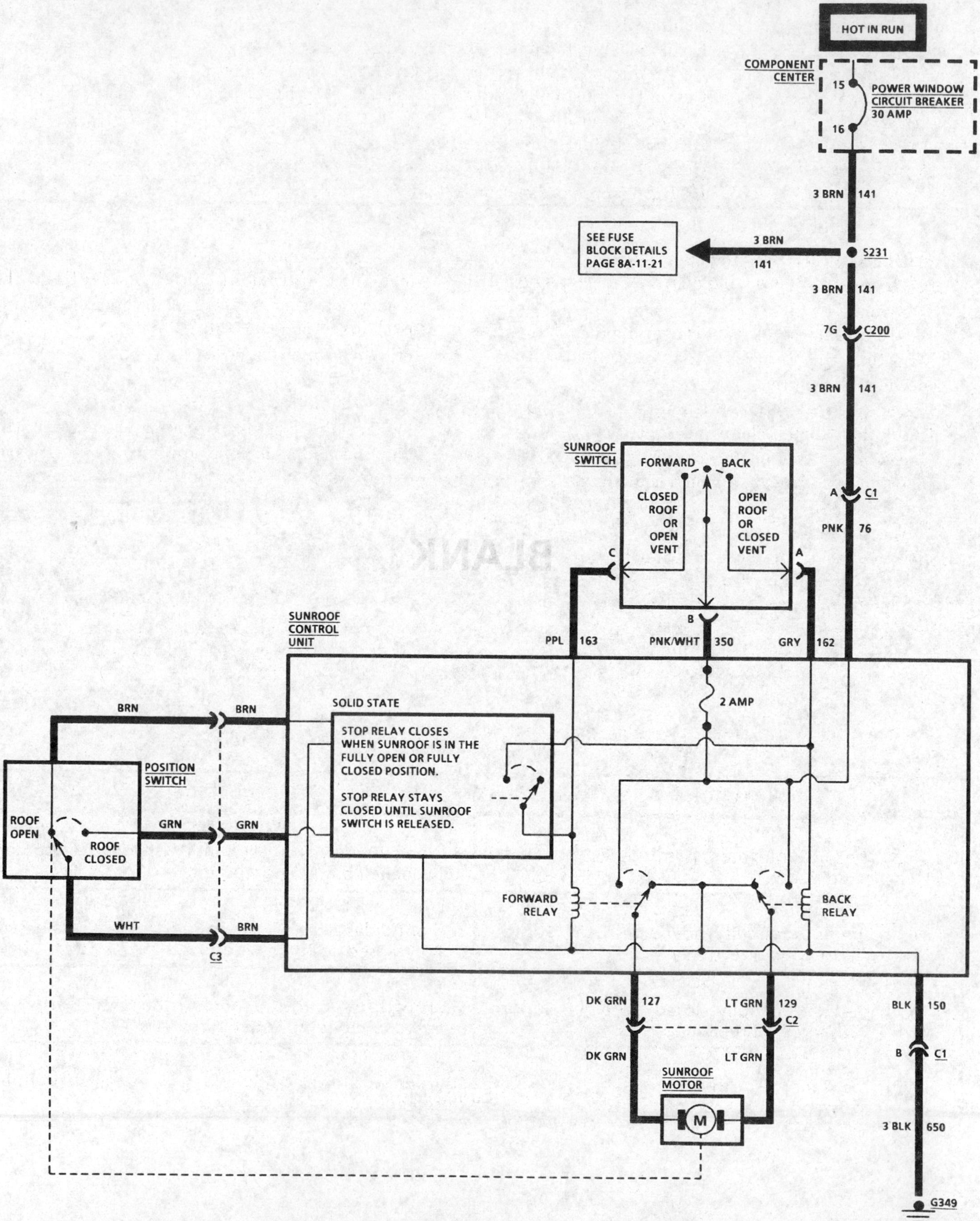
HOT IN RUN
COMPONENT CENTER
15
16
POWER WINDOW CIRCUIT BREAKER 30 AMP
3 BRN 141
SEE FUSE BLOCK DETAILS PAGE 8A-11-21
3 BRN 141
S231
3 BRN 141
7G
C200
3 BRN 141
SUNROOF SWITCH
FORWARD
BACK
CLOSED ROOF OR OPEN VENT
OPEN ROOF OR CLOSED VENT
C
A
B
A
C1
PNK 76
PPL 163
PNK/WHT 350
GRY 162
SUNROOF CONTROL UNIT
2 AMP
SOLID STATE
STOP RELAY CLOSES WHEN SUNROOF IS IN THE FULLY OPEN OR FULLY CLOSED POSITION.
STOP RELAY STAYS CLOSED UNTIL SUNROOF SWITCH IS RELEASED.
BRN
BRN
POSITION SWITCH
ROOF OPEN
ROOF CLOSED
GRN
GRN
WHT
BRN
C3
FORWARD RELAY
BACK RELAY
DK GRN 127
LT GRN 129
C2
DK GRN
LT GRN
SUNROOF MOTOR
M
BLK 150
B
C1
3 BLK 650
G349

COMPONENT	LOCATION	201-PG	FIG.	CONN
Component Center	Behind RH side of I/P	11	36	202-14
Position Switch	Center of windshield header			
Sunroof Control Unit	Center of windshield header	13	45	
Sunroof Motor	Center of windshield header	13	45	
Sunroof Switch	Center of windshield header	12	39	
C200 (102 cavities)	Behind RH side of I/P, near shroud	13	44	202-3
G349	Center of windshield header, near rearview mirror	13	45	
S231	I/P Harn, approx 3 cm from C200			

TROUBLESHOOTING HINTS (Perform before beginning System Diagnosis)

1. Before attempting any electrical diagnosis, make sure that the Sunroof is not binding due to a mechanical failure.
2. Check the Power Window Circuit Breaker.
3. Check that G349 is clean and tight.

- Check for a broken (or partially broken) wire inside of the insulation which could cause system malfunction but prove "GOOD" in a continuity/voltage check with a system disconnected. These circuits may be intermittent or resistive when loaded, and if possible, should be checked by monitoring for a voltage drop with the system operational (under load).
- Check for proper installation of aftermarket electronic equipment which may affect the integrity of other systems (see "Troubleshooting Procedures," page 8A-4-0).
- Refer to System Diagnosis.

SYSTEM DIAGNOSIS

- Perform the System Check and refer to the Symptom Table for the appropriate diagnostic procedure(s).

SYSTEM CHECK

ACTION	NORMAL RESULTS
[1] • With the Sunroof closed, push the Sunroof Switch to back direction.	Sunroof slides open (back) until switch is released or fully opened position is reached.
[2] • With the Sunroof fully open, push the Sunroof Switch in forward direction.	Sunroof slides closed (forward) until switch is released or fully closed position is reached.
[3] • With the Sunroof fully closed, push the Sunroof Switch in forward direction.	Sunroof lifts up into vent position until switch is released or highest position is reached.
[4] • With the Sunroof in the vent position, push the Sunroof Switch in back direction.	Sunroof will lower until switch is released or fully closed position is reached.

SUNROOF

SYMPTOM TABLE

SYMPTOM	PROCEDURE	PAGE NUMBER
Sunroof does not move when switch is pressed.	Chart #1	8A-122-2
Sunroof moves back and forth, but does not stop in the fully open and/or fully closed position.	Chart #2	8A-122-4

CHART #1

SUNROOF DOES NOT MOVE WHEN SWITCH IS PRESSED

NOTICE: The Position Switch generally won't prevent the motor from running

IMPORTANT:

- BEFORE REPLACING THE SUNROOF CONTROL UNIT, CHECK THE UNIT'S EXTERNAL WIRES FOR AN OPEN, SHORT TO GROUND OR BATTERY. IF WIRES ARE OK, CHECK FOR A POOR CONNECTION. IF OK, REPLACE THE UNIT.

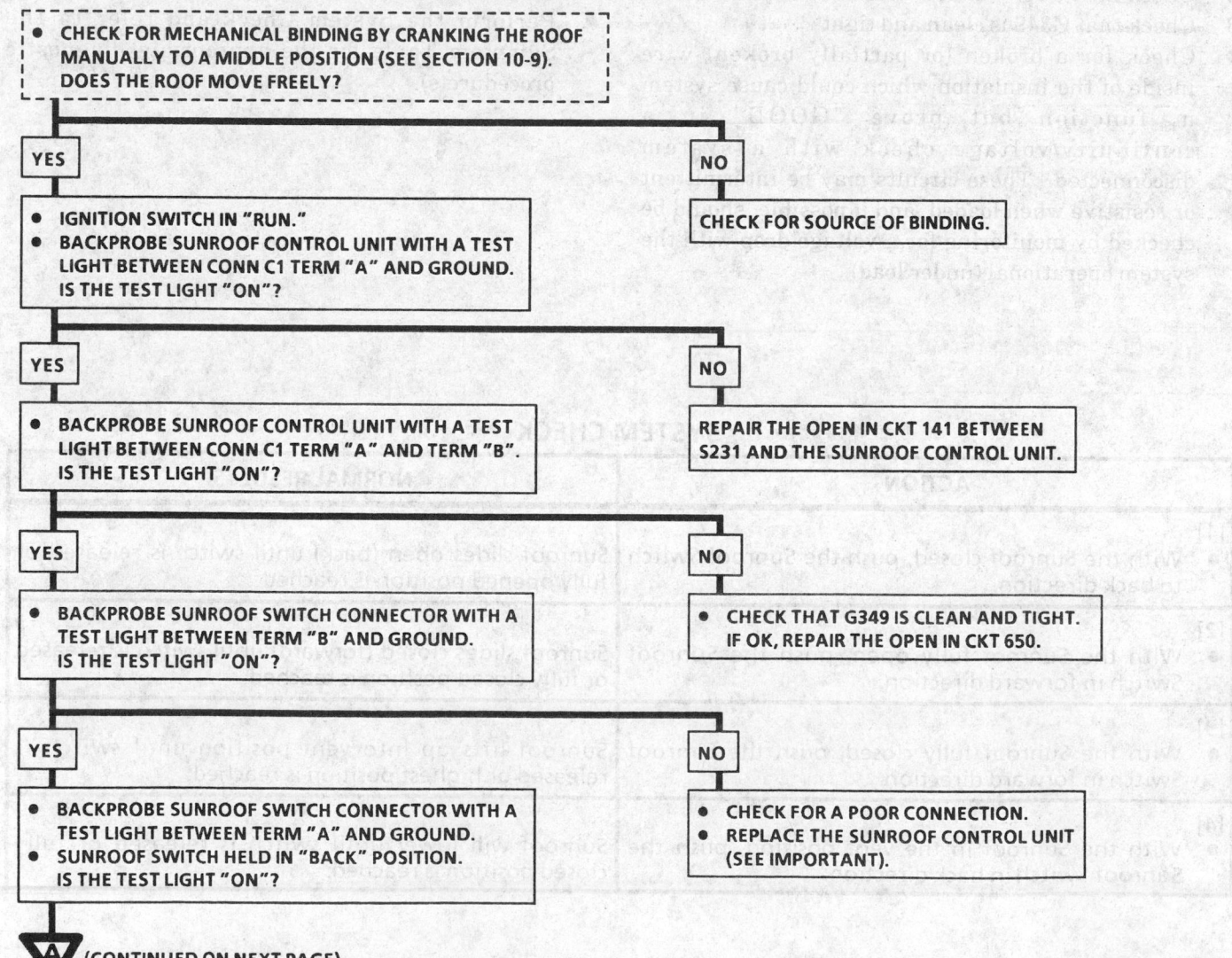

- CHECK FOR MECHANICAL BINDING BY CRANKING THE ROOF MANUALLY TO A MIDDLE POSITION (SEE SECTION 10-9). DOES THE ROOF MOVE FREELY?
  - **NO:** CHECK FOR SOURCE OF BINDING.
  - **YES:**
    - IGNITION SWITCH IN "RUN."
    - BACKPROBE SUNROOF CONTROL UNIT WITH A TEST LIGHT BETWEEN CONN C1 TERM "A" AND GROUND. IS THE TEST LIGHT "ON"?
      - **NO:** REPAIR THE OPEN IN CKT 141 BETWEEN S231 AND THE SUNROOF CONTROL UNIT.
      - **YES:**
        - BACKPROBE SUNROOF CONTROL UNIT WITH A TEST LIGHT BETWEEN CONN C1 TERM "A" AND TERM "B". IS THE TEST LIGHT "ON"?
          - **NO:** CHECK THAT G349 IS CLEAN AND TIGHT. IF OK, REPAIR THE OPEN IN CKT 650.
          - **YES:**
            - BACKPROBE SUNROOF SWITCH CONNECTOR WITH A TEST LIGHT BETWEEN TERM "B" AND GROUND. IS THE TEST LIGHT "ON"?
              - **NO:** CHECK FOR A POOR CONNECTION. REPLACE THE SUNROOF CONTROL UNIT (SEE IMPORTANT).
              - **YES:**
                - BACKPROBE SUNROOF SWITCH CONNECTOR WITH A TEST LIGHT BETWEEN TERM "A" AND GROUND.
                - SUNROOF SWITCH HELD IN "BACK" POSITION. IS THE TEST LIGHT "ON"?
                  - → A

A (CONTINUED ON NEXT PAGE)

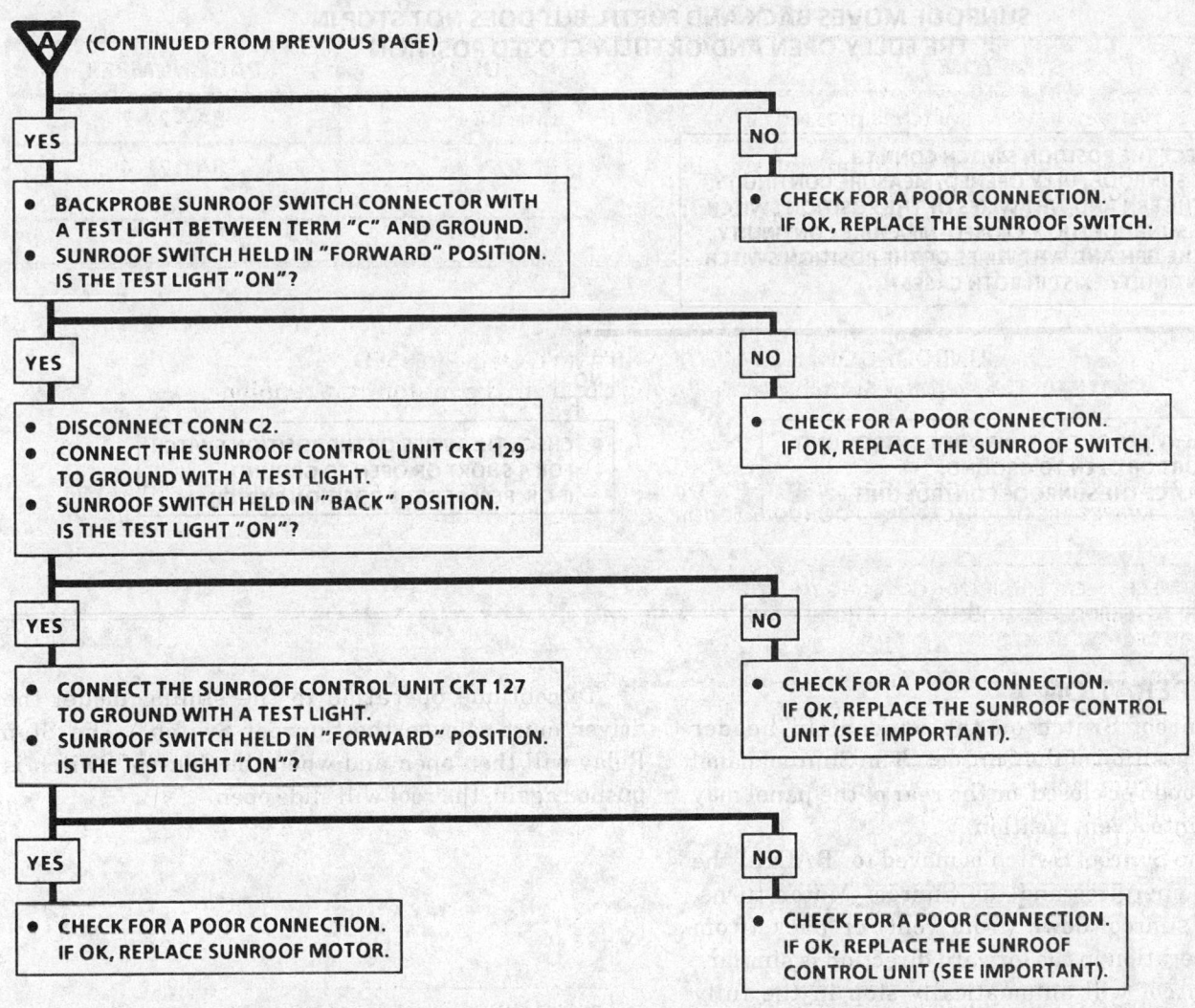

A (CONTINUED FROM PREVIOUS PAGE)

NO
- CHECK FOR A POOR CONNECTION. IF OK, REPLACE THE SUNROOF SWITCH.

YES
- BACKPROBE SUNROOF SWITCH CONNECTOR WITH A TEST LIGHT BETWEEN TERM "C" AND GROUND.
- SUNROOF SWITCH HELD IN "FORWARD" POSITION. IS THE TEST LIGHT "ON"?

NO
- CHECK FOR A POOR CONNECTION. IF OK, REPLACE THE SUNROOF SWITCH.

YES
- DISCONNECT CONN C2.
- CONNECT THE SUNROOF CONTROL UNIT CKT 129 TO GROUND WITH A TEST LIGHT.
- SUNROOF SWITCH HELD IN "BACK" POSITION. IS THE TEST LIGHT "ON"?

NO
- CHECK FOR A POOR CONNECTION. IF OK, REPLACE THE SUNROOF CONTROL UNIT (SEE IMPORTANT).

YES
- CONNECT THE SUNROOF CONTROL UNIT CKT 127 TO GROUND WITH A TEST LIGHT.
- SUNROOF SWITCH HELD IN "FORWARD" POSITION. IS THE TEST LIGHT "ON"?

YES
- CHECK FOR A POOR CONNECTION. IF OK, REPLACE SUNROOF MOTOR.

NO
- CHECK FOR A POOR CONNECTION. IF OK, REPLACE THE SUNROOF CONTROL UNIT (SEE IMPORTANT).

SUNROOF

CHART #2

SUNROOF MOVES BACK AND FORTH, BUT DOES NOT STOP IN THE FULLY OPEN AND/OR FULLY CLOSED POSITION

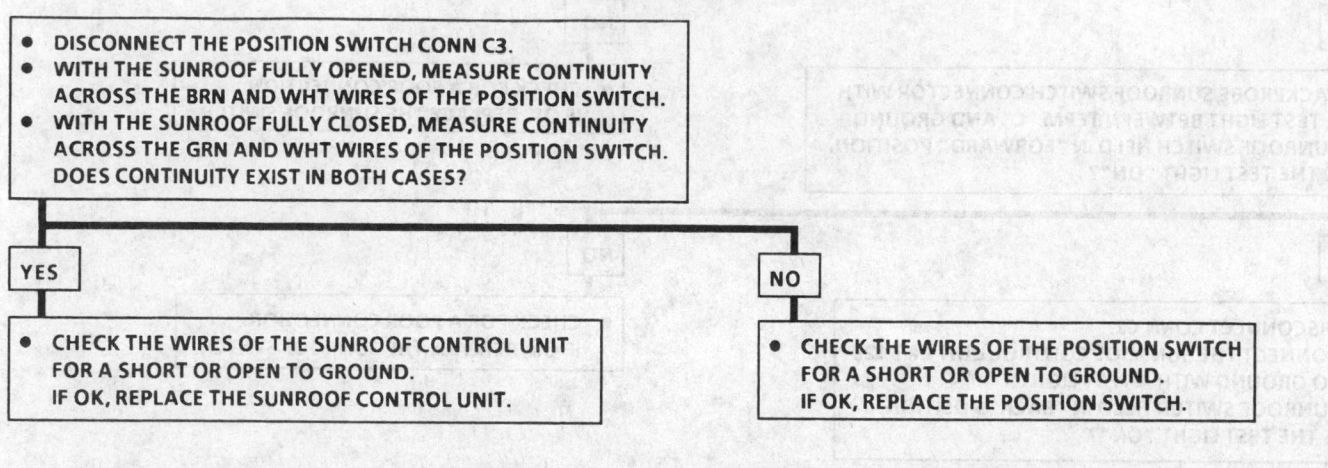

- DISCONNECT THE POSITION SWITCH CONN C3.
- WITH THE SUNROOF FULLY OPENED, MEASURE CONTINUITY ACROSS THE BRN AND WHT WIRES OF THE POSITION SWITCH.
- WITH THE SUNROOF FULLY CLOSED, MEASURE CONTINUITY ACROSS THE GRN AND WHT WIRES OF THE POSITION SWITCH.
  DOES CONTINUITY EXIST IN BOTH CASES?

YES

- CHECK THE WIRES OF THE SUNROOF CONTROL UNIT FOR A SHORT OR OPEN TO GROUND.
  IF OK, REPLACE THE SUNROOF CONTROL UNIT.

NO

- CHECK THE WIRES OF THE POSITION SWITCH FOR A SHORT OR OPEN TO GROUND.
  IF OK, REPLACE THE POSITION SWITCH.

CIRCUIT OPERATION

The Sunroof Switch on the windshield header controls the position of the Sunroof. The Sunroof panel may be slid open or closed, or the rear of the panel may be tilted up into a vent position.

When the Sunroof Switch is moved to "BACK," the Back Relay energizes and the Sunroof Motor turns, driving the sunroof down (from vent) or back (from sliding). Operation in the forward direction is similar.

The Sunroof will automatically stop in the fully open or closed position when approaching from either the vent or sliding positions. The fully open or closed position is sensed by the Position Switch, which remains in the open position, except when the Sunroof is fully open or fully closed. For example, if the roof is closing from the vent position, the back relay will be energized and the Position Switch will be in the open position. When the roof is fully closed, the Position Switch moves to closed. The closed position is sensed by the Stop Relay which in turn energizes the Forward Relay. With both Forward and Back Relays energized, no voltage is applied to the Motor and it stops.

To continue operation to the sliding mode, the driver must release the Sunroof Switch. The Stop Relay will then open and when the Sunroof Switch is pushed again, the roof will slide open.

BLANK

AUTOMATIC DOOR LOCKS

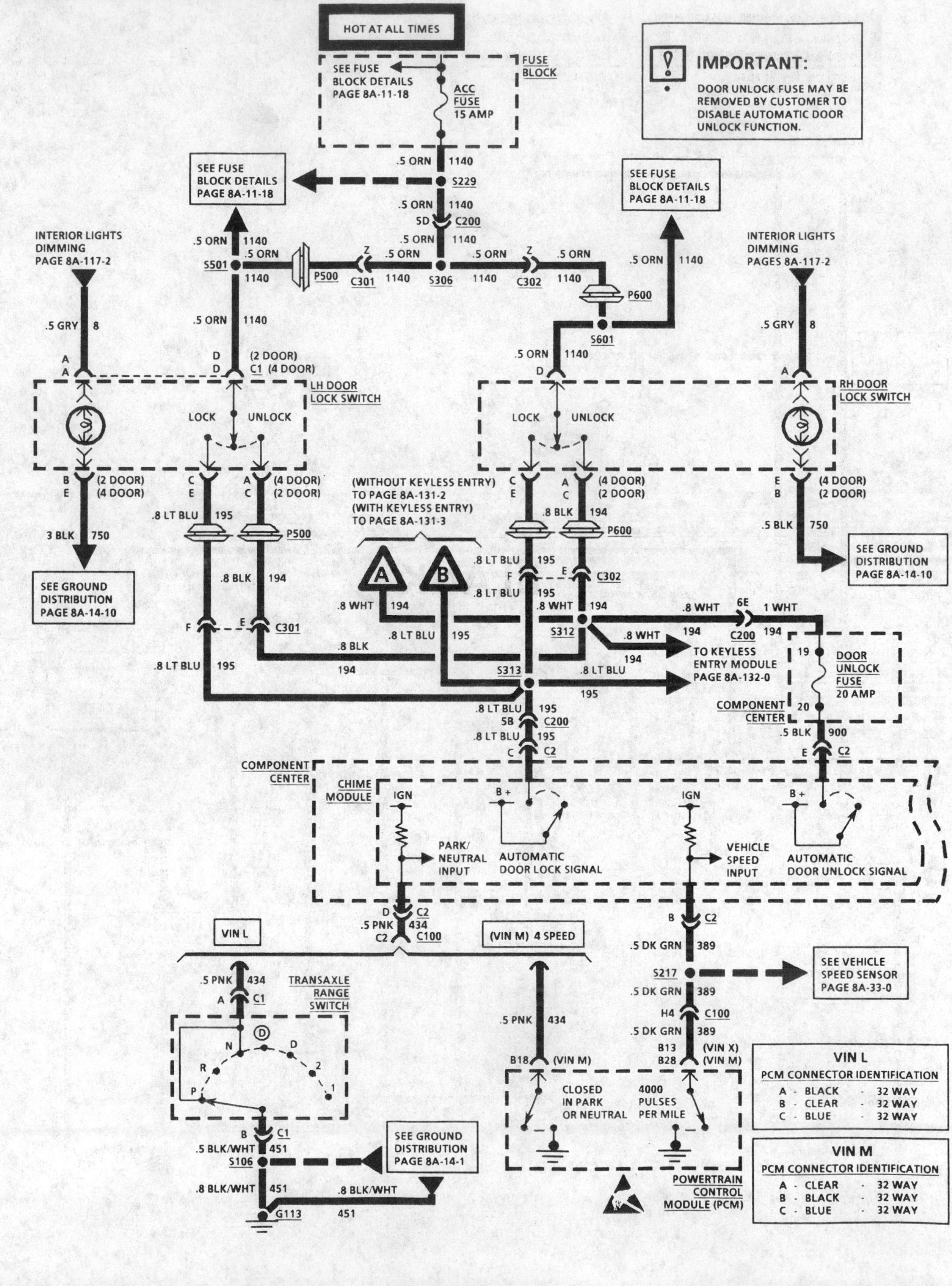
HOT AT ALL TIMES
SEE FUSE BLOCK DETAILS PAGE 8A-11-18
ACC FUSE 15 AMP
FUSE BLOCK
IMPORTANT:
DOOR UNLOCK FUSE MAY BE REMOVED BY CUSTOMER TO DISABLE AUTOMATIC DOOR UNLOCK FUNCTION.
.5 ORN 1140
S229
C200
5D
SEE FUSE BLOCK DETAILS PAGE 8A-11-18
SEE FUSE BLOCK DETAILS PAGE 8A-11-18
INTERIOR LIGHTS DIMMING PAGE 8A-117-2
INTERIOR LIGHTS DIMMING PAGES 8A-117-2
S501
P500
C301
S306
C302
P600
S601
.5 GRY 8
(2 DOOR)
C1 (4 DOOR)
LH DOOR LOCK SWITCH
RH DOOR LOCK SWITCH
LOCK
UNLOCK
(2 DOOR)
(4 DOOR)
3 BLK 750
.5 BLK 750
.8 LT BLU 195
.8 BLK 194
SEE GROUND DISTRIBUTION PAGE 8A-14-10
SEE GROUND DISTRIBUTION PAGE 8A-14-10
(WITHOUT KEYLESS ENTRY) TO PAGE 8A-131-2
(WITH KEYLESS ENTRY) TO PAGE 8A-131-3
A
B
.8 WHT 194
6E
1 WHT 194
S312
C200
TO KEYLESS ENTRY MODULE PAGE 8A-132-0
S313
DOOR UNLOCK FUSE 20 AMP
COMPONENT CENTER
.5 BLK 900
C2
COMPONENT CENTER
CHIME MODULE
IGN
B+
PARK/ NEUTRAL INPUT
AUTOMATIC DOOR LOCK SIGNAL
VEHICLE SPEED INPUT
AUTOMATIC DOOR UNLOCK SIGNAL
.5 PNK 434
C100
VIN L
(VIN M) 4 SPEED
.5 DK GRN 389
S217
SEE VEHICLE SPEED SENSOR PAGE 8A-33-0
TRANSAXLE RANGE SWITCH
C1
P R N D 2 1
.5 BLK/WHT 451
S106
SEE GROUND DISTRIBUTION PAGE 8A-14-1
.8 BLK/WHT 451
G113
H4
B13 (VIN X)
B28 (VIN M)
B18 (VIN M)
CLOSED IN PARK OR NEUTRAL
4000 PULSES PER MILE
POWERTRAIN CONTROL MODULE (PCM)
VIN L
PCM CONNECTOR IDENTIFICATION
A - BLACK - 32 WAY
B - CLEAR - 32 WAY
C - BLUE - 32 WAY
VIN M
PCM CONNECTOR IDENTIFICATION
A - CLEAR - 32 WAY
B - BLACK - 32 WAY
C - BLUE - 32 WAY

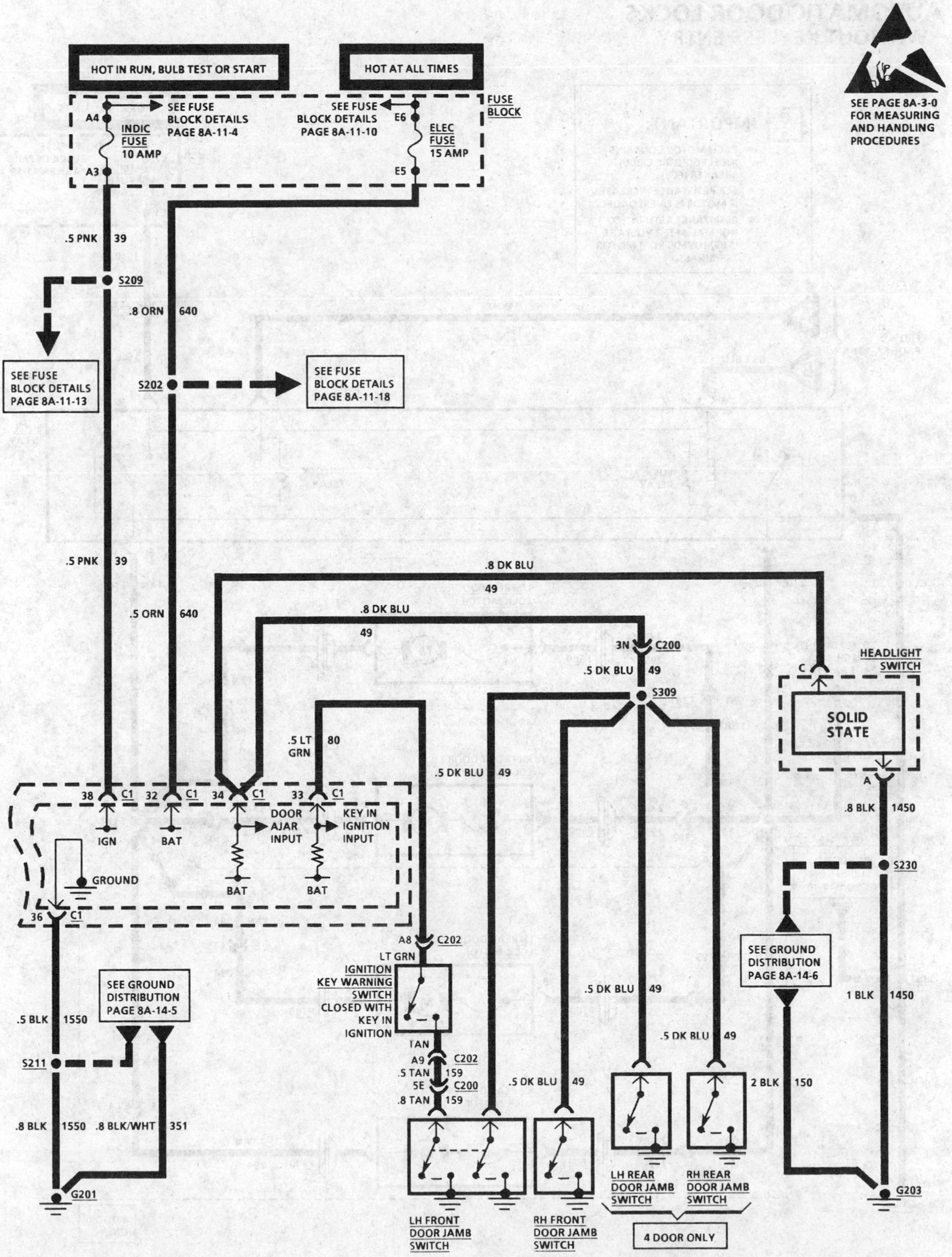

HOT IN RUN, BULB TEST OR START
HOT AT ALL TIMES
FUSE BLOCK
A4
SEE FUSE BLOCK DETAILS PAGE 8A-11-4
INDIC FUSE 10 AMP
A3
SEE FUSE BLOCK DETAILS PAGE 8A-11-10
E6
ELEC FUSE 15 AMP
E5
SEE PAGE 8A-3-0 FOR MEASURING AND HANDLING PROCEDURES
.5 PNK 39
S209
.8 ORN 640
SEE FUSE BLOCK DETAILS PAGE 8A-11-13
S202
SEE FUSE BLOCK DETAILS PAGE 8A-11-18
.5 PNK 39
.5 ORN 640
.8 DK BLU 49
.8 DK BLU 49
3N C200
.5 DK BLU 49
S309
HEADLIGHT SWITCH
C
SOLID STATE
A
.5 LT GRN 80
.5 DK BLU 49
38 C1
32 C1
34 C1
33 C1
IGN
BAT
DOOR AJAR INPUT
KEY IN IGNITION INPUT
GROUND
BAT
BAT
36 C1
.8 BLK 1450
S230
A8 C202
LT GRN
IGNITION KEY WARNING SWITCH CLOSED WITH KEY IN IGNITION
SEE GROUND DISTRIBUTION PAGE 8A-14-6
SEE GROUND DISTRIBUTION PAGE 8A-14-5
.5 BLK 1550
.5 DK BLU 49
1 BLK 1450
TAN
.5 DK BLU 49
S211
A9 C202
.5 TAN 159
5E C200
.8 TAN 159
.5 DK BLU 49
2 BLK 150
.8 BLK 1550
.8 BLK/WHT 351
G201
LH FRONT DOOR JAMB SWITCH
RH FRONT DOOR JAMB SWITCH
LH REAR DOOR JAMB SWITCH
RH REAR DOOR JAMB SWITCH
4 DOOR ONLY
G203

AUTOMATIC DOOR LOCKS
WITHOUT KEYLESS ENTRY

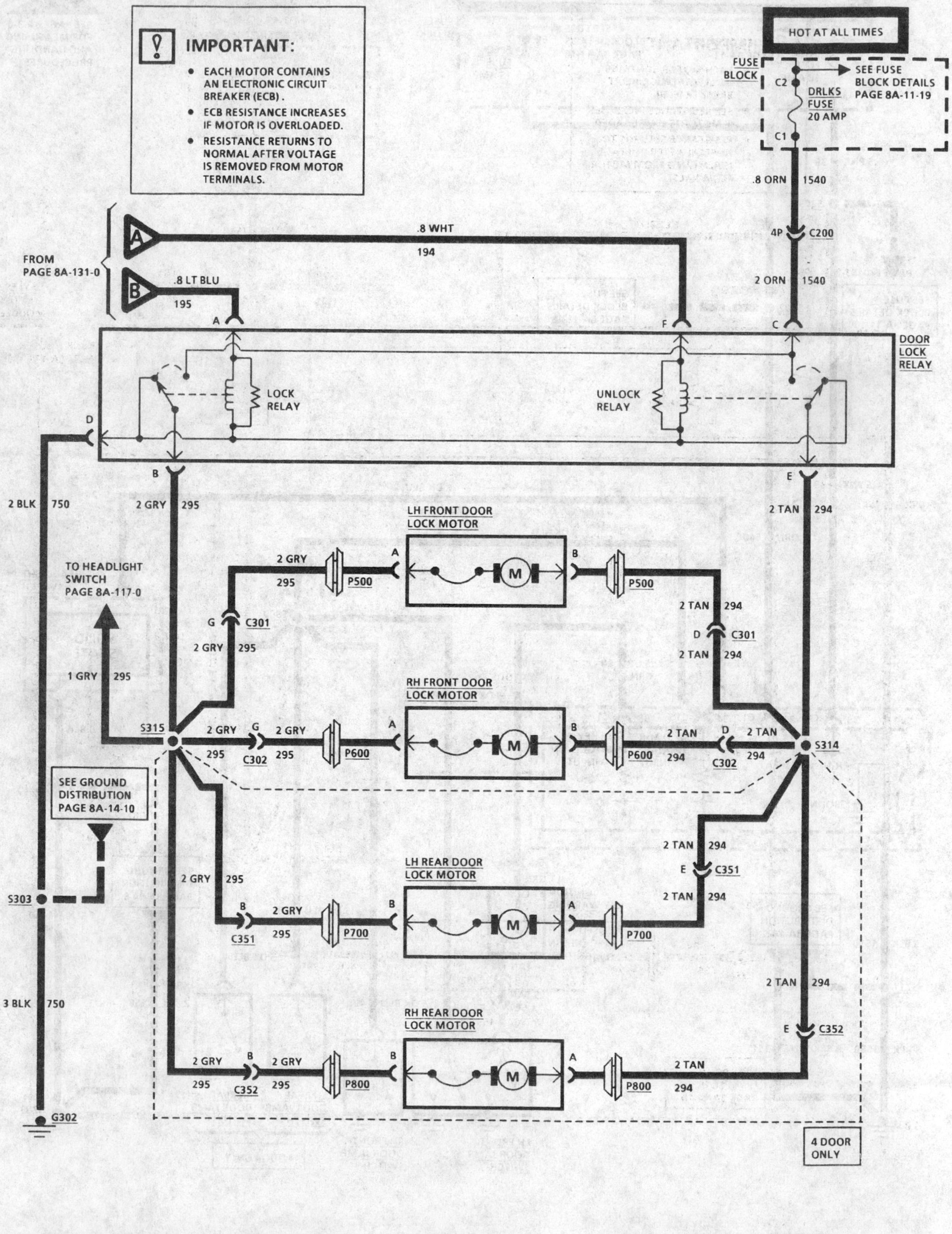

IMPORTANT:
EACH MOTOR CONTAINS AN ELECTRONIC CIRCUIT BREAKER (ECB).
ECB RESISTANCE INCREASES IF MOTOR IS OVERLOADED.
RESISTANCE RETURNS TO NORMAL AFTER VOLTAGE IS REMOVED FROM MOTOR TERMINALS.
HOT AT ALL TIMES
FUSE BLOCK
C2
DRLKS FUSE 20 AMP
C1
SEE FUSE BLOCK DETAILS PAGE 8A-11-19
.8 ORN 1540
4P C200
2 ORN 1540
FROM PAGE 8A-131-0
A
.8 WHT
194
B
.8 LT BLU
195
A
F
C
DOOR LOCK RELAY
LOCK RELAY
UNLOCK RELAY
D
B
E
2 BLK 750
2 GRY 295
2 TAN 294
LH FRONT DOOR LOCK MOTOR
2 GRY 295
P500
A
B
M
P500
TO HEADLIGHT SWITCH PAGE 8A-117-0
2 TAN 294
G C301
D C301
2 GRY 295
2 TAN 294
1 GRY 295
RH FRONT DOOR LOCK MOTOR
S315
2 GRY 295
G C302
2 GRY 295
P600
A
B
P600
2 TAN 294
D C302
2 TAN 294
S314
SEE GROUND DISTRIBUTION PAGE 8A-14-10
2 TAN 294
E C351
LH REAR DOOR LOCK MOTOR
2 TAN 294
2 GRY 295
S303
B C351
2 GRY 295
P700
B
A
P700
3 BLK 750
2 TAN 294
E C352
RH REAR DOOR LOCK MOTOR
2 GRY 295
B C352
2 GRY 295
P800
B
A
P800
2 TAN 294
G302
4 DOOR ONLY

AUTOMATIC DOOR LOCKS
WITH KEYLESS ENTRY

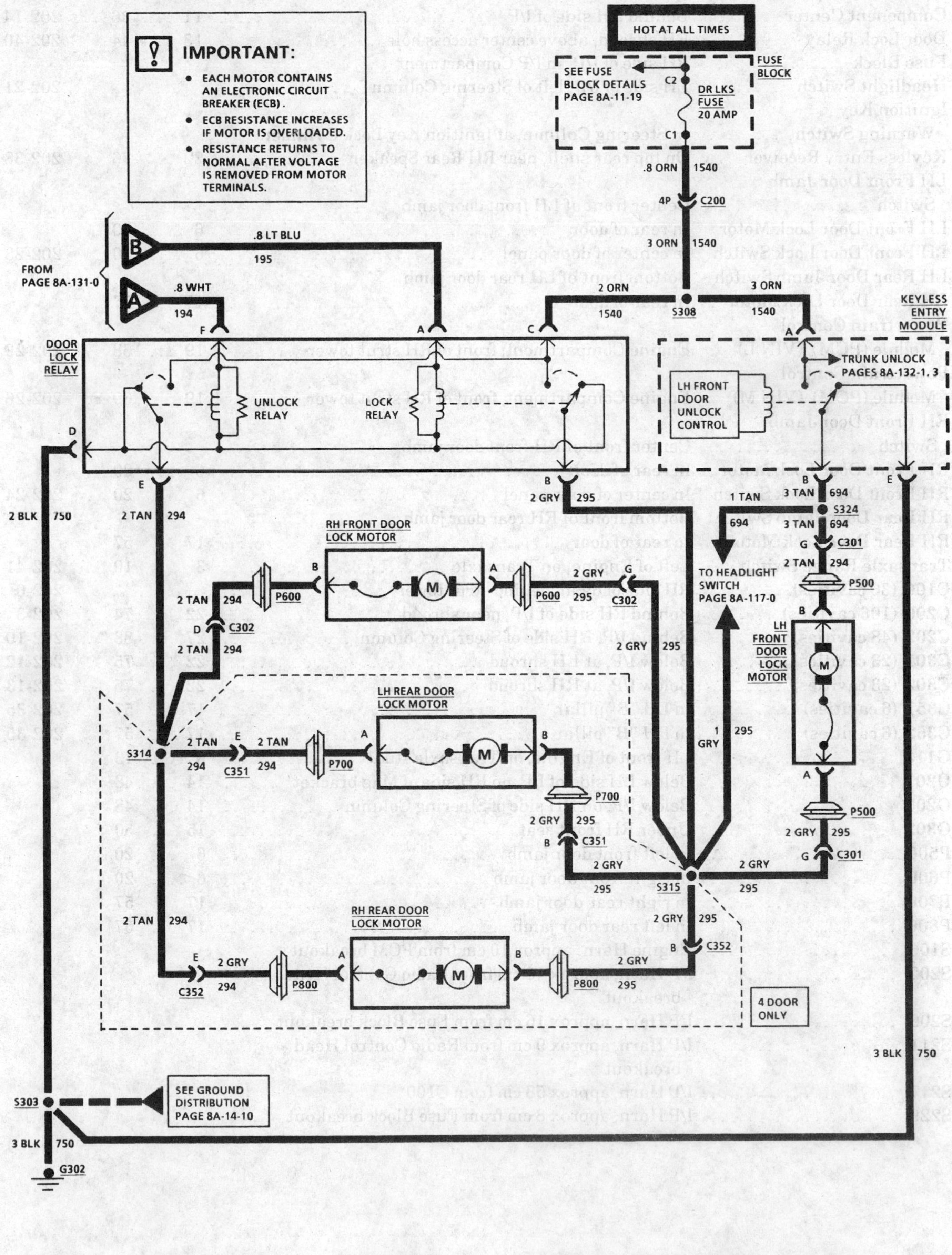
IMPORTANT:
EACH MOTOR CONTAINS AN ELECTRONIC CIRCUIT BREAKER (ECB).
ECB RESISTANCE INCREASES IF MOTOR IS OVERLOADED.
RESISTANCE RETURNS TO NORMAL AFTER VOLTAGE IS REMOVED FROM MOTOR TERMINALS.
HOT AT ALL TIMES
SEE FUSE BLOCK DETAILS PAGE 8A-11-19
FUSE BLOCK
DR LKS FUSE 20 AMP
C2
C1
.8 ORN 1540
4P C200
3 ORN 1540
2 ORN 1540
3 ORN 1540
S308
FROM PAGE 8A-131-0
B
A
.8 LT BLU 195
.8 WHT 194
DOOR LOCK RELAY
UNLOCK RELAY
LOCK RELAY
KEYLESS ENTRY MODULE
TRUNK UNLOCK PAGES 8A-132-1, 3
LH FRONT DOOR UNLOCK CONTROL
2 BLK 750
2 TAN 294
2 GRY 295
1 TAN 694
3 TAN 694
S324
C301
TO HEADLIGHT SWITCH PAGE 8A-117-0
RH FRONT DOOR LOCK MOTOR
P600
C302
LH FRONT DOOR LOCK MOTOR
P500
LH REAR DOOR LOCK MOTOR
S314
C351
P700
1 GRY 295
S315
RH REAR DOOR LOCK MOTOR
C352
P800
4 DOOR ONLY
3 BLK 750
S303
SEE GROUND DISTRIBUTION PAGE 8A-14-10
G302

AUTOMATIC DOOR LOCKS

COMPONENT	LOCATION	201-PG	FIG.	CONN
Component Center	Behind RH side of I/P	11	36	202-14
Door Lock Relay	RH shroud, above center access hole	13	44	202-40
Fuse Block	RH side of I/P, in I/P Compartment			
Headlight Switch	LH side of I/P, left of Steering Column			202-21
Ignition Key Warning Switch	In Steering Column, at Ignition Key Lock Cylinder			
Keyless Entry Receiver	On top rear shelf, near RH Rear Speaker	22	76	202-38
LH Front Door Jamb Switch	Center front of LH front door jamb			
LH Front Door Lock Motor	In rear of door	6	20	
LH Front Door Lock Switch	In center of door panel	6	20	202-23
LH Rear Door Jamb Switch	Bottom front of LH rear door jamb			
LH Rear Door Lock Motor	In rear of door	17	57	
Powertrain Control Module (PCM) (VIN L)	Engine Compartment, front of RH strut tower	19	68	202-29
Powertrain Control Module (PCM) (VIN M)	Engine Compartment, front of RH strut tower	19	69	202-26
RH Front Door Jamb Switch	Center front of RH front door jamb			
RH Front Door Lock Motor	In rear of door	6	20	
RH Front Door Lock Switch	In center of door panel	6	20	202-24
RH Rear Door Jamb Switch	Bottom front of RH rear door jamb			
RH Rear Door Lock Motor	In rear of door	17	57	
Transaxle Range Switch	Left of Engine, on Transaxle	3	10	202-41
C100 (36 cavities)	RH side of dash, behind strut tower			202-0
C200 (106 cavities)	Behind RH side of I/P, near shroud	22	74	202-3
C202 (48 cavities)	Behind I/P, RH side of Steering Column	27	88	202-10
C301 (23 cavities)	Below I/P, at LH shroud	22	75	202-12
C302 (23 cavities)	Below I/P, at RH shroud	22	75	202-13
C351 (6 cavities)	In LH "B" pillar	17	57	202-35
C352 (6 cavities)	In RH "B" pillar	17	57	202-35
G113	LH front of Engine, on Transaxle stud	0	13	
G201	Below LH side of I/P, on RH side of Mag bracket	14	48	
G203	Below I/P, on RH side of Steering Column	14	48	
G302	Under RH front seat	15	50	
P500	In left front door jamb	6	20	
P600	In right front door jamb	6	20	
P700	In right rear door jamb	17	57	
P800	In left rear door jamb	17	57	
S106	Engine Harn, approx 10 cm from PCM breakout			
S202	I/P Harn, approx 13 cm from Radio Control Head breakout			
S209	I/P Harn, approx 16 cm from Fuse Block breakout			
S211	I/P Harn, approx 9 cm from Radio Control Head breakout			
S217	I/P Harn, approx 58 cm from C100			
S229	I/P Harn, approx 8 cm from Fuse Block breakout			

COMPONENT	LOCATION	201-PG	FIG.	CONN
S230	I/P Harn, approx 27 cm from Radio Control Head breakout			
S303	Cross Car Harn, approx 38 cm from Driver Seat Belt Switch breakout			
S306	Cross Car Harn, approx 10 cm from G302 breakout			
S309	Cross Car Harn, approx 13 cm from Driver Seat Belt Switch breakout			
S312 (2 Door)	Cross Car Harn, approx 22 cm from Driver Seat Belt Switch breakout	13	44	
S312 (4 Door)	Cross Car Harn, approx 22 cm from Driver Seat Belt Switch breakout	13	44	
S313 (2 Door)	Cross Car Harn, approx 30 cm from Driver Seat Belt Switch breakout	13	44	
S313 (4 Door)	Cross Car Harn, approx 30 cm from Driver Seat Belt Switch breakout	13	44	
S314	Cross Car Harn, approx 7 cm from Driver Seat Belt Switch breakout	13	44	
S315	Cross Car Harn, approx 14 cm from Driver Seat Belt Switch breakout	13	44	
S501	LH Front Door Harn, approx 10 cm from Door Lock Switch breakout	6	20	
S601	RH Front Door Harn, approx 10 cm from Door Lock Switch breakout	6	20	

AUTOMATIC DOOR LOCKS

TROUBLESHOOTING HINTS (Perform before beginning System Diagnosis)

1. Check the ACC, DRLKS, ELEC and INDIC Fuses by visual inspection.
2. Check for mechanical binds in the Door Lock System.
3. If one of the Door Lock Motors does not operate properly, but the other Door Lock Motors function normally, check the wiring to the suspect motor. If the wiring is correct, check for a poor connection. If OK, replace the motor.
4. Check that grounds G113, G201, G203 and G302 are clean and tight.
5. Check that the Dome Light Switch is in the "OFF" position.

Important:

- For diagnosis of Power Door Locks on vehicles equipped with Keyless Entry, see page 8A-132-0.

- Check for a broken (or partially broken) wire inside of the insulation which could cause system malfunction but prove "GOOD" in a continuity/voltage check with a system disconnected. These circuits may be intermittent or resistive when loaded, and if possible, should be checked by monitoring for a voltage drop with the system operational (under load).
- Check for proper installation of aftermarket electronic equipment which may affect the integrity of other systems (see "Troubleshooting Procedures," page 8A-4-0).
- Refer to System Diagnosis.

SYSTEM DIAGNOSIS

- Refer to the Symptom Table for the appropriate diagnostic procedure(s).

SYMPTOM TABLE

SYMPTOM	PROCEDURE	PAGE NUMBER
Power Door Locks inoperative from both Power Door Lock Switches.	Chart #1	8A-131-7
Power Door Locks operate from one Door Lock Switch only.	Chart #2	8A-131-8
Lock function inoperative (unlock function operative) from both Door Lock Switches.	Chart #3	8A-131-8
Unlock function inoperative (lock function operative) from both Door Lock Switches.	Chart #4	8A-131-8
Lock function inoperative (unlock function operative) from one Door Lock Switch.	Chart #5	8A-131-8
Unlock function inoperative (lock function operative) from one Door Lock Switch.	Chart #6	8A-131-9
One or more Lock Motors inoperative from both switches.	Chart #7	8A-131-9
Automatic Door Lock feature does not operate properly, Power Locks operate normally from Door Lock Switches.	Chart #8	8A-131-10

CHART #1
POWER DOOR LOCKS INOPERATIVE FROM BOTH DOOR LOCK SWITCHES

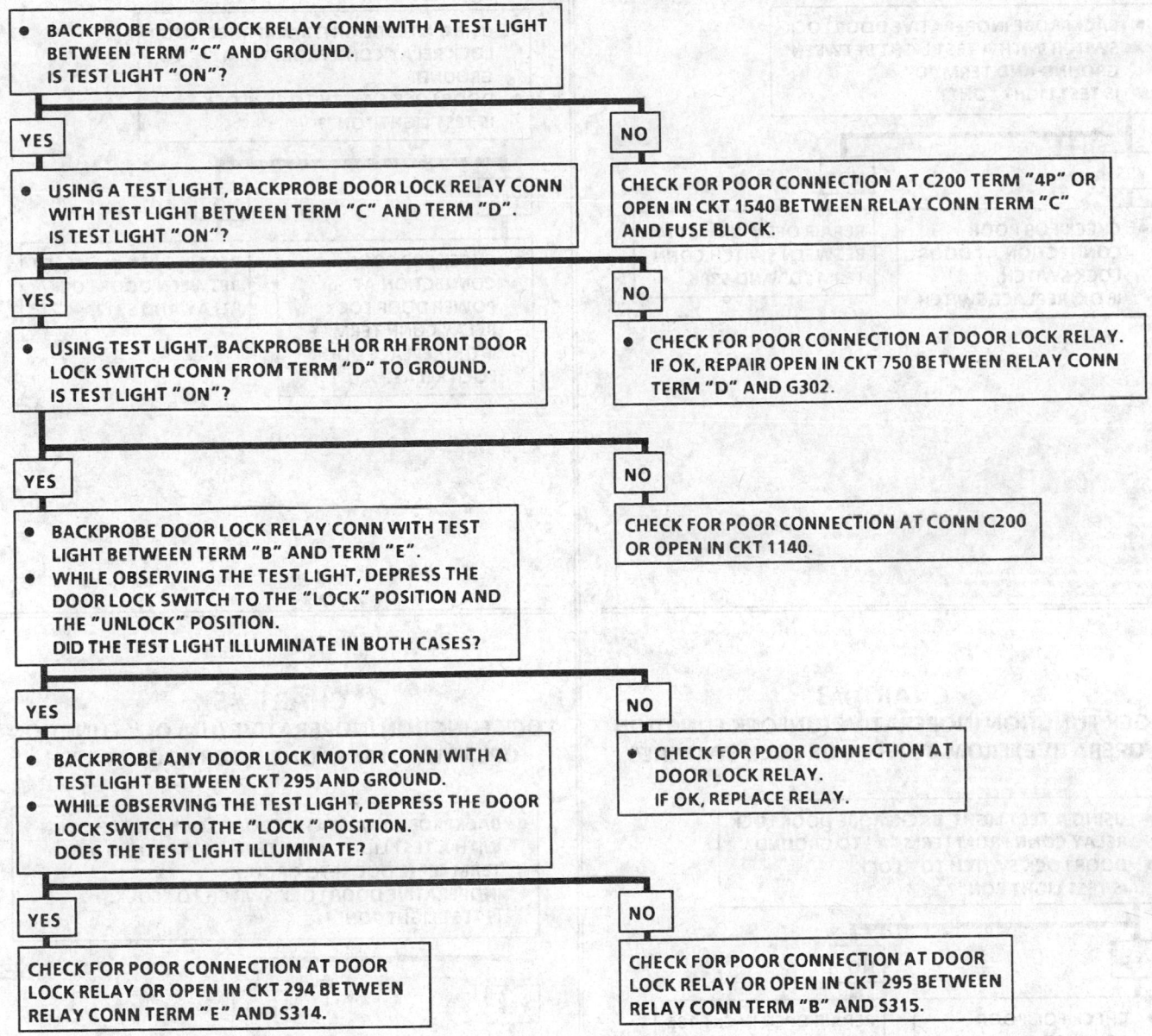

- BACKPROBE DOOR LOCK RELAY CONN WITH A TEST LIGHT BETWEEN TERM "C" AND GROUND.
  IS TEST LIGHT "ON"?

NO: CHECK FOR POOR CONNECTION AT C200 TERM "4P" OR OPEN IN CKT 1540 BETWEEN RELAY CONN TERM "C" AND FUSE BLOCK.

YES:

- USING A TEST LIGHT, BACKPROBE DOOR LOCK RELAY CONN WITH TEST LIGHT BETWEEN TERM "C" AND TERM "D".
  IS TEST LIGHT "ON"?

NO:
- CHECK FOR POOR CONNECTION AT DOOR LOCK RELAY.
  IF OK, REPAIR OPEN IN CKT 750 BETWEEN RELAY CONN TERM "D" AND G302.

YES:

- USING TEST LIGHT, BACKPROBE LH OR RH FRONT DOOR LOCK SWITCH CONN FROM TERM "D" TO GROUND.
  IS TEST LIGHT "ON"?

NO: CHECK FOR POOR CONNECTION AT CONN C200 OR OPEN IN CKT 1140.

YES:

- BACKPROBE DOOR LOCK RELAY CONN WITH TEST LIGHT BETWEEN TERM "B" AND TERM "E".
- WHILE OBSERVING THE TEST LIGHT, DEPRESS THE DOOR LOCK SWITCH TO THE "LOCK" POSITION AND THE "UNLOCK" POSITION.
  DID THE TEST LIGHT ILLUMINATE IN BOTH CASES?

NO:
- CHECK FOR POOR CONNECTION AT DOOR LOCK RELAY.
  IF OK, REPLACE RELAY.

YES:

- BACKPROBE ANY DOOR LOCK MOTOR CONN WITH A TEST LIGHT BETWEEN CKT 295 AND GROUND.
- WHILE OBSERVING THE TEST LIGHT, DEPRESS THE DOOR LOCK SWITCH TO THE "LOCK" POSITION.
  DOES THE TEST LIGHT ILLUMINATE?

YES: CHECK FOR POOR CONNECTION AT DOOR LOCK RELAY OR OPEN IN CKT 294 BETWEEN RELAY CONN TERM "E" AND S314.

NO: CHECK FOR POOR CONNECTION AT DOOR LOCK RELAY OR OPEN IN CKT 295 BETWEEN RELAY CONN TERM "B" AND S315.

AUTOMATIC DOOR LOCKS

CHART #2
POWER DOOR LOCKS OPERATE FROM ONE DOOR LOCK SWITCH ONLY

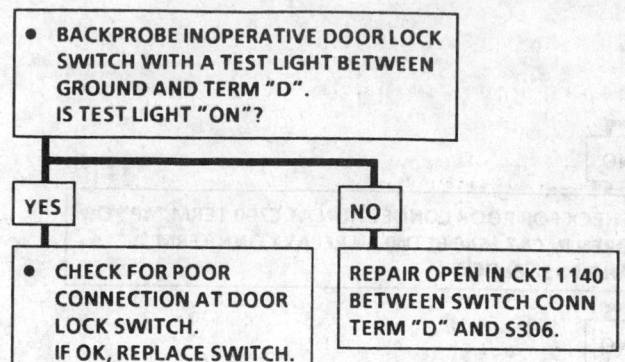

- BACKPROBE INOPERATIVE DOOR LOCK SWITCH WITH A TEST LIGHT BETWEEN GROUND AND TERM "D". IS TEST LIGHT "ON"?

YES
- CHECK FOR POOR CONNECTION AT DOOR LOCK SWITCH. IF OK, REPLACE SWITCH.

NO

REPAIR OPEN IN CKT 1140 BETWEEN SWITCH CONN TERM "D" AND S306.

CHART #4
UNLOCK FUNCTION INOPERATIVE (LOCK FUNCTION OPERATIVE) FROM BOTH DOOR LOCK SWITCHES

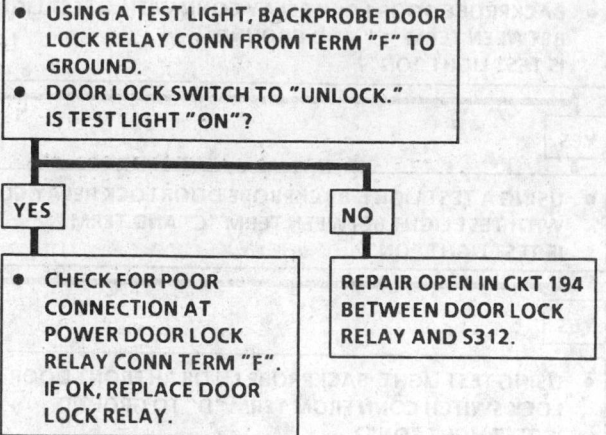

- USING A TEST LIGHT, BACKPROBE DOOR LOCK RELAY CONN FROM TERM "F" TO GROUND.
- DOOR LOCK SWITCH TO "UNLOCK." IS TEST LIGHT "ON"?

YES
- CHECK FOR POOR CONNECTION AT POWER DOOR LOCK RELAY CONN TERM "F". IF OK, REPLACE DOOR LOCK RELAY.

NO

REPAIR OPEN IN CKT 194 BETWEEN DOOR LOCK RELAY AND S312.

CHART #3
LOCK FUNCTION INOPERATIVE (UNLOCK FUNCTION OPERATIVE) FROM BOTH DOOR LOCK SWITCHES

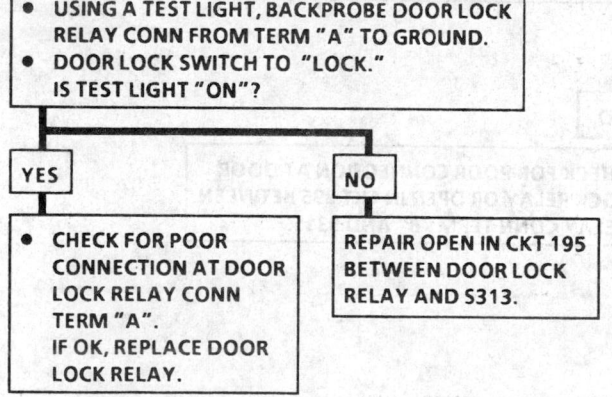

- USING A TEST LIGHT, BACKPROBE DOOR LOCK RELAY CONN FROM TERM "A" TO GROUND.
- DOOR LOCK SWITCH TO "LOCK." IS TEST LIGHT "ON"?

YES
- CHECK FOR POOR CONNECTION AT DOOR LOCK RELAY CONN TERM "A". IF OK, REPLACE DOOR LOCK RELAY.

NO

REPAIR OPEN IN CKT 195 BETWEEN DOOR LOCK RELAY AND S313.

CHART #5
LOCK FUNCTION INOPERATIVE (UNLOCK FUNCTION OPERATIVE) FROM ONE DOOR LOCK SWITCH

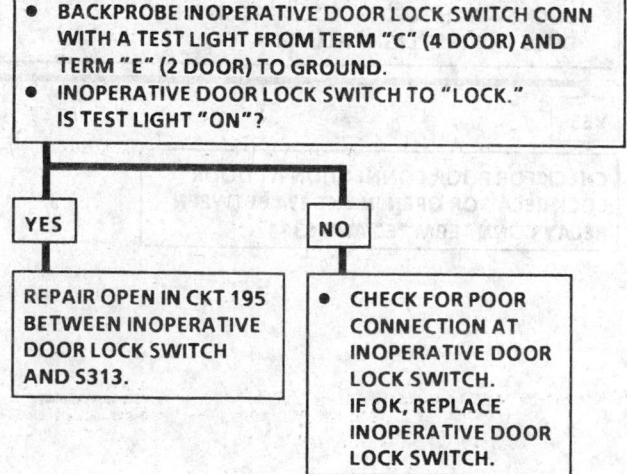

- BACKPROBE INOPERATIVE DOOR LOCK SWITCH CONN WITH A TEST LIGHT FROM TERM "C" (4 DOOR) AND TERM "E" (2 DOOR) TO GROUND.
- INOPERATIVE DOOR LOCK SWITCH TO "LOCK." IS TEST LIGHT "ON"?

YES

REPAIR OPEN IN CKT 195 BETWEEN INOPERATIVE DOOR LOCK SWITCH AND S313.

NO
- CHECK FOR POOR CONNECTION AT INOPERATIVE DOOR LOCK SWITCH. IF OK, REPLACE INOPERATIVE DOOR LOCK SWITCH.

CHART #6

UNLOCK FUNCTION INOPERATIVE (LOCK FUNCTION OPERATIVE) FROM ONE DOOR LOCK SWITCH

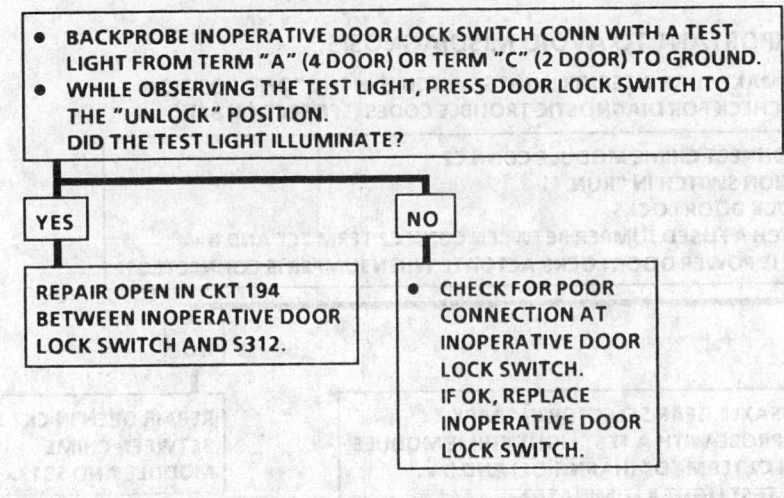

- BACKPROBE INOPERATIVE DOOR LOCK SWITCH CONN WITH A TEST LIGHT FROM TERM "A" (4 DOOR) OR TERM "C" (2 DOOR) TO GROUND.
- WHILE OBSERVING THE TEST LIGHT, PRESS DOOR LOCK SWITCH TO THE "UNLOCK" POSITION.

DID THE TEST LIGHT ILLUMINATE?

YES

REPAIR OPEN IN CKT 194 BETWEEN INOPERATIVE DOOR LOCK SWITCH AND S312.

NO

- CHECK FOR POOR CONNECTION AT INOPERATIVE DOOR LOCK SWITCH.

IF OK, REPLACE INOPERATIVE DOOR LOCK SWITCH.

CHART #7

ONE OR MORE LOCK MOTORS ARE INOPERATIVE FROM BOTH SWITCHES

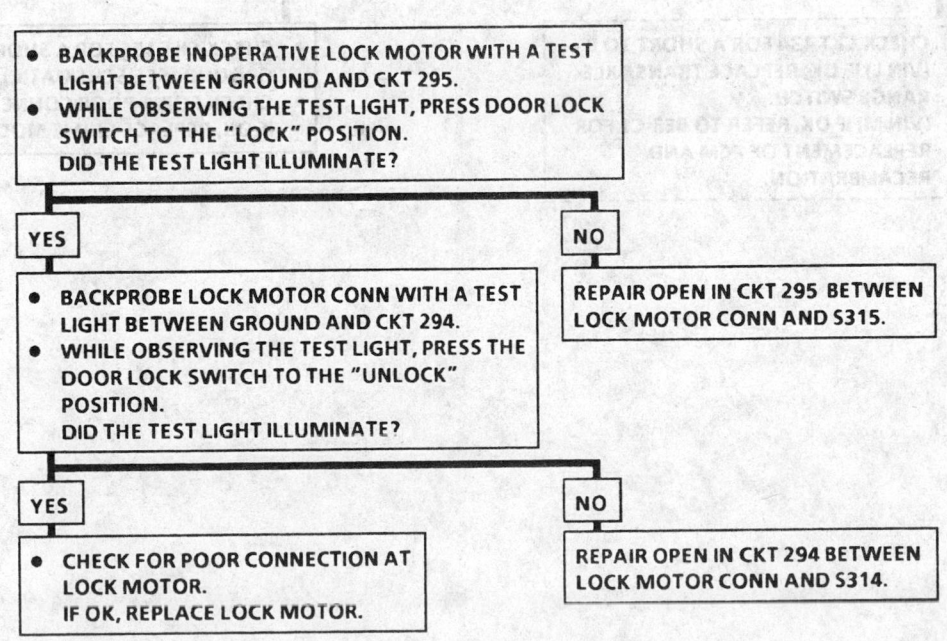

- BACKPROBE INOPERATIVE LOCK MOTOR WITH A TEST LIGHT BETWEEN GROUND AND CKT 295.
- WHILE OBSERVING THE TEST LIGHT, PRESS DOOR LOCK SWITCH TO THE "LOCK" POSITION.

DID THE TEST LIGHT ILLUMINATE?

YES

- BACKPROBE LOCK MOTOR CONN WITH A TEST LIGHT BETWEEN GROUND AND CKT 294.
- WHILE OBSERVING THE TEST LIGHT, PRESS THE DOOR LOCK SWITCH TO THE "UNLOCK" POSITION.

DID THE TEST LIGHT ILLUMINATE?

- **YES**
  - CHECK FOR POOR CONNECTION AT LOCK MOTOR.

  IF OK, REPLACE LOCK MOTOR.
- **NO**

  REPAIR OPEN IN CKT 294 BETWEEN LOCK MOTOR CONN AND S314.

NO

REPAIR OPEN IN CKT 295 BETWEEN LOCK MOTOR CONN AND S315.

AUTOMATIC DOOR LOCKS

CHART #8

AUTOMATIC DOOR LOCK FEATURE DOES NOT OPERATE PROPERLY, POWER LOCKS OPERATE NORMALLY FROM DOOR LOCK SWITCHES

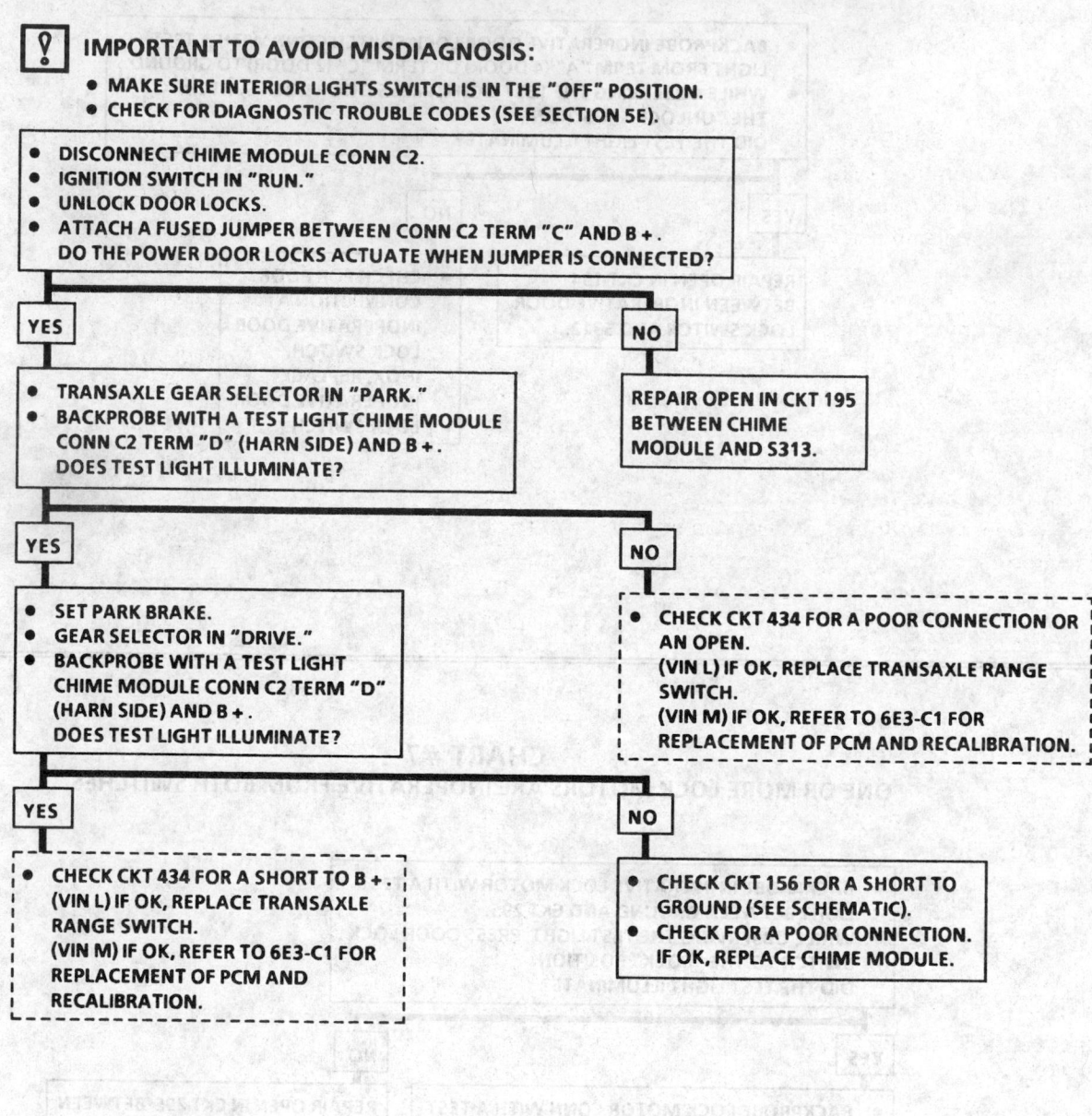

IMPORTANT TO AVOID MISDIAGNOSIS:

- MAKE SURE INTERIOR LIGHTS SWITCH IS IN THE "OFF" POSITION.
- CHECK FOR DIAGNOSTIC TROUBLE CODES (SEE SECTION 5E).

- DISCONNECT CHIME MODULE CONN C2.
- IGNITION SWITCH IN "RUN."
- UNLOCK DOOR LOCKS.
- ATTACH A FUSED JUMPER BETWEEN CONN C2 TERM "C" AND B + .

DO THE POWER DOOR LOCKS ACTUATE WHEN JUMPER IS CONNECTED?

YES

- TRANSAXLE GEAR SELECTOR IN "PARK."
- BACKPROBE WITH A TEST LIGHT CHIME MODULE CONN C2 TERM "D" (HARN SIDE) AND B + .

DOES TEST LIGHT ILLUMINATE?

YES

- SET PARK BRAKE.
- GEAR SELECTOR IN "DRIVE."
- BACKPROBE WITH A TEST LIGHT CHIME MODULE CONN C2 TERM "D" (HARN SIDE) AND B + .

DOES TEST LIGHT ILLUMINATE?

YES

- CHECK CKT 434 FOR A SHORT TO B + .
(VIN L) IF OK, REPLACE TRANSAXLE RANGE SWITCH.
(VIN M) IF OK, REFER TO 6E3-C1 FOR REPLACEMENT OF PCM AND RECALIBRATION.

NO

- CHECK CKT 156 FOR A SHORT TO GROUND (SEE SCHEMATIC).
- CHECK FOR A POOR CONNECTION. IF OK, REPLACE CHIME MODULE.

NO (test light, "PARK")

- CHECK CKT 434 FOR A POOR CONNECTION OR AN OPEN.
(VIN L) IF OK, REPLACE TRANSAXLE RANGE SWITCH.
(VIN M) IF OK, REFER TO 6E3-C1 FOR REPLACEMENT OF PCM AND RECALIBRATION.

NO (door locks, jumper)

REPAIR OPEN IN CKT 195 BETWEEN CHIME MODULE AND S313.

CIRCUIT OPERATION

The Automatic Door Lock feature is controlled by the Chime Module. The Chime Module will send a 400 ms battery voltage signal to the coil of the Door Lock Relay once per Ignition cycle if two conditions are present:

AUTOMATIC TRANSAXLE

The Automatic Door Lock Signal is produced by the Chime Module when all doors are closed and the Transaxle Position Switch is moved out of "PARK" or "NEUTRAL."

WITHOUT KEYLESS ENTRY

When a Door Lock Switch is activated in the Power Door Locks System, all doors lock or unlock in unison. Each lock can also be operated manually from the locking knob. The locks are operated by reversible motors that receive voltage from two relays in the Power Door Lock Relay. These relays operate to turn the motors on by applying a voltage to one of the terminals and a ground to the other terminal. To reverse the motors, the polarity to the terminals must be reversed.

When either Door Lock Switch is moved to the "LOCK" position, it completes a circuit to the coil of the Power Door Lock Relay. The Power Door Lock Relay is energized. Its contact for the Lock Relay closes and is connected to battery voltage through CKT 60, which is the voltage feed for driving the motors.

Voltage is then applied to CKT 295 and to the Door Lock Motors, which are grounded by CKT 294 from the other terminal of the motor through the contact for the Unlock Relay. The motor in each door runs to operate the door lock. When the Door Lock Switch is released, the Lock Relay contact closes to ground again and the motors turn off.

A similar action occurs with the Power Door Lock Relay when it is energized by either of the Door Lock Switches closing to the "UNLOCK" position. Now CKT 294 to the motors carries battery voltage and CKT 295 is grounded. The polarity of the voltage to the motors has reversed. The motors run in the opposite direction to unlock the doors.

The Door Lock Switches are usually closed for just a moment. If they are held closed, a circuit breaker in each motor will open to protect against damage. The circuit breaker resets only after voltage is removed from the motor.

WITH KEYLESS ENTRY

All Door Locks operate the same as without Keyless Entry except the LH Door Lock. When either Door Lock Switch is moved to the "LOCK" position, the Power Door Lock Relay is energized and voltage is applied to the GRY wire and to the Door Lock Motors. The LH Front Door Motor is grounded through the Keyless Entry Receiver terminal "B". The other Door Lock Motors are grounded through the normally open contacts of the Unlock Relay. When either Door Lock Switch is moved to the "UNLOCK" position, voltage is applied to terminal "G" of the Keyless Entry Receiver. This is the Unlock Enable signal that tells the Keyless Entry Receiver to energize terminal "B", which then applies voltage to CKT 294 and to the LH Front Door Lock Motor. The LH Front Door Lock Motor is then grounded through the normally open Lock Relay contacts of the Power Door Lock Relay.

KEYLESS ENTRY

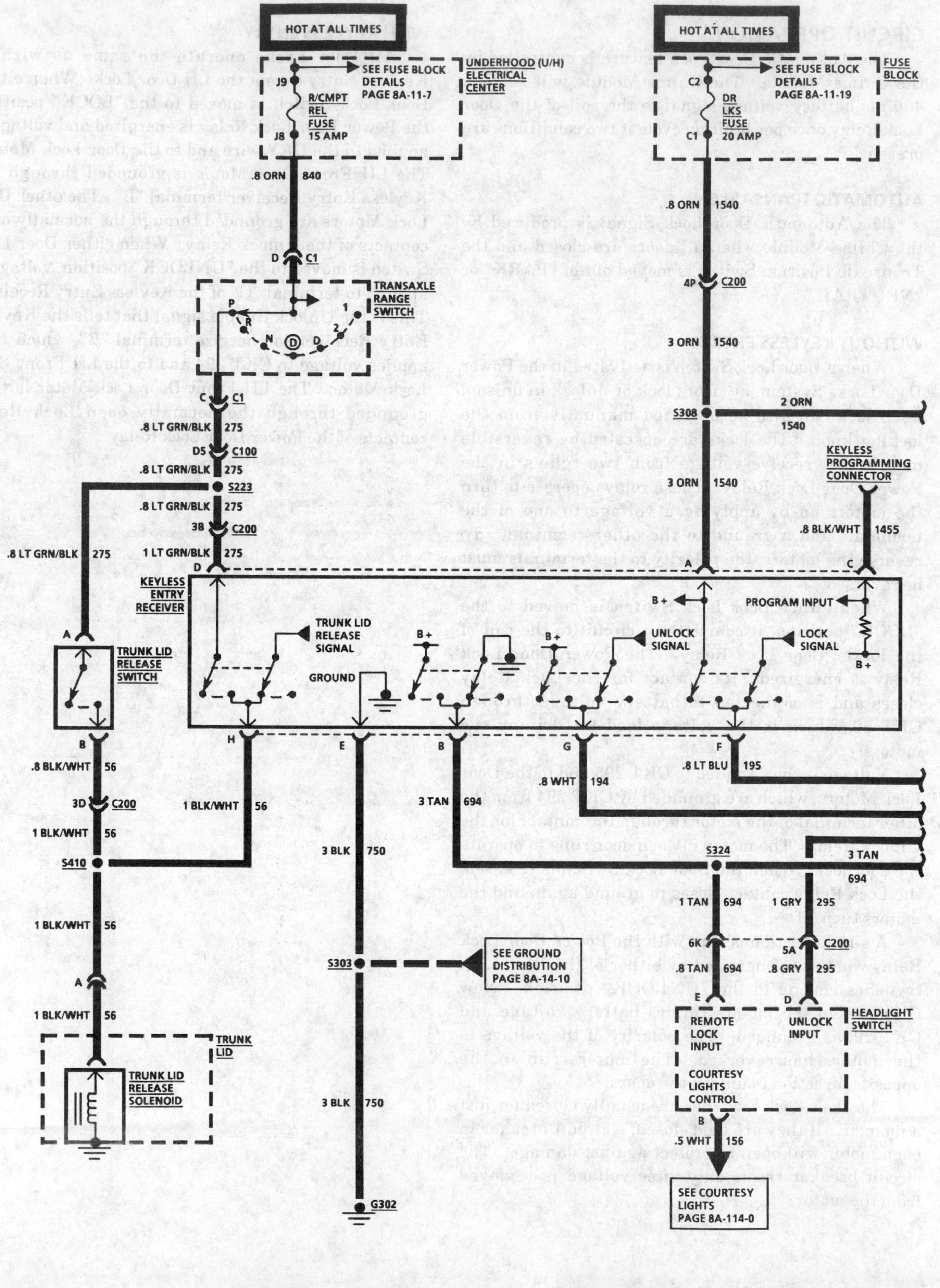

HOT AT ALL TIMES
SEE FUSE BLOCK DETAILS PAGE 8A-11-7
UNDERHOOD (U/H) ELECTRICAL CENTER
J9
R/CMPT REL FUSE 15 AMP
J8
.8 ORN 840
D C1
TRANSAXLE RANGE SWITCH
P R N D D 2 1
C C1
.8 LT GRN/BLK 275
D5 C100
.8 LT GRN/BLK 275
S223
.8 LT GRN/BLK 275
3B C200
1 LT GRN/BLK 275
.8 LT GRN/BLK 275
D
KEYLESS ENTRY RECEIVER
A
TRUNK LID RELEASE SWITCH
TRUNK LID RELEASE SIGNAL
GROUND
B+
B+
UNLOCK SIGNAL
LOCK SIGNAL
PROGRAM INPUT
B+
HOT AT ALL TIMES
SEE FUSE BLOCK DETAILS PAGE 8A-11-19
FUSE BLOCK
C2
DR LKS FUSE 20 AMP
C1
.8 ORN 1540
4P C200
3 ORN 1540
S308
2 ORN 1540
3 ORN 1540
KEYLESS PROGRAMMING CONNECTOR
.8 BLK/WHT 1455
A
C
B
.8 BLK/WHT 56
3D C200
1 BLK/WHT 56
S410
1 BLK/WHT 56
A
1 BLK/WHT 56
TRUNK LID
TRUNK LID RELEASE SOLENOID
H
1 BLK/WHT 56
E
3 BLK 750
S303
SEE GROUND DISTRIBUTION PAGE 8A-14-10
3 BLK 750
G302
B
3 TAN 694
G
.8 WHT 194
F
.8 LT BLU 195
3 TAN 694
S324
1 TAN 694
1 GRY 295
6K
.8 TAN 694
5A C200
.8 GRY 295
E
D
HEADLIGHT SWITCH
REMOTE LOCK INPUT
UNLOCK INPUT
COURTESY LIGHTS CONTROL
B
.5 WHT 156
SEE COURTESY LIGHTS PAGE 8A-114-0

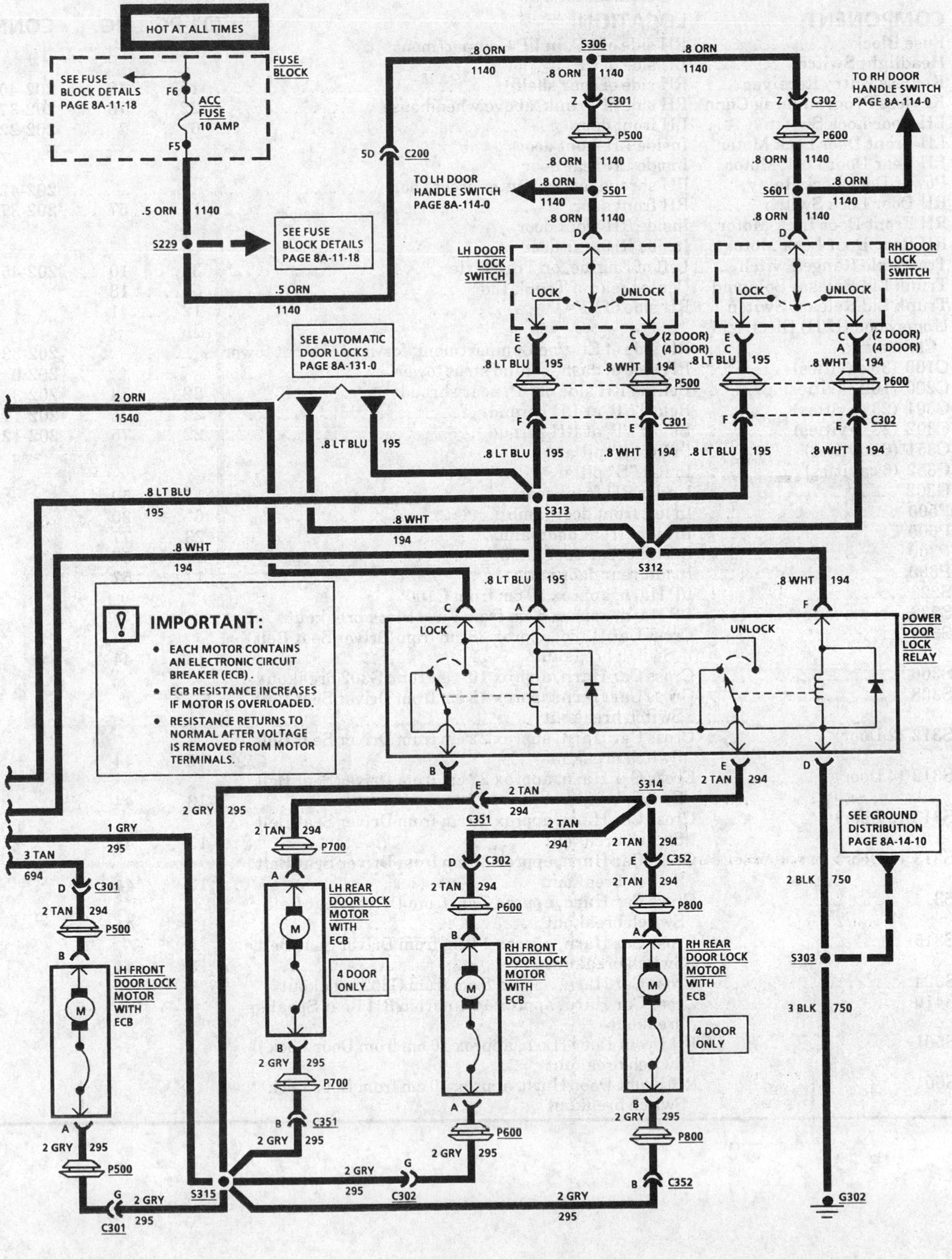
HOT AT ALL TIMES
FUSE BLOCK
SEE FUSE BLOCK DETAILS PAGE 8A-11-18
F6
ACC FUSE 10 AMP
F5
.5 ORN 1140
S229
SEE FUSE BLOCK DETAILS PAGE 8A-11-18
.5 ORN 1140
5D C200
.8 ORN 1140
S306
Z C301
P500
TO LH DOOR HANDLE SWITCH PAGE 8A-114-0
S501
LH DOOR LOCK SWITCH
LOCK
UNLOCK
Z C302
P600
TO RH DOOR HANDLE SWITCH PAGE 8A-114-0
S601
RH DOOR LOCK SWITCH
(2 DOOR)
(4 DOOR)
.8 LT BLU 195
.8 WHT 194
SEE AUTOMATIC DOOR LOCKS PAGE 8A-131-0
2 ORN 1540
S313
S312
POWER DOOR LOCK RELAY
IMPORTANT:
EACH MOTOR CONTAINS AN ELECTRONIC CIRCUIT BREAKER (ECB).
ECB RESISTANCE INCREASES IF MOTOR IS OVERLOADED.
RESISTANCE RETURNS TO NORMAL AFTER VOLTAGE IS REMOVED FROM MOTOR TERMINALS.
2 TAN 294
S314
C351
C352
2 GRY 295
1 GRY 295
3 TAN 694
LH FRONT DOOR LOCK MOTOR WITH ECB
LH REAR DOOR LOCK MOTOR WITH ECB
4 DOOR ONLY
RH FRONT DOOR LOCK MOTOR WITH ECB
RH REAR DOOR LOCK MOTOR WITH ECB
4 DOOR ONLY
P700
P800
S315
SEE GROUND DISTRIBUTION PAGE 8A-14-10
2 BLK 750
S303
3 BLK 750
G302

KEYLESS ENTRY

COMPONENT	LOCATION	201-PG	FIG.	CONN
Fuse Block	RH side of I/P, in I/P Compartment			
Headlight Switch	LH side of I/P			
Keyless Entry Receiver	RH side of rear shelf	15	49	202-40
Keyless Programming Conn	RH side of Trunk, above wheelhouse	22	76	202-37
LH Door Lock Switch	LH front door	6	7	202-22
LH Front Door Lock Motor	Inside LH front door			
LH Rear Door Lock Motor	Inside LH rear door			
Power Door Lock Relay	RH shroud, above center access hole			202-42
RH Door Lock Switch	RH front door	17	57	202-37
RH Front Door Lock Motor	Inside RH front door			
RH Rear Door Lock Motor	Inside RH rear door			
Transaxle Range Switch	Left of Engine, on Transaxle	3	10	202-45
Trunk Lid Release Solenoid	Center rear of Trunk Lid	5	18	
Trunk Lid Release Switch	RH side of I/P	12	41	
Underhood (U/H) Electrical Center #1	RH side of Engine Compartment, forward of strut tower			202-33
C100 (36 cavities)	RH side of dash, behind strut tower			202-0
C200 (102 cavities)	Behind RH side of I/P, near shroud	22	74	202-3
C301 (23 cavities)	Below I/P, at LH shroud	22	75	202-11
C302 (23 cavities)	Below I/P, at RH shroud	22	75	202-12
C351 (6 cavities)	In LH "B" pillar			
C352 (6 cavities)	In RH "B" pillar			
G302	Under RH front seat	15	50	
P500	In left front door jamb	6	20	
P600	In right front door jamb	23	77	
P700	In right rear door jamb	17	57	
P800	In left rear door jamb	17	57	
S223	I/P Harn, approx 50 cm from C100			
S229	I/P Harn, approx 8 cm from Fuse Block breakout			
S303	Cross Car Harn, approx 38 cm from Driver Seat Belt Switch breakout	13	44	
S306	Cross Car Harn, approx 10 cm from G302 breakout			
S308	Cross Car Harn, approx 19 cm from Driver Seat Belt Switch breakout			
S312 (2 Door)	Cross Car Harn, approx 22 cm from Driver Seat Belt Switch breakout	13	44	
S312 (4 Door)	Cross Car Harn, approx 22 cm from Driver Seat Belt Switch breakout	13	44	
S313 (2 Door)	Cross Car Harn, approx 30 cm from Driver Seat Belt Switch breakout	13	44	
S313 (4 Door)	Cross Car Harn, approx 30 cm from Driver Seat Belt Switch breakout	13	44	
S314	Cross Car Harn, approx 7 cm from Driver Seat Belt Switch breakout	13	44	
S315	Cross Car Harn, approx 14 cm from Driver Seat Belt Switch breakout	13	44	
S324	Cross Car Harn, approx 8 cm from G302 breakout			
S410	Cross Car Harn, approx 10 cm from RH Rear Speaker breakout			
S501	LH Front Door Harn, approx 10 cm from Door Lock Switch breakout			
S601	RH Front Door Harn, approx 10 cm from Door Lock Switch breakout			

TROUBLESHOOTING HINTS (Perform before beginning System Diagnosis)

1. Check R/CMPT REL Fuse by visual inspection.
2. Always check terminal contact before replacing any component.
3. Be certain to verify proper Power Door Lock function before beginning Keyless Entry diagnosis. See "Automatic Door Locks," page 8A-131-0.
4. Be certain to verify proper Trunk Lid Release function before beginning Keyless Entry diagnosis. See "Trunk Lid Release," page 8A-134-0.
5. If door locks operate from the Transmitter, but not from the Door Lock Switches, check continuity of Door Lock Switch and associated wiring for an open or a short. Repair/replace as necessary.
6. If a second Transmitter is available, try it. If it works, remove the batteries and install them in the first Transmitter. If the first Transmitter still doesn't work, it is defective.
7. Check Transmitter Battery terminals. They should be clean and make good contact with the Battery.
8. If in doubt as to the condition of the Transmitter batteries, replace them with new ones. Measuring battery voltage with a DVOM may show a weak Battery as being good.

- Check for a broken (or partially broken) wire inside of the insulation which could cause system malfunction but prove "GOOD" in a continuity/voltage check with a system disconnected. These circuits may be intermittent or resistive when loaded, and if possible, should be checked by monitoring for a voltage drop with the system operational (under load).
- Check for proper installation of aftermarket electronic equipment which may affect the integrity of other systems (see "Troubleshooting Procedures," page 8A-4-0).

KEYLESS ENTRY PROGRAMMING PROCEDURE

- **Do the following procedure whenever the Keyless Programming Connector is grounded, the Keyless Entry Receiver is replaced, the Transmitter is replaced or a second Transmitter is added.**

1. Jumper the Keyless Programming Connector to ground (all power door locks will lock and unlock).
2. Operate Transmitter by pressing a single button once (all power door locks will again lock and unlock).
3. To program for a second Portable Transmitter, operate Transmitter 2 by pressing a single button once. In order for programming to be complete, wait for the locks to fully cycle.
4. Disconnect Keyless Programming Connector Jumper after locks have finished cycling.
5. Verify that the Transmitter(s) operate Door Locks and Trunk Lid Release.

- Refer to System Diagnosis.

SYSTEM DIAGNOSIS

- Perform the System Check and refer to the Symptom Table for the appropriate diagnostic procedures.

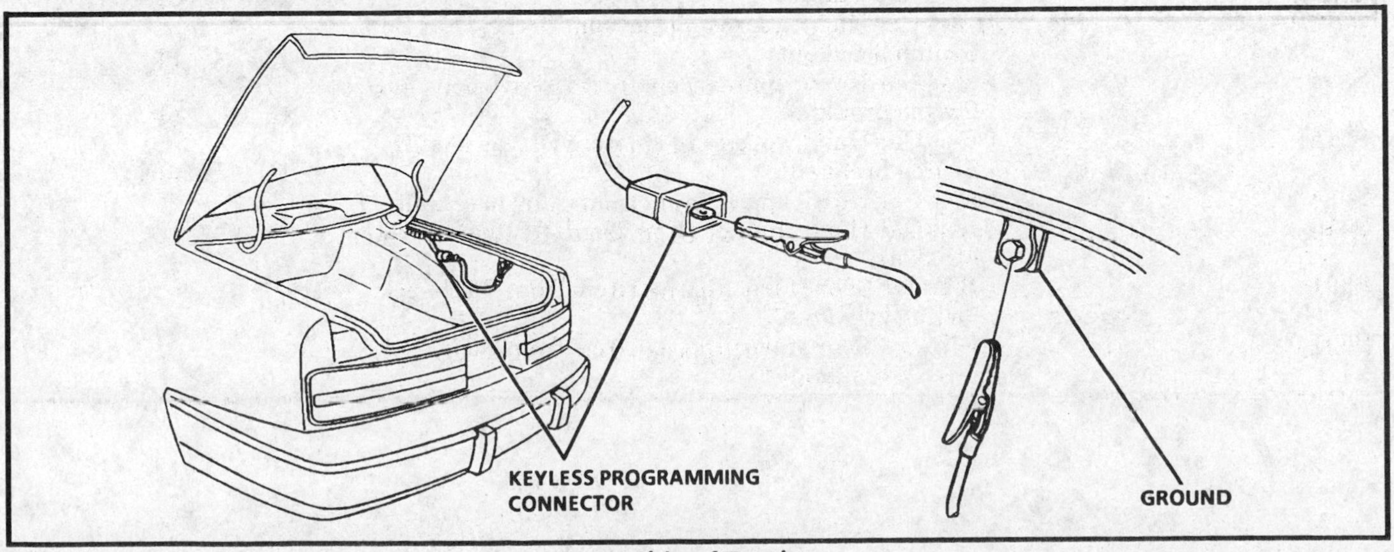
KEYLESS PROGRAMMING CONNECTOR
GROUND

RH Side of Trunk

KEYLESS ENTRY

SYSTEM CHECK

ACTION	NORMAL RESULTS
[1] ● Press Keyless Entry Transmitter "DOOR" button.	All doors lock and Courtesy Lights illuminate for approximately 2 seconds.
[2] ● Press Keyless Entry Transmitter "UNLOCK" button.	Driver's door unlocks and Courtesy Lights illuminate for 40 seconds or until Ignition Switch is turned to "RUN."
[3] ● Press Keyless Entry Transmitter "UNLOCK" button again within 5 seconds of [2].	All doors unlock and Courtesy Lights operate as in [2].
[4] ● Press Keyless Entry Transmitter Trunk Lid Release button.	Trunk Lid releases.

SYMPTOM TABLE

SYMPTOM	PROCEDURE	PAGE NUMBER
No Keyless Entry features operate.	Chart #1	8A-132-5
Keyless Entry Transmitter lock function inoperative.	Chart #2	8A-132-6
Keyless Entry Transmitter unlock function inoperative (driver's door only).	Chart #3	8A-132-6
Keyless Entry Transmitter unlock function inoperative (all passenger doors).	Chart #4	8A-132-7
Keyless Entry Transmitter Trunk Lid Release function inoperative.	Chart #5	8A-132-7
Keyless Entry Receiver/Transmitter will not program.	Chart #6	8A-132-8
Illuminated Entry functions inoperative with Keyless Entry.	Refer to SECTION 8A-114.	

CHART #1
NO KEYLESS ENTRY FEATURES OPERATE

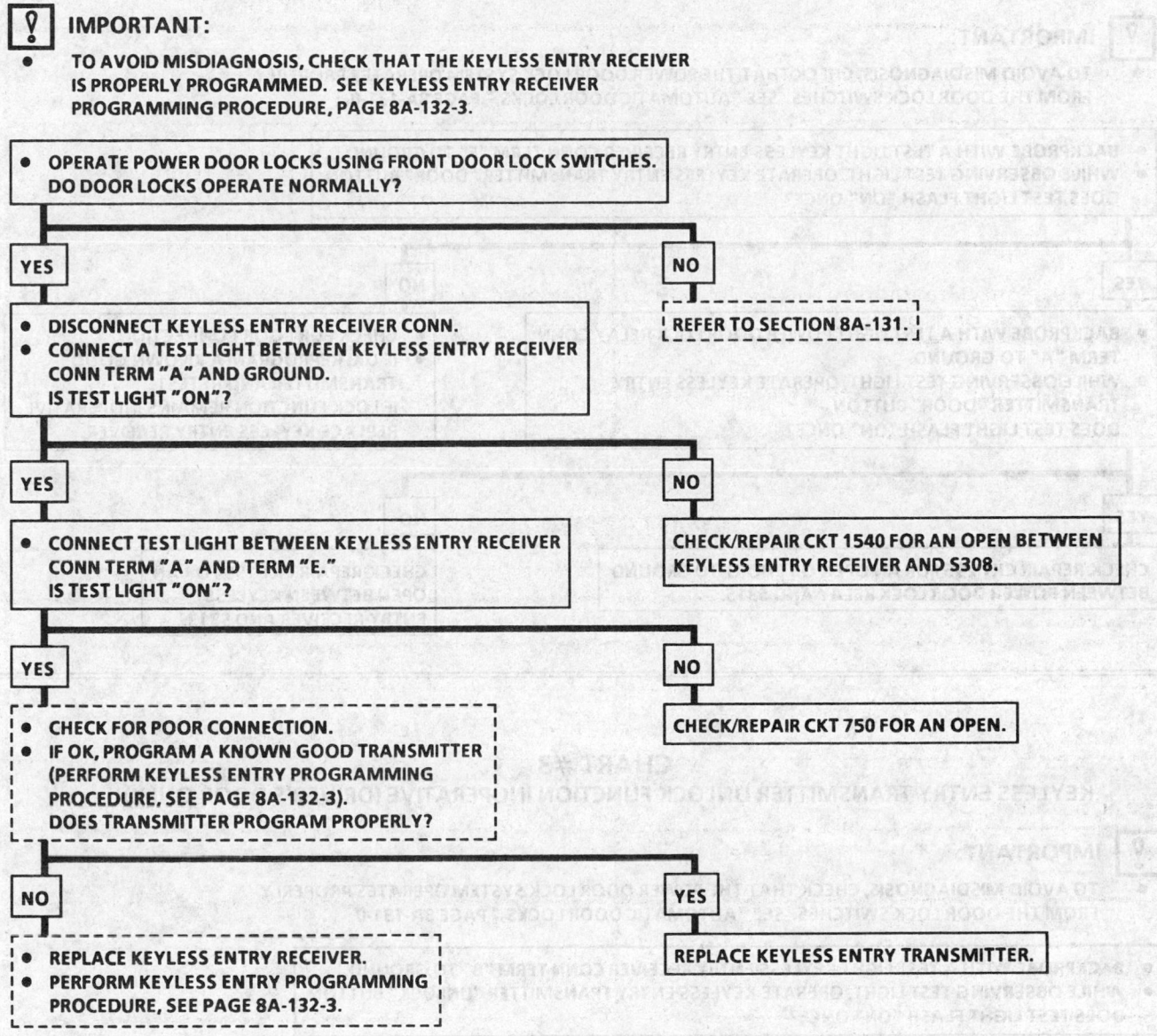

IMPORTANT:

- TO AVOID MISDIAGNOSIS, CHECK THAT THE KEYLESS ENTRY RECEIVER IS PROPERLY PROGRAMMED. SEE KEYLESS ENTRY RECEIVER PROGRAMMING PROCEDURE, PAGE 8A-132-3.

- OPERATE POWER DOOR LOCKS USING FRONT DOOR LOCK SWITCHES.
  DO DOOR LOCKS OPERATE NORMALLY?

YES

- DISCONNECT KEYLESS ENTRY RECEIVER CONN.
- CONNECT A TEST LIGHT BETWEEN KEYLESS ENTRY RECEIVER CONN TERM "A" AND GROUND.
  IS TEST LIGHT "ON"?

  YES

  - CONNECT TEST LIGHT BETWEEN KEYLESS ENTRY RECEIVER CONN TERM "A" AND TERM "E."
    IS TEST LIGHT "ON"?

    YES

    - CHECK FOR POOR CONNECTION.
    - IF OK, PROGRAM A KNOWN GOOD TRANSMITTER (PERFORM KEYLESS ENTRY PROGRAMMING PROCEDURE, SEE PAGE 8A-132-3).
      DOES TRANSMITTER PROGRAM PROPERLY?

      NO

      - REPLACE KEYLESS ENTRY RECEIVER.
      - PERFORM KEYLESS ENTRY PROGRAMMING PROCEDURE, SEE PAGE 8A-132-3.

      YES

      REPLACE KEYLESS ENTRY TRANSMITTER.

    NO

    CHECK/REPAIR CKT 750 FOR AN OPEN.

  NO

  CHECK/REPAIR CKT 1540 FOR AN OPEN BETWEEN KEYLESS ENTRY RECEIVER AND S308.

NO

REFER TO SECTION 8A-131.

KEYLESS ENTRY

CHART #2

KEYLESS ENTRY TRANSMITTER LOCK FUNCTION INOPERATIVE

IMPORTANT:

- TO AVOID MISDIAGNOSIS, CHECK THAT THE POWER DOOR LOCK SYSTEM OPERATES PROPERLY FROM THE DOOR LOCK SWITCHES. SEE "AUTOMATIC DOOR LOCKS," PAGE 8A-131-0.

- BACKPROBE WITH A TEST LIGHT KEYLESS ENTRY RECEIVER CONN TERM "F" TO GROUND.
- WHILE OBSERVING TEST LIGHT, OPERATE KEYLESS ENTRY TRANSMITTER "DOOR" BUTTON.

DOES TEST LIGHT FLASH "ON" ONCE?

YES

- BACKPROBE WITH A TEST LIGHT POWER DOOR LOCK RELAY CONN TERM "A" TO GROUND.
- WHILE OBSERVING TEST LIGHT, OPERATE KEYLESS ENTRY TRANSMITTER "DOOR" BUTTON.

DOES TEST LIGHT FLASH "ON" ONCE?

YES

CHECK/REPAIR CKT 295 FOR AN OPEN OR SHORT TO GROUND BETWEEN POWER DOOR LOCK RELAY AND S315.

NO

CHECK/REPAIR CKT 195 FOR AN OPEN BETWEEN KEYLESS ENTRY RECEIVER AND S313.

NO

- CHECK FOR POOR CONNECTION.
- IF OK, REPROGRAM A KNOWN GOOD TRANSMITTER AND RETEST. IF LOCK FUNCTION REMAINS INOPERATIVE, REPLACE KEYLESS ENTRY RECEIVER.

CHART #3

KEYLESS ENTRY TRANSMITTER UNLOCK FUNCTION INOPERATIVE (DRIVER'S DOOR ONLY)

IMPORTANT:

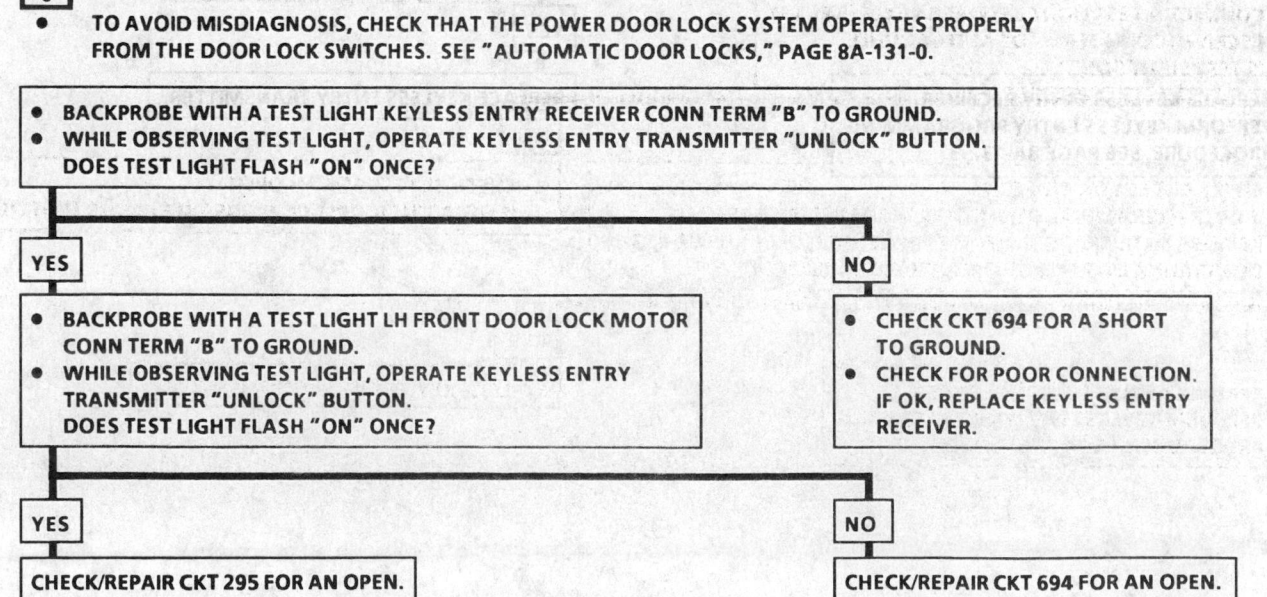

- TO AVOID MISDIAGNOSIS, CHECK THAT THE POWER DOOR LOCK SYSTEM OPERATES PROPERLY FROM THE DOOR LOCK SWITCHES. SEE "AUTOMATIC DOOR LOCKS," PAGE 8A-131-0.

- BACKPROBE WITH A TEST LIGHT KEYLESS ENTRY RECEIVER CONN TERM "B" TO GROUND.
- WHILE OBSERVING TEST LIGHT, OPERATE KEYLESS ENTRY TRANSMITTER "UNLOCK" BUTTON.

DOES TEST LIGHT FLASH "ON" ONCE?

YES

- BACKPROBE WITH A TEST LIGHT LH FRONT DOOR LOCK MOTOR CONN TERM "B" TO GROUND.
- WHILE OBSERVING TEST LIGHT, OPERATE KEYLESS ENTRY TRANSMITTER "UNLOCK" BUTTON.

DOES TEST LIGHT FLASH "ON" ONCE?

YES

CHECK/REPAIR CKT 295 FOR AN OPEN.

NO

CHECK/REPAIR CKT 694 FOR AN OPEN.

NO

- CHECK CKT 694 FOR A SHORT TO GROUND.
- CHECK FOR POOR CONNECTION. IF OK, REPLACE KEYLESS ENTRY RECEIVER.

CHART #4

KEYLESS ENTRY TRANSMITTER UNLOCK FUNCTION INOPERATIVE ALL PASSENGER DOORS

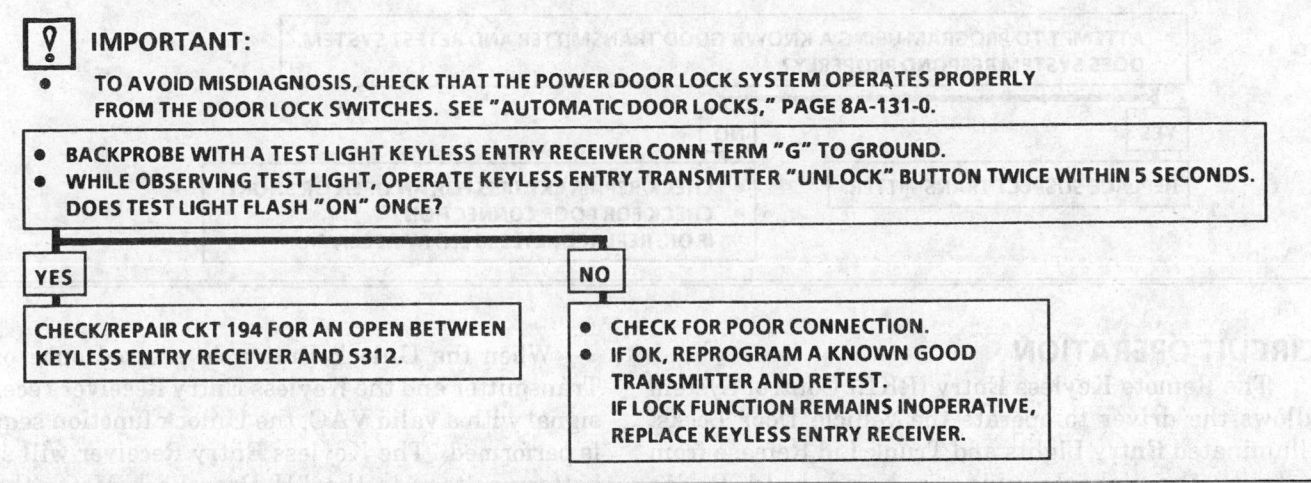

IMPORTANT:

- TO AVOID MISDIAGNOSIS, CHECK THAT THE POWER DOOR LOCK SYSTEM OPERATES PROPERLY FROM THE DOOR LOCK SWITCHES. SEE "AUTOMATIC DOOR LOCKS," PAGE 8A-131-0.

- BACKPROBE WITH A TEST LIGHT KEYLESS ENTRY RECEIVER CONN TERM "G" TO GROUND.
- WHILE OBSERVING TEST LIGHT, OPERATE KEYLESS ENTRY TRANSMITTER "UNLOCK" BUTTON TWICE WITHIN 5 SECONDS.

DOES TEST LIGHT FLASH "ON" ONCE?

YES

CHECK/REPAIR CKT 194 FOR AN OPEN BETWEEN KEYLESS ENTRY RECEIVER AND S312.

NO

- CHECK FOR POOR CONNECTION.
- IF OK, REPROGRAM A KNOWN GOOD TRANSMITTER AND RETEST.

IF LOCK FUNCTION REMAINS INOPERATIVE, REPLACE KEYLESS ENTRY RECEIVER.

CHART #5

KEYLESS ENTRY TRANSMITTER TRUNK LID RELEASE FUNCTION INOPERATIVE

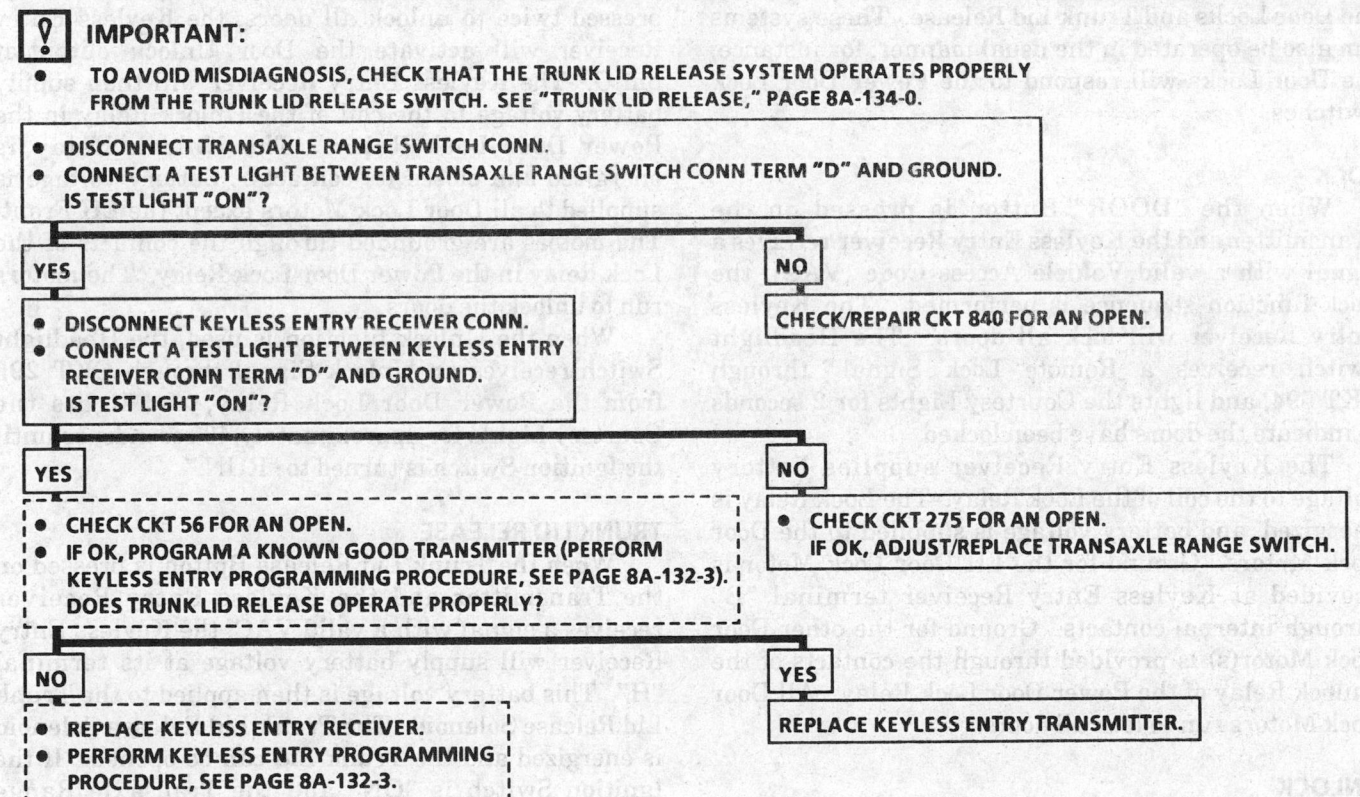

IMPORTANT:

- TO AVOID MISDIAGNOSIS, CHECK THAT THE TRUNK LID RELEASE SYSTEM OPERATES PROPERLY FROM THE TRUNK LID RELEASE SWITCH. SEE "TRUNK LID RELEASE," PAGE 8A-134-0.

- DISCONNECT TRANSAXLE RANGE SWITCH CONN.
- CONNECT A TEST LIGHT BETWEEN TRANSAXLE RANGE SWITCH CONN TERM "D" AND GROUND.

IS TEST LIGHT "ON"?

YES

- DISCONNECT KEYLESS ENTRY RECEIVER CONN.
- CONNECT A TEST LIGHT BETWEEN KEYLESS ENTRY RECEIVER CONN TERM "D" AND GROUND.

IS TEST LIGHT "ON"?

YES

- CHECK CKT 56 FOR AN OPEN.
- IF OK, PROGRAM A KNOWN GOOD TRANSMITTER (PERFORM KEYLESS ENTRY PROGRAMMING PROCEDURE, SEE PAGE 8A-132-3).

DOES TRUNK LID RELEASE OPERATE PROPERLY?

NO

- REPLACE KEYLESS ENTRY RECEIVER.
- PERFORM KEYLESS ENTRY PROGRAMMING PROCEDURE, SEE PAGE 8A-132-3.

YES

REPLACE KEYLESS ENTRY TRANSMITTER.

NO

- CHECK CKT 275 FOR AN OPEN.

IF OK, ADJUST/REPLACE TRANSAXLE RANGE SWITCH.

NO

CHECK/REPAIR CKT 840 FOR AN OPEN.

KEYLESS ENTRY

CHART #6
KEYLESS ENTRY RECEIVER/TRANSMITTER WILL NOT PROGRAM

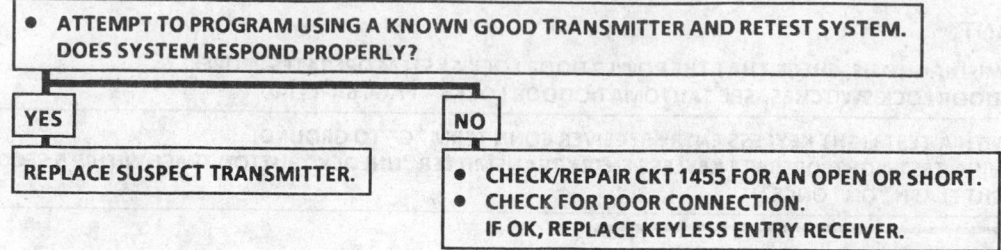

- **ATTEMPT TO PROGRAM USING A KNOWN GOOD TRANSMITTER AND RETEST SYSTEM. DOES SYSTEM RESPOND PROPERLY?**

YES

REPLACE SUSPECT TRANSMITTER.

NO

- **CHECK/REPAIR CKT 1455 FOR AN OPEN OR SHORT.**
- **CHECK FOR POOR CONNECTION.**

IF OK, REPLACE KEYLESS ENTRY RECEIVER.

CIRCUIT OPERATION

The Remote Keyless Entry (RKE) Control System allows the driver to operate the vehicle Door Locks, Illuminated Entry Lights and Trunk Lid Release from outside the vehicle using a hand held Radio Transmitter. The Transmitter operates in the UHF band; it sends digitally coded signals to the Keyless Entry Receiver. The Keyless Entry Receiver detects and decodes the signals and issues signals to control the Door Locks and Trunk Lid Release. These systems can also be operated in the usual manner; for instance, the Door Locks will respond to the Power Door Lock Switches.

LOCK

When the "DOOR" Button is pressed on the Transmitter and the Keyless Entry Receiver receives a signal with a valid Vehicle Access Code (VAC), the Lock function sequence is performed. The Keyless Entry Receiver will lock all doors. The Headlight Switch receives a Remote Lock Signal through CKT 694, and lights the Courtesy Lights for 2 seconds to indicate the doors have been locked.

The Keyless Entry Receiver supplies battery voltage to the coil of the Lock Relay. The Lock Relay is energized, and battery voltage is supplied to the Door Lock Motors. Ground for the LH Door Lock Motor is provided at Keyless Entry Receiver terminal "B" through internal contacts. Ground for the other Door Lock Motor(s) is provided through the contacts of the Unlock Relay of the Power Door Lock Relay. All Door Lock Motors run to lock all doors.

UNLOCK

The Unlock function is separated into two operations depending on how the "UNLOCK" Button is pressed on the Transmitter. If the "UNLOCK" Button is pressed once, only the LH Door is unlocked. If the "UNLOCK" Button is pressed twice within 1 to 5 seconds, all doors will be unlocked.

When the Unlock Button is pressed once on the Transmitter and the Keyless Entry Receiver receives a signal with a valid VAC, the Unlock function sequence is performed. The Keyless Entry Receiver will supply battery voltage to the LH Door Lock Motor through CKT 694. The motor is grounded through the contacts of the Lock Relay in the Power Door Lock Relay. The LH Door Lock Motor runs to unlock the LH door.

If the "UNLOCK" Button on the Transmitter is pressed twice to unlock all doors, the Keyless Entry Receiver will activate the Door Unlock output at pin G. The Keyless Entry Receiver will then supply battery voltage to the coil of the Unlock Relay in the Power Door Lock Relay. The Unlock Relay is energized and closes its contacts. Battery voltage is supplied to all Door Lock Motors except the LH Front. The motors are grounded through the contacts of the Lock Relay in the Power Door Lock Relay. The motors run to unlock the doors.

When the Unlock function is used, the Headlight Switch receives an Unlock Signal through CKT 295 from the Power Door Lock Relay, and lights the Courtesy Lights for approximately 40 seconds, or until the Ignition Switch is turned to "RUN."

TRUNK LID RELEASE

When the Trunk Lid Release Button is pressed on the Transmitter and the Keyless Entry Receiver receives a signal with a valid VAC, the Keyless Entry Receiver will supply battery voltage at its terminal "H". This battery voltage is then applied to the Trunk Lid Release Solenoid. The Trunk Lid Release Solenoid is energized and the Trunk Lid can be opened. If the Ignition Switch is "ON" and the Transaxle Range Switch is not in "PARK," battery voltage is not supplied to Keyless Entry Receiver terminal "C" and the Trunk Lid will not open.

BLANK

THEFT DETERRENT SYSTEM: PASS-Key®II

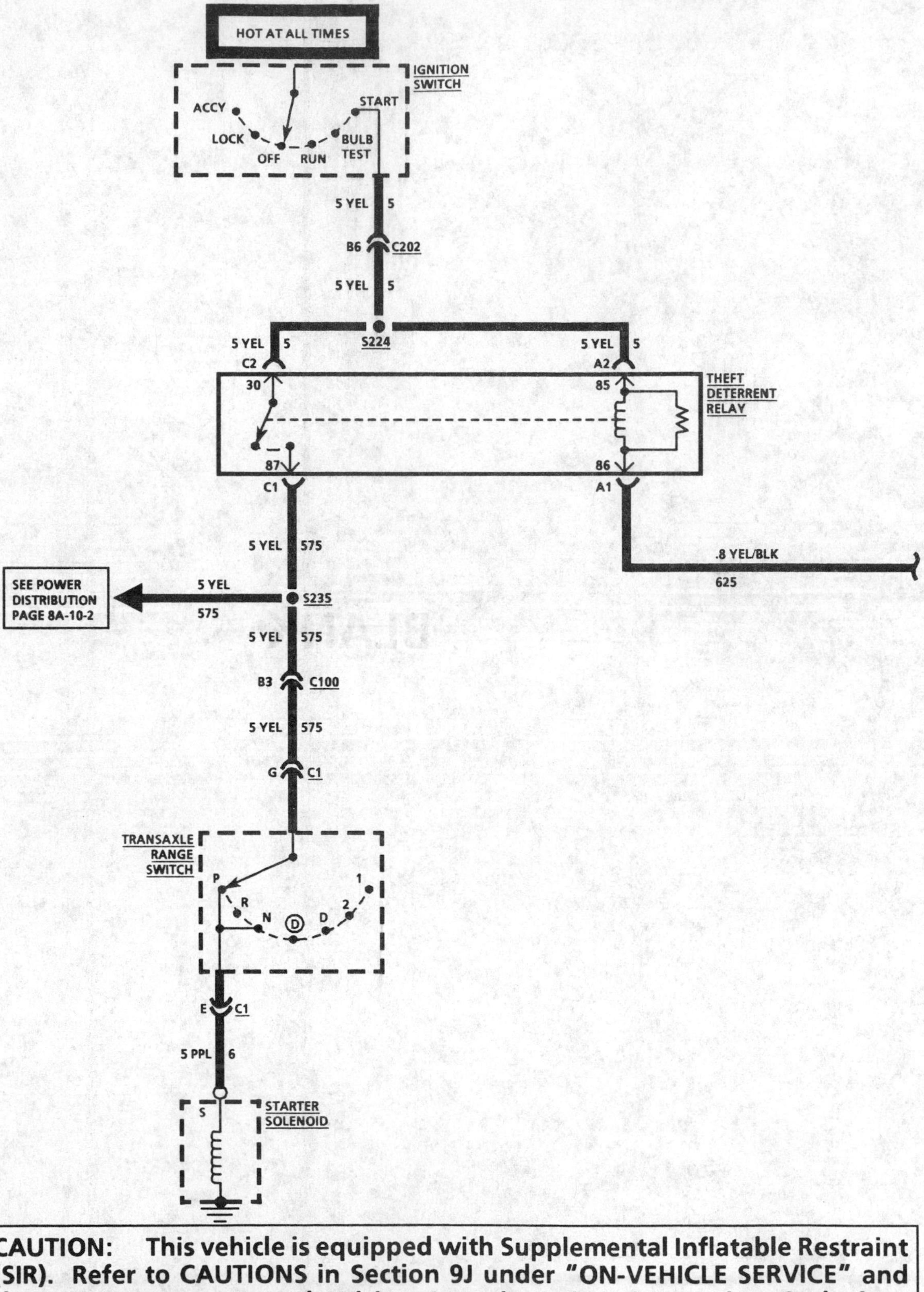

HOT AT ALL TIMES
IGNITION SWITCH
ACCY
LOCK
OFF
RUN
START
BULB TEST
5 YEL 5
B6 C202
5 YEL 5
S224
5 YEL 5
C2
30
5 YEL 5
A2
85
THEFT DETERRENT RELAY
87
C1
86
A1
5 YEL 575
.8 YEL/BLK
625
SEE POWER DISTRIBUTION PAGE 8A-10-2
5 YEL
575
S235
5 YEL 575
B3 C100
5 YEL 575
G C1
TRANSAXLE RANGE SWITCH
P
R
N
D
D
2
1
E C1
5 PPL 6
S
STARTER SOLENOID

SEE PAGE 8A-3-0 FOR PROPER HANDLING PROCEDURES

CAUTION: This vehicle is equipped with Supplemental Inflatable Restraint (SIR). Refer to CAUTIONS in Section 9J under "ON-VEHICLE SERVICE" and the SIR Component and Wiring Location view in Section 9J before performing service on or around SIR components or wiring. Failure to follow CAUTIONS could result in possible air bag deployment, personal injury, or otherwise unneeded SIR system repairs.

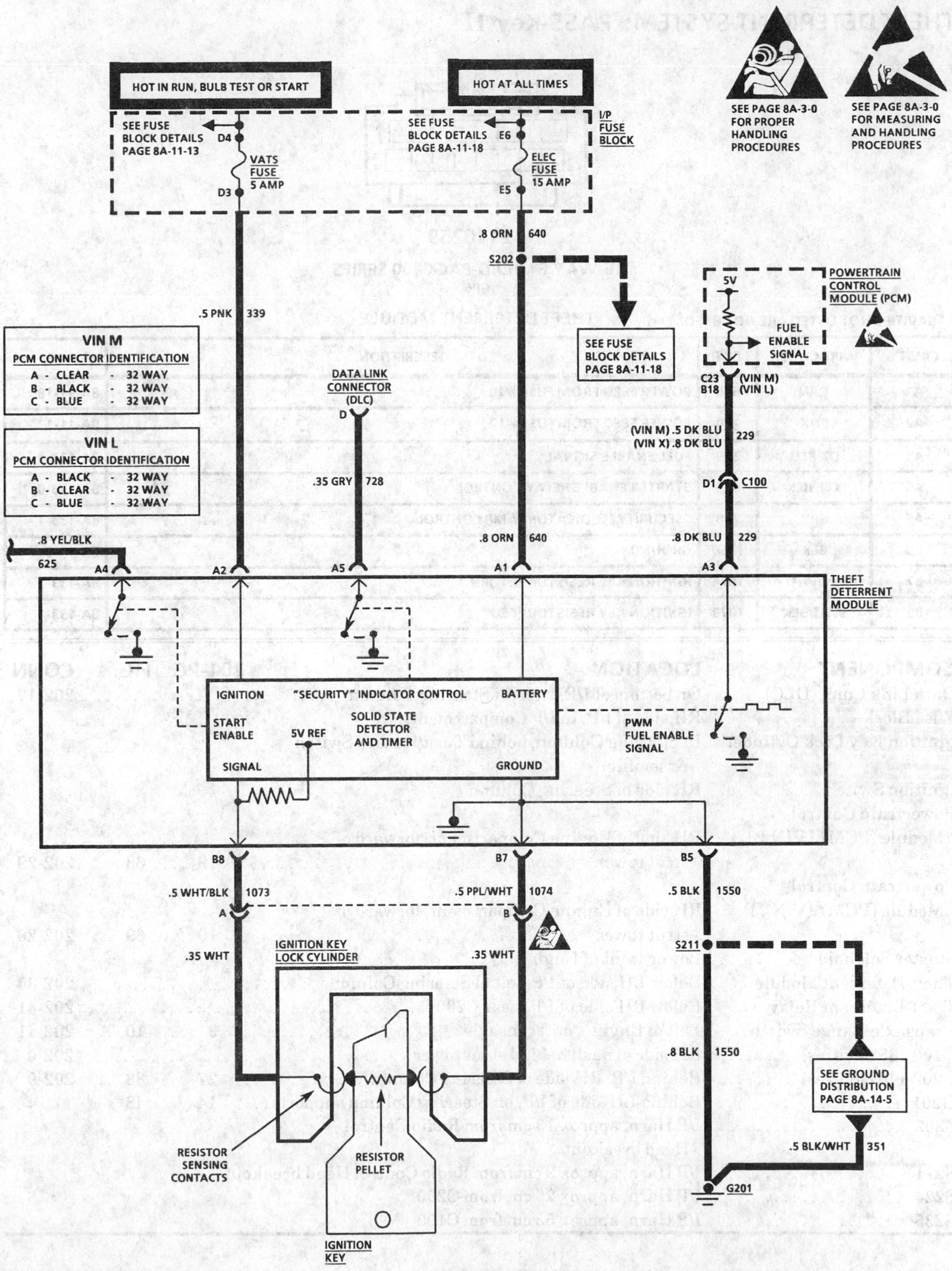
HOT IN RUN, BULB TEST OR START
HOT AT ALL TIMES
SEE FUSE BLOCK DETAILS PAGE 8A-11-13
D4
VATS FUSE 5 AMP
D3
SEE FUSE BLOCK DETAILS PAGE 8A-11-18
E6
ELEC FUSE 15 AMP
E5
I/P FUSE BLOCK
SEE PAGE 8A-3-0 FOR PROPER HANDLING PROCEDURES
SEE PAGE 8A-3-0 FOR MEASURING AND HANDLING PROCEDURES
.8 ORN 640
S202
SEE FUSE BLOCK DETAILS PAGE 8A-11-18
.5 PNK 339
VIN M
PCM CONNECTOR IDENTIFICATION
A - CLEAR - 32 WAY
B - BLACK - 32 WAY
C - BLUE - 32 WAY
VIN L
PCM CONNECTOR IDENTIFICATION
A - BLACK - 32 WAY
B - CLEAR - 32 WAY
C - BLUE - 32 WAY
DATA LINK CONNECTOR (DLC)
D
.35 GRY 728
POWERTRAIN CONTROL MODULE (PCM)
5V
FUEL ENABLE SIGNAL
C23 (VIN M)
B18 (VIN L)
(VIN M) .5 DK BLU
(VIN X) .8 DK BLU
229
D1
C100
.8 YEL/BLK
625
.8 ORN 640
.8 DK BLU 229
A4
A2
A5
A1
A3
THEFT DETERRENT MODULE
IGNITION
"SECURITY" INDICATOR CONTROL
BATTERY
START ENABLE
5V REF
SOLID STATE DETECTOR AND TIMER
PWM FUEL ENABLE SIGNAL
SIGNAL
GROUND
B8
B7
B5
.5 WHT/BLK 1073
.5 PPL/WHT 1074
.5 BLK 1550
A
B
.35 WHT
.35 WHT
IGNITION KEY LOCK CYLINDER
S211
.8 BLK 1550
SEE GROUND DISTRIBUTION PAGE 8A-14-5
.5 BLK/WHT 351
G201
RESISTOR SENSING CONTACTS
RESISTOR PELLET
IGNITION KEY

THEFT DETERRENT SYSTEM: PASS-Key®II

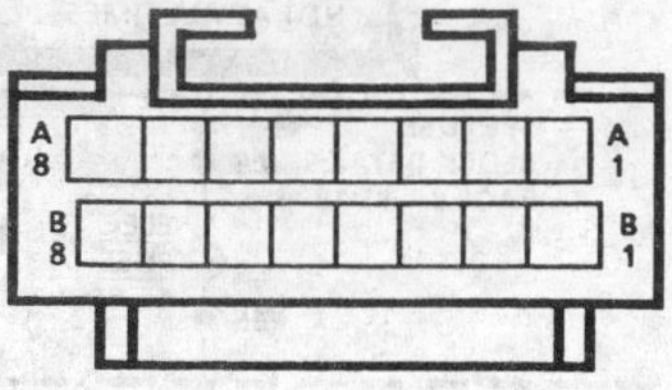
A 8
A 1
B 8
B 1

12110259

16-WAY F MICRO-PACK 100 SERIES

GRN

**CAVITIES NOT LISTED ARE NOT USED

THEFT DETERRENT MODULE

CAVITY	WIRE COLOR	CKT	DESCRIPTION	PAGE
A1	ORN	640	POWER FEED FROM FUSE #10	8A-11-18
A2	PNK	339	POWER FEED FROM FUSE #12	8A-11-13
A3	DK BLU	229	FUEL ENABLE SIGNAL	8A-133-1
A4	YEL/BLK	625	STARTER ENABLE RELAY CONTROL	8A-133-0, 1
A5	GRY	728	"SECURITY" INDICATOR LAMP CONTROL	8A-133-1
B5	BLK	1550	GROUND	8A-14-6
B7	PPL/WHT	1074	IGNITION KEY RESISTOR RETURN	8A-133-1
B8	WHT/BLK	1073	IGNITION KEY RESISTOR FEED	8A-133-1

COMPONENT	LOCATION	201-PG	FIG.	CONN
Data Link Conn (DLC)	On bottom of I/P, right of Steering Column			202-17
Fuse Block	RH side of I/P, in I/P Compartment			
Ignition Key Lock Cylinder	In Steering Column, behind Turn/Hazard Switch Assembly			
Ignition Switch	RH side of Steering Column			
Powertrain Control Module (PCM) (VIN L)	RH side of Engine Compartment, forward of strut tower	19	68	202-29
Powertrain Control Module (PCM) (VIN M)	RH side of Engine Compartment, forward of strut tower	19	69	202-26
Starter Solenoid	Lower front of Engine			
Theft Deterrent Module	Below LH side of I/P, left of Steering Column			202-34
Theft Deterrent Relay	Below RH side of I/P, near C200			202-41
Transaxle Range Switch	Left of Engine, on Transaxle	3	10	202-41
C100 (36 cavities)	RH side of dash behind strut tower			202-0
C202 (48 cavities)	Behind I/P, RH side of Steering Column	27	88	202-9
G201	Behind LH side of I/P, on Steering Column support	14	48	
S202	I/P Harn, approx 13 cm from Radio Control Head breakout			
S211	I/P Harn, approx 9 cm from Radio Control Head breakout			
S224	I/P Harn, approx 25 cm from C200			
S235	I/P Harn, approx 53 cm from C100			

TROUBLESHOOTING HINTS (Perform before beginning System Diagnosis)

1. Check the Ignition Key for a cracked resistor pellet or a pellet that is dirty or coated. Also check that the Ignition Key is free from excess plastic around the resistor pellet contacts.
2. Check owner's Ignition Key using the J 35628 PASS-Key®II Interrogator or equivalent. (See "Duplication of Keys," page 8A-133-10.) If the Key Code window shows "E", replace the owner's key.
3. Check the key pellet sensing contacts in the Ignition Lock Cylinder by looking into the key opening. If the contacts are damaged or not silver in color, replace the Lock Cylinder.
4. Check the VATS Fuse, the ELEC Fuse and the fuse contacts by visual inspection.
5. If the PASS-Key®II system is intermittent, check that the connector to the Theft Deterrent Module is tight and the terminals are clean. Also check G201 and the engine grounds.
6. If the Theft Deterrent Relay must be replaced, also check CKT 6 to the Starter Solenoid for a possible short. A short may have caused the relay to fail.
7. To check the contacts to the key and the wires in the Steering Column, disconnect the connector near the base of the column. Measure the resistance back to the key at this connector while you turn and adjust the Steering Wheel. If there is any change or intermittent reading, replace the Lock Cylinder and the Steering Column wires that come with it. See SECTION 3F5) to .

Important:

- For "SECURITY" Indicator: attach a Tech 1 scan tool to the Data Link Connector (DLC) and monitor "PASS-Key®II System Indicator" (active="ON"; inactive="OFF"). If Tech 1 is unavailable, attach a test light to the DLC between terminal "D" and B+.

- Automatic Transaxle: Check for proper adjustment of the Transaxle Range Switch. See SECTION 7A.
- Check for a broken (or partially broken) wire inside of the insulation which could cause system malfunction but prove "GOOD" in a continuity/voltage check with a system disconnected. These circuits may be intermittent or resistive when loaded, and if possible, should be checked by monitoring for a voltage drop with the system operational (under load).
- Check for proper installation of aftermarket electronic equipment which may affect the integrity of other systems (see "Troubleshooting Procedures," page 8A-4-0).
- Refer to System Diagnosis.

SYSTEM DIAGNOSIS

- Perform the System Check and refer to the Symptom Table for the appropriate diagnostic procedures.

Important:

- Perform the Diagnostic Circuit Check described in DRIVEABILITY & EMISSIONS (SEC 6E) to be certain no trouble codes are stored in PCM memory which may lead to misdiagnosis, specifically any code, indicating a problem in the PASS-Key®II Fuel Enable circuit.

SYSTEM CHECK

ACTION	NORMAL RESULTS
[1] • Observe "SECURITY" Indicator. • Ignition Switch to "RUN."	"SECURITY" Indicator illuminates for approximately 5 seconds then goes "OFF."
[2] • Gear Selector in "PARK." • Ignition Switch to "START."	Engine starts.

(CONTINUED ON NEXT PAGE)

THEFT DETERRENT SYSTEM: PASS-Key®II

Important:

- For "SECURITY" Indicator: attach a Tech 1 scan tool to the Data Link Connector (DLC) and monitor "PASS-Key®II System Indicator" (active="ON"; inactive="OFF"). If Tech 1 is unavailable, attach a test light to the DLC between terminal "D" and B+.

(CONTINUED FROM PREVIOUS PAGE)

SYSTEM CHECK

ACTION	NORMAL RESULTS
[3] • Ignition Switch to "OFF."	Engine stops.
[4] • Disconnect Theft Deterrent Key Resistor Connector at base of Steering Column. **Important** • This vehicle is equipped with Supplemental Inflatable Restraints (SIR). Make sure to differentiate between the 2-way Theft Deterrent Key Resistor Connector and the yellow 2-Way Supplemental Inflatable Restraints (SIR) Connector. • Connect the male and female parts to the mating connectors on the pigtails from the J 35628 Interrogator or equivalent. • Insert the customer's Ignition Key into the Key Code Reader on the J 35628 Interrogator. • Press the On-Off Rocker Switch to the "ON" position. • A number from 1 to 15 will appear on the display of the Interrogator indicating the electrical code of the key ("E" indicates error). • Set the Key Code Selector on the J 35628 Interrogator to a code which is different from the code read on the Key Code Reader display. • Turn Ignition Switch to "START."	Vehicle will not crank. "SECURITY" Indicator is illuminated.
[5] • Ignition Switch to "OFF." • Disconnect and remove the J 35628 Interrogator. • Reconnect connectors at base of Steering Column (within the 3 minute shut-down period). • Turn Ignition Switch to "START."	Vehicle will not crank. "SECURITY" Indicator is illuminated.
[6] • Turn Ignition Switch to "OFF." • Wait 3 to 4 minutes. • Observe the Indicator. • When Indicator goes "OFF," turn Ignition Switch to "START."	Engine starts.

Important:

- For "SECURITY" Indicator: attach a Tech 1 scan tool to the Data Link Connector (DLC) and monitor "PASS-Key®II System Indicator" (active = "ON"; inactive = "OFF"). If Tech 1 is unavailable, attach a test light to the DLC between terminal "D" and B+.

SYMPTOM TABLE

SYMPTOM	PROCEDURE	PAGE NUMBER
Engine does not crank; "SECURITY" Indicator does not illuminate.	• Check for battery voltage at Theft Deterrent Module Connector terminal "A1". • Ignition Switch to "RUN." • Check for battery voltage at Theft Deterrent Module Connector terminal "A2". • Check for ground at Theft Deterrent Module Connector terminal "B5". If power and ground wires to Theft Deterrent Module are OK, replace Theft Deterrent Module.	
Engine does not crank; "SECURITY" Indicator "ON" steady (not flashing).	• Perform Lock Cylinder and Harness Test on page 8A-133-8 (Chart #5).	
Engine does not crank; "SECURITY" Indicator flashing.	• Perform Lock Cylinder and Harness Test on page 8A-133-8 (Chart #5).	
Engine does not crank; "SECURITY" Indicator illuminates for approximately 5 seconds (bulb check).	Chart #1	8A-133-6
Engine cranks but won't start; "SECURITY" Indicator "ON" steady.	• Check for diagnostic trouble codes. (Refer to SECTION 6E). • Check for an open or short on CKT 229 between ECM and Theft Deterrent Module (see schematics).	
Engine cranks but won't start; "SECURITY" Indicator flashing.	• Perform Lock Cylinder and Harness Test on page 8A-133-8 (Chart #5).	
Engine cranks but won't start; "SECURITY" Indicator illuminates for approximately 5 seconds (bulb check).	Chart #2	8A-133-7
"SECURITY" Indicator flashing; Engine starts.	This symptom is present when an unprogrammed module is put in a vehicle that has an open or short to B+ or ground in the Lock Cylinder Contacts or CKTs 1073 or 1074, or with a damaged key. • Perform Lock Cylinder and Harness Test on page 8A-133-8 (Chart #5).	
"SECURITY" Indicator "ON" steady (not flashing); Engine starts.	Chart #3	8A-133-7
"SECURITY" Indicator never illuminates; Engine starts.	Chart #4	8A-133-8

THEFT DETERRENT SYSTEM: PASS-Key®II

CHART #1

ENGINE DOES NOT "CRANK"; "SECURITY" INDICATOR ILLUMINATES FOR APPROXIMATELY 5 SECONDS (BULB CHECK)

IMPORTANT:

- TO AVOID MISDIAGNOSIS, CHECK FOR DIAGNOSTIC TROUBLE CODES. SEE DRIVEABILITY AND EMISSIONS (SEC 6E).
- FOR "SECURITY" INDICATOR: ATTACH A TECH 1 SCAN TOOL TO THE DATA LINK CONNECTOR (DLC) AND MONITOR "PASS-Key®II SYSTEM INDICATOR" (ACTIVE = "ON"; INACTIVE = "OFF"). IF TECH 1 IS UNAVAILABLE, ATTACH A TEST LIGHT TO THE DLC BETWEEN TERMINAL "D" AND B+.

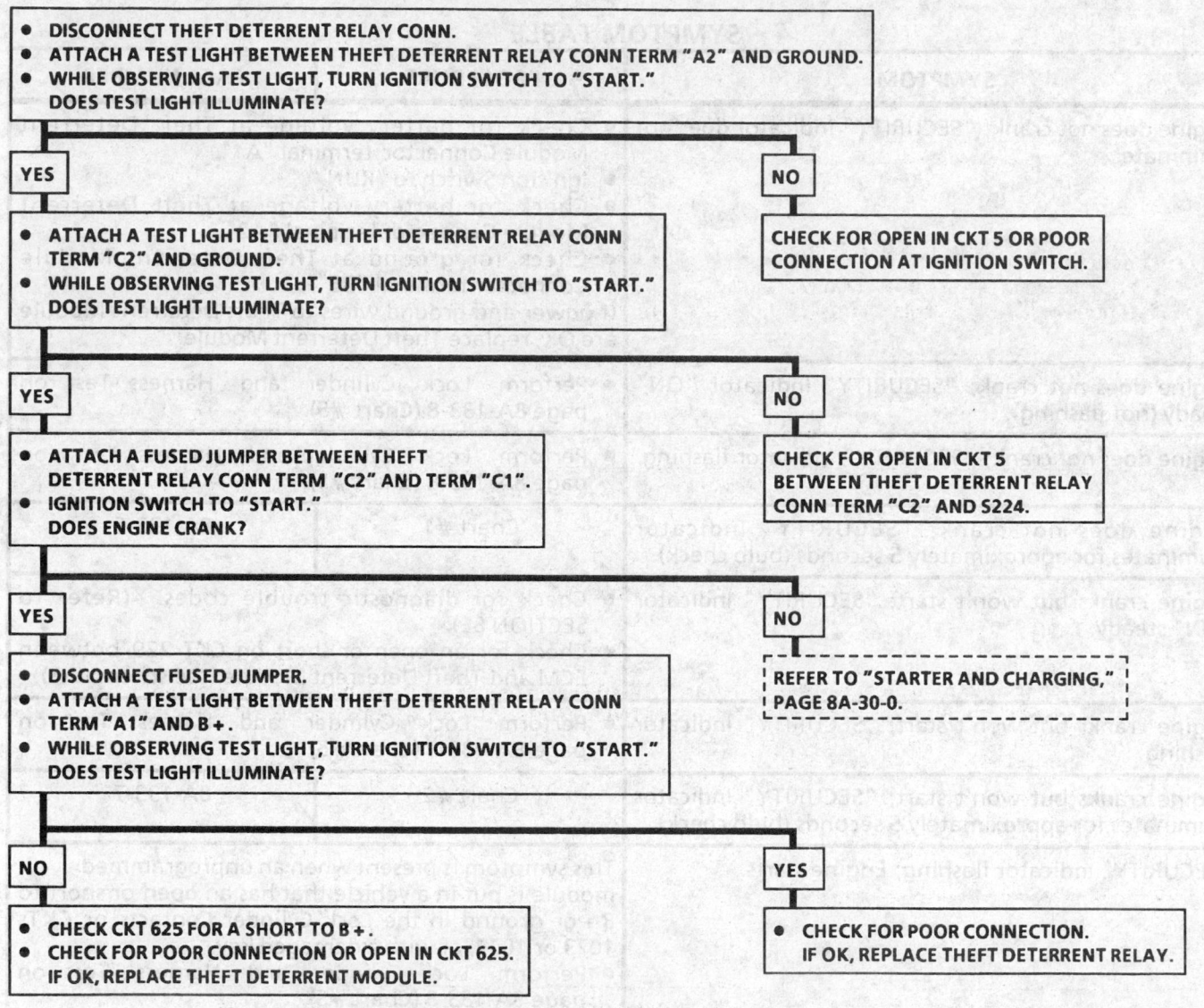

- DISCONNECT THEFT DETERRENT RELAY CONN.
- ATTACH A TEST LIGHT BETWEEN THEFT DETERRENT RELAY CONN TERM "A2" AND GROUND.
- WHILE OBSERVING TEST LIGHT, TURN IGNITION SWITCH TO "START."

DOES TEST LIGHT ILLUMINATE?

YES

- ATTACH A TEST LIGHT BETWEEN THEFT DETERRENT RELAY CONN TERM "C2" AND GROUND.
- WHILE OBSERVING TEST LIGHT, TURN IGNITION SWITCH TO "START."

DOES TEST LIGHT ILLUMINATE?

NO

CHECK FOR OPEN IN CKT 5 OR POOR CONNECTION AT IGNITION SWITCH.

(From "C2" test:)

YES

- ATTACH A FUSED JUMPER BETWEEN THEFT DETERRENT RELAY CONN TERM "C2" AND TERM "C1".
- IGNITION SWITCH TO "START."

DOES ENGINE CRANK?

NO

CHECK FOR OPEN IN CKT 5 BETWEEN THEFT DETERRENT RELAY CONN TERM "C2" AND S224.

(From fused jumper test:)

YES

- DISCONNECT FUSED JUMPER.
- ATTACH A TEST LIGHT BETWEEN THEFT DETERRENT RELAY CONN TERM "A1" AND B+.
- WHILE OBSERVING TEST LIGHT, TURN IGNITION SWITCH TO "START."

DOES TEST LIGHT ILLUMINATE?

NO

REFER TO "STARTER AND CHARGING," PAGE 8A-30-0.

(From "A1" test:)

NO

- CHECK CKT 625 FOR A SHORT TO B+.
- CHECK FOR POOR CONNECTION OR OPEN IN CKT 625.

IF OK, REPLACE THEFT DETERRENT MODULE.

YES

- CHECK FOR POOR CONNECTION.

IF OK, REPLACE THEFT DETERRENT RELAY.

CHART #2
VEHICLE CRANKS BUT WON'T START; "SECURITY" INDICATOR ILLUMINATES FOR APPROX 5 SECONDS (BULB CHECK)

IMPORTANT:
- TO AVOID MISDIAGNOSIS, CHECK FOR DIAGNOSTIC TROUBLE CODES. SEE DRIVEABILITY AND EMISSIONS (SEC 6E).
- FOR "SECURITY" INDICATOR: ATTACH A TECH 1 SCAN TOOL TO THE DATA LINK CONNECTOR (DLC) AND MONITOR "PASS-Key®II SYSTEM INDICATOR" (ACTIVE = "ON"; INACTIVE = "OFF"). IF TECH 1 IS UNAVAILABLE, ATTACH A TEST LIGHT TO THE DLC BETWEEN TERMINAL "D" AND B+.

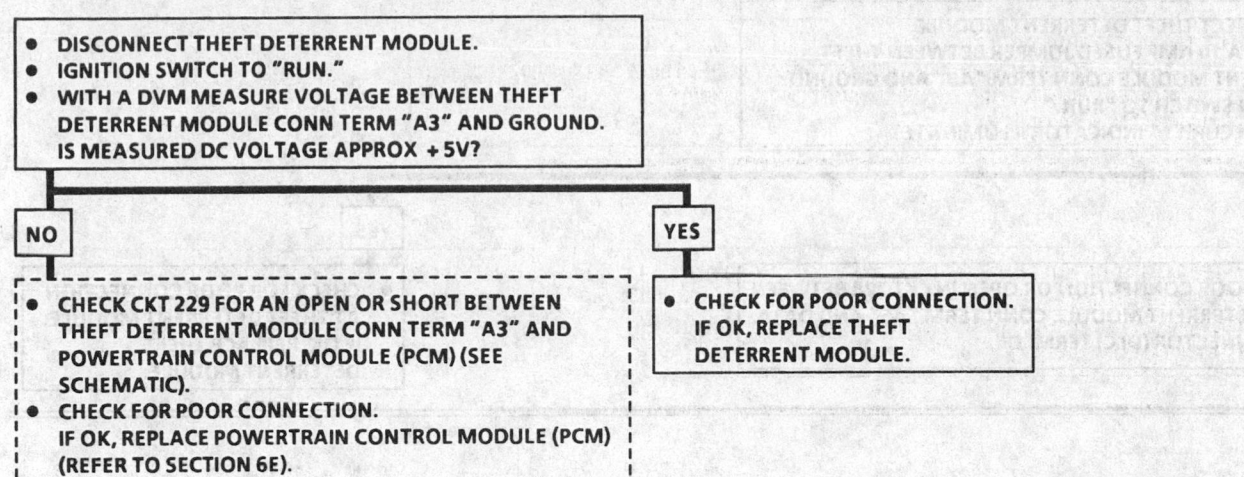

- DISCONNECT THEFT DETERRENT MODULE.
- IGNITION SWITCH TO "RUN."
- WITH A DVM MEASURE VOLTAGE BETWEEN THEFT DETERRENT MODULE CONN TERM "A3" AND GROUND. IS MEASURED DC VOLTAGE APPROX +5V?

NO
- CHECK CKT 229 FOR AN OPEN OR SHORT BETWEEN THEFT DETERRENT MODULE CONN TERM "A3" AND POWERTRAIN CONTROL MODULE (PCM) (SEE SCHEMATIC).
- CHECK FOR POOR CONNECTION. IF OK, REPLACE POWERTRAIN CONTROL MODULE (PCM) (REFER TO SECTION 6E).

YES
- CHECK FOR POOR CONNECTION. IF OK, REPLACE THEFT DETERRENT MODULE.

CHART #3
"SECURITY" INDICATOR "ON" STEADY (NOT FLASHING); VEHICLE STARTS

IMPORTANT:
- TO AVOID MISDIAGNOSIS, CHECK FOR DIAGNOSTIC TROUBLE CODES. SEE DRIVEABILITY AND EMISSIONS (SEC 6E).
- FOR "SECURITY" INDICATOR: ATTACH A TECH 1 SCAN TOOL TO THE DATA LINK CONNECTOR (DLC) AND MONITOR "PASS-Key®II SYSTEM INDICATOR" (ACTIVE = "ON"; INACTIVE = "OFF"). IF TECH 1 IS UNAVAILABLE, ATTACH A TEST LIGHT TO THE DLC BETWEEN TERMINAL "D" AND B+.

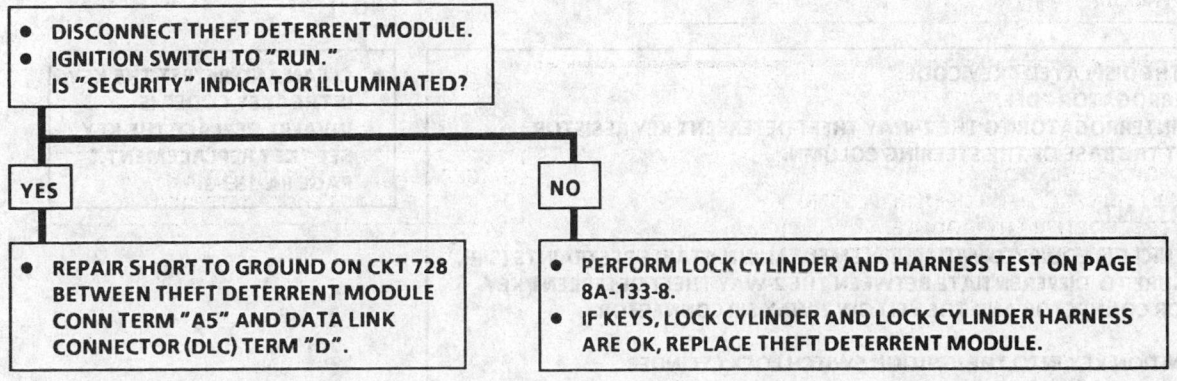

- DISCONNECT THEFT DETERRENT MODULE.
- IGNITION SWITCH TO "RUN." IS "SECURITY" INDICATOR ILLUMINATED?

YES
- REPAIR SHORT TO GROUND ON CKT 728 BETWEEN THEFT DETERRENT MODULE CONN TERM "A5" AND DATA LINK CONNECTOR (DLC) TERM "D".

NO
- PERFORM LOCK CYLINDER AND HARNESS TEST ON PAGE 8A-133-8.
- IF KEYS, LOCK CYLINDER AND LOCK CYLINDER HARNESS ARE OK, REPLACE THEFT DETERRENT MODULE.

THEFT DETERRENT SYSTEM: PASS-Key®II

CHART #4
"SECURITY" INDICATOR NEVER ILLUMINATES; VEHICLE STARTS

IMPORTANT:

- TO AVOID MISDIAGNOSIS, CHECK FOR DIAGNOSTIC TROUBLE CODES. SEE DRIVEABILITY AND EMISSIONS (SEC 6E).
- FOR "SECURITY" INDICATOR: ATTACH A TECH 1 SCAN TOOL TO THE DATA LINK CONNECTOR (DLC) AND MONITOR "PASS-Key®II SYSTEM INDICATOR" (ACTIVE = "ON"; INACTIVE = "OFF"). IF TECH 1 IS UNAVAILABLE, ATTACH A TEST LIGHT TO THE DLC BETWEEN TERMINAL "D" AND B+.

- DISCONNECT THEFT DETERRENT MODULE.
- ATTACH A 10 AMP FUSED JUMPER BETWEEN THEFT DETERRENT MODULE CONN TERM "A5" AND GROUND.
- IGNITION SWITCH TO "RUN."

DOES "SECURITY" INDICATOR ILLUMINATE?

NO

- REPAIR POOR CONNECTION OR OPEN IN CKT 728 BETWEEN THEFT DETERRENT MODULE CONN TERM "A5" AND DATA LINK CONNECTOR (DLC) TERM "D".

YES

- CHECK FOR POOR CONNECTION AT THEFT DETERRENT MODULE. IF OK, REPLACE THEFT DETERRENT MODULE.

CHART #5
LOCK CYLINDER AND HARNESS TEST

IMPORTANT:

- TO AVOID MISDIAGNOSIS, DO NOT PERFORM THIS TEST UNLESS DIRECTED BY SYMPTOM TABLE.
- AFTER A REPAIR TO THE LOCK CYLINDER HARNESS, THE "SECURITY" INDICATOR WILL REMAIN "ON" FOR ONE MINUTE.

- INSERT IGNITION KEY INTO PASS-Key®II INTERROGATOR J 35628.
- TURN THE INTERROGATOR "ON."
- READ THE "KEY CODE" SHOWN ON THE DISPLAY OF THE INTERROGATOR.

IS THE DISPLAYED "KEY CODE" A VALUE OF "1" THROUGH "15"?

YES

- WRITE DOWN THE DISPLAYED "KEY CODE."
- TURN THE INTERROGATOR "OFF."
- CONNECT THE INTERROGATOR TO THE 2-WAY THEFT DETERRENT KEY RESISTOR CONNECTOR AT THE BASE OF THE STEERING COLUMN.

IMPORTANT:

- THIS VEHICLE IS EQUIPPED WITH SUPPLEMENTAL INFLATABLE RESTRAINTS (SIR). MAKE SURE TO DIFFERENTIATE BETWEEN THE 2-WAY THEFT DETERRENT KEY RESISTOR CONNECTOR AND THE YELLOW 2-WAY SIR CONNECTOR.

- INSERT THE IGNITION KEY INTO THE IGNITION SWITCH LOCK CYLINDER.
- TURN THE INTERROGATOR "ON."
- WHILE OBSERVING THE DISPLAY ON THE INTERROGATOR, TURN THE IGNITION SWITCH SLOWLY TO THE "START" POSITION.

DOES THE DISPLAYED "KEY CODE" VALUE MATCH THE VALUE OBSERVED IN STEP 1?

NO

- CLEAN AND RETEST THE KEY. IF THE "KEY CODE" IS INVALID, REPLACE THE KEY. SEE "KEY REPLACEMENT," PAGE 8A-133-9.

A (CONTINUED ON NEXT PAGE)

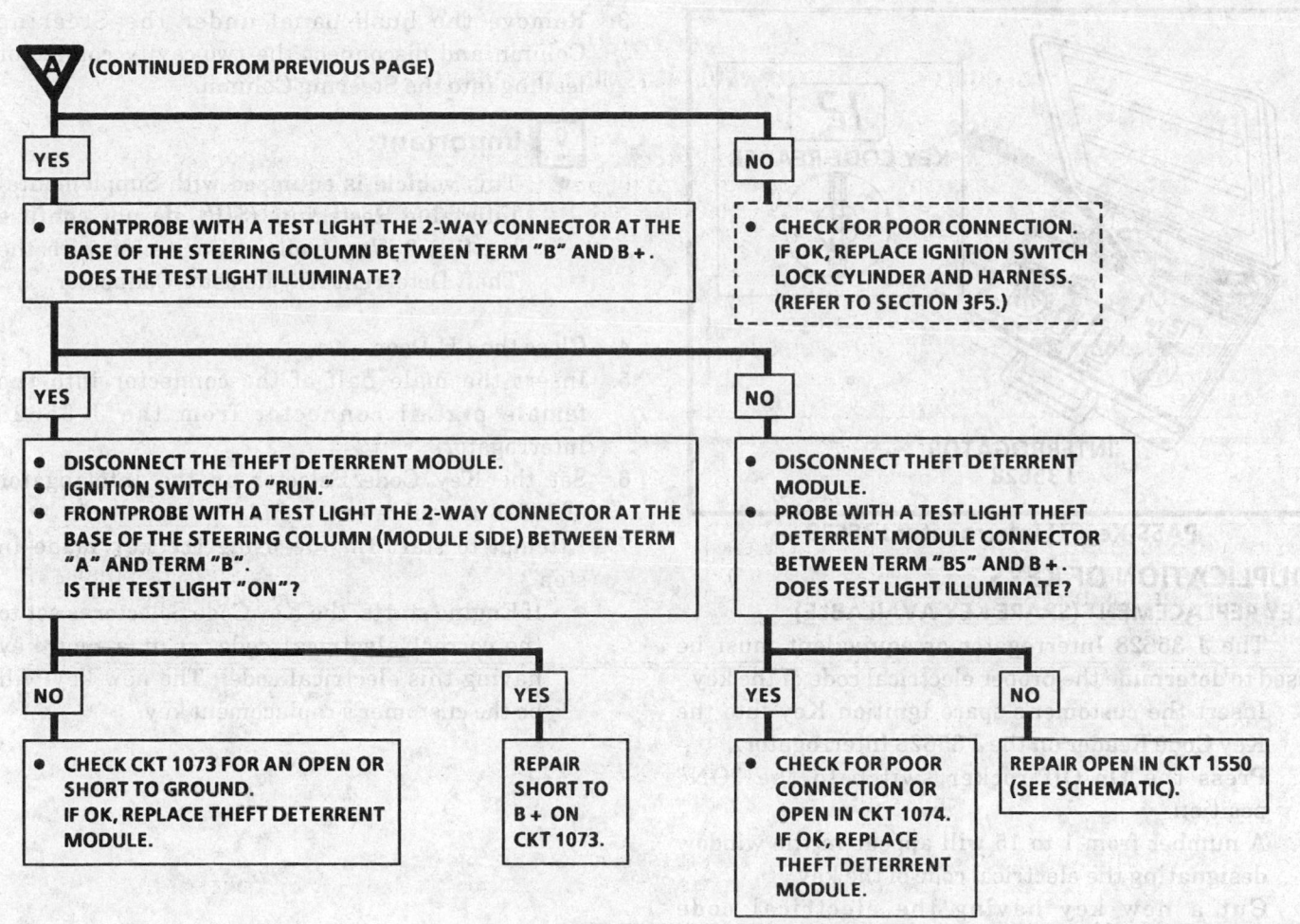

A (CONTINUED FROM PREVIOUS PAGE)

YES

- FRONTPROBE WITH A TEST LIGHT THE 2-WAY CONNECTOR AT THE BASE OF THE STEERING COLUMN BETWEEN TERM "B" AND B +. DOES THE TEST LIGHT ILLUMINATE?

NO

- CHECK FOR POOR CONNECTION. IF OK, REPLACE IGNITION SWITCH LOCK CYLINDER AND HARNESS. (REFER TO SECTION 3F5.)

From the test light question above:

YES

- DISCONNECT THE THEFT DETERRENT MODULE.
- IGNITION SWITCH TO "RUN."
- FRONTPROBE WITH A TEST LIGHT THE 2-WAY CONNECTOR AT THE BASE OF THE STEERING COLUMN (MODULE SIDE) BETWEEN TERM "A" AND TERM "B". IS THE TEST LIGHT "ON"?

NO

- DISCONNECT THEFT DETERRENT MODULE.
- PROBE WITH A TEST LIGHT THEFT DETERRENT MODULE CONNECTOR BETWEEN TERM "B5" AND B +. DOES TEST LIGHT ILLUMINATE?

From "IS THE TEST LIGHT "ON"?":

NO

- CHECK CKT 1073 FOR AN OPEN OR SHORT TO GROUND. IF OK, REPLACE THEFT DETERRENT MODULE.

YES

REPAIR SHORT TO B + ON CKT 1073.

From "DOES TEST LIGHT ILLUMINATE?":

YES

- CHECK FOR POOR CONNECTION OR OPEN IN CKT 1074. IF OK, REPLACE THEFT DETERRENT MODULE.

NO

REPAIR OPEN IN CKT 1550 (SEE SCHEMATIC).

THEFT DETERRENT SYSTEM: PASS-Key®II

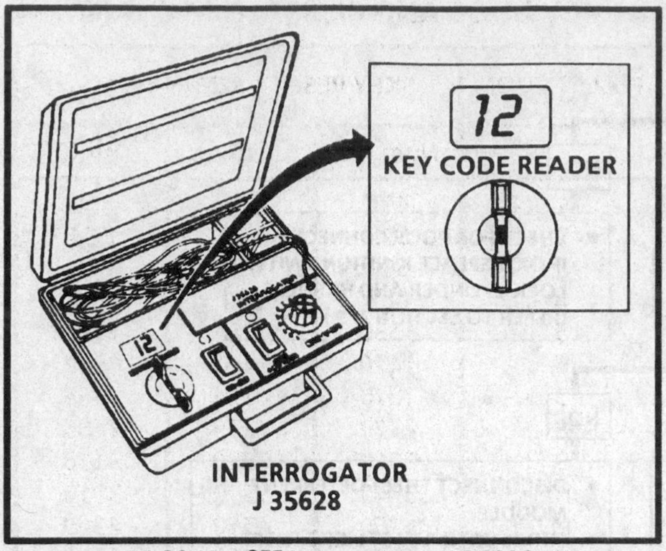
12
KEY CODE READER
INTERROGATOR
J 35628

PASS-Key®II Interrogator J 35628

DUPLICATION OF KEYS

KEY REPLACEMENT (SPARE KEY AVAILABLE)

The J 35628 Interrogator or equivalent must be used to determine the proper electrical code of the key.

1. Insert the customer's spare Ignition Key into the Key Code Reader on the J 35628 Interrogator.
2. Press the On-Off rocker switch to the "ON" position.
3. A number from 1 to 15 will appear in the window designating the electrical code of the key.
4. Cut a new key having the electrical code determined from the J 35628 Interrogator.
5. Start the Engine using the new key to insure that the key is correct both mechanically and electrically.

KEY REPLACEMENT (NO SPARE KEY AVAILABLE)

1. If the Ignition Key is lost and there is no spare key, determine the mechanical code from the code on the Ignition Key Lock Cylinder. The code may also be determined from the dealer invoice for the vehicle.
2. Cut a new key to this mechanical code. Use a blank PASS-Key®II test key which has no resistance pellet. This key will be used to operate the Ignition Switch for the remaining steps.
3. Remove the hush panel under the Steering Column and disconnect the two-cavity connector leading into the Steering Column.

Important:

- This vehicle is equipped with Supplemental Inflatable Restraints (SIR), do not confuse the SIR 2-Way (yellow) Connector with the Theft Deterrent Key Resistor Connector.

4. Close the LH Door.
5. Insert the male half of the connector into the female pigtail connector from the J 35628 Interrogator.
6. Set the Key Code Selector on the Interrogator (J 35628 or equivalent) to "1".
7. Attempt to start Engine using the key made in step 2.
   - If Engine starts, the Key Code Selector is set to the correct electrical code. Cut a new key having this electrical code. The new key will be the customer's replacement key.

- If Engine does not start, turn Ignition Switch to "OFF," then turn the Key Code Selector to the next higher position. Wait four minutes and attempt to start the Engine using the new electrical code. Use the 4-minute Timer on the J 35628 Interrogator to indicate the 4-minute interval. Start the Timer by depressing the "Start" rocker switch. The red indicator will turn off at the end of a four minute interval. This procedure must be repeated until the Engine can be started. Cut a new key having the electrical code which allowed the vehicle to start.

PROGRAMMING A NEW DECODER MODULE

New decoder modules are unprogrammed. Before the system will function properly after a new module has been installed, it must be programmed to the code that matches the customer's keys. Programming a new module is very simple:

1. Install the new, unprogrammed decoder module.
2. Insert one of the customer's keys in the ignition lock cylinder and turn it to the "ON" position. It's a good idea to start the engine at this time to verify system operation.
3. Observe the "SECURITY" Indicator Lamp:

Important:

- For "SECURITY" Indicator: attach a Tech 1 scan tool to the Data Link Connector (DLC) and monitor "PASS-Key®II System Indicator" (active="ON"; inactive="OFF"). If Tech 1 is unavailable, attach a test light to the DLC between terminal "D" and B+.

- The indicator lamp should light for about five seconds and then go out. If the wiring or contacts to the Key Resistance Pellet or the key is defective or intermittent and a new module is installed, the Engine will start but the "SECURITY" Indicator will flash at a rate of one flash per second until the Ignition Switch is turned off. This indicates that the module did not program and that the system components, wiring and contacts should be checked for a fault.

KEY CODE AND RESISTANCE CHART

PELLET CODE	KEY RESISTANCE IN OHMS		
	Nominal	Low	High
1	402	386	438
2	523	502	564
3	681	654	728
4	887	852	942
5	1130	1085	1195
6	1470	1411	1549
7	1870	1795	1965
8	2370	2275	2485
9	3010	2890	3150
10	3740	3590	3910
11	4750	4560	4960
12	6040	5798	6302
13	7500	7200	7820
14	9530	9149	9931
15	11800	11328	12292

Important:

- Before connecting the Interrogator to the ignition lock cylinder circuit, always verify vehicle key code and set the code into the Interrogator using "key code" knob. This will prevent programming an unprogrammed decoder module with an undesired key code.

THEFT DETERRENT SYSTEM: PASS-Key®II

Important:

- For "SECURITY" Indicator: attach a Tech 1 scan tool to the Data Link Connector (DLC) and monitor "PASS-Key®II System Indicator" (active="ON"; inactive="OFF"). If Tech 1 is unavailable, attach a test light to the DLC between terminal "D" and B+.

CIRCUIT OPERATION

PASS-Key®II is a theft deterrent system which prevents the vehicle from starting if the Ignition Key "Resistance Code" is not recognized by the Theft Deterrent Module. If the Resistance Code is not recognized, the Engine is prevented from starting in two ways: battery voltage from the Ignition Switch to the starter is disabled by a Theft Deterrent Relay and fuel to the fuel injectors is stopped without the presence of a fuel enable signal.

Resistor sensing contacts are located in the Ignition Key Lock Cylinder. These contact the Key Resistor Pellet on the key when it is inserted. When the lock is rotated, Ignition voltage is applied to the Theft Deterrent Module and pellet resistance is read at this time. The Pellet resistance is read across terminals "B7" and "B8" which is then compared against the resistance value stored in the Module.

If the Key Resistance Pellet is the proper resistance, terminal "A4" is grounded, energizing the Theft Deterrent Relay. At the same time, a signal is applied at terminal "A3" to enable the Powertrain Control Module (PCM). When this signal is received by the PCM, it allows fuel injector pulses to begin.

If the Key Resistor Pellet is the wrong value, the Theft Deterrent Module will shut down for 3 minutes + or — 18 seconds. During this interval, there will be no output at terminals "A3" or "A4" and the "SECURITY" Indicator will illuminate. The Ignition Switch input is ignored during this shut down period. For this reason, the timer will run and the "SECURITY" Indicator will remain illuminated with Ignition on or off.

Once the timer has completed its 3 minute + or — 18 second shut down, the next time Ignition is cycled from off to on, the Theft Deterrent Module timer is reset. A key having the correct code can then be used to start the Engine.

"SECURITY" INDICATOR OPERATION

The "SECURITY" Indicator is controlled directly by the Theft Deterrent Module. The following describes the modes of indicator operation:

1. When the Ignition is put in "RUN," "BULB TEST," or "START," the "SECURITY" Indicator illuminates for about 5 seconds as a bulb check.
2. If the Theft Deterrent Module is actively in the shut down mode and thus preventing the vehicle from starting, the indicator will be illuminated (grounded) by the Theft Deterrent Module for 3 minutes + or — 18 seconds after Ignition is turned on.
3. If the resistor sensing contacts or CKTs 1073 or 1074 are open or shorted, or if a defective key is being used at the time Ignition is turned on, the "SECURITY" Indicator will flash at a rate of once per second and the Engine will not start; however, the 3 minute + or — 18 second lockout will not be activated. Additionally, if an unprogrammed module is present and there is an open or short, or if a defective key is being used the Theft Deterrent Module will not program a key code, the "SECURITY" Indicator will flash at a rate of once per second, and the Engine will start.
4. Lock Cylinder CKTs 1073 and 1074 are continuously monitored and if a fault is detected in these circuits for 1 minute, the indicator will turn "ON." If the fault condition goes away for 1 minute, the indicator will turn "OFF" and the system will function as normal. If a lock cylinder circuit fault (lock cylinder contacts or wiring becomes open or shorted, or if a defective key is detected) while the Engine is "RUNNING", the vehicle can be restarted. The "SECURITY" Indicator will illuminate during this Ignition cycle while the fault is present. When a fault condition is present at the time Ignition is cycled off, the vehicle will not be protected by the PASS-Key®II System and the indicator will be illuminated whenever the Ignition is on, until the fault is corrected. This is called the Fault Enable Mode. After the fault has been corrected, the "Security" Indicator will remain "ON" for one minute then go "OFF."

BLANK

TRUNK LID RELEASE

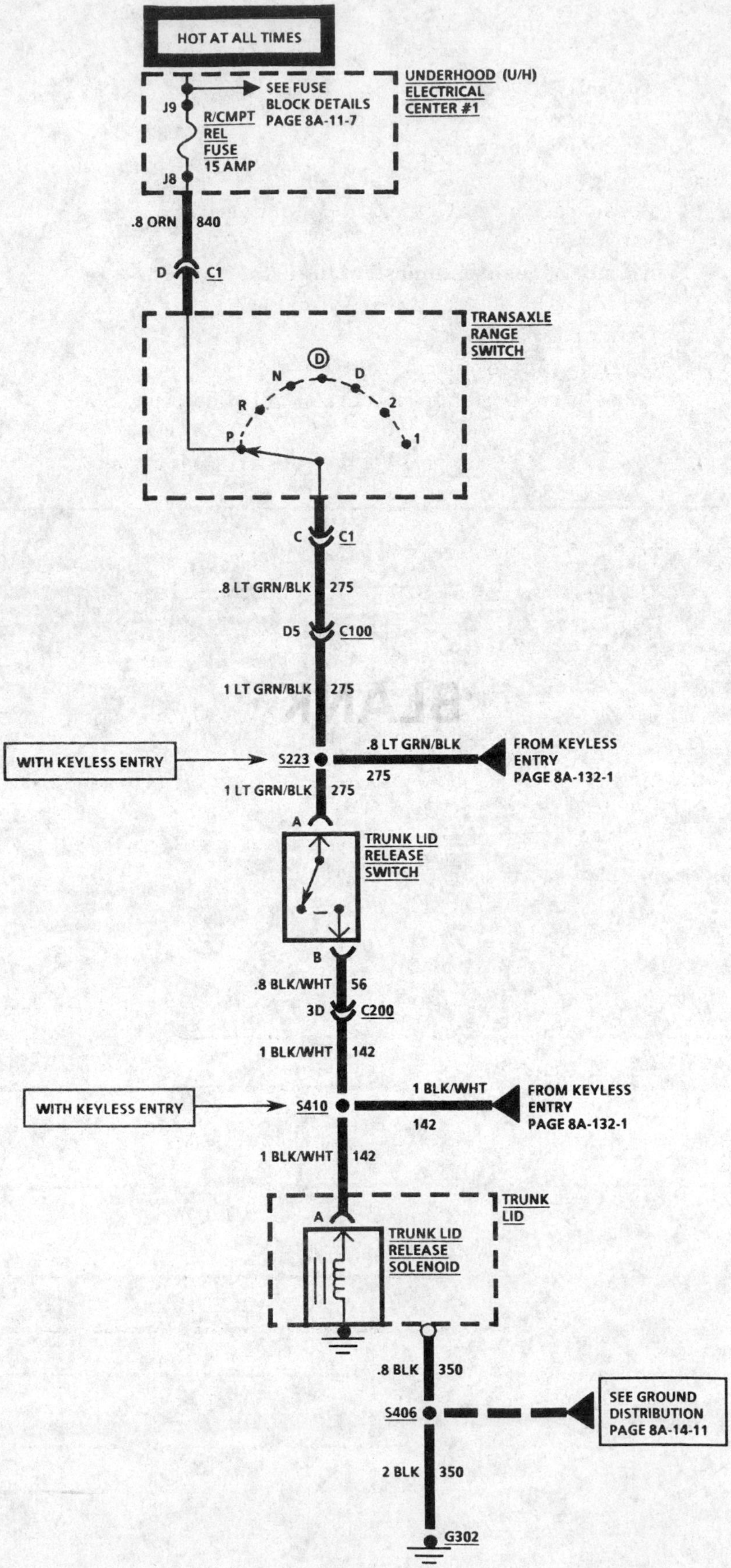

HOT AT ALL TIMES
UNDERHOOD (U/H) ELECTRICAL CENTER #1
SEE FUSE BLOCK DETAILS PAGE 8A-11-7
J9
R/CMPT REL FUSE 15 AMP
J8
.8 ORN 840
D C1
TRANSAXLE RANGE SWITCH
P R N D D 2 1
C C1
.8 LT GRN/BLK 275
D5 C100
1 LT GRN/BLK 275
WITH KEYLESS ENTRY
S223
.8 LT GRN/BLK 275
FROM KEYLESS ENTRY PAGE 8A-132-1
1 LT GRN/BLK 275
A
TRUNK LID RELEASE SWITCH
B
.8 BLK/WHT 56
3D C200
1 BLK/WHT 142
WITH KEYLESS ENTRY
S410
1 BLK/WHT 142
FROM KEYLESS ENTRY PAGE 8A-132-1
1 BLK/WHT 142
TRUNK LID
A
TRUNK LID RELEASE SOLENOID
.8 BLK 350
S406
SEE GROUND DISTRIBUTION PAGE 8A-14-11
2 BLK 350
G302

COMPONENT	LOCATION	201-PG	FIG.	CONN
Transaxle Range Switch	Left of Engine, on Transaxle	3	10	202-41
Trunk Lid Release Solenoid	Center rear of Trunk Lid	5	18	
Trunk Lid Release Switch	I/P Compartment	12	41	
Underhood (U/H) Electrical Center #1	RH side of Engine Compartment, forward of strut tower			202-34
C100 (36 cavities)	RH side of dash, behind strut tower			202-0
C200 (102 cavities)	Behind RH side of I/P, near shroud	13	44	202-7
G302	Under RH front seat			
S223 (with Keyless Entry)	I/P Harn, approx 50 cm from C100			
S406	Cross Car Harn, approx 9 cm from RH Rear Speaker breakout			
S410 (with Keyless Entry)	Cross Car Harn, approx 10 cm from RH Rear Speaker breakout			

TROUBLESHOOTING HINTS (Perform before beginning System Diagnosis)

1. Check that the Trunk Lid Release Solenoid case ground is clean and tight.
2. Check the R/CMPT REL Fuse by visual inspection.

- Check for a broken (or partially broken) wire inside of the insulation which could cause system malfunction but prove "GOOD" in a continuity/voltage check with a system disconnected. These circuits may be intermittent or resistive when loaded, and if possible, should be checked by monitoring for a voltage drop with the system operational (under load).
- Check for proper installation of aftermarket electronic equipment which may affect the integrity of other systems (see "Troubleshooting Procedures," page 8A-4-0).
- Refer to System Diagnosis.

SYSTEM DIAGNOSIS

- Perform the System Check and refer to the Symptom Table for the appropriate diagnostic procedures.

SYSTEM CHECK

ACTION	NORMAL RESULTS
[1] • Press Trunk Lid Release Switch with Gear Selector in "PARK."	Trunk Lid releases.

SYMPTOM TABLE

SYMPTOM	PROCEDURE	PAGE NUMBER
Trunk Lid will not release.	Chart #1	8A-134-2
Trunk Lid will not release using Keyless Entry Remote, releases normally from switch.	See Keyless Entry.	8A-132-0
Trunk Lid does not latch (without Keyless Entry).	Chart #2	8A-134-3
Trunk Lid does not latch (with Keyless Entry).	See Keyless Entry.	8A-132-0

TRUNK LID RELEASE

CHART #1

TRUNK LID WILL NOT RELEASE

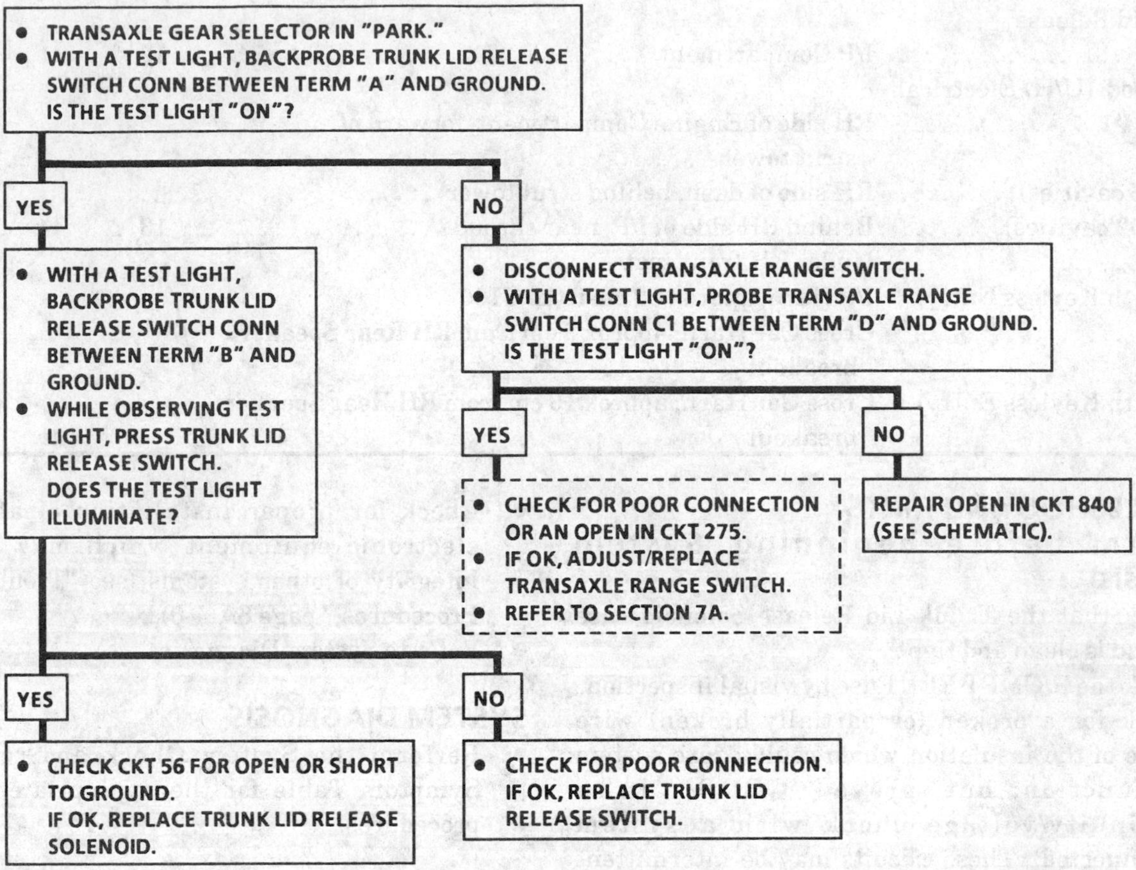
• TRANSAXLE GEAR SELECTOR IN "PARK."
• WITH A TEST LIGHT, BACKPROBE TRUNK LID RELEASE SWITCH CONN BETWEEN TERM "A" AND GROUND.
IS THE TEST LIGHT "ON"?
YES
NO
• WITH A TEST LIGHT, BACKPROBE TRUNK LID RELEASE SWITCH CONN BETWEEN TERM "B" AND GROUND.
• WHILE OBSERVING TEST LIGHT, PRESS TRUNK LID RELEASE SWITCH.
DOES THE TEST LIGHT ILLUMINATE?
• DISCONNECT TRANSAXLE RANGE SWITCH.
• WITH A TEST LIGHT, PROBE TRANSAXLE RANGE SWITCH CONN C1 BETWEEN TERM "D" AND GROUND.
IS THE TEST LIGHT "ON"?
YES
NO
• CHECK FOR POOR CONNECTION OR AN OPEN IN CKT 275.
• IF OK, ADJUST/REPLACE TRANSAXLE RANGE SWITCH.
• REFER TO SECTION 7A.
REPAIR OPEN IN CKT 840 (SEE SCHEMATIC).
YES
NO
• CHECK CKT 56 FOR OPEN OR SHORT TO GROUND.
IF OK, REPLACE TRUNK LID RELEASE SOLENOID.
• CHECK FOR POOR CONNECTION.
IF OK, REPLACE TRUNK LID RELEASE SWITCH.

CHART #2
TRUNK LID DOES NOT LATCH (WITHOUT KEYLESS ENTRY)

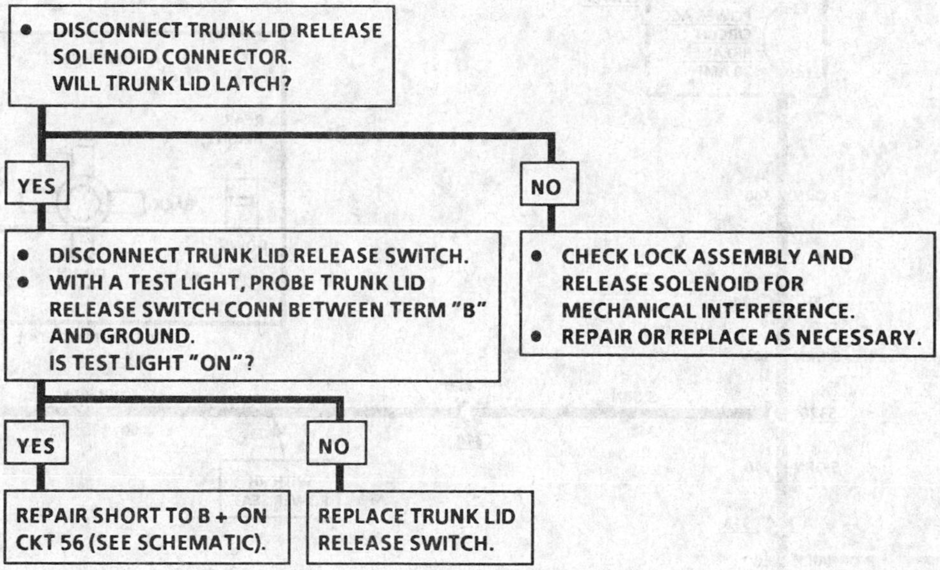
• DISCONNECT TRUNK LID RELEASE SOLENOID CONNECTOR.
WILL TRUNK LID LATCH?
YES
NO
• DISCONNECT TRUNK LID RELEASE SWITCH.
• WITH A TEST LIGHT, PROBE TRUNK LID RELEASE SWITCH CONN BETWEEN TERM "B" AND GROUND.
IS TEST LIGHT "ON"?
• CHECK LOCK ASSEMBLY AND RELEASE SOLENOID FOR MECHANICAL INTERFERENCE.
• REPAIR OR REPLACE AS NECESSARY.
YES
NO
REPAIR SHORT TO B + ON CKT 56 (SEE SCHEMATIC).
REPLACE TRUNK LID RELEASE SWITCH.

CIRCUIT OPERATION

Voltage is applied at all times through the R/CMPT REL Fuse to the Trunk Lid Release Switch. With the Switch closed and the Transaxle Range Switch in "PARK," voltage is applied to the Trunk Lid Release Solenoid, releasing the Trunk Lid.

POWER SEATS

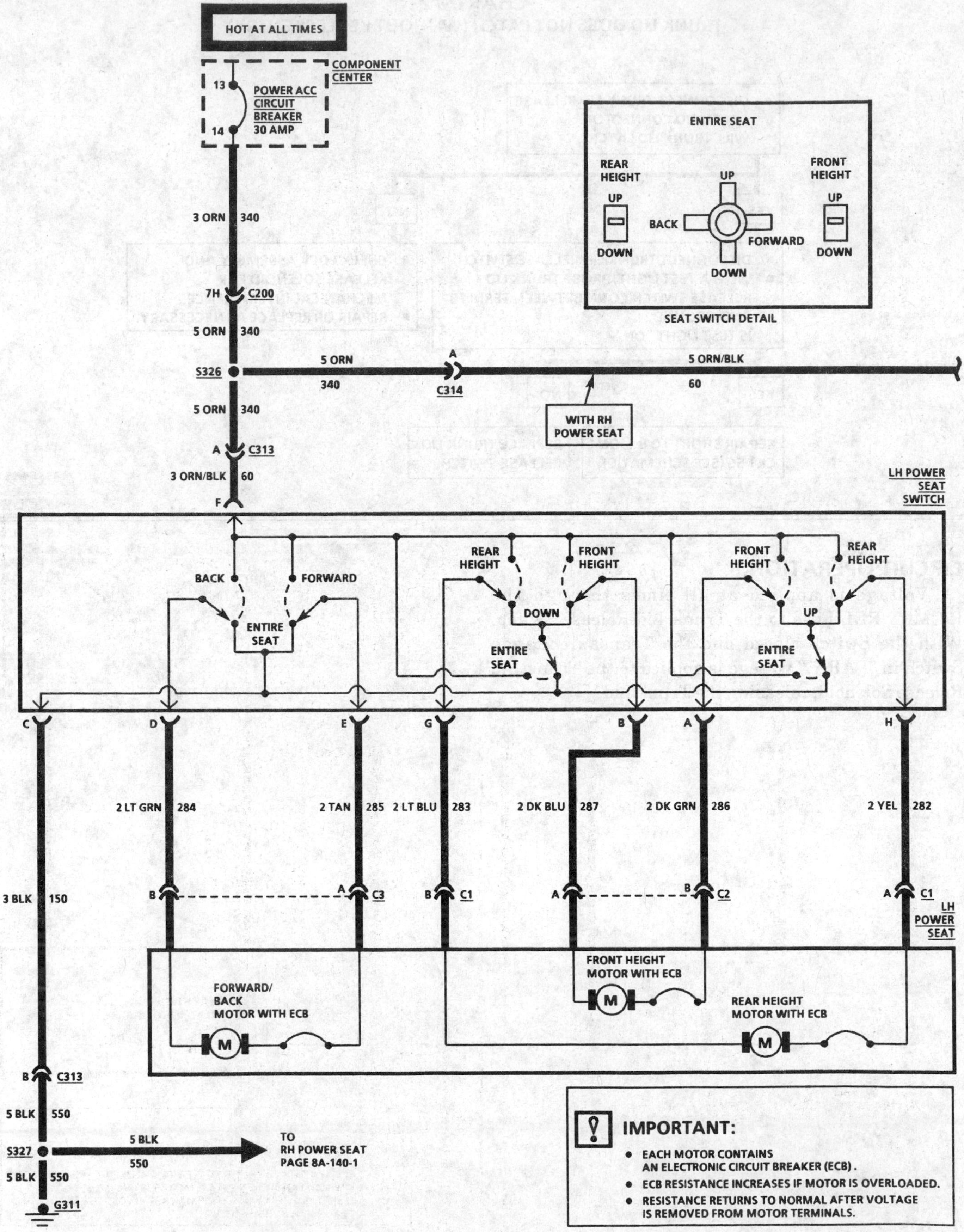

HOT AT ALL TIMES
COMPONENT CENTER
13
POWER ACC CIRCUIT BREAKER 30 AMP
14
3 ORN 340
7H C200
5 ORN 340
S326
5 ORN 340
A C314
5 ORN/BLK 60
WITH RH POWER SEAT
5 ORN 340
A C313
3 ORN/BLK 60
F
LH POWER SEAT SWITCH
ENTIRE SEAT
REAR HEIGHT
UP
DOWN
BACK
FORWARD
FRONT HEIGHT
SEAT SWITCH DETAIL
BACK
FORWARD
ENTIRE SEAT
REAR HEIGHT
FRONT HEIGHT
DOWN
ENTIRE SEAT
FRONT HEIGHT
REAR HEIGHT
UP
ENTIRE SEAT
C D E G B A H
3 BLK 150
2 LT GRN 284
2 TAN 285
2 LT BLU 283
2 DK BLU 287
2 DK GRN 286
2 YEL 282
B A C3
B C1
A B C2
A C1
LH POWER SEAT
FORWARD/ BACK MOTOR WITH ECB
FRONT HEIGHT MOTOR WITH ECB
REAR HEIGHT MOTOR WITH ECB
M
B C313
5 BLK 550
S327
5 BLK 550
TO RH POWER SEAT PAGE 8A-140-1
5 BLK 550
G311

IMPORTANT:

- EACH MOTOR CONTAINS AN ELECTRONIC CIRCUIT BREAKER (ECB).
- ECB RESISTANCE INCREASES IF MOTOR IS OVERLOADED.
- RESISTANCE RETURNS TO NORMAL AFTER VOLTAGE IS REMOVED FROM MOTOR TERMINALS.

POWER SEATS
WITH RH POWER SEAT (AC1/AG2)

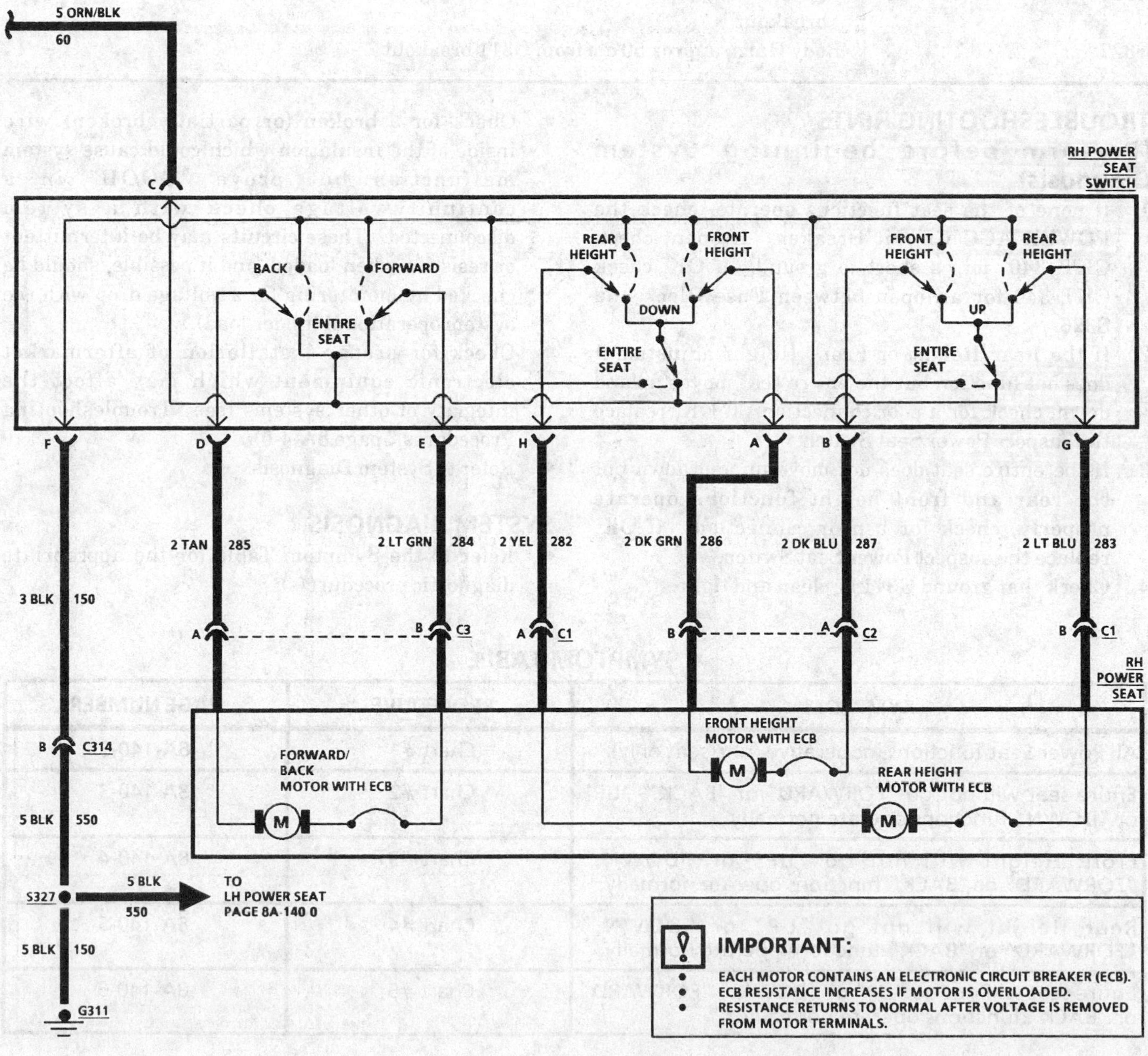

5 ORN/BLK
60
C
RH POWER SEAT SWITCH
BACK
FORWARD
ENTIRE SEAT
REAR HEIGHT
FRONT HEIGHT
DOWN
ENTIRE SEAT
FRONT HEIGHT
REAR HEIGHT
UP
ENTIRE SEAT
F
D
E
H
A
B
G
2 TAN 285
2 LT GRN 284
2 YEL 282
2 DK GRN 286
2 DK BLU 287
2 LT BLU 283
3 BLK 150
A
B C3
A C1
B
A C2
B C1
RH POWER SEAT
FRONT HEIGHT MOTOR WITH ECB
FORWARD/ BACK MOTOR WITH ECB
REAR HEIGHT MOTOR WITH ECB
B C314
5 BLK 550
5 BLK
550
S327
TO LH POWER SEAT PAGE 8A-140-0
5 BLK 150
G311

IMPORTANT:

- EACH MOTOR CONTAINS AN ELECTRONIC CIRCUIT BREAKER (ECB).
- ECB RESISTANCE INCREASES IF MOTOR IS OVERLOADED.
- RESISTANCE RETURNS TO NORMAL AFTER VOLTAGE IS REMOVED FROM MOTOR TERMINALS.

POWER SEATS

COMPONENT	LOCATION	201-PG	FIG.	CONN
Component Center	Behind RH side of I/P	11	36	202-14
LH Forward/Back Motor	Under LH front seat			
LH Front Height Seat Motor	Under LH front seat			
LH Power Seat Switch	On LH side of LH front seat			202-25
LH Rear Height Seat Motor	Under LH front seat			
RH Forward/Back Motor	Under RH front seat			
RH Front Height Seat Motor	Under RH front seat			
RH Power Seat Switch	On RH side of RH front seat			202-25
RH Rear Height Seat Motor	Under RH front seat			
C200 (106 cavities)	Behind RH side of I/P, near shroud	22	74	202-3
C313 (2 cavities)	Under LH front seat	15	50	
C314 (2 cavities)	Under RH front seat			
G311	Under LH front seat			
S326	Body Harn, approx 5 cm from Driver Power Seat breakout			
S327	Body Harn, approx 50 cm from G311 breakout			

TROUBLESHOOTING HINTS (Perform before beginning System Diagnosis)

1. If none of the seat functions operate, check the POWER ACC Circuit Breaker. If open, check CKT 340 for a short to ground. If OK, check CKT 340 for an open between Fuse Block and S326.
2. If the Rear Height or Front Height adjustment does not function but the entire seat moves up and down, check for a poor connection. If OK, replace the suspect Power Seat Switch.
3. If the entire seat does not move up and down but the rear and front height functions operate properly, check for a poor connection. If OK, replace the suspect Power Seat Switch.
4. Check that ground G311 is clean and tight.

- Check for a broken (or partially broken) wire inside of the insulation which could cause system malfunction but prove "GOOD" in a continuity/voltage check with a system disconnected. These circuits may be intermittent or resistive when loaded, and if possible, should be checked by monitoring for a voltage drop with the system operational (under load).
- Check for proper installation of aftermarket electronic equipment which may affect the integrity of other systems (see "Troubleshooting Procedures," page 8A-4-0).
- Refer to System Diagnosis.

SYSTEM DIAGNOSIS

- Refer to the Symptom Table for the appropriate diagnostic procedure(s).

SYMPTOM TABLE

SYMPTOM	PROCEDURE	PAGE NUMBER
All Power Seat functions inoperative (one seat only).	Chart #1	8A-140-3
Entire seat will not go "FORWARD" or "BACK," "UP" or "DOWN" functions operate normally.	Chart #2	8A-140-3
Front Height will not go "UP" or "DOWN," "FORWARD" or "BACK" functions operate normally.	Chart #3	8A-140-4
Rear Height will not go "UP" or "DOWN," "FORWARD" or "BACK" functions operate normally.	Chart #4	8A-140-5
Entire seat will not go "UP" or "DOWN," "FORWARD" or "BACK" functions operate normally.	Chart #5	8A-140-6

CHART #1

ALL POWER SEAT FUNCTIONS INOPERATIVE (ONE SEAT ONLY)

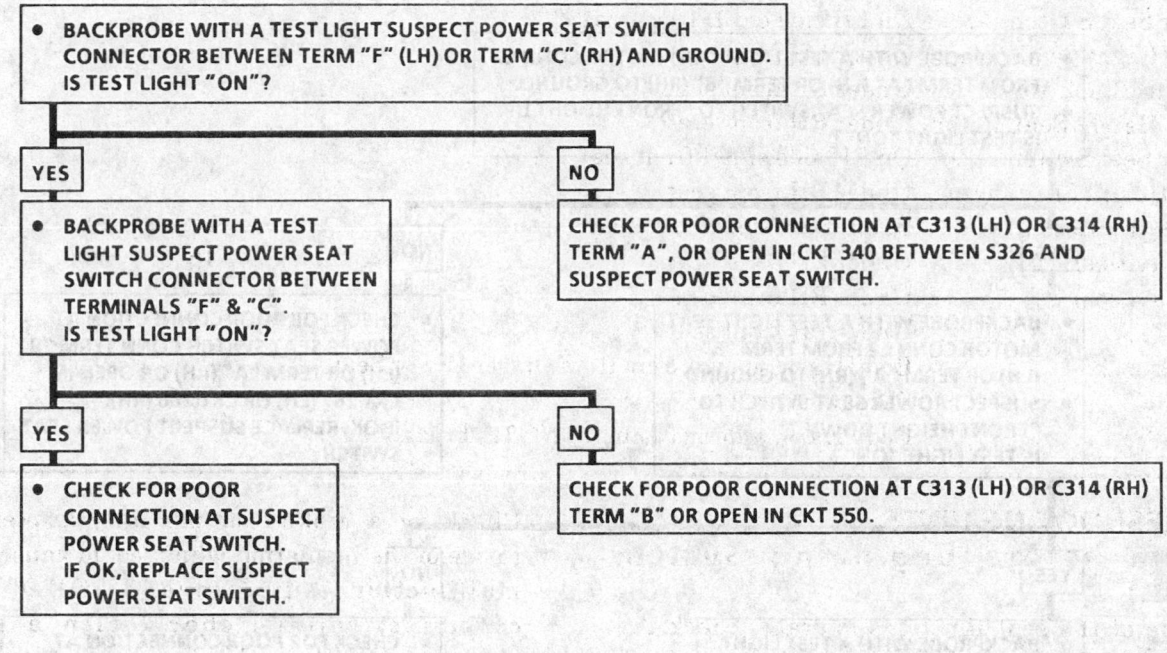

- BACKPROBE WITH A TEST LIGHT SUSPECT POWER SEAT SWITCH CONNECTOR BETWEEN TERM "F" (LH) OR TERM "C" (RH) AND GROUND. IS TEST LIGHT "ON"?

YES

- BACKPROBE WITH A TEST LIGHT SUSPECT POWER SEAT SWITCH CONNECTOR BETWEEN TERMINALS "F" & "C". IS TEST LIGHT "ON"?

  YES

  - CHECK FOR POOR CONNECTION AT SUSPECT POWER SEAT SWITCH. IF OK, REPLACE SUSPECT POWER SEAT SWITCH.

  NO

  CHECK FOR POOR CONNECTION AT C313 (LH) OR C314 (RH) TERM "B" OR OPEN IN CKT 550.

NO

CHECK FOR POOR CONNECTION AT C313 (LH) OR C314 (RH) TERM "A", OR OPEN IN CKT 340 BETWEEN S326 AND SUSPECT POWER SEAT SWITCH.

CHART #2

ENTIRE SEAT WILL NOT GO "FORWARD" OR "BACK," "UP" OR "DOWN" FUNCTIONS OPERATE NORMALLY

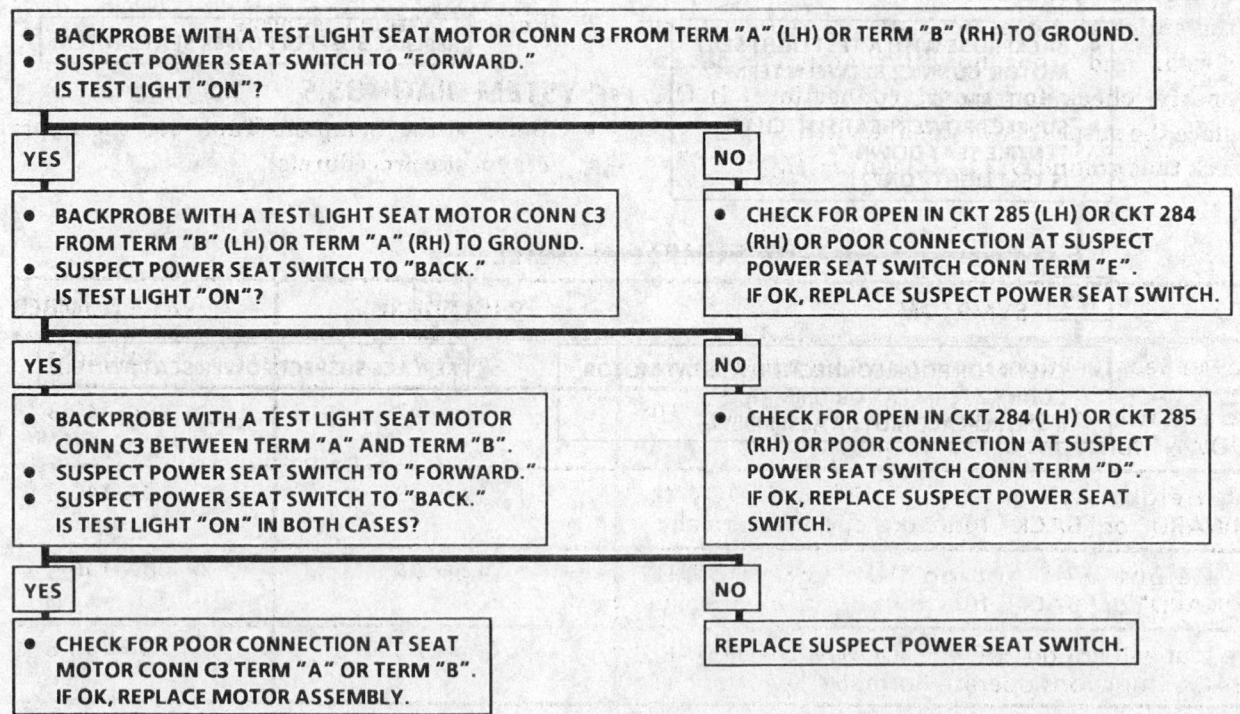

- BACKPROBE WITH A TEST LIGHT SEAT MOTOR CONN C3 FROM TERM "A" (LH) OR TERM "B" (RH) TO GROUND.
- SUSPECT POWER SEAT SWITCH TO "FORWARD."

IS TEST LIGHT "ON"?

YES

- BACKPROBE WITH A TEST LIGHT SEAT MOTOR CONN C3 FROM TERM "B" (LH) OR TERM "A" (RH) TO GROUND.
- SUSPECT POWER SEAT SWITCH TO "BACK."

IS TEST LIGHT "ON"?

  YES

  - BACKPROBE WITH A TEST LIGHT SEAT MOTOR CONN C3 BETWEEN TERM "A" AND TERM "B".
  - SUSPECT POWER SEAT SWITCH TO "FORWARD."
  - SUSPECT POWER SEAT SWITCH TO "BACK."

  IS TEST LIGHT "ON" IN BOTH CASES?

    YES

    - CHECK FOR POOR CONNECTION AT SEAT MOTOR CONN C3 TERM "A" OR TERM "B". IF OK, REPLACE MOTOR ASSEMBLY.

    NO

    REPLACE SUSPECT POWER SEAT SWITCH.

  NO

  - CHECK FOR OPEN IN CKT 284 (LH) OR CKT 285 (RH) OR POOR CONNECTION AT SUSPECT POWER SEAT SWITCH CONN TERM "D". IF OK, REPLACE SUSPECT POWER SEAT SWITCH.

NO

- CHECK FOR OPEN IN CKT 285 (LH) OR CKT 284 (RH) OR POOR CONNECTION AT SUSPECT POWER SEAT SWITCH CONN TERM "E". IF OK, REPLACE SUSPECT POWER SEAT SWITCH.

POWER SEATS

CHART #3
FRONT HEIGHT WILL NOT GO "UP" OR "DOWN," "FORWARD" OR "BACK" FUNCTIONS OPERATE NORMALLY

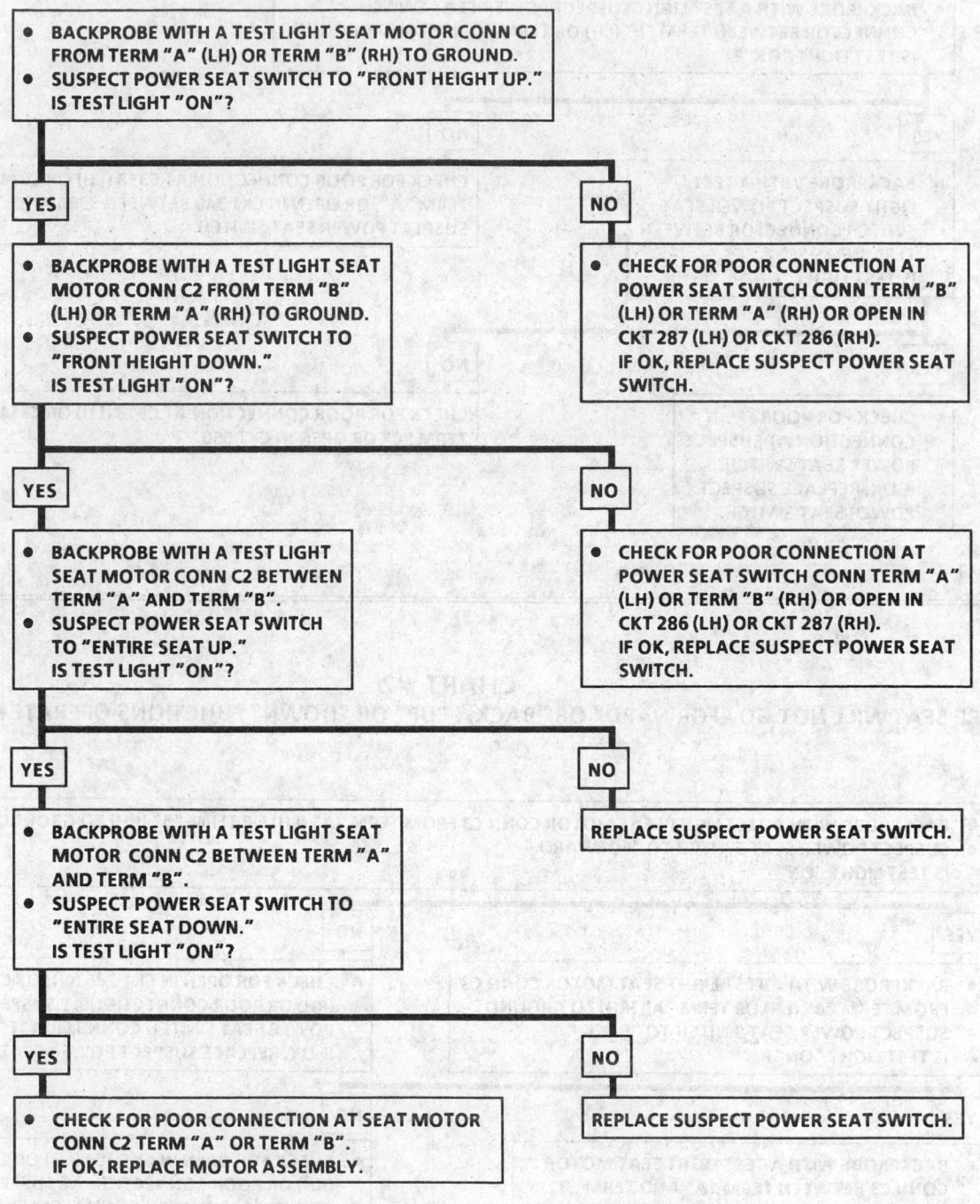

- BACKPROBE WITH A TEST LIGHT SEAT MOTOR CONN C2 FROM TERM "A" (LH) OR TERM "B" (RH) TO GROUND.
- SUSPECT POWER SEAT SWITCH TO "FRONT HEIGHT UP."

IS TEST LIGHT "ON"?

NO:
- CHECK FOR POOR CONNECTION AT POWER SEAT SWITCH CONN TERM "B" (LH) OR TERM "A" (RH) OR OPEN IN CKT 287 (LH) OR CKT 286 (RH). IF OK, REPLACE SUSPECT POWER SEAT SWITCH.

YES:
- BACKPROBE WITH A TEST LIGHT SEAT MOTOR CONN C2 FROM TERM "B" (LH) OR TERM "A" (RH) TO GROUND.
- SUSPECT POWER SEAT SWITCH TO "FRONT HEIGHT DOWN."

IS TEST LIGHT "ON"?

NO:
- CHECK FOR POOR CONNECTION AT POWER SEAT SWITCH CONN TERM "A" (LH) OR TERM "B" (RH) OR OPEN IN CKT 286 (LH) OR CKT 287 (RH). IF OK, REPLACE SUSPECT POWER SEAT SWITCH.

YES:
- BACKPROBE WITH A TEST LIGHT SEAT MOTOR CONN C2 BETWEEN TERM "A" AND TERM "B".
- SUSPECT POWER SEAT SWITCH TO "ENTIRE SEAT UP."

IS TEST LIGHT "ON"?

NO: REPLACE SUSPECT POWER SEAT SWITCH.

YES:
- BACKPROBE WITH A TEST LIGHT SEAT MOTOR CONN C2 BETWEEN TERM "A" AND TERM "B".
- SUSPECT POWER SEAT SWITCH TO "ENTIRE SEAT DOWN."

IS TEST LIGHT "ON"?

NO: REPLACE SUSPECT POWER SEAT SWITCH.

YES:
- CHECK FOR POOR CONNECTION AT SEAT MOTOR CONN C2 TERM "A" OR TERM "B". IF OK, REPLACE MOTOR ASSEMBLY.

CHART #4
REAR HEIGHT WILL NOT GO "UP" OR "DOWN," "FORWARD" OR "BACK" FUNCTIONS OPERATE NORMALLY

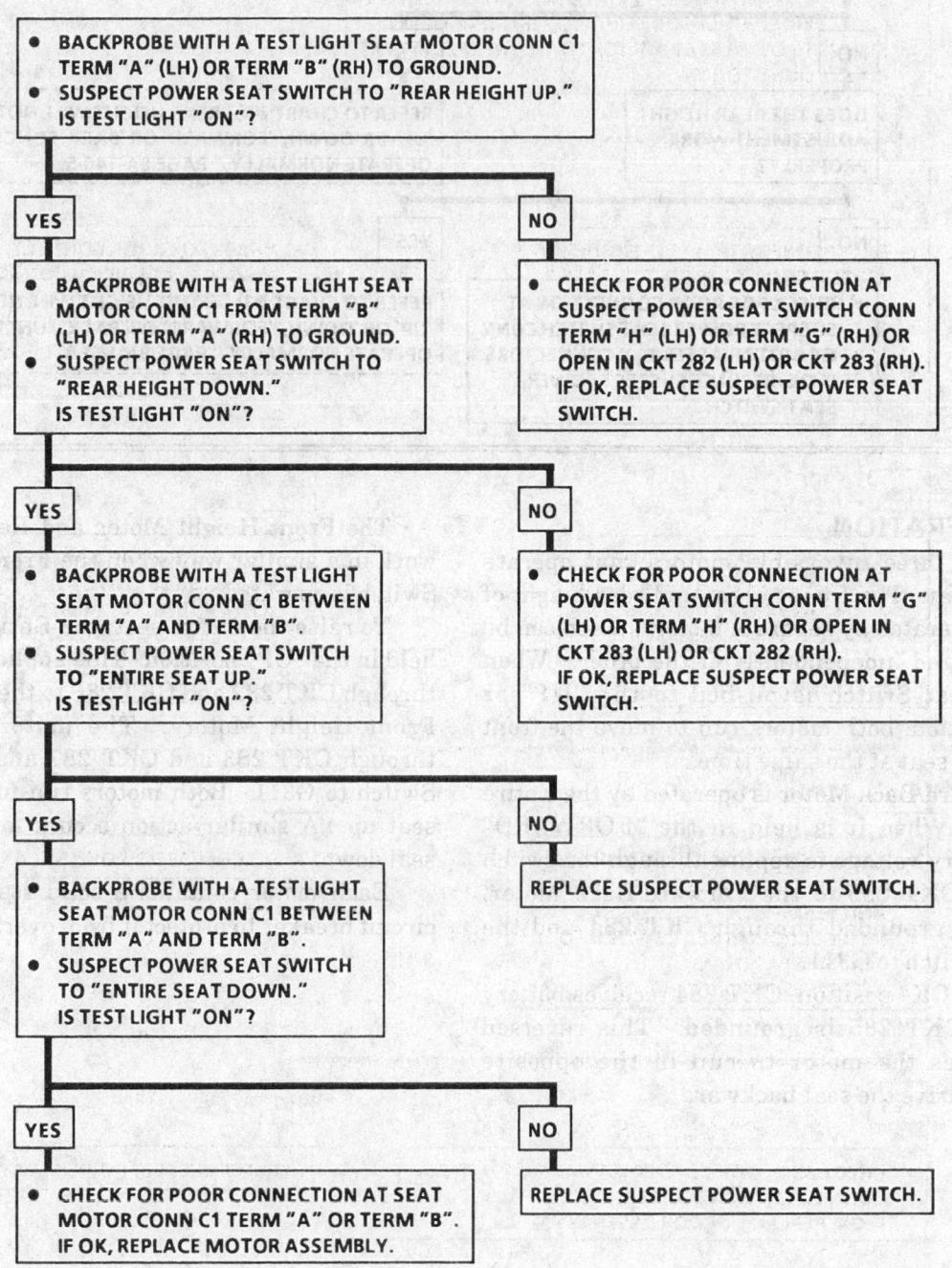

- BACKPROBE WITH A TEST LIGHT SEAT MOTOR CONN C1 TERM "A" (LH) OR TERM "B" (RH) TO GROUND.
- SUSPECT POWER SEAT SWITCH TO "REAR HEIGHT UP."

IS TEST LIGHT "ON"?

NO:

- CHECK FOR POOR CONNECTION AT SUSPECT POWER SEAT SWITCH CONN TERM "H" (LH) OR TERM "G" (RH) OR OPEN IN CKT 282 (LH) OR CKT 283 (RH). IF OK, REPLACE SUSPECT POWER SEAT SWITCH.

YES:

- BACKPROBE WITH A TEST LIGHT SEAT MOTOR CONN C1 FROM TERM "B" (LH) OR TERM "A" (RH) TO GROUND.
- SUSPECT POWER SEAT SWITCH TO "REAR HEIGHT DOWN."

IS TEST LIGHT "ON"?

NO:

- CHECK FOR POOR CONNECTION AT POWER SEAT SWITCH CONN TERM "G" (LH) OR TERM "H" (RH) OR OPEN IN CKT 283 (LH) OR CKT 282 (RH). IF OK, REPLACE SUSPECT POWER SEAT SWITCH.

YES:

- BACKPROBE WITH A TEST LIGHT SEAT MOTOR CONN C1 BETWEEN TERM "A" AND TERM "B".
- SUSPECT POWER SEAT SWITCH TO "ENTIRE SEAT UP."

IS TEST LIGHT "ON"?

NO: REPLACE SUSPECT POWER SEAT SWITCH.

YES:

- BACKPROBE WITH A TEST LIGHT SEAT MOTOR CONN C1 BETWEEN TERM "A" AND TERM "B".
- SUSPECT POWER SEAT SWITCH TO "ENTIRE SEAT DOWN."

IS TEST LIGHT "ON"?

NO: REPLACE SUSPECT POWER SEAT SWITCH.

YES:

- CHECK FOR POOR CONNECTION AT SEAT MOTOR CONN C1 TERM "A" OR TERM "B". IF OK, REPLACE MOTOR ASSEMBLY.

POWER SEATS

CHART #5
ENTIRE SEAT WILL NOT GO "UP" OR "DOWN," "FORWARD" OR "BACK" FUNCTIONS OPERATE NORMALLY

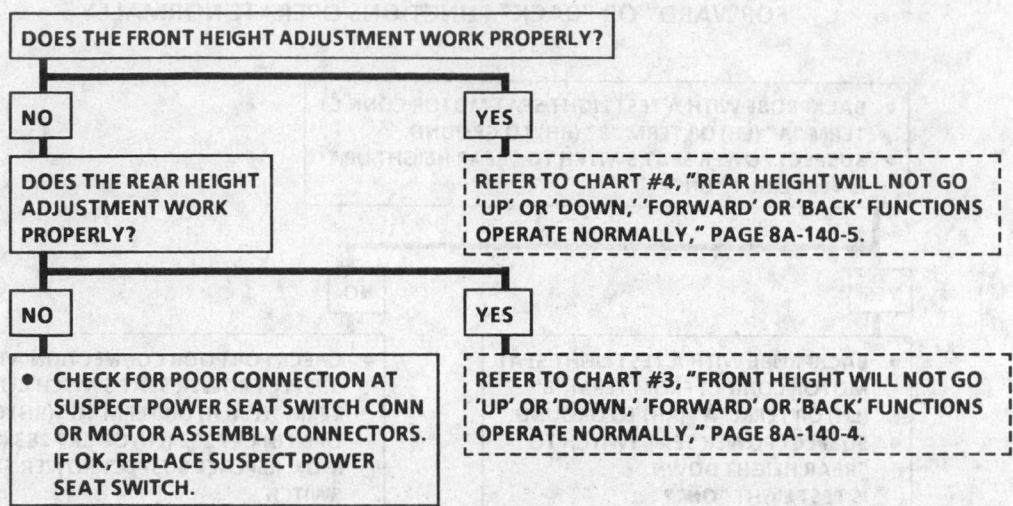

DOES THE FRONT HEIGHT ADJUSTMENT WORK PROPERLY?

- YES: REFER TO CHART #4, "REAR HEIGHT WILL NOT GO 'UP' OR 'DOWN,' 'FORWARD' OR 'BACK' FUNCTIONS OPERATE NORMALLY," PAGE 8A-140-5.
- NO: DOES THE REAR HEIGHT ADJUSTMENT WORK PROPERLY?
  - YES: REFER TO CHART #3, "FRONT HEIGHT WILL NOT GO 'UP' OR 'DOWN,' 'FORWARD' OR 'BACK' FUNCTIONS OPERATE NORMALLY," PAGE 8A-140-4.
  - NO:
    - CHECK FOR POOR CONNECTION AT SUSPECT POWER SEAT SWITCH CONN OR MOTOR ASSEMBLY CONNECTORS. IF OK, REPLACE SUSPECT POWER SEAT SWITCH.

CIRCUIT OPERATION

There are three reversible motors that operate each Power Seat. The front height and rear height of the seat are operated by separate motors. Each can be raised or lowered independently of the other. When the Entire Seat Switch is pushed to the "UP" or "DOWN" position, both motors run to move the front and rear of the seat at the same time.

The Forward/Back Motor is operated by the Entire Seat Switch. When it is held in the "FORWARD" position, battery voltage is applied through the switch contacts and CKT 285 to the Forward/Back Motor. The motor is grounded through CKT 284 and the Power Seat Switch to G311.

In the "BACK" position, CKT 284 receives battery voltage and CKT 285 is grounded. This reversed polarity causes the motor to run in the opposite direction and drive the seat backward.

The Front Height Motor and Rear Height Motor work in a similar way when the Front or Rear Height Switch is operated.

To raise the entire seat, the Entire Seat Switch is held in the "UP" position. This applies battery voltage through CKT 282 and CKT 286 to the Rear Height and Front Height Motors. The motors are grounded through CKT 283 and CKT 287 and the Power Seat Switch to G311. Both motors run to drive the entire seat up. A similar action occurs to move the entire seat down.

Each motor contains a solid state self-resetting circuit breaker to protect it from overload.

BLANK

AUTOMATIC SEAT BELTS

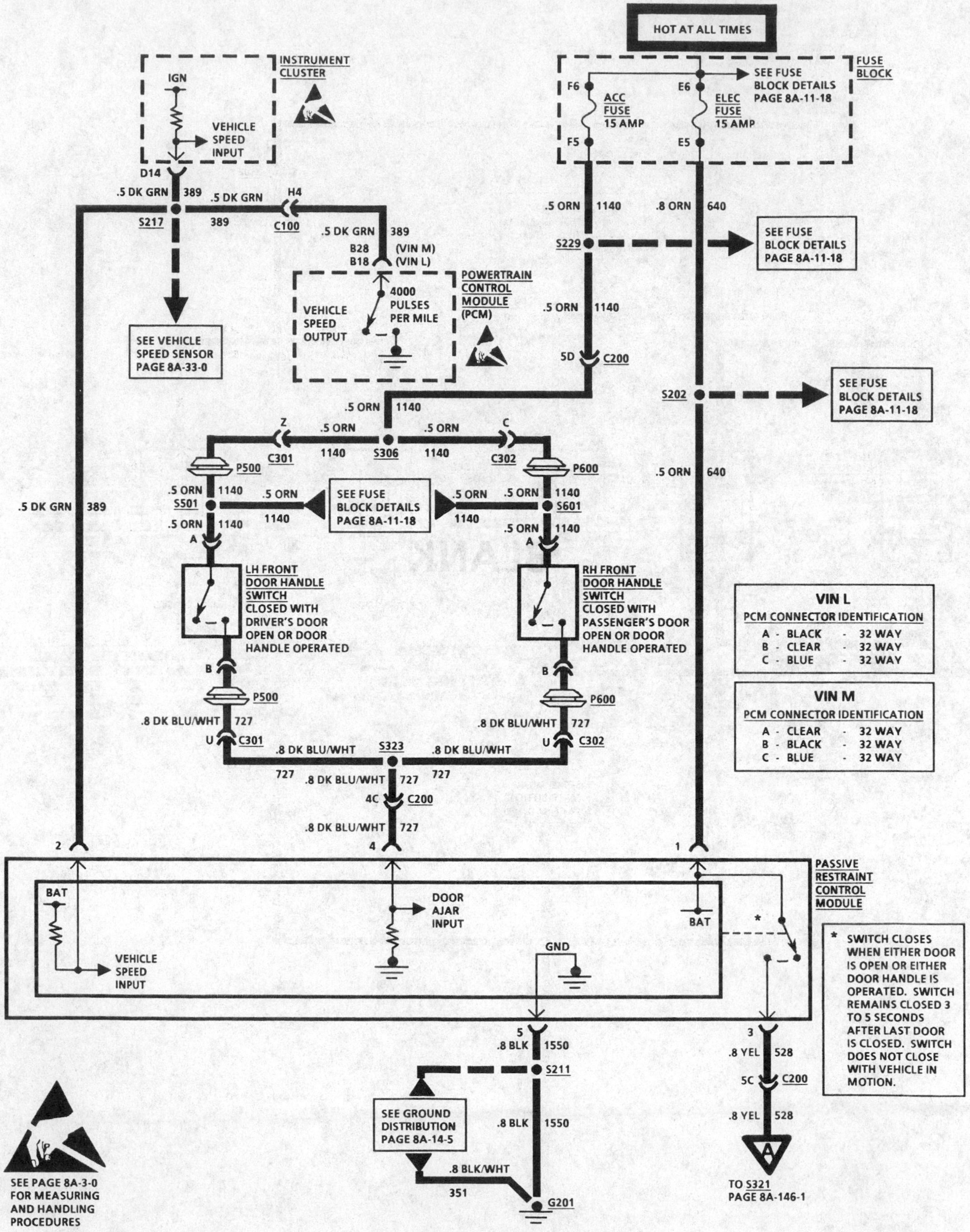
HOT AT ALL TIMES
INSTRUMENT CLUSTER
IGN
VEHICLE SPEED INPUT
D14
.5 DK GRN 389
S217
.5 DK GRN
389
H4
C100
.5 DK GRN 389
B28 (VIN M)
B18 (VIN L)
POWERTRAIN CONTROL MODULE (PCM)
VEHICLE SPEED OUTPUT
4000 PULSES PER MILE
SEE VEHICLE SPEED SENSOR PAGE 8A-33-0
FUSE BLOCK
F6
ACC FUSE 15 AMP
F5
E6
ELEC FUSE 15 AMP
E5
SEE FUSE BLOCK DETAILS PAGE 8A-11-18
.5 ORN 1140
.8 ORN 640
S229
SEE FUSE BLOCK DETAILS PAGE 8A-11-18
.5 ORN 1140
5D
C200
S202
SEE FUSE BLOCK DETAILS PAGE 8A-11-18
.5 ORN 1140
Z
.5 ORN
1140
C301
S306
C
.5 ORN
1140
C302
P500
P600
.5 ORN 640
.5 DK GRN 389
.5 ORN 1140
S501
.5 ORN
1140
SEE FUSE BLOCK DETAILS PAGE 8A-11-18
.5 ORN
1140
.5 ORN 1140
S601
.5 ORN 1140
A
LH FRONT DOOR HANDLE SWITCH CLOSED WITH DRIVER'S DOOR OPEN OR DOOR HANDLE OPERATED
RH FRONT DOOR HANDLE SWITCH CLOSED WITH PASSENGER'S DOOR OPEN OR DOOR HANDLE OPERATED
B
P500
P600
.8 DK BLU/WHT 727
U
C301
C302
.8 DK BLU/WHT
S323
.8 DK BLU/WHT
727
.8 DK BLU/WHT 727
727
4C
C200
.8 DK BLU/WHT 727
2
4
1
PASSIVE RESTRAINT CONTROL MODULE
BAT
VEHICLE SPEED INPUT
DOOR AJAR INPUT
GND
BAT
*
5
.8 BLK 1550
S211
SEE GROUND DISTRIBUTION PAGE 8A-14-5
.8 BLK 1550
.8 BLK/WHT
351
G201
3
.8 YEL 528
5C
C200
.8 YEL 528
A
TO S321 PAGE 8A-146-1
* SWITCH CLOSES WHEN EITHER DOOR IS OPEN OR EITHER DOOR HANDLE IS OPERATED. SWITCH REMAINS CLOSED 3 TO 5 SECONDS AFTER LAST DOOR IS CLOSED. SWITCH DOES NOT CLOSE WITH VEHICLE IN MOTION.
SEE PAGE 8A-3-0 FOR MEASURING AND HANDLING PROCEDURES

VIN L

PCM CONNECTOR IDENTIFICATION

A	BLACK	-	32 WAY
B	CLEAR	-	32 WAY
C	BLUE	-	32 WAY

VIN M

PCM CONNECTOR IDENTIFICATION

A	CLEAR	-	32 WAY
B	BLACK	-	32 WAY
C	BLUE	-	32 WAY

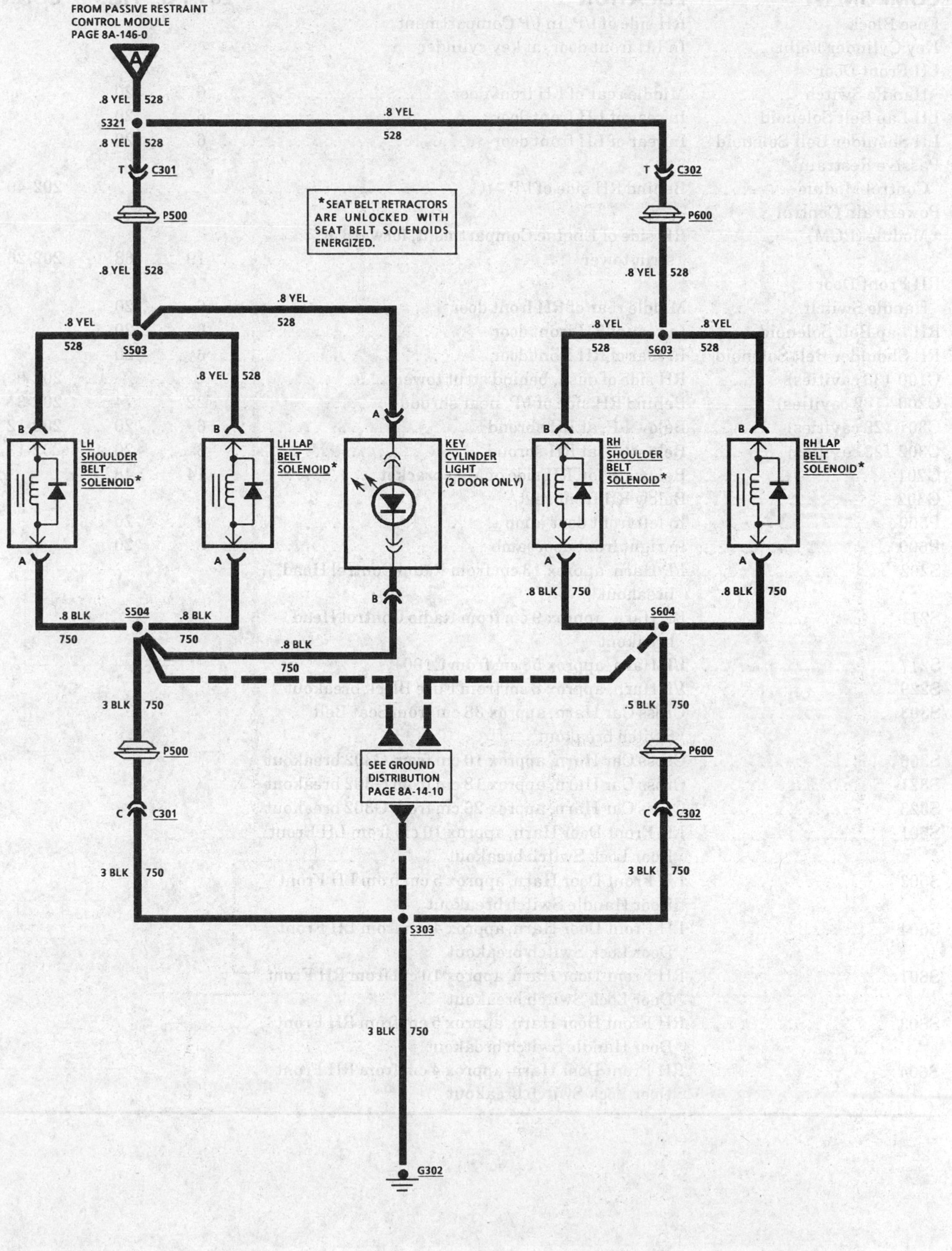

FROM PASSIVE RESTRAINT CONTROL MODULE PAGE 8A-146-0
A
.8 YEL 528
S321
.8 YEL 528
T C301
P500
.8 YEL 528
.8 YEL 528
T C302
P600
.8 YEL 528
*SEAT BELT RETRACTORS ARE UNLOCKED WITH SEAT BELT SOLENOIDS ENERGIZED.
.8 YEL 528
.8 YEL 528
S503
.8 YEL 528
.8 YEL 528
.8 YEL 528
S603
B
LH SHOULDER BELT SOLENOID*
A
B
LH LAP BELT SOLENOID*
A
A
KEY CYLINDER LIGHT (2 DOOR ONLY)
B
B
RH SHOULDER BELT SOLENOID*
A
B
RH LAP BELT SOLENOID*
A
.8 BLK 750
S504
.8 BLK 750
.8 BLK 750
.8 BLK 750
.8 BLK 750
S604
3 BLK 750
P500
.5 BLK 750
P600
SEE GROUND DISTRIBUTION PAGE 8A-14-10
C C301
3 BLK 750
C C302
3 BLK 750
S303
3 BLK 750
G302

AUTOMATIC SEAT BELTS

COMPONENT	LOCATION	201-PG	FIG.	CONN
Fuse Block	RH side of I/P, in I/P Compartment			
Key Cylinder Light	In LH front door, at key cylinder			
LH Front Door Handle Switch	Middle rear of LH front door	6	20	
LH Lap Belt Solenoid	In rear of LH front door	6	20	
LH Shoulder Belt Solenoid	In rear of LH front door	6	20	
Passive Restraint Control Module	Behind RH side of I/P			202-40
Powertrain Control Module (PCM)	RH side of Engine Compartment, forward of strut tower	19	68	202-26
RH Front Door Handle Switch	Middle rear of RH front door	6	20	
RH Lap Belt Solenoid	In rear of RH front door	6	20	
RH Shoulder Belt Solenoid	In rear of RH front door	6	20	
C100 (36 cavities)	RH side of dash, behind strut tower			202-0
C200 (102 cavities)	Behind RH side of I/P, near shroud	22	74	202-3
C301 (23 cavities)	Below I/P, at LH shroud	6	20	202-12
C302 (23 cavities)	Below I/P, at RH shroud	6	20	202-13
G201	Below I/P, on RH side of Mag bracket	14	48	
G302	Below RH front seat			
P500	In left front door jamb	6	20	
P600	In right front door jamb	6	20	
S202	I/P Harn, approx 13 cm from Radio Control Head breakout			
S211	I/P Harn, approx 9 cm from Radio Control Head breakout			
S217	I/P Harn, approx 58 cm from C100			
S229	I/P Harn, approx 8 cm from Fuse Block breakout			
S303	Cross Car Harn, approx 38 cm from Seat Belt Switch breakout			
S306	Cross Car Harn, approx 10 cm from G302 breakout			
S321	Cross Car Harn, approx 18 cm from G302 breakout			
S323	Cross Car Harn, approx 26 cm from G302 breakout			
S501	LH Front Door Harn, approx 10 cm from LH Front Door Lock Switch breakout			
S503	LH Front Door Harn, approx 5 cm from LH Front Door Handle Switch breakout			
S504	LH Front Door Harn, approx 4 cm from LH Front Door Lock Switch breakout			
S601	RH Front Door Harn, approx 10 cm from RH Front Door Lock Switch breakout			
S603	RH Front Door Harn, approx 5 cm from RH Front Door Handle Switch breakout			
S604	RH Front Door Harn, approx 4 cm from RH Front Door Lock Switch breakout			

TROUBLESHOOTING HINTS (Perform before beginning System Diagnosis)

1. Check the ACC and ELEC Fuses by visual inspection.
2. If the Seat Belts remain taut with either front door open, check for a shorted Door Handle Switch.
3. If one belt remains taut with either Door Handle Switch operated, check CKT 528 and CKT 750 to the suspect belt solenoid for an open.
4. The Key Cylinder Light should glow when either Door Handle Switch is operated. If only one switch does not trigger the light, check the associated switch and wiring. The Seat Belt Solenoids should click when the switch is operated.
5. If the Seat Belt Solenoids in both doors do click, but the Key Cylinder Light does not light, check CKT 528 and CKT 750 to the light for an open. If wires are OK, replace the Key Cylinder Light.

- Check for a broken (or partially broken) wire inside of the insulation which could cause system malfunction but prove "GOOD" in a continuity/voltage check with a system disconnected. These circuits may be intermittent or resistive when loaded, and if possible, should be checked by monitoring for a voltage drop with the system operational (under load).
- Check for proper installation of aftermarket electronic equipment which may affect the integrity of other systems (see "Troubleshooting Procedures," page 8A-4-0).
- Refer to System Diagnosis.

SYSTEM DIAGNOSIS

- Perform the System Check and refer to the Symptom Table for the appropriate diagnostic procedures.

SYSTEM CHECK

ACTION	NORMAL RESULTS
[1] ● Buckle the Driver's Seat Belt. ● Open the Driver's Door.	Solenoids click as door handle is operated. Lap and Shoulder Belts extend smoothly. Driver's Door opens freely.
[2] ● Sit in Driver's Seat. ● Close Driver's Door.	Lap and Shoulder Belts retract smoothly to fit the driver. Solenoids click 3 to 5 seconds after door is closed.
[3] ● Repeat steps 1 and 2 from the passenger's side.	System operates similarly from the passenger's side.

SYMPTOM TABLE

SYMPTOM	PROCEDURE	PAGE NUMBER
Seat Belts remain taut at all times.	Chart #1	8A-146-4
Seat Belts remain loose at all times.	Chart #2	8A-146-5

AUTOMATIC SEAT BELTS

CHART #1
SEAT BELTS REMAIN TAUT AT ALL TIMES

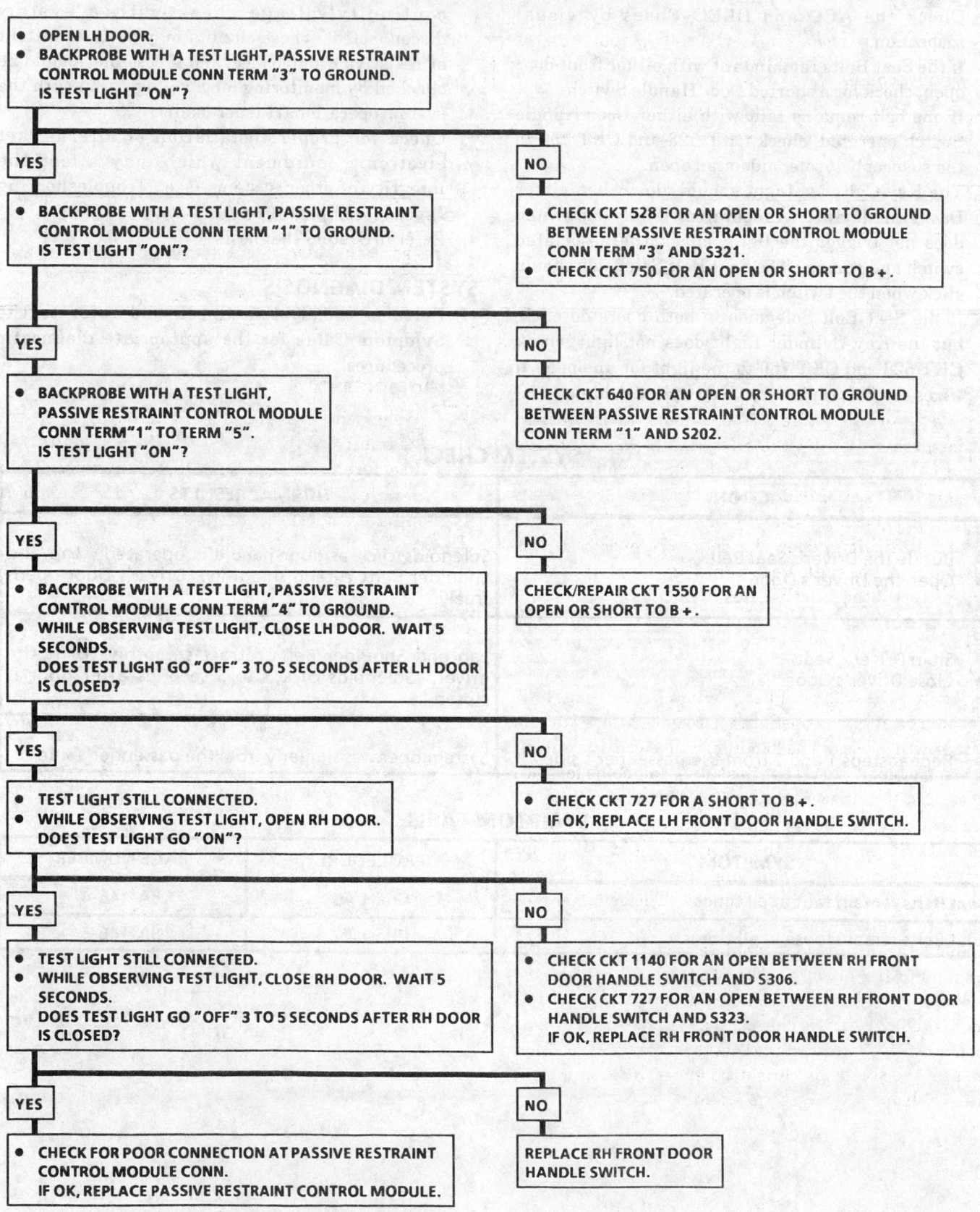

- OPEN LH DOOR.
- BACKPROBE WITH A TEST LIGHT, PASSIVE RESTRAINT CONTROL MODULE CONN TERM "3" TO GROUND.
  IS TEST LIGHT "ON"?

YES

- BACKPROBE WITH A TEST LIGHT, PASSIVE RESTRAINT CONTROL MODULE CONN TERM "1" TO GROUND.
  IS TEST LIGHT "ON"?

NO

- CHECK CKT 528 FOR AN OPEN OR SHORT TO GROUND BETWEEN PASSIVE RESTRAINT CONTROL MODULE CONN TERM "3" AND S321.
- CHECK CKT 750 FOR AN OPEN OR SHORT TO B +.

YES

- BACKPROBE WITH A TEST LIGHT, PASSIVE RESTRAINT CONTROL MODULE CONN TERM "1" TO TERM "5".
  IS TEST LIGHT "ON"?

NO

CHECK CKT 640 FOR AN OPEN OR SHORT TO GROUND BETWEEN PASSIVE RESTRAINT CONTROL MODULE CONN TERM "1" AND S202.

YES

- BACKPROBE WITH A TEST LIGHT, PASSIVE RESTRAINT CONTROL MODULE CONN TERM "4" TO GROUND.
- WHILE OBSERVING TEST LIGHT, CLOSE LH DOOR. WAIT 5 SECONDS.
  DOES TEST LIGHT GO "OFF" 3 TO 5 SECONDS AFTER LH DOOR IS CLOSED?

NO

CHECK/REPAIR CKT 1550 FOR AN OPEN OR SHORT TO B +.

YES

- TEST LIGHT STILL CONNECTED.
- WHILE OBSERVING TEST LIGHT, OPEN RH DOOR.
  DOES TEST LIGHT GO "ON"?

NO

- CHECK CKT 727 FOR A SHORT TO B +.
  IF OK, REPLACE LH FRONT DOOR HANDLE SWITCH.

YES

- TEST LIGHT STILL CONNECTED.
- WHILE OBSERVING TEST LIGHT, CLOSE RH DOOR. WAIT 5 SECONDS.
  DOES TEST LIGHT GO "OFF" 3 TO 5 SECONDS AFTER RH DOOR IS CLOSED?

NO

- CHECK CKT 1140 FOR AN OPEN BETWEEN RH FRONT DOOR HANDLE SWITCH AND S306.
- CHECK CKT 727 FOR AN OPEN BETWEEN RH FRONT DOOR HANDLE SWITCH AND S323.
  IF OK, REPLACE RH FRONT DOOR HANDLE SWITCH.

YES

- CHECK FOR POOR CONNECTION AT PASSIVE RESTRAINT CONTROL MODULE CONN.
  IF OK, REPLACE PASSIVE RESTRAINT CONTROL MODULE.

NO

REPLACE RH FRONT DOOR HANDLE SWITCH.

CHART #2
SEAT BELTS REMAIN LOOSE AT ALL TIMES

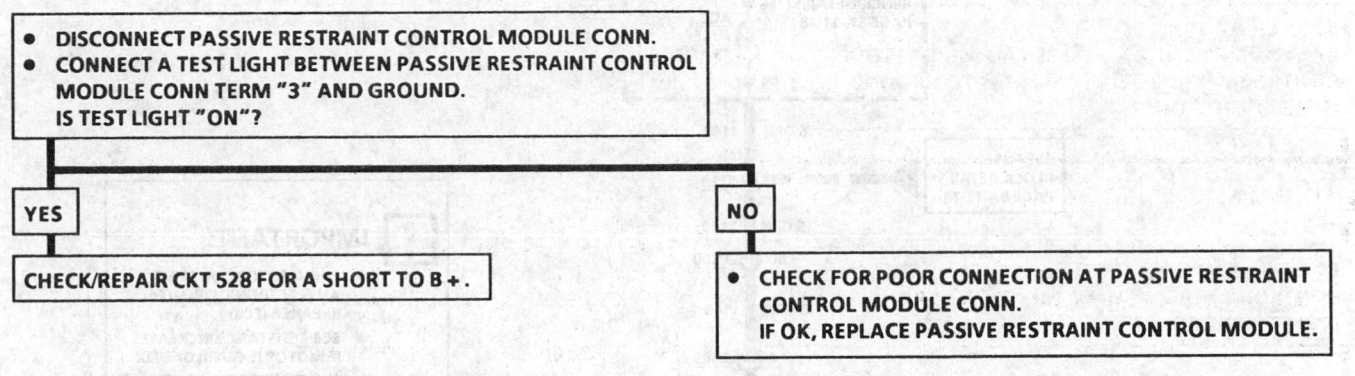

- DISCONNECT PASSIVE RESTRAINT CONTROL MODULE CONN.
- CONNECT A TEST LIGHT BETWEEN PASSIVE RESTRAINT CONTROL MODULE CONN TERM "3" AND GROUND.

IS TEST LIGHT "ON"?

YES

CHECK/REPAIR CKT 528 FOR A SHORT TO B+.

NO

- CHECK FOR POOR CONNECTION AT PASSIVE RESTRAINT CONTROL MODULE CONN.

IF OK, REPLACE PASSIVE RESTRAINT CONTROL MODULE.

CIRCUIT OPERATION

The purpose of the Passive Restraint Control Module is to allow the vehicle doors to be opened without restriction by the Seat Belts. Without this feature, the Retractor Lock Pendulums would lock the belts as they are pulled out of the retractors when a front door is opened for entry or for exit. This would make it difficult to open the door. To overcome this difficulty, the seat belt locking mechanism is controlled by the Passive Restraint Control Module which controls the operation of the Seat Belt Retractor Release Solenoids.

The Passive Restraint Control Module receives power from the ELEC Fuse. When a door handle is operated or a door is open, the associated Door Handle Switch will close. The module will close its output switch and energize all the Seat Belt Solenoids for both doors and illuminate the Key Cylinder Light (2 Door). The door can then be opened without interference from the Seat Belts. When the door is closed, the Door Handle Switch opens again and the solenoids are de-energized after about three seconds. The belts are now ready to protect the wearer. To ensure that the solenoids are released, a vehicle speed signal is also supplied to the Module. The Module will release the solenoids any time the vehicle is moving, even if a Door Handle Switch is closed. If a Latch Switch fails to open and the speed signal causes the solenoids to release, the solenoids cannot be energized again until the switch opens to reset the Module.

Important:

- A shorted Door Handle Switch will keep the Module from resetting, so both Seat Belts will interfere with door opening. An open Door Handle Switch will still allow the system to operate properly when the other door is used.

POWER MIRRORS

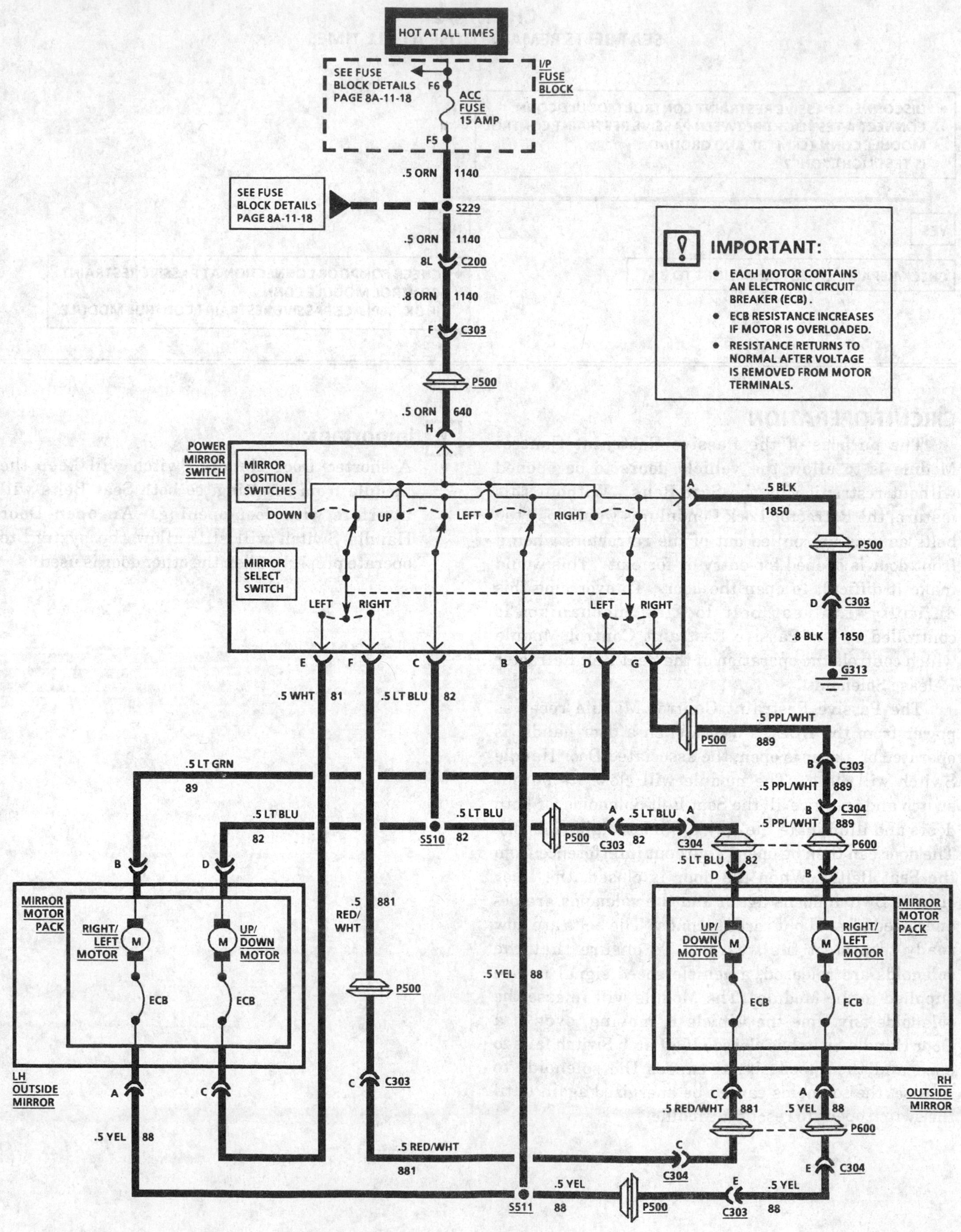
HOT AT ALL TIMES
SEE FUSE BLOCK DETAILS PAGE 8A-11-18
F6
ACC FUSE 15 AMP
F5
I/P FUSE BLOCK
.5 ORN 1140
SEE FUSE BLOCK DETAILS PAGE 8A-11-18
S229
.5 ORN 1140
8L C200
.8 ORN 1140
F C303
P500
.5 ORN 640
H
IMPORTANT:
• EACH MOTOR CONTAINS AN ELECTRONIC CIRCUIT BREAKER (ECB).
• ECB RESISTANCE INCREASES IF MOTOR IS OVERLOADED.
• RESISTANCE RETURNS TO NORMAL AFTER VOLTAGE IS REMOVED FROM MOTOR TERMINALS.
POWER MIRROR SWITCH
MIRROR POSITION SWITCHES
DOWN
UP
LEFT
RIGHT
MIRROR SELECT SWITCH
LEFT
RIGHT
LEFT
RIGHT
A
.5 BLK 1850
P500
D C303
.8 BLK 1850
G313
E F C B D G
.5 WHT 81
.5 LT BLU 82
.5 PPL/WHT 889
P500
B C303
.5 PPL/WHT 889
B C304
.5 PPL/WHT 889
P600
.5 LT GRN 89
.5 LT BLU 82
.5 LT BLU 82
S510
P500
A C303
.5 LT BLU 82
A C304
.5 LT BLU 82
D
B
B
D
MIRROR MOTOR PACK
RIGHT/ LEFT MOTOR
M
UP/ DOWN MOTOR
ECB
ECB
.5 RED/ WHT 881
P500
.5 YEL 88
UP/ DOWN MOTOR
RIGHT/ LEFT MOTOR
MIRROR MOTOR PACK
ECB
ECB
LH OUTSIDE MIRROR
A
C
C C303
RH OUTSIDE MIRROR
C
A
.5 RED/WHT 881
.5 YEL 88
P600
.5 YEL 88
.5 RED/WHT 881
C C304
E C304
S511
.5 YEL 88
P500
E C303
.5 YEL 88

COMPONENT	LOCATION	201-PG	FIG.	CONN
Fuse Block	RH side of I/P, in I/P Compartment			
LH Outside Mirror	On LH front door	17	58	202-39
Power Mirror Switch	Center of LH front door	17	58	202-39
RH Outside Mirror	On RH front door	17	58	202-39
C200 (102 cavities)	Behind RH side of I/P, near shroud	22	74	202-3
C303 (6 cavities)	Below I/P, at LH shroud	17	58	
C304 (6 cavities)	Below I/P, at RH shroud	17	58	
G313	Under LH front seat			
P500	In left front door jamb			
P600	In right front door jamb			
S229	I/P Harn, approx 8 cm from Fuse Block breakout			
S510	LH Front Door Harn, approx 5 cm from LH Outside Mirror breakout			
S511	LH Front Door Harn, approx 5 cm from LH Outside Mirror breakout			

TROUBLESHOOTING HINTS (Perform before beginning System Diagnosis)

1. Check ACC Fuse by visual inspection.
2. Check that G311 is clean and tight.

- Check for a broken (or partially broken) wire inside of the insulation which could cause system malfunction but prove "GOOD" in a continuity/voltage check with a system disconnected. These circuits may be intermittent or resistive when loaded, and if possible, should be checked by monitoring for a voltage drop with the system operational (under load).
- Check for proper installation of aftermarket electronic equipment which may affect the integrity of other systems (see "Troubleshooting Procedures," page 8A-4-0).

SYSTEM DIAGNOSIS

- Perform the System Check and refer to the Symptom Table for the appropriate diagnostic procedure(s).

SYSTEM CHECK

ACTION	NORMAL RESULTS
[1] • Power Mirror Switch to "LEFT" position. • Move Power Mirror Switch to "UP" and "DOWN" positions.	LH Outside Mirror moves smoothly upward and downward.
[2] • Move Power Mirror Switch to the "LEFT" and "RIGHT" positions.	LH Outside Mirror moves smoothly to the left and right.
[3] • Power Mirror Switch to "RIGHT" position. • Move Power Mirror Switch to "UP" and "DOWN" positions.	RH Outside Mirror moves smoothly upward and downward.
[4] • Move Power Mirror Switch to the "LEFT" and "RIGHT" positions.	RH Outside Mirror moves smoothly to the left and right.

POWER MIRRORS

SYMPTOM TABLE

SYMPTOM	PROCEDURE	PAGE NUMBER
Both mirrors inoperative in either "UP/DOWN" or "LEFT/RIGHT" direction.	Chart #1	8A-147-2
One mirror inoperative in the "UP/DOWN" direction, "LEFT/RIGHT" direction operates normally.	Chart #2	8A-147-3
One mirror inoperative in the "LEFT/RIGHT" direction, "UP/DOWN" direction operates normally.	Chart #3	8A-147-3
One mirror inoperative in both "UP/DOWN" and "LEFT/RIGHT" directions.	Chart #4	8A-147-4

CHART #1
BOTH MIRRORS INOPERATIVE IN ALL DIRECTIONS

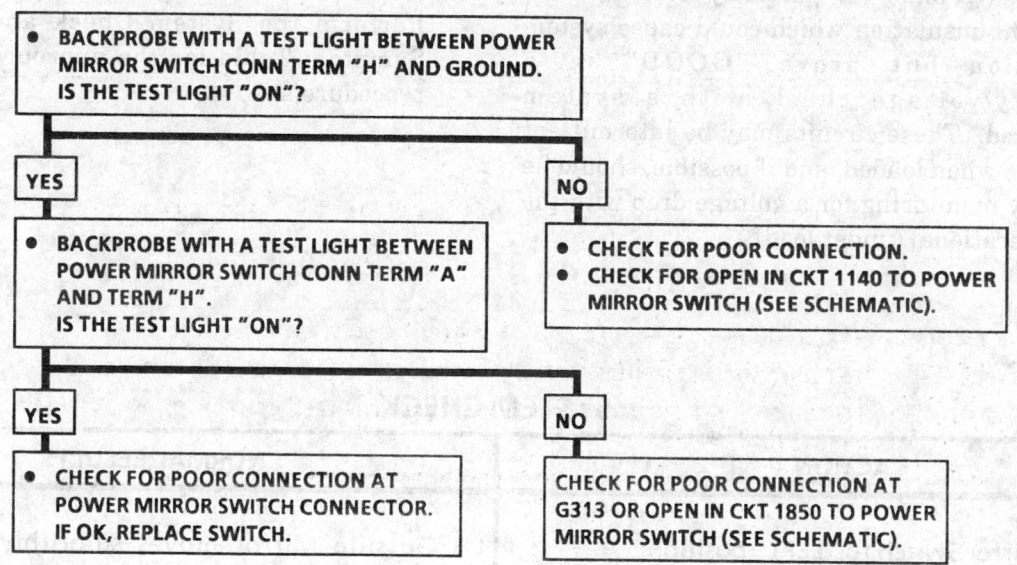

- BACKPROBE WITH A TEST LIGHT BETWEEN POWER MIRROR SWITCH CONN TERM "H" AND GROUND. IS THE TEST LIGHT "ON"?

YES

- BACKPROBE WITH A TEST LIGHT BETWEEN POWER MIRROR SWITCH CONN TERM "A" AND TERM "H". IS THE TEST LIGHT "ON"?

  YES

  - CHECK FOR POOR CONNECTION AT POWER MIRROR SWITCH CONNECTOR. IF OK, REPLACE SWITCH.

  NO

  CHECK FOR POOR CONNECTION AT G313 OR OPEN IN CKT 1850 TO POWER MIRROR SWITCH (SEE SCHEMATIC).

NO

- CHECK FOR POOR CONNECTION.
- CHECK FOR OPEN IN CKT 1140 TO POWER MIRROR SWITCH (SEE SCHEMATIC).

CHART #2
ONE MIRROR INOPERATIVE IN THE "UP/DOWN" DIRECTION, "LEFT/RIGHT" DIRECTION OPERATES NORMALLY

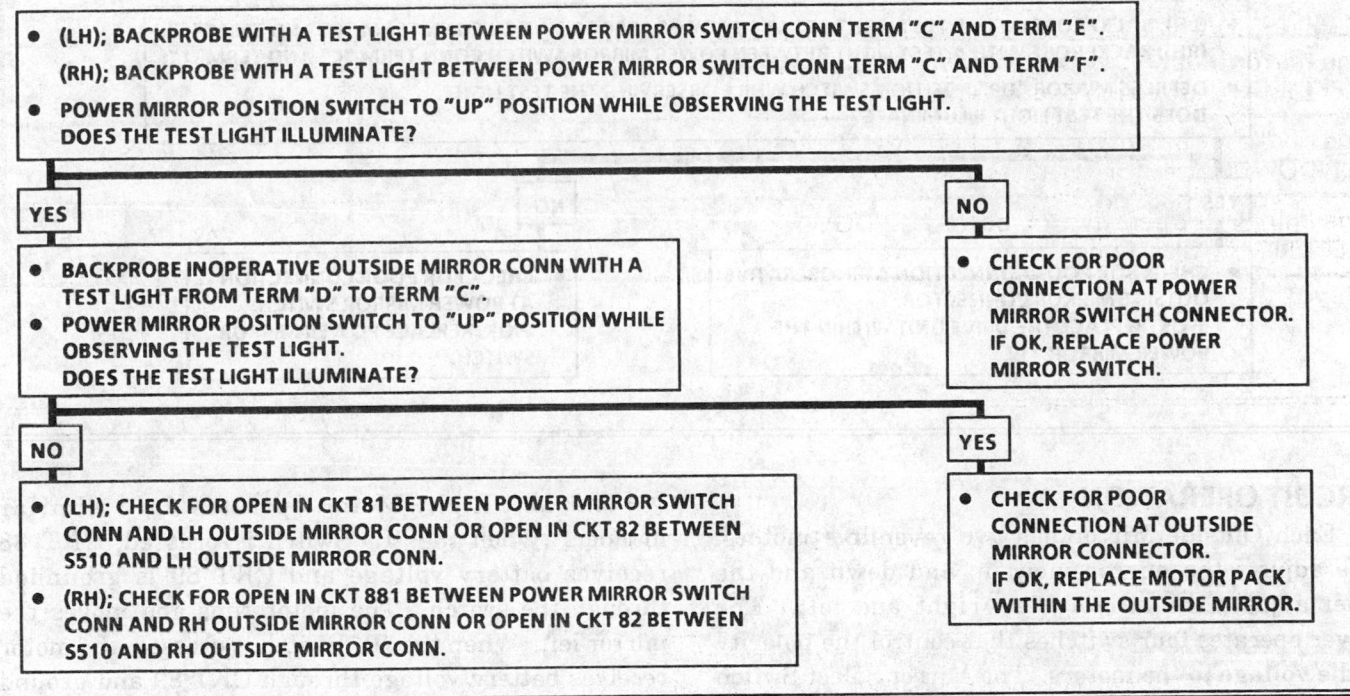

- (LH); BACKPROBE WITH A TEST LIGHT BETWEEN POWER MIRROR SWITCH CONN TERM "C" AND TERM "E".
  (RH); BACKPROBE WITH A TEST LIGHT BETWEEN POWER MIRROR SWITCH CONN TERM "C" AND TERM "F".
- POWER MIRROR POSITION SWITCH TO "UP" POSITION WHILE OBSERVING THE TEST LIGHT.
  DOES THE TEST LIGHT ILLUMINATE?

YES

- BACKPROBE INOPERATIVE OUTSIDE MIRROR CONN WITH A TEST LIGHT FROM TERM "D" TO TERM "C".
- POWER MIRROR POSITION SWITCH TO "UP" POSITION WHILE OBSERVING THE TEST LIGHT.
  DOES THE TEST LIGHT ILLUMINATE?

  NO

  - (LH); CHECK FOR OPEN IN CKT 81 BETWEEN POWER MIRROR SWITCH CONN AND LH OUTSIDE MIRROR CONN OR OPEN IN CKT 82 BETWEEN S510 AND LH OUTSIDE MIRROR CONN.
  - (RH); CHECK FOR OPEN IN CKT 881 BETWEEN POWER MIRROR SWITCH CONN AND RH OUTSIDE MIRROR CONN OR OPEN IN CKT 82 BETWEEN S510 AND RH OUTSIDE MIRROR CONN.

  YES

  - CHECK FOR POOR CONNECTION AT OUTSIDE MIRROR CONNECTOR.
    IF OK, REPLACE MOTOR PACK WITHIN THE OUTSIDE MIRROR.

NO

- CHECK FOR POOR CONNECTION AT POWER MIRROR SWITCH CONNECTOR.
  IF OK, REPLACE POWER MIRROR SWITCH.

CHART #3
ONE MIRROR INOPERATIVE IN THE "LEFT/RIGHT" DIRECTION, "UP/DOWN" DIRECTION OPERATES NORMALLY

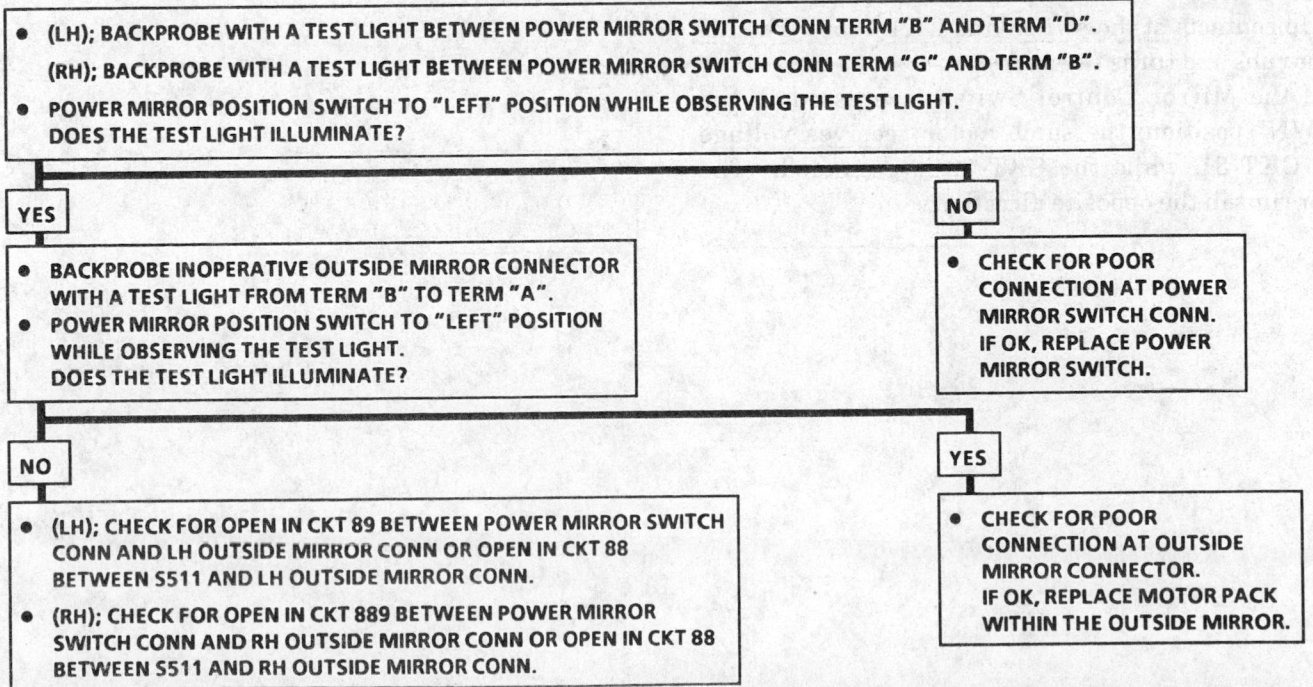

- (LH); BACKPROBE WITH A TEST LIGHT BETWEEN POWER MIRROR SWITCH CONN TERM "B" AND TERM "D".
  (RH); BACKPROBE WITH A TEST LIGHT BETWEEN POWER MIRROR SWITCH CONN TERM "G" AND TERM "B".
- POWER MIRROR POSITION SWITCH TO "LEFT" POSITION WHILE OBSERVING THE TEST LIGHT.
  DOES THE TEST LIGHT ILLUMINATE?

YES

- BACKPROBE INOPERATIVE OUTSIDE MIRROR CONNECTOR WITH A TEST LIGHT FROM TERM "B" TO TERM "A".
- POWER MIRROR POSITION SWITCH TO "LEFT" POSITION WHILE OBSERVING THE TEST LIGHT.
  DOES THE TEST LIGHT ILLUMINATE?

  NO

  - (LH); CHECK FOR OPEN IN CKT 89 BETWEEN POWER MIRROR SWITCH CONN AND LH OUTSIDE MIRROR CONN OR OPEN IN CKT 88 BETWEEN S511 AND LH OUTSIDE MIRROR CONN.
  - (RH); CHECK FOR OPEN IN CKT 889 BETWEEN POWER MIRROR SWITCH CONN AND RH OUTSIDE MIRROR CONN OR OPEN IN CKT 88 BETWEEN S511 AND RH OUTSIDE MIRROR CONN.

  YES

  - CHECK FOR POOR CONNECTION AT OUTSIDE MIRROR CONNECTOR.
    IF OK, REPLACE MOTOR PACK WITHIN THE OUTSIDE MIRROR.

NO

- CHECK FOR POOR CONNECTION AT POWER MIRROR SWITCH CONN.
  IF OK, REPLACE POWER MIRROR SWITCH.

POWER MIRRORS

CHART #4
ONE MIRROR INOPERATIVE IN BOTH "UP/DOWN" AND "LEFT/RIGHT" DIRECTIONS

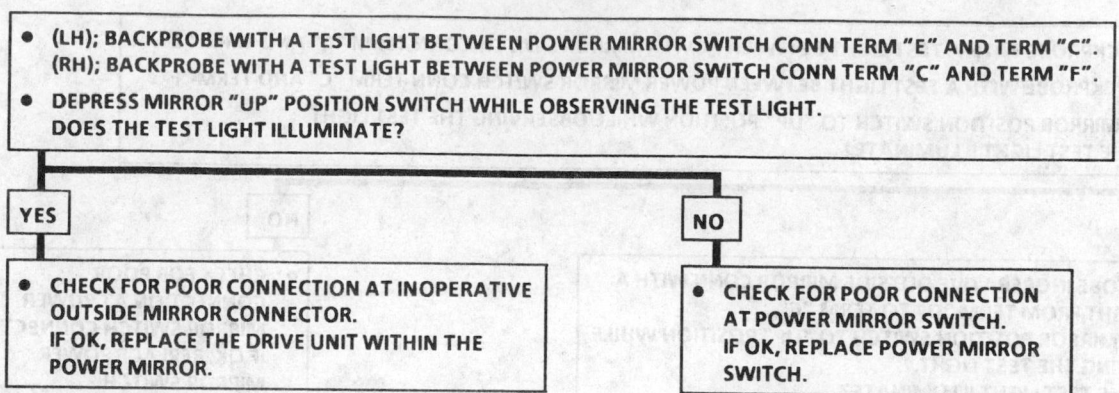

- (LH); BACKPROBE WITH A TEST LIGHT BETWEEN POWER MIRROR SWITCH CONN TERM "E" AND TERM "C".
  (RH); BACKPROBE WITH A TEST LIGHT BETWEEN POWER MIRROR SWITCH CONN TERM "C" AND TERM "F".
- DEPRESS MIRROR "UP" POSITION SWITCH WHILE OBSERVING THE TEST LIGHT.
  DOES THE TEST LIGHT ILLUMINATE?

YES

- CHECK FOR POOR CONNECTION AT INOPERATIVE OUTSIDE MIRROR CONNECTOR.
  IF OK, REPLACE THE DRIVE UNIT WITHIN THE POWER MIRROR.

NO

- CHECK FOR POOR CONNECTION AT POWER MIRROR SWITCH.
  IF OK, REPLACE POWER MIRROR SWITCH.

CIRCUIT OPERATION

Each Outside Mirror has two reversible motors. One adjusts the mirror view up and down and the other adjusts the mirror view right and left. The driver operates four switches that control the polarity of the voltage to the motors. The Mirror Select Switch directs the voltage to either the RH or LH Outside Mirror.

When the LH Outside Mirror is selected and the "UP" position of the switch is pressed, battery voltage from CKT 1140 wire is applied to CKT 82 and the Up/Down Motor in the LH Outside Mirror. The Power Mirror Switch has a path to ground through CKT 81, the Up contacts of the switch and CKT 1850. The LH Motor runs and turns the mirror up.

If the Mirror Control Switch is pressed in the "DOWN" position, the same motor receives voltage from CKT 81, while the CKT 82 is grounded. The motor runs in the opposite direction.

The Left/Right Motor operates in a similar manner. When the "L" Switch is pressed, CKT 88 receives battery voltage and CKT 89 is grounded through the switch. The motor runs and moves the mirror left. When the "R" Switch is pressed, the motor receives battery voltage through CKT 89 and ground through the CKT 88. The motor runs in the opposite direction to move the mirror right.

The RH Outside Mirror works the same way as the LH Outside Mirror when the Mirror Select Switch is moved to the "RH" position and the appropriate position switch is operated.

BLANK

RADIO

AM/FM STEREO WITH CASSETTE AND DIGITAL CLOCK (UM6)
AM/FM STEREO WITH CASSETTE/EQUALIZER AND DIGITAL CLOCK (UX1)
AM/FM STEREO WITH COMPACT DISC PLAYER (U1C)

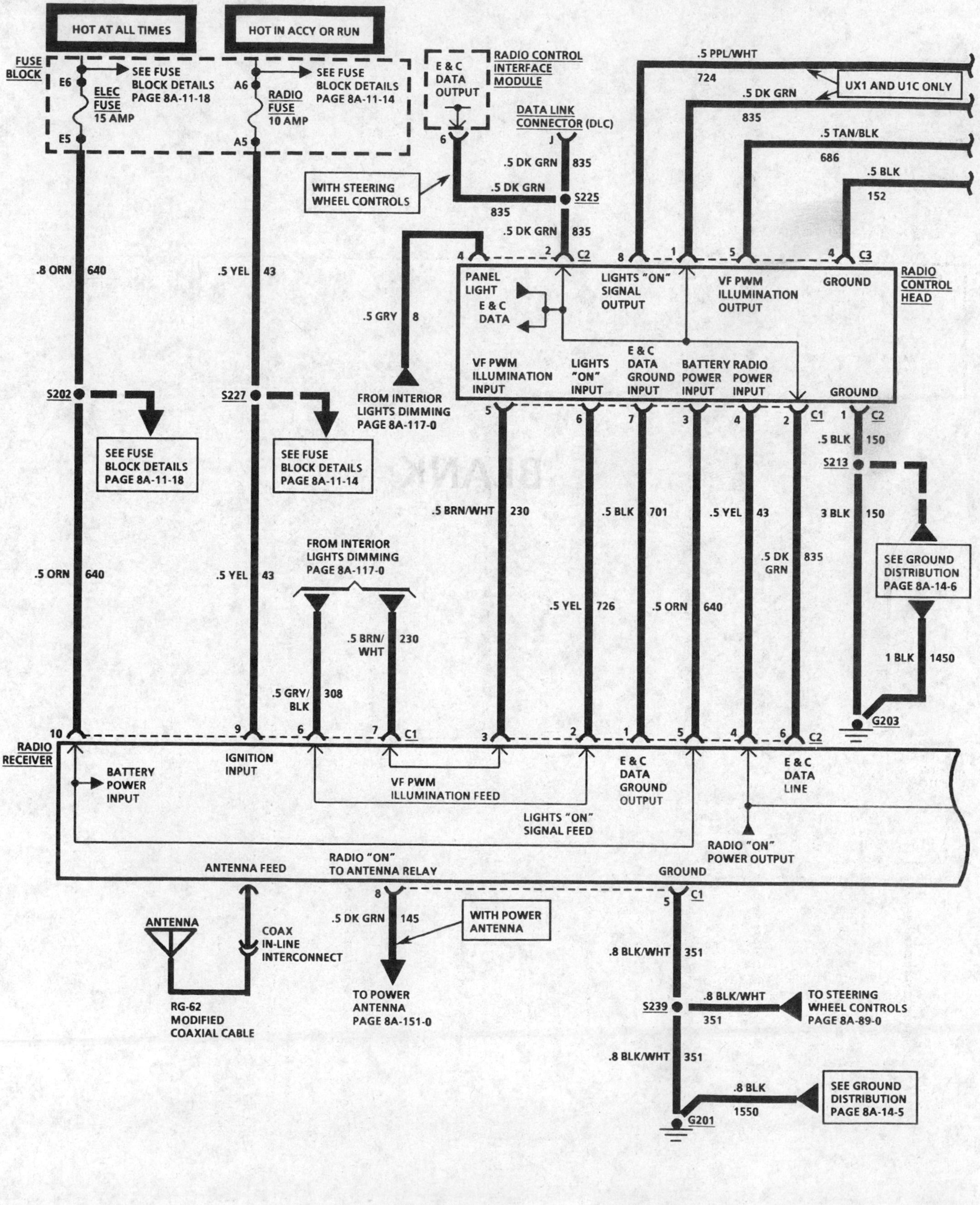

HOT AT ALL TIMES
HOT IN ACCY OR RUN
FUSE BLOCK
E6
SEE FUSE BLOCK DETAILS PAGE 8A-11-18
ELEC FUSE 15 AMP
E5
A6
SEE FUSE BLOCK DETAILS PAGE 8A-11-14
RADIO FUSE 10 AMP
A5
E & C DATA OUTPUT
RADIO CONTROL INTERFACE MODULE
DATA LINK CONNECTOR (DLC)
WITH STEERING WHEEL CONTROLS
.5 DK GRN 835
S225
.5 PPL/WHT 724
.5 DK GRN 835
UX1 AND U1C ONLY
.5 TAN/BLK 686
.5 BLK 152
C2
C3
PANEL LIGHT
E & C DATA
LIGHTS "ON" SIGNAL OUTPUT
VF PWM ILLUMINATION OUTPUT
GROUND
RADIO CONTROL HEAD
VF PWM ILLUMINATION INPUT
LIGHTS "ON" INPUT
E & C DATA GROUND INPUT
BATTERY POWER INPUT
RADIO POWER INPUT
C1
.8 ORN 640
.5 YEL 43
.5 GRY 8
FROM INTERIOR LIGHTS DIMMING PAGE 8A-117-0
S202
S227
SEE FUSE BLOCK DETAILS PAGE 8A-11-18
SEE FUSE BLOCK DETAILS PAGE 8A-11-14
.5 BLK 150
S213
.5 BRN/WHT 230
.5 BLK 701
.5 YEL 43
3 BLK 150
.5 DK GRN 835
SEE GROUND DISTRIBUTION PAGE 8A-14-6
.5 ORN 640
.5 YEL 43
.5 YEL 726
.5 ORN 640
.5 BRN/WHT 230
.5 GRY/BLK 308
1 BLK 1450
G203
RADIO RECEIVER
BATTERY POWER INPUT
IGNITION INPUT
VF PWM ILLUMINATION FEED
E & C DATA GROUND OUTPUT
E & C DATA LINE
LIGHTS "ON" SIGNAL FEED
RADIO "ON" POWER OUTPUT
ANTENNA FEED
RADIO "ON" TO ANTENNA RELAY
GROUND
ANTENNA
COAX IN-LINE INTERCONNECT
.5 DK GRN 145
WITH POWER ANTENNA
TO POWER ANTENNA PAGE 8A-151-0
RG-62 MODIFIED COAXIAL CABLE
.8 BLK/WHT 351
S239
TO STEERING WHEEL CONTROLS PAGE 8A-89-0
.8 BLK 1550
SEE GROUND DISTRIBUTION PAGE 8A-14-5
G201

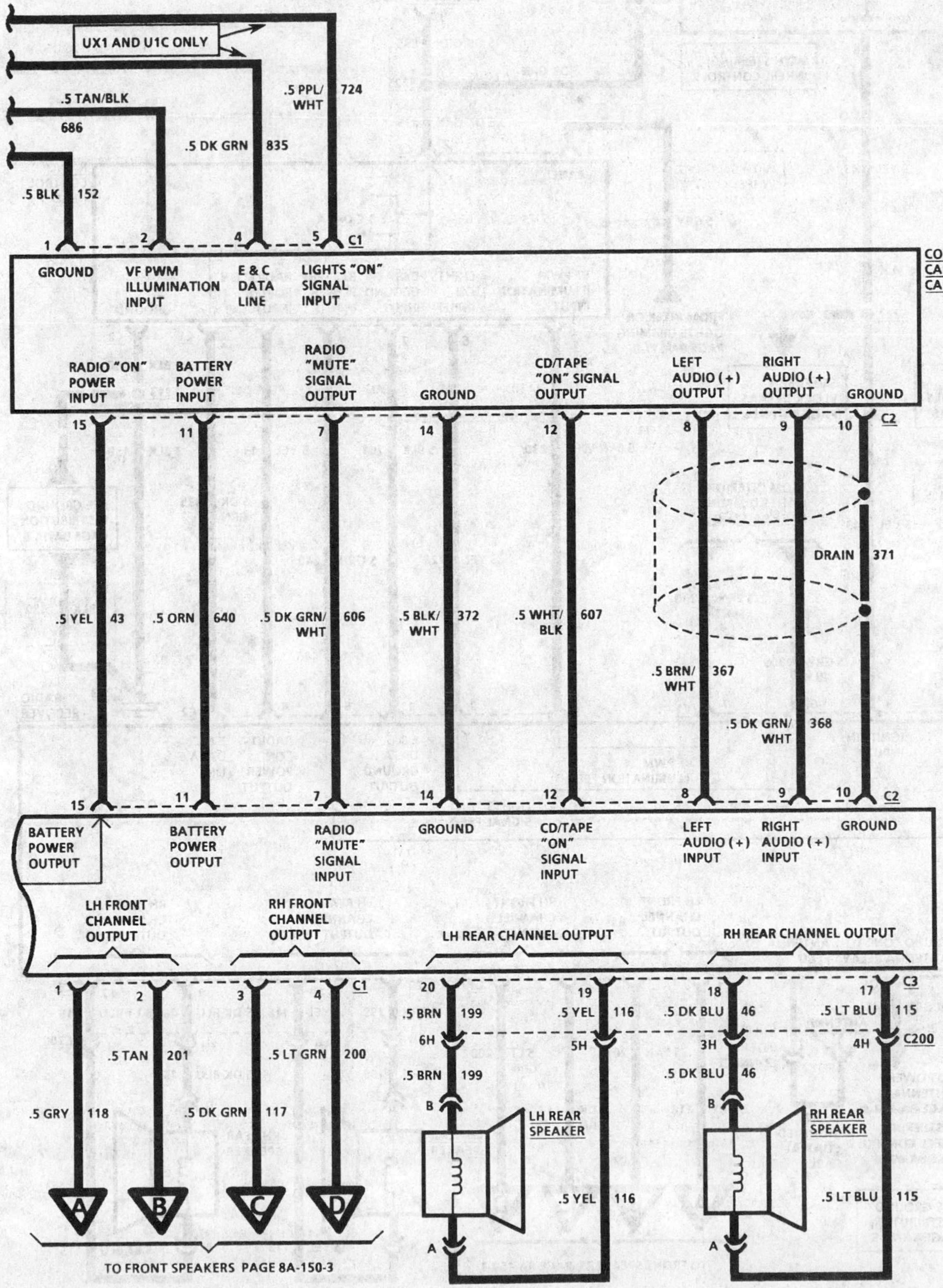

UX1 AND U1C ONLY
.5 PPL/ WHT 724
.5 TAN/BLK 686
.5 DK GRN 835
.5 BLK 152
C1
GROUND
VF PWM ILLUMINATION INPUT
E & C DATA LINE
LIGHTS "ON" SIGNAL INPUT
COMPACT DISC PLAYER (U1C)
CASSETTE/EQUALIZER (UX1)
CASSETTE PLAYER (UM6)
RADIO "ON" POWER INPUT
BATTERY POWER INPUT
RADIO "MUTE" SIGNAL OUTPUT
GROUND
CD/TAPE "ON" SIGNAL OUTPUT
LEFT AUDIO (+) OUTPUT
RIGHT AUDIO (+) OUTPUT
GROUND
C2
DRAIN 371
.5 YEL 43
.5 ORN 640
.5 DK GRN/ WHT 606
.5 BLK/ WHT 372
.5 WHT/ BLK 607
.5 BRN/ WHT 367
.5 DK GRN/ WHT 368
C2
BATTERY POWER OUTPUT
BATTERY POWER OUTPUT
RADIO "MUTE" SIGNAL INPUT
GROUND
CD/TAPE "ON" SIGNAL INPUT
LEFT AUDIO (+) INPUT
RIGHT AUDIO (+) INPUT
GROUND
LH FRONT CHANNEL OUTPUT
RH FRONT CHANNEL OUTPUT
LH REAR CHANNEL OUTPUT
RH REAR CHANNEL OUTPUT
C1
C3
.5 BRN 199
.5 YEL 116
.5 DK BLU 46
.5 LT BLU 115
C200
.5 TAN 201
.5 LT GRN 200
.5 GRY 118
.5 DK GRN 117
LH REAR SPEAKER
RH REAR SPEAKER
A
B
C
D
TO FRONT SPEAKERS PAGE 8A-150-3

RADIO

AM/FM STEREO WITH DIGITAL CLOCK (UM7)

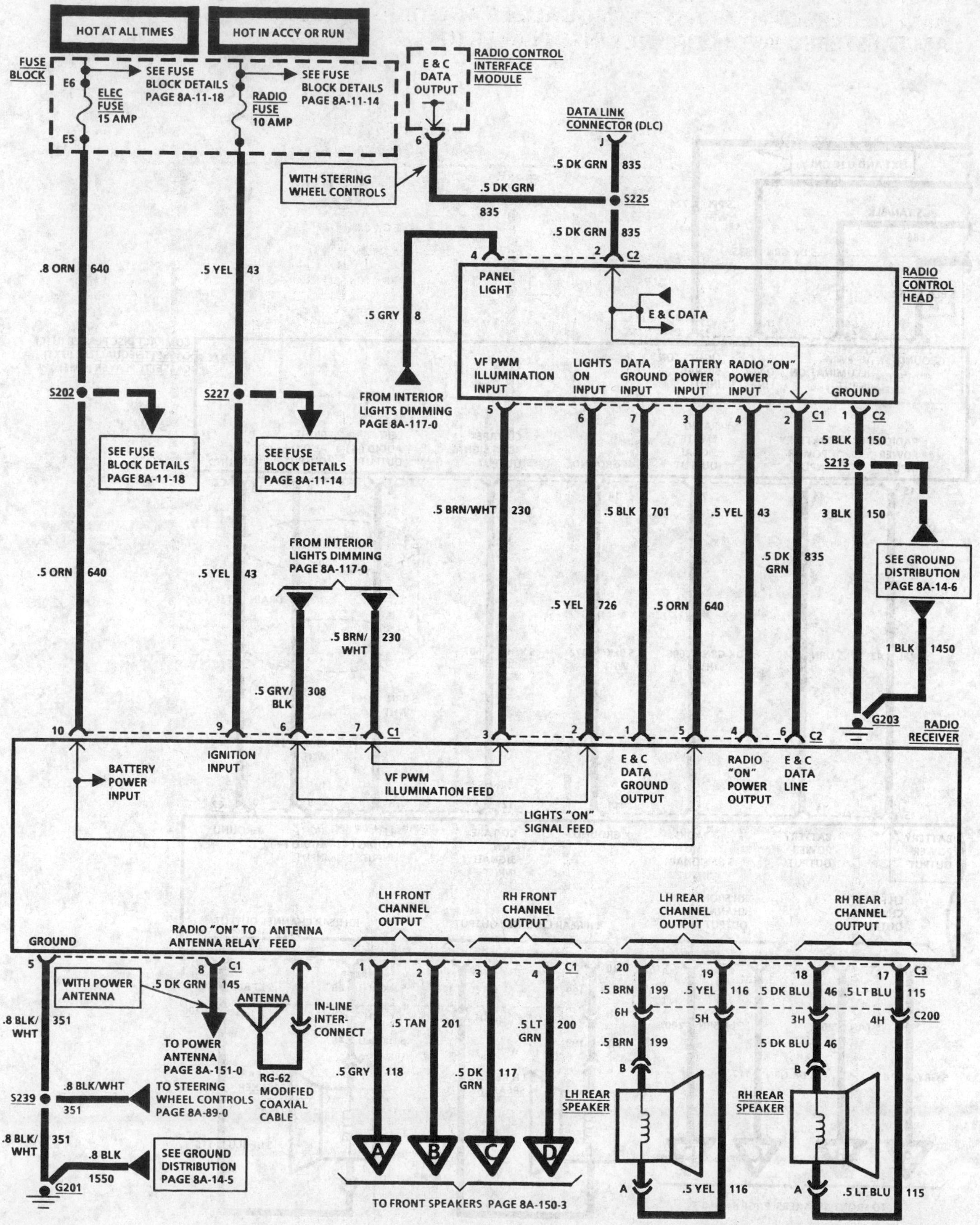

HOT AT ALL TIMES
HOT IN ACCY OR RUN
FUSE BLOCK
E6
E5
ELEC FUSE 15 AMP
SEE FUSE BLOCK DETAILS PAGE 8A-11-18
RADIO FUSE 10 AMP
SEE FUSE BLOCK DETAILS PAGE 8A-11-14
E & C DATA OUTPUT
RADIO CONTROL INTERFACE MODULE
6
WITH STEERING WHEEL CONTROLS
DATA LINK CONNECTOR (DLC)
J
.5 DK GRN 835
.5 DK GRN
835
S225
.5 DK GRN 835
.8 ORN 640
.5 YEL 43
4
2
C2
PANEL LIGHT
RADIO CONTROL HEAD
E & C DATA
.5 GRY 8
FROM INTERIOR LIGHTS DIMMING PAGE 8A-117-0
VF PWM ILLUMINATION INPUT
LIGHTS ON INPUT
DATA GROUND INPUT
BATTERY POWER INPUT
RADIO "ON" POWER INPUT
GROUND
S202
S227
5
6
7
3
4
2
C1
1
C2
.5 BLK 150
S213
SEE FUSE BLOCK DETAILS PAGE 8A-11-18
SEE FUSE BLOCK DETAILS PAGE 8A-11-14
.5 BRN/WHT 230
.5 BLK 701
.5 YEL 43
3 BLK 150
.5 DK GRN 835
.5 ORN 640
.5 YEL 43
SEE GROUND DISTRIBUTION PAGE 8A-14-6
FROM INTERIOR LIGHTS DIMMING PAGE 8A-117-0
.5 YEL 726
.5 ORN 640
.5 BRN/WHT 230
1 BLK 1450
.5 GRY/BLK 308
G203
10
9
6
7
C1
3
2
1
5
4
6
C2
RADIO RECEIVER
BATTERY POWER INPUT
IGNITION INPUT
VF PWM ILLUMINATION FEED
E & C DATA GROUND OUTPUT
RADIO "ON" POWER OUTPUT
E & C DATA LINE
LIGHTS "ON" SIGNAL FEED
LH FRONT CHANNEL OUTPUT
RH FRONT CHANNEL OUTPUT
LH REAR CHANNEL OUTPUT
RH REAR CHANNEL OUTPUT
GROUND
RADIO "ON" TO ANTENNA RELAY
ANTENNA FEED
5
8
C1
1
2
3
4
C1
20
19
18
17
C3
WITH POWER ANTENNA
.5 DK GRN 145
ANTENNA
IN-LINE INTER-CONNECT
.5 BRN 199
.5 YEL 116
.5 DK BLU 46
.5 LT BLU 115
6H
5H
3H
4H
C200
.8 BLK/WHT 351
TO POWER ANTENNA PAGE 8A-151-0
.5 TAN 201
.5 LT GRN 200
.5 BRN 199
.5 DK BLU 46
RG-62 MODIFIED COAXIAL CABLE
.5 GRY 118
.5 DK GRN 117
B
B
S239
.8 BLK/WHT
351
TO STEERING WHEEL CONTROLS PAGE 8A-89-0
LH REAR SPEAKER
RH REAR SPEAKER
.8 BLK/WHT 351
.8 BLK
1550
SEE GROUND DISTRIBUTION PAGE 8A-14-5
A
B
C
D
G201
TO FRONT SPEAKERS PAGE 8A-150-3
A
.5 YEL 116
A
.5 LT BLU 115

RADIO

AM/FM STEREO WITH DIGITAL CLOCK (UM7)
AM/FM STEREO WITH CASSETTE AND DIGITAL CLOCK (UM6)
AM/FM STEREO WITH CASSETTE/EQUALIZER AND DIGITAL CLOCK (UX1)
AM/FM STEREO WITH COMPACT DISC PLAYER (U1C)

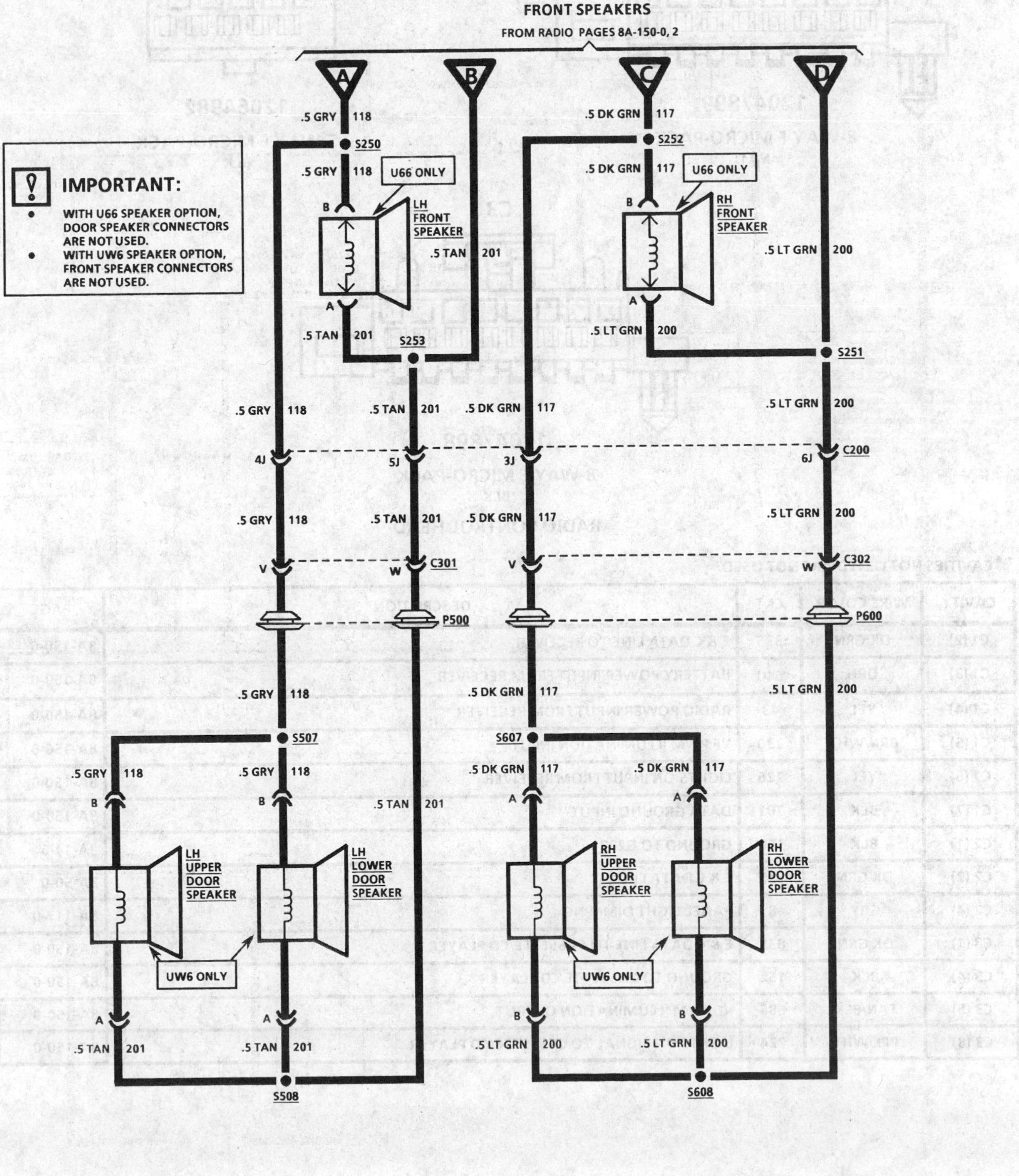
FRONT SPEAKERS
FROM RADIO PAGES 8A-150-0, 2
A
B
C
D
IMPORTANT:
WITH U66 SPEAKER OPTION, DOOR SPEAKER CONNECTORS ARE NOT USED.
WITH UW6 SPEAKER OPTION, FRONT SPEAKER CONNECTORS ARE NOT USED.
.5 GRY 118
S250
U66 ONLY
LH FRONT SPEAKER
.5 TAN 201
S253
.5 DK GRN 117
S252
RH FRONT SPEAKER
.5 LT GRN 200
S251
4J
5J
3J
6J
C200
V
W
C301
C302
P500
P600
S507
S607
LH UPPER DOOR SPEAKER
LH LOWER DOOR SPEAKER
RH UPPER DOOR SPEAKER
RH LOWER DOOR SPEAKER
UW6 ONLY
S508
S608

RADIO

C1

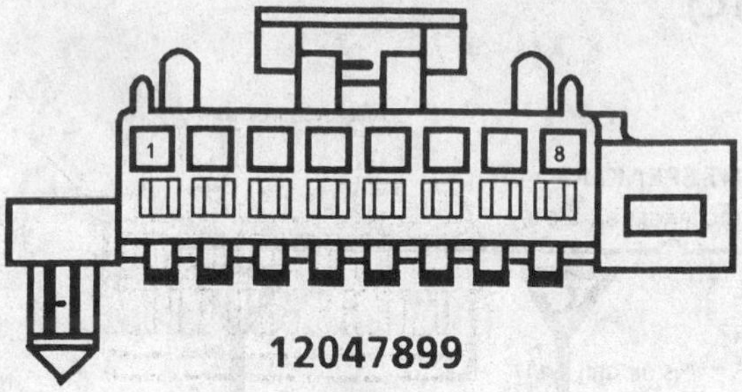
1
8

12047899

8-WAY F MICRO-PACK

NAT

C2

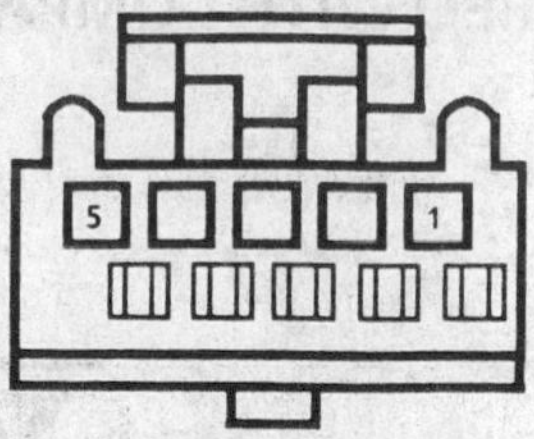
5
1

12064982

5-WAY F MICRO-PACK

BLK

C3

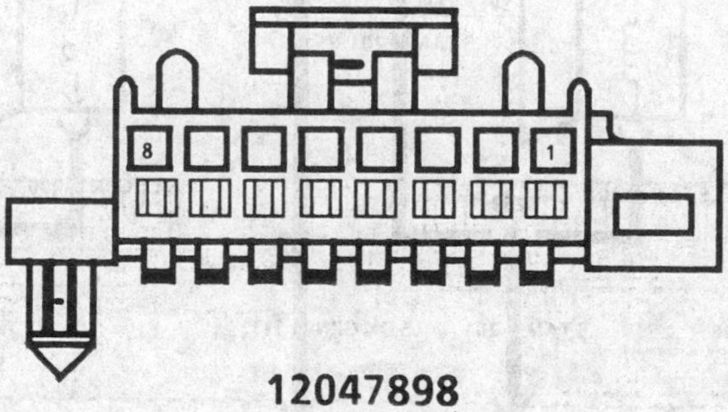
8
1

12047898

8-WAY F MICRO-PACK

BLK

RADIO CONTROL HEAD

**CAVITIES NOT LISTED ARE NOT USED

CAVITY	WIRE COLOR	CKT	DESCRIPTION	PAGE
C1 (2)	DK GRN	835	E & C DATA LINE TO RECEIVER	8A-150-0
C1 (3)	ORN	640	BATTERY POWER INPUT FROM RECEIVER	8A-150-0
C1 (4)	YEL	43	RADIO POWER INPUT FROM RECEIVER	8A-150-0
C1 (5)	BRN/WHT	230	VF PWM ILLUMINATION INPUT	8A-150-0
C1 (6)	YEL	726	LIGHTS ON INPUT FROM RECEIVER	8A-150-0
C1 (7)	BLK	701	DATA GROUND INPUT	8A-150-0
C2 (1)	BLK	150	GROUND TO G203	8A-14-6
C2 (2)	DK GRN	835	E & C DATA LINE	8A-50-0
C2 (4)	GRY	8	PANEL LIGHT DIMMING	8A-117-0
C3 (1)	DK GRN	835	E & C DATA LINE TO CASSETTE/CD PLAYER	8A-150-0
C3 (4)	BLK	152	GROUND TO CASSETTE/CD PLAYER	8A-150-0
C3 (5)	TAN/BLK	686	VF PWM ILLUMINATION OUTPUT	8A-150-0
C3 (8)	PPL/WHT	724	LIGHTS ON SIGNAL TO CASSETTE/CD PLAYER	8A-150-0

C1

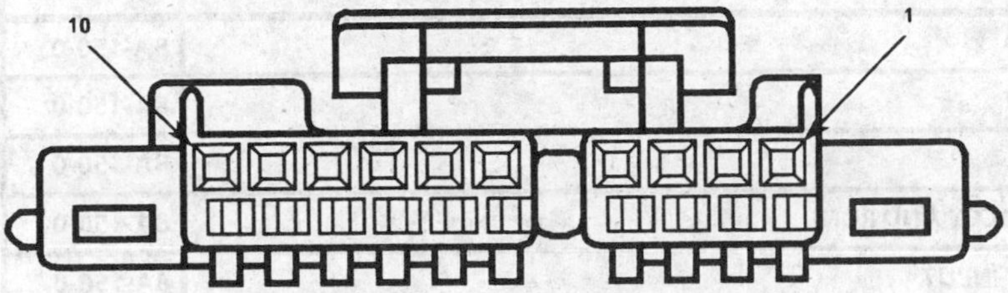
10
1

12047531

10-WAY F MICRO-PACK

BLK

C2 (UM7)

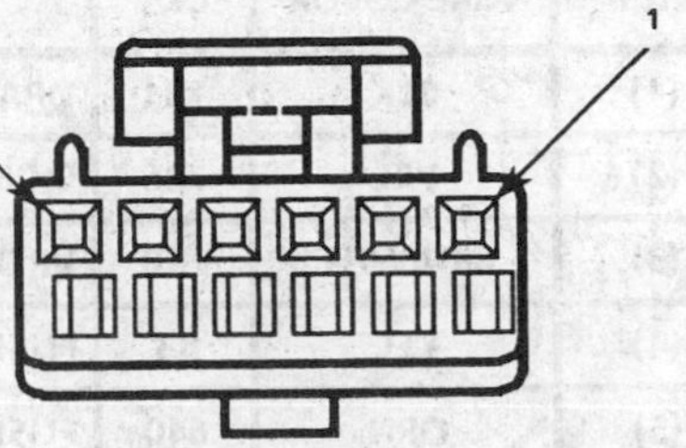
6
1

12064978

6-WAY F MICRO-PACK

GRY

C2 (U1C, UX1, UM6)

1
15

12064984

15-WAY F MICRO-PACK

BLK

C3

11
20

12065785

10-WAY F MICRO-PACK

GRY

RADIO RECEIVER

** CAVITIES NOT LISTED ARE NOT USED

CAVITY	WIRE COLOR	CKT	DESCRIPTION	PAGE
C1 (1)	GRY	118	LH FRONT SPEAKER(S) RETURN	8A-150-0
C1 (2)	TAN	201	LH FRONT SPEAKER(S) RETURN	8A-150-0
C1 (3)	DK GRN	117	RH FRONT SPEAKER(S) RETURN	8A-150-0
C1 (4)	LT GRN	200	RH FRONT SPEAKER(S) RETURN	8A-150-0
C1 (5)	BLK/WHT	351	GROUND TO G201	8A-150-0
C1 (6)	GRY/BLK	308	LIGHTS ON DIM INPUT	8A-150-0
C1 (7)	BRN/WHT	230	VF DIMMING INPUT	8A-150-0
C1 (8)	DK GRN	145	RADIO ON CONTROL FEED	8A-150-0
C1 (9)	YEL	43	FUSED FEED (HOT IN ACCY AND RUN)	8A-150-0
C1 (10)	ORN	640	FUSED FEED BATTERY INPUT	8A-150-0

(CONTINUED ON NEXT PAGE)

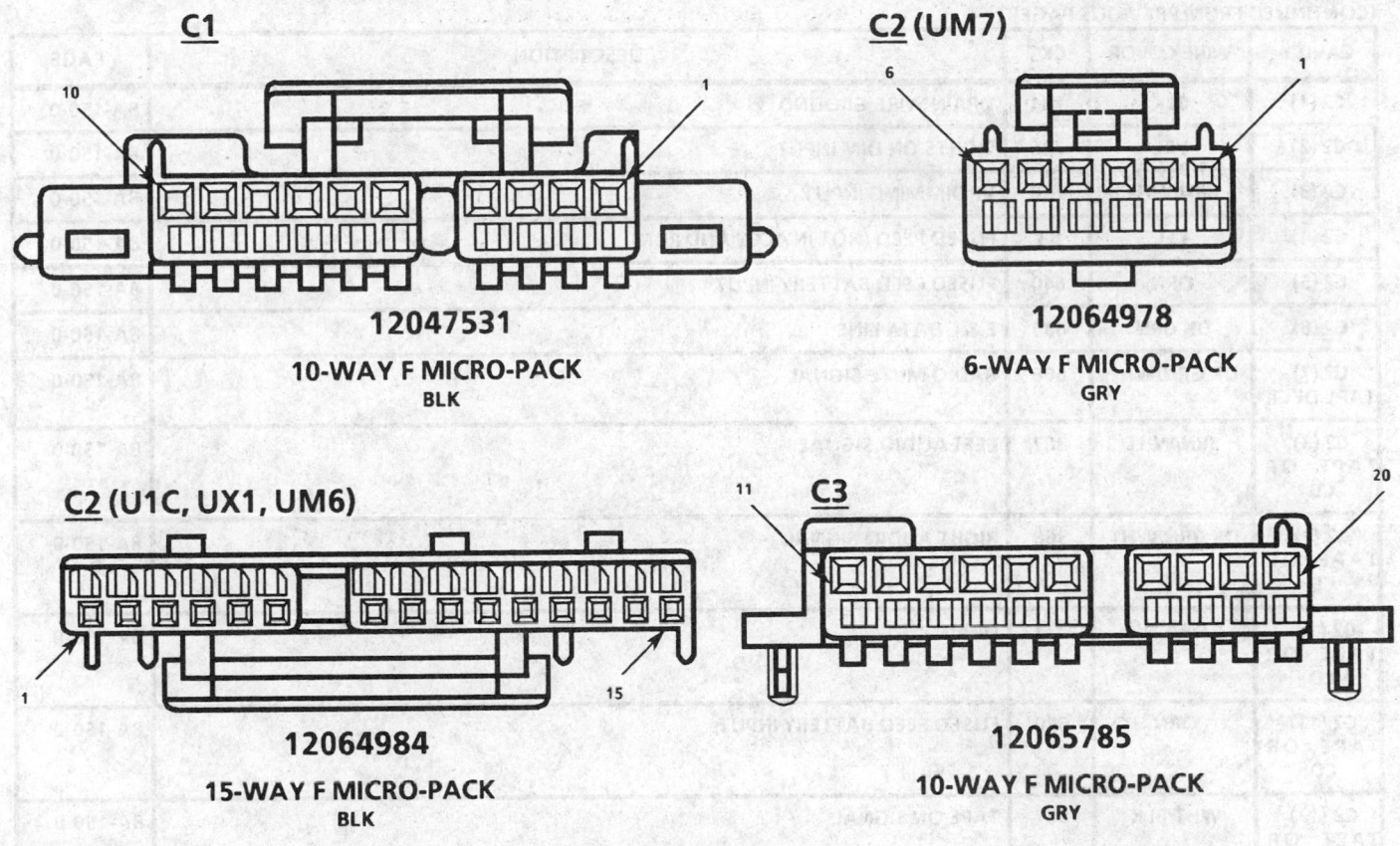

RADIO

(CONTINUED FROM PREVIOUS PAGE)

CAVITY	WIRE COLOR	CKT	DESCRIPTION	PAGE
C2 (1)	BLK	701	DRAIN WIRE GROUND	8A-150-0
C2 (2)	YEL	726	LIGHTS ON DIM INPUT	8A-150-0
C2 (3)	BRN/WHT	230	VF DIMMING INPUT	8A-150-0
C2 (4)	YEL	43	FUSED FEED (HOT IN ACCY AND RUN)	8A-150-0
C2 (5)	ORN	640	FUSED FEED BATTERY INPUT	8A-150-0
C2 (6)	DK GRN	835	E & C DATA LINE	8A-150-0
C2 (7) TAPE DECK	DK GRN/WHT	606	RADIO MUTE SIGNAL	8A-150-0
C2 (8) TAPE OR CD	BRN/WHT	367	LEFT AUDIO SIGNAL	8A-150-0
C2 (9) TAPE OR CD	DK GRN/WHT	368	RIGHT AUDIO SIGNAL	8A-150-0
C2 (10) TAPE OR CD	DRAIN	371	DRAIN	8A-150-0
C2 (11) TAPE OR CD	ORN	640	FUSED FEED BATTERY INPUT	8A-150-0
C2 (12) TAPE OR CD	WHT/BLK	607	TAPE ON SIGNAL	8A-150-0
C2 (14) TAPE OR CD	BLK/WHT	372	HIGH GROUND	8A-150-0
C2 (15) TAPE OR CD	YEL	43	FUSED FEED (HOT IN ACCY AND RUN)	8A-150-0
C3 (17)	LT BLU	115	RIGHT REAR SPEAKER RETURN	8A-150-0
C3 (18)	DK BLU	46	RIGHT REAR SPEAKER FEED	8A-150-0
C3 (19)	YEL	116	LEFT REAR SPEAKER RETURN	8A-150-0
C3 (20)	BRN	199	LEFT REAR SPEAKER FEED	8A-150-0

C1

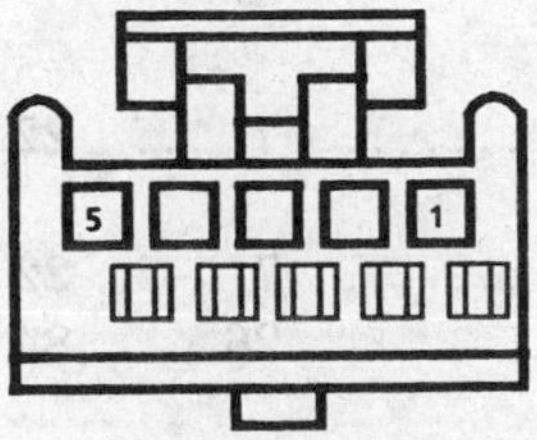
5
1

12064983

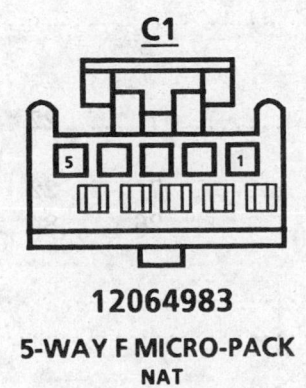

5-WAY F MICRO-PACK
NAT

C2

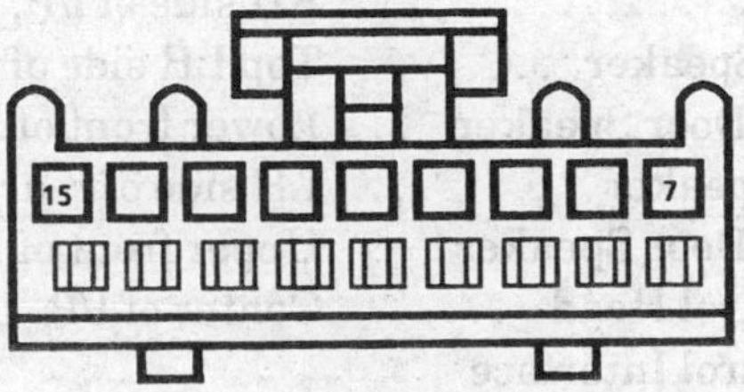
15
7

12064980

9-WAY F MICRO-PACK 100 SERIES
BLK

CASSETTE PLAYER/EQUALIZER OR CD

** CAVITIES NOT LISTED ARE NOT USED

CAVITY	WIRE COLOR	CKT	DESCRIPTION	PAGE
C1 (1)	BLK	152	GROUND TO RADIO CONTROL HEAD	8A-150-1
C1 (2)	TAN/BLK	686	VACUUM FLUORESCENT PWM ILLUMINATION INPUT	8A-150-1
C1 (4)	DK GRN	835	E & C DATA LINE TO RADIO CONTROL HEAD	8A-150-1
C1 (5)	PPL/WHT	724	LIGHTS "ON" SIGNAL	8A-150-1
C2 (7)	DK GRN/WHT	606	RADIO MUTE SIGNAL OUTPUT	8A-150-1
C2 (8)	BRN/WHT	367	LEFT AUDIO OUTPUT	8A-150-1
C2 (9)	DK GRN/WHT	368	RIGHT AUDIO OUTPUT	8A-150-1
C2 (10)	DRAIN	371	GROUND SHIELD	8A-150-1
C2 (11)	ORN	640	BATTERY INPUT FROM RECEIVER	8A-150-1
C2 (12)	WHT/BLK	607	CD/TAPE "ON" SIGNAL	8A-150-1
C2 (14)	BLK/WHT	372	GROUND FROM RECEIVER	8A-150-1
C2 (15)	YEL	43	RADIO "ON" BATTERY INPUT	8A-150-1

RADIO

COMPONENT	LOCATION	201-PG	FIG.	CONN
Cassette/Equalizer	Center of I/P	26	84	
Cassette Player	Center of I/P	26	84	
Compact Disc Player	Center of I/P	26	84	
Data Link Conn (DLC)	On bottom of I/P, right of Steering Column			202-17
Fuse Block	RH side of I/P, in I/P Compartment			
LH Front Speaker	Top LH side of I/P			
LH Lower Door Speaker	Lower front of LH front door	7	22	
LH Rear Speaker	LH side of rear shelf			
LH Upper Door Speaker	Upper front of LH front door	7	22	
Radio Control Head	Center of I/P	26	84	202-40
Radio Control Interface Module	At base of Steering Column			202-40
Radio Receiver	Behind RH side of I/P			202-32
RH Front Speaker	Top RH side of I/P			
RH Lower Door Speaker	Lower front of RH front door	7	22	
RH Rear Speaker	On RH side of rear shelf			
RH Upper Door Speaker	Upper front of RH front door	7	22	
C200 (102 cavities)	Behind RH side of I/P, near shroud	22	74	202-3
C202 (48 cavities)	Behind I/P, RH side of Steering Column	14	48	202-10
C301 (23 cavities)	In LH front door jamb	6	20	202-12
C302 (23 cavities)	In RH front door jamb	6	20	202-13
G201	Behind I/P, on RH side of mag bracket	14	48	
G203	Behind I/P, on RH side of mag bracket	14	48	
P500	In left front door jamb	6	20	
P600	In right front door jamb	6	20	
S202	I/P Harn, approx 51 cm from Instrument Cluster			
S213	I/P Harn, approx 8 cm from HVAC Control breakout			
S225	I/P Harn, approx 25 cm from Radio Control Head			
S227	I/P Harn, approx 3 cm from Fuse Block breakout			
S239	I/P Harn, approx 8 cm from HVAC Control Assembly breakout			
S250	I/P Harn, approx 31 cm from C200			
S251	I/P Harn, approx 18 cm from Radio Receiver			
S252	I/P Harn, approx 11 cm from Radio Receiver breakout			
S253	I/P Harn, approx 12 cm from RH Front Speaker breakout			
S507	LH Front Door Harn, 13 cm from LH Door Speaker breakout			
S508	LH Front Door Harn, 5 cm from LH Door Speaker breakout			
S607	RH Front Door Harn, 13 cm from RH Door Speaker breakout			
S608	RH Front Door Harn, 5 cm from RH Door Speaker breakout			

TROUBLESHOOTING HINTS (Perform before beginning System Diagnosis)

Radio Inoperative:

1. For checking a speaker, use a "C" or "D" cell Battery and momentarily connect and disconnect it across the circuits to that speaker while listening for a slight popping sound or watching for the cone of the speaker to move in and out. If either happens, the speaker and circuitry are usually OK.
2. Check ELEC Fuse. If open, check for a short to ground through CKT 640.
3. Check RADIO Fuse. If open, check for a short to ground through CKT 43.
4. Make sure ground G201 is clean and tight.

Radio Noise:

A noise "sniffer" may be used to aid in troubleshooting Radio noise, see details on page 8A-150-22. (For definitions of the different types of Radio noise, refer to "Noise Entry," page 8A-150-24.)

1. Test the Radio outside with the hood down.
2. Ignition noise on FM indicates a possible defective Electronic Ignition (EI) System. Refer to SECTION 6D4.
3. Check antenna coax connectors for corrosion or bad connections.
4. If a test antenna is used, ground the base of the antenna to the vehicle body.
5. When shielding components, use aluminum foil tape (nickel tape works best for magnetic interference) and ground one end of the shield.
6. Most noise can be found on weak AM Stations near low end of Radio band.
7. Coated screws or bolts can act as poor grounds.
8. Most hoses are conductive unless they have a white stripe.
9. Before removing a speaker, check all accessible wiring and connectors to that speaker.

General:

- Check for a broken (or partially broken) wire inside of the insulation which could cause system malfunction but prove "GOOD" in a continuity/voltage check with a system disconnected. These circuits may be intermittent or resistive when loaded, and if possible, should be checked by monitoring for a voltage drop with the system operational (under load).
- Check for proper installation of aftermarket electronic equipment which may affect the integrity of other systems (see "Troubleshooting Procedures," page 8A-4-0).
- Refer to System Diagnosis.

SYSTEM DIAGNOSIS

- Determine type of audio complaint.
- Try to duplicate condition (listen to AM or FM, start vehicle, put in a good CD or cassette, test switches, etc.).
- Refer to the Symptom Table for the appropriate diagnostic procedure(s).

The purpose of the System Performance Check is to distinguish between noise or poor reception. Some noises induced into the system may not be audible but can cause poor reception.

SYSTEM PERFORMANCE CHECK

ACTION	NORMAL RESULTS
[1] ● Ignition in "ACCESSORY" mode, Radio "ON."	
[2] ● Seek up (88-108 FM) (550-1600 AM). ● Count number of valid Radio Stations tuner stops at. ● Listen for various noise problems.	– A certain number of Radio stations will be received. – Sometimes Radio will stop at dead spots on the display where there is no audible information. These dead spots should not be counted as valid stations.
[3] ● Ignition "ON," Engine off. Repeat step 2.	– Same number of stations are received as above.
[4] ● Ignition "ON," Engine running. Repeat step 2.	– Same number of stations are received as above.

NOTICE TO TECHNICIANS: Electromagnetic interference (EMI) can cause a fewer number of stations to be received in one of the three modes. The EMI can be caused by various vehicle components. This may be the cause of the differences in reception. Check for components powered up in the three various key positions. This may eliminate Engine running components, Ignition on components, etc. For example, if the same number of stations are received with the Engine running as when the Engine was off, the components active with the Engine running are not causing the interference.

RADIO

SYMPTOM TABLE

HARDWARE RELATED FAILURES
(No Audio, Display Problems, Inoperative Functions, etc.)

SYMPTOM	PROCEDURE	PAGE NUMBER
Tech 1: Primary test.	Chart #1	8A-150-11
Tech 1: E & C Bus error.	Chart #2	8A-150-12
Tech 1: E & C Bus intermittent.	Chart #3	8A-150-13
Tech 1: Radio feature inoperative.	Chart #4	8A-150-14
Tech 1: Cassette or CD feature inoperative.	Chart #5	8A-150-15
Tech 1: No audio output.	Chart #6	8A-150-16
Tech 1: Cassette/Compact Disc no audio.	Chart #7	8A-150-17
Tech 1: VF display problem.	Chart #8	8A-150-18
Tech 1: Clock problem.	Chart #9	8A-150-18
Tech 1: One or more speakers inoperative.	Chart #10	8A-150-19
Compact Disc problems.	Chart #11	8A-150-29
Tape problems.	Chart #12	8A-150-29

PERFORMANCE COMPLAINTS
(Noise or Reception Symptoms)

To distinguish between noise or poor reception, perform the System Performance Check on the previous page.

SYMPTOM	PROCEDURE	PAGE NUMBER
Poor reception.	Chart #13	8A-150-30
Radio noise entering through Radio (sideways noise).	Chart #14	8A-150-31
Radio noise entering through harness (backway noise) while Engine not running.	Chart #15	8A-150-32
Radio noise entering through harness (backway noise) while Engine running only.	Chart #16	8A-150-33
Ignition noise.	Chart #17	8A-150-33
Generator whine (varies with Engine speed).	Chart #18	8A-150-34
Radio noise.	Chart #19	8A-150-35
Speaker harness related noise.	Chart #20	8A-150-36
Radio noise entering through antenna system (frontway noise).	Chart #21	8A-150-36
Switch pop or accessory noise.	Chart #22	8A-150-37

CHART #1

TECH 1: PRIMARY TEST

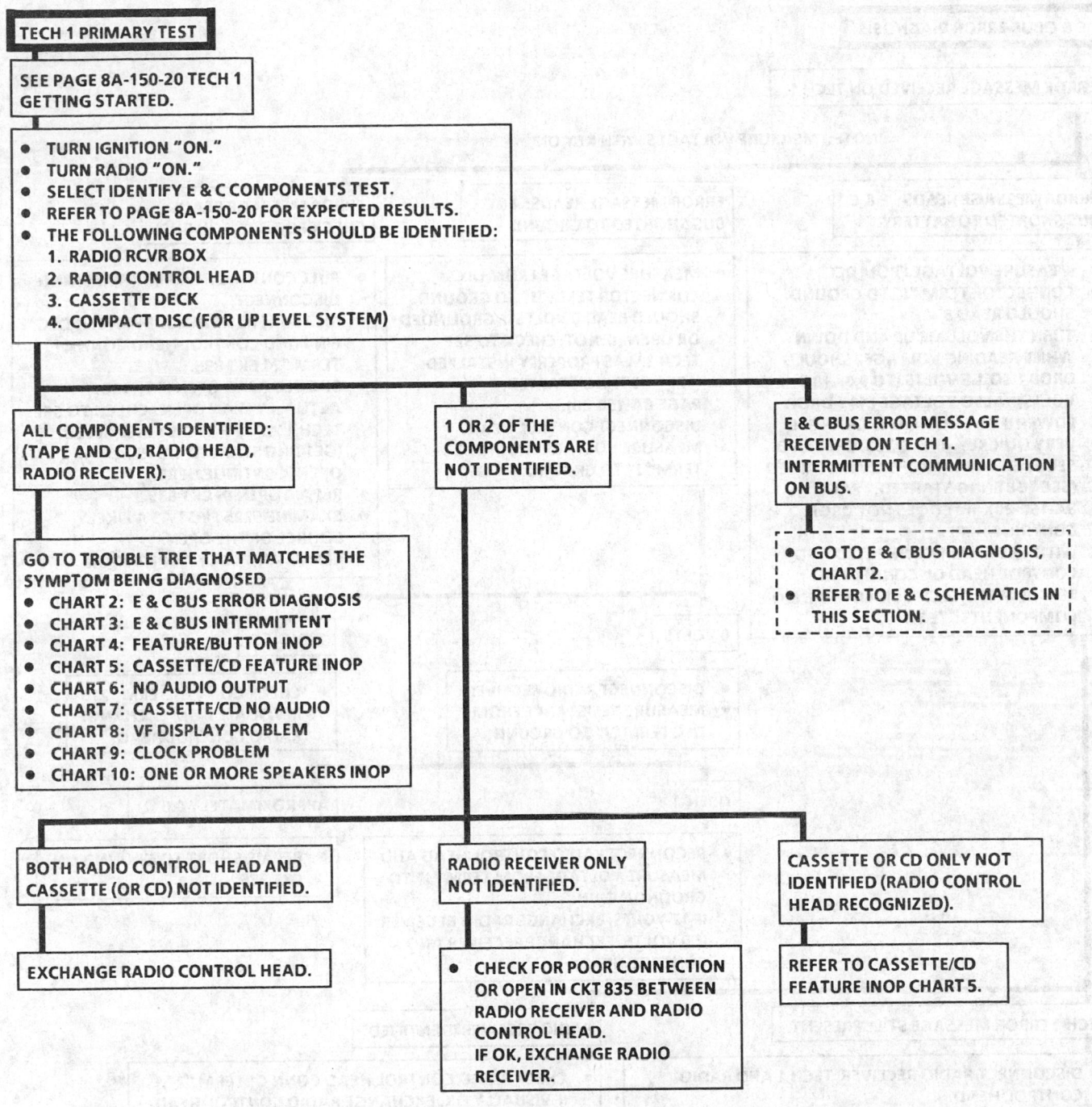

TECH 1 PRIMARY TEST

SEE PAGE 8A-150-20 TECH 1 GETTING STARTED.

- TURN IGNITION "ON."
- TURN RADIO "ON."
- SELECT IDENTIFY E & C COMPONENTS TEST.
- REFER TO PAGE 8A-150-20 FOR EXPECTED RESULTS.
- THE FOLLOWING COMPONENTS SHOULD BE IDENTIFIED:
  1. RADIO RCVR BOX
  2. RADIO CONTROL HEAD
  3. CASSETTE DECK
  4. COMPACT DISC (FOR UP LEVEL SYSTEM)

ALL COMPONENTS IDENTIFIED: (TAPE AND CD, RADIO HEAD, RADIO RECEIVER).

GO TO TROUBLE TREE THAT MATCHES THE SYMPTOM BEING DIAGNOSED

- CHART 2: E & C BUS ERROR DIAGNOSIS
- CHART 3: E & C BUS INTERMITTENT
- CHART 4: FEATURE/BUTTON INOP
- CHART 5: CASSETTE/CD FEATURE INOP
- CHART 6: NO AUDIO OUTPUT
- CHART 7: CASSETTE/CD NO AUDIO
- CHART 8: VF DISPLAY PROBLEM
- CHART 9: CLOCK PROBLEM
- CHART 10: ONE OR MORE SPEAKERS INOP

1 OR 2 OF THE COMPONENTS ARE NOT IDENTIFIED.

- BOTH RADIO CONTROL HEAD AND CASSETTE (OR CD) NOT IDENTIFIED.
  - EXCHANGE RADIO CONTROL HEAD.
- RADIO RECEIVER ONLY NOT IDENTIFIED.
  - CHECK FOR POOR CONNECTION OR OPEN IN CKT 835 BETWEEN RADIO RECEIVER AND RADIO CONTROL HEAD. IF OK, EXCHANGE RADIO RECEIVER.
- CASSETTE OR CD ONLY NOT IDENTIFIED (RADIO CONTROL HEAD RECOGNIZED).
  - REFER TO CASSETTE/CD FEATURE INOP CHART 5.

E & C BUS ERROR MESSAGE RECEIVED ON TECH 1. INTERMITTENT COMMUNICATION ON BUS.

- GO TO E & C BUS DIAGNOSIS, CHART 2.
- REFER TO E & C SCHEMATICS IN THIS SECTION.

RADIO

CHART #2

TECH 1: E & C BUS ERROR

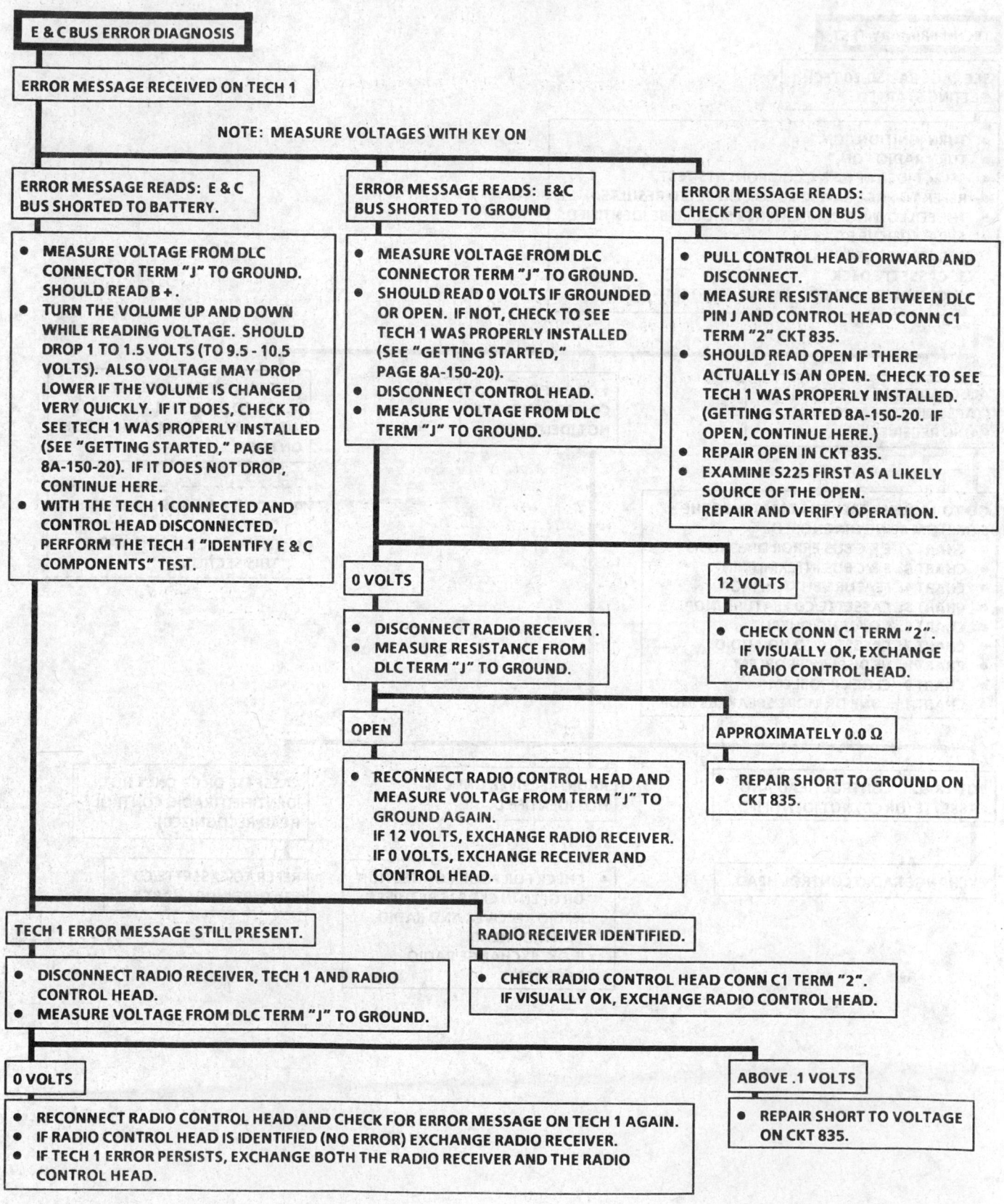

E & C BUS ERROR DIAGNOSIS

ERROR MESSAGE RECEIVED ON TECH 1

NOTE: MEASURE VOLTAGES WITH KEY ON

ERROR MESSAGE READS: E & C BUS SHORTED TO BATTERY.

- MEASURE VOLTAGE FROM DLC CONNECTOR TERM "J" TO GROUND. SHOULD READ B+.
- TURN THE VOLUME UP AND DOWN WHILE READING VOLTAGE. SHOULD DROP 1 TO 1.5 VOLTS (TO 9.5 - 10.5 VOLTS). ALSO VOLTAGE MAY DROP LOWER IF THE VOLUME IS CHANGED VERY QUICKLY. IF IT DOES, CHECK TO SEE TECH 1 WAS PROPERLY INSTALLED (SEE "GETTING STARTED," PAGE 8A-150-20). IF IT DOES NOT DROP, CONTINUE HERE.
- WITH THE TECH 1 CONNECTED AND CONTROL HEAD DISCONNECTED, PERFORM THE TECH 1 "IDENTIFY E & C COMPONENTS" TEST.

ERROR MESSAGE READS: E&C BUS SHORTED TO GROUND

- MEASURE VOLTAGE FROM DLC CONNECTOR TERM "J" TO GROUND.
- SHOULD READ 0 VOLTS IF GROUNDED OR OPEN. IF NOT, CHECK TO SEE TECH 1 WAS PROPERLY INSTALLED (SEE "GETTING STARTED," PAGE 8A-150-20).
- DISCONNECT CONTROL HEAD.
- MEASURE VOLTAGE FROM DLC TERM "J" TO GROUND.

0 VOLTS

- DISCONNECT RADIO RECEIVER.
- MEASURE RESISTANCE FROM DLC TERM "J" TO GROUND.

OPEN

- RECONNECT RADIO CONTROL HEAD AND MEASURE VOLTAGE FROM TERM "J" TO GROUND AGAIN.

IF 12 VOLTS, EXCHANGE RADIO RECEIVER.
IF 0 VOLTS, EXCHANGE RECEIVER AND CONTROL HEAD.

APPROXIMATELY 0.0 Ω

- REPAIR SHORT TO GROUND ON CKT 835.

12 VOLTS

- CHECK CONN C1 TERM "2". IF VISUALLY OK, EXCHANGE RADIO CONTROL HEAD.

ERROR MESSAGE READS: CHECK FOR OPEN ON BUS

- PULL CONTROL HEAD FORWARD AND DISCONNECT.
- MEASURE RESISTANCE BETWEEN DLC PIN J AND CONTROL HEAD CONN C1 TERM "2" CKT 835.
- SHOULD READ OPEN IF THERE ACTUALLY IS AN OPEN. CHECK TO SEE TECH 1 WAS PROPERLY INSTALLED. (GETTING STARTED 8A-150-20. IF OPEN, CONTINUE HERE.)
- REPAIR OPEN IN CKT 835.
- EXAMINE S225 FIRST AS A LIKELY SOURCE OF THE OPEN.

REPAIR AND VERIFY OPERATION.

TECH 1 ERROR MESSAGE STILL PRESENT.

- DISCONNECT RADIO RECEIVER, TECH 1 AND RADIO CONTROL HEAD.
- MEASURE VOLTAGE FROM DLC TERM "J" TO GROUND.

0 VOLTS

- RECONNECT RADIO CONTROL HEAD AND CHECK FOR ERROR MESSAGE ON TECH 1 AGAIN.
- IF RADIO CONTROL HEAD IS IDENTIFIED (NO ERROR) EXCHANGE RADIO RECEIVER.
- IF TECH 1 ERROR PERSISTS, EXCHANGE BOTH THE RADIO RECEIVER AND THE RADIO CONTROL HEAD.

ABOVE .1 VOLTS

- REPAIR SHORT TO VOLTAGE ON CKT 835.

RADIO RECEIVER IDENTIFIED.

- CHECK RADIO CONTROL HEAD CONN C1 TERM "2". IF VISUALLY OK, EXCHANGE RADIO CONTROL HEAD.

CHART #3

TECH 1: E & C BUS INTERMITTENT

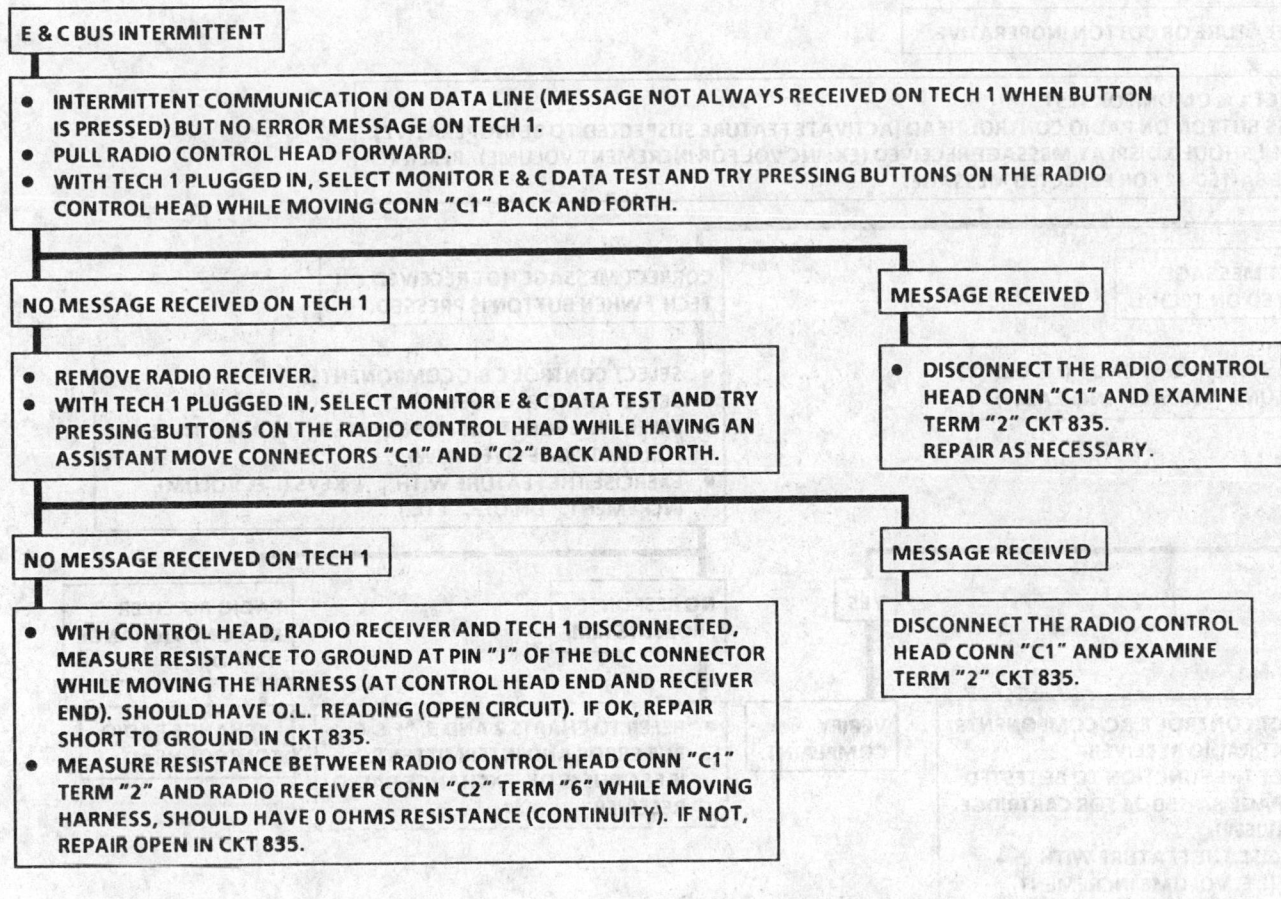

E & C BUS INTERMITTENT

- INTERMITTENT COMMUNICATION ON DATA LINE (MESSAGE NOT ALWAYS RECEIVED ON TECH 1 WHEN BUTTON IS PRESSED) BUT NO ERROR MESSAGE ON TECH 1.
- PULL RADIO CONTROL HEAD FORWARD.
- WITH TECH 1 PLUGGED IN, SELECT MONITOR E & C DATA TEST AND TRY PRESSING BUTTONS ON THE RADIO CONTROL HEAD WHILE MOVING CONN "C1" BACK AND FORTH.

NO MESSAGE RECEIVED ON TECH 1

- REMOVE RADIO RECEIVER.
- WITH TECH 1 PLUGGED IN, SELECT MONITOR E & C DATA TEST AND TRY PRESSING BUTTONS ON THE RADIO CONTROL HEAD WHILE HAVING AN ASSISTANT MOVE CONNECTORS "C1" AND "C2" BACK AND FORTH.

NO MESSAGE RECEIVED ON TECH 1

- WITH CONTROL HEAD, RADIO RECEIVER AND TECH 1 DISCONNECTED, MEASURE RESISTANCE TO GROUND AT PIN "J" OF THE DLC CONNECTOR WHILE MOVING THE HARNESS (AT CONTROL HEAD END AND RECEIVER END). SHOULD HAVE O.L. READING (OPEN CIRCUIT). IF OK, REPAIR SHORT TO GROUND IN CKT 835.
- MEASURE RESISTANCE BETWEEN RADIO CONTROL HEAD CONN "C1" TERM "2" AND RADIO RECEIVER CONN "C2" TERM "6" WHILE MOVING HARNESS, SHOULD HAVE 0 OHMS RESISTANCE (CONTINUITY). IF NOT, REPAIR OPEN IN CKT 835.

MESSAGE RECEIVED

- DISCONNECT THE RADIO CONTROL HEAD CONN "C1" AND EXAMINE TERM "2" CKT 835. REPAIR AS NECESSARY.

MESSAGE RECEIVED

DISCONNECT THE RADIO CONTROL HEAD CONN "C1" AND EXAMINE TERM "2" CKT 835.

RADIO

CHART #4
TECH 1: RADIO FEATURE INOPERATIVE

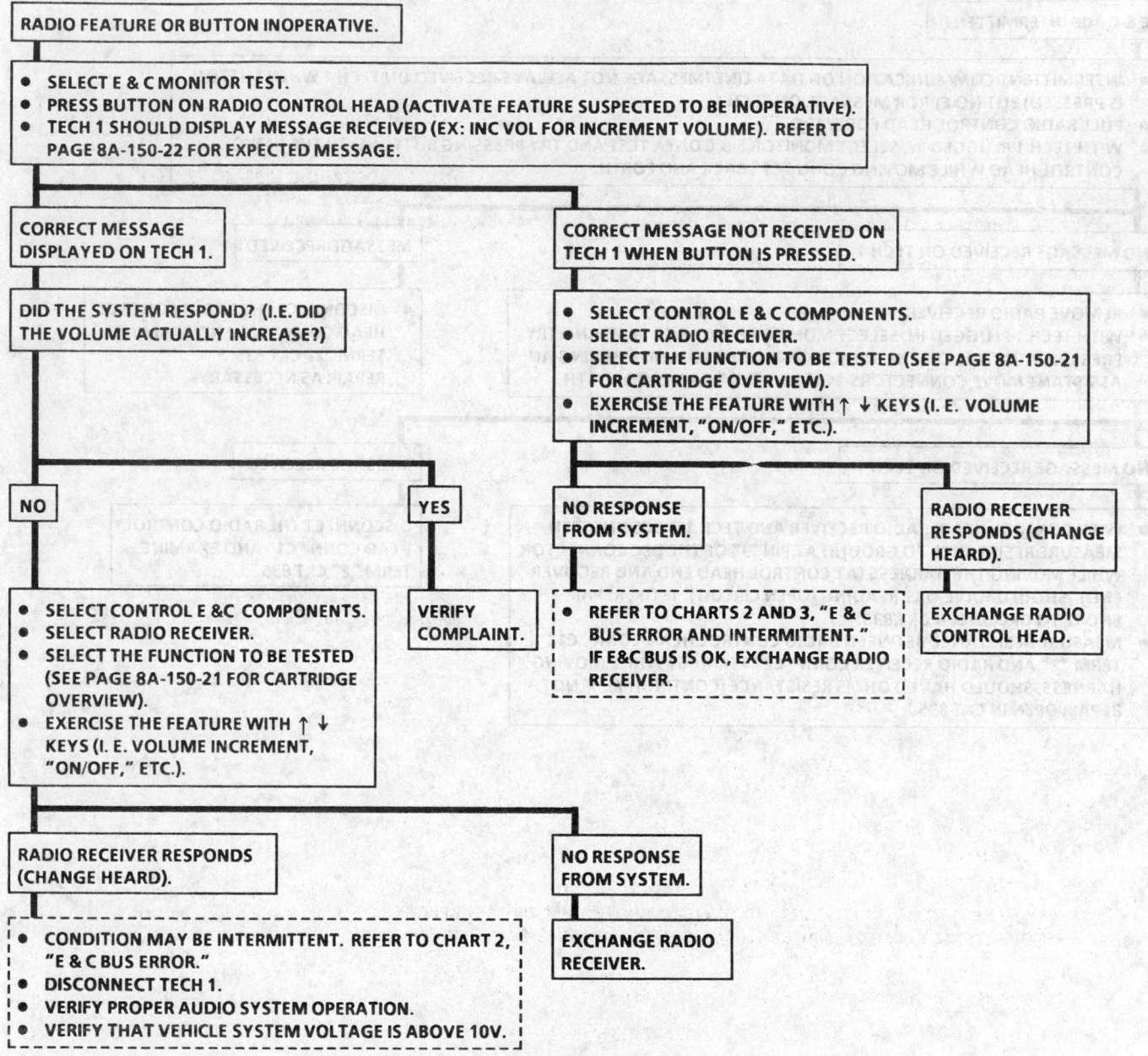

RADIO FEATURE OR BUTTON INOPERATIVE.

- SELECT E & C MONITOR TEST.
- PRESS BUTTON ON RADIO CONTROL HEAD (ACTIVATE FEATURE SUSPECTED TO BE INOPERATIVE).
- TECH 1 SHOULD DISPLAY MESSAGE RECEIVED (EX: INC VOL FOR INCREMENT VOLUME). REFER TO PAGE 8A-150-22 FOR EXPECTED MESSAGE.

CORRECT MESSAGE DISPLAYED ON TECH 1.

DID THE SYSTEM RESPOND? (I.E. DID THE VOLUME ACTUALLY INCREASE?)

NO

- SELECT CONTROL E &C COMPONENTS.
- SELECT RADIO RECEIVER.
- SELECT THE FUNCTION TO BE TESTED (SEE PAGE 8A-150-21 FOR CARTRIDGE OVERVIEW).
- EXERCISE THE FEATURE WITH ↑ ↓ KEYS (I. E. VOLUME INCREMENT, "ON/OFF," ETC.).

RADIO RECEIVER RESPONDS (CHANGE HEARD).

- CONDITION MAY BE INTERMITTENT. REFER TO CHART 2, "E & C BUS ERROR."
- DISCONNECT TECH 1.
- VERIFY PROPER AUDIO SYSTEM OPERATION.
- VERIFY THAT VEHICLE SYSTEM VOLTAGE IS ABOVE 10V.

NO RESPONSE FROM SYSTEM.

EXCHANGE RADIO RECEIVER.

YES

VERIFY COMPLAINT.

CORRECT MESSAGE NOT RECEIVED ON TECH 1 WHEN BUTTON IS PRESSED.

- SELECT CONTROL E & C COMPONENTS.
- SELECT RADIO RECEIVER.
- SELECT THE FUNCTION TO BE TESTED (SEE PAGE 8A-150-21 FOR CARTRIDGE OVERVIEW).
- EXERCISE THE FEATURE WITH ↑ ↓ KEYS (I. E. VOLUME INCREMENT, "ON/OFF," ETC.).

NO RESPONSE FROM SYSTEM.

- REFER TO CHARTS 2 AND 3, "E & C BUS ERROR AND INTERMITTENT." IF E&C BUS IS OK, EXCHANGE RADIO RECEIVER.

RADIO RECEIVER RESPONDS (CHANGE HEARD).

EXCHANGE RADIO CONTROL HEAD.

CHART #5

TECH 1: CASSETTE OR CD FEATURE INOPERATIVE

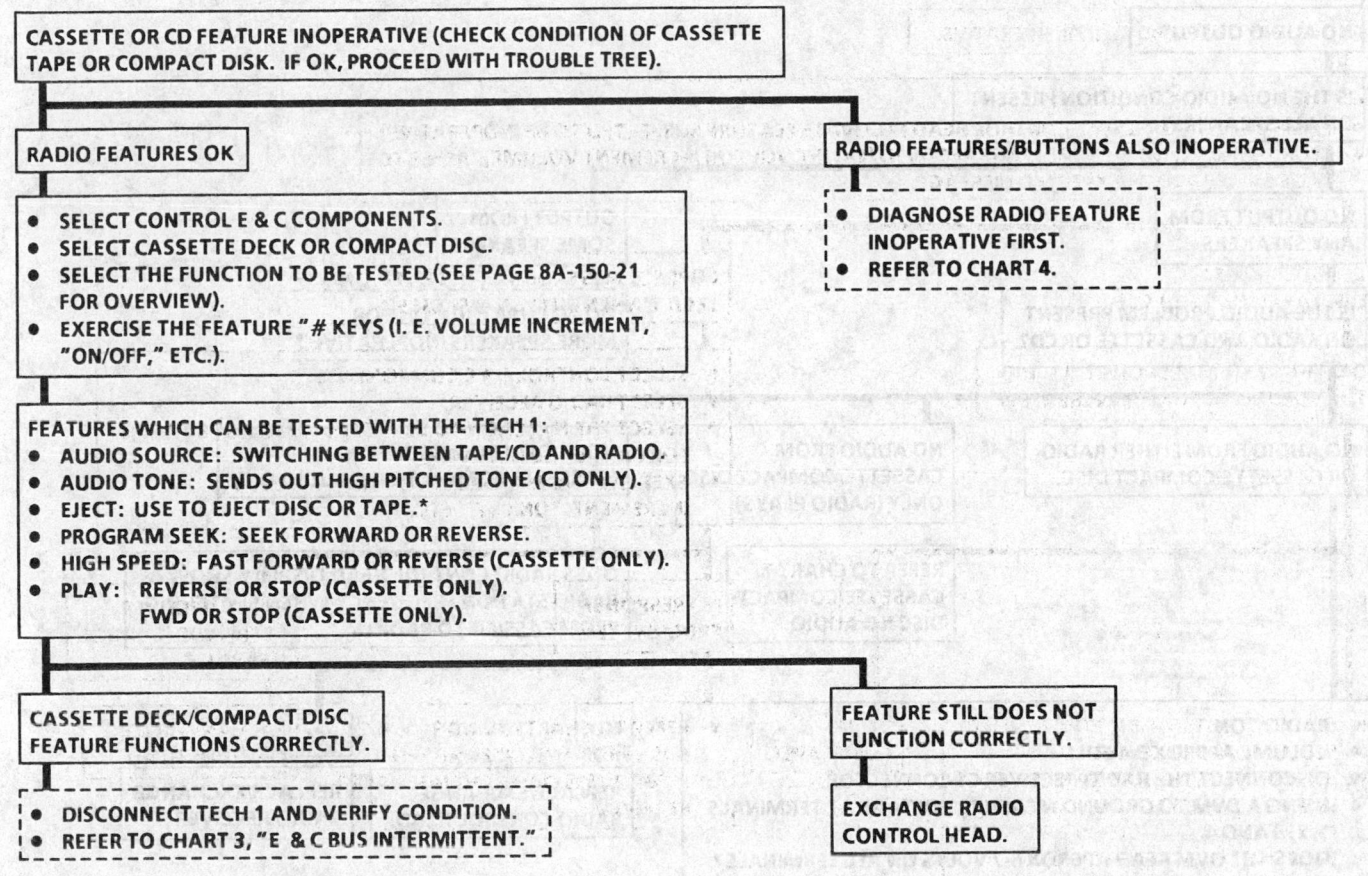

CASSETTE OR CD FEATURE INOPERATIVE (CHECK CONDITION OF CASSETTE TAPE OR COMPACT DISK. IF OK, PROCEED WITH TROUBLE TREE).

RADIO FEATURES OK

- SELECT CONTROL E & C COMPONENTS.
- SELECT CASSETTE DECK OR COMPACT DISC.
- SELECT THE FUNCTION TO BE TESTED (SEE PAGE 8A-150-21 FOR OVERVIEW).
- EXERCISE THE FEATURE "# KEYS (I. E. VOLUME INCREMENT, "ON/OFF," ETC.).

FEATURES WHICH CAN BE TESTED WITH THE TECH 1:

- AUDIO SOURCE: SWITCHING BETWEEN TAPE/CD AND RADIO.
- AUDIO TONE: SENDS OUT HIGH PITCHED TONE (CD ONLY).
- EJECT: USE TO EJECT DISC OR TAPE.*
- PROGRAM SEEK: SEEK FORWARD OR REVERSE.
- HIGH SPEED: FAST FORWARD OR REVERSE (CASSETTE ONLY).
- PLAY: REVERSE OR STOP (CASSETTE ONLY).
  FWD OR STOP (CASSETTE ONLY).

CASSETTE DECK/COMPACT DISC FEATURE FUNCTIONS CORRECTLY.

- DISCONNECT TECH 1 AND VERIFY CONDITION.
- REFER TO CHART 3, "E & C BUS INTERMITTENT."

FEATURE STILL DOES NOT FUNCTION CORRECTLY.

EXCHANGE RADIO CONTROL HEAD.

RADIO FEATURES/BUTTONS ALSO INOPERATIVE.

- DIAGNOSE RADIO FEATURE INOPERATIVE FIRST.
- REFER TO CHART 4.

* MAY BE ABLE TO USE THIS COMMAND TO EJECT OWNERS DISC OR TAPE BEFORE SENDING TO AC-DELCO EXCHANGE CENTER IF EJECT BUTTON IS INOPERATIVE.

RADIO

CHART #6
TECH 1: NO AUDIO OUTPUT

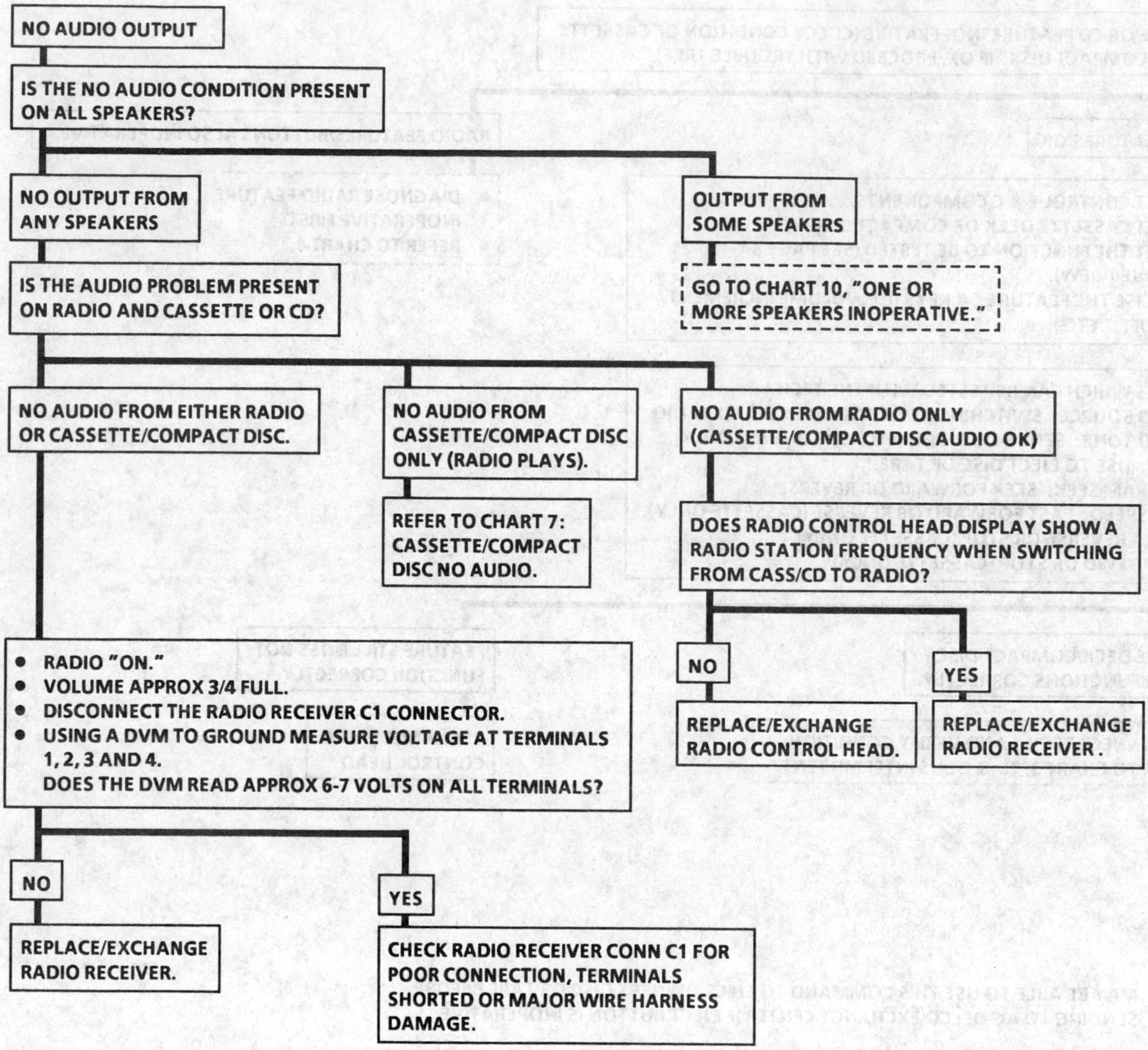
NO AUDIO OUTPUT
IS THE NO AUDIO CONDITION PRESENT ON ALL SPEAKERS?
NO OUTPUT FROM ANY SPEAKERS
OUTPUT FROM SOME SPEAKERS
GO TO CHART 10, "ONE OR MORE SPEAKERS INOPERATIVE."
IS THE AUDIO PROBLEM PRESENT ON RADIO AND CASSETTE OR CD?
NO AUDIO FROM EITHER RADIO OR CASSETTE/COMPACT DISC.
NO AUDIO FROM CASSETTE/COMPACT DISC ONLY (RADIO PLAYS).
NO AUDIO FROM RADIO ONLY (CASSETTE/COMPACT DISC AUDIO OK)
REFER TO CHART 7: CASSETTE/COMPACT DISC NO AUDIO.
DOES RADIO CONTROL HEAD DISPLAY SHOW A RADIO STATION FREQUENCY WHEN SWITCHING FROM CASS/CD TO RADIO?
NO
YES
REPLACE/EXCHANGE RADIO CONTROL HEAD.
REPLACE/EXCHANGE RADIO RECEIVER .
• RADIO "ON."
• VOLUME APPROX 3/4 FULL.
• DISCONNECT THE RADIO RECEIVER C1 CONNECTOR.
• USING A DVM TO GROUND MEASURE VOLTAGE AT TERMINALS 1, 2, 3 AND 4.
DOES THE DVM READ APPROX 6-7 VOLTS ON ALL TERMINALS?
NO
YES
REPLACE/EXCHANGE RADIO RECEIVER.
CHECK RADIO RECEIVER CONN C1 FOR POOR CONNECTION, TERMINALS SHORTED OR MAJOR WIRE HARNESS DAMAGE.

CHART #7

TECH 1: CASSETTE/COMPACT DISC NO AUDIO

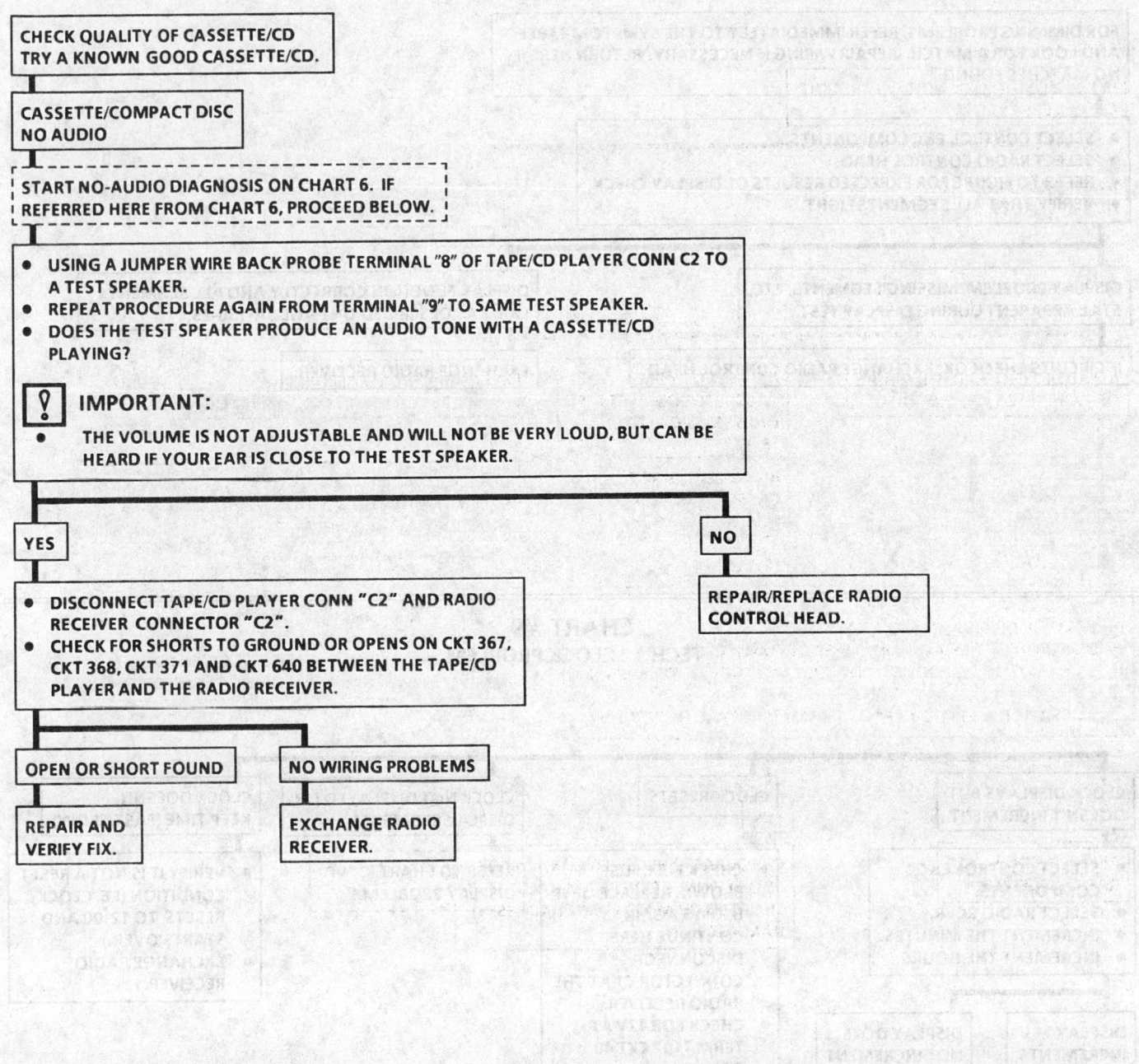

CHECK QUALITY OF CASSETTE/CD
TRY A KNOWN GOOD CASSETTE/CD.

CASSETTE/COMPACT DISC
NO AUDIO

START NO-AUDIO DIAGNOSIS ON CHART 6. IF REFERRED HERE FROM CHART 6, PROCEED BELOW.

- USING A JUMPER WIRE BACK PROBE TERMINAL "8" OF TAPE/CD PLAYER CONN C2 TO A TEST SPEAKER.
- REPEAT PROCEDURE AGAIN FROM TERMINAL "9" TO SAME TEST SPEAKER.
- DOES THE TEST SPEAKER PRODUCE AN AUDIO TONE WITH A CASSETTE/CD PLAYING?

IMPORTANT:

- THE VOLUME IS NOT ADJUSTABLE AND WILL NOT BE VERY LOUD, BUT CAN BE HEARD IF YOUR EAR IS CLOSE TO THE TEST SPEAKER.

YES

- DISCONNECT TAPE/CD PLAYER CONN "C2" AND RADIO RECEIVER CONNECTOR "C2".
- CHECK FOR SHORTS TO GROUND OR OPENS ON CKT 367, CKT 368, CKT 371 AND CKT 640 BETWEEN THE TAPE/CD PLAYER AND THE RADIO RECEIVER.

OPEN OR SHORT FOUND

REPAIR AND VERIFY FIX.

NO WIRING PROBLEMS

EXCHANGE RADIO RECEIVER.

NO

REPAIR/REPLACE RADIO CONTROL HEAD.

RADIO

CHART #8
TECH 1: VF DISPLAY PROBLEM

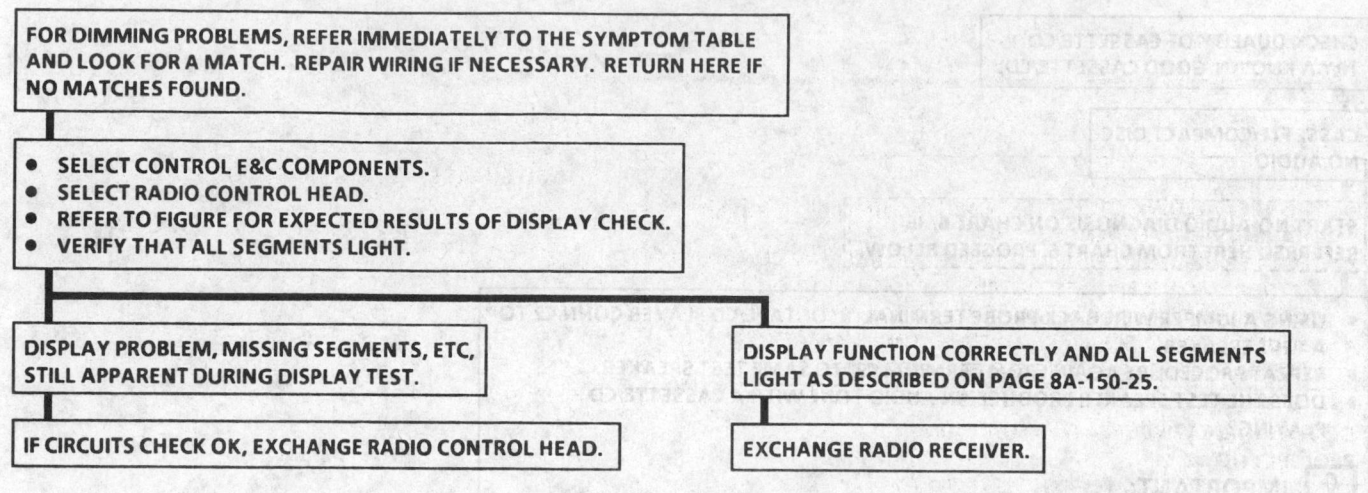

FOR DIMMING PROBLEMS, REFER IMMEDIATELY TO THE SYMPTOM TABLE AND LOOK FOR A MATCH. REPAIR WIRING IF NECESSARY. RETURN HERE IF NO MATCHES FOUND.

- SELECT CONTROL E&C COMPONENTS.
- SELECT RADIO CONTROL HEAD.
- REFER TO FIGURE FOR EXPECTED RESULTS OF DISPLAY CHECK.
- VERIFY THAT ALL SEGMENTS LIGHT.

DISPLAY PROBLEM, MISSING SEGMENTS, ETC, STILL APPARENT DURING DISPLAY TEST.

IF CIRCUITS CHECK OK, EXCHANGE RADIO CONTROL HEAD.

DISPLAY FUNCTION CORRECTLY AND ALL SEGMENTS LIGHT AS DESCRIBED ON PAGE 8A-150-25.

EXCHANGE RADIO RECEIVER.

CHART #9
TECH 1: CLOCK PROBLEM

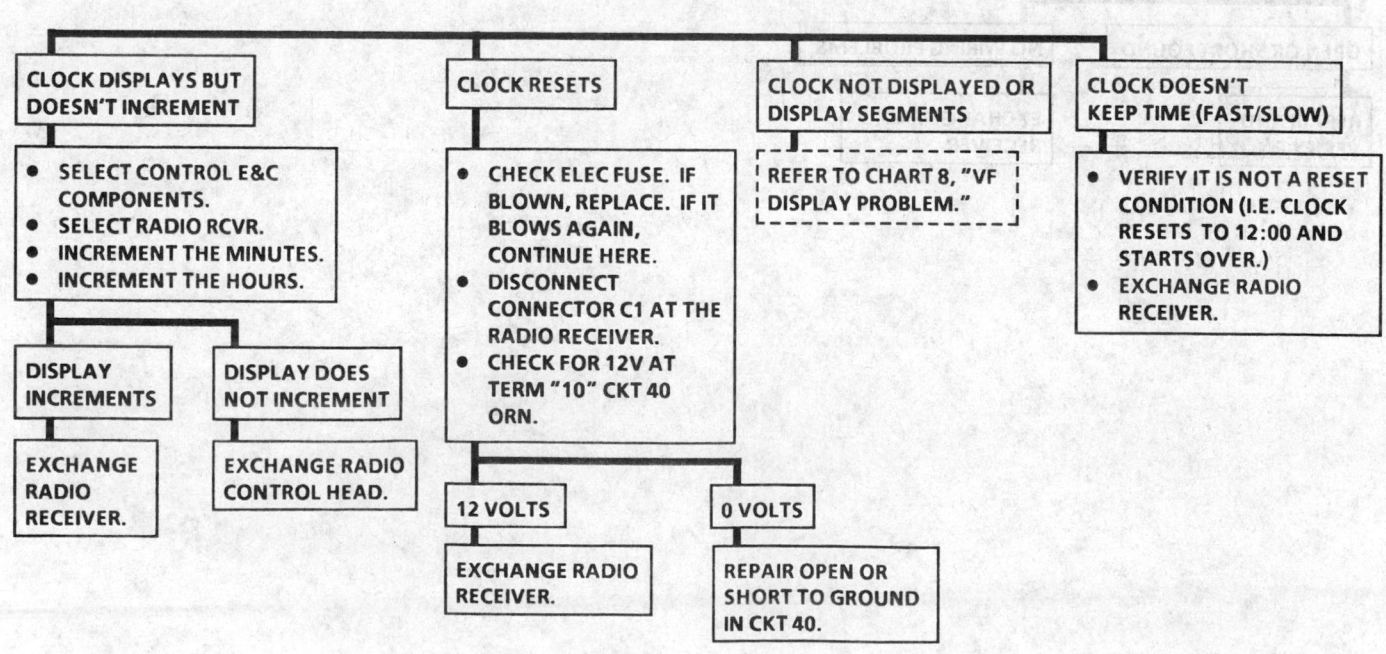

CLOCK DISPLAYS BUT DOESN'T INCREMENT

- SELECT CONTROL E&C COMPONENTS.
- SELECT RADIO RCVR.
- INCREMENT THE MINUTES.
- INCREMENT THE HOURS.

DISPLAY INCREMENTS

EXCHANGE RADIO RECEIVER.

DISPLAY DOES NOT INCREMENT

EXCHANGE RADIO CONTROL HEAD.

CLOCK RESETS

- CHECK ELEC FUSE. IF BLOWN, REPLACE. IF IT BLOWS AGAIN, CONTINUE HERE.
- DISCONNECT CONNECTOR C1 AT THE RADIO RECEIVER.
- CHECK FOR 12V AT TERM "10" CKT 40 ORN.

12 VOLTS

EXCHANGE RADIO RECEIVER.

0 VOLTS

REPAIR OPEN OR SHORT TO GROUND IN CKT 40.

CLOCK NOT DISPLAYED OR DISPLAY SEGMENTS

REFER TO CHART 8, "VF DISPLAY PROBLEM."

CLOCK DOESN'T KEEP TIME (FAST/SLOW)

- VERIFY IT IS NOT A RESET CONDITION (I.E. CLOCK RESETS TO 12:00 AND STARTS OVER.)
- EXCHANGE RADIO RECEIVER.

CHART #10
TECH 1: ONE OR MORE SPEAKERS INOPERATIVE

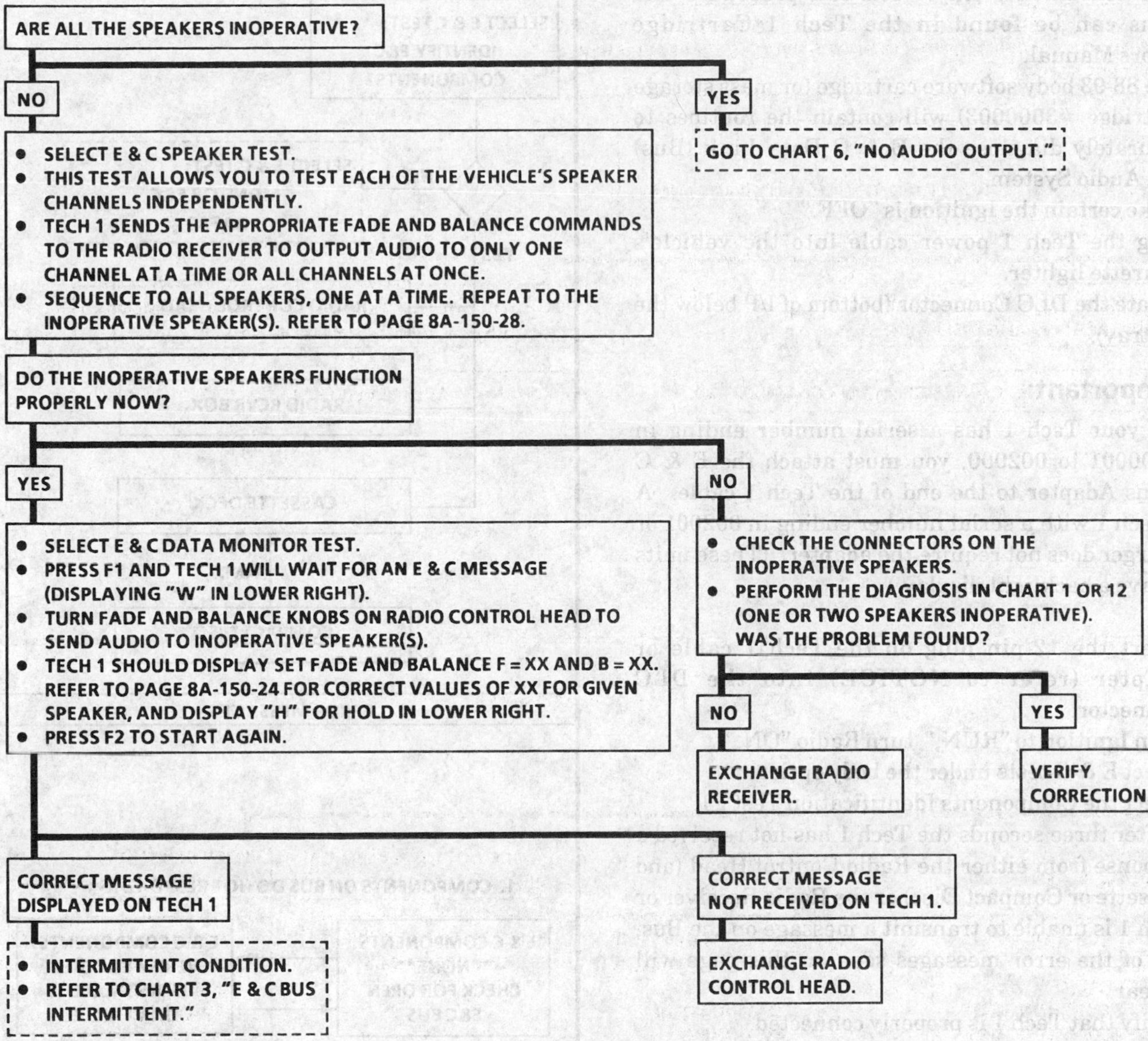
ARE ALL THE SPEAKERS INOPERATIVE?
NO
YES
GO TO CHART 6, "NO AUDIO OUTPUT."
• SELECT E & C SPEAKER TEST.
• THIS TEST ALLOWS YOU TO TEST EACH OF THE VEHICLE'S SPEAKER CHANNELS INDEPENDENTLY.
• TECH 1 SENDS THE APPROPRIATE FADE AND BALANCE COMMANDS TO THE RADIO RECEIVER TO OUTPUT AUDIO TO ONLY ONE CHANNEL AT A TIME OR ALL CHANNELS AT ONCE.
• SEQUENCE TO ALL SPEAKERS, ONE AT A TIME. REPEAT TO THE INOPERATIVE SPEAKER(S). REFER TO PAGE 8A-150-28.
DO THE INOPERATIVE SPEAKERS FUNCTION PROPERLY NOW?
YES
NO
• SELECT E & C DATA MONITOR TEST.
• PRESS F1 AND TECH 1 WILL WAIT FOR AN E & C MESSAGE (DISPLAYING "W" IN LOWER RIGHT).
• TURN FADE AND BALANCE KNOBS ON RADIO CONTROL HEAD TO SEND AUDIO TO INOPERATIVE SPEAKER(S).
• TECH 1 SHOULD DISPLAY SET FADE AND BALANCE F = XX AND B = XX. REFER TO PAGE 8A-150-24 FOR CORRECT VALUES OF XX FOR GIVEN SPEAKER, AND DISPLAY "H" FOR HOLD IN LOWER RIGHT.
• PRESS F2 TO START AGAIN.
• CHECK THE CONNECTORS ON THE INOPERATIVE SPEAKERS.
• PERFORM THE DIAGNOSIS IN CHART 1 OR 12 (ONE OR TWO SPEAKERS INOPERATIVE). WAS THE PROBLEM FOUND?
NO
YES
EXCHANGE RADIO RECEIVER.
VERIFY CORRECTION.
CORRECT MESSAGE DISPLAYED ON TECH 1
CORRECT MESSAGE NOT RECEIVED ON TECH 1.
• INTERMITTENT CONDITION.
• REFER TO CHART 3, "E & C BUS INTERMITTENT."
EXCHANGE RADIO CONTROL HEAD.

RADIO

TECH 1: AUDIO DIAGNOSIS (GETTING STARTED)

The "Getting Started" information is provided here for convenience only. The full procedure and cautions can be found in the Tech 1 Cartridge Operators Manual.

1. The 88-93 body software cartridge (or mass storage cartridge #3000003) will contain the routines to accurately diagnose the E & C Data Link (Bus) and Audio System.
2. Make certain the Ignition is "OFF."
3. Plug the Tech 1 power cable into the vehicle's cigarette lighter.
4. Locate the DLC Connector (bottom of I/P below the ashtray).

Important:

- If your Tech 1 has a serial number ending in 000001 to 002000, you must attach the E & C Bus Adapter to the end of the Tech 1 cable. A Tech 1 with a serial number ending in 002001 or larger does not require the adapter. (These units have a backlight display.)

5. Insert the 12-pin plug on the Tech 1 cable or adapter (refer to NOTICE) into the DLC Connector.
6. Turn Ignition to "RUN," turn Radio "ON."
7. Select E & C tests under the body option.
8. Select the Components Identification Test F1.
9. If after three seconds the Tech 1 has not received a response from either the Radio Control Head (and Cassette or Compact Disc) or the Radio Receiver or Tech 1 is unable to transmit a message on the Bus, one of the error messages seen on this page will appear.
10. Verify that Tech 1 is properly connected.

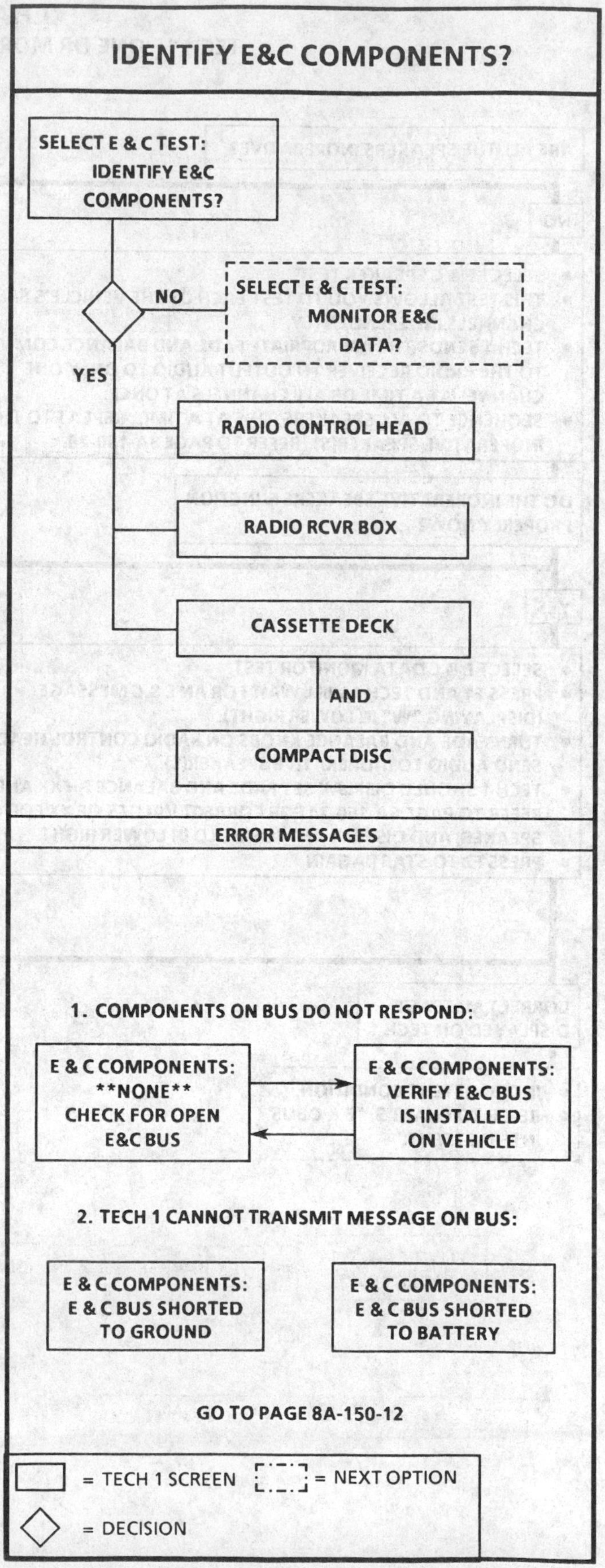
IDENTIFY E&C COMPONENTS?
SELECT E & C TEST: IDENTIFY E&C COMPONENTS?
NO
SELECT E & C TEST: MONITOR E&C DATA?
YES
RADIO CONTROL HEAD
RADIO RCVR BOX
CASSETTE DECK
AND
COMPACT DISC
ERROR MESSAGES
1. COMPONENTS ON BUS DO NOT RESPOND:
E & C COMPONENTS: **NONE** CHECK FOR OPEN E&C BUS
E & C COMPONENTS: VERIFY E&C BUS IS INSTALLED ON VEHICLE
2. TECH 1 CANNOT TRANSMIT MESSAGE ON BUS:
E & C COMPONENTS: E & C BUS SHORTED TO GROUND
E & C COMPONENTS: E & C BUS SHORTED TO BATTERY
GO TO PAGE 8A-150-12
= TECH 1 SCREEN
= NEXT OPTION
= DECISION

TECH 1: E&C CARTRIDGE OVERVIEW

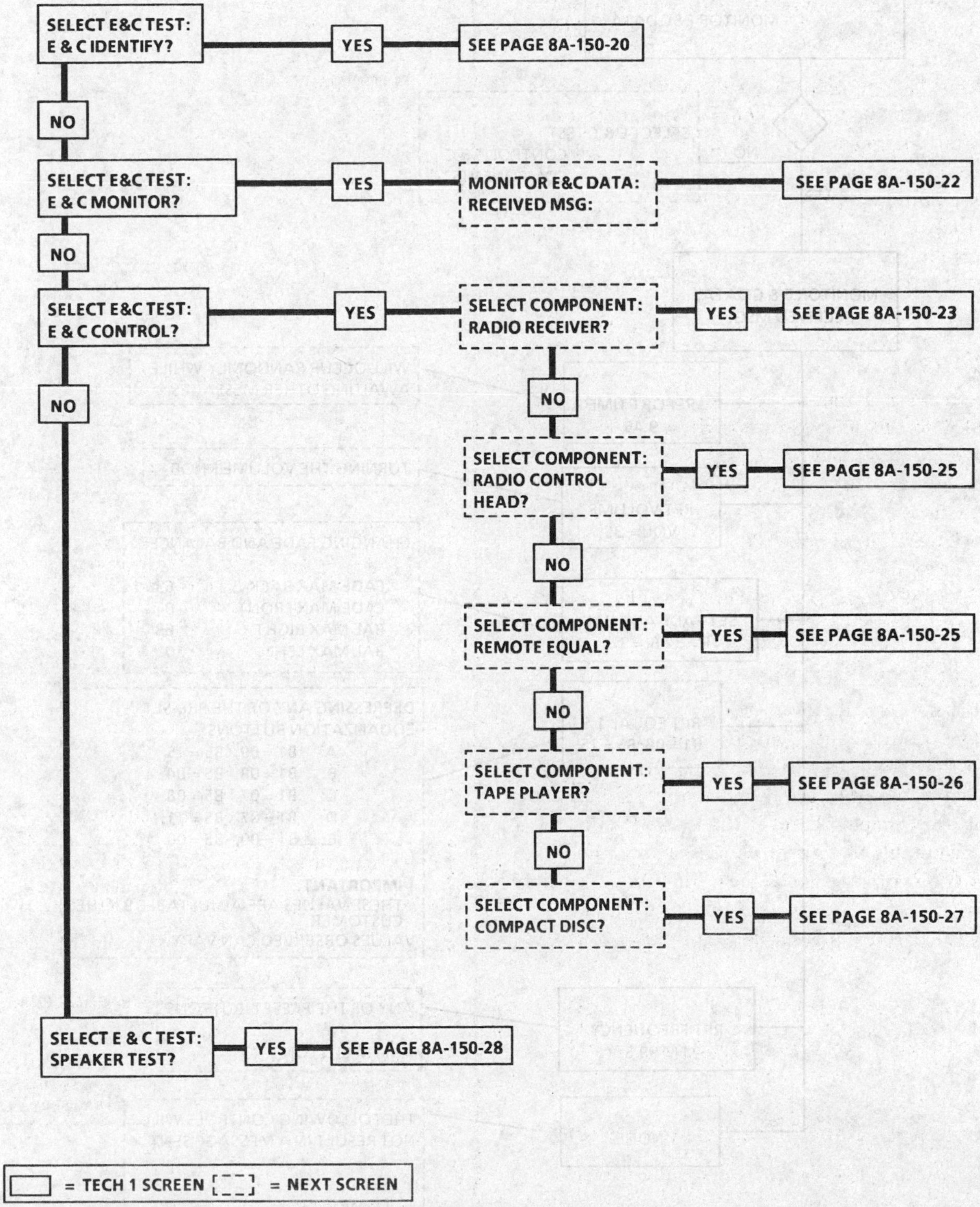
SELECT E&C TEST:
E & C IDENTIFY?
YES
SEE PAGE 8A-150-20
NO
SELECT E&C TEST:
E & C MONITOR?
YES
MONITOR E&C DATA:
RECEIVED MSG:
SEE PAGE 8A-150-22
NO
SELECT E&C TEST:
E & C CONTROL?
YES
SELECT COMPONENT:
RADIO RECEIVER?
YES
SEE PAGE 8A-150-23
NO
NO
SELECT COMPONENT:
RADIO CONTROL
HEAD?
YES
SEE PAGE 8A-150-25
NO
SELECT COMPONENT:
REMOTE EQUAL?
YES
SEE PAGE 8A-150-25
NO
SELECT COMPONENT:
TAPE PLAYER?
YES
SEE PAGE 8A-150-26
NO
SELECT COMPONENT:
COMPACT DISC?
YES
SEE PAGE 8A-150-27
SELECT E & C TEST:
SPEAKER TEST?
YES
SEE PAGE 8A-150-28
= TECH 1 SCREEN
= NEXT SCREEN

RADIO

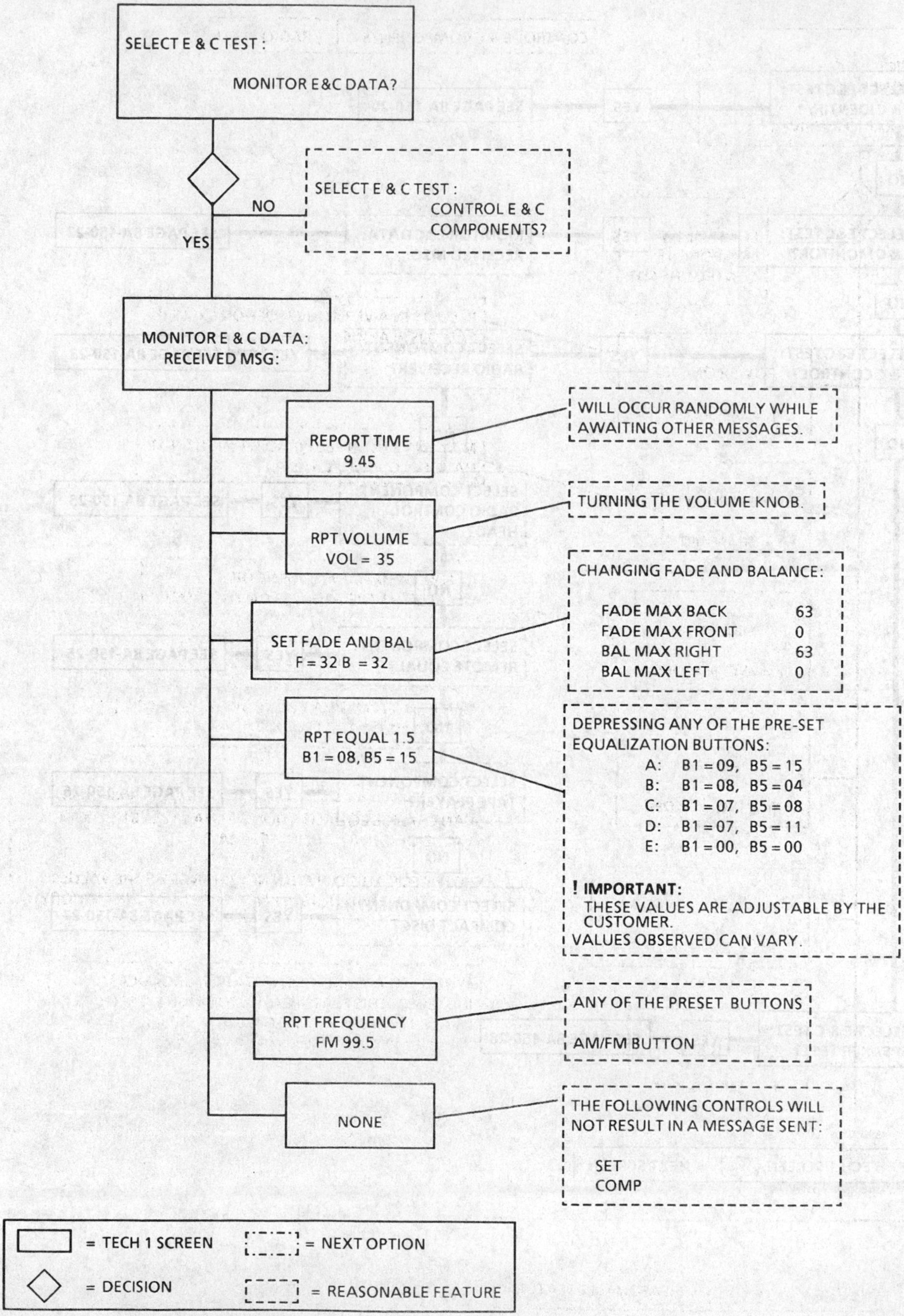
SELECT E & C TEST :
MONITOR E&C DATA?
NO
YES
SELECT E & C TEST :
CONTROL E & C COMPONENTS?
MONITOR E & C DATA:
RECEIVED MSG:
REPORT TIME
9.45
WILL OCCUR RANDOMLY WHILE AWAITING OTHER MESSAGES.
RPT VOLUME
VOL = 35
TURNING THE VOLUME KNOB.
SET FADE AND BAL
F = 32 B = 32
CHANGING FADE AND BALANCE:
FADE MAX BACK 63
FADE MAX FRONT 0
BAL MAX RIGHT 63
BAL MAX LEFT 0
RPT EQUAL 1.5
B1 = 08, B5 = 15
DEPRESSING ANY OF THE PRE-SET EQUALIZATION BUTTONS:
A: B1 = 09, B5 = 15
B: B1 = 08, B5 = 04
C: B1 = 07, B5 = 08
D: B1 = 07, B5 = 11
E: B1 = 00, B5 = 00
! IMPORTANT:
THESE VALUES ARE ADJUSTABLE BY THE CUSTOMER.
VALUES OBSERVED CAN VARY.
RPT FREQUENCY
FM 99.5
ANY OF THE PRESET BUTTONS
AM/FM BUTTON
NONE
THE FOLLOWING CONTROLS WILL NOT RESULT IN A MESSAGE SENT:
SET
COMP
= TECH 1 SCREEN
= NEXT OPTION
= DECISION
= REASONABLE FEATURE

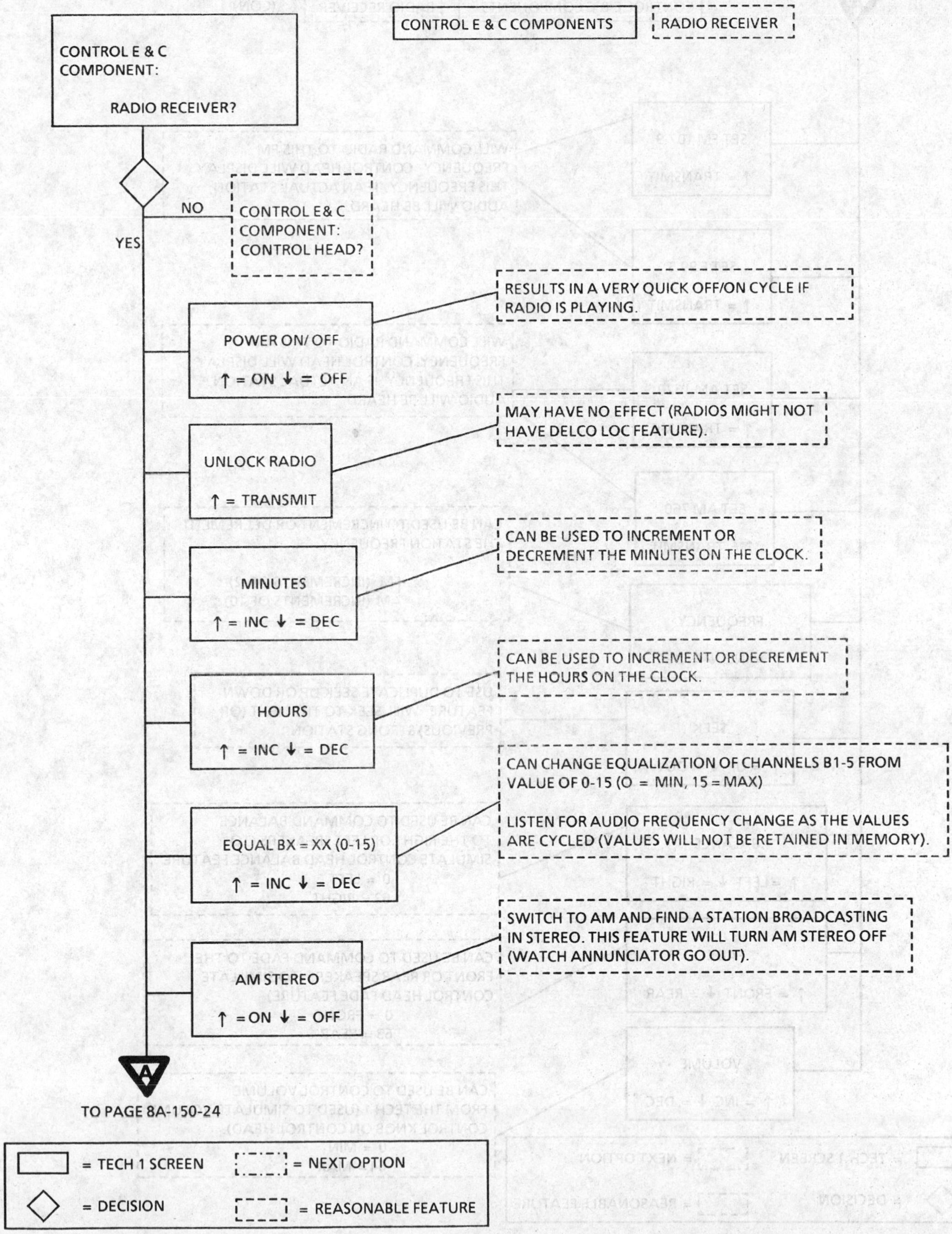
CONTROL E & C COMPONENTS
RADIO RECEIVER
CONTROL E & C COMPONENT: RADIO RECEIVER?
NO
CONTROL E& C COMPONENT: CONTROL HEAD?
YES
POWER ON/ OFF
↑ = ON ↓ = OFF
RESULTS IN A VERY QUICK OFF/ON CYCLE IF RADIO IS PLAYING.
UNLOCK RADIO
↑ = TRANSMIT
MAY HAVE NO EFFECT (RADIOS MIGHT NOT HAVE DELCO LOC FEATURE).
MINUTES
↑ = INC ↓ = DEC
CAN BE USED TO INCREMENT OR DECREMENT THE MINUTES ON THE CLOCK.
HOURS
↑ = INC ↓ = DEC
CAN BE USED TO INCREMENT OR DECREMENT THE HOURS ON THE CLOCK.
EQUAL BX = XX (0-15)
↑ = INC ↓ = DEC
CAN CHANGE EQUALIZATION OF CHANNELS B1-5 FROM VALUE OF 0-15 (O = MIN, 15 = MAX)
LISTEN FOR AUDIO FREQUENCY CHANGE AS THE VALUES ARE CYCLED (VALUES WILL NOT BE RETAINED IN MEMORY).
AM STEREO
↑ = ON ↓ = OFF
SWITCH TO AM AND FIND A STATION BROADCASTING IN STEREO. THIS FEATURE WILL TURN AM STEREO OFF (WATCH ANNUNCIATOR GO OUT).
A
TO PAGE 8A-150-24
= TECH 1 SCREEN
= NEXT OPTION
= DECISION
= REASONABLE FEATURE

RADIO

FROM PAGE 8A-150-23

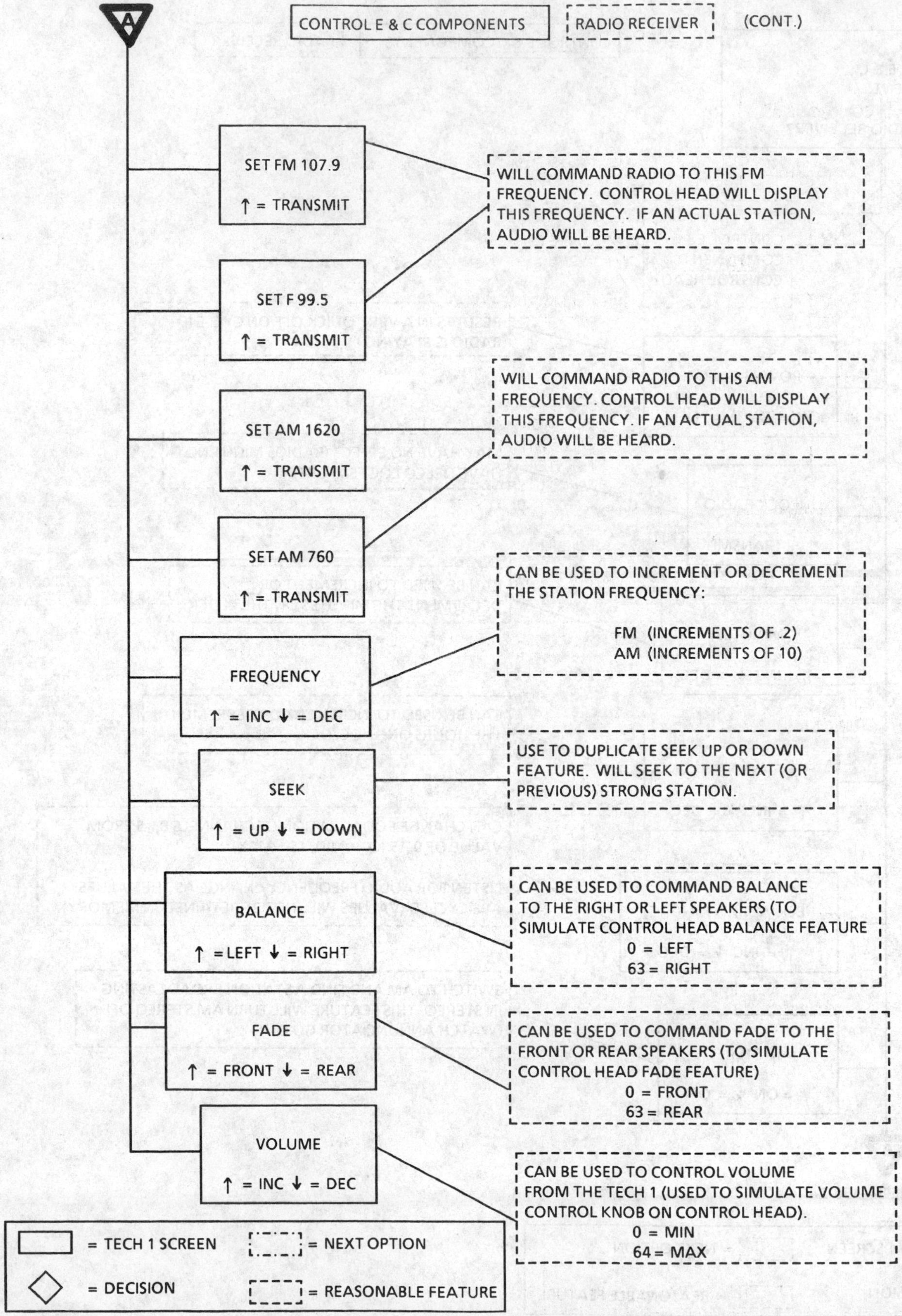
A
CONTROL E & C COMPONENTS
RADIO RECEIVER
(CONT.)
SET FM 107.9
↑ = TRANSMIT
SET F 99.5
↑ = TRANSMIT
WILL COMMAND RADIO TO THIS FM FREQUENCY. CONTROL HEAD WILL DISPLAY THIS FREQUENCY. IF AN ACTUAL STATION, AUDIO WILL BE HEARD.
SET AM 1620
↑ = TRANSMIT
SET AM 760
↑ = TRANSMIT
WILL COMMAND RADIO TO THIS AM FREQUENCY. CONTROL HEAD WILL DISPLAY THIS FREQUENCY. IF AN ACTUAL STATION, AUDIO WILL BE HEARD.
FREQUENCY
↑ = INC ↓ = DEC
CAN BE USED TO INCREMENT OR DECREMENT THE STATION FREQUENCY:
FM (INCREMENTS OF .2)
AM (INCREMENTS OF 10)
SEEK
↑ = UP ↓ = DOWN
USE TO DUPLICATE SEEK UP OR DOWN FEATURE. WILL SEEK TO THE NEXT (OR PREVIOUS) STRONG STATION.
BALANCE
↑ = LEFT ↓ = RIGHT
CAN BE USED TO COMMAND BALANCE TO THE RIGHT OR LEFT SPEAKERS (TO SIMULATE CONTROL HEAD BALANCE FEATURE
0 = LEFT
63 = RIGHT
FADE
↑ = FRONT ↓ = REAR
CAN BE USED TO COMMAND FADE TO THE FRONT OR REAR SPEAKERS (TO SIMULATE CONTROL HEAD FADE FEATURE)
0 = FRONT
63 = REAR
VOLUME
↑ = INC ↓ = DEC
CAN BE USED TO CONTROL VOLUME FROM THE TECH 1 (USED TO SIMULATE VOLUME CONTROL KNOB ON CONTROL HEAD).
0 = MIN
64 = MAX
= TECH 1 SCREEN
= NEXT OPTION
= DECISION
= REASONABLE FEATURE

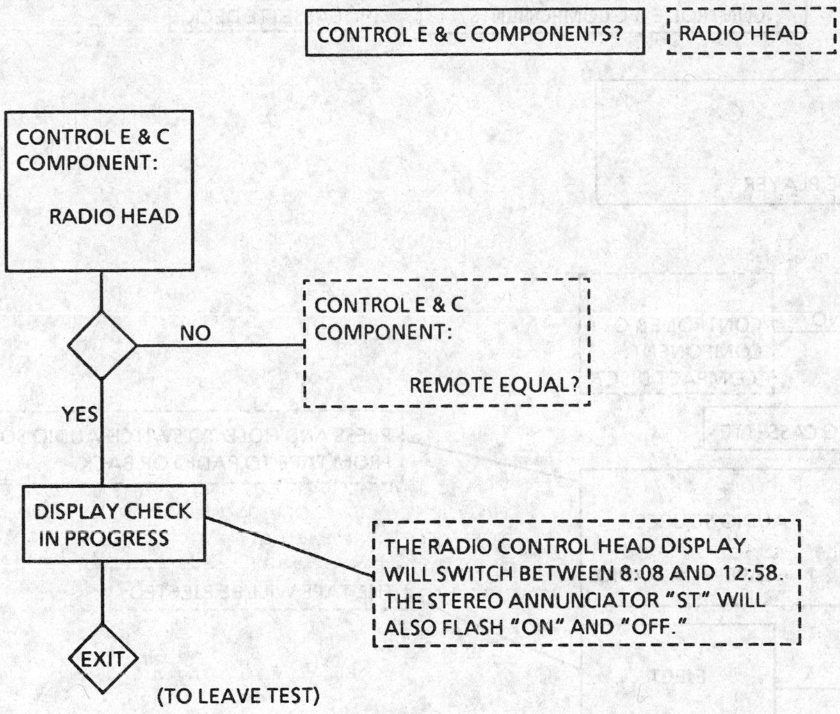
CONTROL E & C COMPONENTS?
RADIO HEAD
CONTROL E & C COMPONENT:
RADIO HEAD
NO
CONTROL E & C COMPONENT:
REMOTE EQUAL?
YES
DISPLAY CHECK IN PROGRESS
THE RADIO CONTROL HEAD DISPLAY WILL SWITCH BETWEEN 8:08 AND 12:58. THE STEREO ANNUNCIATOR "ST" WILL ALSO FLASH "ON" AND "OFF."
EXIT
(TO LEAVE TEST)

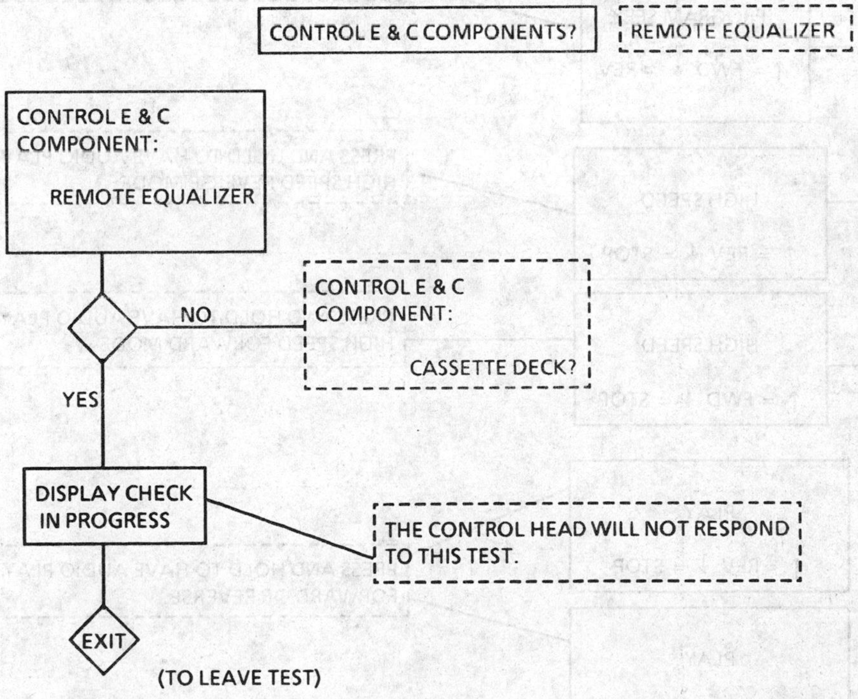
CONTROL E & C COMPONENTS?
REMOTE EQUALIZER
CONTROL E & C COMPONENT:
REMOTE EQUALIZER
NO
CONTROL E & C COMPONENT:
CASSETTE DECK?
YES
DISPLAY CHECK IN PROGRESS
THE CONTROL HEAD WILL NOT RESPOND TO THIS TEST.
EXIT
(TO LEAVE TEST)

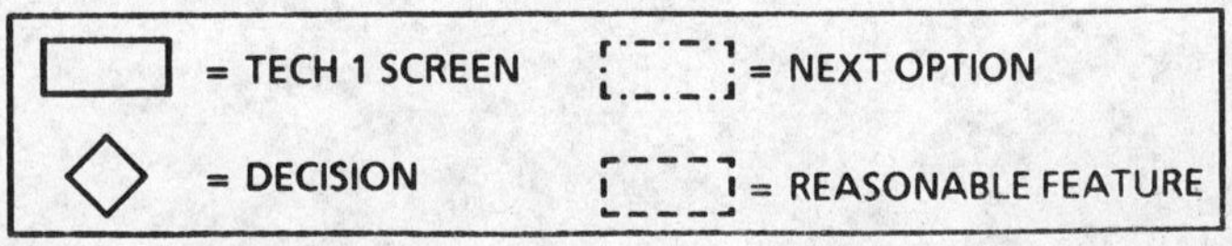
= TECH 1 SCREEN
= NEXT OPTION
= DECISION
= REASONABLE FEATURE

RADIO

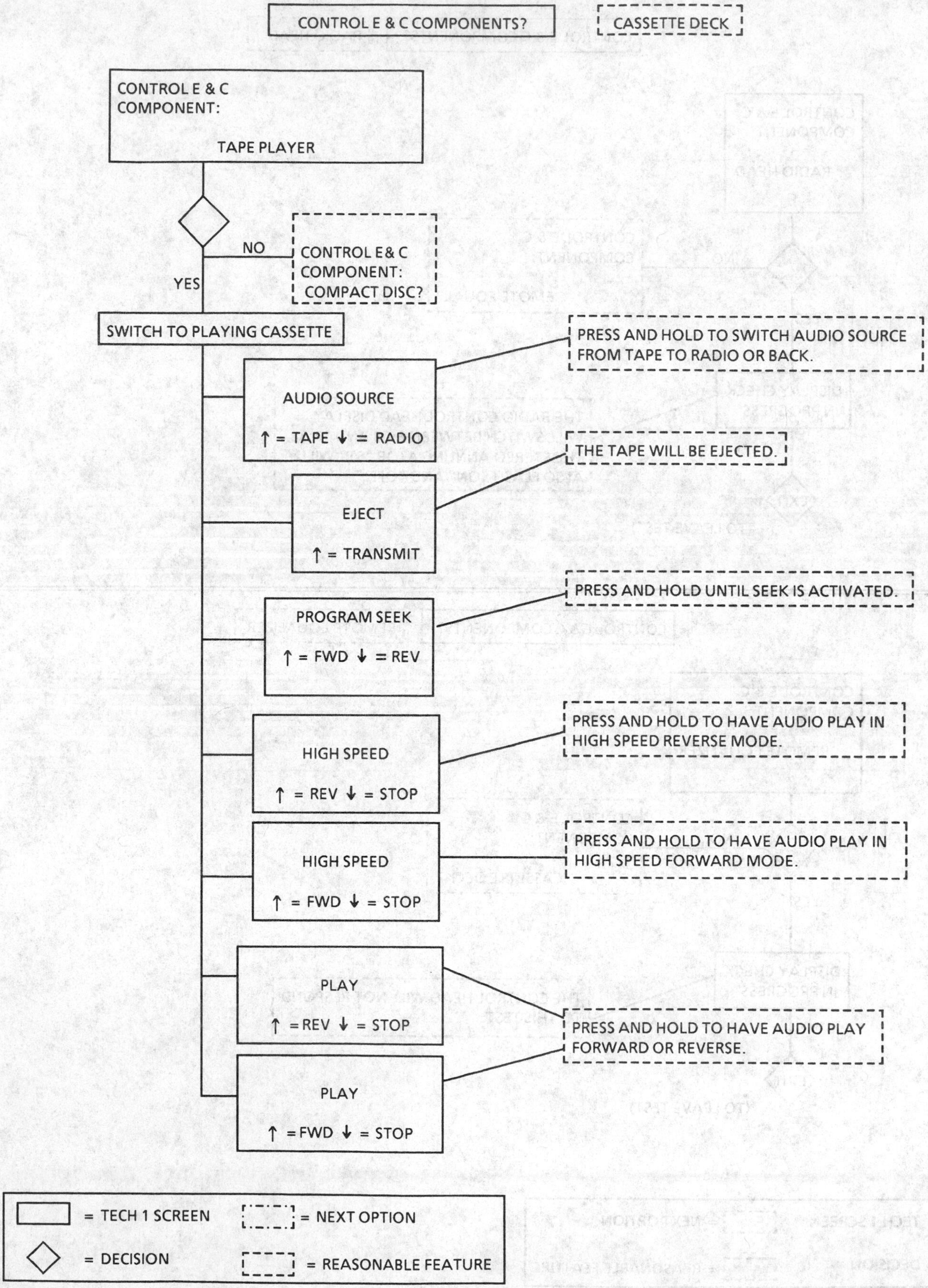

CONTROL E & C COMPONENTS?
CASSETTE DECK
CONTROL E & C COMPONENT:
TAPE PLAYER
NO
YES
CONTROL E& C COMPONENT: COMPACT DISC?
SWITCH TO PLAYING CASSETTE
AUDIO SOURCE
↑ = TAPE ↓ = RADIO
PRESS AND HOLD TO SWITCH AUDIO SOURCE FROM TAPE TO RADIO OR BACK.
EJECT
↑ = TRANSMIT
THE TAPE WILL BE EJECTED.
PROGRAM SEEK
↑ = FWD ↓ = REV
PRESS AND HOLD UNTIL SEEK IS ACTIVATED.
HIGH SPEED
↑ = REV ↓ = STOP
PRESS AND HOLD TO HAVE AUDIO PLAY IN HIGH SPEED REVERSE MODE.
HIGH SPEED
↑ = FWD ↓ = STOP
PRESS AND HOLD TO HAVE AUDIO PLAY IN HIGH SPEED FORWARD MODE.
PLAY
↑ = REV ↓ = STOP
PLAY
↑ = FWD ↓ = STOP
PRESS AND HOLD TO HAVE AUDIO PLAY FORWARD OR REVERSE.
= TECH 1 SCREEN
= NEXT OPTION
= DECISION
= REASONABLE FEATURE

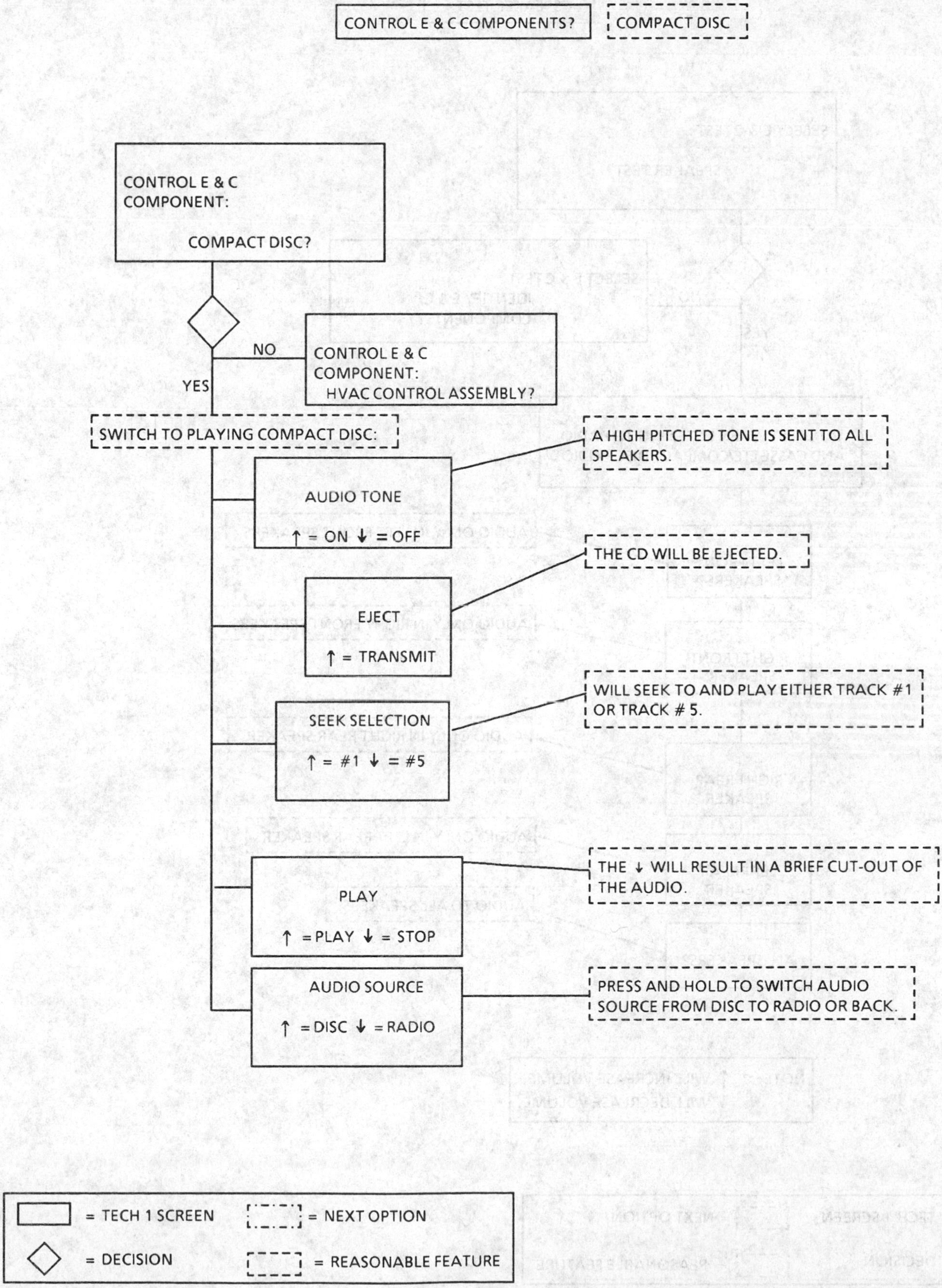
CONTROL E & C COMPONENTS?
COMPACT DISC
CONTROL E & C COMPONENT: COMPACT DISC?
NO
YES
CONTROL E & C COMPONENT: HVAC CONTROL ASSEMBLY?
SWITCH TO PLAYING COMPACT DISC:
AUDIO TONE
↑ = ON ↓ = OFF
A HIGH PITCHED TONE IS SENT TO ALL SPEAKERS.
EJECT
↑ = TRANSMIT
THE CD WILL BE EJECTED.
SEEK SELECTION
↑ = #1 ↓ = #5
WILL SEEK TO AND PLAY EITHER TRACK #1 OR TRACK # 5.
PLAY
↑ = PLAY ↓ = STOP
THE ↓ WILL RESULT IN A BRIEF CUT-OUT OF THE AUDIO.
AUDIO SOURCE
↑ = DISC ↓ = RADIO
PRESS AND HOLD TO SWITCH AUDIO SOURCE FROM DISC TO RADIO OR BACK.
= TECH 1 SCREEN
= NEXT OPTION
= DECISION
= REASONABLE FEATURE

RADIO

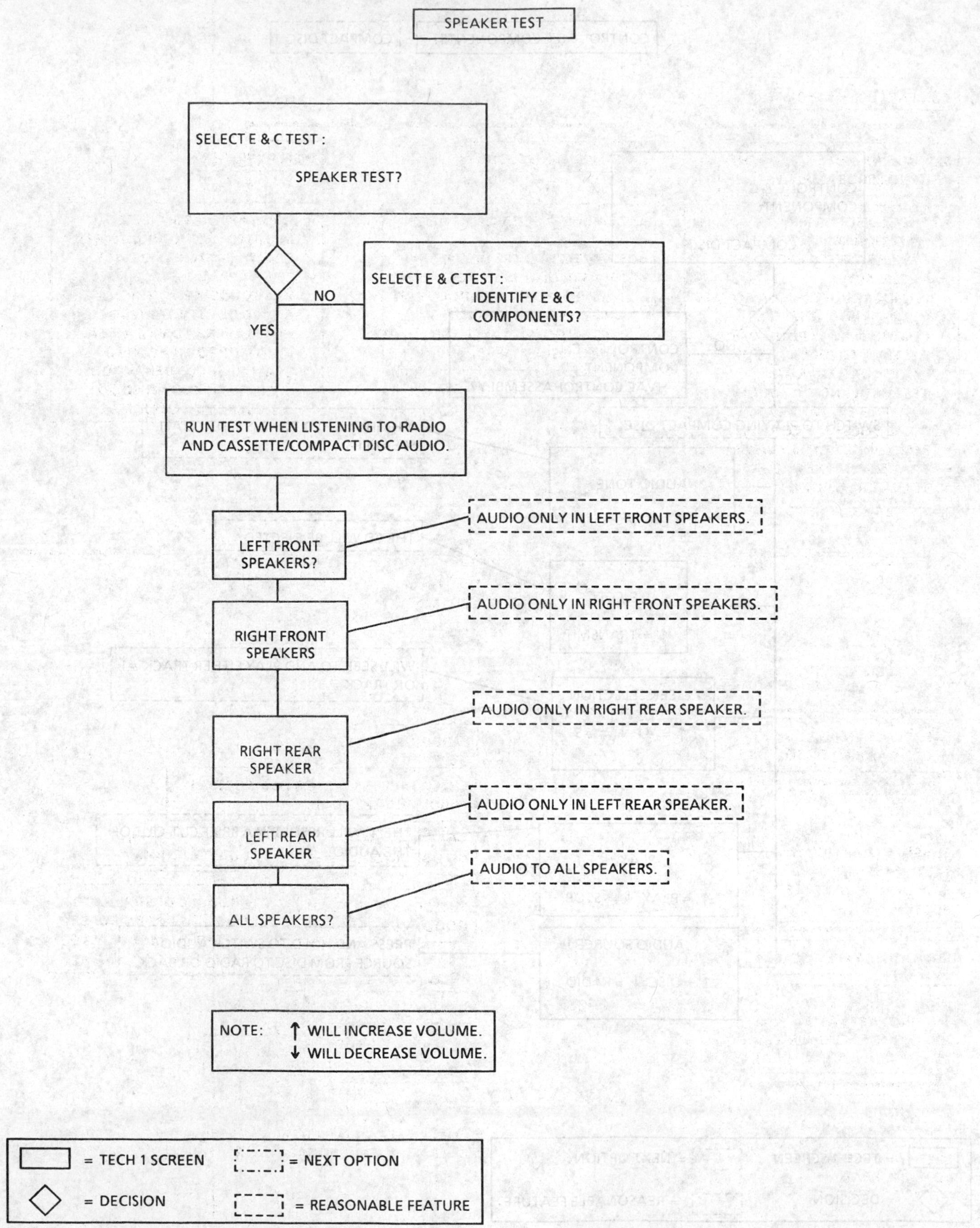
SPEAKER TEST
SELECT E & C TEST :
SPEAKER TEST?
NO
SELECT E & C TEST :
IDENTIFY E & C
COMPONENTS?
YES
RUN TEST WHEN LISTENING TO RADIO
AND CASSETTE/COMPACT DISC AUDIO.
LEFT FRONT
SPEAKERS?
AUDIO ONLY IN LEFT FRONT SPEAKERS.
RIGHT FRONT
SPEAKERS
AUDIO ONLY IN RIGHT FRONT SPEAKERS.
RIGHT REAR
SPEAKER
AUDIO ONLY IN RIGHT REAR SPEAKER.
LEFT REAR
SPEAKER
AUDIO ONLY IN LEFT REAR SPEAKER.
ALL SPEAKERS?
AUDIO TO ALL SPEAKERS.
NOTE: ↑ WILL INCREASE VOLUME.
↓ WILL DECREASE VOLUME.
= TECH 1 SCREEN
= NEXT OPTION
= DECISION
= REASONABLE FEATURE

CHART #11
COMPACT DISC PROBLEMS

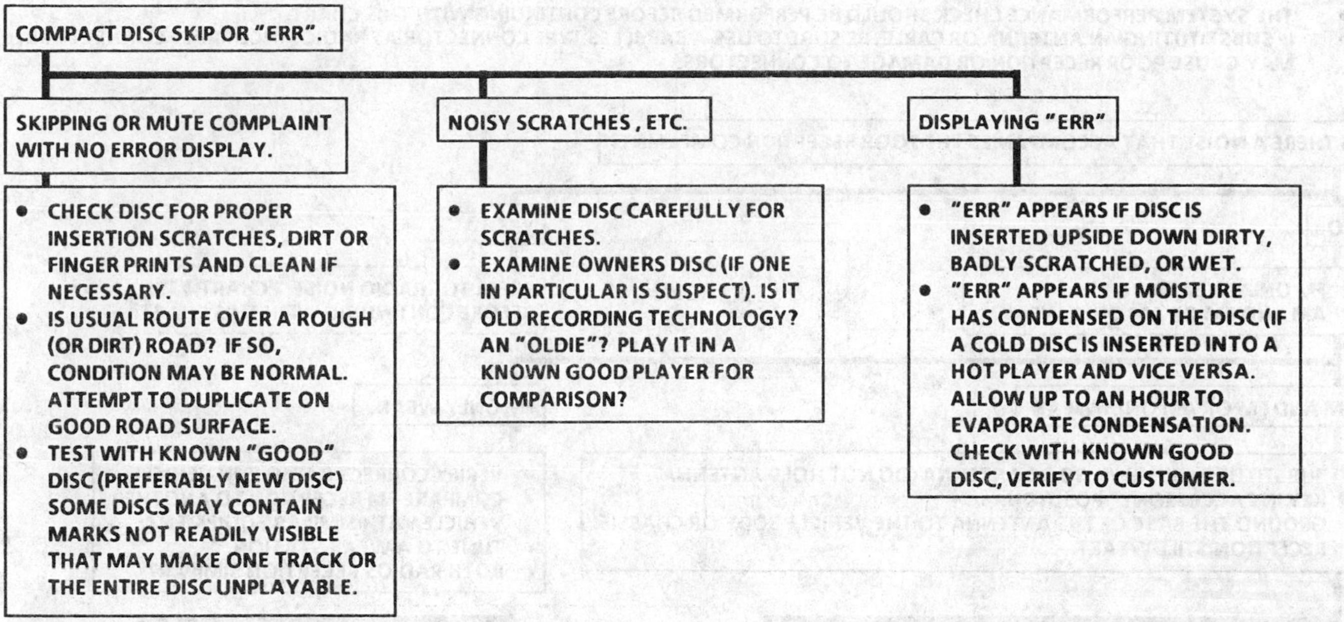
COMPACT DISC SKIP OR "ERR".
SKIPPING OR MUTE COMPLAINT WITH NO ERROR DISPLAY.
NOISY SCRATCHES , ETC.
DISPLAYING "ERR"
• CHECK DISC FOR PROPER INSERTION SCRATCHES, DIRT OR FINGER PRINTS AND CLEAN IF NECESSARY.
• IS USUAL ROUTE OVER A ROUGH (OR DIRT) ROAD? IF SO, CONDITION MAY BE NORMAL. ATTEMPT TO DUPLICATE ON GOOD ROAD SURFACE.
• TEST WITH KNOWN "GOOD" DISC (PREFERABLY NEW DISC) SOME DISCS MAY CONTAIN MARKS NOT READILY VISIBLE THAT MAY MAKE ONE TRACK OR THE ENTIRE DISC UNPLAYABLE.
• EXAMINE DISC CAREFULLY FOR SCRATCHES.
• EXAMINE OWNERS DISC (IF ONE IN PARTICULAR IS SUSPECT). IS IT OLD RECORDING TECHNOLOGY? AN "OLDIE"? PLAY IT IN A KNOWN GOOD PLAYER FOR COMPARISON?
• "ERR" APPEARS IF DISC IS INSERTED UPSIDE DOWN DIRTY, BADLY SCRATCHED, OR WET.
• "ERR" APPEARS IF MOISTURE HAS CONDENSED ON THE DISC (IF A COLD DISC IS INSERTED INTO A HOT PLAYER AND VICE VERSA. ALLOW UP TO AN HOUR TO EVAPORATE CONDENSATION. CHECK WITH KNOWN GOOD DISC, VERIFY TO CUSTOMER.

CHART #12
TAPE PROBLEMS

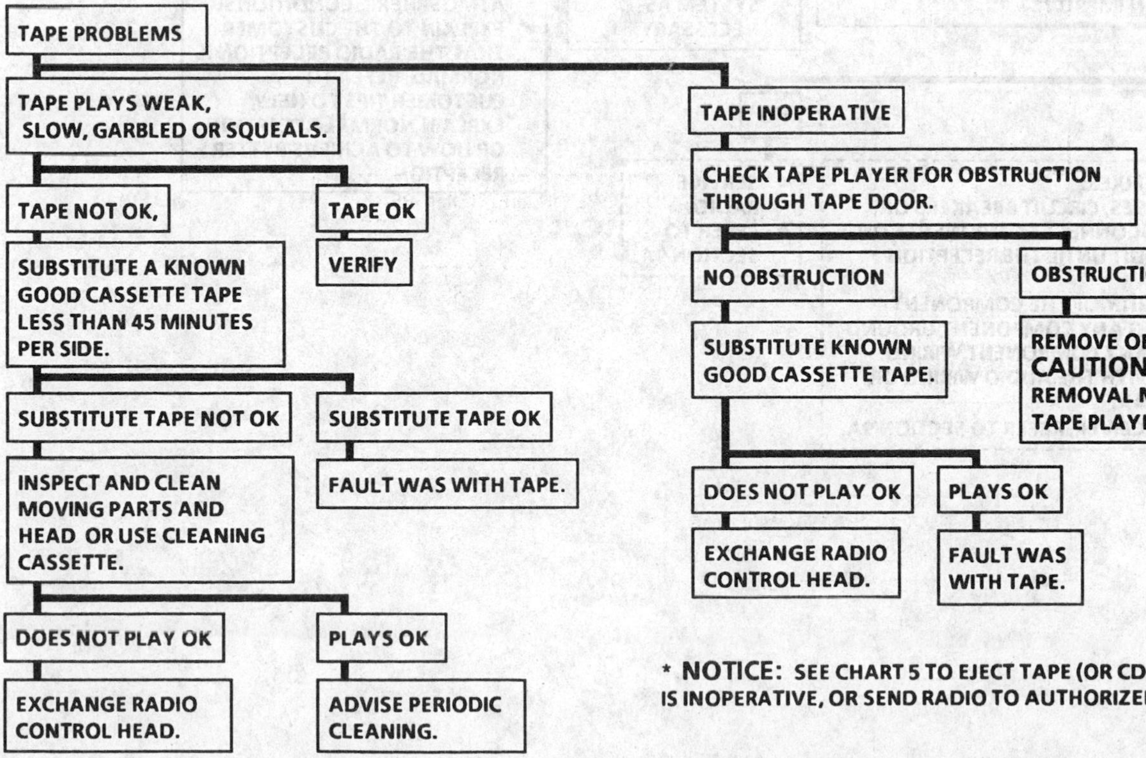
TAPE PROBLEMS
TAPE PLAYS WEAK, SLOW, GARBLED OR SQUEALS.
TAPE NOT OK,
TAPE OK
VERIFY
SUBSTITUTE A KNOWN GOOD CASSETTE TAPE LESS THAN 45 MINUTES PER SIDE.
SUBSTITUTE TAPE NOT OK
SUBSTITUTE TAPE OK
FAULT WAS WITH TAPE.
INSPECT AND CLEAN MOVING PARTS AND HEAD OR USE CLEANING CASSETTE.
DOES NOT PLAY OK
PLAYS OK
EXCHANGE RADIO CONTROL HEAD.
ADVISE PERIODIC CLEANING.
TAPE INOPERATIVE
CHECK TAPE PLAYER FOR OBSTRUCTION THROUGH TAPE DOOR.
NO OBSTRUCTION
OBSTRUCTION
SUBSTITUTE KNOWN GOOD CASSETTE TAPE.
REMOVE OBSTRUCTION CAUTION: IMPROPER REMOVAL MAY DAMAGE TAPE PLAYER. *
DOES NOT PLAY OK
PLAYS OK
EXCHANGE RADIO CONTROL HEAD.
FAULT WAS WITH TAPE.

* **NOTICE:** SEE CHART 5 TO EJECT TAPE (OR CD) IF EJECT BUTTON IS INOPERATIVE, OR SEND RADIO TO AUTHORIZED AC-DELCO SHOP.

RADIO

CHART #13
POOR RECEPTION

IMPORTANT:

- THE SYSTEM PERFORMANCE CHECK SHOULD BE PERFORMED BEFORE CONTINUING WITH THIS CHART.
- IF SUBSTITUTING AN ANTENNA OR CABLE, BE SURE TO USE A BARBLESS TYPE CONNECTOR AT RADIO. INCORRECT CONNECTORS MAY CAUSE POOR RECEPTION OR DAMAGE TO CONNECTORS.

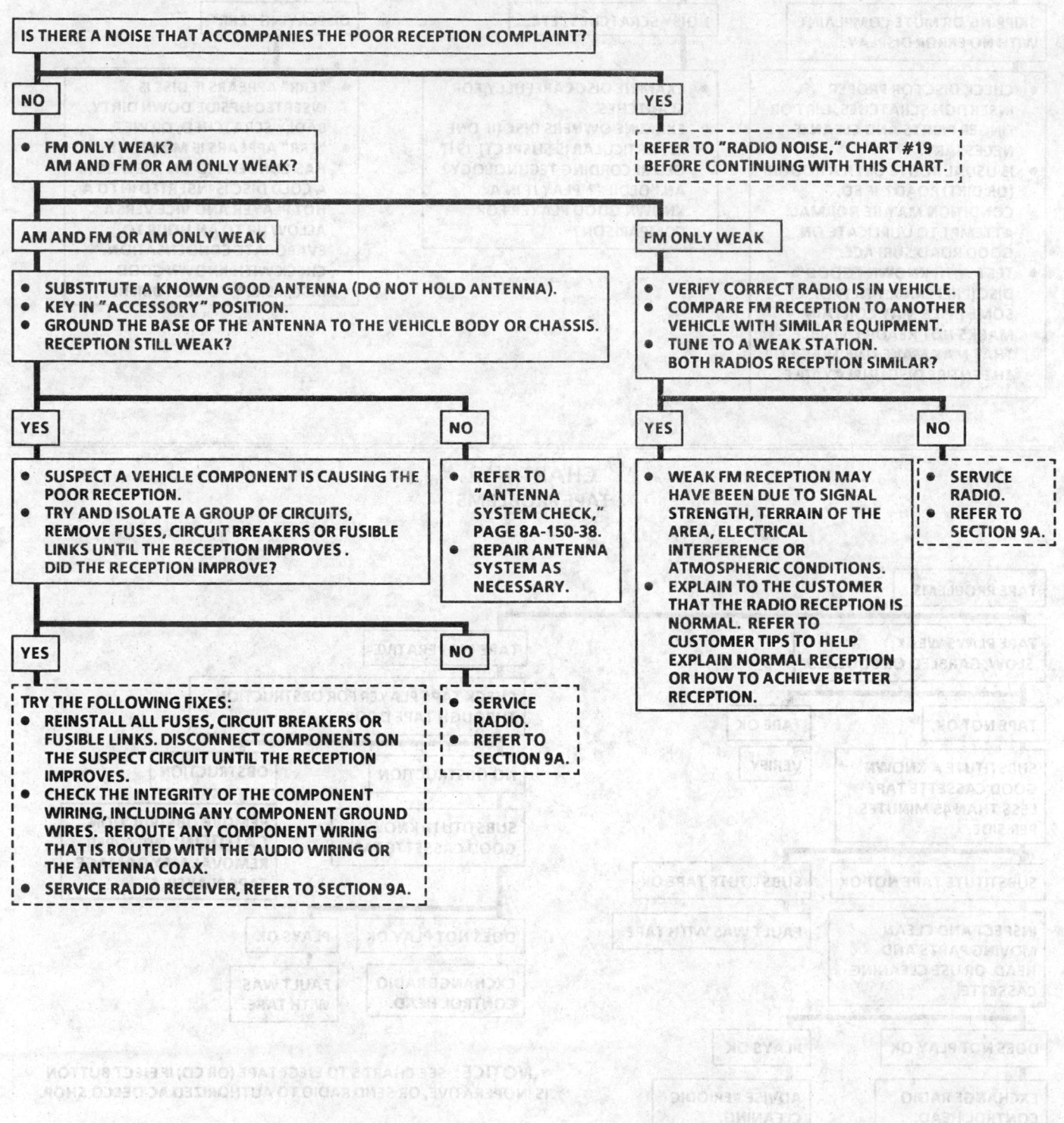

IS THERE A NOISE THAT ACCOMPANIES THE POOR RECEPTION COMPLAINT?

YES

REFER TO "RADIO NOISE," CHART #19 BEFORE CONTINUING WITH THIS CHART.

NO

- FM ONLY WEAK?
  AM AND FM OR AM ONLY WEAK?

AM AND FM OR AM ONLY WEAK

- SUBSTITUTE A KNOWN GOOD ANTENNA (DO NOT HOLD ANTENNA).
- KEY IN "ACCESSORY" POSITION.
- GROUND THE BASE OF THE ANTENNA TO THE VEHICLE BODY OR CHASSIS.
  RECEPTION STILL WEAK?

YES

- SUSPECT A VEHICLE COMPONENT IS CAUSING THE POOR RECEPTION.
- TRY AND ISOLATE A GROUP OF CIRCUITS, REMOVE FUSES, CIRCUIT BREAKERS OR FUSIBLE LINKS UNTIL THE RECEPTION IMPROVES.
  DID THE RECEPTION IMPROVE?

YES

TRY THE FOLLOWING FIXES:
- REINSTALL ALL FUSES, CIRCUIT BREAKERS OR FUSIBLE LINKS. DISCONNECT COMPONENTS ON THE SUSPECT CIRCUIT UNTIL THE RECEPTION IMPROVES.
- CHECK THE INTEGRITY OF THE COMPONENT WIRING, INCLUDING ANY COMPONENT GROUND WIRES. REROUTE ANY COMPONENT WIRING THAT IS ROUTED WITH THE AUDIO WIRING OR THE ANTENNA COAX.
- SERVICE RADIO RECEIVER, REFER TO SECTION 9A.

NO

- SERVICE RADIO.
- REFER TO SECTION 9A.

NO (reception not still weak)

- REFER TO "ANTENNA SYSTEM CHECK," PAGE 8A-150-38.
- REPAIR ANTENNA SYSTEM AS NECESSARY.

FM ONLY WEAK

- VERIFY CORRECT RADIO IS IN VEHICLE.
- COMPARE FM RECEPTION TO ANOTHER VEHICLE WITH SIMILAR EQUIPMENT.
- TUNE TO A WEAK STATION.
  BOTH RADIOS RECEPTION SIMILAR?

YES

- WEAK FM RECEPTION MAY HAVE BEEN DUE TO SIGNAL STRENGTH, TERRAIN OF THE AREA, ELECTRICAL INTERFERENCE OR ATMOSPHERIC CONDITIONS.
- EXPLAIN TO THE CUSTOMER THAT THE RADIO RECEPTION IS NORMAL. REFER TO CUSTOMER TIPS TO HELP EXPLAIN NORMAL RECEPTION OR HOW TO ACHIEVE BETTER RECEPTION.

NO

- SERVICE RADIO.
- REFER TO SECTION 9A.

CHART #14
RADIO NOISE ENTERING THROUGH RADIO (SIDEWAYS NOISE)

IMPORTANT:
- ONLY PERFORM THIS CHART IF SENT HERE FROM CHART #19, " RADIO NOISE."

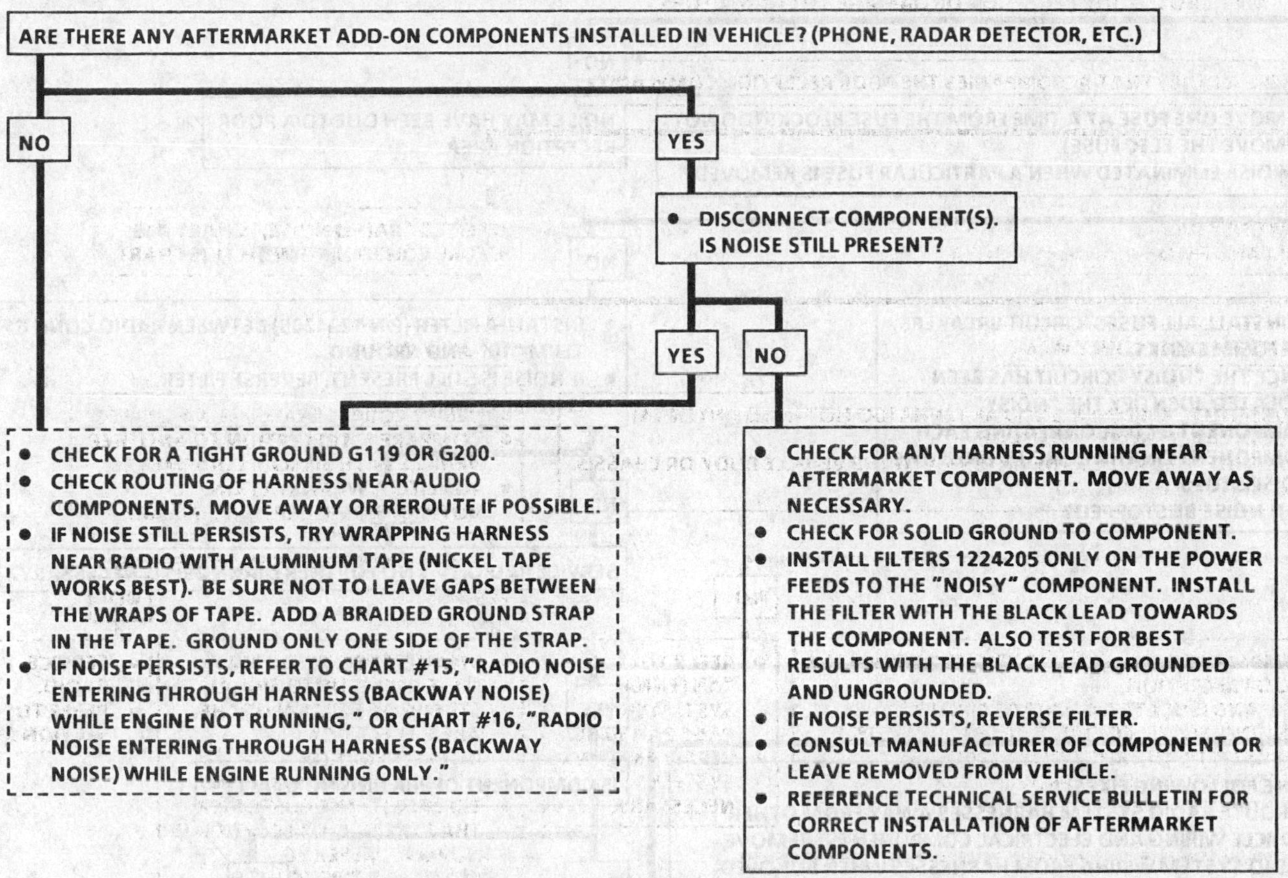
ARE THERE ANY AFTERMARKET ADD-ON COMPONENTS INSTALLED IN VEHICLE? (PHONE, RADAR DETECTOR, ETC.)
NO
YES
• DISCONNECT COMPONENT(S). IS NOISE STILL PRESENT?
YES
NO
• CHECK FOR A TIGHT GROUND G119 OR G200.
• CHECK ROUTING OF HARNESS NEAR AUDIO COMPONENTS. MOVE AWAY OR REROUTE IF POSSIBLE.
• IF NOISE STILL PERSISTS, TRY WRAPPING HARNESS NEAR RADIO WITH ALUMINUM TAPE (NICKEL TAPE WORKS BEST). BE SURE NOT TO LEAVE GAPS BETWEEN THE WRAPS OF TAPE. ADD A BRAIDED GROUND STRAP IN THE TAPE. GROUND ONLY ONE SIDE OF THE STRAP.
• IF NOISE PERSISTS, REFER TO CHART #15, "RADIO NOISE ENTERING THROUGH HARNESS (BACKWAY NOISE) WHILE ENGINE NOT RUNNING," OR CHART #16, "RADIO NOISE ENTERING THROUGH HARNESS (BACKWAY NOISE) WHILE ENGINE RUNNING ONLY."
• CHECK FOR ANY HARNESS RUNNING NEAR AFTERMARKET COMPONENT. MOVE AWAY AS NECESSARY.
• CHECK FOR SOLID GROUND TO COMPONENT.
• INSTALL FILTERS 1224205 ONLY ON THE POWER FEEDS TO THE "NOISY" COMPONENT. INSTALL THE FILTER WITH THE BLACK LEAD TOWARDS THE COMPONENT. ALSO TEST FOR BEST RESULTS WITH THE BLACK LEAD GROUNDED AND UNGROUNDED.
• IF NOISE PERSISTS, REVERSE FILTER.
• CONSULT MANUFACTURER OF COMPONENT OR LEAVE REMOVED FROM VEHICLE.
• REFERENCE TECHNICAL SERVICE BULLETIN FOR CORRECT INSTALLATION OF AFTERMARKET COMPONENTS.

RADIO

CHART #15

RADIO NOISE ENTERING THROUGH HARNESS (BACKWAY NOISE) WHILE ENGINE NOT RUNNING

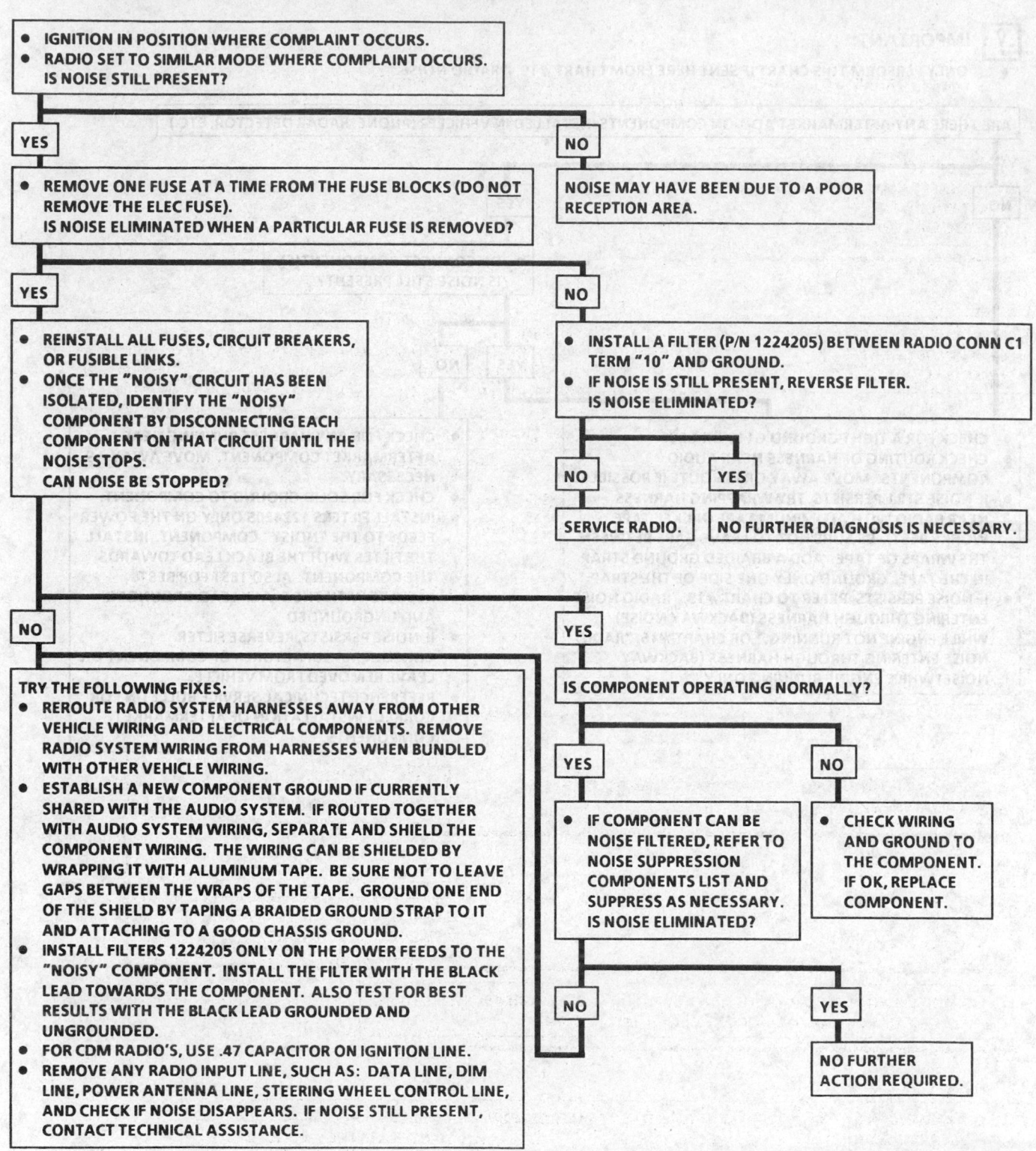

- IGNITION IN POSITION WHERE COMPLAINT OCCURS.
- RADIO SET TO SIMILAR MODE WHERE COMPLAINT OCCURS.
  IS NOISE STILL PRESENT?

YES

- REMOVE ONE FUSE AT A TIME FROM THE FUSE BLOCKS (DO NOT REMOVE THE ELEC FUSE).
  IS NOISE ELIMINATED WHEN A PARTICULAR FUSE IS REMOVED?

NO

NOISE MAY HAVE BEEN DUE TO A POOR RECEPTION AREA.

YES

- REINSTALL ALL FUSES, CIRCUIT BREAKERS, OR FUSIBLE LINKS.
- ONCE THE "NOISY" CIRCUIT HAS BEEN ISOLATED, IDENTIFY THE "NOISY" COMPONENT BY DISCONNECTING EACH COMPONENT ON THAT CIRCUIT UNTIL THE NOISE STOPS.
  CAN NOISE BE STOPPED?

NO

- INSTALL A FILTER (P/N 1224205) BETWEEN RADIO CONN C1 TERM "10" AND GROUND.
- IF NOISE IS STILL PRESENT, REVERSE FILTER.
  IS NOISE ELIMINATED?

NO

SERVICE RADIO.

YES

NO FURTHER DIAGNOSIS IS NECESSARY.

NO

TRY THE FOLLOWING FIXES:

- REROUTE RADIO SYSTEM HARNESSES AWAY FROM OTHER VEHICLE WIRING AND ELECTRICAL COMPONENTS. REMOVE RADIO SYSTEM WIRING FROM HARNESSES WHEN BUNDLED WITH OTHER VEHICLE WIRING.
- ESTABLISH A NEW COMPONENT GROUND IF CURRENTLY SHARED WITH THE AUDIO SYSTEM. IF ROUTED TOGETHER WITH AUDIO SYSTEM WIRING, SEPARATE AND SHIELD THE COMPONENT WIRING. THE WIRING CAN BE SHIELDED BY WRAPPING IT WITH ALUMINUM TAPE. BE SURE NOT TO LEAVE GAPS BETWEEN THE WRAPS OF THE TAPE. GROUND ONE END OF THE SHIELD BY TAPING A BRAIDED GROUND STRAP TO IT AND ATTACHING TO A GOOD CHASSIS GROUND.
- INSTALL FILTERS 1224205 ONLY ON THE POWER FEEDS TO THE "NOISY" COMPONENT. INSTALL THE FILTER WITH THE BLACK LEAD TOWARDS THE COMPONENT. ALSO TEST FOR BEST RESULTS WITH THE BLACK LEAD GROUNDED AND UNGROUNDED.
- FOR CDM RADIO'S, USE .47 CAPACITOR ON IGNITION LINE.
- REMOVE ANY RADIO INPUT LINE, SUCH AS: DATA LINE, DIM LINE, POWER ANTENNA LINE, STEERING WHEEL CONTROL LINE, AND CHECK IF NOISE DISAPPEARS. IF NOISE STILL PRESENT, CONTACT TECHNICAL ASSISTANCE.

YES

IS COMPONENT OPERATING NORMALLY?

YES

- IF COMPONENT CAN BE NOISE FILTERED, REFER TO NOISE SUPPRESSION COMPONENTS LIST AND SUPPRESS AS NECESSARY.
  IS NOISE ELIMINATED?

NO (go to TRY THE FOLLOWING FIXES)

YES

NO FURTHER ACTION REQUIRED.

NO

- CHECK WIRING AND GROUND TO THE COMPONENT. IF OK, REPLACE COMPONENT.

CHART #16

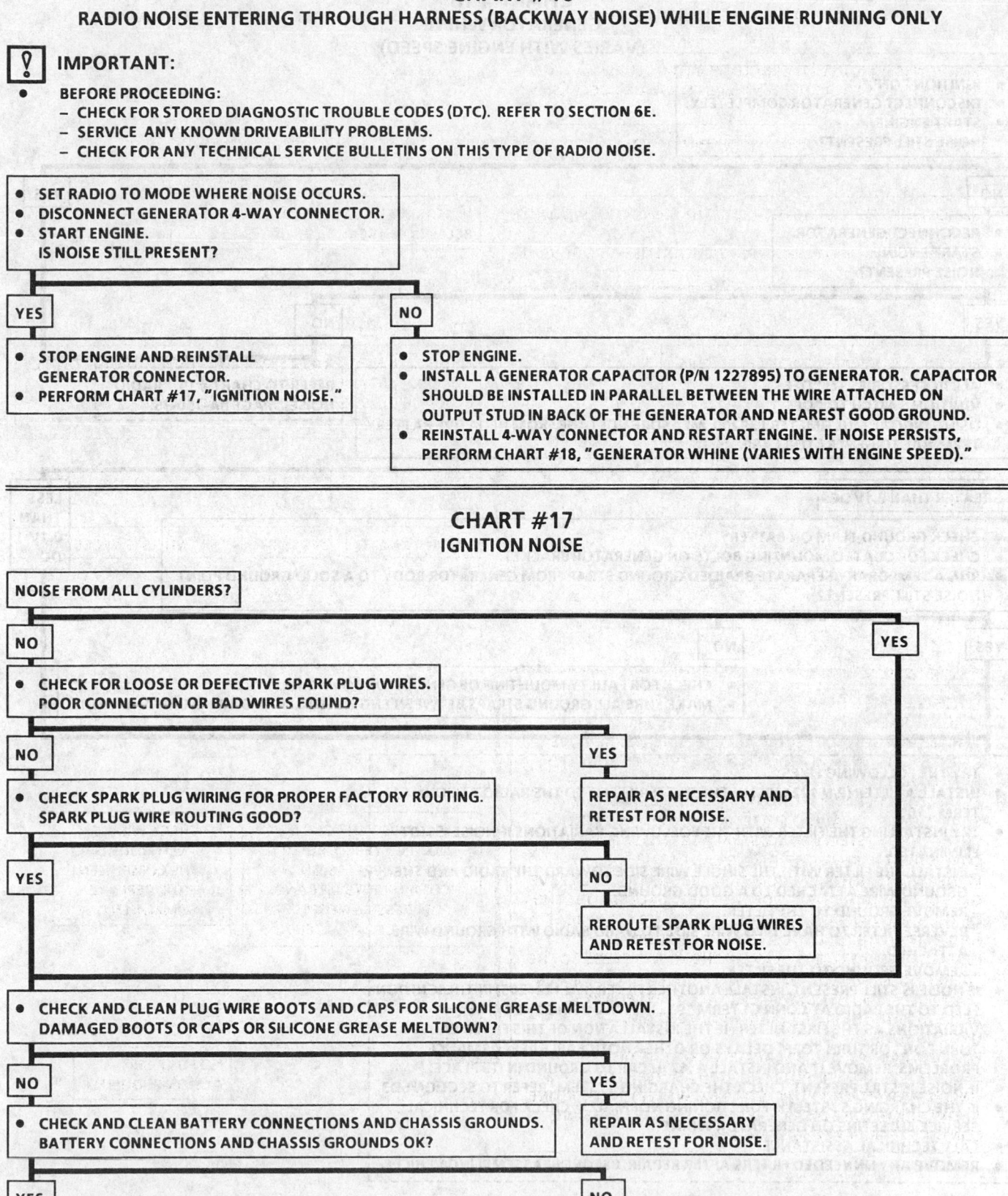

RADIO NOISE ENTERING THROUGH HARNESS (BACKWAY NOISE) WHILE ENGINE RUNNING ONLY

IMPORTANT:

- BEFORE PROCEEDING:
  - CHECK FOR STORED DIAGNOSTIC TROUBLE CODES (DTC). REFER TO SECTION 6E.
  - SERVICE ANY KNOWN DRIVEABILITY PROBLEMS.
  - CHECK FOR ANY TECHNICAL SERVICE BULLETINS ON THIS TYPE OF RADIO NOISE.

- SET RADIO TO MODE WHERE NOISE OCCURS.
- DISCONNECT GENERATOR 4-WAY CONNECTOR.
- START ENGINE.

IS NOISE STILL PRESENT?

YES

- STOP ENGINE AND REINSTALL GENERATOR CONNECTOR.
- PERFORM CHART #17, "IGNITION NOISE."

NO

- STOP ENGINE.
- INSTALL A GENERATOR CAPACITOR (P/N 1227895) TO GENERATOR. CAPACITOR SHOULD BE INSTALLED IN PARALLEL BETWEEN THE WIRE ATTACHED ON OUTPUT STUD IN BACK OF THE GENERATOR AND NEAREST GOOD GROUND.
- REINSTALL 4-WAY CONNECTOR AND RESTART ENGINE. IF NOISE PERSISTS, PERFORM CHART #18, "GENERATOR WHINE (VARIES WITH ENGINE SPEED)."

CHART #17

IGNITION NOISE

NOISE FROM ALL CYLINDERS?

NO

- CHECK FOR LOOSE OR DEFECTIVE SPARK PLUG WIRES.

POOR CONNECTION OR BAD WIRES FOUND?

NO

- CHECK SPARK PLUG WIRING FOR PROPER FACTORY ROUTING.

SPARK PLUG WIRE ROUTING GOOD?

YES (go to "CHECK AND CLEAN PLUG WIRE BOOTS")

NO

REROUTE SPARK PLUG WIRES AND RETEST FOR NOISE.

YES (poor connection or bad wires found)

REPAIR AS NECESSARY AND RETEST FOR NOISE.

YES (noise from all cylinders)

- CHECK AND CLEAN PLUG WIRE BOOTS AND CAPS FOR SILICONE GREASE MELTDOWN.

DAMAGED BOOTS OR CAPS OR SILICONE GREASE MELTDOWN?

NO

- CHECK AND CLEAN BATTERY CONNECTIONS AND CHASSIS GROUNDS.

BATTERY CONNECTIONS AND CHASSIS GROUNDS OK?

YES

INSTALL P/N 3906145 IN POWER FEED TO ELECTRONIC IGNITION MODULE.

NO

REPAIR AS NECESSARY AND RETEST FOR NOISE.

YES (damaged boots or caps)

REPAIR AS NECESSARY AND RETEST FOR NOISE.

RADIO

CHART #18
GENERATOR WHINE
(VARIES WITH ENGINE SPEED)

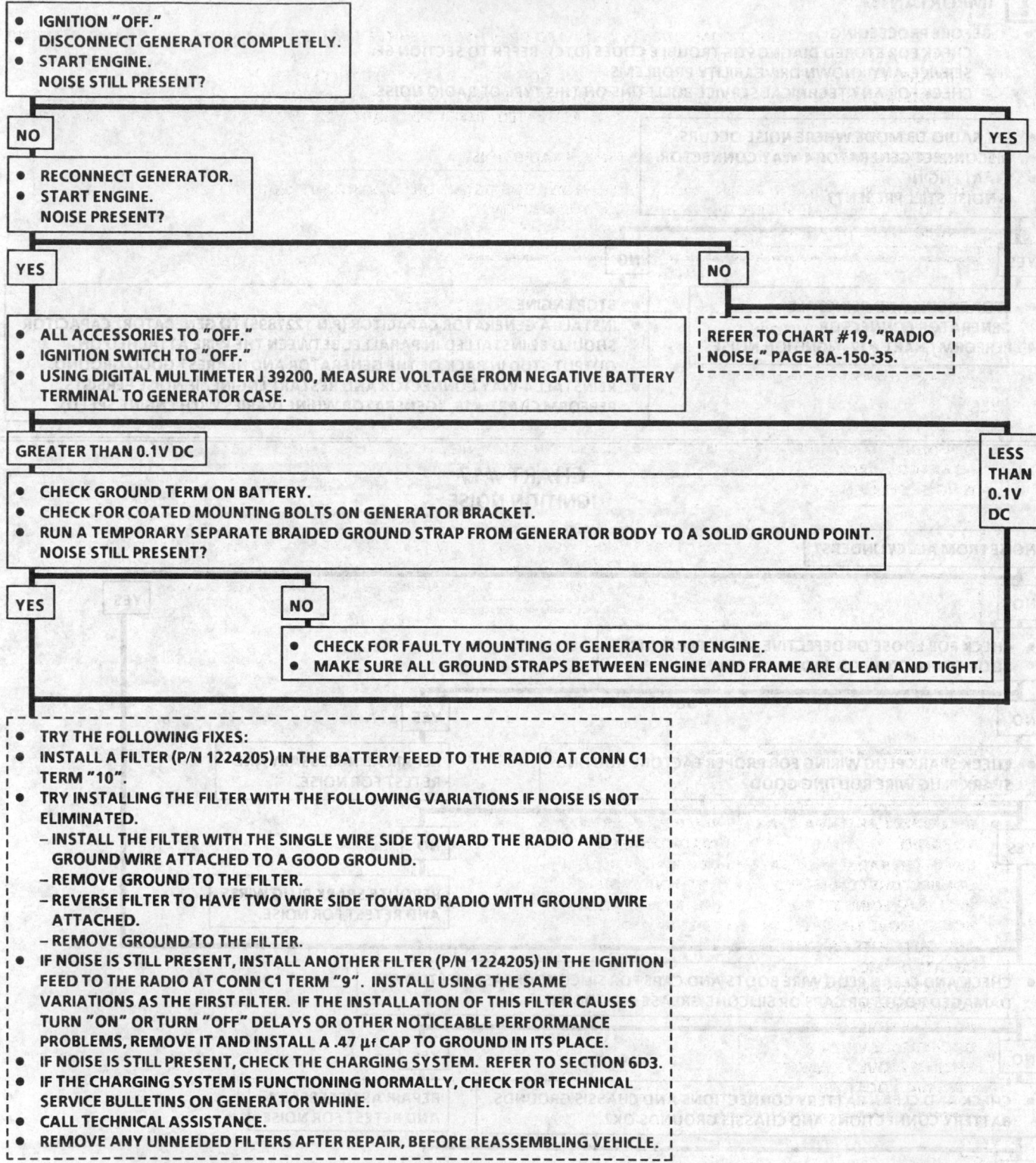

- IGNITION "OFF."
- DISCONNECT GENERATOR COMPLETELY.
- START ENGINE.

NOISE STILL PRESENT?

NO

- RECONNECT GENERATOR.
- START ENGINE.

NOISE PRESENT?

YES

- ALL ACCESSORIES TO "OFF."
- IGNITION SWITCH TO "OFF."
- USING DIGITAL MULTIMETER J 39200, MEASURE VOLTAGE FROM NEGATIVE BATTERY TERMINAL TO GENERATOR CASE.

NO

REFER TO CHART #19, "RADIO NOISE," PAGE 8A-150-35.

GREATER THAN 0.1V DC

- CHECK GROUND TERM ON BATTERY.
- CHECK FOR COATED MOUNTING BOLTS ON GENERATOR BRACKET.
- RUN A TEMPORARY SEPARATE BRAIDED GROUND STRAP FROM GENERATOR BODY TO A SOLID GROUND POINT.

NOISE STILL PRESENT?

NO

- CHECK FOR FAULTY MOUNTING OF GENERATOR TO ENGINE.
- MAKE SURE ALL GROUND STRAPS BETWEEN ENGINE AND FRAME ARE CLEAN AND TIGHT.

YES (from first question) / **LESS THAN 0.1V DC** / **YES**

- TRY THE FOLLOWING FIXES:
- INSTALL A FILTER (P/N 1224205) IN THE BATTERY FEED TO THE RADIO AT CONN C1 TERM "10".
- TRY INSTALLING THE FILTER WITH THE FOLLOWING VARIATIONS IF NOISE IS NOT ELIMINATED.
  - INSTALL THE FILTER WITH THE SINGLE WIRE SIDE TOWARD THE RADIO AND THE GROUND WIRE ATTACHED TO A GOOD GROUND.
  - REMOVE GROUND TO THE FILTER.
  - REVERSE FILTER TO HAVE TWO WIRE SIDE TOWARD RADIO WITH GROUND WIRE ATTACHED.
  - REMOVE GROUND TO THE FILTER.
- IF NOISE IS STILL PRESENT, INSTALL ANOTHER FILTER (P/N 1224205) IN THE IGNITION FEED TO THE RADIO AT CONN C1 TERM "9". INSTALL USING THE SAME VARIATIONS AS THE FIRST FILTER. IF THE INSTALLATION OF THIS FILTER CAUSES TURN "ON" OR TURN "OFF" DELAYS OR OTHER NOTICEABLE PERFORMANCE PROBLEMS, REMOVE IT AND INSTALL A .47 µf CAP TO GROUND IN ITS PLACE.
- IF NOISE IS STILL PRESENT, CHECK THE CHARGING SYSTEM. REFER TO SECTION 6D3.
- IF THE CHARGING SYSTEM IS FUNCTIONING NORMALLY, CHECK FOR TECHNICAL SERVICE BULLETINS ON GENERATOR WHINE.
- CALL TECHNICAL ASSISTANCE.
- REMOVE ANY UNNEEDED FILTERS AFTER REPAIR, BEFORE REASSEMBLING VEHICLE.

CHART #19
RADIO NOISE

IMPORTANT:

- IF THERE ARE AFTERMARKET COMPONENTS INSTALLED OR IN USE IN VEHICLE THAT MAY BE CAUSING COMPLAINT, REFER TO CHART #14 THEN RETURN TO THIS CHART.
- IF NOISE IS IN CONJUNCTION WITH POOR RECEPTION, GO TO CHART #13, "POOR RECEPTION."
- TO DISTINGUISH BETWEEN NOISE OR POOR RECEPTION, PERFORM THE SYSTEM PERFORMANCE CHECK ON PAGE 8A-150-9*
- IF NOISE IS ONLY PRESENT WHEN A SWITCH IS ACTIVATED, REFER TO CHART #22, "SWITCH POP OR ACCESSORY NOISE," BEFORE PROCEEDING.
- CHECK FOR ANY TECHNICAL SERVICE BULLETINS ON RADIO NOISE.

- PUT RADIO AND VEHICLE IN SIMILAR MODE WHERE NOISE OCCURS (AM OR FM, STATION FREQUENCY, ETC.).
- IF A VEHICLE SYSTEM IS SUSPECTED, IT SHOULD BE TURNED "ON."

IS NOISE IN ALL SPEAKERS?

NO: REFER TO CHART #20, "SPEAKER HARNESS RELATED NOISE" PAGE 8A-150-36.

YES:

- PUT IGNITION IN "ACCESSORY."

DOES NOISE OCCUR IN THE "ACCESSORY" MODE?

NO: WITH THE IGNITION "ON" AND ENGINE "OFF," IS THE NOISE PRESENT?

- **YES:** REFER TO CHART #15, "RADIO NOISE ENTERING THROUGH HARNESS (BACKWAY NOISE) WHILE ENGINE NOT RUNNING" PAGE 8A-150-32.
- **NO:** WITH THE ENGINE "ON" AND THE ENGINE "RUNNING," IS THE NOISE PRESENT?
  - **NO:** REFER TO CHART #13, "POOR RECEPTION" PAGE 8A-150-30.
  - **YES:** REFER TO CHART #16, "RADIO NOISE ENTERING THROUGH HARNESS (BACKWAY NOISE) WHILE ENGINE RUNNING ONLY" PAGE 8A-150-33.

YES:

- DISCONNECT ANTENNA COAX FROM RADIO.

IS NOISE STILL PRESENT?

NO: REFER TO CHART #21, "RADIO NOISE ENTERING THROUGH ANTENNA SYSTEM (FRONTWAY NOISE)" PAGE 8A-150-36.

YES:

- RECONNECT ANTENNA COAX TO RADIO.
- UNFASTEN RADIO AND LEAVE CONNECTORS CONNECTED.
- WHILE LISTENING TO THE NOISE: MOVE THE RADIO IN AND OUT OF ITS ORIGINAL LOCATION. MOVE HARNESSES AWAY FROM RADIO IF NECESSARY.

DOES THE NOISE DISAPPEAR OR DECREASE WHEN THE RADIO IS MOVED FROM ITS ORIGINAL LOCATION?

- **YES:** REFER TO CHART #14, "RADIO NOISE ENTERING THROUGH RADIO (SIDEWAYS NOISE)" PAGE 8A-150-31.
- **NO:** REFER TO CHART #15, "RADIO NOISE ENTERING THROUGH HARNESS (BACKWAY NOISE) WHILE ENGINE NOT RUNNING" PAGE 8A-150-32.

RADIO

CHART #20
SPEAKER HARNESS RELATED NOISE

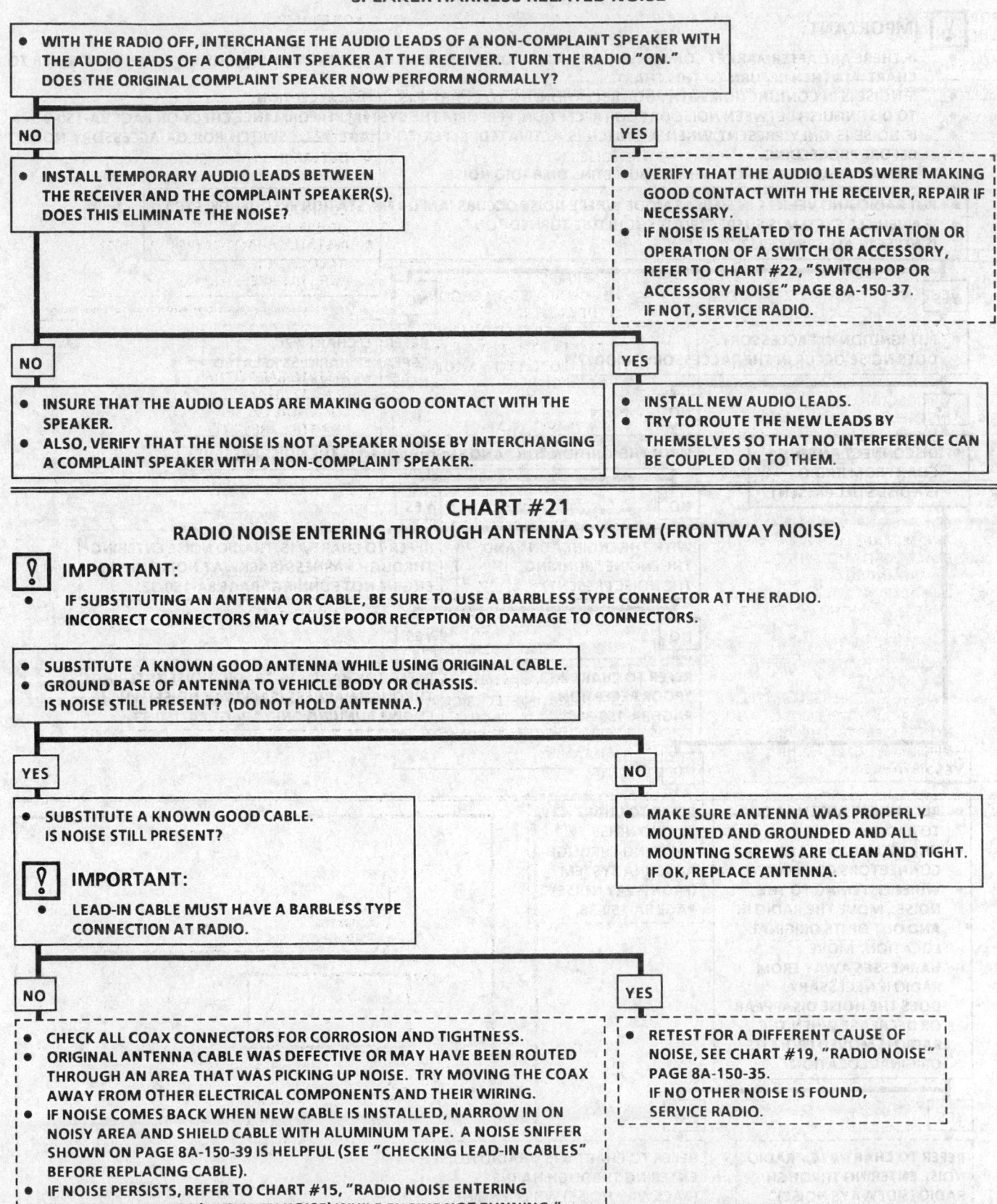

- WITH THE RADIO OFF, INTERCHANGE THE AUDIO LEADS OF A NON-COMPLAINT SPEAKER WITH THE AUDIO LEADS OF A COMPLAINT SPEAKER AT THE RECEIVER. TURN THE RADIO "ON." DOES THE ORIGINAL COMPLAINT SPEAKER NOW PERFORM NORMALLY?

NO

- INSTALL TEMPORARY AUDIO LEADS BETWEEN THE RECEIVER AND THE COMPLAINT SPEAKER(S). DOES THIS ELIMINATE THE NOISE?

NO

- INSURE THAT THE AUDIO LEADS ARE MAKING GOOD CONTACT WITH THE SPEAKER.
- ALSO, VERIFY THAT THE NOISE IS NOT A SPEAKER NOISE BY INTERCHANGING A COMPLAINT SPEAKER WITH A NON-COMPLAINT SPEAKER.

YES

- INSTALL NEW AUDIO LEADS.
- TRY TO ROUTE THE NEW LEADS BY THEMSELVES SO THAT NO INTERFERENCE CAN BE COUPLED ON TO THEM.

YES

- VERIFY THAT THE AUDIO LEADS WERE MAKING GOOD CONTACT WITH THE RECEIVER, REPAIR IF NECESSARY.
- IF NOISE IS RELATED TO THE ACTIVATION OR OPERATION OF A SWITCH OR ACCESSORY, REFER TO CHART #22, "SWITCH POP OR ACCESSORY NOISE" PAGE 8A-150-37. IF NOT, SERVICE RADIO.

CHART #21
RADIO NOISE ENTERING THROUGH ANTENNA SYSTEM (FRONTWAY NOISE)

IMPORTANT:
- IF SUBSTITUTING AN ANTENNA OR CABLE, BE SURE TO USE A BARBLESS TYPE CONNECTOR AT THE RADIO. INCORRECT CONNECTORS MAY CAUSE POOR RECEPTION OR DAMAGE TO CONNECTORS.

- SUBSTITUTE A KNOWN GOOD ANTENNA WHILE USING ORIGINAL CABLE.
- GROUND BASE OF ANTENNA TO VEHICLE BODY OR CHASSIS.

IS NOISE STILL PRESENT? (DO NOT HOLD ANTENNA.)

YES

- SUBSTITUTE A KNOWN GOOD CABLE.

IS NOISE STILL PRESENT?

IMPORTANT:
- LEAD-IN CABLE MUST HAVE A BARBLESS TYPE CONNECTION AT RADIO.

NO

- CHECK ALL COAX CONNECTORS FOR CORROSION AND TIGHTNESS.
- ORIGINAL ANTENNA CABLE WAS DEFECTIVE OR MAY HAVE BEEN ROUTED THROUGH AN AREA THAT WAS PICKING UP NOISE. TRY MOVING THE COAX AWAY FROM OTHER ELECTRICAL COMPONENTS AND THEIR WIRING.
- IF NOISE COMES BACK WHEN NEW CABLE IS INSTALLED, NARROW IN ON NOISY AREA AND SHIELD CABLE WITH ALUMINUM TAPE. A NOISE SNIFFER SHOWN ON PAGE 8A-150-39 IS HELPFUL (SEE "CHECKING LEAD-IN CABLES" BEFORE REPLACING CABLE).
- IF NOISE PERSISTS, REFER TO CHART #15, "RADIO NOISE ENTERING THROUGH HARNESS (BACKWAY NOISE) WHILE ENGINE NOT RUNNING."

YES

- RETEST FOR A DIFFERENT CAUSE OF NOISE, SEE CHART #19, "RADIO NOISE" PAGE 8A-150-35. IF NO OTHER NOISE IS FOUND, SERVICE RADIO.

NO

- MAKE SURE ANTENNA WAS PROPERLY MOUNTED AND GROUNDED AND ALL MOUNTING SCREWS ARE CLEAN AND TIGHT. IF OK, REPLACE ANTENNA.

CHART #22
SWITCH POP OR ACCESSORY NOISE

(FOR NOISE RELATED TO THE ACTIVATION OR OPERATION OF A SWITCH OR ACCESSORY. FOR EXAMPLE, A POP WHEN THE BRAKES ARE APPLIED OR A HUM WHEN THE A/C IS USED.)

DOES NOISE OCCUR ONLY WHEN TURNING A SWITCH ON OR OFF?

NO

- DETERMINE WHICH ACCESSORY IS CAUSING THE NOISE. IS A MOTOR NOISE SUSPECTED?

NO

TRY THESE REPAIRS:
- CHECK THE GROUND CIRCUIT FOR THE SUSPECT MODULE OR COMPONENT.
- REROUTE ANY AUDIO HARNESSES OR THE ANTENNA COAX AWAY FROM THE MODULE OR COMPONENT.
- INSTALL A FILTER PACKAGE 1224205 ONLY IN THE POWER FEED TO THE MODULE OR COMPONENT. INSTALL THE FILTER WITH THE BLACK LEAD AWAY FROM THE MODULE OR COMPONENT. ALSO, TEST FOR THE BEST RESULTS WITH THE BLACK LEAD GROUNDED AND UNGROUNDED.
- INSTALL A .47 µf CAPACITOR IN THE B + AND IGNITION FEEDS TO THE RADIO.
- IF NOISE IS STILL PRESENT TRY A KNOWN GOOD MODULE OR COMPONENT.
- IF NOISE STILL PERSISTS, REFER TO "BACKWAY/ELECTRICAL NOISE" CHARTS, THEN IF NECESSARY CALL TECHNICAL ASSISTANCE.

YES

TRY THESE REPAIRS:
- CHECK FOR A GOOD GROUND TO THE MOTOR.
- INSTALL A CAPACITOR (P/N 3906145) AT THE POWER FEED TO THE MOTOR TO A KNOWN GOOD GROUND.

IMPORTANT:
FOR A BLOWER MOTOR NOISE INSTALL A "FEED THROUGH" CAPACITOR (P/N 3906187) IN THE POWER FEED TO THE BLOWER MOTOR.

- TRY INSTALLING A .47 µf CAPACITOR (IN PARALLEL TO GROUND) AT THE B + AND IGNITION FEEDS TO THE RADIO.
- IF NOISE IS STILL PRESENT, TRY A KNOWN GOOD MOTOR.
- IF NOISE STILL PERSISTS, REFER TO "BACKWAY/ELECTRICAL NOISE" CHARTS, THEN IF NECESSARY CALL TECHNICAL ASSISTANCE.

YES

- DETERMINE WHICH SWITCH IS CAUSING A POP WHEN ACTIVATED.
- DETERMINE SWITCH CONFIGURATION, SEE FIGURE 1 OR FIGURE 2.
- INSTALL CAPACITOR (P/N 1227894) AT LOCATION ①. POP STILL PRESENT?

YES

- INSTALL CAPACITOR (P/N 1227894) AT LOCATION ②. POP STILL PRESENT?

YES

- INSTALL CAPACITOR (P/N 1227894) AT LOCATION ③. POP STILL PRESENT?

YES

CHECK FOR TECHNICAL SERVICE BULLETINS ON SWITCH POP.

NO (at any step)

RETEST FOR NOISE.

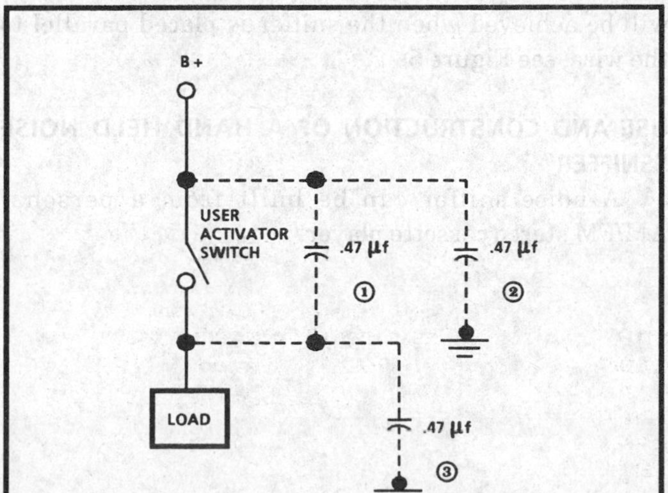
B +
USER
ACTIVATOR
SWITCH
.47 µf
①
.47 µf
②
LOAD
.47 µf
③

Figure 1 - Direct Switch Activated Device

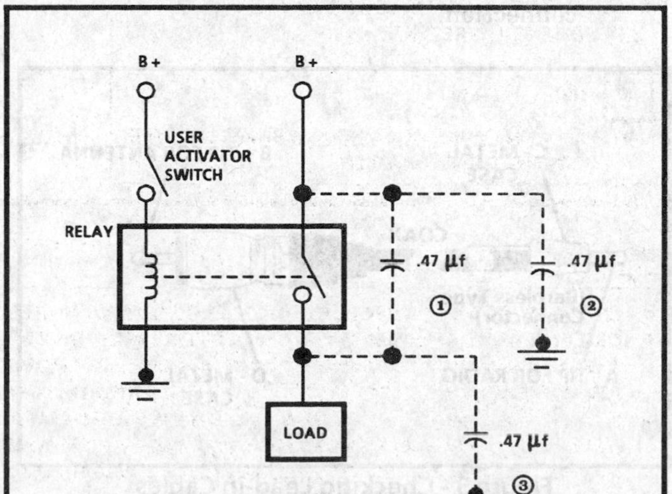
B +
B +
USER
ACTIVATOR
SWITCH
RELAY
.47 µf
①
.47 µf
②
LOAD
.47 µf
③

Figure 2 - Relay Activated Device

RADIO

ANTENNA SYSTEM CHECK

CHECKING RADIO MAST ANTENNAS

Unplug antenna lead-in at back of Radio and plug a test antenna into Radio. Make sure test antenna base is grounded to the vehicle chassis. Do not touch the mast. Check Radio reception in an area away from tall buildings, metal structures, power lines, fluorescent lighting and power tools. Tune to high and low ends of the dial on both AM and FM, checking weak and strong station reception. See "System Performance Check," page 8A-150-9. If reception is OK, the problem exists with antenna and/or its lead-in cable. If reception is still poor with test antenna, check for aftermarket equipment that may be causing complaint. If OK, service Radio.

CHECKING LEAD-IN CABLES

In case of continued reception or noise complaints, always check the lead-in with a digital multimeter, see Figure 3 and Table 1. If long jumper leads are not available, check center conductor continuity by jumping the antenna mast to ground and checking for continuity from the center conductor at Radio to ground.

When checking resistance, cautiously wiggle the lead-in tip and cable. Consistent readings from Table 1 should always be obtained. If not, some portion of the lead-in is intermittent and lead-in should be replaced. Also try:

1. Running a braided ground strap to the antenna lead-in.
2. Changing the antenna lead-in.
3. Disconnecting the lead-in to check resistance.
4. Check in-line connection for corrosion or poor connection.

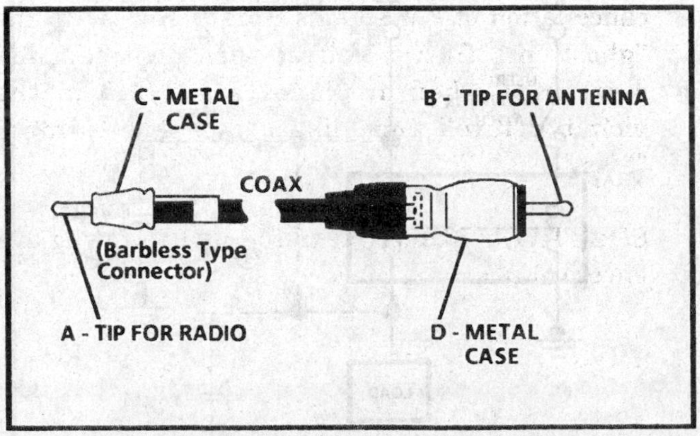
C - METAL CASE
B - TIP FOR ANTENNA
COAX
(Barbless Type Connector)
A - TIP FOR RADIO
D - METAL CASE

Figure 3 - Checking Lead-in Cables

Table 1 - Lead-in Cable Resistance Checks

Digital Multimeter probes at points:	Resistance measured in ohms
A and B	less than 3.5
C and D	less than 0.2
A and D	infinite
C and B	infinite
A and C	infinite
B and D	infinite

USE AND CONSTRUCTION OF A NOISE "SNIFFER"

The antenna sniffer can be used along with the vehicle's Radio to locate "hot spots" which are generating Radio noise interference. These "hot spots" can be found in the harnesses, in the upper part of the dash or even between the hood and windshield.

The sniffer can be made from an old piece of antenna lead-in from a mast or power antenna. The longer the lead-in the better.

Make the antenna sniffer as shown in Figure 4. The 2" section with the black coating and braided shield stripped back becomes the antenna when the sniffer is plugged into the Radio's antenna socket. It can then be used to probe and search out "hot spots."

To use the noise sniffer:

1. While listening to the complaint noise, disconnect the antenna and plug the sniffer into the antenna socket.
2. Turn the Radio volume up.
3. Search for the noise source, keeping fingers off the 2" probe.

When checking for noise on a wire, the best results will be achieved when the sniffer is placed parallel to the wire, see Figure 5.

USE AND CONSTRUCTION OF A HAND HELD NOISE "SNIFFER"

A noise sniffer can be built from a personal AM/FM stereo cassette player.

EQUIPMENT

- Personal AM/FM stereo cassette tape player with headphones
- Four feet of 75 ohm antenna coax
- One-half inch heat shrink tube the same diameter as the coax
- A drill and bit the same diameter as the coax
- Book of matches or hair dryer
- Soldering iron and solder

INSTRUCTION FOR THE PERSONAL TYPE RADIO

1. Strip 1/4" off both ends of the coax.
2. Place the heat shrink over one end of the bare wire. Fasten the heat shrink to the wire by heating it (a match or a hair dryer).
3. Disassemble the Radio and locate the antenna.
4. Disconnect the antenna and fasten the bare end of the coax to the antenna mount. A soldering iron may be needed.
5. Feed the coax to the exterior of the Radio. Drill a feed hole if necessary.
6. Reassemble the Radio.

To use the Radio sniffer, turn the Radio on AM and select an appropriate station.

INSTRUCTION FOR THE PERSONAL TYPE CASSETTE

1. Strip 1/4" off each end of coax.
2. Disassemble the cassette deck and locate the tape head.
3. Remove the head and mount one end of the coax to this point. A soldering iron may be needed.
4. Feed the coax to the exterior of the cassette deck. Drill a feed hole if necessary.
5. Reassemble the cassette deck.
6. Feed the heat shrink tube through the other end of the coax. DO NOT FASTEN THE HEAT SHRINK.

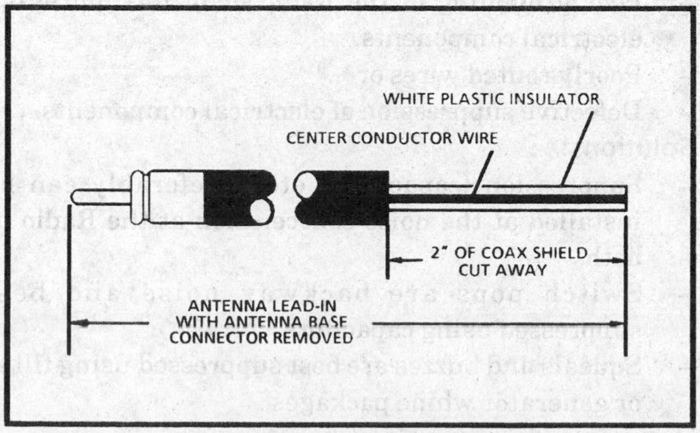
WHITE PLASTIC INSULATOR
CENTER CONDUCTOR WIRE
2" OF COAX SHIELD CUT AWAY
ANTENNA LEAD-IN WITH ANTENNA BASE CONNECTOR REMOVED

Figure 4 - Antenna Sniffer

7. Fasten the head to the open end of the coax. Use a soldering iron.
8. Cover the exposed wires between the head and the wire by positioning the heat shrink tube and heating it.

To use the cassette sniffer, push "play." It will work on the same idea as a metal detector.

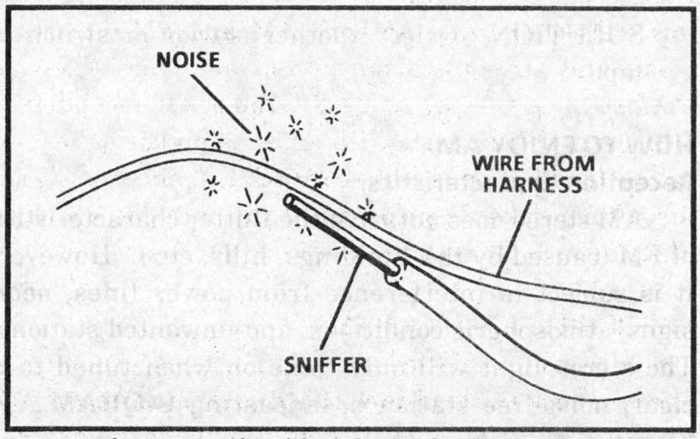
NOISE
WIRE FROM HARNESS
SNIFFER

Figure 5 - Checking for Noise on a Wire

CUSTOMER'S TIPS

HOW TO ENJOY FM STEREO

A. Select Stations Within Range – The best FM fidelity will be obtained from stations within a 10-40 mile range. Beyond that "noise" or "flutter" may begin to appear due to the "line of sight" range limitations of FM signals.

   SOLUTION: Reduce treble response by moving the treble control down (or to the left) in fringe areas. On EQ Radios, slowly slide the 10K control down.

B. Realize Tall Structures Can Interfere – Tall buildings or hills may cause "shadows" or cancellation of FM signals (this is similar to the "ghost" or "flutter" effect seen on television sometimes when airplanes are flying in the vicinity). It will sound like a "pop" or momentary "hiss."

   SOLUTION: Reduce the treble or 10K setting to a lower volume.

RADIO

C. Interference From Another Station – Although the circuits in Delco receivers are the most advanced available, there are rare instances where a station being listened to will be interfered with by another station. This only happens when the stations are on almost the same frequency and certain geographical criteria are present.

SOLUTION: Select another station or switch to tape.

HOW TO ENJOY AM

Reception Characteristics

AM stereo does not have the flutter characteristics of FM (caused by tall buildings, hills, etc.). However, it is subject to interference from power lines, neon signs, atmospheric conditions, and unwanted stations. The stereo light will only come on when tuned to a clear, noise-free station broadcasting C-QUAM AM Stereo.

Finding Stereo Stations

1. Depress AM Stereo-Mono button to inward position.
2. Consult directory, or use Seek or Scan.
3. Watch for stereo light to come on, indicating you are tuned to stereo.

Important:

- After tuning to a stereo station, there is a one or two second delay before the stereo light comes on.

WAYS TO REDUCE NOISE

1. Press AM Stereo button to switch to mono.
2. Move treble control down.
3. Tune to a stronger station.

AM STEREO

The AM Stereo-Mono button has no effect on FM reception.

Most AM Stereo stations broadcast in C-Quam, but some do not. Check with your local station to determine compatibility in your area. **C-Quam** is a registered trademark of Motorola Inc.

NOISE ENTRY

FRONTWAY NOISE

Any noise which is brought into the Radio system through the antenna. (Noise can be eliminated by unplugging the antenna from the back of the Radio.)

Some Causes:

- Poor grounding or missing grounds of: the antenna base; the receiver; some electrical components; body parts.
- Defective or marginal components: relays, solenoid, switches and electric motors.
- Something near the antenna coax or corrosion at antenna coax connections.

Solutions:

- Always verify grounding first. If more than one component interferes, a poor ground probably exists.
- Pinpoint the source: suppress, shield or replace.
- Reroute noisy wires if necessary.

SIDEWAYS NOISE

Any noise that enters the audio component by a radiated field through the component case. (Noise is reduced or eliminated when slowly removing the audio component from its fastened location.)

Some Causes:

Noisy wires or hoses behind or on top of the Radio or antenna coax lead-in.

Solutions:

- Suppress or shield the noisy wire or hose or reroute it.
- Shield the Radio case.
- Use aluminum or nickel tape and ground the tape whenever shielding. (Nickel tape will also stop magnetic interference, aluminum will not.)

BACKWAY NOISE

Noise that enters the audio component through its wiring harness, most commonly detected in the power and ground circuits. (Noise that can be heard at minimum volume and not frontway or sideway noise.)

Some Causes:

- Poor grounding of the Radio or of unsuppressed electrical components.
- Poorly routed wires or
- Defective suppression of electrical components.

Solutions:

- Suppression (capacitors, etc.) preferably can be installed at the noise source, then at the Radio or both.
- Switch pops are backway noise and best suppressed using capacitors.
- Squeals and buzzes are best suppressed using filter or generator whine packages.

HARNESS RELATED NOISE

Noise induced into speaker wires or any low level audio signal wire used as an interconnect between the various audio components.

Some Causes:

- Broken, pinched or shorted audio wires.
- Screw through wire harness.
- Faulty shield wires.

Solutions:

- Localize problem to left, right side, front or back speaker location. Preferably done by using the fade and balance controls; if not, try reversing the speaker leads at the Radio connector.
- Check wiring for defects, breaks, pinches or shorts.
- Check wiring near known noisy components.

CIRCUIT OPERATION

The Radio with a remote Radio Control Head and Remote Cassette/Equalizer or Compact Disc Player (optional) uses a Serial Data Line to coordinate the operation of several independent units into a sound system. The E & C Line allows each of the units to communicate with the others by digitally encoded pulse streams or serial data. This is referred to as the Entertainment and Comfort (E & C) Data Line. Access to the E & C Data is available at the Data Link Connector (DLC). The E & C Data can be read by a bi-directional scan tool.

RADIO RECEIVER

The Radio Receiver incorporates most of the circuitry found in an ordinary Radio including the tuner and amplifier. Instead of manually operated controls, however, it utilizes an E & C Data input/output port to control its functions. E & C Data is sent to this port from the Radio Control Head. The Radio Receiver responds to these signals by adjusting its frequency, changing its output to the speakers and so on.

RADIO CONTROL HEAD

The Radio Control Head contains all the control switches and the display. It controls the Radio Receiver by sending E & C Data to it, causing the Radio Receiver to adjust its output accordingly. The Radio Control Head displays the selected receiving frequency and other operating information.

CASSETTE/EQUALIZER (UX1)

The Cassette/Equalizer is used to provide two functions. The Equalizer portion modifies the Radio's response to each of the five audio frequency bands as selected by the operator. The required signals are sent to the Radio Receiver over the E & C Data Line, similar to that described earlier. The cassette portion derives a signal from cassette tapes and sends this signal to the Radio Receiver which amplifies it and drives the speakers. In addition, a mute signal is sent from the Cassette/Equalizer to the Radio Receiver to switch its program source from the internal tuner to the Cassette Player. The Cassette signals are not encoded.

POWER ANTENNA

When the receiver is turned "ON," battery voltage is applied to CKT 143 to energize the Antenna Relay.

ILLUMINATION

The Radio Control Head and Cassette/Equalizer or Compact Disc Player utilize a Vacuum Fluorescent (VF) display to provide the vehicle occupants with time and sound system information. With the Radio turned on, the VF displays light to a fixed brightness. When the Park Lights or Headlights are turned on, battery voltage is applied to the Radio Control Head via the Radio Receiver from the "Lights on input." This lights on signal is sent to the Cassette/Equalizer or Compact Disc Player through the Radio Control Head. The VF display then dims to the present dimmer control setting. With the lights on, the Radio Control Head receives a Pulse Width Modulated (PWM) illumination signal from the Light Switch through the Radio Receiver. A PWM signal is then sent to the Cassette/Equalizer or Compact Disc Player from the Radio Control Head. These PWM signals control the VF illumination which varies as the dimmer control is adjusted.

The Radio Control Head buttons and face illumination is incandescent. They are illuminated when the lights are turned on, receiving power from the Panel Light input. The Radio Control Head incandescent illumination brightness is controlled by the variable voltage panel light input. The Cassette Player, Compact Disc Player and the Cassette/Equalizer buttons and face are also incandescent. They receive their illumination signal from the PWM signal that comes from the Radio Control Head. The brightness of the incandescent bulbs is controlled by this PWM signal.

RADIO

CASSETTE PLAYER (UM6)

The Cassette Player derives a signal from cassette tapes and sends the signal to the Radio Receiver which amplifies it and drives the speakers. In addition, a mute signal is sent from the Cassette Player to the Radio Receiver to switch its program source from the internal tuner to the Cassette Player. The Cassette signals are not digitally encoded.

COMPACT DISC (U1C)

The Compact Disc Player operates similarly to the Cassette Player.

STEERING WHEEL CONTROLS

Steering Wheel Radio Controls are available and send control signals over the E & C Data Line via the Radio Control Interface Module.

TECH 1 DIAGNOSIS

As described in the General Information section, the Radio Receiver and Radio Control Head have separate and distinct roles, but they work together to achieve Entertainment System operation. To work together, the Radio Control Head, and the Radio Receiver communicate information with one another electronically over the Entertainment Data Link. Access to the E & C Data Link for diagnostic purposes is available at pin "J" of the DLC Connector. Using a Tech 1 scan tool equipped with the appropriate cartridge (mass storage cartridge #3000003), a technician can plug into the DLC Connector and monitor the information being exchanged on the Data Link between the Radio Control Head, and the Radio Receiver.

The Tech 1 may be used to exercise the Radio Control Head displays, send the audio signal to the audio channels, monitor or send commands to the Radio Receiver, etc. Using the trouble trees found in this section (starting on page 8A-150-11), it can be quickly determined whether the Radio Control Head, Radio Receiver, speakers or wiring should be serviced.

Detailed instructions, cautions and schematics for Tech 1 E & C Data Link (Bus) diagnosis can also be found in the Cartridge User's Manual. If unfamiliar with the Tech 1 take time to look at the Operator's Manual.

TECH 1 DIAGNOSTIC CHARTS

The basic theory behind the Tech 1 diagnostic charts presented in this section is very simple. If this theory is understood, the trouble trees can be used simply as a general outline.

The Tech 1 is used to listen on the data link to see if the Radio Control Head is sending the right message on the data link to the Radio Receiver. The trouble tree will refer to Figure 12 and monitor E & C Data for the correct messages to expect if the Radio Control Head is functioning correctly.

If the Radio Control Head is not sending the right message, the Tech 1 is used to send the message directly from the Tech 1 to the Radio Receiver to verify that the Radio Receiver is OK and can respond to the messages. If the Radio Receiver does respond, the problem is either in the Radio Control Head, or in the wiring. (The diagnostic charts will refer to page 8A-150-23, Control E & C Components for the procedure and correct responses if the radio receiver is OK.)

If the Radio Control Head is sending the right message when the suspected button or feature is pressed, the Tech 1 is used to verify that the Radio Receiver may have failed by sending the message directly from the Tech 1. If the Radio Receiver still does not respond, the Radio Control Head is OK, and the problem is either in the Radio Receiver or in the wiring. (The trouble tree will refer to page 8A-150-23, Control E & C Components for the procedure and correct response if the Radio Receiver is actually OK.)

BLANK

POWER ANTENNA

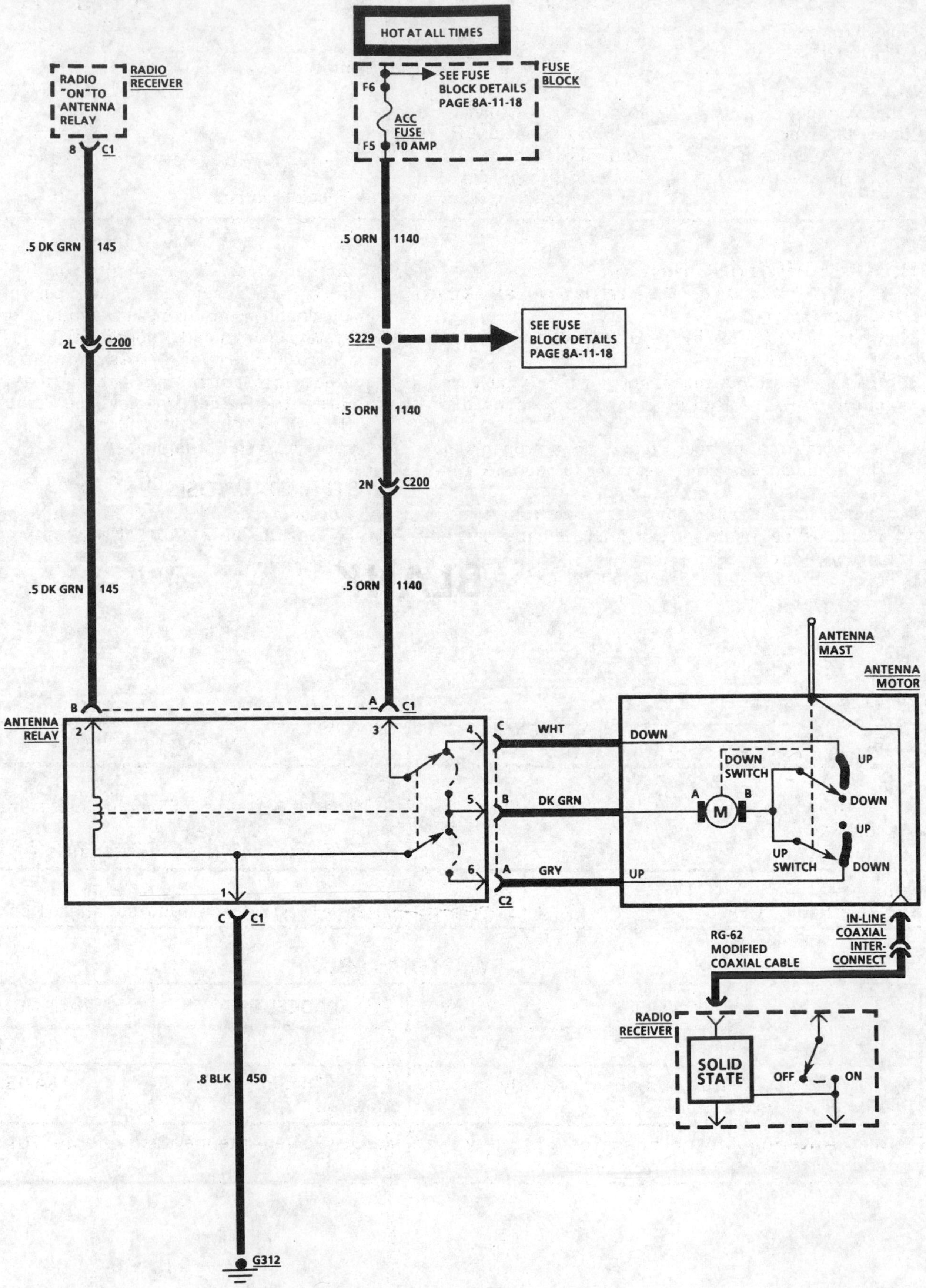
HOT AT ALL TIMES
RADIO "ON" TO ANTENNA RELAY
RADIO RECEIVER
8 C1
F6
SEE FUSE BLOCK DETAILS PAGE 8A-11-18
FUSE BLOCK
ACC FUSE
F5 10 AMP
.5 DK GRN 145
.5 ORN 1140
2L C200
S229
SEE FUSE BLOCK DETAILS PAGE 8A-11-18
.5 ORN 1140
2N C200
.5 DK GRN 145
.5 ORN 1140
ANTENNA MAST
ANTENNA MOTOR
B
A C1
ANTENNA RELAY
2
3
4
C
WHT
DOWN
UP
DOWN SWITCH
A
M
B
DOWN
5
B
DK GRN
UP
UP SWITCH
DOWN
6
A
GRY
UP
C2
1
C C1
IN-LINE COAXIAL INTER-CONNECT
RG-62 MODIFIED COAXIAL CABLE
RADIO RECEIVER
SOLID STATE
OFF
ON
.8 BLK 450
G312

COMPONENT	LOCATION	201-PG	FIG.	CONN
Antenna Motor	RH side of Trunk	12	38	
Antenna Relay	RH side of Trunk	12	38	
Fuse Block	RH side of I/P, in I/P Compartment			
In-Line Coaxial Interconnect	Behind RH kickpad			
Radio Receiver	Behind RH side of I/P	16	53	202-32
C200 (102 cavities)	Behind RH side of I/P, near shroud	22	74	202-3
G312	Under RH front seat			
S229	I/P Harn, approx 8 cm from Fuse Block breakout			

TROUBLESHOOTING HINTS (Perform before beginning System Diagnosis)

1. Check RADIO Fuse by visual inspection.
2. Check ACC Fuse.
3. If Power Antenna goes up or down only part way, check Power Antenna Mast for bent or dirty condition.
4. If Power Antenna goes up and down properly, but the Radio does not receive, refer to page 8A-150-0 for diagnosis.

- Check for a broken (or partially broken) wire inside of the insulation which could cause system malfunction but prove "GOOD" in a continuity/voltage check with a system disconnected. These circuits may be intermittent or resistive when loaded, and if possible, should be checked by monitoring for a voltage drop with the system operational (under load).
- Check for proper installation of aftermarket electronic equipment which may affect the integrity of other systems (see "Troubleshooting Procedures," page 8A-4-0).
- Refer to System Diagnosis.

SYSTEM DIAGNOSIS

- Perform the System Check and refer to the Symptom Table for the proper diagnostic procedure(s).

SYSTEM CHECK

ACTION	NORMAL RESULTS
[1] • With Ignition Switch in "RUN" or "ACCY," turn the Radio "ON." Tune in a local station.	Antenna Mast rises to full height (approximately three feet). Radio receives strong broadcast signals.
[2] • Turn Radio "OFF."	Antenna Mast retracts into right quarter panel.

SYMPTOM TABLE

SYMPTOM	PROCEDURE	PAGE NUMBER
Power Antenna is inoperative.	Chart #1	8A-151-2
Power Antenna goes up and down properly, but the Radio will not receive signals.	Refer to "Radio: Diagnosis."	8A-150-0
Power Antenna Motor operates normally but Antenna Mast will not extend or retract.	Replace Power Antenna Mast; refer to SECTION 9A.	

POWER ANTENNA

CHART #1
POWER ANTENNA IS INOPERATIVE

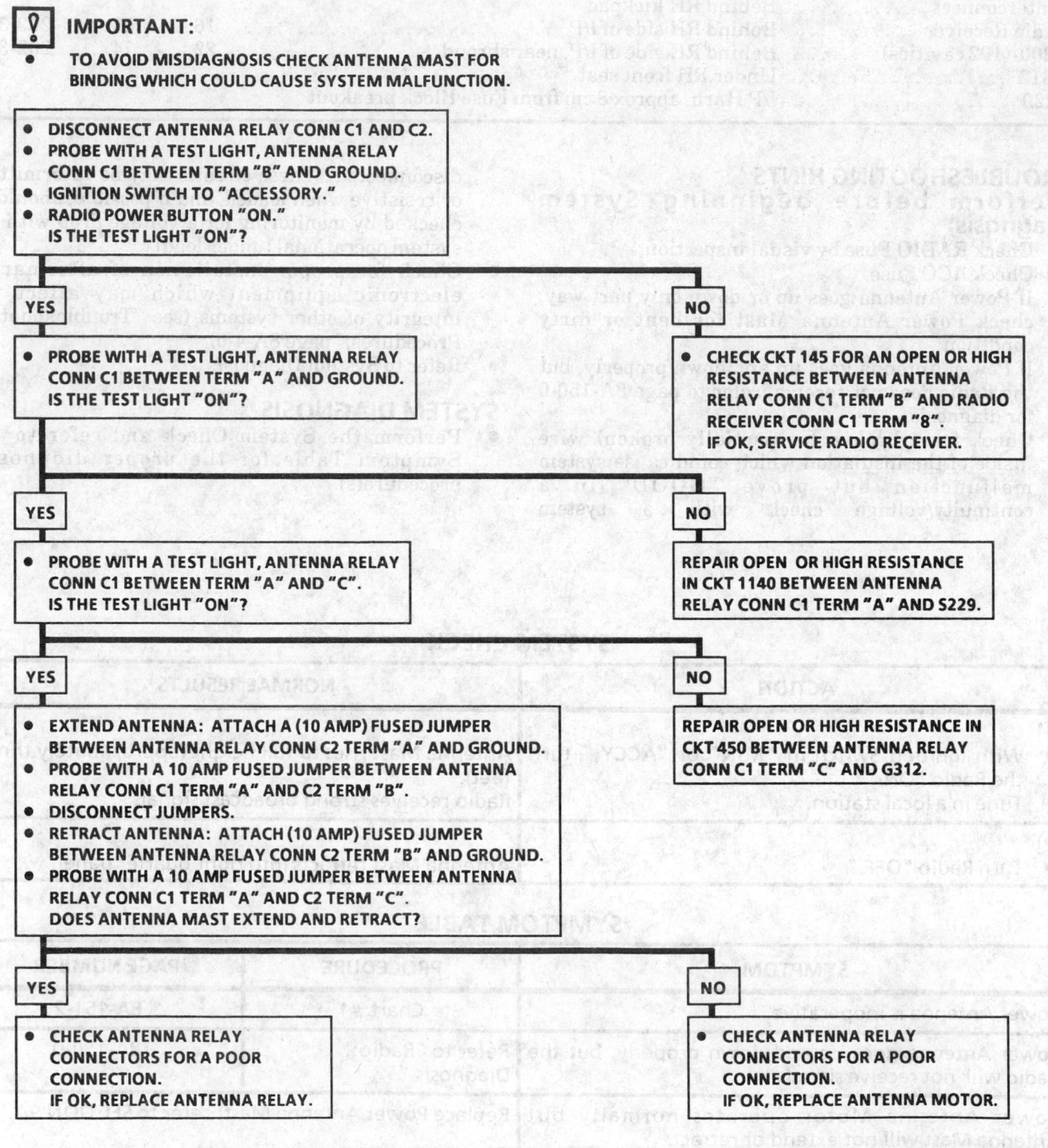

IMPORTANT:
- TO AVOID MISDIAGNOSIS CHECK ANTENNA MAST FOR BINDING WHICH COULD CAUSE SYSTEM MALFUNCTION.

- DISCONNECT ANTENNA RELAY CONN C1 AND C2.
- PROBE WITH A TEST LIGHT, ANTENNA RELAY CONN C1 BETWEEN TERM "B" AND GROUND.
- IGNITION SWITCH TO "ACCESSORY."
- RADIO POWER BUTTON "ON."

IS THE TEST LIGHT "ON"?

YES

- PROBE WITH A TEST LIGHT, ANTENNA RELAY CONN C1 BETWEEN TERM "A" AND GROUND.

IS THE TEST LIGHT "ON"?

NO

- CHECK CKT 145 FOR AN OPEN OR HIGH RESISTANCE BETWEEN ANTENNA RELAY CONN C1 TERM "B" AND RADIO RECEIVER CONN C1 TERM "8".

IF OK, SERVICE RADIO RECEIVER.

YES

- PROBE WITH A TEST LIGHT, ANTENNA RELAY CONN C1 BETWEEN TERM "A" AND "C".

IS THE TEST LIGHT "ON"?

NO

REPAIR OPEN OR HIGH RESISTANCE IN CKT 1140 BETWEEN ANTENNA RELAY CONN C1 TERM "A" AND S229.

YES

- EXTEND ANTENNA: ATTACH A (10 AMP) FUSED JUMPER BETWEEN ANTENNA RELAY CONN C2 TERM "A" AND GROUND.
- PROBE WITH A 10 AMP FUSED JUMPER BETWEEN ANTENNA RELAY CONN C1 TERM "A" AND C2 TERM "B".
- DISCONNECT JUMPERS.
- RETRACT ANTENNA: ATTACH (10 AMP) FUSED JUMPER BETWEEN ANTENNA RELAY CONN C2 TERM "B" AND GROUND.
- PROBE WITH A 10 AMP FUSED JUMPER BETWEEN ANTENNA RELAY CONN C1 TERM "A" AND C2 TERM "C".

DOES ANTENNA MAST EXTEND AND RETRACT?

NO

REPAIR OPEN OR HIGH RESISTANCE IN CKT 450 BETWEEN ANTENNA RELAY CONN C1 TERM "C" AND G312.

YES

- CHECK ANTENNA RELAY CONNECTORS FOR A POOR CONNECTION.

IF OK, REPLACE ANTENNA RELAY.

NO

- CHECK ANTENNA RELAY CONNECTORS FOR A POOR CONNECTION.

IF OK, REPLACE ANTENNA MOTOR.

CIRCUIT OPERATION

When the Radio is turned "ON," voltage from CKT 43 is applied from the Radio Receiver and CKT 145 to the Antenna Relay coil. The relay contacts close and battery voltage is supplied through the DK GRN wire to the Antenna Motor. The Antenna Motor is grounded through the Up Switch, the GRY wire, and the relay contacts. The Motor drives the Antenna up. When the Antenna is at its full height, the Up Switch opens and the Motor stops.

When the Radio or Ignition Switch is turned "OFF," the circuit through the Antenna Relay coil is opened. The Antenna Relay contacts open to the position shown in the schematic, applying battery voltage to the WHT wire. The DK GRN wire is now grounded. Since the Down Switch at the Antenna is now making contact to the WHT wire, the voltage to the Motor has reversed polarity. It runs in the opposite direction and drives the Antenna down.

At the end of the Antenna's travel, the Down Switch opens and breaks the current flow. Both sets of switches are now in the positions shown in the schematic, the Radio is "OFF," and the Antenna is down.

The Antenna is connected to the Radio by coaxial cable.

COMPONENT LOCATION VIEWS

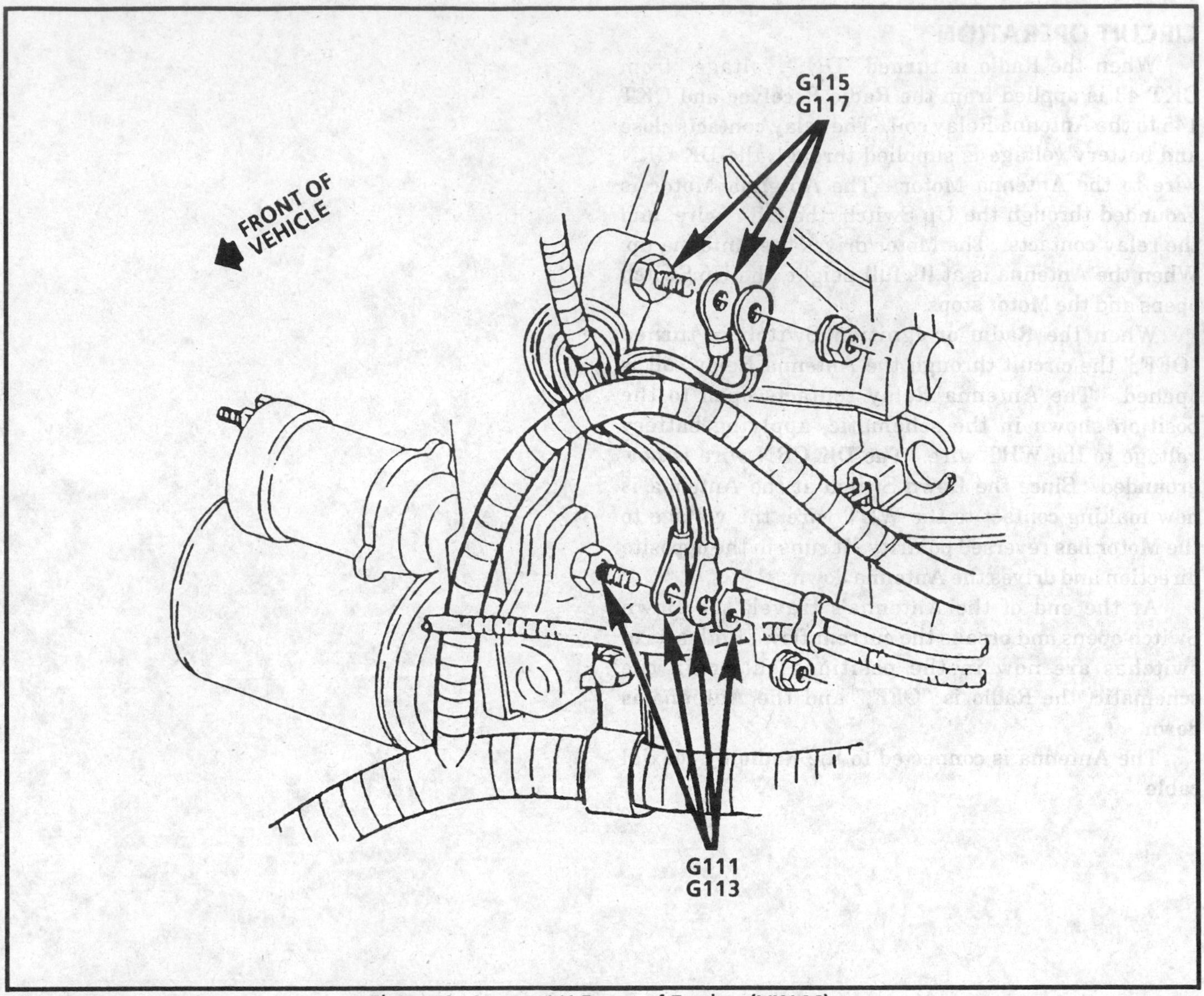
G115
G117
FRONT OF VEHICLE
G111
G113

Figure 1 - Lower LH Front of Engine (VIN M)

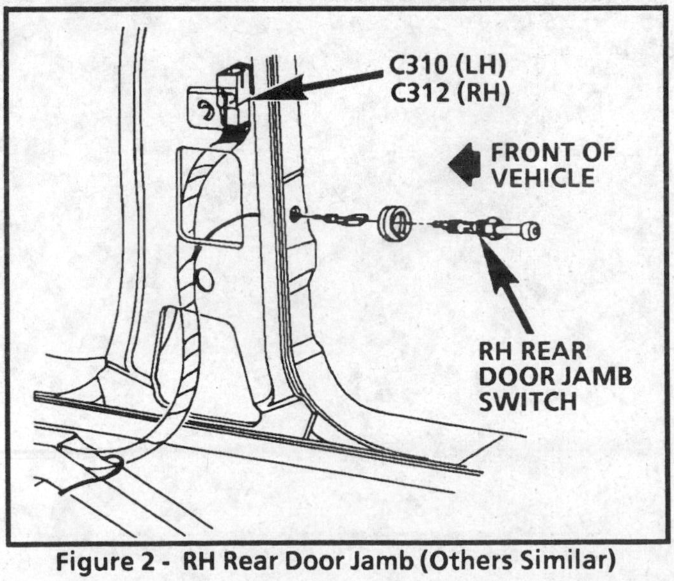
C310 (LH)
C312 (RH)
FRONT OF VEHICLE
RH REAR DOOR JAMB SWITCH

Figure 2 - RH Rear Door Jamb (Others Similar)

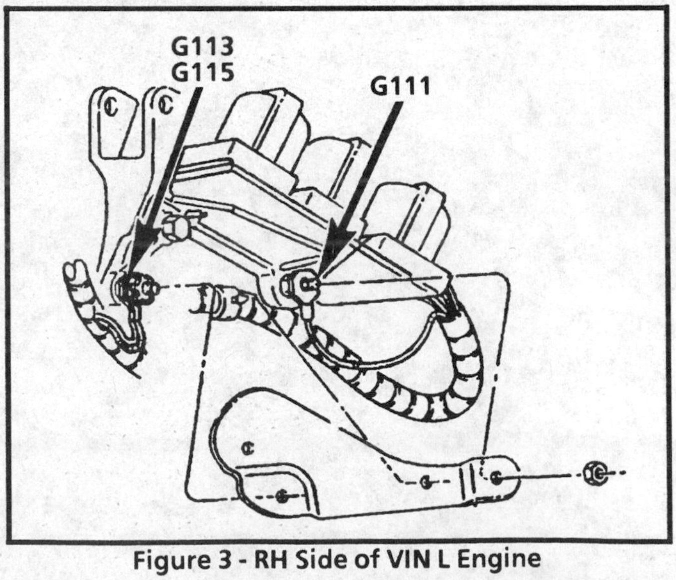
G113
G115
G111

Figure 3 - RH Side of VIN L Engine

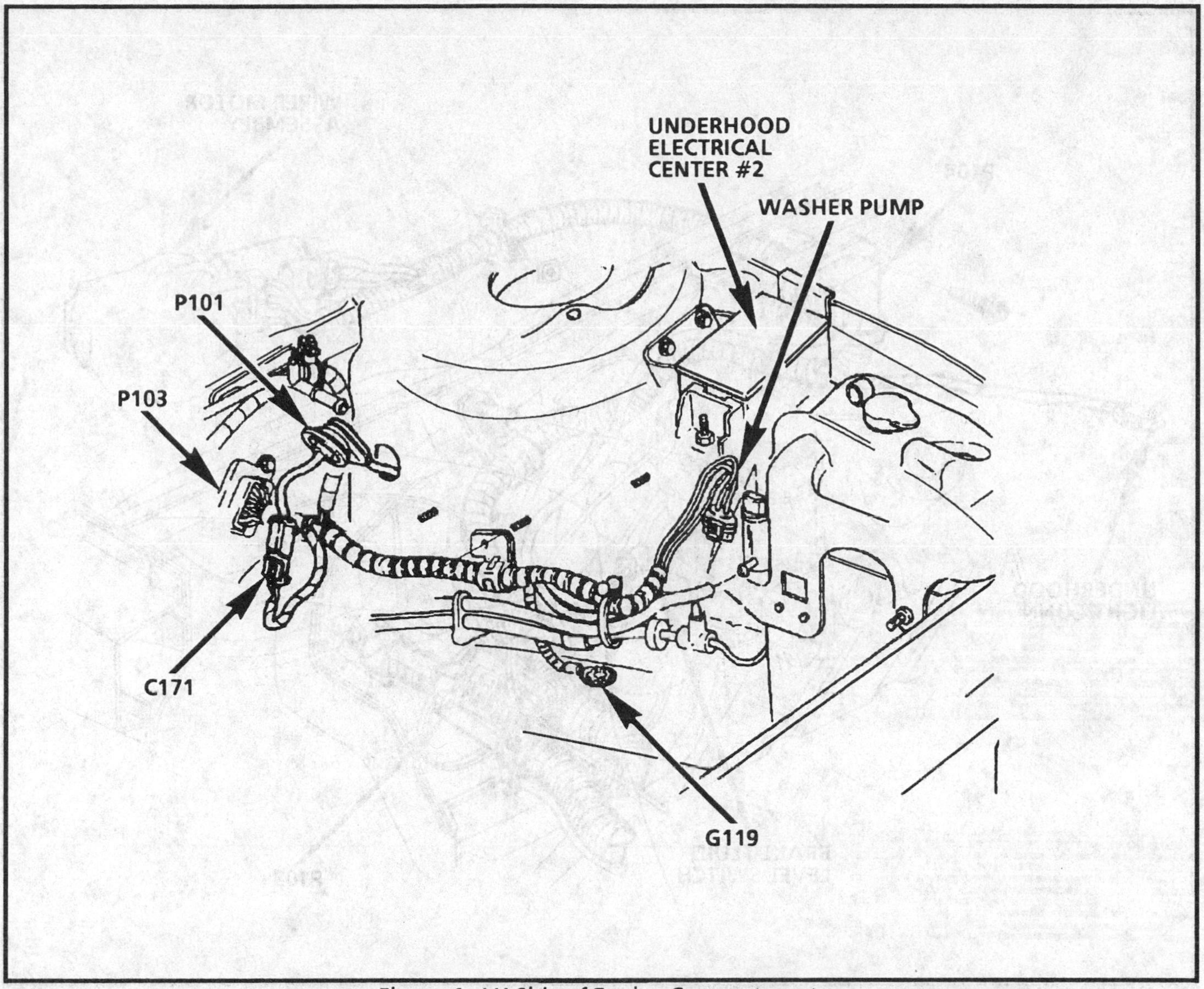
UNDERHOOD
ELECTRICAL
CENTER #2
WASHER PUMP
P101
P103
C171
G119

Figure 4 - LH Side of Engine Compartment

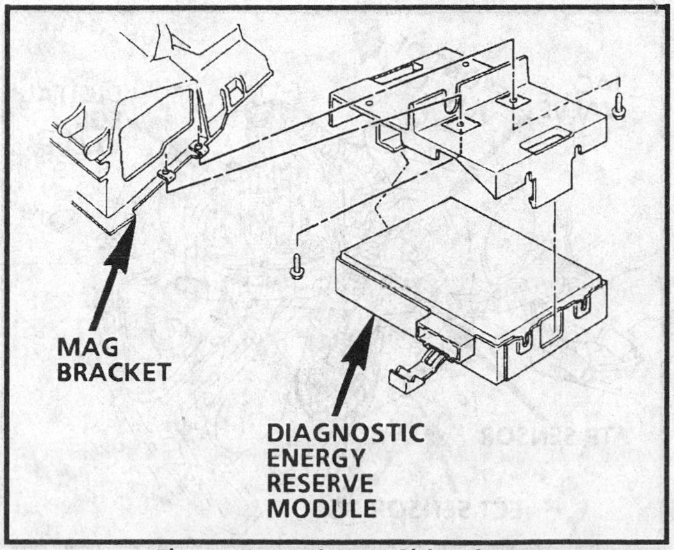
MAG
BRACKET
DIAGNOSTIC
ENERGY
RESERVE
MODULE

Figure 5 - Under LH Side of I/P

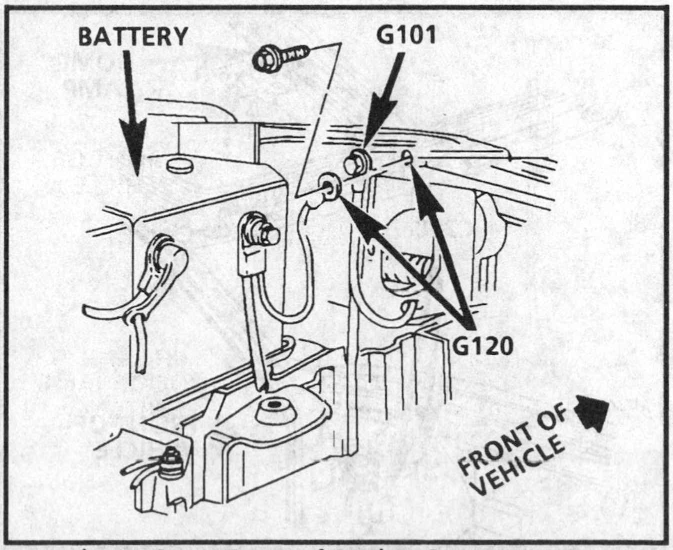
BATTERY
G101
G120
FRONT OF
VEHICLE

Figure 6 - LH Front of Engine Compartment

COMPONENT LOCATION VIEWS

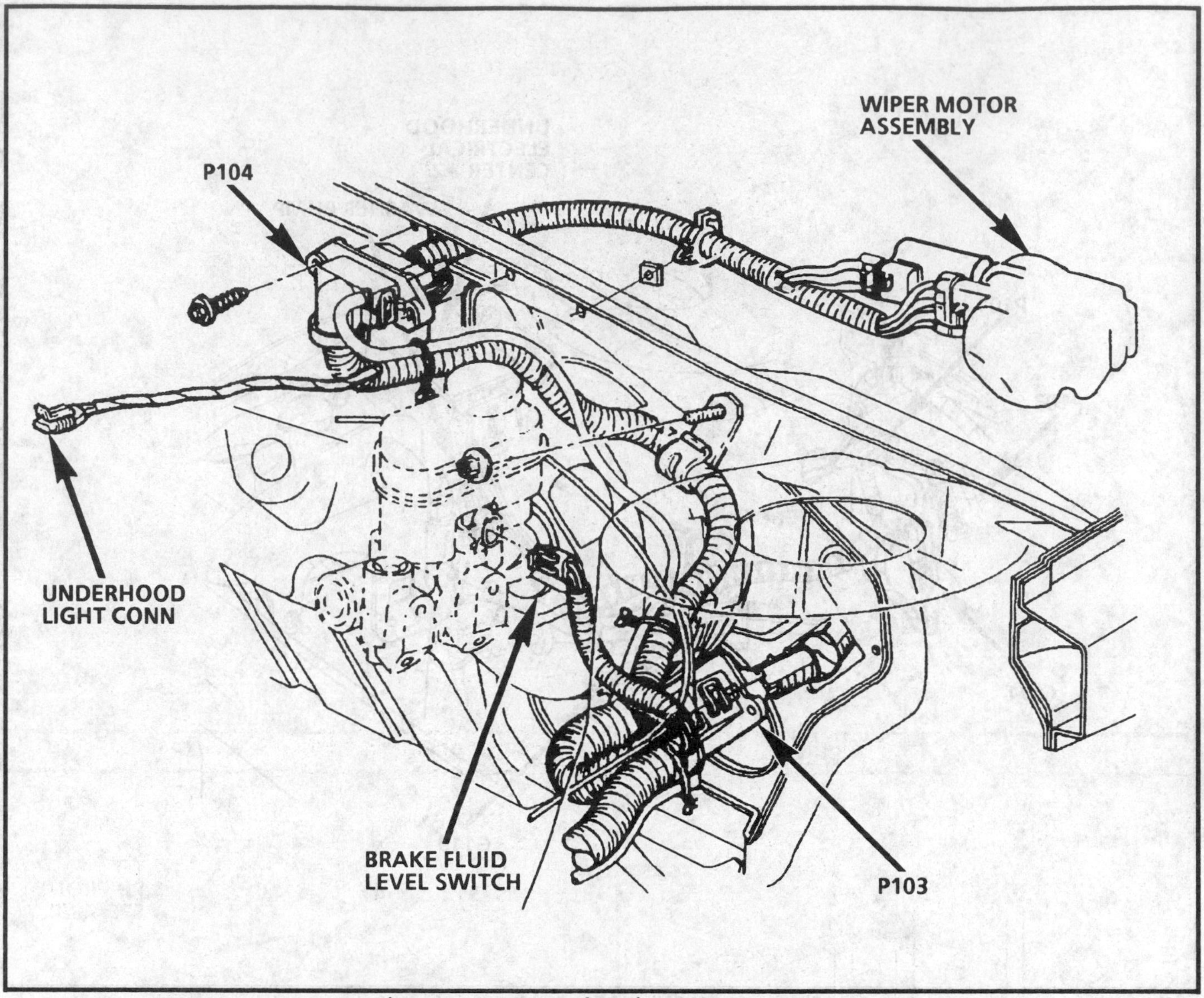
WIPER MOTOR
ASSEMBLY
P104
UNDERHOOD
LIGHT CONN
BRAKE FLUID
LEVEL SWITCH
P103

Figure 7 - LH Rear of Engine Compartment

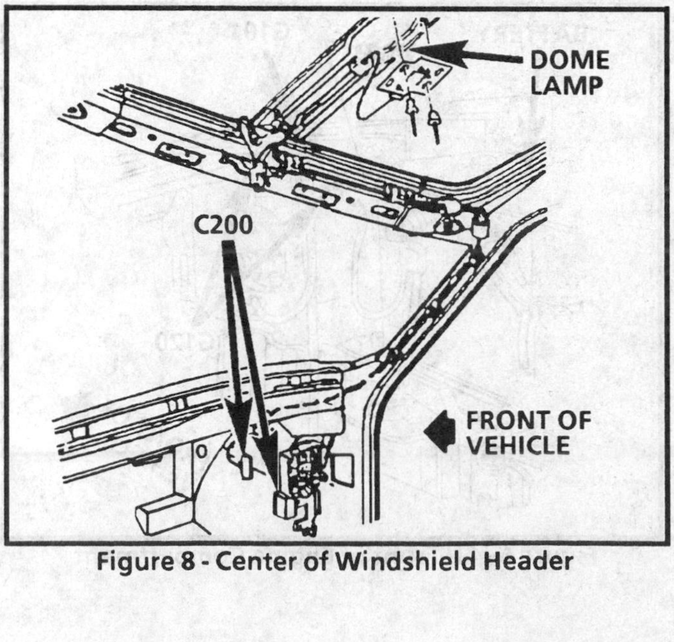
DOME
LAMP
C200
FRONT OF
VEHICLE

Figure 8 - Center of Windshield Header

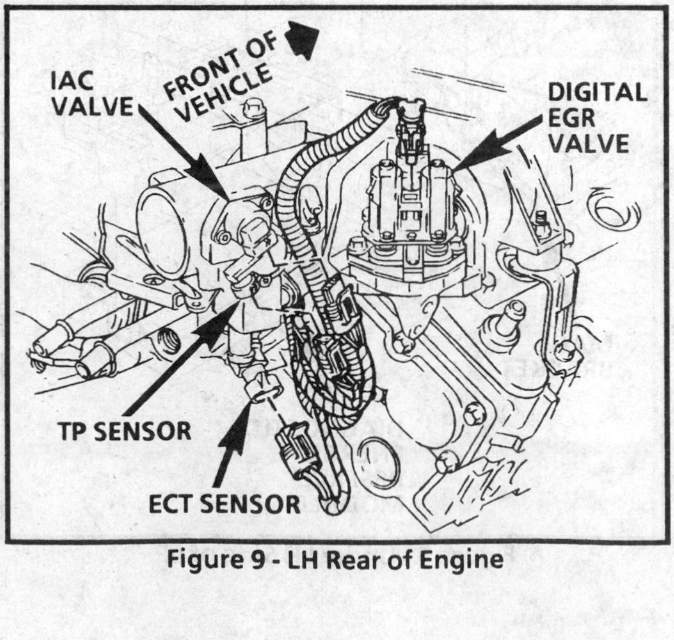
IAC
VALVE
FRONT OF
VEHICLE
DIGITAL
EGR
VALVE
TP SENSOR
ECT SENSOR

Figure 9 - LH Rear of Engine

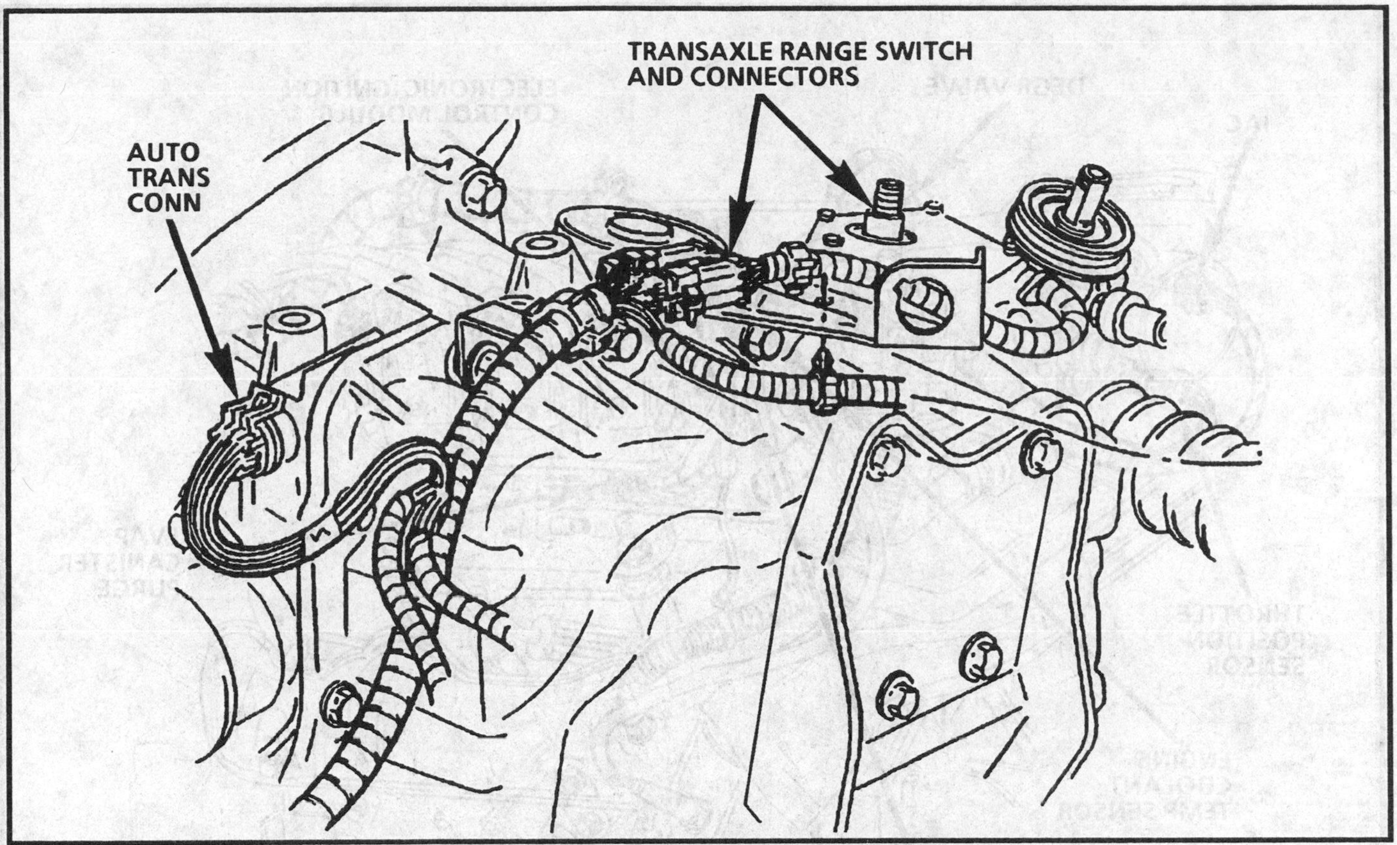
TRANSAXLE RANGE SWITCH
AND CONNECTORS
AUTO
TRANS
CONN

Figure 10 - Lower LH Side of Engine Compartment

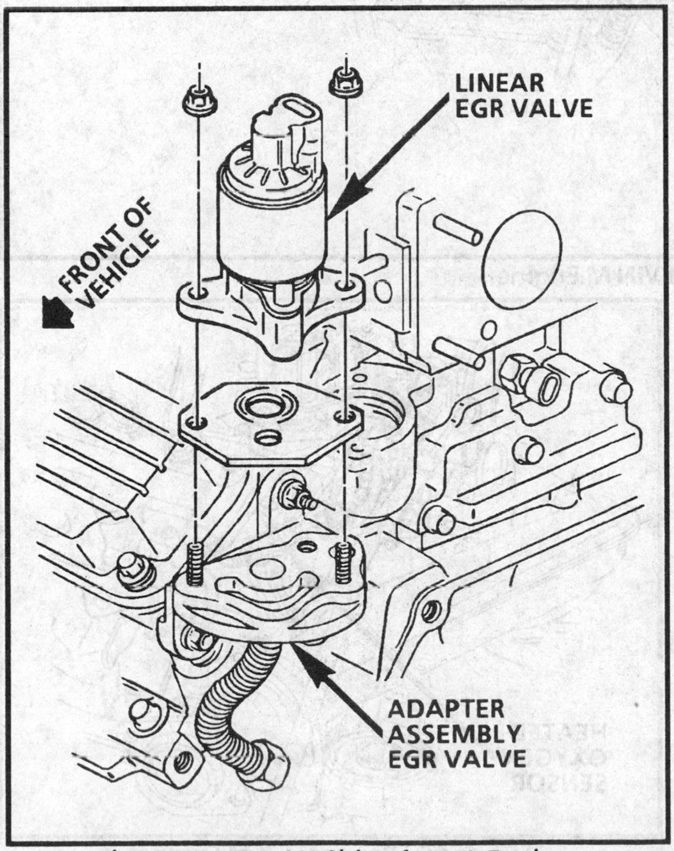
LINEAR
EGR VALVE
FRONT OF
VEHICLE
ADAPTER
ASSEMBLY
EGR VALVE

Figure 11 - Top LH Side of VIN L Engine

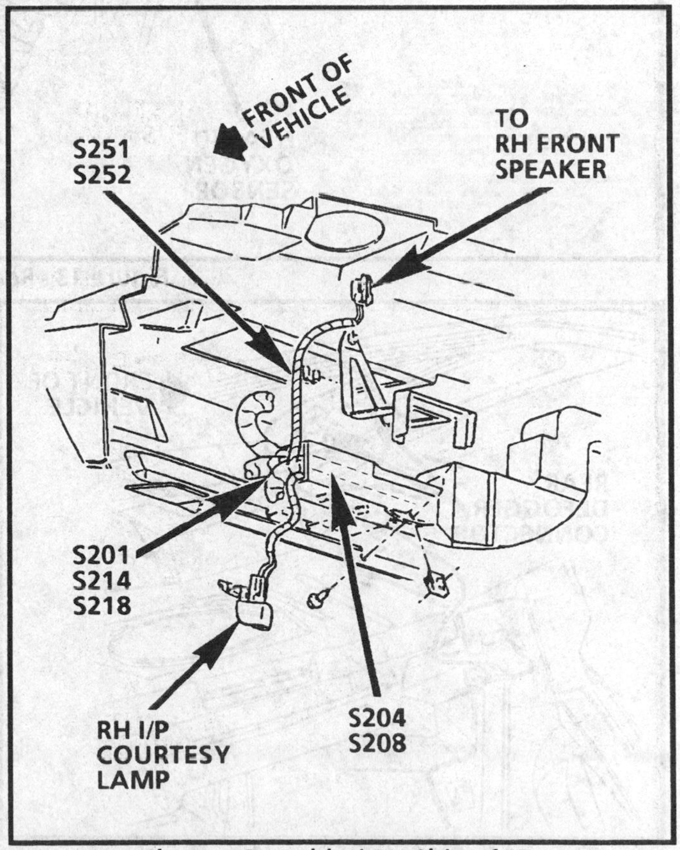
FRONT OF
VEHICLE
S251
S252
TO
RH FRONT
SPEAKER
S201
S214
S218
RH I/P
COURTESY
LAMP
S204
S208

Figure 12 - Behind RH Side of I/P

COMPONENT LOCATION VIEWS

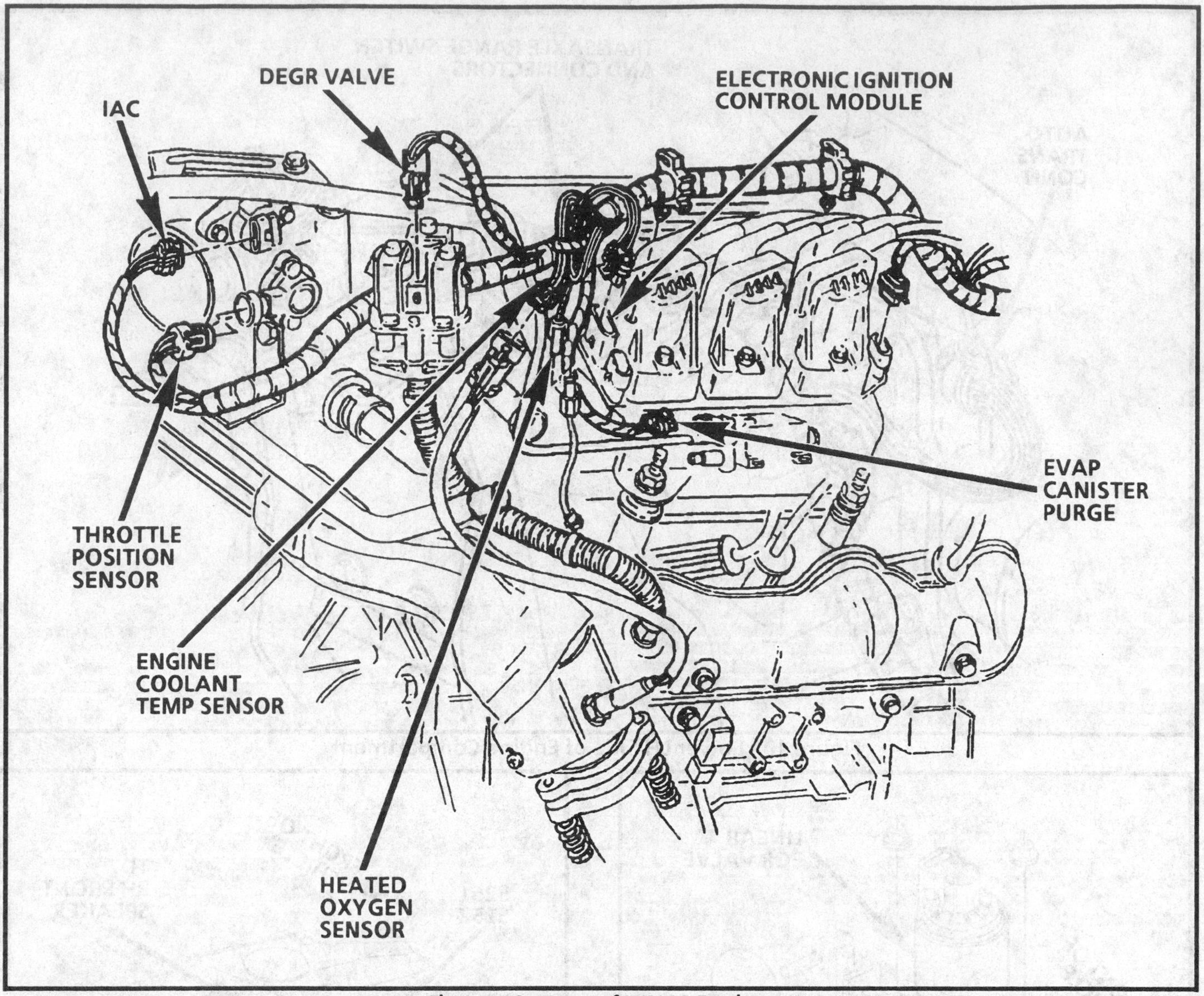
DEGR VALVE
IAC
ELECTRONIC IGNITION
CONTROL MODULE
EVAP
CANISTER
PURGE
THROTTLE
POSITION
SENSOR
ENGINE
COOLANT
TEMP SENSOR
HEATED
OXYGEN
SENSOR

Figure 13 - Rear of VIN M Engine

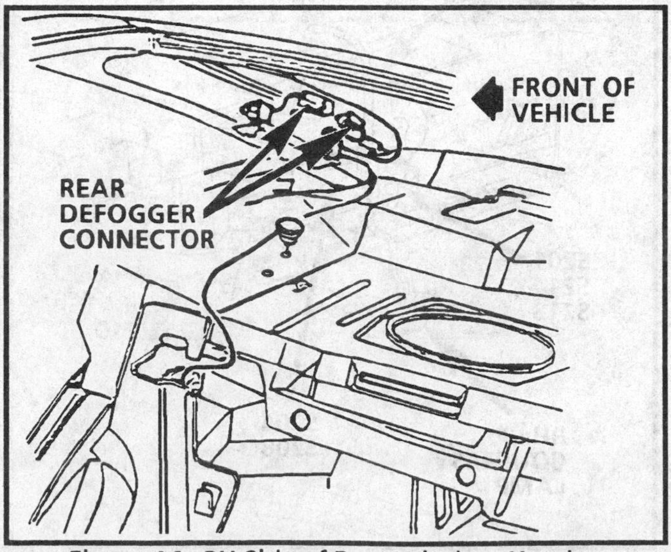
FRONT OF
VEHICLE
REAR
DEFOGGER
CONNECTOR

Figure 14 - RH Side of Rear Window Header

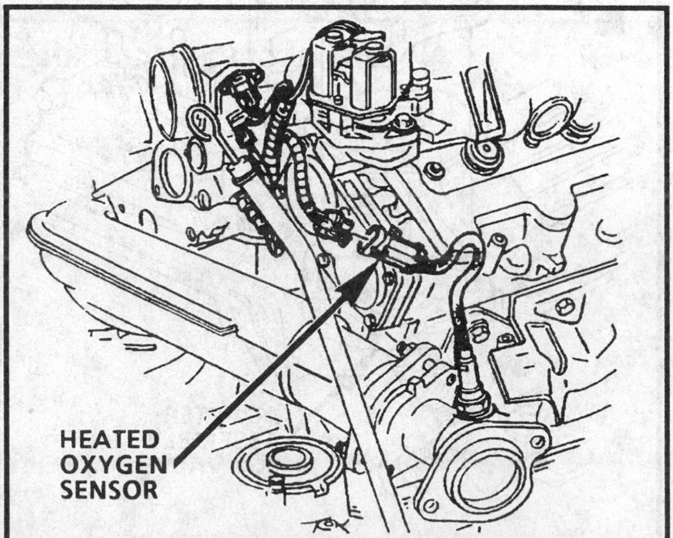
HEATED
OXYGEN
SENSOR

Figure 15 - Rear of VIN M Engine

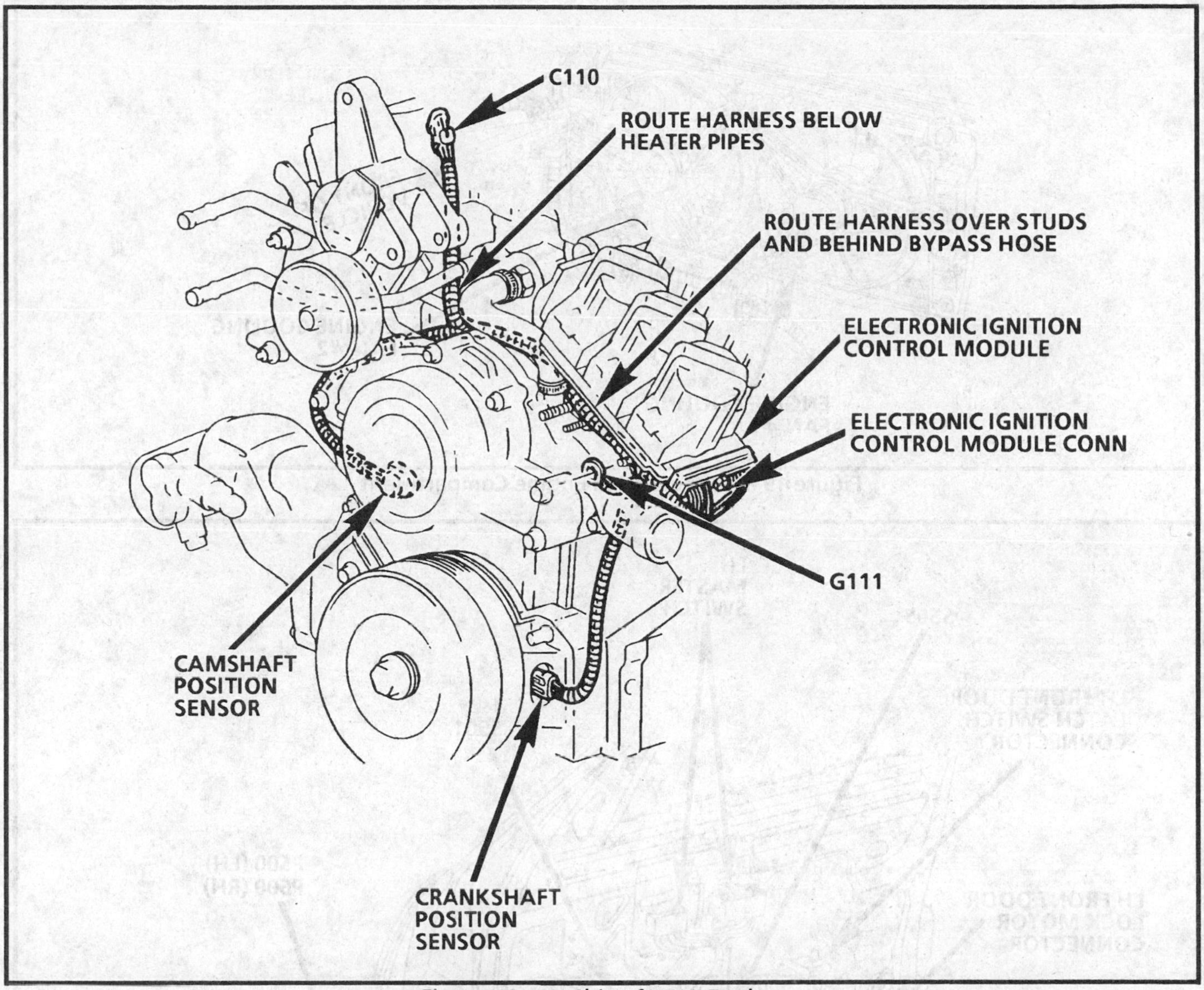
C110
ROUTE HARNESS BELOW
HEATER PIPES
ROUTE HARNESS OVER STUDS
AND BEHIND BYPASS HOSE
ELECTRONIC IGNITION
CONTROL MODULE
ELECTRONIC IGNITION
CONTROL MODULE CONN
G111
CAMSHAFT
POSITION
SENSOR
CRANKSHAFT
POSITION
SENSOR

Figure 16 - RH Side of VIN L Engine

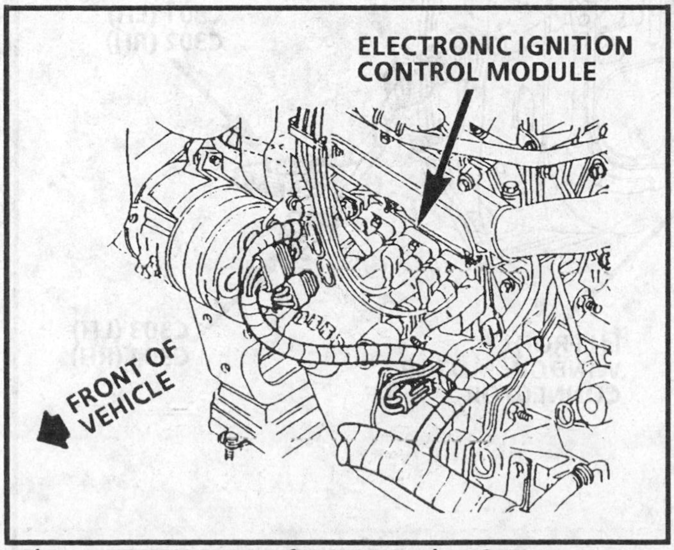
ELECTRONIC IGNITION
CONTROL MODULE
FRONT OF
VEHICLE

Figure 17 - RH Front of VIN M Engine Compartment

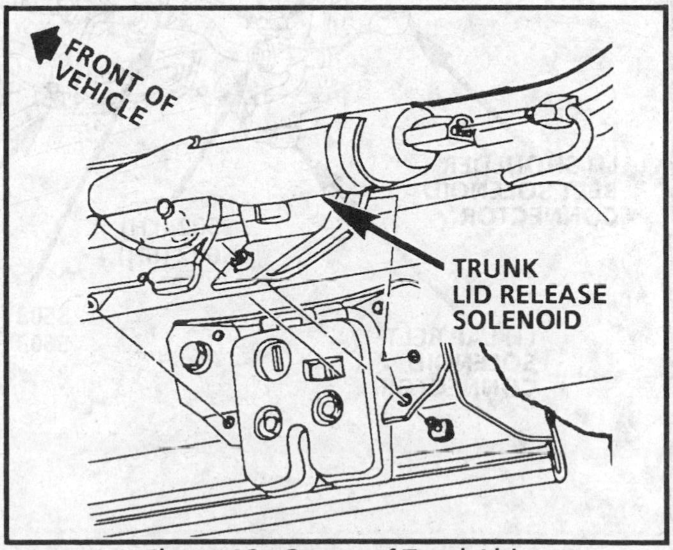
FRONT OF
VEHICLE
TRUNK
LID RELEASE
SOLENOID

Figure 18 - Center of Trunk Lid

COMPONENT LOCATION VIEWS

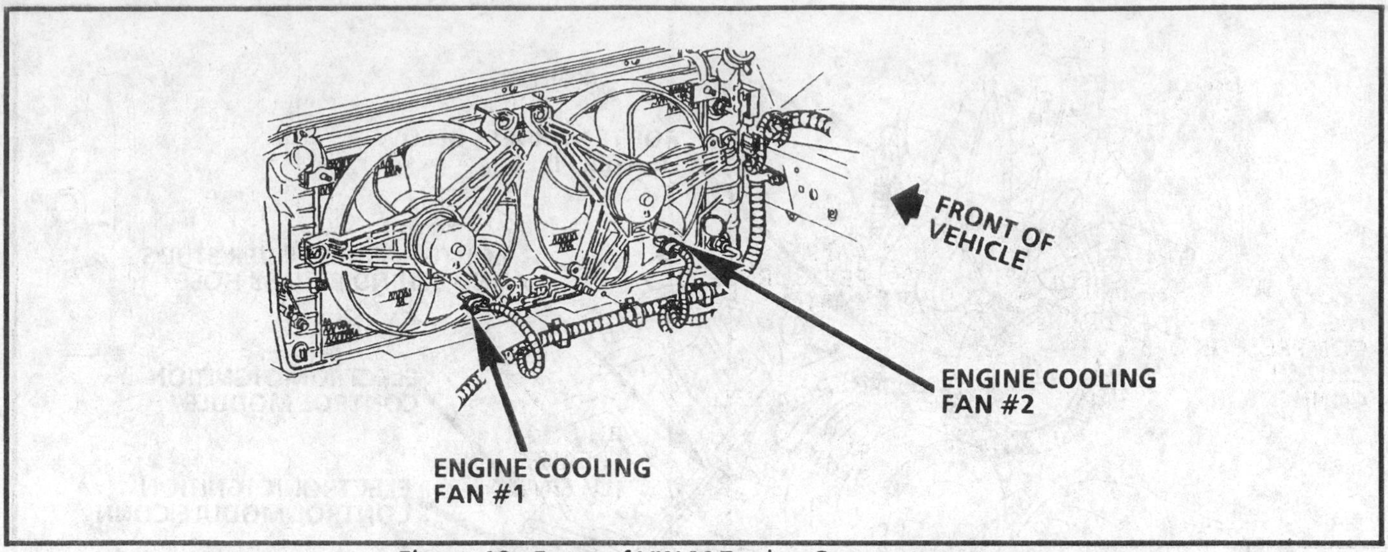
FRONT OF VEHICLE
ENGINE COOLING FAN #2
ENGINE COOLING FAN #1

Figure 19 - Front of VIN M Engine Compartment

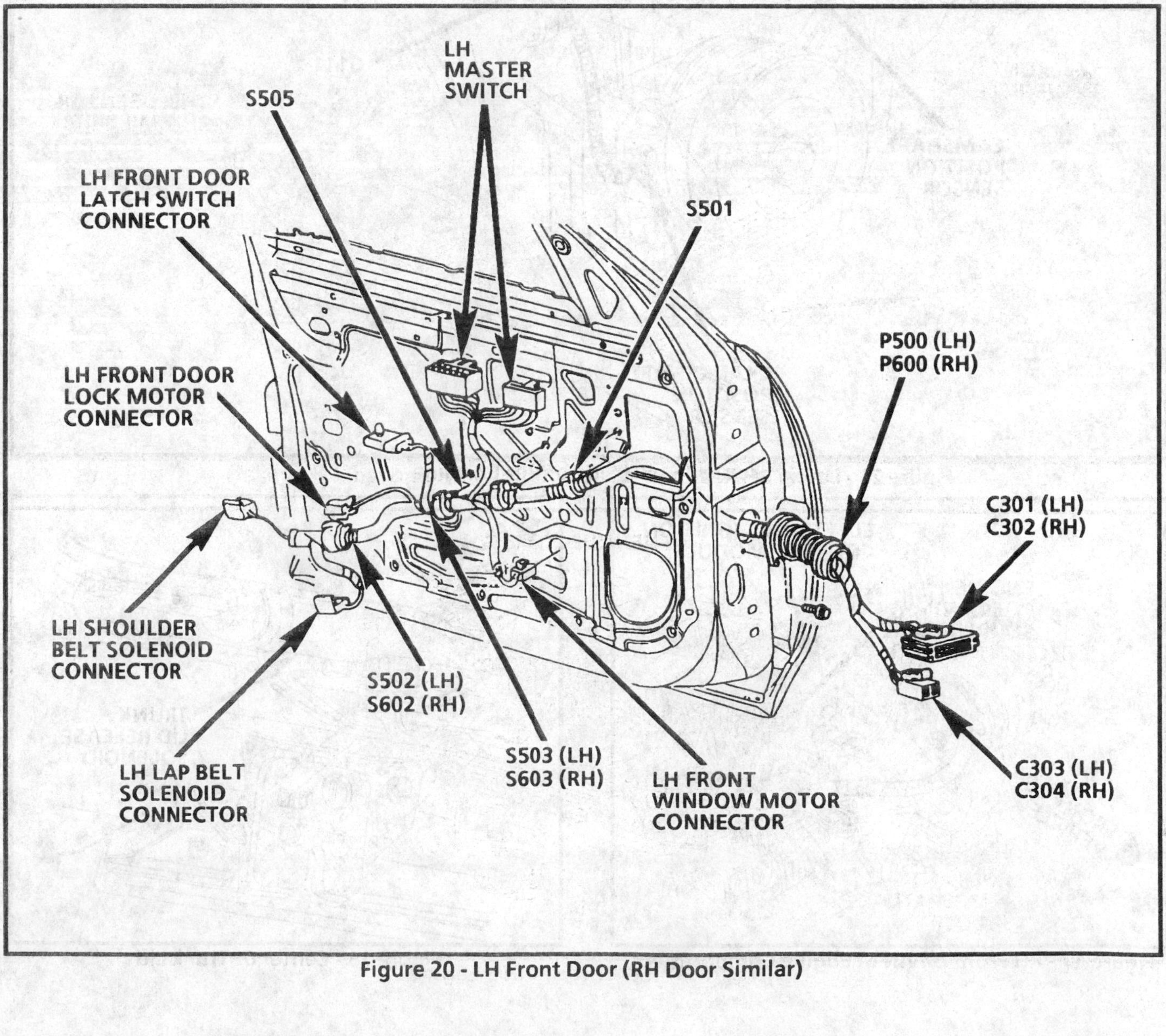
LH MASTER SWITCH
S505
LH FRONT DOOR LATCH SWITCH CONNECTOR
S501
LH FRONT DOOR LOCK MOTOR CONNECTOR
P500 (LH)
P600 (RH)
C301 (LH)
C302 (RH)
LH SHOULDER BELT SOLENOID CONNECTOR
S502 (LH)
S602 (RH)
S503 (LH)
S603 (RH)
LH LAP BELT SOLENOID CONNECTOR
LH FRONT WINDOW MOTOR CONNECTOR
C303 (LH)
C304 (RH)

Figure 20 - LH Front Door (RH Door Similar)

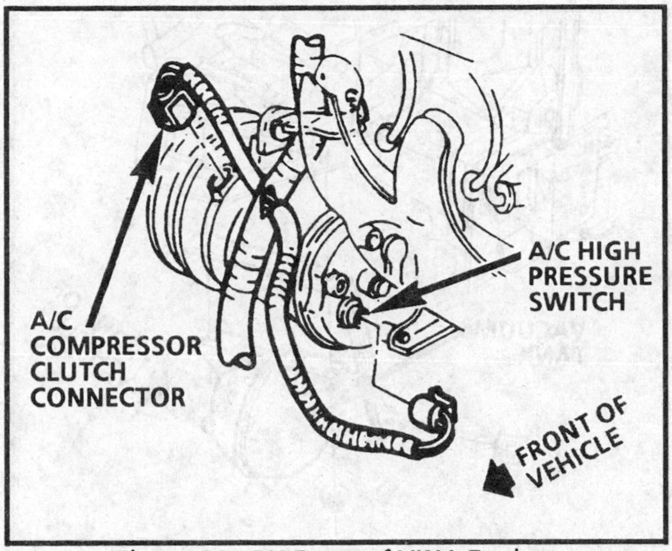
A/C COMPRESSOR CLUTCH CONNECTOR
A/C HIGH PRESSURE SWITCH
FRONT OF VEHICLE

Figure 21 - RH Front of VIN L Engine

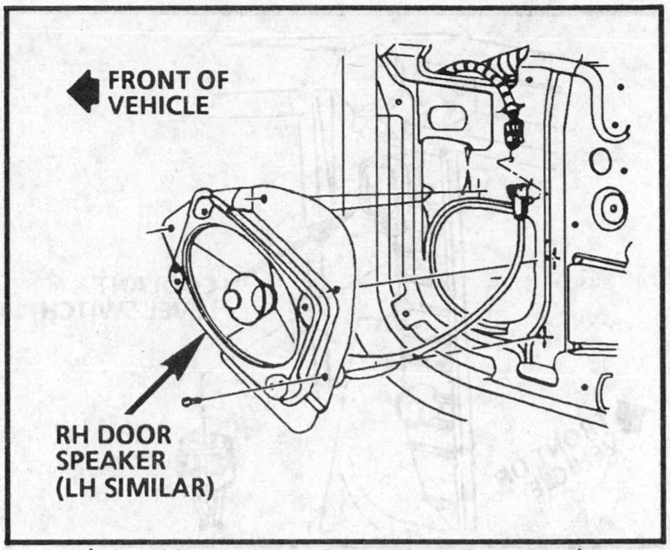
FRONT OF VEHICLE
RH DOOR SPEAKER (LH SIMILAR)

Figure 22 - RH Front Door, Near Door Jamb

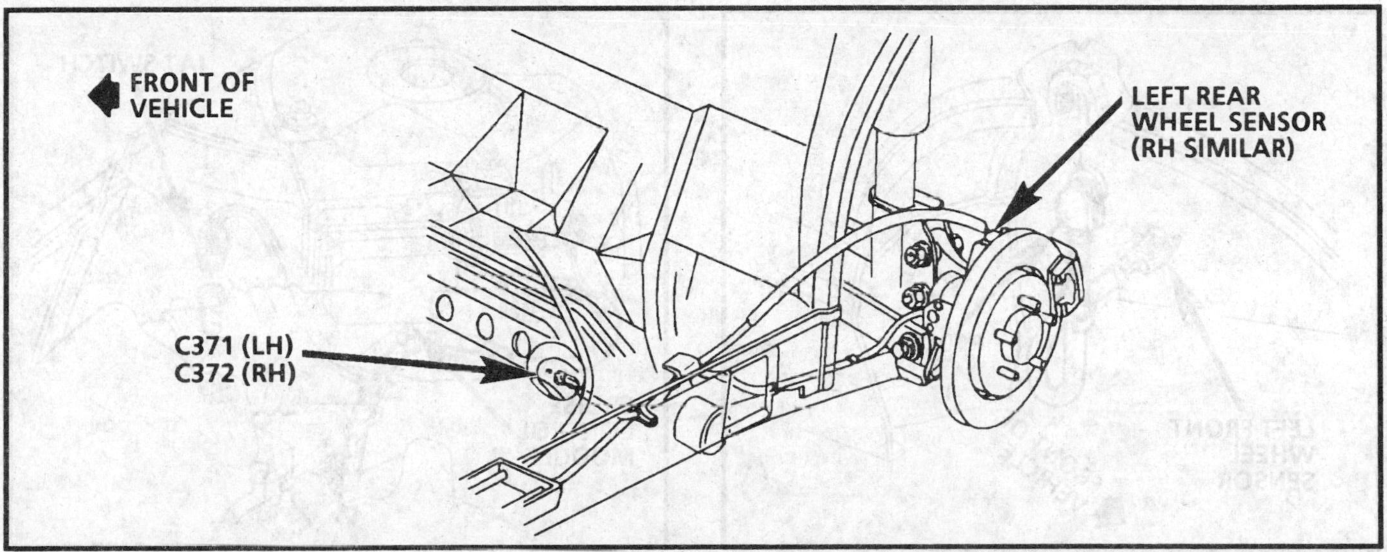
FRONT OF VEHICLE
LEFT REAR WHEEL SENSOR (RH SIMILAR)
C371 (LH)
C372 (RH)

Figure 23 - Lower LH Rear of Vehicle with Wheel Removed (RH Similar)

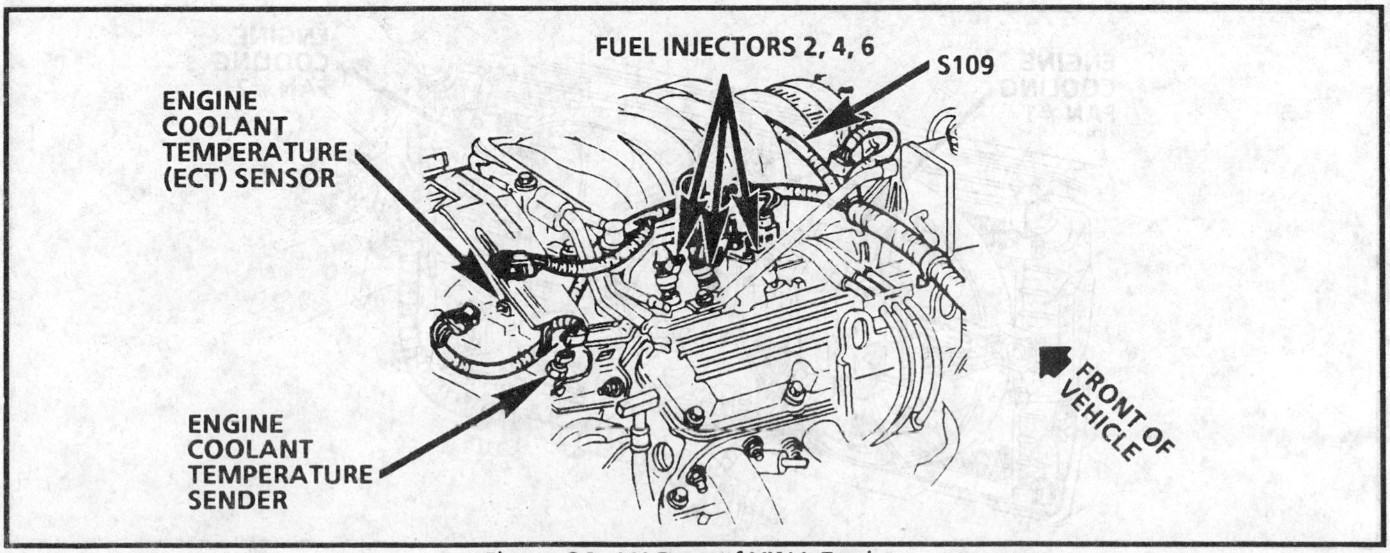
FUEL INJECTORS 2, 4, 6
S109
ENGINE COOLANT TEMPERATURE (ECT) SENSOR
ENGINE COOLANT TEMPERATURE SENDER
FRONT OF VEHICLE

Figure 24 - LH Rear of VIN L Engine

COMPONENT LOCATION VIEWS

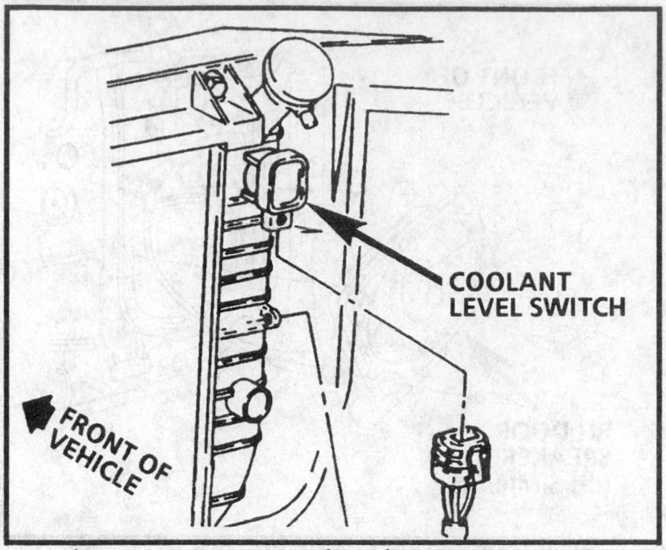
COOLANT
LEVEL SWITCH
FRONT OF
VEHICLE
Figure 25 - RH Front of Engine Compartment

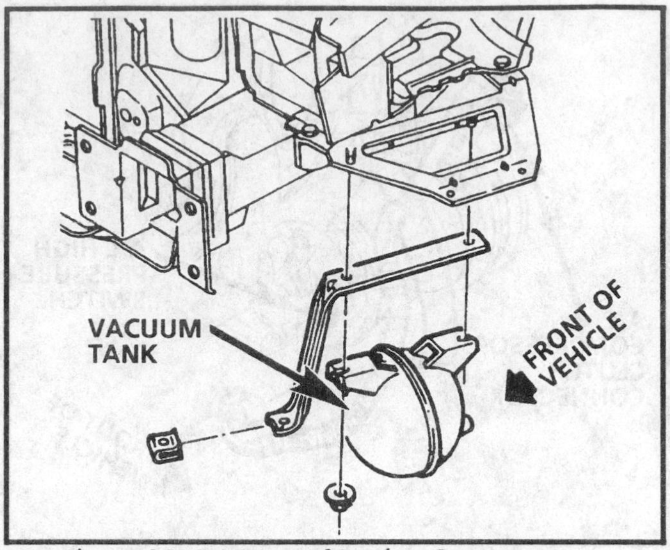
VACUUM
TANK
FRONT OF
VEHICLE
Figure 27 - LH Front of Engine Compartment

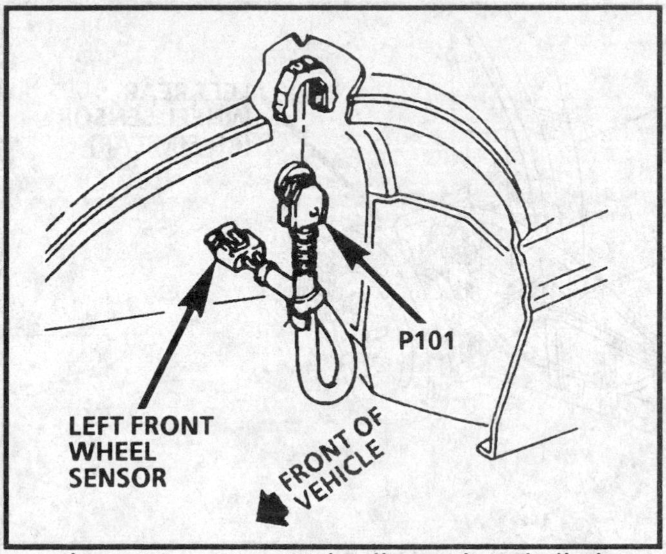
P101
LEFT FRONT
WHEEL
SENSOR
FRONT OF
VEHICLE
Figure 26 - LH Front Wheelhouse (RH Similar)

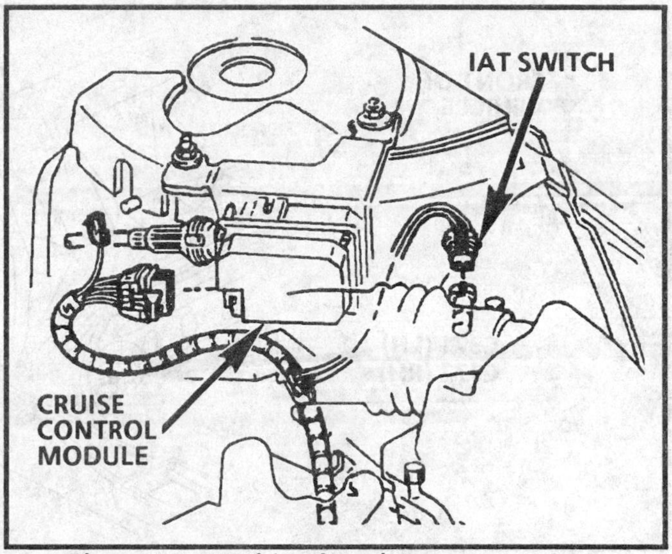
IAT SWITCH
CRUISE
CONTROL
MODULE
Figure 28 - LH Side of Engine Compartment

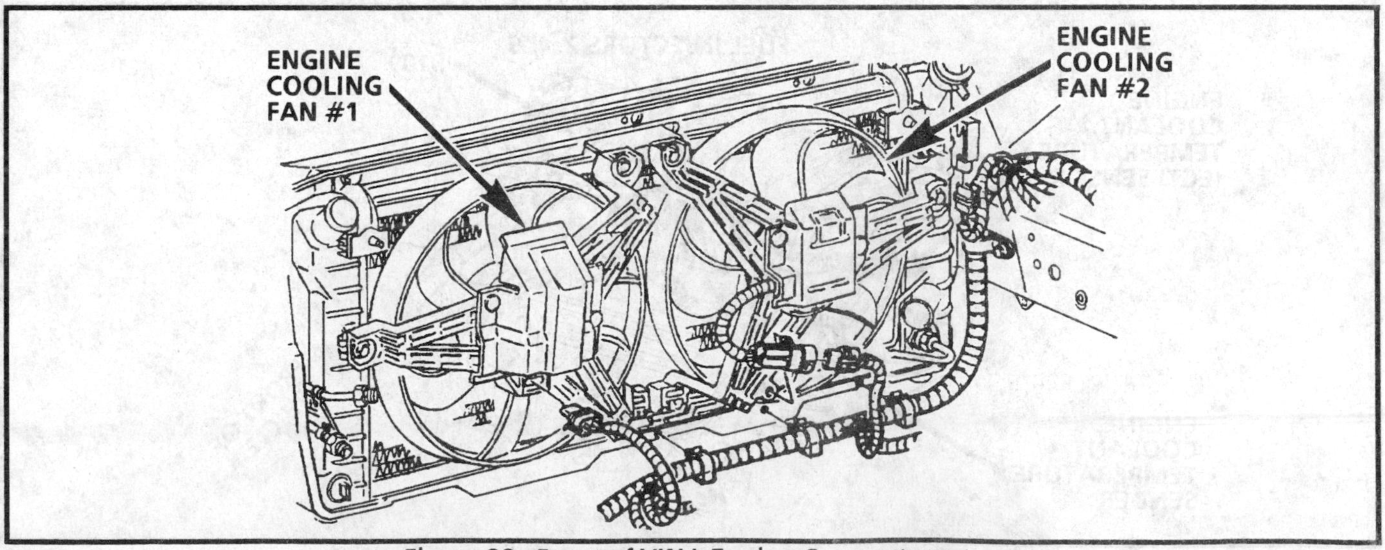
ENGINE
COOLING
FAN #1
ENGINE
COOLING
FAN #2
Figure 29 - Front of VIN L Engine Compartment

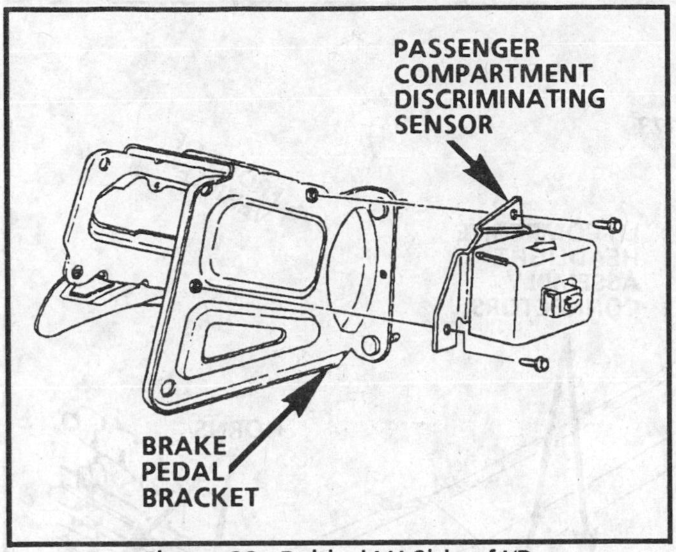
PASSENGER
COMPARTMENT
DISCRIMINATING
SENSOR
BRAKE
PEDAL
BRACKET

Figure 30 - Behind LH Side of I/P

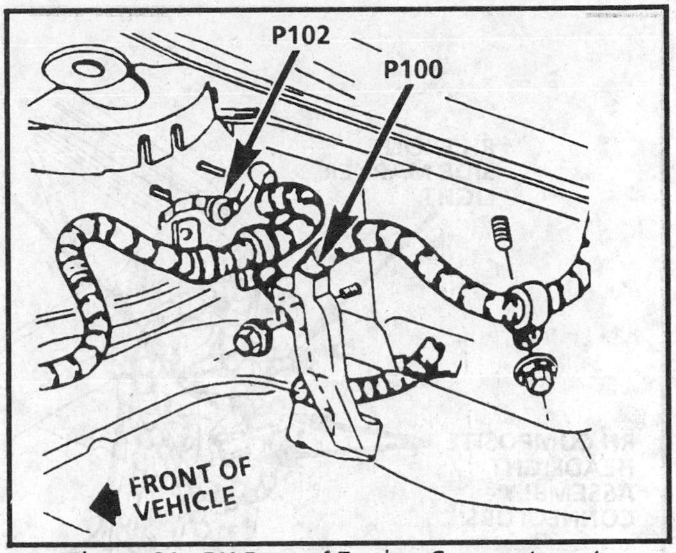
P102
P100
FRONT OF
VEHICLE

Figure 31 - RH Rear of Engine Compartment

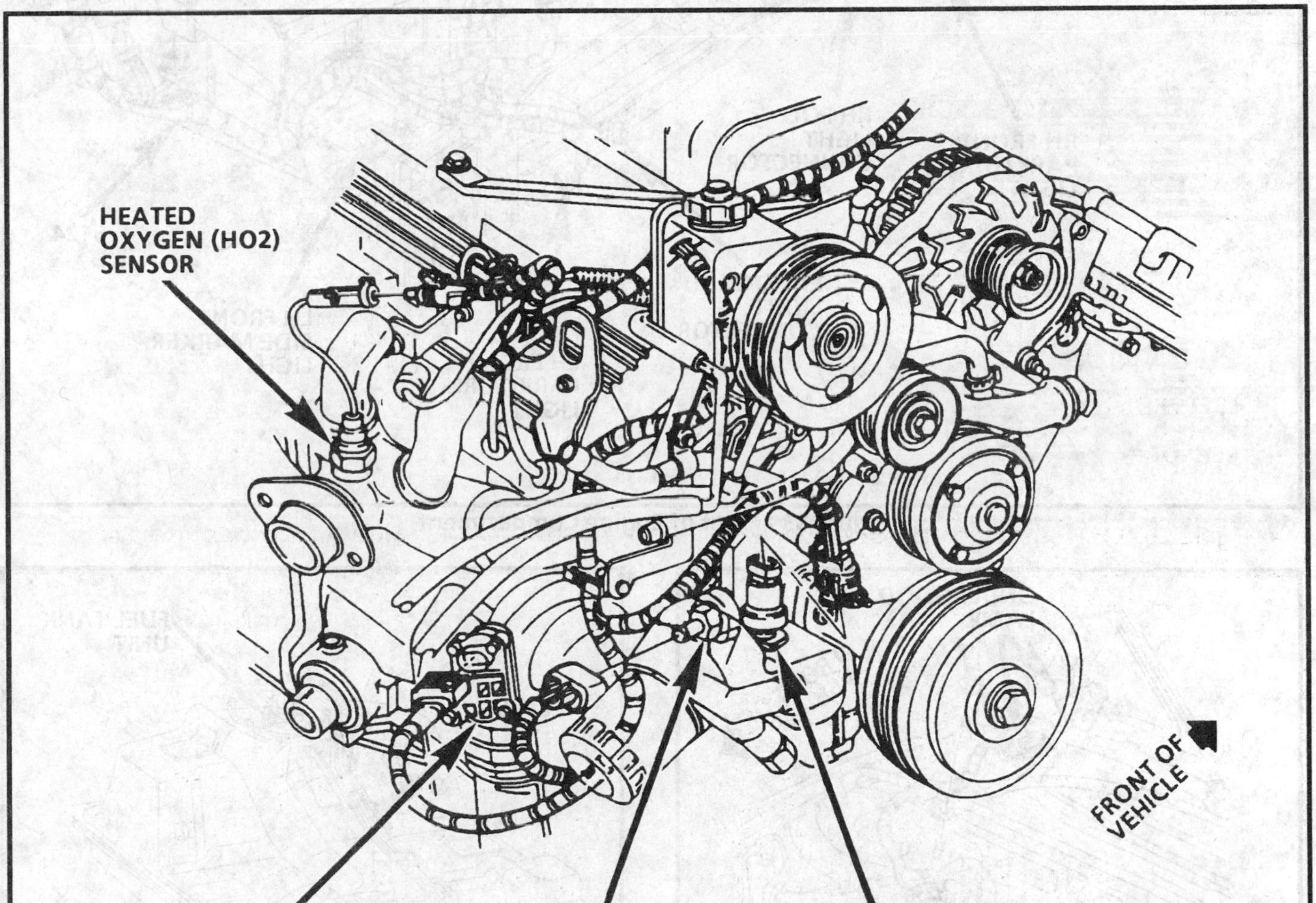
HEATED
OXYGEN (HO2)
SENSOR
FRONT OF
VEHICLE
VEHICLE SPEED
SENSOR (VSS)
KNOCK
SENSOR (KS)
FUEL PUMP/OIL
PRESSURE SWITCH

Figure 32 - RH Rear of VIN L Engine

COMPONENT LOCATION VIEWS

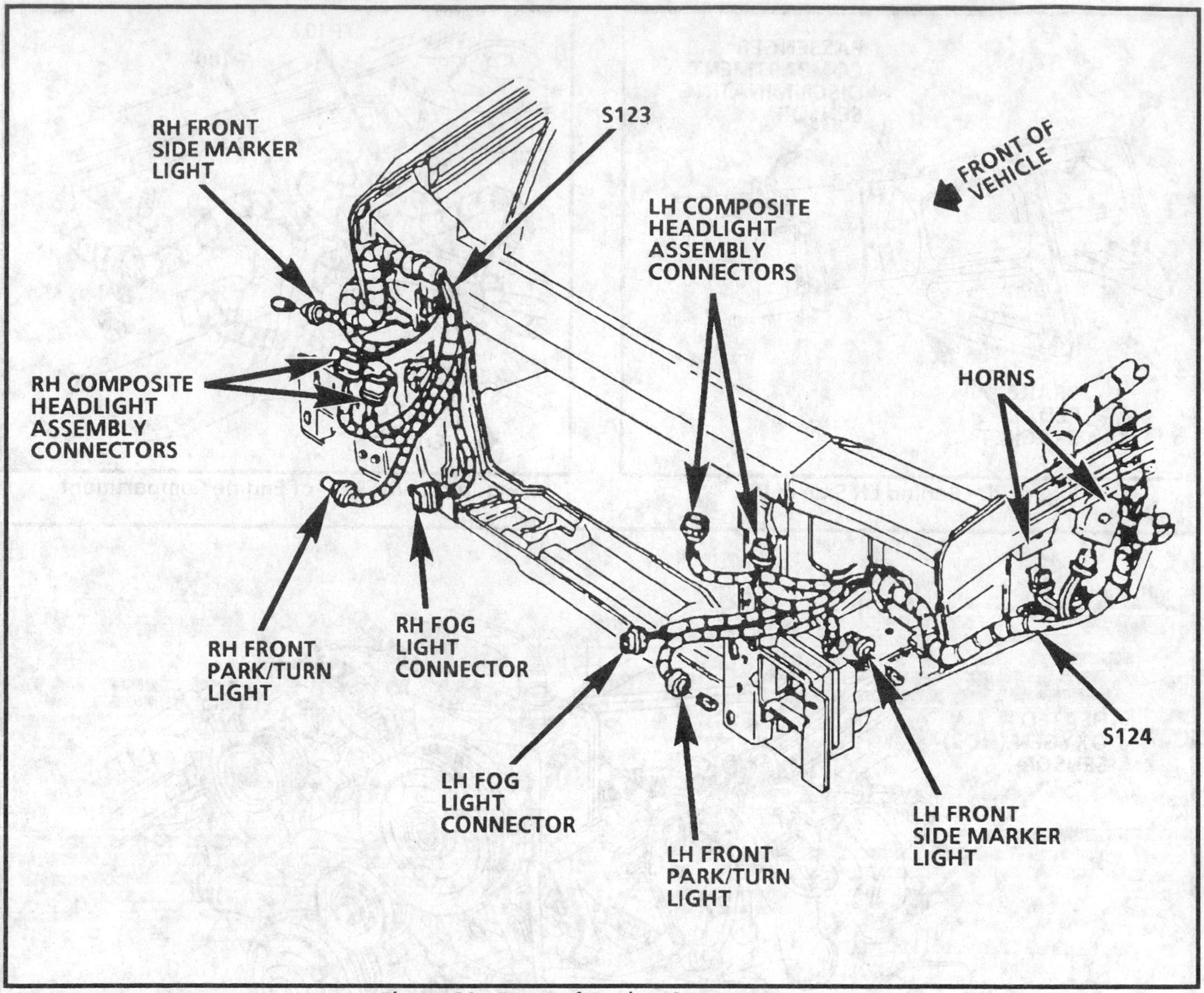

RH FRONT SIDE MARKER LIGHT
S123
FRONT OF VEHICLE
LH COMPOSITE HEADLIGHT ASSEMBLY CONNECTORS
RH COMPOSITE HEADLIGHT ASSEMBLY CONNECTORS
HORNS
RH FRONT PARK/TURN LIGHT
RH FOG LIGHT CONNECTOR
S124
LH FOG LIGHT CONNECTOR
LH FRONT SIDE MARKER LIGHT
LH FRONT PARK/TURN LIGHT

Figure 33 - Front of Engine Compartment

UNDERHOOD LAMP
FRONT OF VEHICLE
P104

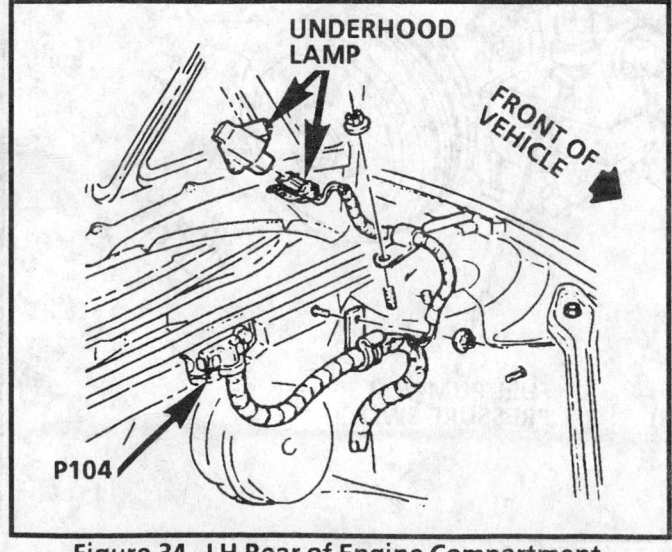

Figure 34 - LH Rear of Engine Compartment

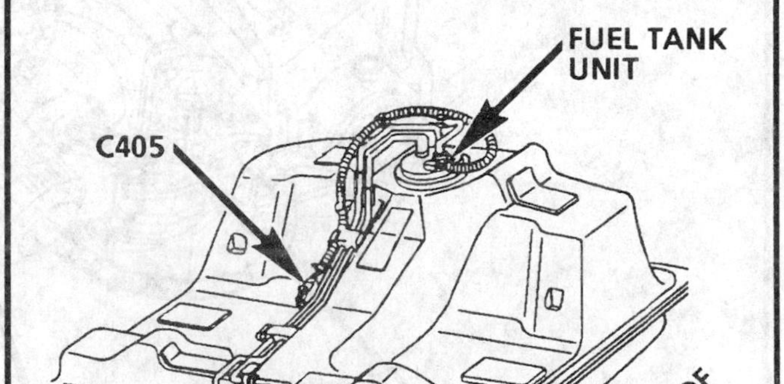

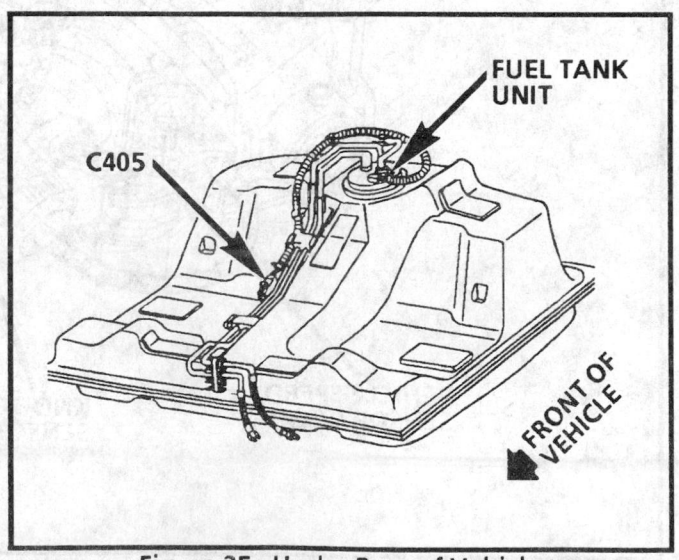

FUEL TANK UNIT
C405
FRONT OF VEHICLE

Figure 35 - Under Rear of Vehicle

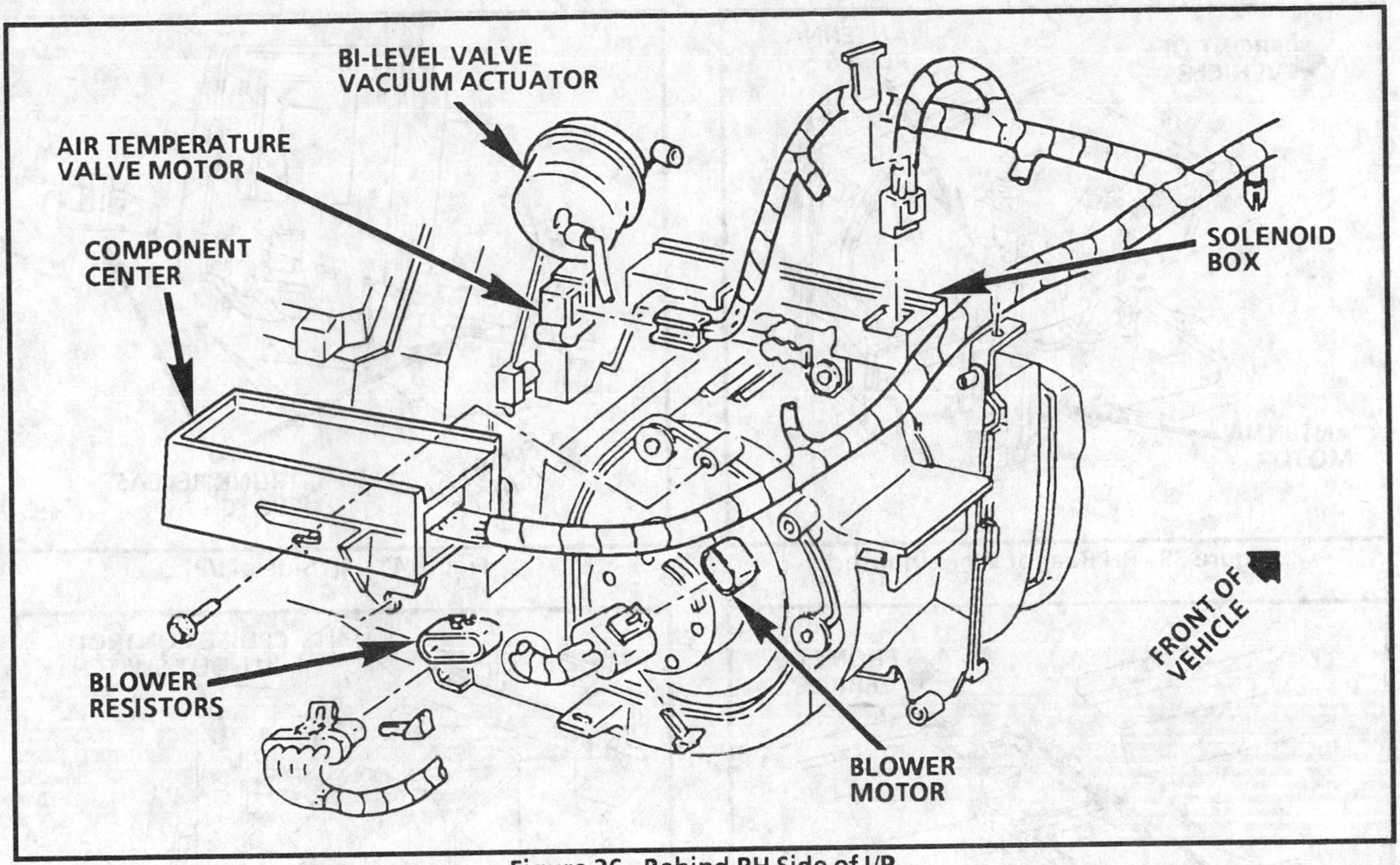
BI-LEVEL VALVE
VACUUM ACTUATOR
AIR TEMPERATURE
VALVE MOTOR
COMPONENT
CENTER
SOLENOID
BOX
FRONT OF
VEHICLE
BLOWER
RESISTORS
BLOWER
MOTOR

Figure 36 - Behind RH Side of I/P

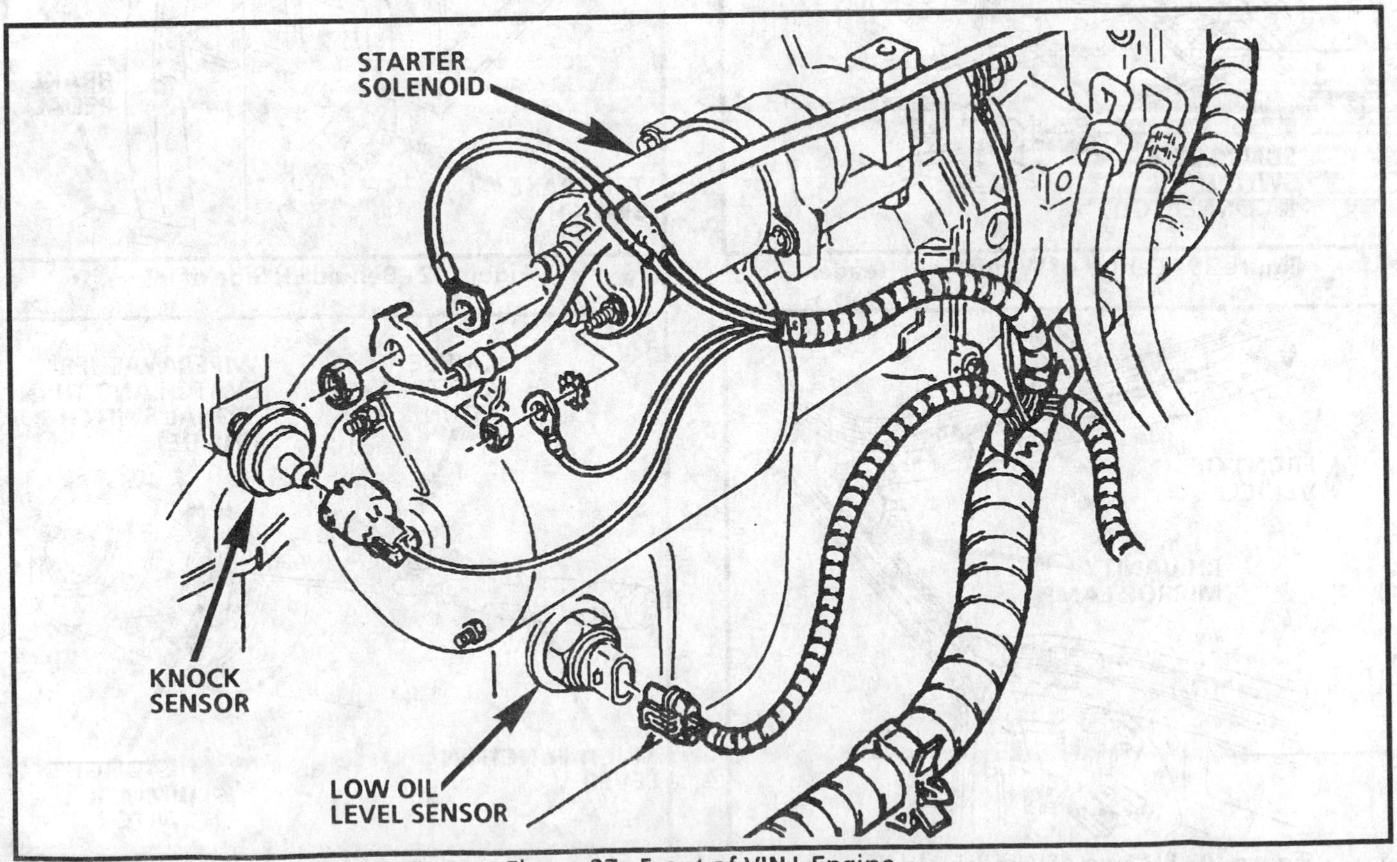
STARTER
SOLENOID
KNOCK
SENSOR
LOW OIL
LEVEL SENSOR

Figure 37 - Front of VIN L Engine

COMPONENT LOCATION VIEWS

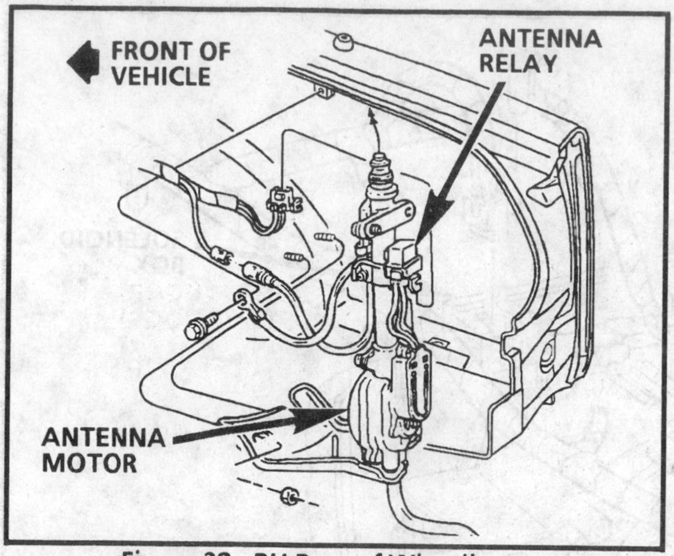
FRONT OF
VEHICLE
ANTENNA
RELAY
ANTENNA
MOTOR

Figure 38 - RH Rear of Wheelhouse

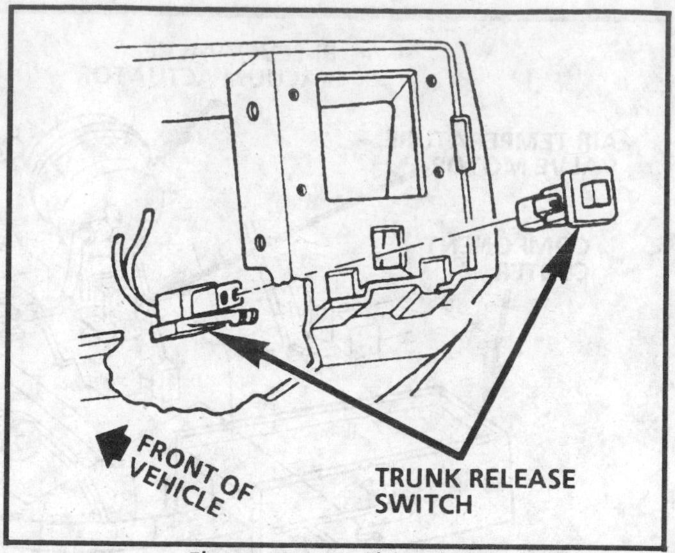
FRONT OF
VEHICLE
TRUNK RELEASE
SWITCH

Figure 41 - RH Side of I/P

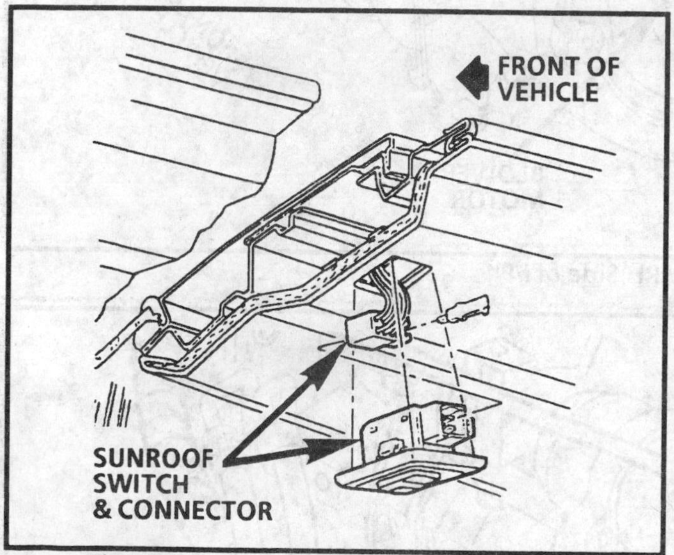
FRONT OF
VEHICLE
SUNROOF
SWITCH
& CONNECTOR

Figure 39 - Center of Windshield Header

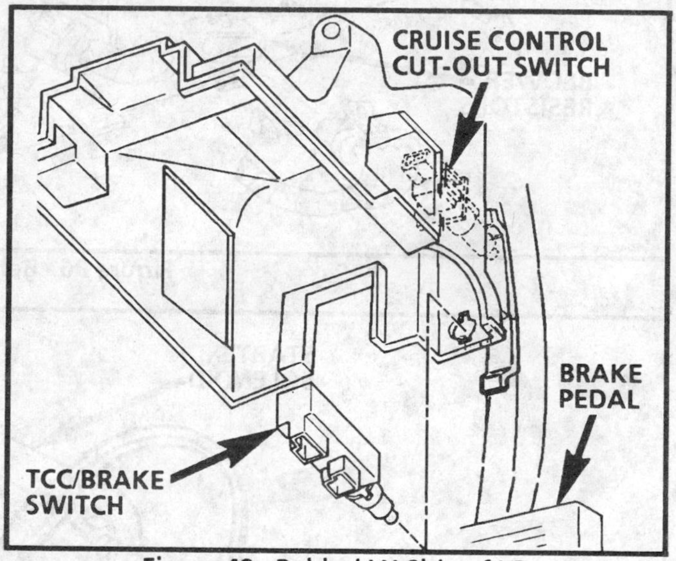
CRUISE CONTROL
CUT-OUT SWITCH
BRAKE
PEDAL
TCC/BRAKE
SWITCH

Figure 42 - Behind LH Side of I/P

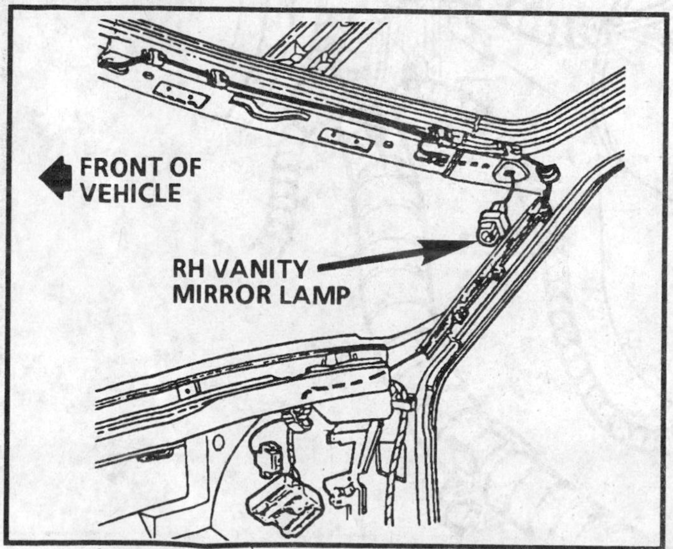
FRONT OF
VEHICLE
RH VANITY
MIRROR LAMP

Figure 40 - RH Side of Windshield Header

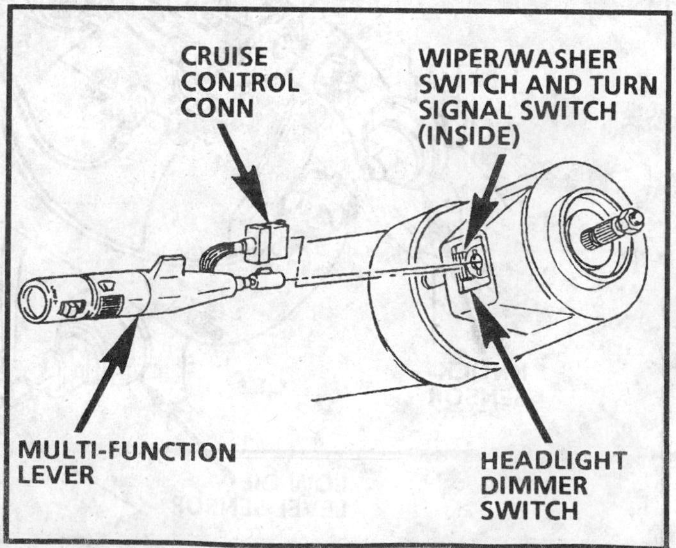
CRUISE
CONTROL
CONN
WIPER/WASHER
SWITCH AND TURN
SIGNAL SWITCH
(INSIDE)
MULTI-FUNCTION
LEVER
HEADLIGHT
DIMMER
SWITCH

Figure 43 - Top of Steering Column

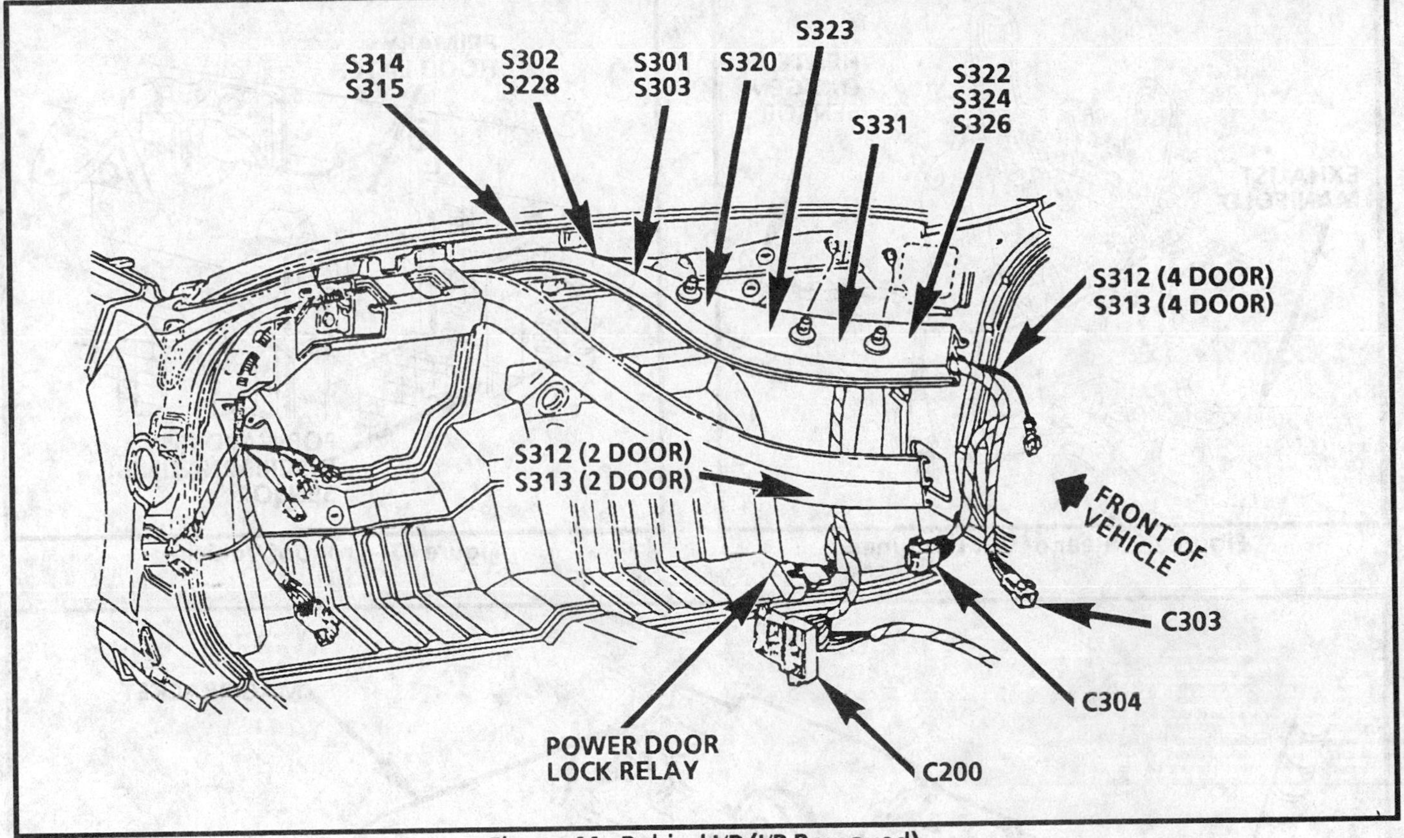
S314
S315
S302
S228
S301
S303
S320
S323
S331
S322
S324
S326
S312 (4 DOOR)
S313 (4 DOOR)
S312 (2 DOOR)
S313 (2 DOOR)
FRONT OF VEHICLE
C303
C304
POWER DOOR LOCK RELAY
C200

Figure 44 - Behind I/P (I/P Removed)

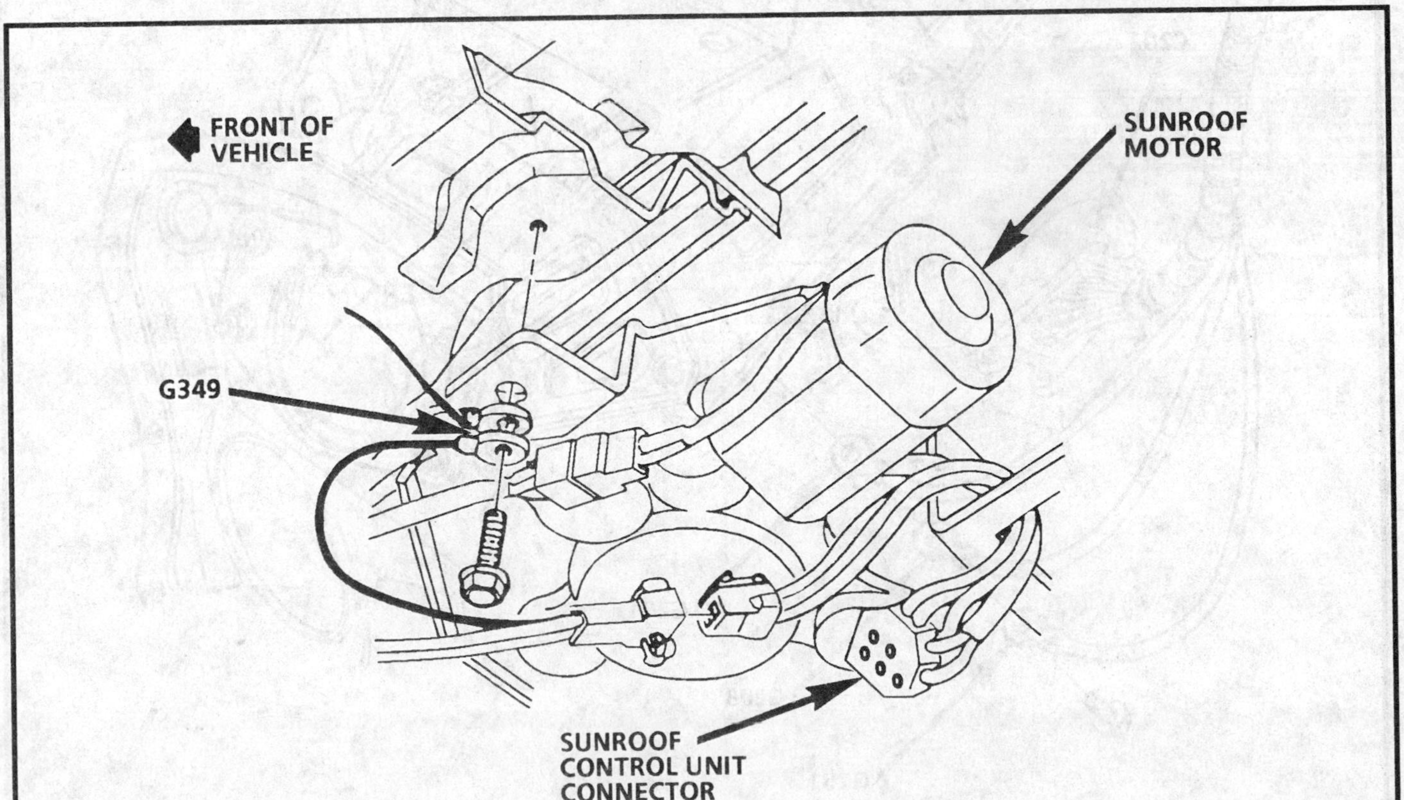
FRONT OF VEHICLE
SUNROOF MOTOR
G349
SUNROOF CONTROL UNIT CONNECTOR

Figure 45 - Center of Windshield Header

COMPONENT LOCATION VIEWS

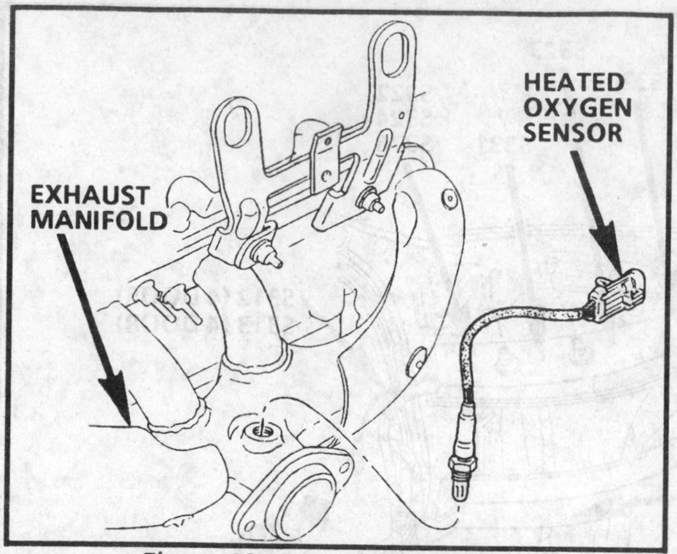
HEATED
OXYGEN
SENSOR
EXHAUST
MANIFOLD

Figure 46 - Rear of VIN L Engine

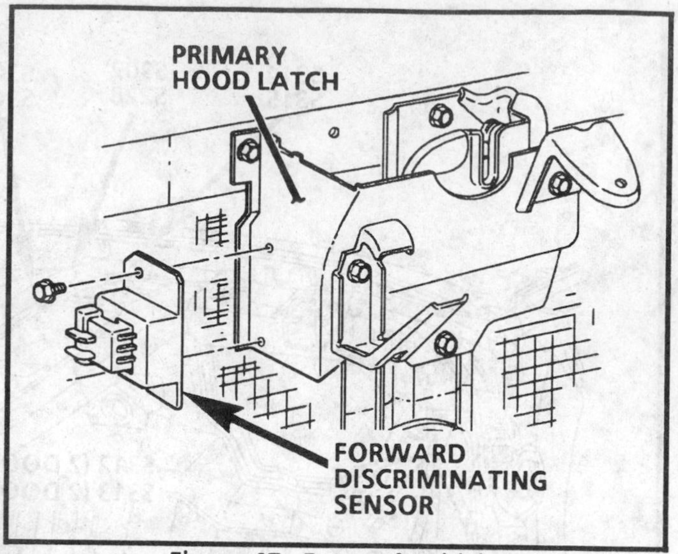
PRIMARY
HOOD LATCH
FORWARD
DISCRIMINATING
SENSOR

Figure 47 - Front of Vehicle

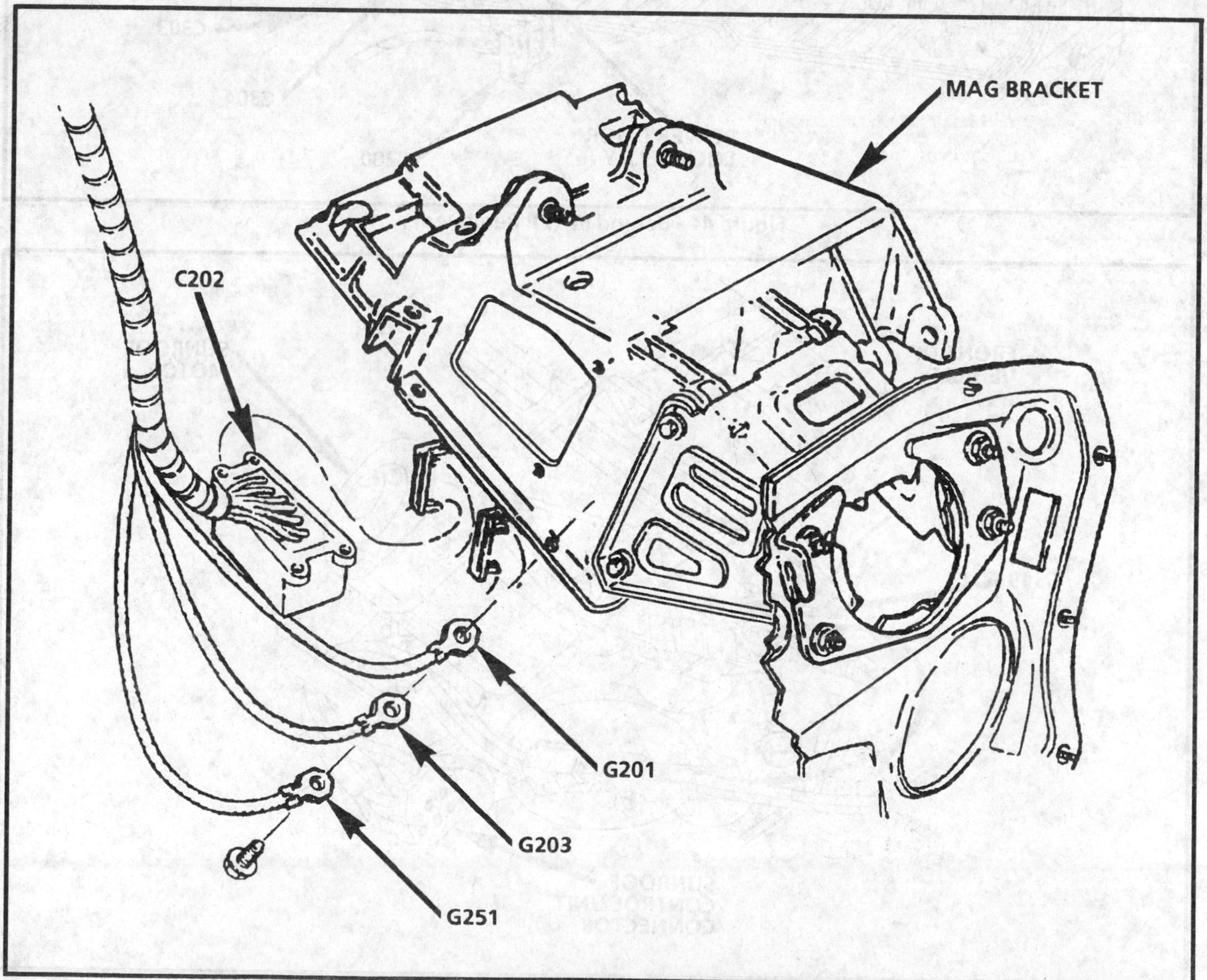
MAG BRACKET
C202
G201
G203
G251

Figure 48 - Behind LH Side of I/P

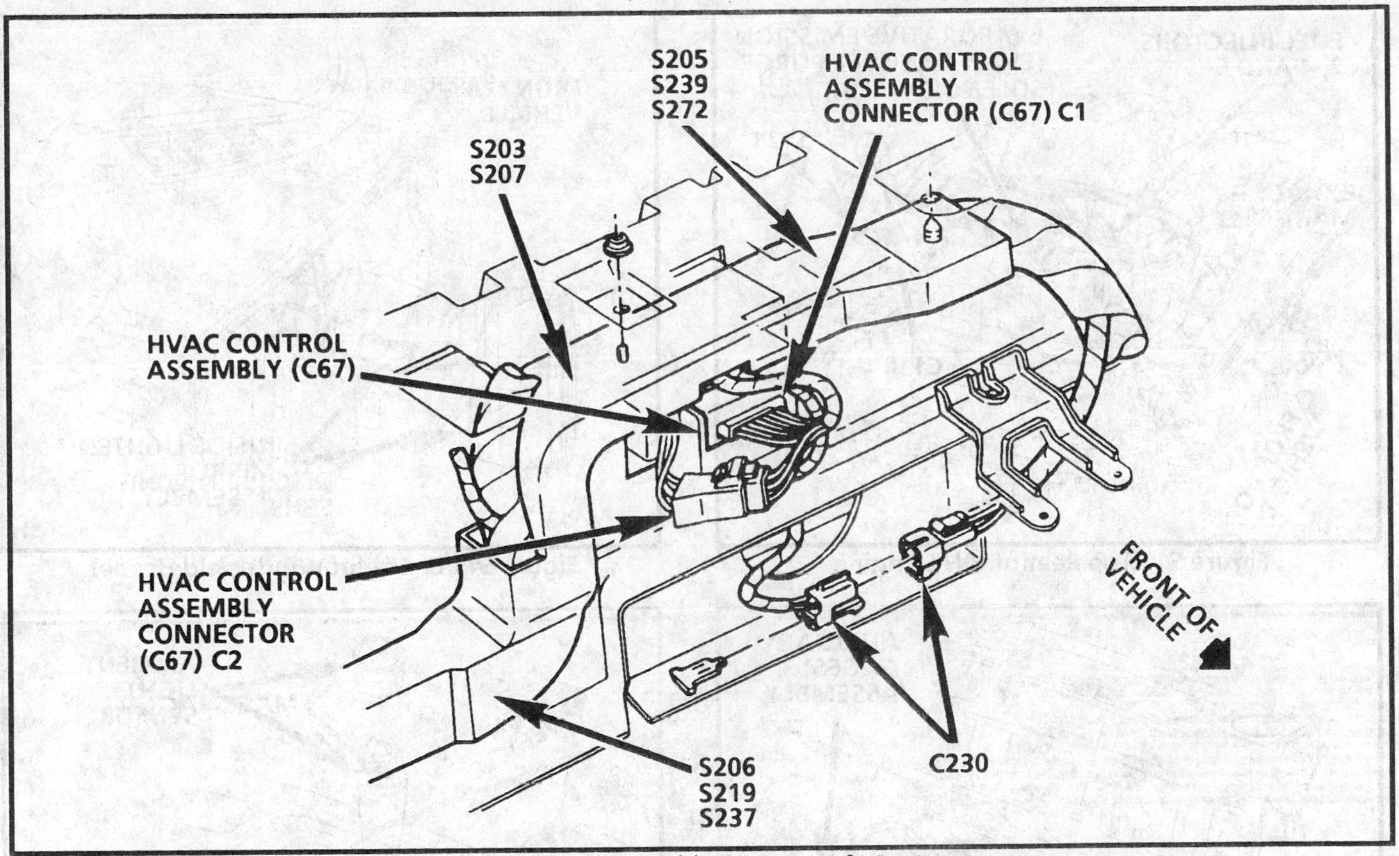
S205
S239
S272
HVAC CONTROL
ASSEMBLY
CONNECTOR (C67) C1
S203
S207
HVAC CONTROL
ASSEMBLY (C67)
HVAC CONTROL
ASSEMBLY
CONNECTOR
(C67) C2
FRONT OF
VEHICLE
S206
S219
S237
C230

Figure 49 - Behind Center of I/P

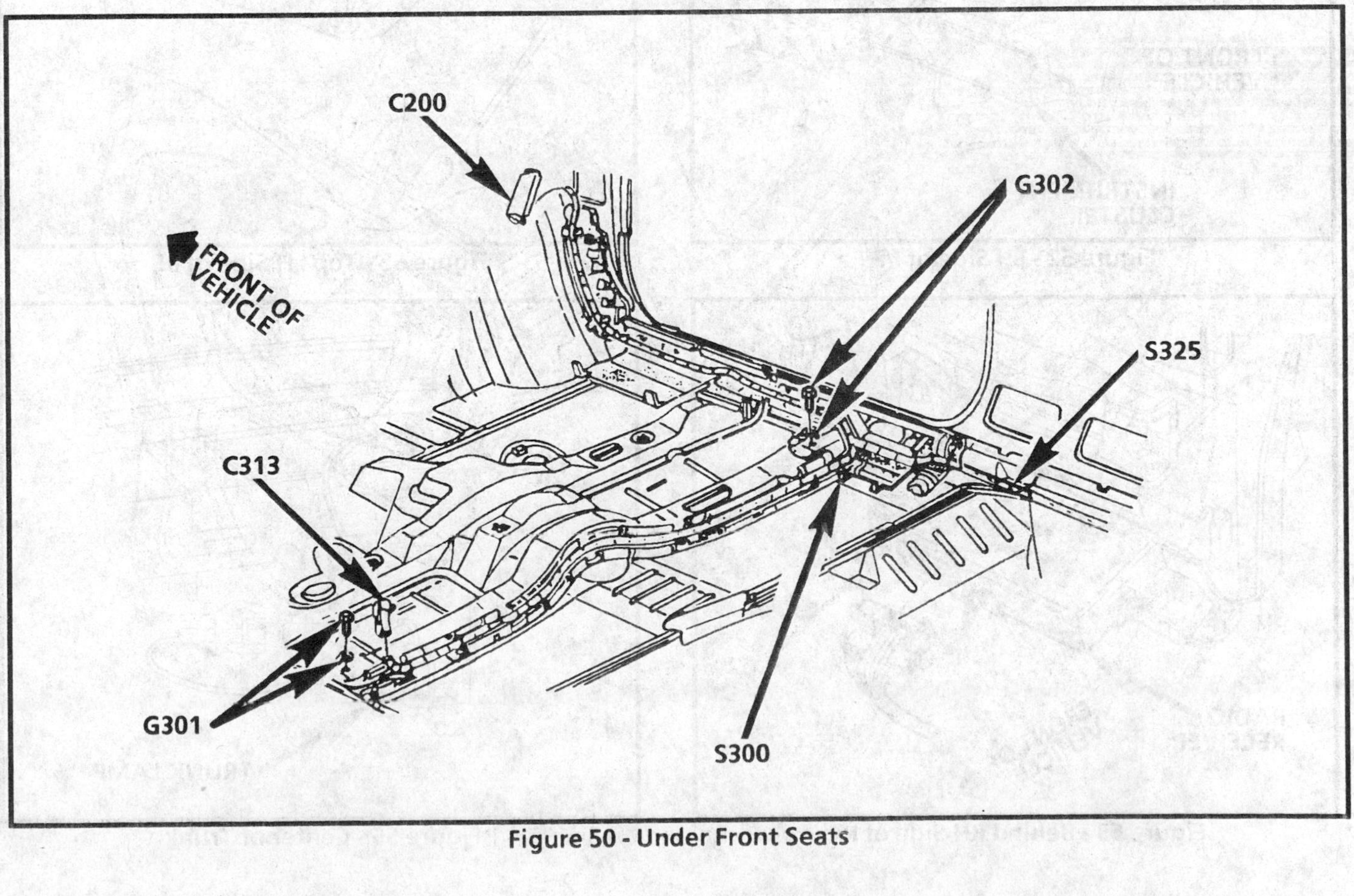
C200
FRONT OF
VEHICLE
G302
S325
C313
G301
S300

Figure 50 - Under Front Seats

COMPONENT LOCATION VIEWS

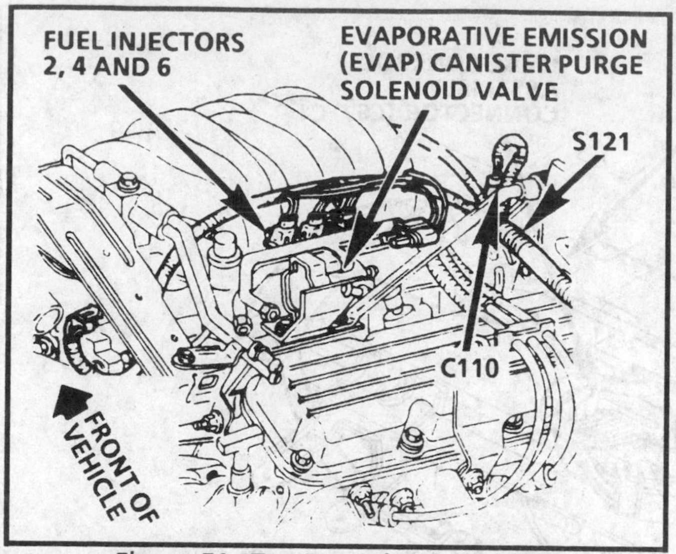
FUEL INJECTORS
2, 4 AND 6
EVAPORATIVE EMISSION
(EVAP) CANISTER PURGE
SOLENOID VALVE
S121
C110
FRONT OF
VEHICLE

Figure 51 - Top Rear of VIN L Engine

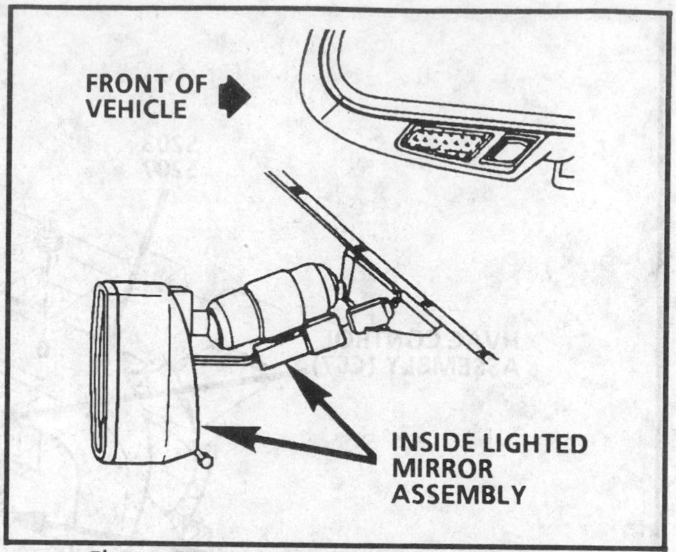
FRONT OF
VEHICLE
INSIDE LIGHTED
MIRROR
ASSEMBLY

Figure 54 - Center of Windshield Header

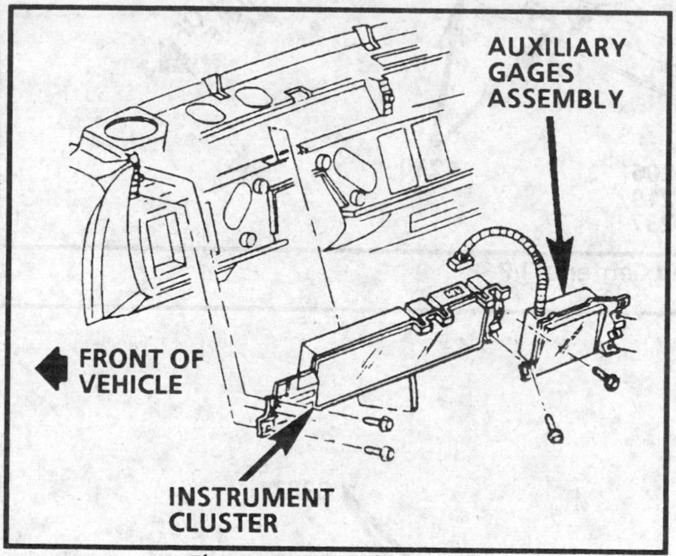
AUXILIARY
GAGES
ASSEMBLY
FRONT OF
VEHICLE
INSTRUMENT
CLUSTER

Figure 52 - LH Side of I/P

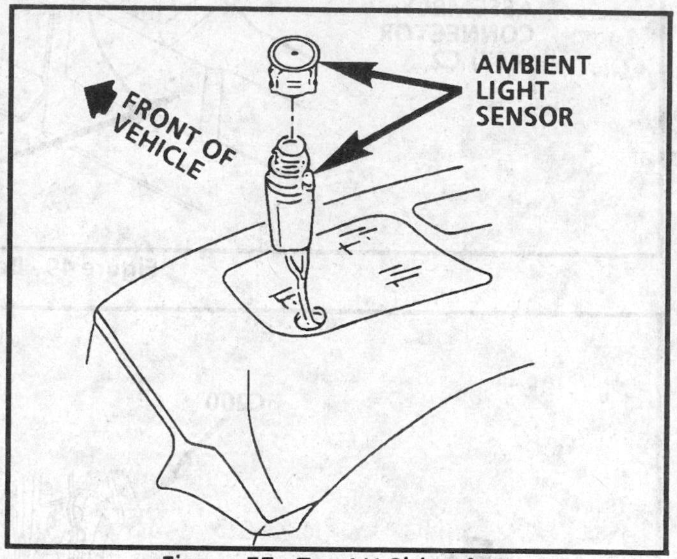
AMBIENT
LIGHT
SENSOR
FRONT OF
VEHICLE

Figure 55 - Top LH Side of I/P

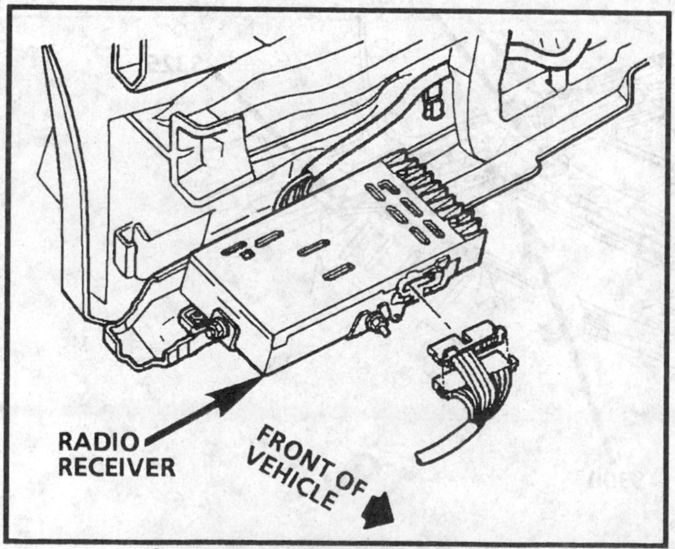
RADIO
RECEIVER
FRONT OF
VEHICLE

Figure 53 - Behind RH Side of I/P

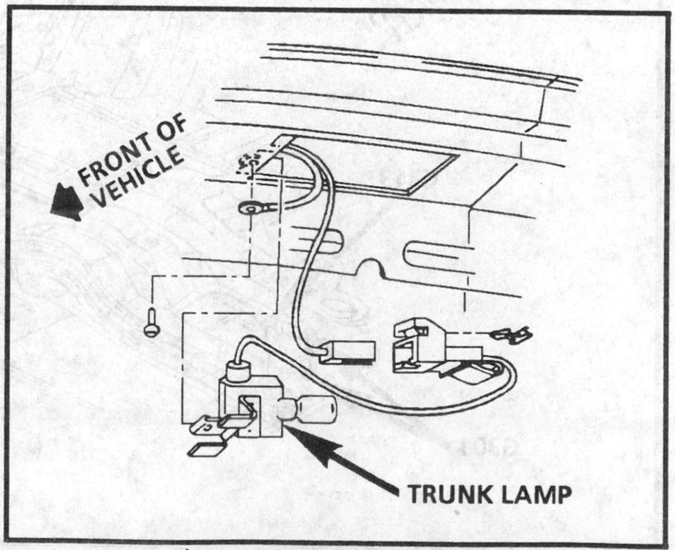
FRONT OF
VEHICLE
TRUNK LAMP

Figure 56 - Center of Trunk

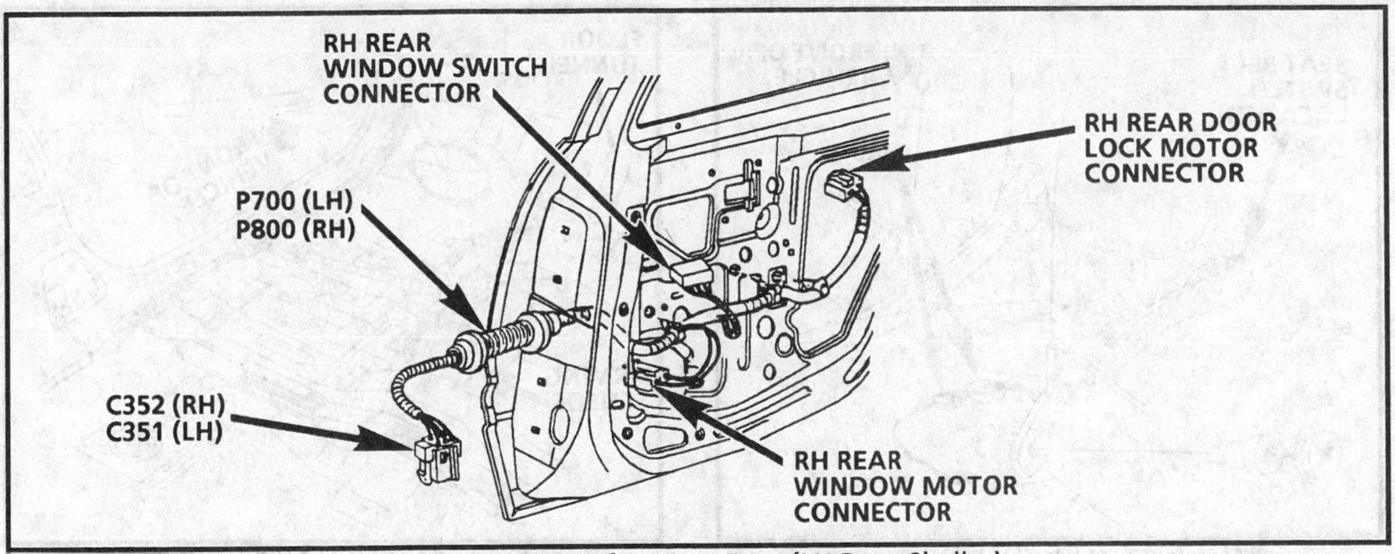
RH REAR
WINDOW SWITCH
CONNECTOR
RH REAR DOOR
LOCK MOTOR
CONNECTOR
P700 (LH)
P800 (RH)
C352 (RH)
C351 (LH)
RH REAR
WINDOW MOTOR
CONNECTOR

Figure 57 - Front of RH Rear Door (LH Door Similar)

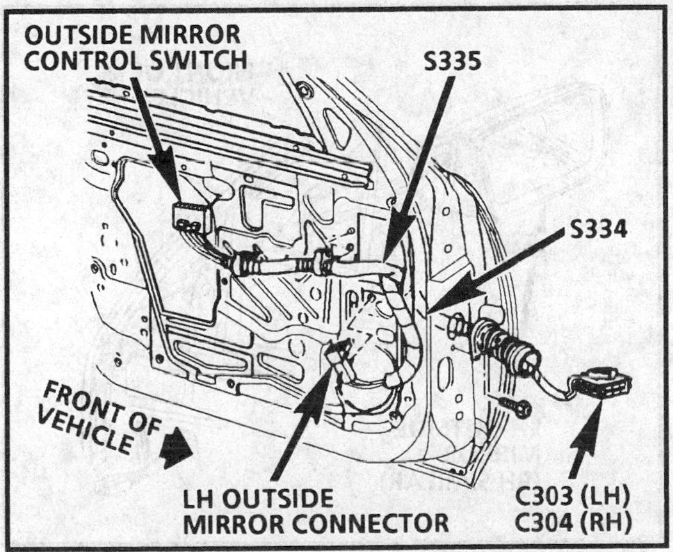
OUTSIDE MIRROR
CONTROL SWITCH
S335
S334
FRONT OF
VEHICLE
LH OUTSIDE
MIRROR CONNECTOR
C303 (LH)
C304 (RH)

Figure 58 - Front of LH Front Door (RH Door Similar)

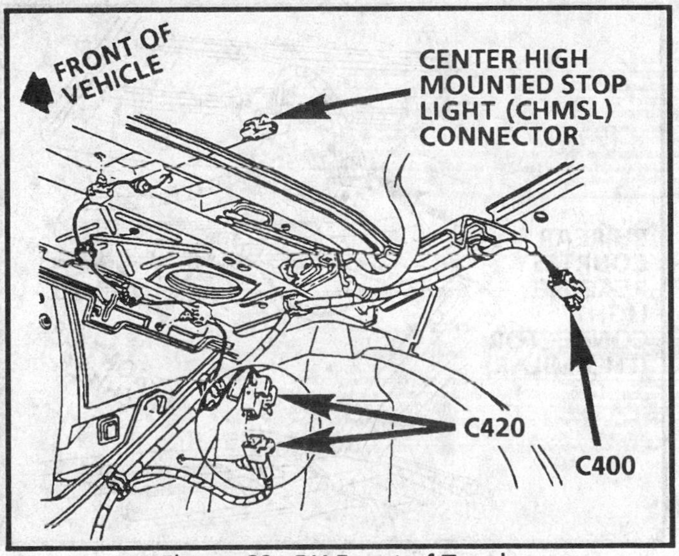
FRONT OF
VEHICLE
CENTER HIGH
MOUNTED STOP
LIGHT (CHMSL)
CONNECTOR
C420
C400

Figure 60 - RH Front of Trunk

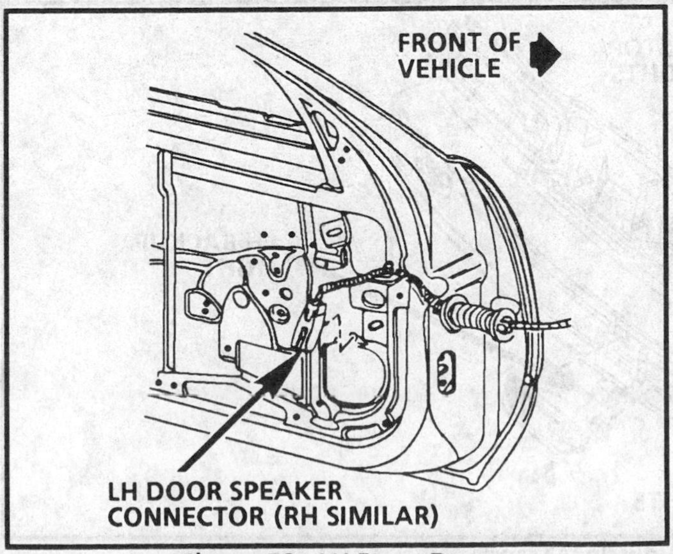
FRONT OF
VEHICLE
LH DOOR SPEAKER
CONNECTOR (RH SIMILAR)

Figure 59 - LH Front Door

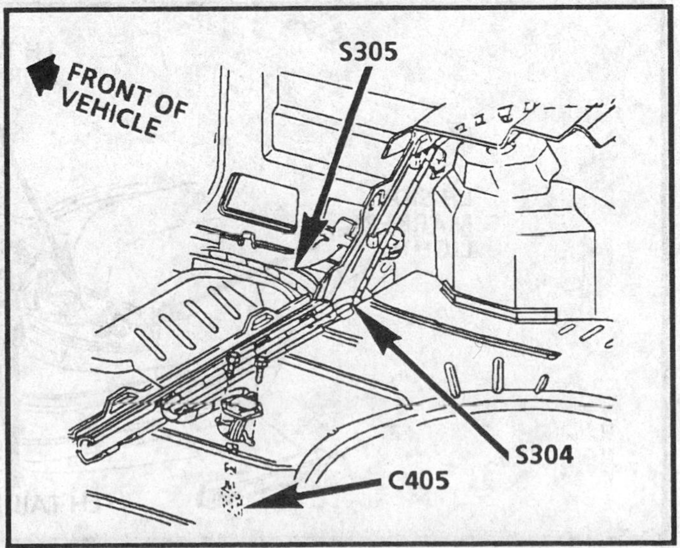
S305
FRONT OF
VEHICLE
S304
C405

Figure 61 - RH Front of Trunk

COMPONENT LOCATION VIEWS

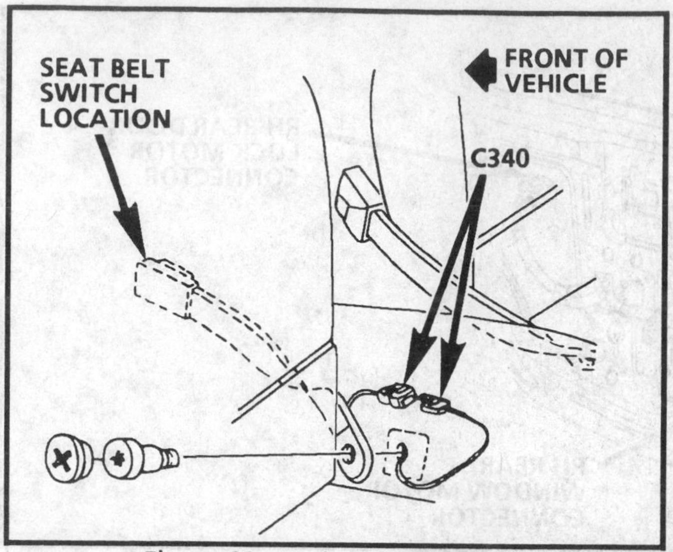
SEAT BELT
SWITCH
LOCATION
FRONT OF
VEHICLE
C340

Figure 62 - Under LH Front Seat

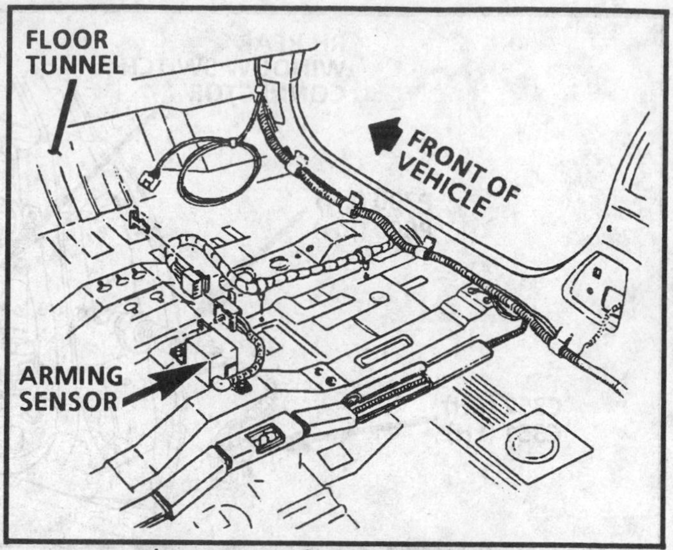
FLOOR
TUNNEL
FRONT OF
VEHICLE
ARMING
SENSOR

Figure 64 - Below RH Front Seat

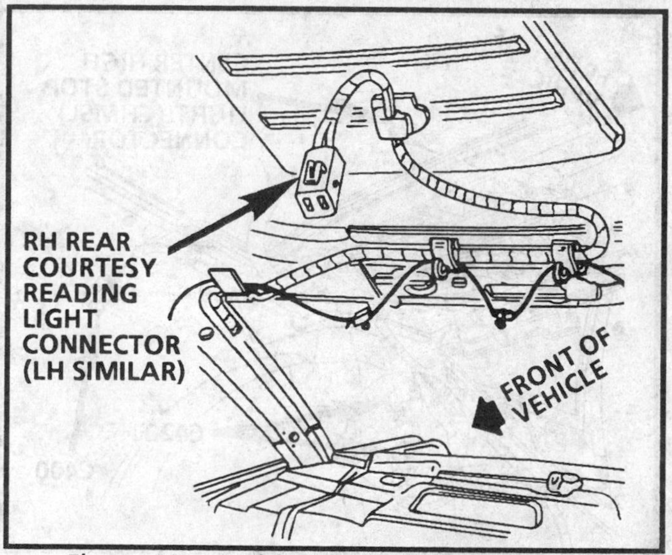
RH REAR
COURTESY
READING
LIGHT
CONNECTOR
(LH SIMILAR)
FRONT OF
VEHICLE

Figure 63 - RH Side of Rear Window Header

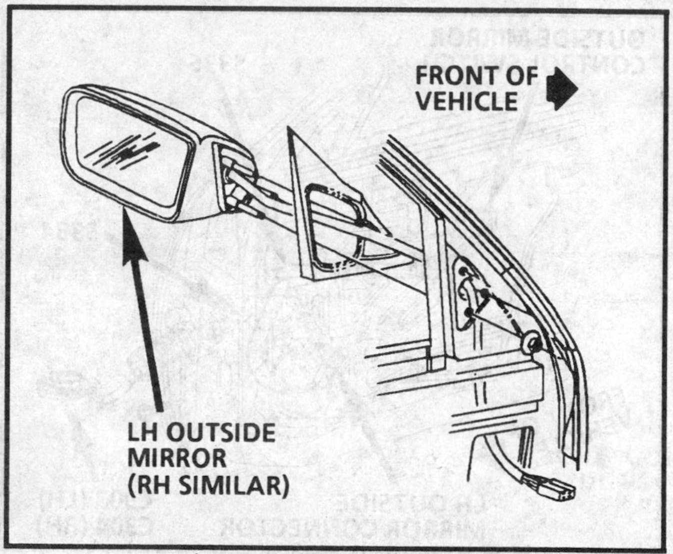
FRONT OF
VEHICLE
LH OUTSIDE
MIRROR
(RH SIMILAR)

Figure 65 - LH Front Door

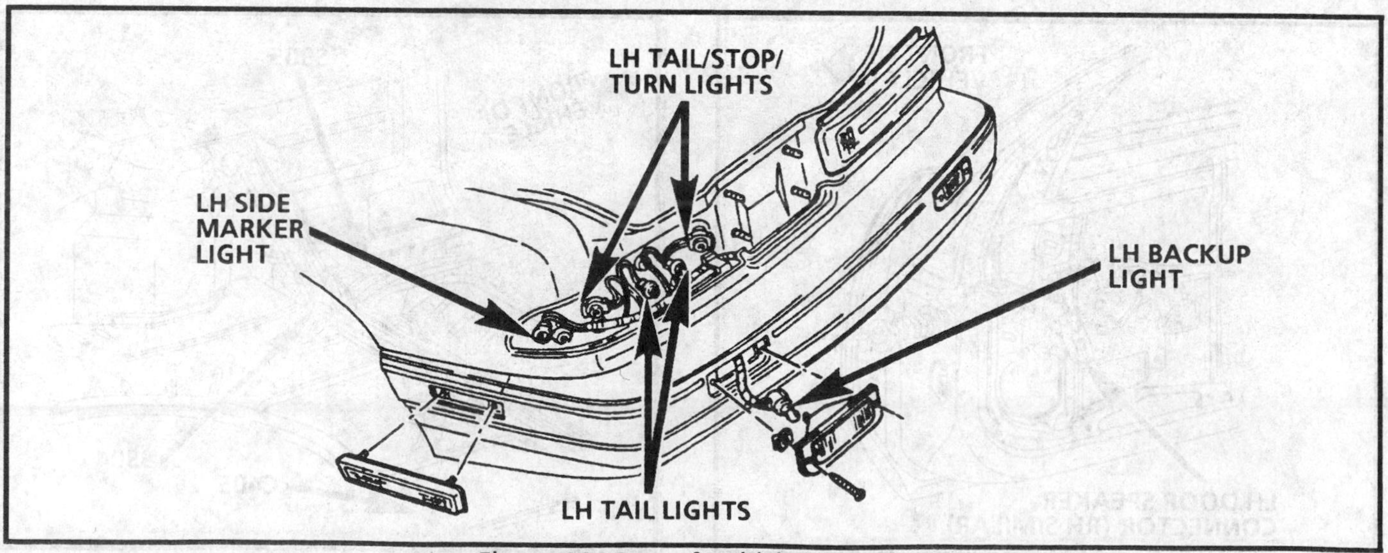
LH TAIL/STOP/
TURN LIGHTS
LH SIDE
MARKER
LIGHT
LH BACKUP
LIGHT
LH TAIL LIGHTS

Figure 66 - Rear of Vehicle (4 Door)

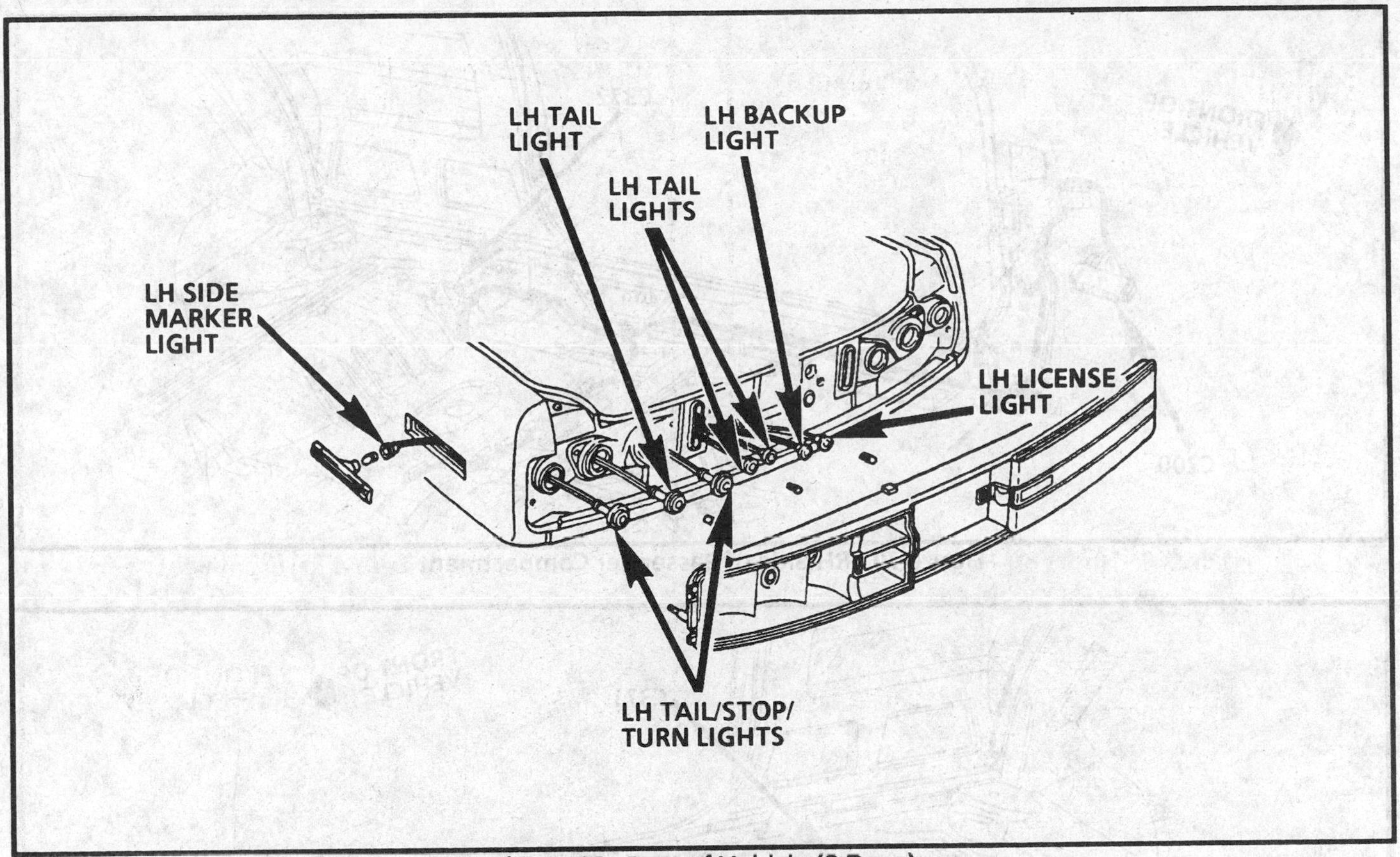
LH TAIL
LIGHT
LH BACKUP
LIGHT
LH TAIL
LIGHTS
LH SIDE
MARKER
LIGHT
LH LICENSE
LIGHT
LH TAIL/STOP/
TURN LIGHTS

Figure 67 - Rear of Vehicle (2 Door)

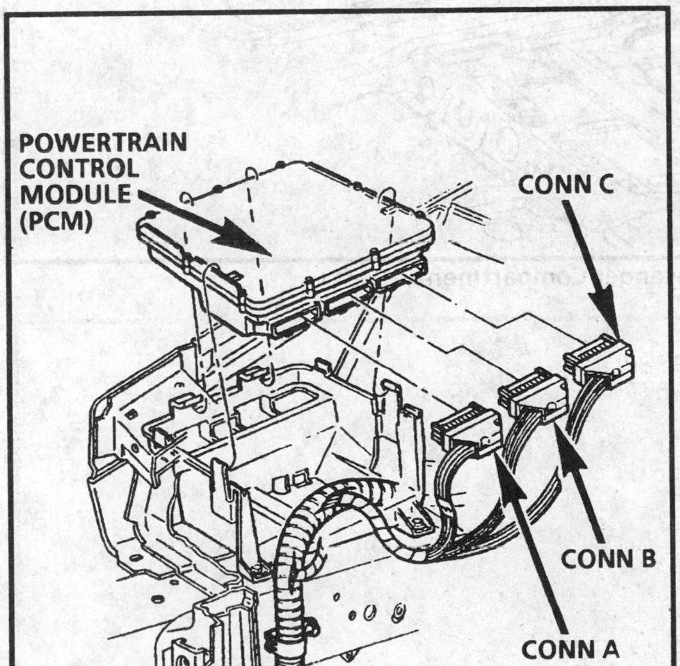
POWERTRAIN
CONTROL
MODULE
(PCM)
CONN C
CONN B
CONN A

Figure 68 - RH Front of VIN L Engine Compartment

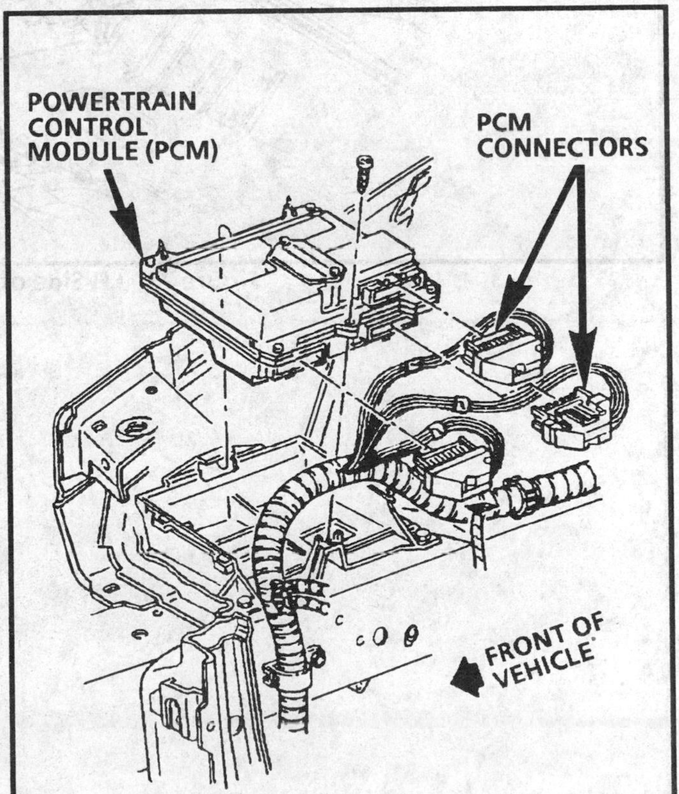
POWERTRAIN
CONTROL
MODULE (PCM)
PCM
CONNECTORS
FRONT OF
VEHICLE

Figure 69 - RH Front of VIN M Engine Compartment

COMPONENT LOCATION VIEWS

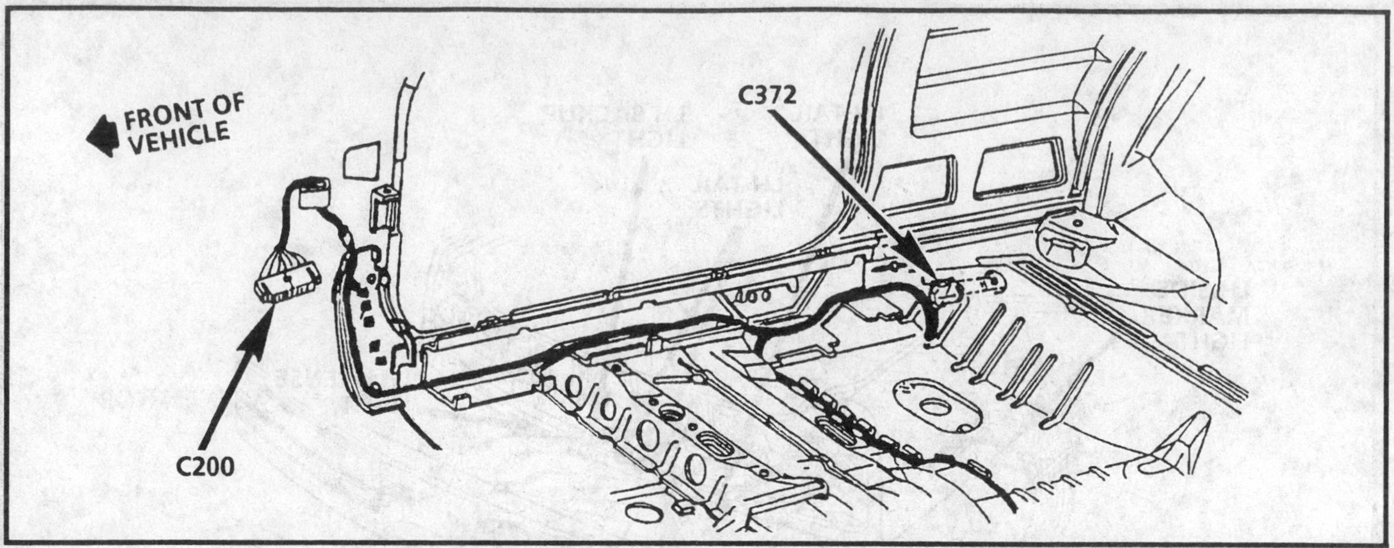
FRONT OF VEHICLE
C372
C200

Figure 70 - RH Side of Passenger Compartment

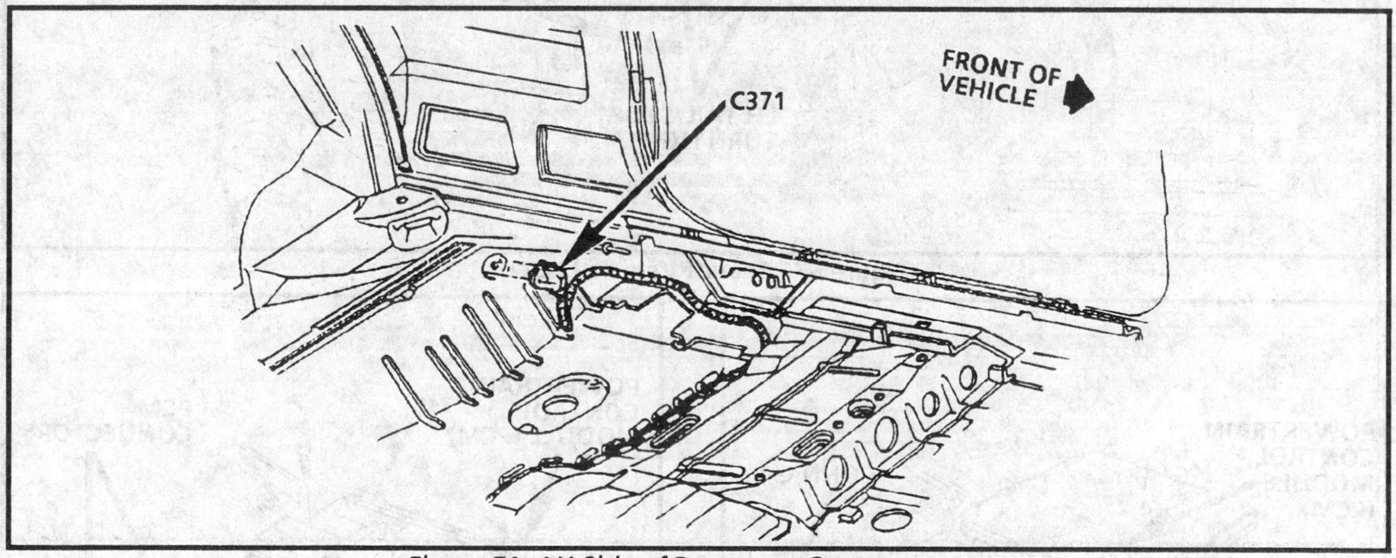
FRONT OF VEHICLE
C371

Figure 71 - LH Side of Passenger Compartment

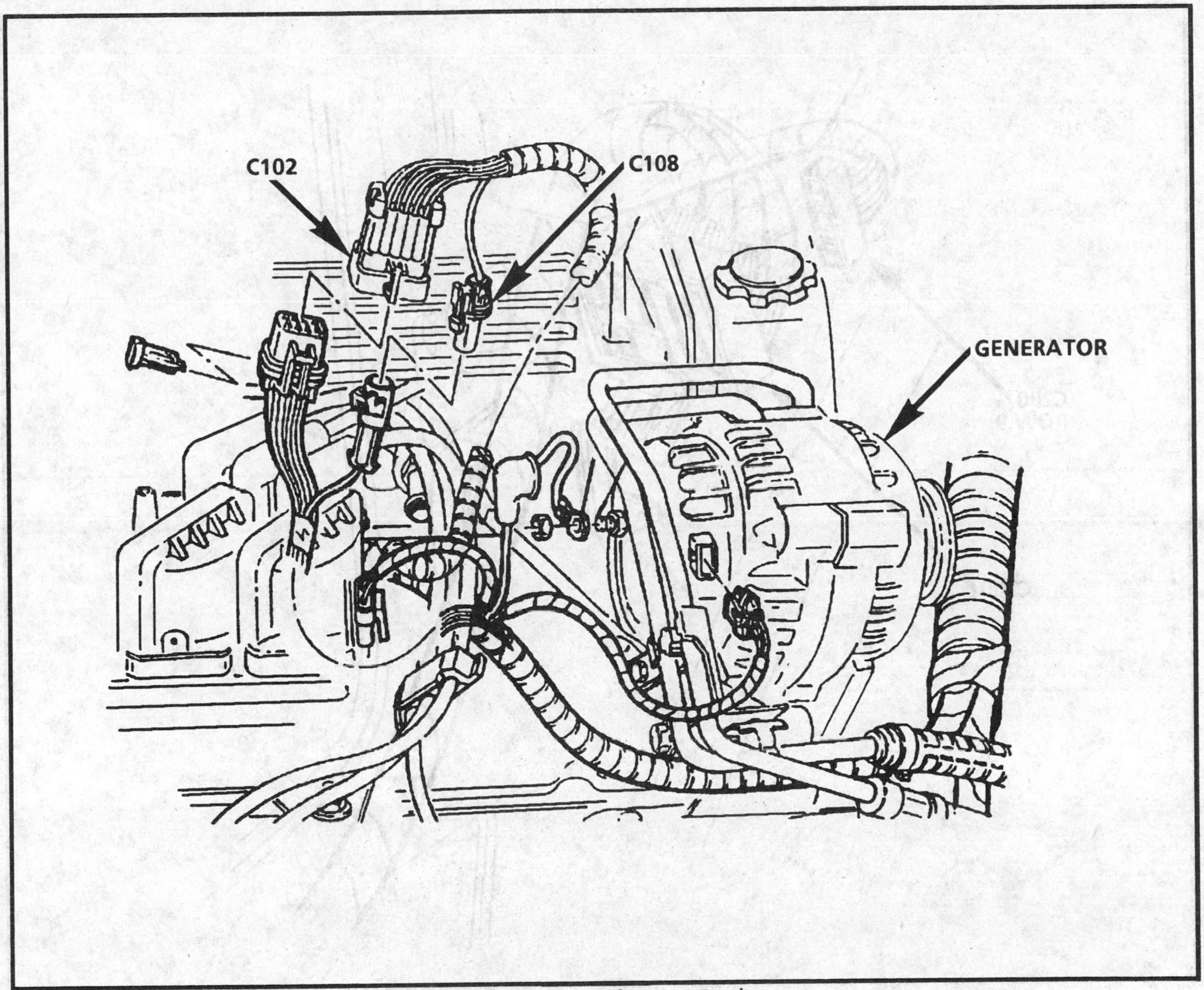
C102
C108
GENERATOR

Figure 72 - Rear of VIN M Engine

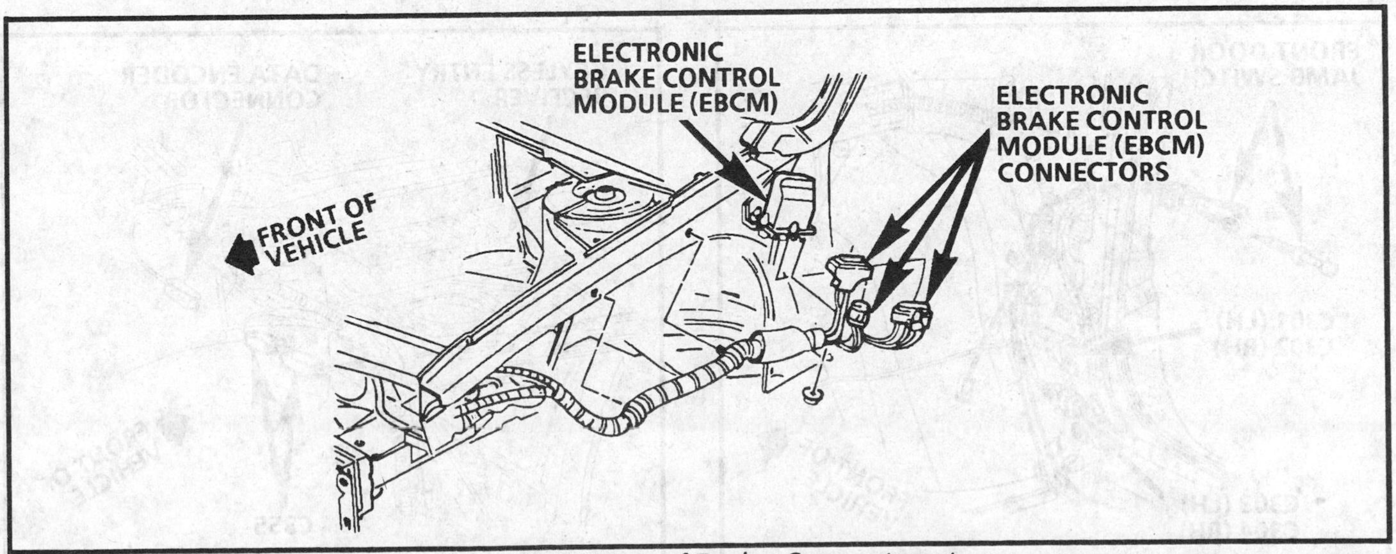
ELECTRONIC BRAKE CONTROL MODULE (EBCM)
ELECTRONIC BRAKE CONTROL MODULE (EBCM) CONNECTORS
FRONT OF VEHICLE

Figure 73 - LH Rear of Engine Compartment

COMPONENT LOCATION VIEWS

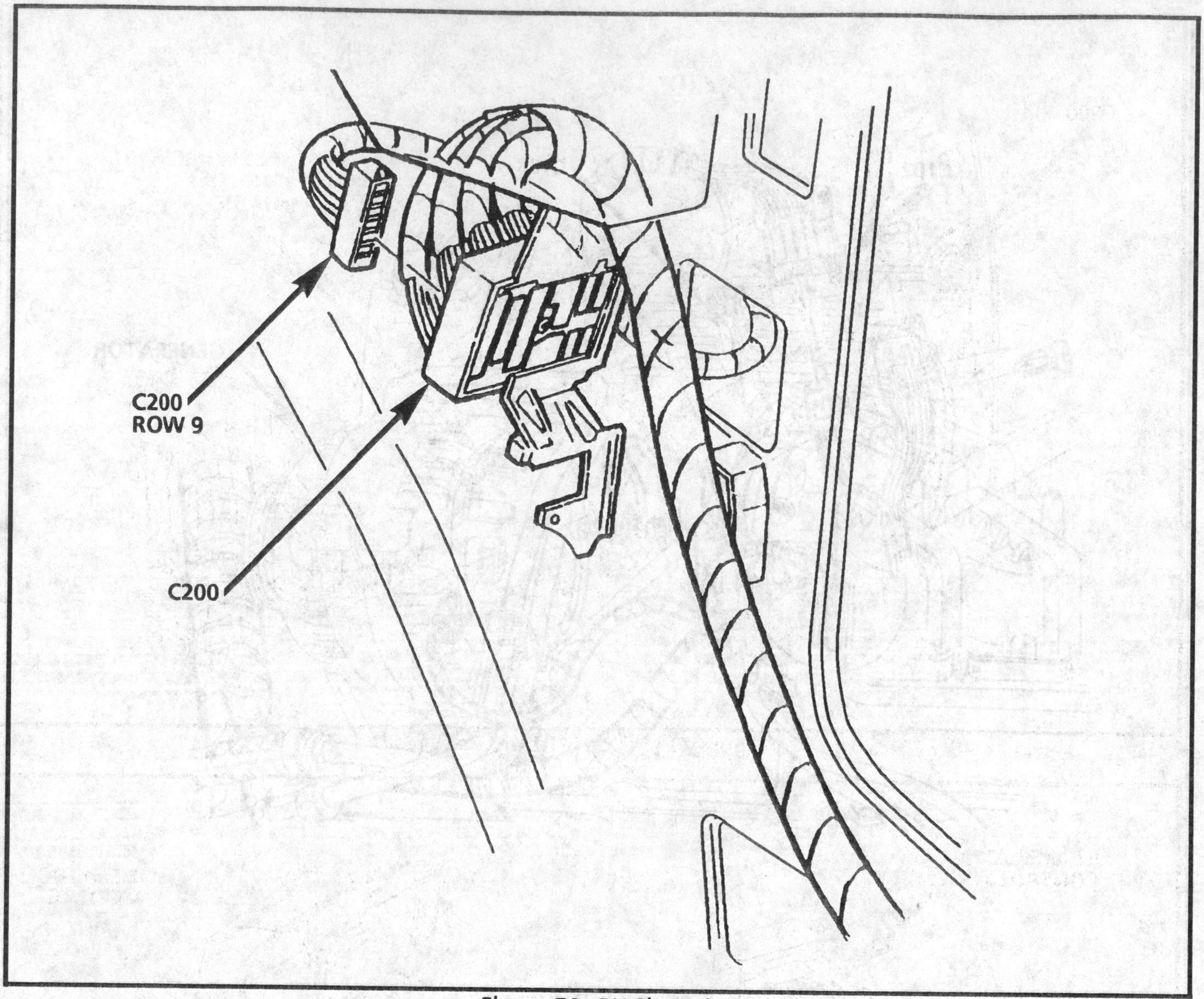
C200
ROW 9
C200

Figure 74 - RH Shroud

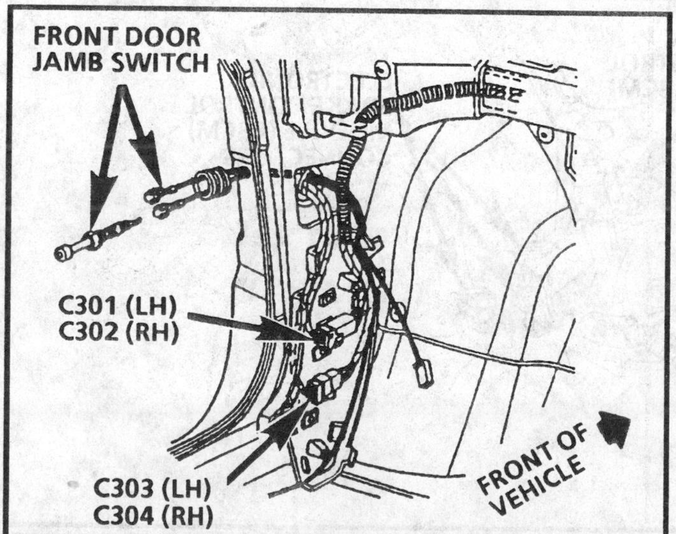
FRONT DOOR
JAMB SWITCH
C301 (LH)
C302 (RH)
C303 (LH)
C304 (RH)
FRONT OF
VEHICLE

Figure 75 - LH Shroud (RH Similar)

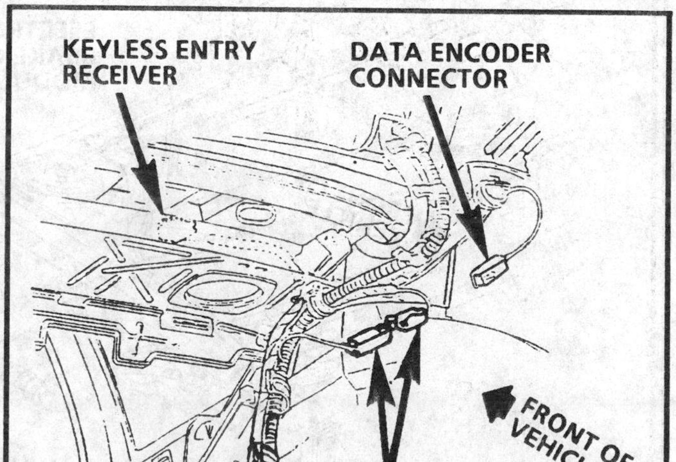
KEYLESS ENTRY
RECEIVER
DATA ENCODER
CONNECTOR
FRONT OF
VEHICLE
C355

Figure 76 - RH Front of Trunk

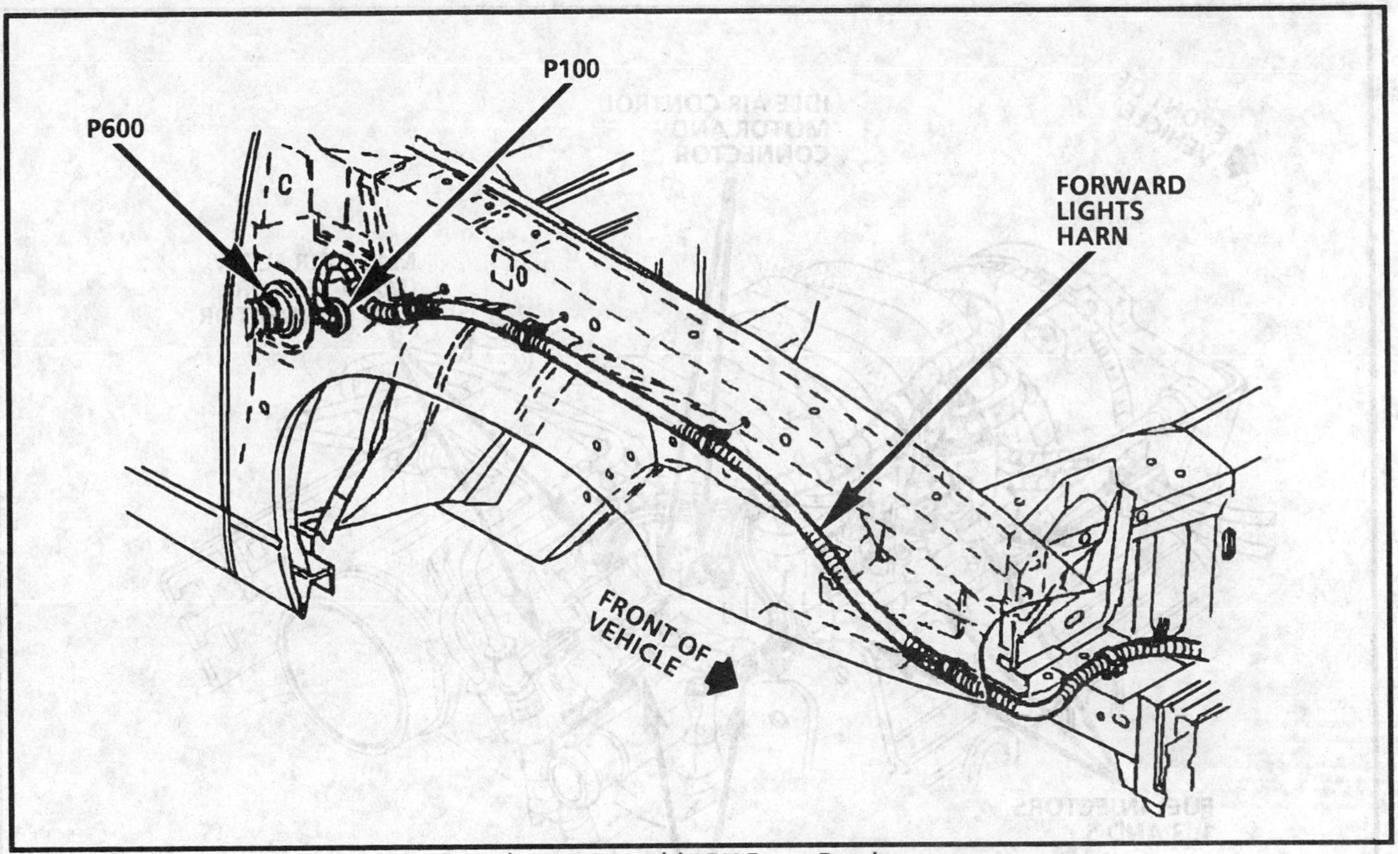
P100
P600
FORWARD
LIGHTS
HARN
FRONT OF
VEHICLE

Figure 77 - Inside RH Front Fender

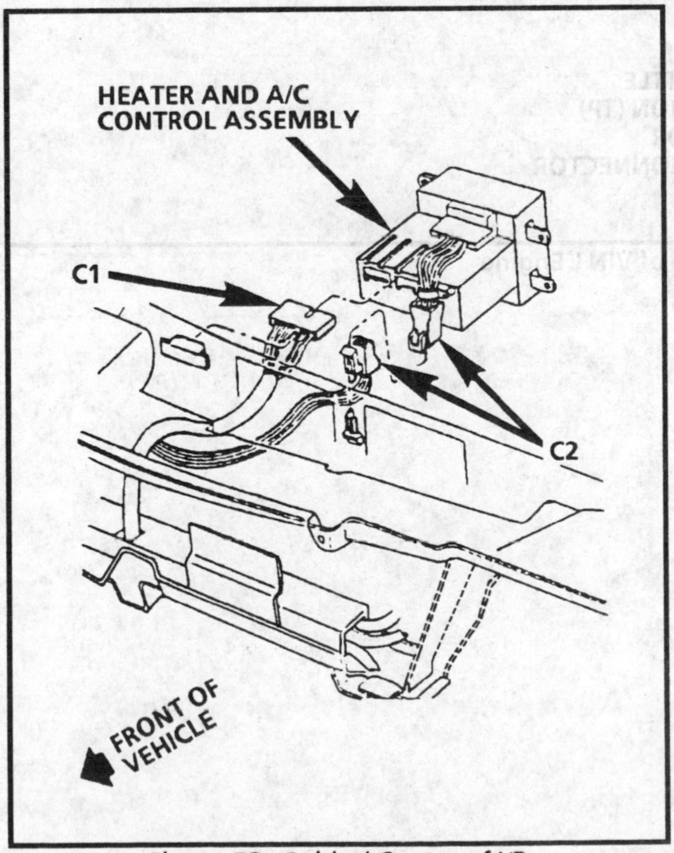
HEATER AND A/C
CONTROL ASSEMBLY
C1
C2
FRONT OF
VEHICLE

Figure 78 - Behind Center of I/P

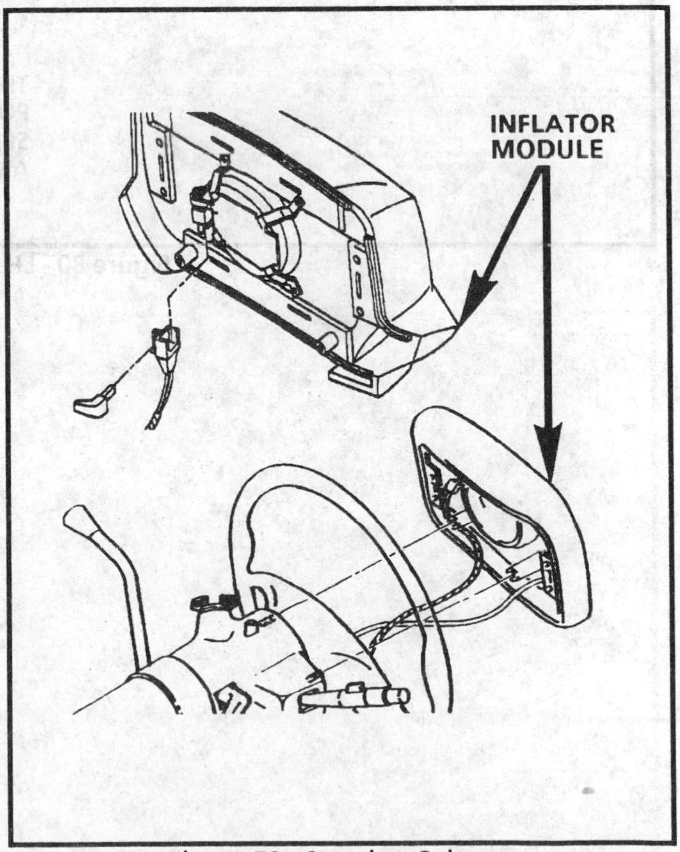
INFLATOR
MODULE

Figure 79 - Steering Column

COMPONENT LOCATION VIEWS

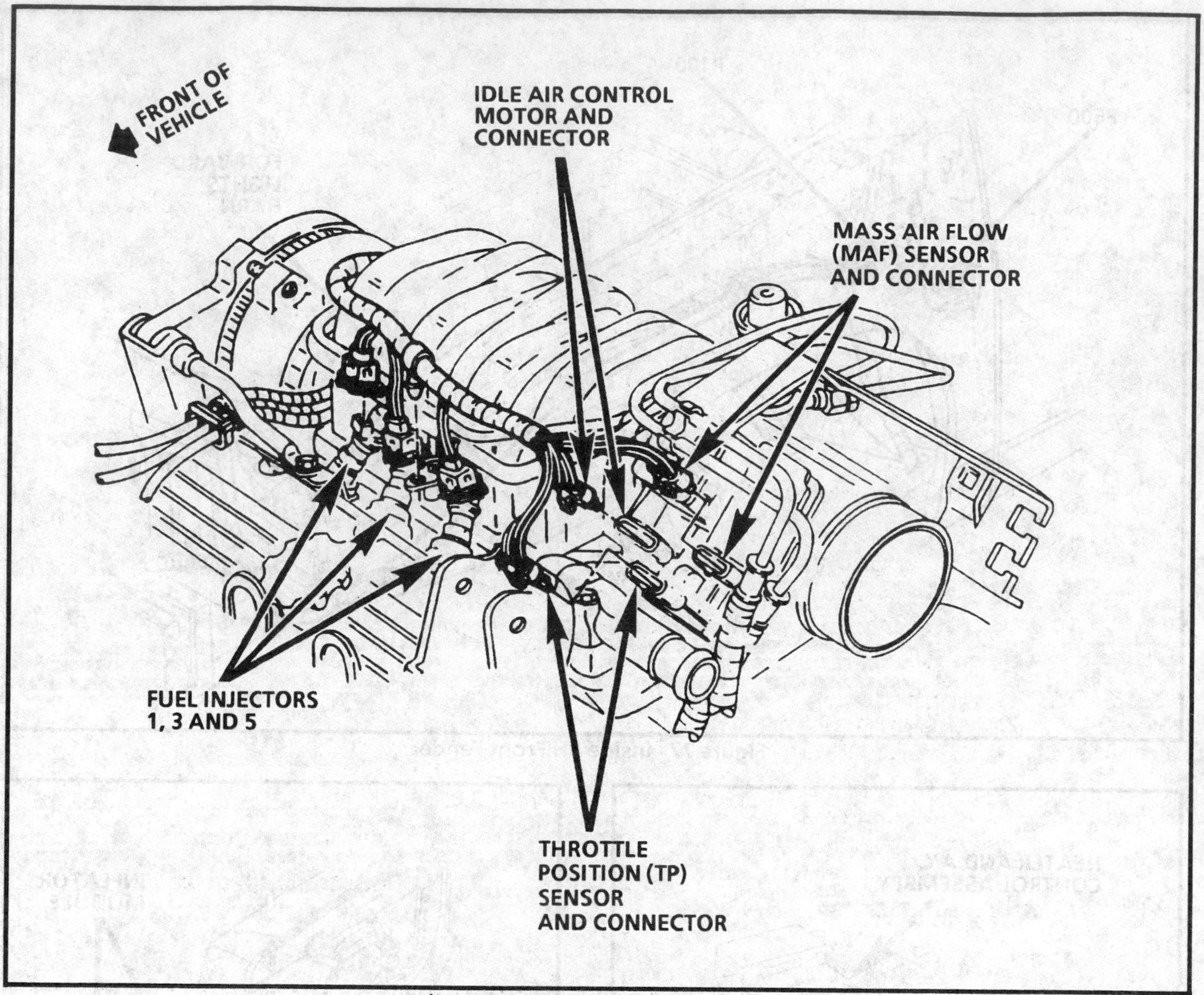
FRONT OF VEHICLE
IDLE AIR CONTROL MOTOR AND CONNECTOR
MASS AIR FLOW (MAF) SENSOR AND CONNECTOR
FUEL INJECTORS 1, 3 AND 5
THROTTLE POSITION (TP) SENSOR AND CONNECTOR

Figure 80 - LH Top of VIN L Engine

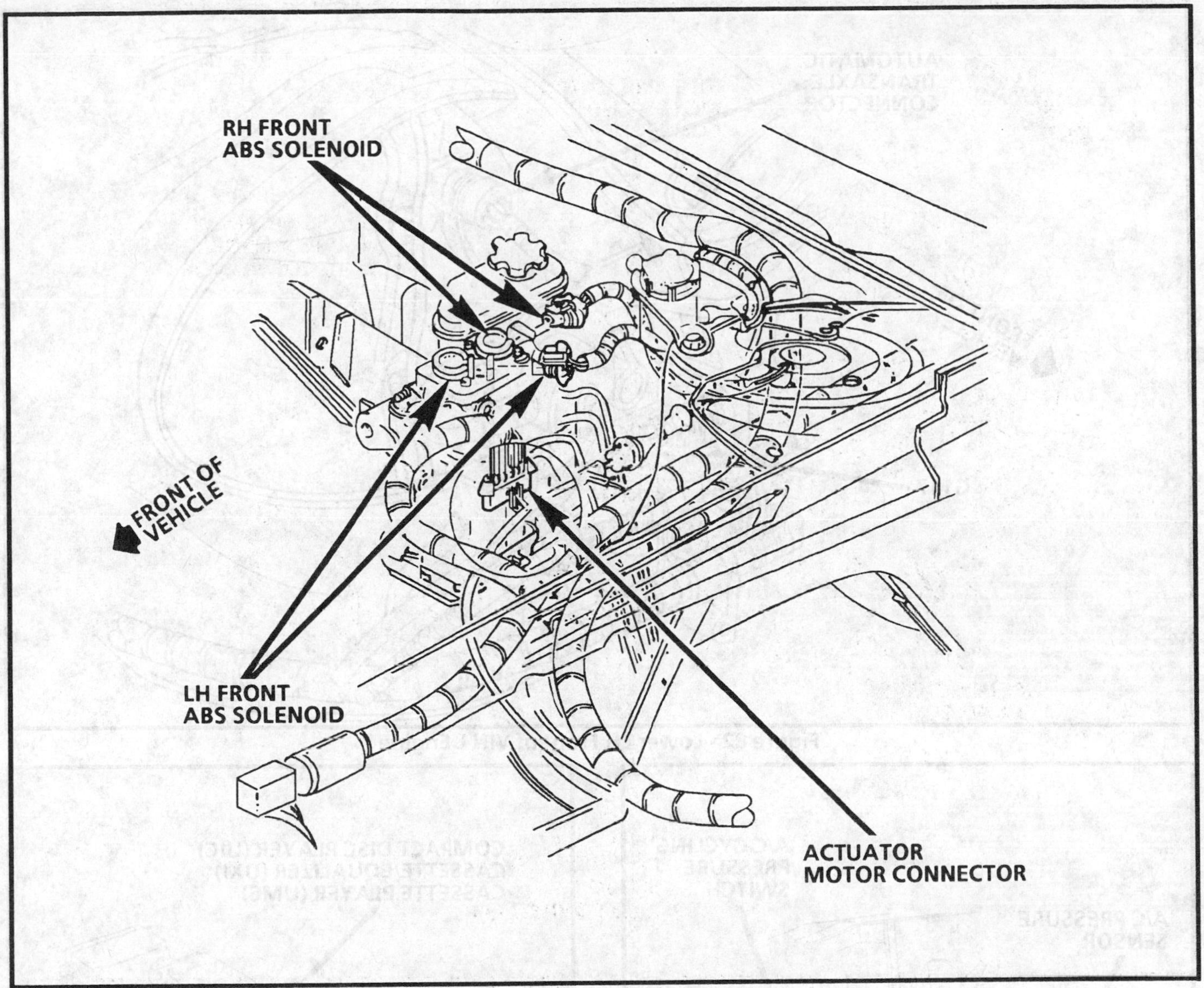
RH FRONT
ABS SOLENOID
FRONT OF
VEHICLE
LH FRONT
ABS SOLENOID
ACTUATOR
MOTOR CONNECTOR

Figure 81 - LH Rear of Engine Compartment

COMPONENT LOCATION VIEWS

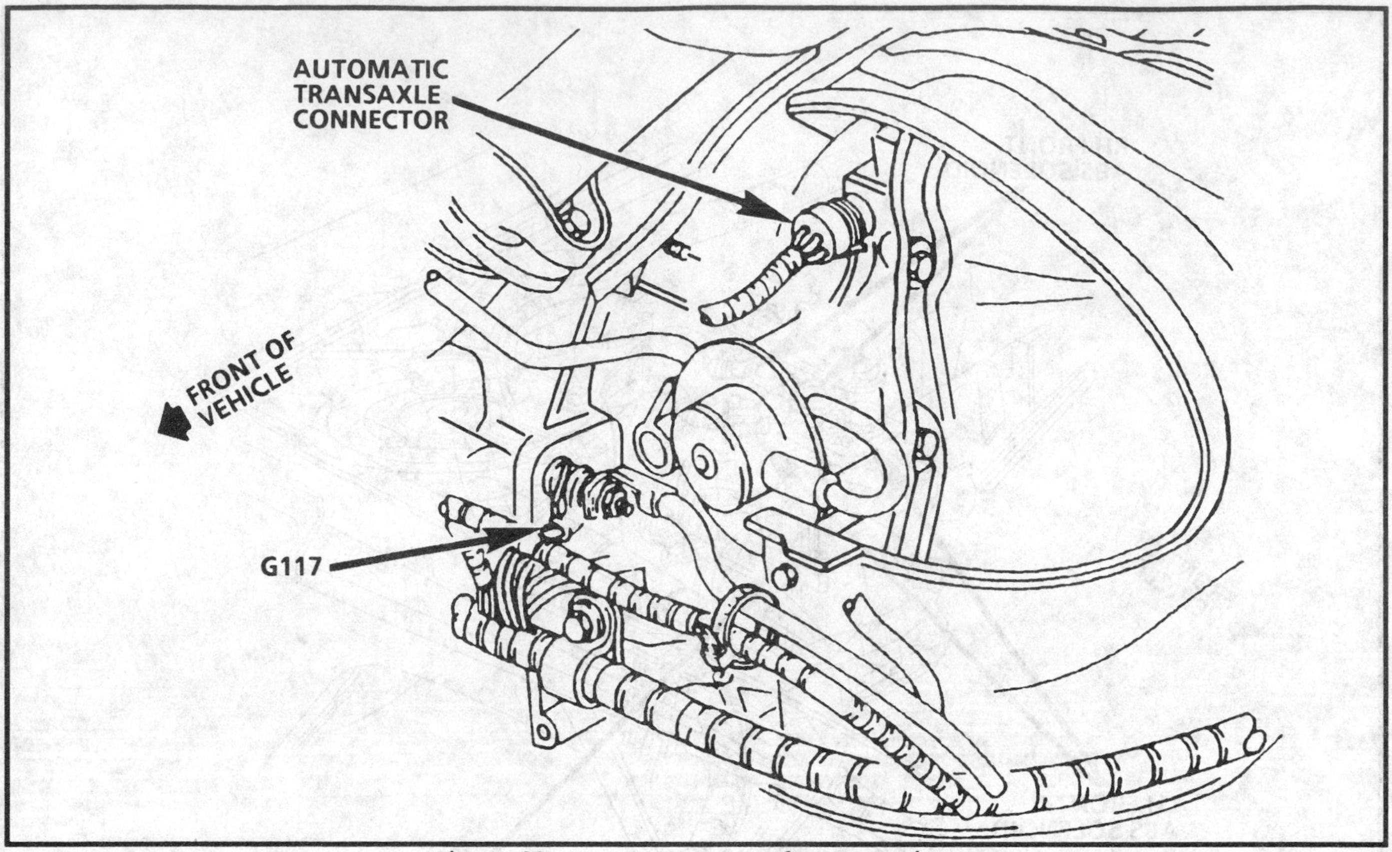
AUTOMATIC
TRANSAXLE
CONNECTOR
FRONT OF
VEHICLE
G117

Figure 82 - Lower LH Front of VIN L Engine

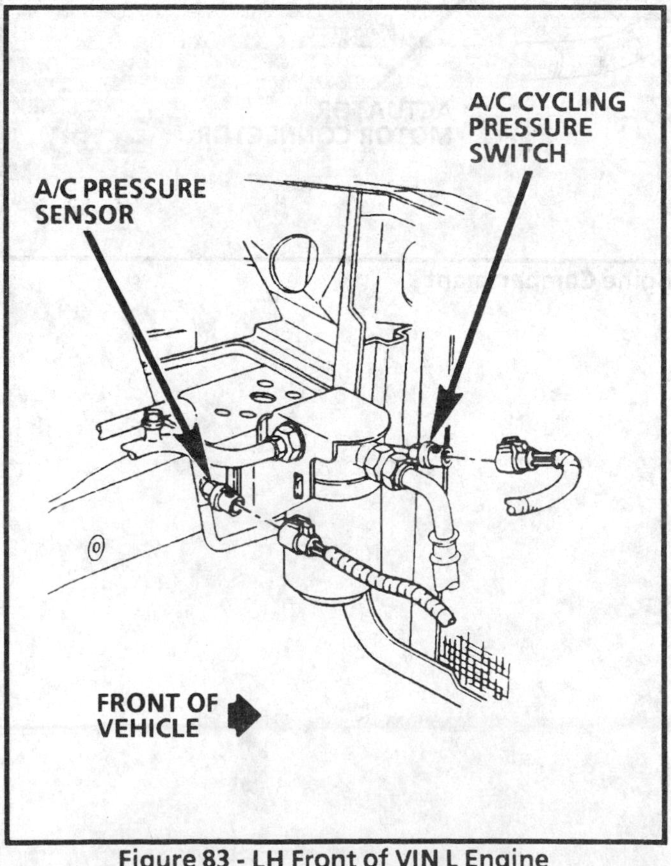
A/C CYCLING
PRESSURE
SWITCH
A/C PRESSURE
SENSOR
FRONT OF
VEHICLE

Figure 83 - LH Front of VIN L Engine Compartment (VIN M Similar)

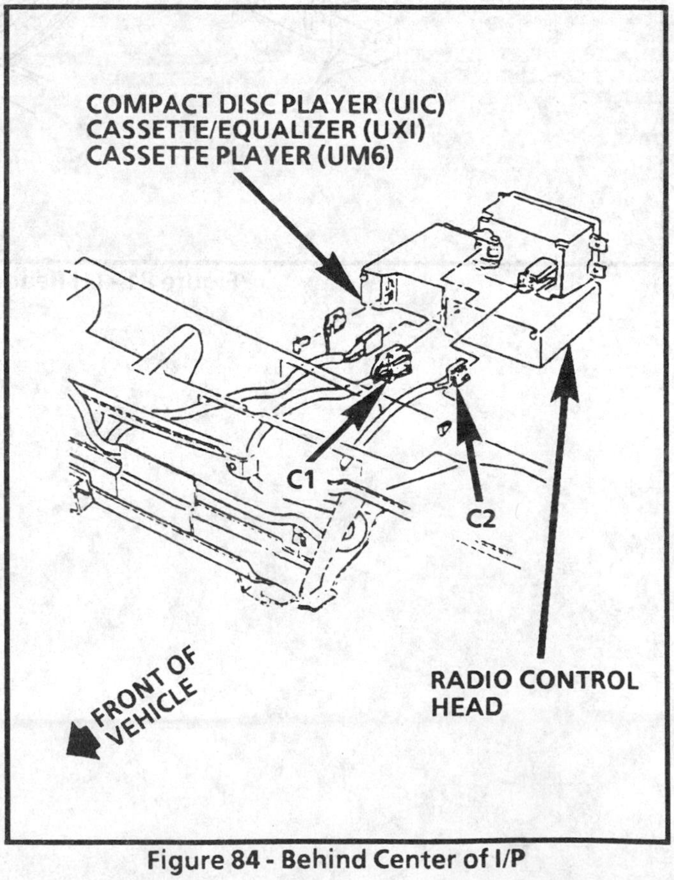
COMPACT DISC PLAYER (UIC)
CASSETTE/EQUALIZER (UXI)
CASSETTE PLAYER (UM6)
C1
C2
RADIO CONTROL
HEAD
FRONT OF
VEHICLE

Figure 84 - Behind Center of I/P

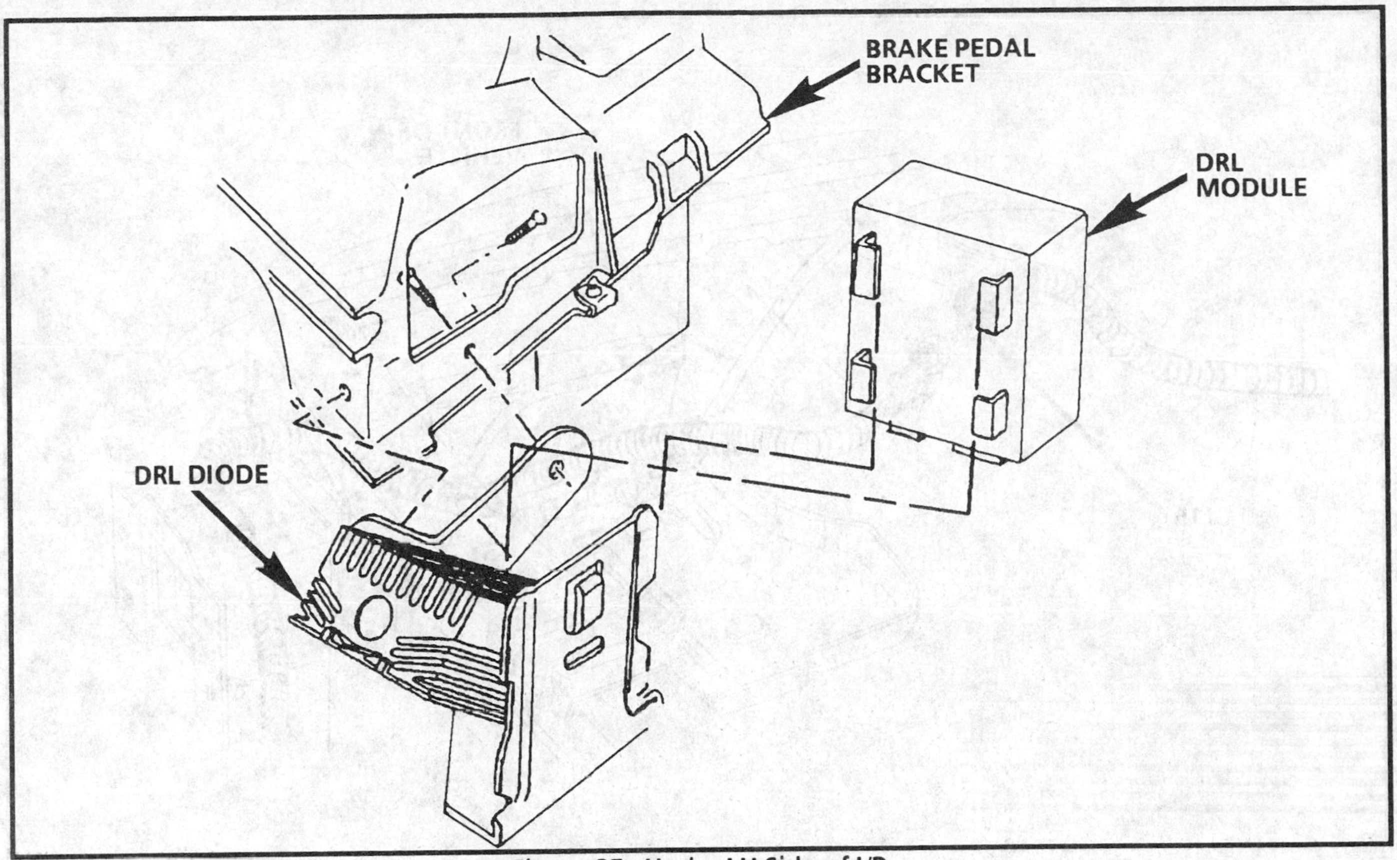
BRAKE PEDAL
BRACKET
DRL
MODULE
DRL DIODE
Figure 85 - Under LH Side of I/P

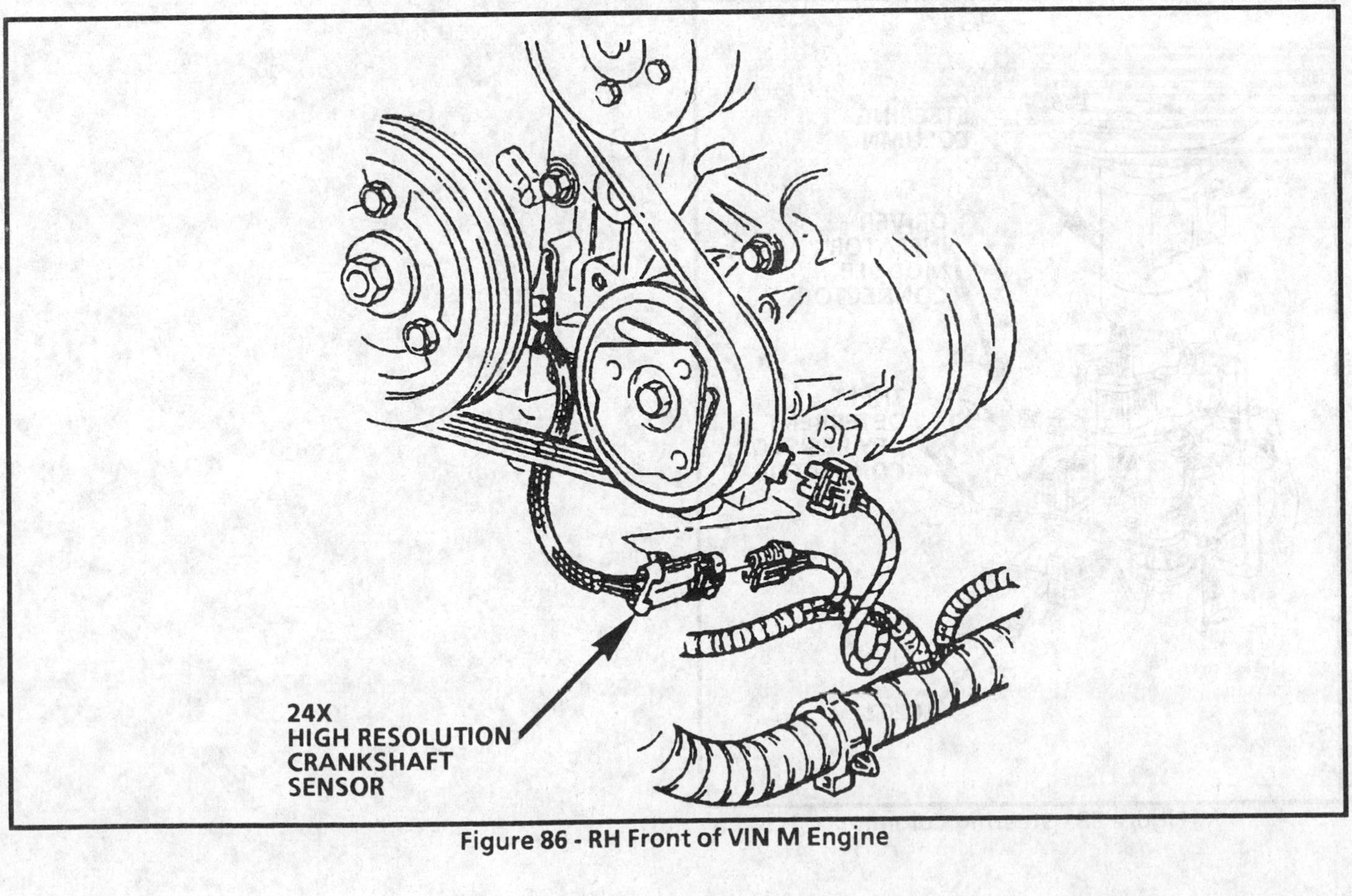
24X
HIGH RESOLUTION
CRANKSHAFT
SENSOR
Figure 86 - RH Front of VIN M Engine

COMPONENT LOCATION VIEWS

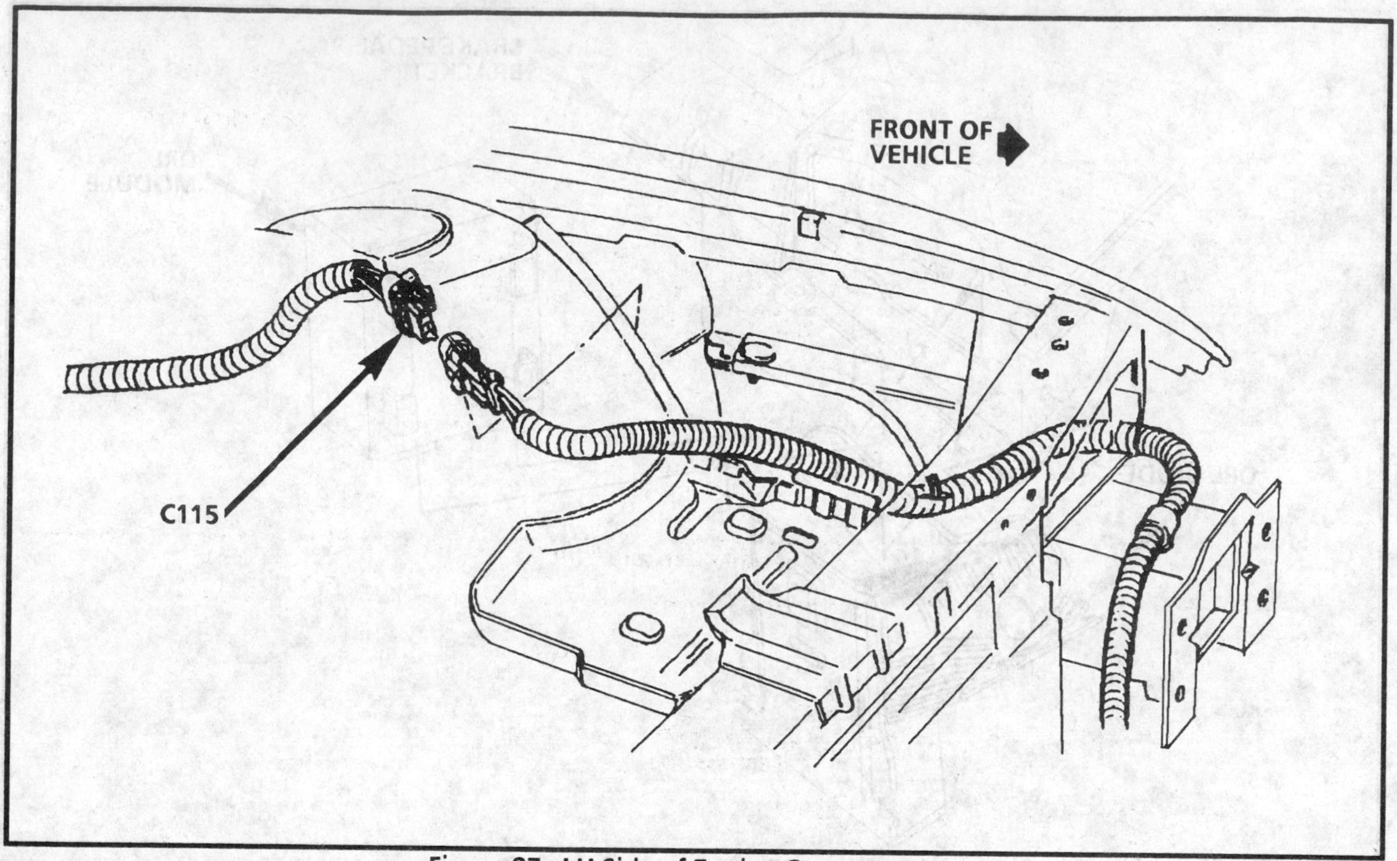
FRONT OF VEHICLE
C115

Figure 87 - LH Side of Engine Compartment

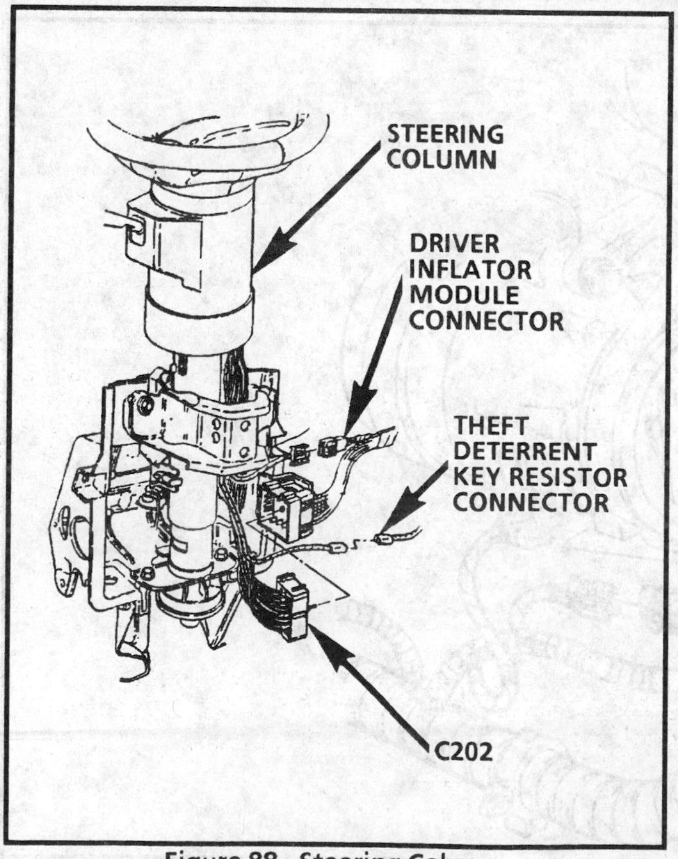
STEERING COLUMN
DRIVER INFLATOR MODULE CONNECTOR
THEFT DETERRENT KEY RESISTOR CONNECTOR
C202

Figure 88 - Steering Column

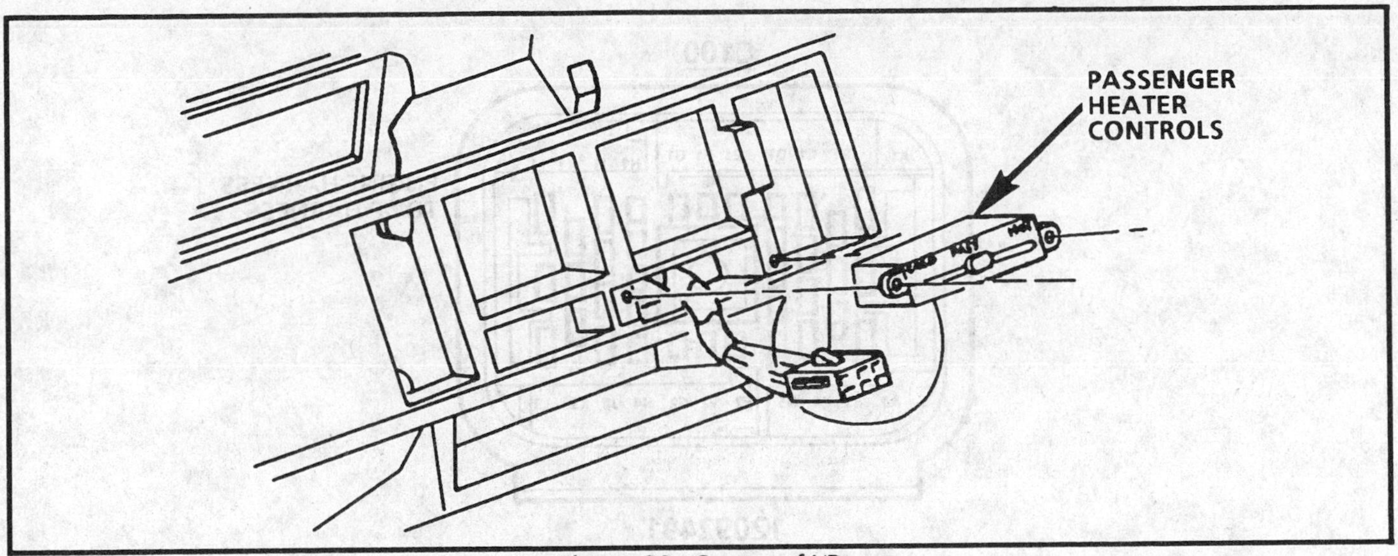
PASSENGER
HEATER
CONTROLS

Figure 89 - Center of I/P

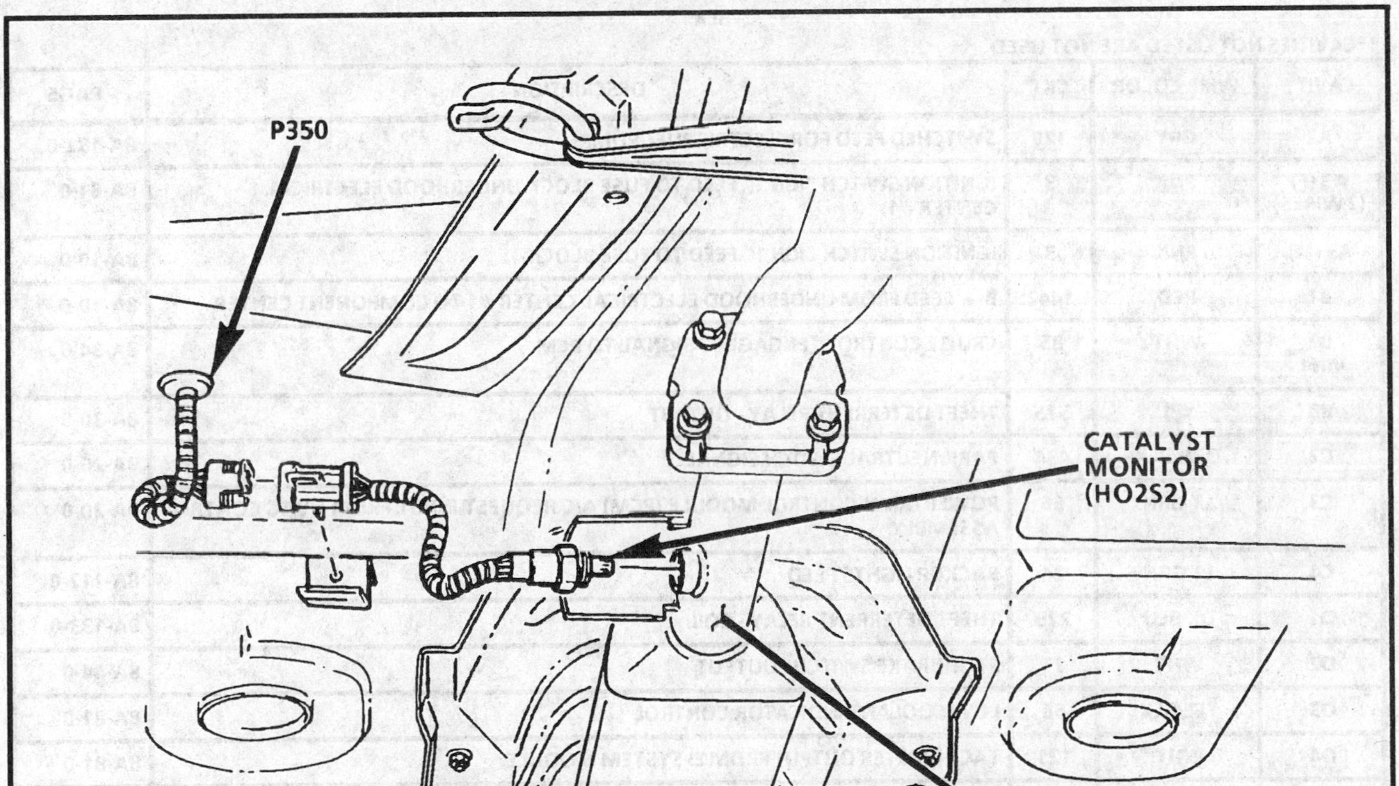
P350
CATALYST
MONITOR
(HO2S2)
EXHAUST
SYSTEM
CATALYTIC
CONVERTER
FRONT OF
VEHICLE

Figure 90 - Below Center of Vehicle

HARNESS CONNECTOR FACES

C100

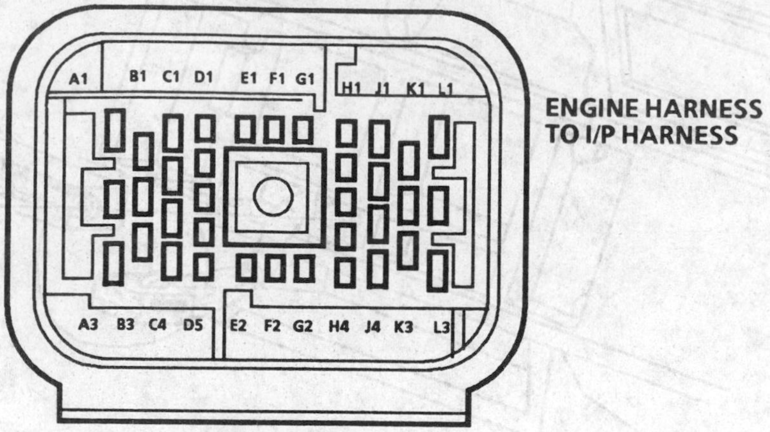
A1
B1
C1
D1
E1
F1
G1
H1
J1
K1
L1
A3
B3
C4
D5
E2
F2
G2
H4
J4
K3
L3
ENGINE HARNESS TO I/P HARNESS

12092491

36-WAY F METRI-PACK MIXED SERIES

BLK

**CAVITIES NOT LISTED ARE NOT USED

CAVITY	WIRE COLOR	CKT	DESCRIPTION	PAGE
A2	GRY	120	SWITCHED FEED FOR ELECTRIC FUEL PUMP	8A-132-0
A3 (F) (2 WIRES)	PNK	3	IGNITION SWITCH "IGN 1" FEED TO FUSE BLOCK/UNDERHOOD ELECTRICAL CENTER #1	8A-81-0
A3 (M)	PNK	3	IGNITION SWITCH "IGN 1" FEED TO FUSE BLOCK	8A-10-0
B1	RED	1442	B + FEED FROM UNDERHOOD ELECTRICAL CENTER #1 TO COMPONENT CENTER	8A-10-0
B2 VIN L	WHT	85	CRUISE CONTROL "ENGAGED" SIGNAL TO PCM	8A-34-0
B3	YEL	575	THEFT DETERRENT RELAY - OUTPUT	8A-30-0
C2	ORN/BLK	434	PARK/NEUTRAL SWITCH SIGNAL	8A-20-0
C3	LT GRN	66	POWERTRAIN CONTROL MODULE (PCM) A/C REQUEST INPUT FROM HVAC CONTROL ASSEMBLY	8A-20-0
C4	LT GRN	24	BACKUP LIGHTS FEED	8A-112-0
D1	DK BLU	229	THEFT DETERRENT RELAY - COIL	8A-133-0
D2	WHT	17	STOP BRAKE SWITCH - OUTPUT	8A-44-0
D3	YEL/BLK	68	LOW COOLANT INDICATOR CONTROL	8A-81-0
D4	WHT	121	TACHOMETER OUTPUT FROM EI SYSTEM MODULE	8A-81-0
D5	LT GRN	275	TRANSAXLE POSITION SWITCH INPUT TO KEYLESS ENTRY RECEIVER	8A-132-0
E1 VIN L	BRN	1174	LOW OIL LEVEL SWITCH OUTPUT	8A-81-0
E2	BRN/WHT	25	SWITCHED GROUND FOR CHECK GAGES INDICATOR	8A-81-0
F1 VIN M	BRN/WHT	1173	LOW OIL LEVEL SWITCH - OUTPUT	8A-81-0
F2	TAN	31	OIL PRESSURE GAGE/INDICATOR CONTROL	8A-81-0
G1	BRN	86	CRUISE CONTROL CUT-OFF SWITCH - OUTPUT	8A-34-0

(CONTINUED ON NEXT PAGE)

(CONTINUED FROM PREVIOUS PAGE)

CAVITY	WIRE COLOR	CKT	DESCRIPTION	PAGE
G2	DK GRN	135	COOLANT TEMPERATURE GAGE/INDICATOR CONTROL	8A-81-0
H1	GRY/BLK	87	CRUISE CONTROL SWITCH - RESUME/ACCEL	8A-34-0
H2	DK BLU	84	CRUISE CONTROL SWITCH - SET/COAST	8A-34-0
H3	BRN/WHT	419	POWERTRAIN CONTROL MODULE (PCM) MALFUNCTION INDICATOR LAMP (MIL) CONTROL	8A-81-0
H4	DK GRN	389	POWERTRAIN CONTROL MODULE (PCM) VSS OUTPUT	8A-33-0
H5	GRY	397	CRUISE CONTROL SWITCH - ON/OFF	8A-34-0
J1	WHT/BLK	1493	TRANSMISSION SELECT SWITCH - OUTPUT (NOT USED)	8A-20-8, 8A-21-8
J1 VIN L	PPL/WHT	1668	CATALYST MONITOR (HO2S2) INPUT HIGH	8A-21-0
J2 VIN L	TAN/WHT	1669	CATALYST MONITOR (HO2S2) INPUT LOW	8A-21-0
J3	PPL	420	BRAKE SWITCH FEED TO AUTOMATIC TRANSAXLE	8A-20-0
J4	ORN	800	SERIAL DATA SIGNAL -UART	8A-50-0
K1	RED	242	BATTERY FUSED FEED	8A-10-0
K2	ORN	704	IGNITION "3" FEED TO UNDERHOOD ELECTRICAL CENTER #2	8A-10-0
L1	RED	42	BATTERY FUSED FEED	8A-10-0

M = MALE SIDE OF CONNECTOR
F = FEMALE SIDE OF CONNECTOR

HARNESS CONNECTOR FACES

C102 (VIN M)

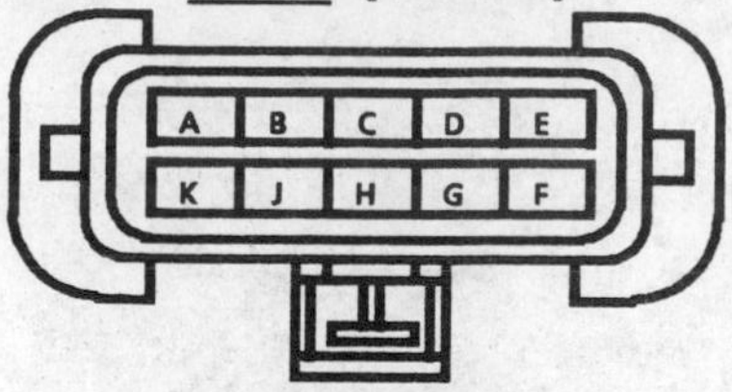
A
B
C
D
E
K
J
H
G
F

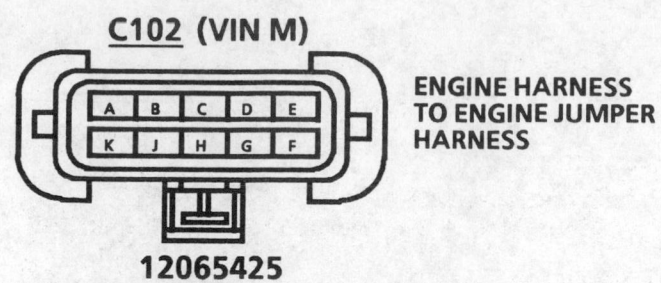

ENGINE HARNESS TO ENGINE JUMPER HARNESS

12065425

10-WAY F METRI-PACK 150 SERIES

BLK

**CAVITIES NOT LISTED ARE NOT USED

CAVITY	WIRE COLOR	CKT	DESCRIPTION	PAGE
A	BLK	1744	FUEL INJECTOR #1 CONTROL	8A-20-0
B	LT GRN/BLK	1745	FUEL INJECTOR #2 CONTROL	8A-20-0
C	PNK/BLK	1746	FUEL INJECTOR #3 CONTROL	8A-20-0
D	PNK	639	FUEL INJECTOR FEED	8A-20-0
E	YEL	410	ENGINE COOLANT TEMPERATURE (ECT) SENSOR	8A-20-0
F	BLK	808	MAP AND ECT GROUND	8A-20-0
G	LT GRN	432	MAP SENSOR	8A-20-0
H	YEL/BLK	846	FUEL INJECTOR #6 CONTROL	8A-20-0
J	BLK/WHT	845	FUEL INJECTOR #5 CONTROL	8A-20-0
K	LT BLU/BLK	844	FUEL INJECTOR #4 CONTROL	8A-20-0

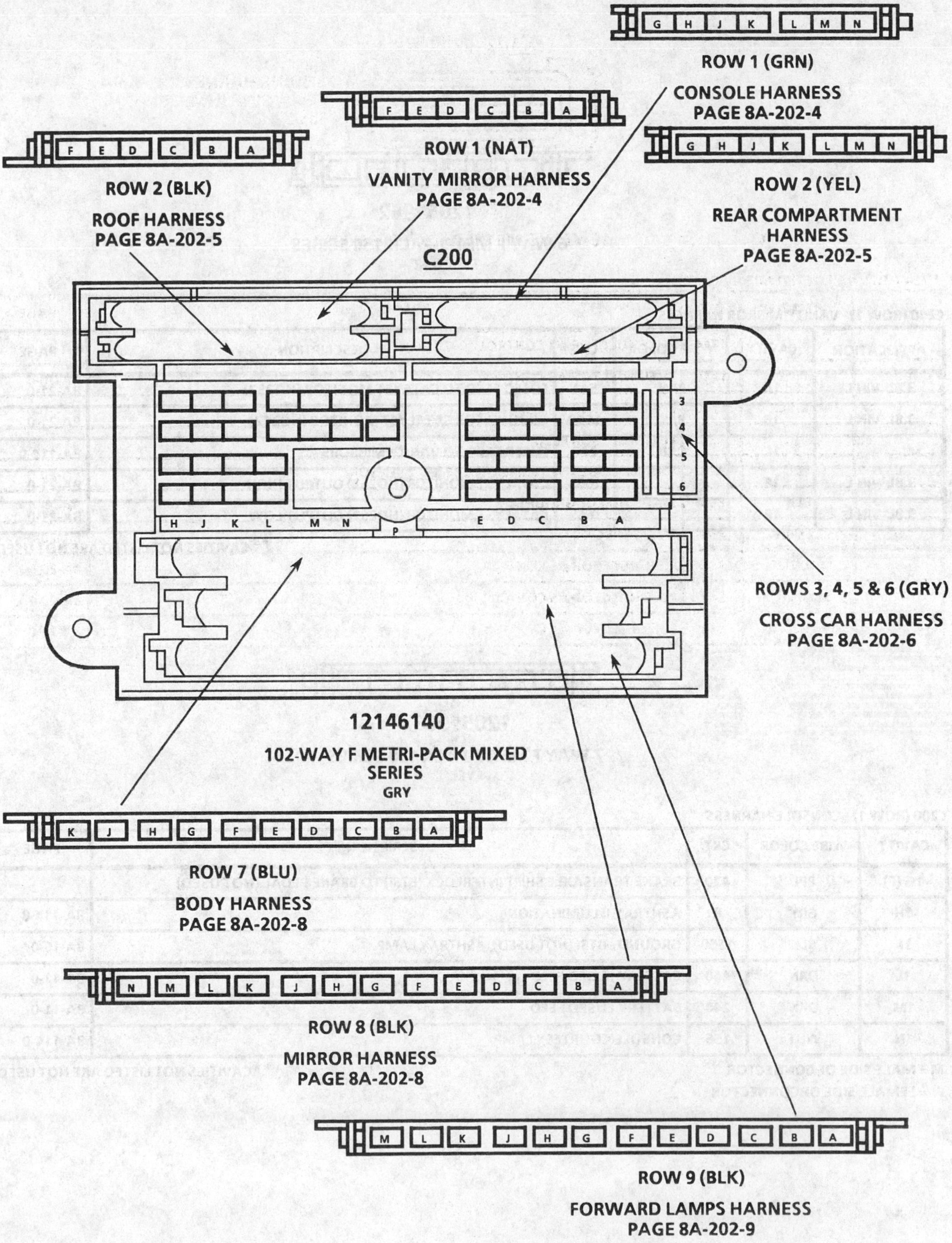
G H J K L M N
ROW 1 (GRN)
CONSOLE HARNESS
PAGE 8A-202-4
F E D C B A
ROW 1 (NAT)
VANITY MIRROR HARNESS
PAGE 8A-202-4
F E D C B A
ROW 2 (BLK)
ROOF HARNESS
PAGE 8A-202-5
G H J K L M N
ROW 2 (YEL)
REAR COMPARTMENT
HARNESS
PAGE 8A-202-5
C200
3
4
5
6
H J K L M N
P
E D C B A
ROWS 3, 4, 5 & 6 (GRY)
CROSS CAR HARNESS
PAGE 8A-202-6
12146140
102-WAY F METRI-PACK MIXED
SERIES
GRY
K J H G F E D C B A
ROW 7 (BLU)
BODY HARNESS
PAGE 8A-202-8
N M L K J H G F E D C B A
ROW 8 (BLK)
MIRROR HARNESS
PAGE 8A-202-8
M L K J H G F E D C B A
ROW 9 (BLK)
FORWARD LAMPS HARNESS
PAGE 8A-202-9

HARNESS CONNECTOR FACES

F
E
D
C
B
A

12059962

6-WAY F METRI-PACK 150 SERIES
NAT

C200 (ROW 1) - VANITY MIRROR HARNESS

APPLICATION	CAVITY	WIRE COLOR	CKT	DESCRIPTION	PAGE
3.8L VIN L	1A	BRN	541	FUSED FEED TO CATAYST MONITOR (HO2S2)	8A-21-0
3.8L VIN L	1B	BLK	1050	GROUND FOR CATALYST MONITOR (HO2S2)	8A-21-0
	1C	ORN	240	FUSED FEED TO VANITY MIRRORS	8A-114-0
3.8L VIN L	1E		1668	CATALYST MONITOR (HO2S2) OUTPUT HIGH	8A-21-0
3.8L VIN L	1F		1669	CATALYST MONITOR (HO2S2) OUTPUT LOW	8A-21-0

**CAVITIES NOT LISTED ARE NOT USED

G
H
J
K
L
M
N

12059968

7-WAY F METRI-PACK 150 SERIES
YEL

C200 (ROW 1) - CONSOLE HARNESS

CAVITY	WIRE COLOR	CKT	DESCRIPTION	PAGE
1G (F)	PPL	420	BRAKE TRANSAXLE SHIFT INTERLOCK (BTSI) TO BRAKE PEDAL (NOT USED)	
1H	GRY	8	ASHTRAY ILLUMINATION	8A-114-0
1K	BLK	1550	GROUND - BTSI (NOT USED), ASHTRAY LAMP	8A-10-0
1L	ORN	440	BATTERY FUSED FEED	8A-11-0
1M	ORN	240	BATTERY FUSED FEED	8A-11-0
1N	WHT	156	CONSOLE COURTESY LAMP	8A-114-0

M = MALE SIDE OF CONNECTOR
F = FEMALE SIDE OF CONNECTOR

**CAVITIES NOT LISTED ARE NOT USED

F
E
D
C
B
A

12059964

6-WAY F METRI-PACK 150 SERIES

BLK

C200 (ROW 2) - ROOF HARNESS

CAVITY	WIRE COLOR	CKT	DESCRIPTION	PAGE
2B	ORN	240	INTERIOR ILLUMINATION FEED	8A-114-0
2C	WHT	156	INTERIOR ILLUMINATION RETURN	8A-114-0
2D	BLK	150	COURTESY LIGHTS GROUND	8A-114-0

**CAVITIES NOT LISTED ARE NOT USED

M = MALE SIDE OF CONNECTOR

F = FEMALE SIDE OF CONNECTOR

G
H
J
K
L
M
N

12059968

7-WAY F METRI-PACK 150 SERIES

YEL

C200 (ROW 2) - REAR COMPARTMENT HARNESS

APPLICATION	CAVITY	WIRE COLOR	CKT	DESCRIPTION	PAGE
	2L	DK GRN	145	POWER ANTENNA RELAY COIL - FEED	8A-150-0
	2N	ORN	1140	FUSED FEED TO POWER ANTENNA	8A-150-0

**CAVITIES NOT LISTED ARE NOT USED

HARNESS CONNECTOR FACES

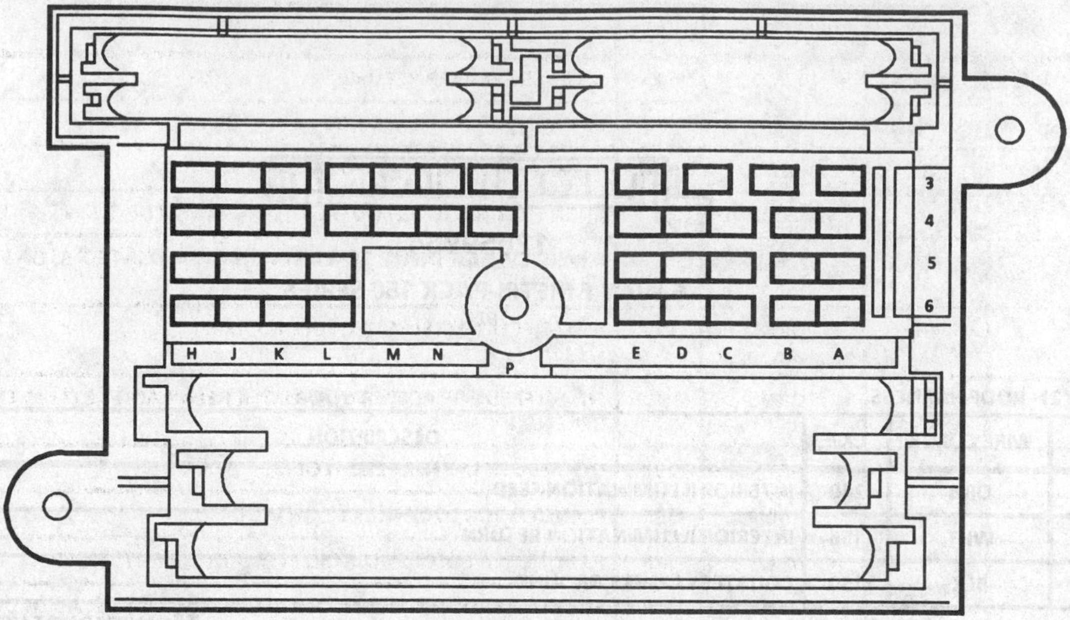
3
4
5
6
H J K L M N
P
E D C B A

12146138

41-WAY F METRI-PACK MIXED SERIES

GRY

C200 (ROWS 3, 4, 5, 6) - CROSS CAR HARNESS

APPLICATION	CAVITY	WIRE COLOR	CKT	DESCRIPTION	PAGE
8 CIRCUIT BUS TO 2A	3A	GRY	8	LIGHT SWITCH PWM ILLUMINATION FEED FOR LH AND RH WINDOW/DOOR LOCK SWITCH	8A-117-0
KEYLESS ENTRY ONLY	3B	LT GRN	275	KEYLESS ENTRY RECEIVER "PARK" INPUT	8A-132-0
	3C	ORN	240	FUSED FEED FOR LH AND RH WINDOW/DOOR LOCK SWITCH AND TRUNK COURTESY LIGHT	8A-11-0, 8A-131-0
	3D	BLK/WHT	56	TRUNK RELEASE FEED	8A-134-0
	3H	DK BLU	46	RH REAR SPEAKER FEED	8A-150-0
	3J	DK GRN	117	RH FRONT SPEAKER RETURN	8A-150-0
	3K	PPL	30	FUEL LEVEL SENDER INPUT TO INSTRUMENT CLUSTER	8A-81-0
	3L	BLK/WHT	238	SEAT BELT SWITCH INPUT TO CHIME MODULE	8A-76-0
	3M	PPL	293	REAR DEFOGGER FEED	8A-61-0
	3N	DK BLU	49	DOOR HANDLE SWITCH SIGNAL TO HEADLIGHT SWITCH	8A-114-0
	3P	BRN	141	FUSED FEED FOR LH AND RH FRONT DOOR LOCK/WINDOW SWITCH	8A-120-0
	4B	GRY/BLK	745	LH FRONT DOOR AJAR SWITCH	8A-114-0
	4C	DK BLU/WHT	727	PASSIVE RESTRAINT MODULE DOOR AJAR INPUT	8A-146-0
	4D	BLK/WHT	746	RH FRONT DOOR AJAR SIGNAL	8A-114-0

(CONTINUED ON NEXT PAGE)

(CONTINUED FROM PREVIOUS PAGE)

APPLICATION	CAVITY	WIRE COLOR	CKT	DESCRIPTION	PAGE
	4H	LT BLU	115	RH REAR SPEAKER RETURN	8A-150-0
	4J	GRY	118	LH FRONT SPEAKER RETURN	8A-150-0
	4K	WHT	156	DOOR AJAR SIGNAL TO DOME LAMPS	8A-114-0
	4L	DK GRN	19	TURN SIGNAL SWITCH OUTPUT TO RH TAIL/STOP-TURN LIGHTS	8A-110-0
	4M	WHT	17	BRAKE SWITCH INPUT TO CENTER HIGH MOUNTED STOP LIGHT (CHMSL)	8A-110-0
	4N	GRY	120	SWITCH FEED TO ELECTRIC FUEL PUMP	8A-20-0, 8A-131-0
	4P	ORN	1540	FUSED FEED FOR POWER DOOR LOCK RELAY AND KEYLESS ENTRY RECEIVER	8A-131-0, 8A-132-0
	5A	GRY	295	DOOR LOCK MOTOR FEED - LOCK	8A-131-0
	5B	LT BLU	195	POWER DOOR LOCK RELAY CONTROL	8A-131-0
	5C	YEL	528	PASSIVE SEAT BELT SOLENOID FEED AND KEY CYLINDER	8A-146-0
	5D	ORN	1140	FUSED FEED TO DOOR HANDLE SWITCHES AND DOOR LOCK/WINDOW SWITCH	8A-146-0
	5E	TAN	159	IGNITION KEY BUZZER GROUND	8A-76-0
	5H	YEL	116	LH REAR SPEAKER RETURN	8A-150-0
	5J	TAN	201	LH FRONT SPEAKER FEED	8A-150-0
	5K	LT GRN	24	BACKUP LIGHTS FEED	8A-112-0
	5L	YEL	18	TURN SIGNAL SWITCH OUTPUT TO LH TAIL/STOP-TURN LIGHTS	8A-110-0
	6A	BRN	882	ELECTRONIC BRAKE CONTROL MODULE (EBCM) (+) CONTROL TO RIGHT REAR WHEEL SPEED SENSOR	8A-44-0
	6B	WHT	883	ELECTRONIC BRAKE CONTROL MODULE (EBCM) (-) CONTROL TO RIGHT REAR WHEEL SPEED SENSOR	8A-44-0
	6C	BLK	884	ELECTRONIC BRAKE CONTROL MODULE (EBCM) (+) CONTROL TO LEFT REAR WHEEL SPEED SENSOR	8A-44-0
	6D	RED	885	ELECTRONIC BRAKE CONTROL MODULE (EBCM) (-) CONTROL TO LEFT REAR WHEEL SPEED SENSOR	8A-44-0
	6E	WHT	194	DOOR LOCK RELAY FEED - UNLOCK	8A-131-0
	6H	BRN	199	LH REAR SPEAKER FEED	8A-150-0
	6J	LT GRN	200	RH FRONT SPEAKER FEED	8A-150-0
	6K	TAN	694	DOOR LOCK MOTOR FEED - DRIVER DOOR UNLOCK	8A-131-0
	6L	BRN	9	TAIL, MARKER, LICENSE LIGHT FEED	8A-110-0

M = MALE SIDE OF CONNECTOR

F = FEMALE SIDE OF CONNECTOR

HARNESS CONNECTOR FACES

K
J
H
G
F
E
D
C
B
A

12059972

10-WAY F METRI-PACK MIXED SERIES
BLU

C200 (ROW 7) - BODY HARNESS

APPLICATION	CAVITY	WIRE COLOR	CKT	DESCRIPTION	PAGE
WITH SUNROOF	7G	BRN	141	POWER FEED FOR SUNROOF	8A-122-0
	7H	ORN	340	FUSED FEED FOR LH AND RH POWER SEAT SWITCH	8A-140-0

**CAVITIES NOT LISTED ARE NOT USED

N
M
L
K
J
H
G
F
E
D
C
B
A

12059965

13-WAY F METRI-PACK 150 SERIES
BLK

C200 (ROW 8) - MIRROR HARNESS

APPLICATION	CAVITY	WIRE COLOR	CKT	DESCRIPTION	PAGE
	8L	ORN	1140	BATTERY FUSED FEED FOR POWER MIRRORS	8A-147-0

**CAVITIES NOT LISTED ARE NOT USED

M
L
K
J
H
G
F
E
D
C
B
A

12146070

12-WAY F METRI-PACK 150 SERIES

BLK

C200 (ROW 9) - FORWARD LAMPS HARNESS

CAVITY	WIRE COLOR	CKT	DESCRIPTION	PAGE
9C	TAN	12	(2 DOOR) SWITCHED FEED FOR "LO BEAM" HEADLIGHTS	8A-100-0, 8A-102-0
9D	LT GRN	11	SWITCHED FEED FOR "HI BEAM" HEADLIGHTS	8A-100-0, 8A-102-0
9E	BRN	9	HEADLIGHT SWITCH "PARK OR HEAD" ILLUMINATION FEED	8A-110-0
9F	LT BLU	14	TURN SIGNAL SWITCH OUTPUT TO LH FRONT TURN LIGHTS	8A-110-0
9G	DK BLU	15	TURN SIGNAL SWITCH OUTPUT TO RH FRONT TURN LIGHTS	8A-110-0
9J	GRY	349	LEFT FRONT DISCRIMINATING SENSOR	8A-47-0
9K	BLK/WHT	1751	SIR GROUND FOR LEFT FRONT DISCRIMINATING SENSOR	8A-47-0

**CAVITIES NOT LISTED ARE NOT USED

C202

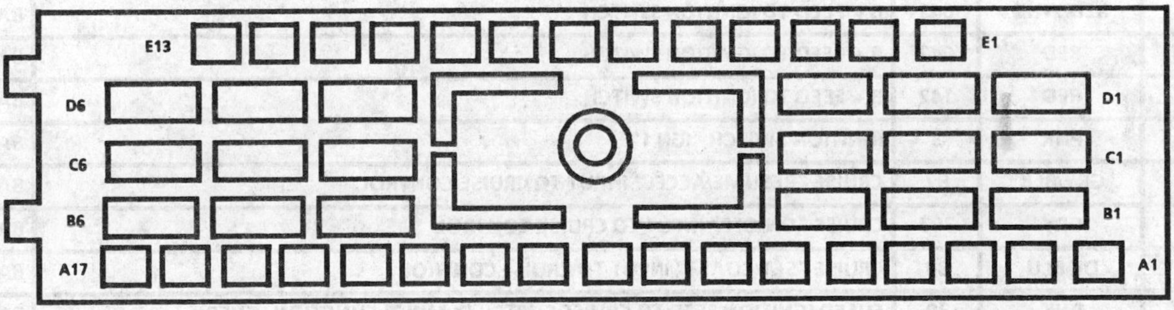
E13
E1
D6
D1
C6
C1
B6
B1
A17
A1

12077822

48-WAY M METRI-PACK MIXED SERIES

BLK

I/P HARNESS TO STEERING COLUMN HARNESS

**CAVITIES NOT LISTED ARE NOT USED

CAVITY	WIRE COLOR	CKT	DESCRIPTION	PAGE
A1 (F)	PPL	16	TURN FLASHER JUMPER TO TURN SIGNAL SWITCH	8A-110-0
A1(M)	LT BLU	1508	TURN FLASHER JUMPER TO TURN SIGNAL SWITCH	8A-110-0
A2	LT BLU	14	TURN SIGNAL OUTPUT TO LH TURN INDICATOR AND LH FRONT TURN LIGHTS	8A-110-0
A3	DK GRN	15	TURN SIGNAL OUTPUT TO RH TURN INDICATOR AND RH FRONT TURN LIGHTS	8A-110-0
A4	YEL	18	TURN SIGNAL OUTPUT TO LH REAR TURN LIGHTS	8A-110-0
A5	DK GRN	19	TURN SIGNAL OUTPUT TO RH REAR TURN LIGHTS	8A-110-0
A6	WHT	17	BRAKE SWITCH FEED TO TURN SIGNAL SWITCH	8A-110-0

(CONTINUED ON NEXT PAGE)

HARNESS CONNECTOR FACES

(CONTINUED FROM PREVIOUS PAGE)

CAVITY	WIRE COLOR	CKT	DESCRIPTION	PAGE
A7	BLK	28	HORN RELAY SWITCHED GROUND	8A-40-0
A8	LT GRN	80	CHIME MODULE IGNITION KEY WARNING SWITCH INPUT	8A-76-0
A9	TAN	159	SWITCH GROUND FROM LH DOOR JAM SWITCH: IGNITION KEY WARNING	8A-76-0
A11 (F)	ORN	1840	HAZARD FLASHER INPUT TO TURN SIGNAL SWITCH	8A-110-0
A11 (M)	BRN	27	HAZARD FLASHER INPUT TO TURN SIGNAL SWITCH	8A-110-0
A12 (F)	PNK	539	TURN FLASHER INPUT TO TURN SIGNAL SWITCH	8A-110-0
A12 (M)	PPL	16	TURN FLASHER INPUT TO TURN SIGNAL SWITCH	8A-110-0
A13 (F)	DK BLU	1508	TURN FLASHER JUMPER TO TURN SIGNAL SWITCH	8A-110-0
A13 (M)	LT BLU	1508	TURN FLASHER JUMPER TO TURN SIGNAL SWITCH	8A-110-0
A14	YEL	43	FUSED B + TO STEERING WHEEL CONTROLS	8A-89-0
A15	GRY	8	ILLUMINATION FEED TO STEERING WHEEL CONTROLS	8A-117-0
A16 (F)	LT GRN	1011	REMOTE RADIO CONTROL SIGNAL FROM STEERING WHEEL CONTROLS	8A-89-0
A16 (M)	DK BLU	596	REMOTE RADIO CONTROL SIGNAL FROM STEERING WHEEL CONTROLS	8A-89-0
A17	BLK	1450	ILLUMINATION GROUND FROM STEERING WHEEL CONTROLS	8A-117-0
B2	ORN	300	IGNITION SWITCH "ACCESSORY 2"	8A-10-0
B3	TAN/WHT	33	IGNITION SWITCH "BULB TEST" GROUND	8A-81-0
B6	YEL	5	IGNITION SWITCH "START" FEED TO THEFT DETERRENT RELAY	8A-133-0
C2	PPL	704	IGNITION SWITCH "IGN 3"	8A-10-0
C6	BRN	4	IGNITION SWITCH "ACCESSORY 1"	8A-10-0
D2 (F)	RED/WHT	642	B + FEED TO IGNITION SWITCH	8A-10-0
D2 (M)	RED	642	B + FEED TO IGNITION SWITCH	8A-10-0
D5	RED	142	B + FEED TO IGNITION SWITCH	8A-10-0
D6	PNK	3	IGNITION SWITCH "IGN 1"	8A-10-0
E1	GRY/BLK	87	CRUISE "RESUME/ACCEL" INPUT TO CRUISE CONTROL	8A-34-0
E2	GRY	397	CRUISE "ON/OFF" INPUT TO CRUISE CONTROL	8A-34-0
E3	DK BLU	84	CRUISE "SET/COAST" INPUT TO CRUISE CONTROL	8A-34-0
E4 (F)	PNK	39	FUSED IGNITION FEED TO CRUISE SWITCH IN MULTI-FUNCTION LEVER	8A-34-0
E4 (M)	BRN	541	FUSED IGNITION FEED TO CRUISE SWITCH IN MULTI-FUNCTION LEVER	8A-34-0
E5	LT GRN	11	SWITCHED FEED FOR "HI BEAM" HEADLIGHTS	8A-100-0, 8A-102-0
E6	TAN	12	SWITCHED FEED FOR "LO BEAM" HEADLIGHTS	8A-100-0, 8A-102-0
E7	YEL	10	HEADLIGHT DIMMER FEED	8A-100-0, 8A-102-0
E9 (F)	YEL/WHT	243	FUSED B + TO WIPER/WASHER SWITCH	8A-91-0
E9 (M)	YEL	243	FUSED B + TO WIPER/WASHER SWITCH	8A-91-0
E10	GRY	91	"MIST," "PULSE," "LO" AND "WASH" OUTPUT TO WIPER MOTOR	8A-91-0
E11	DK GRN	95	LO SPEED OUTPUT TO WIPER MOTOR	8A-91-0
E12	PPL	92	HI SPEED OUTPUT TO WIPER MOTOR	8A-91-0
E13	PNK	94	WASH OUTPUT TO WIPER MOTOR AND WASHER	8A-91-0

M = MALE SIDE OF CONNECTOR
F = FEMALE SIDE OF CONNECTOR

C215

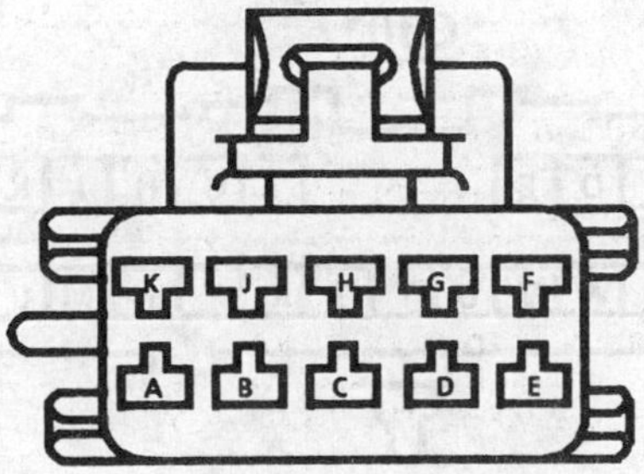
K
J
H
G
F
A
B
C
D
E
I/P TO WIPER HARNESS

12064769

10-WAY F METRI-PACK 150 SERIES
NAT

** CAVITIES NOT LISTED ARE NOT USED

CAVITY	WIRE COLOR	CKT	DESCRIPTION	PAGE
A	BRN	882	ELECTRONIC BRAKE CONTROL MODULE (EBCM) (+) CONTROL TO RH REAR WHEEL SPEED SENSOR	8A-44-0
B	WHT	17	BRAKE SWITCH FEED TO EBCM	8A-44-0
D	BRN	341	FUSED IGNITION FEED	8A-44-0
E	WHT	883	EBCM (-) CONTROL TO RH REAR WHEELS SPEED SENSOR	8A-44-0
F	BLK	884	EBCM (+) CONTROL TO LH REAR WHEELS SPEED SENSOR	8A-44-0
G	ORN	640	FUSED B + FEED	8A-44-0
H	TAN	800	SERIAL DATA LINE FROM EBCM TO DLC	8A-44-0
J	WHT	852	ABS INDICATOR SIGNAL	8A-44-0
K	RED	885	EBCM (-) CONTROL TO LH REAR WHEEL SPEED SENSOR	8A-44-0

HARNESS CONNECTOR FACES

C301

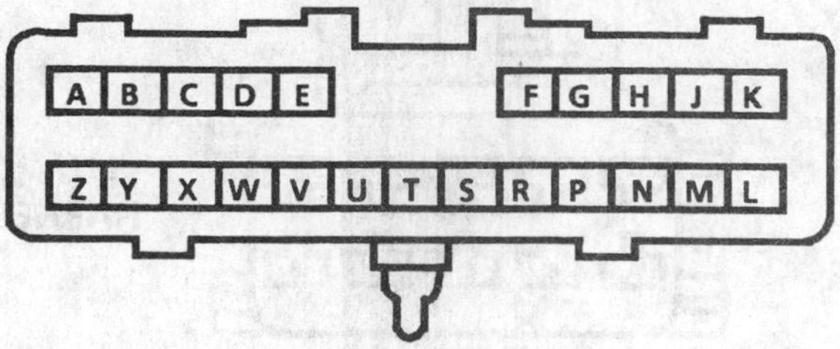
A B C D E
F G H J K
Z Y X W V U T S R P N M L

CROSS CAR HARNESS TO LEFT FRONT DOOR HARNESS

12092248
23-WAY M METRI-PACK ACT 280
BLK

** CAVITIES NOT LISTED ARE NOT USED

CAVITY	WIRE COLOR	CKT	DESCRIPTION	PAGE
A	LT GRN	170	RH REAR WINDOW UP FROM LH FRONT SWITCH	8A-120-0
B	LT BLU	166	RH FRONT WINDOW UP FROM LH FRONT SWITCH	8A-120-0
C	BLK	750	GROUND TO LH FRONT DOOR LOCK/WINDOW SWITCH, DOOR HANDLE SWITCH, LAP BELT AND SHOULDER BELT SOLENOID	8A-14-0
D	TAN	294	RH FRONT DOOR LOCK MOTOR FEED - UNLOCK	8A-131-0
E	WHT	194	RH FRONT DOOR LOCK RELAY FEED - UNLOCK COIL	8A-131-0
F	LT BLU	195	RH FRONT DOOR LOCK RELAY FEED - LOCK COIL	8A-131-0
G	GRY	295	RH FRONT DOOR LOCK MOTOR FEED - LOCK	8A-131-0
H	BRN	141	FUSED FEED TO LH FRONT DOOR SWITCH ASSEMBLY	8A-11-0
J	TAN	167	RH FRONT WINDOW DOWN FROM LH FRONT SWITCH	8A-120-0
K	ORN	240	FUSED FEED TO LH FRONT DOOR - NOT USED ON DOOR	8A-11-0
L	PPL	169	LH REAR WINDOW DOWN FROM LH FRONT SWITCH	8A-120-0
M	DK GRN	168	LH REAR WINDOW UP FROM LH FRONT SWITCH	8A-120-0
N	DK BLU	1307	WINDOW LOCK OUT CONTROL	8A-120-0
P	GRY/BLK	745	DOOR AJAR SWITCH SIGNAL TO CHIME MODULE	8A-76-0
R	DK BLU	49	DOOR HANDLE SWITCH SIGNAL TO HEADLIGHT SWITCH	8A-114-0
S	GRY	8	LH FRONT DOOR SWITCH ILLUMINATION	8A-120-0
T	YEL	528	PASSIVE SEAT BELT SOLENOID FEED AND KEY CYLINDER LIGHT	8A-146-0
U	DK BLU/WHT	727	DOOR AJAR SWITCH SIGNAL TO CHIME MODULE SECONDARY	8A-76-0
V	GRY	118	LH FRONT SPEAKER RETURN	8A-150-0
W	TAN	201	LH FRONT SPEAKER FEED	8A-150-0
X	WHT	156	LH FRONT DOOR COURTESY LAMP	8A-114-0
Y	PPL	171	RH REAR WINDOW DOWN FROM LH FRONT SWITCH	8A-120-0
Z	ORN	1140	FUSED FEED TO DOOR HANDLE SWITCH AND DOOR LOCK/WINDOW SWITCH	8A-146-0

M = MALE SIDE OF CONNECTOR
F = FEMALE SIDE OF CONNECTOR

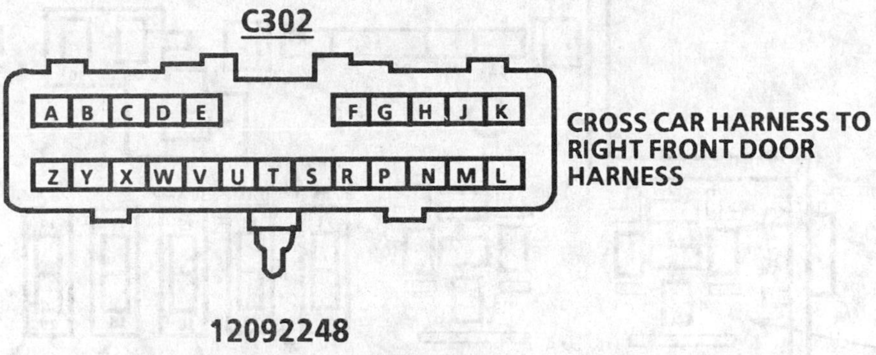
C302
A B C D E
F G H J K
Z Y X W V U T S R P N M L
CROSS CAR HARNESS TO RIGHT FRONT DOOR HARNESS
12092248

23-WAY M METRI-PACK ACT 280
BLK

** CAVITIES NOT LISTED ARE NOT USED

CAVITY	WIRE COLOR	CKT	DESCRIPTION	PAGE
B	LT BLU	166	RH FRONT WINDOW UP FROM LH FRONT SWITCH	8A-120-0
C	BLK	750	GROUND TO RH FRONT DOOR LOCK/WINDOW SWITCH, DOOR HANDLE SWITCH, LAP AND SHOULDER BELT SOLENOID	8A-14-0
D	TAN	294	RH FRONT DOOR LOCK MOTOR FEED - UNLOCK	8A-131-0
E	WHT	194	RH FRONT DOOR LOCK RELAY FEED - UNLOCK COIL	8A-131-0
F	LT BLU	195	RH FRONT DOOR LOCK RELAY FEED - LOCK COIL	8A-131-0
G	GRY	295	RH FRONT DOOR LOCK MOTOR FEED - LOCK	8A-131-0
J	TAN	167	RH FRONT WINDOW DOWN FROM LH FRONT SWITCH	8A-120-0
K	ORN	240	FUSED FEED TO RH FRONT DOOR - NOT USED ON DOOR	8A-11-0
N	DK BLU	1307	WINDOW LOCK OUT CONTROL	8A-120-0
P	BLK/WHT	746	RH FRONT DOOR AJAR SIGNAL	8A-114-0
R	DK BLU	49	DOOR HANDLE SWITCH SIGNAL TO HEADLIGHT SWITCH	8A-114-0
S	GRY	8	RH FRONT DOOR SWITCH ILLUMINATION	8A-120-0
T	YEL	528	PASSIVE SEAT BELT SOLENOID FEED AND KEY CYLINDER LIGHT (2 DOOR)	8A-146-0
U	DK/BLU	727	DOOR AJAR SWITCH SIGNAL TO CHIME MODULE SECONDARY	8A-76-0
V	DK GRN	117	RH FRONT SPEAKER RETURN	8A-150-0
W	LT GRN	200	RH FRONT SPEAKER FEED	8A-150-0
X	WHT	156	RH FRONT DOOR COURTESY LAMP	8A-114-0
Z	ORN	1140	FUSED FEED TO DOOR HANDLE SWITCH AND DOOR LOCK/WINDOW SWITCH	8A-146-0

M = MALE SIDE OF CONNECTOR
F = FEMALE SIDE OF CONNECTOR

HARNESS CONNECTOR FACES

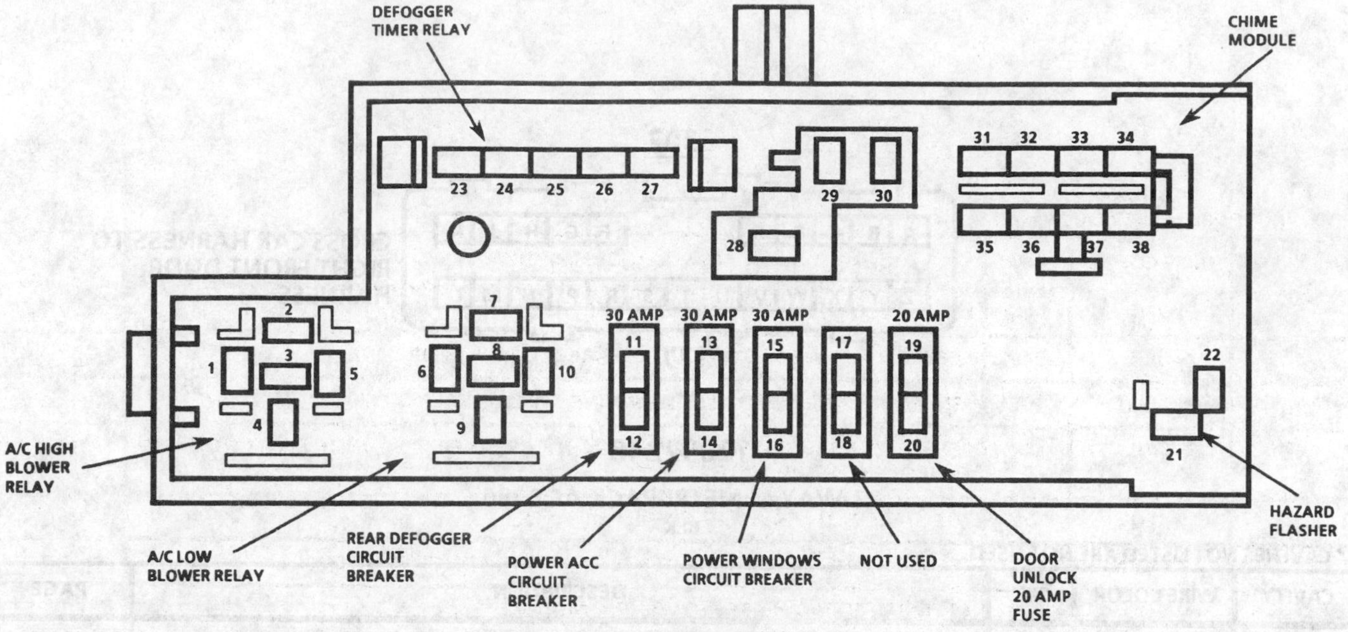
DEFOGGER TIMER RELAY
CHIME MODULE
23 24 25 26 27
29 30
28
31 32 33 34
35 36 37 38
2
1 3 5
4
7
6 8 10
9
30 AMP 11 12
30 AMP 13 14
30 AMP 15 16
17 18
20 AMP 19 20
22
21
A/C HIGH BLOWER RELAY
A/C LOW BLOWER RELAY
REAR DEFOGGER CIRCUIT BREAKER
POWER ACC CIRCUIT BREAKER
POWER WINDOWS CIRCUIT BREAKER
NOT USED
DOOR UNLOCK 20 AMP FUSE
HAZARD FLASHER

12064880
METRI-PACK 630 SERIES
BLK
COMPONENT CENTER

** CAVITIES NOT LISTED ARE NOT USED

CAVITY	WIRE COLOR	CKT	DESCRIPTION	PAGE
1	BLK	150	HIGH BLOWER RELAY COIL GROUND	8A-63-0
2	RED	40	FUSED FEED FOR BLOWER MOTOR (HIGH SPEED)	8A-63-0
3	DK BLU	101	BLOWER MOTOR FEED FOR LO, M1 AND M2 SPEEDS	8A-63-0
4	PPL	65	BLOWER MOTOR FEED FROM HIGH BLOWER RELAY	8A-63-0
5	ORN	52	HIGH SPEED FEED FROM BLOWER SWITCH	8A-63-0
6	BLK	150	LOW BLOWER RELAY COIL GROUND	8A-63-0
8	BRN	41	FUSED FEED TO LOW BLOWER RELAY	8A-63-0
9	YEL (2 WIRES)	51	LOW BLOWER RELAY FEED TO BLOWER SWITCH AND BLOWER RESISTORS	8A-63-0
10	YEL	770	"OFF" FEED FROM HVAC CONTROL ASSEMBLY	8A-63-0
11	RED	1442	FUSED FEED TO REAR DEFOG CIRCUIT BREAKER	8A-63-0
12	RED/BLK	1040	FEED FROM REAR DEFOG CIRCUIT BREAKER TO REAR DEFOGGER TIMER RELAY	8A-10-0, 8A-61-0

(CONTINUED ON NEXT PAGE)

(CONTINUED FROM PREVIOUS PAGE)

CAVITY	WIRE COLOR	CKT	DESCRIPTION	PAGE
13	RED	1442	FUSED FEED TO POWER ACC CIRCUIT BREAKER	8A-11-0
14	ORN	340	FEED FROM POWER ACC CIRCUIT BREAKER TO POWER OPTIONS	8A-11-0
15	LT BLU	706	IGNITION SWITCH FEED TO POWER WINDOW CIRCUIT BREAKER	8A-11-0
16	BRN	141	FEED FROM POWER WINDOWS CIRCUIT BREAKER TO DOOR SWITCHES AND SUNROOF CONTROL UNIT	8A-11-0
17	RED	1445	FUSED FEED TO HEADLIGHT CIRCUIT BREAKER	8A-10-0
18	DK GRN	860	FEED FROM HEADLIGHT CIRCUIT BREAKER TO HEADLIGHT SWITCH	8A-11-0
19	BLK	900	400 MILLISECOND PULSE FROM CHIME MODULE	8A-131-0
20	WHT	194	FEED FROM DOOR UNLOCK FUSE TO DOOR LOCK RELAY	8A-131-0
21	BRN	27	HAZARD FLASHER OUTPUT TO TURN SIGNAL SWITCH	8A-110-0
22	ORN	140	FUSED FEED TO HAZARD FLASHER	8A-110-0
23	BLK	150	GROUND FOR REAR DEFOGGER TIMER RELAY	8A-61-0
24	LT BLU	292	REAR DEFOGGER "ON" INPUT	8A-61-0
25	PNK/BLK	39	IGNITION INPUT FUSED TO REAR DEFOGGER TIMER RELAY	8A-61-0
26	PPL/WHT	293	POWER OUTPUT FROM REAR DEFOGGER TIMER RELAY TO REAR DEFOGGER AND REAR DEFOGGER "ON" INDICATOR	8A-61-0
27	ORN	1040	REAR DEFOG CIRCUIT BREAKER POWER INPUT TO REAR DEFOGGER TIMER RELAY	8A-61-0
31	BRN	9	LIGHTS ON INPUT TO CHIME MODULE	8A-76-0
32	ORN	640	BATTERY INPUT TO CHIME MODULE	8A-76-0
33	LT GRN	80	IGNITION KEY WARNING INPUT TO CHIME MODULE	8A-76-0
34	WHT	156	CHIME MODULE COURTESY LIGHTS GROUND	8A-114-0
35	BLK	238	SEAT BELT INPUT TO CHIME MODULE	8A-76-0
36	BLK	1550	GROUND FOR CHIME MODULE	8A-14-0
37	YEL	237	OUTPUT FROM CHIME MODULE TO "FASTEN BELTS" INDICATOR	8A-76-0
38	PNK/BLK	39	IGNITION INPUT TO CHIME MODULE	8A-76-0

HARNESS CONNECTOR FACES

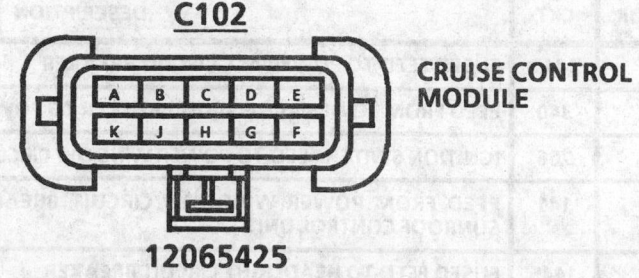

C102

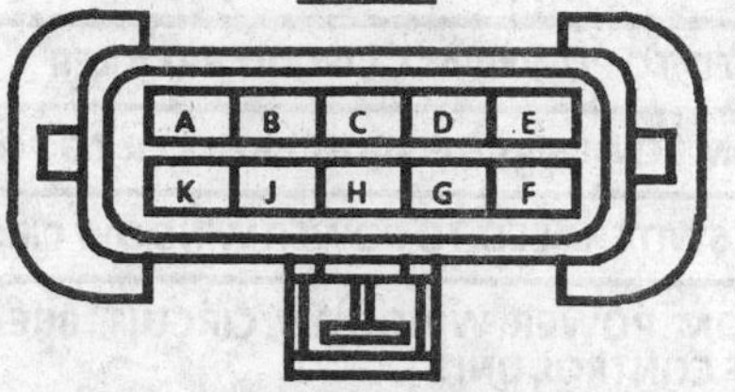
A B C D E
K J H G F

CRUISE CONTROL MODULE

12065425

10-WAY F METRI-PACK 150 SERIES

BLK

CAVITY	WIRE COLOR	CKT	DESCRIPTION	PAGE
A	GRY	397	CRUISE "ON/OFF" INPUT	8A-34-0
B	DK BLU	84	CRUISE "SET/COAST" INPUT	8A-34-0
C	GRY/BLK	87	CRUISE "RESUME/ACCEL" INPUT	8A-34-0
D	BRN	86	CRUISE CUT-OFF SWITCH	8A-34-0
E	BLK	1050	GROUND	8A-34-0
F	PNK	739	FUSED FEED	8A-34-0
G	WHT	17	CRUISE/STOP BRAKE SWITCH	8A-34-0
H	DK GRN	83	CRUISE "INHIBIT" SIGNAL	8A-34-0
J	WHT	85	CRUISED "ENGAGED" SIGNAL	8A-34-0
K	DK GRN	389	VSS INPUT	8A-34-0

M = MALE SIDE OF CONNECTOR
F = FEMALE SIDE OF CONNECTOR

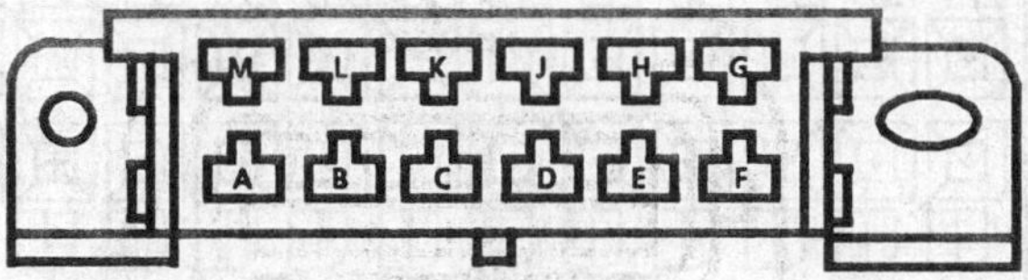
M
L
K
J
H
G
A
B
C
D
E
F

12020043

12-WAY F METRI-PACK 280 SERIES

BLK

DATA LINK CONNECTOR (DLC)

** CAVITIES NOT LISTED ARE NOT USED

CAVITY	WIRE COLOR	CKT	DESCRIPTION	PAGE
A	BLK	1550	GROUND TO G201	8A-50-0
D	GRY	728	SECURITY INDICATOR SIGNAL	8A-133-1
J	DK GRN	835	SERIAL DATA: RADIO, C68 HVAC CONTROL ASSEMBLY	8A-150-0, 8A-63-0
K	PPL	326	DIAGNOSTIC REQUEST TO DIAGNOSTIC ENERGY RESERVE MODULE (DERM)	8A-50-0
M	TAN	800	SERIAL DATA: INPUT/OUTPUT	8A-50-0

HARNESS CONNECTOR FACES

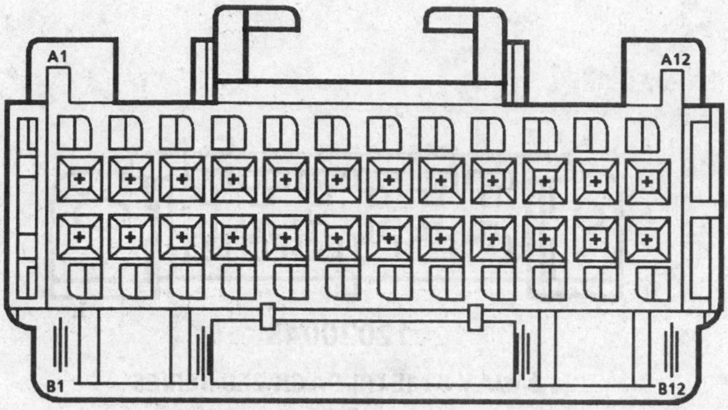
A1
A12
B1
B12

12092689
24-WAY F MICRO-PACK 100 SERIES
YEL

DIAGNOSTIC ENERGY RESERVE MODULE (DERM)

** CAVITIES NOT LISTED ARE NOT USED

CAVITY	WIRE COLOR	CKT	DESCRIPTION	PAGE
A1	BLK	1751	GROUND TO G251	8A-47-0
A2	BLK	1550	REDUNDANT INDICATOR GROUND TO G201	8A-47-0
A4	YEL/BLK	236	36 VOLT LOOP RESERVE (VLR) TO ARMING SENSOR	8A-47-0
A5	LT GRN	1400	DRIVER SOURCE SENSE FROM ARMING SENSOR	8A-47-0
A8	PPL	326	DIAGNOSTIC REQUEST INPUT FROM DLC	8A-47-0
A9	YEL	1139	FUSED IGNITION FEED	8A-47-0
A10	YEL	1139	FUSED IGNITION FEED	8A-47-0
A12	BLK	1751	TO GROUND G251	8A-47-0
B1	BRN	358	TO "AIR BAG" INDICATOR	8A-47-0
B2	PNK	39	FUSED IGNITION FEED	8A-47-0
B5	BLK/WHT	238	SEAT BELT INPUT FROM SEAT BELT SWITCH	8A-76-0
B8	DK GRN	348	INFLATOR OUTPUT TO DRIVER INFLATOR MODULE	8A-47-0
B9	WHT	347	INFLATOR FEED TO DRIVER INFLATOR MODULE	8A-47-0
B10	PPL	806	FUSED CRANK FEED	8A-47-0
B11	TAN	800	SERIAL DATA LINE TO DLC	8A-47-0

C1

A
B

12110637

2-WAY F METRI-PACK 480 SERIES

GRY

C2

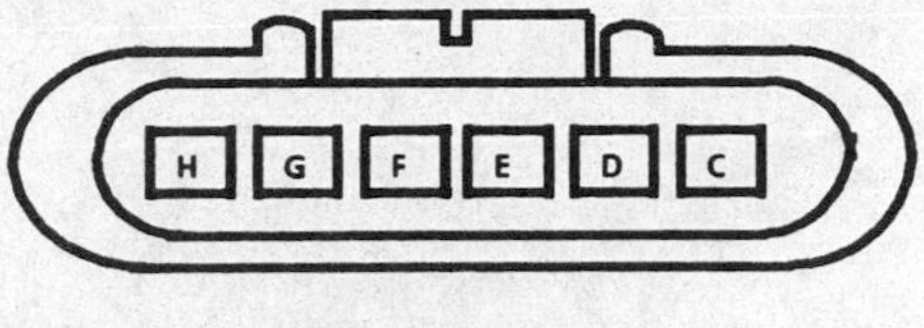
H
G
F
E
D
C

12110635

6-WAY F METRI-PACK 280 SERIES

GRY

C3

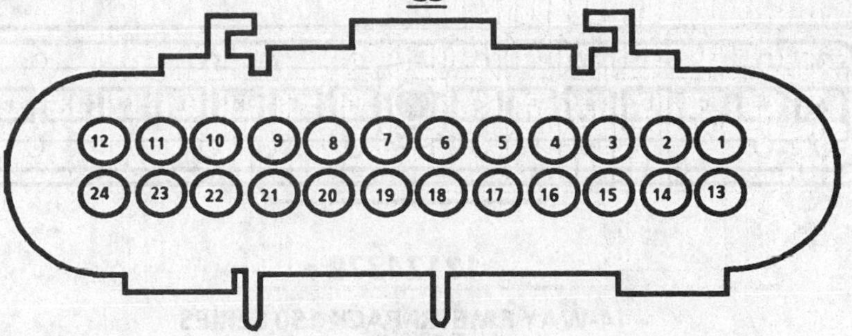
12 11 10 9 8 7 6 5 4 3 2 1
24 23 22 21 20 19 18 17 16 15 14 13

12129183

24-WAY F MICRO-PACK 100 SERIES

CLR

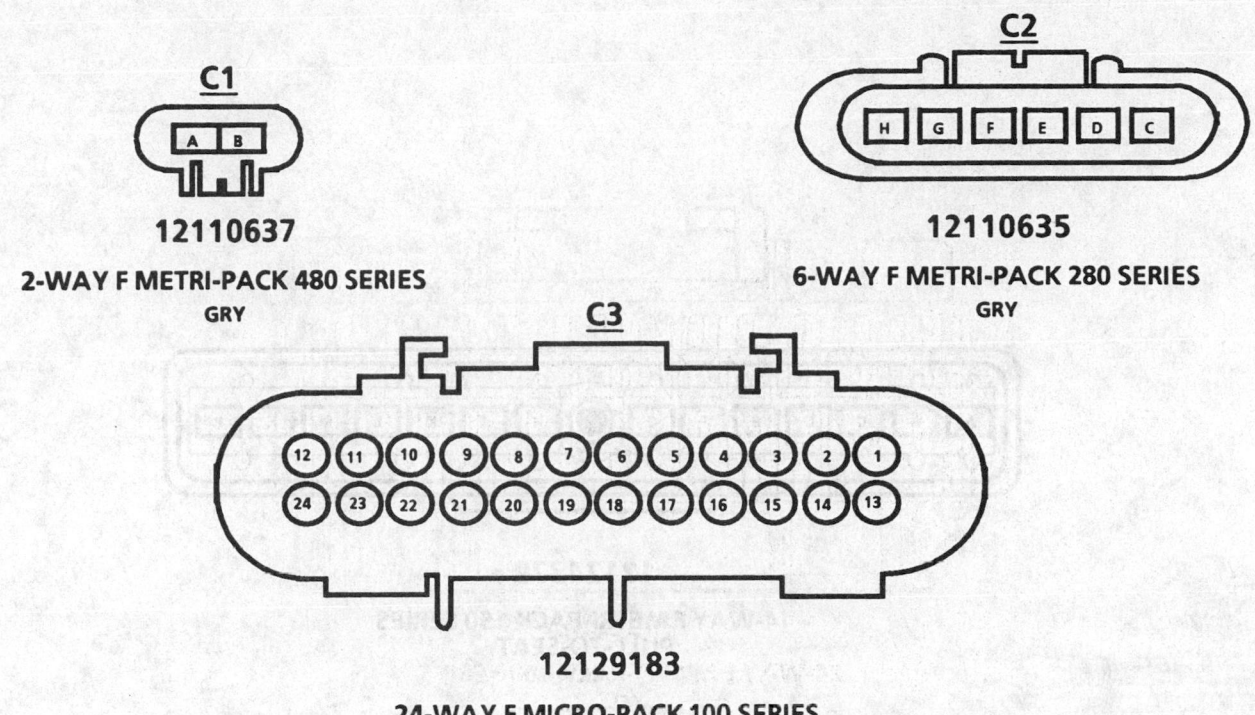

ELECTRONIC BRAKE CONTROL MODULE (EBCM) CONNECTORS

** CAVITIES NOT LISTED ARE NOT USED

CAVITY	WIRE COLOR	CKT	DESCRIPTION	PAGE
C3 (2)	TAN	800	SERIAL DATA: INPUT/OUTPUT	8A-44-0
C3 (4)	LT BLU/BLK	1289	EBCM RF SOLENOID CONTROL	8A-44-0
C3 (5)	LT BLU	830	EBCM (-) INPUT TO LF WHEEL SPEED SENSOR	8A-44-0
C3 (6)	YEL	873	EBCM (+) RETURN FROM LF WHEEL SPEED SENSOR	8A-44-0
C3 (7)	BRN	882	EBCM (+) INPUT TO RR WHEEL SPEED SENSOR	8A-44-0
C3 (8)	WHT	883	EBCM (-) RETURN FROM RR WHEEL SPEED SENSOR	8A-44-0
C3 (9)	DK GRN	872	EBCM (+) INPUT TO RF WHEEL SPEED SENSOR	8A-44-0
C3 (10)	TAN	833	EBCM (-) RETURN FROM RF WHEEL SPEED SENSOR	8A-44-0
C3 (11)	RED	885	EBCM (-) RETURN FROM LR WHEEL SPEED SENSOR	8A-44-0
C3 (12)	BLK	884	EBCM (+) INPUT TO LR WHEEL SPEED SENSOR	8A-44-0
C3 (13)	WHT	17	EBCM BRAKE SWITCH INPUT	8A-44-0
C3 (14)	BRN	341	FUSED FEED TO EBCM	8A-44-0
C3 (15)	ORN	640	FUSED FEED TO EBCM	8A-44-0
C3 (21)	TAN/WHT	33	EBCM BRAKE INDICATOR CONTROL	8A-44-0
C3 (22)	PNK	1632	EBCM ABS RELAY A CONTROL	8A-44-0
C3 (23)	WHT	852	EBCM ABS INDICATOR CONTROL TO LAMP DRIVER MODULE	8A-44-0
C3 (24)	DK GRN/YEL	1288	EBCM LF SOLENOID CONTROL	8A-44-0

HARNESS CONNECTOR FACES

A
B
C
D
E
F
G
H
J
K
L
M
N
P

12124379

14-WAY F METRI-PACK 150 SERIES
PULL-TO-SEAT
GRY

ELECTRONIC IGNITION CONTROL MODULE (VIN L)

** CAVITIES NOT LISTED ARE NOT USED

CAVITY	WIRE COLOR	CKT	DESCRIPTION	PAGE
A	WHT	423	IGNITION CONTROL (IC) INPUT	8A-21-0
B	TAN/BLK	424	IGNITION MODULE BYPASS	8A-21-0
C	LT BLU/BLK	647	CRANKSHAFT REFERENCE HI	8A-21-0
D	PPL/WHT	430	FUEL CONTROL REFERENCE HI	8A-21-0
E	WHT	121	RPM SIGNAL TO TACHOMETER	8A-21-0
F	BLK	630	CAMSHAFT REFERENCE OUTPUT	8A-21-0
G	YEL	573	CRANKSHAFT POSITION SENSOR SIGNAL	8A-21-0
H	LT BLU/WHT	646	CRANKSHAFT POSITION SENSOR SIGNAL	8A-21-0
J	BRN/WHT	633	CAMSHAFT POSITION SENSOR SIGNAL	8A-21-0
K	BLK/WHT	451	GROUND TO G111	8A-21-0
L	RED/BLK	453	FUEL CONTROL REFERNECE OUTPUT LO	8A-21-0
M	RED/BLK	645	SENSOR GROUND	8A-21-0
N	WHT/BLK	644	10V REFERENCE	8A-21-0
P	PNK	839	FUSED IGNITION	8A-21-0

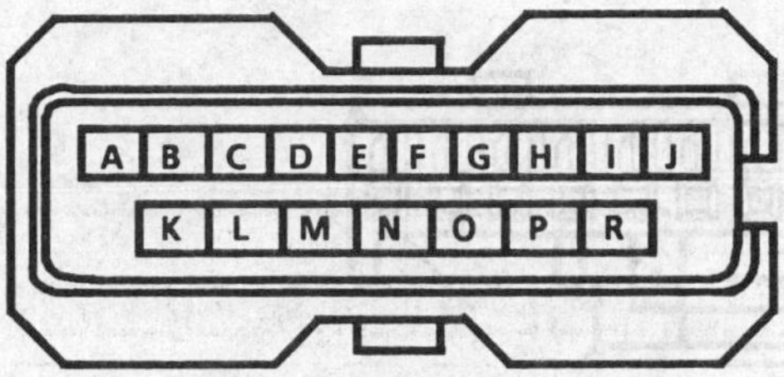
A B C D E F G H I J
K L M N O P R

12059993

17-WAY F METRI-PACK MIXED SERIES

BLK

HEADLIGHT SWITCH

** CAVITIES NOT LISTED ARE NOT USED

CAVITY	WIRE COLOR	CKT	DESCRIPTION	PAGE
A	BLK	1450	GROUND TO G203	8A-14-6
B	WHT	156	DOME LIGHT	8A-114-0
C	DK BLU	49	DOOR OPEN INPUT	8A-114-0
D	GRY	295	DOOR LOCK MOTOR "LOCK" SIGNAL	8A-131-0
E	TAN	694	DRIVER DOOR "UNLOCK" SIGNAL	8A-131-0
F	PNK	39	FUSED IGNITION FEED FROM INDIC FUSE	8A-11-13
G	BRN/WHT	230	VACUUM FLUORESCENT DIMMING SIGNAL	8A-117-0
H	GRY	8	ANALOG PWM ILLUMINATION TO I/P LIGHTS	8A-117-0
I	GRY/BLK	308	PARK LIGHTS "ON" SIGNAL	8A-117-0
K	DK GRN	306	HEADLIGHTS "OFF" SIGNAL TO DAYTIME RUNNING LIGHTS MODULE	8A-102-0
L	YEL	10	HEADLIGHTS "ON" FEED TO DIMMER SWITCH	8A-100-0 8A-102-0
N	RED	442	B + FROM HD LPS MAXI CIRCUIT BREAKER	8A-10-0
O	ORN	1340	FUSED B + FROM PARK LPS FUSE	8A-11-12
P	LT BLU	1872	PARK LIGHTS "OFF" SIGNAL TO DRL MODULE	8A-102-0
R	BRN	9	PARK LIGHTS FEED	8A-110-0

HARNESS CONNECTOR FACES

C1

1
15

12064984

15-WAY F MICRO-PACK

BLK

C2

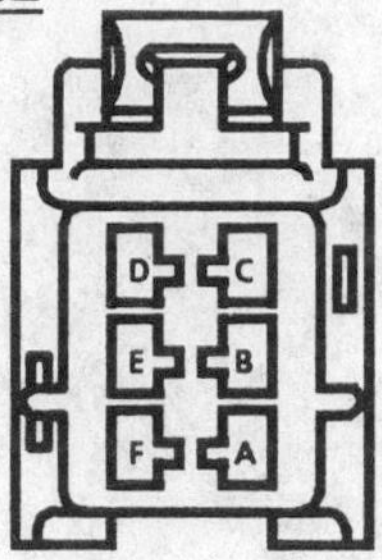
D
C
E
B
F
A

12064752

6-WAY F METRI-PACK 280 SERIES

BLK

HVAC CONTROL ASSEMBLY (C67)

**CAVITIES NOT LISTED ARE NOT USED

CAVITY	WIRE COLOR	CKT	DESCRIPTION	PAGE
C1 (1)	PPL	361	SWITCHED GROUND BI-LEVEL SOLENOID	8A-65-0
C1 (2)	RED	362	SWITCHED GROUND FOR HEATER SOLENOID	8A-65-0
C1 (3)	LT GRN/BLK	366	SWITCHED GROUND FOR DEFROST SOLENOID	8A-65-0
C1 (4)	BRN	541	FUSED FEED TO HVAC CONTROL ASSEMBLY	8A-65-0
C1 (5)	LT BLU	706	SWITCHED GROUND FOR RECIRC SOLENOID	8A-65-0
C1 (6)	LT GRN	66	SWITCHED FEED FOR A/C REQUEST INPUT TO ECM	8A-64-0
C1 (8)	YEL	770	SWITCHED FEED TO LOW BLOWER RELAY	8A-66-0
C1 (9)	LT BLU	292	SWITCHED FEED TO REAR DEFOGGER TIMER RELAY	8A-61-0
C1 (10)	GRY	8	PANEL ILLUMINATION FEED	8A-117-0
C1 (11)	LT BLU	733	AIR TEMPERATURE VALVE MOTOR CONTROL OUTPUT	8A-65-0
C1 (12)	BLK	150	GROUND TO G203	8A-14-0
C1 (13)	PPL/WHT	293	REAR DEFOGGER ON INDICATOR INPUT	8A-61-0
C1 (14)	BRN	9	HEADLIGHT SWITCH FEED FOR HVAC CONTROL ASSEMBLY ILLUMINATION	8A-61-0, 8A-63-0, 8A-65-0
C1 (15)	TAN	363	SWITCH GROUND FOR A/C SOLENOID	8A-65-0

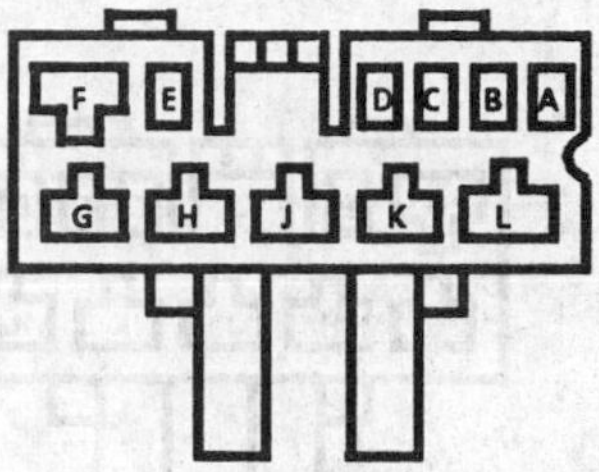
F
E
D
C
B
A
G
H
J
K
L

12084617

11-WAY F METRI-PACK MIXED SERIES

BLK

LH WINDOW/DOOR LOCK SWITCH (2 DOOR)

CAVITY	WIRE COLOR	CKT	DESCRIPTION	PAGE
A	GRY	8	PWM ILLUMINATION FEED	8A-117-0
B	BLK	750	GROUND TO G302	8A-131-0
C	BLK	194	UNLOCK OUTPUT TO POWER DOOR LOCK RELAY	8A-131-0
D	ORN	1140	FUSED BATTERY FEED	8A-120-0, 8A-131-0
E	LT BLU	195	LOCK OUTPUT TO POWER DOOR LOCK RELAY	8A-131-0
F	BRN	141	FUSED IGNITION FEED	8A-120-0
G	TAN	167	DOWN OUTPUT TO RH WINDOW/DOOR LOCK SWITCH	8A-120-0
H	DK BLU/WHT	166	UP OUTPUT TO RH WINDOW/DOOR LOCK SWITCH	8A-120-0
J	BRN	165	DOWN OUTPUT TO LH FRONT WINDOW MOTOR	8A-120-0
K	DK BLU	164	UP OUTPUT TO LH FRONT WINDOW MOTOR	8A-120-0
L	BLK	750	GROUND TO G302	8A-120-0

HARNESS CONNECTOR FACES

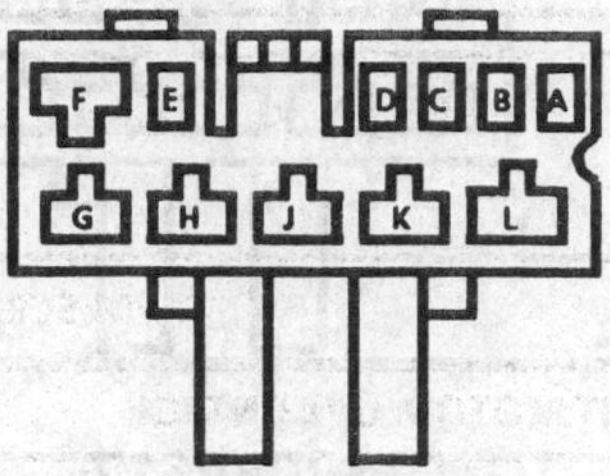
F
E
D
C
B
A
G
H
J
K
L

12084617

11-WAY F MICRO-PACK MIXED SERIES

BLK

RH WINDOW/DOOR LOCK SWITCH (2 DOOR)

CAVITY	WIRE COLOR	CKT	DESCRIPTION	PAGE
A	GRY	8	PWM ILLUMINATION FEED	8A-117-0
B	BLK	750	GROUND TO G305	8A-120-0
C	BLK	194	UNLOCK OUTPUT TO POWER DOOR LOCK RELAY	8A-131-0
D	ORN	1140	FUSED FEED FOR RH SWITCH ASSEMBLY	8A-120-0, 8A-131-0
E	LT BLU	195	LOCK OUTPUT TO POWER DOOR LOCK RELAY	8A-131-0
F	PNK	141	FUSED FEED TO RH WINDOW/DOOR LOCK SWITCH	8A-120-0
H	DK BLU	666	UP OUTPUT TO RH FRONT WINDOW MOTOR	8A-120-0
L	DK BLU/WHT	166	UP INPUT FROM LH WINDOW/DOOR LOCK SWITCH	8A-120-0
G	BRN	667	DOWN OUTPUT TO RH FRONT WINDOW MOTOR	8A-120-0
K	TAN	167	DOWN INPUT FROM LH WINDOW/DOOR LOCK SWITCH	8A-120-0

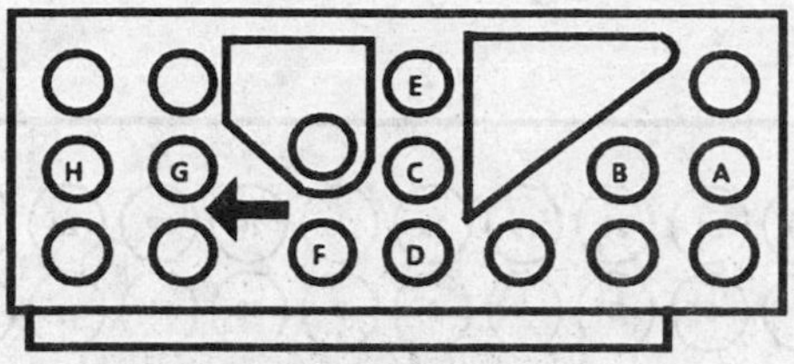
E
H
G
C
B
A
F
D

12066386
8-WAY F PIN GRIP SERIES
GRY
LH POWER SEAT SWITCH

** CAVITIES NOT LISTED ARE NOT USED

CAVITY	WIRE COLOR	CKT	DESCRIPTION	PAGE
A	YEL	282	REAR HEIGHT MOTOR: UP CONTROL	8A-140-0
B	LT BLU	283	REAR HEIGHT MOTOR: DOWN CONTROL	8A-140-0
C	BLK	150	LH POWER SEAT SWITCH GROUND TO G304	8A-140-0
D	LT GRN	284	FORWARD BACK MOTOR: ENTIRE SEAT BACK	8A-140-0
E	TAN	285	FORWARD BACK MOTOR: ENTIRE SEAT FORWARD	8A-140-0
F	ORN/BLK	60	CIRCUIT BREAKER PROTECTED FEED TO LH POWER SEAT SWITCH	8A-140-0
G	DK GRN	286	FRONT HEIGHT MOTOR: FRONT HEIGHT UP	8A-140-0
H	DK BLU	287	FRONT HEIGHT MOTOR: FRONT HEIGHT DOWN	8A-140-0

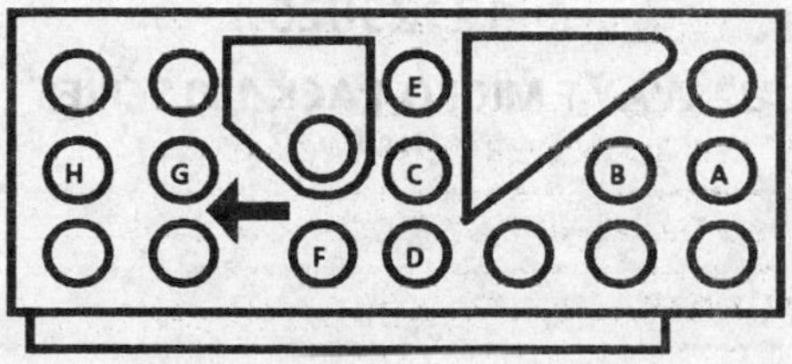
E
H
G
C
B
A
F
D

12066386
8-WAY F PIN GRIP SERIES
GRY
RH POWER SEAT SWITCH

** CAVITIES NOT LISTED ARE NOT USED

CAVITY	WIRE COLOR	CKT	DESCRIPTION	PAGE
A	DK GRN	286	FRONT HEIGHT MOTOR: FRONT HEIGHT UP	8A-140-0
B	DK BLU	287	FRONT HEIGHT MOTOR: FRONT HEIGHT DOWN	8A-140-0
C	ORN/BLK	60	CIRCUIT BREAKER PROTECTED FEED TO LH POWER SEAT SWITCH	8A-140-0
D	TAN	285	FORWARD BACK MOTOR: ENTIRE SEAT FORWARD	8A-140-0
E	LT GRN	284	FORWARD BACK MOTOR: ENTIRE SEAT BACK	8A-140-0
F	BLK	150	LH POWER SEAT SWITCH GROUND TO G304	8A-140-0
G	LT BLU	283	REAR HEIGHT MOTOR: DOWN CONTROL	8A-140-0
H	YEL	282	REAR HEIGHT MOTOR: UP CONTROL	8A-140-0

HARNESS CONNECTORS FACES

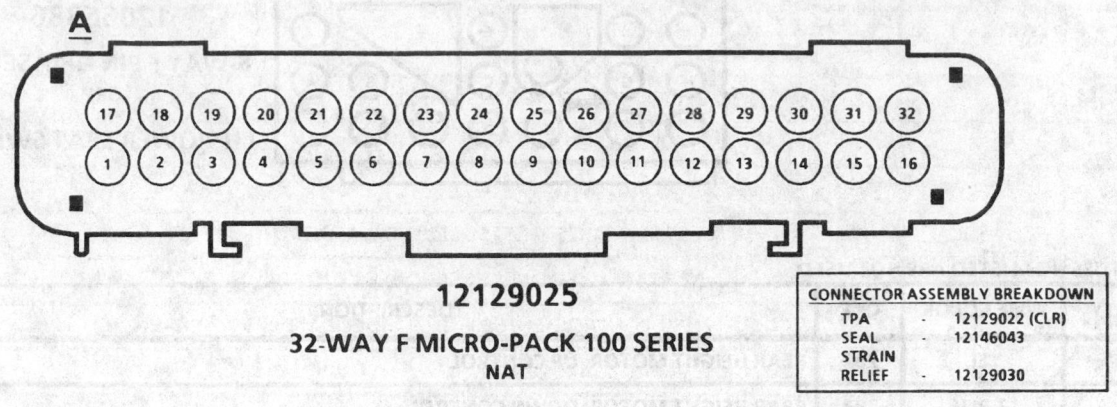

A

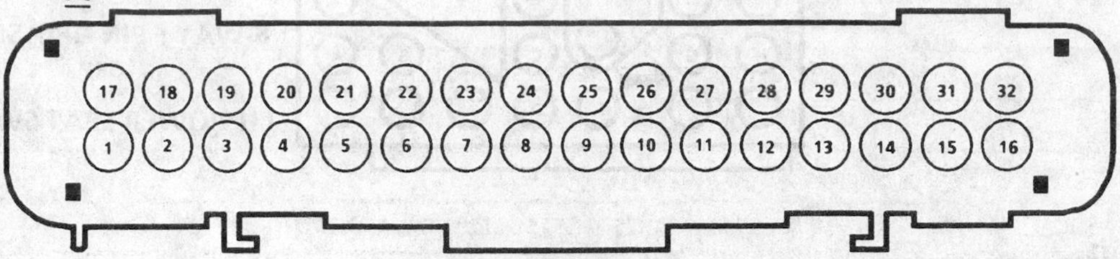
17 18 19 20 21 22 23 24 25 26 27 28 29 30 31 32
1 2 3 4 5 6 7 8 9 10 11 12 13 14 15 16

12129025

32-WAY F MICRO-PACK 100 SERIES
NAT

CONNECTOR ASSEMBLY BREAKDOWN		
TPA	-	12129022 (CLR)
SEAL	-	12146043
STRAIN RELIEF	-	12129030

B

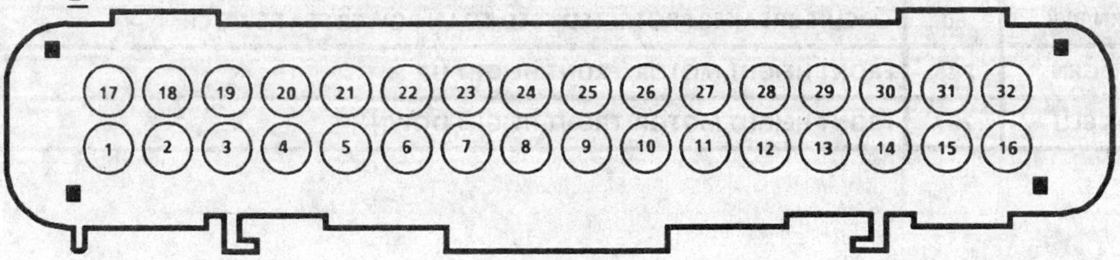
17 18 19 20 21 22 23 24 25 26 27 28 29 30 31 32
1 2 3 4 5 6 7 8 9 10 11 12 13 14 15 16

12129025

32-WAY F MICRO-PACK 100 SERIES
NAT

CONNECTOR ASSEMBLY BREAKDOWN		
TPA	-	12129021 (BLK)
SEAL	-	12146043
STRAIN RELIEF	-	12129030

C

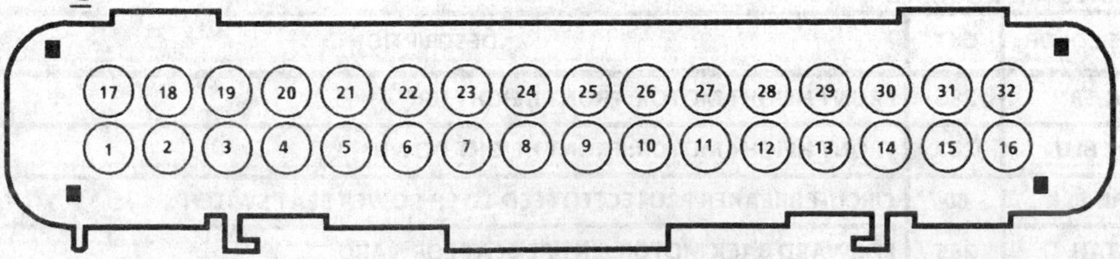
17 18 19 20 21 22 23 24 25 26 27 28 29 30 31 32
1 2 3 4 5 6 7 8 9 10 11 12 13 14 15 16

12129025

32-WAY F MICRO-PACK 100 SERIES
NAT

CONNECTOR ASSEMBLY BREAKDOWN		
TPA	-	12129023 (BLU)
SEAL	-	12146043
STRAIN RELIEF	-	12129028

POWERTRAIN CONTROL MODULE (PCM) CONNECTORS
(3.1L VIN M)

** CAVITIES NOT LISTED ARE NOT USED

CAVITY	WIRE COLOR	CKT	DESCRIPTION	PAGE
A2	LT GRN	66	A/C REQUEST INPUT	8A-20-0, 8A-64-0
A5	RED/BLK	380	A/C REFRIGERANT PRESSURE SENSOR SIGNAL	8A-20-0
A6	GRY	120	FUEL PUMP MOTOR FEED	8A-20-0
A8	DK GRN/WHT	465	FUEL PUMP RELAY CONTROL	8A-20-0
A11	LT GRN	1222	AUTOMATIC TRANSAXLE SHIFT SOLENOID A CONTROL	8A-20-0
A12	YEL/BLK	1223	AUTOMATIC TRANSAXLE SHIFT SOLENOID B CONTROL	8A-20-0
A13	BRN	418	TCC SOLENOID CONTROL (PULSE WIDTH MODULATED)	8A-20-0
A14	BRN/WHT	1173	LOW OIL LEVEL INDICATOR LAMP	8A-20-0
A15	TAN/BLK	422	TCC SOLENOID CONTROL	8A-20-0
A17	BLK	808	SENSOR GROUND	8A-20-0
A18	PPL	420	TCC/BRAKE INPUT	8A-20-0
A19	WHT	776	TRANSMISSION RANGE SWITCH PARITY INPUT	8A-20-0
A21	DK BLU	1493	TRANSMISSION SELECT INDICATOR LAMP	8A-20-0
A24	BRN	1174	OIL LEVEL SENSOR	8A-20-0
A25	GRY	773	TRANSMISSION RANGE SWITCH INPUT C	8A-20-0
A26	YEL	772	TRANSMISSION RANGE SWITCH INPUT B	8A-20-0
A27	BLK/WHT	771	TRANSMISSION RANGE SWITCH INPUT A	8A-20-0
A29	LT GRN	432	MANIFOLD ABSOLUTE PRESSURE (MAP) SENSOR INPUT	8A-20-0
A30	DK BLU	417	THROTTLE POSITION (TP) SENSOR INPUT	8A-20-0
A31	YEL	410	ENGINE COOLANT TEMPERATURE (ECT) INPUT	8A-20-0
A32	YEL/BLK	1227	TRANSMISSION FLUID TEMPERATURE SENSOR INPUT	8A-20-0
B1	DK BLU/WHT	473	ENGINE COOLING FAN #2 RELAY CONTROL	8A-20-0, 8A-31-0
B2	DK GRN/WHT	335	ENGINE COOLING FAN #1 RELAY CONTROL	8A-20-0, 8A-31-0
B4	DK GRN/YEL	428	EVAPORATIVE EMISSIONS (EVAP) CANISTER PURGE SOLENOID CONTROL	8A-20-0
B6	DK GRN/WHT	459	A/C COMPRESSOR CONTROL	8A-20-0, 8A-64-0, 8A-67-0
B7	BRN/WHT	419	MALFUNCTION INDICATOR LAMP (MIL) CONTROL	8A-20-0, 8A-81-0
B10	DK GRN	83	CRUISE CONTROL "INHIBIT" SIGNAL TO CRUISE MODULE	8A-20-0, 8A-34-0
B11	LT BLU	697	DEGR SOLENOID A CONTROL	8A-20-0
B12	BRN	698	DEGR SOLENOID B CONTROL	8A-20-0
B13	RED	699	DEGR SOLENOID C CONTROL	8A-20-0
B14/B15	ORN	540	FUSED FEED TO PCM	8A-20-0
B16	TAN/WHT	551	PCM GROUND	8A-20-0

(CONTINUED ON NEXT PAGE)

HARNESS CONNECTORS FACES

(CONTINUED FROM PREVIOUS PAGE)

CAVITY	WIRE COLOR	CKT	DESCRIPTION	PAGE
B18	ORN/BLK	434	NEUTRAL SAFETY SWITCH	8A-20-0
B19	ORN	800	DATA LINK CONNECTOR (DLC) SERIAL DATA: INPUT/OUTPUT	8A-20-0, 8A-50-0
B22	PPL	412	HEATED OXYGEN SENSOR (HO2S) INPUT HIGH	8A-20-0
B23	TAN	413	HEATED OXYGEN SENSOR (HO2S) INPUT LOW	8A-20-0
B24	LT GRN/WHT	1749	IDLE AIR CONTROL (IAC) MOTOR	8A-20-0
B25	LT GRN/BLK	444	IDLE AIR CONTROL (IAC) MOTOR	8A-20-0
B26	LT BLU/BLK	1748	IDLE AIR CONTROL (IAC) MOTOR	8A-20-0
B27	LT BLU/WHT	1747	IDLE AIR CONTROL (IAC) MOTOR	8A-20-0
B28	DK GRN	389	VSS OUTPUT	8A-20-0, 8A-33-0
B29	PPL	401	VSS RETURN	8A-20-0, 8A-33-0
B30	YEL	400	VSS INPUT	8A-20-0, 8A-33-0
B31	GRY	416	5 VOLT REF	8A-20-0
B32	BLK/WHT	451	PCM GROUND	8A-20-0
C1	BLK/WHT	451	PCM GROUND	8A-20-0
C3	PNK/BLK	439	FUSED FEED TO PCM	8A-20-0
C8	WHT	85	CRUISE "ENGAGED" SIGNAL FROM CRUISE MODULE	8A-20-0, 8A-34-0
C11	ORN/BLK	434	NEUTRAL SAFETY SWITCH	8A-20-0
C12	BLK/PNK	1746	INJECTOR #3 CONTROL	8A-20-0
C13	LT GRN/BLK	1745	INJECTOR #2 CONTROL	8A-20-0
C14	BLK	1744	INJECTOR #1 CONTROL	8A-20-0
C15	BLK/YEL	846	INJECTOR #6 CONTROL	8A-20-0
C16	BLK/WHT	845	INJECTOR #5 CONTROL	8A-20-0
C17	TAN/WHT	551	PCM GROUND	8A-20-0
C18	BLK/PNK	632	CAMSHAFT POSITION SENSOR RETURN	8A-20-0
C20	DK BLU	496	KNOCK SENSOR (KS) INPUT	8A-20-0
C21	LT BLU/BLK	647	HIGH RESOLUTION 24X CRANKSHAFT POSITION SENSOR SIGNAL	8A-20-0
C23	DK BLU	229	THEFT DETERRENT - FUEL ENABLE	8A-20-0, 8A-133-0
C25	BRN/WHT	633	CAMSHAFT POSITION SENSOR SIGNAL	8A-20-0
C27	WHT	423	IGNITION CONTROL INPUT	8A-20-0
C28	TAN/BLK	424	IGNITION CONTROL BYPASS CONTROL	8A-20-0
C29	TAN	472	INTAKE AIR TEMPERATURE (IAT) SENSOR INPUT	8A-20-0
C30	PPL/WHT	430	IGNITION REFERENCE PULSE HIGH	8A-20-0
C31	BLK/RED	453	IGNITION REFERENCE LOW	8A-20-0
C32	BLK/LT BLU	844	INJECTOR #4 CONTROL	8A-20-0

A

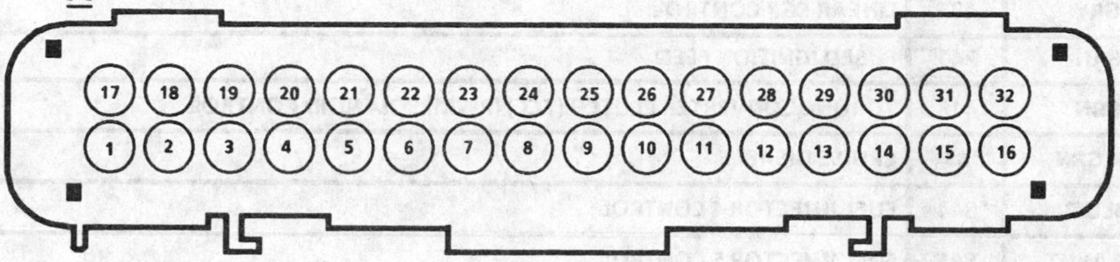
17 18 19 20 21 22 23 24 25 26 27 28 29 30 31 32
1 2 3 4 5 6 7 8 9 10 11 12 13 14 15 16

12129025

32-WAY F MICRO-PACK 100 SERIES

NAT

CONNECTOR ASSEMBLY BREAKDOWN		
TPA	-	12129021 (BLK)
SEAL	-	12146043
STRAIN RELIEF	-	12129030

B

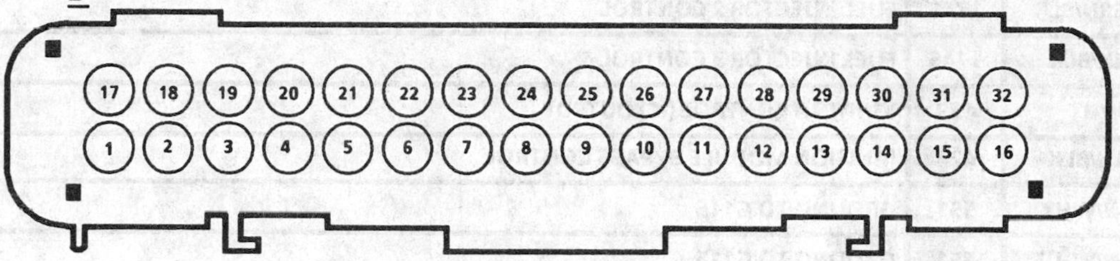
17 18 19 20 21 22 23 24 25 26 27 28 29 30 31 32
1 2 3 4 5 6 7 8 9 10 11 12 13 14 15 16

12129025

32-WAY F MICRO-PACK 100 SERIES

NAT

CONNECTOR ASSEMBLY BREAKDOWN		
TPA	-	12129022 (CLR)
SEAL	-	12146043
STRAIN RELIEF	-	12129030

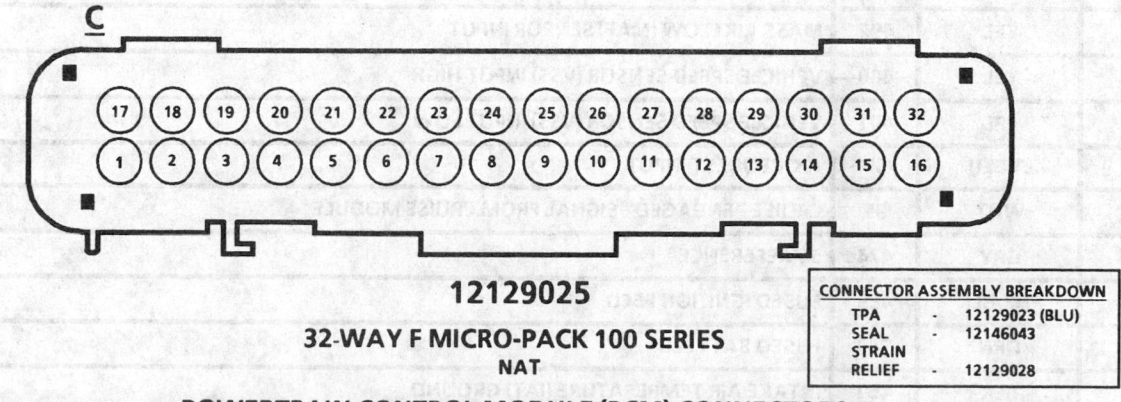

C

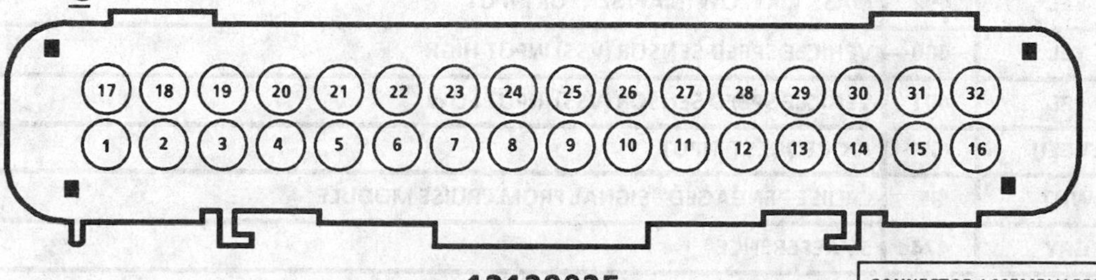
17 18 19 20 21 22 23 24 25 26 27 28 29 30 31 32
1 2 3 4 5 6 7 8 9 10 11 12 13 14 15 16

12129025

32-WAY F MICRO-PACK 100 SERIES

NAT

CONNECTOR ASSEMBLY BREAKDOWN		
TPA	-	12129023 (BLU)
SEAL	-	12146043
STRAIN RELIEF	-	12129028

POWERTRAIN CONTROL MODULE (PCM) CONNECTORS

(3.8L VIN L)

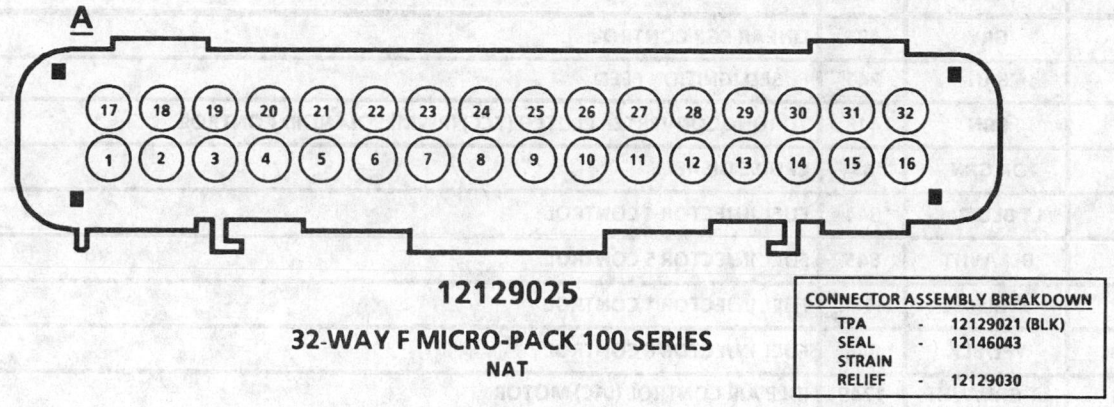

HARNESS CONNECTOR FACES

CAVITY	WIRE COLOR	CKT	DESCRIPTION	PAGE
A1	GRY	435	LINEAR EGR CONTROL	8A-21-0
A2	BRN	241	FUSED IGNITION FEED	8A-21-0
A4	BRN	418	TORQUE CONVERTER CLUTCH (TCC) (PWM) SOLENOID CONTROL	8A-21-0
A5	DK GRN	83	CRUISE DISABLE	8A-21-0
A7	LT BLU/BLK	844	FUEL INJECTOR 4 CONTROL	8A-21-0
A8	BLK/WHT	845	FUEL INJECTOR 5 CONTROL	8A-21-0
A9	BLK	1744	FUEL INJECTOR 1 CONTROL	8A-21-0
A10	YEL/BLK	846	FUEL INJECTOR 6 CONTROL	8A-21-0
A11	LT GRN/WHT	1749	IDLE AIR CONTROL (IAC) MOTOR	8A-21-0
A12	LT GRN/BLK	444	IDLE AIR CONTROL (IAC) MOTOR	8A-21-0
A13	LT BLU/BLK	1748	IDLE AIR CONTROL (IAC) MOTOR	8A-21-0
A14	LT BLU/WHT	1747	IDLE AIR CONTROL (IAC) MOTOR	8A-21-0
A15	LT GRN/BLK	1745	FUEL INJECTOR 2 CONTROL	8A-21-0
A16	PNK/BLK	1746	FUEL INJECTOR 3 CONTROL	8A-21-0
A17	WHT	423	IGNITION CONTROL (IC) OUTPUT	8A-21-0
A18	TAN/BLK	424	IGNITION MODULE BYPASS CONTROL	8A-21-0
A19	TAN/WHT	551	GROUND TO G115	8A-21-0
A20	TAN/WHT	551	GROUND TO G115	8A-21-0
A21	BLK/WHT	451	GROUND TO G113	8A-21-0
A22	BLK/WHT	451	GROUND TO G113	8A-21-0
A24	BLK	630	CAMSHAFT REFERENCE INPUT	8A-21-0
A25	PPL/WHT	430	FUEL CONTROL REFERENCE INPUT HI	8A-21-0
A26	RED/BLK	453	FUEL CONTROL REFERENCE INPUT LO	8A-21-0
A27	LT BLU/BLK	647	CRANKSHAFT REFERENCE INPUT HI	8A-21-0
A28	YEL	492	MASS AIR FLOW (MAF) SENSOR INPUT	8A-21-0
A30	YEL	400	VEHICLE SPEED SENSOR (VSS) INPUT HIGH	8A-21-0
A31	PPL	401	VEHICLE SPEED SENSOR (VSS) INPUT LOW	8A-21-0
B1	LT BLU	67	A/C REQUEST INPUT	8A-21-0
B2	WHT	85	CRUISE "ENGAGED" SIGNAL FROM CRUISE MODULE	8A-34-0
B7	GRY	474	5V REFERENCE	8A-21-0
B8	PNK/BLK	439	FUSED IGNITION FEED	8A-21-0
B10	ORN	540	FUSED BAT FEED	8A-21-0
B11	BLK	452	INTAKE AIR TEMPERATURE (IAT) GROUND	8A-21-0
B17	DK GRN/WHT	465	FUEL PUMP RELAY CONTROL	8A-21-0
B18	DK GRN	389	VEHICLE SPEED SENSOR (VSS) OUTPUT - 4000 PULSE PER MILE	8A-21-0
B19	DK BLU	229	FUEL INJECTOR ENABLE	8A-21-0

(CONTINUED ON NEXT PAGE)

(CONTINUED FROM PREVIOUS PAGE)

CAVITY	WIRE COLOR	CKT	DESCRIPTION	PAGE
B20	BRN/WHT	419	MALFUNCTION INDICATOR LAMP (MIL) CONTROL	8A-21-0
B21	DK GRN/WHT	459	A/C COMPRESSOR CONTROL	8A-21-0
B22	DK GRN	335	ENGINE COOLING FAN #1 RELAY CONTROL	8A-21-0
B23	DK BLU	473	ENGINE COOLING FAN #2 RELAY CONTROL	8A-21-0
B30	RED/BLK	380	COOLING FAN REQUEST	8A-21-0
B32	TAN	800	SERIAL DATA LINE	8A-21-0
C2	YEL/BLK	1223	TRANSAXLE SHIFT SOLENOID B CONTROL	8A-21-0
C3	LT GRN	1222	TRANSAXLE SHIFT SOLENOID A CONTROL	8A-21-0
C5	TAN/BLK	422	TORQUE CONVERTER CLUTCH (TCC) SOLENOID CONTROL	8A-21-0
C8	DK GRN/WHT	428	EVAPORATIVE EMISSIONS (EVAP) CANISTER PURGE SOLENOID CONTROL	8A-21-0
C9	BLK/WHT	771	TRANS RANGE SWITCH INPUT A	8A-21-0
C10	YEL	772	TRANS RANGE SWITCH INPUT B	8A-21-0
C11	GRY	416	5V REFERENCE	8A-21-0
C12	BLK	808	ENGINE DATA SENSOR GROUND	8A-21-0
C14	WHT	776	TRANS RANGE SWITCH PARITY INPUT	8A-21-0
C15	GRY	773	TRANS RANGE SWITCH INPUT C	8A-21-0
C18	DK BLU	496	KNOCK SENSOR (KS) INPUT	8A-21-0
C19	YEL	1227	TRANSMISSION TEMPERATURE INPUT	8A-21-0
C20	YEL	410	ENGINE COOLANT TEMPERATURE (ECT) INPUT	8A-21-0
C21	BRN	1456	LINEAR EGR PINTLE POSITION INPUT	8A-21-0
C22	DK BLU	417	THROTTLE POSITION SENSOR (TP) INPUT	8A-21-0
C23	TAN	413	HEATED OXYGEN SENSOR (HO2S1) INPUT LOW	8A-21-0
C24	PPL	412	HEATED OXYGEN SENSOR (HO2S1) INPUT HIGH	8A-21-0
C26	TAN	472	INTAKE AIR TEMPERATURE (IAT) INPUT	8A-21-0
C30	PPL	420	BRAKE SWITCH INPUT	8A-21-0
C31	TAN/WHT	1669	CATALYST MONITOR (HO2S2) INPUT LOW	8A-21-0
C32	PPL/WHT	1668	CATALYST MONITOR (HO2S2) INPUT HIGH	8A-21-0

HARNESS CONNECTOR FACES

C1

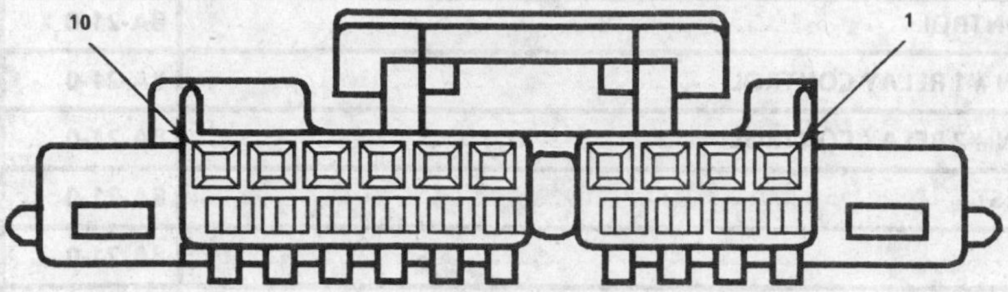
10
1

12047531

10-WAY F MICRO-PACK

BLK

C2 (UM7)

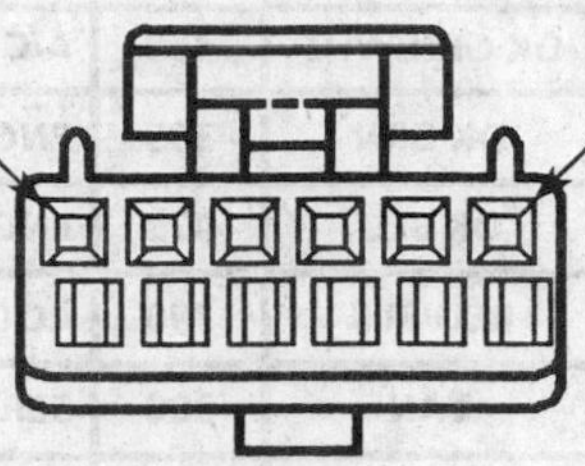
6
1

12064978

6-WAY F MICRO-PACK

GRY

C2 (U1C, UX1, UM6)

1
15

12064984

15-WAY F MICRO-PACK

BLK

C3

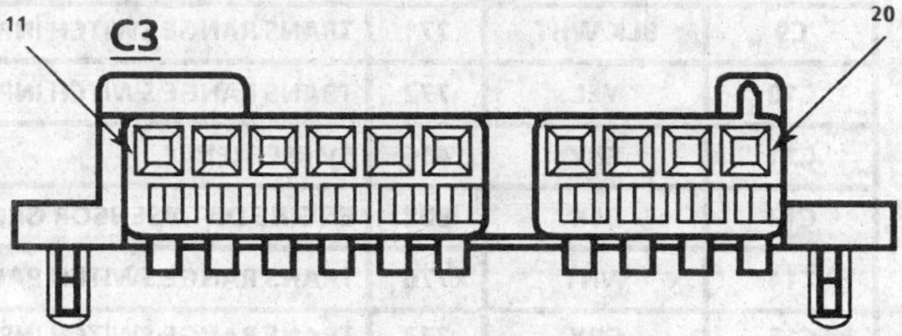
11
20

12065785

10-WAY F MICRO-PACK

GRY

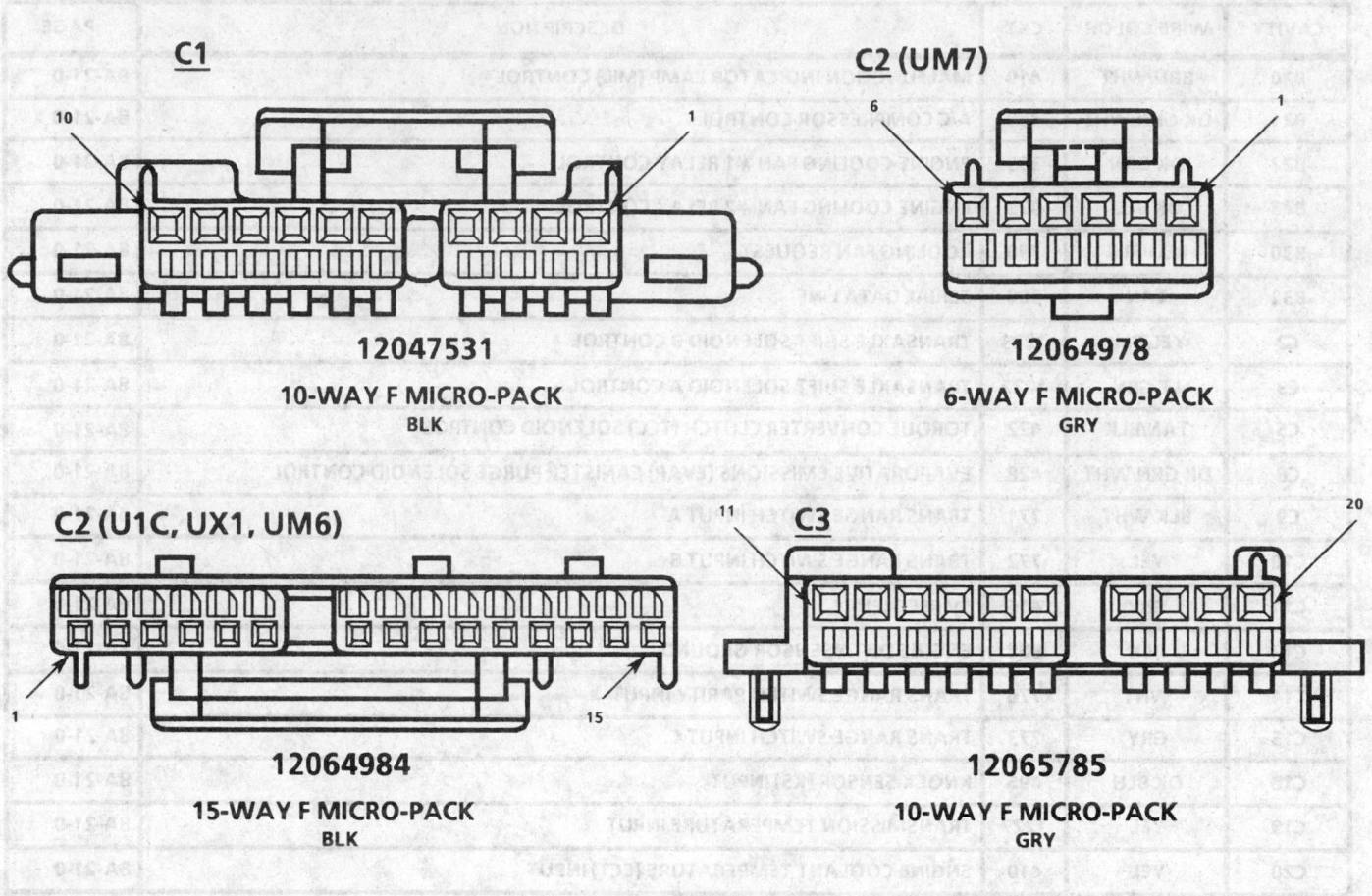

RADIO RECEIVER

** CAVITIES NOT LISTED ARE NOT USED

CAVITY	WIRE COLOR	CKT	DESCRIPTION	PAGE
C1 (1)	GRY	118	LH FRONT SPEAKER(S) RETURN	8A-150-0
C1 (2)	TAN	201	LH FRONT SPEAKER(S) RETURN	8A-150-0
C1 (3)	DK GRN	117	RH FRONT SPEAKER(S) RETURN	8A-150-0
C1 (4)	LT GRN	200	RH FRONT SPEAKER(S) RETURN	8A-150-0
C1 (5)	BLK/WHT	351	GROUND TO G201	8A-150-0
C1 (6)	GRY/BLK	308	LIGHTS ON DIM INPUT	8A-150-0
C1 (7)	BRN/WHT	230	VF DIMMING INPUT	8A-150-0
C1 (8)	DK GRN	145	RADIO ON CONTROL FEED	8A-150-0
C1 (9)	YEL	43	FUSED FEED (HOT IN ACCY AND RUN)	8A-150-0
C1 (10)	ORN	640	FUSED FEED BATTERY INPUT	8A-150-0

(CONTINUED ON NEXT PAGE)

(CONTINUED FROM PREVIOUS PAGE)

CAVITY	WIRE COLOR	CKT	DESCRIPTION	PAGE
C2 (1)	BLK	701	DRAIN WIRE GROUND	8A-150-0
C2 (2)	YEL	726	LIGHTS ON DIM INPUT	8A-150-0
C2 (3)	BRN/WHT	230	VF DIMMING INPUT	8A-150-0
C2 (4)	YEL	43	FUSED FEED (HOT IN ACCY AND RUN)	8A-150-0
C2 (5)	ORN	640	FUSED FEED BATTERY INPUT	8A-150-0
C2 (6)	DK GRN	835	DATA LINE	8A-150-0
C2 (7) TAPE DECK OR CD	DK GRN/WHT	606	RADIO MUTE SIGNAL	8A-150-0
C2 (8) TAPE OR CD	BRN/WHT	367	LEFT AUDIO SIGNAL	8A-150-0
C2 (9) TAPE OR CD	DK GRN/WHT	368	RIGHT AUDIO SIGNAL	8A-150-0
C2 (10) TAPE OR CD	DRAIN	371	DRAIN	8A-150-0
C2 (11) TAPE OR CD	ORN	640	FUSED FEED BATTERY INPUT	8A-150-0
C2 (12) TAPE OR CD	WHT/BLK	607	TAPE ON SIGNAL	8A-150-0
C2 (14) TAPE OR CD	BLK/WHT	372	HIGH GROUND	8A-150-0
C2 (15) TAPE OR CD	YEL	43	FUSED FEED (HOT IN ACCY AND RUN)	8A-150-0
C3 (17)	LT BLU	115	RIGHT REAR SPEAKER RETURN	8A-150-0
C3 (18)	DK BLU	46	RIGHT REAR SPEAKER FEED	8A-150-0
C3 (19)	YEL	116	LEFT REAR SPEAKER RETURN	8A-150-0
C3 (20)	BRN	199	LEFT REAR SPEAKER FEED	8A-150-0

HARNESS CONNECTOR FACES

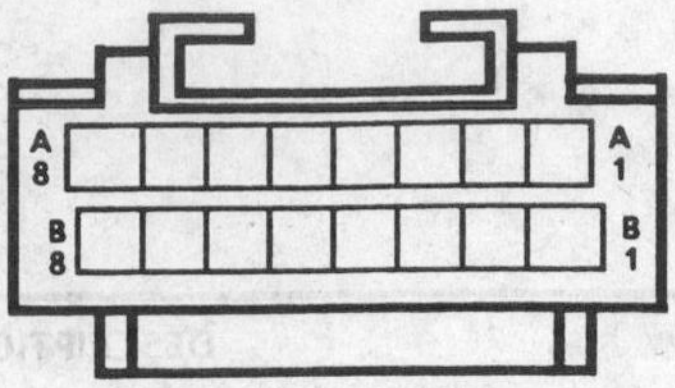
A
8
A
1
B
8
B
1

12110259

16-WAY F MICRO-PACK 100 SERIES

GRN

THEFT DETERRENT MODULE

**CAVITIES NOT LISTED ARE NOT USED

CAVITY	WIRE COLOR	CKT	DESCRIPTION	PAGE
A1	ORN	640	POWER FEED FROM ELEC FUSE	8A-11-18
A2	PNK	339	POWER FEED FROM VATS FUSE	8A-11-13
A3	DK BLU	229	FUEL ENABLE SIGNAL	8A-133-1
A4	YEL/BLK	625	THEFT DETERRENT RELAY CONTROL	8A-133-0, 1
A5	GRY	728	"SECURITY" INDICATOR LAMP CONTROL	8A-133-1
B5	BLK	1550	GROUND TO G201	8A-14-6
B7	PPL/WHT	1074	IGNITION KEY RESISTOR RETURN	8A-133-1
B8	WHT/BLK	1073	IGNITION KEY RESISTOR FEED	8A-133-1

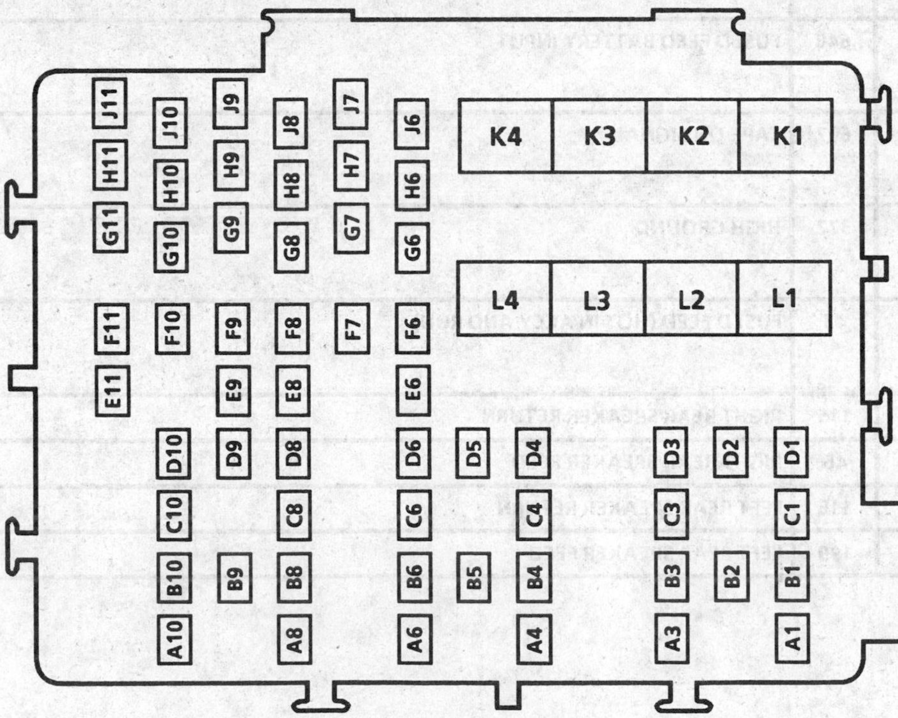
J11
J10
J9
J8
J7
J6
K4
K3
K2
K1
H11
H10
H9
H8
H7
H6
G11
G10
G9
G8
G7
G6
L4
L3
L2
L1
F11
F10
F9
F8
F7
F6
E11
E9
E8
E6
D10
D9
D8
D6
D5
D4
D3
D2
D1
C10
C8
C6
C4
C3
C1
B10
B9
B8
B6
B5
B4
B3
B2
B1
A10
A8
A6
A4
A3
A1

12146180

UNDERHOOD ELECTRICAL CENTER #1

12146179

UNDERHOOD ELECTRICAL CENTER #2

BLK

C110

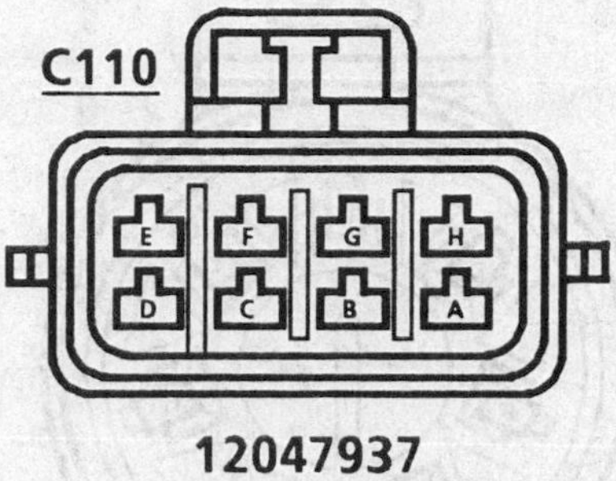
E F G H
D C B A

12047937

8-WAY F METRI-PACK 150 SERIES

BLK

ENGINE HARNESS TO IGNITION JUMPER HARNESS
(3.8L VIN L)

C211

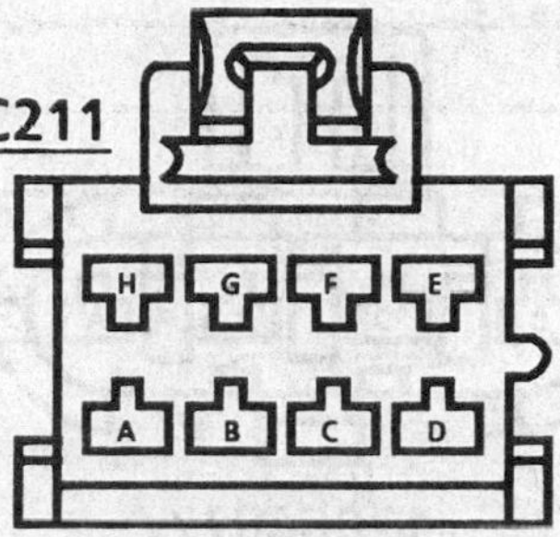
H G F E
A B C D

12064998

8-WAY F METRI-PACK 280 SERIES

BLK

I/P HARNESS TO WIPER/WASHER HARNESS

C213

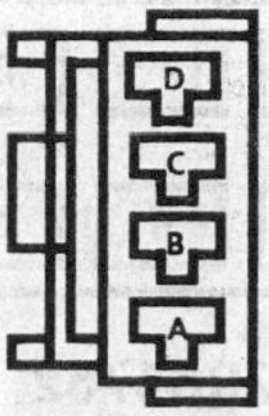
D
C
B
A

12015664

4-WAY F METRI-PACK 630 SERIES

BLK

I/P HARNESS TO WIPER HARNESS

C303
C304
C349

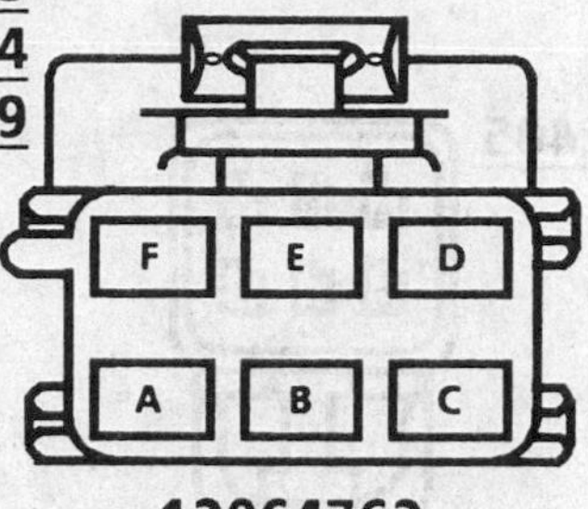
F E D
A B C

12064762

6-WAY F METRI-PACK 150 SERIES

GRY

CROSS CAR HARNESS TO CONSOLE HARNESS
MIRROR HARNESS TO LH OUTSIDE MIRROR JUMPER
MIRROR HARNESS TO RH OUTSIDE MIRROR JUMPER

C351
C352
C400

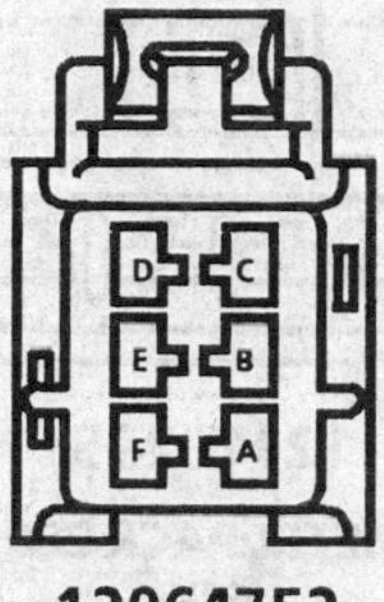
D C
E B
F A

12064752

6-WAY F METRI-PACK 280 SERIES

BLK

CROSS CAR HARNESS TO RH REAR DOOR HARNESS
CROSS CAR HARNESS TO LH REAR DOOR HARNESS
CROSS CAR HARNESS TO BODY REAR HARNESS

C353
C354

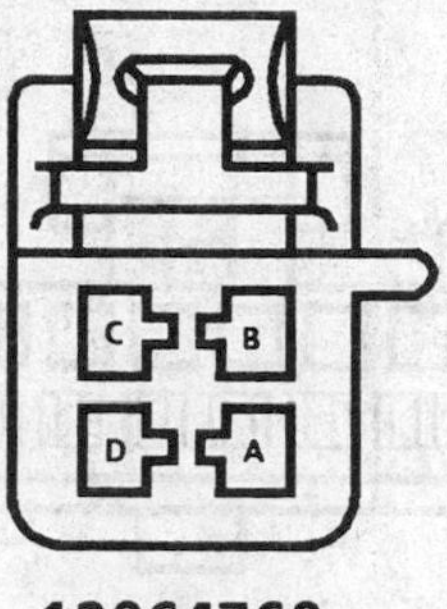
C B
D A

12064760

4-WAY F METRI-PACK 150 SERIES

BLK

CROSS CAR HARNESS TO RH REAR DOOR HARNESS
CROSS CAR HARNESS TO LH REAR DOOR HARNESS

HARNESS CONNECTOR FACES

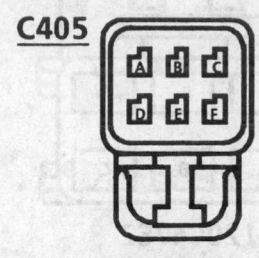

C405

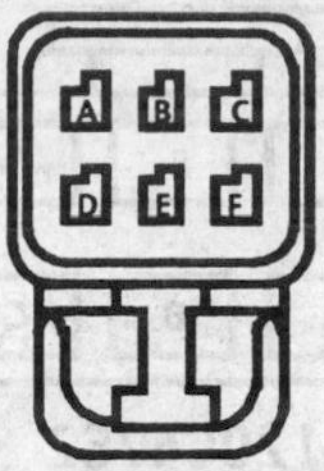
A B C
D E F

12089872

6-WAY F METRI-PACK 150 SERIES
PULL-TO-SEAT
BLK

CROSS CAR HARNESS TO FUEL TANK HARNESS

E
D
C
F
G
A
B

12129508

7-WAY F METRI-PACK 150 SERIES
BLK

AUTOMATIC TRANSAXLE

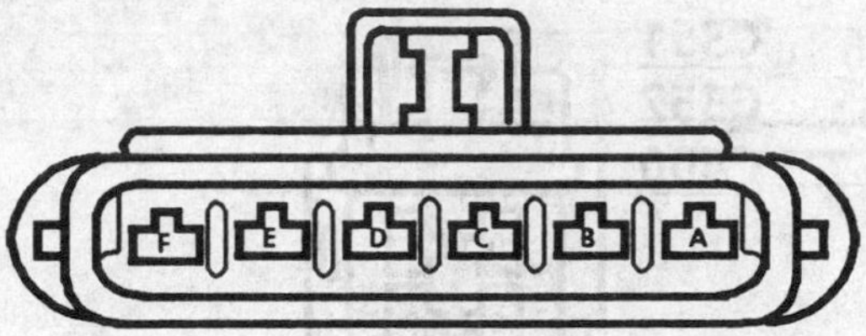
F E D C B A

12110295

6-WAY F METRI-PACK 280 SERIES
GRY

ACTUATOR MOTOR ASSEMBLY

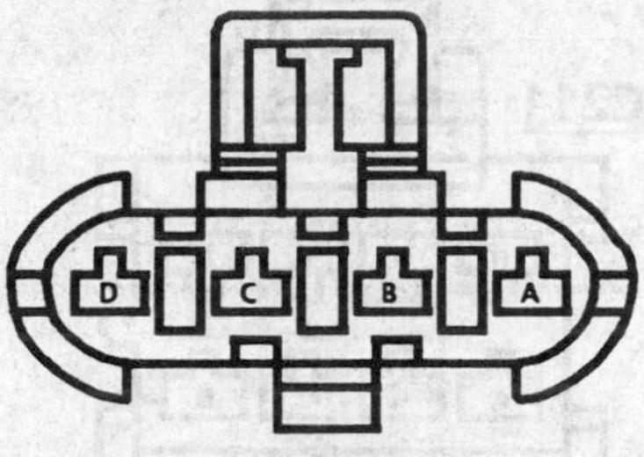
D C B A

12064877

4-WAY F METRI-PACK 480 SERIES
BLK

BLOWER RESISTORS

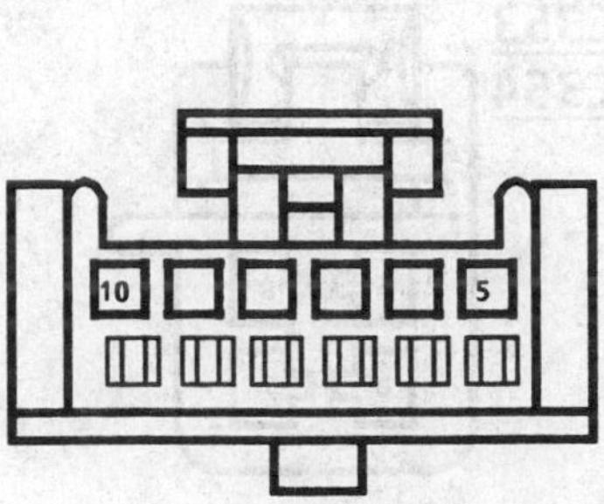
10
5

12064993

6-WAY F MICRO-PACK
BLK

AIR TEMPERATURE VALVE MOTOR

C2

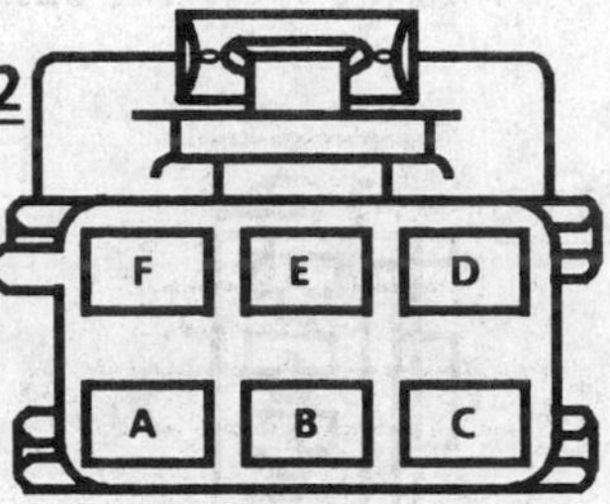
F E D
A B C

12064762

6-WAY F METRI-PACK 150 SERIES
GRY

CHIME MODULE

C1

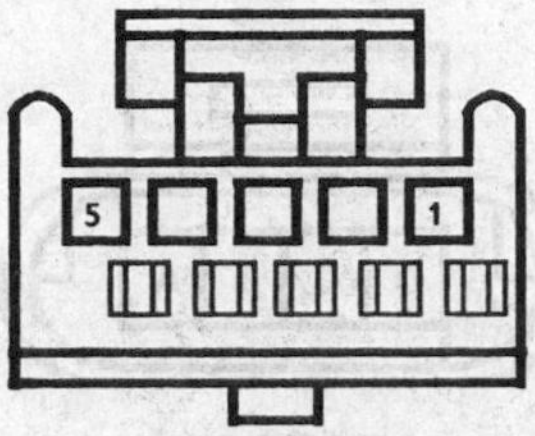
5
1

12064983

5-WAY F MICRO-PACK

NAT

C2

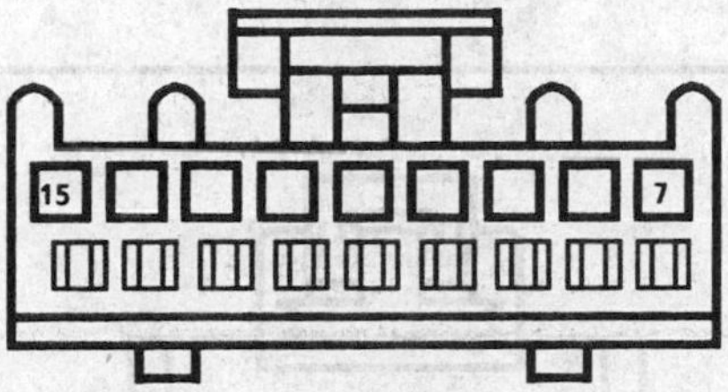
15
7

12064980

9-WAY F MICRO-PACK 100 SERIES

BLK

CASSETTE PLAYER/EQUALIZER OR CD

C1

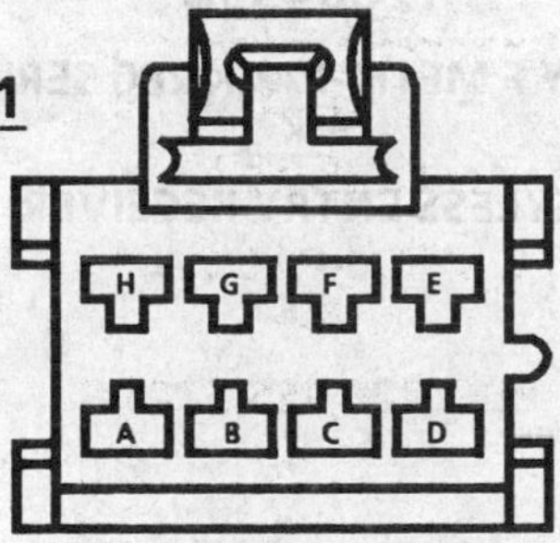
H
G
F
E
A
B
C
D

12064998

8-WAY F METRI-PACK 280 SERIES

BLK

C2

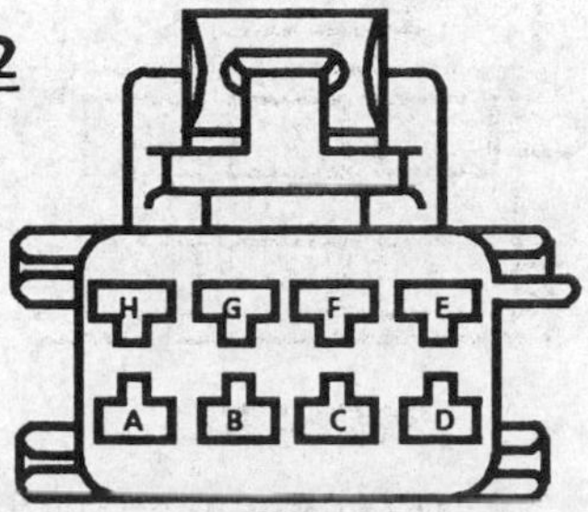
H
G
F
E
A
B
C
D

12064766

8-WAY F METRI-PACK 150 SERIES

BLU

DAYTIME RUNNING LIGHTS
(DRL) MODULE

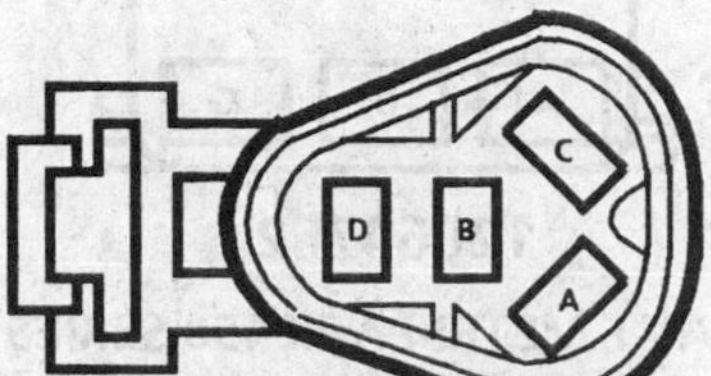
C
D
B
A

12065292

4-WAY F METRI-PACK 150 PULL-TO-SEAT

BLK

DIGITAL EXHAUST GAS RECIRCULATION
(DEGR) ASSEMBLY
(3.1L VIN M)

C1

B
A

12078084

2-WAY F METRI-PACK 150 PULL-TO-SEAT

BLK

C2

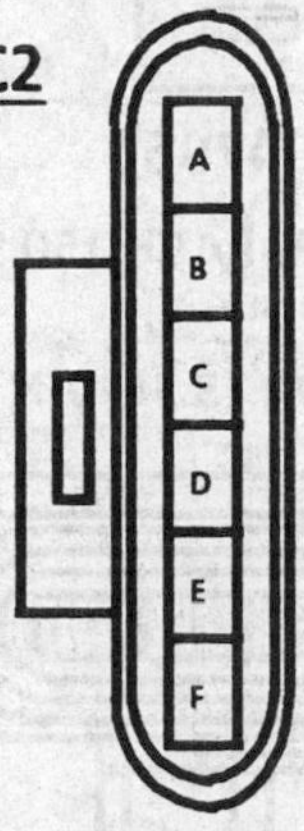
A
B
C
D
E
F

12084420

6-WAY F METRI-PACK 150 PULL-TO-SEAT

BLK

ELECTRONIC IGNITION (EI) CONTROL MODULE
(3.1L VIN M)

HARNESS CONNECTOR FACES

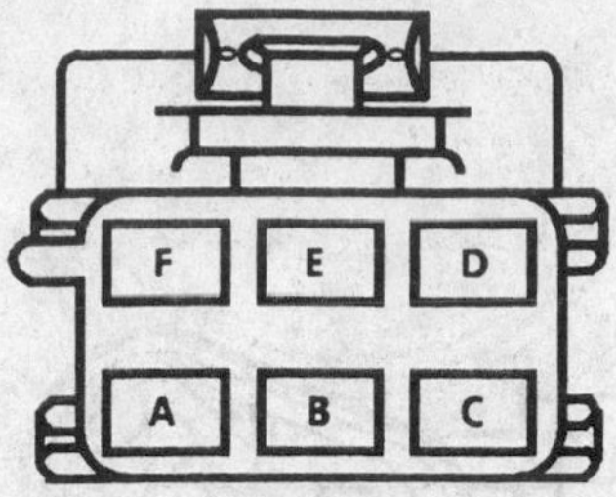
F
E
D
A
B
C

12064762

6-WAY F METRI-PACK 150 SERIES
GRY

FRONT DOOR LOCK SWITCH (LH AND RH)
(4 DOOR)

D
C
B
A

12078082

4-WAY F METRI-PACK 150 SERIES
PULL-TO-SEAT
BLK

IDLE AIR CONTROL MOTOR

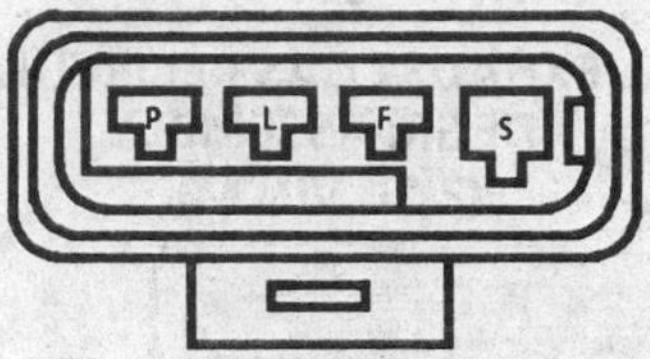
P
L
F
S

12045896
12129068

4-WAY F METRI-PACK MIXED SERIES
BLK

GENERATOR (3.8L VIN L)

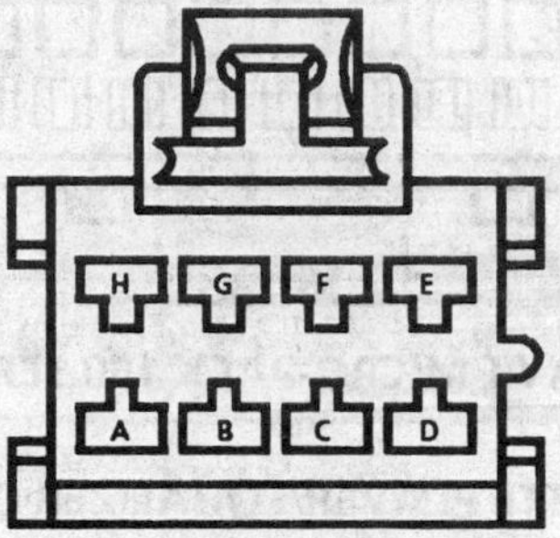
H
G
F
E
A
B
C
D

12064998

8-WAY F METRI-PACK 280 SERIES
BLK

KEYLESS ENTRY RECEIVER

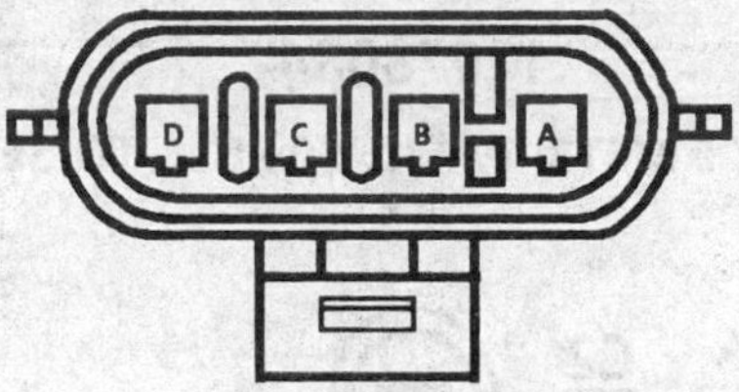
D
C
B
A

12047950

4-WAY F METRI-PACK 150 SERIES
BLK

GENERATOR (3.1L VIN M)

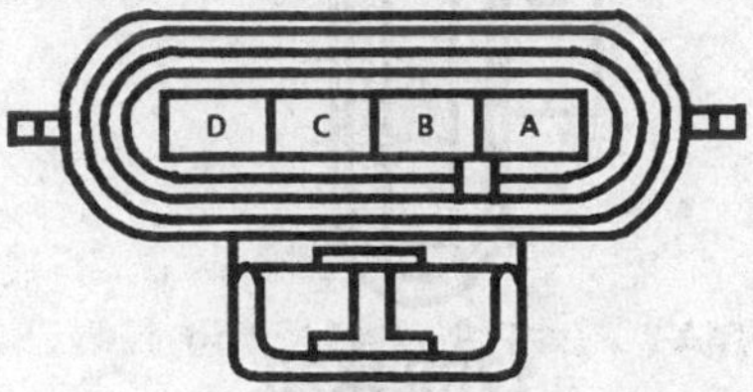
D
C
B
A

12059870

4-WAY F METRI-PACK 150 SERIES
BLK

HEATED OXYGEN SENSOR (HO2S)

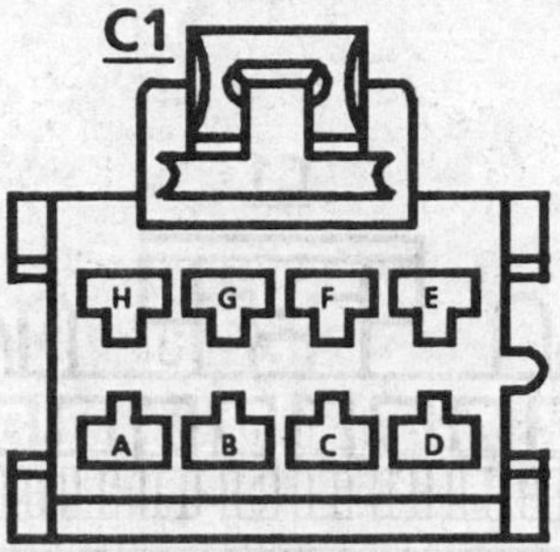
C1
H
G
F
E
A
B
C
D

12064998

8-WAY F METRI-PACK 280 SERIES
BLK

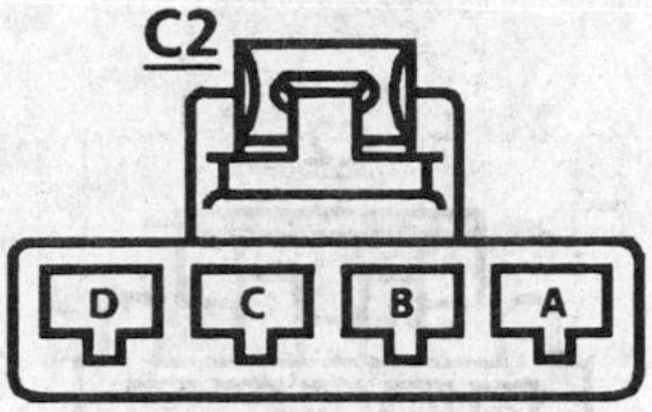
C2
D
C
B
A

12066571

4-WAY F METRI-PACK 480 SERIES
BLK

LH MASTER SWITCH (4 DOOR)
RH POWER WINDOW SWITCH (4 DOOR)

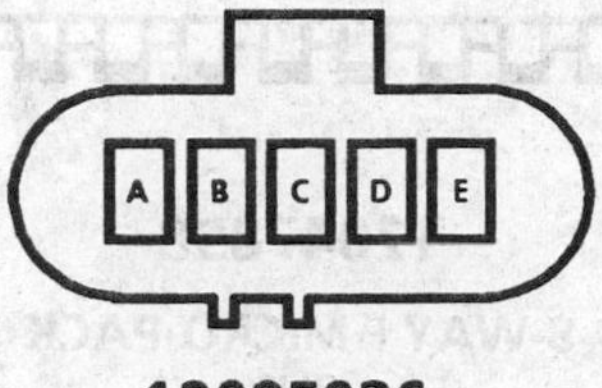
A
B
C
D
E

12085036

5-WAY M METRI-PACK 280 SERIES
GRY

LINEAR EXHAUST GAS RECIRCULATION VALVE

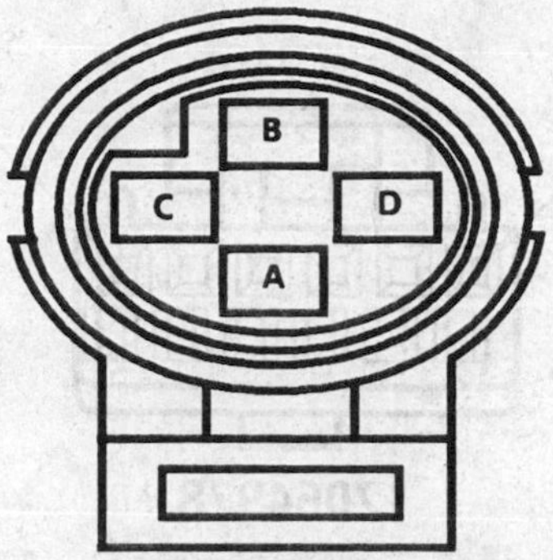
B
C
D
A

12065298

4-WAY F METRI-PACK 150 SERIES
BLK

OIL PRESSURE SWITCH (V6 VIN L)

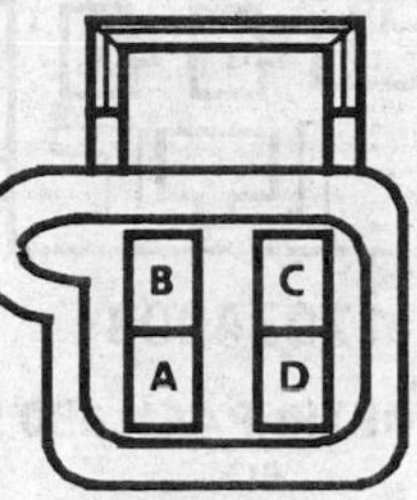
B
C
A
D

12065658

4-WAY M METRI-PACK 150 SERIES
BLK

OUTSIDE MIRROR (LH & RH)

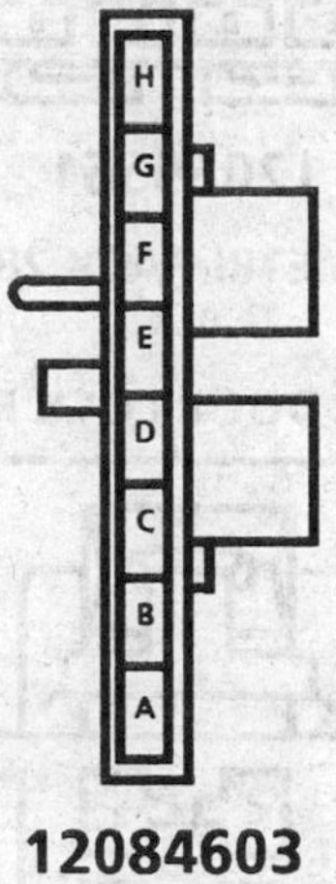
H
G
F
E
D
C
B
A

12084603

8-WAY F METRI-PACK 150 SERIES
BLK

OUTSIDE MIRROR CONTROL SWITCH

HARNESS CONNECTOR FACES

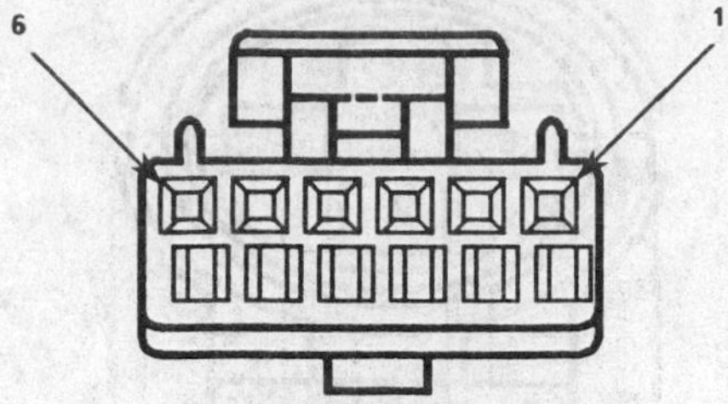
6
1

12064978

6-WAY F MICRO-PACK
GRY

PASSENGER TEMPERATURE CONTROL

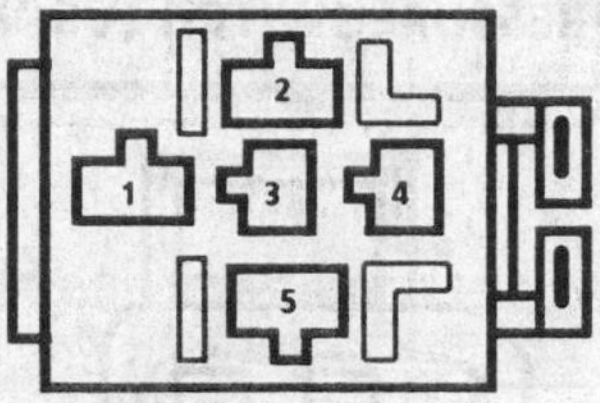
2
1
3
4
5

12034003

5-WAY F METRI-PACK 630 SERIES
BLK

PASSIVE RESTRAINT CONTROL MODULE
HEADLIGHT RELAY

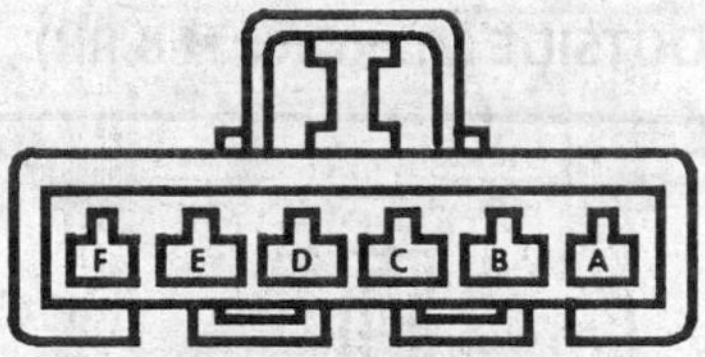
F
E
D
C
B
A

12059561

6-WAY F METRI-PACK 280 SERIES
BLK

POWER DOOR LOCK RELAY

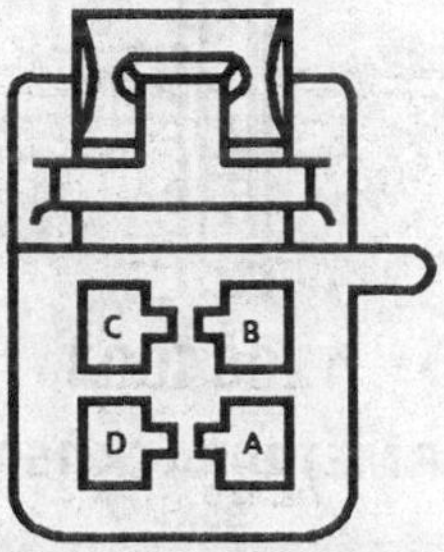
C
B
D
A

12064760

4-WAY F METRI-PACK 150 SERIES
BLK

RADIO CONTROL INTERFACE MODULE

C1

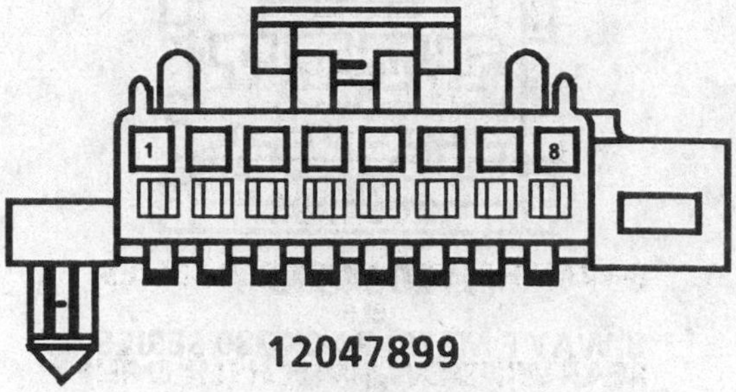
1
8

12047899

8-WAY F MICRO-PACK
NAT

C2

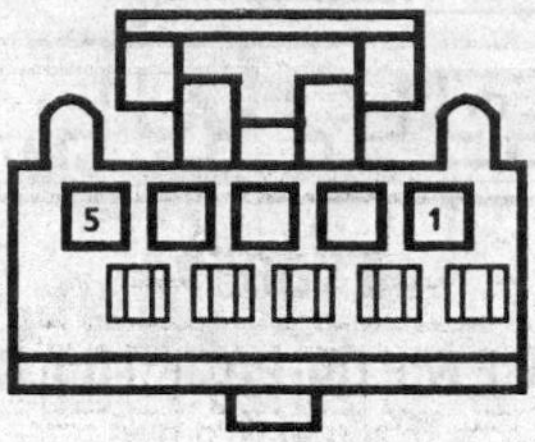
5
1

12064982

5-WAY F MICRO-PACK
BLK

C3

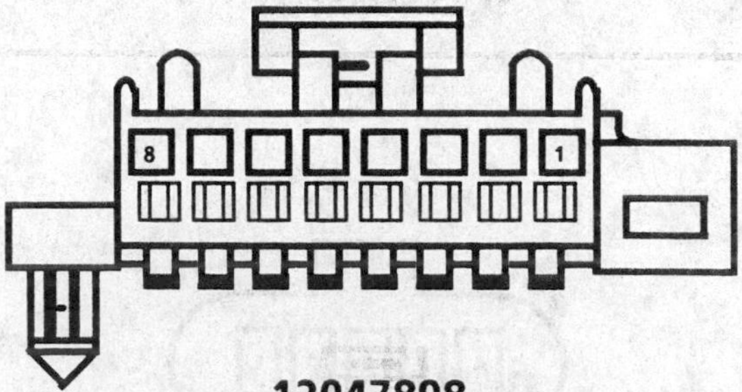
8
1

12047898

8-WAY F MICRO-PACK
BLK

RADIO CONTROL HEAD

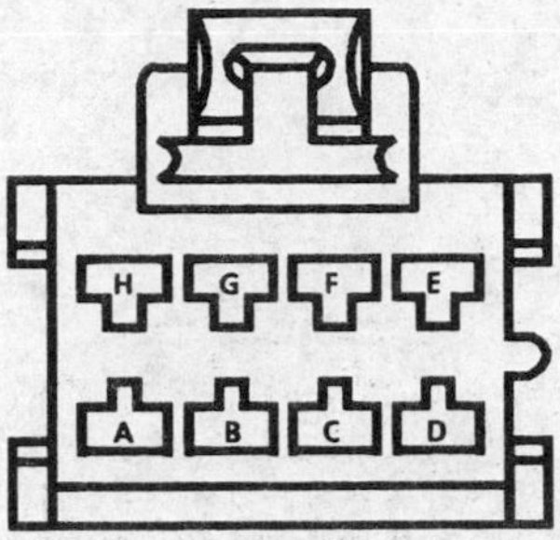
H
G
F
E
A
B
C
D

12064998

8-WAY F METRI-PACK 280 SERIES

BLK

REAR WINDOW SWITCH (LH & RH)

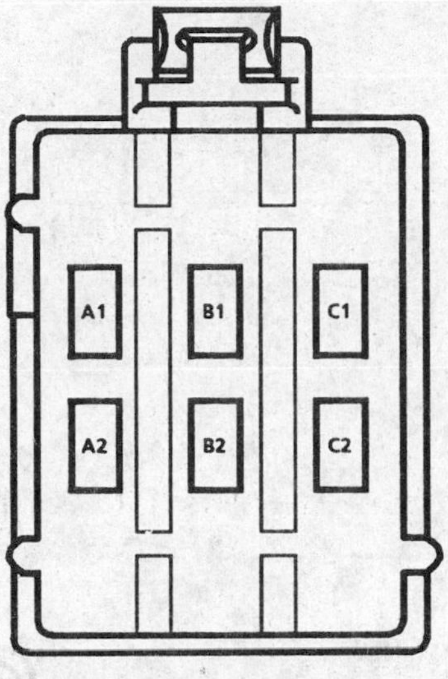
A1
B1
C1
A2
B2
C2

12110541

6-WAY F METRI-PACK 280 FLX LK

BLK

THEFT DETERRENT RELAY

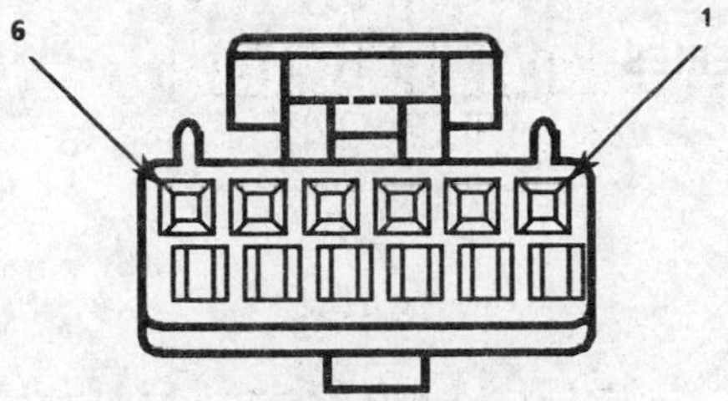
6
1

12064978

6-WAY F MICRO-PACK

GRY

SOLENOID BOX

C1

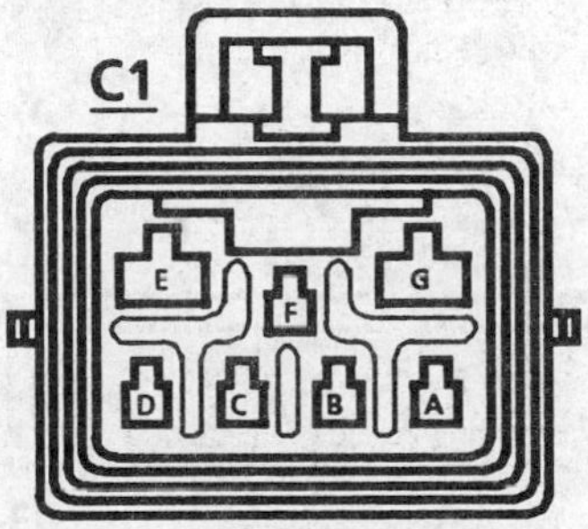
E
F
G
D
C
B
A

12059472

7-WAY F METRI-PACK MIXED SERIES

BLK

C2

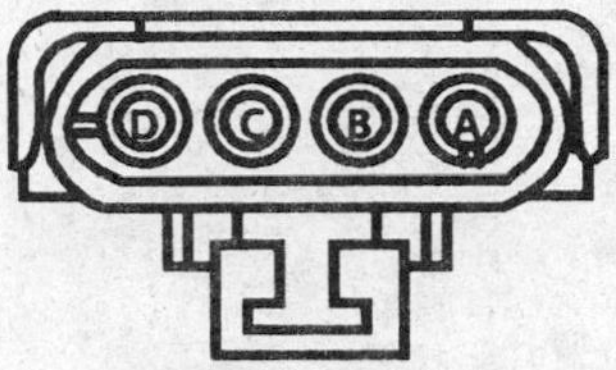
D
C
B
A

12020832

4-WAY F WEATHER PACK

BLK

TRANSAXLE POSITION SWITCH
(V6 VIN L)

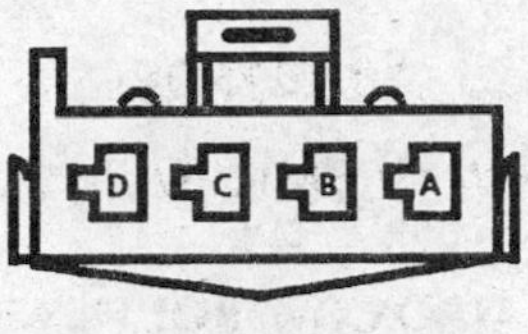
D
C
B
A

12033704

4-WAY F METRI-PACK 280 SERIES

BLK

TCC/BRAKE SWITCH

HARNESS CONNECTOR FACES

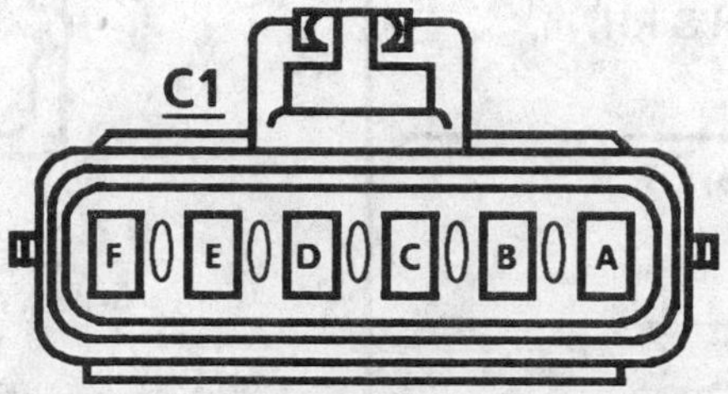
C1
F
E
D
C
B
A

12059573

6-WAY F METRI-PACK 280 SERIES

BLK

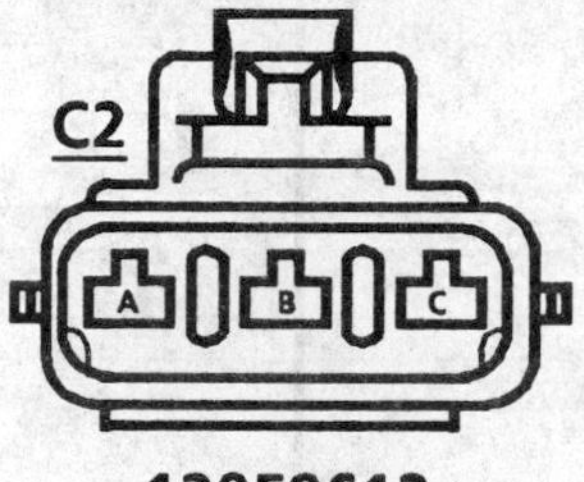
C2
A
B
C

12059612

3-WAY F METRI-PACK 280 SERIES

BLK

WIPER MOTOR ASSEMBLY

BLANK

HARNESS ROUTING VIEWS

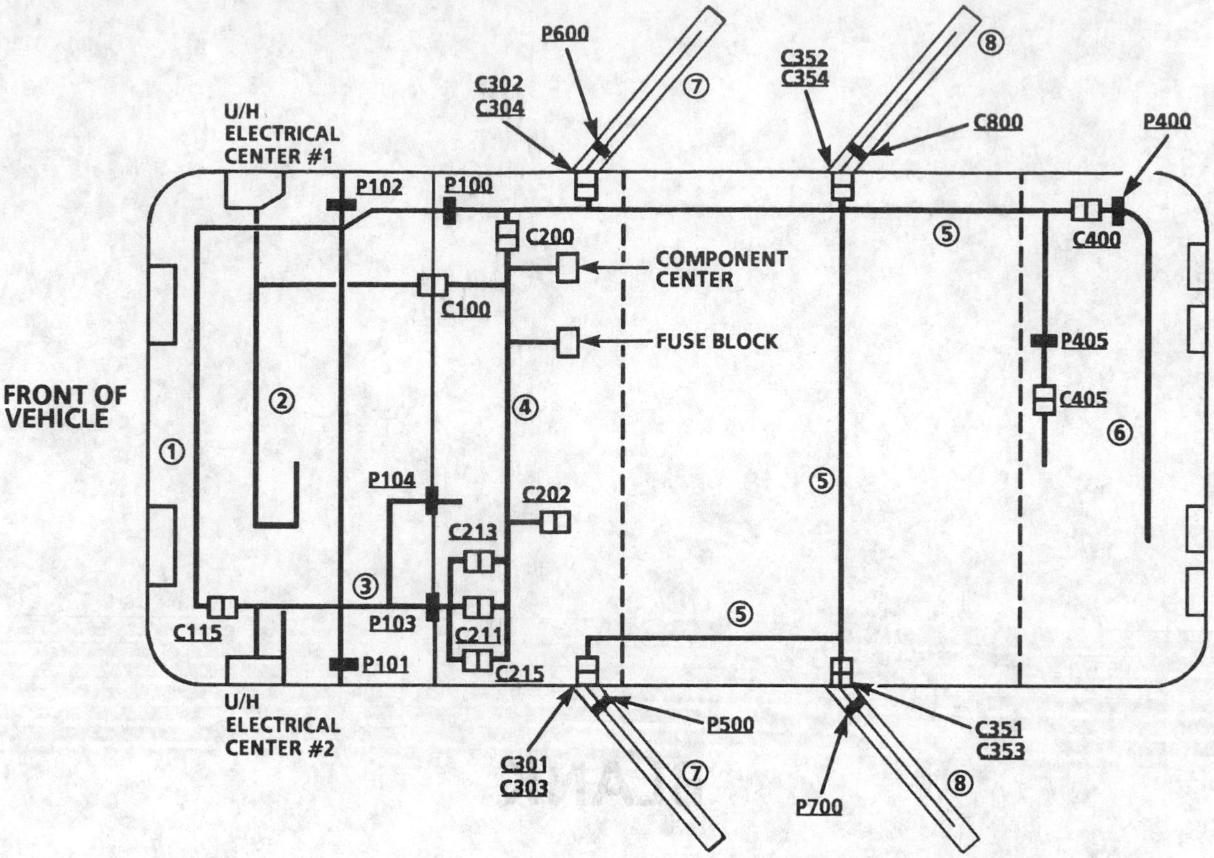
P600
C302
C304
U/H
ELECTRICAL
CENTER #1
P102
P100
C352
C354
C800
P400
C200
COMPONENT
CENTER
C100
FUSE BLOCK
C400
P405
C405
FRONT OF
VEHICLE
P104
C202
C213
C115
P103
C211
P101
C215
P500
C351
C353
U/H
ELECTRICAL
CENTER #2
C301
C303
P700

NUMBER	WIRING HARNESS	DETAIL VIEW PAGE-FIGURE
1	Forward Light	201-10-33 201-23-77
2	Engine	201-4-13 201-5-16 201-7-24 201-9-32 201-19-68, 69 201-20-70
3	Windshield Wiper	201-1-4 201-2-7
4	I/P	201-3-11, 12 201-11-36 201-14-48 201-15-49
5	Cross Car	201-0-2 201-15-50 201-23-78
6	Rear Body	201-18-66 201-19-67
7	Front Door	201-6-20
8	Rear Door	201-17-57

SYMBOLS

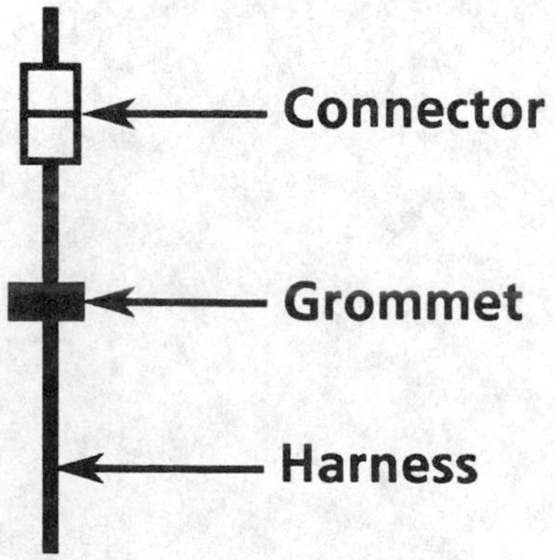
Connector
Grommet
Harness

BLANK

SECTION 8B

LIGHTING SYSTEMS AND HORNS

CAUTION: Before removing or installing any electrical unit(s), disconnect the negative battery cable to help prevent personal injury and/or damage to the vehicle or its components.

NOTICE: When fasteners are removed, always reinstall them at the same location from which they were removed. If a fastener needs to be replaced, use the correct part number fastener for that application. If the correct part number fastener is not available, a fastener of equal size and strength (or stronger) may be used. Fasteners that are not reused, and those requiring thread locking compound will be called out. The correct torque value must be used when installing fasteners that require it. If the above conditions are not followed, parts or system damage could result.

CONTENTS

GENERAL DESCRIPTION

HALOGEN BULBS

Some lamps in this vehicle (such as the headlamps) contain halogen bulbs.

CAUTION: Halogen bulbs contain a gas under pressure. Handling a bulb improperly could cause it to shatter into flying glass fragments. To help avoid personal injury:

- **Turn off the light switch and allow bulb to cool before changing bulbs. Leave the switch off until bulb change is complete.**
- **Always wear eye protection when changing a halogen bulb.**
- **Handle the bulb only by its base. Avoid touching the glass.**
- **Do not drop or scratch the bulb.**
- **Keep moisture away.**
- **Place the used bulb in the new bulb's carton and dispose of it properly. Keep halogen bulbs out of the reach of children.**

DIAGNOSIS

Wiring diagrams and other diagnosis information is given in ELECTRICAL DIAGNOSIS (SECTION 8A). Information on properly repairing wiring harnesses, connectors, etc. is on 8A-5-0 ELECTRICAL DIAGNOSIS (SECTION 8A).

LIGHTING SYSTEMS

Most lighting problems are caused by loose connectors, open or shorted wiring, burned-out bulbs, bad switches, inadequate ground or blown fuses. Many of these require only replacing a defective part. When replacing a part that requires a special procedure (such as sealing washers), be sure to reinstall those items when replacing the part. Also, if any body sealing items (grommets, etc.) are disturbed, be sure to repair them so the passenger compartment remains properly sealed.

HORNS

If the horns do not blow, or blow constantly, follow the diagnostic procedures in 8A-40-0 ELECTRICAL DIAGNOSIS (SECTION 8A).

Horn Tone Poor

1. **Horn Tone Poor** — Tighten bolts in mounting area, or correct poor connections or ground.
2. **Low-Pitched Moan** — Sounds like "mooing." Caused by current too high.
3. **Weak Tone** — Current too low. Correct poor connections or ground.
4. **Weak, Strained Tone** — Remove foreign object in horn.
5. **Harsh Vibration** — Bend bracket so horn is not touching sheet metal.

Current Draw Diagnosis

Current draw for a horn while operating should be 4.5 to 5.5 amperes at 11.5 to 12.5 volts. High current (more than 20 amperes) indicates an overheated winding or shorted horn; replace the horn. A current reading of about 18 amperes means the contact points are not opening; replace the horn.

No current reading indicates a broken connection, or an open circuit due to a broken lead or overheated horn. An overheated horn must be replaced. No current reading may also mean the contact points are open, replace the horn.

EXTERIOR LAMPS

The exterior lighting system includes the headlamps, foglamps, front parking/turn signal lamps, tail/stop/turn signal lamps, backup lamps, license plate lamps, opera lamps, sidemarker lamps, rear compartment lamp, underhood lamp, and the center high-mounted stoplamp; it also includes all associated wiring, controls and related hardware for these lamps.

BACKUP LAMPS

The backup lamps are part of the taillamp assembly on coupes and are in the rear fascia on sedans. The backup lamps are activated by the neutral start switch.

To replace a backup lamp bulb on coupes, refer to "Tail/Stop/Turn Signal Lamps" in this section. For information on the backup lamp switch, refer to SECTION 7A.

Assembly or Bulb Replacement (Sedan)

Remove or Disconnect

1. Two screws.
2. Assembly.
3. Socket from assembly.
4. Bulb from socket, if replacing.

Install or Connect

1. Bulb into socket, if removed.
2. Socket into assembly.
3. Assembly.
4. Screws.

Tighten

- Screws to 2 N·m (18 lb. in.).

CENTER HIGH-MOUNTED STOPLAMP

The center high-mounted stoplamp is in the center of the filler panel between the rear seat and the rear window. On vehicles with an optional rear compartment lid luggage carrier, the lamp is suspended from the rear crossbar. It will come on whenever the brake pedal is pushed down. The lamp is powered separately from the rear tail/stop/turn signal lamps through a separate circuit in the stoplamp switch, refer to 8A-110-0 ELECTRICAL DIAGNOSIS (SECTION 8A).

Assembly Replacement — Interior

Refer to SECTION 10-8 for assembly replacement on coupes or SECTION 10-9 on sedans.

Bulb Replacement — Interior

Remove or Disconnect

1. Center high mounted stoplamp. Refer to SECTION 10-8.
2. Socket assembly by carefully opening tab and pulling assembly out.
3. Bulb(s) from socket(s).

Install or Connect

1. Bulb(s) into socket(s).
2. Socket assembly making sure the wires are out of the way and the tabs lock.
3. Center high mounted stoplamp. Refer to SECTION 10-8.

Assembly or Bulb Replacement – Luggage Carrier

Remove or Disconnect

1. Luggage carrier. Refer to SECTION 10-8.
2. Two screws at bottom front of assembly.
3. Cover by sliding forward.
4. Socket assembly.
5. Bulb from socket, if replacing.

Install or Connect

1. Bulb into socket, if removed.
2. Socket assembly.
3. Cover by engaging tab with slot and sliding rearward.
4. Screws.

   Tighten
   - Screws to 3 N·m (27 lb. in.).

5. Luggage carrier. Refer to SECTION 10-8.

FRONT PARKING/TURN SIGNAL LAMPS

The lamp switches are to the left of the instrument cluster. Push the right button to turn on the parking lamps. Push it again to turn the lamps off.

If the parking lamps are on and the ignition is off, a warning chime will sound as a reminder to turn the lamps off. Refer to 8A-110-0 ELECTRICAL DIAGNOSIS (SECTION 8A).

When the turn signals are activated, the appropriate front parking lamp flashes to signal a turn. The turn signals work only when the ignition is on, and the hazard flashers are turned off.

The turn signals are controlled by the turn signal lever on the left side of the steering column. Moving the lever all the way up or down (past the detent) will turn on the turn signals. When the turn is completed, the lever will return to neutral and the turn signals will stop flashing.

For changing lanes or shallow turns where the steering wheel does not turn far enough to cancel the signal, move the turn signal lever only to the first detent and hold it there. When the lever is released, it will return to neutral and the turn signal will cancel. For more information, refer to ELECTRICAL DIAGNOSIS (SECTION 8A).

Assembly or Bulb Replacement (Coupe)

Figure 1

See caution under "Halogen Bulbs" in this section.

Remove or Disconnect

1. Raise hood.
2. Cover over headlamps by turning knob and folding back.
3. Two nuts holding lamp housing.
4. Housing.
5. Sockets from housing.
6. Bulb(s) from socket(s), if replacing.

Install or Connect

1. Bulb(s) into socket(s), if removed.
2. Sockets into housing.
3. Housing.
4. Two nuts.

   Tighten
   - Nuts to 7 N·m (62 lb. in.).

5. Headlamp cover.
6. Close hood.

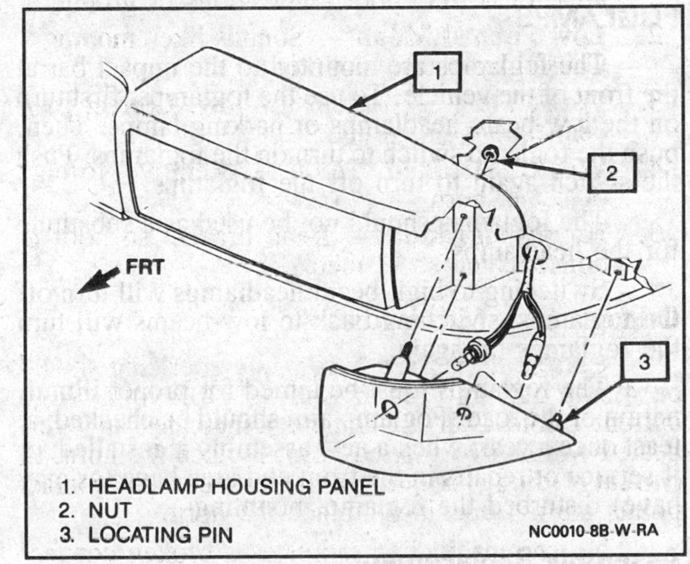
1
2
3
FRT
1. HEADLAMP HOUSING PANEL
2. NUT
3. LOCATING PIN
NC0010-8B-W-RA

Figure 1 Front Parking/Turn Signal Lamp (Coupe)

Assembly or Bulb Replacement (Sedan)

Figure 2

Remove or Disconnect

1. Two screws.
2. Assembly.
3. Socket from assembly.
4. Bulb from socket, if replacing.

Install or Connect

1. Bulb into socket, if removed.
2. Socket into assembly.
3. Assembly.
4. Screws.

   Tighten
   - Screws to 2 N·m (18 lb. in.).

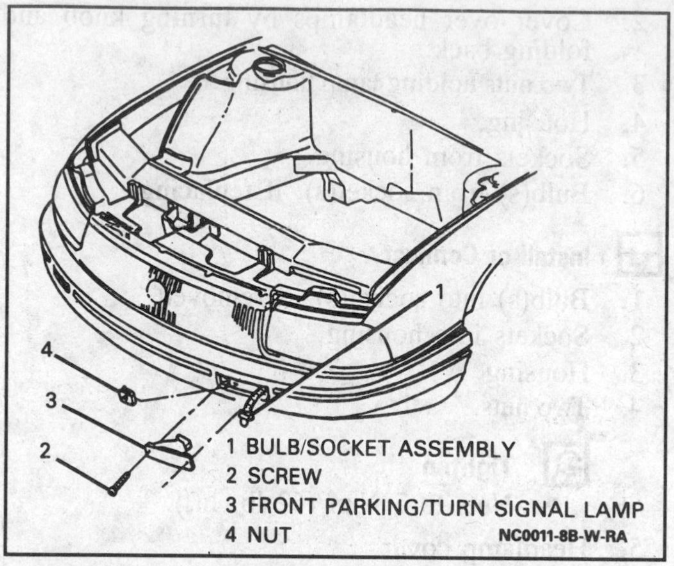
1
2
3
4
1 BULB/SOCKET ASSEMBLY
2 SCREW
3 FRONT PARKING/TURN SIGNAL LAMP
4 NUT
NC0011-8B-W-RA

Figure 2 Front Parking/Turn Signal Lamp (Sedan)

FOGLAMPS

The foglamps are mounted to the impact bar at the front of the vehicle. To use the foglamps, first turn on the low-beam headlamps or parking lamps. Then, push the foglamp switch to turn on the foglamps. Push the switch again to turn off the foglamps.

The foglamps should not be used as a substitute for the headlamps.

Switching to high-beam headlamps will turn off the foglamps; switching back to low-beams will turn the foglamps on again.

The foglamps must be aimed for proper illumination of the road. Foglamp aim should be checked: at least once a year; when a new assembly is installed; or if service or repairs in the front end area have (or may have) disturbed the foglamp mountings.

Assembly Replacement

Figure 3

Remove or Disconnect

1. Electrical connector.
2. Bolts.
3. Assembly.

Install or Connect

1. Assembly.
2. Bolts.

Tighten

- Bolts to 10 N·m (89 lb. in.).

3. Electrical connector.

Bulb Replacement

See caution under "Halogen Bulbs" in this section.

Remove or Disconnect

1. Electrical connector.
2. Bulb/socket assembly from foglamp assembly.

Install or Connect

1. Bulb/socket assembly into foglamp assembly.
2. Electrical connector.

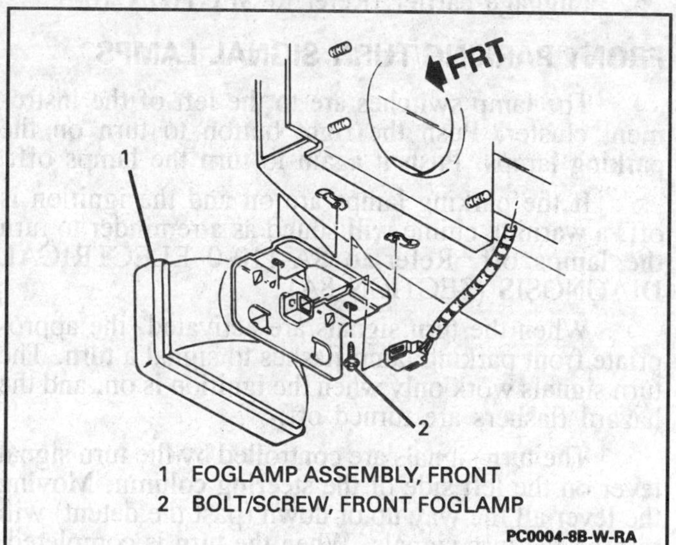
FRT
1
2
1 FOGLAMP ASSEMBLY, FRONT
2 BOLT/SCREW, FRONT FOGLAMP
PC0004-8B-W-RA

Figure 3 Foglamps

FOGLAMP AIMING STANDARD PROCEDURE

Figure 4

If a vehicle is equipped with foglamps, they should be properly aimed. The movable horizontal and vertical lines on the aiming screen should be located so they cross at the "straight ahead" positions of the centerline of each foglamp, whether symmetrical or non-symmetrical.

Foglamp Inspection

Procedure: With vehicle properly located and loaded (the same as for headlamp aiming) switch on the foglamps and observe the location of the high intensity zone on the screen.

Symmetrical Beam

Procedure: When properly aimed, the top edge of the high intensity zone is set 102 mm (4 inches) below horizontal centerline of foglamp, and the center of the high intensity zone is set on the vertical centerline (see Figure 4).

Foglamp Not Within Specifications: If center of high intensity zone is more than:

Horizontally:

- 102 mm (4 inches) LEFT, or
- 102 mm (4 inches) RIGHT of straight ahead line, and

Foglamp Not Within Specifications: If top edge is:

- Vertically ABOVE centerline level.

Non-Symmetrical Beam

Procedure: When properly aimed, the top edge of the high intensity zone is set at the horizontal centerline of the foglamp, and the left edge of the high intensity zone is set at the vertical centerline.

Foglamp Not Within Specifications: If left edge of high intensity zone is:

Horizontally more than:

- 102 mm (4 inches) LEFT, or
- 102 mm (4 inches) RIGHT of straight ahead line.

Foglamp Not Within Specifications: If top edge is:

Vertically more than:

- 102 mm (4 inches) ABOVE, or
- 102 mm (4 inches) BELOW the horizontal line.

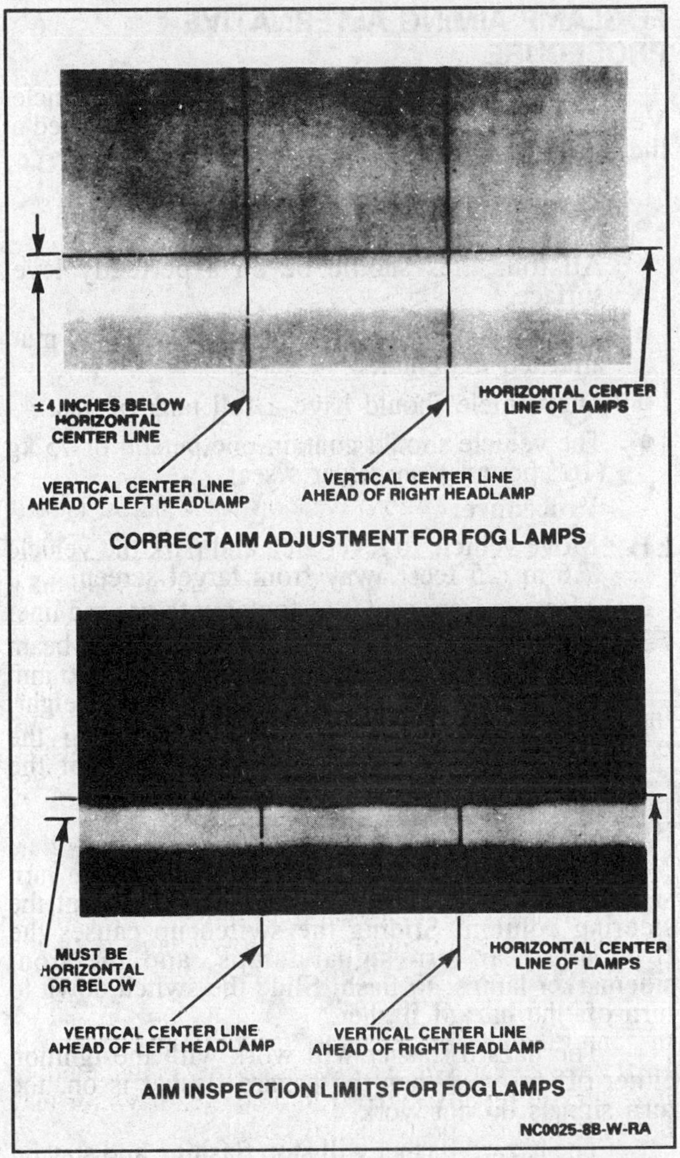
±4 INCHES BELOW HORIZONTAL CENTER LINE
HORIZONTAL CENTER LINE OF LAMPS
VERTICAL CENTER LINE AHEAD OF LEFT HEADLAMP
VERTICAL CENTER LINE AHEAD OF RIGHT HEADLAMP
CORRECT AIM ADJUSTMENT FOR FOG LAMPS
MUST BE HORIZONTAL OR BELOW
HORIZONTAL CENTER LINE OF LAMPS
VERTICAL CENTER LINE AHEAD OF LEFT HEADLAMP
VERTICAL CENTER LINE AHEAD OF RIGHT HEADLAMP
AIM INSPECTION LIMITS FOR FOG LAMPS
NC0025-8B-W-RA

Figure 4 Visual Aim Adjustment and Inspection Limits For Foglamp

FOGLAMP AIMING ALTERNATIVE PROCEDURE

Horizontal aim is not adjustable on this vehicle. Vertical aim is done by an adjusting screw located at the top right side of the foglamp.

Preparation:

- Tires should be properly inflated.
- All four tires should be on a perfectly level surface.
- There should not be any snow, ice or mud attached to vehicle.
- The vehicle should have a full tank of gas.
- The vehicle should contain one person or 75 kg (165 pounds) on driver's seat.

Procedure:

1. Move vehicle to level area and park the vehicle 7.6 m (25 feet) away from target screen.
2. Measure from center of foglamp to ground line.
3. Turn foglamps on, the top of the foglamp beam image on the target screen should be 101.6 mm (4 inches) below center of foglamp lens height.
4. Adjust the foglamp as required, using the adjusting screw at the top right side of the foglamp assembly.

HAZARD FLASHER

The hazard warning flasher is part of the turn signal circuit. The switch is on the right side of the steering column. Sliding the switch up causes the front and rear turn signal lamps, and the front sidemarker lamps, to flash. Slide the switch down to turn off the hazard flasher.

The hazard flasher will work with the ignition either off or on. When the hazard flasher is on, the turn signals do not work.

The hazard flasher will stop flashing and stay on brightly if the brake pedal is pushed down.

The hazard flasher is in the convenience center, behind the right side of the instrument panel. To remove it, refer to SECTION 8C. For information on the hazard flasher switch refer to SECTION 3F1 or SECTION 3F2.

HEADLAMPS

The headlamps are controlled by the switches on the instrument panel (to the left of the speedometer). They will come on whether or not the ignition is turned on. Pushing the left button turns on the headlamps. Pushing the button again turns the lamps off.

If the ignition is off and the headlamps are on, a warning chime will sound as a reminder to turn the lamps off. For more information, refer to 8A-100-0 ELECTRICAL DIAGNOSIS (SECTION 8A).

Headlamp low-beam and high-beam are controlled by the turn signal lever on the left side of the steering column. When the headlamps are on, pull the lever toward you until the switch clicks; the lamps will change from low-beam to high-beam, or from high-beam to low-beam. An indicator lamp on the center instrument cluster will come on when the high-beam headlamps are on.

With flash-to-pass, the driver can flash the high-beam headlamps briefly to warn other drivers. The headlamps must be off to use this feature (the parking lamps may be either off or on). Pull the turn signal lever toward the driver; the high-beam headlamps will come on. They will stay on until the turn signal lever is released. (If the headlamps are on, pulling the turn signal lever will merely switch between high-beam and low-beam headlamps.)

Moisture may appear in the headlamp capsule from condensation; this is normal. To remove it, turn on the headlamps until the capsule dries.

See Caution under "Halogen Bulbs" in this section.

The headlamps must be aimed for proper illumination of the road. Headlamp aim should be checked: at least once a year; when a new headlamp assembly is installed; or if service or repairs to the front end area have (or may have) disturbed the headlamps or their mountings.

Headlamp focus is set when the unit is made; no adjustment for focus is necessary or possible.

Some state and local laws specify requirements for headlamp aim; these laws must be followed.

Assembly Replacement

Figures 5 and 6

See Caution under "Halogen Bulbs" in this section.

Remove or Disconnect

1. Open hood.
2. Headlamp cover by turning knob and folding back.
3. Nuts (if Sedan) and bolts holding headlamp assembly.
4. Bulb/socket assemblies.
5. Headlamp assembly.

Install or Connect

1. Headlamp assembly, making sure to align guide post on back of assembly with hole in headlamp housing panel.
2. Bulb/socket assemblies.
3. Nuts (if Sedan) and bolts to assembly.

Tighten

- Bolts (Sedan) to 8 N·m (71 lb. in.).
- Bolts (Coupe) to 7 N·m (62 lb. in.).

4. Headlamp cover.
5. Close hood.

Adjust

- Headlamp aim.

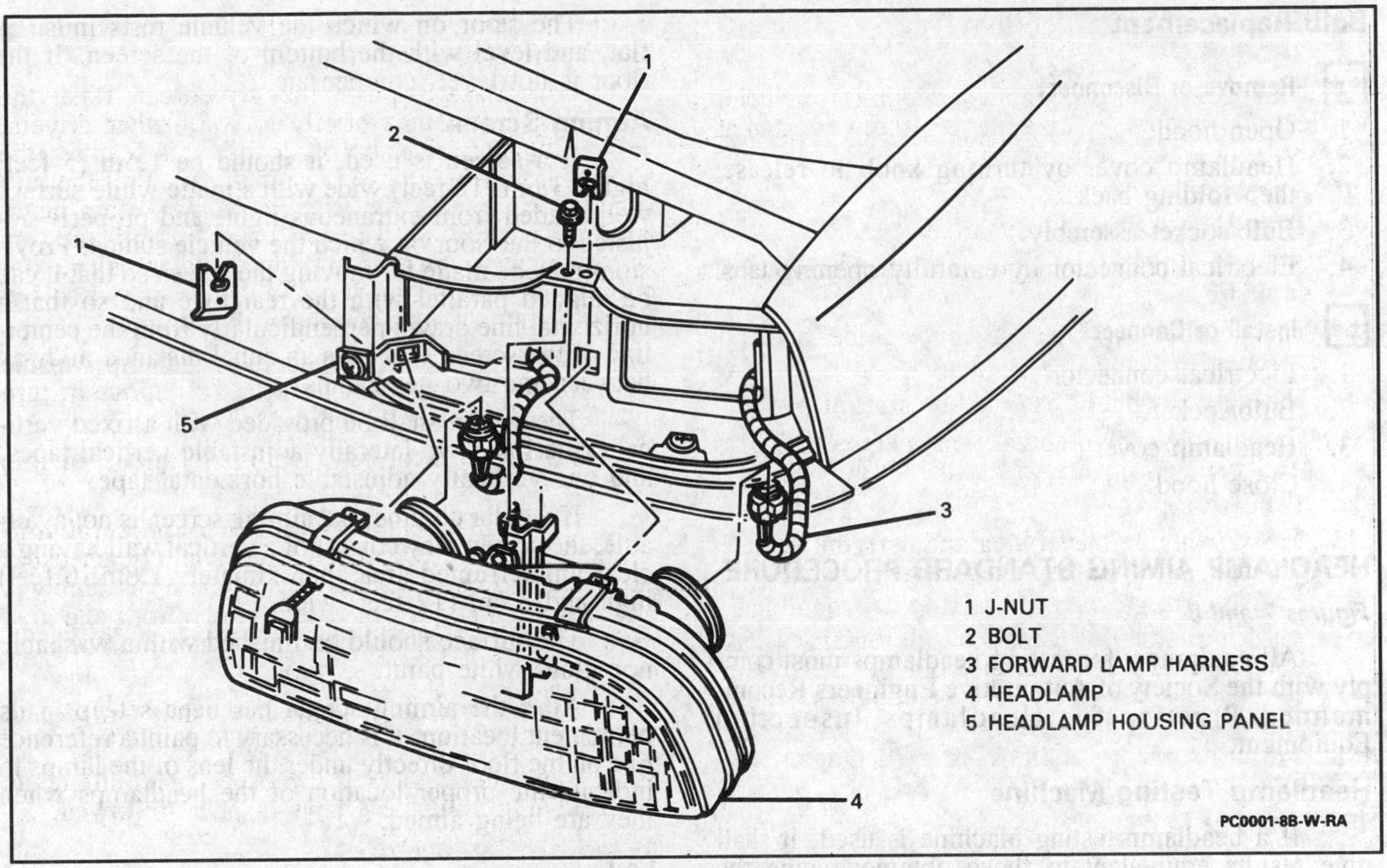
1
2
1
5
3
1 J-NUT
2 BOLT
3 FORWARD LAMP HARNESS
4 HEADLAMP
5 HEADLAMP HOUSING PANEL
4
PC0001-8B-W-RA

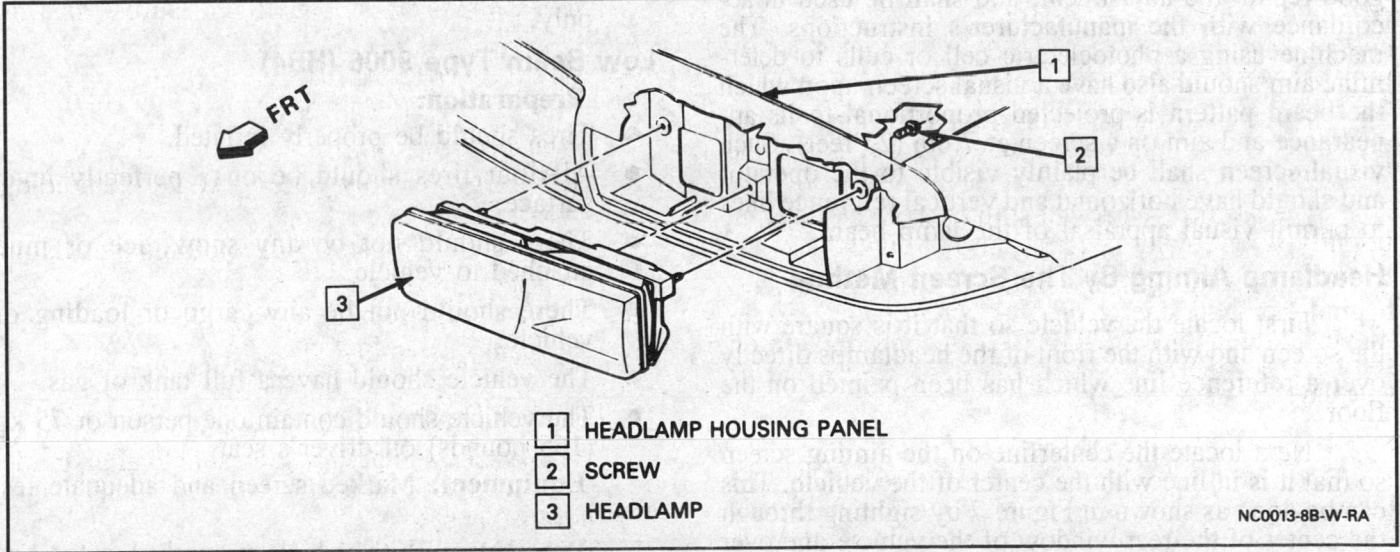

Figure 5 Headlamp Assembly (Sedan)

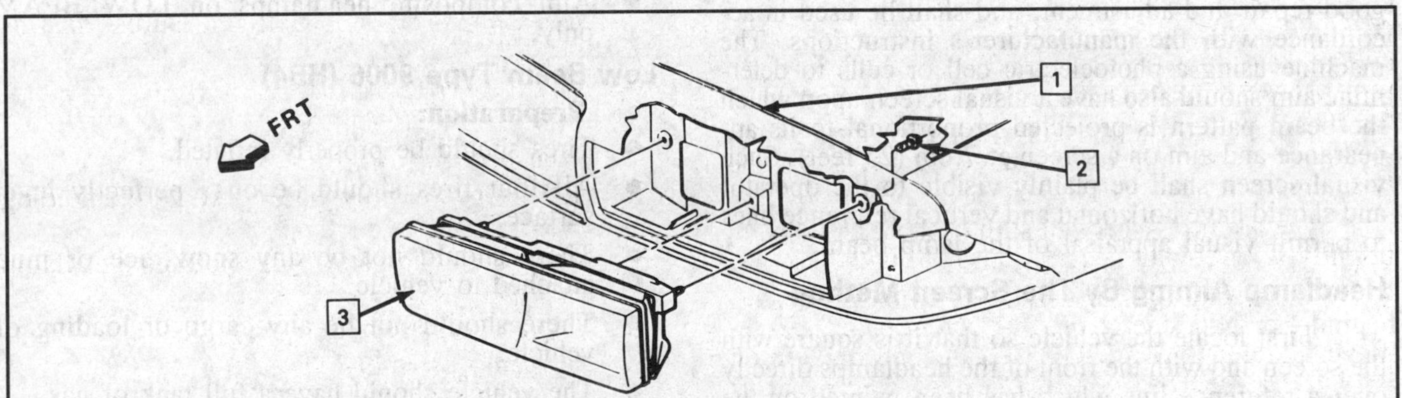
FRT
1
2
3
1 HEADLAMP HOUSING PANEL
2 SCREW
3 HEADLAMP
NC0013-8B-W-RA

Figure 6 Headlamp Assembly (Coupe)

Bulb Replacement

Remove or Disconnect

1. Open hood.
2. Headlamp cover by turning knob to release, then folding back.
3. Bulb/socket assembly.
4. Electrical connector by carefully opening tabs.

Install or Connect

1. Electrical connector.
2. Bulb/socket.
3. Headlamp cover.
4. Close hood.

HEADLAMP AIMING STANDARD PROCEDURE

Figures 7 and 8

All equipment for testing headlamps must comply with the Society of Automotive Engineers Recommended Practice for Headlamps Inspection Equipment.

Headlamp Testing Machine

If a headlamp testing machine is used, it shall give results equivalent to those obtained using the screen procedure shown in Figure 7. It shall be in good repair and adjustment, and shall be used in accordance with the manufacturer's instructions. The machine using a photoelectric cell or cells to determine aim should also have a visual screen upon which the beam pattern is projected proportional to its appearance and aim on a screen at 7.6m (25 feet). Such visual screen shall be plainly visible to the operator and should have horizontal and vertical reference lines to permit visual appraisal of the lamp beam.

Headlamp Aiming By The Screen Method

First locate the vehicle so that it is square with the screen and with the front of the headlamps directly over a reference line which has been painted on the floor.

Next locate the centerline on the aiming screen so that it is in line with the center of the vehicle. This can be done as shown in Figure 7 by sighting through the center of the rear window of the vehicle and over the hood ornament; have vehicle moved until it is in alignment with these two points. If there is no center hood ornament, mark the center of the front and rear windows with narrow strips of masking tape. Use these "sights" to locate the center line of the aiming screen directly in line with the vehicle axis.

Aiming Area Required

It is desirable to have a specific aiming area in a darkened location. This should be sufficient for the vehicle and an additional 7.6m (25 feet) measured from face of lamps to the front of the visual screen.

The floor on which the vehicle rests must be flat, and level with the bottom of the screen. If the floor is not level, compensate.

Aiming Screen

If a screen is used, it should be 1.5m (5 feet) high x 3.6m (12 feet) wide with a matte white surface well shaded from extraneous light, and properly adjusted to the floor on which the vehicle stands. Provisions may be made for moving the screen so that it can be aligned parallel with the rear axle and so that a horizontal line drawn perpendicularly from the centerline of the screen will pass an equal distance midway between the two headlamps.

The screen shall be provided with a fixed vertical centerline, two laterally adjustable vertical tapes, and one vertically adjustable horizontal tape.

If regular commercial aiming screen is not available, the screen may consist of a vertical wall having a clear uninterrupted area approximately 1.8m (6 feet) high and 3.6m (12 feet) wide.

The surface should be finished with a washable non-gloss white paint.

After the aiming screen has been set up in its permanent location, it is necessary to paint a reference line on the floor directly under the lens of the lamps to indicate the proper location of the headlamps when they are being aimed.

Important

- Aim composite headlamps on LOW BEAM only.

Low Beam Type 9006 (HB4)

Preparation:

- Tires should be properly inflated.
- All four tires should be on a perfectly level surface.
- There should not be any snow, ice or mud attached to vehicle.
- There should not be any cargo or loading of vehicle.
- The vehicle should have a full tank of gas.
- The vehicle should contain one person or 75 kg (165 pounds) on driver's seat.

Equipment: Marked screen and adequate test area.

Procedure: With vehicle properly located and loaded, switch headlamps to low beam and observe left and top edges of high intensity zone on the screen.

Headlamp Not Within Specifications: If left edge is horizontally more than:

- 102 mm (4 inches) LEFT, or
- 102 mm (4 inches) RIGHT of straight ahead

Headlamp Not Within Specifications: If top edge is vertically more than:

- 102 mm (4 inches) ABOVE, or
- 102 mm (4 inches) BELOW the horizontal line.

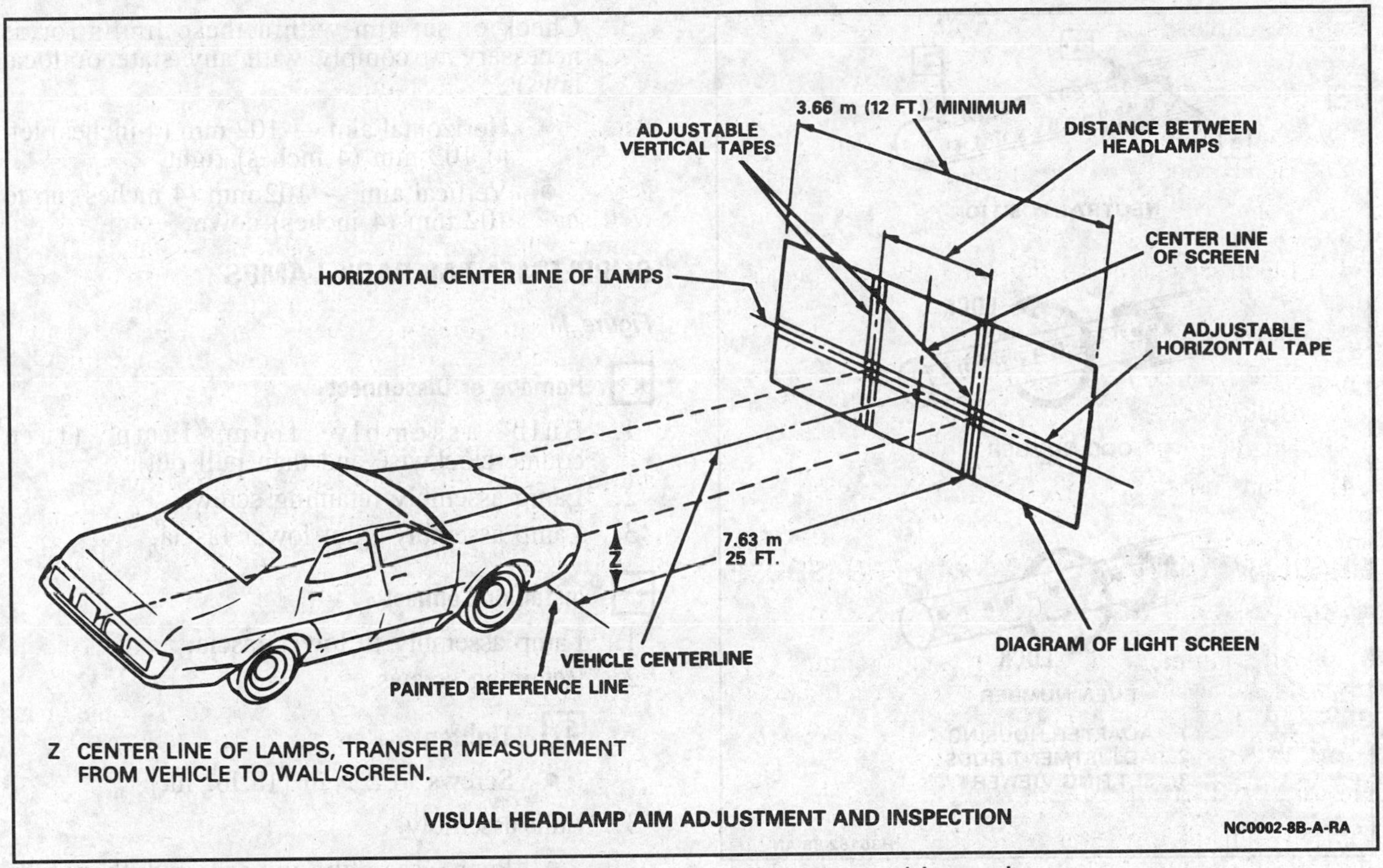
3.66 m (12 FT.) MINIMUM
ADJUSTABLE VERTICAL TAPES
DISTANCE BETWEEN HEADLAMPS
CENTER LINE OF SCREEN
HORIZONTAL CENTER LINE OF LAMPS
ADJUSTABLE HORIZONTAL TAPE
Z
7.63 m 25 FT.
DIAGRAM OF LIGHT SCREEN
VEHICLE CENTERLINE
PAINTED REFERENCE LINE
Z CENTER LINE OF LAMPS, TRANSFER MEASUREMENT FROM VEHICLE TO WALL/SCREEN.
VISUAL HEADLAMP AIM ADJUSTMENT AND INSPECTION
NC0002-8B-A-RA

Figure 7 Visual Headlamp Aim Adjustment and Inspection

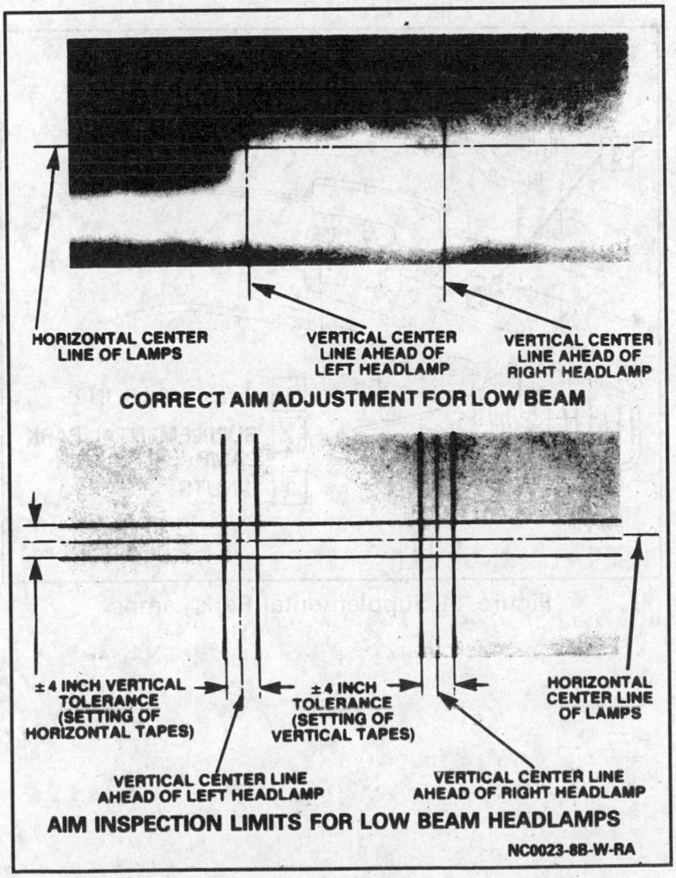
HORIZONTAL CENTER LINE OF LAMPS
VERTICAL CENTER LINE AHEAD OF LEFT HEADLAMP
VERTICAL CENTER LINE AHEAD OF RIGHT HEADLAMP
CORRECT AIM ADJUSTMENT FOR LOW BEAM
± 4 INCH VERTICAL TOLERANCE (SETTING OF HORIZONTAL TAPES)
± 4 INCH TOLERANCE (SETTING OF VERTICAL TAPES)
HORIZONTAL CENTER LINE OF LAMPS
VERTICAL CENTER LINE AHEAD OF LEFT HEADLAMP
VERTICAL CENTER LINE AHEAD OF RIGHT HEADLAMP
AIM INSPECTION LIMITS FOR LOW BEAM HEADLAMPS
NC0023-8B-W-RA

Figure 8 Visual Headlamp Aim Adjustment and Inspection Limits

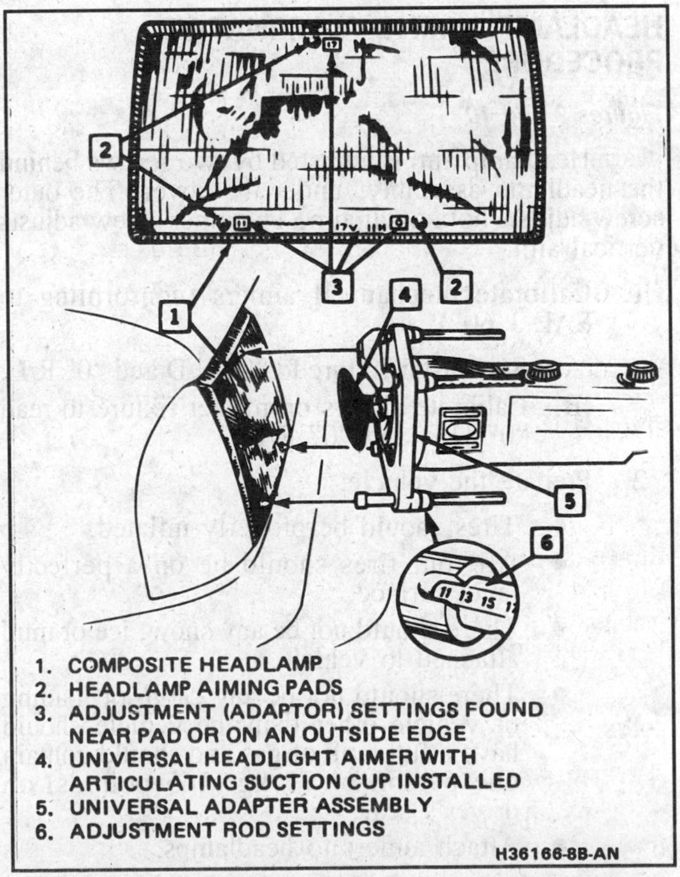
1
2
3
4
5
6
11 13 15
1. COMPOSITE HEADLAMP
2. HEADLAMP AIMING PADS
3. ADJUSTMENT (ADAPTOR) SETTINGS FOUND NEAR PAD OR ON AN OUTSIDE EDGE
4. UNIVERSAL HEADLIGHT AIMER WITH ARTICULATING SUCTION CUP INSTALLED
5. UNIVERSAL ADAPTER ASSEMBLY
6. ADJUSTMENT ROD SETTINGS
H36166-8B-AN

Figure 9 Composite Headlamp Aiming (Typical)

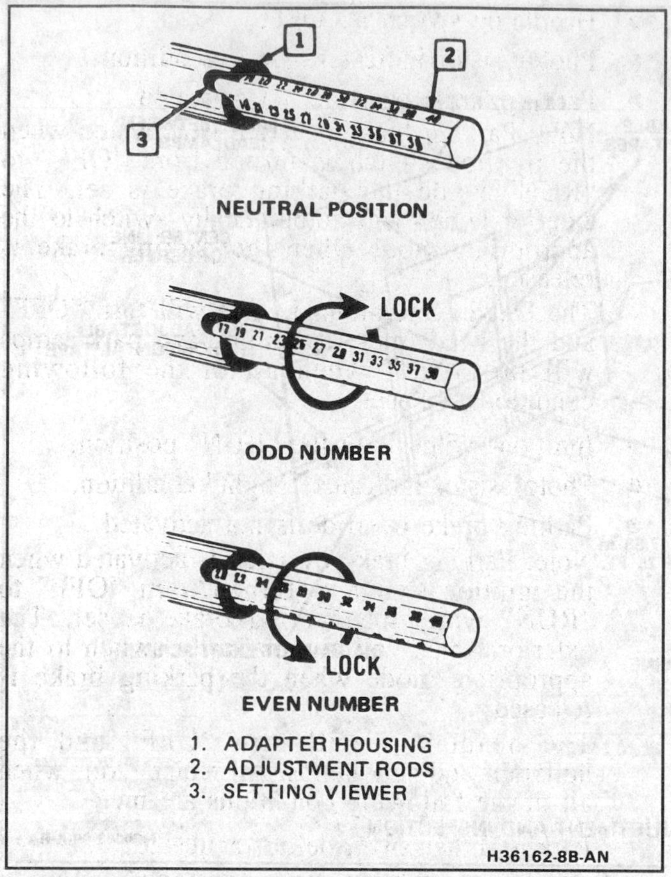
NEUTRAL POSITION
LOCK
ODD NUMBER
LOCK
EVEN NUMBER
1. ADAPTER HOUSING
2. ADJUSTMENT RODS
3. SETTING VIEWER
H36162-8B-AN

Figure 10 Composite Light Aiming Rods (Typical)

HEADLAMP AIMING ALTERNATIVE PROCEDURE

Figures 9 and 10

Headlamp aim is adjusted by two screws behind the headlamp assembly, under the cover. The outer screw adjusts horizontal aim. The inner screw adjusts vertical aim.

1. Calibrate mechanical aimers (conforming to SAE J 602):
   A. Set master fixture to "0" U/D and "0" R/L.
   B. Calibrate aimers on master fixture to read "0" U/D and "0" R/L.
2. Prepare the vehicle:
   - Tires should be properly inflated.
   - All four tires should be on a perfectly level surface.
   - There should not be any snow, ice or mud attached to vehicle.
   - There should not be any cargo or loading of vehicle other than the vehicle should have a full tank of gas and should contain one person or 75 kg (165 pounds) on driver's seat.
   - Attach aimers to headlamps.
3. Check or set aim within these limits (or as necessary to comply with any state or local laws):
   - Horizontal aim — 102 mm (4 inches) left to 102 mm (4 inches) right.
   - Vertical aim — 102 mm (4 inches) up to 102 mm (4 inches) down.

SUPPLEMENTAL PARK LAMPS

Figure 11

Remove or Disconnect

1. Bulb assembly from lamp (turn counterclockwise and then pull out).
2. Lamp assembly retaining screws.
3. Lamp assembly from lower fascia.

Install or Connect

1. Lamp assembly to lower fascia.
2. Retaining screws.

Tighten

- Screws to 2 N·m (18 lb. in.)

3. Bulb assembly.
   - Push assembly inward and then turn clockwise.

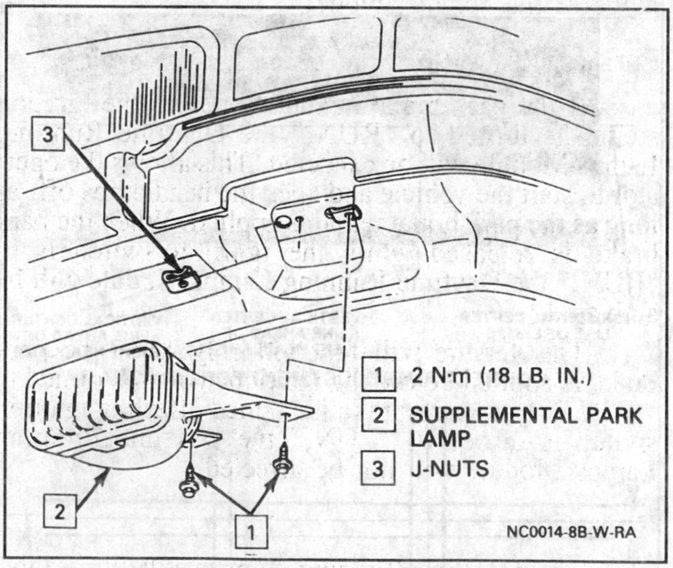
1 2 N·m (18 LB. IN.)
2 SUPPLEMENTAL PARK LAMP
3 J-NUTS
NC0014-8B-W-RA

Figure 11 Supplemental Park Lamps

DAYTIME RUNNING LAMPS (CANADA ONLY)

Module

The Daytime Running Lamps Module is designed to automatically operate certain lamps depending on outside light conditions. The module operates in two modes. In the "Day" mode, the low beam headlamps are on at reduced brilliance. In the "Night" mode, the headlamps are on at full brilliance and the front marker, park, and taillamps are lit.

When the Daytime Running Lamps Module is in the "Day" mode, the Daytime Running Lamp DRL Switch is closed, applying voltage to the Dropping Diodes and the low beam headlamps. The Dropping Diode reduces the voltage applied to the headlamps, reducing the headlamp brilliance.

When the Photoresistor senses darkness, the Daytime Running Lamps Module operates in the "Night" mode. The Daytime Running Lamp DRL Switch opens and the headlamp switch and Park Lights Switch close. Voltage is applied to the headlamps and other exterior lamps through the same circuit path as when the headlamp switch is on.

Sensor Input

The photoresistor is a light sensitive variable resistor. Its resistance decreases as outside light intensity increases. The Daytime Running Lamps Module measures the voltage drop across the photoresistor and determines whether it should operate in the "Day" mode or the "Night" mode.

Park Brake Input

If the park brake is applied before the ignition switch is turned to "RUN," the Daytime Running Lamps Module will be canceled. This allows the operator to start the vehicle and keep the headlamps off, as long as the park brake remains applied. When the park brake is released while the ignition switch is in "RUN," the Daytime Running Lamps Module will be activated.

This feature will function only when the park brake is applied before the ignition switch is turned to "RUN." If the park brake is applied after the ignition switch is turned to "RUN," the Daytime Running Lamps Module will not be affected.

Operation

The Daytime Running Lamps will turn "ON" when all of the following conditions are met.

- Ignition switch is in the "RUN" position.
- Headlamp switch is "OFF."
- Photoresistor indicates "Day" condition.
- Parking brake override not activated.

  Note: Parking brake override is activated when the ignition switch is turned from "OFF" to "RUN" while the parking brake is set. The exterior lamps will automatically switch to the appropriate mode when the parking brake is released.

  The Daytime Running Lamps will turn "OFF" and the headlamps, taillamps, and park lamps will turn "ON" when all of the following conditions are met:

- Ignition switch is in the "RUN" position.
- Photoresistor indicates "Night" condition.
- Parking brake override is not activated.

  Note: Parking brake override is activated when the ignition switch is turned from "OFF" to "RUN" while the parking brake is set. The exterior lamps will automatically switch to the appropriate mode when the parking brake is released.

  The headlamps will turn "OFF" and the taillamps and park lamps will remain "on" when all of the following conditions are met:

- Parking brake override not activated.

  Note: Parking brake override is activated when the ignition switch is turned from "OFF" to "RUN" while the parking brake is set. The exterior lamps will automatically switch to the appropriate mode when the parking brake is released.

- Ignition switch is turned from "RUN" to "CRANK."

SENSOR REPLACEMENT

Figure 12

Remove or Disconnect

1. Left front speaker grille.
2. Electrical connector from speaker grille.
3. Sensor.

Install or Connect

1. Sensor.
2. Electrical connector to speaker grille.
3. Left front speaker grille.

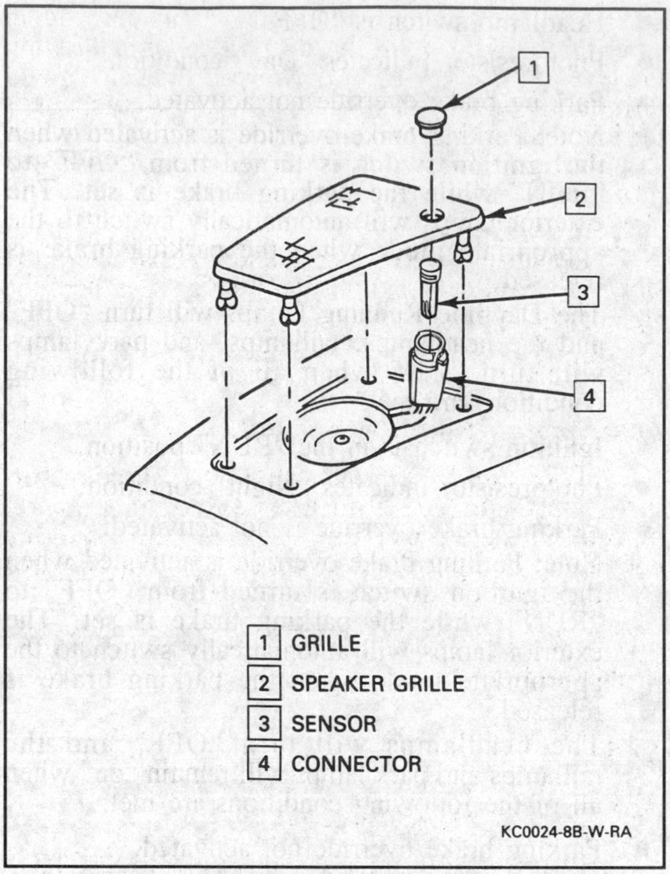
1
2
3
4
1 GRILLE
2 SPEAKER GRILLE
3 SENSOR
4 CONNECTOR
KC0024-8B-W-RA

Figure 12 Daytime Running Lamps Sensor (Canada Only)

MODULE REPLACEMENT

Figure 13

Remove or Disconnect

1. Trim panel below steering column. Refer to SECTION 8C.
2. Electrical connectors from module (located on brake pedal bracket).
3. Module from bracket.

Install or Connect

1. Module to bracket.
2. Electrical connectors to module.
3. Trim panel below steering column. Refer to SECTION 8C.

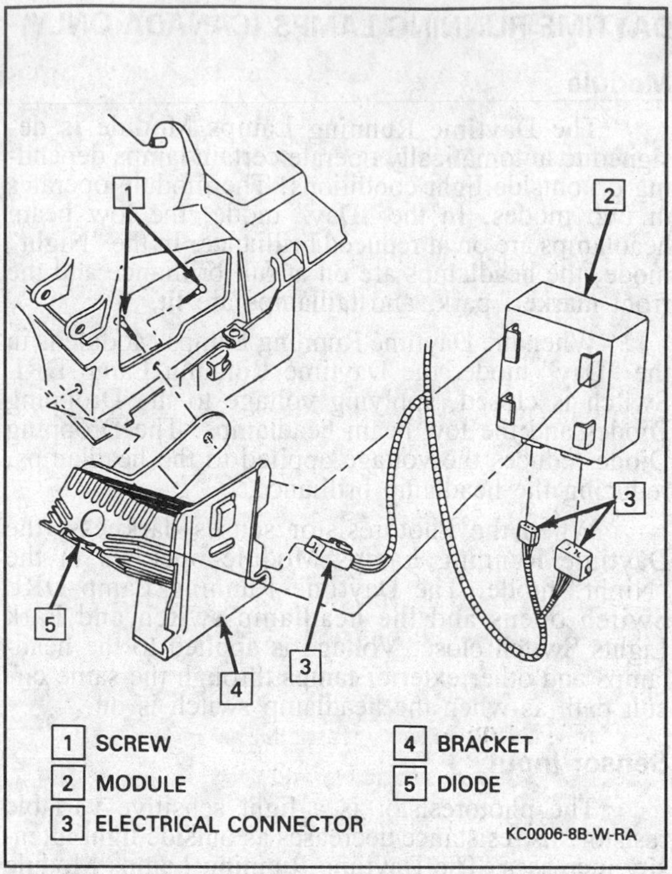
1
2
3
3
4
5
1 SCREW
2 MODULE
3 ELECTRICAL CONNECTOR
4 BRACKET
5 DIODE
KC0006-8B-W-RA

Figure 13 Module and Diode Assembly

DIODE ASSEMBLY REPLACEMENT

Figure 13

Remove or Disconnect

1. Trim panel below steering column. Refer to SECTION 8C.
2. Electrical connector from diode assembly.
3. Screws holding diode assembly to brake pedal bracket.
4. Module from diode assembly.

Install or Connect

1. Module to diode assembly.
2. Diode assembly to brake pedal bracket.
3. Screws to bracket.

Tighten

- Screws to 2 N·m (18 lb. in.).

4. Electrical connector to diode assembly.
5. Trim panel below steering column. Refer to SECTION 8C.

LICENSE PLATE LAMPS

The license plate lamps will come on when the headlamps or parking lamps are on.

Assembly or Bulb Replacement

Sedan

Remove or Disconnect

1. Open rear compartment lid.
2. Screws.
3. Assembly.
4. Socket from assembly.
5. Bulb (if replacing).

Install or Connect

1. Bulb, if removed.
2. Socket into assembly.
3. Assembly into position.
4. Screws.

Tighten

- Screws to 2 N·m (18 lb. in.).

5. Close rear compartment lid.

Coupe

Remove or Disconnect

1. Screw.
2. Assembly.
3. Socket from assembly.
4. Bulb (if replacing).

Install or Connect

1. Bulb (if removed).
2. Socket into assembly.
3. Assembly into position.
4. Screw.

Tighten

- Screw to 2 N•m (18 lb. in.).

TAIL/STOP/TURN SIGNAL LAMPS

The tail/stop/turn signal lamps, and the backup lamps (on coupes), are part of the same lamp assembly. Pushing either the headlamps or parking lamps button will turn on the taillamps. When the brake pedal is pushed down, the outer lamps glow brighter to serve as stoplamps. (The lamps above and below the backup lamps (on coupes) serve as taillamps only.)

The turn signals are controlled by the turn signal lever on the left side of the steering column. Moving the lever all the way up or down (past the detent) will turn on the turn signals. When the turn is completed, the lever will return to neutral and the turn signals will stop flashing. (If the brake pedal is held down when a turn is signaled, one side will flash and the other will stay on brightly.)

For changing lanes or shallow turns where the steering wheel does not turn far enough to cancel the signal, move the turn signal lever only to the first detent. When a lever is released, it will return to neutral and the turn signals will cancel.

Assembly or Bulb Replacement

Take care to prevent waterleaks if sealing surfaces are disturbed. Damaged gaskets must be replaced. If necessary, use sealer (body caulking compound or equivalent) in critical areas or any area where the gasket doesn't scal properly.

On coupes, see Caution under "Halogen Bulbs" in this section.

Sedan

Remove or Disconnect

1. Rear compartment trim panel. Refer to SECTION 10-8.
2. Taillamp assembly.
3. Sockets from assembly.
4. Bulb(s) from socket(s), if replacing.

Install or Connect

1. Bulb(s) into socket(s), if removed.
2. Sockets into assembly.
3. Taillamp assembly.
4. Rear compartment trim panel. Refer to SECTION 10-8.

Coupe

Remove or Disconnect

1. Rear compartment trim panel. Refer to SECTION 10-8.
2. Socket assembly.
3. Bulb from socket.

Install or Connect

1. Bulb into socket.
2. Socket assembly.
3. Rear compartment trim panel. Refer to SECTION 10-8.

SIDEMARKER LAMPS AND REFLECTORS

The front and rear sidemarker lamps will come on when the headlamps or parking lamps are on. There are also front and rear reflectors that will shine when struck by light, whether or not the vehicle's lamps are on.

If the headlamps or parking lamps are off when a turn is signaled, the appropriate front sidemarker lamp will flash in unison with the front turn signal lamp on the same side. If the lamps are on when a turn is signaled, the front sidemarker lamp and front turn signal lamp flash alternately.

The front sidemarker lamps are part of the front parking/turn signal assembly on coupes. See "Front Parking/Turn Signal Lamps" in this section. On sedans they are just in front of the front wheel opening.

The rear sidemarker lamps are just behind the rear wheel opening on coupes.

Front Sidemarker Assembly or Bulb Replacement (Sedan)

Remove or Disconnect

1. Electrical connector.
2. Nuts.
3. Assembly.
4. Bulb/socket assembly from lamp assembly, if replacing.

Install or Connect

1. Bulb/socket assembly, if removed.
2. Assembly.
3. Nuts.

Tighten

- Nuts to 2 N·m (18 lb. in.).

4. Electrical connector.

Rear Sidemarker Assembly or Bulb Replacement

Figure 14

Remove or Disconnect

1. Screws.
2. Assembly.
3. Socket from assembly.
4. Bulb from socket, if replacing.

Install or Connect

1. Bulb into socket (if replacing).
2. Socket into assembly.
3. Assembly.
4. Screws.

Tighten

- Screws to 2 N·m (18 lb. in.).

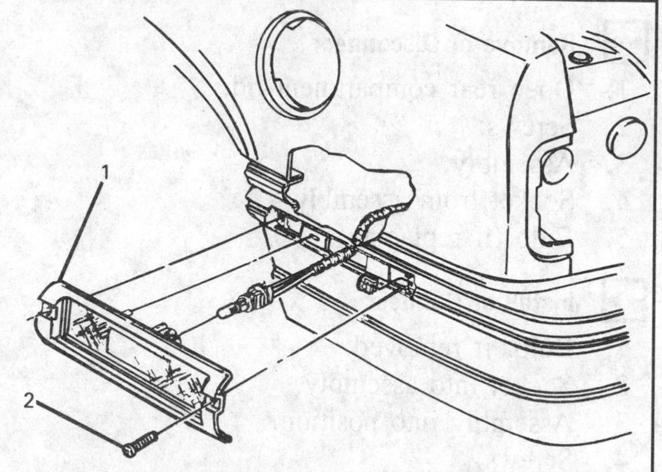
1
2

1 LAMP, REAR SIDEMARKER
2 BOLT/SCREW, REAR SIDEMARKER LAMP PC0003-8B-W-RA

Figure 14 Rear Sidemarker Lamp

Front Reflector Assembly Replacement (Coupe)

Remove or Disconnect

1. Nuts.
2. Assembly.

Install or Connect

1. Assembly.
2. Nuts.

Tighten

- Nuts to 2 N·m (18 lb. in.).

Rear Reflector Assembly Replacement (Sedan)

Remove or Disconnect

1. Nuts.
2. Assembly.

Install or Connect

1. Assembly.
2. Nuts.

Tighten

- Nuts to 2 N·m (18 lb. in.).

REAR COMPARTMENT LAMP

The rear compartment lamp will come on whenever the lid is opened, even if the headlamps or parking lamps are not on.

Assembly Replacement

Remove or Disconnect

1. Open rear compartment lid.
2. Bolt and ground wire.
3. Assembly by sliding loose the clip.
4. Slide loose the clip holding the connector.
5. Electrical connector.

Install or Connect

1. Electrical connector.
2. Connector clip.
3. Assembly by sliding clip onto lid.
4. Bolt with ground wire.

Tighten

- Bolt to 3 N·m (27 lb. in.).

5. Close rear compartment lid.

Bulb Replacement

Remove or Disconnect

1. Open rear compartment lid.
2. Bulb retainer.
3. Bulb from socket.

Install or Connect

1. Bulb into socket.
2. Bulb retainer.
3. Close rear compartment lid.

TURN SIGNAL FLASHER

The turn signal flasher is behind the instrument panel, to the right of the steering column. Refer to SECTION 8C.

UNDERHOOD LAMP

The underhood lamp will come on when the hood is raised, whether or not the parking lamps or headlamps are on.

Assembly Replacement

Refer to SECTION 10-5 for assembly replacement.

Bulb Replacement

Remove or Disconnect

1. Open hood.
2. Lens by squeezing ends.
3. Bulb by sliding off contacts.

Install or Connect

1. Bulb.
2. Lens by snapping into place.
3. Close hood.

INTERIOR LAMPS

The interior lighting systems include courtesy lamps, dome lamps, reading lamps, door lamps, and convenience lamps (such as the lower compartment lamp or lighted visor mirror); also included are all associated wiring, controls and related hardware for these lamps.

For information on indicator lights, instrument cluster lighting, etc., refer to SECTION 8C.

For circuit information, refer to 8A-114-0 ELECTRICAL DIAGNOSIS (SECTION 8A).

INSTRUMENT PANEL COURTESY LAMPS

Two courtesy lamps under the instrument panel will come on when a door is opened, or when the inside lamps are turned on. To turn on the inside lamps, slide the brightness lever (under the lamp buttons) all the way to the right, past the detent. Slide the lever back past the detent to turn off the lamps.

Left Lamp Replacement

Remove or Disconnect

1. Two retainers holding left sound insulator.
2. Left sound insulator.
3. One bolt holding courtesy lamp.
4. Courtesy lamp.

Install or Connect

1. Courtesy lamp.
2. One bolt.

Tighten

- Bolt to 2 N·m (18 lb. in.).

3. Sound insulator.
4. Two retainers holding sound insulator.

Right Lamp Replacement

Remove or Disconnect

1. One bolt and one retainer holding right sound insulator.
2. Sound insulator by pushing rearward then down.
3. One bolt holding courtesy lamp.
4. Courtesy lamp.

Install or Connect

1. Courtesy lamp.
2. One bolt to courtesy lamp.

Tighten

- Bolt to 2 N·m (18 lb. in.).

3. Sound insulator.
4. One bolt and one retainer to sound insulator.

Tighten

- Bolt to 2 N·m (18 lb. in.).

DOME AND READING LAMPS

The dome lamp is on the roof between the front seats. It will come on when a door is opened, or when the inside lamps are turned on. To turn on the inside lamps, slide the lever under the lamp buttons all the way to the right, past the detent. To turn them off, slide the lever back to the left, just past the detent.

If so equipped, the reading lamps are part of the courtesy lamp assembly. Push the switch to turn a lamp on or off.

Assembly Replacement

Refer to SECTION 10-9 for assembly replacement.

Bulb Replacement

Remove or Disconnect

1. Lens by pulling down.
2. Bulb(s) by releasing contacts.

Install or Connect

1. Bulb(s).
2. Lens by snapping into place.

LOWER COMPARTMENT LAMP

When the ignition is on, a lamp in the lower compartment will come on when the door is opened.

Assembly or Bulb Replacement

Remove or Disconnect

1. Lower compartment. Refer to SECTION 8C.
2. Bulb from socket, if replacing.
3. Socket (if removing) by turning it to align tabs with holes and pushing out.

Install or Connect

1. Socket, if removed.
2. Bulb, if removed.
3. Lower compartment. Refer to SECTION 8C.

LIGHTED VISOR MIRROR

The optional lighted visor mirror is on the rear of the passenger's sunshade. The lamps will come on when the cover is raised.

Assembly Replacement

Refer to SECTION 10-9 for assembly replacement.

Bulb Replacement

Remove or Disconnect

1. Lens by prying carefully, using a small screwdriver in the slot in the bottom of the lens.
2. Bulb by prying carefully with a small screwdriver.

Install or Connect

1. Bulb.
2. Lens by snapping into place.

DOOR COURTESY LAMP

Remove or Disconnect

1. Door courtesy lamp lens.
   - Unsnap lens from door trim panel.
2. Bulb from socket.

Install or Connect

1. Bulb to socket.
2. Door courtesy lamp lens.
   - Snap lens into door trim panel.

QUARTER COURTESY LAMP

Remove or Disconnect

1. Quarter upper trim panel. Refer to SECTION 10-7.
2. Quarter courtesy lamp.
   A. Press tabs inward.
   B. Push lamp through opening in quarter upper trim panel.
3. Electrical connector.
4. Bulb/socket from lamp.

Install or Connect

1. Bulb/socket to lamp.
2. Electrical connector.
3. Quarter courtesy lamp to quarter upper trim panel.
4. Quarter upper trim panel. Refer to SECTION 10-7.

LAMP SWITCHES

Most inside and outside lamps are controlled by the lamp switches to the left of the instrument cluster. For more information on these buttons, refer to SECTION 8C and ELECTRICAL DIAGNOSIS (SECTION 8A).

Push the right button (marked with a **"P"**) to turn on the parking lamps, taillamps, sidemarker lamps, and the instrument panel lamps. Push the button again to turn the lamps off.

Push the left button (marked with the headlamp symbol) to turn on all these lamps plus the headlamps. Push the button again to turn off all lamps. Headlamp low-beam/high-beam is controlled by the turn signal lever on the left side of the steering column. With the headlamps on, pull the lever toward you until you hear a click. The lamps will change from low-beam to high-beam, or from high-beam to low-beam.

The lever under the buttons controls the inside lamps, and the brightness of the instrument panel lamps. Slide it to the left to dim the instrument panel lamps. Slide it all the way to the right, past the detent, to turn on the inside lights.

HORNS

The horns are mounted on the radiator support and hood latch support. Pushing the pad in the center of the steering wheel sounds the horns by closing the horn relay. The horn relay is under the right electrical center (underhood) in the forward lamp electrical center. The horns use a solenoid-operated diaphragm to generate sound. For wiring and circuit information, refer to 8A-40-0 ELECTRICAL DIAGNOSIS (SECTION 8A).

HORN ASSEMBLY

Figure 15

Remove or Disconnect

1. Open hood.
2. Headlamp housing panel.
3. One bolt holding horn.
4. Electrical connector to horn.
5. Horn.

Install or Connect

1. Electrical connector to horn.
2. Horn.
3. Bolt.

Tighten

- Bolt to 10 N•m (89 lb. in.).

4. Headlamp housing panel.
5. Close hood.

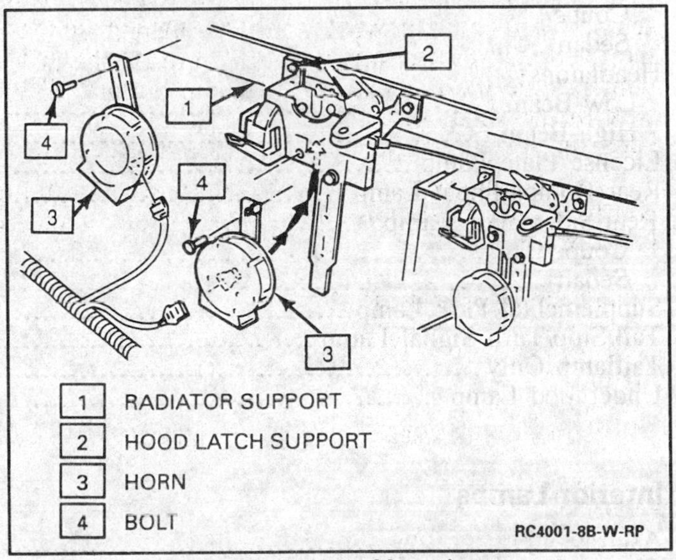
1
2
3
4
1 RADIATOR SUPPORT
2 HOOD LATCH SUPPORT
3 HORN
4 BOLT
RC4001-8B-W-RP

Figure 15 Horn Mounting

HORN RELAY

The horn relay is under the right electrical center (underhood) in the forward lamp electrical center. For more information, refer to SECTION 8C.

SPECIFICATIONS

REPLACEMENT BULBS

Exterior Lamps

	Trade No.
Backup Lamps	
Coupe	892
Sedan	3057
Center High-Mounted Stoplamp	
Except Luggage Carrier Mounted	3155
Luggage Carrier Mounted	891
Foglamp	H3
Front Parking/Turn Signal Lamps	
Coupe	890
Sedan	3157NA
Front Sidemarker Lamp	
Coupe	194NA
Sedan	194
Headlamps	
Low-Beam	9006
High-Beam	9005
License Plate Lamp	194
Rear Compartment Lamp	920
Rear Sidemarker Lamp	
Coupe	24
Sedan	24
Supplemental Park Lamp	3057
Tail/Stop/Turn Signal Lamp	3057
Taillamp Only	194
Underhood Lamp	561

Interior Lamps

	Trade No.
Ashtray	194
Cluster Lighting	160, 161, 194, 194G
Dome Lamp	561
Dome Lamp with Reading Lamps	211-2
Reading Lamps	24
Door Courtesy Lamp	212-2
Gear Selector Indicator	73, 161
Headlamp High-Beam Indicator	161
Indicator Lamp	161
Instrument Panel Courtesy Lamp	194
Lighted Rearview Mirror Lamp	212-2
Lower Compartment Lamp	1816
Turn Signal Indicators	194
Quarter Courtesy Lamp	562
Visor Vanity Mirror Lamp	TS-14VICP

FASTENER TIGHTENING SPECIFICATIONS

Backup Lamp Screw (Sedan) .... 2 N·m (18 lb. in.)
Cross Brace Bolt (Front) .... 25 N·m (18 lb. ft.)
Cross Brace Bolt (Rear) .... 47 N·m (35 lb. ft.)
Daytime Running Lamps Diode Screw .... 2 N·m (18 lb. in.)
Foglamp Bolt .... 10 N·m (89 lb. in.)
Front Parking/Turn Signal Lamp Nut (Coupe) .... 7 N·m (62 lb. in.)
Front Parking/Turn
Signal Lamp Screw (Sedan) .... 2 N·m (18 lb. in.)

Front Reflector Nut .... 2 N·m (18 lb. in.)
Front Sidemarker Nut (Sedan) .... 2 N·m (18 lb. in.)
Headlamp Bolt (Coupe) .... 7 N·m (62 lb. in.)
Headlamp Bolt (Sedan) .... 8 N·m (71 lb. in.)
Horn Mounting Bolt .... 10 N•m (89 lb. in.)
Instrument Panel Courtesy Lamp Bolt .... 2 N·m (18 lb. in.)
License Plate Lamp Screw (Sedan) .... 2 N·m (18 lb. in.)

Luggage Carrier Center
High-Mounted Stoplamp Screw .... 3 N·m (27 lb. in.)
Rear Compartment Lamp Bolt .... 3 N·m (27 lb. in.)
Rear Reflector Nut .... 2 N·m (18 lb. in.)
Rear Sidemarker Screw .... 2 N·m (18 lb. in.)
Right Sound Insulator Bolt .... 2 N·m (18 lb. in.)
Supplemental Park Lamp Screw .... 2 N·m (18 lb. in.)

SECTION 8C

INSTRUMENT PANEL, GAGES AND CONSOLE

CAUTION: This vehicle is equipped with Supplemental Inflatable Restraint (SIR). Refer to CAUTIONS in Section 9J under "ON-VEHICLE SERVICE" and the SIR component and wiring location view in Section 9J before performing service on or around SIR components or wiring. Failure to follow CAUTIONS could result in possible air bag deployment, personal injury, or otherwise unneeded SIR system repairs.

NOTICE: When fasteners are removed, always reinstall them at the same location from which they were removed. If a fastener needs to be replaced, use the correct part number fastener for that application. If the correct part number fastener is not available, a fastener of equal size and strength (or stronger) may be used. Fasteners that are not reused, and those requiring thread locking compound will be called out. The correct torque value must be used when installing fasteners that require it. If the above conditions are not followed, parts or system damage could result.

CONTENTS

GENERAL DESCRIPTION

INSTRUMENT PANEL, GAGES AND CONSOLE

This vehicle is equipped with driver side Supplemental Inflatable Restraint (SIR). This system includes a Diagnostic Energy Reserve Module (DERM) and also a sensor in the right side of the instrument panel.

ON-VEHICLE SERVICE

This section covers the removal and replacement of the instrument panel, instrument cluster and console, and their various components. Operating information on these components is included in other sections. Electrical diagnosis, circuit diagrams, etc., are covered in ELECTRICAL DIAGNOSIS (SECTION 8A).

CAUTION: Refer to "When to Disconnect the Negative Battery Cable" in GENERAL INFORMATION (SECTION 0A).

As a courtesy, reset the clock after disconnecting the negative battery cable.

SERVICE PRECAUTIONS

CAUTION: When performing service on or around SIR components or SIR wiring, follow the procedures listed below to temporarily disable the SIR system. Failure to follow procedures could result in possible air bag deployment, personal injury or otherwise unneeded SIR system repairs.

The DERM in 1993 and previous Driver-Only SIR systems can maintain sufficient voltage to cause a deployment for up to ten minutes after the ignition switch is turned "OFF," the battery is disconnected, or the fuse powering the DERM is removed.

The DERM in 1993 1/2 and later Driver-Only and the DERM in all Driver-Passenger SIR systems can maintain sufficient voltage to cause a deployment for up to two minutes after the ignition switch is turned "OFF," the battery is disconnected, or the fuse powering the DERM is removed.

Many of the service procedures require removal of the "ARBG1" fuse, and the disconnection of the inflator module from the deployment loop to avoid an accidental deployment. If the inflator module is disconnected from the deployment loop as noted in the "Disabling the SIR System" procedure that follows, service can begin immediately without waiting for the ten-minute or two-minute time period to expire.

DISABLING THE SIR SYSTEM

Figures 1 and 2

↔ Remove or Disconnect

Important

- Turn the steering wheel so that the vehicle's wheels are pointing straight ahead.
- Turn the ignition switch to "LOCK" and remove key.

1. 15A "ARBG1" fuse from instrument panel fuse block.
2. Left sound insulator. Refer to "Sound Insulators" in this section.
3. Connector Position Assurance (CPA) and yellow 2-way connector at base of steering column.

Important

- With the "ARBG1" fuse removed and ignition switch "ON," the "AIR BAG" warning lamp will be "ON." This is normal operation and does not indicate a SIR system malfunction.

ENABLING THE SIR SYSTEM

Figures 1 and 2

→← Install or Connect

Important

- Turn ignition switch to "LOCK" and remove key.

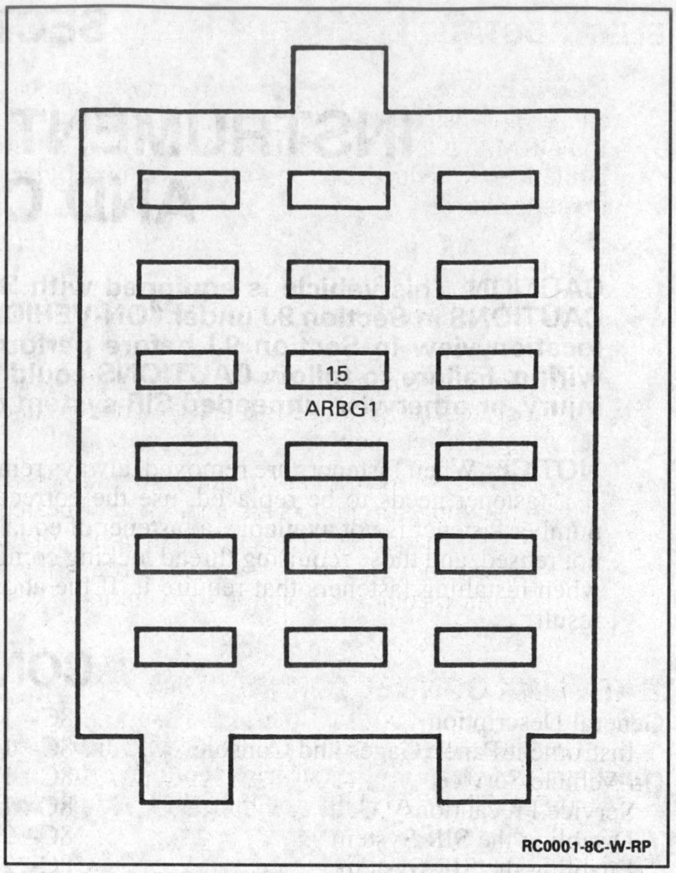
15
ARBG1
RC0001-8C-W-RP

Figure 1 "ARBG1" Fuse Location

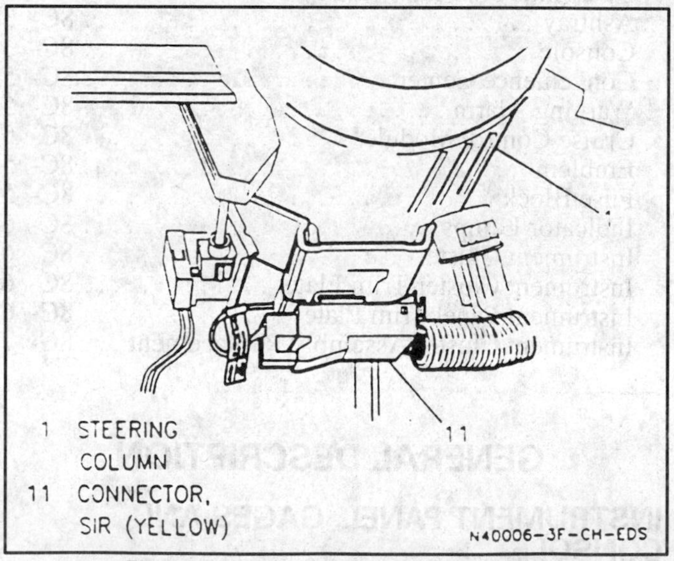
1
11
1 STEERING COLUMN
11 CONNECTOR, SIR (YELLOW)
N40006-3F-CH-EDS

Figure 2 Yellow 2-Way SIR Connector

1. Yellow 2-way connector and Connector Position Assurance (CPA) at base of steering column.
2. Left sound insulator. Refer to "Sound Insulators" in this section.
3. 15A "ARBG1" fuse to instrument panel fuse block.

Inspect

- Turn ignition switch to "RUN" and verify that the "AIR BAG" warning lamp flashes seven times and then turns "OFF."

ELECTROSTATIC DISCHARGE (ESD)

NOTICE: When handling an electronic part that has an ESD-sensitive sticker, refer to GENERAL INFORMATION (SECTION 0A). Follow these guidelines to reduce any possible build-up of electrostatic charge:

- Do not open the package until time to install the part.
- Avoid touching electrical terminals of the part.
- Before removing the part from its package, ground the package to a known good ground on the vehicle.
- Always touch a known good ground before handling the part. This should be repeated while handling the part; do it more often after sliding across the seat, sitting down from a standing position, or walking a distance.

DATA LINK CONNECTOR (DLC)

The data link connector is under the instrument panel, to the right of the steering column. Refer to 8A-51-0 ELECTRICAL DIAGNOSIS (SECTION 8A).

Figure 3

Remove or Disconnect

1. Two bolts/screws holding data link connector.
2. Lower data link connector.

Install or Connect

1. Data link connector into position.
2. Two bolts/screws.

Tighten

- Bolts/screws to 2 N•m (18 lb. in.).

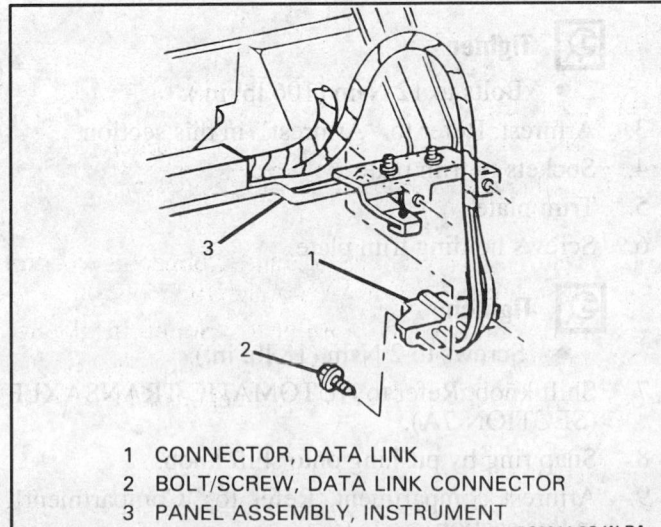

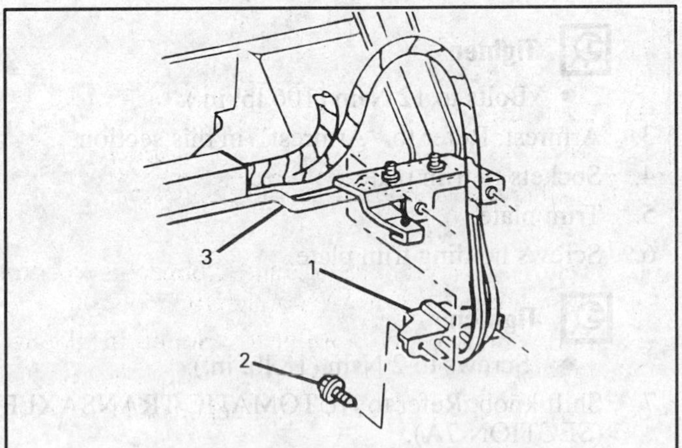
3
1
2
1 CONNECTOR, DATA LINK
2 BOLT/SCREW, DATA LINK CONNECTOR
3 PANEL ASSEMBLY, INSTRUMENT
PC0014-8C-W-RA

Figure 3 Data Link Connector

ASHTRAY

The front seat ashtray is on the bottom of the instrument panel, in the center. Slide the ashtray out to use it; push it in to close. To remove the ashtray, slide it out, push down the metal tab in the top center and slide it the rest of the way out. To put it back, slide it in, push down the metal tab, then push it closed.

Assembly Replacement

Remove or Disconnect

1. Ashtray.
2. Four bolts holding the ashtray slide bracket.
3. Bracket.
4. Electrical connector.

Install or Connect

1. Electrical connector.
2. Bracket.
3. Four bolts.
4. Ashtray.

CONSOLE

Figure 4

Armrest

Remove or Disconnect

1. Lift armrest.
2. Screws holding armrest to hinge.
3. Armrest.
4. Screws holding hinge to console, if replacing.

Install or Connect

1. Screws holding hinge to console, if removed.
2. Armrest.
3. Screws to armrest.
4. Lower armrest.

Rear Compartment

Remove or Disconnect

1. Raise armrest.
2. Screws.
3. Compartment.

Install or Connect

1. Compartment.
2. Screws.
3. Close armrest.

Front Compartment

To remove front compartment, lift it up and out.

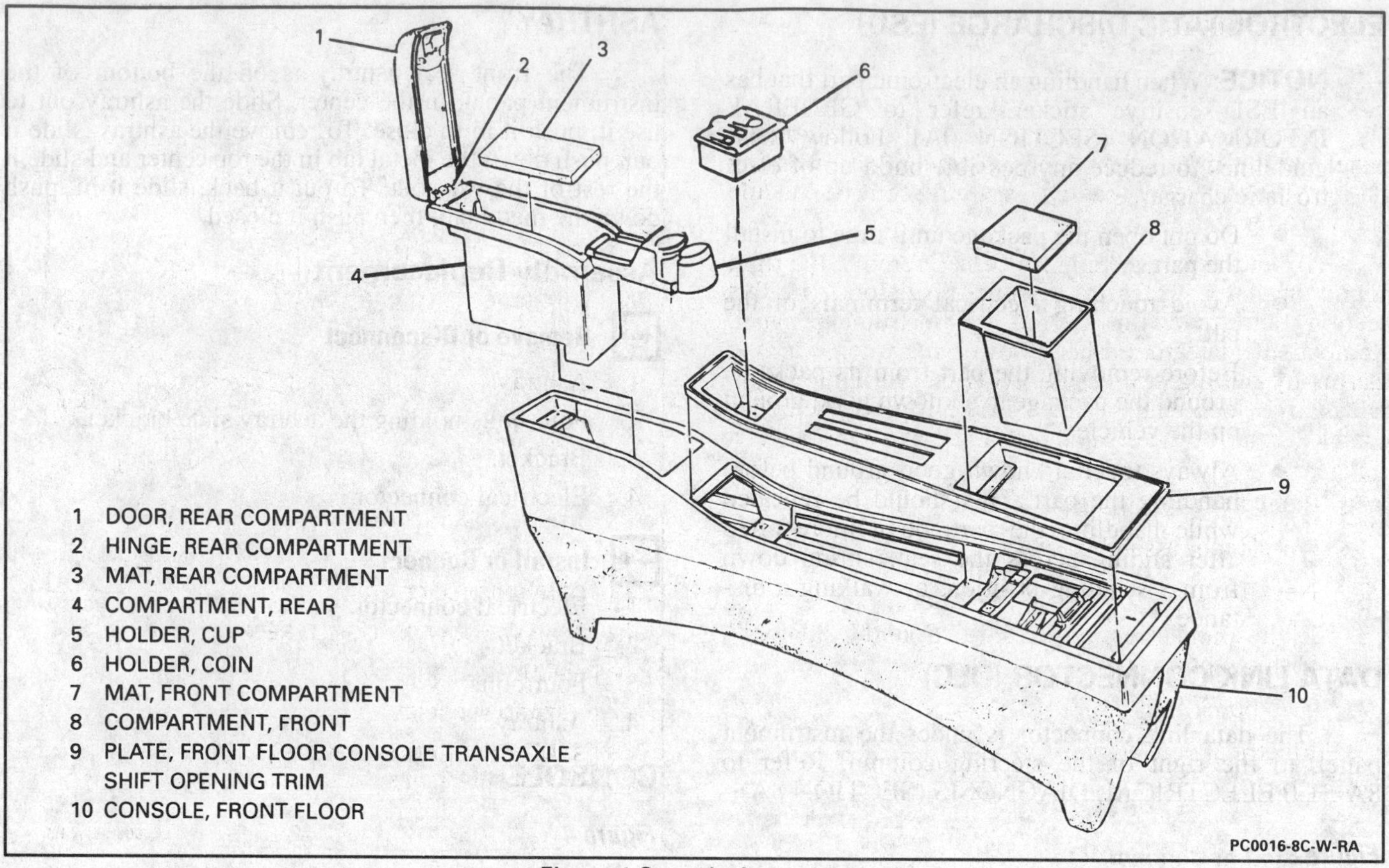
1
2
3
4
5
6
7
8
9
10
1 DOOR, REAR COMPARTMENT
2 HINGE, REAR COMPARTMENT
3 MAT, REAR COMPARTMENT
4 COMPARTMENT, REAR
5 HOLDER, CUP
6 HOLDER, COIN
7 MAT, FRONT COMPARTMENT
8 COMPARTMENT, FRONT
9 PLATE, FRONT FLOOR CONSOLE TRANSAXLE SHIFT OPENING TRIM
10 CONSOLE, FRONT FLOOR
PC0016-8C-W-RA

Figure 4 Console Assembly

Cup Holder

Remove or Disconnect

1. Open console.
2. Cup holder.

Install or Connect

1. Cup holder.
2. Close console.

Coin Holder

To remove coin holder, lift it up and out.

Console Assembly

Remove or Disconnect

1. Apply parking brake.
2. Shift transaxle to neutral.
3. Armrest compartment. Refer to "Compartment" in this section.
4. Snap ring holding shift knob by prying with a screwdriver.
5. Shift knob. Refer to AUTOMATIC TRANSAXLE (SECTION 7A).
6. Screws holding trim plate.
7. Trim plate.
8. Sockets from trim plate.
9. Armrest. Refer to "Armrest" in this section.
10. Four bolts.
11. Console.

Install or Connect

1. Console into position.
2. Four bolts.

Tighten

- Bolts to 12 N•m (106 lb. in.).

3. Armrest. Refer to "Armrest" in this section.
4. Sockets to trim plate.
5. Trim plate.
6. Screws holding trim plate.

Tighten

- Screws to 2 N•m (18 lb. in.).

7. Shift knob. Refer to AUTOMATIC TRANSAXLE (SECTION 7A).
8. Snap ring by pushing onto shift knob.
9. Armrest compartment. Refer to "Compartment" in this section.
10. Transaxle into park.

CONVENIENCE CENTER

Figure 5

The convenience center is behind the instrument panel, on the right side. It contains the hazard warning flasher, blower relay, passive restraint control module and warning alarms.

To reach the convenience center, remove the right sound insulator (refer to "Sound Insulators" in this section) and reach up behind the instrument panel. Remove the hazard flasher, blower relay, or warning alarms by pulling straight out. (On the warning alarm, release the locking tab first.) Lower the convenience center to remove the passive restraint control module.

Remove or Disconnect

1. Air cleaner assembly.
2. Negative battery cable.
3. Right sound insulator. Refer to "Sound Insulators" in this section.
4. Two bolts.
5. Electrical connectors.
6. Convenience center.

Install or Connect

1. Electrical connectors.
2. Convenience center into position.
3. Two bolts.

Tighten

- Bolts to 2 N•m (18 lb. in.).

4. Right sound insulator. Refer to "Sound Insulators" in this section.
5. Negative battery cable.
6. Air cleaner assembly.

WARNING ALARM

Seat Belt, Key, Lights, and Turn Signal Alarm

Remove or Disconnect

1. Convenience center. Refer to "Convenience Center" in this section.
2. Alarm, by lifting up on retaining tab and pulling out.

Install or Connect

1. Alarm to convenience center.
   - Make sure alarm is seated in retaining tab.
2. Convenience center. Refer to "Convenience Center" in this section.

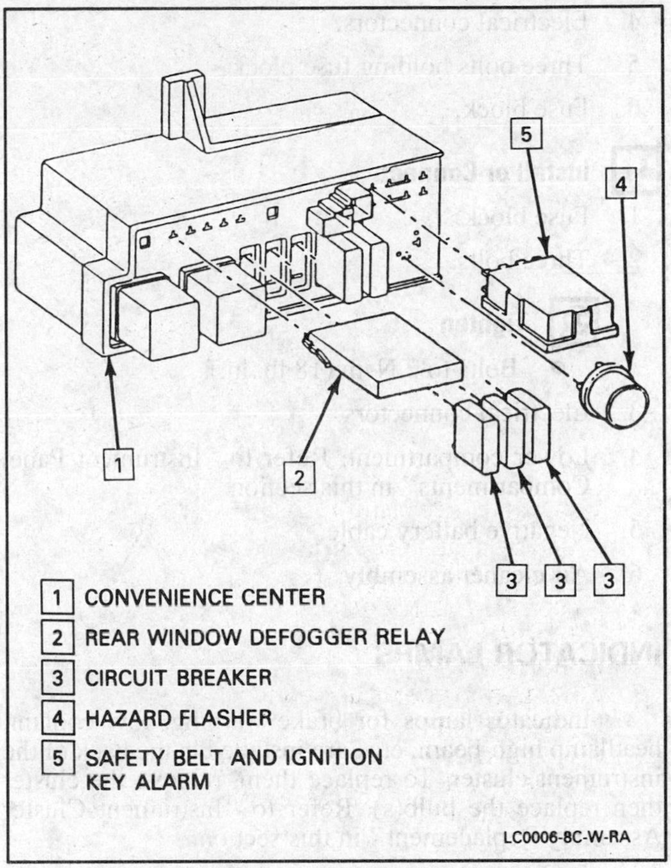
5
4
1
2
3
3
3
1 CONVENIENCE CENTER
2 REAR WINDOW DEFOGGER RELAY
3 CIRCUIT BREAKER
4 HAZARD FLASHER
5 SAFETY BELT AND IGNITION KEY ALARM
LC0006-8C-W-RA

Figure 5 Convenience Center Components

CRUISE CONTROL MODULE

For the removal and installation procedures of the Cruise Control Module, refer to CRUISE CONTROL (SECTION 9B).

EMBLEM

The Buick Regal emblem is on the right side of the instrument panel, above the lower compartment.

Remove or Disconnect

1. Gently pry up on edge of emblem with flat blade.
2. Lift out of locking snaps.

Install or Connect

1. Emblem to instrument panel.
2. Snap to secure.

FUSE BLOCK

The fuse block is inside the lower compartment. Refer to 8A-11-0 ELECTRICAL DIAGNOSIS (SECTION 8A).

Remove or Disconnect

1. Air cleaner assembly.
2. Negative battery cable.
3. Lower compartment. Refer to "Instrument Panel Compartments" in this section.

4. Electrical connectors.
5. Three bolts holding fuse block.
6. Fuse block.

Install or Connect

1. Fuse block.
2. Three bolts.

Tighten

- Bolts to 2 N•m (18 lb. in.).

3. Electrical connectors.
4. Lower compartment. Refer to "Instrument Panel Compartments" in this section.
5. Negative battery cable.
6. Air cleaner assembly.

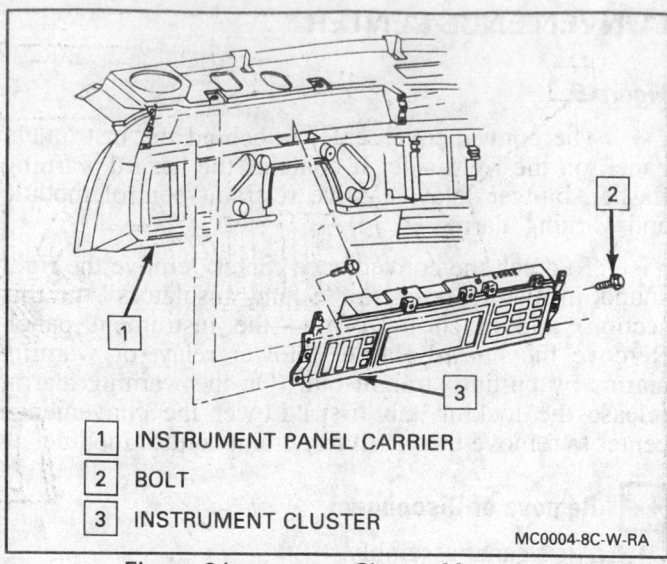

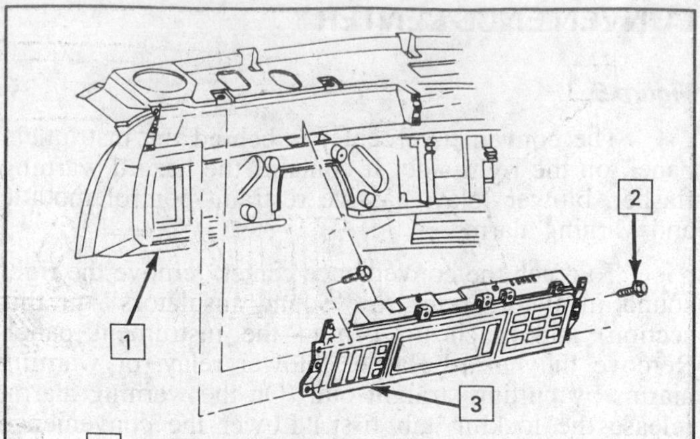
1 INSTRUMENT PANEL CARRIER
2 BOLT
3 INSTRUMENT CLUSTER
MC0004-8C-W-RA

Figure 6 Instrument Cluster Mounting

INDICATOR LAMPS

Indicator lamps for brake warning, low coolant, headlamp high-beam, etc., are installed in the back of the instrument cluster. To replace them, remove the cluster then replace the bulb(s). Refer to "Instrument Cluster Assembly Replacement" in this section.

For a list of indicator lamp bulbs. Refer to LIGHTING SYSTEMS AND HORNS (SECTION 8B).

INSTRUMENT CLUSTER

Figure 6

The instrument cluster contains all the displays, lights and indicators which provide normal operating information to the driver. Refer to 8A-80-0 or 8A-81-0 ELECTRICAL DIAGNOSIS (SECTION 8A).

INSTRUMENT CLUSTER TRIM PLATE

Figure 7

Remove or Disconnect

1. Instrument panel pad. Refer to "Instrument Panel Pad Cover" in this section.
2. One bolt holding trim plate (on left side).
3. Trim plate.

Install or Connect

1. Trim plate.
2. One bolt.

Tighten

- Bolts to 2 N•m (18 lb. in.).

3. Instrument panel pad. Refer to "Instrument Panel Pad Cover" in this section.

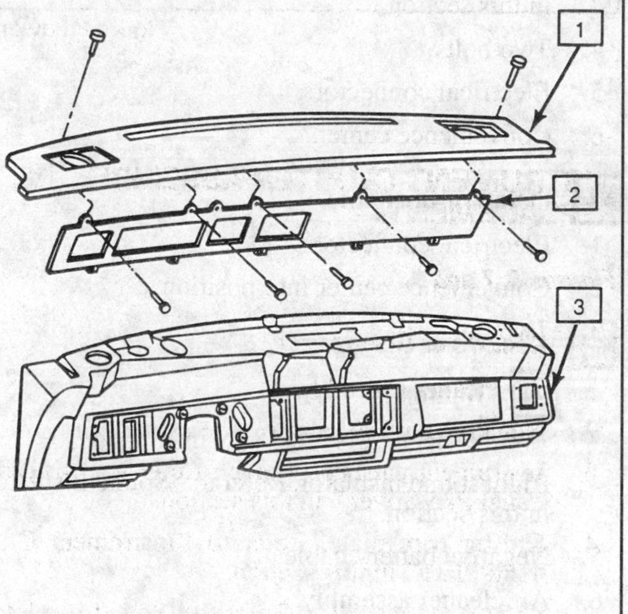
1 INSTRUMENT PANEL PAD
2 INSTRUMENT CLUSTER TRIM PLATE
3 INSTRUMENT PANEL CARRIER
RC4010-8C-W-RP

Figure 7 Instrument Panel Assembly and Cluster Trim Plate

INSTRUMENT PANEL TRIM PLATE

Figure 8

Remove or Disconnect

- Instrument panel trim plate by unsnapping.

Install or Connect

- Instrument panel trim plate by snapping into place.

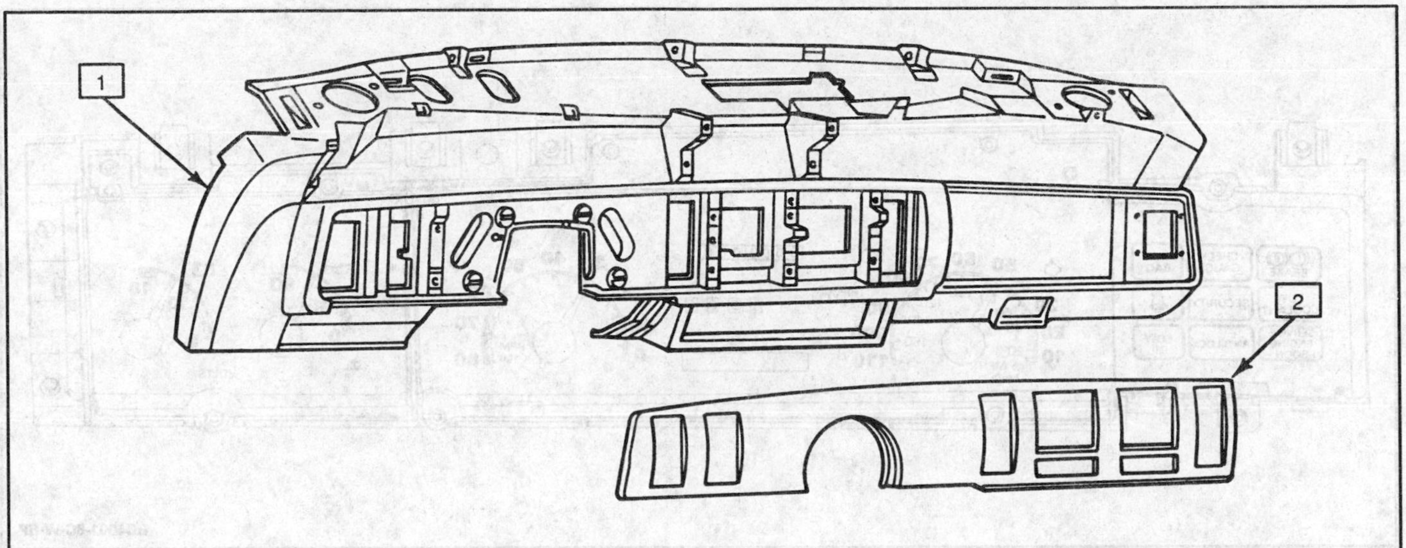
1
2
1 INSTRUMENT PANEL PAD ASSEMBLY
2 TRIM PLATE
RC4020-8C-W-RP

Figure 8 Lower Instrument Panel Trim Plate

INSTRUMENT CLUSTER ASSEMBLY REPLACEMENT

Figures 6, 7 and 9

Remove or Disconnect

1. Air cleaner assembly.
2. Negative battery cable.
3. Instrument panel pad cover. Refer to "Instrument Panel Pad Cover" in this section.
4. Cluster trim plate. Refer to "Instrument Cluster Trim Plate" in this section.
5. Left sound insulator. Refer to "Sound Insulators" in this section.
6. Steering column knee bolster trim panel. Refer to "Knee Bolster Trim Panel" in this section.
7. Shift control cable at bracket and lever.
8. Shift indicator cable.
9. Electrical connectors.
10. Bolts holding cluster.
11. Cluster.

Install or Connect

1. Cluster.
2. Six bolts.

Tighten

- Bolts to 2 N•m (18 lb. in.).

3. Electrical connector.
4. Shift indicator cable.
5. Shift control cable at bracket and lever.
6. Steering column knee bolster trim panel. Refer to "Knee Bolster Trim Panel" in this section.
7. Left sound insulator. Refer to "Sound Insulators" in this section.
8. Cluster trim plate. Refer to "Instrument Cluster Trim Plate" in this section.
9. Instrument panel pad cover. Refer to "Instrument Panel Pad Cover" in this section.
10. Negative battery cable.
11. Air cleaner assembly.

INSTRUMENT CLUSTER LENS

Remove or Disconnect

1. Instrument cluster. Refer to "Instrument Cluster Assembly Replacement" in this section.
2. Instrument cluster lens bolts/screws.
3. Instrument cluster lens.

Install or Connect

1. Instrument cluster lens.
2. Instrument cluster lens bolts/screws.

Tighten

- Bolts/screws to 1 N•m (9 lb. in.).

3. Instrument cluster. Refer to "Instrument Cluster Assembly Replacement" in this section.

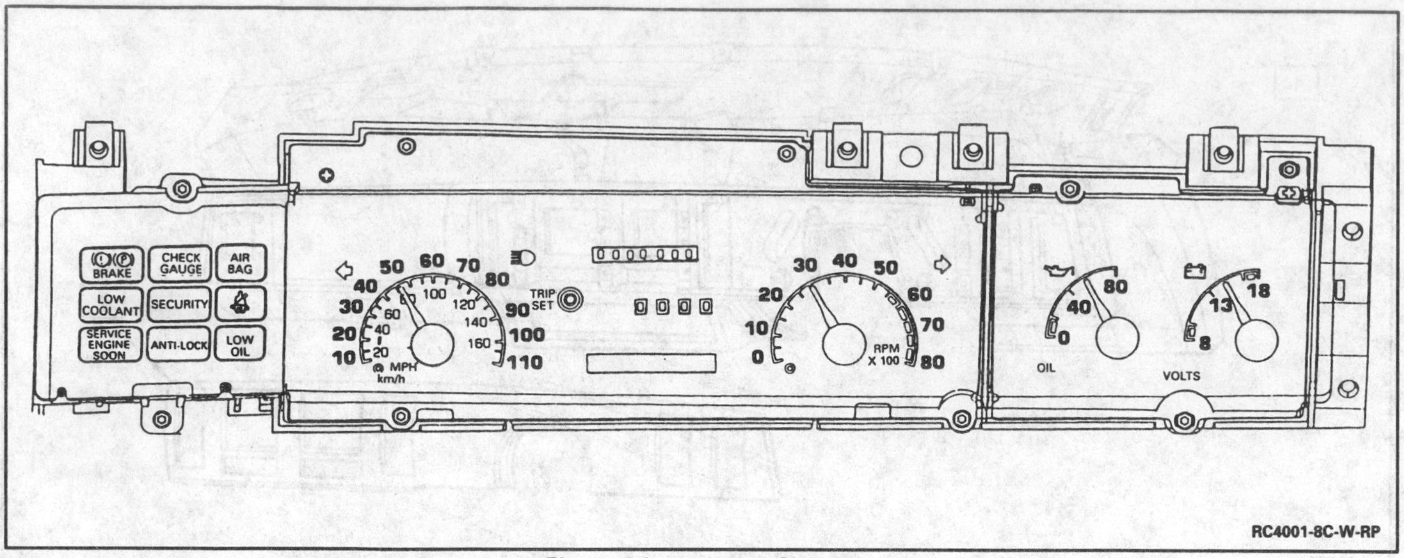
BRAKE
CHECK GAUGE
AIR BAG
LOW COOLANT
SECURITY
SERVICE ENGINE SOON
ANTI-LOCK
LOW OIL
10
20
30
40
50
60
70
80
90
100
110
20
40
60
100
120
140
160
MPH
km/h
TRIP SET
30 40 50
20
60
10
70
0
80
RPM X 100
40
80
0
OIL
13
18
8
VOLTS
RC4001-8C-W-RP
Figure 9 Instrument Cluster

OIL PRESSURE SENSOR OR SWITCH

For information on the oil pressure sensor or switch, refer to DRIVEABILITY AND EMISSIONS (SECTION 6E3-C2).

INSTRUMENT PANEL ASSEMBLY

The instrument panel contains the operating instruments used by the driver when operating the vehicle (speedometer, etc.), the ventilation and audio system controls, and convenience items such as the lower compartment and heating/air conditioning outlets. It is designed for easy removal of all switches and instruments. Trim covers are held in place by screws and clips.

INSTRUMENT PANEL PAD COVER

Figures 7, 10 and 11

Remove or Disconnect

1. Speaker grilles by prying carefully and disconnect Daytime Running Lamp Sensor connector (if equipped). Refer to LIGHTING SYSTEMS AND HORNS (SECTION 8B).
2. One screw under each speaker grille. Refer to "Speakers" in this section.
3. Five screws under lower edge of instrument panel pad.
4. Pad by lifting front, pulling rearward to release, then lifting up and out.

Install or Connect

1. Pad.
2. Five screws under lower edge.

Tighten

- Screws to 2 N•m (18 lb. in.).

3. One screw under speaker grille. Refer to "Speakers" in this section.
4. Daytime Running Lamp Sensor connector (if removed). Refer to LIGHTING SYSTEMS AND HORNS (SECTION 8B).
5. Speaker grille by pushing firmly into place. Refer to "Speakers" in this section.

INSTRUMENT PANEL ACCESSORY TRIM PLATE

Figures 10 and 11

Remove or Disconnect

- Gently pull out on plate evenly and gradually.

Install or Connect

- Snap plate into position.

INSTRUMENT PANEL CARRIER ASSEMBLY

Figures 10 and 11

Remove or Disconnect

1. Instrument panel pad cover. Refer to "Instrument Panel Pad Cover" in this section.
2. Speakers. Refer to "Speakers" in this section.
3. Instrument cluster. Refer to "Instrument Cluster" in this section.
4. Lower compartment. Refer to "Instrument Panel Compartment" in this section.
5. Right sound insulator. Refer to "Sound Insulators" in this section.
6. Ventilation system controls. Refer to "Ventilation System" in this section.
7. Audio system controls. Refer to "Audio System" in this section.

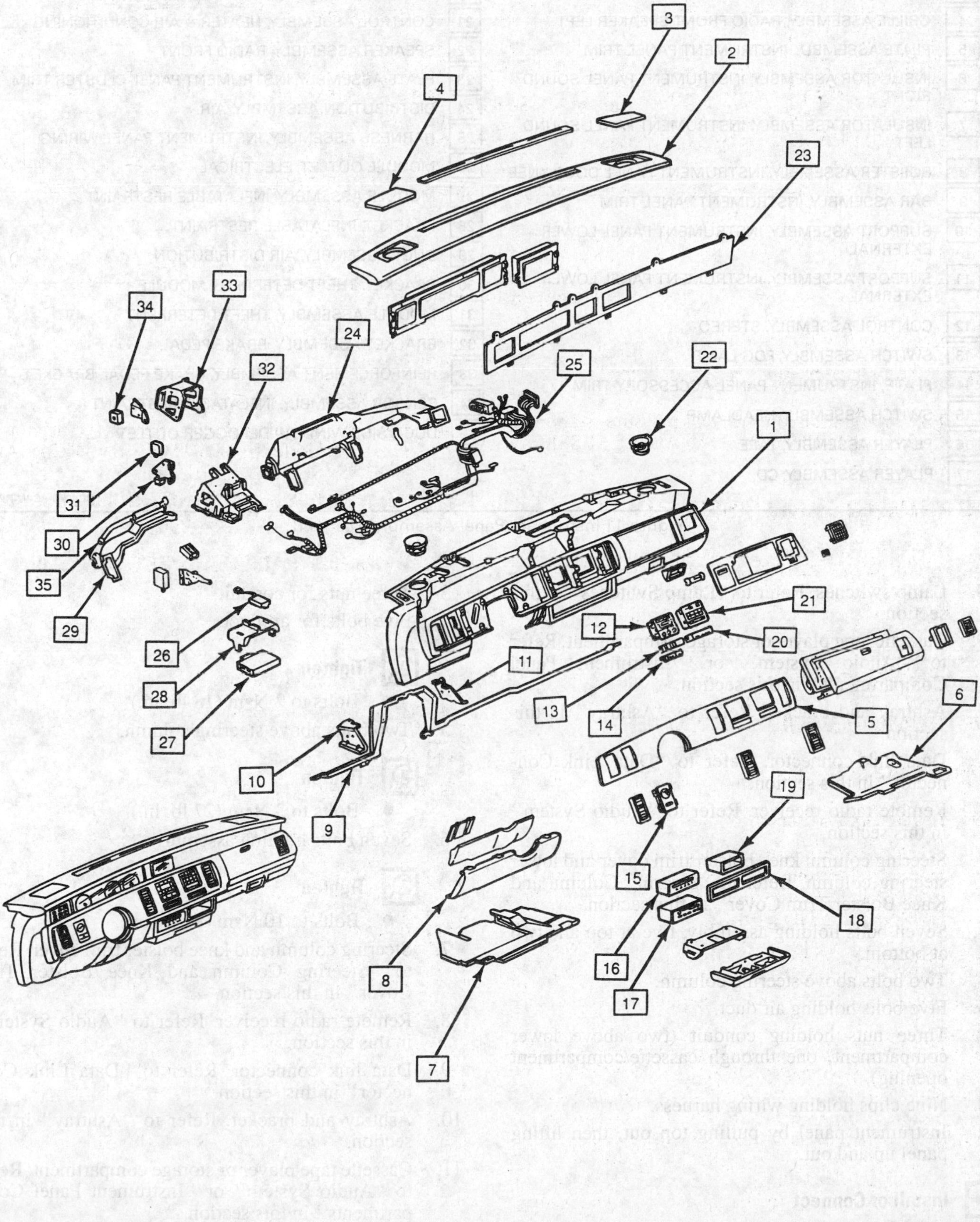
3
2
4
23
33
34
24
32
25
22
1
31
30
35
29
21
12
20
11
26
28
27
13
14
5
6
10
9
19
15
18
8
16
17
7

RC4030-8C-W-RP

Figure 10 Instrument Panel Assembly

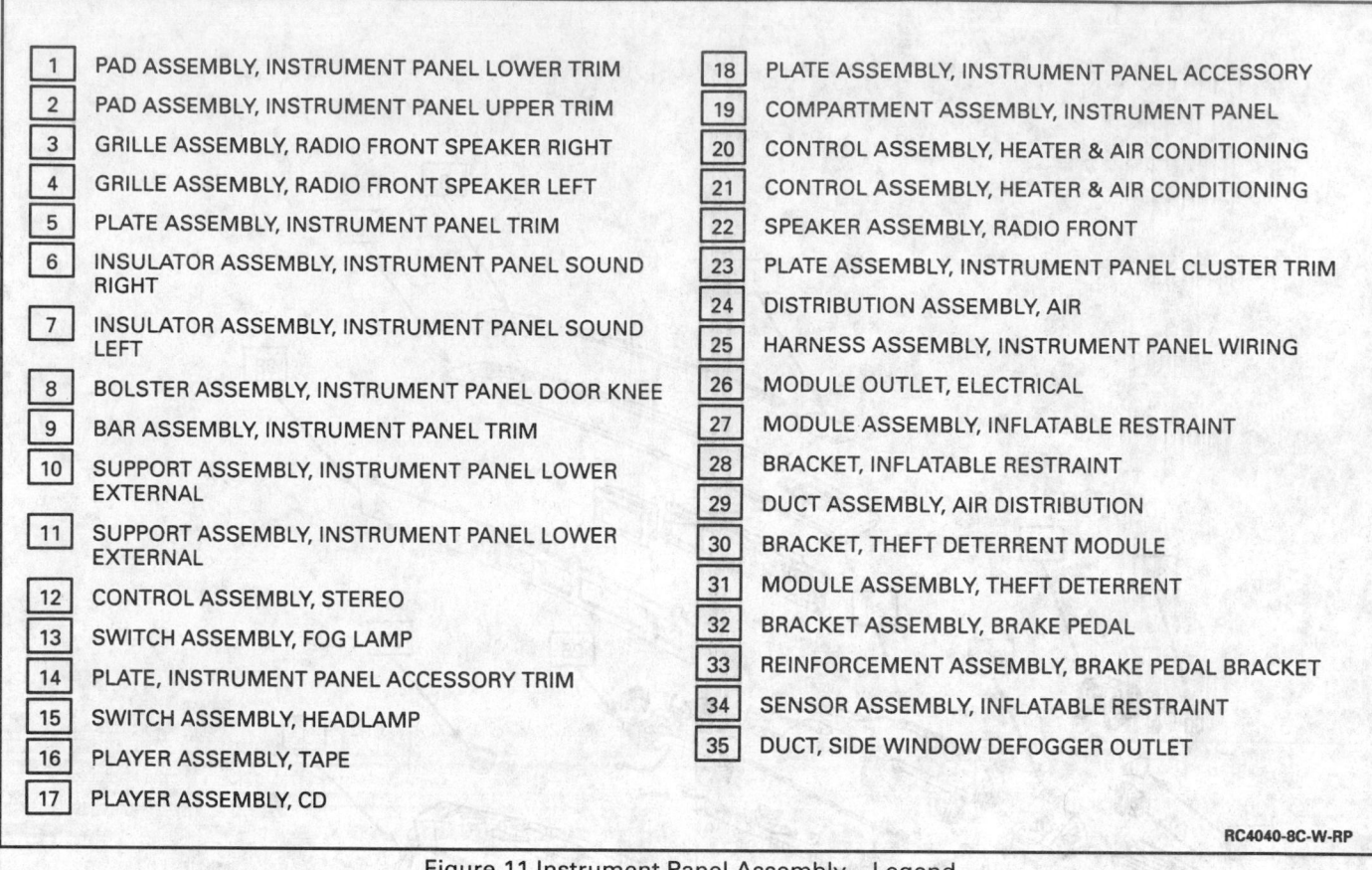

1	PAD ASSEMBLY, INSTRUMENT PANEL LOWER TRIM	18	PLATE ASSEMBLY, INSTRUMENT PANEL ACCESSORY
2	PAD ASSEMBLY, INSTRUMENT PANEL UPPER TRIM	19	COMPARTMENT ASSEMBLY, INSTRUMENT PANEL
3	GRILLE ASSEMBLY, RADIO FRONT SPEAKER RIGHT	20	CONTROL ASSEMBLY, HEATER & AIR CONDITIONING
4	GRILLE ASSEMBLY, RADIO FRONT SPEAKER LEFT	21	CONTROL ASSEMBLY, HEATER & AIR CONDITIONING
5	PLATE ASSEMBLY, INSTRUMENT PANEL TRIM	22	SPEAKER ASSEMBLY, RADIO FRONT
6	INSULATOR ASSEMBLY, INSTRUMENT PANEL SOUND RIGHT	23	PLATE ASSEMBLY, INSTRUMENT PANEL CLUSTER TRIM
7	INSULATOR ASSEMBLY, INSTRUMENT PANEL SOUND LEFT	24	DISTRIBUTION ASSEMBLY, AIR
8	BOLSTER ASSEMBLY, INSTRUMENT PANEL DOOR KNEE	25	HARNESS ASSEMBLY, INSTRUMENT PANEL WIRING
9	BAR ASSEMBLY, INSTRUMENT PANEL TRIM	26	MODULE OUTLET, ELECTRICAL
10	SUPPORT ASSEMBLY, INSTRUMENT PANEL LOWER EXTERNAL	27	MODULE ASSEMBLY, INFLATABLE RESTRAINT
11	SUPPORT ASSEMBLY, INSTRUMENT PANEL LOWER EXTERNAL	28	BRACKET, INFLATABLE RESTRAINT
12	CONTROL ASSEMBLY, STEREO	29	DUCT ASSEMBLY, AIR DISTRIBUTION
13	SWITCH ASSEMBLY, FOG LAMP	30	BRACKET, THEFT DETERRENT MODULE
14	PLATE, INSTRUMENT PANEL ACCESSORY TRIM	31	MODULE ASSEMBLY, THEFT DETERRENT
15	SWITCH ASSEMBLY, HEADLAMP	32	BRACKET ASSEMBLY, BRAKE PEDAL
16	PLAYER ASSEMBLY, TAPE	33	REINFORCEMENT ASSEMBLY, BRAKE PEDAL BRACKET
17	PLAYER ASSEMBLY, CD	34	SENSOR ASSEMBLY, INFLATABLE RESTRAINT
		35	DUCT, SIDE WINDOW DEFOGGER OUTLET

RC4040-8C-W-RP

Figure 11 Instrument Panel Assembly – Legend

8. Lamp switches. Refer to "Lamp Switches" in this section.
9. Cassette tape player or storage compartment. Refer to "Audio System" or "Instrument Panel Compartments" in this section.
10. Ashtray and bracket. Refer to "Ashtray" in this section.
11. Data link connector. Refer to "Data Link Connector" in this section.
12. Remote radio receiver. Refer to "Audio System" in this section.
13. Steering column knee bolster trim cover and lower steering column. Refer to "Steering Column and Knee Bolster Trim Cover" in this section.
14. Seven bolts holding assembly, five at top and two at bottom.
15. Two bolts above steering column.
16. Five bolts holding air duct.
17. Three nuts holding conduit (two above lower compartment, one through cassette/compartment opening).
18. Nine clips holding wiring harness.
19. Instrument panel by pulling top out, then lifting panel up and out.

Install or Connect

1. Instrument panel into position.
2. Nine clips for wiring harness.
3. Three nuts for conduit.
4. Five bolts for air duct.

Tighten

- Bolts to 2 N•m (18 lb. in.).

5. Two bolts above steering column.

Tighten

- Bolts to 3 N•m (27 lb. in.).

6. Seven bolts holding assembly.

Tighten

- Bolts to 10 N•m (89 lb. in.).

7. Steering column and knee bolster trim cover. Refer to "Steering Column and Knee Bolster Trim Cover" in this section.
8. Remote radio receiver. Refer to "Audio System" in this section.
9. Data link connector. Refer to "Data Link Connector" in this section.
10. Ashtray and bracket. Refer to "Ashtray" in this section.
11. Cassette tape player or storage compartment. Refer to "Audio System" or "Instrument Panel Compartments" in this section.
12. Lamp switches. Refer to "Lamp Switches" in this section.

13. Audio system controls. Refer to "Audio Systems" in this section.
14. Ventilation system controls. Refer to "Ventilation System" in this section.
15. Right sound insulator. Refer to "Sound Insulators" in this section.
16. Lower compartment. Refer to "Instrument Panel Compartment" in this section.
17. Instrument cluster. Refer to "Instrument Cluster" in this section.
18. Speakers. Refer to "Speakers" in this section.
19. Instrument panel pad cover. Refer to "Instrument Panel Pad Cover" in this cover.

INSTRUMENT PANEL COMPARTMENTS

Lower Compartment

The lower compartment is on the right side of the instrument panel. To open, lift the handle; to close, simply push it shut. The lower compartment door can be locked or unlocked using the oval-head key.

Air Deflector

An air deflector in the door covers the air outlet on the end of the instrument panel.

Remove or Disconnect

1. Open lower compartment.
2. Two screws holding air deflector.
3. Air deflector by pushing out from rear.

Install or Connect

1. Air deflector.
2. Two screws.
3. Close lower compartment.

Assembly Replacement

Remove or Disconnect

1. Open lower compartment door.
2. Gasket around air outlet.
3. Two screws behind gasket.
4. Open fuse block cover.
5. Two screws holding left side of lower compartment.
6. Lower compartment.
7. Electrical connector.

Install or Connect

1. Electrical connector.
2. Lower compartment.
3. Two screws at left.

Tighten

- Screws to 2 N•m (18 lb. in.).

4. Fuse block cover.
5. Two screws at right.
6. Gasket.
7. Close door.

Door Replacement

Remove or Disconnect

1. Lower compartment assembly. Refer to "Assembly Replacement" above.
2. Four bolts at hinge.
3. Screw and strap.
4. Door.

Install or Connect

1. Door.
2. Four bolts.
3. Strap and screw.
4. Lower compartment assembly. Refer to "Assembly Replacement" above.

Handle/Lock Replacement

Remove or Disconnect

1. Open lower compartment door.
2. Screws holding inner door panel.
3. Screw and strap.
4. Inner door panel.
5. Bolts holding the handle and lock assembly.
6. Assembly by pushing out from the rear.

Install or Connect

1. Assembly.
2. Three bolts.
3. Inner door panel.
4. Screws to inner panel.
5. Strap and screw.
6. Close door.

Hinge

Remove or Disconnect

1. Open lower compartment.
2. Screw and strap.
3. Screws holding inner door panel.
4. Inner door panel.
5. Bolts holding hinge to door.
6. Bolts holding hinge to instrument panel.
7. Hinge.

Install or Connect

1. Hinge.
2. Bolts to instrument panel.
3. Bolts to door.
4. Inner door panel.
5. Strap and screw.
6. Screws to panel.
7. Close lower compartment.

Center Compartment

On vehicles without a cassette player or compact disc player, there is a small storage compartment in the center bottom of the instrument panel.

Remove or Disconnect

1. Trim panel by prying carefully.
2. Four screws.
3. Compartment.

Install or Connect

1. Compartment.
2. Four screws.
3. Trim panel.

LAMP SWITCHES

The switches for the headlamps, parking lamps, and interior lamps are on the left side of the instrument cluster. The switch for the fog lamps is on the right side of the instrument cluster, below the radio. For operating information, as well as information on replacing inside and outside lamps, refer to LIGHTING SYSTEMS AND HORNS (SECTION 8B).

Headlamp

Figure 12

Remove or Disconnect

1. Instrument panel trim plate. Refer to "Instrument Panel Trim Plate" in this section.
2. Bolts holding switch assembly.
3. Electrical connector.
4. Switch assembly.

Install or Connect

1. Electrical connector.
2. Switch assembly.
3. Bolts to switch assembly.

Tighten

- Bolts to 1.5 N•m (13 lb. in.).

4. Instrument panel trim plate. Refer to "Instrument Panel Trim Plate" in this section.

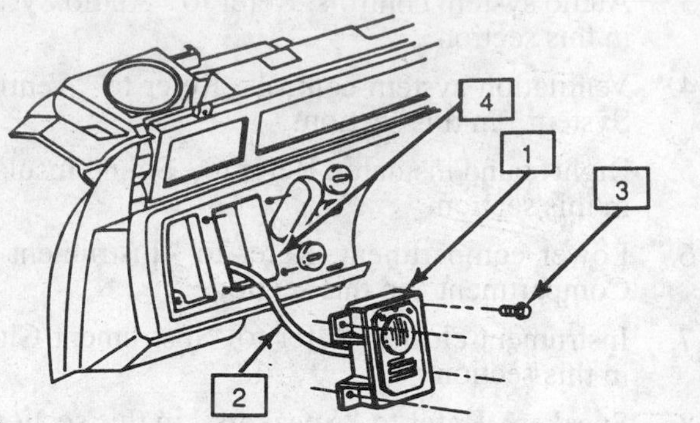
4
1
3
2

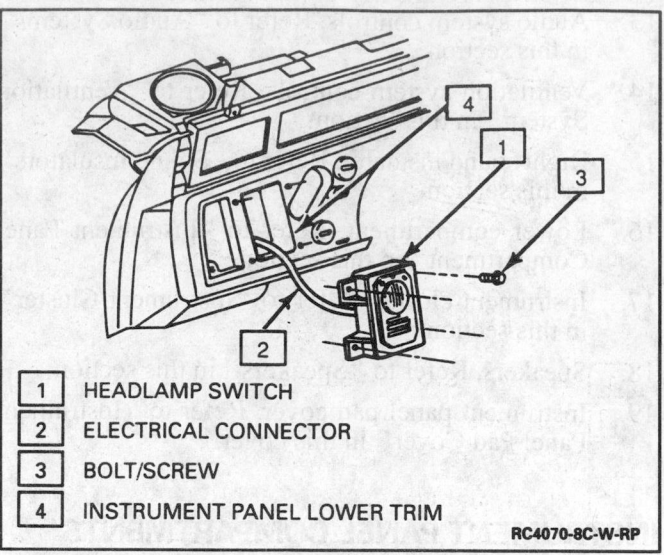

1 HEADLAMP SWITCH
2 ELECTRICAL CONNECTOR
3 BOLT/SCREW
4 INSTRUMENT PANEL LOWER TRIM

RC4070-8C-W-RP

Figure 12 Headlamp Switch

Foglamp Switch

Figure 13

Remove or Disconnect

1. Instrument panel trim plate. Refer to "Instrument Panel Trim Plate" in this section.
2. Bolts holding switch assembly.
3. Electrical connector.
4. Switch assembly.

Install or Connect

1. Switch assembly.
2. Electrical connector.
3. Bolts to switch assembly.

Tighten

- Bolts/screws to 1.5 N•m (13 lb. in.).

4. Instrument panel trim plate. Refer to "Instrument Panel Trim Plate" in this section.

LIGHTER

The lighter is part of the ashtray assembly. Refer to "Ashtray" in this section.

To use a cigarette lighter, push it in all the way. When it is heated enough to use, it will "snap" back to normal position with a slight sound. Do not hold the lighter in while it is heating.

If a lighter does not work, check the fuse. If the fuse is OK, check the element in the lighter. Replace the lighter if the element is burned out.

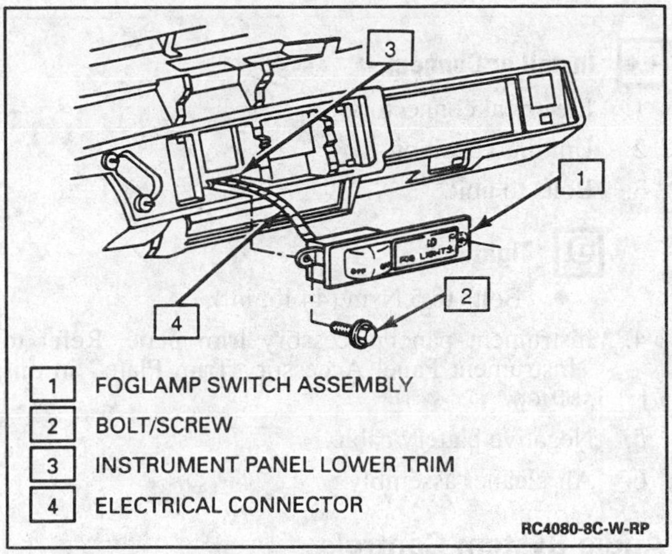
3
1
2
4
1 FOGLAMP SWITCH ASSEMBLY
2 BOLT/SCREW
3 INSTRUMENT PANEL LOWER TRIM
4 ELECTRICAL CONNECTOR
RC4080-8C-W-RP

Figure 13 Foglamp Switch

TURN SIGNAL FLASHER

The turn signal flasher is mounted in a clip next to the steering column. For more information, refer to LIGHTING SYSTEMS AND HORNS (SECTION 8B) and ELECTRICAL DIAGNOSIS (SECTION 8A).

Figure 14

Remove or Disconnect

1. Left sound insulator panel. Refer to "Sound Insulators" in this section.
2. Flasher from clip.
3. Electrical connector from flasher.

Install or Connect

1. Electrical connector to flasher.
2. Flasher to clip.
3. Left sound insulator. Refer to "Sound Insulators" in this section.

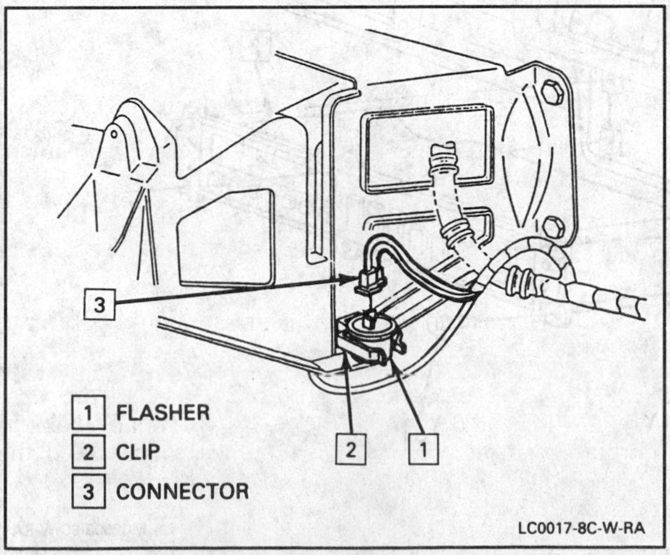
3
2
1
1 FLASHER
2 CLIP
3 CONNECTOR
LC0017-8C-W-RA

Figure 14 Turn Signal Flasher Installation

REAR COMPARTMENT LID RELEASE SWITCH

The rear compartment lid release switch is inside the lower compartment. With the ignition on, push the button to release the lid.

Remove or Disconnect

1. Air cleaner assembly.
2. Negative battery cable.
3. Open lower compartment.
4. Switch by prying carefully.
5. Electrical connector.

Install or Connect

1. Electrical connector.
2. Switch by pushing into place.
3. Close lower compartment.
4. Negative battery cable.
5. Air cleaner assembly.

SOUND INSULATORS

Sound insulators under the instrument panel help isolate the passenger compartment from noise.

Left Insulator

1. Nut near the cowl.
2. Retainers.
3. Insulator.

Install or Connect

1. Insulator.
2. Retainers.
3. Nut.

Right Insulator

Remove or Disconnect

1. Screw and retainer holding insulator.
2. Insulator by pushing toward front of vehicle, then pulling down.

Install or Connect

1. Insulator.
2. Screw and retainer.

Tighten

- Screw to 2 N•m (18 lb. in.).

AUDIO SYSTEM

The audio system controls are in the center of the instrument panel, to the right of the steering column. The radio receiver is mounted remotely, behind the right side of the instrument panel. The optional cassette player and compact disc player are below the audio system controls.

For operating information, refer to AUDIO SYSTEM (SECTION 9A).

Cassette Player/Equalizer Replacement

Figure 15

Remove or Disconnect

1. Air cleaner assembly.
2. Negative battery cable.
3. Instrument panel accessory trim plate. Refer to "Instrument Panel Accessory Trim Plate" in this section.
4. Bolts holding unit.
5. Pull unit ahead and remove electrical connectors.
6. Unit.

Important

- When installing unit, do not pinch wires or a short circuit to ground may happen and cause damage to the unit.

Install or Connect

1. Electrical connectors.
2. Unit into position.
3. Bolts to unit.

Tighten

- Bolts to 5 N•m (44 lb. in.).

4. Instrument panel accessory trim plate. Refer to "Instrument Panel Accessory Trim Plate" in this section.
5. Negative battery cable.
6. Air cleaner assembly.

Audio System Controls

Figure 16

1. Air cleaner assembly.
2. Negative battery cable.
3. Instrument panel accessory trim plate. Refer to "Instrument Panel Accessory Trim Plate" in this section.
4. Bolts holding audio system.
5. Audio system.
6. Electrical connectors.

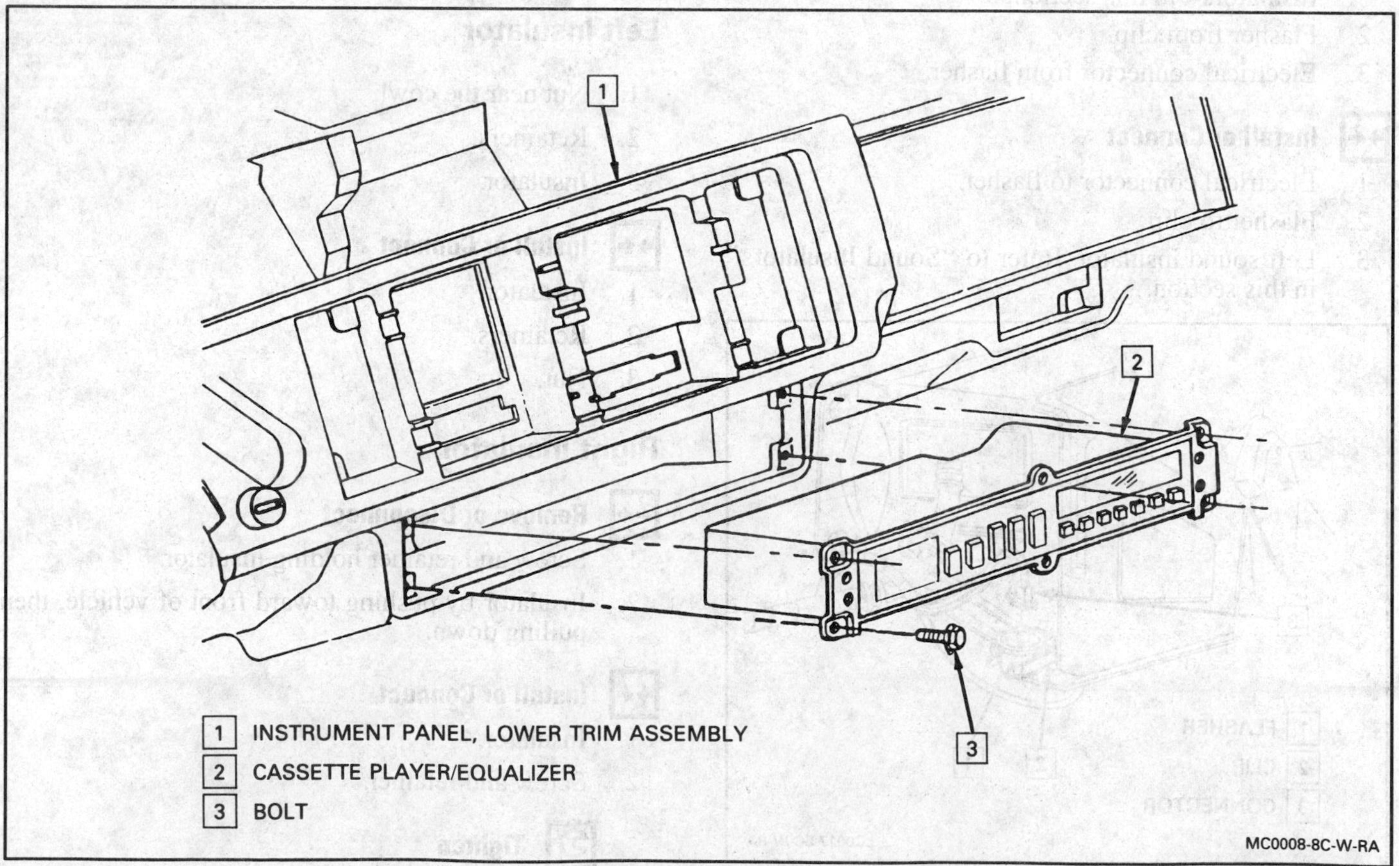
1
2
3
1 INSTRUMENT PANEL, LOWER TRIM ASSEMBLY
2 CASSETTE PLAYER/EQUALIZER
3 BOLT
MC0008-8C-W-RA

Figure 15 Cassette and Equalizer

Important

- When installing unit, do not pinch wires or a short circuit to ground may happen and cause damage to the unit.

Install or Connect

1. Electrical connectors.
2. Audio system.
3. Bolts to audio system.

Tighten

- Bolts to 2 N•m (18 lb. in.).

4. Instrument panel accessory trim plate. Refer to "Instrument Panel Accessory Trim Plate" in this section.
5. Negative battery cable.
6. Air cleaner assembly.

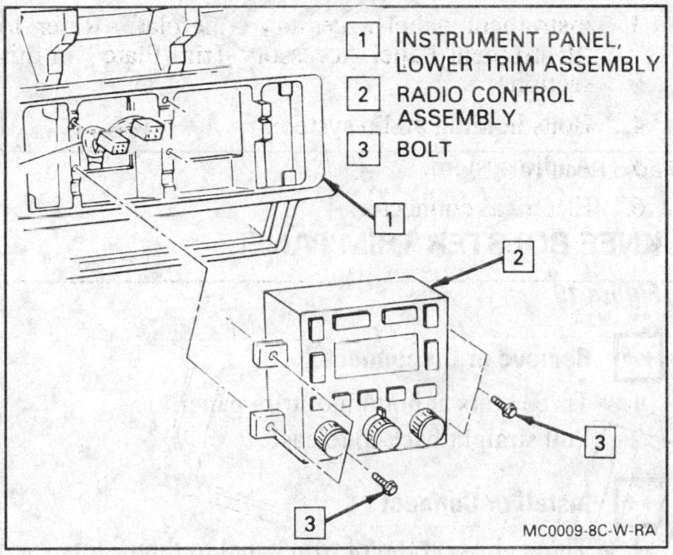
1 INSTRUMENT PANEL, LOWER TRIM ASSEMBLY
2 RADIO CONTROL ASSEMBLY
3 BOLT
1
2
3
3
MC0009-8C-W-RA
Figure 16 Audio System

Radio Receiver

Figure 17

Remove or Disconnect

1. Air cleaner assembly.
2. Negative battery cable.
3. Right sound insulator. Refer to "Sound Insulators" in this section.
4. Bolt holding courtesy lamp.
5. Courtesy lamp and connector.
6. Bolts holding receiver.
7. Receiver.
8. Electrical connectors.
9. Antenna connector.

Install or Connect

1. Antenna connector.
2. Electrical connectors.
3. Receiver.
4. Bolts.

Tighten

- Bolts to 3 N•m (27 lb. in.).

5. Courtesy lamp and connector.
6. Bolt to courtesy lamp.
7. Sound insulator. Refer to "Sound Insulators" in this section.
8. Negative battery cable.
9. Air cleaner assembly.

SPEAKERS

The front speakers are on the ends of the instrument panel, on top. All Delco audio systems have ungrounded speakers, installing add on components which use the vehicle speakers may damage the audio system.

The following procedure applies to both the left and right front speakers.

Speaker Replacement

Remove or Disconnect

1. Instrument panel pad cover. Refer to "Instrument Panel Pad Cover" in this section.
2. Bolts holding speaker.
3. Speaker.
4. Connectors.

Install or Connect

1. Connectors.
2. Speaker.
3. Bolts to speakers.

Tighten

- Bolts to 2 N•m (18 lb. in.).

4. Instrument panel pad cover. Refer to "Instrument Panel Pad Cover" in this section.

Speaker Cover Replacement

To remove a speaker cover, pry carefully to release it. Snap it back into place to reinstall.

STEERING COLUMN AND KNEE BOLSTER TRIM PANEL

For more information on the steering column. Refer to STEERING WHEEL AND COLUMN (SECTION 3F).

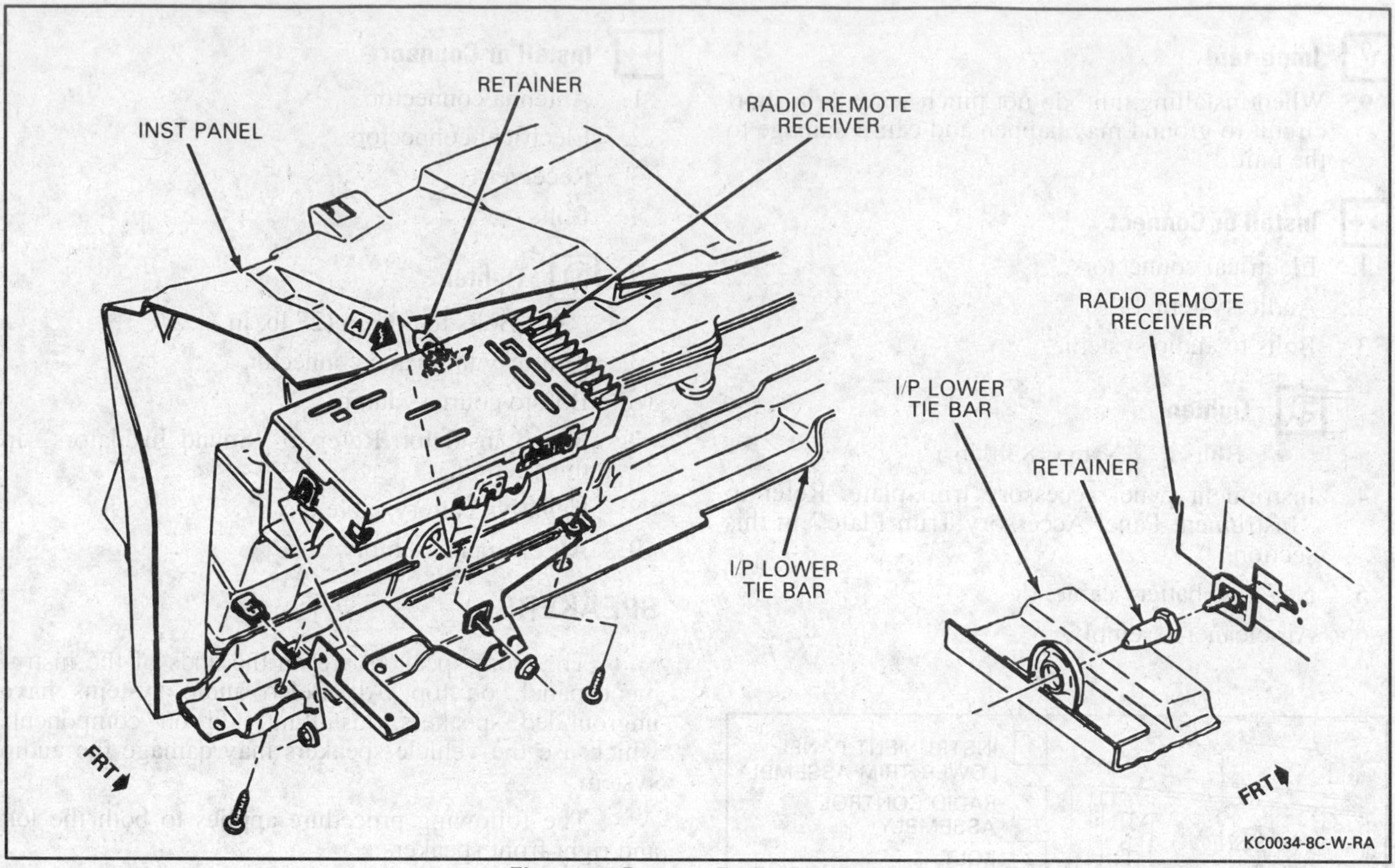
RETAINER
INST PANEL
RADIO REMOTE RECEIVER
RADIO REMOTE RECEIVER
I/P LOWER TIE BAR
RETAINER
I/P LOWER TIE BAR
FRT
FRT
KC0034-8C-W-RA

Figure 17 Remote Radio Receiver

Lower Steering Column

Figure 18

Remove or Disconnect

1. Left sound insulator. Refer to "Sound Insulators" in this section.
2. Steering column knee bolster trim panel. Refer to "Knee Bolster Trim Panel" in this section.
3. Two bolts at upper part of column.
4. Two bolts at bottom part of column.
5. Lower column.

Install or Connect

1. Raise column into position.
2. Two bolts at bottom.

Tighten

- Bolts to 24 N•m (18 lb. ft.).

3. Two bolts at top.

Tighten

- Bolts to 24 N•m (18 lb. ft.).

4. Knee bolster trim panel. Refer to "Knee Bolster Trim Panel" in this section.
5. Left sound insulator. Refer to "Sound Insulators" in this section.

KNEE BOLSTER TRIM PANEL

Figure 19

Remove or Disconnect

1. Three bolts at bottom of trim panel.
2. Pull straight back to release.

Install or Connect

1. Three clips on top of trim panel to three slots.
2. Three bolts at bottom of trim panel.

Tighten

- Bolts/screws to 2 N•m (18 lb. in.).

VENTILATION SYSTEM

Ventilation Controls

The ventilation system controls are in the center of the instrument panel, to the right of the audio system controls. For operating information, refer to GENERAL AIR CONDITIONING (SECTION 1B).

Remove or Disconnect

1. Instrument panel trim plate. Refer to "Instrument Panel Trim Plate" in this section.
2. Bolts.
3. Control assembly.
4. Connectors.

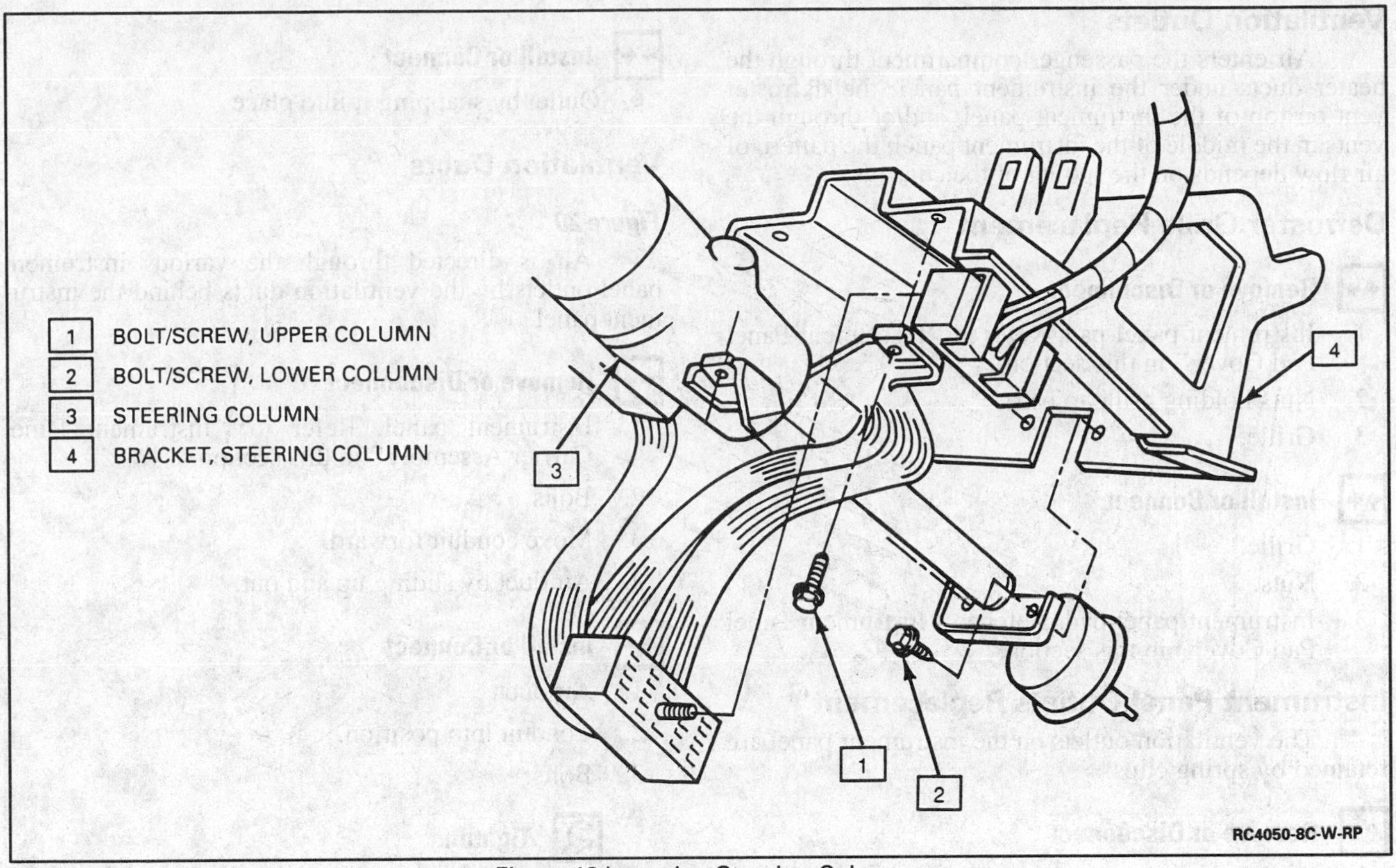
1 BOLT/SCREW, UPPER COLUMN
2 BOLT/SCREW, LOWER COLUMN
3 STEERING COLUMN
4 BRACKET, STEERING COLUMN
3
4
1
2
RC4050-8C-W-RP

Figure 18 Lowering Steering Column

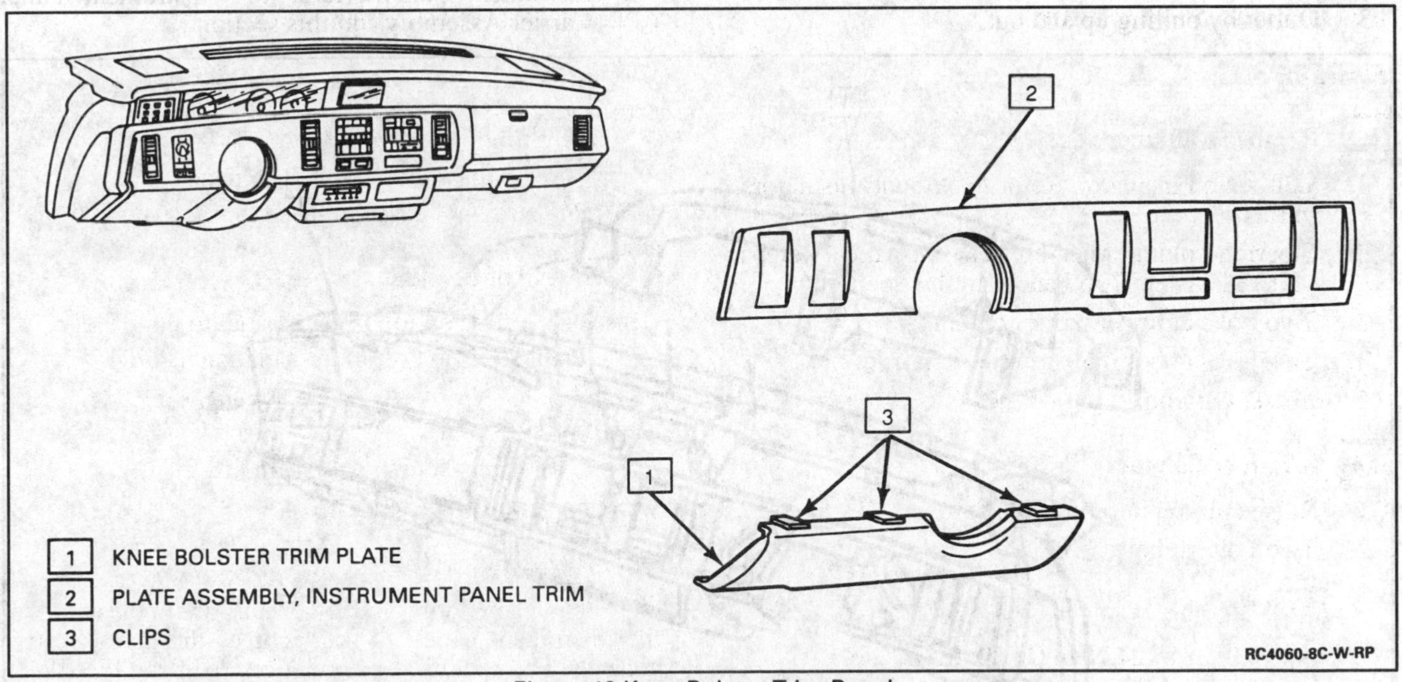
2
3
1
1 KNEE BOLSTER TRIM PLATE
2 PLATE ASSEMBLY, INSTRUMENT PANEL TRIM
3 CLIPS
RC4060-8C-W-RP

Figure 19 Knee Bolster Trim Panel

Install or Connect

1. Connectors.
2. Control assembly.
3. Bolts.

Tighten

- Bolts to 2 N•m (18 lb. in.).

4. Instrument panel trim plate. Refer to "Instrument Panel Trim Panel" in this section.

Ventilation Outlets

Air enters the passenger compartment through the heater ducts under the instrument panel, the defroster vent on top of the instrument panel, and/or through the vents in the middle of the instrument panel; the pattern of air flow depends on the setting of the controls.

Defroster Grille Replacement

Remove or Disconnect

1. Instrument panel pad. Refer to "Instrument Panel Pad Cover" in this section.
2. Nuts holding grille to pad.
3. Grille.

Install or Connect

1. Grille.
2. Nuts.
3. Instrument panel pad. Refer to "Instrument Panel Pad Cover" in this section.

Instrument Panel Outlets Replacement

The ventilation outlets on the instrument panel are retained by spring clips.

Remove or Disconnect

1. Straighten outlet so it faces directly into the vehicle.
2. Pry carefully at the top of the outlet, to pop it out.
3. Outlet by pulling up and out.

Install or Connect

- Outlet by snapping it into place.

Ventilation Ducts

Figure 20

Air is directed through the various instrument panel outlets by the ventilation ducts behind the instrument panel.

Remove or Disconnect

1. Instrument panel. Refer to "Instrument Panel Carrier Assembly" in this section.
2. Bolts.
3. Move conduit forward.
4. Air duct by sliding up and out.

Install or Connect

1. Air duct.
2. Conduit into position.
3. Bolts.

Tighten

- Bolts to 2 N•m (18 lb. in.).

4. Instrument panel. Refer to "Instrument Panel Carrier Assembly" in this section.

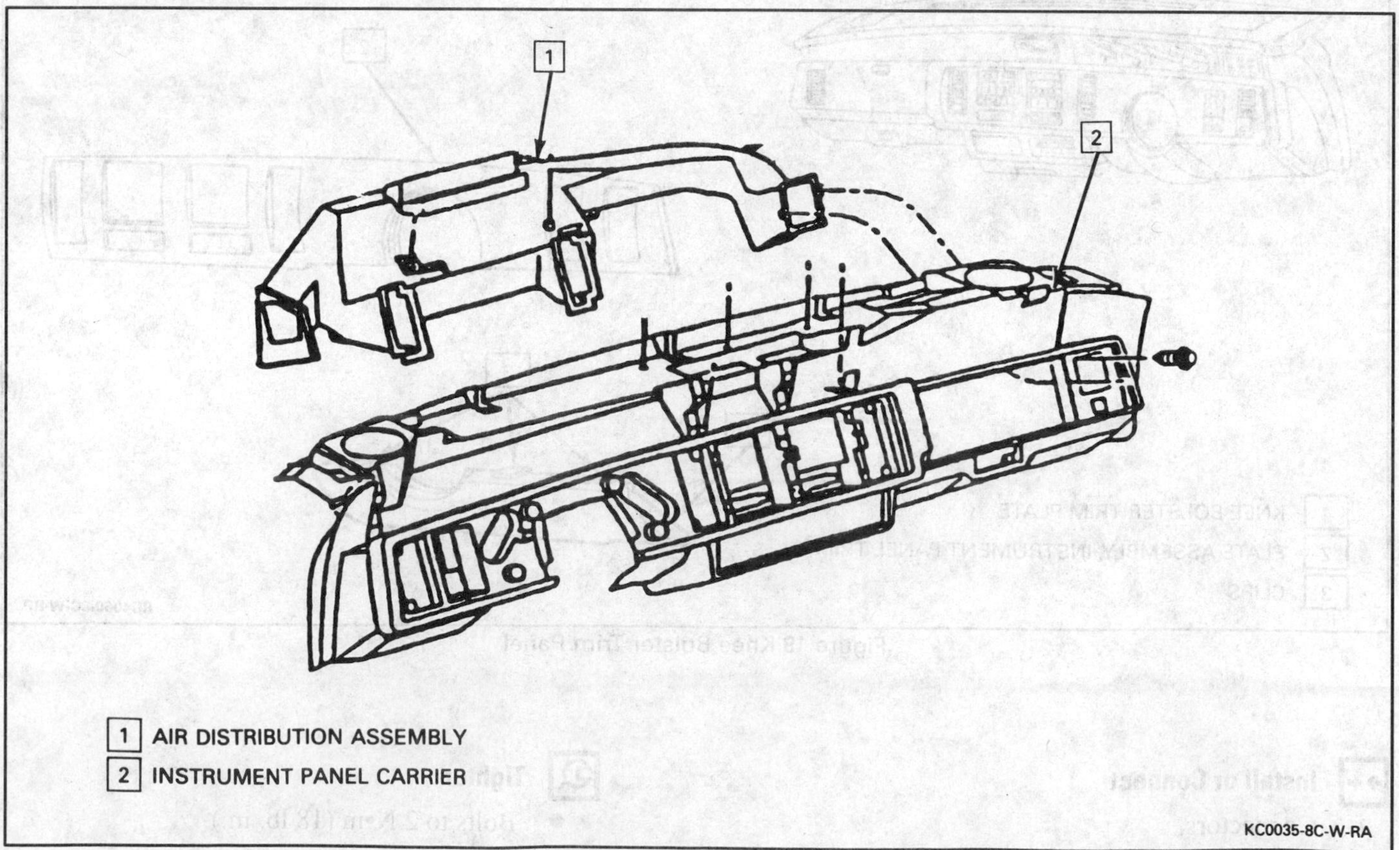
1
2
1 AIR DISTRIBUTION ASSEMBLY
2 INSTRUMENT PANEL CARRIER
KC0035-8C-W-RA

Figure 20 Ventilation Ducts

SPECIFICATIONS

FASTENER TIGHTENING SPECIFICATIONS

Audio System Bolt	2 N•m (18 lb. in.)
Cassette Player/Equalizer Bolt	5 N•m (44 lb. in.)
Cluster Trim Plate Bolt	2 N•m (18 lb. in.)
Cluster Bolt	2 N•m (18 lb. in.)
Cluster Lens Bolt/Screw	1 N•m (9 lb. in.)
Console Bolt	12 N•m (106 lb. in.)
Console Trim Plate Screw	2 N•m (18 lb. in.)
Convenience Center Bolt	2 N•m (18 lb. in.)
Data Link Connector Bolt/Screw	2 N•m (18 lb. in.)
Foglamp Switch Screw	1.5 N•m (13 lb. in.)
Fuse Block Bolt	2 N•m (18 lb. in.)
Headlamp Switch Screw	1.5 N•m (13 lb. in.)
Instrument Panel Bolt	10 N•m (89 lb. in.)
Instrument Panel Pad Screw	2 N•m (18 lb. in.)
Lower Compartment Screw	2 N•m (18 lb. in.)
Radio Receiver Bolt	3 N•m (27 lb. in.)
Sound Insulator Screw	2 N•m (18 lb. in.)
Speaker Bolt	2 N•m (18 lb. in.)
Steering Column Bolt	24 N•m (18 lb. ft.)
Steering Column Trim Panel Screw	2 N•m (18 lb. in.)
Ventilation Controls Bolt	2 N•m (18 lb. in.)
Ventilation Duct Bolt	2 N•m (18 lb. in.)

SECTION 8E

WINDSHIELD WIPER/WASHER SYSTEM (PULSE)

NOTICE: Refer to battery disconnect caution in Section 0A.

NOTICE: When fasteners are removed, always reinstall them at the same location from which they were removed. If a fastener needs to be replaced, use the correct part number fastener for that application. If the correct part number fastener is not available, a fastener of equal size and strength (or stronger) may be used. The correct torque value must be used when installing fasteners that require it. If the above conditions are not followed, parts or system damage could result.

CONTENTS

GENERAL DESCRIPTION

A modular depressed park, non-articulating arm wiper/washer system is used on this vehicle. The system produces a symmetrical overlapping wipe pattern. 20-inch wiper blade assemblies are used. The wiper/washer switch assembly, washer pump and washer solvent container also are components of the system.

The wiper drive system is installed in the vehicle as a module (see Figure 1) that includes the wiper motor and transmission assemblies attached to a carrier plate, which is attached to the cowl panel by six screws. The module must be removed from the vehicle as a unit for component bench service.

A centrally located bell crank has been added to the conventional symmetrical overlap system to maintain wiper blade separation in the wipe mode.

The wiper/washer system is a pulse (delay) type. Pulse timing and demand wash functions are controlled electronically.

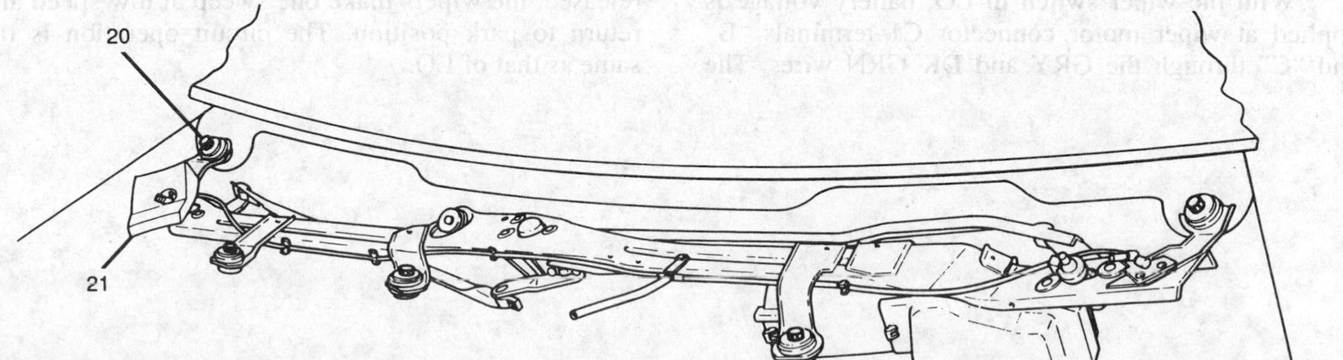
20
21

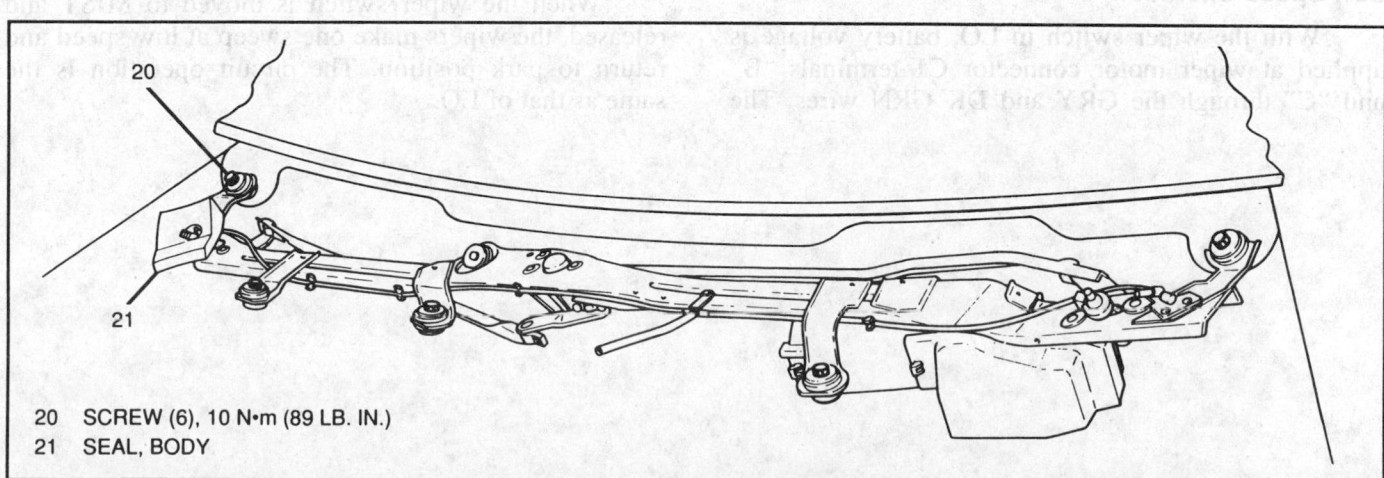

20 SCREW (6), 10 N•m (89 LB. IN.)
21 SEAL, BODY

Figure 1 – Wiper Drive System Module

CIRCUIT OPERATION

Figure 2

In addition to the features of a conventional (non-pulse) wiper system (low and high speeds), the pulse type windshield wiper/washer system includes an operating mode in which the wipers make single sweeps with an adjustable time interval between sweeps. The time interval is controlled by a solid state timer in the wiper motor assembly. The duration of the delay interval is determined by the delay rheostat in the wiper/washer switch assembly.

The wiper motor is protected by a circuit breaker. If the wipers are blocked (by snow or ice, for example) the circuit breaker will open the circuit. The circuit breaker resets automatically when it cools.

Pulse Operation

With the wiper switch in DELAY (pulse), battery voltage is applied to the wiper motor at terminal "B" of connector C1 through the GRY wire. Voltage also is applied to terminal "F" through the PNK wire and the pulse delay resistor in the wiper/washer switch assembly. The battery voltage at terminal "B" energizes the park switch coil, which closes its contacts. In response to the voltage at terminal "F", the solid state timer momentarily closes contact "A" in wiper motor cover assembly which applies battery voltage at terminal "B" to the contacts of the park switch, starting the wiper motor.

A mechanical arm (end of sweep input) operates contacts in the cover assembly, which causes contact "A" to open when the wipers have completed their sweep. Since the park switch coil remains energized, the wipers do not park but remain just above the park position until the cover assembly closes contact "A" again to start another sweep.

The length of delay time between sweeps is controlled by the variable pulse delay resistor. The delay is adjustable from 0 to 25 seconds.

Low Speed Operation

With the wiper switch in LO, battery voltage is applied at wiper motor connector C1 terminals "B" and "C" through the GRY and DK GRN wires. The park switch coil is again energized and battery voltage is applied to the park switch contacts and the wiper motor, which runs continuously.

High Speed Operation

With the wiper switch in the HI position, battery voltage is applied directly to wiper motor terminal "A" of connector C2 without passing through the park switch contacts. Terminal "A" is connected to a separate wiper motor brush for high speed operation. The park switch coil remains energized in the HI position because of the voltage present at the low speed wiper motor brush when voltage is applied to the high speed brush. The current path from the low speed brush to the park switch coil is completed through the wiper/washer switch assembly. An open in this circuit will cause the wipers to cycle in and out of park position in HI and possibly prevent LO speed operation.

When turned off from HI, the wipers complete the last sweep at low speed and park. To do this, the wiper motor receives voltage in the OFF position of the wiper switch, which is applied through the DK GRN wire to terminal "C" of connector C1. The park switch is de-energized when the wiper switch is moved to OFF, but the contacts remain closed until the wipers reach park position.

Washer Operation

When the washer switch is held ON, battery voltage is applied to the wiper motor cover assembly through the PNK and GRY wires. The park switch is energized by the battery voltage at terminal "B" of connector C1. Cover assembly circuitry turns on the washer pump and wiper motor by closing contacts "A" and "B". The cover assembly circuitry turns the wiper motor off approximately six seconds after it interrupts power to the washer pump. If the wipers had been in DELAY, LO, or HI, they will return to that operation after the wash cycle.

Mist Operation

When the wiper switch is moved to MIST and released, the wipers make one sweep at low speed and return to park position. The circuit operation is the same as that of LO.

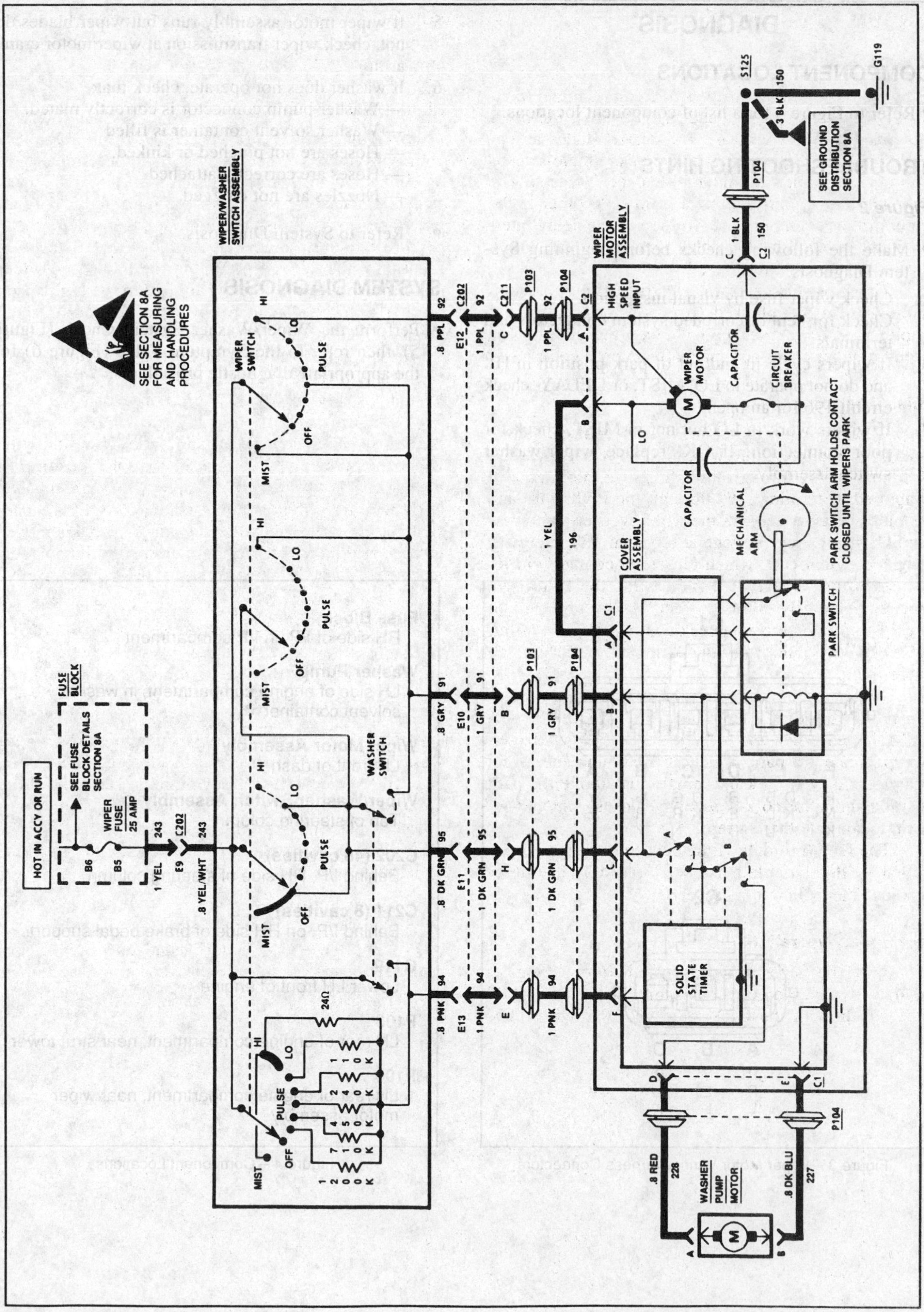
HOT IN ACCY OR RUN
FUSE BLOCK
SEE FUSE BLOCK DETAILS SECTION 8A
WIPER FUSE 25 AMP
SEE SECTION 8A FOR MEASURING AND HANDLING PROCEDURES
WIPER/WASHER SWITCH ASSEMBLY
WIPER SWITCH
WASHER SWITCH
MIST
OFF
PULSE
LO
HI
24Ω
C202
C211
P103
P104
E9
E10
E11
E12
E13
1 YEL
.8 YEL/WHT
243
.8 PNK
1 PNK
94
.8 DK GRN
1 DK GRN
95
.8 GRY
1 GRY
91
.8 PPL
1 PPL
92
196
WIPER MOTOR ASSEMBLY
HIGH SPEED INPUT
WIPER MOTOR
CAPACITOR
CIRCUIT BREAKER
MECHANICAL ARM
PARK SWITCH ARM HOLDS CONTACT CLOSED UNTIL WIPERS PARK
COVER ASSEMBLY
PARK SWITCH
SOLID STATE TIMER
1 BLK
150
3 BLK
S125
G119
SEE GROUND DISTRIBUTION SECTION 8A
WASHER PUMP MOTOR
.8 RED
228
.8 DK BLU
227

Figure 2 – Wiper/Washer System Electrical Schematic

DIAGNOSIS

COMPONENT LOCATIONS

- Refer to Figure 4 for a list of component locations.

TROUBLESHOOTING HINTS

Figure 2

- Make the following checks before beginning System Diagnosis.

1. Check wiper fuse by visual inspection.
2. Check for bent or corroded system connectors and terminals.
3. If wipers cycle in and out of park position in HI, and do not operate in LO, MIST, or DELAY, check circuit 196 for an open.
4. If wipers work in LO but not in MIST, check for poor connection. If OK, replace wiper/washer switch assembly.
5. If wiper motor assembly runs but wiper blades do not, check wiper transmission at wiper motor crank arm.
6. If washer does not operate, check that:
   — Washer pump connector is correctly mated.
   — Washer solvent container is filled.
   — Hoses are not pinched or kinked.
   — Hoses are correctly attached.
   — Nozzles are not clogged.

- Refer to System Diagnosis.

SYSTEM DIAGNOSIS

- Perform the Wiper/Washer System Check (Figure 5), then refer to the Symptom Table (Figure 6) for the appropriate diagnostic procedures.

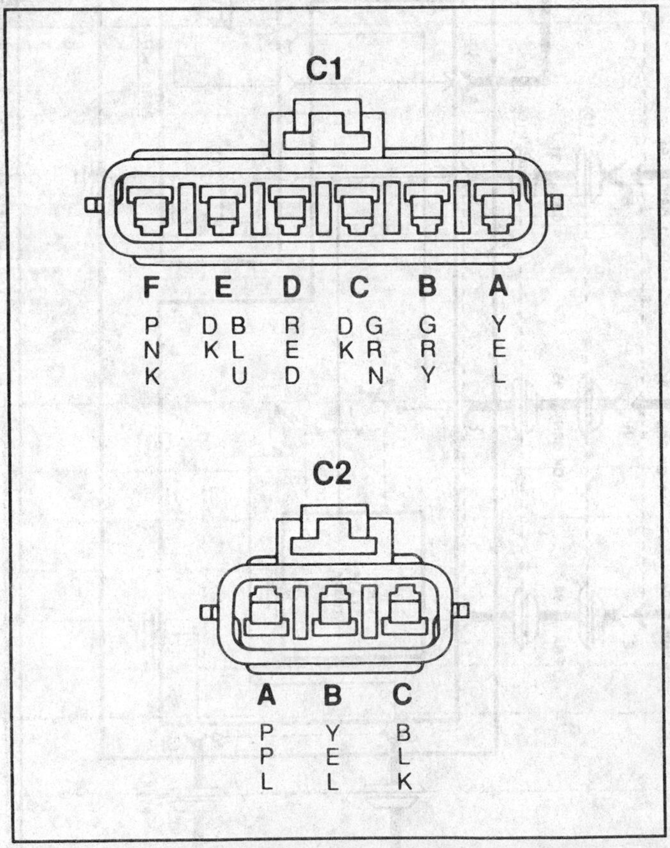
C1
F E D C B A
PNK DK BLU RED DK GRN GRY YEL
C2
A B C
PPL YEL BLK

Figure 3 – Wiper Motor Wiring Harness Connectors

Fuse Block
RH side of I/P, in I/P compartment

Washer Pump
LH side of engine compartment, in washer solvent container

Wiper Motor Assembly
LH front of dash

Wiper/Washer Switch Assembly
Top of steering column

C202 (48 cavities)
Behind I/P, RH side of steering column

C211 (8 cavities)
Behind I/P, on RH side of brake pedal support

G119
Lower LH front of engine

P103
LH rear of engine compartment, near strut tower

P104
LH rear of engine compartment, near wiper motor assembly

Figure 4 – Component Locations

ACTION	NORMAL OPERATION
[1] • Ignition switch in ACCY or RUN. • Hold washer switch ON for 1 to 2 seconds.	Washer sprays windshield until switch is released. Wipers run at low speed and continue to run for approximately 6 seconds after wash cycle is complete, then return to park position.
[2] • Turn wiper switch to DELAY (pulse mode). • Activate delay time by turning wiper switch through delay range.	Wipers make one complete sweep, then pause for 0 to 25 seconds before making next sweep.
[3] • Wiper switch in DELAY. • Push wiper switch ON for 1 to 2 seconds.	Washer sprays as long as washer switch is held ON. Wipers run at low speed during spray period and continue for approximately 6 seconds after wash cycle. Wipers return to pulse operation.
[4] • Turn wiper switch to LO.	Wipers run continuously at low speed.
[5] • Turn wiper switch to HI.	Wipers run continuously at high speed.
[6] • Turn wiper switch to OFF.	Wipers return to park position at low speed.
[7] • Turn wiper switch to MIST and release.	Wipers make one complete sweep at low speed and park.

Figure 5 – Wiper/Washer System Check

SYMPTOM	PROCEDURE	PAGE
Wipers do not operate in any mode.	Chart 1	8E-6
Wipers run at high speed only (low speed inoperative).	Chart 2	8E-7
Wipers run at low speed only (high speed inoperative).	Chart 3	8E-7
Wipers run intermittently in low or high speed settings.	Chart 4	8E-8
Wipers will not turn off.	Chart 5	8E-8
Wipers cycle in and out of park position after wipers are shut off.	Chart 6	8E-9
Pulse delay operates incorrectly or not at all.	Chart 7	8E-9
Washer will not operate.	Chart 8	8E-10
Washer will not shut off.	Chart 9	8E-10

Figure 6 – Symptom Table

CHART 1
WIPERS DO NOT OPERATE IN ANY MODE

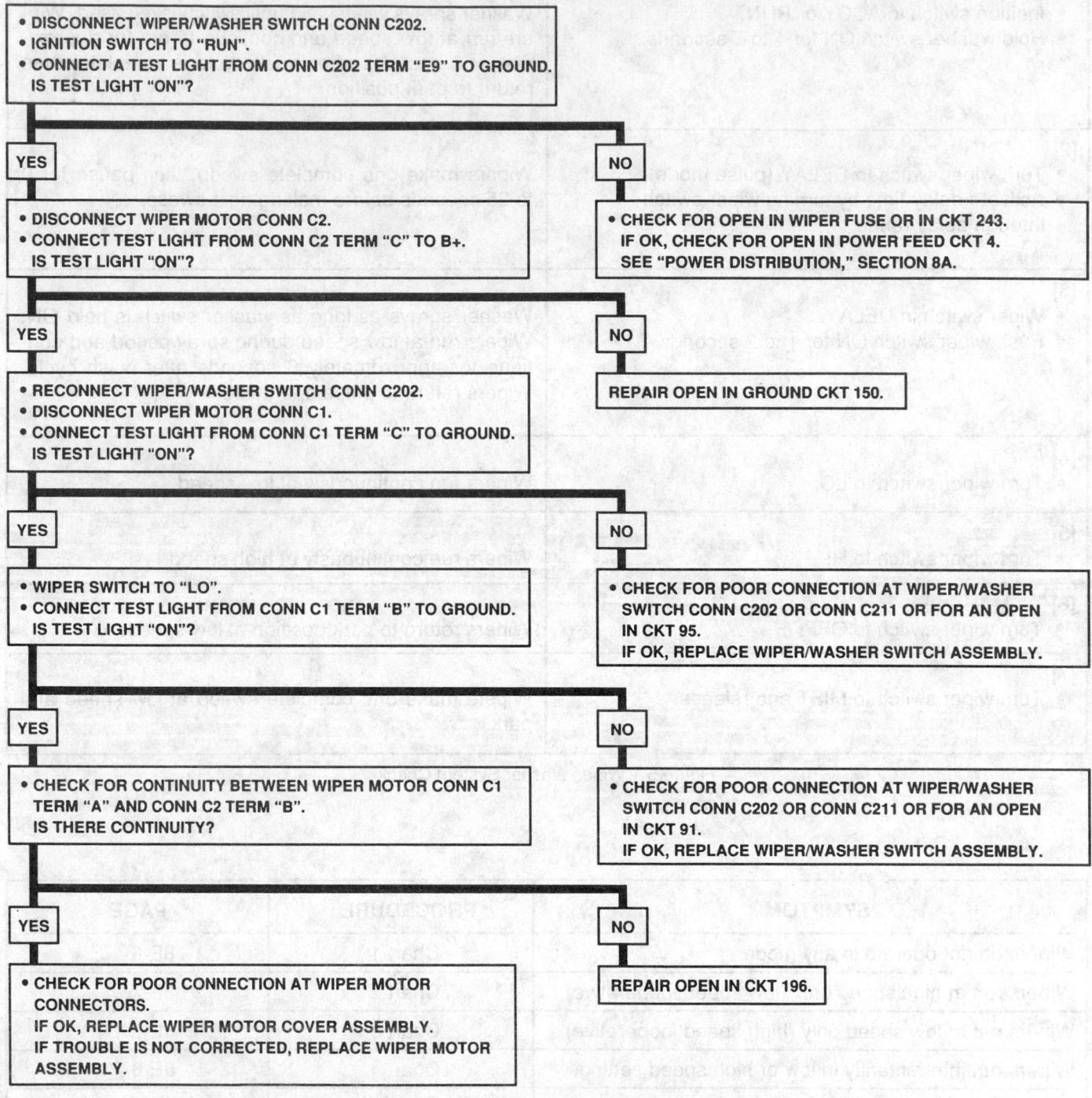

- DISCONNECT WIPER/WASHER SWITCH CONN C202.
- IGNITION SWITCH TO "RUN".
- CONNECT A TEST LIGHT FROM CONN C202 TERM "E9" TO GROUND.

IS TEST LIGHT "ON"?

NO
- CHECK FOR OPEN IN WIPER FUSE OR IN CKT 243.
IF OK, CHECK FOR OPEN IN POWER FEED CKT 4.
SEE "POWER DISTRIBUTION," SECTION 8A.

YES
- DISCONNECT WIPER MOTOR CONN C2.
- CONNECT TEST LIGHT FROM CONN C2 TERM "C" TO B+.

IS TEST LIGHT "ON"?

NO
REPAIR OPEN IN GROUND CKT 150.

YES
- RECONNECT WIPER/WASHER SWITCH CONN C202.
- DISCONNECT WIPER MOTOR CONN C1.
- CONNECT TEST LIGHT FROM CONN C1 TERM "C" TO GROUND.

IS TEST LIGHT "ON"?

NO
- CHECK FOR POOR CONNECTION AT WIPER/WASHER SWITCH CONN C202 OR CONN C211 OR FOR AN OPEN IN CKT 95.
IF OK, REPLACE WIPER/WASHER SWITCH ASSEMBLY.

YES
- WIPER SWITCH TO "LO".
- CONNECT TEST LIGHT FROM CONN C1 TERM "B" TO GROUND.

IS TEST LIGHT "ON"?

NO
- CHECK FOR POOR CONNECTION AT WIPER/WASHER SWITCH CONN C202 OR CONN C211 OR FOR AN OPEN IN CKT 91.
IF OK, REPLACE WIPER/WASHER SWITCH ASSEMBLY.

YES
- CHECK FOR CONTINUITY BETWEEN WIPER MOTOR CONN C1 TERM "A" AND CONN C2 TERM "B".

IS THERE CONTINUITY?

NO
REPAIR OPEN IN CKT 196.

YES
- CHECK FOR POOR CONNECTION AT WIPER MOTOR CONNECTORS.
IF OK, REPLACE WIPER MOTOR COVER ASSEMBLY.
IF TROUBLE IS NOT CORRECTED, REPLACE WIPER MOTOR ASSEMBLY.

CHART 2
WIPERS RUN AT HIGH SPEED ONLY
(LOW SPEED INOPERATIVE)

- DISCONNECT WIPER MOTOR CONN C1.
- IGNITION SWITCH TO "RUN".
- WIPER SWITCH TO "LO".
- CONNECT A TEST LIGHT FROM CONN C1 TERM "B" TO GROUND.

IS TEST LIGHT "ON"?

YES

- CONNECT TEST LIGHT FROM CONN C1 TERM "C" TO GROUND.

IS TEST LIGHT "ON"?

YES

- CHECK FOR CONTINUITY THROUGH CKT 196.

IS THERE CONTINUITY?

YES

- CHECK FOR POOR CONNECTION AT CONN C1.

IF OK, REPLACE WIPER MOTOR COVER ASSEMBLY.
IF TROUBLE IS NOT CORRECTED, REPLACE WIPER MOTOR ASSEMBLY.

NO

REPAIR OPEN IN CKT 196.

NO

- CHECK CKT 95 FOR POOR CONNECTIONS OR OPEN.

IF OK, REPLACE WIPER/WASHER SWITCH ASSEMBLY.

NO

- CHECK FOR OPEN IN CKT 91 OR POOR CONNECTION AT WIPER/WASHER SWITCH CONN C202 OR CONN C211.

IF OK, REPLACE WIPER/WASHER SWITCH ASSEMBLY.

CHART 3
WIPERS RUN AT LOW SPEED ONLY
(HIGH SPEED INOPERATIVE)

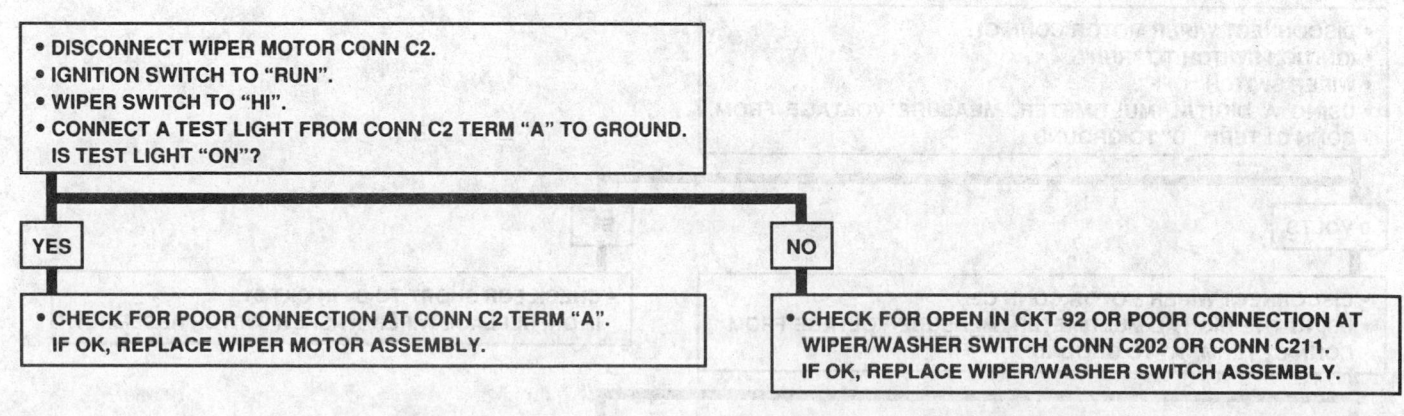

- DISCONNECT WIPER MOTOR CONN C2.
- IGNITION SWITCH TO "RUN".
- WIPER SWITCH TO "HI".
- CONNECT A TEST LIGHT FROM CONN C2 TERM "A" TO GROUND.

IS TEST LIGHT "ON"?

YES

- CHECK FOR POOR CONNECTION AT CONN C2 TERM "A".

IF OK, REPLACE WIPER MOTOR ASSEMBLY.

NO

- CHECK FOR OPEN IN CKT 92 OR POOR CONNECTION AT WIPER/WASHER SWITCH CONN C202 OR CONN C211.

IF OK, REPLACE WIPER/WASHER SWITCH ASSEMBLY.

CHART 4
WIPERS RUN INTERMITTENTLY IN LOW OR HIGH SPEED SETTINGS

- REMOVE WIPER FUSE AND CONNECT AN AMMETER (0-30 AMP) ACROSS FUSE BLOCK TERMINALS.
- IGNITION SWITCH TO "RUN".
- WIPER SWITCH TO "LO".
- OBSERVE LOWEST CURRENT DRAW WHILE WIPERS ARE RUNNING ON DRY GLASS (CURRENT DRAW WILL FLUCTUATE). IS LOWEST CURRENT DRAW LESS THAN 3.5 AMPS?

YES → REPLACE WIPER MOTOR ASSEMBLY.

NO → IS LOWEST CURRENT DRAW MORE THAN 6.5 AMPS?

- NO → END OF TEST.
- YES →
  - REPLACE WIPER BLADE ELEMENTS AND REPEAT TEST. IS LOWEST CURRENT DRAW STILL MORE THAN 6.5 AMPS?
  - NO → END OF TEST.
  - YES →
    - DISCONNECT WIPER TRANSMISSION DRIVE LINK FROM WIPER MOTOR CRANK ARM AND REPEAT TEST. IS LOWEST CURRENT DRAW STILL MORE THAN 6.5 AMPS?
    - YES → REPLACE WIPER MOTOR ASSEMBLY.
    - NO → WIPER TRANSMISSION ASSEMBLY IS BINDING. REPLACE OR REPAIR AS REQUIRED.

CHART 5
WIPERS WILL NOT TURN OFF

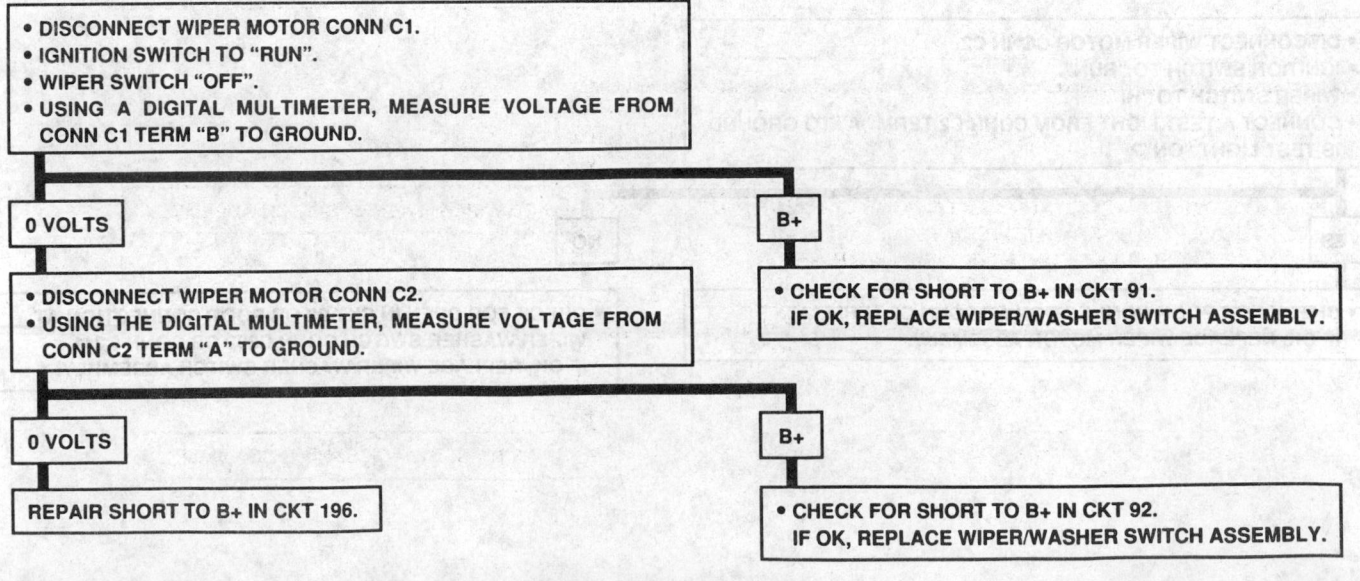

- DISCONNECT WIPER MOTOR CONN C1.
- IGNITION SWITCH TO "RUN".
- WIPER SWITCH "OFF".
- USING A DIGITAL MULTIMETER, MEASURE VOLTAGE FROM CONN C1 TERM "B" TO GROUND.

B+ →
- CHECK FOR SHORT TO B+ IN CKT 91. IF OK, REPLACE WIPER/WASHER SWITCH ASSEMBLY.

0 VOLTS →
- DISCONNECT WIPER MOTOR CONN C2.
- USING THE DIGITAL MULTIMETER, MEASURE VOLTAGE FROM CONN C2 TERM "A" TO GROUND.

  0 VOLTS → REPAIR SHORT TO B+ IN CKT 196.

  B+ →
  - CHECK FOR SHORT TO B+ IN CKT 92. IF OK, REPLACE WIPER/WASHER SWITCH ASSEMBLY.

CHART 6
WIPERS CYCLE IN AND OUT OF PARK POSITION AFTER WIPERS ARE SHUT OFF

- DOES WIPER MOTOR ASSEMBLY OPERATE IN "LO"?

YES → REPLACE PARK SWITCH ASSEMBLY. IS TROUBLE CORRECTED?

- YES → END OF TEST.
- NO → REPLACE WIPER MOTOR ASSEMBLY.

NO → REFER TO CHART 2, "WIPERS RUN AT HIGH SPEED ONLY".

CHART 7
PULSE DELAY OPERATES INCORRECTLY OR NOT AT ALL

- IGNITION SWITCH "OFF".
- DISCONNECT WIPER/WASHER SWITCH CONN C202.
- WIPER SWITCH TO "DELAY".
- WITH A DIGITAL MULTIMETER SET TO OHMS SCALE, MEASURE RESISTANCE THROUGH WIPER/WASHER SWITCH AT CONN C202 FROM TERM "E9" TO TERM "E13".
- MOVE WIPER SWITCH THROUGH ENTIRE DELAY RANGE.

DOES RESISTANCE VARY FROM APPROXIMATELY 1200 K OHMS TO 110 K OHMS?

NO → REPLACE WIPER/WASHER SWITCH ASSEMBLY.

YES →

- MEASURE RESISTANCE THROUGH CONN C202 FROM TERM "E9" TO TERM "E10".

IS RESISTANCE LESS THAN 3 OHMS?

NO → REPLACE WIPER/WASHER SWITCH ASSEMBLY.

YES →

- CHECK CKTS 91 AND 94 FOR AN OPEN OR POOR CONNECTION.
- IF OK, REMOVE WIPER MOTOR COVER ASSEMBLY.

ARE PARK SWITCH PULSE CONTACTS TOUCHING PADS ON CIRCUIT BOARD?

- YES → REPLACE WIPER MOTOR COVER ASSEMBLY.
- NO → REPLACE PARK SWITCH SPRING CONTACTS.

CHART 8
WASHER WILL NOT OPERATE

- DISCONNECT WASHER PUMP CONNECTOR.
- IGNITION SWITCH TO "RUN".
- CONNECT A TEST LIGHT BETWEEN TERMINALS "A" AND "B" OF WASHER PUMP CONNECTOR.
- ACTIVATE WASHER SWITCH WHILE OBSERVING TEST LIGHT.

IS TEST LIGHT "ON"?

YES

- CHECK FOR POOR CONNECTION AT WASHER PUMP CONNECTOR.

IF OK, REPLACE WASHER PUMP.

NO

- CONNECT TEST LIGHT FROM WASHER PUMP CONN TERM "A" TO GROUND.
- ACTIVATE WASHER SWITCH WHILE OBSERVING TEST LIGHT.

IS TEST LIGHT "ON"?

YES

- CHECK FOR POOR CONNECTION OR OPEN IN CKT 227.

IF OK, REPLACE WIPER MOTOR ASSEMBLY (INTERNAL GROUND CKT OPEN).

NO

- CONNECT TEST LIGHT FROM WIPER MOTOR CONN C1 TERM "D" TO GROUND.

IS TEST LIGHT "ON"?

YES

CHECK FOR POOR CONNECTION OR OPEN IN CKT 228.

NO

- IGNITION SWITCH TO "RUN".
- USING A DIGITAL MULTIMETER, BACKPROBE WIPER/WASHER SWITCH CONN C202 FROM TERM "E13" TO GROUND.
- ACTIVATE WASHER SWITCH WHILE OBSERVING THE DIGITAL MULTIMETER.

0 VOLTS

REPLACE WIPER/WASHER SWITCH ASSEMBLY.

B+

- CHECK FOR POOR CONNECTION AT WIPER/WASHER SWITCH CONN C202, CONN C211 AND WIPER MOTOR ASSEMBLY; OR OPEN IN CKT 94.

IF OK, REPLACE WIPER MOTOR ASSEMBLY.

CHART 9
WASHER WILL NOT SHUT OFF

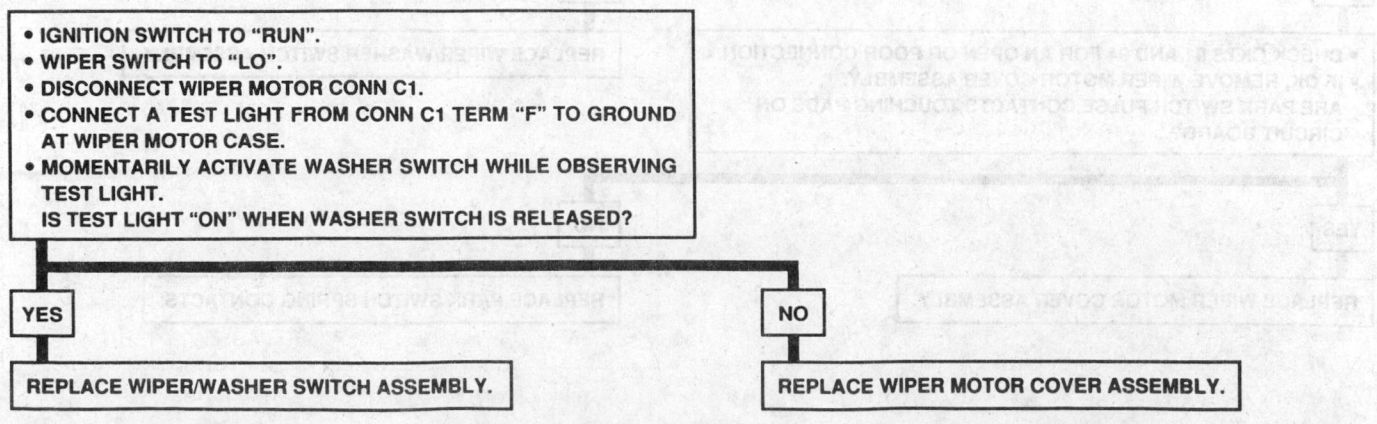

- IGNITION SWITCH TO "RUN".
- WIPER SWITCH TO "LO".
- DISCONNECT WIPER MOTOR CONN C1.
- CONNECT A TEST LIGHT FROM CONN C1 TERM "F" TO GROUND AT WIPER MOTOR CASE.
- MOMENTARILY ACTIVATE WASHER SWITCH WHILE OBSERVING TEST LIGHT.

IS TEST LIGHT "ON" WHEN WASHER SWITCH IS RELEASED?

YES

REPLACE WIPER/WASHER SWITCH ASSEMBLY.

NO

REPLACE WIPER MOTOR COVER ASSEMBLY.

ON-VEHICLE SERVICE

WASHER PUMP REPLACEMENT

Figure 7

Remove or Disconnect

1. Negative battery cable.
2. Washer solvent.
3. Electrical connector (1) and washer hose (5).
4. Two screws (3).
5. Washer solvent container (2).
6. Washer pump (4) from container.

Install or Connect

NOTICE: See fastener "Notice" on page 8E-1 of this section.

1. Washer pump (4) in solvent container (2).

Important

- Make sure washer pump is pushed all the way into the solvent container recess and seal.

2. Solvent container and two screws (3).
3. Electrical connector (1) and washer hose (5).
4. Washer solvent.
5. Negative battery cable.

WIPER ARM ASSEMBLY REPLACEMENT

Figures 8 through 14

Remove or Disconnect

1. Washer hose (8, Figure 8), protective cap (6) and nut (7) from wiper arm assembly (9 or 10) with wipers in park position and hood raised.
2. Lift wiper arm assembly and insert a suitable pin or pop rivet completely through the two holes located next to pivot of arm (see Figure 9). Then, lift arm assembly off its transmission drive shaft using a battery terminal puller.
3. Wiper blade assembly, if required. See "Wiper Blade Assembly Replacement".

Clean

- Any metal shavings from knurls of transmission drive shaft with a wire brush.

Install or Connect

NOTICE: See fastener "Notice" on page 8E-1 of this section.

1. Wiper blade assembly, if removed. See "Wiper Blade Assembly Replacement".
2. Arm assembly (9 or 10, Figure 8) on transmission drive shaft, then remove pivot pin or pop rivet from arm.
   - If installing LH arm and blade assembly, the blade tip must be 53 mm (approx. 2 in.) from bottom edge of glass (see Figure 10).
   - If installing RH arm and blade assembly, the blade tip must be 231 mm (approx. 9-1/8 in.) from bottom edge of glass (see Figure 11).
3. Nut (7, Figure 8).

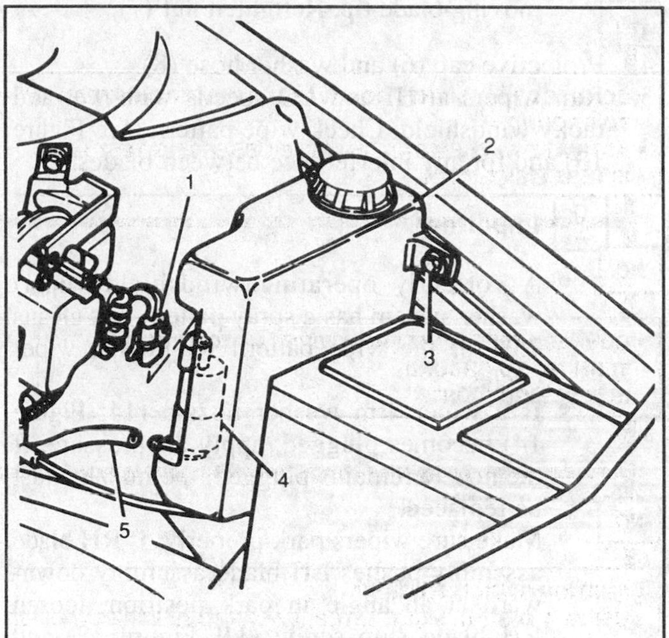
1
2
3
4
5

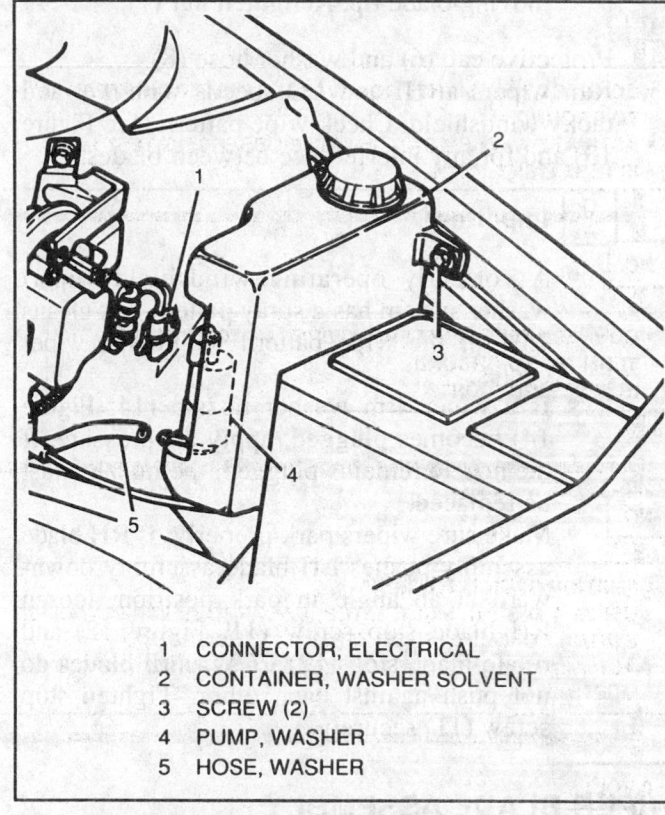

1 CONNECTOR, ELECTRICAL
2 CONTAINER, WASHER SOLVENT
3 SCREW (2)
4 PUMP, WASHER
5 HOSE, WASHER

Figure 7 – Washer Pump and Solvent Container

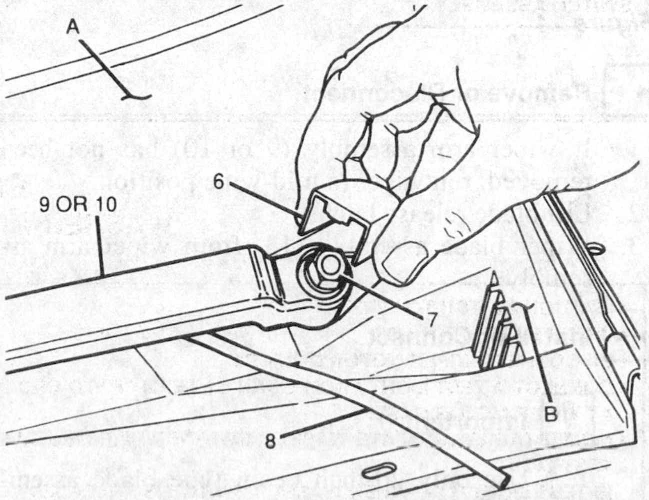
A
6
9 OR 10
7
B
8

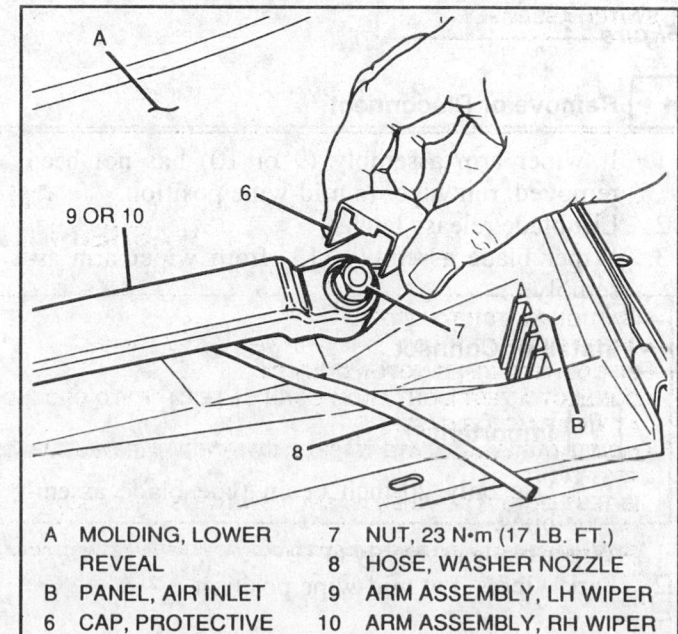

A MOLDING, LOWER REVEAL	7 NUT, 23 N•m (17 LB. FT.)
	8 HOSE, WASHER NOZZLE
B PANEL, AIR INLET	9 ARM ASSEMBLY, LH WIPER
6 CAP, PROTECTIVE	10 ARM ASSEMBLY, RH WIPER

Figure 8 – Hose, Cap and Nut Removal

Tighten

- Nut (7) to 23 N•m (17 lb. ft.) while holding blade tip in position.

Important

- It may be necessary to allow for some movement of arm when nut is being tightened. If arm moves away from desired alignment mark, loosen nut (7) and reposition arm by moving blade tip. Retighten nut (7).

4. Protective cap (6) and washer hose (8).
5. Run wipers at HI and LO speeds with wet and tacky windshield. Check wipe pattern (see Figure 13) and for any interference between blades.

Important

- A correctly operating windshield wiper/washer system has a spray pattern that cleans 75% of the wipe pattern within ten wiper cycles.
- If a wiper arm washer nozzle (14, Figure 14) becomes plugged, apply air pressure. If the nozzle remains plugged, the nozzle must be replaced.
- Make sure wipers park properly. If RH blade assembly pushes LH blade assembly downward at an angle in park position, loosen RH blade stop screw (11, Figure 12) and rotate blade stop (12) CCW until blades do not push against each other. Tighten stop screw (11) securely.

WIPER BLADE ASSEMBLY REPLACEMENT

Figure 14

Remove or Disconnect

1. If wiper arm assembly (9 or 10) has not been removed, run wiper to mid-wipe position.
2. Lift blade release latch.
3. Wiper blade assembly (13) from wiper arm assembly.

Install or Connect

Important

- Use only 20-inch beam type blade assemblies.

1. Wiper blade assembly (13).
2. Park wipers if at mid-wipe position.

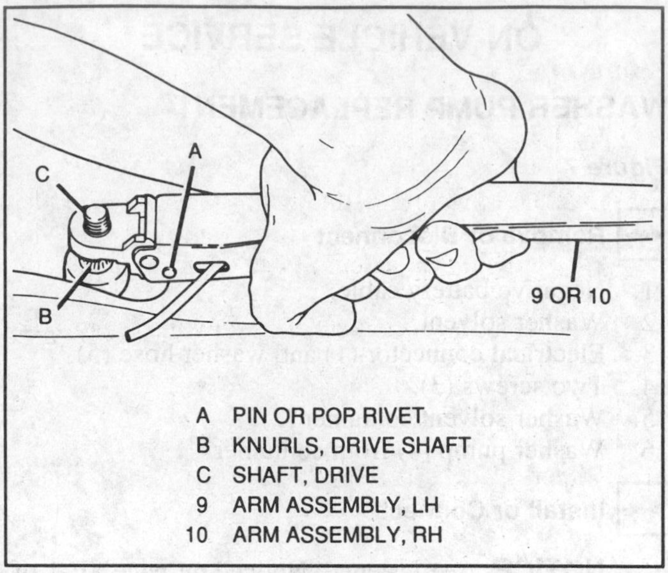
A
C
B
9 OR 10
A PIN OR POP RIVET
B KNURLS, DRIVE SHAFT
C SHAFT, DRIVE
9 ARM ASSEMBLY, LH
10 ARM ASSEMBLY, RH

Figure 9 – Wiper Arm Assembly Removal

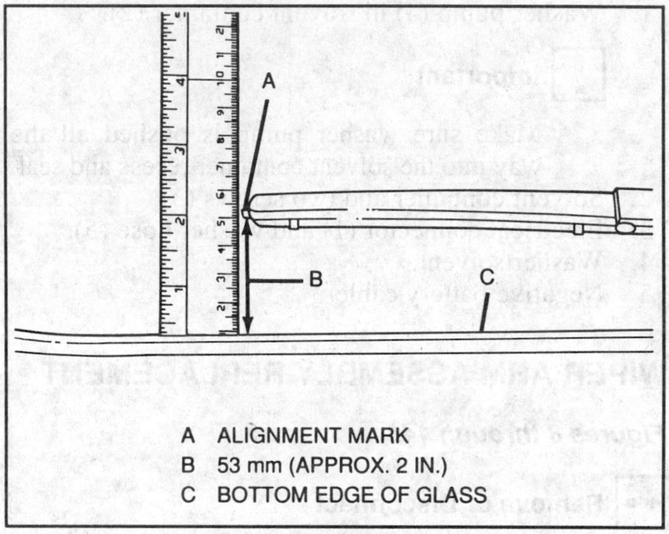
A
B
C
A ALIGNMENT MARK
B 53 mm (APPROX. 2 IN.)
C BOTTOM EDGE OF GLASS

Figure 10 – Left-Hand Wiper Arm Alignment

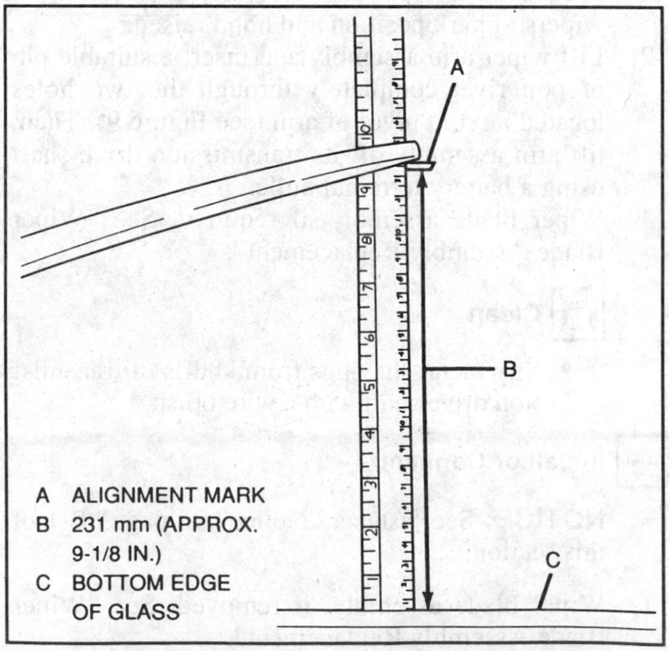
A
B
C
A ALIGNMENT MARK
B 231 mm (APPROX. 9-1/8 IN.)
C BOTTOM EDGE OF GLASS

Figure 11 – Right-Hand Wiper Arm Alignment

WIPER BLADE ELEMENT REPLACEMENT

Figure 14

Important

- To prevent possible windshield damage, the blade assembly should be removed from the wiper arm assembly to replace the blade element.
- If a blade element is removed, it must be replaced.

Remove or Disconnect

1. Wiper blade assembly (13). See "Wiper Blade Assembly Replacement".

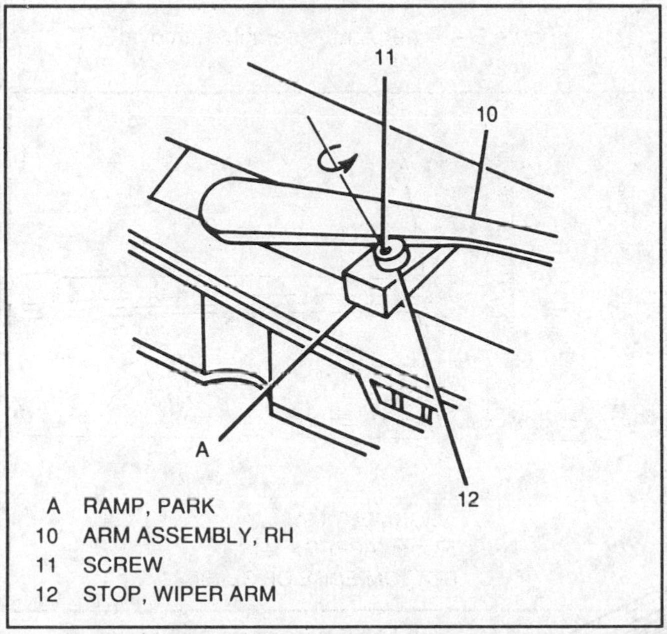
11
10
A
12
A RAMP, PARK
10 ARM ASSEMBLY, RH
11 SCREW
12 STOP, WIPER ARM

Figure 12 – Right-Hand Wiper Arm Stop Adjustment

2. Insert a small coin between edge of blade superstructure and blade element (15) beside claw. Press slowly until blade element clears one side of claw set (see View A).
3. Blade element from other claw sets.

Install or Connect

1. Blade element (15) into claws, starting with second set from outer end (see View B).
2. Engage blade element into one side of remaining claw set and, with a rocking motion, push blade element upward until it snaps into place (see View C).
3. Wiper blade assembly (13). See "Wiper Blade Assembly Replacement".

WIPER DRIVE SYSTEM MODULE REMOVAL AND INSTALLATION

Figures 1 and 15 through 21

Remove or Disconnect

1. Negative battery cable.
2. Wiper arm and blade assemblies. See "Wiper Arm Assembly Replacement".
3. Lower reveal molding screws. Then, lower hood and remove lower reveal molding (see Figure 8) in direction shown in Figure 15.
4. Air inlet panel screws, underhood lamp switch (if equipped) and air inlet panel (Figure 16) with hood raised.

Important

- If wiper motor assembly can run, place in inner wipe position as shown in Figure 17.

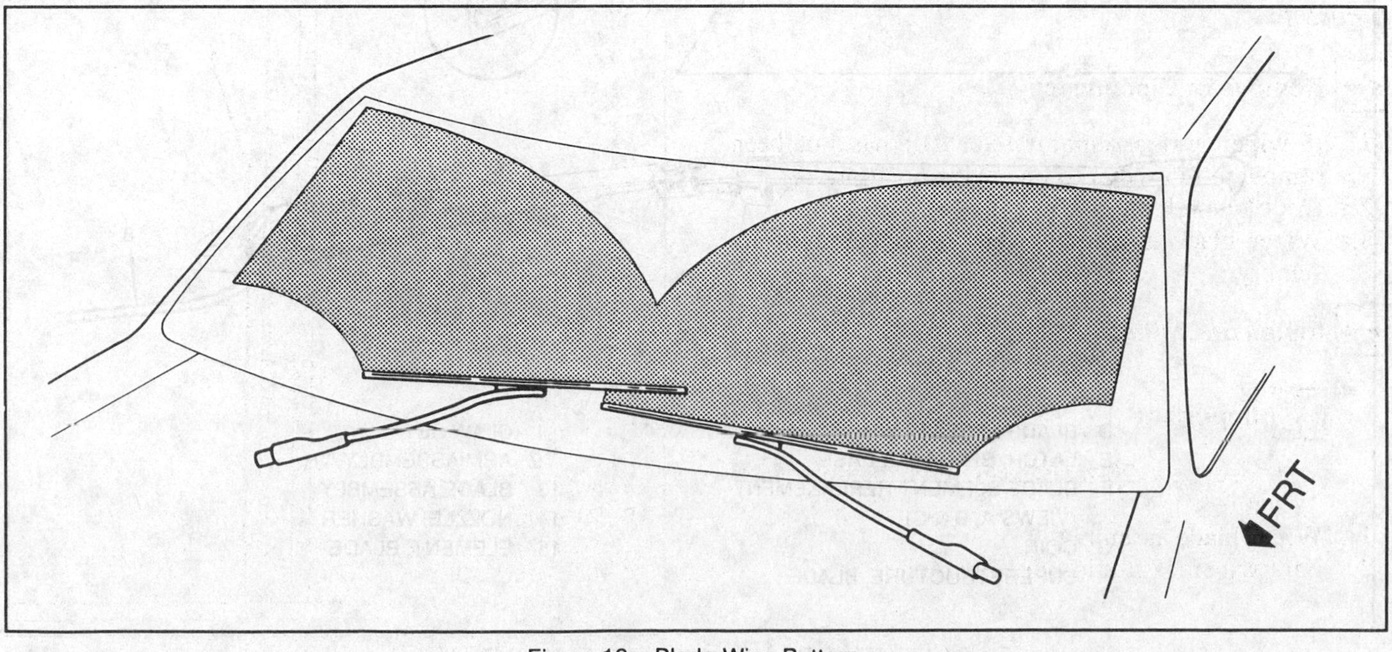
FRT

Figure 13 – Blade Wipe Pattern

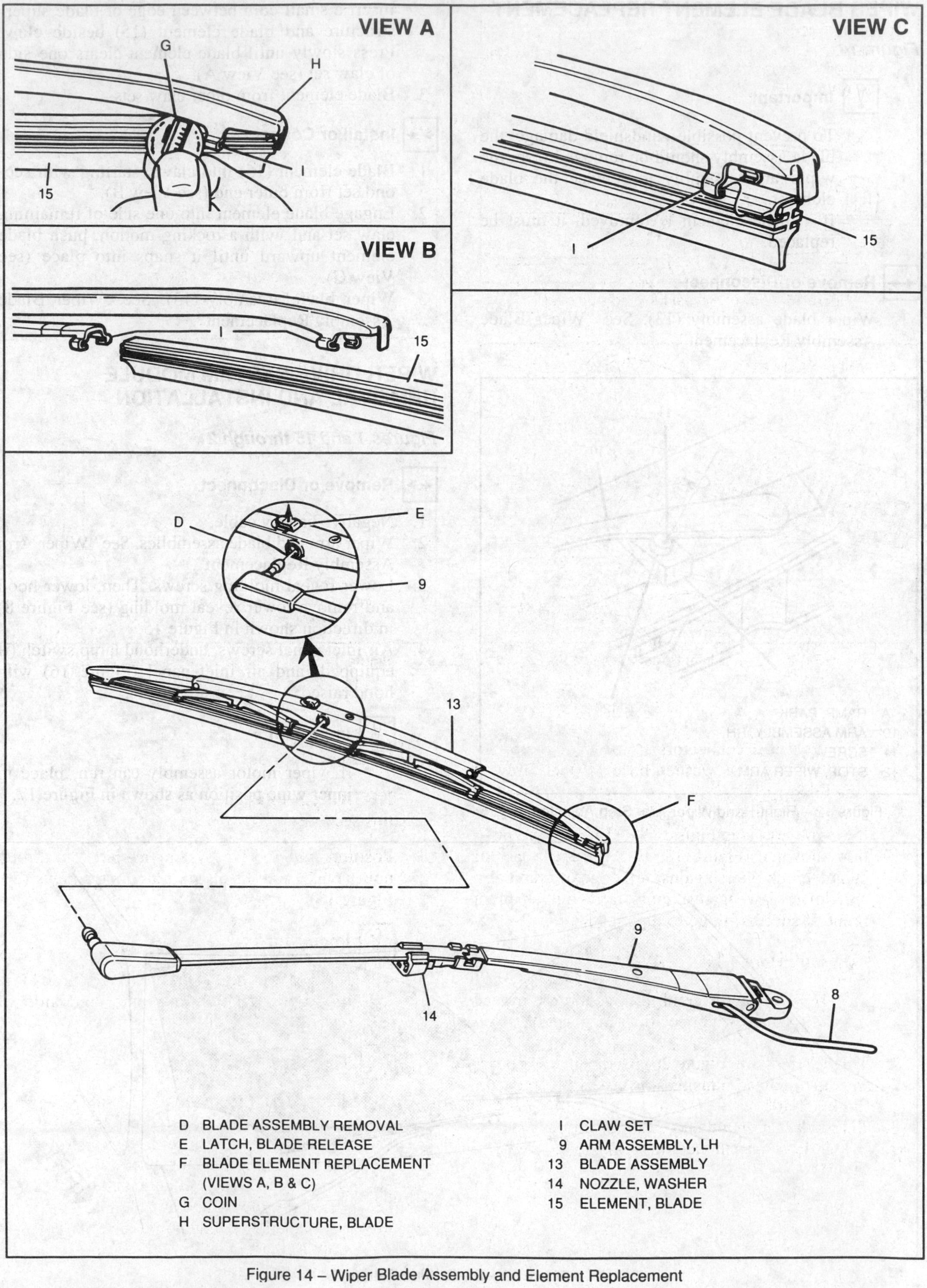
VIEW A
G
H
15
VIEW B
I
15
VIEW C
I
15
D
E
9
13
F
9
14
8
D BLADE ASSEMBLY REMOVAL
E LATCH, BLADE RELEASE
F BLADE ELEMENT REPLACEMENT (VIEWS A, B & C)
G COIN
H SUPERSTRUCTURE, BLADE
I CLAW SET
9 ARM ASSEMBLY, LH
13 BLADE ASSEMBLY
14 NOZZLE, WASHER
15 ELEMENT, BLADE

Figure 14 – Wiper Blade Assembly and Element Replacement

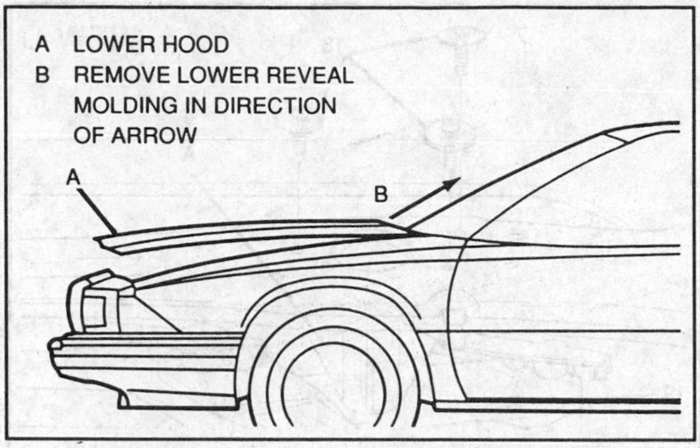
A LOWER HOOD
B REMOVE LOWER REVEAL MOLDING IN DIRECTION OF ARROW
A
B

Figure 15 – Lower Reveal Molding Removal

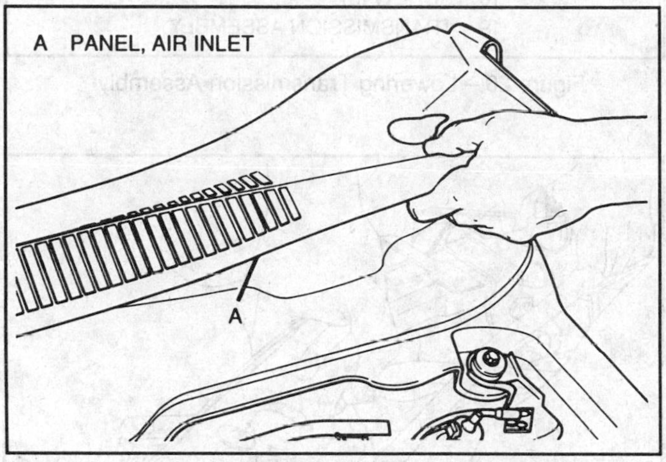
A PANEL, AIR INLET
A

Figure 16 – Air Inlet Panel Removal

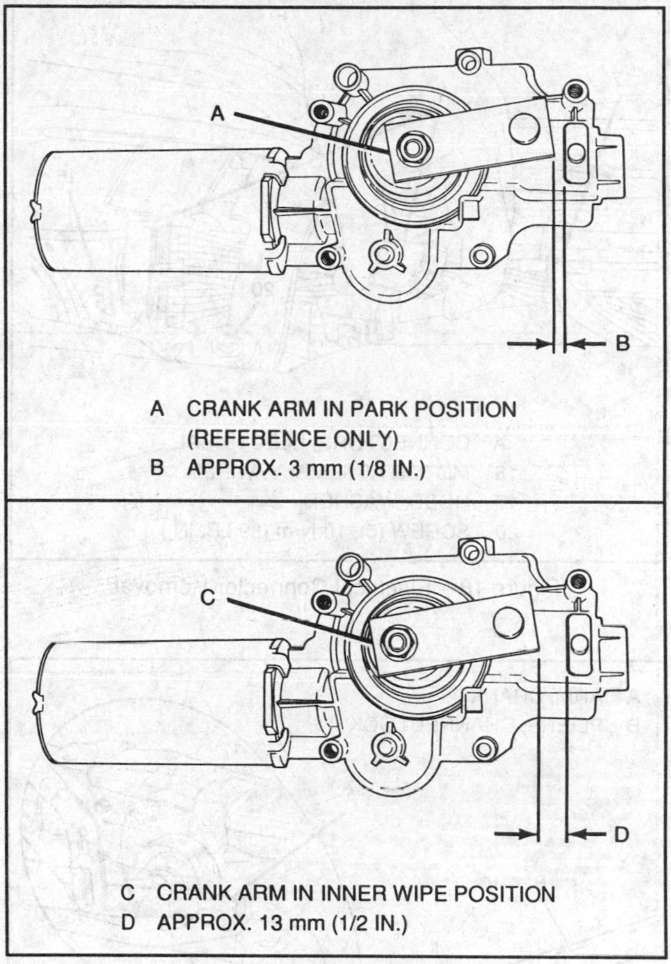
A
B
A CRANK ARM IN PARK POSITION (REFERENCE ONLY)
B APPROX. 3 mm (1/8 IN.)
C
D
C CRANK ARM IN INNER WIPE POSITION
D APPROX. 13 mm (1/2 IN.)

Figure 17 – Wiper Motor Crank Arm in Inner Wipe and Park Positions

5. Two electrical connectors from wiper motor assembly (16), and washer hose (17) at firewall (see Figure 18).
6. If wiper motor assembly is inoperative, rotate motor crank arm (see Figure 19) to inner wipe position shown in Figure 17. Engage upper jaw of channel lock pliers against top edge of crank arm and lower jaw against crank arm nut as pivot point. If successful, go to Step 8.

Important

- If wiper motor crank arm cannot be moved into inner wipe position in Step 6, go to Step 7.

7. Three screws (18, Figure 20) from bell crank housing, then lower transmission assembly (19) for module removal.
8. Six module mounting screws (20, Figure 18).
9. Wiper drive system module from vehicle (see Figure 21).

Install or Connect

NOTICE: See fastener "Notice" on page 8E-1 of this section.

1. Position wiper drive system module on shroud upper panel and install six mounting screws (20, Figure 18).

Important

- Make sure body seal (21, Figure 1) is in proper position on right-hand side of module.

Tighten

- Screws (20, Figure 18) to 10 N•m (89 lb. in.).

2. Electrical connectors to wiper motor assembly (16).
3. Washer hose (17) to hose connector at firewall.
4. Air inlet panel and attaching screws.
5. Underhood lamp switch (if equipped).
6. Lower reveal molding and attaching screws.
7. Wiper arm and blade assemblies. See "Wiper Arm Assembly Replacement".
8. Negative battery cable.

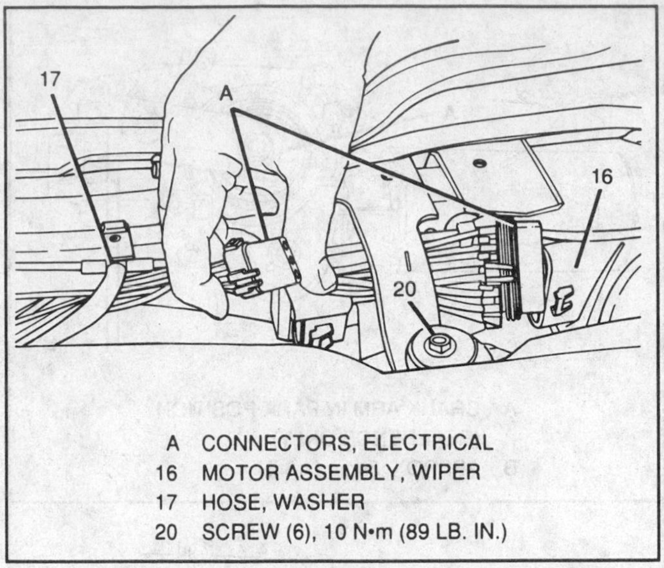
17
A
16
20
A CONNECTORS, ELECTRICAL
16 MOTOR ASSEMBLY, WIPER
17 HOSE, WASHER
20 SCREW (6), 10 N•m (89 LB. IN.)

Figure 18 – Electrical Connector Removal

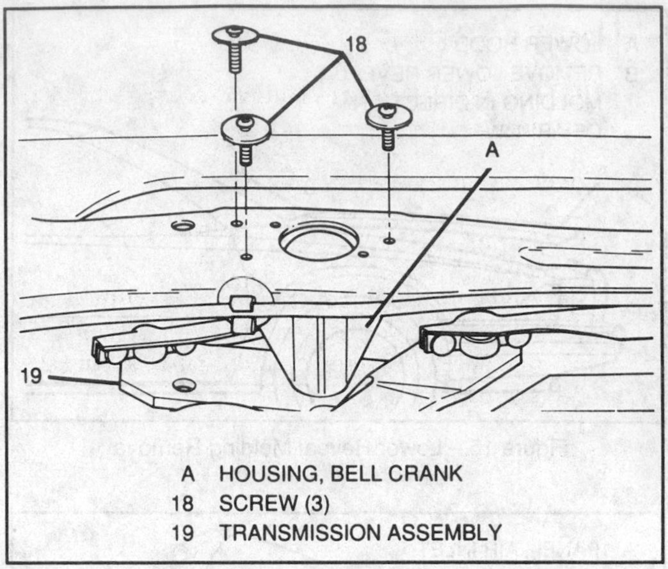
18
A
19
A HOUSING, BELL CRANK
18 SCREW (3)
19 TRANSMISSION ASSEMBLY

Figure 20 – Lowering Transmission Assembly

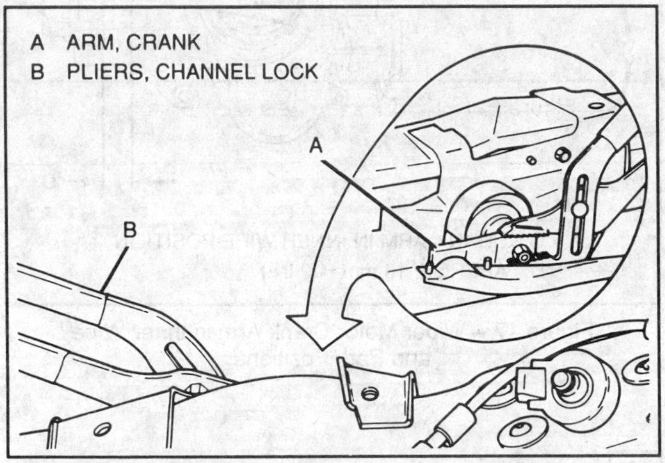
A ARM, CRANK
B PLIERS, CHANNEL LOCK
A
B

Figure 19 – Moving Crank Arm to Inner Wipe Position

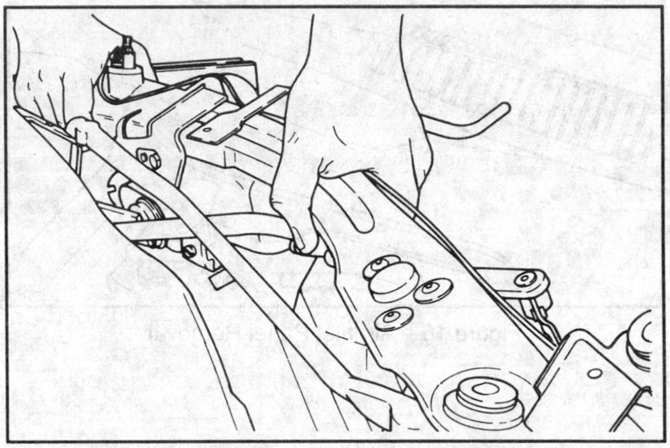

Figure 21 – Wiper Drive System Removal

OFF-VEHICLE SERVICE

WIPER MOTOR ASSEMBLY REPLACEMENT

Figure 22

Remove or Disconnect

1. Nut (22) and crank arm (23) from wiper motor assembly (16).

Important

- Crank arm **MUST** be removed from **WIPER MOTOR ONLY.** Do **NOT** remove crank arm from transmission assembly because of factory preset adjustment.

2. Three screws (24), then remove wiper motor assembly for repair or replacement.

Install or Connect

NOTICE: See fastener "Notice" on page 8E-1 of this section.

1. Wiper motor assembly (16) and three screws (24).
2. Crank arm (23) and nut (22).

Tighten

- Nut (22) to 43 N•m (32 lb. ft.).

WIPER MOTOR COVER ASSEMBLY REPLACEMENT

Figure 23

Remove or Disconnect

1. Three screws (25).
2. Cover assembly (26).

Install or Connect

NOTICE: See fastener "Notice" on page 8E-1 of this section.

1. Cover assembly (26).

Important

- Always install cover assembly with wiper motor in park position and with drive pin in open area of the cam as shown in Figure 23.

2. Three screws (25).

Tighten

- Screws (25) to 2 N•m (18 lb. in.).

PARK SWITCH ASSEMBLY REPLACEMENT

Figures 23 and 24

Remove or Disconnect

1. Three screws (25, Figure 24) and cover assembly (26).

Important

- If wiper motor assembly is in park position (see Figure 23), operate wiper motor assembly as required to remove pawl from relay slot.

2. Park switch assembly (27, Figure 24) and screw (28).

Install or Connect

NOTICE: See fastener "Notice" on page 8E-1 of this section.

1. New park switch assembly (27) and screw (28).
2. Follow "Wiper Motor Cover Assembly Replacement" procedure carefully.

WIPER TRANSMISSION ASSEMBLY REPLACEMENT

Figures 17 and 25 through 27

Remove or Disconnect

1. Two drive link socket screws (Figure 25), then remove socket from crank arm ball.
2. Nine screws (18, Figure 26) to detach transmission assembly (19) from module.

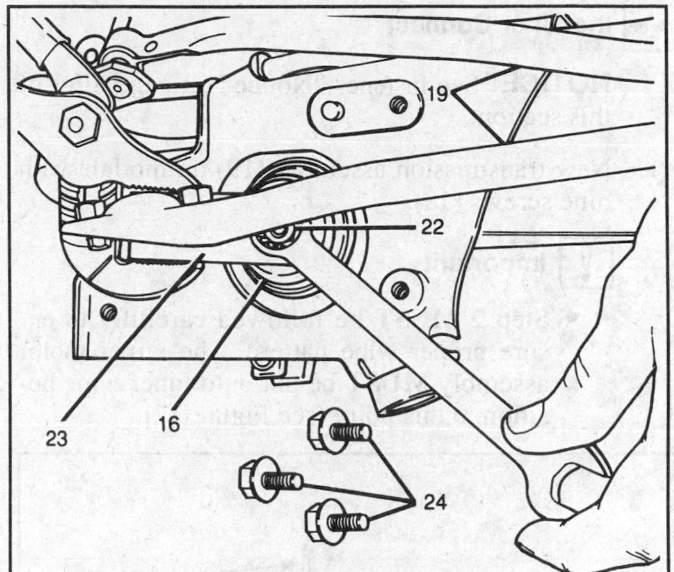
19
22
23
16
24

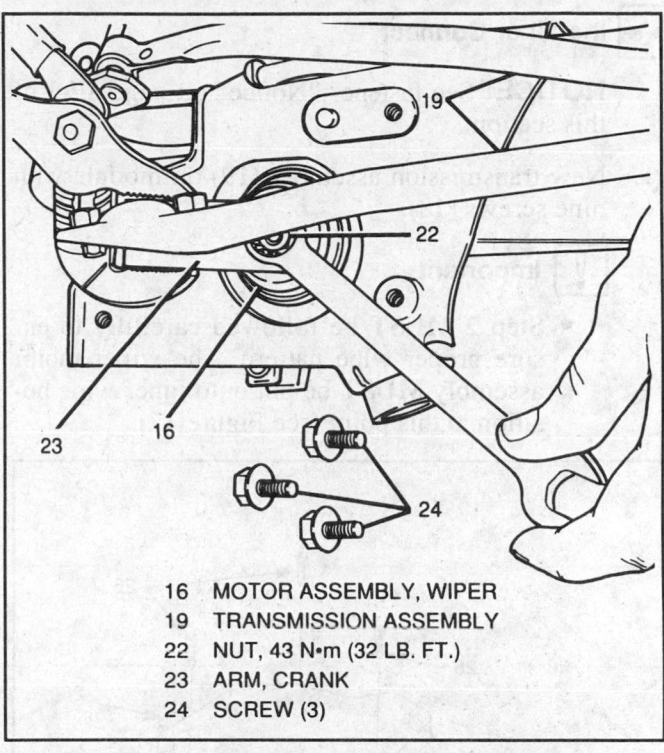

16 MOTOR ASSEMBLY, WIPER
19 TRANSMISSION ASSEMBLY
22 NUT, 43 N•m (32 LB. FT.)
23 ARM, CRANK
24 SCREW (3)

Figure 22 – Wiper Motor Crank Arm Removal

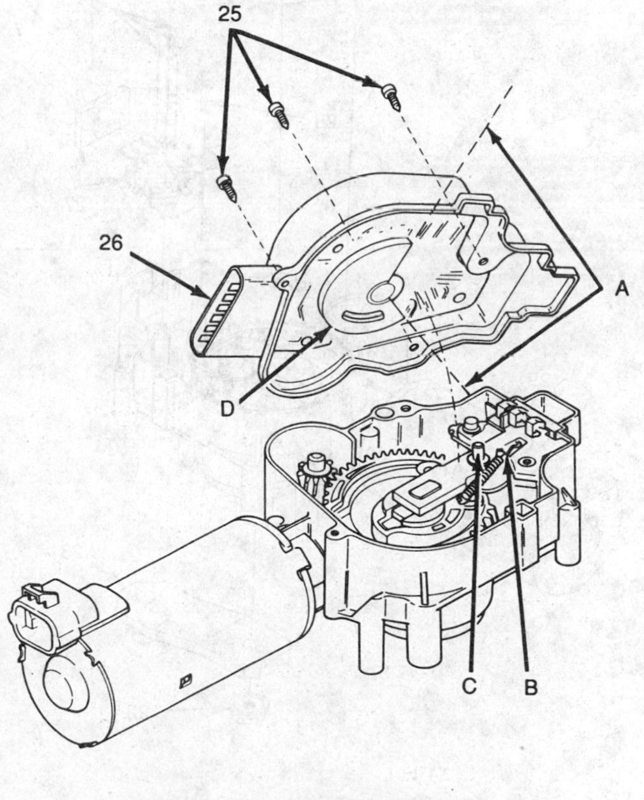
25
26
A
D
C
B

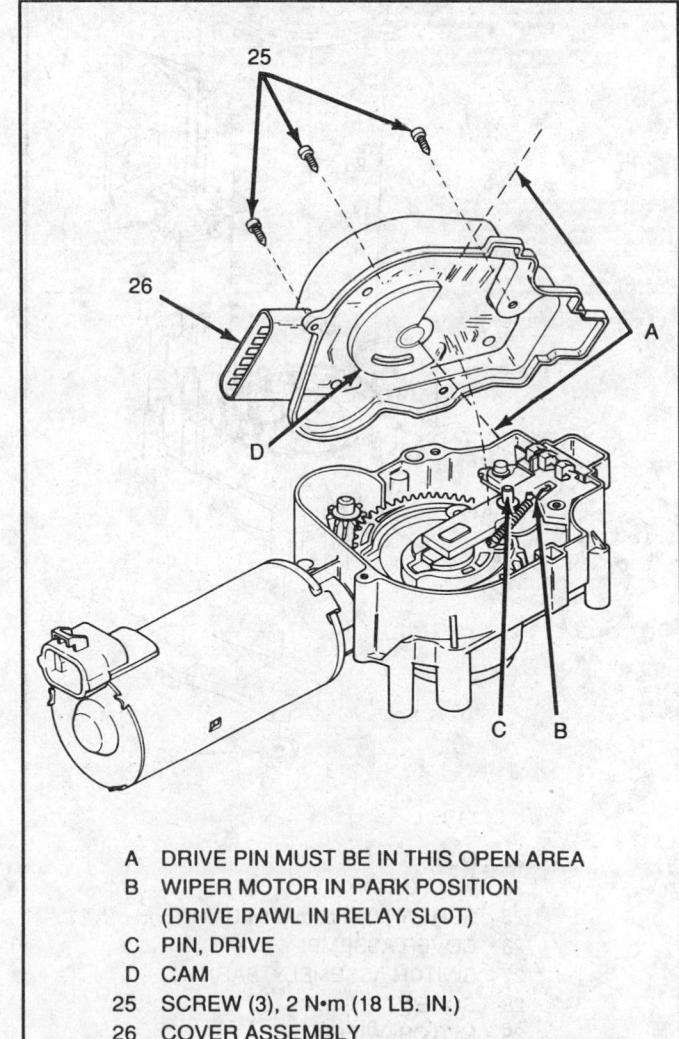

A DRIVE PIN MUST BE IN THIS OPEN AREA
B WIPER MOTOR IN PARK POSITION (DRIVE PAWL IN RELAY SLOT)
C PIN, DRIVE
D CAM
25 SCREW (3), 2 N•m (18 LB. IN.)
26 COVER ASSEMBLY

Figure 23 – Wiper Motor Cover Assembly Removal

Install or Connect

NOTICE: See fastener "Notice" on page 8E-1 of this section.

1. New transmission assembly (19) on module with nine screws (18).

Important

- Step 2 **MUST** be followed carefully to ensure proper wipe pattern. The wiper motor assembly **MUST** be put onto inner wipe position at this point (see Figure 17).

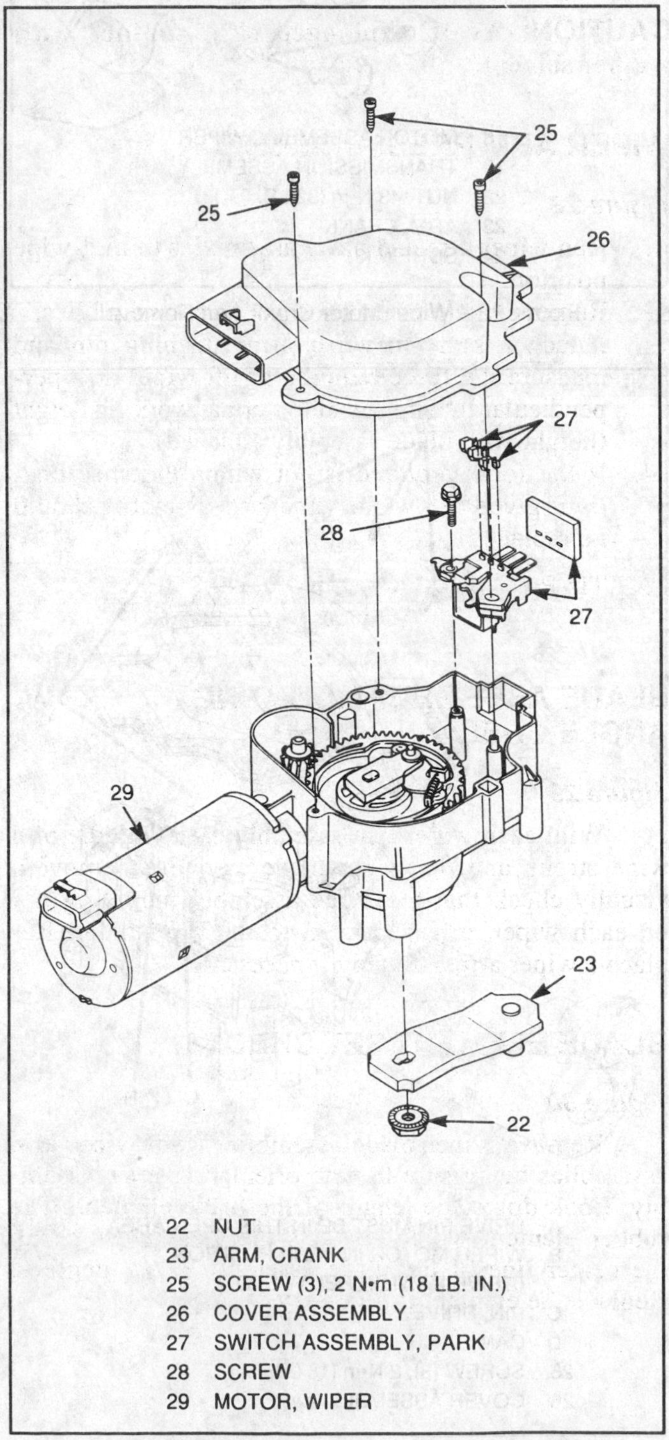
25
25
26
27
28
27
29
23
22
22 NUT
23 ARM, CRANK
25 SCREW (3), 2 N•m (18 LB. IN.)
26 COVER ASSEMBLY
27 SWITCH ASSEMBLY, PARK
28 SCREW
29 MOTOR, WIPER

Figure 24 – Wiper Motor Assembly Components

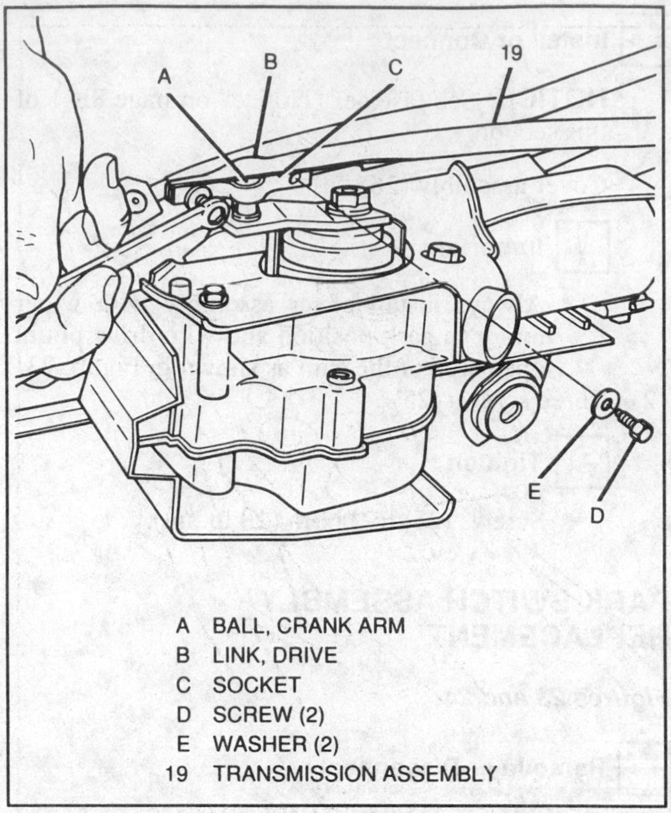
A
B
C
19
E
D
A BALL, CRANK ARM
B LINK, DRIVE
C SOCKET
D SCREW (2)
E WASHER (2)
19 TRANSMISSION ASSEMBLY

Figure 25 – Transmission Socket Removal

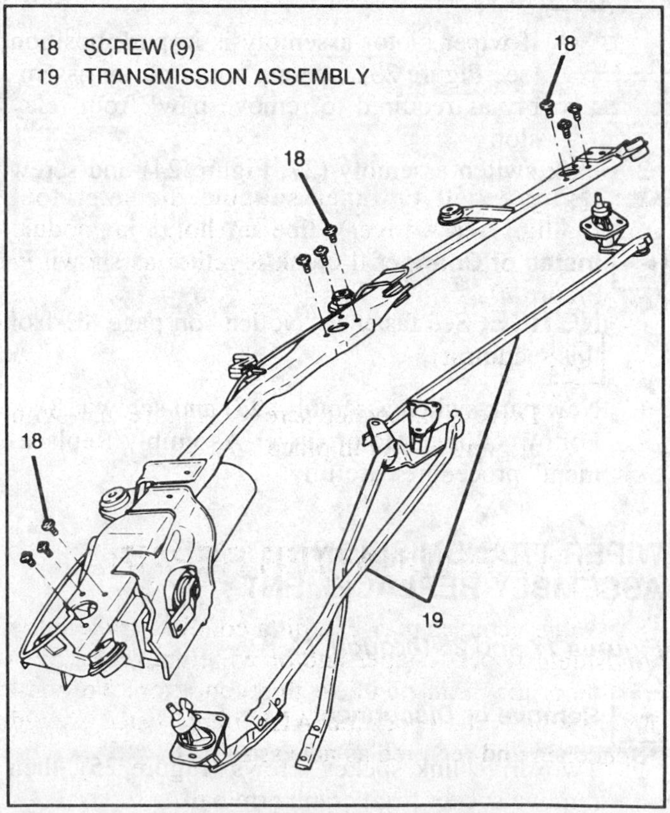
18 SCREW (9)
19 TRANSMISSION ASSEMBLY
18
18
18
19

Figure 26 – Transmission Assembly Removed from Module

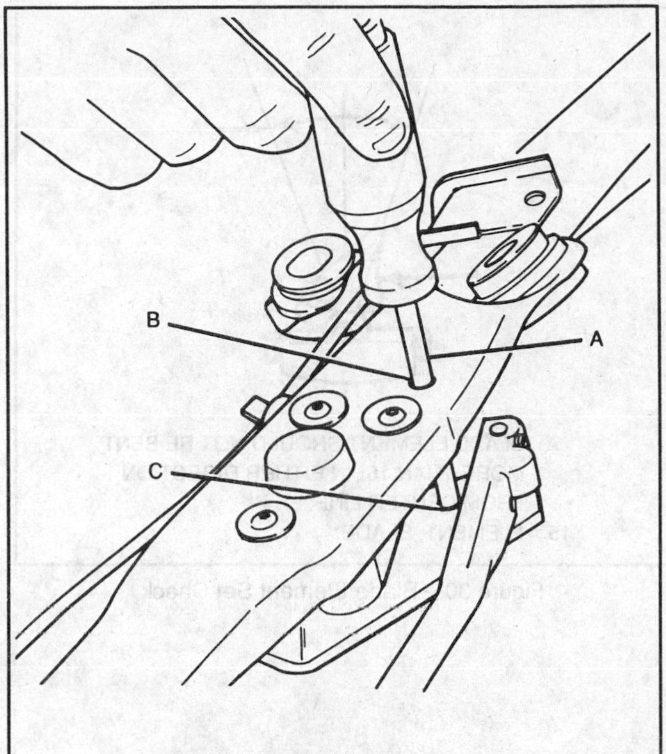
B
A
C
A TOOL, ALIGNMENT
B HOLE IN MODULE CARRIER PLATE
C HOLE IN BELL CRANK

Figure 27 – Module and Bell Crank Hole Alignment

2. Using a bolt or other suitable diameter tool (Phillips screwdriver), line up holes in module carrier plate and bell crank together as shown in Figure 27.

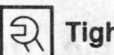

Tighten

- Drive link socket screws (Figure 25) with alignment tool in place.

WIPER CHATTER REPAIR

Some vehicles may exhibit a condition where the windshield wipers chatter and/or wipe unevenly. Several items may contribute to this condition. To completely repair this condition **ALL** items listed should be checked and repaired as necessary.

WINDSHIELD GLASS CLEANING

Clean windshield with windshield cleaner, GM PN 1050011 or equivalent. The cleaner used should be one which will not harm paint finish or scratch glass. The glass is clean when water no longer beads, but sheets across entire glass surface.

BLADE ELEMENT CLEANING

Lift each blade assembly off windshield and clean element with a cloth saturated in full strength washer solvent. Rinse blade assemblies with water.

CAUTION: Avoid prolonged skin contact with washer solvent.

WIPER ARM PRESSURE CHECK

Figure 28

1. Run wiper arm and blade assemblies to mid-wipe position.
2. Remove blade assemblies from arm assemblies.
3. Attach a scale to wiper arm attaching pin and measure the force required to lift wiper arm perpendicular to windshield to normal working height (height with blade assembly attached).
4. If the force required is not within the specifications given below, the wiper arm assembly should be replaced.

Tip Pressure — Newtons – 7.5-9.3
(Ounces) – (27-33)

BLADE ASSEMBLY MOUNTING ANGLE CHECK

Figure 29

With each wiper arm assembly in the middle of a wipe stroke and the wiper blade assembly removed, visually check that the blade assembly mounting pin on each wiper arm is parallel to the windshield. Replace a wiper arm assembly if necessary.

BLADE ELEMENT SET CHECK

Figure 30

Remove wiper blade assemblies from wiper arm assemblies being sure to note orientation for reassembly. Look down the length of the blade element. The rubber element which contacts the glass must be on the center line of the blade assembly +/–15 degrees. Replace the element if necessary.

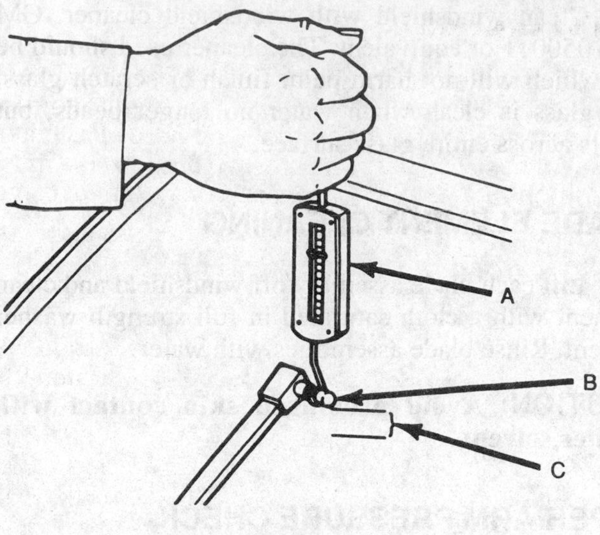
A
B
C

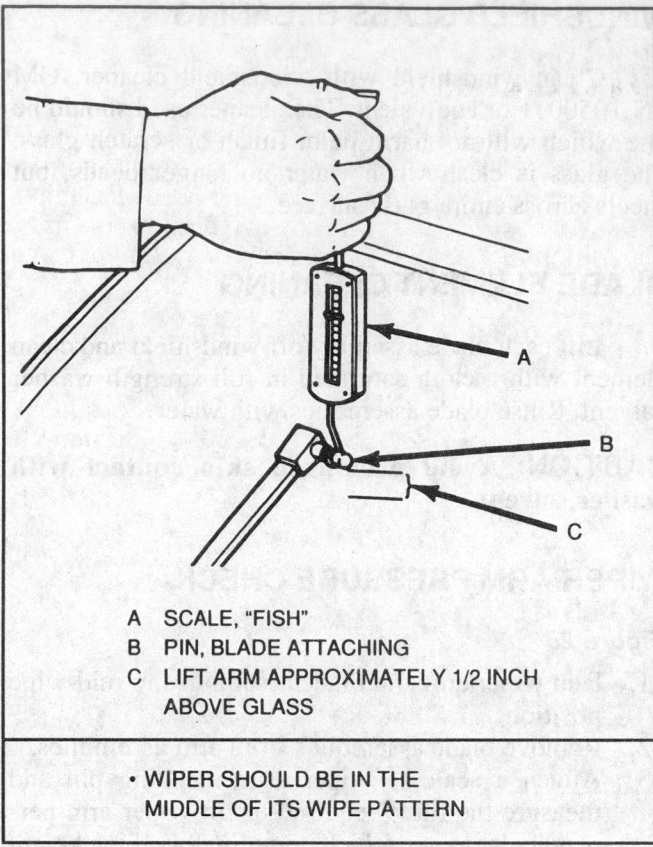

A SCALE, "FISH"
B PIN, BLADE ATTACHING
C LIFT ARM APPROXIMATELY 1/2 INCH ABOVE GLASS

• WIPER SHOULD BE IN THE MIDDLE OF ITS WIPE PATTERN

Figure 28 – Wiper Arm Pressure Check

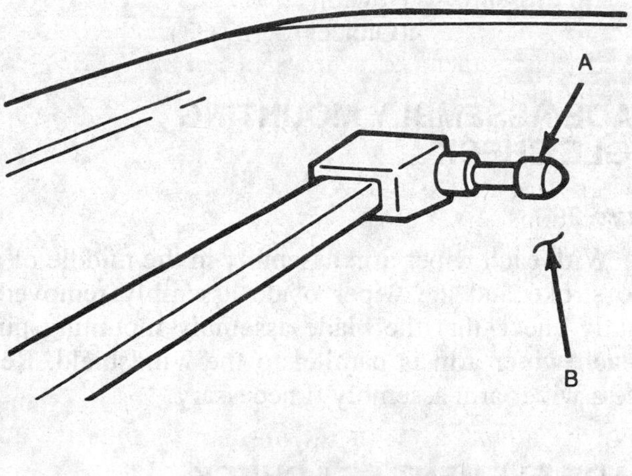
A
B

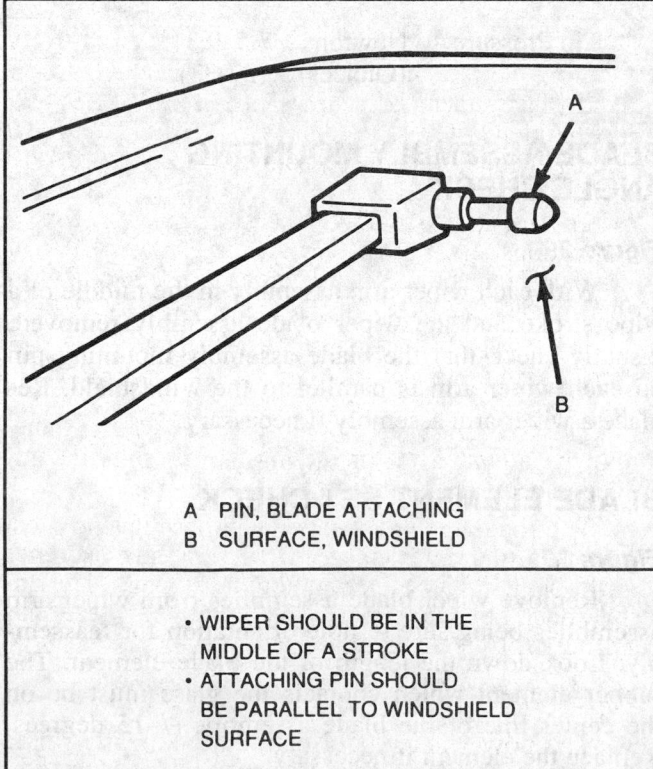

A PIN, BLADE ATTACHING
B SURFACE, WINDSHIELD

• WIPER SHOULD BE IN THE MIDDLE OF A STROKE
• ATTACHING PIN SHOULD BE PARALLEL TO WINDSHIELD SURFACE

Figure 29 – Blade Assembly Mounting Angle Check

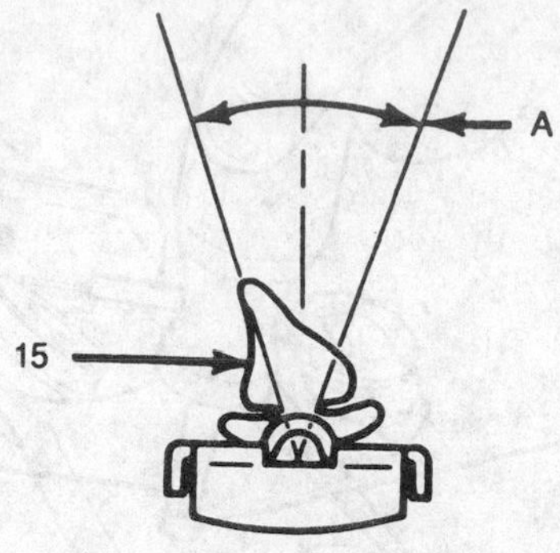
A
15

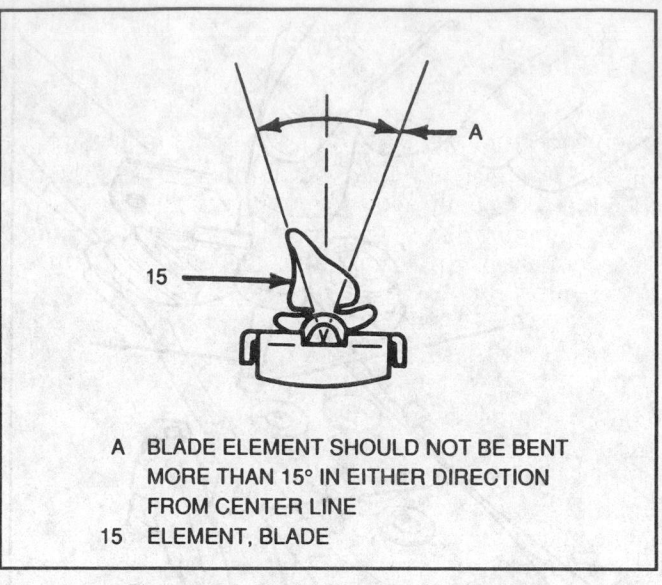

A BLADE ELEMENT SHOULD NOT BE BENT MORE THAN 15° IN EITHER DIRECTION FROM CENTER LINE
15 ELEMENT, BLADE

Figure 30 – Blade Element Set Check

SPECIFICATIONS

FASTENER TIGHTENING SPECIFICATIONS

Wiper Arm Assembly Nut (7) . . . . 23 N•m (17 lb. ft.)
Wiper Drive System Module
  Screws (20) . . . . 10 N•m (89 lb. in.)
Wiper Motor Cover Assembly
  Screws (25) . . . . 2 N•m (18 lb. in.)
Wiper Motor Crank Arm
  Nut (22) .43 N•m (32 lb. ft.)

ACCESSORIES

NOTICE: When fasteners are removed, always reinstall them at the same location from which they were removed. If a fastener needs to be replaced, use the correct part number fastener for that application. If the correct part number fastener is not available, a fastener of equal size and strength (or stronger) may be used. Fasteners that are not reused, and those requiring thread locking compound will be called out. The correct torque value must be used when installing fasteners that require it. If the above conditions are not followed, parts or system damage could result.

CONTENTS

SECTION 9A

AUDIO SYSTEM

CONTENTS

GENERAL DESCRIPTION

RADIOS

Four different radios are available as options, beginning with the Options UM6, UM7 and U1C, and feature AM/FM stereo, Electronically Tuned Receiver (ETR), Seek/Scan tuning and a clock. Option UX1 features AM Stereo/FM Stereo, Electronically Tuned Receiver (ETR), Seek/Scan tuning and clock.

TAPE PLAYERS

The UM6 option also features an auto reverse cassette tape player with Dynamic Noise Reduction (DNR). The UX1 option adds a "Music Search" feature plus a Graphic Equalizer.

COMPACT DISC PLAYER

The U1C option also has a Compact Disc Player.

FIXED ANTENNA

The fixed antenna on the right rear quarter panel cannot be adjusted up or down. It may provide improved reception in rural areas.

The fixed antenna is designed to withstand most car washes without damage. If the antenna becomes slightly bent, it can be straightened by hand. The antenna must be replaced if severely bent. Antennas must be kept clean for good performance.

POWER ANTENNA

The power antenna system automatically raises the antenna when the radio is turned on and the ignition switch is in the run or accessory position and automatically lowers the antenna when the radio or ignition switch is turned off. The antenna is replaceable.

The power antenna system does not utilize a relay or limit switches. The system consists of a solid state module integral with the motor. Output from the radio and an "ignition crank" signal to control the antenna up or down functions. A B+ feed and ground circuit to the module/motor drive the antenna.

Power Antenna Operation

Up:

With the radio switch on and the ignition switch off, the antenna is in the down position. When the ignition switch is in the run or accessory position, the antenna will go up immediately when the radio is turned on.

If the antenna is cycling up and it is mechanically prevented from reaching its full up position (ice buildup, an obstruction, etc.), it will recycle in thirty seconds and attempt to reach the full up position for one second. If the mechanical obstruction remains, cycling will continue every thirty seconds.

Down:

When the antenna has reached a full up position, it will cycle down if the radio is turned off or if the ignition switch is taken out of the run or accessory positions.

If the antenna is obstructed during its downward cycle, it will stop where the obstruction occurred. No recycling will occur as in the up cycle. If the antenna is then cycled according to the up parameters, it will complete its up cycle providing the obstruction has been eliminated.

OPERATING INSTRUCTIONS

UM7, AM/FM STEREO WITH SEEK AND SCAN

Figure 1

To Play the Radio

1. Left Knob – The left knob does these things:
   - It turns the system on and off.
   - It controls the volume.
   - It allows you to recall the frequency when the radio is playing. Press the knob.
2. BALANCE – The control behind the center knob allows you to **BAL**ance the sound between the right and left speakers.
3. FADE – The center knob **FADES** the sound between your front and rear speakers.
4. Right Knob – Turn the right knob to **TUNE** radio stations.
5. SEEK – Pressing the **SEEK** button will cause the receiver to seek the next higher station and stop.
6. SCAN – Press **SCAN** once to listen for a few seconds to stations higher on the AM or FM band. The radio will continue to scan stations every few seconds until you press **SCAN** again to stop on a station.
7. Pushbuttons – The five pushbuttons let you return to stations. You can set the pushbuttons for up to ten stations (5 AM and 5 FM). Just:
   A. Tune in the station you want to listen to.
   B. Press the **SET** pushbutton. (NOTE: the display will show SET for about 5 seconds.)
   C. Within the 5 seconds, push one of the five pushbuttons. Whenever you press that button, the preset station will return.
8. Clock – To set the clock, just:
   A. Press the **SET** pushbutton.
   B. Within 5 seconds, press and hold **SCAN** until the correct minute appears on the display.
   C. Press and hold **SEEK** until the correct hour appears on the display.
9. TREBLE – Press **TRB** + to increase the treble response. If station is weak or noisy, press **TRB** – to reduce the noise.
10. BASS – Press **BAS** + or – to increase or decrease the bass response.
11. AM/FM – Press **AM FM** to select either the AM or FM band. The band you select will be displayed on the VF display along with the frequency of the station. If the station is in stereo, a STEREO indicator will also be displayed.

UM6, AM/FM STEREO CASSETTE WITH SEEK AND SCAN

Figure 1

To Play the Radio

1. Left Knob – The left knob does these things:
   - It turns the system on and off.
   - It controls the volume.
   - It allows you to recall the frequency when the radio is playing. Press the knob.
2. BALANCE – The control behind the center knob allows you to **BAL**ance the sound between the right and left speakers.
3. FADE – The center knob **FADES** the sound between your front and rear speakers.
4. Right Knob – Turn the right knob to **TUNE** radio stations.
5. SEEK – Pressing the **SEEK** button will cause the receiver to seek the next higher station and stop.
6. SCAN – Press **SCAN** once to listen for a few seconds to stations higher on the AM or FM band. The radio will continue to scan stations every few seconds until you press **SCAN** again to stop on a station.

7. Pushbuttons – The five pushbuttons let you return to stations. You can set the pushbuttons for up to ten stations (5 AM and 5 FM). Just:
   A. Tune in the station you want to listen to.
   B. Press the **SET** pushbutton. (NOTE: the display will show SET for about 5 seconds.)
   C. Within the 5 seconds, push one of the five pushbuttons. Whenever you press that button, the preset station will return.
8. Clock – To set the clock, just:
   A. Press the **SET** pushbutton.
   B. Within 5 seconds, press and hold **SCAN** until the correct minute appears on the display.
   C. Press and hold **SEEK** until the correct hour appears on the display.
9. TREBLE – Press **TRB** + to increase the treble response. If station is weak or noisy, press **TRB** – to reduce the noise.
10. BASS – Press **BAS** + or – to increase or decrease the bass response.
11. AM/FM – Press **AM FM** to select either the AM or FM band. The band you select will be displayed on the VF display along with the frequency of the station. If the station is in stereo, a STEREO indicator will also be displayed.

To Play A Cassette

Your tape player is built to work best with tapes that are 30 to 45 minutes long on each side. Tapes longer than that are so thin they may not work well in this player.

Once the tape is playing, use the upper and lower knobs for volume balance and fade just as you did for radio. The arrows indicate which side of the tape is being played.

1. FORWARD – To rapidly advance the tape, press **FWD** and the tape will rapidly go forward until you press the **REV** button lightly.
2. REVERSE – To rapidly reverse the tape, press **REV** and the tape will rapidly reverse until you press the **FWD** button lightly.
3. PROGRAM – To go from one side of the tape to the other, press **PROG**.
4. EJECT – To remove the tape, press the **EJCT** button.

UX1, AM/FM STEREO/CASSETTE WITH EQUALIZER

Figure 2

The VF display is a source of information for many functions. These include the clock, radio station frequency, which radio band (AM or FM) is selected, whether an FM station is in stereo, and more.

To Play the Radio

1. Left Knob – The left knob does these things:
   - It turns the system on and off.
   - It controls the volume.
   - It allows you to recall the frequency when the radio is playing. Press the knob.
2. BALANCE – The control behind the center knob allows you to **BAL**ance the sound between the right and left speakers.
3. FADE – The center knob **FADES** the sound between your front and rear speakers.
4. Right Knob – Turn the right knob to **TUNE** radio stations.
5. SEEK – Pressing the **SEEK** button will cause the receiver to seek the next higher station and stop.
6. SCAN – Press **SCAN** once to listen for a few seconds to stations higher on the AM or FM band. The radio will continue to scan stations every few seconds until you press **SCAN** again to stop on a station.
7. Pushbuttons – The five pushbuttons let you return to stations. You can set the pushbuttons for up to ten stations (5 AM and 5 FM). Just:
   A. Tune in the station you want to listen to.
   B. Press the **SET** pushbutton. (NOTE: the display will show SET for about 5 seconds.)
   C. Within the 5 seconds, push one of the five pushbuttons. Whenever you press that button, the preset station will return.
8. Clock – To set the clock, just:
   A. Press the **SET** pushbutton.
   B. Within 5 seconds, press and hold **SCAN** until the correct minute appears on the display.
   C. Press and hold **SEEK** until the correct hour appears on the display.
9. Equalizer – Press an **EQUALIZER** control + to emphasize a frequency or – to de-emphasize it.
10. MUTE – Press **MUTE** to silence the speakers without turning the unit off. Press **MUTE** again to resume sound in the speakers.
11. LOUD – Press **LD** to increase the bass response. On some systems, **LD** must be pressed for the subwoofer to work properly.
12. AM/FM – Press **AM FM** to select either the AM or FM band. The band you select will be displayed on the VF display along with the frequency of the station. If the station is in stereo, a STEREO indicator will also be displayed.

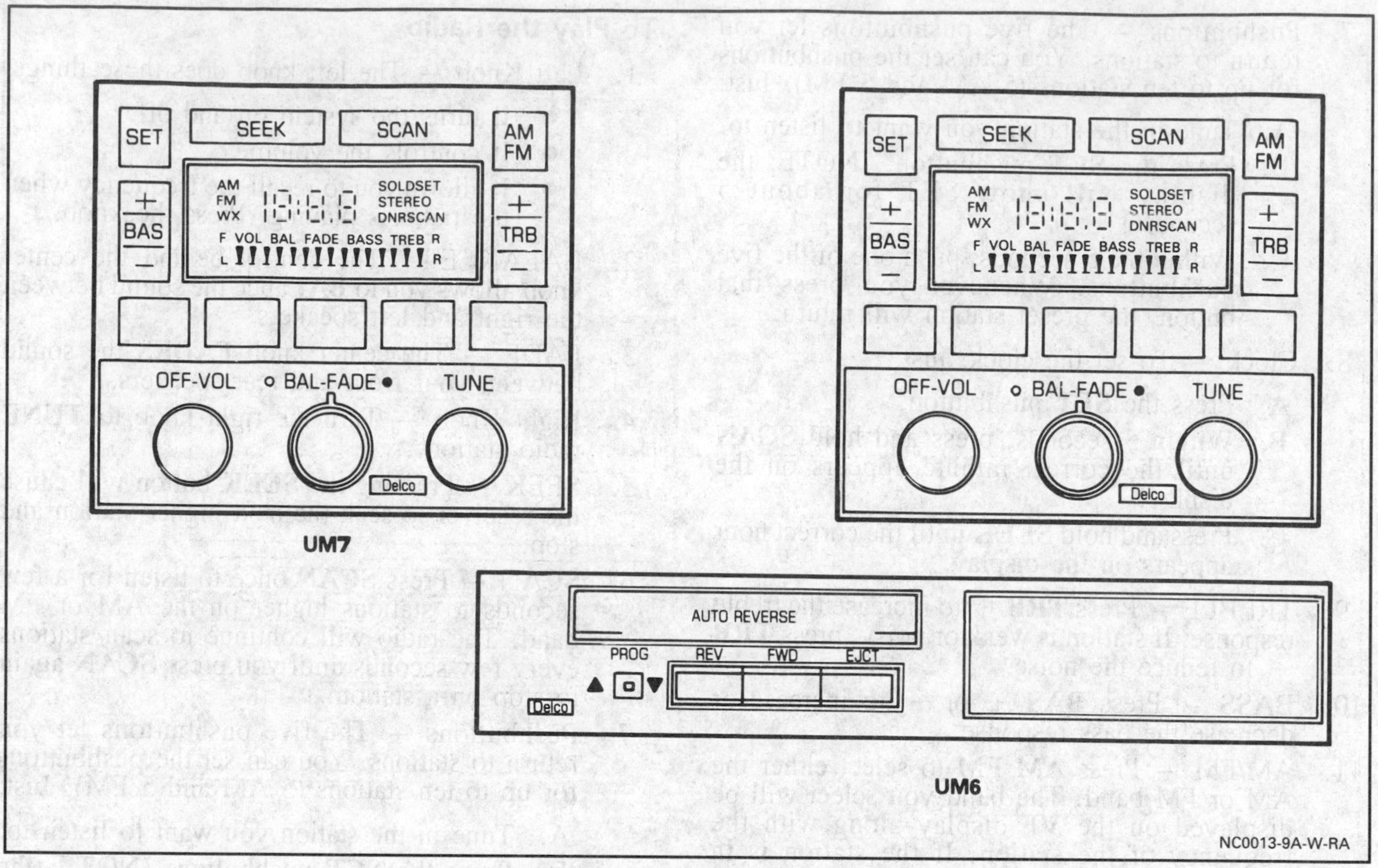
SET
SEEK
SCAN
AM FM
AM FM WX
SOLDSET STEREO DNRSCAN
BAS
TRB
F VOL BAL FADE BASS TREB R
L R
OFF-VOL
BAL-FADE
TUNE
Delco
UM7
AUTO REVERSE
PROG
REV
FWD
EJCT
Delco
UM6
NC0013-9A-W-RA

Figure 1 Audio Systems (1 of 2)

To Play A Cassette

Turn the power on. The radio will play until a cassette is pushed into the cassette entry door (the tape side goes in first). Do not use tapes that are longer than 90 minutes (45 minutes on each side).

1. FORWARD – Press **FWD** to advance the tape rapidly. The button will illuminate while in fast forward mode. Press again to play the tape. (The radio plays while a tape is advancing.)
2. REVERSE – Press to **REV**erse the tape rapidly. The button will illuminate while in the fast reverse mode. Press again to play the tape. (The radio plays while a tape is rewinding.)
3. SEEK – To search for the next selection on the tape, press **SEEK**; then press either **FWD** or **REV**. For the **SEEK** to stop, there must be at least a 3-second gap between selections on the tape. (The radio does not play during **SEEK**.)
4. PROGRAM – Press **PROG** to change the side of the tape being played. When ▲ is lighted, the selections listed on the top side of the tape are played. When ▼ is lighted, selections listed on the bottom side of the tape are played. When the end of a tape is reached, the other side will then play.
5. Dolby Noise Reduction – Press to reduce noise on dolby tapes.
6. CrO_2 – This button sets tape bias. When playing high bias chrome or metal tapes, press **CrO_2** (the L.E.D. in the button will light). When playing standard tapes, press again (the light will go out).
7. EJECT – Press **EJCT** to eject the cassette tape from the tape player (the radio will then play).

U1C, AM/FMS CD

Figure 2

To Play the Radio

1. Left Knob – The left knob does these things:
   - It turns the system on and off.
   - It controls the volume.
   - It allows you to recall the frequency when the radio is playing. Press the knob.
2. BALANCE – The control behind the center knob allows you to **BAL**ance the sound between the right and left speakers.
3. FADE – The center knob **FADES** the sound between your front and rear speakers.
4. Right Knob – Turn the right knob to **TUNE** radio stations.
5. SEEK – Pressing the **SEEK** button will cause the receiver to seek the next higher station and stop.

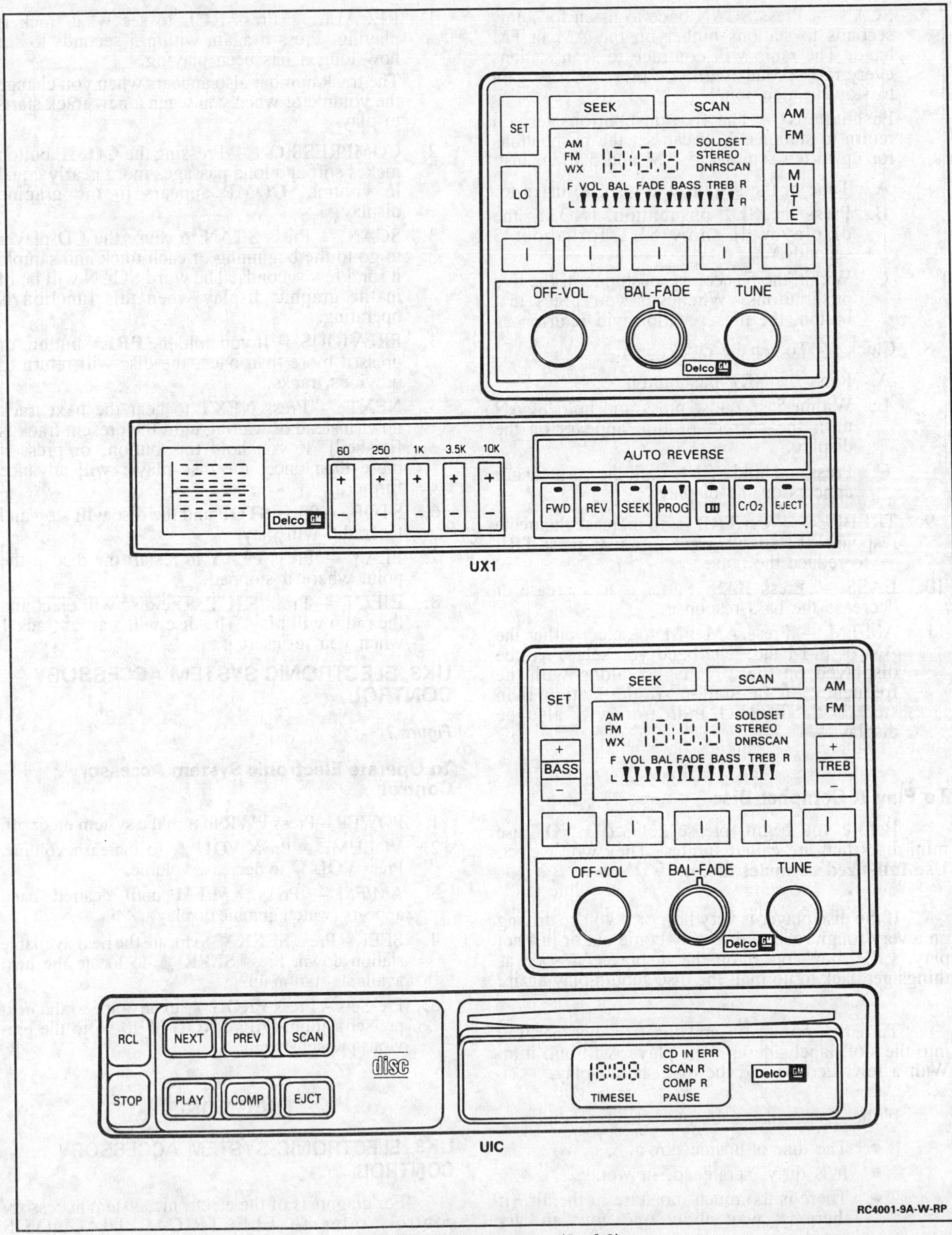
SET
SEEK
SCAN
AM
FM
AM
FM
WX
SOLDSET
STEREO
DNRSCAN
LO
MUTE
F VOL BAL FADE BASS TREB R
L
R
OFF-VOL
BAL-FADE
TUNE
Delco GM
60
250
1K
3.5K
10K
AUTO REVERSE
FWD
REV
SEEK
PROG
CrO2
EJECT
UX1
SET
SEEK
SCAN
AM
FM
BASS
TREB
OFF-VOL
BAL-FADE
TUNE
RCL
NEXT
PREV
SCAN
STOP
PLAY
COMP
EJCT
disc
CD IN ERR
SCAN R
COMP R
TIMESEL
PAUSE
UIC
RC4001-9A-W-RP

Figure 2 Audio Systems (2 of 2)

6. SCAN – Press **SCAN** once to listen for a few seconds to stations higher on the AM or FM band. The radio will continue to scan stations every few seconds until you press **SCAN** again to stop on a station.
7. Pushbuttons – The five pushbuttons let you return to stations. You can set the pushbuttons for up to ten stations (5 AM and 5 FM). Just:
   A. Tune in the station you want to listen to.
   B. Press the **SET** pushbutton. (NOTE: the display will show SET for about 5 seconds.)
   C. Within the 5 seconds, push one of the five pushbuttons. Whenever you press that button, the preset station will return.
8. Clock – To set the clock, just:
   A. Press the **SET** pushbutton.
   B. Within 5 seconds, press and hold **SCAN** until the correct minute appears on the display.
   C. Press and hold **SEEK** until the correct hour appears on the display.
9. TREBLE – Press **TRB** + to increase the treble response. If station is weak or noisy, press **TRB** – to reduce the noise.
10. BASS – Press **BAS** + or – to increase or decrease the bass response.
11. AM/FM – Press **AM FM** to select either the AM or FM band. The band you select will be displayed on the VF display along with the frequency of the station. If the station is in stereo, a STEREO indicator will also be displayed.

To Play A Compact Disc

Before you begin, please note: **DO NOT** use mini-discs that are called singles. They won't eject. **Use full-sized compact discs.**

If the disc player is very hot, or if you're driving on a very rough road, a disc may come out or just not play. ERR may appear on the display. As soon as things get back to normal, the disc should play again.

Turn the system on and insert a disc partway into the slot, label side up. The player will pull it in. Wait a few seconds and the disc should play.

If the disc comes back out, check whether:

- The disc is upside down.
- It is dirty, scratched, or wet.
- There is too much moisture in the air. (If there is, wait about one hour and try again.)

1. RECALL – Press **RCL** to see what track is playing. Press it again within 5 seconds to see how long it has been playing.
   The track number also appears when you change the volume or when you when a new track starts to play.
2. COMPRESSION – Pressing the **COMP** button makes soft and loud passages more nearly equal in volume. **COMP** appears in the graphic display.
3. SCAN – Press **SCAN** to cause the CD player to go to the beginning of each track and sample it for a few seconds. The word **SCAN** will be lit in the graphic display when this function is operating.
4. PREVIOUS – If you hold the **PREV** button, or press it more than once, the disc will return to previous tracks.
5. NEXT – Press **NEXT** to hear the next track now (instead of waiting until the present track is finished). If you hold this button, or press it more than once, the disc player will advance further.
6. STOP – Press **STOP** and the disc will stop and the radio will play.
7. PLAY – Press **PLAY** to restart the disc at the point where it stopped.
8. EJECT – Press **EJCT**. The disc will eject and the radio will play. The disc will start at track 1 when you re-insert it.

UK3, ELECTRONIC SYSTEM ACCESSORY CONTROL

Figure 3

To Operate Electronic System Accessory Control

1. POWER – Press **PWR** to turn the system on or off.
2. VOLUME – Press **VOL ▲** to increase volume. Press **VOL ▼** to decrease volume.
3. AM/FM – Press **AM/FM** until desired band appears (watch graphic display).
4. SEEK – Press **SEEK ▼** to locate the next available station down. Press **SEEK ▲** to locate the next available station up.
5. Pre-Sets – Press **PROG ▲** to advance to the next pre-set station. Press **PROG ▼** to go to the previous pre-set station.

DIAGNOSIS

UK3, ELECTRONIC SYSTEM ACCESSORY CONTROL

For diagnosis of the electronic system accessory control, refer to ELECTRICAL DIAGNOSIS (SECTION 8A).

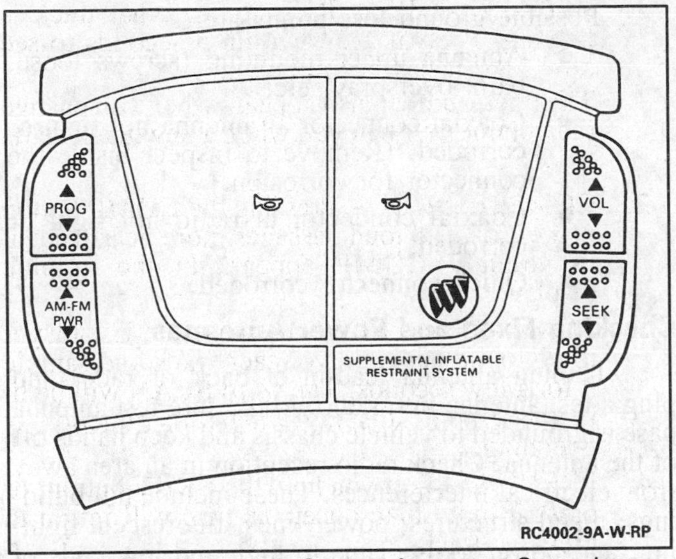
PROG
VOL
AM-FM PWR
SEEK
SUPPLEMENTAL INFLATABLE RESTRAINT SYSTEM
RC4002-9A-W-RP

Figure 3 Electronic System Accessory Control

TAPE PLAYER

For diagnosis of the tape player, refer to Figure 4. For electrical diagnosis, refer to ELECTRICAL DIAGNOSIS (SECTION 8A).

RADIO

Static and Noise

Ground strap connections must be clean and tight; spark plug cables must be TVRS-type and in good condition; and resistance-type spark plugs must be used. Capacitors are used in the generator, heating/air conditioning system, and fuse panel to reduce noise entering the radio through the feed wires. If the vehicle has a heater only, the capacitor is in the blower motor feed wire. If equipped with A/C, the blower motor has a built-in capacitor. Extra electrical equipment added to the vehicle could cause static if not properly grounded or wiring was improperly routed.

Weak FM station reception will be affected by nearby buildings, vehicle speed and direction. These "flutter" and "fading" conditions are characteristic of weak FM signals.

Popping Noise

Operating devices such as turn signals, operating stoplamps, pushing in cigarette lighter, etc., may cause a popping noise on distant (weak) AM signals.

Preliminary Diagnostics

Always determine the exact nature of the radio problem. Is the condition intermittent or constant? Does it occur with the engine off or running, and whether it occurs with vehicle parked or moving will help to pinpoint the problem. Radio diagnostic information is in ELECTRICAL DIAGNOSIS (SECTION 8A).

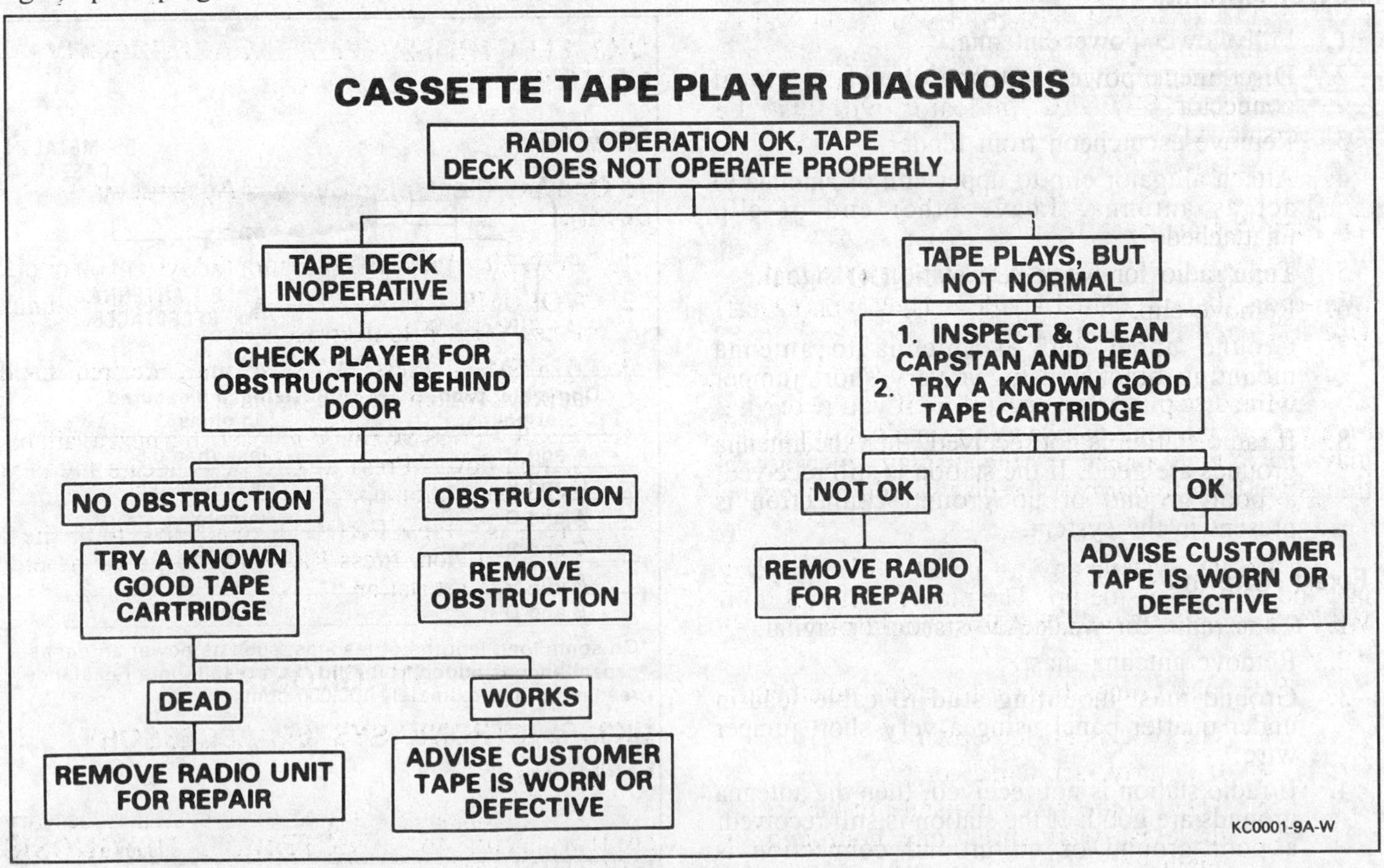
CASSETTE TAPE PLAYER DIAGNOSIS
RADIO OPERATION OK, TAPE DECK DOES NOT OPERATE PROPERLY
TAPE DECK INOPERATIVE
CHECK PLAYER FOR OBSTRUCTION BEHIND DOOR
NO OBSTRUCTION
OBSTRUCTION
TRY A KNOWN GOOD TAPE CARTRIDGE
REMOVE OBSTRUCTION
DEAD
WORKS
REMOVE RADIO UNIT FOR REPAIR
ADVISE CUSTOMER TAPE IS WORN OR DEFECTIVE
TAPE PLAYS, BUT NOT NORMAL
1. INSPECT & CLEAN CAPSTAN AND HEAD
2. TRY A KNOWN GOOD TAPE CARTRIDGE
NOT OK
OK
REMOVE RADIO FOR REPAIR
ADVISE CUSTOMER TAPE IS WORN OR DEFECTIVE
KC0001-9A-W

Figure 4 Tape Player Diagnosis

Follow these quick checks before removing the radio for repair.

1. Turn ignition to the accessory position and turn radio on.
2. On AM-FM radios, if the radio is inoperative on FM but the AM plays normally, the radio should be removed for repair. (The reverse of this condition does not necessarily call for radio removal.) Refer to ELECTRICAL DIAGNOSIS (SECTION 8A).
3. On combination radio/tape player units, if the radio operates properly but the tape player does not, the unit should be removed for repair. (The reverse of this condition does not necessarily call for radio/tape player removal.) Refer to ELECTRICAL DIAGNOSIS (SECTION 8A).

FIXED AND POWER ANTENNA

Testing For Good Ground of Antenna Mounting and Connections

Poor grounding of the antenna, either at the antenna mounting or at any other connection in the antenna/lead-in system, can result in reduced radio performance. A poor ground can cause excess ignition noise in AM reception, or erratic sound.

To check for a poor ground of the antenna, do the following:

Power Antenna

1. Fully lower power antenna.
2. Disconnect power antenna motor electrical connector.
3. Remove escutcheon from fender.
4. Attach alligator clip to upper end of antenna to act as antenna. Leave other end of clip unattached.
5. Tune radio for weak AM station or signal.
6. Remove clip.
7. Ground upper end of antenna to antenna mounting bracket using a very short jumper wire.
8. If radio station is not received, then the antenna grounds are good. If the station is still received, a poor ground or no ground connection is present in the system.

Fixed Antenna

1. Tune radio for weak AM station or signal.
2. Remove antenna mast.
3. Ground mast mounting stud to cable lead-in under quarter panel using a very short jumper wire.
4. If radio station is not received, then the antenna grounds are good. If the station is still received, a poor ground or no ground connection is present in the system.

Possible ground loss points are:

- Antenna upper mounting (screws loose, paint overspray, etc.).
- Coaxial connector at antenna not tight or corroded. (Remove to inspect inside the connector for corrosion.)
- Coaxial connector at radio not tight or corroded.
- Quick connector corroded.

Checking Fixed and Power Antennas

Unplug antenna lead-in at back of radio and plug a test antenna into radio. Make sure test antenna base is grounded to vehicle chassis and keep hands off of the antenna. Check radio reception in an area away from electrical interferences. These include tall buildings, metal structures, power lines, fluorescent lighting, and power tools. Tune to high and low ends of the dial on both AM and FM checking weak and strong station reception. If reception is OK, problem exists with antenna and/or its lead-in cable. If reception is still poor, refer to ELECTRICAL DIAGNOSIS (SECTION 8A).

Checking Lead-In Cables

Figure 5

Usually symptoms of broken center conductor of the lead-in cable will result in no AM and weak FM. In case of continued reception or noise com-

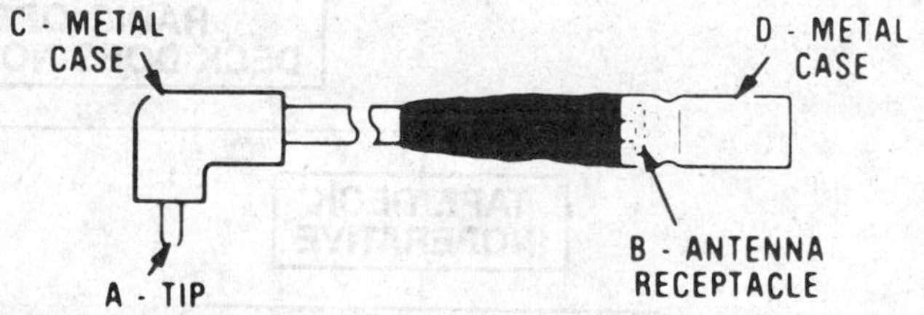
C - METAL CASE
D - METAL CASE
B - ANTENNA RECEPTACLE
A - TIP

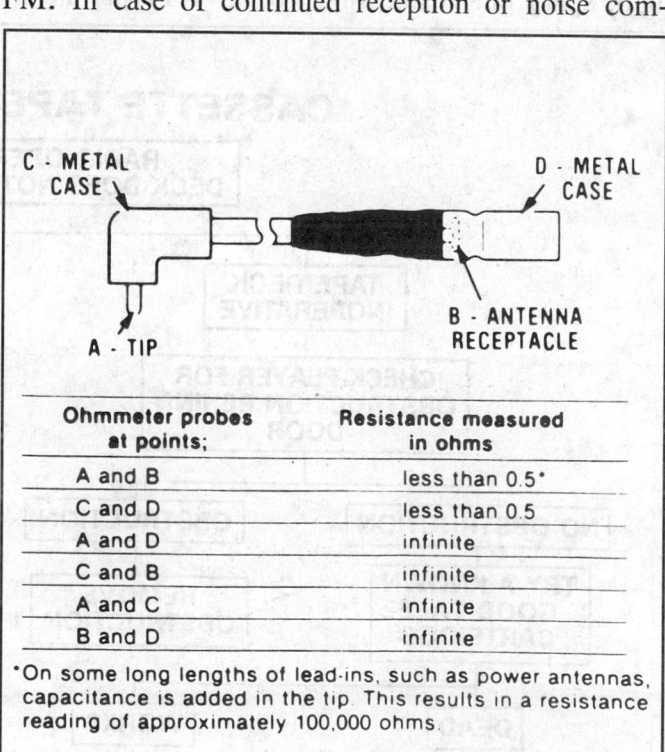

Ohmmeter probes at points;	Resistance measured in ohms
A and B	less than 0.5*
C and D	less than 0.5
A and D	infinite
C and B	infinite
A and C	infinite
B and D	infinite

*On some long lengths of lead-ins, such as power antennas, capacitance is added in the tip. This results in a resistance reading of approximately 100,000 ohms.

G35209-9-E

Figure 5 Lead-in Cable Diagnosis

plaints, always check the lead-in with an ohmmeter. Twist and pull antenna lead-in cable to disconnect. The chart and diagram show readings which should be obtained. When checking resistance, carefully wiggle the lead-in tip and cable. If the readings shown are not obtained, some portion of the lead-in is intermittent and the lead-in should be replaced. Twist and pull antenna lead-in to disconnect.

POWER ANTENNA

For diagnosis of the power antenna, refer to 8A-151-0 ELECTRICAL DIAGNOSIS (SECTION 8A). For removal and installation procedures, refer to "On-Vehicle Service" in this section.

RADIO NOISE SUPPRESSION EQUIPMENT

When installing a new radio, or when noise is a problem, make sure that radio suppression equipment is present and properly installed. Refer to 8A-150-0 ELECTRICAL DIAGNOSIS (SECTION 8A).

STEREO CASSETTE TAPE PLAYER CARE

Figure 6

Optimum performance can be maintained by cleaning the internal tape head, capstan, and pinch roller periodically. Clean the tape head every 15 hours for optimum audio performance. Cleaning at least every 50 hours will help prevent damage to the playback unit. This can be done by inserting a nonabrasive cleaning cassette in place of the music tape.

- DO NOT USE silicone spray lubricants for switch, plunger or tape head lubrication.
- NO LUBRICANTS should be used because they cause the tape player to operate improperly, especially at extreme temperatures.
- Do not bring any magnetized tools near the tape head. If the head becomes magnetized, every cassette played will be degraded.

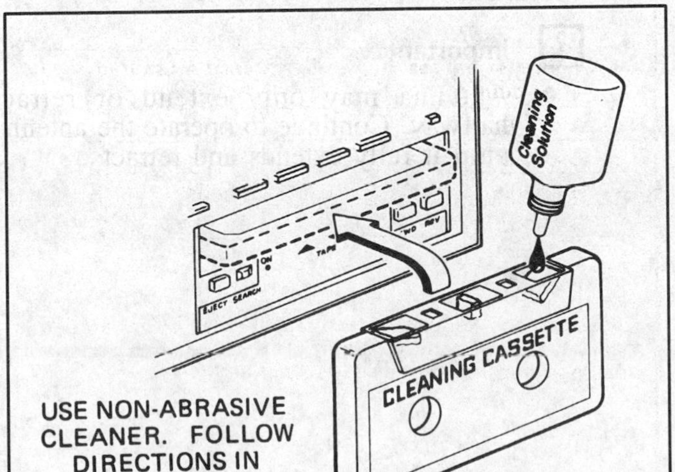
Cleaning Solution
CLEANING CASSETTE
USE NON-ABRASIVE CLEANER. FOLLOW DIRECTIONS IN PACKAGE.
G20003-9A

Figure 6 Cleaning the Cassette Player

Store cassettes away from extreme heat or direct sunlight. Protect the open ends from dirt or damage; store them in their original cases or other protective cases. For best results, do not use tapes longer than 60 minutes total (30 minutes per side).

When leaving the vehicle, cassettes may be left in the tape player (tapes are either automatically ejected or internally protected).

CLEANING OF POWER ANTENNA MAST

- Periodic cleaning may be necessary to assure proper radio and power antenna operation.
- Do not lubricate the antenna mast. Lubrication will cause a collection of dust that will cause damage to the antenna operation.

Recommended cleaning procedures:

1. Actuate antenna to full mast extension.
2. Dampen clean cloth with mineral spirits.
3. Wipe cloth over antenna mast sections removing any dirt.
4. Actuate antenna through one complete retraction and extension cycle.
5. Repeat steps 1-4 at least two times.

ON-VEHICLE SERVICE

For removal and installation procedures of front speakers, refer to INSTRUMENT PANEL, GAGES AND CONSOLE (SECTION 8C).

For removal and installation procedures of door speakers, refer to DOORS (SECTION 10-6).

For removal and installation procedures of rear speakers, refer to BODY REAR END (SECTION 10-8).

For removal and installation procedures of radio assembly, refer to INSTRUMENT PANEL, GAGES AND CONSOLE (SECTION 8C).

For removal and installation procedures of UQ3, low frequency audio amplifier assembly, refer to INSTRUMENT PANEL, GAGES AND CONSOLE (SECTION 8C).

FIXED MAST ANTENNA

Figures 7 and 8

Remove or Disconnect

- Antenna mast by unscrewing.

Install or Connect

- Antenna mast.

Tighten

- Mast to 5 N·m (44 lb. in.).

FIXED ANTENNA CABLE (SEDAN)

Figure 7

Tool Required:

J 38536 Antenna Bezel Socket

Remove or Disconnect

1. Fixed antenna mast. Refer to "Fixed Antenna Mast" in this section.
2. Nut using J 38536.
3. Antenna cable.

Install or Connect

1. Antenna cable.
2. Nut using J 38536.

Tighten

- Nut to 4 N·m (35 lb. in.).

3. Fixed antenna mast. Refer to "Fixed Antenna Mast" in this section.

FIXED ANTENNA ASSEMBLY (COUPE)

Figure 8

Remove or Disconnect

1. Open rear compartment lid.
2. Rear quarter trim cover.
3. Fixed antenna mast. Refer to "Fixed Antenna Mast" in this section.
4. Bolt and nuts.
5. Fixed antenna assembly.

Install or Connect

1. Fixed antenna assembly.
2. Bolt and nuts.

Tighten

- Bolt to 3 N·m (27 lb. in.).
- Nuts to 5 N·m (44 lb. in.).

3. Fixed antenna mast. Refer to "Fixed Antenna Mast" in this section.
4. Rear quarter trim cover.
5. Close rear compartment lid.

POWER ANTENNA

Figure 9

The antenna may be replaced separately from the motor. The antenna should be cleaned when it becomes dirty. Do not lubricate the antenna.

Remove or Disconnect

1. Antenna nut.
2. With the ignition switch on, turn on the radio to raise the antenna.
   - Do not pull the antenna up by hand.
   - The antenna contact spring, located on the bottom of the antenna, will be reused. Clean the contact spring with contact cleaner and set aside for later use.

Install or Connect

1. Insert plastic cable into housing and stop when about 304.8 mm (12 inches) resistance is felt.

Important

- Serrated side of the plastic cable must face the antenna motor.

2. With the ignition on, turn off the radio to lower the antenna.
3. If the plastic cable does not retract into the housing, rotate the cable until the cable retracts into the housing with the motor operating.
4. Contact spring on the antenna. Make certain the flanged end of the contact spring faces upward.
5. Antenna nut.

Tighten

- Nut to 2 N·m (18 lb. in.).

6. Cycle the antenna several times to check the operation.

Important

- Antenna may only extend or retract halfway. Continue to operate the antenna until it fully extends and retracts.

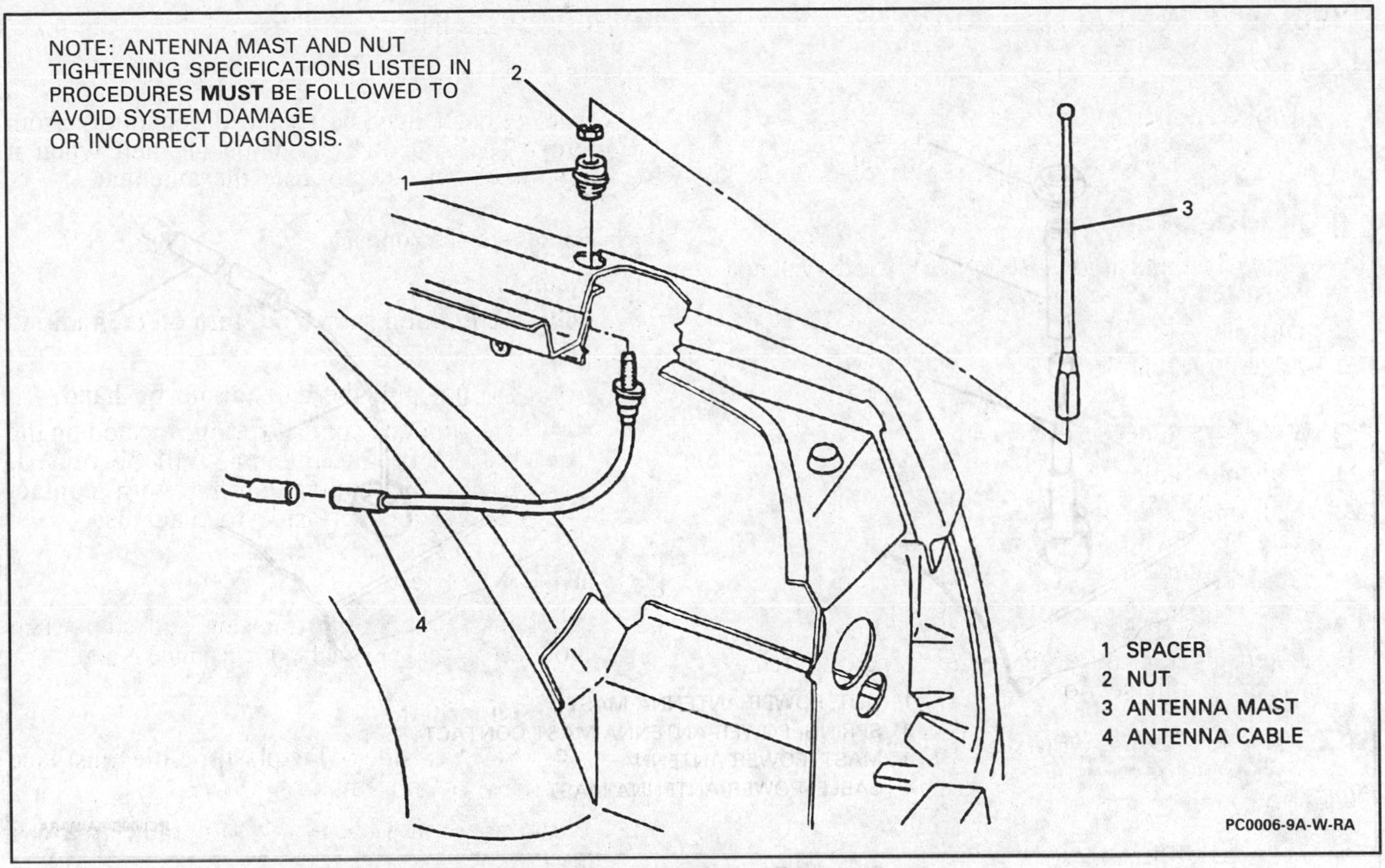
NOTE: ANTENNA MAST AND NUT TIGHTENING SPECIFICATIONS LISTED IN PROCEDURES **MUST** BE FOLLOWED TO AVOID SYSTEM DAMAGE OR INCORRECT DIAGNOSIS.
1
2
3
4
1 SPACER
2 NUT
3 ANTENNA MAST
4 ANTENNA CABLE
PC0006-9A-W-RA

Figure 7 Fixed Antenna Replacement (Sedan)

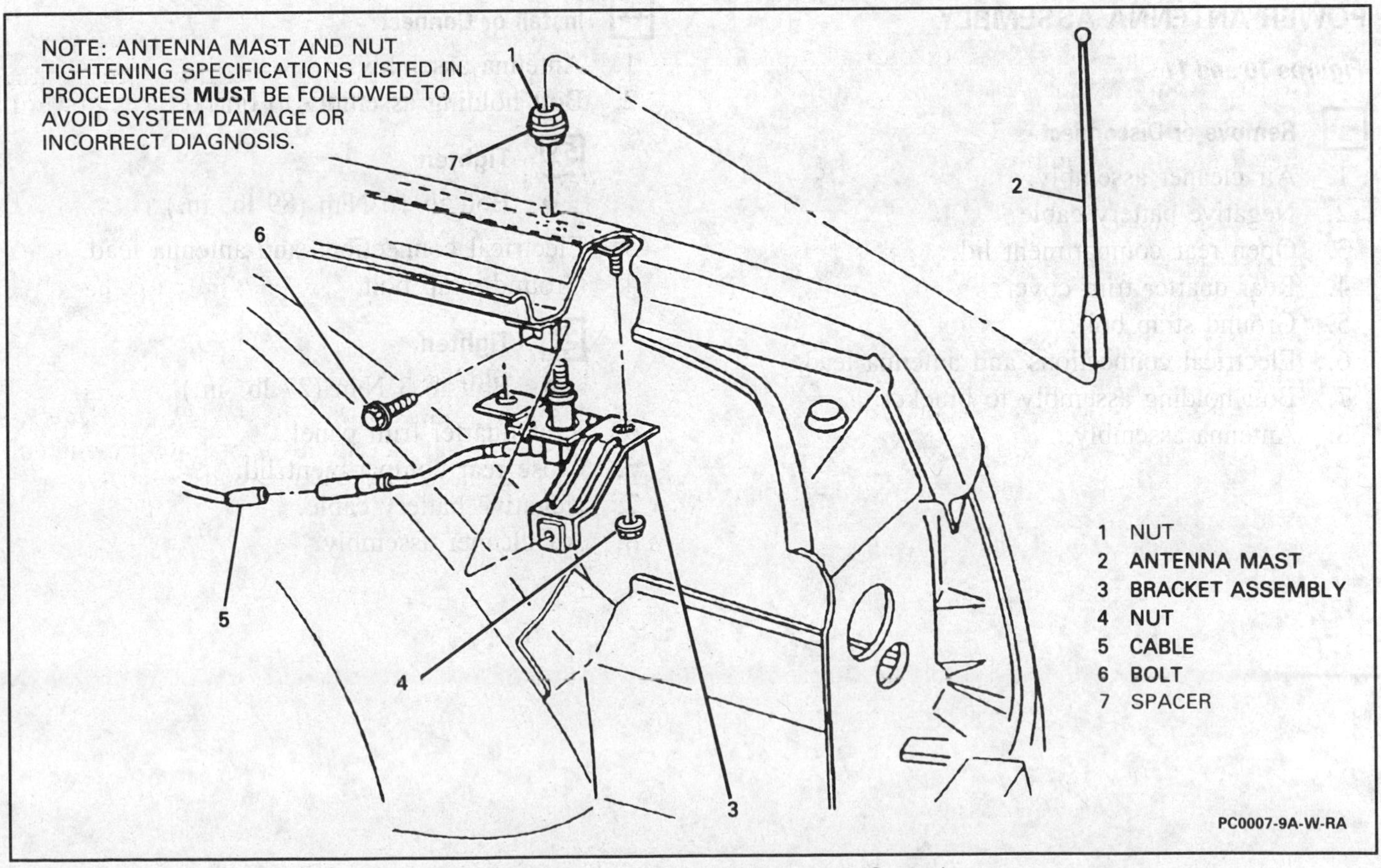
NOTE: ANTENNA MAST AND NUT TIGHTENING SPECIFICATIONS LISTED IN PROCEDURES **MUST** BE FOLLOWED TO AVOID SYSTEM DAMAGE OR INCORRECT DIAGNOSIS.
1
2
3
4
5
6
7
1 NUT
2 ANTENNA MAST
3 BRACKET ASSEMBLY
4 NUT
5 CABLE
6 BOLT
7 SPACER
PC0007-9A-W-RA

Figure 8 Fixed Antenna Replacement (Coupe)

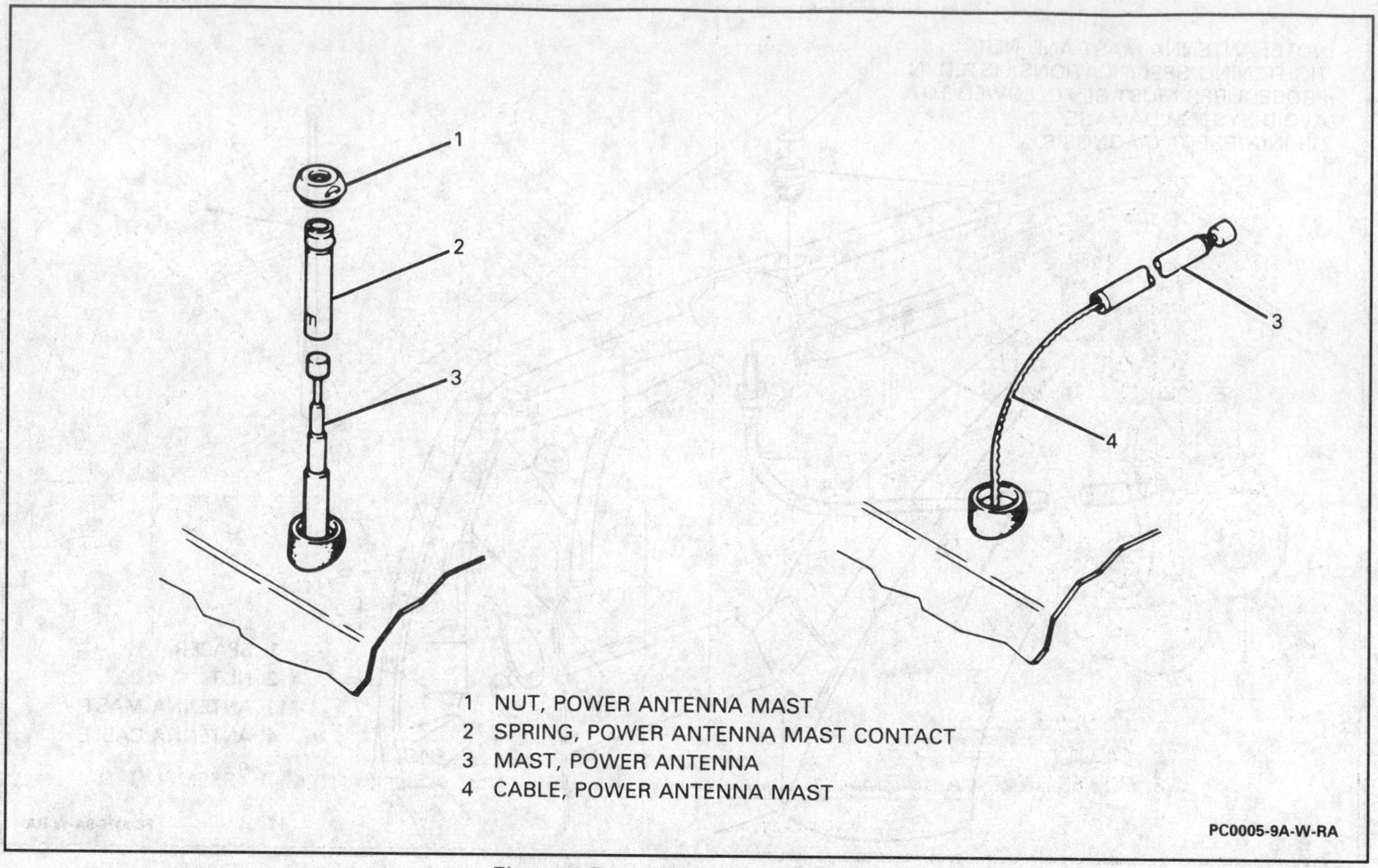
1
2
3
3
4
1 NUT, POWER ANTENNA MAST
2 SPRING, POWER ANTENNA MAST CONTACT
3 MAST, POWER ANTENNA
4 CABLE, POWER ANTENNA MAST
PC0005-9A-W-RA

Figure 9 Power Mast Replacement

POWER ANTENNA ASSEMBLY

Figures 10 and 11

↔ Remove or Disconnect

1. Air cleaner assembly.
2. Negative battery cable.
3. Open rear compartment lid.
4. Rear quarter trim cover.
5. Ground strap bolt.
6. Electrical connections and antenna lead.
7. Bolt holding assembly to bracket.
8. Antenna assembly.

→← Install or Connect

1. Antenna assembly.
2. Bolt holding assembly to bracket.

Tighten

- Bolt to 10 N·m (89 lb. in.).

3. Electrical connections and antenna lead.
4. Ground strap bolt.

Tighten

- Bolt to 3 N·m (27 lb. in.).

5. Rear quarter trim panel.
6. Close rear compartment lid.
7. Negative battery cable.
8. Air cleaner assembly.

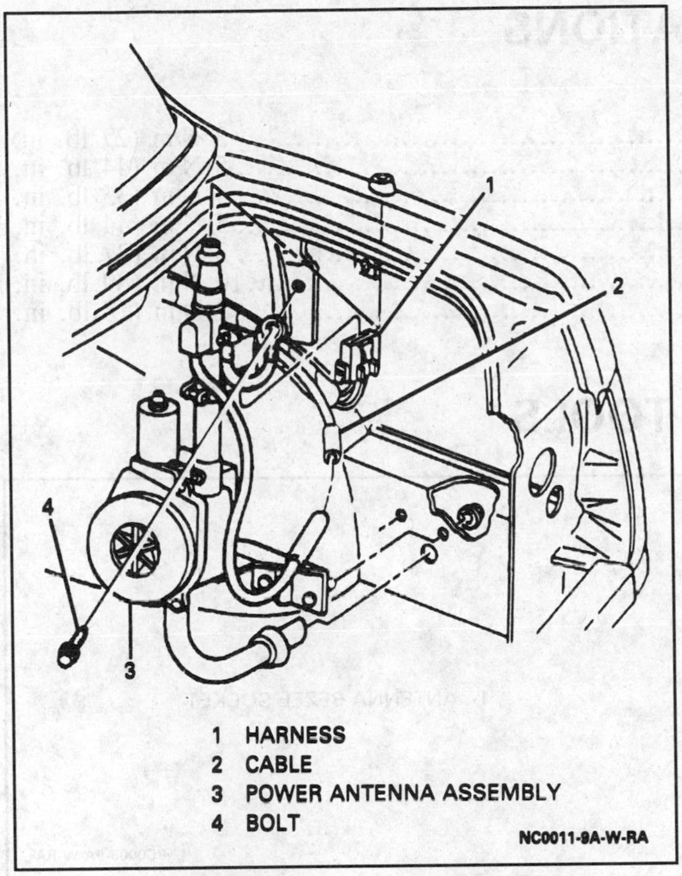
1 HARNESS
2 CABLE
3 POWER ANTENNA ASSEMBLY
4 BOLT
NC0011-9A-W-RA

Figure 10 Power Antenna Assembly (Sedan)

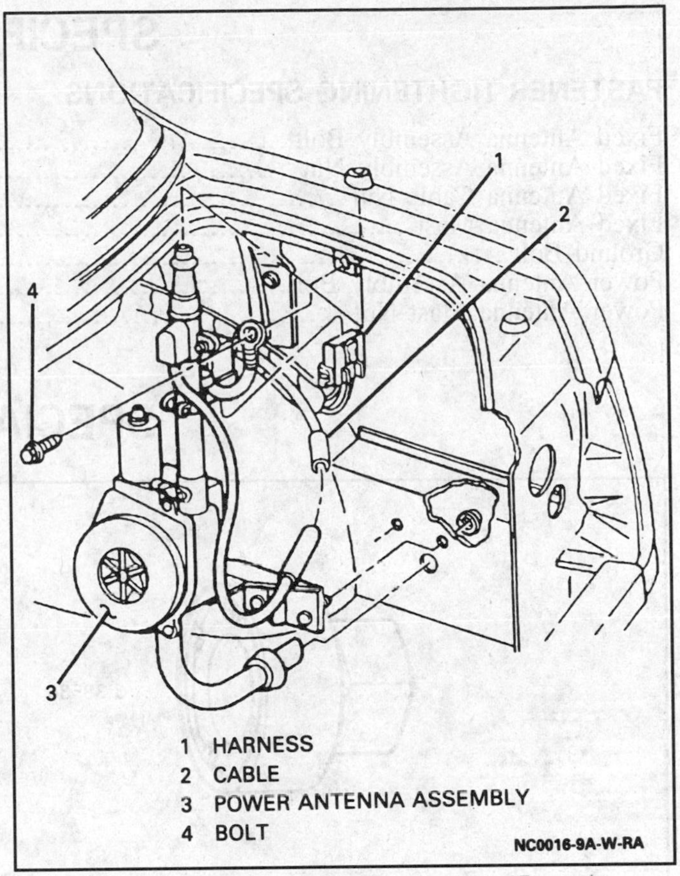
1 HARNESS
2 CABLE
3 POWER ANTENNA ASSEMBLY
4 BOLT
NC0016-9A-W-RA

Figure 11 Power Antenna Assembly (Coupe)

SPECIFICATIONS

FASTENER TIGHTENING SPECIFICATIONS

Fixed Antenna Assembly Bolt	3 N·m (27 lb. in.)
Fixed Antenna Assembly Nut	5 N·m (44 lb. in.)
Fixed Antenna Cable Nut	4 N·m (35 lb. in.)
Fixed Antenna Mast	5 N·m (44 lb. in.)
Ground Bolt	3 N·m (27 lb. in.)
Power Antenna Assembly Bolt	10 N·m (89 lb. in.)
Power Antenna Mast Nut	2 N·m (18 lb. in.)

SPECIAL TOOLS

1 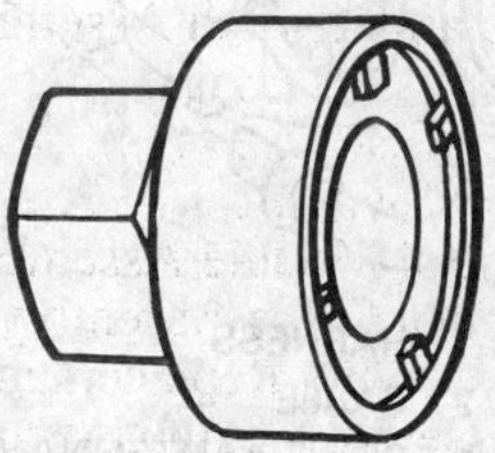 J 38536

1 ANTENNA BEZEL SOCKET

PC0003-9A-W-RA

SECTION 9B

CRUISE CONTROL

NOTICE: When fasteners are removed, always reinstall them at the same location from which they were removed. If a fastener needs to be replaced, use the correct part number fastener for that application. If the correct part number fastener is not available, a fastener of equal size and strength (or stronger) may be used. Fasteners that are not reused, and those requiring thread locking compound will be called out. The correct torque value must be used when installing fasteners that require it. If the above conditions are not followed, parts or system damage could result.

CONTENTS

GENERAL DESCRIPTION

Cruise control is a speed control system that maintains a desired vehicle speed under normal driving conditions. However, steep grades up or down may cause variations in the selected speeds. The electronic cruise control system has the capability to cruise, coast, resume speed, accelerate and "tap-up" and "tap-down."

The main parts of the cruise control system are the functional control switches, cruise control module assembly, vehicle speed sensor and cruise control release switch and stoplamp switch assemblies.

The cruise control system uses a cruise control module assembly to obtain the desired vehicle cruise operation. Two important components in the module assembly help to do this. One is an electronic controller and the second is an electric stepper motor. The controller monitors vehicle speed and operates the electric stepper motor. The motor moves a band and throttle linkage, in response to the controller, to maintain the desired cruise speed. The cruise control module assembly contains a low speed limit which will prevent system engagement below a minimum speed of 40 km/h (25 mph). The operation of the controller is controlled by functional control switches located on the multifunctional turn signal lever.

Cruise control release switch and stoplamp switch assemblies are provided to disengage the cruise system. The switch assemblies are mounted on the brake pedal bracket assembly. When the brake pedal assembly is depressed, the cruise control system is electrically disengaged and the throttle is returned to the idle position.

CRUISE CONTROL MODULE ASSEMBLY

The cruise control module assembly is mounted on the left strut tower. The module assembly has an electronic controller and an electric stepper motor to vary the throttle with each different cruise control mode. The module assembly is not serviceable.

CRUISE CONTROL RELEASE SWITCH AND STOPLAMP SWITCH ASSEMBLIES

The cruise control release switch and stoplamp switch assemblies are used to disengage the cruise control system. A release switch assembly and a stoplamp switch assembly mounted on the brake pedal bracket assembly disengage the system electrically when the brake pedal assembly is depressed. This is done by activating the brake cut-out input to the cruise control module assembly. The speed of the vehicle at brake actuation will be stored in the memory of the system.

SPEED SENSOR

Vehicle Speed Sensor (VSS) Buffer Assembly

The vehicle speed sensor (VSS) buffer assembly receives a signal from the VSS (permanent magnet generator) indicating the speed of the vehicle. This signal is then processed by the VSS buffer assembly and supplied to the engine control module (ECM), the cruise control module assembly and the speedometer assembly.

Refer to SECTION 8A to troubleshoot the VSS buffer assembly and to SECTION 8C to remove and replace the VSS buffer assembly.

Vehicle Speed Sensor (VSS)

The vehicle speed sensor (VSS) is mounted to the automatic transmission assembly and produces an AC signal. The frequency of this signal is proportional to the speed at which the automatic transmission assembly output shaft rotates, which in turn, is proportional to the speed of the vehicle.

The AC signal produced by the VSS is amplified and converted by the VSS buffer assembly. The signal is supplied to the ECM, cruise control module assembly and speedometer assembly by the VSS buffer. The VSS buffer assembly produces the signal by opening and closing internal solid state switches to ground.

The signal to the ECM, cruise control module assembly and speedometer assembly is at a rate of 4000 pulses per mile. The ECM, cruise control module assembly and speedometer assembly internally convert the number of pulses per mile per second to determine vehicle speed.

For removal procedure, refer to SECTION 7A or to SECTION 8A for diagnostic information.

CRUISE CONTROL OPERATION

Figure 1

With cruise control, you can maintain a speed of about 25 mph (40 km/h) or more without keeping your foot on the accelerator. This can really help on long trips.

Cruise control does not work at speeds below about 25 mph (40 km/h).

When you apply your brakes, the cruise control shuts off.

To Set Cruise Control

1. Move the cruise control switch to **ON**.

   CAUTION: Cruise Control can be dangerous where you can't drive safely at a steady speed. So, don't use your Cruise Control on winding roads or in heavy traffic.

   Cruise Control can be dangerous on slippery roads. On such roads, fast changes in tire traction can cause needless wheel spinning, and you could lose control. Don't use Cruise Control on slippery roads.

2. Get up to the speed you want.
3. Push in the **SET** button at the end of the lever and release it.
4. Take your foot off the accelerator pedal.

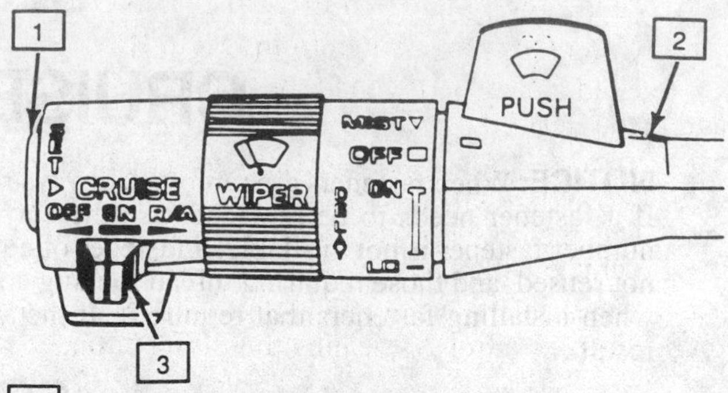

1
2
PUSH
MIST
OFF
ON
CRUISE
OFF ON R/A
WIPER
LO
3

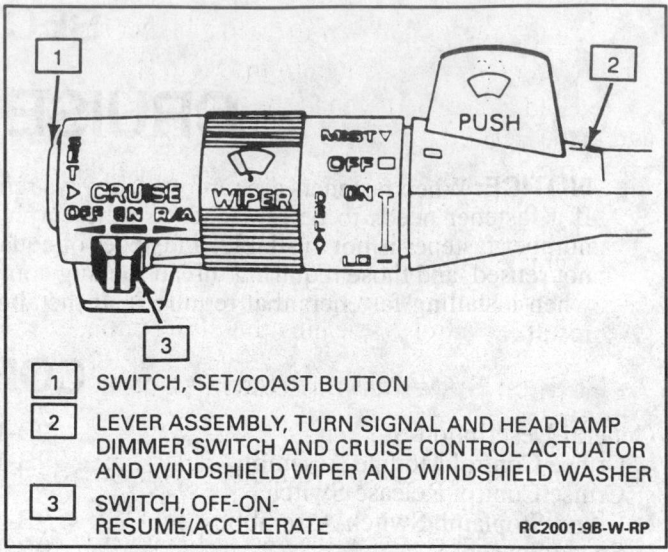

1 SWITCH, SET/COAST BUTTON
2 LEVER ASSEMBLY, TURN SIGNAL AND HEADLAMP DIMMER SWITCH AND CRUISE CONTROL ACTUATOR AND WINDSHIELD WIPER AND WINDSHIELD WASHER
3 SWITCH, OFF-ON-RESUME/ACCELERATE

RC2001-9B-W-RP

Figure 1 Multifunctional Turn Signal Lever

CAUTION: If you leave your Cruise Control switch on when you're not using Cruise, you might hit a button and go into Cruise when you don't want to. You could be startled and even lose control. Keep the Cruise Control switch OFF until you want to use it.

To Resume a Set Speed

Suppose you set your cruise control at a desired speed with the **SET** button and then you apply the brake. This, of course, shuts off the cruise control. But you don't need to reset it. Once you're going about 25 mph (40 km/h) or more, you can move the cruise control switch from **ON** to **R/A** (which stands for Resume/Accelerate) for about half a second.

You'll go right back up to your chosen speed and stay there.

If you shift into **P** (Park) after you set a cruise control speed, you'll erase the system's memory. Moving the switch to **R/A** won't restore the speed you set.

To Increase Speed While Using Cruise Control

There are two ways to go to a higher speed. Here's the first:

1. Use the accelerator pedal to get to the higher speed.
2. Push the button at the end of the lever, then release the button and the accelerator pedal.

You'll now cruise at the higher speed.

Here's the second way to go to a higher speed:

1. Move the cruise switch from **ON** to **R/A**.

   Hold it there until you get up to the speed you want, and then release the switch.

2. To increase your speed in very small amounts, move the switch to R/A for less than half a second and then release it. Each time you do this, your vehicle will go about 1 mph (1.6 km/h) faster.

The accelerate feature will only work after you turn on the cruise control by pushing the **SET** button.

To Reduce Speed While Using Cruise Control

There are two ways to reduce your speed while using cruise control:

- Push in the button at the end of the lever until you reach the lower speed you want, then release it.
- To slow down in very small amounts, push the button for less than half a second. Each time you do this, you'll go 1 mph (1.6 km/h) slower.

Passing Another Vehicle While Using Cruise Control

Use the accelerator pedal to increase your speed. When you take your foot off the pedal, your vehicle will slow down to the cruise control speed you set earlier.

Using Cruise Control on Hills

How well your cruise control will work on hills depends upon your speed, load, and the steepness of the hills. When going up steep hills, you may have to step on the accelerator pedal to maintain your speed. When going downhill, you may have to brake or shift to a lower gear to keep your speed down. Of course, applying the brake takes you out of cruise control. Many drivers find this to be too much trouble and don't use cruise control on steep hills.

To Get Out of Cruise Control

There are two ways to turn off the cruise control:

- Step lightly on the brake pedal; OR
- Move the cruise switch to **OFF**.

To Erase Cruise Speed Memory

When you turn off the cruise control or the ignition, or shift into **P** (Park), your cruise control set speed memory is erased.

DIAGNOSIS

IMPROPER CRUISE CONTROL OPERATION

In resolving any cruise system malfunction, first make a visual inspection. Check the system to ensure there are no bare, broken or disconnected wires. If preliminary inspection reveals no solution and the system is inoperative, use diagnostic information in ELECTRICAL DIAGNOSIS (SECTION 8A).

ON-VEHICLE SERVICE

CRUISE CONTROL RELEASE SWITCH AND STOPLAMP SWITCH ASSEMBLIES

Figures 2 and 3

Adjustment

The release switch assembly and the stoplamp switch assembly cannot be adjusted until after the brake booster pushrod is assembled to brake pedal assembly. The cruise control release switch and the stoplamp switch are adjusted together. Incorrect adjustment could cause the cruise control system to not work properly. For more information about the stoplamp switch adjustment refer to BRAKES (SECTION 5).

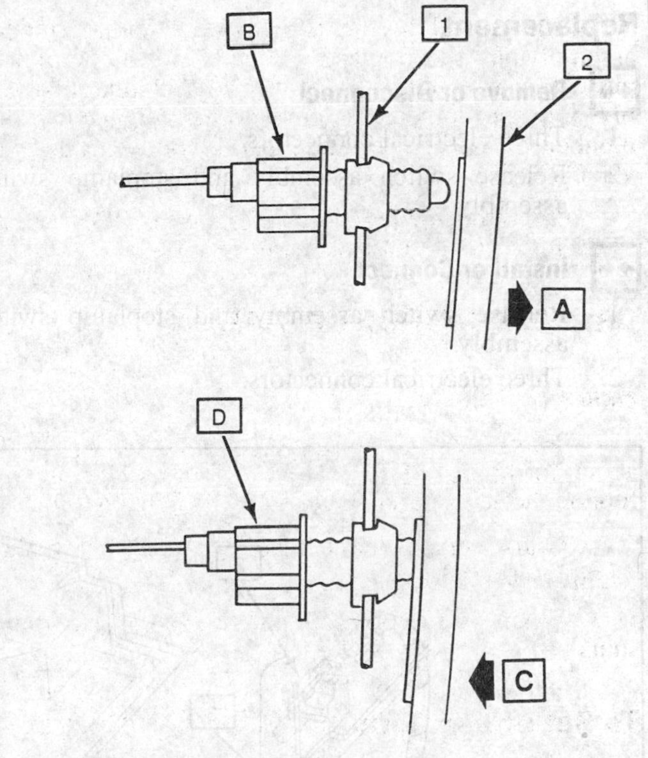
B
1
2
A
D
C

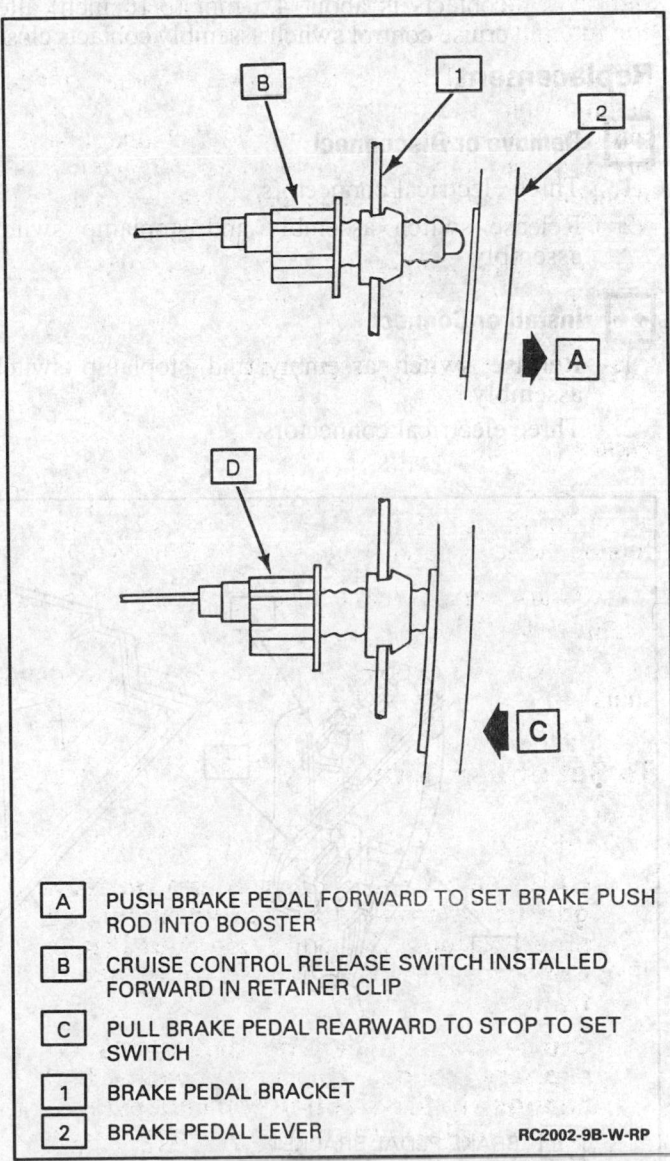

A	PUSH BRAKE PEDAL FORWARD TO SET BRAKE PUSH ROD INTO BOOSTER
B	CRUISE CONTROL RELEASE SWITCH INSTALLED FORWARD IN RETAINER CLIP
C	PULL BRAKE PEDAL REARWARD TO STOP TO SET SWITCH
1	BRAKE PEDAL BRACKET
2	BRAKE PEDAL LEVER

RC2002-9B-W-RP

Figure 2 Cruise Control Release Switch Adjustment

Adjust

1. Press brake pedal assembly and insert release switch assembly and stoplamp switch assembly into retainers until fully seated.

2. Slowly release brake pedal assembly back to its fully retracted position. The release switch assembly and stoplamp switch assembly will move within retainers to their "adjusted" position.

Measure

- The following brake pedal assembly travel distances can be used to check for properly adjusted release switch assembly and stoplamp switch assembly.
    - Release switch assembly and stoplamp switch assembly contacts must be open at 3.5 to 12.5 mm (1/8 to 1/2 inch) brake pedal assembly travel, measured at the centerline of the brake pedal assembly pad. Nominal actuation of the stoplamp switch assembly contacts is about 4.5 mm (3/16 inch) after cruise control switch assembly contacts close.

Replacement

Remove or Disconnect

1. Three electrical connectors.
2. Release switch assembly and stoplamp switch assembly.

Install or Connect

1. Release switch assembly and stoplamp switch assembly.
2. Three electrical connectors.

Adjust

- Release switch assembly and stoplamp switch assembly as outlined above.

ENGAGEMENT SWITCH

Figure 1

The engagement switch cannot be serviced. The complete multifunctional turn signal lever must be replaced as an assembly.

Remove or Disconnect

1. Battery negative cable.
2. Electrical connector from backside of switch.

Important

- Make sure windshield wiper switch is in "OFF" position.

3. Lever assembly by pulling it straight out.

Install or Connect

1. Lever assembly by pushing it in.
2. Electrical connector at backside of switch.
3. Battery negative cable.

Tighten

- Bolt to 15 N•m (11 lb. ft.).

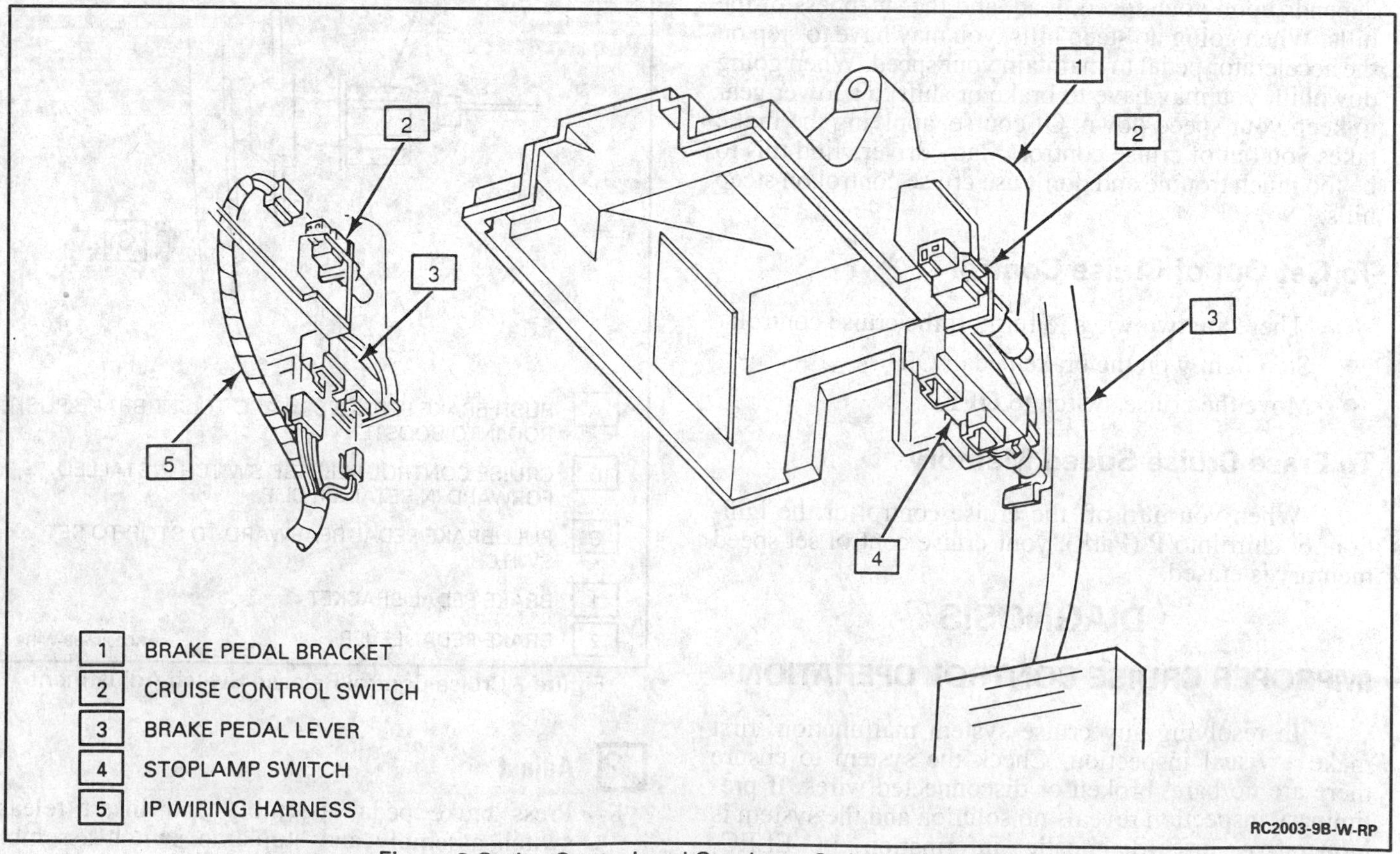
2
3
5
1
2
3
4
1 BRAKE PEDAL BRACKET
2 CRUISE CONTROL SWITCH
3 BRAKE PEDAL LEVER
4 STOPLAMP SWITCH
5 IP WIRING HARNESS
RC2003-9B-W-RP

Figure 3 Cruise Control and Stoplamp Switches Installed

CRUISE CONTROL MODULE ASSEMBLY

Figures 4 through 7

The cruise control module assembly is mounted on the left shock tower in the engine compartment.

Remove or Disconnect

1. Battery negative cable.
2. Cruise control cable at engine bracket and TBI cam.
3. Cruise control cable from module assembly.
4. Electrical connector from module assembly.
5. Three nuts from mounting studs.
6. Module assembly.

Install or Connect

1. Module assembly on mounting stuck.
2. Three nuts.

Tighten

- Nuts to 4 N•m (36 lb. in.).

3. Electrical connector to module.
4. Cruise control cable to module assembly.
5. Cruise control cable to engine bracket and TBI cam.

Adjust

- Cruise control cable:

A. Disengage adjustment lock on cruise control cable (cable will move freely in and out of adjuster when lock is disengaged).

B. Hold TBI at closed position.

C. Engage adjustment lock.

6. Battery negative cable.

Tighten

- Bolt to 15 N•m (11 lb. ft.).

CRUISE CONTROL CABLE ASSEMBLY

Cable Assembly Replacement

Figures 5 through 9

Remove or Disconnect

1. Cruise control cable at TBI cam and engine bracket.
2. Cruise control cable from cruise control module.

Important

- Note cable routing for replacement.

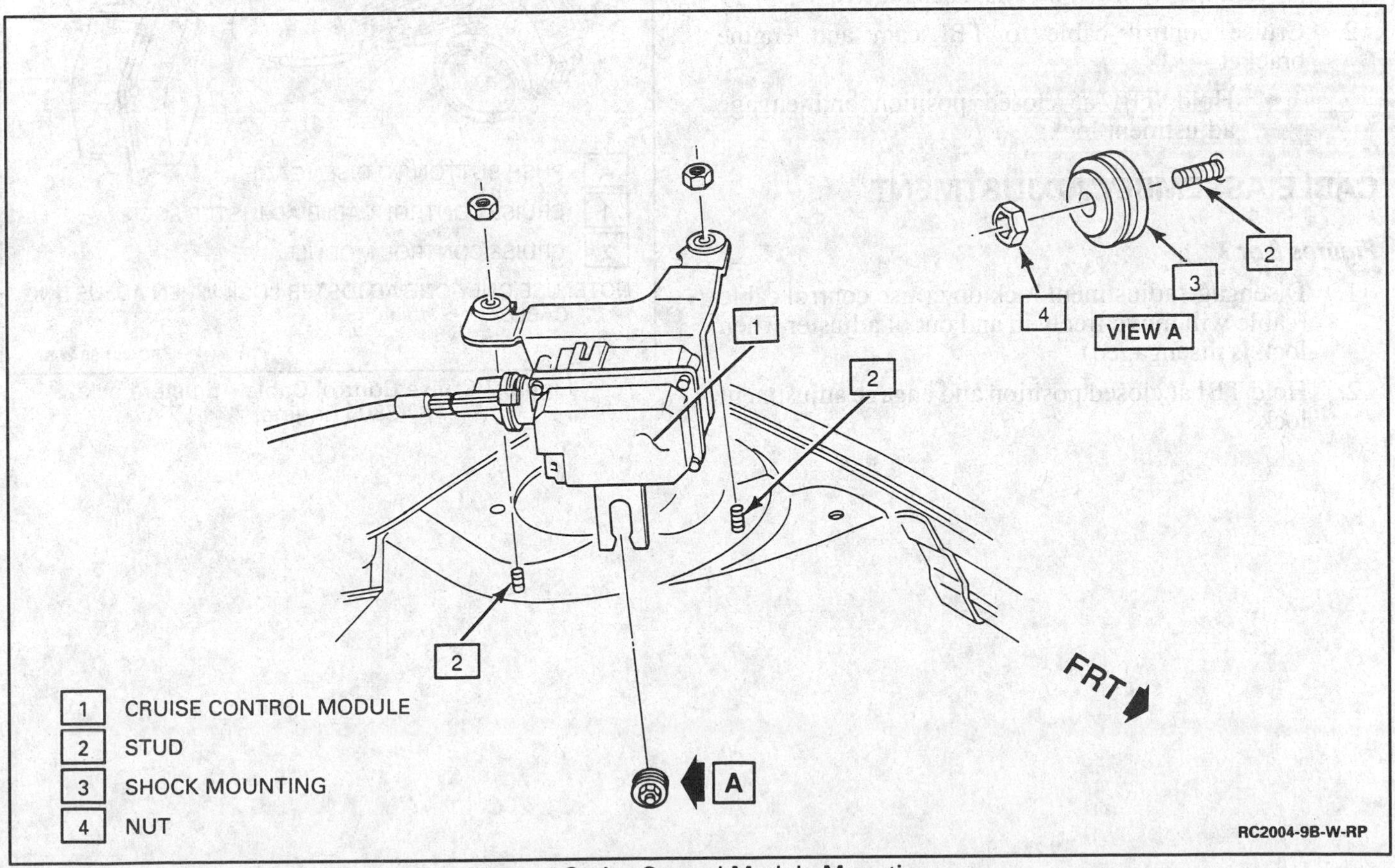
1
2
3
4
VIEW A
FRT
A
1 CRUISE CONTROL MODULE
2 STUD
3 SHOCK MOUNTING
4 NUT
RC2004-9B-W-RP

Figure 4 Cruise Control Module Mounting

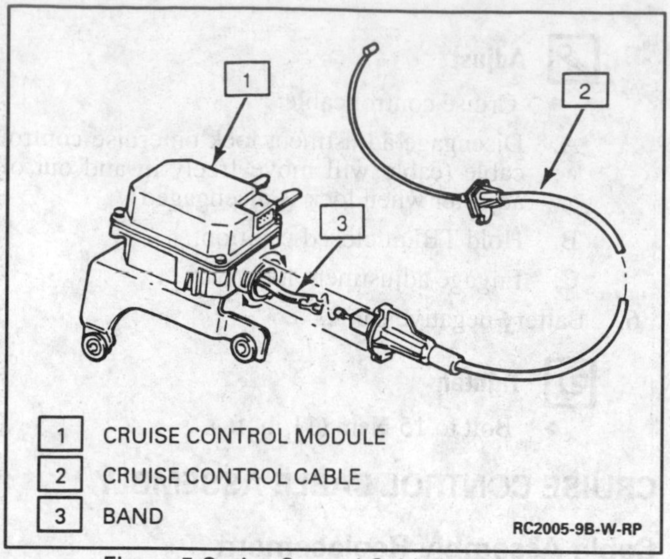
1
2
3
1 CRUISE CONTROL MODULE
2 CRUISE CONTROL CABLE
3 BAND
RC2005-9B-W-RP

Figure 5 Cruise Control Cable Installation

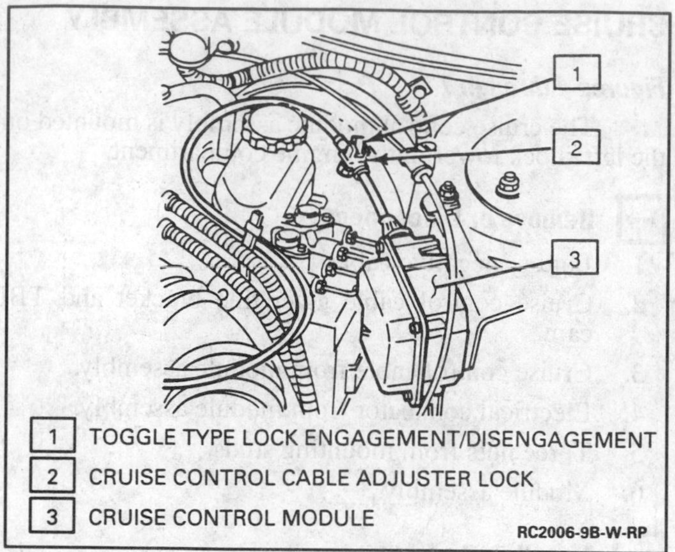
1
2
3
1 TOGGLE TYPE LOCK ENGAGEMENT/DISENGAGEMENT
2 CRUISE CONTROL CABLE ADJUSTER LOCK
3 CRUISE CONTROL MODULE
RC2006-9B-W-RP

Figure 6 Cruise Control Cable Adjuster Lock (3.1L Engine)

Install or Connect

1. Cruise control cable to cruise control module.

Important

- Disengage adjustment lock on cruise control cable (cable will move freely in and out of adjuster when lock is disengaged).

2. Cruise control cable to TBI cam and engine bracket.
   - Hold TBI at closed position and engage adjustment lock.

CABLE ASSEMBLY ADJUSTMENT

Figures 6 or 7

1. Disengage adjustment lock on cruise control cable (cable will move freely in and out of adjuster when lock is disengaged).
2. Hold TBI at closed position and engage adjustment lock.

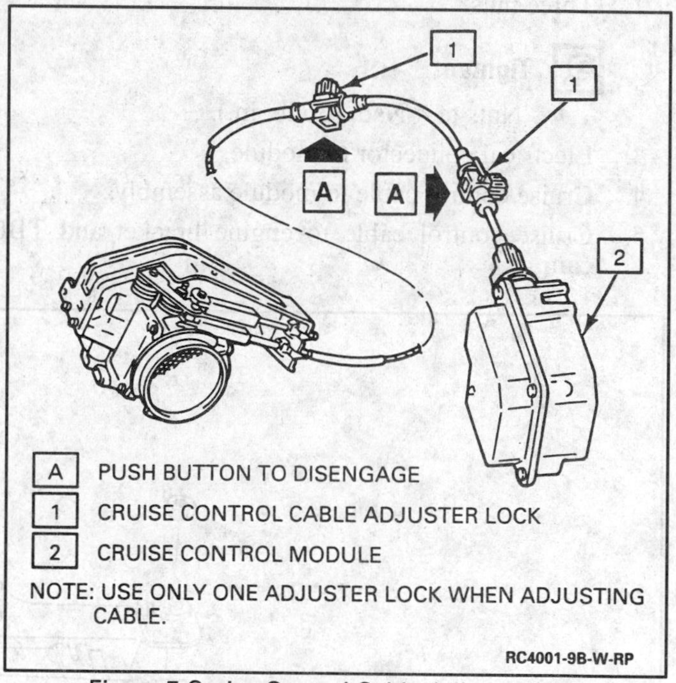
1
1
A
A
2
A PUSH BUTTON TO DISENGAGE
1 CRUISE CONTROL CABLE ADJUSTER LOCK
2 CRUISE CONTROL MODULE
NOTE: USE ONLY ONE ADJUSTER LOCK WHEN ADJUSTING CABLE.
RC4001-9B-W-RP

Figure 7 Cruise Control Cable Adjuster Lock (3800 Engine)

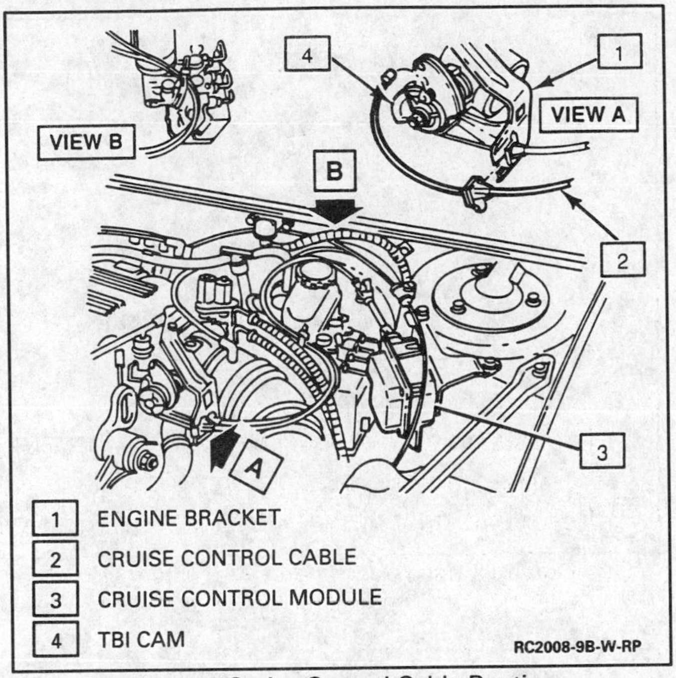
VIEW B
4
1
VIEW A
B
2
3
A
1 ENGINE BRACKET
2 CRUISE CONTROL CABLE
3 CRUISE CONTROL MODULE
4 TBI CAM
RC2008-9B-W-RP

Figure 8 Cruise Control Cable Routing (3.1L Engine)

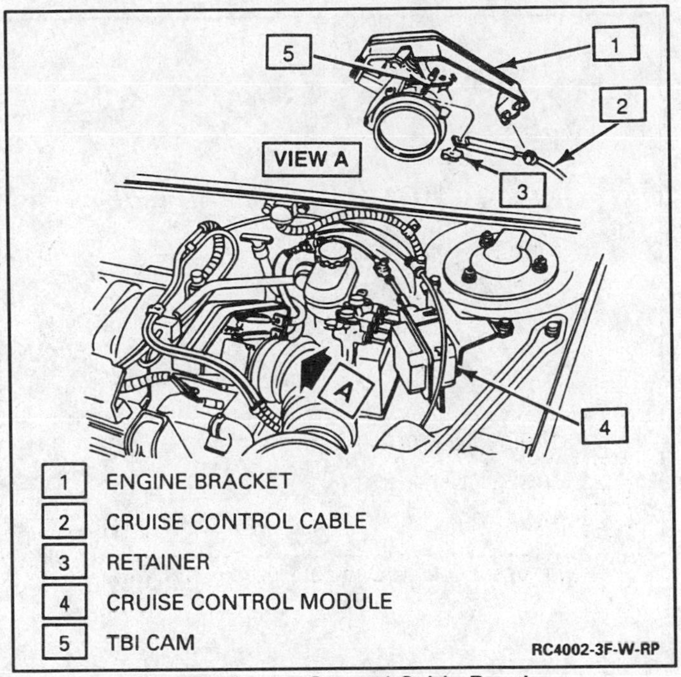
5
1
2
VIEW A
3
A
4
1 ENGINE BRACKET
2 CRUISE CONTROL CABLE
3 RETAINER
4 CRUISE CONTROL MODULE
5 TBI CAM
RC4002-3F-W-RP

Figure 9 Cruise Control Cable Routing (3800 Engine)

SPECIFICATIONS

FASTENER TIGHTENING SPECIFICATIONS

Cruise Control Module Assembly .... 4 N•m (36 lb. in.)

SECTION 9D
THEFT DETERRENT SYSTEMS

CAUTION: This vehicle is equipped with the Supplemental Inflatable Restraint (SIR). Refer to CAUTIONS in Section 9J under "ON-VEHICLE SERVICE" and the SIR Component and Wiring Location view in Section 9J before performing service on or around SIR components or wiring. Failure to follow CAUTIONS could result in possible air bag deployment, personal injury, or otherwise unneeded SIR system repairs.

NOTICE: When fasteners are removed, always reinstall them at the same location from which they were removed. If a fastener needs to be replaced, use the correct part number fastener for that application. If the correct part number is not available, a fastener of equal size and strength (or stronger) may be used. Fasteners that are not reused, and those requiring thread locking compound will be called out. The correct torque value must be used when installing fasteners that require it. If the above conditions are not followed, parts or system damage could result.

CONTENTS

GENERAL DESCRIPTION

PASS-Key II® SYSTEM

The personal automatic security system (PASS-Key II®) is standard equipment on this vehicle. The system is designed to prevent vehicle theft by disabling the engine unless an ignition key assembly with a specific electrical resistance is used in the ignition cylinder assembly. The components of the system are the ignition key assembly, the ignition cylinder assembly, the theft deterrent module assembly, the theft deterrent relay assembly, and the engine control module (ECM).

SYSTEM OPERATION

The PASS-Key II® system is designed to prevent the engine from starting if the proper resistance is not sensed from the ignition key assembly. Of the 15 key codes (resistance values) available, only one will work with each theft deterrent module assembly.

The PASS-Key II® system prevents the engine from starting by controlling the theft deterrent relay assembly and the ECM fuel enable input. If the ECM does not sense the proper pulse width modulate (PWM) signal on the fuel enable output, it will not provide fuel to the engine.

If the wrong resistance value is sensed when the ignition switch is in the "RUN" position, the theft deterrent module assembly will not ground the starter enable circuit and will not ouput the fuel enable PWM signal for approximately three minutes. This prevents the engine from starting and discourages the thief from trying key codes (resistance values) at random.

If the correct resistance value is sensed when the ignition switch is in the "RUN" position, the theft deterrent module assembly will ground the starter enable circuit and output the fuel enable PWM signal. This will allow the engine to start normally.

SYSTEM COMPONENTS

Figure 1

Ignition Key Assembly

The ignition key assembly for vehicles equipped with the PASS-Key II® system is an assembly of a typical square ignition key blank and resistor assembly. The ignition key blank and resistor assembly are not serviceable separately. There are 15 different ignition key assemblies, each with a different resistance value. The ignition key assembly also has mechanical cuts similar to non-PASS-Key II® ignition key assemblies.

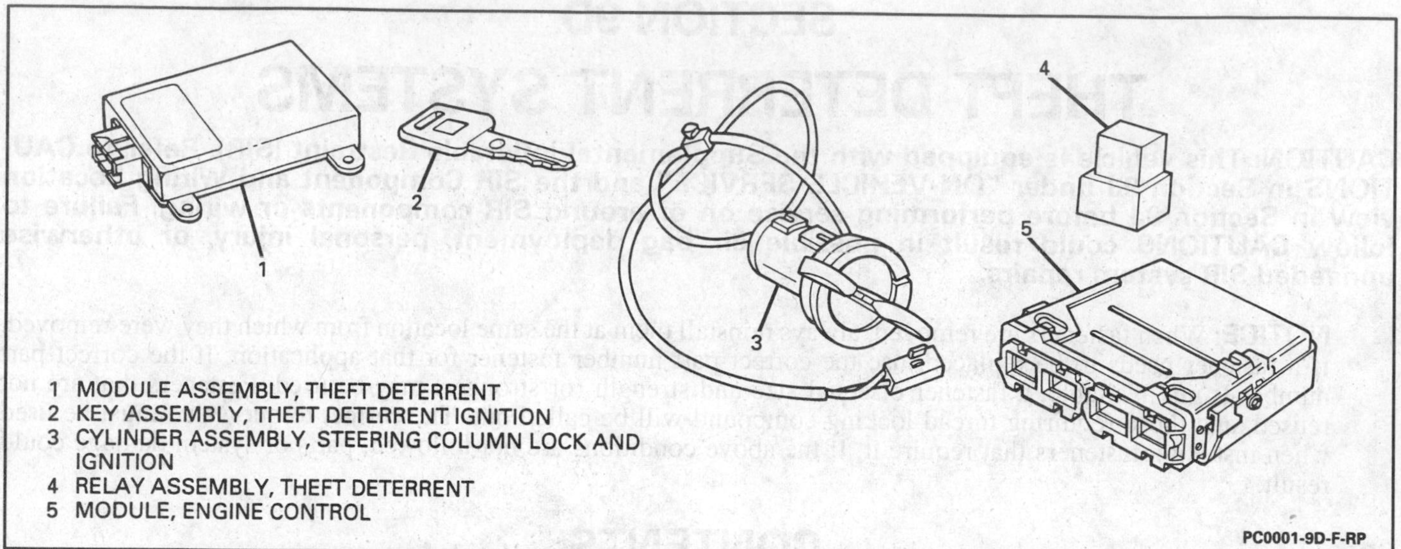
1
2
3
4
5
1 MODULE ASSEMBLY, THEFT DETERRENT
2 KEY ASSEMBLY, THEFT DETERRENT IGNITION
3 CYLINDER ASSEMBLY, STEERING COLUMN LOCK AND IGNITION
4 RELAY ASSEMBLY, THEFT DETERRENT
5 MODULE, ENGINE CONTROL
PC0001-9D-F-RP

Figure 1 PASS-Key II® System Components (Typical)

Important

- When servicing the PASS-Key II® system, obtain all ignition key assemblies, if possible, and verify proper values with tool J 35628-A, VATS/PASS Interrogator. Refer to "Copying Ignition Key Assemblies" in this section.

Steering Column Lock and Ignition Cylinder Assembly

Figure 2

The ignition cylinder assembly in vehicles equipped with the PASS-Key II® system contains a set of electrical contacts used to measure the resistor assembly in the ignition key assembly. When servicing the ignition cylinder assembly, be certain to maintain proper wire routing. A two pin connector at the base of the steering column assembly connects the contacts to the vehicle wiring. The connector is also used for diagnostic purposes. This ignition cylinder assembly also performs all functions of ignition cylinder assemblies on non-PASS-Key II® vehicles. When replacing an ignition cylinder assembly, it will be necessary to make new ignition key assemblies which match the PASS-Key II® key code of the theft deterrent module assembly and the mechanical cut of the new ignition cylinder assembly.

Important

- The wire routing for the contacts inside the steering column assembly is critical.

Theft Deterrent Module Assembly

The theft deterrent module assembly contains the logic of the PASS-Key II® system. The theft deterrent module assembly has inputs from the ignition circuit and the resistor assembly. The theft deterrent module assembly has outputs to the starter enable circuit, the fuel enable circuit, and the security lamp circuit.

Important

- This vehicle is not equipped with a SECURITY telltale lamp on the instrument cluster. For proper diagnostic procedures, refer to SECTION 8A.

Ignition Input

The ignition input is used to turn the theft deterrent module assembly on. When the theft deterrent module assembly is turned on, it will read the resistor assembly and control the outputs accordingly. When the theft deterrent module assembly is turned off the resistor assembly is not read, and the theft deterrent relay assembly and fuel enable output will not allow the engine to start. When the ignition switch is in the "OFF" position, the battery input to the theft deterrent module assembly will draw about 1 milli-amp.

Key Resistor Inputs

The key resistor inputs are used to determine if the correct ignition key assembly is being used to start the vehicle. The key resistor inputs are read when the theft deterrent module assembly is first turned on. If the key code (resistance value) of the ignition key assembly matches the value stored in the theft deterrent module assembly, the theft deterrent relay assembly and fuel enable output will allow the vehicle to start. If the resistance value of the ignition key assembly does not match the value stored in the theft deterrent module assembly, the relay assembly and fuel enable ouput will not allow the vehicle to start.

Starter Enable Output

The starter enable circuit controls the theft deterrent relay assembly. When the theft deterrent module assembly sees the proper resistance at the ignition key assembly, it grounds the starter enable circuit which allows the engine to be cranked. If the theft deterrent module assembly does not see the proper resistance at the

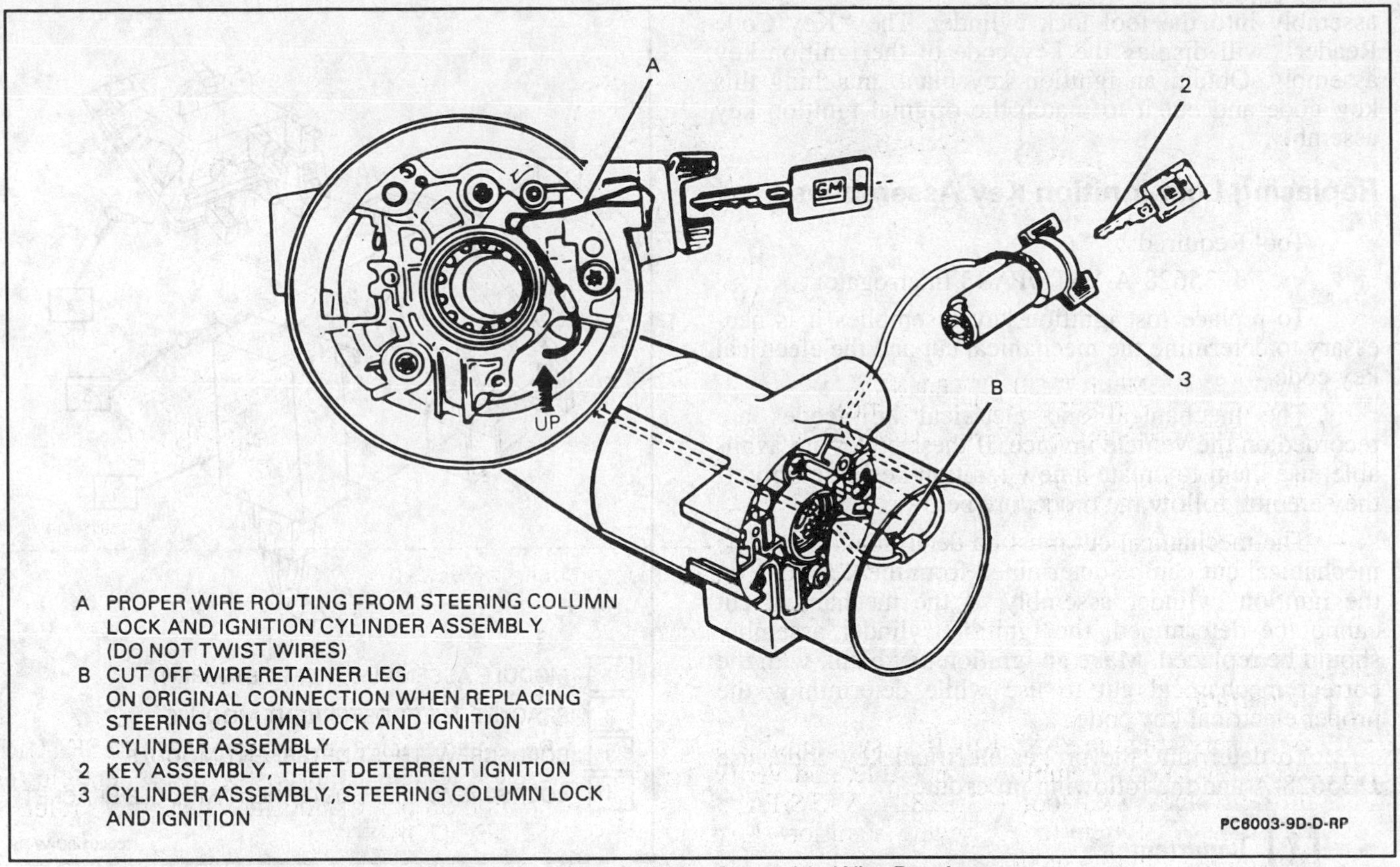
A
2
3
B
UP
GM
A PROPER WIRE ROUTING FROM STEERING COLUMN LOCK AND IGNITION CYLINDER ASSEMBLY (DO NOT TWIST WIRES)
B CUT OFF WIRE RETAINER LEG ON ORIGINAL CONNECTION WHEN REPLACING STEERING COLUMN LOCK AND IGNITION CYLINDER ASSEMBLY
2 KEY ASSEMBLY, THEFT DETERRENT IGNITION
3 CYLINDER ASSEMBLY, STEERING COLUMN LOCK AND IGNITION
PC8003-9D-D-RP

Figure 2 Ignition Cylinder Assembly Wire Routing

ignition key assembly, it will not ground the starter enable circuit.

Fuel Enable Output

The fuel enable circuit is an output from the theft deterrent module assembly and an input to the ECM. When the theft deterrent module assembly sees the proper resistance at the ignition key assembly, it will output a pulse width modulated (PWM) signal to the ECM. If the theft deterrent module assembly does not see the proper resistance at the ignition key assembly, it will not output the PWM signal to the ECM

Security Indicator Lamp Output

The "SECURITY" lamp circuit is an indicator lamp output. For further information, refer to SECTION 8A.

Important

- This vehicle is not equipped with a SECURITY telltalc lamp on the instrument cluster. For proper diagnostic procedure, refer to SECTION 8A.

Theft Deterrent Relay Assembly

The relay assembly is used to stop the engine from cranking if the correct resistance is not sensed at the ignition key assembly. It prevents the engine from cranking by opening the circuit to the starter solenoid switch.

Engine Control Module (ECM)

The ECM reads the fuel enable circuit to determine if fuel injection should be allowed. If the fuel enable PWM signal is not present, the ECM will not allow fuel injection. If the PWM signal is present, the ECM will allow fuel injection and normal engine operation.

The ECM has some diagnostic features associated with the fuel enable input, including diagnostic trouble codes. For details, refer to SECTION 6E.

DIAGNOSIS

For theft deterrent system diagnosis, use diagnostic information in ELECTRICAL DIAGNOSIS (SECTION 8A).

ON-VEHICLE SERVICE

IGNITION KEY ASSEMBLY

Copying Ignition Key Assemblies

Tool Required:

J 35628-A VATS/PASS Interrogator

To copy an ignition key assembly, it is necessary to first determine which PASS-Key II® key code (resistance value) is needed. The ignition key assembly being copied must be tested to determine the key code. The ignition key assembly may be tested using J 35628-A. To use J 35628-A, turn the tool on, make sure the tool wiring connectors are disconnected and insert the ignition key assembly into the tool lock cylinder. The "Key Code Reader" will display the key code of the ignition key assembly. Obtain an ignition key blank matching this key code and cut it to match the original ignition key assembly.

Replacing Lost Ignition Key Assemblies

Tool Required:

J 35628-A VATS/PASS Interrogator

To replace lost ignition key assemblies it is necessary to determine the mechanical cut and the electrical key code.

The mechanical and electrical key codes are recorded on the vehicle invoice. If these codes are available, use them to create a new ignition key assembly. If they are not, follow the procedure below.

The mechanical cut must be determined first. The mechanical cut can be determined from the key code on the ignition cylinder assembly. If the mechanical cut cannot be determined, the ignition cylinder assembly should be replaced. Make an ignition key blank with the correct mechanical cut to use while determining the proper electrical key code.

To determine the proper electrical key code, use J 35628-A and the following procedure:

Important

- Do not disconnect yellow two-way SIR connector.

1. Connect J 35628-A wiring to PASS–Key II® dash connector at base of steering column assembly. Do not connect to steering column wiring.
2. Turn J 35628-A on and place key code switch to "I" and attempt to start the engine with proper mechanically cut key. It engine starts, key code is "I."
3. If engine does not start, turn the ignition off and press 4-minute timer on J 35628-A.
4. When timer light goes out, place key code switch to "2" and attempt to start engine. If engine starts, key code is "2."
5. Continue trying different key codes until proper key code is found.
6. Make new ignition key assembly with proper key code and mechanical cut.

THEFT DETERRENT MODULE ASSEMBLY

Figure 3

Remove or Disconnect

1. Lower sound insulator panel. Refer to SECTION 8C.
2. Diagnostic energy reserve module (DERM) and bracket. Refer to SECTION 9J.
3. Theft deterrent module screw from bracket.
4. Theft deterrent module.
5. Electrical connector from theft deterrent module.

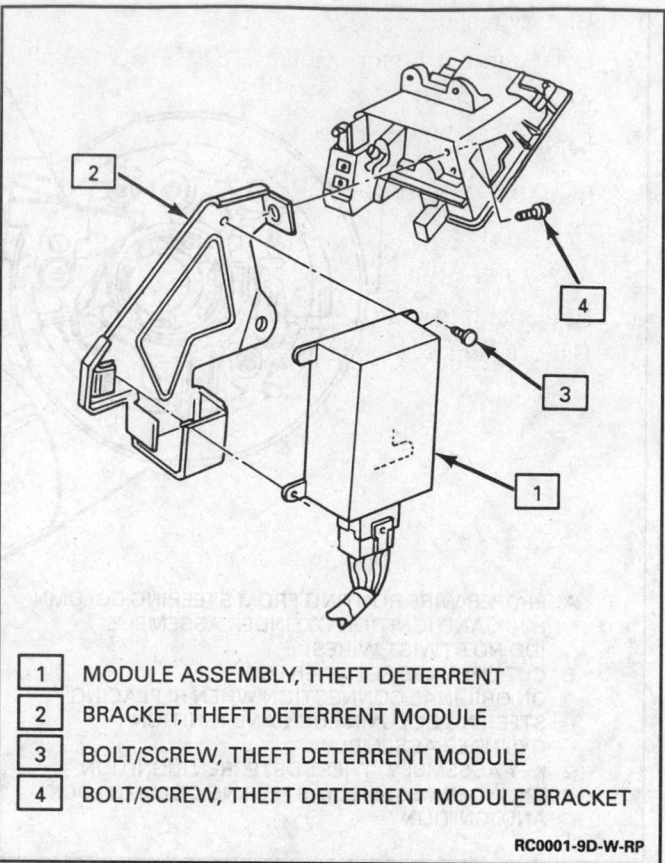

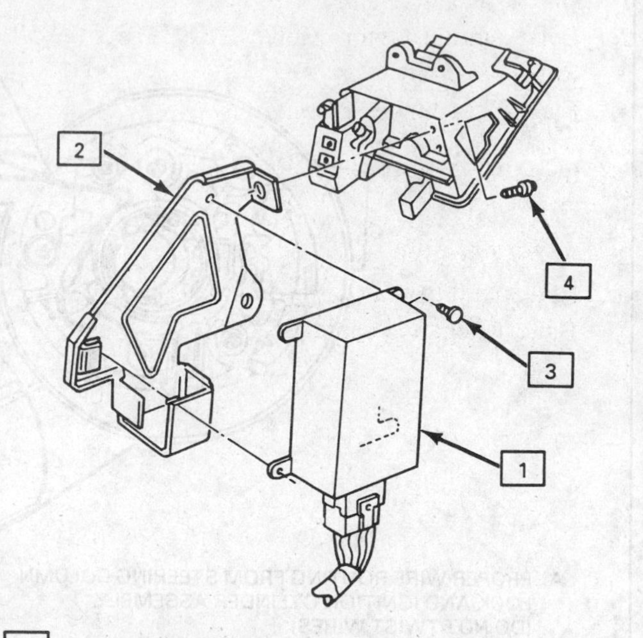
2
4
3
1
1 MODULE ASSEMBLY, THEFT DETERRENT
2 BRACKET, THEFT DETERRENT MODULE
3 BOLT/SCREW, THEFT DETERRENT MODULE
4 BOLT/SCREW, THEFT DETERRENT MODULE BRACKET
RC0001-9D-W-RP

Figure 3 Theft Deterrent Module Assembly

Install or Connect

NOTICE: See "Notice" on page 9D-1 of this section.

1. Electrical connector.
2. Slide lower left hand tab on theft deterrent module into bracket slot.
3. Theft deterrent module screw.

Tighten

- Screw to 1.9 N•m (17 lb. in.).

4. Diagnostic energy reserve module (DERM) and bracket. Refer to SECTION 9J.
5. Lower sound insulator panel. Refer to SECTION 8C.

THEFT DETERRENT RELAY ASSEMBLY

Figure 4

If the relay assembly is determined to be inoperative, it should be replaced.

Remove or Disconnect

CAUTION: Refer to "Caution" under "Disconnecting the Battery Negative Cable Assemblv" in SECTION 0A.

1. Battery negative cable assembly.
2. Left sound insulator . Refer to SECTION 8C.
3. Relay assembly.
4. Electrical connector from relay assembly.

Install or Connect

1. Electrical connector to relay assembly.
2. Relay assembly.
3. Left sound insulator. Refer to SECTION 8C.
4. Battery negative cable assembly.

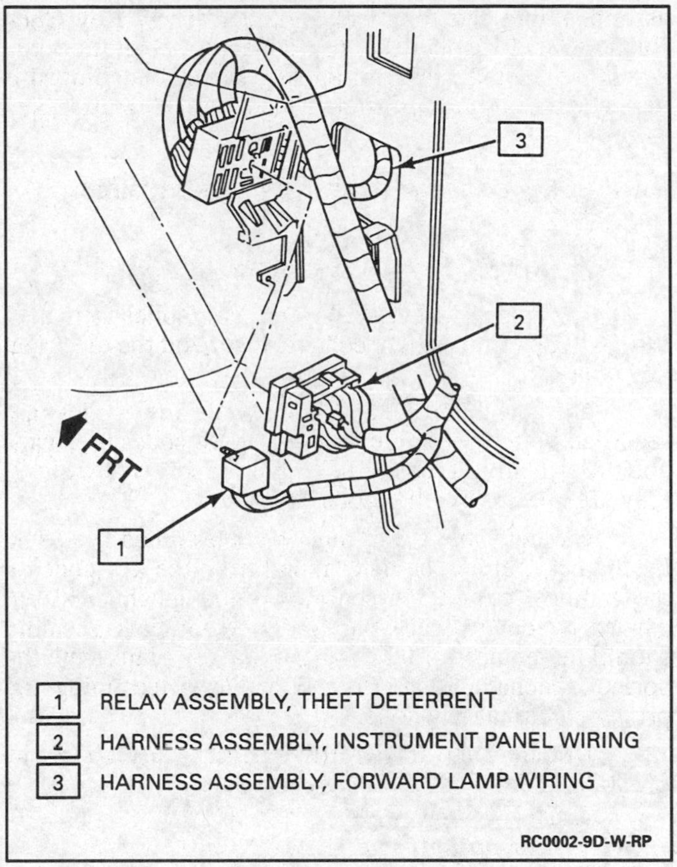
3
2
FRT
1
1 RELAY ASSEMBLY, THEFT DETERRENT
2 HARNESS ASSEMBLY, INSTRUMENT PANEL WIRING
3 HARNESS ASSEMBLY, FORWARD LAMP WIRING
RC0002-9D-W-RP

Figure 4 Theft Deterrent Relay Assembly

SPECIFICATIONS

FASTENER TIGHTENING SPECIFICATIONS

Theft Deterrent Module Bolt/Screw .... 1.9 N•m (17 lb. in.)

SPECIAL TOOLS

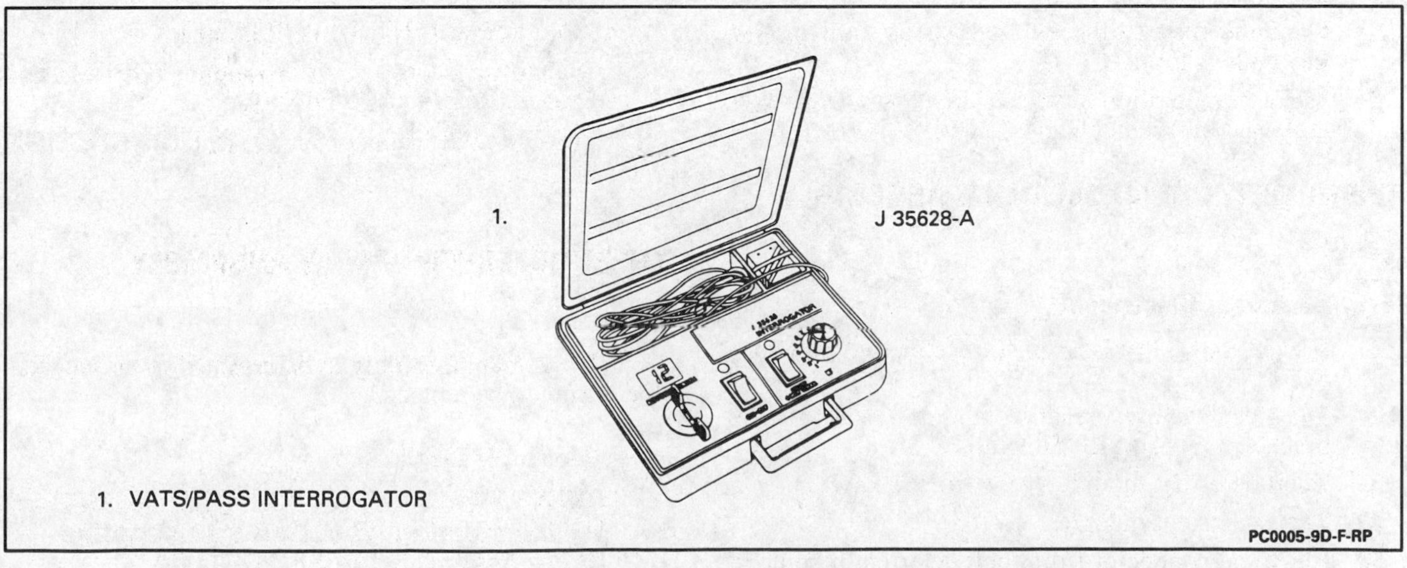
1.
J 35628-A
1. VATS/PASS INTERROGATOR
PC0005-9D-F-RP

SECTION 9E

ENGINE BLOCK HEATER

CAUTION: This vehicle is equipped with Supplemental Inflatable Restraint (SIR). Refer to CAUTIONS in Section 9J under "ON-VEHICLE SERVICE" and the SIR Component and Wiring Location view in Section 9J before performing service on or around SIR components or wiring. Failure to follow CAUTIONS could result in possible air bag deployment, personal injury, or otherwise unneeded SIR system repairs.

NOTICE: When fasteners are removed, always reinstall them at the same location from which they were removed. If a fastener needs to be replaced, use the correct part number fastener for that application. If the correct part number fastener is not available, a fastener of equal size and strength (or stronger) may be used. Fasteners that are not reused, and those requiring thread locking compound will be called out. The correct torque value must be used when installing fasteners that require it. If the above conditions are not followed, parts or system damage could result.

CONTENTS

GENERAL DESCRIPTION

The heating element for the engine block heater (option K05) is installed into the water jacket of the engine block. The 600 watt heating coil is powered by a 110-volt AC external power source.

The unit has a detachable electrical cord. If engine block heater fails to operate, check cord, connections and power supply before replacing the heating element.

ON-VEHICLE SERVICE

ENGINE BLOCK HEATER

Figures 1 and 2

Remove or Disconnect

1. Drain coolant. Refer to COOLING AND RADIATOR (SECTION 6B).
2. Raise vehicle and suitably support. Refer to GENERAL INFORMATION (SECTION 0A).
3. Cord from engine block heater.
4. Loosen screw.
5. Engine block heater.

Clean

- Core plug hole.

Install or Connect

1. Coat of lubricant to the gasket and the cleaned surface of the plug hole.
2. Engine block heater assembly with cord connector in downward position.
3. Hand start screw in engine block heater assembly.

   Tighten

   - Screw to 2 N·m (18 lb. in.).
4. Heater cord to engine block heater.

   Important

   - Cord must not contact engine, hot pipes, manifold or any moving parts.
5. Lower vehicle.
6. Coolant. Refer to COOLING AND RADIATOR (SECTION 6B).

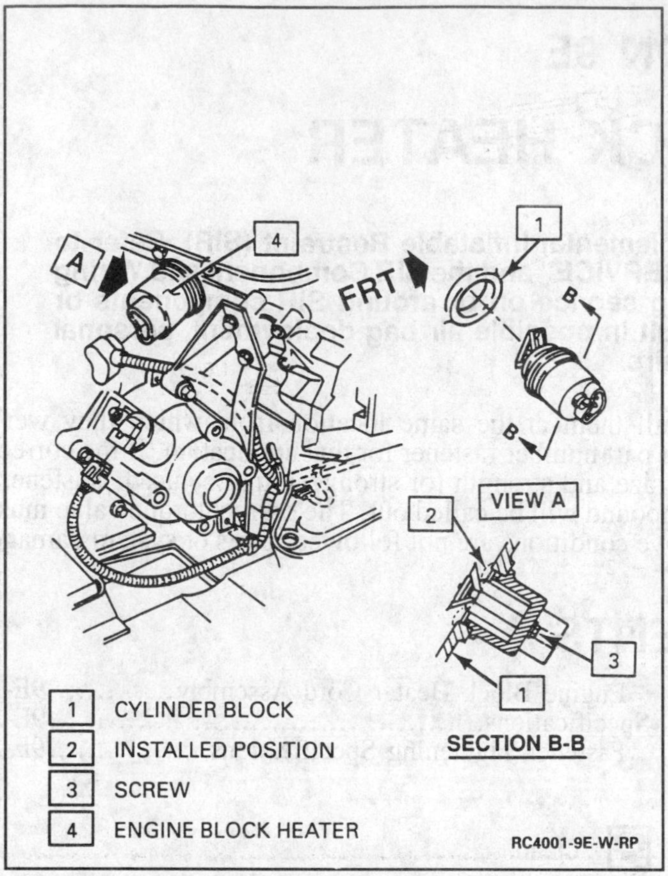

A
4
FRT
1
B
B
VIEW A
2
3
1
SECTION B-B
1 CYLINDER BLOCK
2 INSTALLED POSITION
3 SCREW
4 ENGINE BLOCK HEATER
RC4001-9E-W-RP

Figure 1 Engine Block Heater Mounting (3.1L Engine)

ENGINE BLOCK HEATER CORD ASSEMBLY

Figures 1 through 3

Remove or Disconnect

1. Raise vehicle and suitably support. Refer to GENERAL INFORMATION (SECTION 0A).
2. Heater cord from engine block heater.
3. Straps.
4. Heater cord.

Install or Connect

1. Heater cord.

Important

- Cord must not contact engine, hot pipes, manifold or any moving parts.

2. Straps.
3. Heater cord to engine block heater.
4. Lower vehicle.

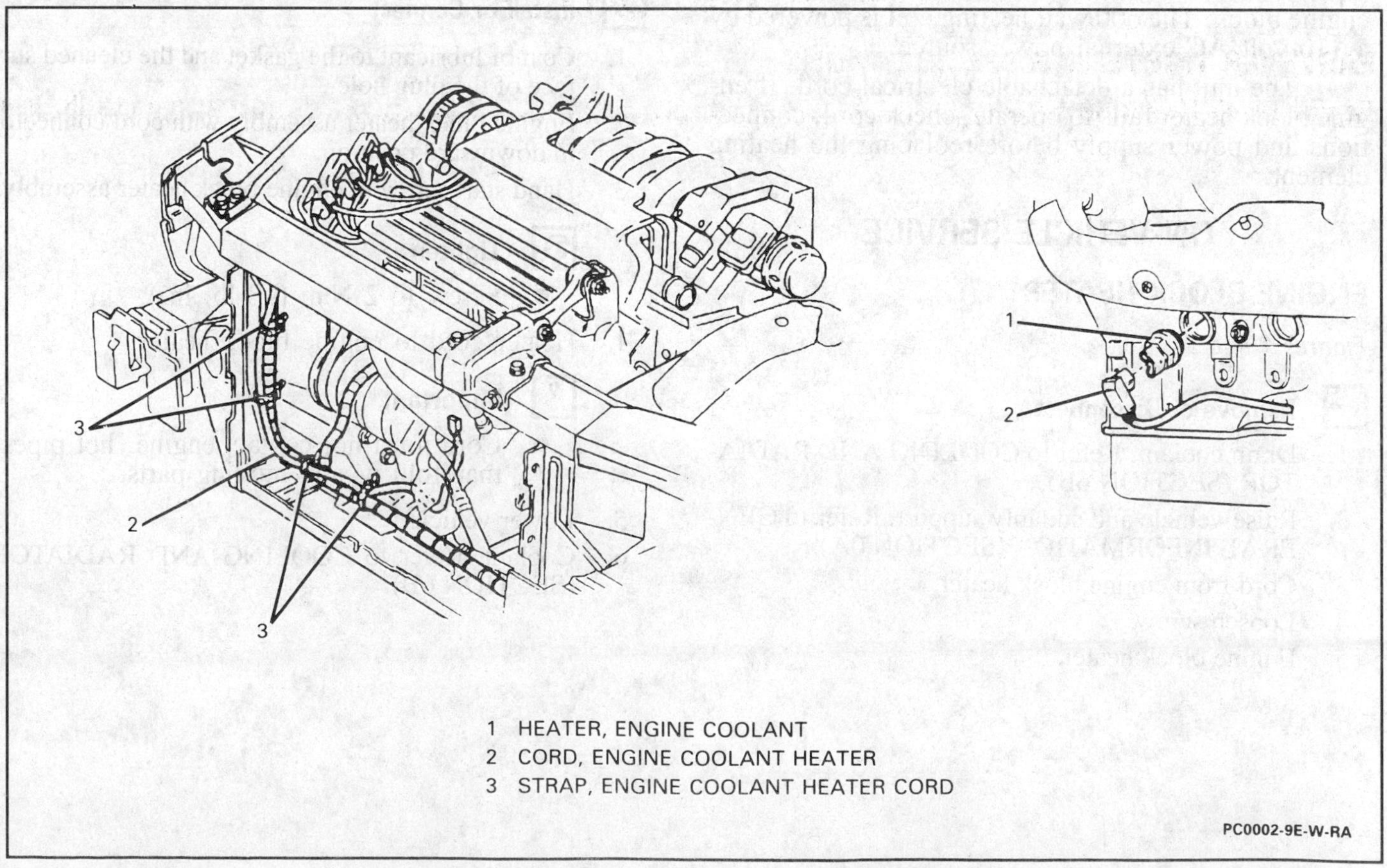

3
2
3
1
2
1 HEATER, ENGINE COOLANT
2 CORD, ENGINE COOLANT HEATER
3 STRAP, ENGINE COOLANT HEATER CORD
PC0002-9E-W-RA

Figure 2 Engine Block Heater Mounting (3800 Engine)

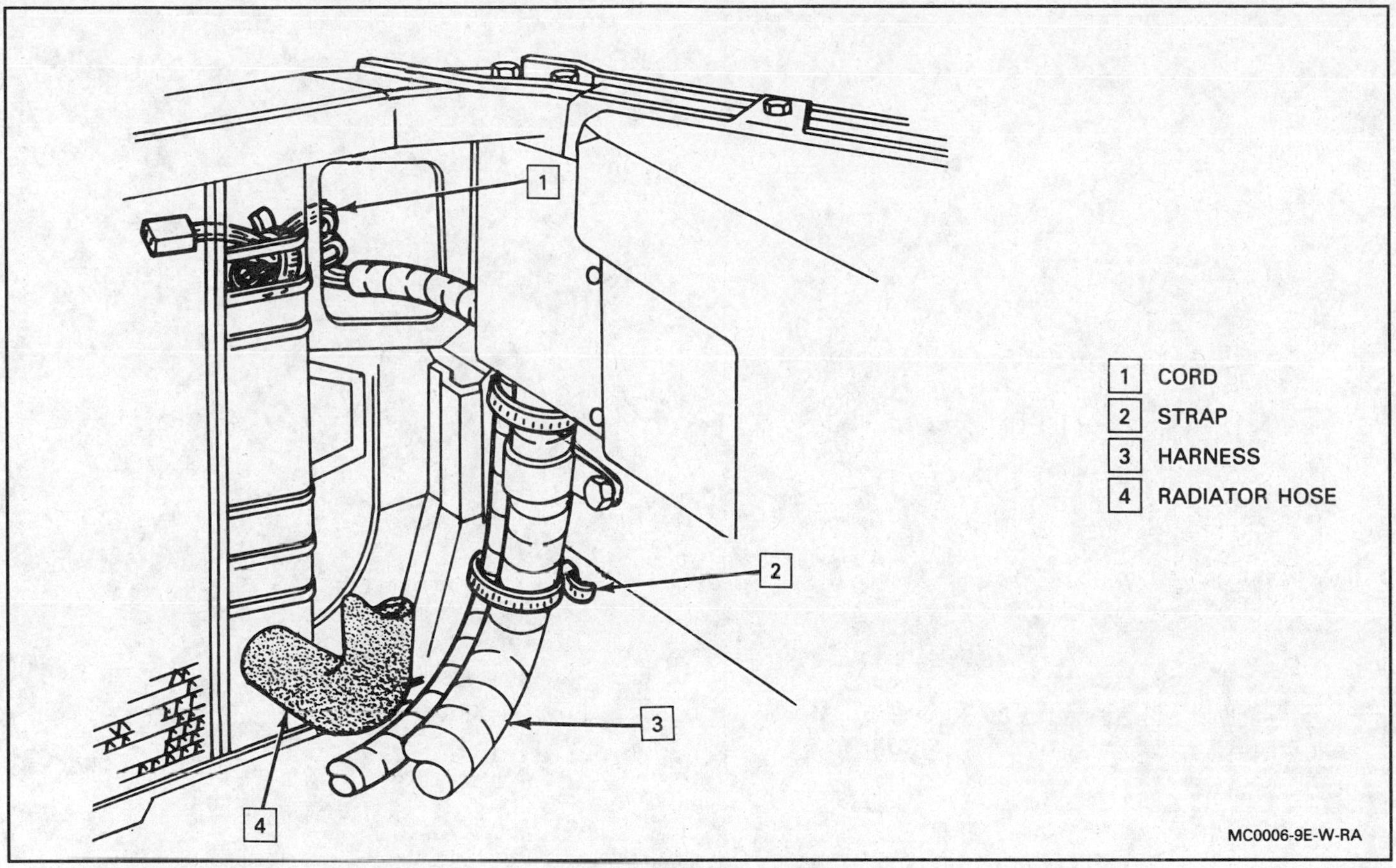
1
2
3
4
1 CORD
2 STRAP
3 HARNESS
4 RADIATOR HOSE
MC0006-9E-W-RA

Figure 3 Cord Storage

SPECIFICATIONS

FASTENER TIGHTENING SPECIFICATIONS

Engine Block Heater Screw .... 2 N·m (18 lb. in.)

SECTION 9J

SUPPLEMENTAL INFLATABLE RESTRAINT (SIR) SYSTEM

CAUTION: This vehicle is equipped with Supplemental Inflatable Restraint (SIR). Refer to CAUTIONS in this section under "ON-VEHICLE SERVICE" and the SIR Component and Wiring Location view in this section before performing service on or around SIR components or wiring. Failure to follow CAUTIONS could result in possible air bag deployment, personal injury, or otherwise unneeded SIR system repairs.

NOTICE: When fasteners are removed, always reinstall them at the same location from which they were removed. If a fastener needs to be replaced, use the correct part number fastener for that application. If the correct part number fastener is not available, a fastener of equal size and strength (or stronger) may be used. Fasteners that are not reused, and those requiring thread-locking compound will be called out. The correct torque value must be used when installing fasteners that require it. If the above conditions are not followed, parts or system damage could result.

CONTENTS

GENERAL DESCRIPTION

RESTRAINT DEVICES
Figure 1

The Supplemental Inflatable Restraint (SIR) system helps supplement the protection offered by the driver's seat belt by deploying an air bag from the center of the steering wheel during certain frontal crashes. The air bag deploys when the vehicle is involved in a frontal crash of sufficient force up to 30 degrees off the centerline of the vehicle. To further absorb the crash energy there is a knee bolster located beneath the instrument panel in the driver's area and the steering column is collapsible.

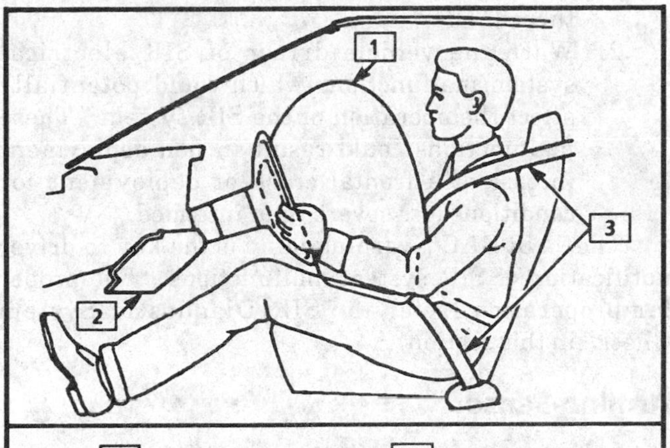
1
2
3
1 DEPLOYED AIR BAG
2 KNEE BOLSTER
3 SEAT BELT
9S 6227-9J

Figure 1 - Restraint Devices

SYSTEM DESCRIPTION
Figures 2 and 3

The main portions of the SIR system are the deployment loop and the Diagnostic Energy Reserve Module (DERM). The main function of the deployment loop is to supply current through the inflator module in the steering wheel, which will cause deployment of the air bag in the event of a frontal crash of sufficient force, up to 30 degrees off the centerline of the vehicle.

The arming sensor, SIR coil assembly, inflator module, and discriminating sensors make up the deployment loop. The arming sensor switches power to the inflator module on the high side (power side) of the deployment loop. Either of the discriminating sensors can supply ground to the inflator module on the low side (ground side) of the loop. The inflator module is only supplied sufficient current to deploy when the arming sensor and at least one of the two discriminating sensors are closed simultaneously.

A function of the DERM is to supply the deployment loop with a 36 Volt Loop Reserve (36 VLR) to ensure sufficient energy to deploy the air bag if the

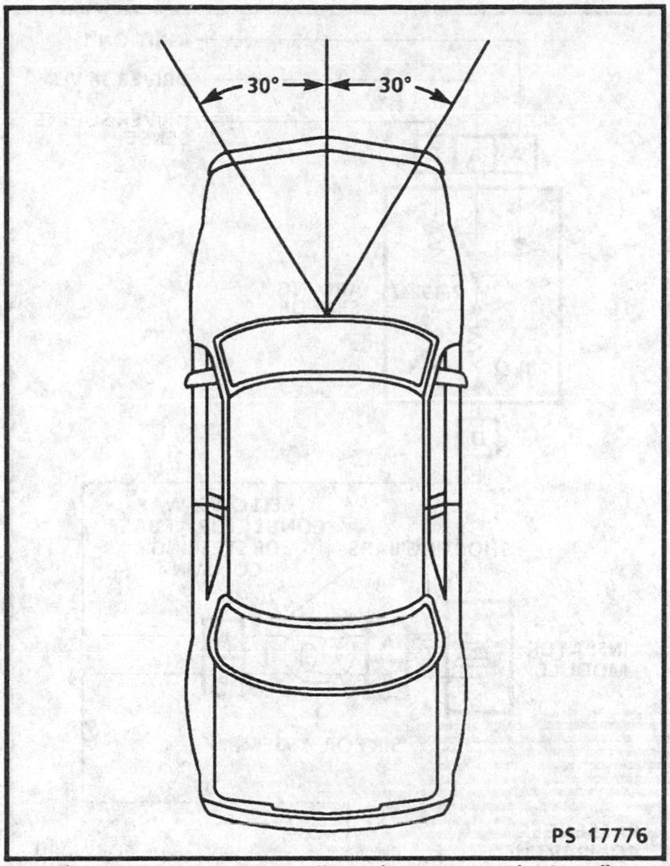
30°
30°
PS 17776

Figure 2 - SIR System "Deployment Window"

ignition feed to the arming sensor is lost during a frontal crash.

Another function of the DERM is electrical system diagnostics. The DERM monitors the deployment loop in conjunction with the resistors in the arming sensor and discriminating sensors. These resistors make it possible for the DERM to detect circuit and component malfunctions within the deployment loop. The DERM monitors the voltage drop across each component within the loop during normal non-deployment conditions. If the monitored voltages fall outside of expected limits, the DERM will indicate a malfunction through the storage of a diagnostic trouble code and the illumination of the "AIR BAG" warning lamp.

COMPONENT DESCRIPTION
Figure 4

DERM

NOTICE: Do not open the DERM case for any reason. Touching the connector pins or soldered components may cause electrostatic discharge damage. Repair of a malfunctioning DERM is by replacement only.

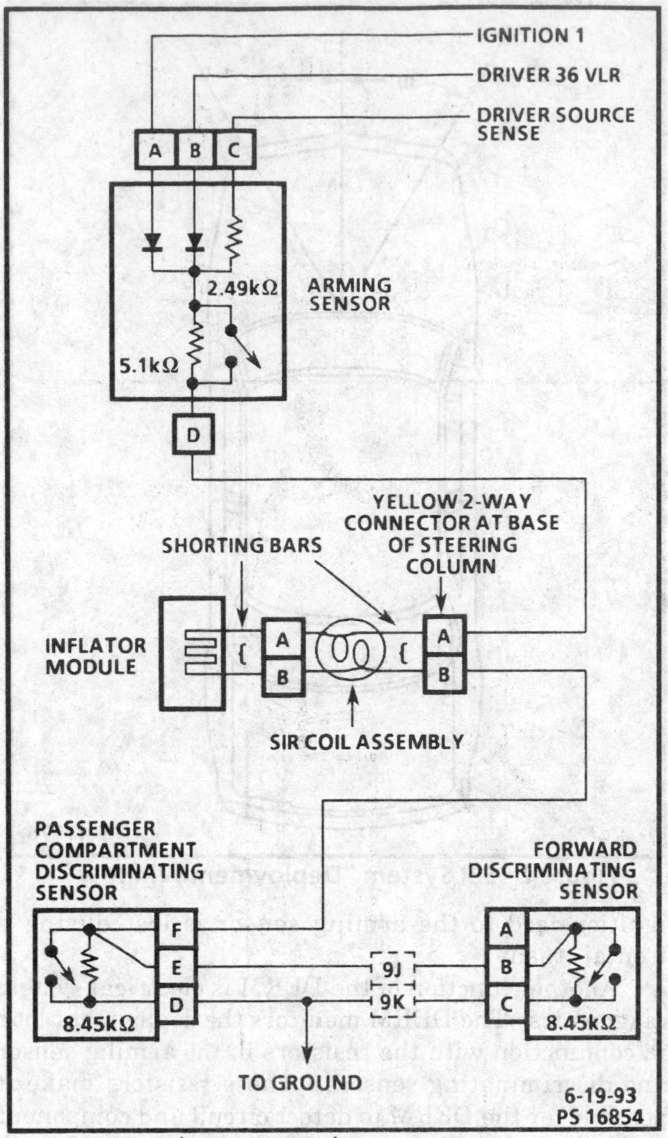
IGNITION 1
DRIVER 36 VLR
DRIVER SOURCE SENSE
A
B
C
2.49kΩ
ARMING SENSOR
5.1kΩ
D
YELLOW 2-WAY CONNECTOR AT BASE OF STEERING COLUMN
SHORTING BARS
INFLATOR MODULE
A
B
SIR COIL ASSEMBLY
PASSENGER COMPARTMENT DISCRIMINATING SENSOR
FORWARD DISCRIMINATING SENSOR
F
E
D
9J
9K
8.45kΩ
TO GROUND
6-19-93
PS 16854

Figure 3 - Deployment Loop

The DERM is designed to perform the following functions in the SIR system:

1. Energy Reserve - The DERM maintains a 36 Volt Loop Reserve (36 VLR) energy supply to provide deployment energy when the vehicle voltage is low or lost in a frontal crash.
2. Malfunction Detection - The DERM performs diagnostic monitoring of SIR system electrical components.
3. Malfunction Recording - The DERM provides SIR system diagnostic trouble code information through a scan tool.
4. Driver Notification - The DERM warns the vehicle driver of SIR system malfunctions by controlling the "AIR BAG" warning lamp.
5. Frontal Crash Recording - The DERM records the SIR system status during a frontal crash.

The DERM is connected to the SIR wiring harness by a 24-way connector. This harness connector uses a shorting bar across certain terminals in the contact area. This shorting bar connects the "AIR BAG" warning lamp to ground when the DERM harness connector is disconnected. This will cause the "AIR BAG" warning lamp to come "ON" steady whenever the ignition switch is at the RUN, BULB TEST or START positions with the DERM disconnected.

"AIR BAG" Warning Lamp

Ignition voltage is applied to the "AIR BAG" warning lamp when the ignition switch is at the RUN, BULB TEST or START positions. The DERM controls the lamp by providing ground with a lamp driver. The "AIR BAG" warning lamp is used in the SIR system to do the following:

1. Verify lamp and DERM operation by flashing seven times when the ignition switch is first turned "ON."
2. Warn the vehicle driver of SIR electrical system malfunctions which could potentially affect the operation of the SIR system. These malfunctions could result in non-deployment in case of a frontal crash or deployment for conditions less severe than intended.

The "AIR BAG" warning lamp is the key to driver notification of SIR system malfunctions. For proper lamp operation, refer to "SIR Diagnostic System Check" in this section.

Arming Sensor

The arming sensor is a protective switch located in the high side (power side) of the deployment loop. The arming sensor is calibrated to close at low level velocity changes (lower than the discriminating sensors). This ensures that the inflator module is connected directly to the "36 VLR" output of the DERM or "Ignition 1" voltage when either of the discriminating sensors closes.

The arming sensor consists of: a sensing element, normally open switch contacts, two diagnostic resistors, and two diodes. The sensing element closes the switch contacts when the velocity of the vehicle changes at a rate indicating a potential need for deployment.

The 5.1kΩ diagnostic resistor is connected in parallel with the switch contacts allowing a small amount of current to flow through the deployment loop during normal, non-deployment operation. This current flow results in voltage drops across each component within the deployment loop. The DERM monitors these voltage drops to detect circuit or component malfunctions. The 2.49kΩ diagnostic resistor is connected in parallel with the diodes allowing the DERM to monitor the voltage applied to the high side of the deployment loop. The two diodes in the arming sensor provide isolation between the "36 VLR" output of the DERM and "Ignition 1" voltage.

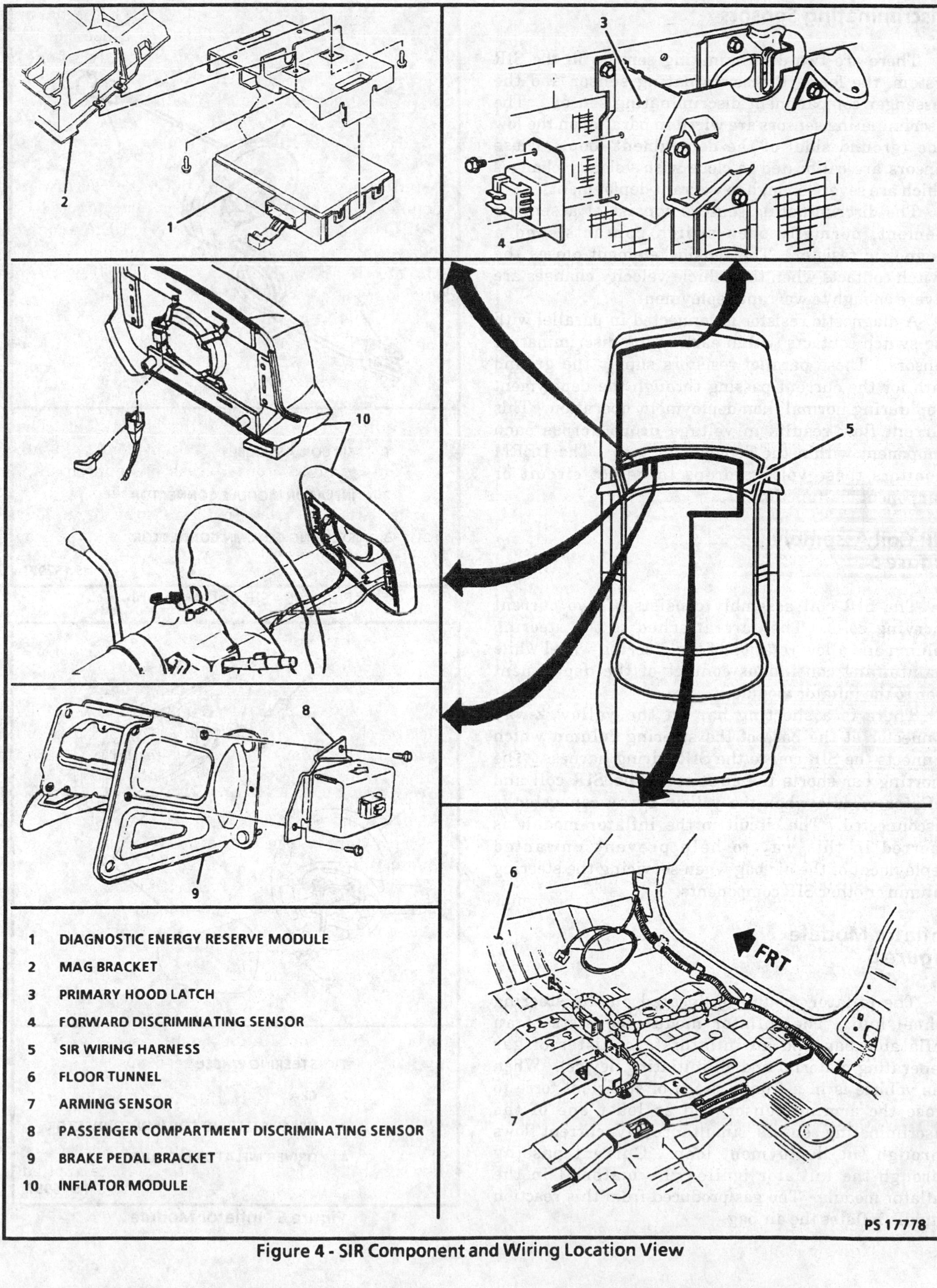
1
2
3
4
5
6
7
8
9
10
FRT
PS 17778

1 DIAGNOSTIC ENERGY RESERVE MODULE
2 MAG BRACKET
3 PRIMARY HOOD LATCH
4 FORWARD DISCRIMINATING SENSOR
5 SIR WIRING HARNESS
6 FLOOR TUNNEL
7 ARMING SENSOR
8 PASSENGER COMPARTMENT DISCRIMINATING SENSOR
9 BRAKE PEDAL BRACKET
10 INFLATOR MODULE

Figure 4 - SIR Component and Wiring Location View

Discriminating Sensors

There are two discriminating sensors in the SIR system, the forward discriminating sensor and the passenger compartment discriminating sensor. The discriminating sensors are wired in parallel on the low side (ground side) of the deployment loop. These sensors are calibrated to close with velocity changes which are severe enough to warrant deployment.

The discriminating sensors consist of a sensing element, normally open switch contacts, and a diagnostic resistor. The sensing element closes the switch contacts when the vehicle velocity changes are severe enough to warrant deployment.

A diagnostic resistor is connected in parallel with the switch contacts within each of the discriminating sensors. These parallel resistors supply the ground path for the current passing through the deployment loop during normal, non-deployment operation. This current flow results in voltage drops across each component within the deployment loop. The DERM monitors these voltage drops to detect circuit or component malfunctions.

SIR Coil Assembly
Figure 5

The SIR coil assembly consists of two current carrying coils. They are attached to the steering column and allow rotation of the steering wheel while maintaining continuous contact of the deployment loop to the inflator module.

There is a shorting bar on the yellow 2-way connector at the base of the steering column which connects the SIR coil to the SIR wiring harness. The shorting bar shorts the circuits to the SIR coil and inflator module when the yellow 2-way connector is disconnected. The circuit to the inflator module is shorted in this way to help prevent unwanted deployment of the air bag when servicing the steering column or other SIR components.

Inflator Module
Figure 6

The inflator module is located on the steering wheel hub. The inflator module consists of an inflatable bag and an inflator (a canister of gas generating material and an initiating device). When the vehicle is in a frontal crash of sufficient force to close the arming sensor and at least one of the discriminating sensors, simultaneously, current flows through the deployment loop. Current passing through the initiator ignites the material in the inflator module. The gas produced from this reaction rapidly inflates the air bag.

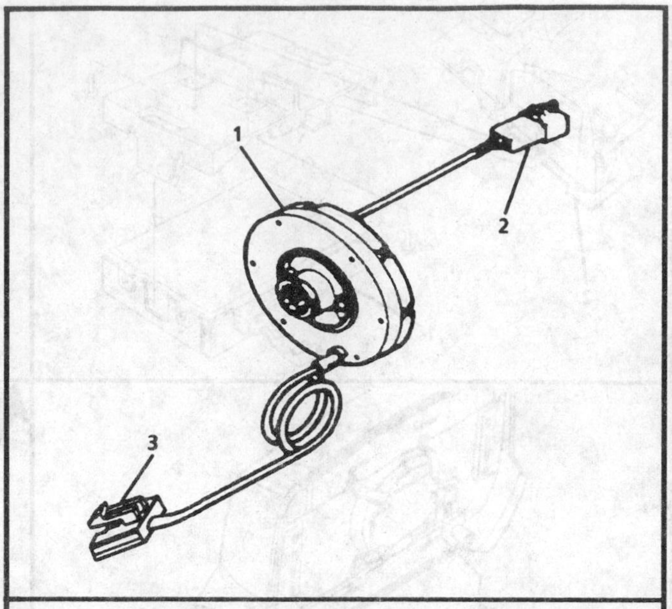
1
2
3

1 SIR COIL ASSEMBLY

2 INFLATOR MODULE CONNECTOR

3 STEERING COLUMN CONNECTOR

NS 15297

Figure 5 - SIR Coil Assembly

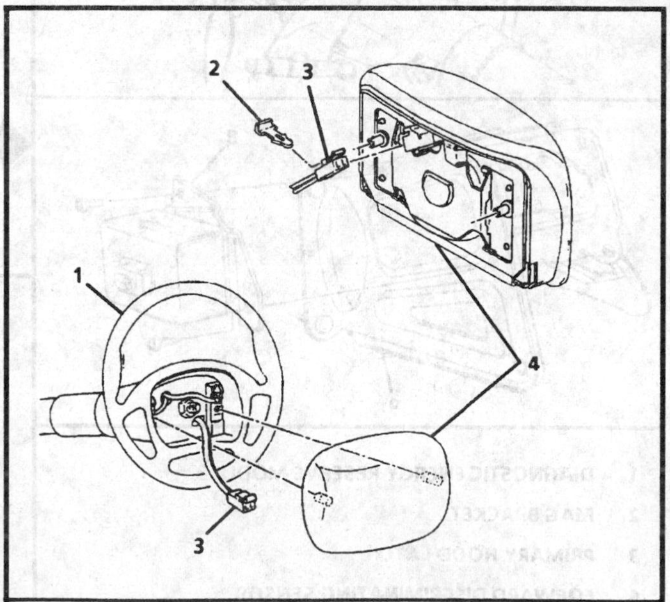
2
3
1
4
3

1 STEERING WHEEL

2 CPA

3 UPPER STEERING COLUMN CONNECTOR

4 DRIVER INFLATOR MODULE

PS 16957

Figure 6 - Inflator Module

There is a shorting bar on the inflator module side of the upper steering column connector which connects the SIR coil to the inflator module. The shorting bar shorts the inflator module circuit when the upper steering column connector is disconnected. The circuit to the inflator module is shorted in this way to help prevent unwanted deployment of the air bag when servicing the inflator module or steering column.

Steering Column

The steering column is energy absorbing and designed to compress in a frontal crash to decrease the chance of injury to the driver.

Knee Bolster

The knee bolster is used to absorb energy and control the driver's forward movement during a frontal crash by limiting leg movement.

DEFINITIONS:

AIR BAG - An inflatable cloth cushion designed to deploy in certain frontal crashes. It supplements the protection offered by the seat belts by distributing the impact load more evenly over the vehicle occupant's head and torso.

ARMING SENSOR - A sensor on the high side (power side) of the deployment loop that is calibrated to supply voltage to the inflator module when the vehicle velocity changes are severe enough to warrant arming of the air bag in preparation for deployment.

B+ - Battery voltage, the voltage available at the battery at the time of the indicated measurement. With the ignition switch "ON" and the engine not running, system voltage will likely be between 12 and 12.5 volts. At idle the voltage may be 14 to 16 volts. The voltage could be as low as 10 volts during engine cranking.

BULB CHECK - The DERM will cause the "AIR BAG" warning lamp to flash seven times and then go "OFF" whenever the ignition switch transitions to the RUN position from any other ignition switch position and no malfunctions are detected.

"CONTINUOUS MONITORING" - Tests performed by the DERM on the SIR system every 100 milliseconds while "Ignition 1" voltage is in the normal operating voltage range at the DERM.

DATA LINK CONNECTOR (DLC) - Formerly "ALDL", a connector which is connected by wires to multiple on-board computers allowing communication with an off-board computer, such as a scan tool.

DATUM LINE - A base line parallel to the plane of the underbody or frame from which all vertical measurements originate.

DEPLOY - To inflate the air bag.

DEPLOYMENT LOOP - The circuits which supply current to the inflator module to deploy the air bag.

DERM - Diagnostic energy reserve module which provides reserve energy to the deployment loop and performs diagnostic monitoring of all SIR system components.

DIAGNOSTIC TROUBLE CODE (DTC) - A numerical designator used by the DERM to indicate specific SIR system malfunctions.

DRIVER CURRENT SOURCE - An output of the DERM which injects current into the driver inflator module circuit during the "Initiator Assembly Resistance Test."

FORWARD DISCRIMINATING SENSOR - A sensor on the low side (ground side) of the deployment loop that is calibrated to supply ground to the inflator module when the vehicle velocity changes are severe enough to warrant deployment of the air bag.

HIGHER PRIORITY FAULT - Each diagnostic trouble code is assigned a priority based on the detectability with other DTCs present. The priority corresponds to the detectability of the malfunction ONLY, and does NOT relate to the criticality of the malfunction with respect to deployment or non-deployment under any given condition.

IGNITION CYCLE - The voltage at the DERM "Ignition 1" inputs, with ignition switch "ON," is within the normal operating voltage range for at least ten seconds before turning ignition switch "OFF."

IGNITION 1 - A battery voltage (B+) circuit which is only powered with the ignition switch in the RUN, BULB TEST or START positions.

INFLATOR MODULE - An assembly located in the steering wheel hub consisting of an inflatable bag, inflator, and initiator.

INITIATOR - The electrical component inside the inflator module which, when sufficient current flows, sets off the chemical reaction that inflates the air bag.

"INITIATOR ASSEMBLY RESISTANCE TEST" - Tests performed once each ignition cycle when no malfunctions are detected during "Turn-ON" or "Continuous Monitoring." This test checks for the correct DERM configuration for the vehicle, shorts to "Ignition 1" in the deployment loop, high resistance or opens in the "Driver Side High" and "Driver Side Low" circuits, and measures the resistance of the inflator assembly consisting of: 1) Initiator, 2) SIR coil assembly, 3) Connectors and associated wiring.

NORMAL OPERATING VOLTAGE RANGE - The voltage measured between the DERM "Ignition 1" terminals and "Ground" terminals is between 7.25 and 16 volts.

PASSENGER COMPARTMENT DISCRIMINATING SENSOR - A sensor on the low side (ground side) of the deployment loop that is calibrated to supply ground to the inflator module when the vehicle velocity changes are severe enough to warrant deployment of the air bag.

SCAN TOOL - An off-board computer used to read diagnostic information from on-board computer via the data link connector.

SERIAL DATA - Information representing the status of the SIR system.

SIR - Supplemental inflatable restraint.

SIR COIL ASSEMBLY - An assembly of two current-carrying coils in the deployment loop that allows the rotation of the steering wheel while maintaining the continuous contact of the deployment loop to the inflator module.

SIR WIRING HARNESS - The wires and connectors that electrically connect the components in the SIR system.

SYSTEM VOLTAGE - Voltage available at the battery at the time of the indicated voltage measurement. With the ignition switch "ON" and engine not running, system voltage will likely be between 12 and 12.5 volts. At idle the voltage may be 14 to 16 volts. The voltage could be as low as 10 volts during engine cranking.

"10 MINUTE LOOP TEST" - Portions of the "Initiator Assembly Resistance Test" are repeated every ten minutes during an ignition cycle. This is the check for shorts to "Ignition 1" in the deployment loop.

"TURN-ON" - Test which the DERM performs on the SIR system once during each ignition cycle immediately after "Ignition 1" voltage is applied to the DERM and before "Continuous Monitoring."

36 VLR - The 36 volt loop reserve energy supply from the DERM which provides deployment power when vehicle voltage is low or lost in a frontal crash.

36 VLR DELAY - Charging of the 36 VLR power supply is inhibited briefly during "Turn-ON." This allows detection of certain malfunctions related to "Ignition 1" voltage which cannot be tested with 36 volts present.

DIAGNOSIS

CAUTION: To avoid deployment when troubleshooting the SIR system, do not use electrical test equipment such as a battery powered or ac powered voltmeter, ohmmeter, etc., or any type of electrical equipment other than that specified in this manual. Do not use a non-powered probe type tester. Instructions in this manual must be followed carefully, otherwise personal injury may result.

DIAGNOSTIC TROUBLE CODES

The "SIR Diagnostic System Check" must always be the starting point of any SIR system diagnosis. The "SIR Diagnostic System Check" checks for proper "AIR BAG" warning lamp operation and checks for SIR diagnostic trouble codes using the scan tool.

1. Current diagnostic trouble codes - Malfunctions that are presently being detected. Current diagnostic trouble codes are stored in RAM (Random Access Memory).
2. History diagnostic trouble codes - All malfunctions detected since the last time the history memory was cleared. History diagnostic trouble codes are stored in EEPROM (Electrically Erasable Programmable Read-Only Memory).

Scan Tool Diagnostics

A scan tool is used to read current and history diagnostic trouble codes and to clear all diagnostic trouble codes after a repair is completed. The scan tool may need to be updated to communicate with the SIR system through a replaceable cartridge before it can be used for SIR diagnostics. To use the scan tool, connect it to the data link connector and turn the ignition switch "ON." The scan tool reads serial data from the DERM "Serial Data" output terminal "B11" at the data link connector.

A scan tool can also provide SIR system circuit values using the "Data List" function. These values are referred to in the diagnostic trouble code charts to aid in diagnosing certain SIR system malfunctions. For additional information, refer to the scan tool instruction manual.

USE OF SPECIAL TOOLS

CAUTION: To avoid deployment when troubleshooting the SIR system, do not use electrical test equipment such as a battery powered or ac powered voltmeter, ohmmeter, etc., or any type of electrical equipment other than that specified in this manual. Do not use a non-powered probe type tester. Instructions in this manual must be followed carefully, otherwise personal injury may result.

You should be familiar with the tools listed in this section under the heading "SIR SPECIAL TOOLS." You should be able to measure voltage and resistance. You should be familiar with proper use of a scan tool such as the Tech 1 Diagnostic Computer TK-0 or the T-100, the SIR Driver/Passenger Load Tool J 38715, Connector Test Adapter Kit J 35616-A, and the DVM (Digital Multimeter) J 39200.

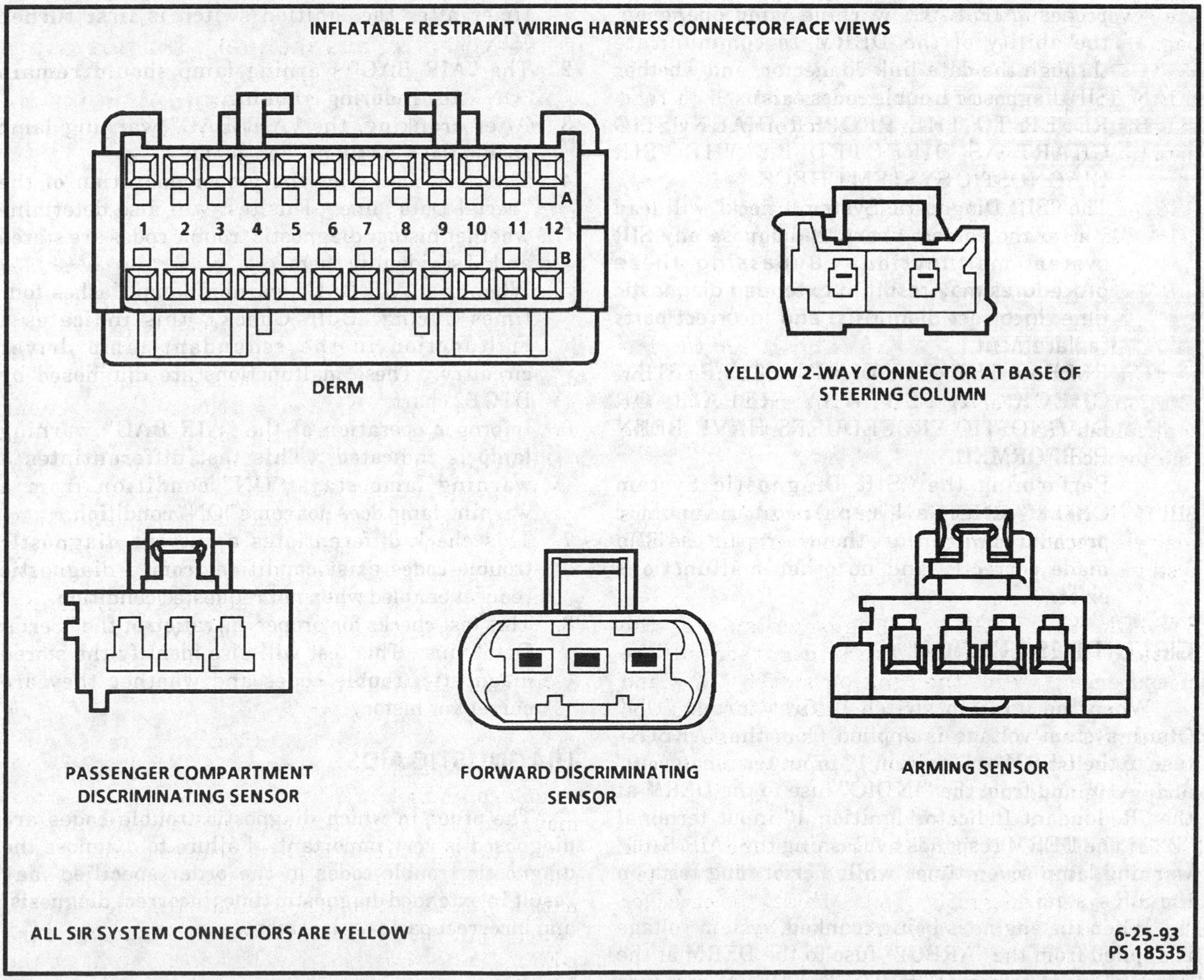
INFLATABLE RESTRAINT WIRING HARNESS CONNECTOR FACE VIEWS
A
1
2
3
4
5
6
7
8
9
10
11
12
B
DERM
YELLOW 2-WAY CONNECTOR AT BASE OF STEERING COLUMN
PASSENGER COMPARTMENT DISCRIMINATING SENSOR
FORWARD DISCRIMINATING SENSOR
ARMING SENSOR
ALL SIR SYSTEM CONNECTORS ARE YELLOW
6-25-93
PS 18535

CAUTION: To avoid deployment when troubleshooting the SIR system, do not use electrical test equipment such as a battery powered or ac powered voltmeter, ohmmeter, etc., or any type of electrical equipment other than that specified in this manual. Do not use a non-powered probe type tester. Instructions in this manual must be followed carefully, otherwise personal injury may result.

SIR DIAGNOSTIC SYSTEM CHECK

The diagnostic procedures used in this section are designed to find and repair SIR system malfunctions. To get the best results, it is important to use the diagnostic charts and follow the sequence listed below:

A. PERFORM THE "SIR DIAGNOSTIC SYSTEM CHECK."
The "SIR Diagnostic System Check" must be the starting point of any SIR diagnostics. The "SIR Diagnostic System Check" checks for proper "AIR BAG" warning lamp operation, the ability of the DERM to communicate through the data link connector, and whether SIR diagnostic trouble codes exist.

B. REFER TO THE PROPER DIAGNOSTIC CHART AS DIRECTED BY THE "SIR DIAGNOSTIC SYSTEM CHECK."
The "SIR Diagnostic System Check" will lead you to the correct chart to diagnose any SIR system malfunction. **Bypassing these procedures may result in extended diagnostic time, incorrect diagnosis, and incorrect parts replacement.**

C. REPEAT THE "SIR DIAGNOSTIC SYSTEM CHECK" AFTER ANY REPAIR OR DIAGNOSTIC PROCEDURES HAVE BEEN PERFORMED.
Performing the "SIR Diagnostic System Check" after all repair or diagnostic procedures will ensure that the repair has been made correctly and no other malfunctions exist.

CIRCUIT DESCRIPTION

When the ignition switch is first turned "ON" (Run), system voltage is applied from the "ARBG1" fuse to the DERM at "Ignition 1" input terminals "A9" and "A10" and from the "INDIC" fuse to the DERM at the "Redundant Indicator Ignition 1" input terminal "B2". The DERM responds by flashing the "AIR BAG" warning lamp seven times while performing tests on the SIR system.

When the engine is being cranked, system voltage is applied from the "ARBG2" fuse to the DERM at the "Crank" input terminal "B10". The DERM responds by grounding the "SIR Indicator" output terminal "B1" until system voltage is removed from the "Crank" input. This results in the "AIR BAG" warning lamp being "ON" steady during cranking.

After cranking, the DERM will flash the "AIR BAG" warning lamp six times and perform tests on the SIR system.

NOTES ON SYSTEM CHECK CHART:

1. The "AIR BAG" warning lamp should flash seven times after the ignition switch is first turned "ON."
2. The "AIR BAG" warning lamp should remain "ON" steady during cranking.
3. After cranking, the "AIR BAG" warning lamp should flash six times then go "OFF."
4. This test checks for the proper operation of the "Serial Data" line. This test will also determine whether history diagnostic trouble codes are stored and, if so, identify them.
5. When the "AIR BAG" warning lamp flashes four times during "Bulb Check," this indicates a malfunction in the redundant lamp driver circuitry. These malfunctions are diagnosed by DTC 62 chart.
6. Improper operation of the "AIR BAG" warning lamp is indicated. This test differentiates a warning lamp stays "ON" condition from a warning lamp does not come "ON" condition.
7. This check differentiates a current diagnostic trouble codes exist condition from a diagnostic request enabled when not requested condition.
8. This test checks for proper operation of the "Serial Data" line. This test will also identify the stored diagnostic trouble codes and whether they are current or history.

DIAGNOSTIC AIDS:

The order in which diagnostic trouble codes are diagnosed is very important. Failure to diagnose the diagnostic trouble codes in the order specified may result in extended diagnostic time, incorrect diagnosis, and incorrect parts replacement.

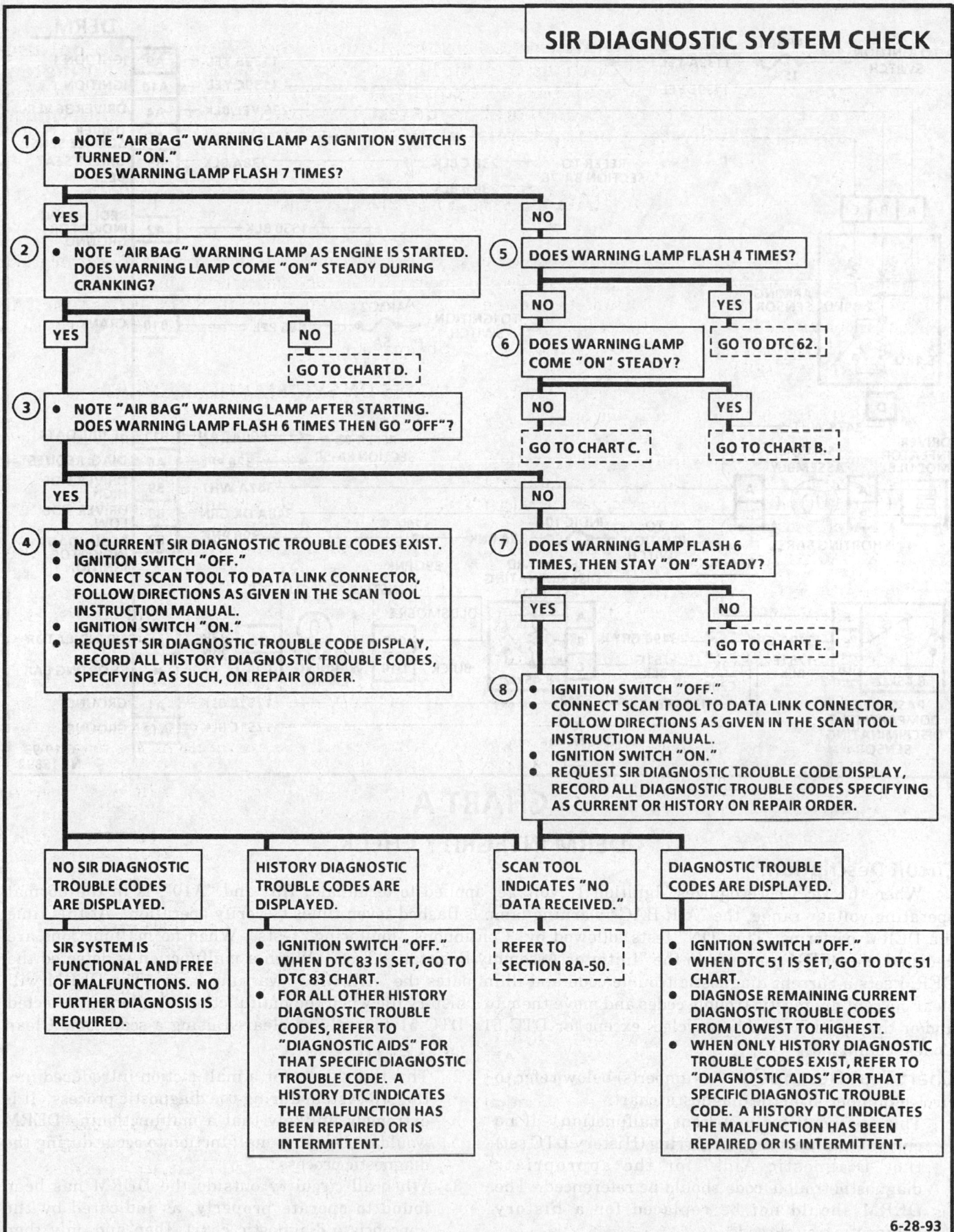

SIR DIAGNOSTIC SYSTEM CHECK

(1)
- NOTE "AIR BAG" WARNING LAMP AS IGNITION SWITCH IS TURNED "ON."
  DOES WARNING LAMP FLASH 7 TIMES?

YES → 2 | NO → 5

(2)
- NOTE "AIR BAG" WARNING LAMP AS ENGINE IS STARTED.
  DOES WARNING LAMP COME "ON" STEADY DURING CRANKING?

YES → 3 | NO → GO TO CHART D.

(3)
- NOTE "AIR BAG" WARNING LAMP AFTER STARTING.
  DOES WARNING LAMP FLASH 6 TIMES THEN GO "OFF"?

YES → 4 | NO → 7

(4)
- NO CURRENT SIR DIAGNOSTIC TROUBLE CODES EXIST.
- IGNITION SWITCH "OFF."
- CONNECT SCAN TOOL TO DATA LINK CONNECTOR, FOLLOW DIRECTIONS AS GIVEN IN THE SCAN TOOL INSTRUCTION MANUAL.
- IGNITION SWITCH "ON."
- REQUEST SIR DIAGNOSTIC TROUBLE CODE DISPLAY, RECORD ALL HISTORY DIAGNOSTIC TROUBLE CODES, SPECIFYING AS SUCH, ON REPAIR ORDER.

(5) DOES WARNING LAMP FLASH 4 TIMES?

NO → 6 | YES → GO TO DTC 62.

(6) DOES WARNING LAMP COME "ON" STEADY?

NO → GO TO CHART C. | YES → GO TO CHART B.

(7) DOES WARNING LAMP FLASH 6 TIMES, THEN STAY "ON" STEADY?

YES → 8 | NO → GO TO CHART E.

(8)
- IGNITION SWITCH "OFF."
- CONNECT SCAN TOOL TO DATA LINK CONNECTOR, FOLLOW DIRECTIONS AS GIVEN IN THE SCAN TOOL INSTRUCTION MANUAL.
- IGNITION SWITCH "ON."
- REQUEST SIR DIAGNOSTIC TROUBLE CODE DISPLAY, RECORD ALL DIAGNOSTIC TROUBLE CODES SPECIFYING AS CURRENT OR HISTORY ON REPAIR ORDER.

NO SIR DIAGNOSTIC TROUBLE CODES ARE DISPLAYED.

SIR SYSTEM IS FUNCTIONAL AND FREE OF MALFUNCTIONS. NO FURTHER DIAGNOSIS IS REQUIRED.

HISTORY DIAGNOSTIC TROUBLE CODES ARE DISPLAYED.

- IGNITION SWITCH "OFF."
- WHEN DTC 83 IS SET, GO TO DTC 83 CHART.
- FOR ALL OTHER HISTORY DIAGNOSTIC TROUBLE CODES, REFER TO "DIAGNOSTIC AIDS" FOR THAT SPECIFIC DIAGNOSTIC TROUBLE CODE. A HISTORY DTC INDICATES THE MALFUNCTION HAS BEEN REPAIRED OR IS INTERMITTENT.

SCAN TOOL INDICATES "NO DATA RECEIVED."

REFER TO SECTION 8A-50.

DIAGNOSTIC TROUBLE CODES ARE DISPLAYED.

- IGNITION SWITCH "OFF."
- WHEN DTC 51 IS SET, GO TO DTC 51 CHART.
- DIAGNOSE REMAINING CURRENT DIAGNOSTIC TROUBLE CODES FROM LOWEST TO HIGHEST.
- WHEN ONLY HISTORY DIAGNOSTIC TROUBLE CODES EXIST, REFER TO "DIAGNOSTIC AIDS" FOR THAT SPECIFIC DIAGNOSTIC TROUBLE CODE. A HISTORY DTC INDICATES THE MALFUNCTION HAS BEEN REPAIRED OR IS INTERMITTENT.

6-28-93
MS 13305

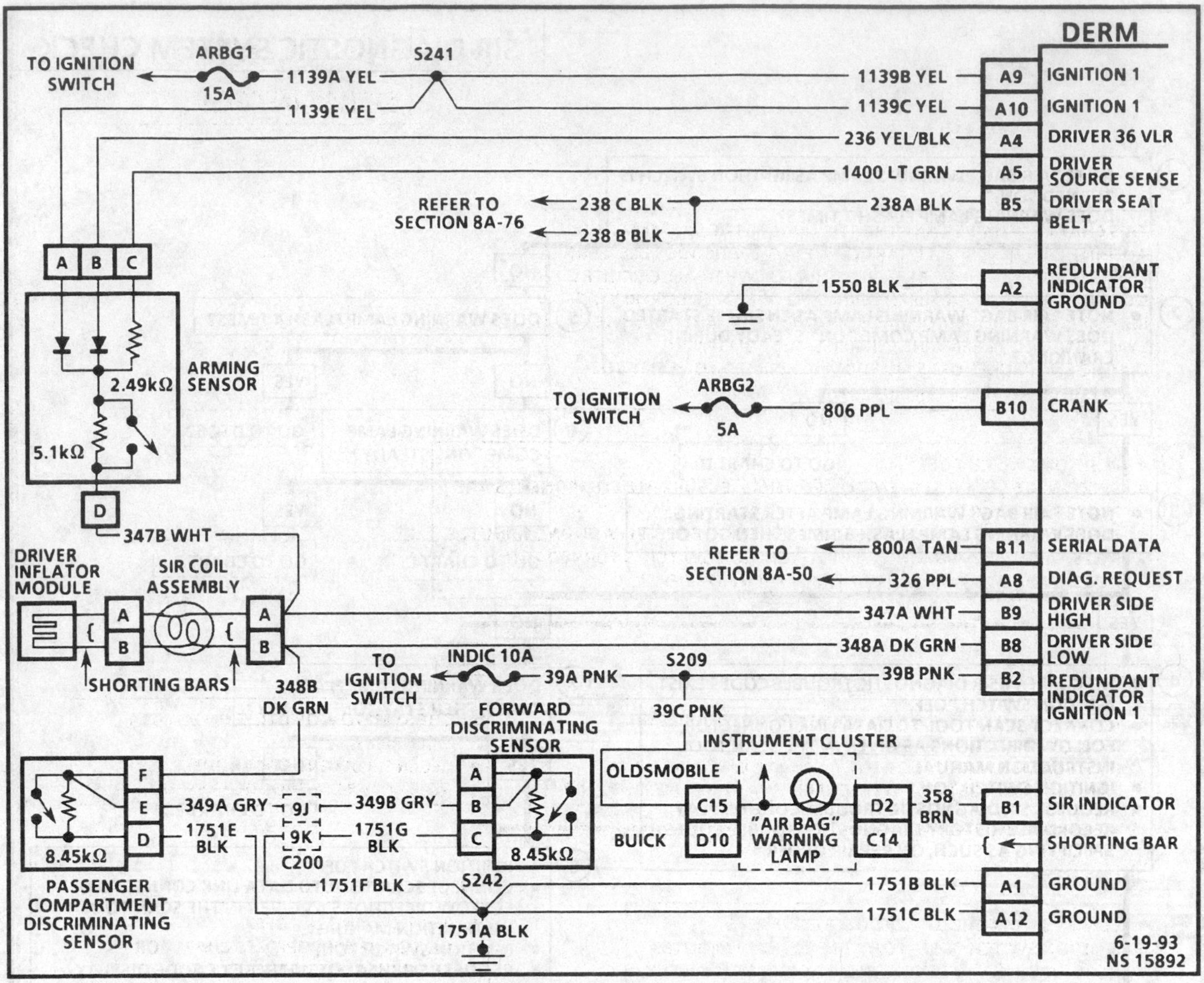
DERM
TO IGNITION SWITCH
ARBG1
15A
S241
1139A YEL
1139E YEL
1139B YEL
A9
IGNITION 1
1139C YEL
A10
IGNITION 1
236 YEL/BLK
A4
DRIVER 36 VLR
1400 LT GRN
A5
DRIVER SOURCE SENSE
REFER TO SECTION 8A-76
238 C BLK
238 B BLK
238A BLK
B5
DRIVER SEAT BELT
A
B
C
1550 BLK
A2
REDUNDANT INDICATOR GROUND
2.49kΩ
ARMING SENSOR
TO IGNITION SWITCH
ARBG2
5A
806 PPL
B10
CRANK
5.1kΩ
D
347B WHT
DRIVER INFLATOR MODULE
SIR COIL ASSEMBLY
REFER TO SECTION 8A-50
800A TAN
B11
SERIAL DATA
326 PPL
A8
DIAG. REQUEST
347A WHT
B9
DRIVER SIDE HIGH
348A DK GRN
B8
DRIVER SIDE LOW
SHORTING BARS
348B DK GRN
TO IGNITION SWITCH
INDIC 10A
39A PNK
S209
39B PNK
B2
REDUNDANT INDICATOR IGNITION 1
FORWARD DISCRIMINATING SENSOR
39C PNK
INSTRUMENT CLUSTER
OLDSMOBILE
F
E
D
349A GRY
9J
9K
C200
349B GRY
1751E BLK
1751G BLK
8.45kΩ
C15
D10
"AIR BAG" WARNING LAMP
D2
C14
358 BRN
B1
SIR INDICATOR
BUICK
SHORTING BAR
PASSENGER COMPARTMENT DISCRIMINATING SENSOR
1751F BLK
S242
1751A BLK
1751B BLK
A1
GROUND
1751C BLK
A12
GROUND
6-19-93
NS 15892

CHART A

DERM INTEGRITY CHECK

Circuit Description:

When the DERM recognizes "Ignition 1" voltage, applied to terminals "A9" and "A10", is in the normal operating voltage range, the "AIR BAG" warning lamp is flashed seven times to verify operation. At this time the DERM performs "Turn-ON" tests followed by "Continuous Monitoring" tests. When no malfunctions are detected the DERM proceeds to the "Initiator Assembly Resistance Test." When a malfunction is detected the DERM sets a current diagnostic trouble code and illuminates the "AIR BAG" warning lamp. The DERM will clear current diagnostic trouble codes and move them to a history file when the malfunction is no longer detected and/or the ignition switch is cycled, except for DTC 51. DTC 51 can only be cleared using a scan tool "Clear Codes" command.

Chart Test Description: Number(s) below refer to circled number(s) on the diagnostic chart.

1. This test confirms a current malfunction. If no current malfunction is occurring (History DTC set) the "Diagnostic Aids" for the appropriate diagnostic trouble code should be referenced. The DERM should not be replaced for a history diagnostic trouble code.
2. This test checks for a malfunction introduced into the SIR system during the diagnostic process. It is extremely unlikely that a malfunctioning DERM would cause a new malfunction to occur during the diagnostic process.
3. When all circuitry outside the DERM has been found to operate properly, as indicated by the appropriate diagnostic chart, then and only then should the DERM be replaced.

CHART A
DERM INTEGRITY CHECK

THIS CHART ASSUMES THAT THE "SIR DIAGNOSTIC SYSTEM CHECK" AND EITHER A SYMPTOM CHART OR A DIAGNOSTIC TROUBLE CODE CHART DIAGNOSIS HAVE BEEN PERFORMED. WHEN ALL CIRCUITRY OUTSIDE THE DERM HAS BEEN FOUND TO OPERATE PROPERLY, AS INDICATED BY THE APPROPRIATE DIAGNOSTIC CHART, AND THE SYMPTOM OR DTC REMAINS CURRENT, THE FOLLOWING DIAGNOSTIC PROCEDURES MUST BE PERFORMED TO VERIFY THE NEED FOR DERM REPLACEMENT.

(1)
- IGNITION SWITCH "OFF."
- RECONNECT ALL SIR SYSTEM COMPONENTS, ENSURE ALL COMPONENTS ARE PROPERLY MOUNTED.
- ENSURE THE IGNITION SWITCH HAS BEEN "OFF" FOR AT LEAST TWO MINUTES.
- NOTE "AIR BAG" WARNING LAMP AS IGNITION SWITCH IS TURNED "ON." DOES WARNING LAMP FLASH 7 TIMES THEN GO "OFF"?

NO

(2)
- USING A SCAN TOOL REQUEST DIAGNOSTIC TROUBLE CODE DISPLAY.
  IS THE SAME SYMPTOM OR DTC OCCURRING AS WAS WHEN THE "SIR DIAGNOSTIC SYSTEM CHECK" WAS FIRST PERFORMED?

YES

- THE SYMPTOM OR DTC IS NO LONGER OCCURRING.
- CLEAR SIR DIAGNOSTIC TROUBLE CODES.
- REPEAT "SIR DIAGNOSTIC SYSTEM CHECK."

(From 2:)

YES

(3)
- CLEAR "SIR DIAGNOSTIC TROUBLE CODES."
- IGNITION SWITCH "OFF" FOR AT LEAST TWO MINUTES.
- NOTE "AIR BAG" WARNING LAMP AS IGNITION SWITCH IS TURNED "ON."
  DOES WARNING LAMP FLASH 7 TIMES THEN GO "OFF"?

NO

- IGNITION SWITCH "OFF."
- GO TO THE APPROPRIATE CHART FOR THE INDICATED MALFUNCTION.

(From 3:)

YES

SIR SYSTEM IS FUNCTIONAL AND FREE OF MALFUNCTIONS. NO FURTHER DIAGNOSIS IS REQUIRED.

NO

- IGNITION SWITCH "OFF."
- REPLACE DERM.
- RECONNECT ALL SIR SYSTEM COMPONENTS, ENSURE ALL COMPONENTS ARE PROPERLY MOUNTED.
- REPEAT "SIR DIAGNOSTIC SYSTEM CHECK."

4-6-93
NS 15420

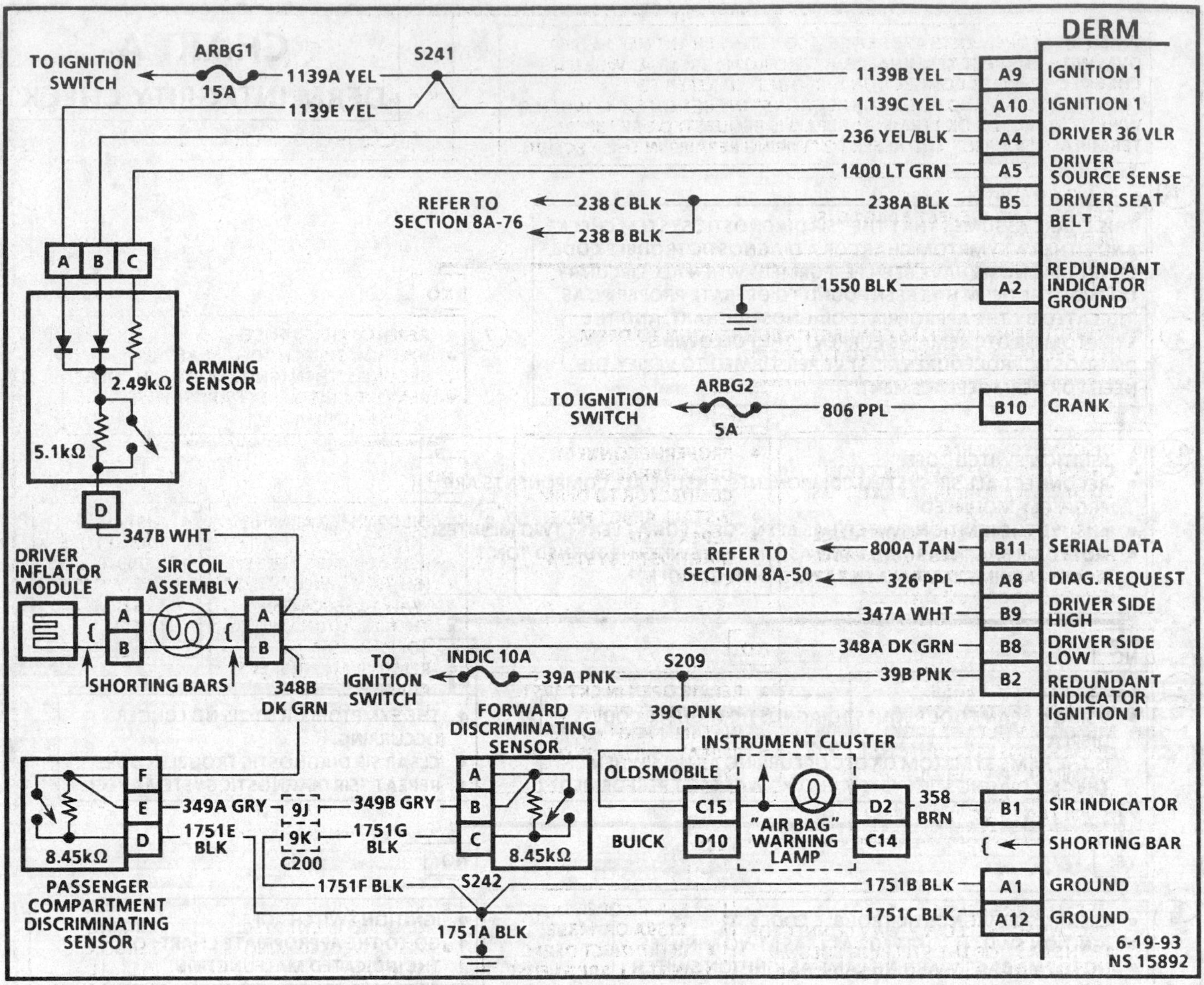
DERM
TO IGNITION SWITCH
ARBG1
15A
S241
1139A YEL
1139E YEL
1139B YEL
1139C YEL
236 YEL/BLK
1400 LT GRN
A9
A10
A4
A5
B5
IGNITION 1
IGNITION 1
DRIVER 36 VLR
DRIVER SOURCE SENSE
DRIVER SEAT BELT
REFER TO SECTION 8A-76
238 C BLK
238 B BLK
238A BLK
A B C
1550 BLK
A2
REDUNDANT INDICATOR GROUND
2.49kΩ
ARMING SENSOR
5.1kΩ
D
TO IGNITION SWITCH
ARBG2
5A
806 PPL
B10
CRANK
347B WHT
DRIVER INFLATOR MODULE
SIR COIL ASSEMBLY
SHORTING BARS
348B DK GRN
REFER TO SECTION 8A-50
800A TAN
326 PPL
347A WHT
348A DK GRN
39B PNK
B11
A8
B9
B8
B2
SERIAL DATA
DIAG. REQUEST
DRIVER SIDE HIGH
DRIVER SIDE LOW
REDUNDANT INDICATOR IGNITION 1
TO IGNITION SWITCH
INDIC 10A
39A PNK
S209
39C PNK
FORWARD DISCRIMINATING SENSOR
INSTRUMENT CLUSTER
OLDSMOBILE
BUICK
C15
D10
D2
C14
"AIR BAG" WARNING LAMP
358 BRN
B1
SIR INDICATOR
SHORTING BAR
349A GRY
349B GRY
9J
9K
C200
1751E BLK
1751G BLK
8.45kΩ
8.45kΩ
F
E
D
A
B
C
1751F BLK
S242
1751B BLK
1751C BLK
1751A BLK
A1
A12
GROUND
GROUND
PASSENGER COMPARTMENT DISCRIMINATING SENSOR
6-19-93
NS 15892

CHART B

"AIR BAG" WARNING LAMP COMES "ON" STEADY

Circuit Description:

When the ignition switch is first turned "ON," "Ignition 1" voltage is applied from the "INDIC" fuse to "Redundant Indicator Ignition 1," terminal "B2", and to the "AIR BAG" warning lamp which is connected to "SIR Indicator," terminal "B1". The "ARBG1" fuse applies system voltage to the "Ignition 1" inputs, terminals "A9" and "A10". The DERM responds by flashing the "AIR BAG" warning lamp seven times. If "Ignition 1" is outside of the normal operating voltage range, the "AIR BAG" warning lamp will come "ON" solid with no DTCs set.

When the engine is being cranked, "Ignition 1" voltage is applied from the "ARBG2" fuse to the DERM at the "Crank" input. The DERM responds by grounding the "SIR Indicator" output until "Ignition 1" voltage is removed from the "Crank" input. This results in the "AIR BAG" warning lamp being "ON" during cranking.

After cranking, the DERM will flash the "AIR BAG" warning lamp six times.

Chart Test Description: Number(s) below refer to circled number(s) on the diagnostic chart.

1. An open "ARBG1" fuse would cause the "AIR BAG" warning lamp to come "ON" steady.
2. A disconnected DERM harness connector will cause the warning lamp to come "ON" steady via the shorting bar from terminal "A1" to terminal "B1".
3. This test checks for an open in the "Ground" circuitry to the DERM.
4. This test checks for an open in the "Ignition 1" circuitry to the DERM.
5. This test checks for a short from the "SIR Indicator" circuit to ground.
6. This test checks for a short from the "Crank" input circuit to B+.
7. This test checks whether a short to ground caused the "ARBG1" fuse to open.
8. This test determines whether the short to ground is due to a malfunctioning arming sensor or a short in the wiring.

WHEN MEASUREMENTS ARE REQUESTED IN THIS CHART USE J 39200 DVM WITH CORRECT TERMINAL ADAPTER FROM J 35616-A. WHEN A CHECK FOR PROPER CONNECTION IS REQUESTED REFER TO "INTERMITTENTS AND POOR CONNECTIONS" IN SECTION 8A-4. WHEN A WIRE, CONNECTOR OR TERMINAL REPAIR IS REQUESTED USE J 38125-A TERMINAL REPAIR KIT AND REFER TO "WIRING REPAIR" IN THIS SECTION.

CHART B

"AIR BAG" WARNING LAMP COMES "ON" STEADY

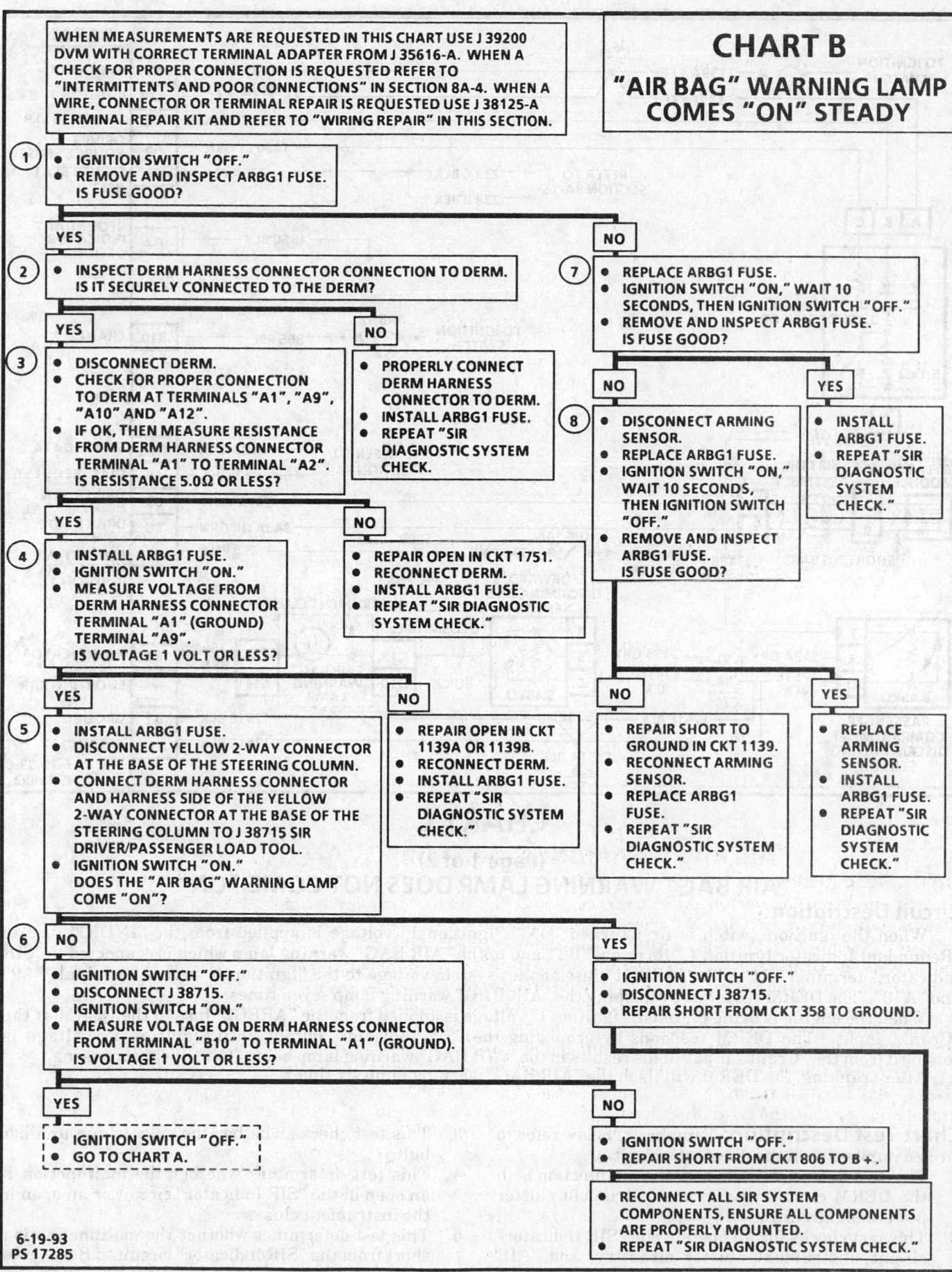

(1)
- IGNITION SWITCH "OFF."
- REMOVE AND INSPECT ARBG1 FUSE.

IS FUSE GOOD?

YES →

(2)
- INSPECT DERM HARNESS CONNECTOR CONNECTION TO DERM.

IS IT SECURELY CONNECTED TO THE DERM?

YES →

(3)
- DISCONNECT DERM.
- CHECK FOR PROPER CONNECTION TO DERM AT TERMINALS "A1", "A9", "A10" AND "A12".
- IF OK, THEN MEASURE RESISTANCE FROM DERM HARNESS CONNECTOR TERMINAL "A1" TO TERMINAL "A2".

IS RESISTANCE 5.0Ω OR LESS?

YES →

(4)
- INSTALL ARBG1 FUSE.
- IGNITION SWITCH "ON."
- MEASURE VOLTAGE FROM DERM HARNESS CONNECTOR TERMINAL "A1" (GROUND) TERMINAL "A9".

IS VOLTAGE 1 VOLT OR LESS?

YES →

(5)
- INSTALL ARBG1 FUSE.
- DISCONNECT YELLOW 2-WAY CONNECTOR AT THE BASE OF THE STEERING COLUMN.
- CONNECT DERM HARNESS CONNECTOR AND HARNESS SIDE OF THE YELLOW 2-WAY CONNECTOR AT THE BASE OF THE STEERING COLUMN TO J 38715 SIR DRIVER/PASSENGER LOAD TOOL.
- IGNITION SWITCH "ON."

DOES THE "AIR BAG" WARNING LAMP COME "ON"?

NO →

(6)
- IGNITION SWITCH "OFF."
- DISCONNECT J 38715.
- IGNITION SWITCH "ON."
- MEASURE VOLTAGE ON DERM HARNESS CONNECTOR FROM TERMINAL "B10" TO TERMINAL "A1" (GROUND).

IS VOLTAGE 1 VOLT OR LESS?

YES →
- IGNITION SWITCH "OFF."
- GO TO CHART A.

NO →
- IGNITION SWITCH "OFF."
- REPAIR SHORT FROM CKT 806 TO B+.

(5) YES →
- IGNITION SWITCH "OFF."
- DISCONNECT J 38715.
- REPAIR SHORT FROM CKT 358 TO GROUND.

(4) NO →
- REPAIR OPEN IN CKT 1139A OR 1139B.
- RECONNECT DERM.
- INSTALL ARBG1 FUSE.
- REPEAT "SIR DIAGNOSTIC SYSTEM CHECK."

(3) NO →
- REPAIR OPEN IN CKT 1751.
- RECONNECT DERM.
- INSTALL ARBG1 FUSE.
- REPEAT "SIR DIAGNOSTIC SYSTEM CHECK."

(2) NO →
- PROPERLY CONNECT DERM HARNESS CONNECTOR TO DERM.
- INSTALL ARBG1 FUSE.
- REPEAT "SIR DIAGNOSTIC SYSTEM CHECK.

(1) NO →

(7)
- REPLACE ARBG1 FUSE.
- IGNITION SWITCH "ON," WAIT 10 SECONDS, THEN IGNITION SWITCH "OFF."
- REMOVE AND INSPECT ARBG1 FUSE.

IS FUSE GOOD?

YES →
- INSTALL ARBG1 FUSE.
- REPEAT "SIR DIAGNOSTIC SYSTEM CHECK."

NO →

(8)
- DISCONNECT ARMING SENSOR.
- REPLACE ARBG1 FUSE.
- IGNITION SWITCH "ON," WAIT 10 SECONDS, THEN IGNITION SWITCH "OFF."
- REMOVE AND INSPECT ARBG1 FUSE.

IS FUSE GOOD?

NO →
- REPAIR SHORT TO GROUND IN CKT 1139.
- RECONNECT ARMING SENSOR.
- REPLACE ARBG1 FUSE.
- REPEAT "SIR DIAGNOSTIC SYSTEM CHECK."

YES →
- REPLACE ARMING SENSOR.
- INSTALL ARBG1 FUSE.
- REPEAT "SIR DIAGNOSTIC SYSTEM CHECK."

Final step (after repairs from CKT 358 / CKT 806):
- RECONNECT ALL SIR SYSTEM COMPONENTS, ENSURE ALL COMPONENTS ARE PROPERLY MOUNTED.
- REPEAT "SIR DIAGNOSTIC SYSTEM CHECK."

6-19-93
PS 17285

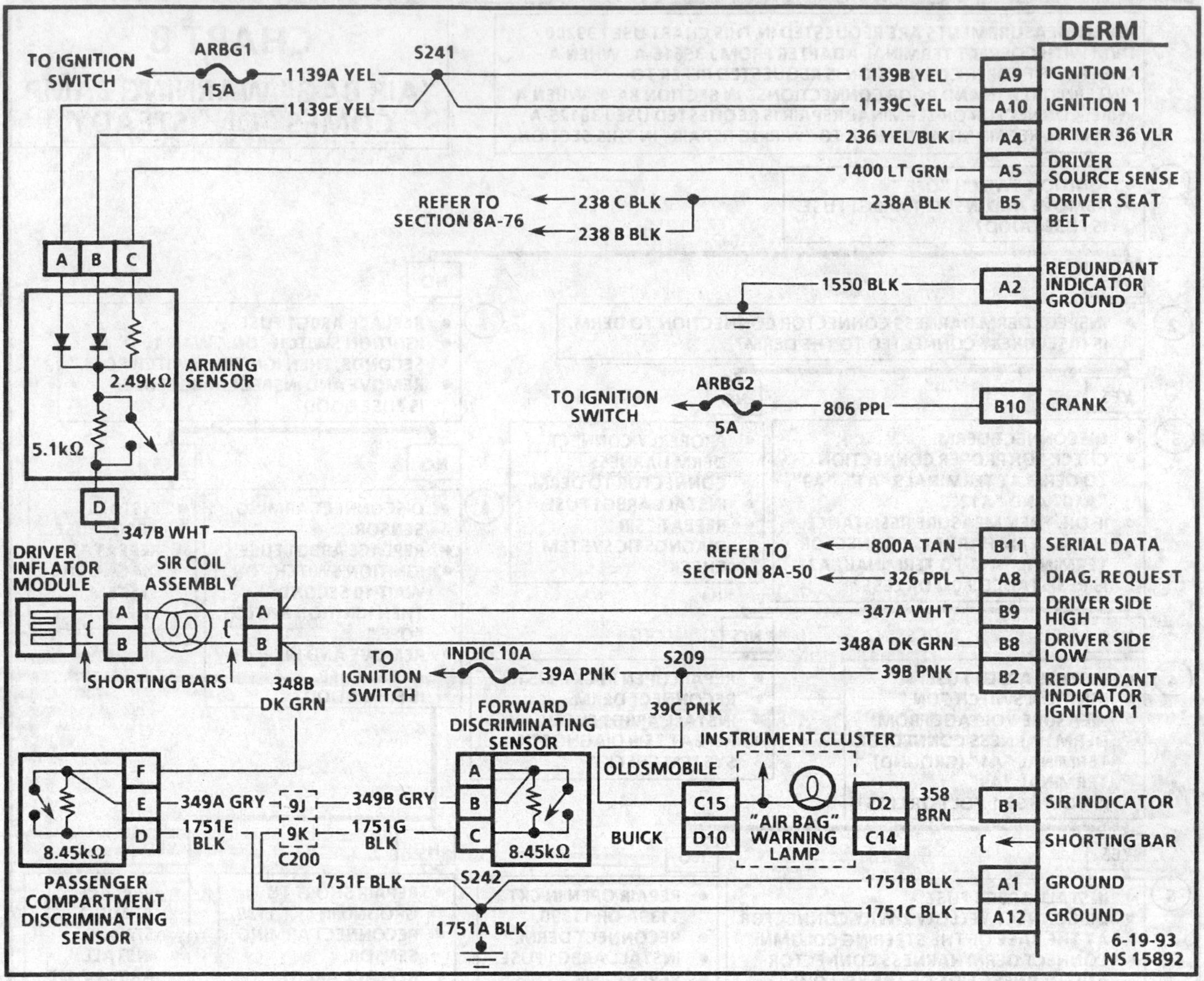
DERM
TO IGNITION SWITCH
ARBG1
15A
1139A YEL
1139E YEL
S241
1139B YEL
A9
IGNITION 1
1139C YEL
A10
IGNITION 1
236 YEL/BLK
A4
DRIVER 36 VLR
1400 LT GRN
A5
DRIVER SOURCE SENSE
REFER TO SECTION 8A-76
238 C BLK
238 B BLK
238A BLK
B5
DRIVER SEAT BELT
A B C
1550 BLK
A2
REDUNDANT INDICATOR GROUND
ARMING SENSOR
2.49kΩ
5.1kΩ
TO IGNITION SWITCH
ARBG2
5A
806 PPL
B10
CRANK
D
347B WHT
DRIVER INFLATOR MODULE
SIR COIL ASSEMBLY
REFER TO SECTION 8A-50
800A TAN
B11
SERIAL DATA
326 PPL
A8
DIAG. REQUEST
347A WHT
B9
DRIVER SIDE HIGH
348A DK GRN
B8
DRIVER SIDE LOW
SHORTING BARS
348B DK GRN
TO IGNITION SWITCH
INDIC 10A
39A PNK
S209
39B PNK
B2
REDUNDANT INDICATOR IGNITION 1
39C PNK
FORWARD DISCRIMINATING SENSOR
INSTRUMENT CLUSTER
OLDSMOBILE
F
E
D
349A GRY
9J
9K
349B GRY
1751E BLK
1751G BLK
C200
8.45kΩ
C15
D10
BUICK
"AIR BAG" WARNING LAMP
D2
C14
358 BRN
B1
SIR INDICATOR
SHORTING BAR
PASSENGER COMPARTMENT DISCRIMINATING SENSOR
1751F BLK
S242
1751B BLK
A1
GROUND
1751A BLK
1751C BLK
A12
GROUND
6-19-93
NS 15892

CHART C

(Page 1 of 2)

"AIR BAG" WARNING LAMP DOES NOT COME "ON"

Circuit Description:

When the ignition switch is first turned "ON," "Ignition 1" voltage is applied from the "INDIC" fuse to "Redundant Indicator Ignition 1," terminal "B2", and to the "AIR BAG" warning lamp which is connected to "SIR Indicator," terminal "B1". The "ARBG1" fuse applies system voltage to the "Ignition 1" inputs, terminals "A9" and "A10". The DERM responds by flashing the "AIR BAG" warning lamp seven times.

When the engine is being cranked, "Ignition 1" voltage is applied from the "ARBG2" fuse to the DERM at the "Crank" input. The DERM responds by grounding the "SIR Indicator" output until "Ignition 1" voltage is removed from the "Crank" input. This results in the "AIR BAG" warning lamp being "ON" during cranking.

After cranking, the DERM will flash the "AIR BAG" warning lamp six times.

Chart Test Description: Number(s) below refer to circled number(s) on the diagnostic chart.

1. This test determines whether the malfunction is in the DERM circuitry or in the instrument cluster power feed circuitry.
2. This test checks for an open in the "SIR Indicator" circuit, instrument cluster circuitry, and "AIR BAG" warning lamp bulb.
3. This test checks whether the open is due to a bad bulb.
4. This test determines whether the malfunction is an open in the "SIR Indicator" circuit or an open in the instrument cluster.
5. This test determines whether the malfunction is a short from the "SIR Indicator" circuit to B+.

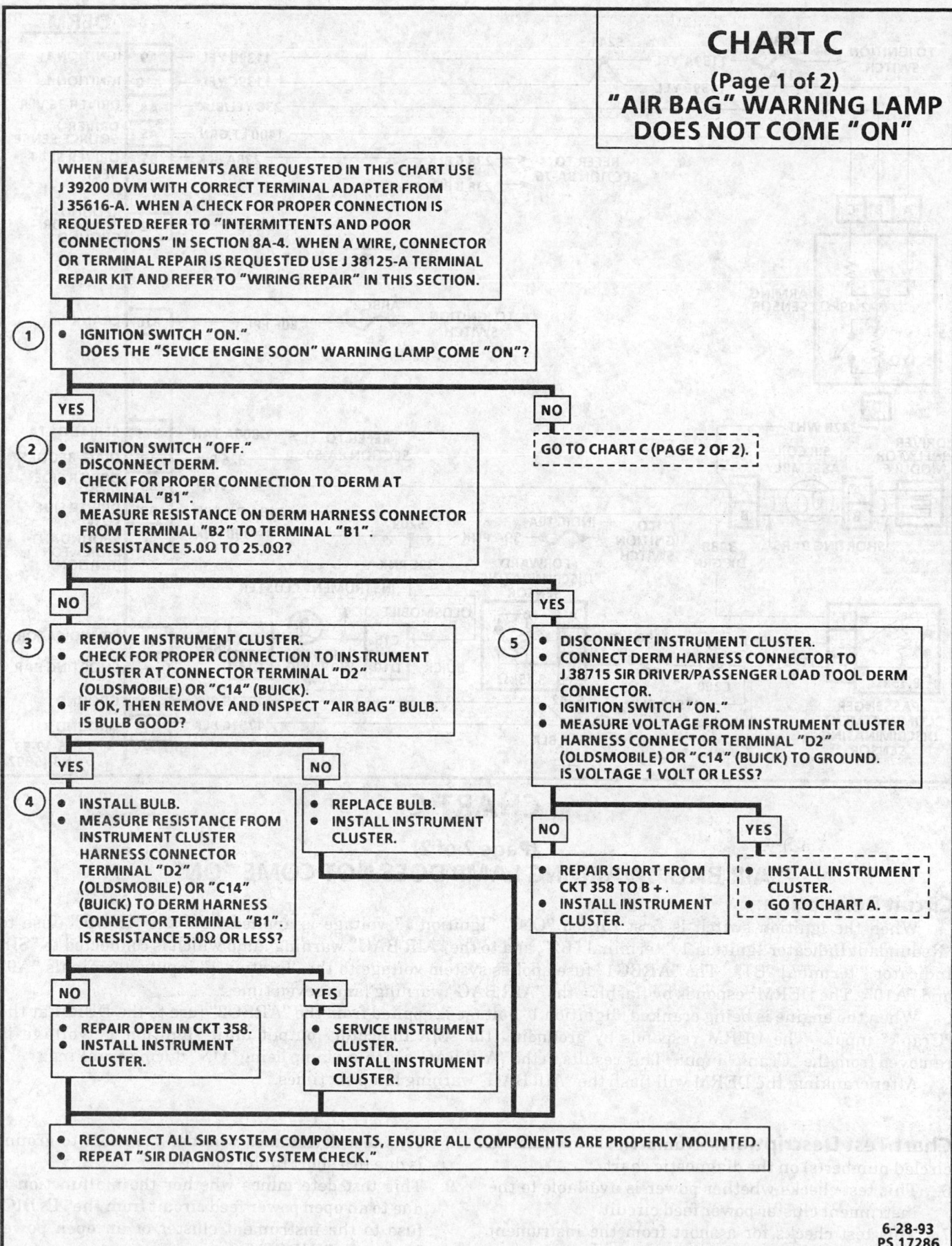

CHART C

(Page 1 of 2)

"AIR BAG" WARNING LAMP DOES NOT COME "ON"

WHEN MEASUREMENTS ARE REQUESTED IN THIS CHART USE J 39200 DVM WITH CORRECT TERMINAL ADAPTER FROM J 35616-A. WHEN A CHECK FOR PROPER CONNECTION IS REQUESTED REFER TO "INTERMITTENTS AND POOR CONNECTIONS" IN SECTION 8A-4. WHEN A WIRE, CONNECTOR OR TERMINAL REPAIR IS REQUESTED USE J 38125-A TERMINAL REPAIR KIT AND REFER TO "WIRING REPAIR" IN THIS SECTION.

1
- IGNITION SWITCH "ON."
  DOES THE "SEVICE ENGINE SOON" WARNING LAMP COME "ON"?

YES → 2

NO → GO TO CHART C (PAGE 2 OF 2).

2
- IGNITION SWITCH "OFF."
- DISCONNECT DERM.
- CHECK FOR PROPER CONNECTION TO DERM AT TERMINAL "B1".
- MEASURE RESISTANCE ON DERM HARNESS CONNECTOR FROM TERMINAL "B2" TO TERMINAL "B1".
  IS RESISTANCE 5.0Ω TO 25.0Ω?

NO → 3

YES → 5

3
- REMOVE INSTRUMENT CLUSTER.
- CHECK FOR PROPER CONNECTION TO INSTRUMENT CLUSTER AT CONNECTOR TERMINAL "D2" (OLDSMOBILE) OR "C14" (BUICK).
- IF OK, THEN REMOVE AND INSPECT "AIR BAG" BULB.
  IS BULB GOOD?

YES → 4

NO →
- REPLACE BULB.
- INSTALL INSTRUMENT CLUSTER.

4
- INSTALL BULB.
- MEASURE RESISTANCE FROM INSTRUMENT CLUSTER HARNESS CONNECTOR TERMINAL "D2" (OLDSMOBILE) OR "C14" (BUICK) TO DERM HARNESS CONNECTOR TERMINAL "B1".
  IS RESISTANCE 5.0Ω OR LESS?

NO →
- REPAIR OPEN IN CKT 358.
- INSTALL INSTRUMENT CLUSTER.

YES →
- SERVICE INSTRUMENT CLUSTER.
- INSTALL INSTRUMENT CLUSTER.

5
- DISCONNECT INSTRUMENT CLUSTER.
- CONNECT DERM HARNESS CONNECTOR TO J 38715 SIR DRIVER/PASSENGER LOAD TOOL DERM CONNECTOR.
- IGNITION SWITCH "ON."
- MEASURE VOLTAGE FROM INSTRUMENT CLUSTER HARNESS CONNECTOR TERMINAL "D2" (OLDSMOBILE) OR "C14" (BUICK) TO GROUND.
  IS VOLTAGE 1 VOLT OR LESS?

NO →
- REPAIR SHORT FROM CKT 358 TO B+.
- INSTALL INSTRUMENT CLUSTER.

YES →
- INSTALL INSTRUMENT CLUSTER.
- GO TO CHART A.

- RECONNECT ALL SIR SYSTEM COMPONENTS, ENSURE ALL COMPONENTS ARE PROPERLY MOUNTED.
- REPEAT "SIR DIAGNOSTIC SYSTEM CHECK."

6-28-93
PS 17286

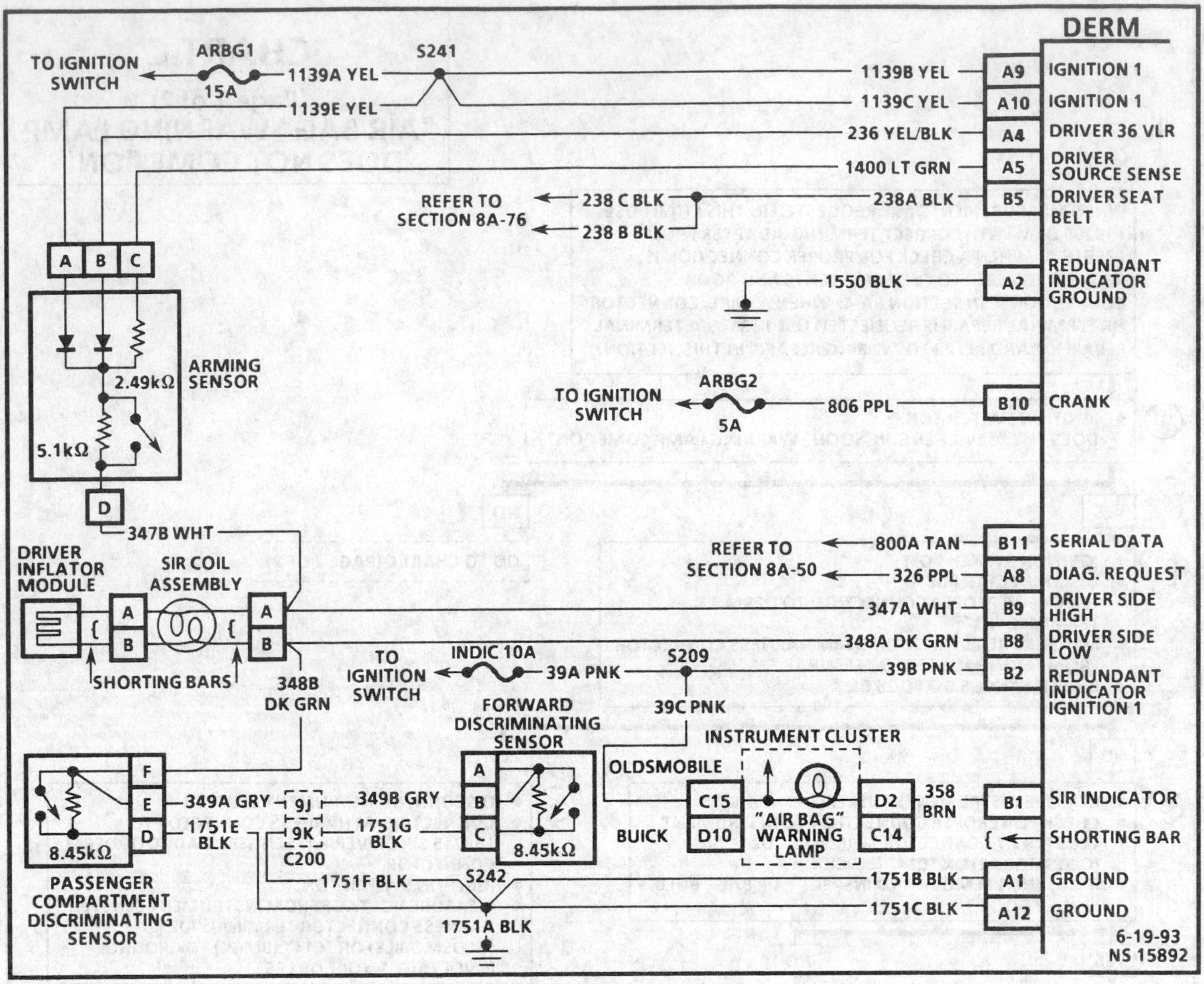
DERM
TO IGNITION SWITCH
ARBG1
15A
1139A YEL
1139E YEL
S241
1139B YEL
A9
IGNITION 1
1139C YEL
A10
IGNITION 1
236 YEL/BLK
A4
DRIVER 36 VLR
1400 LT GRN
A5
DRIVER SOURCE SENSE
REFER TO SECTION 8A-76
238 C BLK
238 B BLK
238A BLK
B5
DRIVER SEAT BELT
A B C
1550 BLK
A2
REDUNDANT INDICATOR GROUND
ARMING SENSOR
2.49kΩ
5.1kΩ
TO IGNITION SWITCH
ARBG2
5A
806 PPL
B10
CRANK
D
347B WHT
DRIVER INFLATOR MODULE
SIR COIL ASSEMBLY
REFER TO SECTION 8A-50
800A TAN
B11
SERIAL DATA
326 PPL
A8
DIAG. REQUEST
347A WHT
B9
DRIVER SIDE HIGH
348A DK GRN
B8
DRIVER SIDE LOW
SHORTING BARS
348B DK GRN
TO IGNITION SWITCH
INDIC 10A
39A PNK
S209
39B PNK
B2
REDUNDANT INDICATOR IGNITION 1
FORWARD DISCRIMINATING SENSOR
39C PNK
INSTRUMENT CLUSTER
OLDSMOBILE
C15
"AIR BAG" WARNING LAMP
D2
358 BRN
B1
SIR INDICATOR
349A GRY
9J
349B GRY
1751E BLK
9K
1751G BLK
C200
BUICK
D10
C14
SHORTING BAR
8.45kΩ
8.45kΩ
1751F BLK
S242
1751B BLK
A1
GROUND
1751C BLK
A12
GROUND
PASSENGER COMPARTMENT DISCRIMINATING SENSOR
1751A BLK
6-19-93
NS 15892

CHART C

(Page 2 of 2)

"AIR BAG" WARNING LAMP DOES NOT COME "ON"

Circuit Description:

When the ignition switch is first turned "ON," "Ignition 1" voltage is applied from the "INDIC" fuse to "Redundant Indicator Ignition 1," terminal "B2", and to the "AIR BAG" warning lamp which is connected to "SIR Indicator," terminal "B1". The "ARBG1" fuse applies system voltage to the "Ignition 1" inputs, terminals "A9" and "A10". The DERM responds by flashing the "AIR BAG" warning lamp seven times.

When the engine is being cranked, "Ignition 1" voltage is applied from the "ARBG2" fuse to the DERM at the "Crank" input. The DERM responds by grounding the "SIR Indicator" output until "Ignition 1" voltage is removed from the "Crank" input. This results in the "AIR BAG" warning lamp being "ON" during cranking.

After cranking, the DERM will flash the "AIR BAG" warning lamp six times.

Chart Test Description: Number(s) below refer to circled number(s) on the diagnostic chart.

6. This test checks whether power is available to the instrument cluster power feed circuit.
7. This test checks for a short from the instrument cluster power feed circuit to ground.
8. This test determines whether the short to ground is due to a short in the wiring.
9. This test determines whether the malfunction is due to an open power feed circuit from the "INDIC" fuse to the instrument cluster or an open power feed to the "INDIC" fuse.

CHART C

(Page 2 of 2)

"AIR BAG" WARNING LAMP DOES NOT COME "ON"

WERE YOU SENT HERE FROM CHART C (PAGE 1 OF 2)?

NO

GO TO CHART C (PAGE 1 OF 2).

YES

6
- IGNITION SWITCH "OFF."
- REMOVE AND INSPECT INDIC FUSE.
  IS FUSE GOOD?

YES

9
- DISCONNECT INSTRUMENT CLUSTER.
- CHECK FOR PROPER CONNECTION TO INSTRUMENT CLUSTER AT TERMINAL "C15" (OLDSMOBILE) OR "D10" (BUICK).
- IF OK THEN MEASURE RESISTANCE FROM INSTRUMENT CLUSTER HARNESS CONNECTOR TERMINAL "C15" (OLDSMOBILE) OR "D10" (BUICK) TO EACH TERMINAL OF THE INDIC FUSE FUSE HOLDER.
  IS EITHER MEASUREMENT 5.0Ω OR LESS?

NO
- REPAIR OPEN IN CKT 39A OR CKT 39C.
- INSTALL INDIC FUSE.

YES
- REPAIR OPEN IN POWER FEED TO INDIC FUSE.
- INSTALL INDIC FUSE.

NO

7
- REPLACE INDIC FUSE.
- IGNITION SWITCH "ON," WAIT 10 SECONDS, THEN IGNITION SWITCH "OFF."
- REMOVE AND INSPECT INDIC FUSE.
  IS FUSE GOOD?

YES

INSTALL INDIC FUSE.

NO

8
- DISCONNECT YELLOW 2-WAY CONNECTOR AT THE BASE OF THE STEERING COLUMN.
- DISCONNECT DERM.
- REPLACE INDIC FUSE.
- IGNITION SWITCH "ON," WAIT 10 SECONDS.
- IGNITION SWITCH "OFF."
- REMOVE AND INSPECT INDIC FUSE.
  IS FUSE GOOD?

NO
- REPAIR SHORT TO GROUND IN CKT 39 OR INSTRUMENT CLUSTER.
- REPLACE INDIC FUSE.

YES
- INSTALL INDIC FUSE.
- GO TO CHART A.

- RECONNECT ALL SIR SYSTEM COMPONENTS, ENSURE ALL COMPONENTS ARE PROPERLY MOUNTED.
- REPEAT "SIR DIAGNOSTIC SYSTEM CHECK."

6-18-93
PS 17287

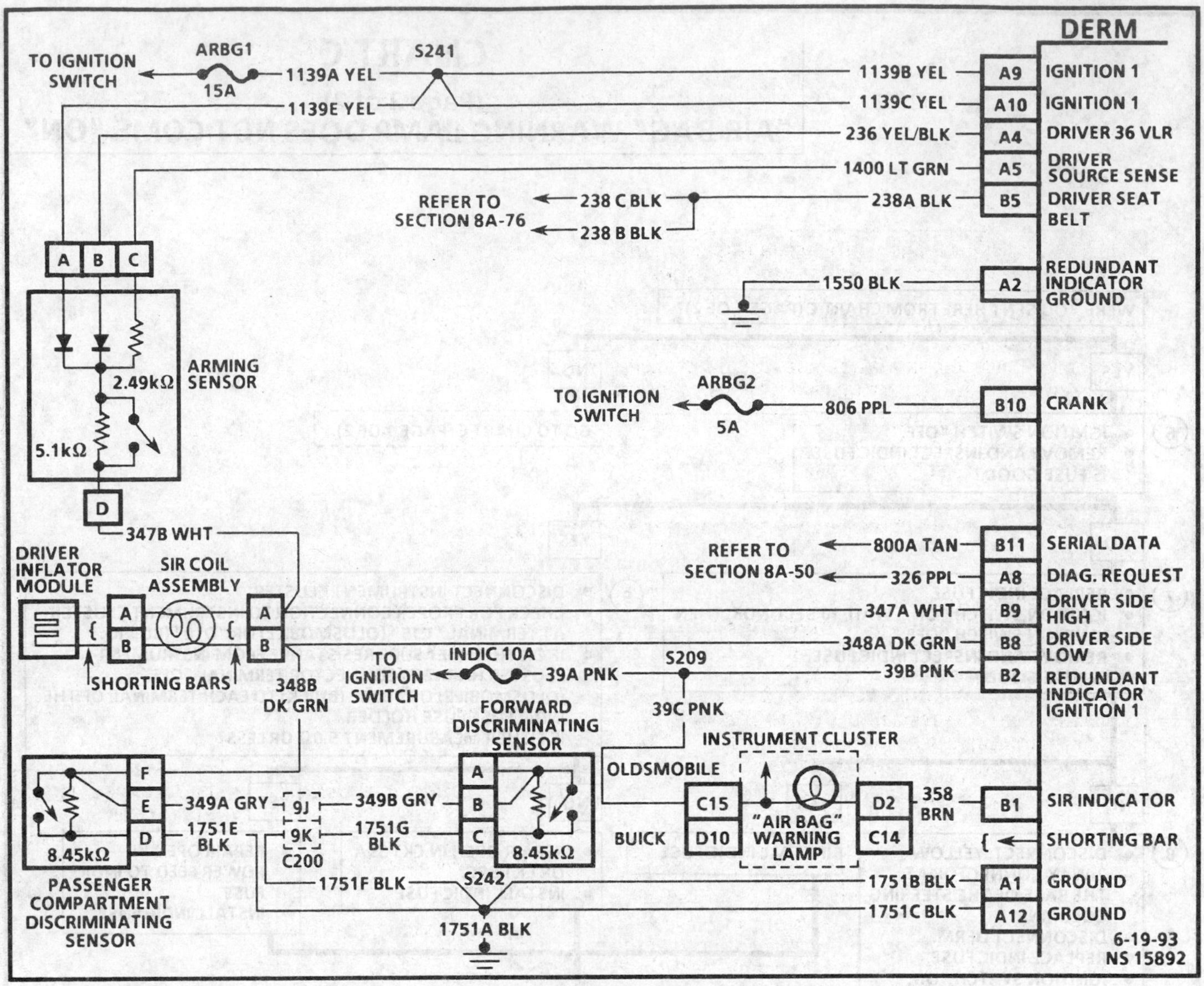
DERM
TO IGNITION SWITCH
ARBG1
15A
S241
1139A YEL
1139E YEL
1139B YEL
A9
IGNITION 1
1139C YEL
A10
IGNITION 1
236 YEL/BLK
A4
DRIVER 36 VLR
1400 LT GRN
A5
DRIVER SOURCE SENSE
REFER TO SECTION 8A-76
238 C BLK
238 B BLK
238A BLK
B5
DRIVER SEAT BELT
A B C
1550 BLK
A2
REDUNDANT INDICATOR GROUND
ARMING SENSOR
2.49kΩ
5.1kΩ
TO IGNITION SWITCH
ARBG2
5A
806 PPL
B10
CRANK
D
347B WHT
DRIVER INFLATOR MODULE
SIR COIL ASSEMBLY
REFER TO SECTION 8A-50
800A TAN
B11
SERIAL DATA
326 PPL
A8
DIAG. REQUEST
347A WHT
B9
DRIVER SIDE HIGH
348A DK GRN
B8
DRIVER SIDE LOW
SHORTING BARS
348B DK GRN
TO IGNITION SWITCH
INDIC 10A
39A PNK
S209
39B PNK
B2
REDUNDANT INDICATOR IGNITION 1
FORWARD DISCRIMINATING SENSOR
39C PNK
INSTRUMENT CLUSTER
OLDSMOBILE
F
E
D
349A GRY
9J
349B GRY
C15
D2
358 BRN
B1
SIR INDICATOR
1751E BLK
9K
1751G BLK
BUICK
D10
"AIR BAG" WARNING LAMP
C14
SHORTING BAR
8.45kΩ
C200
8.45kΩ
1751F BLK
S242
1751B BLK
A1
GROUND
1751C BLK
A12
GROUND
PASSENGER COMPARTMENT DISCRIMINATING SENSOR
1751A BLK
6-19-93
NS 15892

CHART D

"AIR BAG" WARNING LAMP DOES NOT COME "ON" STEADY DURING CRANK

Circuit Description:

When the ignition switch is first turned "ON," "Ignition 1" voltage is applied from the "INDIC" fuse to "Redundant Indicator Ignition 1," terminal "B2", and to the "AIR BAG" warning lamp which is connected to "SIR Indicator," terminal "B1". The "ARBG1" fuse applies system voltage to the "Ignition 1" inputs, terminals "A9" and "A10". The DERM responds by flashing the "AIR BAG" warning lamp seven times.

When the engine is being cranked, "Ignition 1" voltage is applied from the "ARBG2" fuse to the DERM at the "Crank" input. The DERM responds by grounding the "SIR Indicator" output until "Ignition 1" voltage is removed from the "Crank" input. This results in the "AIR BAG" warning lamp being "ON" during cranking.

After cranking, the DERM will flash the "AIR BAG" warning lamp six times.

Chart Test Description: Number(s) below refer to circled number(s) on the diagnostic chart.

1. This test checks whether the malfunction is due to an open "ARBG2" fuse.
2. This test checks for a proper signal to the "Crank" input during cranking.
3. This test determines whether the lack of a proper crank signal is due to an open "Crank" input circuit or an open power feed to the "ARBG2" fuse.
4. This test checks whether the "ARBG2" fuse is open due to a short to ground in the "Crank" input circuit.
5. This test determines whether the short to ground is in the wiring harness.

CHART D

"AIR BAG" WARNING LAMP DOES NOT COME "ON" STEADY DURING CRANK

WHEN MEASUREMENTS ARE REQUESTED IN THIS CHART USE J 39200 DVM WITH CORRECT TERMINAL ADAPTER FROM J 35616-A. WHEN A CHECK FOR PROPER CONNECTION IS REQUESTED REFER TO "INTERMITTENTS AND POOR CONNECTIONS" IN SECTION 8A-4. WHEN A WIRE, CONNECTOR OR TERMINAL REPAIR IS REQUESTED USE J 38125-A TERMINAL REPAIR KIT AND REFER TO "WIRING REPAIR" IN THIS SECTION.

1
- IGNITION SWITCH "OFF."
- REMOVE AND INSPECT ARBG2 FUSE.

IS FUSE GOOD?

YES →

2
- INSTALL ARBG2 FUSE.
- DISCONNECT YELLOW 2-WAY CONNECTOR AT THE BASE OF THE STEERING COLUMN.
- DISCONNECT DERM.
- MEASURE VOLTAGE ON DERM HARNESS CONNECTOR FROM TERMINAL "B10" TO TERMINAL "A1" (GROUND) WHILE STARTING ENGINE.

IS VOLTAGE GREATER THAN 7.25 VOLTS?

NO →

3
- IGNITION SWITCH "OFF."
- REMOVE ARBG2 FUSE.
- MEASURE RESISTANCE FROM EACH TERMINAL OF THE ARBG2 FUSE, FUSE HOLDER TO DERM HARNESS CONNECTOR TERMINAL "B10".

IS EITHER MEASUREMENT 5.0Ω OR LESS?

NO →
- REPAIR OPEN IN CKT 806.
- INSTALL ARBG2 FUSE.

YES →
- REPAIR OPEN IN POWER FEED TO ARBG2 FUSE.
- INSTALL ARBG2 FUSE.

YES (from 2) →
- IGNITION SWITCH "OFF."
- CHECK FOR PROPER CONNECTION AT DERM HARNESS CONNECTOR TERMINAL "B10".
- IF CONNECTION IS GOOD, GO TO CHART A.

NO (from 1) →

4
- REPLACE ARBG2 FUSE.
- START ENGINE, THEN IGNITION SWITCH "OFF."
- REMOVE AND INSPECT ARBG2 FUSE.

IS FUSE GOOD?

NO →

5
- DISCONNECT YELLOW 2-WAY CONNECTOR AT THE BASE OF THE STEERING COLUMN.
- DISCONNECT DERM.
- REPLACE ARBG2 FUSE.
- START ENGINE, THEN IGNITION SWITCH "OFF."
- REMOVE AND INSPECT ARBG2 FUSE.

IS FUSE GOOD?

NO →
- REPAIR SHORT FROM CKT 806 TO GROUND.
- REPLACE ARBG2 FUSE.

YES →
- INSTALL ARBG2 FUSE.
- GO TO CHART A.

YES (from 4) →
- INSTALL ARBG2 FUSE.
- REPEAT "SIR DIAGNOSTIC SYSTEM CHECK."

- RECONNECT ALL SIR SYSTEM COMPONENTS, ENSURE ALL COMPONENTS ARE PROPERLY MOUNTED.
- REPEAT "SIR DIAGNOSTIC SYSTEM CHECK."

6-21-93
PS 17764

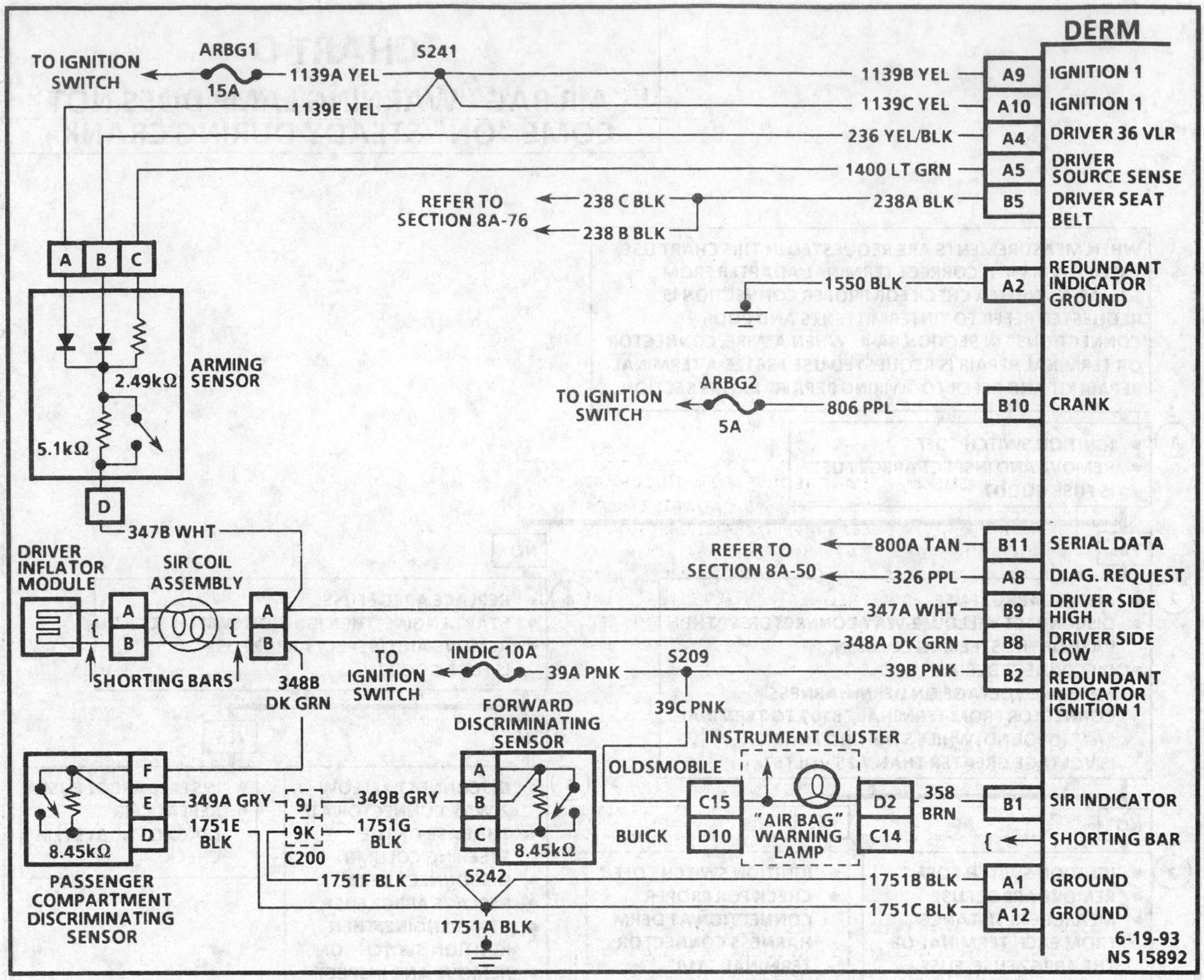
DERM
TO IGNITION SWITCH
ARBG1
15A
S241
1139A YEL
1139E YEL
1139B YEL
1139C YEL
A9 IGNITION 1
A10 IGNITION 1
236 YEL/BLK
A4 DRIVER 36 VLR
1400 LT GRN
A5 DRIVER SOURCE SENSE
REFER TO SECTION 8A-76
238 C BLK
238 B BLK
238A BLK
B5 DRIVER SEAT BELT
1550 BLK
A2 REDUNDANT INDICATOR GROUND
ARMING SENSOR
2.49kΩ
5.1kΩ
TO IGNITION SWITCH
ARBG2
5A
806 PPL
B10 CRANK
347B WHT
DRIVER INFLATOR MODULE
SIR COIL ASSEMBLY
REFER TO SECTION 8A-50
800A TAN
B11 SERIAL DATA
326 PPL
A8 DIAG. REQUEST
347A WHT
B9 DRIVER SIDE HIGH
348A DK GRN
B8 DRIVER SIDE LOW
SHORTING BARS
348B DK GRN
TO IGNITION SWITCH
INDIC 10A
39A PNK
S209
39B PNK
B2 REDUNDANT INDICATOR IGNITION 1
FORWARD DISCRIMINATING SENSOR
39C PNK
INSTRUMENT CLUSTER
OLDSMOBILE
C15
D10
BUICK
"AIR BAG" WARNING LAMP
D2
C14
358 BRN
B1 SIR INDICATOR
SHORTING BAR
349A GRY
9J
349B GRY
1751E BLK
9K
1751G BLK
C200
8.45kΩ
8.45kΩ
S242
1751F BLK
1751B BLK
A1 GROUND
1751C BLK
A12 GROUND
1751A BLK
PASSENGER COMPARTMENT DISCRIMINATING SENSOR
6-19-93
NS 15892

CHART E

"AIR BAG" WARNING LAMP FLASHES DTC 12

Circuit Description:

When the ignition switch is first turned "ON," "Ignition 1" voltage is applied from the "INDIC" fuse to "Redundant Indicator Ignition 1," terminal "B2", and to the "AIR BAG" warning lamp which is connected to "SIR Indicator," terminal "B1". The "ARBG1" fuse applies system voltage to the "Ignition 1" inputs, terminals "A9" and "A10". The DERM responds by flashing the "AIR BAG" warning lamp seven times.

When the engine is being cranked, "Ignition 1" voltage is applied from the "ARBG2" fuse to the DERM at the "Crank" input. The DERM responds by grounding the "SIR Indicator" output until "Ignition 1" voltage is removed from the "Crank" input. This results in the "AIR BAG" warning lamp being "ON" during cranking. After cranking, the DERM will flash the "AIR BAG" warning lamp six times.

This chart diagnoses the situation where, after "Bulb Check" (six or seven flashes), the "AIR BAG" warning lamp is "OFF" for one second and then begins to flash. The sequence is as follows: the lamp will flash once, pause for one second, then flash twice. After a three second pause the previous sequence may repeat or a new pattern may occur. This condition will continue as long as the ignition switch is "ON."

Chart Test Description: Number(s) below refer to circled number(s) on the diagnostic chart.

1. This test checks for a short to ground on the "Diagnostic Request" circuit. Since grounding of the "Diagnostic Request" circuit flashes DTC 12, this ground must be supplied by the DERM or the wiring.

CHART E
"AIR BAG" WARNING LAMP FLASHES DTC 12

WHEN MEASUREMENTS ARE REQUESTED IN THIS CHART USE J 39200 DVM WITH CORRECT TERMINAL ADAPTER FROM J 35616-A. WHEN A CHECK FOR PROPER CONNECTION IS REQUESTED REFER TO "INTERMITTENTS AND POOR CONNECTIONS" IN SECTION 8A-4. WHEN A WIRE, CONNECTOR OR TERMINAL REPAIR IS REQUESTED USE J 38125-A TERMINAL REPAIR KIT AND REFER TO "WIRING REPAIR" IN THIS SECTION.

(1)
- IGNITION SWITCH "OFF."
- DISCONNECT YELLOW 2-WAY CONNECTOR AT THE BASE OF THE STEERING COLUMN.
- DISCONNECT DERM.
- MEASURE RESISTANCE ON DERM HARNESS CONNECTOR FROM TERMINAL "A8" TO TERMINAL "A1" (GROUND). IS RESISTANCE 10.0Ω OR LESS?

YES
- REPAIR SHORT FROM CKT 326 TO GROUND.
- RECONNECT ALL SIR SYSTEM COMPONENTS, ENSURE ALL COMPONENTS ARE PROPERLY MOUNTED.
- REPEAT "SIR DIAGNOSTIC SYSTEM CHECK."

NO

GO TO CHART A.

4-30-93
PS 17765

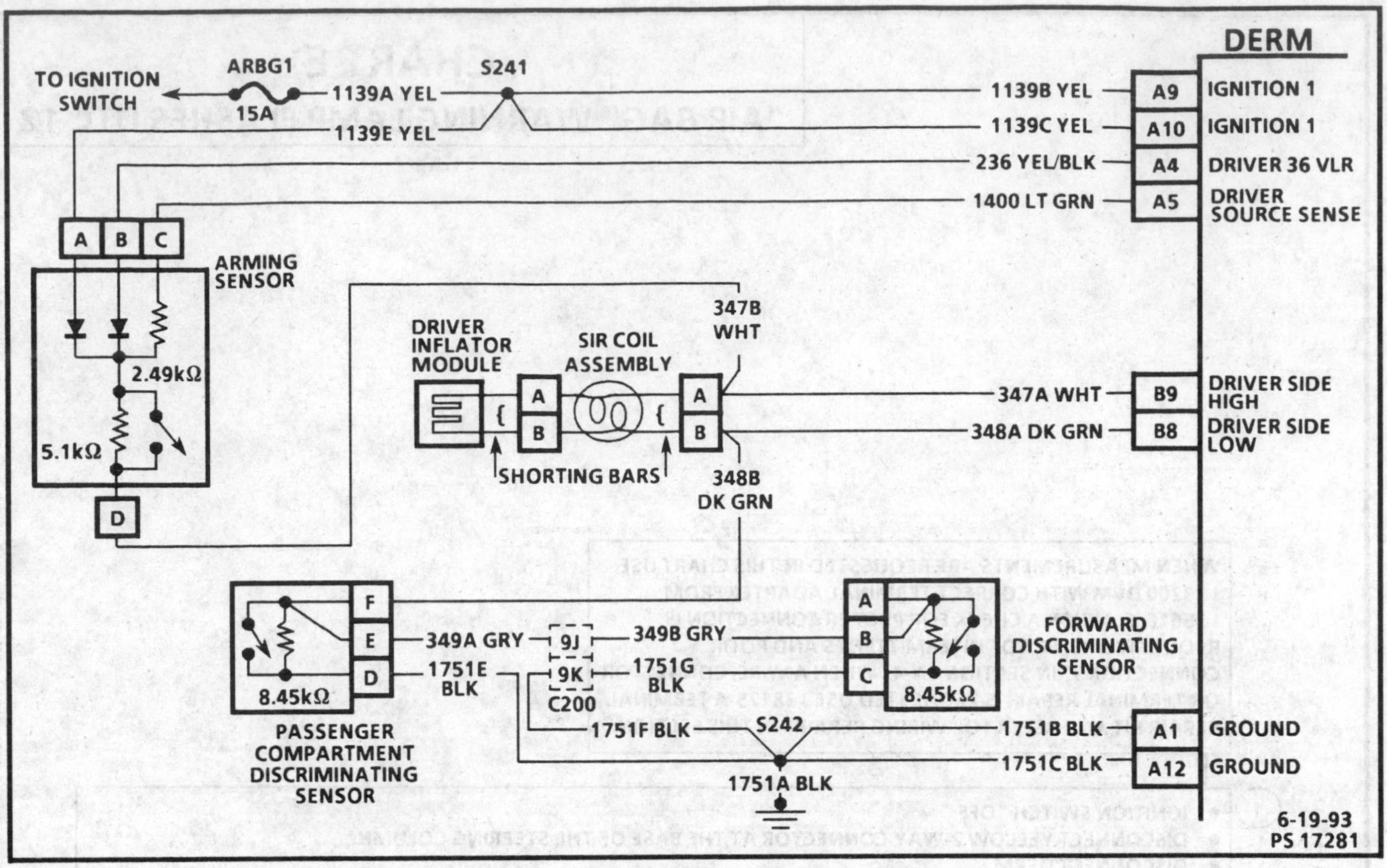
DERM
TO IGNITION SWITCH
ARBG1
15A
S241
1139A YEL
1139E YEL
1139B YEL
1139C YEL
236 YEL/BLK
1400 LT GRN
A9
A10
A4
A5
IGNITION 1
IGNITION 1
DRIVER 36 VLR
DRIVER SOURCE SENSE
A
B
C
ARMING SENSOR
2.49kΩ
5.1kΩ
D
DRIVER INFLATOR MODULE
SIR COIL ASSEMBLY
347B WHT
SHORTING BARS
348B DK GRN
347A WHT
348A DK GRN
B9
B8
DRIVER SIDE HIGH
DRIVER SIDE LOW
F
E
D
349A GRY
9J
9K
C200
349B GRY
1751E BLK
1751G BLK
8.45kΩ
PASSENGER COMPARTMENT DISCRIMINATING SENSOR
FORWARD DISCRIMINATING SENSOR
8.45kΩ
1751F BLK
S242
1751A BLK
1751B BLK
1751C BLK
A1
A12
GROUND
GROUND
6-19-93
PS 17281

DTC 14

ARMING SENSOR DISCONNECTED

Circuit Description:

The DERM monitors the voltage at the "Driver Source Sense" terminal "A5", the "Driver Side High" terminal "B9" and the "Driver Side Low" terminal "B8" during the "Continuous Monitoring" tests. When all voltages are simultaneously below a specified value for 500 milliseconds DTC 14 sets.

DTC Will Set When: The voltages at terminals "A5", "B9" and "B8" of the DERM harness connector are simultaneously below a specified value for 500 milliseconds.

Action Taken: DERM turns "ON" the "AIR BAG" warning lamp and sets a diagnostic trouble code.

DTC Will Clear When: The voltage at terminal "A5", "B9" or "B8" of DERM harness connector is above a specified value for 500 milliseconds.

DTC Chart Test Description: Number(s) below refer to circled number(s) on the diagnostic chart.

1. This test checks for a situation which prevents a proper connection of the arming sensor to the SIR wiring harness.

Diagnostic Aids: It is highly unlikely that an intermittent condition has set this diagnostic trouble code as this would require a poor connection at terminals "A" and "B" or at terminals "C" and "D".

DTC 14
ARMING SENSOR DISCONNECTED

WAS THE "SIR DIAGNOSTIC SYSTEM CHECK" PERFORMED?

NO

GO TO THE "SIR DIAGNOSTIC SYSTEM CHECK."

YES

WHEN MEASUREMENTS ARE REQUESTED IN THIS CHART USE J 39200 DVM WITH CORRECT TERMINAL ADAPTER FROM J 35616-A. WHEN A CHECK FOR PROPER CONNECTION IS REQUESTED REFER TO "INTERMITTENTS AND POOR CONNECTIONS" IN SECTION 8A-4. WHEN A WIRE, CONNECTOR OR TERMINAL REPAIR IS REQUESTED USE J 38125-A TERMINAL REPAIR KIT AND REFER TO "WIRING REPAIR" IN THIS SECTION.

1
- IGNITION SWITCH "OFF."
- DISCONNECT YELLOW 2-WAY CONNECTOR AT THE BASE OF THE STEERING COLUMN.
- DISCONNECT ARMING SENSOR HARNESS CONNECTOR FROM ARMING SENSOR AND RECONNECT.
- RECONNECT YELLOW 2-WAY CONNECTOR AT THE BASE OF THE STEERING COLUMN.
- IGNITION SWITCH "ON."

IS DTC 14 CURRENT?

YES

- IGNITION SWITCH "OFF."
- GO TO CHART A.

NO

- CLEAR SIR DIAGNOSTIC TROUBLE CODES.
- REPEAT "SIR DIAGNOSTIC SYSTEM CHECK."

4-29-93
PS 17748

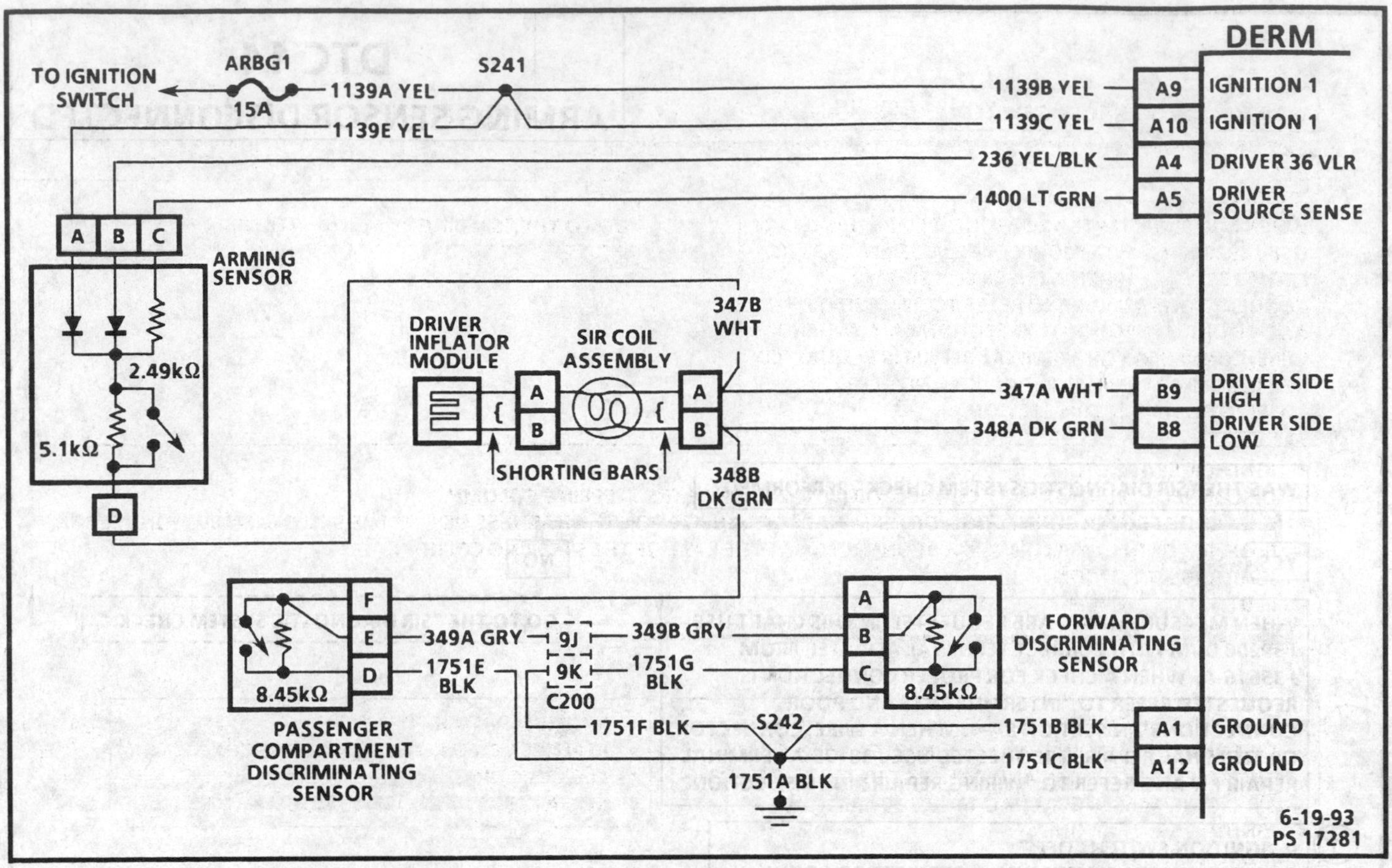
DERM
TO IGNITION SWITCH
ARBG1
15A
1139A YEL
S241
1139E YEL
1139B YEL
1139C YEL
236 YEL/BLK
1400 LT GRN
A9
A10
A4
A5
IGNITION 1
IGNITION 1
DRIVER 36 VLR
DRIVER SOURCE SENSE
A
B
C
ARMING SENSOR
2.49kΩ
5.1kΩ
D
DRIVER INFLATOR MODULE
SIR COIL ASSEMBLY
347B WHT
SHORTING BARS
348B DK GRN
347A WHT
348A DK GRN
B9
B8
DRIVER SIDE HIGH
DRIVER SIDE LOW
F
E
D
8.45kΩ
PASSENGER COMPARTMENT DISCRIMINATING SENSOR
349A GRY
9J
9K
C200
349B GRY
1751E BLK
1751G BLK
FORWARD DISCRIMINATING SENSOR
8.45kΩ
1751F BLK
S242
1751B BLK
1751C BLK
1751A BLK
A1
A12
GROUND
GROUND
6-19-93
PS 17281

DTC 21

DRIVER INITIATOR CIRCUIT RESISTANCE HIGH

Circuit Description:

During the "Initiator Assembly Resistance Test" the DERM grounds the "Driver Side Low" terminal "B8" and turns "ON" the driver current source at the "Driver Side High" terminal "B9". This causes a known amount of current to flow through the driver initiator circuit. By monitoring the difference between the voltage at the "Driver Side High" terminal "B9" and the "Driver Side Low" terminal "B8" the DERM calculates the combined resistance of the driver inflator module, SIR coil assembly, harness wiring CKTs 347A and 348A and connector terminal contact.

DTC Will Set When: The combined resistance of the driver inflator module, SIR coil assembly, harness wiring CKTs 347A and 348A and connector terminal contact is above a specified value. This test is run once each ignition cycle during the "Initiator Assembly Resistance Test" when: 1) No "higher priority faults" are detected during "Turn-ON," 2) No "higher priority faults" are detected during "Continuous Monitoring" for one second, 3) No "Crank" signal present, 4) "Ignition 1" voltage is above a specified value.

Action Taken: DERM turns "ON" the "AIR BAG" warning lamp and sets a diagnostic trouble code.

DTC Will Clear When: The ignition switch is turned "OFF."

DTC Chart Test Description: Number(s) below refer to circled number(s) on the diagnostic chart.

1. This test checks for terminal deformation or contamination.
2. This test determines whether the malfunction is in the driver inflator module circuitry or in the DERM wiring harness circuitry.
3. This test checks for high resistance in the "Driver Side Low" circuit.
4. This test checks for high resistance in the "Driver Side High" circuit.
5. This test determines whether the malfunction is in the driver inflator module or in the SIR coil assembly.

Diagnostic Aids: An intermittent condition is likely to be caused by a poor connection at: the yellow 2-way connector at base of steering column, DERM terminals "B8" or "B9", or the connection at the top of steering column to the driver inflator module. The test for this diagnostic trouble code is only run while the "AIR BAG" warning lamp is performing the bulb check. When a scan tool "Clear Codes" command is issued and the malfunction is still present, the DTC will not reappear until the next ignition cycle.

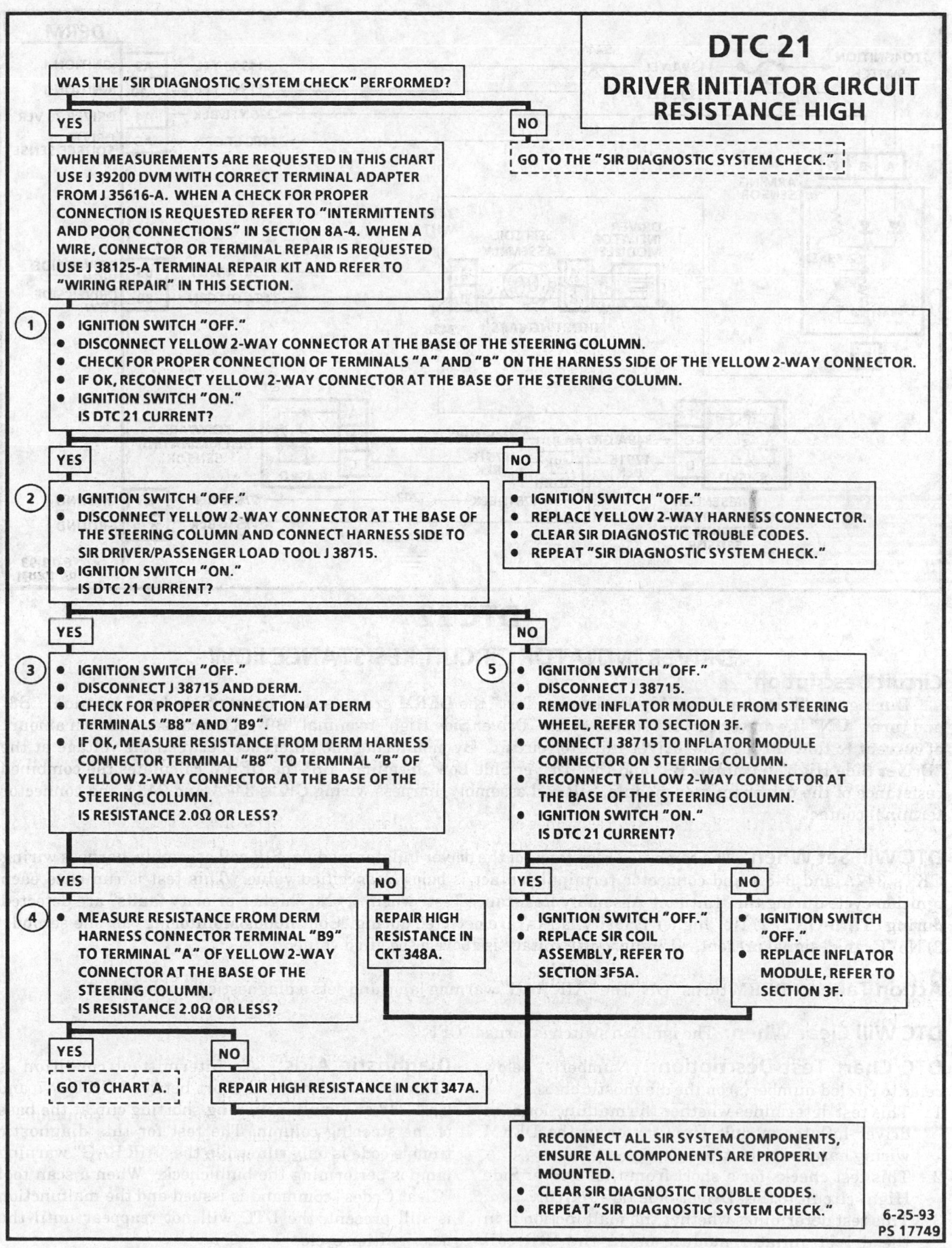

DTC 21
DRIVER INITIATOR CIRCUIT RESISTANCE HIGH

WAS THE "SIR DIAGNOSTIC SYSTEM CHECK" PERFORMED?

- **NO:** GO TO THE "SIR DIAGNOSTIC SYSTEM CHECK."
- **YES:** WHEN MEASUREMENTS ARE REQUESTED IN THIS CHART USE J 39200 DVM WITH CORRECT TERMINAL ADAPTER FROM J 35616-A. WHEN A CHECK FOR PROPER CONNECTION IS REQUESTED REFER TO "INTERMITTENTS AND POOR CONNECTIONS" IN SECTION 8A-4. WHEN A WIRE, CONNECTOR OR TERMINAL REPAIR IS REQUESTED USE J 38125-A TERMINAL REPAIR KIT AND REFER TO "WIRING REPAIR" IN THIS SECTION.

(1)
- IGNITION SWITCH "OFF."
- DISCONNECT YELLOW 2-WAY CONNECTOR AT THE BASE OF THE STEERING COLUMN.
- CHECK FOR PROPER CONNECTION OF TERMINALS "A" AND "B" ON THE HARNESS SIDE OF THE YELLOW 2-WAY CONNECTOR.
- IF OK, RECONNECT YELLOW 2-WAY CONNECTOR AT THE BASE OF THE STEERING COLUMN.
- IGNITION SWITCH "ON."

IS DTC 21 CURRENT?

- **NO:**
  - IGNITION SWITCH "OFF."
  - REPLACE YELLOW 2-WAY HARNESS CONNECTOR.
  - CLEAR SIR DIAGNOSTIC TROUBLE CODES.
  - REPEAT "SIR DIAGNOSTIC SYSTEM CHECK."
- **YES:** go to (2).

(2)
- IGNITION SWITCH "OFF."
- DISCONNECT YELLOW 2-WAY CONNECTOR AT THE BASE OF THE STEERING COLUMN AND CONNECT HARNESS SIDE TO SIR DRIVER/PASSENGER LOAD TOOL J 38715.
- IGNITION SWITCH "ON."

IS DTC 21 CURRENT?

- **YES:** go to (3).
- **NO:** go to (5).

(3)
- IGNITION SWITCH "OFF."
- DISCONNECT J 38715 AND DERM.
- CHECK FOR PROPER CONNECTION AT DERM TERMINALS "B8" AND "B9".
- IF OK, MEASURE RESISTANCE FROM DERM HARNESS CONNECTOR TERMINAL "B8" TO TERMINAL "B" OF YELLOW 2-WAY CONNECTOR AT THE BASE OF THE STEERING COLUMN.

IS RESISTANCE 2.0Ω OR LESS?

- **NO:** REPAIR HIGH RESISTANCE IN CKT 348A.
- **YES:** go to (4).

(4)
- MEASURE RESISTANCE FROM DERM HARNESS CONNECTOR TERMINAL "B9" TO TERMINAL "A" OF YELLOW 2-WAY CONNECTOR AT THE BASE OF THE STEERING COLUMN.

IS RESISTANCE 2.0Ω OR LESS?

- **YES:** GO TO CHART A.
- **NO:** REPAIR HIGH RESISTANCE IN CKT 347A.

(5)
- IGNITION SWITCH "OFF."
- DISCONNECT J 38715.
- REMOVE INFLATOR MODULE FROM STEERING WHEEL, REFER TO SECTION 3F.
- CONNECT J 38715 TO INFLATOR MODULE CONNECTOR ON STEERING COLUMN.
- RECONNECT YELLOW 2-WAY CONNECTOR AT THE BASE OF THE STEERING COLUMN.
- IGNITION SWITCH "ON."

IS DTC 21 CURRENT?

- **YES:**
  - IGNITION SWITCH "OFF."
  - REPLACE SIR COIL ASSEMBLY, REFER TO SECTION 3F5A.
- **NO:**
  - IGNITION SWITCH "OFF."
  - REPLACE INFLATOR MODULE, REFER TO SECTION 3F.

After repair (from CKT 348A repair, CKT 347A repair, and step (5) outcomes):
- RECONNECT ALL SIR SYSTEM COMPONENTS, ENSURE ALL COMPONENTS ARE PROPERLY MOUNTED.
- CLEAR SIR DIAGNOSTIC TROUBLE CODES.
- REPEAT "SIR DIAGNOSTIC SYSTEM CHECK."

6-25-93
PS 17749

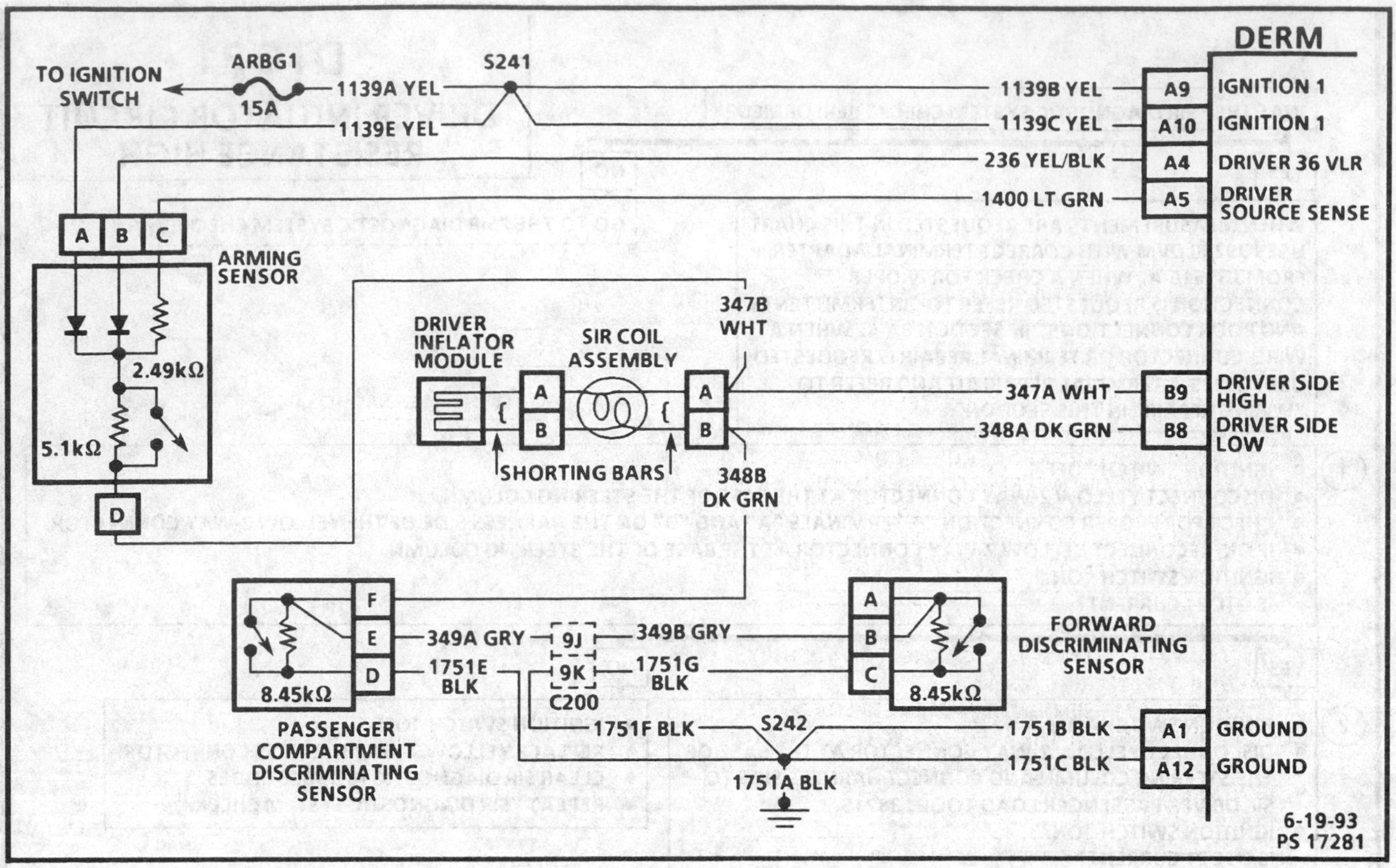

DERM
TO IGNITION SWITCH
ARBG1
15A
1139A YEL
S241
1139E YEL
1139B YEL
A9
IGNITION 1
1139C YEL
A10
IGNITION 1
236 YEL/BLK
A4
DRIVER 36 VLR
1400 LT GRN
A5
DRIVER SOURCE SENSE
A B C
ARMING SENSOR
2.49kΩ
5.1kΩ
D
347B WHT
DRIVER INFLATOR MODULE
SIR COIL ASSEMBLY
A
B
347A WHT
B9
DRIVER SIDE HIGH
348A DK GRN
B8
DRIVER SIDE LOW
SHORTING BARS
348B DK GRN
F
E
D
349A GRY
9J
349B GRY
1751E BLK
9K
1751G BLK
C200
8.45kΩ
PASSENGER COMPARTMENT DISCRIMINATING SENSOR
A
B
C
FORWARD DISCRIMINATING SENSOR
8.45kΩ
1751F BLK
S242
1751B BLK
A1
GROUND
1751C BLK
A12
GROUND
1751A BLK
6-19-93
PS 17281

DTC 22

DRIVER INITIATOR CIRCUIT RESISTANCE LOW

Circuit Description:

During the "Initiator Assembly Resistance Test" the DERM grounds the "Driver Side Low" terminal "B8" and turns "ON" the driver current source at the "Driver Side High" terminal "B9". This causes a known amount of current to flow through the driver initiator circuit. By monitoring the difference between the voltage at the "Driver Side High" terminal "B9" and the "Driver Side Low" terminal "B8" the DERM calculates the combined resistance of the driver inflator module, SIR coil assembly, harness wiring CKTs 347A and 348A and connector terminal contact.

DTC Will Set When: The combined resistance of the driver inflator module, SIR coil assembly, harness wiring CKTs 347A and 348A and connector terminal contact is below a specified value. This test is run once each ignition cycle during the "Initiator Assembly Resistance Test" when: 1) No "higher priority faults" are detected during "Turn-ON," 2) No "higher priority faults" are detected during "Continuous Monitoring" for one second, 3) No "Crank" signal present, 4) "Ignition 1" voltage is above a specified value.

Action Taken: DERM turns "ON" the "AIR BAG" warning lamp and sets a diagnostic trouble code.

DTC Will Clear When: The ignition switch is turned "OFF."

DTC Chart Test Description: Number(s) below refer to circled number(s) on the diagnostic chart.

1. This test determines whether the malfunction is in driver inflator module circuitry or in the DERM wiring harness circuitry.
2. This test checks for a short from the "Driver Side High" circuit to the "Driver Side Low" circuit.
3. This test determines whether the malfunction is in the driver inflator module or in the SIR coil assembly.

Diagnostic Aids: An intermittent condition is likely to be caused by a short between CKT 347 and CKT 348 or a malfunctioning shorting clip at the base of the steering column. The test for this diagnostic trouble code is only run while the "AIR BAG" warning lamp is performing the bulb check. When a scan tool "Clear Codes" command is issued and the malfunction is still present, the DTC will not reappear until the next ignition cycle.

DTC 22
DRIVER INITIATOR CIRCUIT RESISTANCE LOW

WAS THE "SIR DIAGNOSTIC SYSTEM CHECK" PERFORMED?

- NO: GO TO THE "SIR DIAGNOSTIC SYSTEM CHECK."
- YES:

WHEN MEASUREMENTS ARE REQUESTED IN THIS CHART USE J 39200 DVM WITH CORRECT TERMINAL ADAPTER FROM J 35616-A. WHEN A CHECK FOR PROPER CONNECTION IS REQUESTED REFER TO "INTERMITTENTS AND POOR CONNECTIONS" IN SECTION 8A-4. WHEN A WIRE, CONNECTOR OR TERMINAL REPAIR IS REQUESTED USE J 38125-A TERMINAL REPAIR KIT AND REFER TO "WIRING REPAIR" IN THIS SECTION.

(1)
- IGNITION SWITCH "OFF."
- DISCONNECT YELLOW 2-WAY CONNECTOR AT THE BASE OF THE STEERING COLUMN.
- CONNECT J 38715 SIR DRIVER/PASSENGER LOAD TOOL TO HARNESS SIDE OF THE YELLOW 2-WAY CONNECTOR AT THE BASE OF THE STEERING COLUMN.
- IGNITION SWITCH "ON."

IS DTC 22 CURRENT?

YES:

(2)
- IGNITION SWITCH "OFF."
- DISCONNECT J 38715.
- DISCONNECT DERM.
- MEASURE RESISTANCE ON DERM HARNESS CONNECTOR FROM TERMINAL "B8" TO TERMINAL "B9".

DOES J 39200 DISPLAY "OL" (INFINITE)?

- YES: GO TO CHART A.
- NO: REPAIR SHORT FROM CKT 347 TO CKT 348 OR CKT 349.

NO:

(3)
- IGNITION SWITCH "OFF."
- DISCONNECT J 38715.
- REMOVE INFLATOR MODULE FROM STEERING WHEEL, REFER TO SECTION 3F.
- CONNECT J 38715 TO INFLATOR MODULE CONNECTOR ON STEERING COLUMN.
- RECONNECT YELLOW 2-WAY CONNECTOR AT THE BASE OF THE STEERING COLUMN.
- IGNITION SWITCH "ON."

IS DTC 22 CURRENT?

- YES:
  - IGNITION SWITCH "OFF."
  - REPLACE SIR COIL ASSEMBLY, REFER TO SECTION 3F5A.
- NO:
  - IGNITION SWITCH "OFF."
  - REPLACE INFLATOR MODULE, REFER TO SECTION 3F.

(After repair:)
- RECONNECT ALL SIR SYSTEM COMPONENTS, ENSURE ALL COMPONENTS ARE PROPERLY MOUNTED.
- CLEAR SIR DIAGNOSTIC TROUBLE CODES.
- REPEAT "SIR DIAGNOSTIC SYSTEM CHECK."

4-29-93
PS 17750

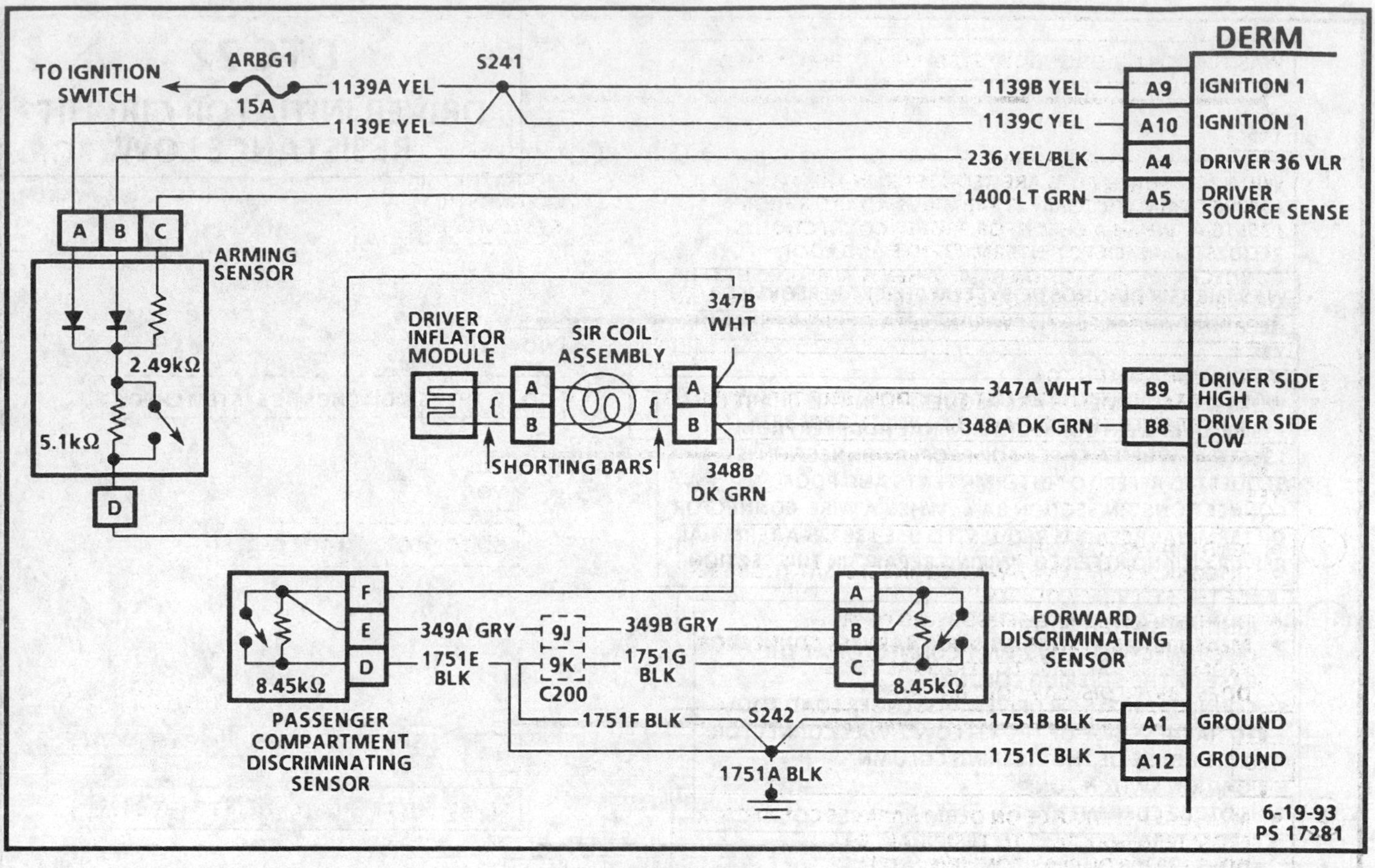

DERM
TO IGNITION SWITCH
ARBG1
15A
S241
1139A YEL
1139E YEL
1139B YEL
1139C YEL
236 YEL/BLK
1400 LT GRN
A9 IGNITION 1
A10 IGNITION 1
A4 DRIVER 36 VLR
A5 DRIVER SOURCE SENSE
A B C
ARMING SENSOR
2.49kΩ
5.1kΩ
D
347B WHT
DRIVER INFLATOR MODULE
SIR COIL ASSEMBLY
SHORTING BARS
348B DK GRN
347A WHT
348A DK GRN
B9 DRIVER SIDE HIGH
B8 DRIVER SIDE LOW
F
E
D
349A GRY
9J
9K
C200
349B GRY
1751E BLK
1751G BLK
8.45kΩ
PASSENGER COMPARTMENT DISCRIMINATING SENSOR
FORWARD DISCRIMINATING SENSOR
1751F BLK
S242
1751B BLK
1751C BLK
1751A BLK
A1 GROUND
A12 GROUND
6-19-93
PS 17281

DTC 23

(Page 1 of 2)

DRIVER INITIATOR CIRCUIT VOLTAGE HIGH

Circuit Description:

During normal, non-deployment operation of the SIR system, a small amount of current flows through the driver deployment loop. The diagnostic resistors within the arming sensor and the discriminating sensors along with the resistance of the inflator module cause voltage drops within the deployment loop. The DERM monitors the voltage at "Driver Side Low" terminal "B8" to detect shorts or opens within the driver deployment loop. When the measured voltage is above a specified percentage of "Driver 36 VLR" for 500 milliseconds DTC 23 is set.

DTC Will Set When: The voltage measured at "Driver Side Low" terminal "B8" is above a specified percentage of "Driver 36 VLR" for 500 milliseconds during "Continuous Monitoring" and DTC 35 is not set.

Action Taken: DERM turns "ON" the "AIR BAG" warning lamp and sets a diagnostic trouble code.

DTC Will Clear When: The voltage measured at "Driver Side Low" terminal "B8" is within a specified percentage of "Driver 36 VLR" for 500 milliseconds during "Continuous Monitoring."

DTC Chart Test Description: Number(s) below refer to circled number(s) on the diagnostic chart.

1. This test, essentially, determines whether the malfunction is due to a component or the wiring.
2. This test checks for a short from the "Driver 36 VLR " circuit to the "Driver Side Low" circuit.
3. This test checks for a short from the "Driver 36 VLR" circuit to the "Driver Side High" circuit.
4. This test checks for an open between the driver inflator module and the discriminating sensor network.
5. This test checks for an open in the passenger compartment discriminating sensor between terminal "F" and the splice.
6. This test checks for a short inside the arming sensor.

Diagnostic Aids: Refer to DTC 23 (Page 2 of 2).

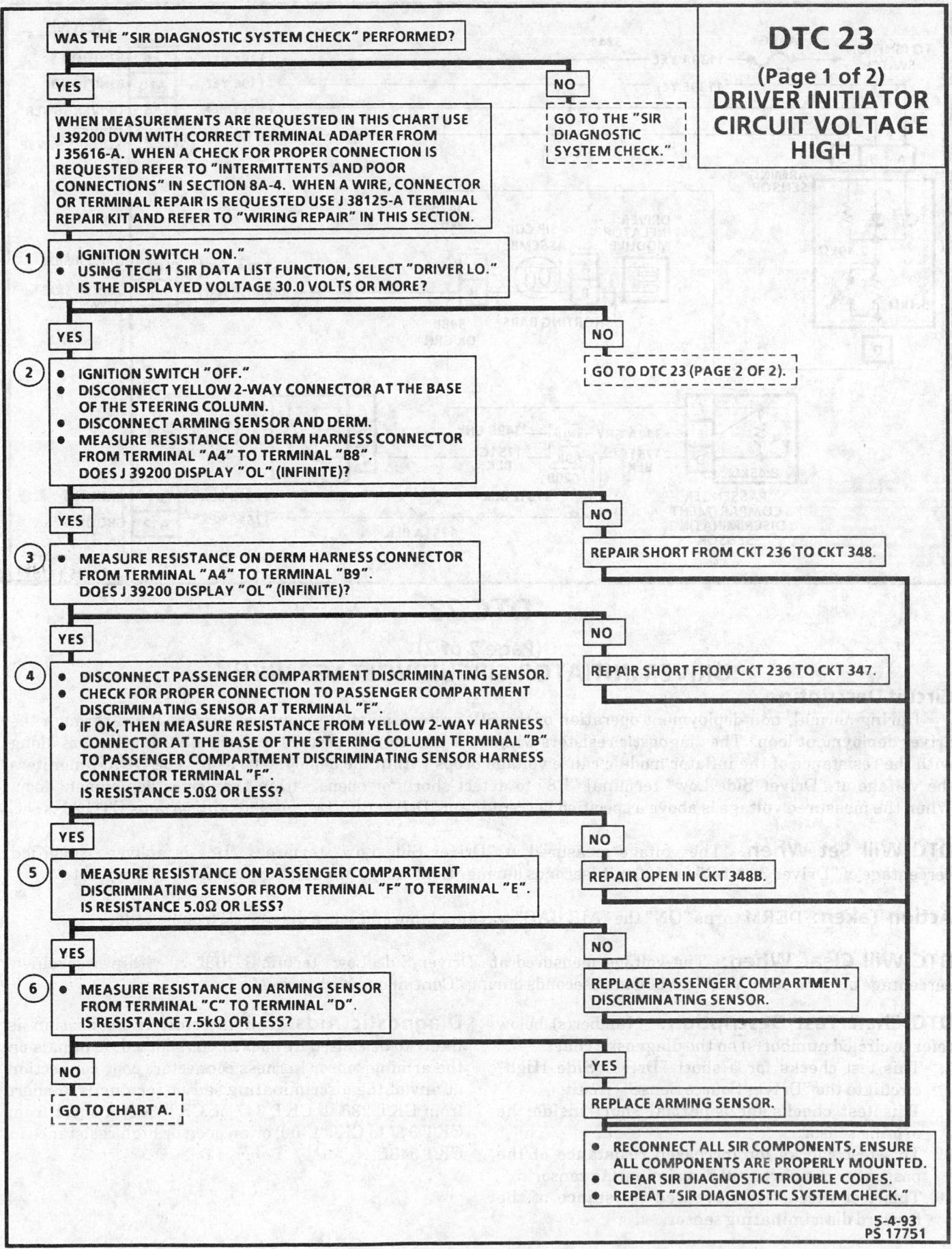

DTC 23
(Page 1 of 2)
DRIVER INITIATOR CIRCUIT VOLTAGE HIGH

WAS THE "SIR DIAGNOSTIC SYSTEM CHECK" PERFORMED?

- **NO** → GO TO THE "SIR DIAGNOSTIC SYSTEM CHECK."
- **YES** ↓

WHEN MEASUREMENTS ARE REQUESTED IN THIS CHART USE J 39200 DVM WITH CORRECT TERMINAL ADAPTER FROM J 35616-A. WHEN A CHECK FOR PROPER CONNECTION IS REQUESTED REFER TO "INTERMITTENTS AND POOR CONNECTIONS" IN SECTION 8A-4. WHEN A WIRE, CONNECTOR OR TERMINAL REPAIR IS REQUESTED USE J 38125-A TERMINAL REPAIR KIT AND REFER TO "WIRING REPAIR" IN THIS SECTION.

(1)
- IGNITION SWITCH "ON."
- USING TECH 1 SIR DATA LIST FUNCTION, SELECT "DRIVER LO."

IS THE DISPLAYED VOLTAGE 30.0 VOLTS OR MORE?

- **NO** → GO TO DTC 23 (PAGE 2 OF 2).
- **YES** ↓

(2)
- IGNITION SWITCH "OFF."
- DISCONNECT YELLOW 2-WAY CONNECTOR AT THE BASE OF THE STEERING COLUMN.
- DISCONNECT ARMING SENSOR AND DERM.
- MEASURE RESISTANCE ON DERM HARNESS CONNECTOR FROM TERMINAL "A4" TO TERMINAL "B8".

DOES J 39200 DISPLAY "OL" (INFINITE)?

- **NO** → REPAIR SHORT FROM CKT 236 TO CKT 348.
- **YES** ↓

(3)
- MEASURE RESISTANCE ON DERM HARNESS CONNECTOR FROM TERMINAL "A4" TO TERMINAL "B9".

DOES J 39200 DISPLAY "OL" (INFINITE)?

- **NO** → REPAIR SHORT FROM CKT 236 TO CKT 347.
- **YES** ↓

(4)
- DISCONNECT PASSENGER COMPARTMENT DISCRIMINATING SENSOR.
- CHECK FOR PROPER CONNECTION TO PASSENGER COMPARTMENT DISCRIMINATING SENSOR AT TERMINAL "F".
- IF OK, THEN MEASURE RESISTANCE FROM YELLOW 2-WAY HARNESS CONNECTOR AT THE BASE OF THE STEERING COLUMN TERMINAL "B" TO PASSENGER COMPARTMENT DISCRIMINATING SENSOR HARNESS CONNECTOR TERMINAL "F".

IS RESISTANCE 5.0Ω OR LESS?

- **NO** → REPAIR OPEN IN CKT 348B.
- **YES** ↓

(5)
- MEASURE RESISTANCE ON PASSENGER COMPARTMENT DISCRIMINATING SENSOR FROM TERMINAL "F" TO TERMINAL "E".

IS RESISTANCE 5.0Ω OR LESS?

- **NO** → REPLACE PASSENGER COMPARTMENT DISCRIMINATING SENSOR.
- **YES** ↓

(6)
- MEASURE RESISTANCE ON ARMING SENSOR FROM TERMINAL "C" TO TERMINAL "D".

IS RESISTANCE 7.5kΩ OR LESS?

- **NO** → GO TO CHART A.
- **YES** → REPLACE ARMING SENSOR.

After repair / replacement:
- RECONNECT ALL SIR COMPONENTS, ENSURE ALL COMPONENTS ARE PROPERLY MOUNTED.
- CLEAR SIR DIAGNOSTIC TROUBLE CODES.
- REPEAT "SIR DIAGNOSTIC SYSTEM CHECK."

5-4-93
PS 17751

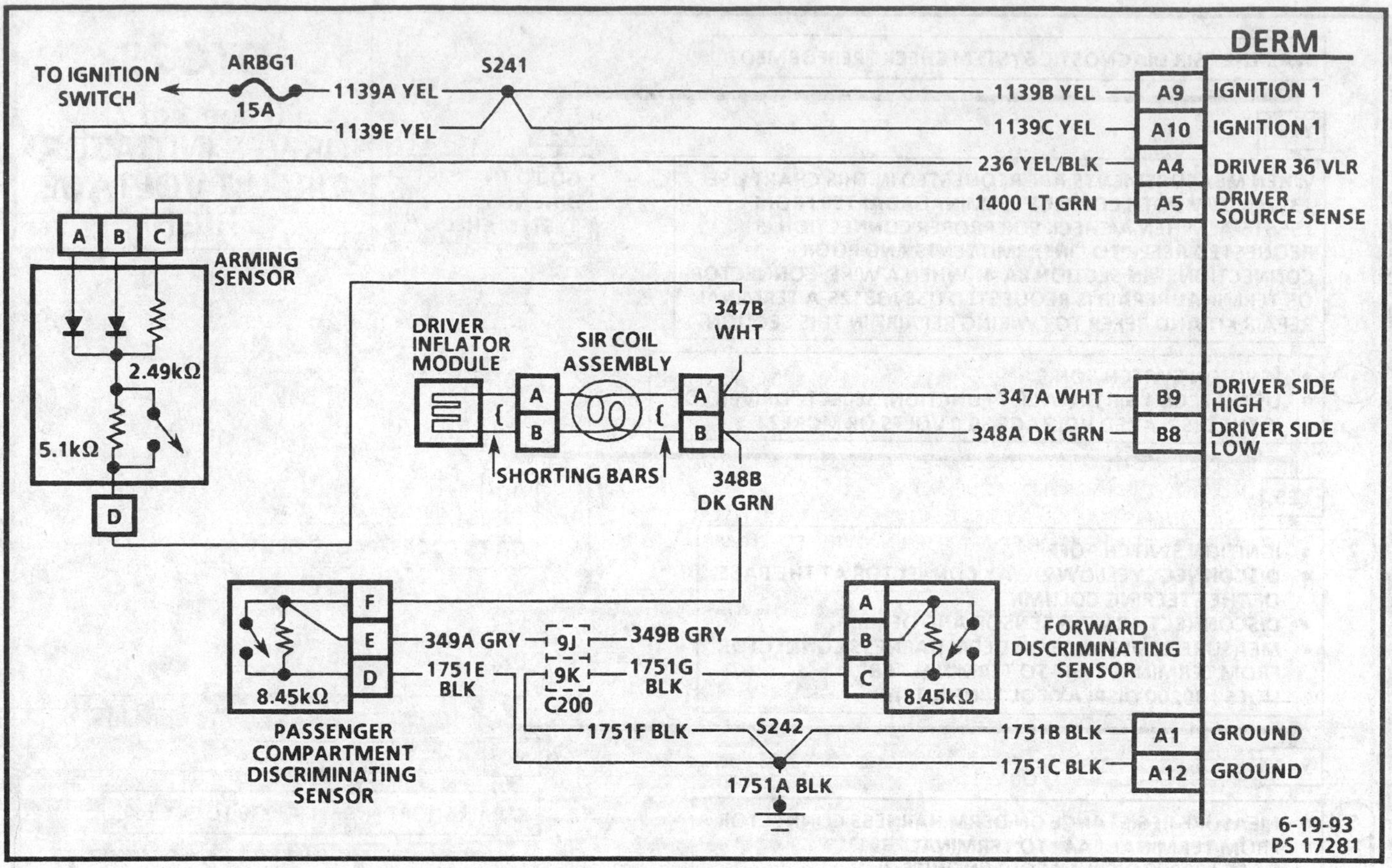
DERM
TO IGNITION SWITCH
ARBG1
15A
1139A YEL
S241
1139E YEL
1139B YEL
1139C YEL
236 YEL/BLK
1400 LT GRN
A9
A10
A4
A5
IGNITION 1
IGNITION 1
DRIVER 36 VLR
DRIVER SOURCE SENSE
A
B
C
ARMING SENSOR
2.49kΩ
5.1kΩ
D
347B WHT
DRIVER INFLATOR MODULE
SIR COIL ASSEMBLY
SHORTING BARS
348B DK GRN
347A WHT
348A DK GRN
B9
B8
DRIVER SIDE HIGH
DRIVER SIDE LOW
F
E
D
349A GRY
9J
9K
C200
349B GRY
1751E BLK
1751G BLK
8.45kΩ
PASSENGER COMPARTMENT DISCRIMINATING SENSOR
FORWARD DISCRIMINATING SENSOR
1751F BLK
S242
1751A BLK
1751B BLK
1751C BLK
A1
A12
GROUND
GROUND
6-19-93
PS 17281

DTC 23

(Page 2 of 2)

DRIVER INITIATOR CIRCUIT VOLTAGE HIGH

Circuit Description:

During normal, non-deployment operation of the SIR system, a small amount of current flows through the driver deployment loop. The diagnostic resistors within the arming sensor and the discriminating sensors along with the resistance of the inflator module cause voltage drops within the deployment loop. The DERM monitors the voltage at "Driver Side Low" terminal "B8" to detect shorts or opens within the driver deployment loop. When the measured voltage is above a specified percentage of "Driver 36 VLR" for 500 milliseconds DTC 23 is set.

DTC Will Set When: The voltage measured at "Driver Side Low" terminal "B8" is above a specified percentage of "Driver 36 VLR" for 500 milliseconds during "Continuous Monitoring" and DTC 35 is not set.

Action Taken: DERM turns "ON" the "AIR BAG" warning lamp and sets a diagnostic trouble code.

DTC Will Clear When: The voltage measured at "Driver Side Low" terminal "B8" is within a specified percentage of "Driver 36 VLR" for 500 milliseconds during "Continuous Monitoring."

DTC Chart Test Description: Number(s) below refer to circled number(s) on the diagnostic chart.

7. This test checks for a short "Driver Side High" circuit to the "Driver Source Sense" circuit.
8. This test checks for a partial short inside the arming sensor.
9. This test checks for increased resistance of the passenger compartment discriminating sensor.
10. This test checks for increased resistance of the forward discriminating sensor.

Diagnostic Aids: An intermittent condition is likely to be caused by backed out/shorted terminals on the arming sensor harness connector, poor connection at any of the discriminating sensor terminals, a short from CKT 236 to CKT 347 or CKT 348, a short from CKT 347 to CKT 1400, or an open or high resistance in CKT 348B.

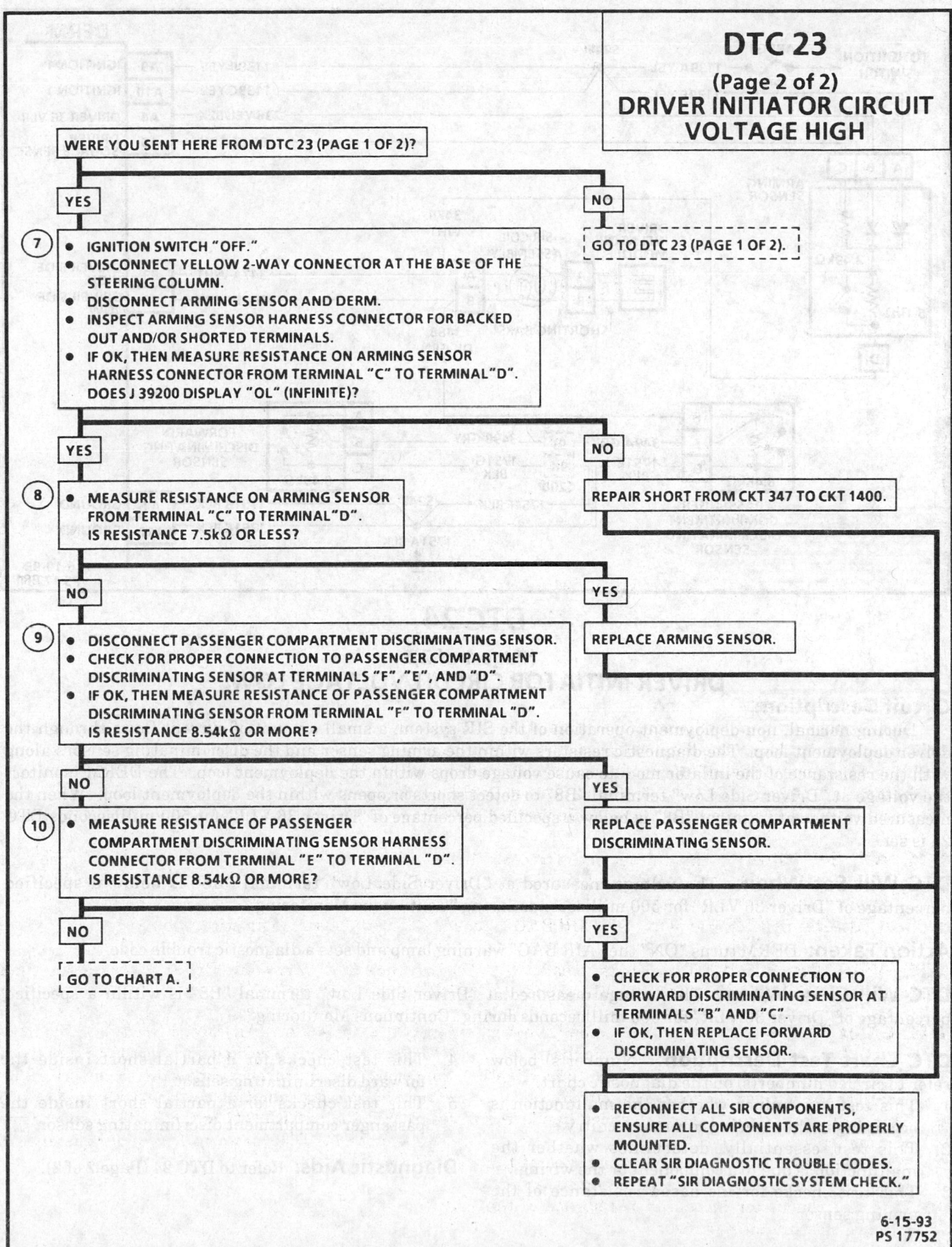

DTC 23
(Page 2 of 2)
DRIVER INITIATOR CIRCUIT VOLTAGE HIGH

WERE YOU SENT HERE FROM DTC 23 (PAGE 1 OF 2)?

- NO: GO TO DTC 23 (PAGE 1 OF 2).
- YES:

7
- IGNITION SWITCH "OFF."
- DISCONNECT YELLOW 2-WAY CONNECTOR AT THE BASE OF THE STEERING COLUMN.
- DISCONNECT ARMING SENSOR AND DERM.
- INSPECT ARMING SENSOR HARNESS CONNECTOR FOR BACKED OUT AND/OR SHORTED TERMINALS.
- IF OK, THEN MEASURE RESISTANCE ON ARMING SENSOR HARNESS CONNECTOR FROM TERMINAL "C" TO TERMINAL "D". DOES J 39200 DISPLAY "OL" (INFINITE)?

- NO: REPAIR SHORT FROM CKT 347 TO CKT 1400.
- YES:

8
- MEASURE RESISTANCE ON ARMING SENSOR FROM TERMINAL "C" TO TERMINAL "D". IS RESISTANCE 7.5kΩ OR LESS?

- YES: REPLACE ARMING SENSOR.
- NO:

9
- DISCONNECT PASSENGER COMPARTMENT DISCRIMINATING SENSOR.
- CHECK FOR PROPER CONNECTION TO PASSENGER COMPARTMENT DISCRIMINATING SENSOR AT TERMINALS "F", "E", AND "D".
- IF OK, THEN MEASURE RESISTANCE OF PASSENGER COMPARTMENT DISCRIMINATING SENSOR FROM TERMINAL "F" TO TERMINAL "D". IS RESISTANCE 8.54kΩ OR MORE?

- YES: REPLACE PASSENGER COMPARTMENT DISCRIMINATING SENSOR.
- NO:

10
- MEASURE RESISTANCE OF PASSENGER COMPARTMENT DISCRIMINATING SENSOR HARNESS CONNECTOR FROM TERMINAL "E" TO TERMINAL "D". IS RESISTANCE 8.54kΩ OR MORE?

- NO: GO TO CHART A.
- YES:
  - CHECK FOR PROPER CONNECTION TO FORWARD DISCRIMINATING SENSOR AT TERMINALS "B" AND "C".
  - IF OK, THEN REPLACE FORWARD DISCRIMINATING SENSOR.

After repair (REPAIR SHORT, REPLACE ARMING SENSOR, REPLACE PASSENGER COMPARTMENT DISCRIMINATING SENSOR, REPLACE FORWARD DISCRIMINATING SENSOR):

- RECONNECT ALL SIR COMPONENTS, ENSURE ALL COMPONENTS ARE PROPERLY MOUNTED.
- CLEAR SIR DIAGNOSTIC TROUBLE CODES.
- REPEAT "SIR DIAGNOSTIC SYSTEM CHECK."

6-15-93
PS 17752

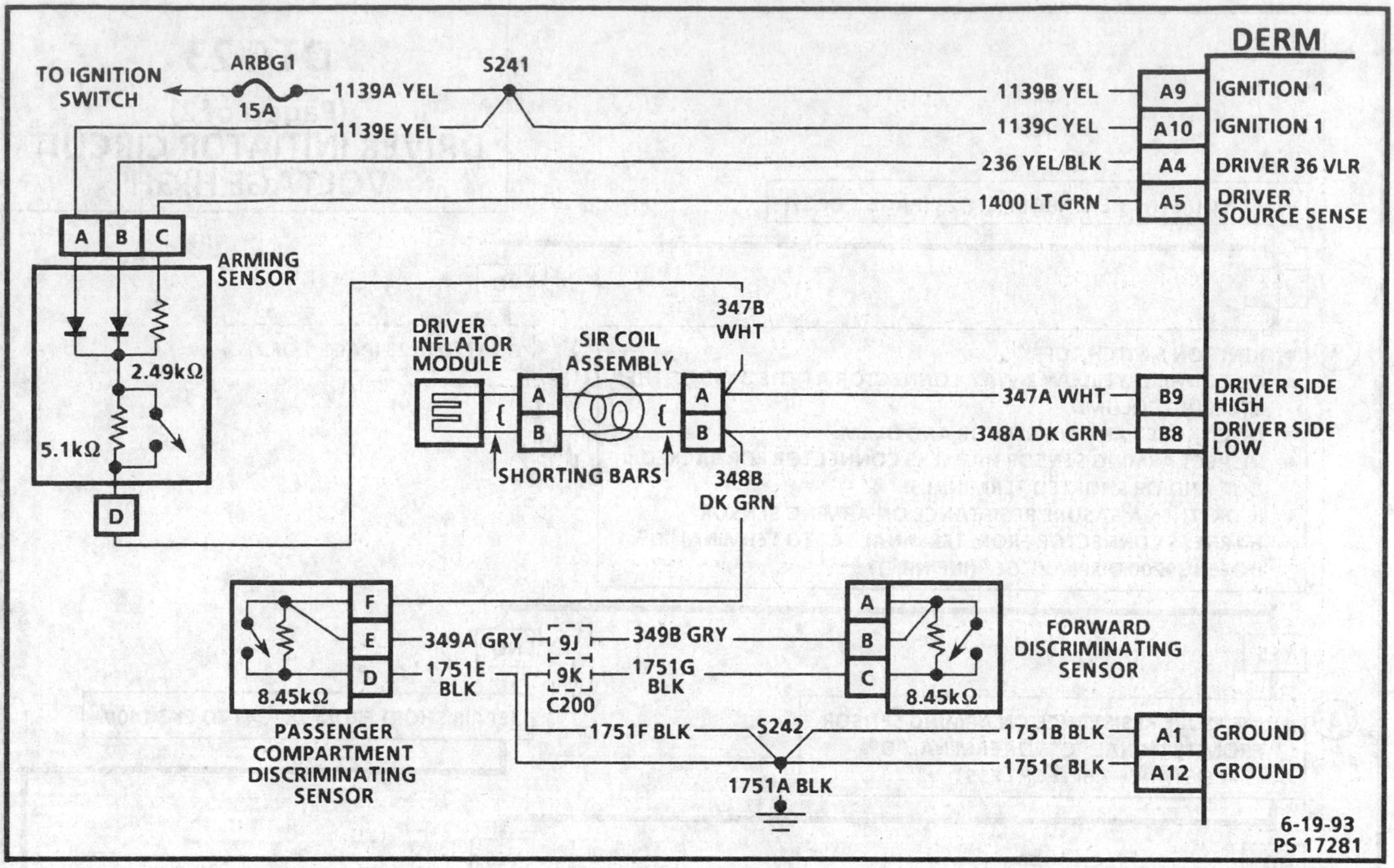

DERM
TO IGNITION SWITCH
ARBG1
15A
1139A YEL
S241
1139E YEL
1139B YEL
1139C YEL
236 YEL/BLK
1400 LT GRN
A9
A10
A4
A5
IGNITION 1
IGNITION 1
DRIVER 36 VLR
DRIVER SOURCE SENSE
A B C
ARMING SENSOR
2.49kΩ
5.1kΩ
D
347B WHT
DRIVER INFLATOR MODULE
SIR COIL ASSEMBLY
SHORTING BARS
348B DK GRN
347A WHT
348A DK GRN
B9
B8
DRIVER SIDE HIGH
DRIVER SIDE LOW
F
E
D
349A GRY
9J
9K
C200
1751E BLK
349B GRY
1751G BLK
8.45kΩ
PASSENGER COMPARTMENT DISCRIMINATING SENSOR
FORWARD DISCRIMINATING SENSOR
1751F BLK
S242
1751A BLK
1751B BLK
1751C BLK
A1
A12
GROUND
GROUND
6-19-93
PS 17281

DTC 24

(Page 1 of 2)

DRIVER INITIATOR CIRCUIT VOLTAGE LOW

Circuit Description:

During normal, non-deployment operation of the SIR system, a small amount of current flows through the driver deployment loop. The diagnostic resistors within the arming sensor and the discriminating sensors along with the resistance of the inflator module cause voltage drops within the deployment loop. The DERM monitors the voltage at "Driver Side Low" terminal "B8" to detect shorts or opens within the deployment loop. When the measured voltage at terminal "B8" is below a specified percentage of "Driver 36 VLR" for 500 milliseconds DTC 24 is set.

DTC Will Set When: The voltage measured at "Driver Side Low" terminal "B8" is below a specified percentage of "Driver 36 VLR" for 500 milliseconds during "Continuous Monitoring."

Action Taken: DERM turns "ON" the "AIR BAG" warning lamp and sets a diagnostic trouble code.

DTC Will Clear When: The voltage measured at "Driver Side Low" terminal "B8" is within a specified percentage of "Driver 36 VLR" for 500 milliseconds during "Continuous Monitoring."

DTC Chart Test Description: Number(s) below refer to circled number(s) on the diagnostic chart.

1. This test determines whether the malfunction is occurring in the steering column circuitry.
2. This test, essentially, determines whether the malfunction is due to a component or the wiring.
3. This test checks for increased resistance of the arming sensor.
4. This test checks for a partial short inside the forward discriminating sensor.
5. This test checks for a partial short inside the passenger compartment discriminating sensor.

Diagnostic Aids: Refer to DTC 24 (Page 2 of 2).

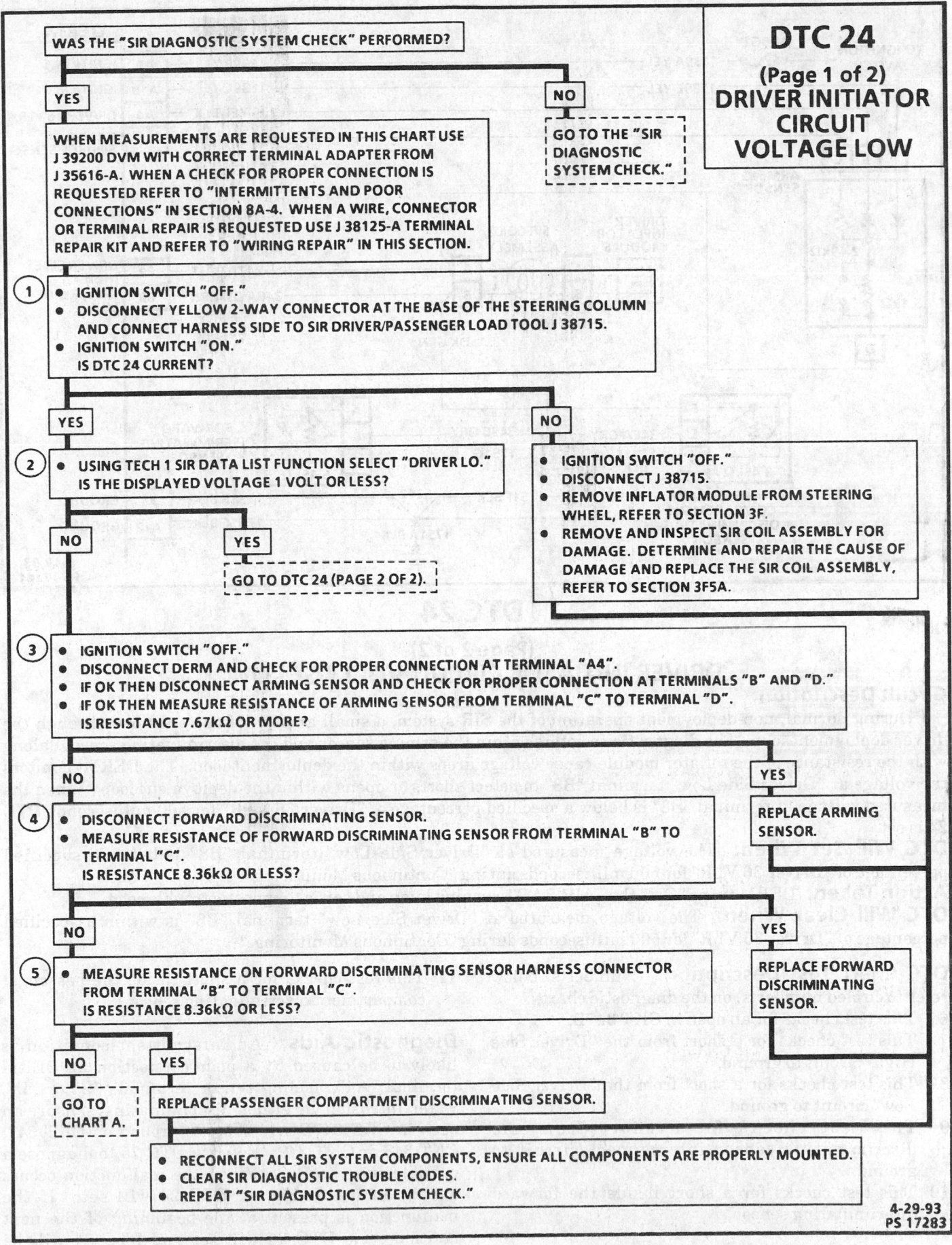

DTC 24
(Page 1 of 2)
DRIVER INITIATOR CIRCUIT VOLTAGE LOW

WAS THE "SIR DIAGNOSTIC SYSTEM CHECK" PERFORMED?

- NO: GO TO THE "SIR DIAGNOSTIC SYSTEM CHECK."
- YES:

WHEN MEASUREMENTS ARE REQUESTED IN THIS CHART USE J 39200 DVM WITH CORRECT TERMINAL ADAPTER FROM J 35616-A. WHEN A CHECK FOR PROPER CONNECTION IS REQUESTED REFER TO "INTERMITTENTS AND POOR CONNECTIONS" IN SECTION 8A-4. WHEN A WIRE, CONNECTOR OR TERMINAL REPAIR IS REQUESTED USE J 38125-A TERMINAL REPAIR KIT AND REFER TO "WIRING REPAIR" IN THIS SECTION.

1
- IGNITION SWITCH "OFF."
- DISCONNECT YELLOW 2-WAY CONNECTOR AT THE BASE OF THE STEERING COLUMN AND CONNECT HARNESS SIDE TO SIR DRIVER/PASSENGER LOAD TOOL J 38715.
- IGNITION SWITCH "ON."

IS DTC 24 CURRENT?

- NO:
  - IGNITION SWITCH "OFF."
  - DISCONNECT J 38715.
  - REMOVE INFLATOR MODULE FROM STEERING WHEEL, REFER TO SECTION 3F.
  - REMOVE AND INSPECT SIR COIL ASSEMBLY FOR DAMAGE. DETERMINE AND REPAIR THE CAUSE OF DAMAGE AND REPLACE THE SIR COIL ASSEMBLY, REFER TO SECTION 3F5A.
- YES:

2
- USING TECH 1 SIR DATA LIST FUNCTION SELECT "DRIVER LO."

IS THE DISPLAYED VOLTAGE 1 VOLT OR LESS?

- YES: GO TO DTC 24 (PAGE 2 OF 2).
- NO:

3
- IGNITION SWITCH "OFF."
- DISCONNECT DERM AND CHECK FOR PROPER CONNECTION AT TERMINAL "A4".
- IF OK THEN DISCONNECT ARMING SENSOR AND CHECK FOR PROPER CONNECTION AT TERMINALS "B" AND "D."
- IF OK THEN MEASURE RESISTANCE OF ARMING SENSOR FROM TERMINAL "C" TO TERMINAL "D".

IS RESISTANCE 7.67kΩ OR MORE?

- YES: REPLACE ARMING SENSOR.
- NO:

4
- DISCONNECT FORWARD DISCRIMINATING SENSOR.
- MEASURE RESISTANCE OF FORWARD DISCRIMINATING SENSOR FROM TERMINAL "B" TO TERMINAL "C".

IS RESISTANCE 8.36kΩ OR LESS?

- YES: REPLACE FORWARD DISCRIMINATING SENSOR.
- NO:

5
- MEASURE RESISTANCE ON FORWARD DISCRIMINATING SENSOR HARNESS CONNECTOR FROM TERMINAL "B" TO TERMINAL "C".

IS RESISTANCE 8.36kΩ OR LESS?

- NO: GO TO CHART A.
- YES: REPLACE PASSENGER COMPARTMENT DISCRIMINATING SENSOR.

(All repair paths then:)
- RECONNECT ALL SIR SYSTEM COMPONENTS, ENSURE ALL COMPONENTS ARE PROPERLY MOUNTED.
- CLEAR SIR DIAGNOSTIC TROUBLE CODES.
- REPEAT "SIR DIAGNOSTIC SYSTEM CHECK."

4-29-93
PS 17283

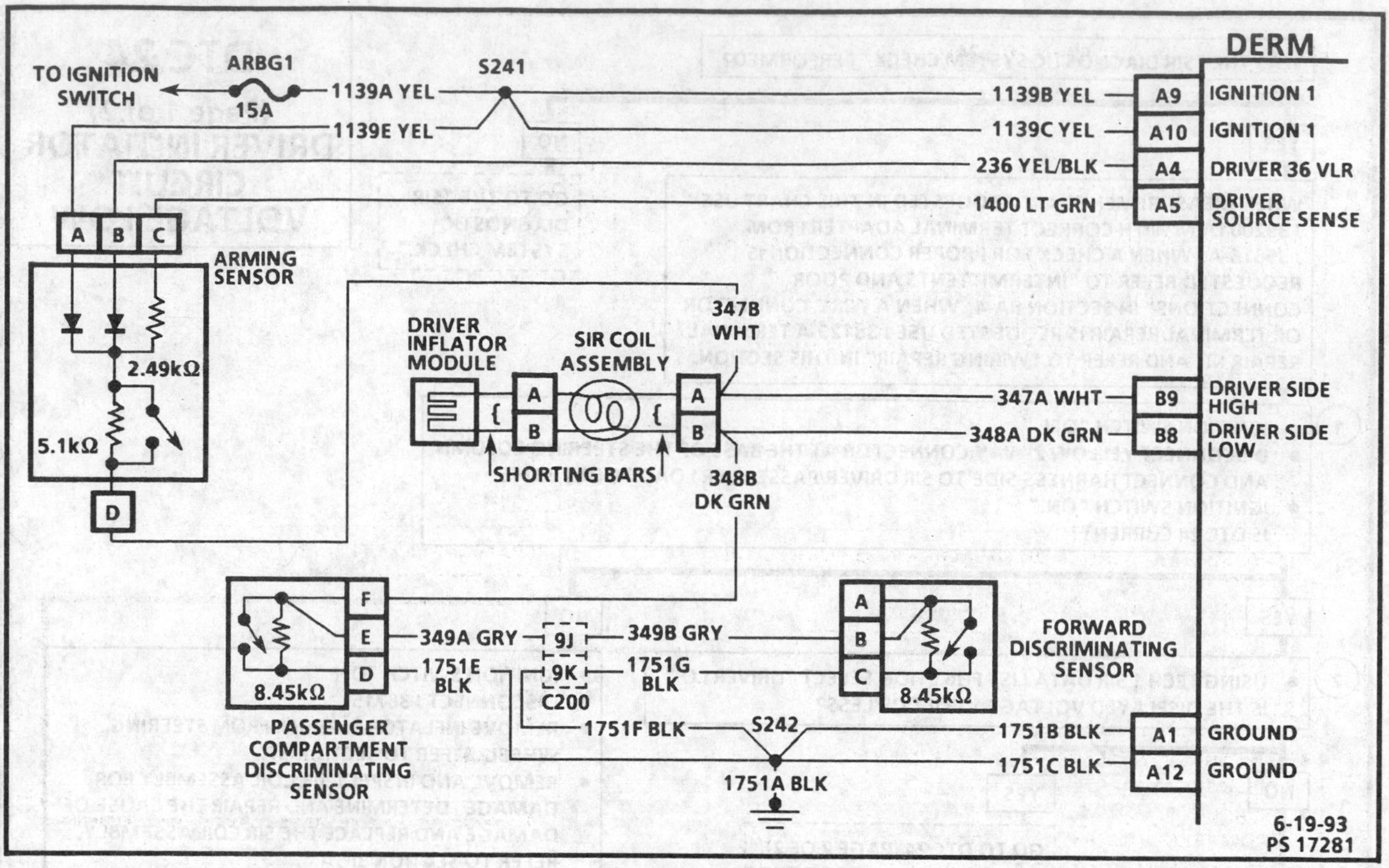
DERM
TO IGNITION SWITCH
ARBG1
15A
S241
1139A YEL
1139E YEL
1139B YEL
1139C YEL
236 YEL/BLK
1400 LT GRN
A9
A10
A4
A5
IGNITION 1
IGNITION 1
DRIVER 36 VLR
DRIVER SOURCE SENSE
A
B
C
ARMING SENSOR
2.49kΩ
5.1kΩ
D
347B WHT
DRIVER INFLATOR MODULE
SIR COIL ASSEMBLY
SHORTING BARS
347A WHT
348A DK GRN
B9
B8
DRIVER SIDE HIGH
DRIVER SIDE LOW
348B DK GRN
F
E
D
349A GRY
9J
9K
C200
349B GRY
1751E BLK
1751G BLK
8.45kΩ
PASSENGER COMPARTMENT DISCRIMINATING SENSOR
FORWARD DISCRIMINATING SENSOR
1751F BLK
S242
1751A BLK
1751B BLK
1751C BLK
A1
A12
GROUND
GROUND
6-19-93
PS 17281

DTC 24

(Page 2 of 2)

DRIVER INITIATOR CIRCUIT VOLTAGE LOW

Circuit Description:

During normal, non-deployment operation of the SIR system, a small amount of current flows through the driver deployment loop. The diagnostic resistors within the arming sensor and the discriminating sensors along with the resistance of the inflator module cause voltage drops within the deployment loop. The DERM monitors the voltage at "Driver Side Low" terminal "B8" to detect shorts or opens within the deployment loop. When the measured voltage at terminal "B8" is below a specified percentage of "Driver 36 VLR" for 500 milliseconds DTC 24 is set.

DTC Will Set When: The voltage measured at "Driver Side Low" terminal "B8" is below a specified percentage of "Driver 36 VLR" for 500 milliseconds during "Continuous Monitoring."

Action Taken: DERM turns "ON" the "AIR BAG" warning lamp and sets a diagnostic trouble code.

DTC Will Clear When: The voltage measured at "Driver Side Low" terminal "B8" is within a specified percentage of "Driver 36 VLR" for 500 milliseconds during "Continuous Monitoring."

DTC Chart Test Description: Number(s) below refer to circled number(s) on the diagnostic chart.

6. This test checks for an open in CKT 347B.
7. This test checks for a short from the "Driver Side High" circuit to ground.
8. This test checks for a short from the "Driver Side Low" circuit to ground.
9. This test checks for a short from the discriminating sensor interconnect circuit to ground.
10. This test checks for a short inside the forward discriminating sensor.
11. This test checks for a short inside the passenger compartment discriminating sensor.

Diagnostic Aids: An intermittent condition is likely to be caused by a poor connection at DERM terminal "A4", arming sensor terminals "B" or "D", water intrusion in either discriminating sensor, an open in CKT 347B or a short to ground on CKT 347, CKT 348 or CKT 349. Refer to DTC 25 to diagnose a possible short to B+. When the malfunction occurs during an ignition cycle DTC 24 will set. If the malfunction is present at the beginning of the next ignition cycle DTC 25 will set and DTC 24 will be moved to a history file.

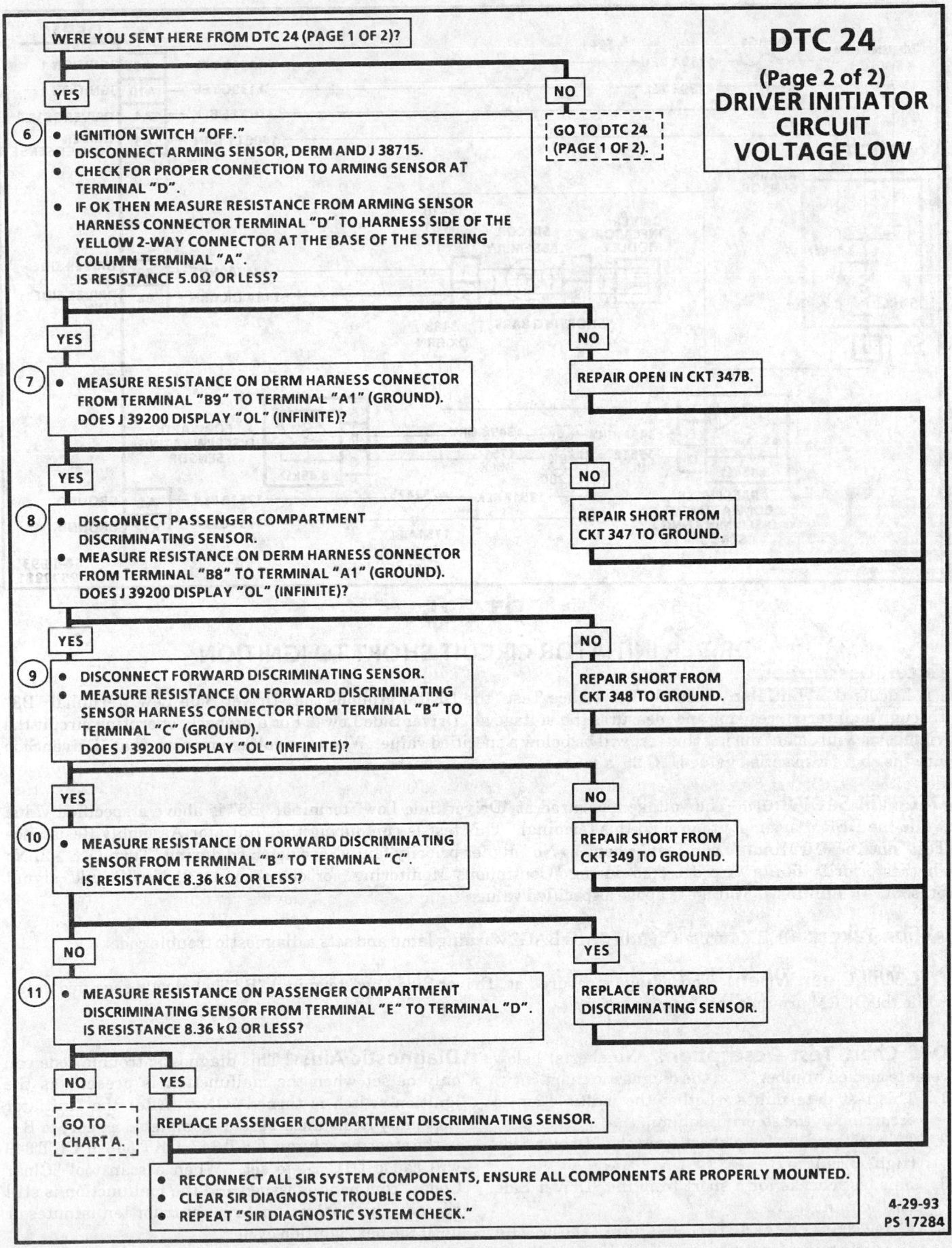

DTC 24

(Page 2 of 2) DRIVER INITIATOR CIRCUIT VOLTAGE LOW

WERE YOU SENT HERE FROM DTC 24 (PAGE 1 OF 2)?

- **NO:** GO TO DTC 24 (PAGE 1 OF 2).
- **YES:** go to step 6.

6
- IGNITION SWITCH "OFF."
- DISCONNECT ARMING SENSOR, DERM AND J 38715.
- CHECK FOR PROPER CONNECTION TO ARMING SENSOR AT TERMINAL "D".
- IF OK THEN MEASURE RESISTANCE FROM ARMING SENSOR HARNESS CONNECTOR TERMINAL "D" TO HARNESS SIDE OF THE YELLOW 2-WAY CONNECTOR AT THE BASE OF THE STEERING COLUMN TERMINAL "A".

IS RESISTANCE 5.0Ω OR LESS?

- **NO:** REPAIR OPEN IN CKT 347B.
- **YES:** go to step 7.

7
- MEASURE RESISTANCE ON DERM HARNESS CONNECTOR FROM TERMINAL "B9" TO TERMINAL "A1" (GROUND).

DOES J 39200 DISPLAY "OL" (INFINITE)?

- **NO:** REPAIR SHORT FROM CKT 347 TO GROUND.
- **YES:** go to step 8.

8
- DISCONNECT PASSENGER COMPARTMENT DISCRIMINATING SENSOR.
- MEASURE RESISTANCE ON DERM HARNESS CONNECTOR FROM TERMINAL "B8" TO TERMINAL "A1" (GROUND).

DOES J 39200 DISPLAY "OL" (INFINITE)?

- **NO:** REPAIR SHORT FROM CKT 348 TO GROUND.
- **YES:** go to step 9.

9
- DISCONNECT FORWARD DISCRIMINATING SENSOR.
- MEASURE RESISTANCE ON FORWARD DISCRIMINATING SENSOR HARNESS CONNECTOR FROM TERMINAL "B" TO TERMINAL "C" (GROUND).

DOES J 39200 DISPLAY "OL" (INFINITE)?

- **NO:** REPAIR SHORT FROM CKT 349 TO GROUND.
- **YES:** go to step 10.

10
- MEASURE RESISTANCE ON FORWARD DISCRIMINATING SENSOR FROM TERMINAL "B" TO TERMINAL "C".

IS RESISTANCE 8.36 kΩ OR LESS?

- **YES:** REPLACE FORWARD DISCRIMINATING SENSOR.
- **NO:** go to step 11.

11
- MEASURE RESISTANCE ON PASSENGER COMPARTMENT DISCRIMINATING SENSOR FROM TERMINAL "E" TO TERMINAL "D".

IS RESISTANCE 8.36 kΩ OR LESS?

- **NO:** GO TO CHART A.
- **YES:** REPLACE PASSENGER COMPARTMENT DISCRIMINATING SENSOR.

After all repairs/replacements:
- RECONNECT ALL SIR SYSTEM COMPONENTS, ENSURE ALL COMPONENTS ARE PROPERLY MOUNTED.
- CLEAR SIR DIAGNOSTIC TROUBLE CODES.
- REPEAT "SIR DIAGNOSTIC SYSTEM CHECK."

4-29-93
PS 17284

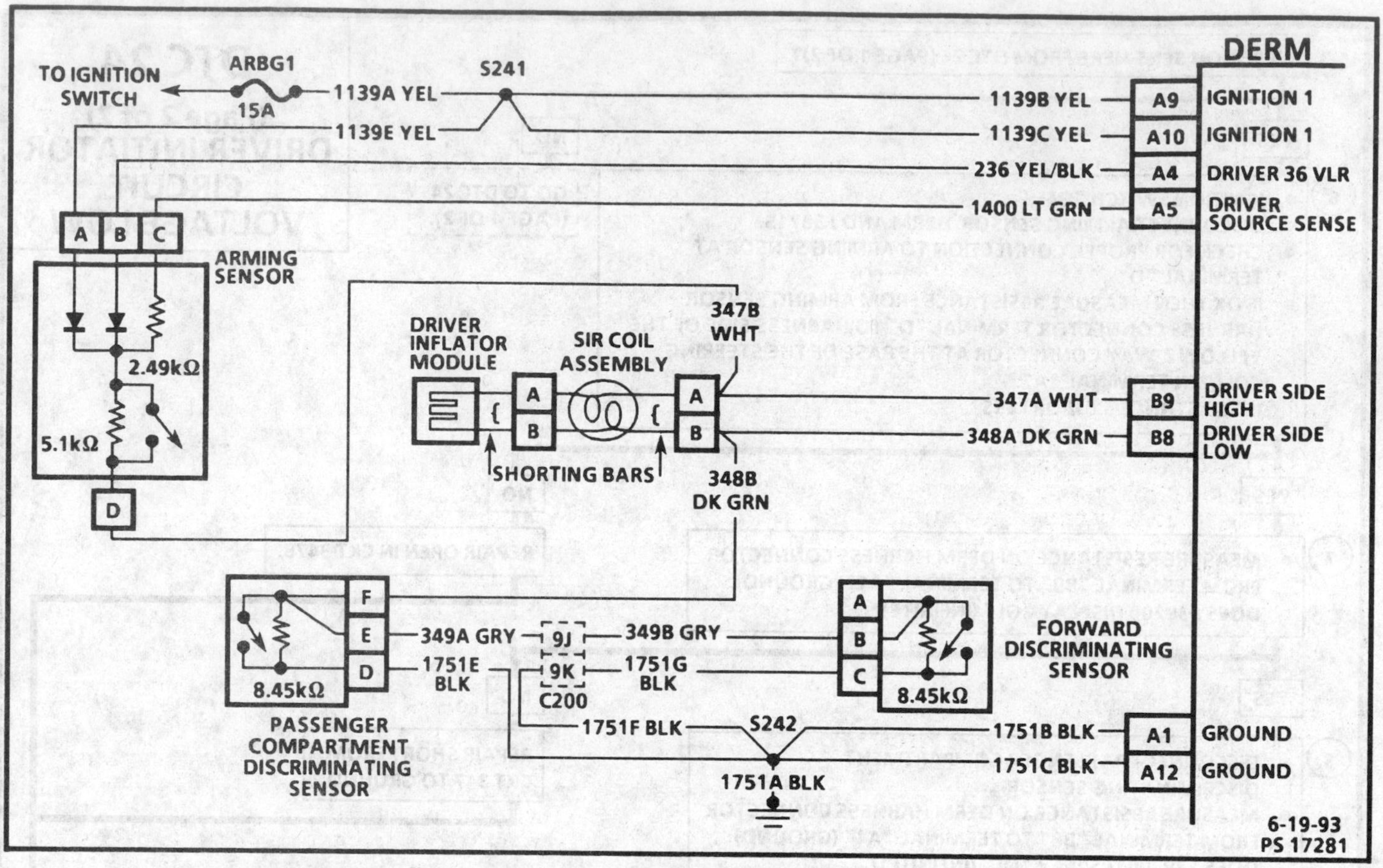
DERM
TO IGNITION SWITCH
ARBG1
15A
S241
1139A YEL
1139E YEL
1139B YEL
1139C YEL
236 YEL/BLK
1400 LT GRN
A9
A10
A4
A5
IGNITION 1
IGNITION 1
DRIVER 36 VLR
DRIVER SOURCE SENSE
A
B
C
ARMING SENSOR
2.49kΩ
5.1kΩ
D
347B WHT
DRIVER INFLATOR MODULE
SIR COIL ASSEMBLY
SHORTING BARS
348B DK GRN
347A WHT
348A DK GRN
B9
B8
DRIVER SIDE HIGH
DRIVER SIDE LOW
F
E
D
8.45kΩ
349A GRY
9J
9K
C200
349B GRY
1751E BLK
1751G BLK
FORWARD DISCRIMINATING SENSOR
8.45kΩ
PASSENGER COMPARTMENT DISCRIMINATING SENSOR
1751F BLK
S242
1751B BLK
1751C BLK
1751A BLK
A1
A12
GROUND
GROUND
6-19-93
PS 17281

DTC 25

DRIVER INITIATOR CIRCUIT SHORT TO IGNITION

Circuit Description:

During the "Initiator Assembly Resistance Test" the DERM grounds the "Driver Side Low" terminal "B8" through an internal resistor and measures the voltage at "Driver Side Low." For a properly operating circuit the voltage measurement during this test will be below a specified value. When the voltage measured at "Driver Side Low" is above a specified value DTC 25 is set.

DTC Will Set When: The voltage measured at "Driver Side Low" terminal "B8" is above a specified value while the DERM attempts to ground this terminal. This test is run during the "Initiator Assembly Resistance Test" and the "10 Minute Loop Test" when: 1) No "higher priority faults" are detected during "Turn-ON," 2) No "higher priority faults" are detected during "Continuous Monitoring" for one second, 3) No "Crank" signal present, 4) "Ignition 1" voltage is above a specified value.

Action Taken: DERM turns "ON" the "AIR BAG" warning lamp and sets a diagnostic trouble code.

DTC Will Clear When: The voltage measured at "Driver Side Low" terminal "B8" is below a specified value while the DERM grounds this terminal.

DTC Chart Test Description: Number(s) below refer to circled number(s) on the diagnostic chart.

1. This test determines whether the malfunction is occurring in the steering column.
2. This test checks for a short from the "Driver Side High" circuit to B+.
3. This test checks for a short from the "Driver Side Low" circuit to B+.
4. This test checks for a short from the discriminating sensor interconnect circuit to B+.

Diagnostic Aids: This diagnostic trouble code can only be set when the malfunction is present as the ignition switch is turned "ON." After the "Initiator Assembly Resistance Test" is completed a short to B+ in the steering column, CKT 347, CKT 348 or CKT 349 will cause DTC 24 to set. When a scan tool "Clear Codes" command is issued and the malfunction is still present, the DTC will not reappear for ten minutes or until the next ignition cycle.

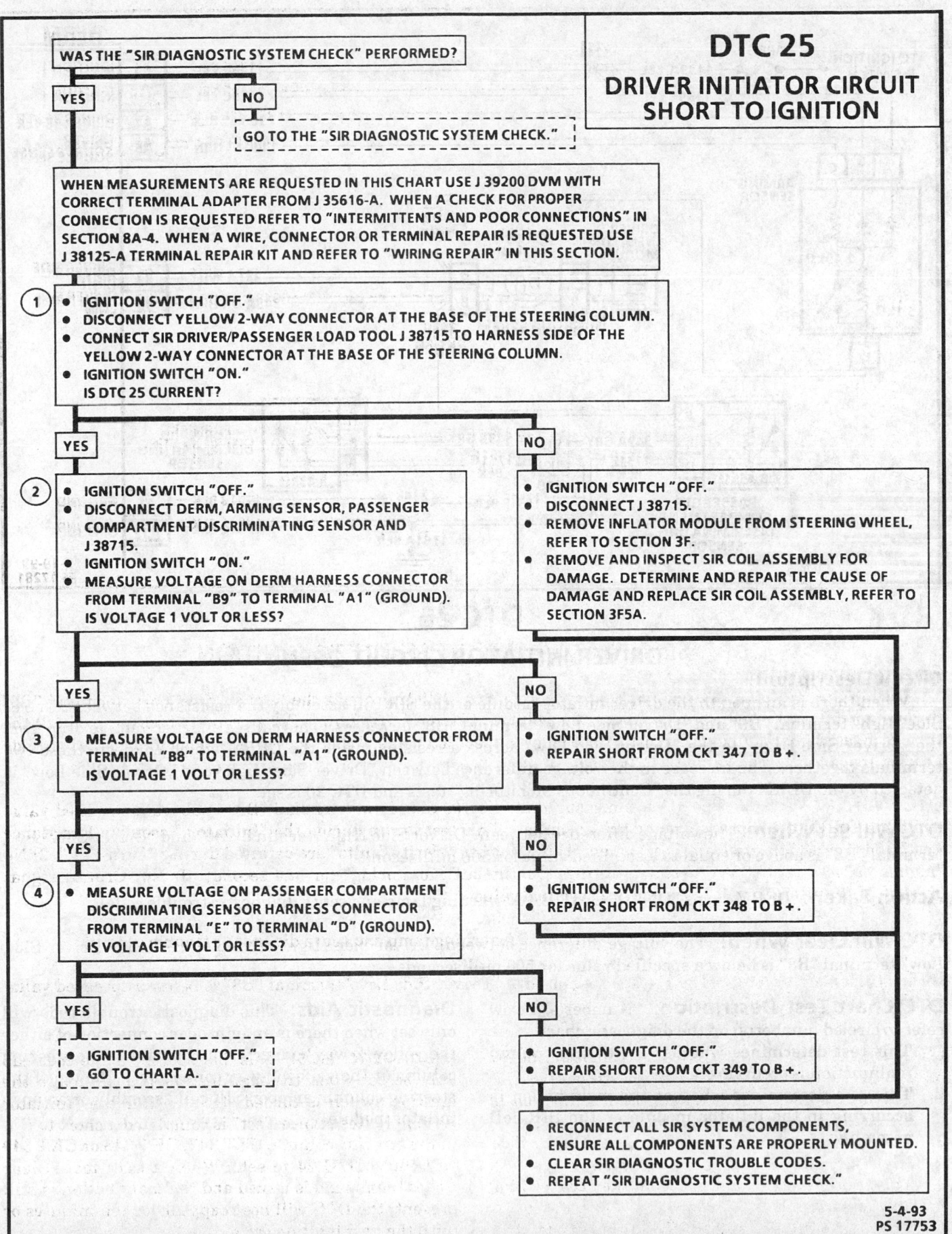

DTC 25

DRIVER INITIATOR CIRCUIT SHORT TO IGNITION

WAS THE "SIR DIAGNOSTIC SYSTEM CHECK" PERFORMED?

- YES: continue below.
- NO: GO TO THE "SIR DIAGNOSTIC SYSTEM CHECK."

WHEN MEASUREMENTS ARE REQUESTED IN THIS CHART USE J 39200 DVM WITH CORRECT TERMINAL ADAPTER FROM J 35616-A. WHEN A CHECK FOR PROPER CONNECTION IS REQUESTED REFER TO "INTERMITTENTS AND POOR CONNECTIONS" IN SECTION 8A-4. WHEN A WIRE, CONNECTOR OR TERMINAL REPAIR IS REQUESTED USE J 38125-A TERMINAL REPAIR KIT AND REFER TO "WIRING REPAIR" IN THIS SECTION.

(1)
- IGNITION SWITCH "OFF."
- DISCONNECT YELLOW 2-WAY CONNECTOR AT THE BASE OF THE STEERING COLUMN.
- CONNECT SIR DRIVER/PASSENGER LOAD TOOL J 38715 TO HARNESS SIDE OF THE YELLOW 2-WAY CONNECTOR AT THE BASE OF THE STEERING COLUMN.
- IGNITION SWITCH "ON."

IS DTC 25 CURRENT?

- YES: go to step 2.
- NO:
  - IGNITION SWITCH "OFF."
  - DISCONNECT J 38715.
  - REMOVE INFLATOR MODULE FROM STEERING WHEEL, REFER TO SECTION 3F.
  - REMOVE AND INSPECT SIR COIL ASSEMBLY FOR DAMAGE. DETERMINE AND REPAIR THE CAUSE OF DAMAGE AND REPLACE SIR COIL ASSEMBLY, REFER TO SECTION 3F5A.

(2)
- IGNITION SWITCH "OFF."
- DISCONNECT DERM, ARMING SENSOR, PASSENGER COMPARTMENT DISCRIMINATING SENSOR AND J 38715.
- IGNITION SWITCH "ON."
- MEASURE VOLTAGE ON DERM HARNESS CONNECTOR FROM TERMINAL "B9" TO TERMINAL "A1" (GROUND).

IS VOLTAGE 1 VOLT OR LESS?

- YES: go to step 3.
- NO:
  - IGNITION SWITCH "OFF."
  - REPAIR SHORT FROM CKT 347 TO B +.

(3)
- MEASURE VOLTAGE ON DERM HARNESS CONNECTOR FROM TERMINAL "B8" TO TERMINAL "A1" (GROUND).

IS VOLTAGE 1 VOLT OR LESS?

- YES: go to step 4.
- NO:
  - IGNITION SWITCH "OFF."
  - REPAIR SHORT FROM CKT 348 TO B +.

(4)
- MEASURE VOLTAGE ON PASSENGER COMPARTMENT DISCRIMINATING SENSOR HARNESS CONNECTOR FROM TERMINAL "E" TO TERMINAL "D" (GROUND).

IS VOLTAGE 1 VOLT OR LESS?

- YES:
  - IGNITION SWITCH "OFF."
  - GO TO CHART A.
- NO:
  - IGNITION SWITCH "OFF."
  - REPAIR SHORT FROM CKT 349 TO B +.

After each repair:
- RECONNECT ALL SIR SYSTEM COMPONENTS, ENSURE ALL COMPONENTS ARE PROPERLY MOUNTED.
- CLEAR SIR DIAGNOSTIC TROUBLE CODES.
- REPEAT "SIR DIAGNOSTIC SYSTEM CHECK."

5-4-93
PS 17753

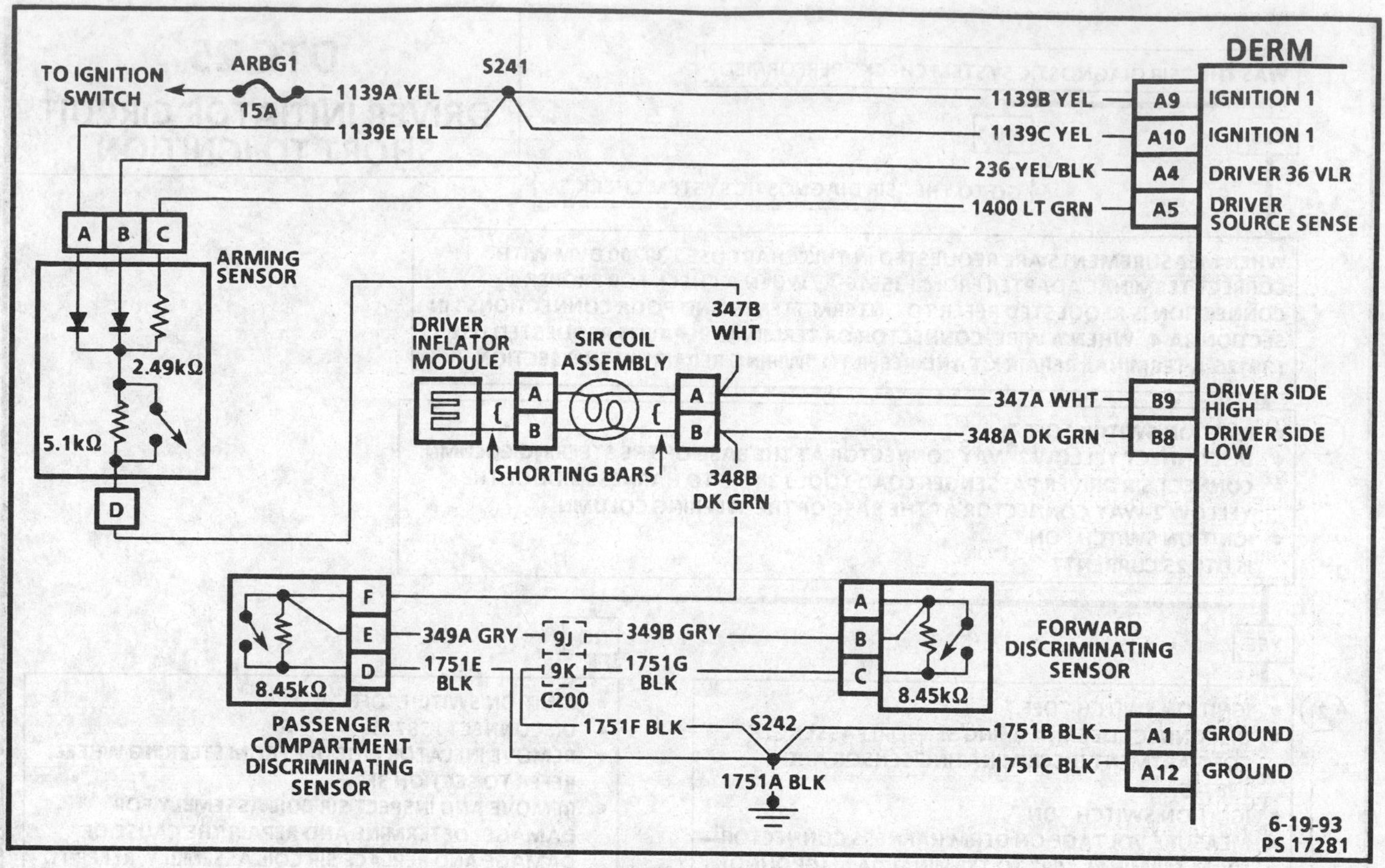

DERM
TO IGNITION SWITCH
ARBG1
15A
S241
1139A YEL
1139E YEL
1139B YEL
1139C YEL
236 YEL/BLK
1400 LT GRN
A9
A10
A4
A5
IGNITION 1
IGNITION 1
DRIVER 36 VLR
DRIVER SOURCE SENSE
A B C
ARMING SENSOR
2.49kΩ
5.1kΩ
D
DRIVER INFLATOR MODULE
SIR COIL ASSEMBLY
SHORTING BARS
347B WHT
347A WHT
348A DK GRN
348B DK GRN
B9
B8
DRIVER SIDE HIGH
DRIVER SIDE LOW
F
E
D
349A GRY
9J
9K
C200
349B GRY
1751E BLK
1751G BLK
1751F BLK
S242
1751B BLK
1751C BLK
1751A BLK
A1
A12
GROUND
GROUND
8.45kΩ
8.45kΩ
PASSENGER COMPARTMENT DISCRIMINATING SENSOR
FORWARD DISCRIMINATING SENSOR
6-19-93
PS 17281

DTC 26

DRIVER INITIATOR CIRCUIT OPEN

Circuit Description:

When there is an open in the driver inflator module or the SIR coil assembly the resistance between "Driver Side High" terminal "B9" and "Driver Side Low" terminal "B8" increases. This causes a larger voltage drop from the "Driver Side High" to the "Driver Side Low" across a resistor inside the DERM which connects these two terminals together. The increase in the voltage difference between "Driver Side High" and "Driver Side Low" is detected by the DERM during the "Continuous Monitoring" tests and DTC 26 is set.

DTC Will Set When: The voltage difference between "Driver Side High" terminal "B9" and "Driver Side Low" terminal "B8" is above or equal to a specified value for 500 milliseconds.

Action Taken: DERM turns "ON" the "AIR BAG" warning lamp and sets a diagnostic trouble code.

DTC Will Clear When: The voltage difference between "Driver Side High" terminal "B9" and "Driver Side Low" terminal "B8" is below a specified value for 500 milliseconds.

DTC Chart Test Description: Number(s) below refer to circled number(s) on the diagnostic chart.

1. This test determines whether a steering column malfunction is occurring.
2. This test determines whether the malfunction is occurring in the inflator module or the SIR coil assembly.

Diagnostic Aids: This diagnostic trouble code will only set when there is an improper connection of either the yellow 2-way connector at the base of the steering column or the yellow 2-way connector at the top of the steering column, an open SIR coil assembly or an open inflator module.

DTC 26
DRIVER INITIATOR CIRCUIT OPEN

WAS THE "SIR DIAGNOSTIC SYSTEM CHECK" PERFORMED?

NO
- GO TO THE "SIR DIAGNOSTIC SYSTEM CHECK."

YES

WHEN MEASUREMENTS ARE REQUESTED IN THIS CHART USE J 39200 DVM WITH CORRECT TERMINAL ADAPTER FROM J 35616-A. WHEN A CHECK FOR PROPER CONNECTION IS REQUESTED REFER TO "INTERMITTENTS AND POOR CONNECTIONS" IN SECTION 8A-4. WHEN A WIRE, CONNECTOR OR TERMINAL REPAIR IS REQUESTED USE J 38125-A TERMINAL REPAIR KIT AND REFER TO "WIRING REPAIR" IN THIS SECTION.

(1)
- IGNITION SWITCH "OFF."
- DISCONNECT YELLOW 2-WAY CONNECTOR AT THE BASE OF THE STEERING COLUMN.
- CHECK FOR PROPER CONNECTION TO YELLOW 2-WAY CONNECTOR AT TERMINALS "A" AND "B".
- CONNECT J 38715 SIR DRIVER/PASSENGER LOAD TOOL TO YELLOW 2-WAY CONNECTOR AT THE BASE OF THE STEERING COLUMN.
- IGNITION SWITCH "ON."

IS DTC 26 CURRENT?

YES
- IGNITION SWITCH "OFF."
- GO TO CHART A.

NO

(2)
- IGNITION SWITCH "OFF."
- DISCONNECT J 38715.
- REMOVE DRIVER INFLATOR MODULE FROM STEERING WHEEL, REFER TO SECTION 3F.
- CONNECT J 38715 TO INFLATOR MODULE CONNECTOR ON STEERING COLUMN.
- RECONNECT YELLOW 2-WAY CONNECTOR AT THE BASE OF THE STEERING COLUMN.
- IGNITION SWITCH "ON."

IS DTC 26 CURRENT?

NO
- IGNITION SWITCH "OFF."
- REPLACE DRIVER INFLATOR MODULE, REFER TO SECTION 3F.
- RECONNECT ALL SIR SYSTEM COMPONENTS, ENSURE ALL COMPONENTS ARE PROPERLY MOUNTED.
- CLEAR SIR DIAGNOSTIC TROUBLE CODES.
- REPEAT "SIR DIAGNOSTIC SYSTEM CHECK."

YES
- IGNITION SWITCH "OFF."
- REPLACE SIR COIL ASSEMBLY, REFER TO SECTION 3F5A.
- RECONNECT ALL SIR SYSTEM COMPONENTS, ENSURE ALL COMPONENTS ARE PROPERLY MOUNTED.
- CLEAR SIR DIAGNOSTIC TROUBLE CODES.
- REPEAT "SIR DIAGNOSTIC SYSTEM CHECK."

4-29-93
PS 17754

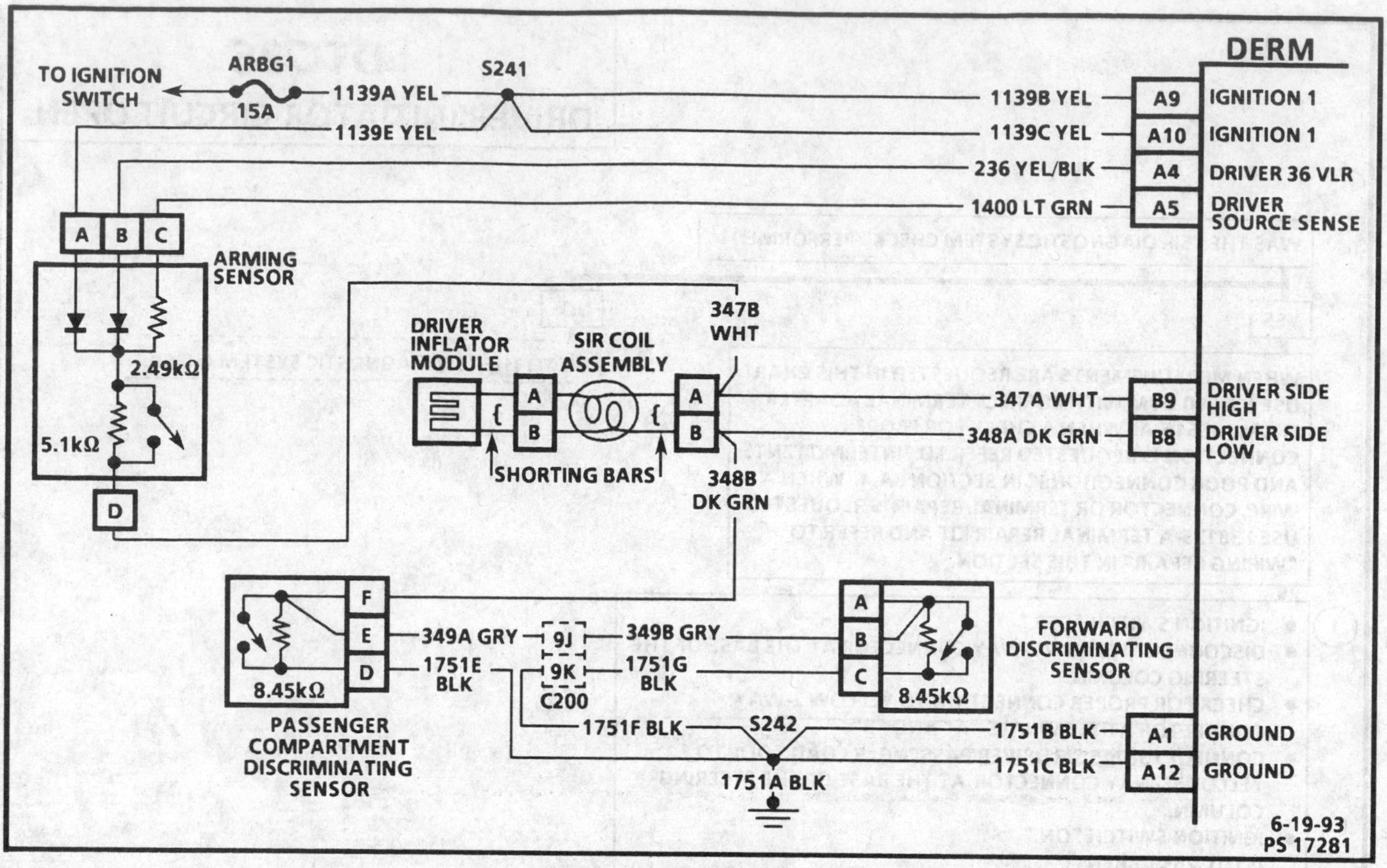
DERM
TO IGNITION SWITCH
ARBG1
15A
S241
1139A YEL
1139E YEL
1139B YEL
1139C YEL
236 YEL/BLK
1400 LT GRN
A9 IGNITION 1
A10 IGNITION 1
A4 DRIVER 36 VLR
A5 DRIVER SOURCE SENSE
A B C
ARMING SENSOR
2.49kΩ
5.1kΩ
D
DRIVER INFLATOR MODULE
SIR COIL ASSEMBLY
347B WHT
347A WHT
348A DK GRN
B9 DRIVER SIDE HIGH
B8 DRIVER SIDE LOW
SHORTING BARS
348B DK GRN
F
E
D
8.45kΩ
PASSENGER COMPARTMENT DISCRIMINATING SENSOR
349A GRY
1751E BLK
9J
9K
C200
349B GRY
1751G BLK
FORWARD DISCRIMINATING SENSOR
8.45kΩ
1751F BLK
S242
1751A BLK
1751B BLK
1751C BLK
A1 GROUND
A12 GROUND
6-19-93
PS 17281

DTC 28

CURRENT SINK OR SOURCE FAILURE

Circuit Description:

During the "Initiator Assembly Resistance Test" the DERM grounds the "Driver Side Low" terminal "B8" and turns "ON" the driver current source at the "Driver Side High" terminal "B9". During this test the DERM monitors voltage at "Driver Side Low" and the difference between "Driver Side High" and "Driver Side Low." When the measured values are outside the expected range DTC 28 is set.

DTC Will Set When: The voltage measured at "Driver Side Low" is below a specified value while its initiator resistance is in range or when the voltage measured at "Driver Side Low" is above a specified value. This test is run once each ignition cycle during the "Initiator Assembly Resistance Test" when: 1) No "higher priority faults" are detected during "Turn-ON," 2) No "higher priority faults" are detected during "Continuous Monitoring" for one second, 3) No "Crank" signal present, 4) "Ignition 1" voltage is above a specified value.

Action Taken: DERM turns "ON" the "AIR BAG" warning lamp and sets a diagnostic trouble code.

DTC Will Clear When: The ignition switch is turned "OFF."

DTC Chart Test Description: None.

Diagnostic Aids: During the "Initiator Assembly Resistance Test" the DERM checks for proper resistance of CKT 347A, CKT 348A, the SIR coil assembly and the inflator module. This test is performed by causing a known amount of current through a known amount of resistance causing a known amount of voltage at "Driver Side Low." When the measured resistance is in range and the voltage at "Driver Side Low" is too high or too low, DTC 28 is set.

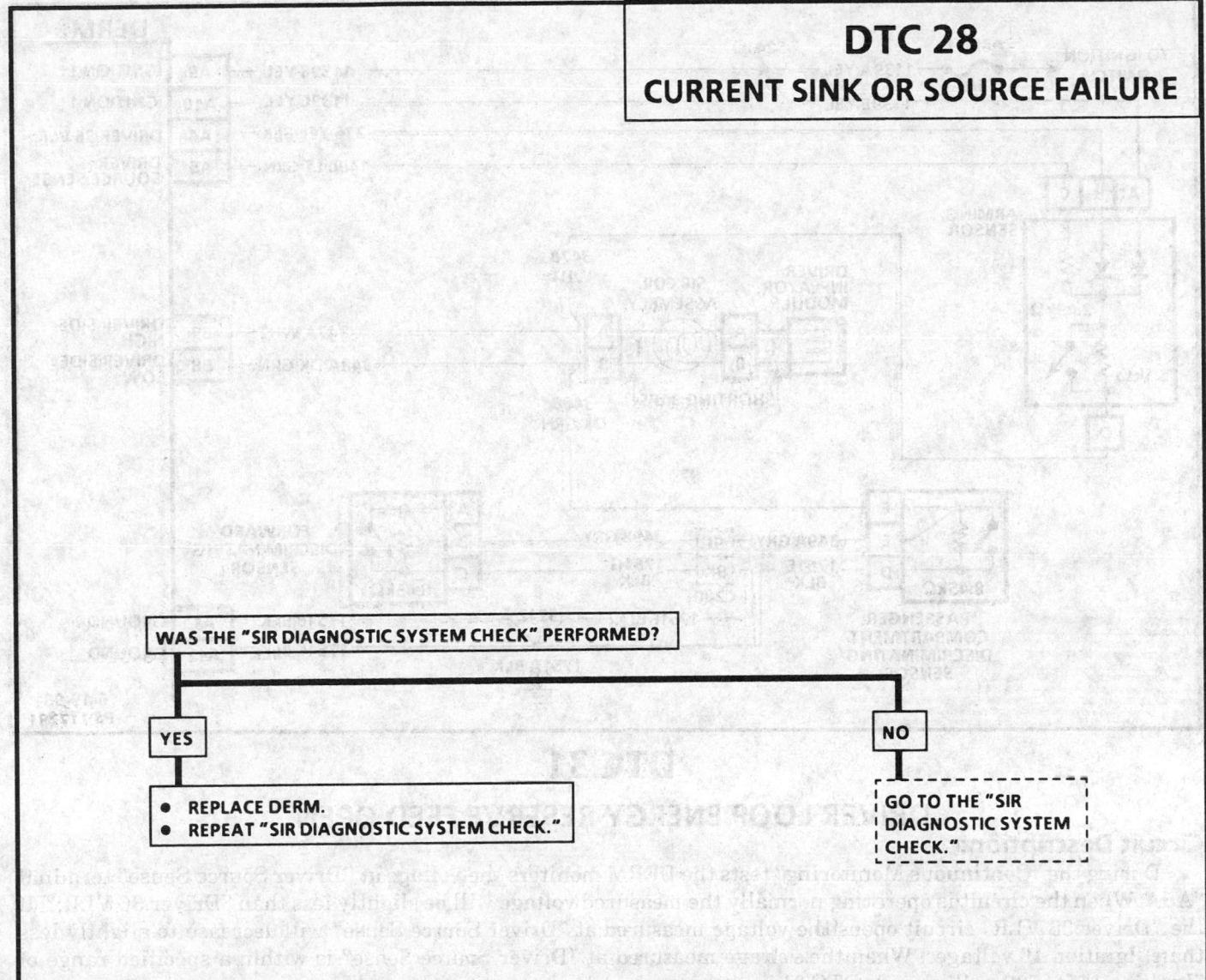

DTC 28
CURRENT SINK OR SOURCE FAILURE

WAS THE "SIR DIAGNOSTIC SYSTEM CHECK" PERFORMED?

YES

- REPLACE DERM.
- REPEAT "SIR DIAGNOSTIC SYSTEM CHECK."

NO

GO TO THE "SIR DIAGNOSTIC SYSTEM CHECK."

2-16-93
PS 16666

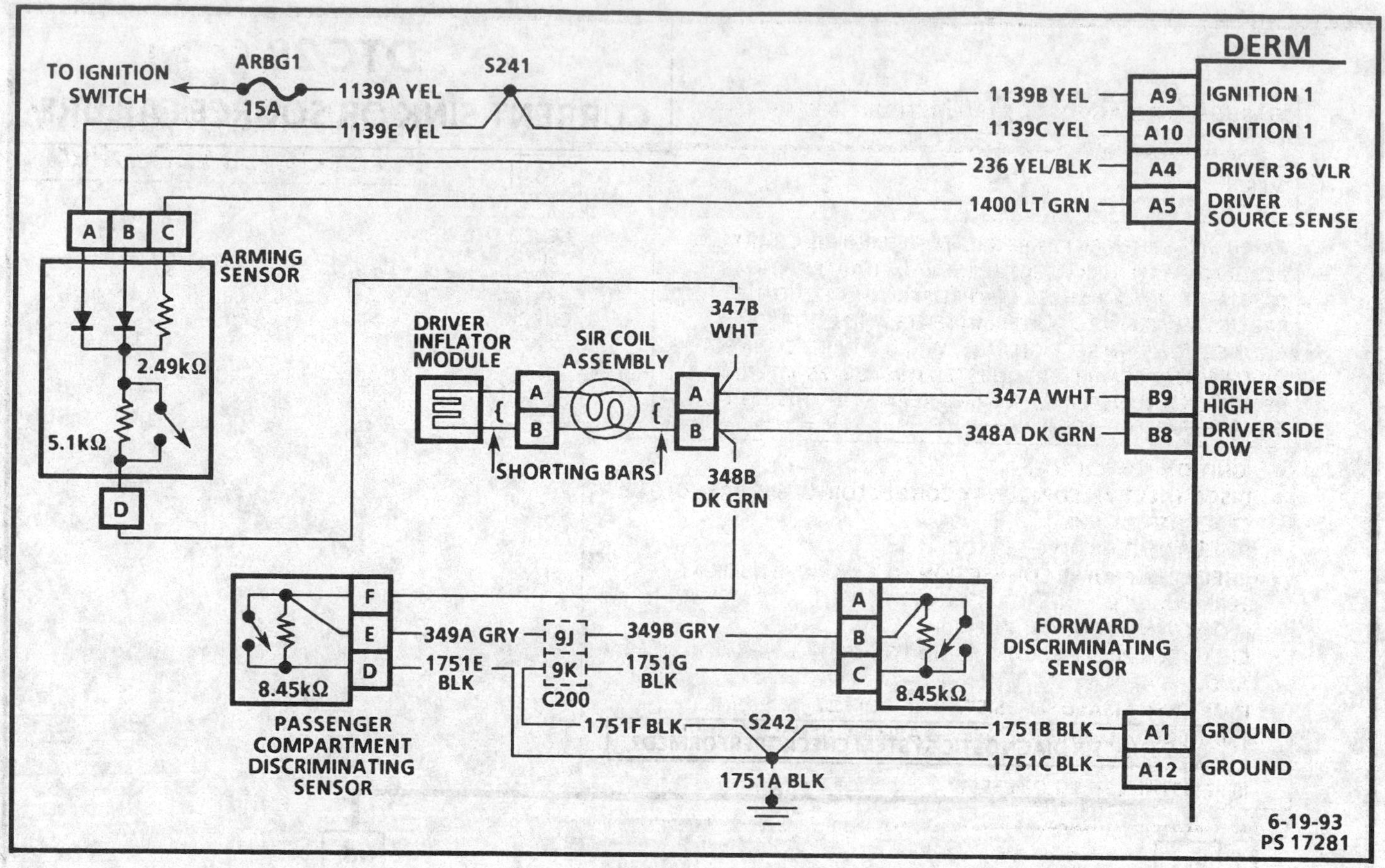
DERM
TO IGNITION SWITCH
ARBG1
15A
1139A YEL
S241
1139E YEL
1139B YEL
A9
IGNITION 1
1139C YEL
A10
IGNITION 1
236 YEL/BLK
A4
DRIVER 36 VLR
1400 LT GRN
A5
DRIVER SOURCE SENSE
A B C
ARMING SENSOR
2.49kΩ
5.1kΩ
D
DRIVER INFLATOR MODULE
SIR COIL ASSEMBLY
347B WHT
347A WHT
B9
DRIVER SIDE HIGH
348A DK GRN
B8
DRIVER SIDE LOW
SHORTING BARS
348B DK GRN
F
E
D
8.45kΩ
PASSENGER COMPARTMENT DISCRIMINATING SENSOR
349A GRY
9J
349B GRY
1751E BLK
9K
1751G BLK
C200
FORWARD DISCRIMINATING SENSOR
8.45kΩ
1751F BLK
S242
1751B BLK
A1
GROUND
1751C BLK
A12
GROUND
1751A BLK
6-19-93
PS 17281

DTC 31

DRIVER LOOP ENERGY RESERVE FEED OPEN

Circuit Description:

During the "Continuous Monitoring" tests the DERM monitors the voltage at "Driver Source Sense" terminal "A5." When the circuit is operating normally the measured voltage will be slightly less than "Driver 36 VLR." If the "Driver 36 VLR" circuit opens the voltage measured at "Driver Source Sense" will decrease to slightly less than "Ignition 1" voltage. When the voltage measured at "Driver Source Sense" is within a specified range of "Ignition 1" for 500 milliseconds DTC 31 is set.

DTC Will Set When: The voltage measured at "Driver Source Sense" terminal "A5" is within a specified range of "Ignition 1" for 500 milliseconds during "Continuous Monitoring."

Action Taken: DERM turns "ON" the "AIR BAG" warning lamp and sets a diagnostic trouble code.

DTC Will Clear When: The voltage measured at "Driver Source Sense" terminal "A5" is outside the specified range of "Ignition 1" which sets the diagnostic trouble code, for 500 milliseconds.

DTC Chart Test Description: Number(s) below refer to circled number(s) on the diagnostic chart.

1. This test checks for an open in the "Driver 36 VLR" circuit.
2. This test checks for high resistance, but not an open, in the "Driver Source Sense" circuit.
3. This test checks for a short from the "Driver Source Sense" circuit to B+.

Diagnostic Aids: An intermittent condition is likely to be caused by a poor connection at arming sensor terminal "B" or "C", poor connection at DERM terminal "A4" or "A5", an open in CKT 236 or CKT 1400, a short from CKT 1400 to B+ or an open inside the arming sensor.

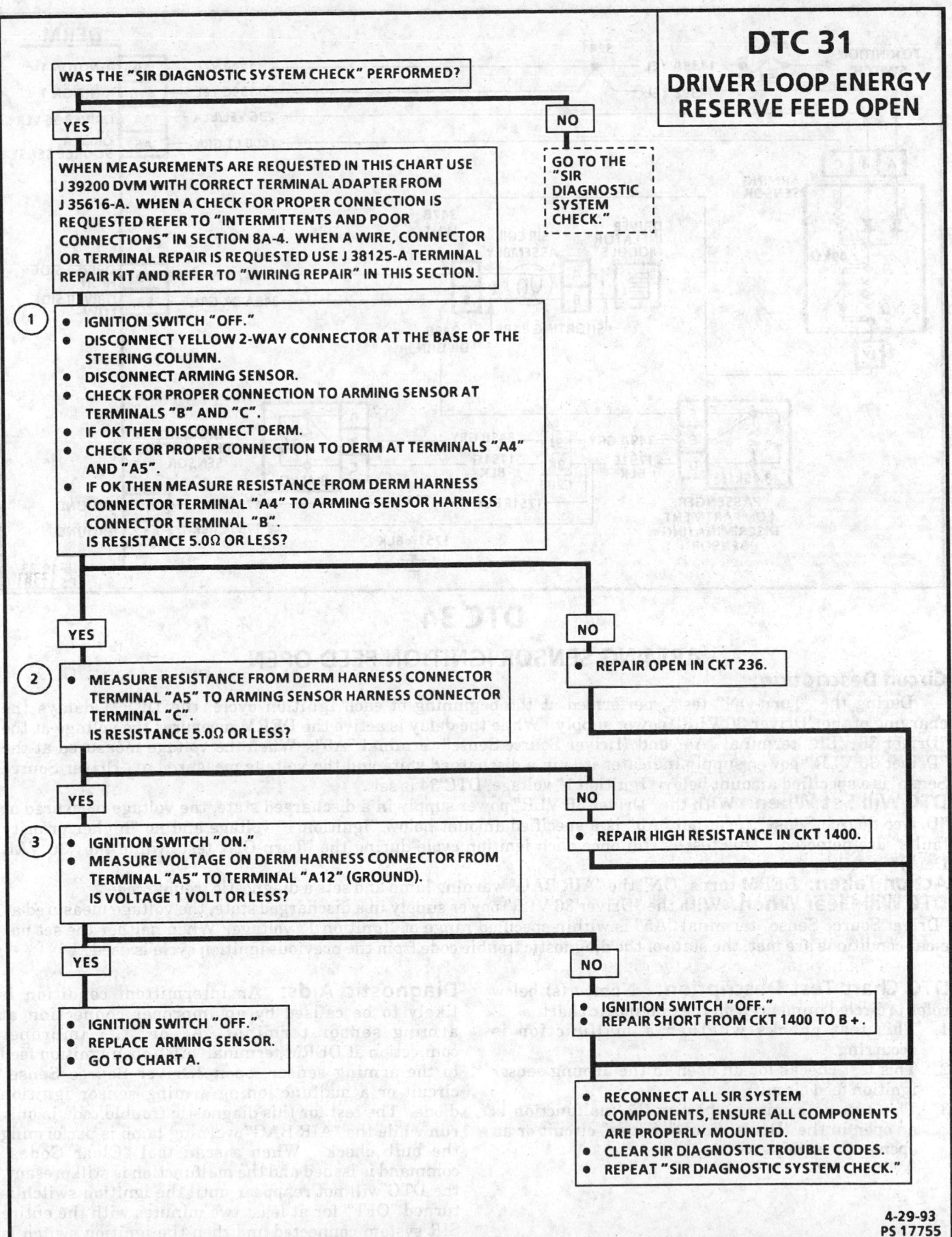

DTC 31
DRIVER LOOP ENERGY RESERVE FEED OPEN

WAS THE "SIR DIAGNOSTIC SYSTEM CHECK" PERFORMED?

- **NO** → GO TO THE "SIR DIAGNOSTIC SYSTEM CHECK."
- **YES** ↓

WHEN MEASUREMENTS ARE REQUESTED IN THIS CHART USE J 39200 DVM WITH CORRECT TERMINAL ADAPTER FROM J 35616-A. WHEN A CHECK FOR PROPER CONNECTION IS REQUESTED REFER TO "INTERMITTENTS AND POOR CONNECTIONS" IN SECTION 8A-4. WHEN A WIRE, CONNECTOR OR TERMINAL REPAIR IS REQUESTED USE J 38125-A TERMINAL REPAIR KIT AND REFER TO "WIRING REPAIR" IN THIS SECTION.

1
- IGNITION SWITCH "OFF."
- DISCONNECT YELLOW 2-WAY CONNECTOR AT THE BASE OF THE STEERING COLUMN.
- DISCONNECT ARMING SENSOR.
- CHECK FOR PROPER CONNECTION TO ARMING SENSOR AT TERMINALS "B" AND "C".
- IF OK THEN DISCONNECT DERM.
- CHECK FOR PROPER CONNECTION TO DERM AT TERMINALS "A4" AND "A5".
- IF OK THEN MEASURE RESISTANCE FROM DERM HARNESS CONNECTOR TERMINAL "A4" TO ARMING SENSOR HARNESS CONNECTOR TERMINAL "B".

IS RESISTANCE 5.0Ω OR LESS?

- **NO** → REPAIR OPEN IN CKT 236.
- **YES** ↓

2
- MEASURE RESISTANCE FROM DERM HARNESS CONNECTOR TERMINAL "A5" TO ARMING SENSOR HARNESS CONNECTOR TERMINAL "C".

IS RESISTANCE 5.0Ω OR LESS?

- **NO** → REPAIR HIGH RESISTANCE IN CKT 1400.
- **YES** ↓

3
- IGNITION SWITCH "ON."
- MEASURE VOLTAGE ON DERM HARNESS CONNECTOR FROM TERMINAL "A5" TO TERMINAL "A12" (GROUND).

IS VOLTAGE 1 VOLT OR LESS?

- **YES** →
  - IGNITION SWITCH "OFF."
  - REPLACE ARMING SENSOR.
  - GO TO CHART A.
- **NO** →
  - IGNITION SWITCH "OFF."
  - REPAIR SHORT FROM CKT 1400 TO B+.

(After repairs:)
- RECONNECT ALL SIR SYSTEM COMPONENTS, ENSURE ALL COMPONENTS ARE PROPERLY MOUNTED.
- CLEAR SIR DIAGNOSTIC TROUBLE CODES.
- REPEAT "SIR DIAGNOSTIC SYSTEM CHECK."

4-29-93
PS 17755

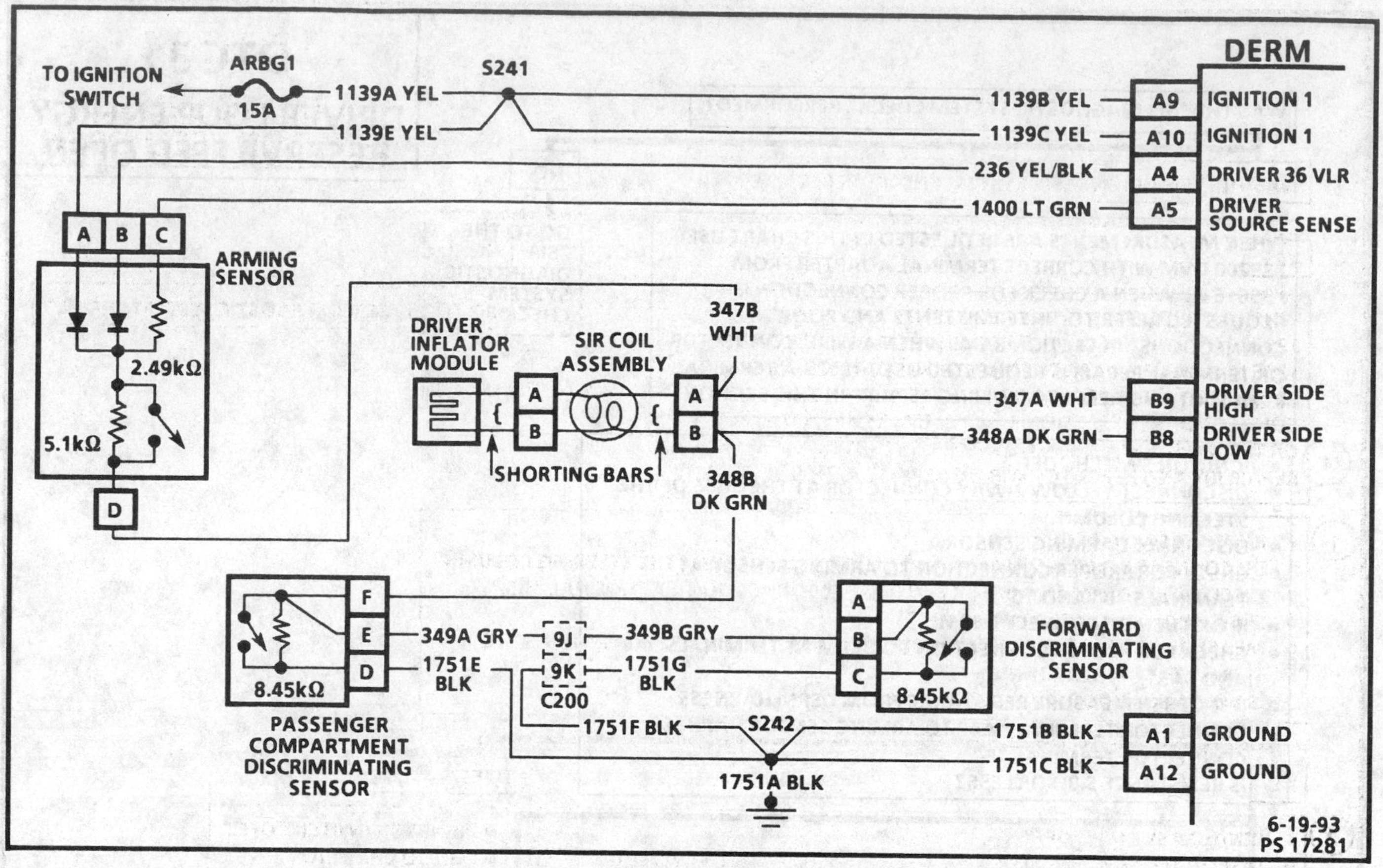

DERM
TO IGNITION SWITCH
ARBG1
15A
1139A YEL
1139E YEL
S241
1139B YEL
1139C YEL
236 YEL/BLK
1400 LT GRN
A9
A10
A4
A5
IGNITION 1
IGNITION 1
DRIVER 36 VLR
DRIVER SOURCE SENSE
A B C
ARMING SENSOR
2.49kΩ
5.1kΩ
D
DRIVER INFLATOR MODULE
SIR COIL ASSEMBLY
347B WHT
347A WHT
348A DK GRN
B9
B8
DRIVER SIDE HIGH
DRIVER SIDE LOW
SHORTING BARS
348B DK GRN
PASSENGER COMPARTMENT DISCRIMINATING SENSOR
8.45kΩ
F
E
D
349A GRY
9J
9K
C200
349B GRY
1751E BLK
1751G BLK
FORWARD DISCRIMINATING SENSOR
8.45kΩ
1751F BLK
S242
1751B BLK
1751C BLK
1751A BLK
A1
A12
GROUND
GROUND
6-19-93
PS 17281

DTC 34

ARMING SENSOR IGNITION FEED OPEN

Circuit Description:

During the "Turn-ON" tests, performed at the beginning of each ignition cycle, the DERM delays the charging of the "Driver 36 VLR" power supply. While the delay is active the DERM measures the voltage at the "Driver 36 VLR" terminal "A4" and "Driver Source Sense" terminal "A5". When the voltage measured at the "Driver 36 VLR" power supply indicates it is in a discharged state and the voltage measured at "Driver Source Sense" is a specified amount below "Ignition 1" voltage, DTC 34 is set.

DTC Will Set When: With the "Driver 36 VLR" power supply in a discharged state, the voltage measured at "Driver Source Sense" terminal "A5" is a specified amount below "Ignition 1" voltage and no "higher priority faults" are detected. This test is run once each ignition cycle during the "Turn-ON" tests while the "36 VLR Delay" is active.

Action Taken: DERM turns "ON" the "AIR BAG" warning lamp and sets a diagnostic trouble code.

DTC Will Clear When: With the "Driver 36 VLR" power supply in a discharged state, the voltage measured at "Driver Source Sense" terminal "A5" is within specified range of "Ignition 1" voltage. When neither the set nor clear conditions are met, the state of the diagnostic trouble code from the previous ignition cycle is used.

DTC Chart Test Description: Number(s) below refer to circled number(s) on the diagnostic chart.

1. This test checks whether a malfunction is occurring.
2. This test checks for an open in the arming sensor ignition feed circuit.
3. This test determines whether the malfunction is an open in the "Driver Source Sense" circuit or an open in the arming sensor.

Diagnostic Aids: An intermittent condition is likely to be caused by an improper connection at arming sensor terminal "A" or "C", improper connection at DERM terminal "A5", open ignition feed to the arming sensor, open "Driver Source Sense" circuit or a malfunctioning arming sensor ignition diode. The test for this diagnostic trouble code is only run while the "AIR BAG" warning lamp is performing the bulb check. When a scan tool "Clear Codes" command is issued and the malfunction is still present, the DTC will not reappear until the ignition switch is turned "OFF" for at least two minutes with the entire SIR system connected and then the ignition switch is turned "ON."

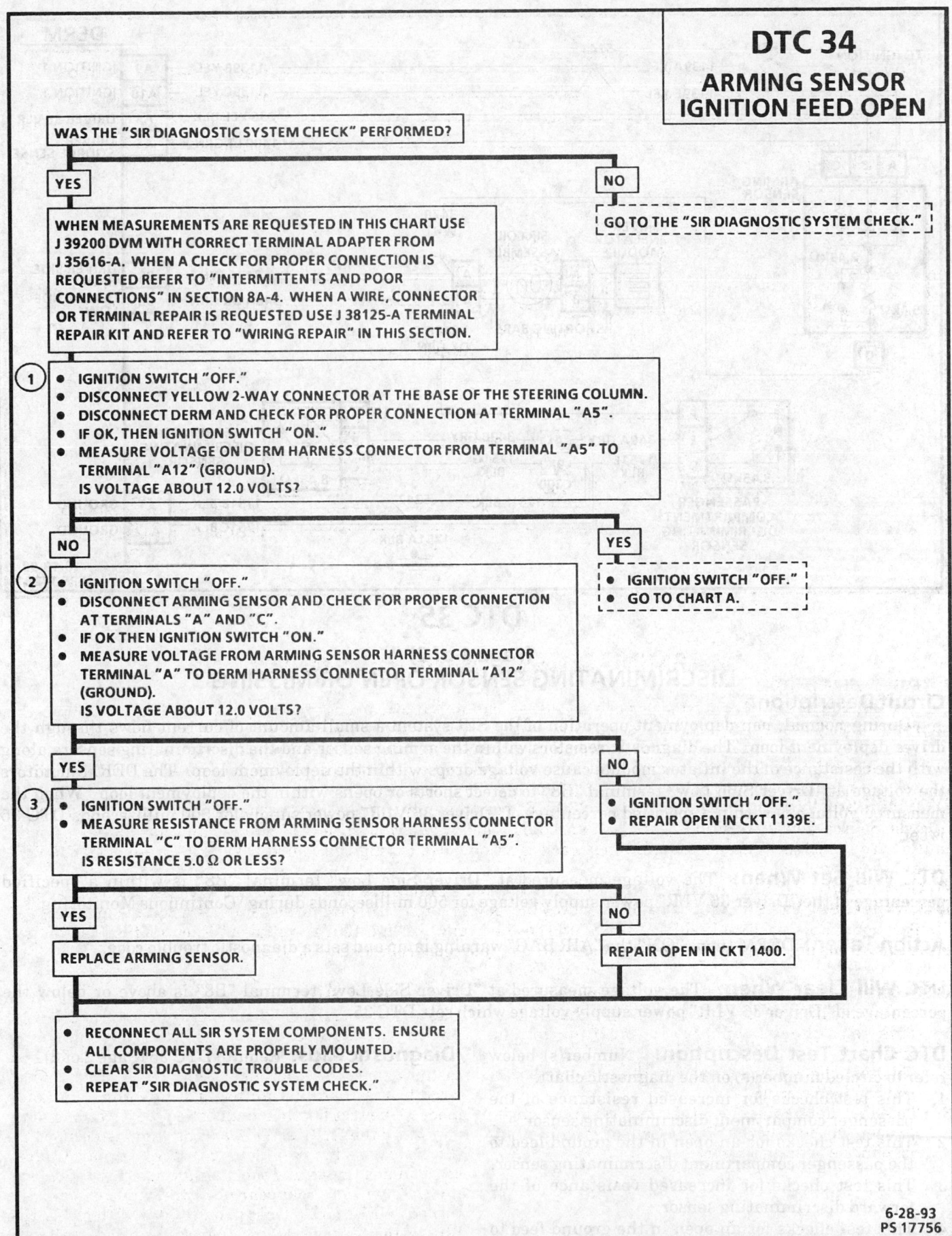

DTC 34

ARMING SENSOR IGNITION FEED OPEN

WAS THE "SIR DIAGNOSTIC SYSTEM CHECK" PERFORMED?

YES

WHEN MEASUREMENTS ARE REQUESTED IN THIS CHART USE J 39200 DVM WITH CORRECT TERMINAL ADAPTER FROM J 35616-A. WHEN A CHECK FOR PROPER CONNECTION IS REQUESTED REFER TO "INTERMITTENTS AND POOR CONNECTIONS" IN SECTION 8A-4. WHEN A WIRE, CONNECTOR OR TERMINAL REPAIR IS REQUESTED USE J 38125-A TERMINAL REPAIR KIT AND REFER TO "WIRING REPAIR" IN THIS SECTION.

NO

GO TO THE "SIR DIAGNOSTIC SYSTEM CHECK."

(1)
- IGNITION SWITCH "OFF."
- DISCONNECT YELLOW 2-WAY CONNECTOR AT THE BASE OF THE STEERING COLUMN.
- DISCONNECT DERM AND CHECK FOR PROPER CONNECTION AT TERMINAL "A5".
- IF OK, THEN IGNITION SWITCH "ON."
- MEASURE VOLTAGE ON DERM HARNESS CONNECTOR FROM TERMINAL "A5" TO TERMINAL "A12" (GROUND).

  IS VOLTAGE ABOUT 12.0 VOLTS?

NO

(2)
- IGNITION SWITCH "OFF."
- DISCONNECT ARMING SENSOR AND CHECK FOR PROPER CONNECTION AT TERMINALS "A" AND "C".
- IF OK THEN IGNITION SWITCH "ON."
- MEASURE VOLTAGE FROM ARMING SENSOR HARNESS CONNECTOR TERMINAL "A" TO DERM HARNESS CONNECTOR TERMINAL "A12" (GROUND).

  IS VOLTAGE ABOUT 12.0 VOLTS?

YES

- IGNITION SWITCH "OFF."
- GO TO CHART A.

(2) → **YES**

(3)
- IGNITION SWITCH "OFF."
- MEASURE RESISTANCE FROM ARMING SENSOR HARNESS CONNECTOR TERMINAL "C" TO DERM HARNESS CONNECTOR TERMINAL "A5".

  IS RESISTANCE 5.0 Ω OR LESS?

(2) → **NO**

- IGNITION SWITCH "OFF."
- REPAIR OPEN IN CKT 1139E.

(3) → **YES**

REPLACE ARMING SENSOR.

(3) → **NO**

REPAIR OPEN IN CKT 1400.

- RECONNECT ALL SIR SYSTEM COMPONENTS. ENSURE ALL COMPONENTS ARE PROPERLY MOUNTED.
- CLEAR SIR DIAGNOSTIC TROUBLE CODES.
- REPEAT "SIR DIAGNOSTIC SYSTEM CHECK."

6-28-93
PS 17756

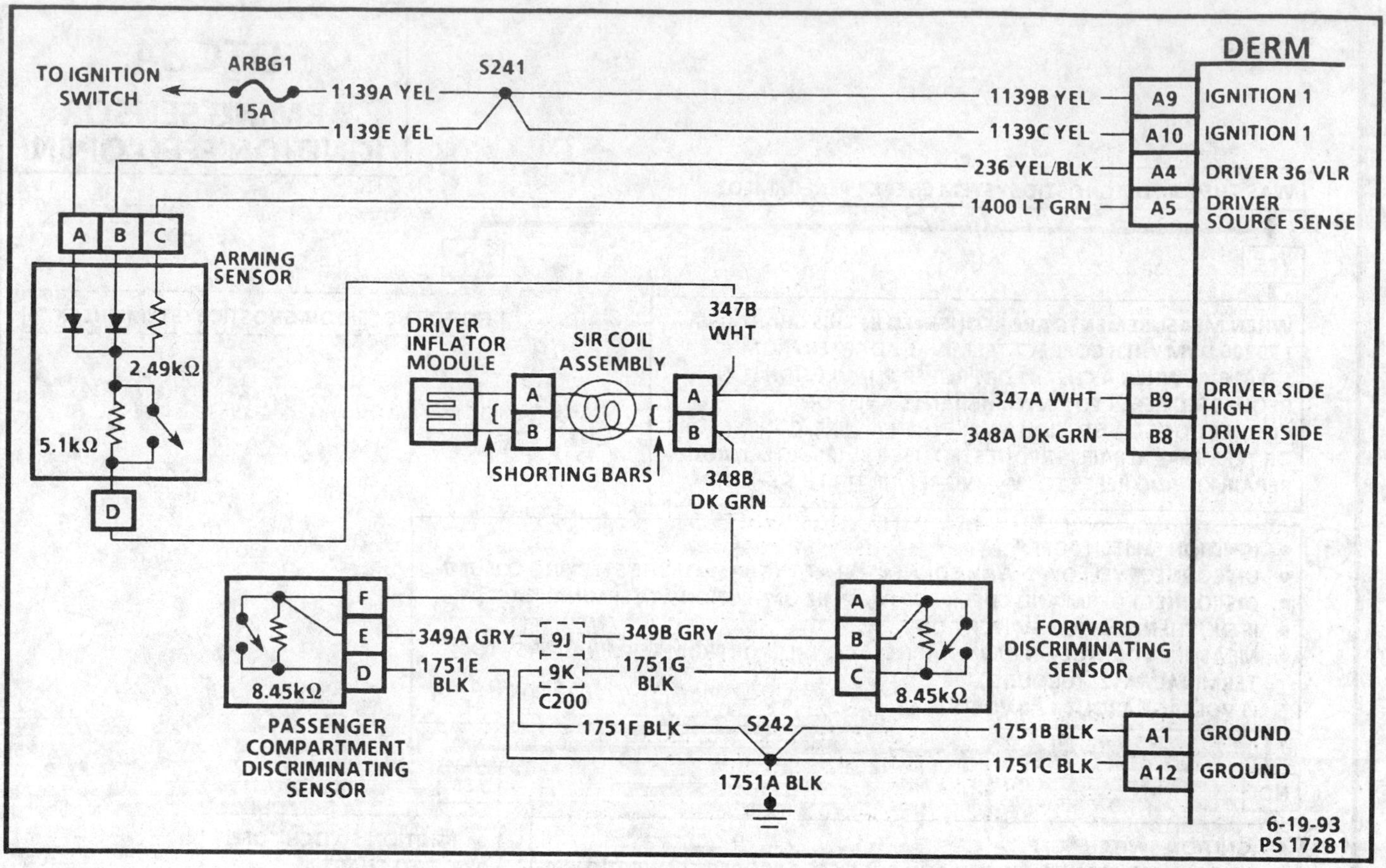
DERM
TO IGNITION SWITCH
ARBG1
15A
1139A YEL
S241
1139E YEL
1139B YEL
A9
IGNITION 1
1139C YEL
A10
IGNITION 1
236 YEL/BLK
A4
DRIVER 36 VLR
1400 LT GRN
A5
DRIVER SOURCE SENSE
A B C
ARMING SENSOR
2.49kΩ
5.1kΩ
D
DRIVER INFLATOR MODULE
SIR COIL ASSEMBLY
347B WHT
347A WHT
B9
DRIVER SIDE HIGH
348A DK GRN
B8
DRIVER SIDE LOW
SHORTING BARS
348B DK GRN
F
E
D
349A GRY
9J
9K
C200
349B GRY
1751E BLK
1751G BLK
8.45kΩ
PASSENGER COMPARTMENT DISCRIMINATING SENSOR
FORWARD DISCRIMINATING SENSOR
1751F BLK
S242
1751B BLK
A1
GROUND
1751C BLK
A12
GROUND
1751A BLK
6-19-93
PS 17281

DTC 35

(Page 1 of 2)
DISCRIMINATING SENSOR OPEN OR MISSING

Circuit Description:

During normal, non-deployment operation of the SIR system a small amount of current flows through the driver deployment loop. The diagnostic resistors within the arming sensor and the discriminating sensors along with the resistance of the inflator module cause voltage drops within the deployment loop. The DERM monitors the voltage at "Driver Side Low" terminal "B8" to detect shorts or opens within the deployment loop. When the measured voltage is within a specified percentage of "Driver 36 VLR" power supply for 500 milliseconds DTC 35 is set.

DTC Will Set When: The voltage measured at "Driver Side Low" terminal "B8" is within a specified percentage of the "Driver 36 VLR" power supply voltage for 500 milliseconds during "Continuous Monitoring."

Action Taken: DERM turns "ON" the "AIR BAG" warning lamp and sets a diagnostic trouble code.

DTC Will Clear When: The voltage measured at "Driver Side Low" terminal "B8" is above or below the percentage of "Driver 36 VLR" power supply voltage which sets DTC 35.

DTC Chart Test Description: Number(s) below refer to circled number(s) on the diagnostic chart.

1. This test checks for increased resistance of the passenger compartment discriminating sensor.
2. This test checks for an open in the ground feed to the passenger compartment discriminating sensor.
3. This test checks for increased resistance of the forward discriminating sensor.
4. This test checks for an open in the ground feed to the forward discriminating sensor.

Diagnostic Aids: Refer to DTC 35 (Page 2 of 2).

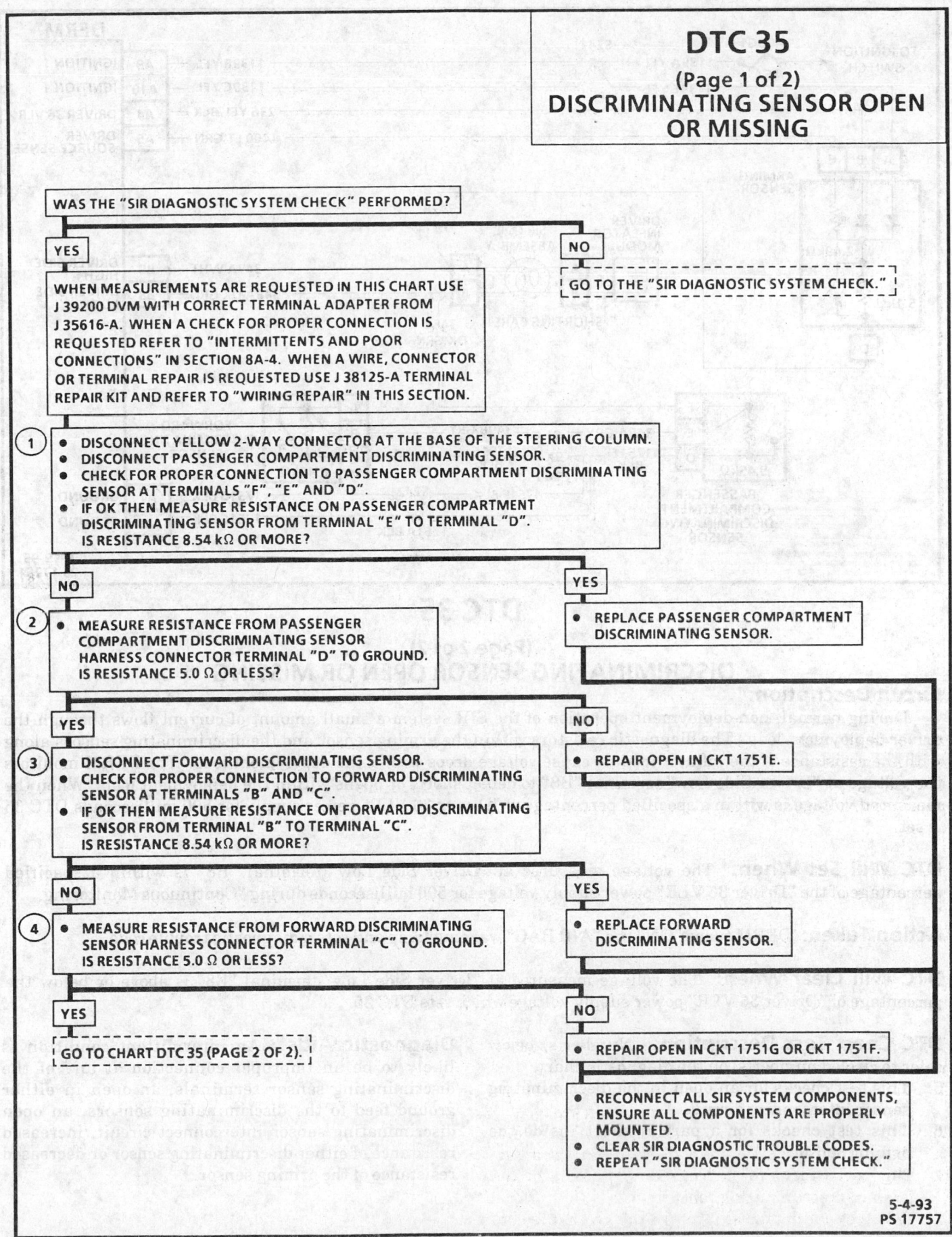

DTC 35

(Page 1 of 2)

DISCRIMINATING SENSOR OPEN OR MISSING

WAS THE "SIR DIAGNOSTIC SYSTEM CHECK" PERFORMED?

- NO → GO TO THE "SIR DIAGNOSTIC SYSTEM CHECK."
- YES →

WHEN MEASUREMENTS ARE REQUESTED IN THIS CHART USE J 39200 DVM WITH CORRECT TERMINAL ADAPTER FROM J 35616-A. WHEN A CHECK FOR PROPER CONNECTION IS REQUESTED REFER TO "INTERMITTENTS AND POOR CONNECTIONS" IN SECTION 8A-4. WHEN A WIRE, CONNECTOR OR TERMINAL REPAIR IS REQUESTED USE J 38125-A TERMINAL REPAIR KIT AND REFER TO "WIRING REPAIR" IN THIS SECTION.

1
- DISCONNECT YELLOW 2-WAY CONNECTOR AT THE BASE OF THE STEERING COLUMN.
- DISCONNECT PASSENGER COMPARTMENT DISCRIMINATING SENSOR.
- CHECK FOR PROPER CONNECTION TO PASSENGER COMPARTMENT DISCRIMINATING SENSOR AT TERMINALS "F", "E" AND "D".
- IF OK THEN MEASURE RESISTANCE ON PASSENGER COMPARTMENT DISCRIMINATING SENSOR FROM TERMINAL "E" TO TERMINAL "D". IS RESISTANCE 8.54 kΩ OR MORE?

YES →
- REPLACE PASSENGER COMPARTMENT DISCRIMINATING SENSOR.

NO →

2
- MEASURE RESISTANCE FROM PASSENGER COMPARTMENT DISCRIMINATING SENSOR HARNESS CONNECTOR TERMINAL "D" TO GROUND. IS RESISTANCE 5.0 Ω OR LESS?

NO →
- REPAIR OPEN IN CKT 1751E.

YES →

3
- DISCONNECT FORWARD DISCRIMINATING SENSOR.
- CHECK FOR PROPER CONNECTION TO FORWARD DISCRIMINATING SENSOR AT TERMINALS "B" AND "C".
- IF OK THEN MEASURE RESISTANCE ON FORWARD DISCRIMINATING SENSOR FROM TERMINAL "B" TO TERMINAL "C". IS RESISTANCE 8.54 kΩ OR MORE?

YES →
- REPLACE FORWARD DISCRIMINATING SENSOR.

NO →

4
- MEASURE RESISTANCE FROM FORWARD DISCRIMINATING SENSOR HARNESS CONNECTOR TERMINAL "C" TO GROUND. IS RESISTANCE 5.0 Ω OR LESS?

YES → GO TO CHART DTC 35 (PAGE 2 OF 2).

NO →
- REPAIR OPEN IN CKT 1751G OR CKT 1751F.

After repair:
- RECONNECT ALL SIR SYSTEM COMPONENTS, ENSURE ALL COMPONENTS ARE PROPERLY MOUNTED.
- CLEAR SIR DIAGNOSTIC TROUBLE CODES.
- REPEAT "SIR DIAGNOSTIC SYSTEM CHECK."

5-4-93
PS 17757

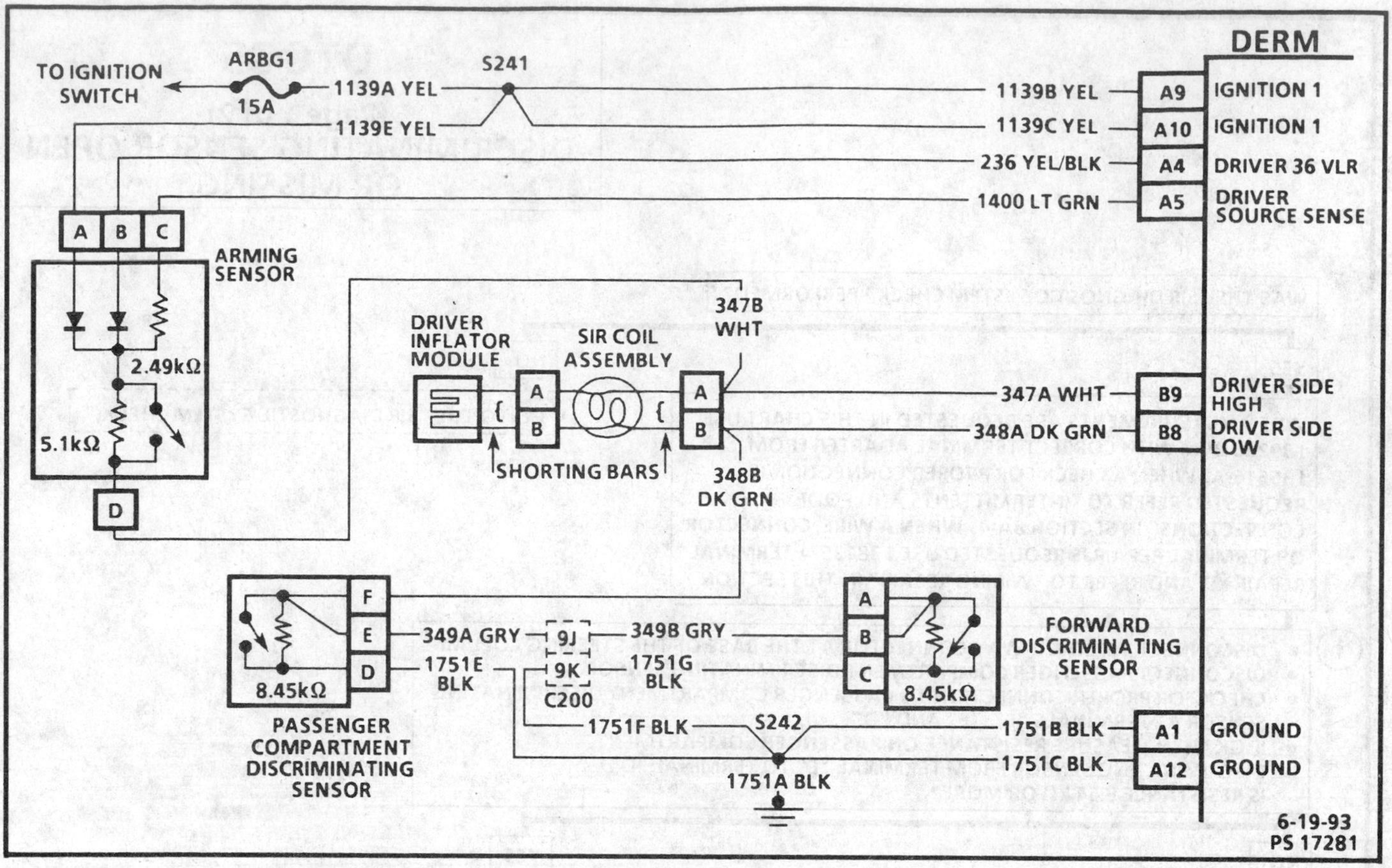
DERM
TO IGNITION SWITCH
ARBG1
15A
1139A YEL
S241
1139E YEL
1139B YEL
A9
IGNITION 1
1139C YEL
A10
IGNITION 1
236 YEL/BLK
A4
DRIVER 36 VLR
1400 LT GRN
A5
DRIVER SOURCE SENSE
ARMING SENSOR
2.49kΩ
5.1kΩ
347B WHT
DRIVER INFLATOR MODULE
SIR COIL ASSEMBLY
347A WHT
B9
DRIVER SIDE HIGH
348A DK GRN
B8
DRIVER SIDE LOW
SHORTING BARS
348B DK GRN
349A GRY
9J
349B GRY
1751E BLK
9K
1751G BLK
C200
8.45kΩ
PASSENGER COMPARTMENT DISCRIMINATING SENSOR
FORWARD DISCRIMINATING SENSOR
8.45kΩ
1751F BLK
S242
1751B BLK
A1
GROUND
1751C BLK
A12
GROUND
1751A BLK
6-19-93
PS 17281

DTC 35

(Page 2 of 2)

DISCRIMINATING SENSOR OPEN OR MISSING

Circuit Description:

During normal, non-deployment operation of the SIR system a small amount of current flows through the driver deployment loop. The diagnostic resistors within the arming sensor and the discriminating sensors along with the resistance of the inflator module cause voltage drops within the deployment loop. The DERM monitors the voltage at "Driver Side Low" terminal "B8" to detect shorts or opens within the deployment loop. When the measured voltage is within a specified percentage of "Driver 36 VLR" power supply for 500 milliseconds DTC 35 is set.

DTC Will Set When: The voltage measured at "Driver Side Low" terminal "B8" is within a specified percentage of the "Driver 36 VLR" power supply voltage for 500 milliseconds during "Continuous Monitoring."

Action Taken: DERM turns "ON" the "AIR BAG" warning lamp and sets a diagnostic trouble code.

DTC Will Clear When: The voltage measured at "Driver Side Low" terminal "B8" is above or below the percentage of "Driver 36 VLR" power supply voltage which sets DTC 35.

DTC Chart Test Description: Number(s) below refer to circled number(s) on the diagnostic chart.

5. This test checks for an open in the discriminating sensor interconnect circuit.
6. This test checks for a partial short inside the arming sensor.

Diagnostic Aids: An intermittent condition is likely to be an improper connection at any of the discriminating sensor terminals, an open in either ground feed to the discriminating sensors, an open discriminating sensor interconnect circuit, increased resistance of either discriminating sensor or decreased resistance of the arming sensor.

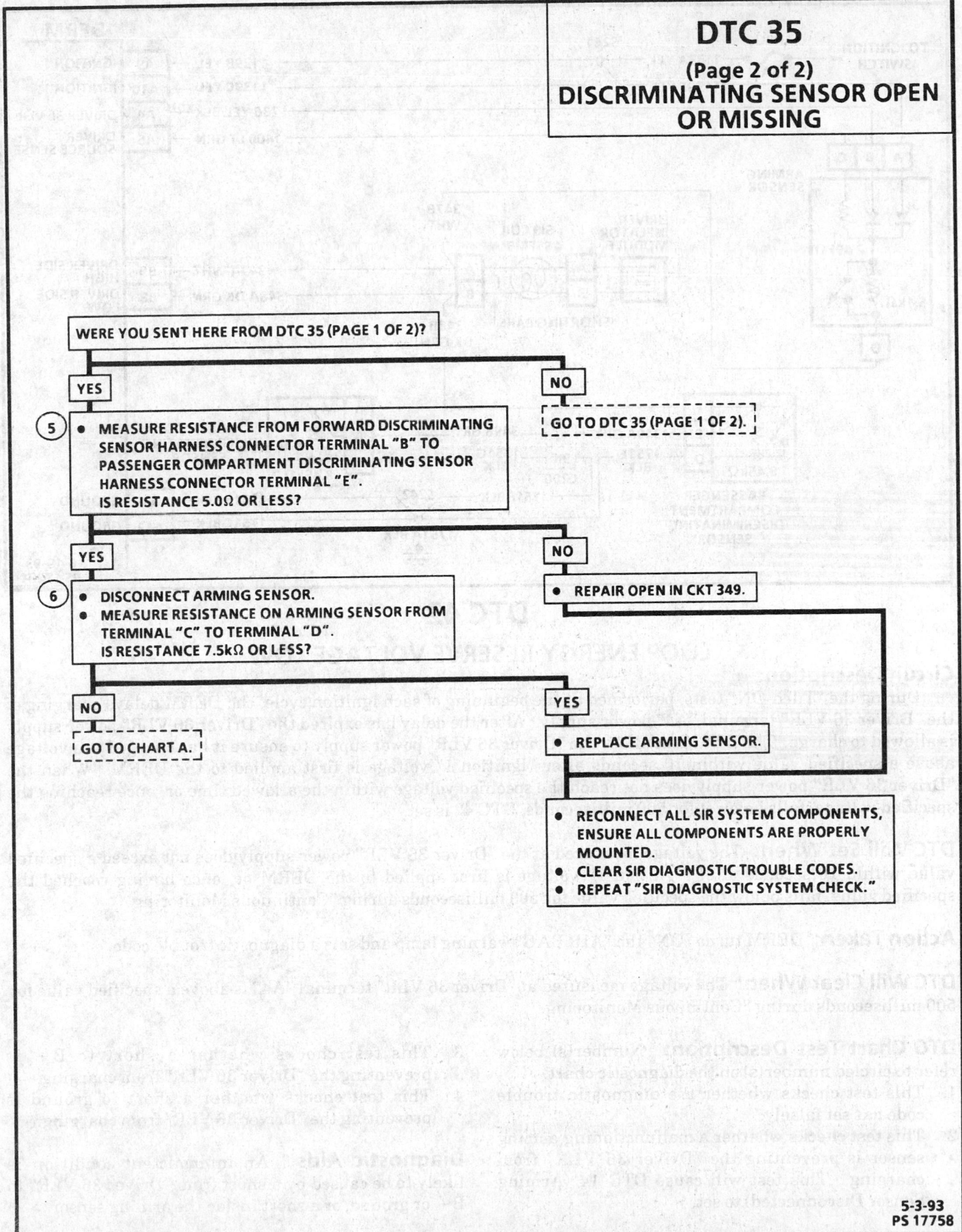

DTC 35
(Page 2 of 2)
DISCRIMINATING SENSOR OPEN OR MISSING

WERE YOU SENT HERE FROM DTC 35 (PAGE 1 OF 2)?

NO → GO TO DTC 35 (PAGE 1 OF 2).

YES ↓

5
- MEASURE RESISTANCE FROM FORWARD DISCRIMINATING SENSOR HARNESS CONNECTOR TERMINAL "B" TO PASSENGER COMPARTMENT DISCRIMINATING SENSOR HARNESS CONNECTOR TERMINAL "E".

IS RESISTANCE 5.0Ω OR LESS?

NO →
- REPAIR OPEN IN CKT 349.

YES ↓

6
- DISCONNECT ARMING SENSOR.
- MEASURE RESISTANCE ON ARMING SENSOR FROM TERMINAL "C" TO TERMINAL "D".

IS RESISTANCE 7.5kΩ OR LESS?

NO → GO TO CHART A.

YES →
- REPLACE ARMING SENSOR.

- RECONNECT ALL SIR SYSTEM COMPONENTS, ENSURE ALL COMPONENTS ARE PROPERLY MOUNTED.
- CLEAR SIR DIAGNOSTIC TROUBLE CODES.
- REPEAT "SIR DIAGNOSTIC SYSTEM CHECK."

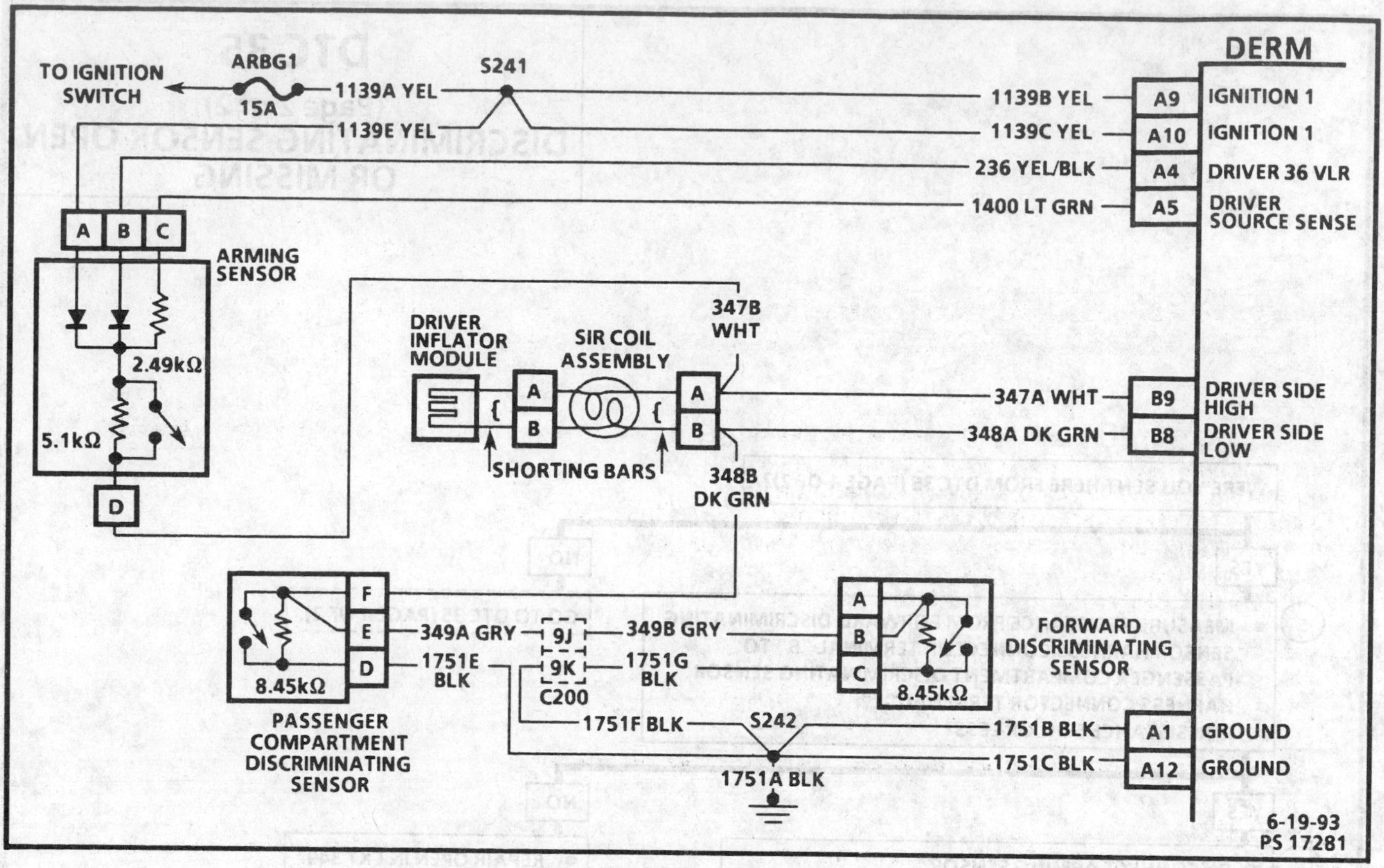
DERM
TO IGNITION SWITCH
ARBG1
15A
S241
1139A YEL
1139E YEL
1139B YEL
1139C YEL
236 YEL/BLK
1400 LT GRN
A9
A10
A4
A5
IGNITION 1
IGNITION 1
DRIVER 36 VLR
DRIVER SOURCE SENSE
A B C
ARMING SENSOR
2.49kΩ
5.1kΩ
D
DRIVER INFLATOR MODULE
SIR COIL ASSEMBLY
347B WHT
347A WHT
348A DK GRN
B9
B8
DRIVER SIDE HIGH
DRIVER SIDE LOW
SHORTING BARS
348B DK GRN
F
E
D
349A GRY
9J
349B GRY
1751E BLK
9K
1751G BLK
C200
8.45kΩ
PASSENGER COMPARTMENT DISCRIMINATING SENSOR
A
B
C
FORWARD DISCRIMINATING SENSOR
8.45kΩ
1751F BLK
S242
1751B BLK
1751C BLK
A1
A12
GROUND
GROUND
1751A BLK
6-19-93
PS 17281

DTC 42

LOOP ENERGY RESERVE VOLTAGE LOW

Circuit Description:

During the "Turn-ON" tests, performed at the beginning of each ignition cycle, the DERM delays charging of the "Driver 36 VLR" terminal "A4" power supply. After the delay has expired the "Driver 36 VLR" power supply is allowed to charge. The DERM monitors the "Driver 36 VLR" power supply to ensure it has charged to a voltage above a specified value within 10 seconds after "Ignition 1" voltage is first applied to the DERM. When the "Driver 36 VLR" power supply does not reach the specified voltage within the allowed time or, once reaching the specified voltage, falls below it for 500 milliseconds, DTC 42 is set.

DTC Will Set When: The voltage measured at the "Driver 36 VLR" power supply does not exceed a specified value within 10 seconds after "Ignition 1" voltage is first applied to the DERM or, once having reached the specified value, falls below the specified value for 500 milliseconds during "Continuous Monitoring."

Action Taken: DERM turns "ON" the "AIR BAG" warning lamp and sets a diagnostic trouble code.

DTC Will Clear When: The voltage measured at "Driver 36 VLR" terminal "A4" is above a specified value for 500 milliseconds during "Continuous Monitoring."

DTC Chart Test Description: Number(s) below refer to circled number(s) on the diagnostic chart.

1. This test checks whether the diagnostic trouble code has set falsely.
2. This test checks whether a malfunctioning arming sensor is preventing the "Driver 36 VLR" from charging. This test will cause DTC 14 (Arming Sensor Disconnected) to set.
3. This test checks whether a short to B+ is preventing the "Driver 36 VLR" from charging.
4. This test checks whether a short to ground is preventing the "Driver 36 VLR" from charging.

Diagnostic Aids: An intermittent condition is likely to be caused by a short from "Driver 36 VLR" to B+ or ground, or a short inside the arming sensor.

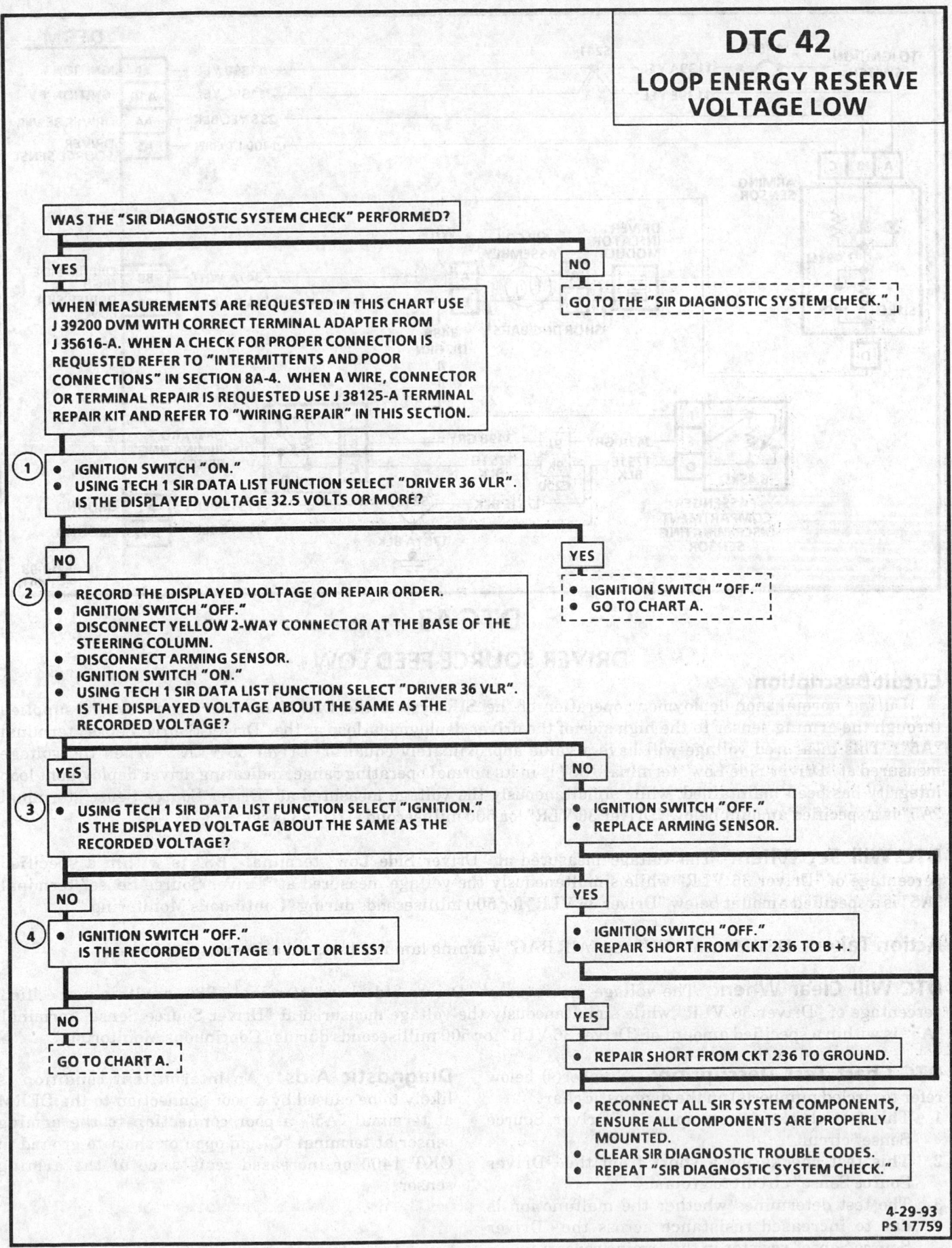

DTC 42
LOOP ENERGY RESERVE VOLTAGE LOW

WAS THE "SIR DIAGNOSTIC SYSTEM CHECK" PERFORMED?

NO

GO TO THE "SIR DIAGNOSTIC SYSTEM CHECK."

YES

WHEN MEASUREMENTS ARE REQUESTED IN THIS CHART USE J 39200 DVM WITH CORRECT TERMINAL ADAPTER FROM J 35616-A. WHEN A CHECK FOR PROPER CONNECTION IS REQUESTED REFER TO "INTERMITTENTS AND POOR CONNECTIONS" IN SECTION 8A-4. WHEN A WIRE, CONNECTOR OR TERMINAL REPAIR IS REQUESTED USE J 38125-A TERMINAL REPAIR KIT AND REFER TO "WIRING REPAIR" IN THIS SECTION.

1
- IGNITION SWITCH "ON."
- USING TECH 1 SIR DATA LIST FUNCTION SELECT "DRIVER 36 VLR". IS THE DISPLAYED VOLTAGE 32.5 VOLTS OR MORE?

YES

- IGNITION SWITCH "OFF."
- GO TO CHART A.

NO

2
- RECORD THE DISPLAYED VOLTAGE ON REPAIR ORDER.
- IGNITION SWITCH "OFF."
- DISCONNECT YELLOW 2-WAY CONNECTOR AT THE BASE OF THE STEERING COLUMN.
- DISCONNECT ARMING SENSOR.
- IGNITION SWITCH "ON."
- USING TECH 1 SIR DATA LIST FUNCTION SELECT "DRIVER 36 VLR". IS THE DISPLAYED VOLTAGE ABOUT THE SAME AS THE RECORDED VOLTAGE?

NO

- IGNITION SWITCH "OFF."
- REPLACE ARMING SENSOR.

YES

3
- USING TECH 1 SIR DATA LIST FUNCTION SELECT "IGNITION." IS THE DISPLAYED VOLTAGE ABOUT THE SAME AS THE RECORDED VOLTAGE?

YES

- IGNITION SWITCH "OFF."
- REPAIR SHORT FROM CKT 236 TO B+.

NO

4
- IGNITION SWITCH "OFF." IS THE RECORDED VOLTAGE 1 VOLT OR LESS?

YES

- REPAIR SHORT FROM CKT 236 TO GROUND.

NO

GO TO CHART A.

- RECONNECT ALL SIR SYSTEM COMPONENTS, ENSURE ALL COMPONENTS ARE PROPERLY MOUNTED.
- CLEAR SIR DIAGNOSTIC TROUBLE CODES.
- REPEAT "SIR DIAGNOSTIC SYSTEM CHECK."

4-29-93
PS 17759

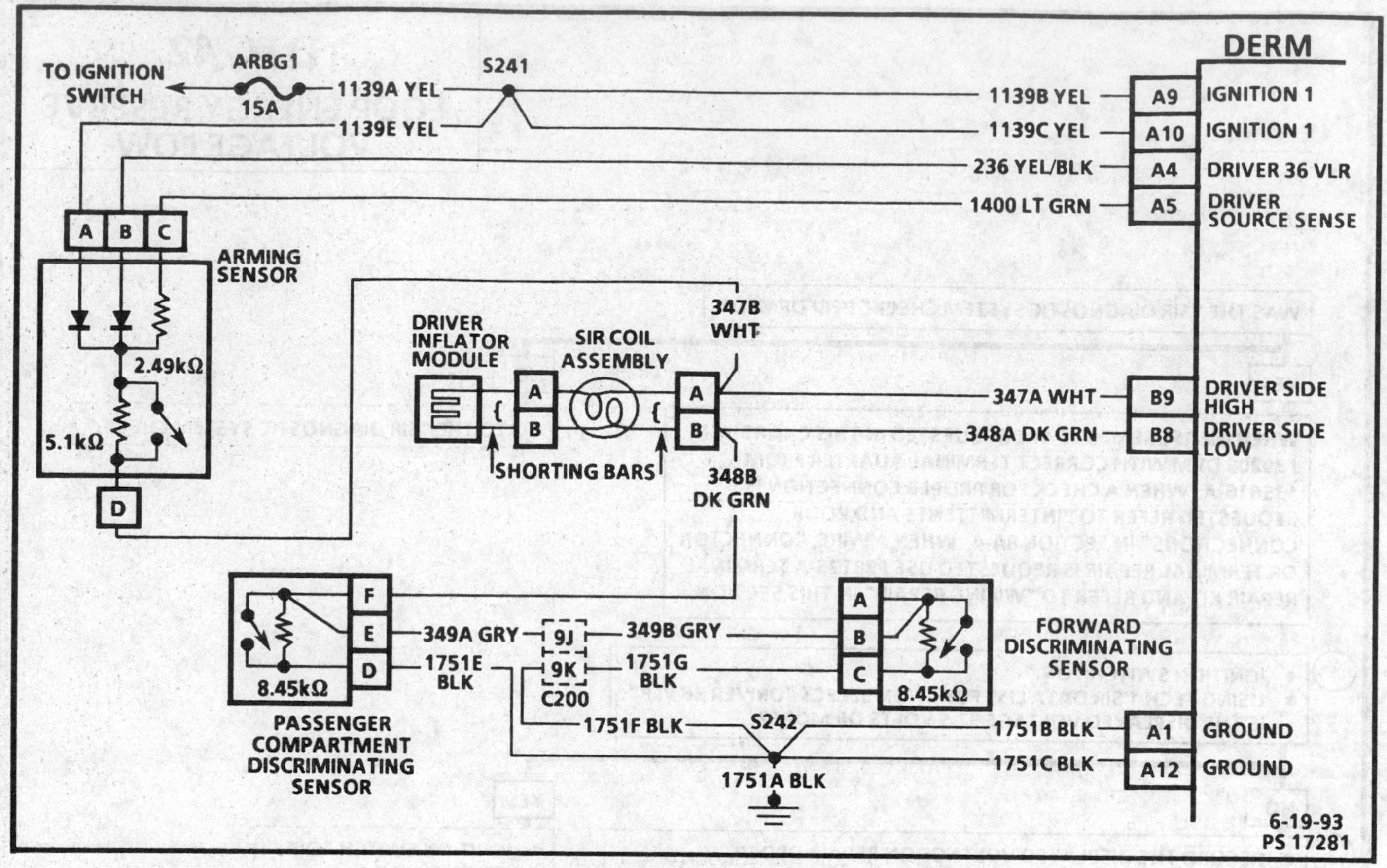
DERM
TO IGNITION SWITCH
ARBG1
15A
1139A YEL
S241
1139E YEL
1139B YEL
1139C YEL
236 YEL/BLK
1400 LT GRN
A9 IGNITION 1
A10 IGNITION 1
A4 DRIVER 36 VLR
A5 DRIVER SOURCE SENSE
ARMING SENSOR
2.49kΩ
5.1kΩ
347B WHT
DRIVER INFLATOR MODULE
SIR COIL ASSEMBLY
SHORTING BARS
348B DK GRN
347A WHT
348A DK GRN
B9 DRIVER SIDE HIGH
B8 DRIVER SIDE LOW
349A GRY
349B GRY
1751E BLK
1751G BLK
9J
9K
C200
8.45kΩ
PASSENGER COMPARTMENT DISCRIMINATING SENSOR
FORWARD DISCRIMINATING SENSOR
1751F BLK
S242
1751A BLK
1751B BLK
1751C BLK
A1 GROUND
A12 GROUND
6-19-93
PS 17281

DTC 43

DRIVER SOURCE FEED LOW

Circuit Description:

During normal, non-deployment operation of the SIR system the DERM monitors the voltage supplied through the arming sensor to the high side of the driver deployment loop at the "Driver Source Sense" terminal "A5". This measured voltage will have a value approximately equal to "Driver 36 VLR." When the voltage measured at "Driver Side Low" terminal "B8" is in its normal operating range, indicating driver deployment loop integrity has been maintained, while simultaneously the voltage measured at "Driver Source Sense" terminal "A5" is a specified amount below "Driver 36 VLR" for 500 milliseconds DTC 43 is set.

DTC Will Set When: The voltage measured at "Driver Side Low" terminal "B8" is within a specified percentage of "Driver 36 VLR" while simultaneously the voltage measured at "Driver Source Sense" terminal "A5" is a specified amount below "Driver 36 VLR" for 500 milliseconds during "Continuous Monitoring."

Action Taken: DERM turns "ON" the "AIR BAG" warning lamp and sets a diagnostic trouble code.

DTC Will Clear When: The voltage measured at "Driver Side Low" terminal "B8" is within a specified percentage of "Driver 36 VLR" while simultaneously the voltage measured at "Driver Source Sense" terminal "A5" is within a specified amount of "Driver 36 VLR" for 500 milliseconds during "Continuous Monitoring."

DTC Chart Test Description: Number(s) below refer to circled number(s) on the diagnostic chart.

1. This test checks for an open in "Driver Source Sense" circuit.
2. This test checks for a short from the "Driver Source Sense" circuit to ground.
3. The test determines whether the malfunction is due to increased resistance across the "Driver Source Sense" resistor in the arming sensor.

Diagnostic Aids: An intermittent condition is likely to be caused by a poor connection to the DERM at terminal "A5", a poor connection to the arming sensor at terminal "C", an open or short to ground in CKT 1400 or increased resistance of the arming sensor.

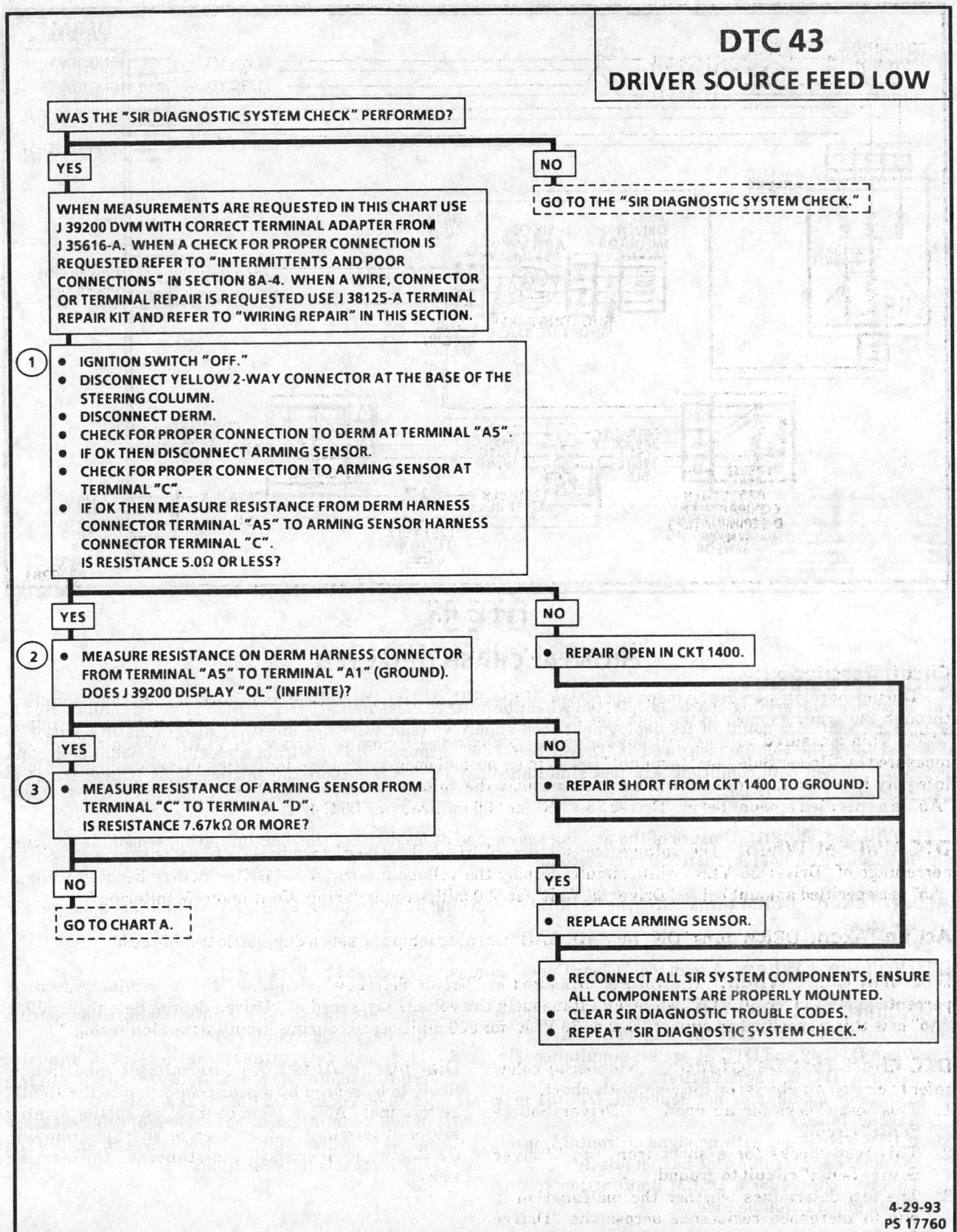

DTC 43
DRIVER SOURCE FEED LOW

WAS THE "SIR DIAGNOSTIC SYSTEM CHECK" PERFORMED?

NO
GO TO THE "SIR DIAGNOSTIC SYSTEM CHECK."

YES

WHEN MEASUREMENTS ARE REQUESTED IN THIS CHART USE J 39200 DVM WITH CORRECT TERMINAL ADAPTER FROM J 35616-A. WHEN A CHECK FOR PROPER CONNECTION IS REQUESTED REFER TO "INTERMITTENTS AND POOR CONNECTIONS" IN SECTION 8A-4. WHEN A WIRE, CONNECTOR OR TERMINAL REPAIR IS REQUESTED USE J 38125-A TERMINAL REPAIR KIT AND REFER TO "WIRING REPAIR" IN THIS SECTION.

(1)
- IGNITION SWITCH "OFF."
- DISCONNECT YELLOW 2-WAY CONNECTOR AT THE BASE OF THE STEERING COLUMN.
- DISCONNECT DERM.
- CHECK FOR PROPER CONNECTION TO DERM AT TERMINAL "A5".
- IF OK THEN DISCONNECT ARMING SENSOR.
- CHECK FOR PROPER CONNECTION TO ARMING SENSOR AT TERMINAL "C".
- IF OK THEN MEASURE RESISTANCE FROM DERM HARNESS CONNECTOR TERMINAL "A5" TO ARMING SENSOR HARNESS CONNECTOR TERMINAL "C".

IS RESISTANCE 5.0Ω OR LESS?

NO
- REPAIR OPEN IN CKT 1400.

YES

(2)
- MEASURE RESISTANCE ON DERM HARNESS CONNECTOR FROM TERMINAL "A5" TO TERMINAL "A1" (GROUND).

DOES J 39200 DISPLAY "OL" (INFINITE)?

NO
- REPAIR SHORT FROM CKT 1400 TO GROUND.

YES

(3)
- MEASURE RESISTANCE OF ARMING SENSOR FROM TERMINAL "C" TO TERMINAL "D".

IS RESISTANCE 7.67kΩ OR MORE?

NO
GO TO CHART A.

YES
- REPLACE ARMING SENSOR.

- RECONNECT ALL SIR SYSTEM COMPONENTS, ENSURE ALL COMPONENTS ARE PROPERLY MOUNTED.
- CLEAR SIR DIAGNOSTIC TROUBLE CODES.
- REPEAT "SIR DIAGNOSTIC SYSTEM CHECK."

4-29-93
PS 17760

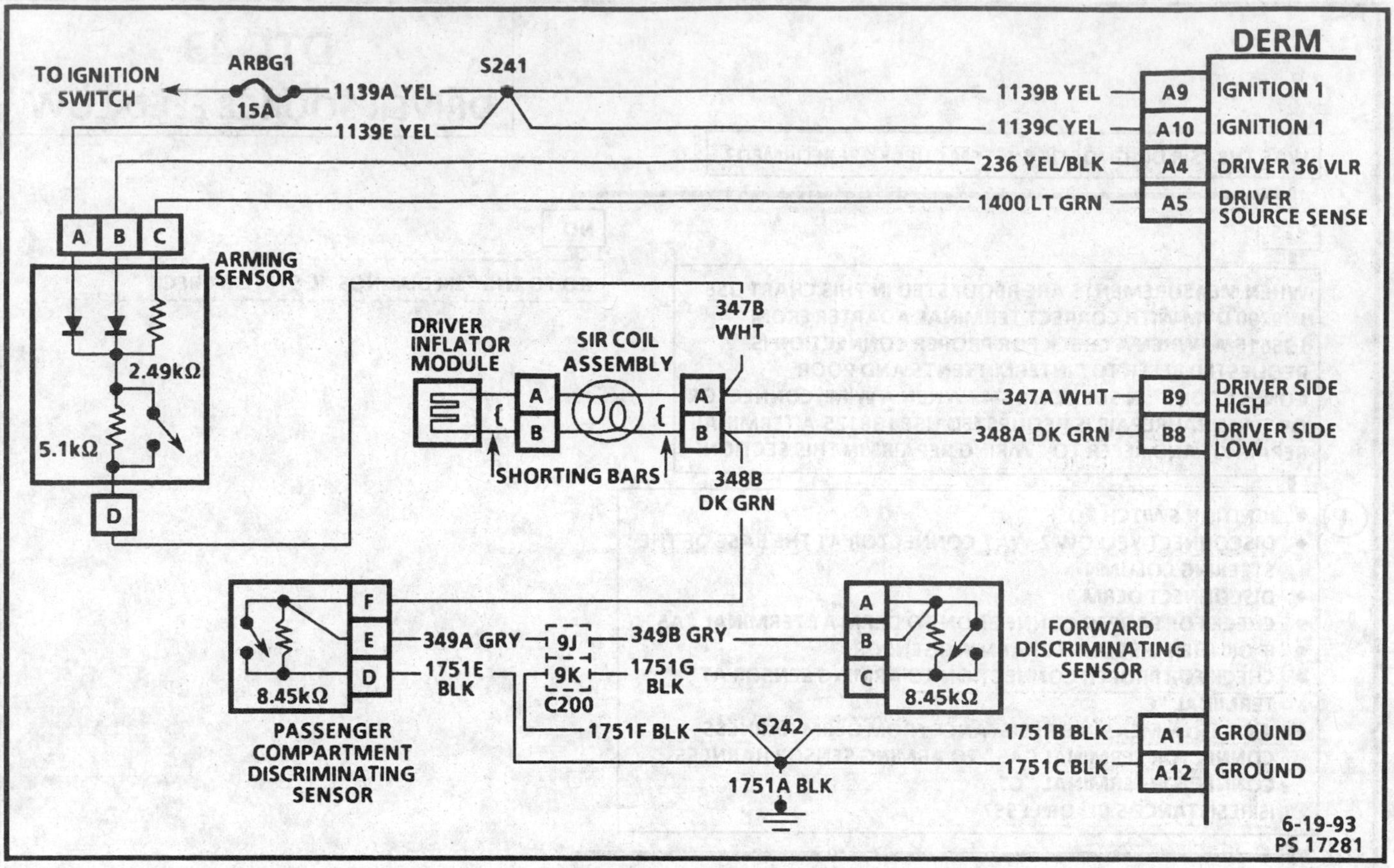
DERM
TO IGNITION SWITCH
ARBG1
15A
S241
1139A YEL
1139E YEL
1139B YEL
1139C YEL
236 YEL/BLK
1400 LT GRN
A9 IGNITION 1
A10 IGNITION 1
A4 DRIVER 36 VLR
A5 DRIVER SOURCE SENSE
ARMING SENSOR
2.49kΩ
5.1kΩ
DRIVER INFLATOR MODULE
SIR COIL ASSEMBLY
SHORTING BARS
347B WHT
348B DK GRN
347A WHT
348A DK GRN
B9 DRIVER SIDE HIGH
B8 DRIVER SIDE LOW
349A GRY
349B GRY
1751E BLK
1751G BLK
9J
9K
C200
8.45kΩ
PASSENGER COMPARTMENT DISCRIMINATING SENSOR
FORWARD DISCRIMINATING SENSOR
1751F BLK
S242
1751B BLK
1751C BLK
1751A BLK
A1 GROUND
A12 GROUND
6-19-93
PS 17281

DTC 51
FRONTAL CRASH DETECTED

Circuit Description:

Closure of the arming sensor is detected when the voltage measured at "Driver Side High" terminal "B9" is within a specified amount of its deployment loop supply voltage. Closure of either discriminating sensor is detected when the voltage measured at "Driver Side Low" terminal "B8" is within a specified amount of ground potential. When both conditions are met simultaneously for not less than 250 microseconds "Crash Data" is recorded and DTC 51 is set.

DTC Will Set When: Closure of the arming sensor and at least one of the discriminating sensors is detected simultaneously for not less than 250 microseconds.

Action Taken: DERM turns "ON" the "AIR BAG" warning lamp, records "Crash Data," and sets a diagnostic trouble code.

DTC Will Clear When: A scan tool "Clear Codes" command is received by the DERM.

DTC Chart Test Description: Number(s) below refer to circled number(s) on the diagnostic chart.

1. When DTC 42 and DTC 51 are set simultaneously, perform DTC 42 diagnosis first.
2. If inflator module has not deployed, DTC 51 may have set falsely.
3. If DTC 51 has set with no signs of frontal impact, the diagnostic trouble code has set falsely.
4. This test checks for a DERM malfunction setting the diagnostic trouble code.
5. This test checks for a DERM malfunction setting the diagnostic trouble code.
6. This test determines whether the diagnostic trouble code was set inadvertently during diagnosis or by a DERM malfunction.
7. When a frontal crash has occurred, it is necessary to perform the indicated procedures to ensure the SIR system is fully functional.

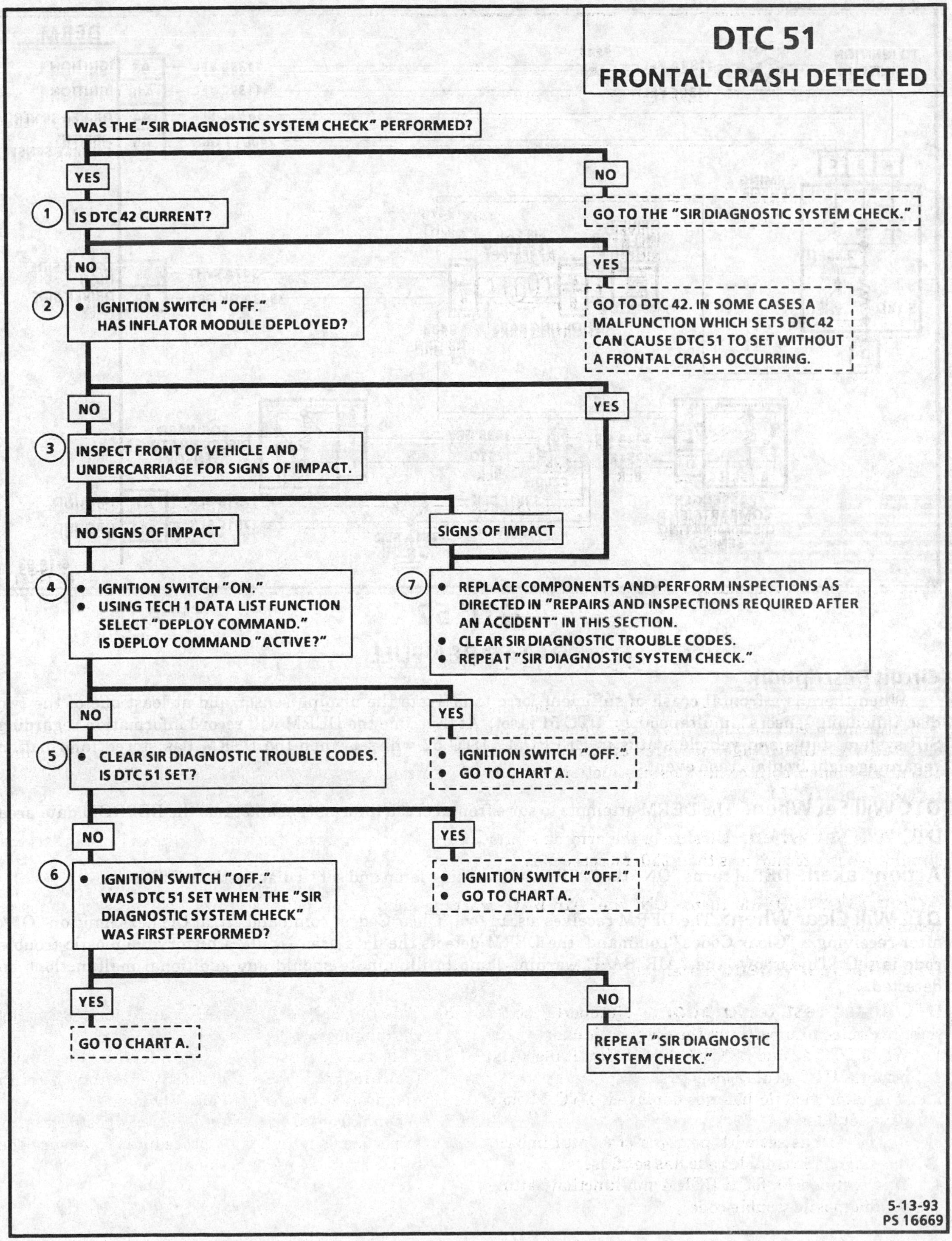
DTC 51
FRONTAL CRASH DETECTED
WAS THE "SIR DIAGNOSTIC SYSTEM CHECK" PERFORMED?
YES
NO
GO TO THE "SIR DIAGNOSTIC SYSTEM CHECK."
1
IS DTC 42 CURRENT?
NO
YES
GO TO DTC 42. IN SOME CASES A MALFUNCTION WHICH SETS DTC 42 CAN CAUSE DTC 51 TO SET WITHOUT A FRONTAL CRASH OCCURRING.
2
• IGNITION SWITCH "OFF."
HAS INFLATOR MODULE DEPLOYED?
NO
YES
3
INSPECT FRONT OF VEHICLE AND UNDERCARRIAGE FOR SIGNS OF IMPACT.
NO SIGNS OF IMPACT
SIGNS OF IMPACT
4
• IGNITION SWITCH "ON."
• USING TECH 1 DATA LIST FUNCTION SELECT "DEPLOY COMMAND."
IS DEPLOY COMMAND "ACTIVE?"
7
• REPLACE COMPONENTS AND PERFORM INSPECTIONS AS DIRECTED IN "REPAIRS AND INSPECTIONS REQUIRED AFTER AN ACCIDENT" IN THIS SECTION.
• CLEAR SIR DIAGNOSTIC TROUBLE CODES.
• REPEAT "SIR DIAGNOSTIC SYSTEM CHECK."
NO
YES
5
• CLEAR SIR DIAGNOSTIC TROUBLE CODES.
IS DTC 51 SET?
• IGNITION SWITCH "OFF."
• GO TO CHART A.
NO
YES
6
• IGNITION SWITCH "OFF."
WAS DTC 51 SET WHEN THE "SIR DIAGNOSTIC SYSTEM CHECK" WAS FIRST PERFORMED?
• IGNITION SWITCH "OFF."
• GO TO CHART A.
YES
NO
GO TO CHART A.
REPEAT "SIR DIAGNOSTIC SYSTEM CHECK."
5-13-93
PS 16669

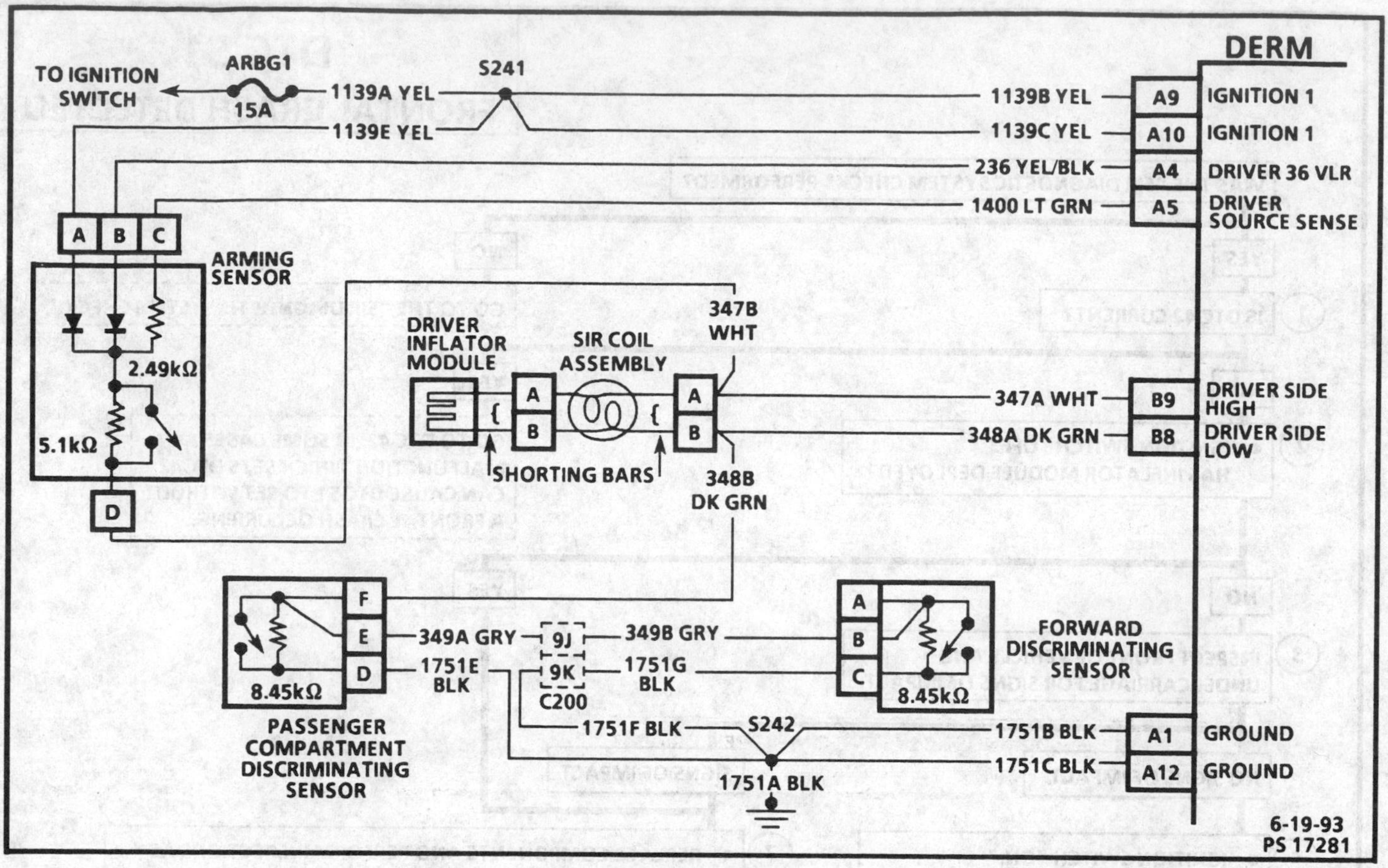
DERM
TO IGNITION SWITCH
ARBG1
15A
S241
1139A YEL
1139E YEL
1139B YEL
1139C YEL
A9 IGNITION 1
A10 IGNITION 1
236 YEL/BLK
A4 DRIVER 36 VLR
1400 LT GRN
A5 DRIVER SOURCE SENSE
A B C
ARMING SENSOR
2.49kΩ
5.1kΩ
D
347B WHT
DRIVER INFLATOR MODULE
SIR COIL ASSEMBLY
A
B
SHORTING BARS
348B DK GRN
347A WHT
B9 DRIVER SIDE HIGH
348A DK GRN
B8 DRIVER SIDE LOW
F
E
D
8.45kΩ
PASSENGER COMPARTMENT DISCRIMINATING SENSOR
349A GRY
9J
9K
C200
349B GRY
1751E BLK
1751G BLK
A
B
C
FORWARD DISCRIMINATING SENSOR
8.45kΩ
1751F BLK
S242
1751A BLK
1751B BLK
A1 GROUND
1751C BLK
A12 GROUND
6-19-93
PS 17281

DTC 52

DATA AREA FULL

Circuit Description:

When there is a frontal crash of sufficient force to activate the arming sensor and at least one of the two discriminating sensors simultaneously, DTC 51 is set. At this time the DERM will record information regarding SIR system status and vehicle status in EEPROM. DTC 52 will set when the DERM has stored information regarding eight frontal crash events.

DTC Will Set When: The DERM attempts to store frontal crash information and finds the EEPROM data area full.

Action Taken: DERM turns "ON" the "AIR BAG" warning lamp and sets a diagnostic trouble code.

DTC Will Clear When: The DERM receives a scan tool "Clear Codes" command. If, at the next ignition "ON" after receiving a "Clear Codes" command, the DERM detects the data area is full, a history diagnostic trouble code is set. This allows the "AIR BAG" warning lamp to illuminate should any additional malfunctions be detected.

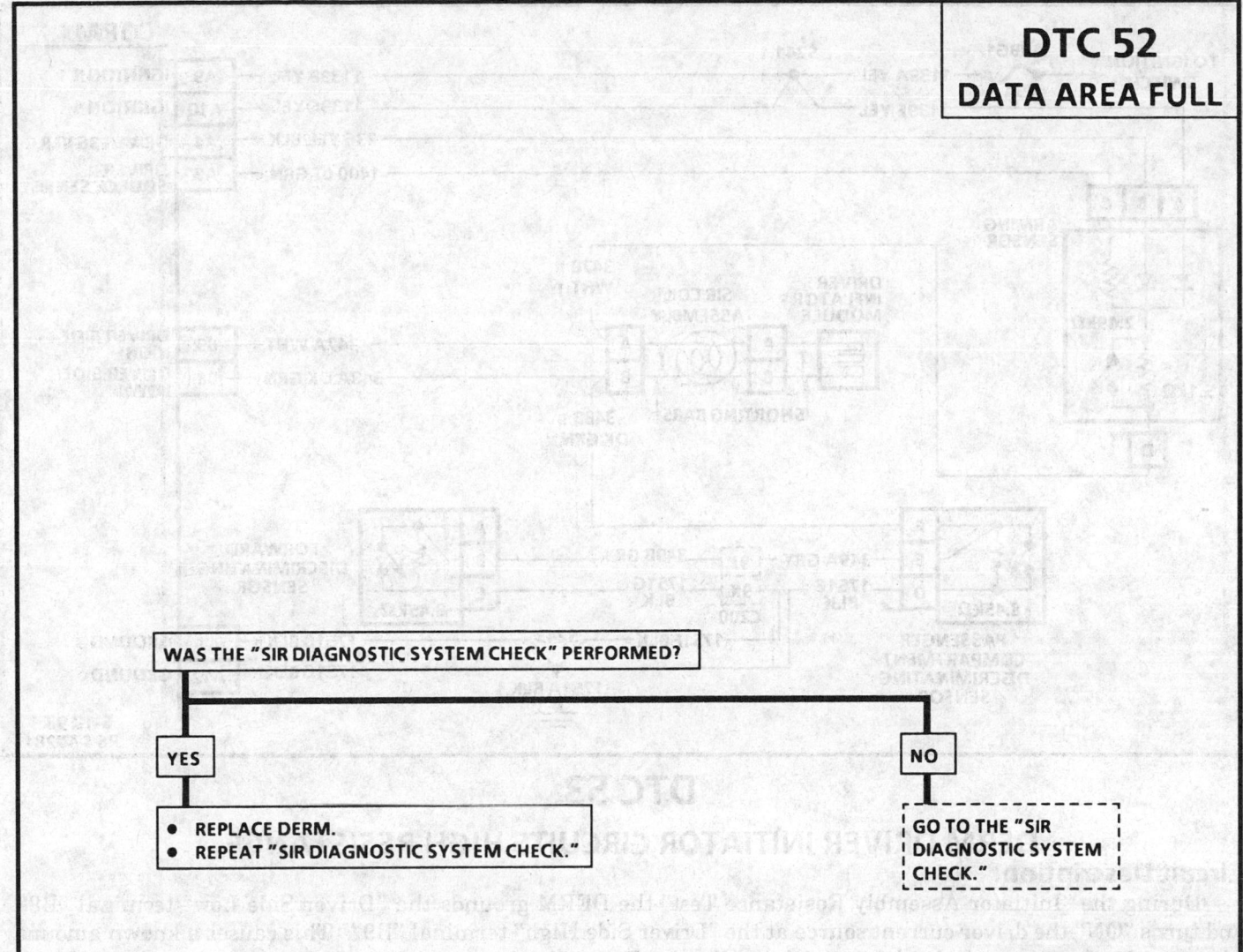

DTC 52
DATA AREA FULL

WAS THE "SIR DIAGNOSTIC SYSTEM CHECK" PERFORMED?

YES

- REPLACE DERM.
- REPEAT "SIR DIAGNOSTIC SYSTEM CHECK."

NO

GO TO THE "SIR DIAGNOSTIC SYSTEM CHECK."

2-16-93
PS 16666

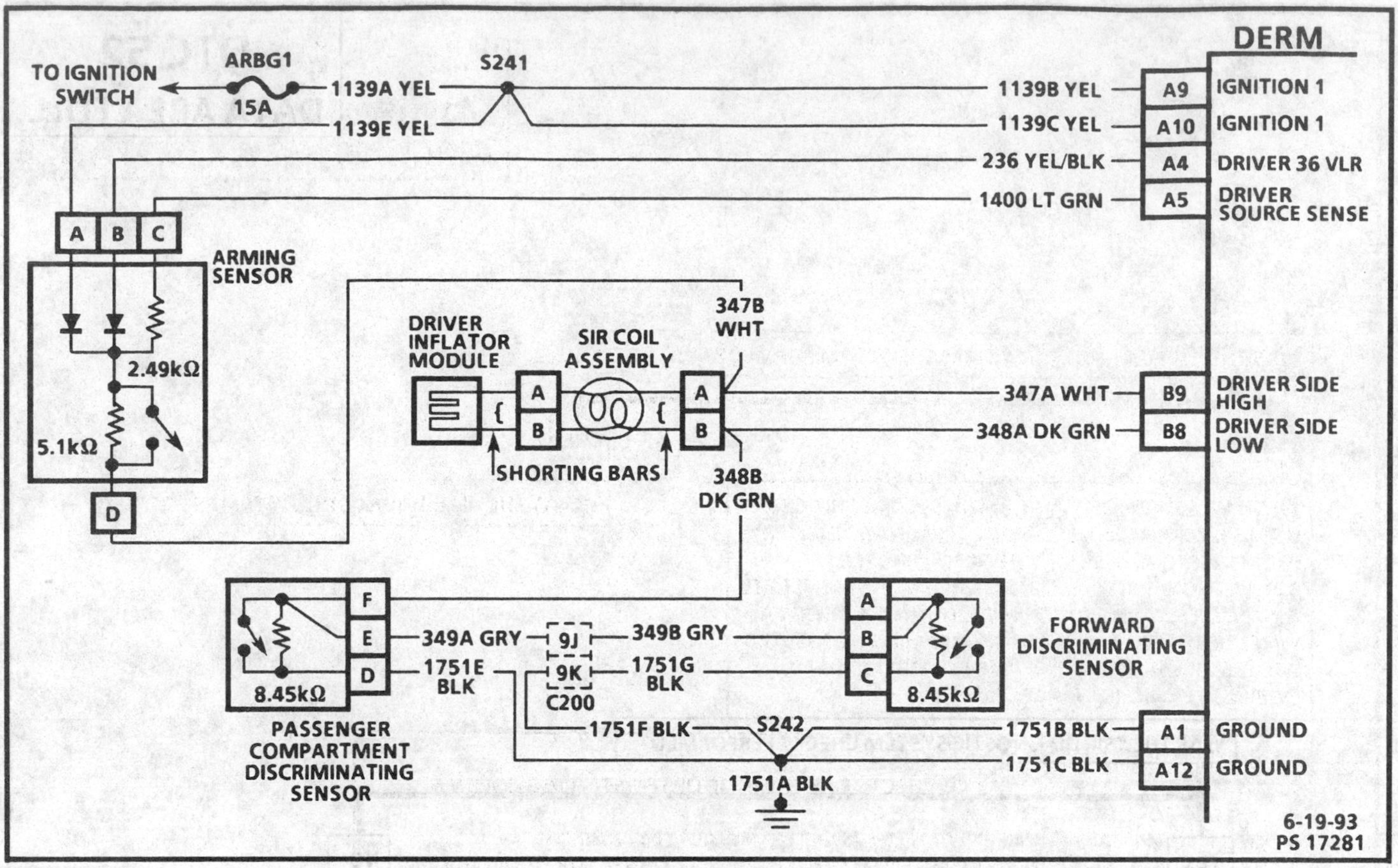
DERM
TO IGNITION SWITCH
ARBG1
15A
S241
1139A YEL
1139E YEL
1139B YEL
1139C YEL
236 YEL/BLK
1400 LT GRN
A9 IGNITION 1
A10 IGNITION 1
A4 DRIVER 36 VLR
A5 DRIVER SOURCE SENSE
ARMING SENSOR
2.49kΩ
5.1kΩ
DRIVER INFLATOR MODULE
SIR COIL ASSEMBLY
SHORTING BARS
347B WHT
348B DK GRN
347A WHT
348A DK GRN
B9 DRIVER SIDE HIGH
B8 DRIVER SIDE LOW
349A GRY
349B GRY
1751E BLK
1751G BLK
9J
9K
C200
8.45kΩ
PASSENGER COMPARTMENT DISCRIMINATING SENSOR
FORWARD DISCRIMINATING SENSOR
1751F BLK
S242
1751A BLK
1751B BLK
1751C BLK
A1 GROUND
A12 GROUND
6-19-93
PS 17281

DTC 53

DERM DRIVER INITIATOR CIRCUITS HIGH RESISTANCE

Circuit Description:

During the "Initiator Assembly Resistance Test" the DERM grounds the "Driver Side Low" terminal "B8" and turns "ON" the driver current source at the "Driver Side High" terminal "B9". This causes a known amount of current to flow through the driver initiator circuit. By monitoring the difference between the voltage at the "Driver Side High" terminal "B9" and the "Driver Side Low" terminal "B8" the DERM calculates the combined resistance of the driver inflator module, SIR coil assembly, harness wiring CKTs 347A and 348A and connector terminal contact.

DTC Will Set When: The voltage difference between "Driver Side High" terminal "B9" and "Driver Side Low" terminal "B8" is above a specified value and the voltage at "Driver Side Low" is within a specified range. This test is run once each ignition cycle during the "Initiator Assembly Resistance Test" when: 1) No "higher priority faults" are detected during "Turn-ON," 2) No "higher priority faults" are detected during "Continuous Monitoring" for one second, 3) No "Crank" signal present, 4) "Ignition 1" voltage is above a specified value.

Action Taken: DERM turns "ON" the "AIR BAG" warning lamp and sets a diagnostic trouble code.

DTC Will Clear When: The ignition switch is turned "OFF."

DTC Chart Test Description: Number(s) below refer to circled number(s) on the diagnostic chart.

1. This test checks whether the malfunction is due to a high resistance or open in the "Driver Side Low" circuit.
2. This test checks whether the malfunction is due to a high resistance or open in the "Driver Side High" circuit.

Diagnostic Aids: An intermittent condition is likely to be caused by a poor connection at DERM terminal "B8" or "B9", an open in CKT 347A or an open in CKT 348A. The test for this diagnostic trouble code is only run while the "AIR BAG" warning lamp is performing the bulb check. When a scan tool "Clear Codes" command is issued and the malfunction is still present, the DTC will not reappear until the next ignition cycle.

DTC 53
DERM DRIVER INITIATOR CIRCUITS HIGH RESISTANCE

WAS THE "SIR DIAGNOSTIC SYSTEM CHECK" PERFORMED?

- YES →
- NO → GO TO THE "SIR DIAGNOSTIC SYSTEM CHECK."

WHEN MEASUREMENTS ARE REQUESTED IN THIS CHART USE J 39200 DVM WITH CORRECT TERMINAL ADAPTER FROM J 35616-A. WHEN A CHECK FOR PROPER CONNECTION IS REQUESTED REFER TO "INTERMITTENTS AND POOR CONNECTIONS" IN SECTION 8A-4. WHEN A WIRE, CONNECTOR OR TERMINAL REPAIR IS REQUESTED USE J 38125-A TERMINAL REPAIR KIT AND REFER TO "WIRING REPAIR" IN THIS SECTION.

1
- IGNITION SWITCH "OFF."
- DISCONNECT YELLOW 2-WAY CONNECTOR AT THE BASE OF THE STEERING COLUMN.
- DISCONNECT DERM.
- CHECK FOR PROPER CONNECTION TO DERM AT TERMINALS "B8" AND "B9".
- IF OK, THEN MEASURE RESISTANCE FROM DERM HARNESS CONNECTOR TERMINAL "B8" TO YELLOW 2-WAY CONNECTOR AT THE BASE OF THE STEERING COLUMN TERMINAL "B". IS RESISTANCE 5.0Ω OR LESS?

YES →

2
- MEASURE RESISTANCE FROM DERM HARNESS CONNECTOR TERMINAL "B9" TO YELLOW 2-WAY CONNECTOR AT THE BASE OF THE STEERING COLUMN TERMINAL "A". IS RESISTANCE 5.0Ω OR LESS?

NO →
- REPAIR OPEN OR HIGH RESISTANCE IN CKT 348A.
- RECONNECT ALL SIR SYSTEM COMPONENTS, ENSURE ALL COMPONENTS ARE PROPERLY MOUNTED.
- CLEAR SIR DIAGNOSTIC TROUBLE CODES.
- REPEAT "SIR DIAGNOSTIC SYSTEM CHECK."

YES → GO TO CHART A.

NO →
- REPAIR OPEN OR HIGH RESISTANCE IN CKT 347A.
- RECONNECT ALL SIR SYSTEM COMPONENTS, ENSURE ALL COMPONENTS ARE PROPERLY MOUNTED.
- CLEAR SIR DIAGNOSTIC TROUBLE CODES.
- REPEAT "SIR DIAGNOSTIC SYSTEM CHECK."

4-30-93
PS 17761

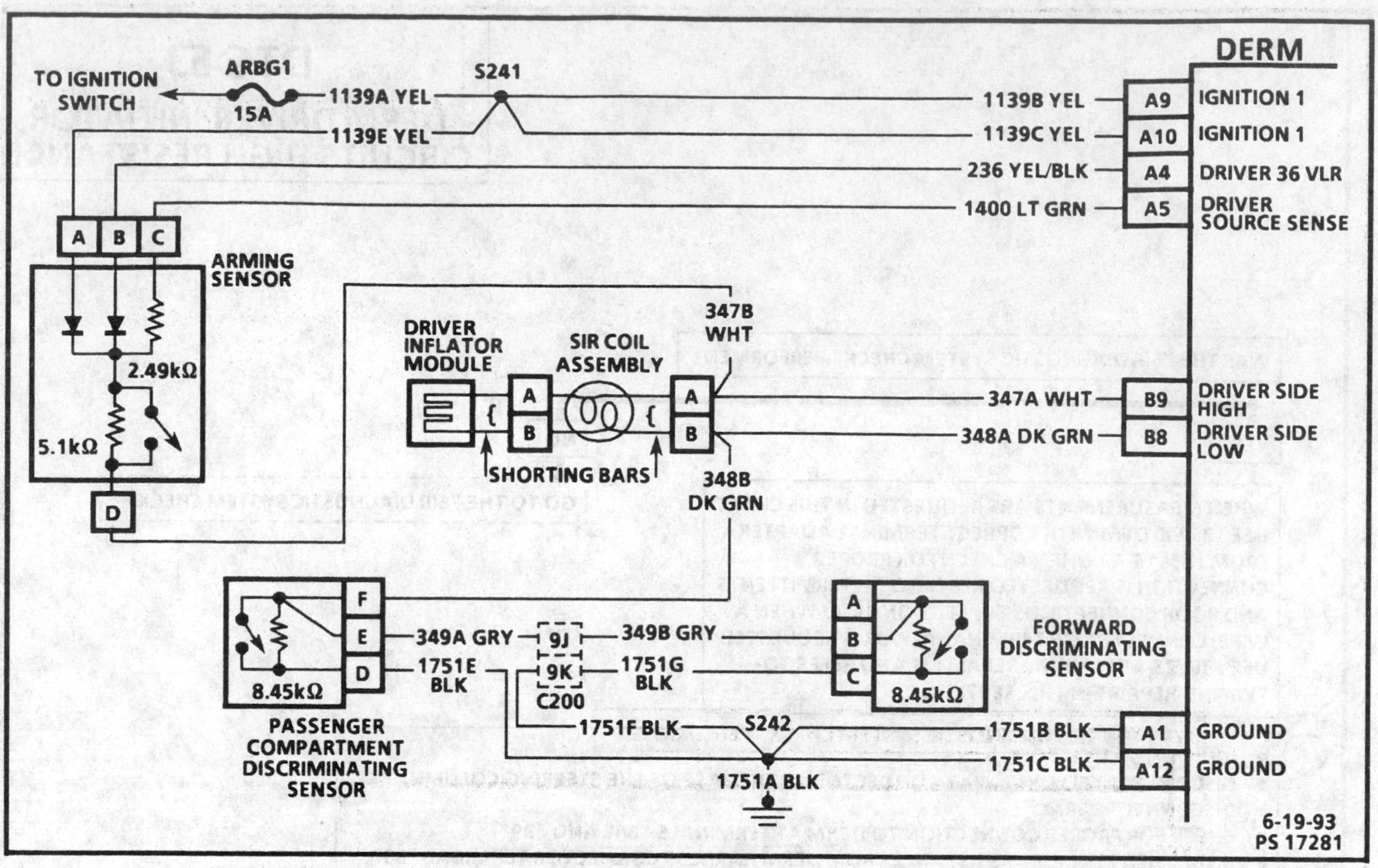
DERM
TO IGNITION SWITCH
ARBG1
15A
1139A YEL
1139E YEL
S241
1139B YEL
1139C YEL
236 YEL/BLK
1400 LT GRN
A9
A10
A4
A5
IGNITION 1
IGNITION 1
DRIVER 36 VLR
DRIVER SOURCE SENSE
A
B
C
ARMING SENSOR
2.49kΩ
5.1kΩ
D
DRIVER INFLATOR MODULE
SIR COIL ASSEMBLY
SHORTING BARS
347B WHT
348B DK GRN
347A WHT
348A DK GRN
B9
B8
DRIVER SIDE HIGH
DRIVER SIDE LOW
F
E
D
8.45kΩ
349A GRY
1751E BLK
9J
9K
C200
349B GRY
1751G BLK
PASSENGER COMPARTMENT DISCRIMINATING SENSOR
FORWARD DISCRIMINATING SENSOR
8.45kΩ
1751F BLK
S242
1751B BLK
1751C BLK
1751A BLK
A1
A12
GROUND
GROUND
6-19-93
PS 17281

DTC 55

DERM INCOMPATIBILITY

Circuit Description:

When "Ignition 1" voltage is first applied to the DERM it will perform "Turn-ON" tests followed by "Continuous Monitoring" for one second. The DERM also monitors "Driver Side Low" terminal "B8" to ensure that voltage is being applied to the inflator module and monitors "Driver Source Sense" terminal "A5" to ensure that "Driver 36 VLR" is supplying voltage to the deployment loop. Ground is applied at terminal "B7" (passenger side low for a driver/passenger DERM) and the voltage is measured at "Driver Side Low" and at terminal "A6" (passenger source sense for a driver/passenger DERM). When grounding terminal "B7" grounds "Driver Side Low" or voltage is measured at terminal "A6", DTC 55 is set.

DTC Will Set When: The conditions described above indicate a driver/passenger DERM has been installed in the vehicle. This test is run once each ignition cycle during the "Initiator Assembly Resistance Test" when: 1) No "higher priority faults" are detected during "Turn-ON," 2) No "higher priority faults" are detected during "Continuous Monitoring" for one second, 3) No "Crank" signal present, 4) "Ignition 1" voltage is above a specified value.

Action Taken: DERM turns "ON" the "AIR BAG" warning lamp and sets a diagnostic trouble code.

DTC Will Clear When: The ignition switch is turned "OFF."

DTC 55
DERM INCOMPATIBILITY

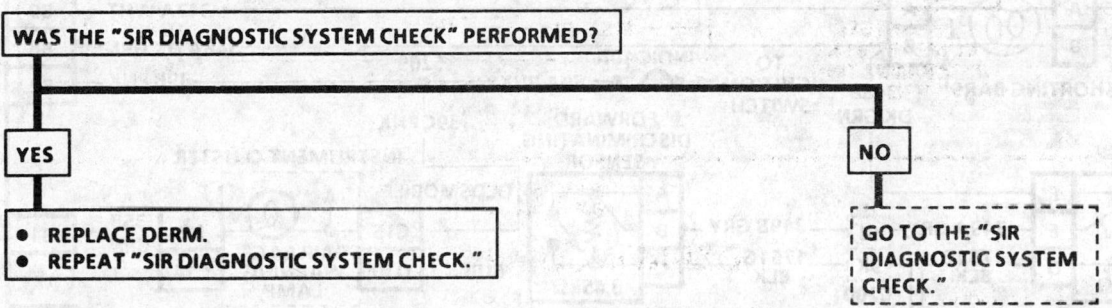

WAS THE "SIR DIAGNOSTIC SYSTEM CHECK" PERFORMED?

YES

- **REPLACE DERM.**
- **REPEAT "SIR DIAGNOSTIC SYSTEM CHECK."**

NO

GO TO THE "SIR DIAGNOSTIC SYSTEM CHECK."

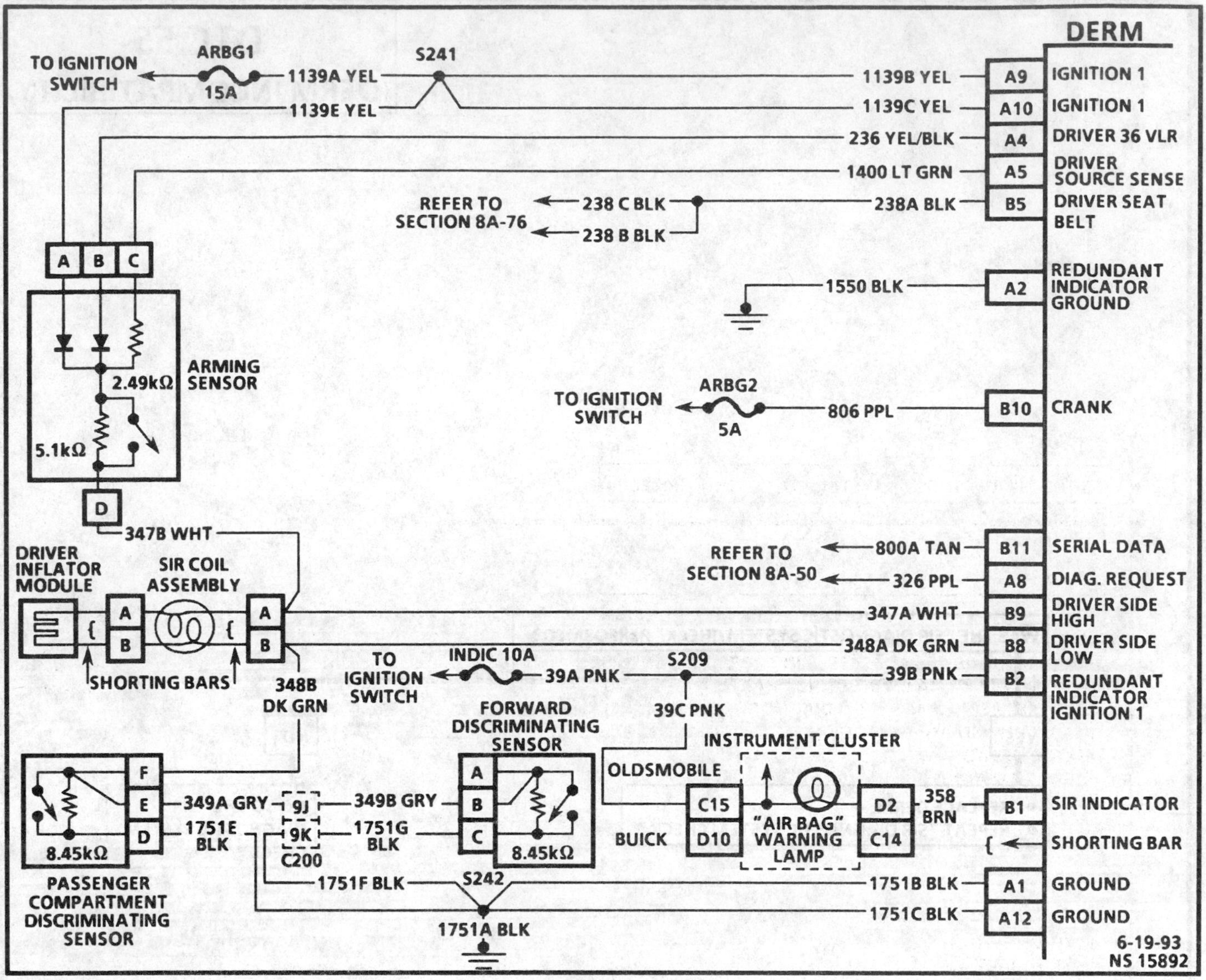
DERM
TO IGNITION SWITCH
ARBG1
15A
1139A YEL
1139E YEL
S241
1139B YEL
1139C YEL
A9
A10
IGNITION 1
IGNITION 1
236 YEL/BLK
A4
DRIVER 36 VLR
1400 LT GRN
A5
DRIVER SOURCE SENSE
REFER TO SECTION 8A-76
238 C BLK
238 B BLK
238A BLK
B5
DRIVER SEAT BELT
A
B
C
1550 BLK
A2
REDUNDANT INDICATOR GROUND
2.49kΩ
ARMING SENSOR
5.1kΩ
TO IGNITION SWITCH
ARBG2
5A
806 PPL
B10
CRANK
D
347B WHT
DRIVER INFLATOR MODULE
SIR COIL ASSEMBLY
REFER TO SECTION 8A-50
800A TAN
B11
SERIAL DATA
326 PPL
A8
DIAG. REQUEST
347A WHT
B9
DRIVER SIDE HIGH
348A DK GRN
B8
DRIVER SIDE LOW
SHORTING BARS
348B DK GRN
TO IGNITION SWITCH
INDIC 10A
39A PNK
S209
39B PNK
B2
REDUNDANT INDICATOR IGNITION 1
39C PNK
FORWARD DISCRIMINATING SENSOR
INSTRUMENT CLUSTER
OLDSMOBILE
F
E
349A GRY
9J
349B GRY
B
C15
D2
358 BRN
B1
SIR INDICATOR
1751E BLK
9K
1751G BLK
C
BUICK
D10
"AIR BAG" WARNING LAMP
C14
SHORTING BAR
8.45kΩ
C200
8.45kΩ
PASSENGER COMPARTMENT DISCRIMINATING SENSOR
1751F BLK
S242
1751B BLK
A1
GROUND
1751C BLK
A12
GROUND
1751A BLK
6-19-93
NS 15892

DTC 61

SIR INDICATOR CIRCUIT FAILURE

Circuit Description:

When the ignition switch is first turned "ON" battery voltage is applied to the "AIR BAG" warning lamp and to the "Ignition 1" input terminals "A9" and "A10". The DERM responds by flashing the "AIR BAG" warning lamp seven times alternating between the primary and redundant lamp drivers. The DERM monitors the primary lamp driver output by comparing the output state at "SIR Indicator" terminal "B1" to the microprocessor commanded state. When "Ignition 1" is above a specified value and the output state does not match the commanded state of the primary lamp driver for 400 milliseconds DTC 61 is set.

DTC Will Set When: "Ignition 1" voltage is above a specified value and the output state at the "SIR Indicator" terminal "B1" does not match the commanded state of the primary lamp driver for 400 milliseconds during "Continuous Monitoring."

Action Taken: DERM attempts to turn "ON" the "AIR BAG" warning lamp using the redundant lamp driver and sets a diagnostic trouble code.

DTC Will Clear When: The ignition switch is turned "OFF."

DTC Chart Test Description: Number(s) below refer to circled number(s) on the diagnostic chart.

1. When the DERM is configured for a serial data controlled warning lamp (smart cluster) DTC 61 will set. Clearing SIR diagnostic trouble codes will reset the DERM allowing the lamp driver in the DERM to control the "AIR BAG" warning lamp.

Diagnostic Aids: Refer to CHART B and CHART C to diagnose warning lamp circuit malfunctions.

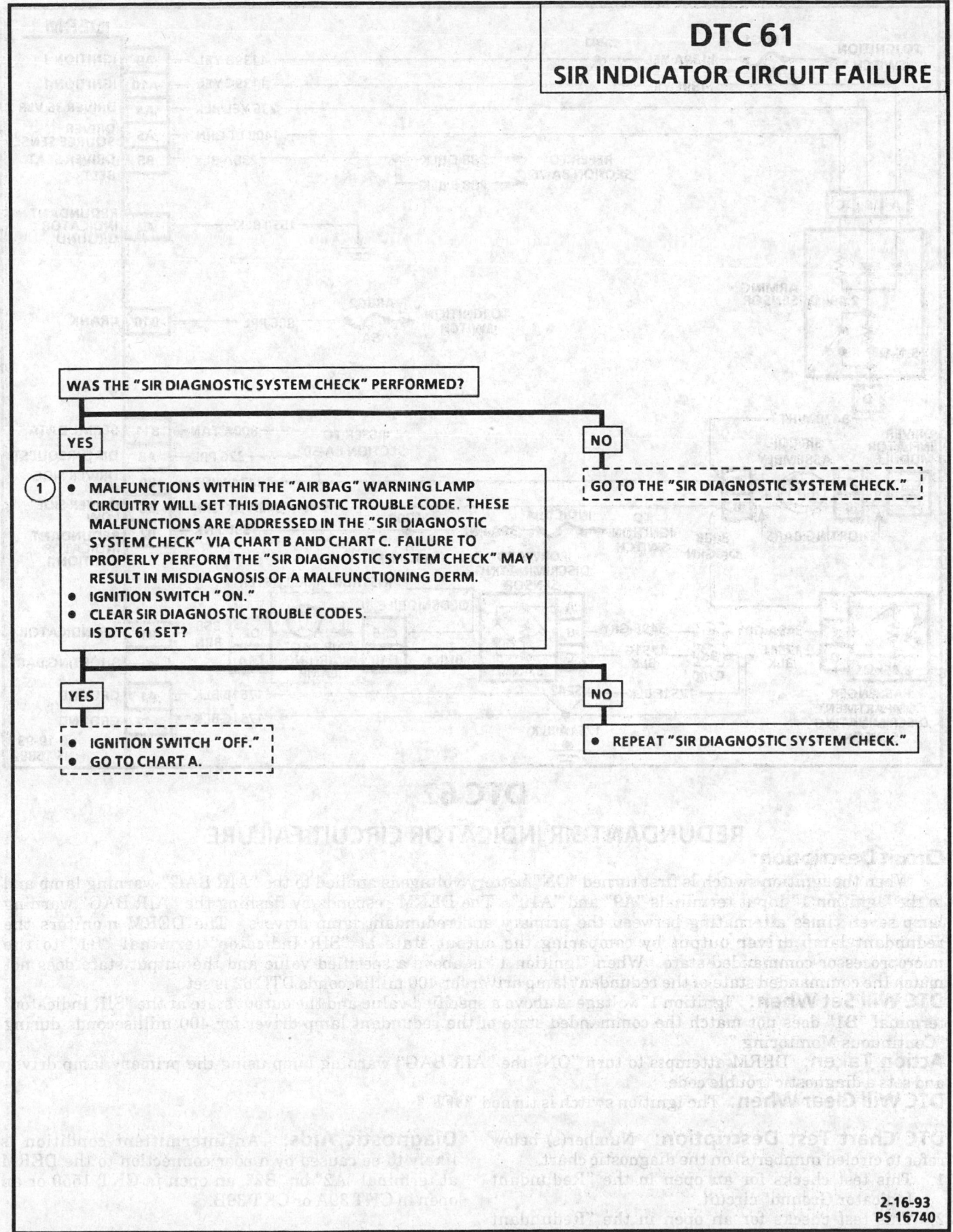

DTC 61
SIR INDICATOR CIRCUIT FAILURE

WAS THE "SIR DIAGNOSTIC SYSTEM CHECK" PERFORMED?

NO
- GO TO THE "SIR DIAGNOSTIC SYSTEM CHECK."

YES

(1)
- MALFUNCTIONS WITHIN THE "AIR BAG" WARNING LAMP CIRCUITRY WILL SET THIS DIAGNOSTIC TROUBLE CODE. THESE MALFUNCTIONS ARE ADDRESSED IN THE "SIR DIAGNOSTIC SYSTEM CHECK" VIA CHART B AND CHART C. FAILURE TO PROPERLY PERFORM THE "SIR DIAGNOSTIC SYSTEM CHECK" MAY RESULT IN MISDIAGNOSIS OF A MALFUNCTIONING DERM.
- IGNITION SWITCH "ON."
- CLEAR SIR DIAGNOSTIC TROUBLE CODES.

IS DTC 61 SET?

YES
- IGNITION SWITCH "OFF."
- GO TO CHART A.

NO
- REPEAT "SIR DIAGNOSTIC SYSTEM CHECK."

2-16-93
PS 16740

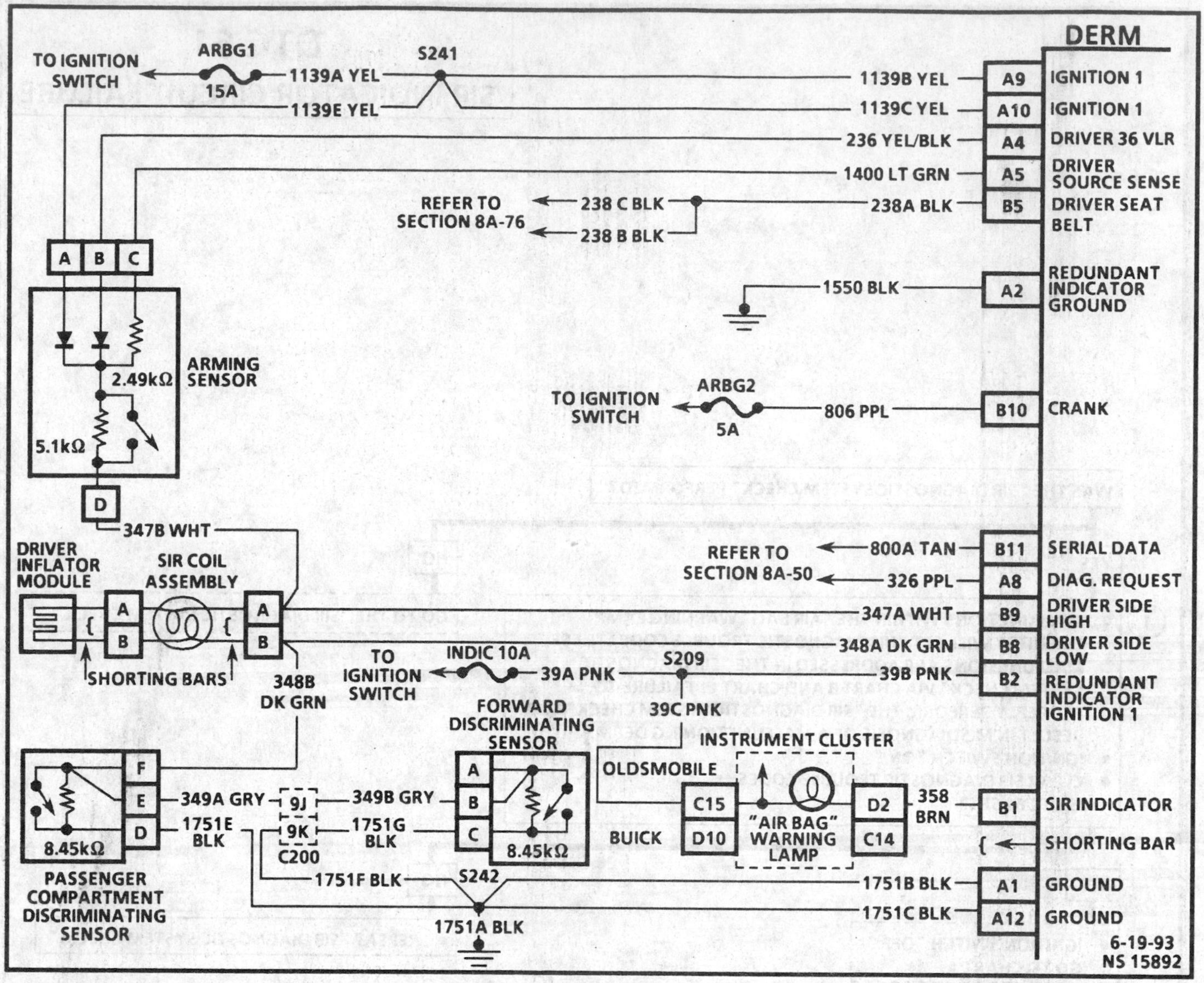
DERM
TO IGNITION SWITCH
ARBG1
15A
1139A YEL
1139E YEL
S241
1139B YEL
1139C YEL
236 YEL/BLK
1400 LT GRN
REFER TO SECTION 8A-76
238 C BLK
238 B BLK
238A BLK
A9
A10
A4
A5
B5
IGNITION 1
IGNITION 1
DRIVER 36 VLR
DRIVER SOURCE SENSE
DRIVER SEAT BELT
A
B
C
1550 BLK
A2
REDUNDANT INDICATOR GROUND
ARMING SENSOR
2.49kΩ
5.1kΩ
TO IGNITION SWITCH
ARBG2
5A
806 PPL
B10
CRANK
D
347B WHT
DRIVER INFLATOR MODULE
SIR COIL ASSEMBLY
SHORTING BARS
REFER TO SECTION 8A-50
800A TAN
326 PPL
347A WHT
348A DK GRN
39B PNK
B11
A8
B9
B8
B2
SERIAL DATA
DIAG. REQUEST
DRIVER SIDE HIGH
DRIVER SIDE LOW
REDUNDANT INDICATOR IGNITION 1
348B DK GRN
TO IGNITION SWITCH
INDIC 10A
39A PNK
S209
39C PNK
FORWARD DISCRIMINATING SENSOR
INSTRUMENT CLUSTER
OLDSMOBILE
BUICK
C15
D10
"AIR BAG" WARNING LAMP
D2
C14
358 BRN
B1
SIR INDICATOR
SHORTING BAR
F
E
D
349A GRY
9J
9K
C200
349B GRY
1751E BLK
1751G BLK
8.45kΩ
8.45kΩ
PASSENGER COMPARTMENT DISCRIMINATING SENSOR
1751F BLK
S242
1751A BLK
1751B BLK
1751C BLK
A1
A12
GROUND
GROUND
6-19-93
NS 15892

DTC 62

REDUNDANT SIR INDICATOR CIRCUIT FAILURE

Circuit Description:

When the ignition switch is first turned "ON" battery voltage is applied to the "AIR BAG" warning lamp and to the "Ignition 1" input terminals "A9" and "A10". The DERM responds by flashing the "AIR BAG" warning lamp seven times alternating between the primary and redundant lamp drivers. The DERM monitors the redundant lamp driver output by comparing the output state at "SIR Indicator" terminal "B1" to the microprocessor commanded state. When "Ignition 1" is above a specified value and the output state does not match the commanded state of the redundant lamp driver for 400 milliseconds DTC 62 is set.

DTC Will Set When: "Ignition 1" voltage is above a specified value and the output state at the "SIR Indicator" terminal "B1" does not match the commanded state of the redundant lamp driver for 400 milliseconds during "Continuous Monitoring."

Action Taken: DERM attempts to turn "ON" the "AIR BAG" warning lamp using the primary lamp driver and sets a diagnostic trouble code.

DTC Will Clear When: The ignition switch is turned "OFF."

DTC Chart Test Description: Number(s) below refer to circled number(s) on the diagnostic chart.

1. This test checks for an open in the "Redundant Indicator Ground" circuit.
2. This test checks for an open in the "Redundant Indicator Ignition 1" circuit.

Diagnostic Aids: An intermittent condition is likely to be caused by a poor connection to the DERM at terminal "A2" or "B2", an open in CKT 1550 or an open in CKT 39A or CKT 39B.

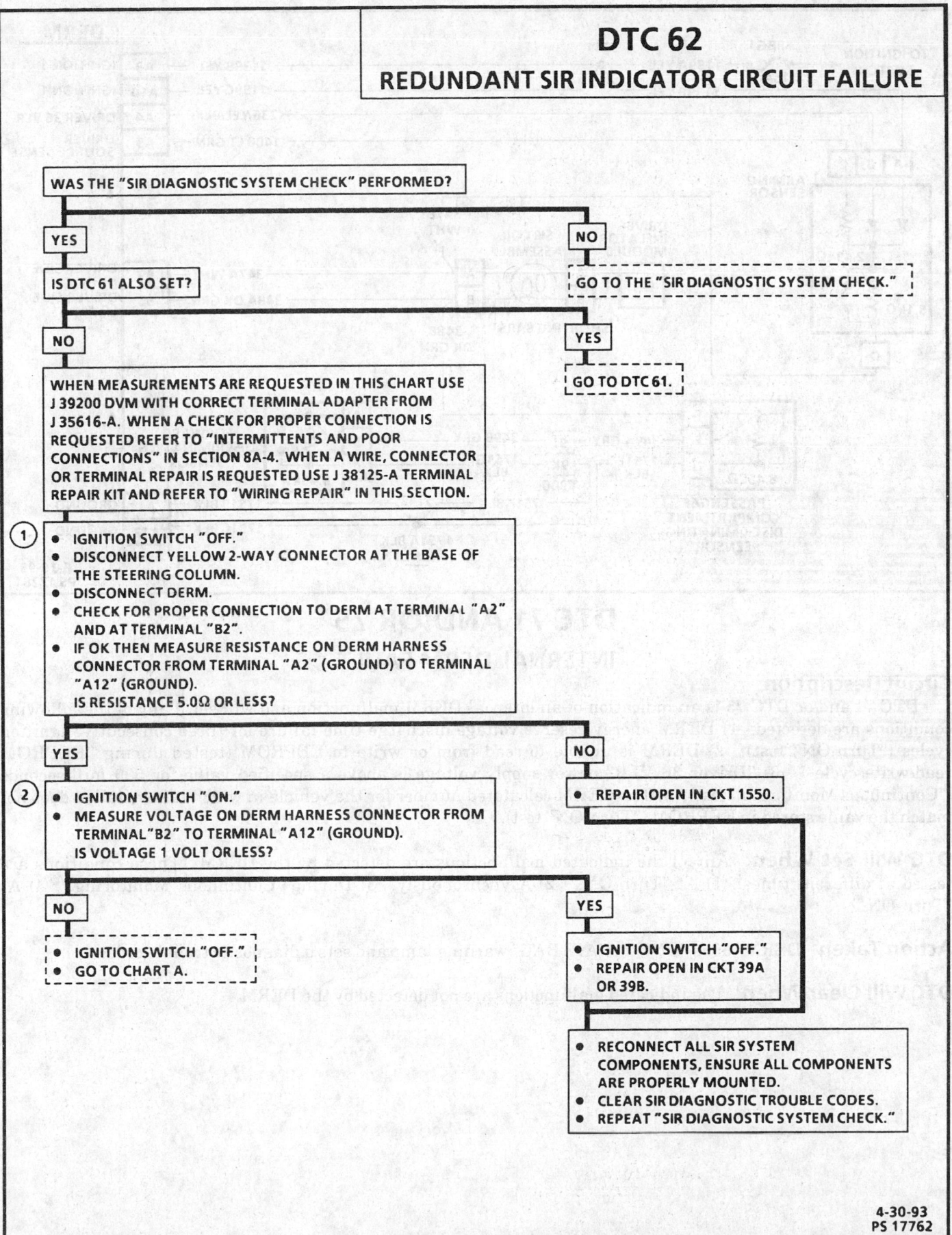

DTC 62
REDUNDANT SIR INDICATOR CIRCUIT FAILURE

WAS THE "SIR DIAGNOSTIC SYSTEM CHECK" PERFORMED?

NO → GO TO THE "SIR DIAGNOSTIC SYSTEM CHECK."

YES → IS DTC 61 ALSO SET?

YES → GO TO DTC 61.

NO →

WHEN MEASUREMENTS ARE REQUESTED IN THIS CHART USE J 39200 DVM WITH CORRECT TERMINAL ADAPTER FROM J 35616-A. WHEN A CHECK FOR PROPER CONNECTION IS REQUESTED REFER TO "INTERMITTENTS AND POOR CONNECTIONS" IN SECTION 8A-4. WHEN A WIRE, CONNECTOR OR TERMINAL REPAIR IS REQUESTED USE J 38125-A TERMINAL REPAIR KIT AND REFER TO "WIRING REPAIR" IN THIS SECTION.

(1)
- IGNITION SWITCH "OFF."
- DISCONNECT YELLOW 2-WAY CONNECTOR AT THE BASE OF THE STEERING COLUMN.
- DISCONNECT DERM.
- CHECK FOR PROPER CONNECTION TO DERM AT TERMINAL "A2" AND AT TERMINAL "B2".
- IF OK THEN MEASURE RESISTANCE ON DERM HARNESS CONNECTOR FROM TERMINAL "A2" (GROUND) TO TERMINAL "A12" (GROUND).

IS RESISTANCE 5.0Ω OR LESS?

NO →
- REPAIR OPEN IN CKT 1550.

YES →

(2)
- IGNITION SWITCH "ON."
- MEASURE VOLTAGE ON DERM HARNESS CONNECTOR FROM TERMINAL "B2" TO TERMINAL "A12" (GROUND).

IS VOLTAGE 1 VOLT OR LESS?

NO →
- IGNITION SWITCH "OFF."
- GO TO CHART A.

YES →
- IGNITION SWITCH "OFF."
- REPAIR OPEN IN CKT 39A OR 39B.

(After repair:)
- RECONNECT ALL SIR SYSTEM COMPONENTS, ENSURE ALL COMPONENTS ARE PROPERLY MOUNTED.
- CLEAR SIR DIAGNOSTIC TROUBLE CODES.
- REPEAT "SIR DIAGNOSTIC SYSTEM CHECK."

4-30-93
PS 17762

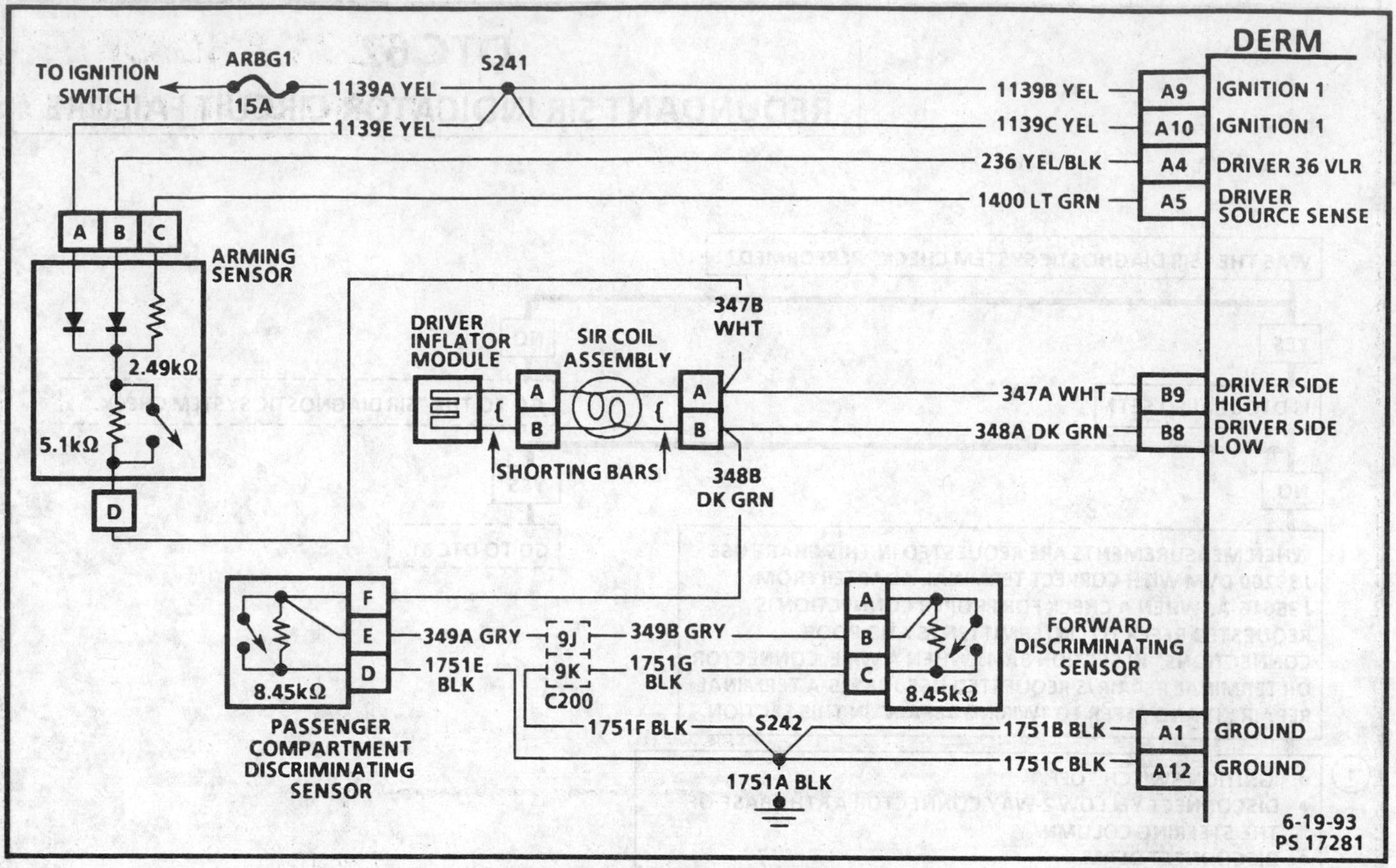

DERM
TO IGNITION SWITCH
ARBG1
15A
1139A YEL
S241
1139E YEL
1139B YEL
A9
IGNITION 1
1139C YEL
A10
IGNITION 1
236 YEL/BLK
A4
DRIVER 36 VLR
1400 LT GRN
A5
DRIVER SOURCE SENSE
A B C
ARMING SENSOR
2.49kΩ
5.1kΩ
D
DRIVER INFLATOR MODULE
SIR COIL ASSEMBLY
347B WHT
347A WHT
B9
DRIVER SIDE HIGH
348A DK GRN
B8
DRIVER SIDE LOW
SHORTING BARS
348B DK GRN
F
E
D
349A GRY
9J
349B GRY
1751E BLK
9K
1751G BLK
C200
8.45kΩ
PASSENGER COMPARTMENT DISCRIMINATING SENSOR
FORWARD DISCRIMINATING SENSOR
8.45kΩ
1751F BLK
S242
1751B BLK
A1
GROUND
1751C BLK
A12
GROUND
1751A BLK
6-19-93
PS 17281

DTC 71 AND/OR 75

INTERNAL DERM FAULT

Circuit Description:

DTC 71 and/or DTC 75 is an indication of an internal DERM malfunction and will set if any of the following conditions are detected: 1) DERM energy reserve voltage discharge time failure for three consecutive ignition cycles ("Turn-ON" test), 2) DERM is unable to read from or write to EEPROM (tested during "EEPROM read/write cycle"), 3) "Driver 36 VLR" power supply voltage is above a specified value for 500 milliseconds ("Continuous Monitoring" test), 4) The DERM calculated number for the vehicle in which it is installed does not match the value stored in EEPROM ("Turn-ON" test).

DTC Will Set When: Any of the indicated malfunctions are detected by the DERM. These conditions are tested at different times: 1) At "Turn-ON," 2) Asynchronously, 3) During "Continuous Monitoring," 4) At "Turn-ON."

Action Taken: DERM turns "ON" the "AIR BAG" warning lamp and sets a diagnostic trouble code.

DTC Will Clear When: The indicated malfunctions are not detected by the DERM.

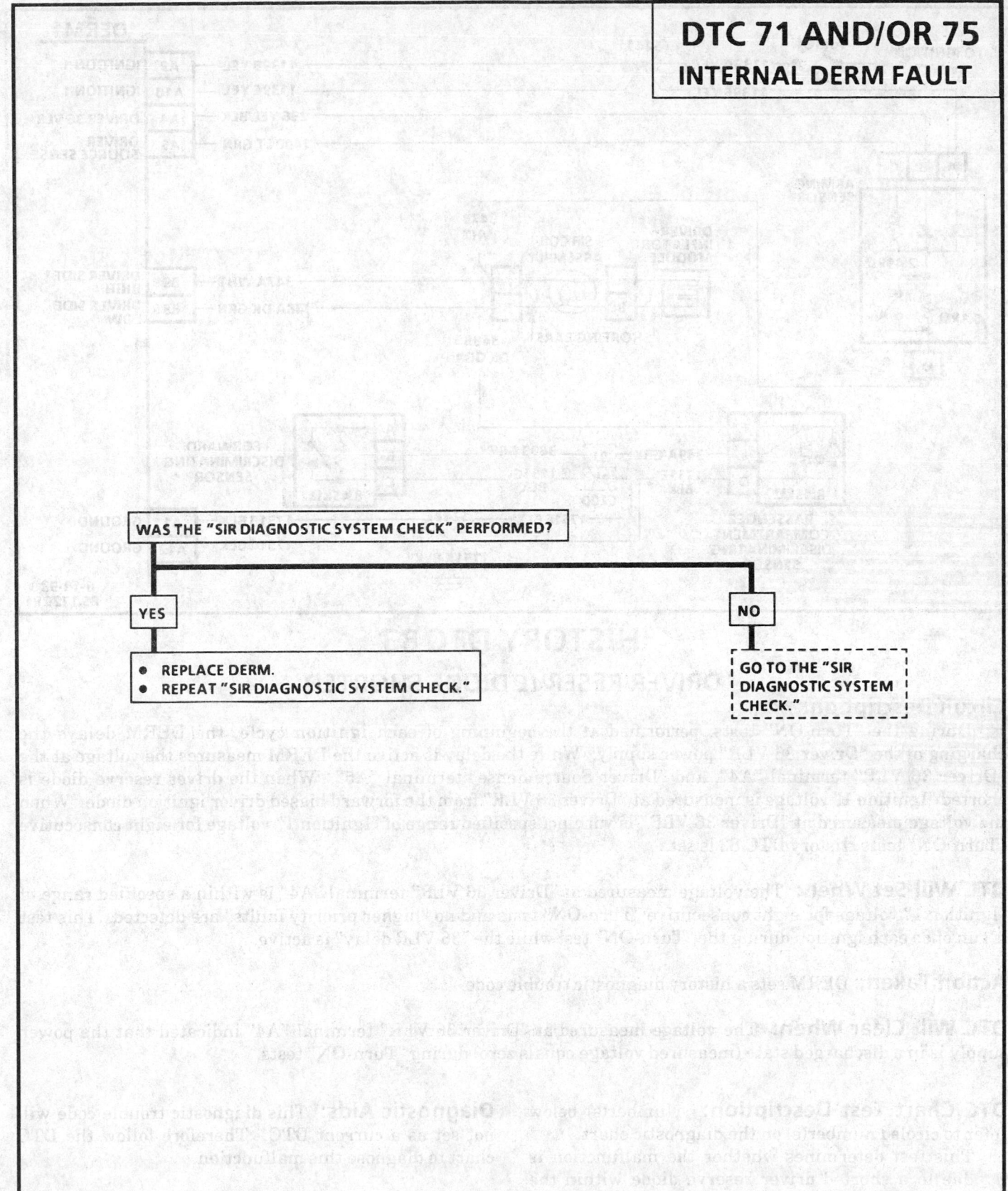

DTC 71 AND/OR 75
INTERNAL DERM FAULT

WAS THE "SIR DIAGNOSTIC SYSTEM CHECK" PERFORMED?

YES

- REPLACE DERM.
- REPEAT "SIR DIAGNOSTIC SYSTEM CHECK."

NO

GO TO THE "SIR DIAGNOSTIC SYSTEM CHECK."

2-16-93
PS 16666

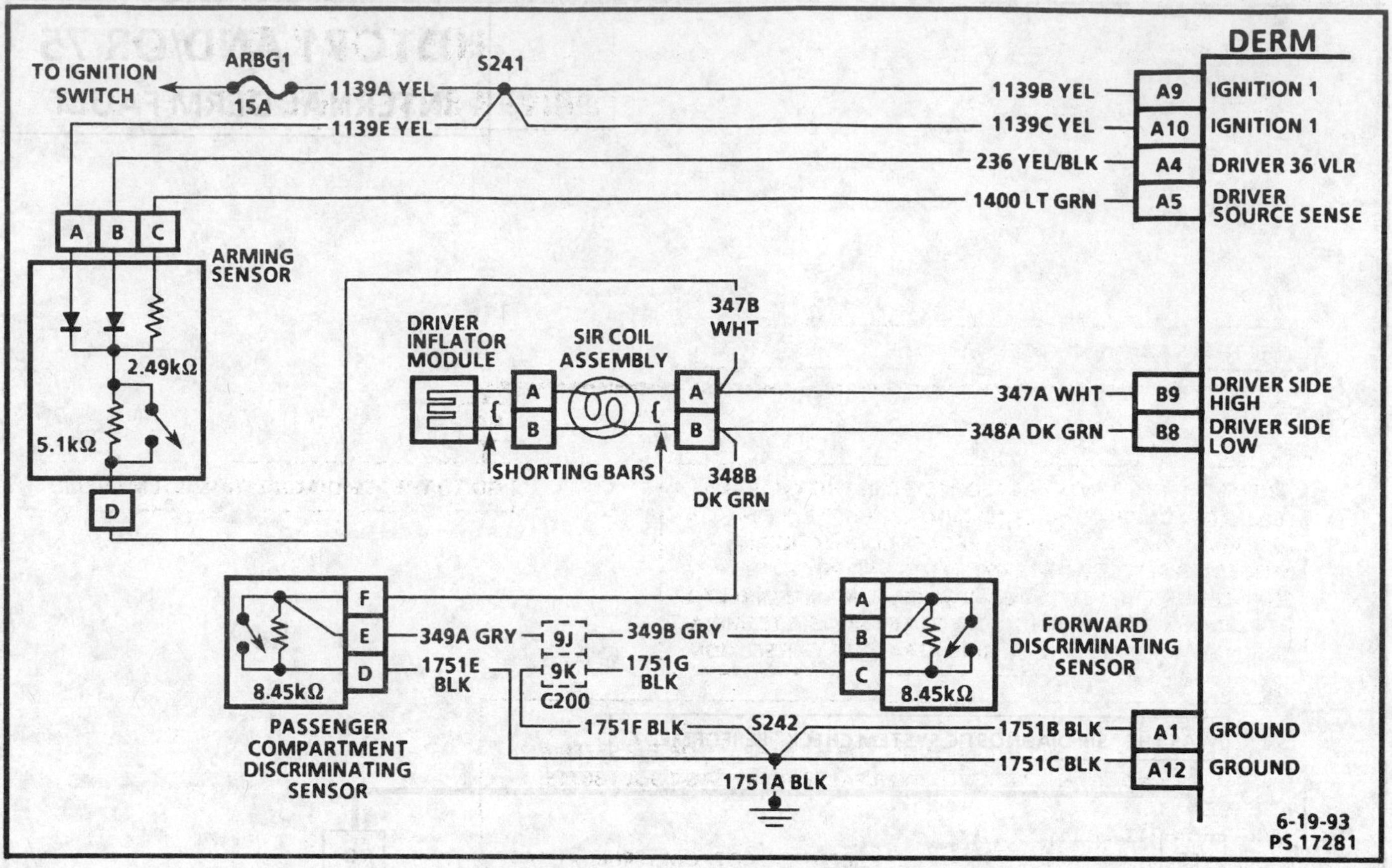
DERM
TO IGNITION SWITCH
ARBG1
15A
S241
1139A YEL
1139E YEL
1139B YEL
1139C YEL
236 YEL/BLK
1400 LT GRN
A9
A10
A4
A5
IGNITION 1
IGNITION 1
DRIVER 36 VLR
DRIVER SOURCE SENSE
A
B
C
ARMING SENSOR
2.49kΩ
5.1kΩ
D
347B WHT
DRIVER INFLATOR MODULE
SIR COIL ASSEMBLY
SHORTING BARS
348B DK GRN
347A WHT
348A DK GRN
B9
B8
DRIVER SIDE HIGH
DRIVER SIDE LOW
F
E
D
8.45kΩ
349A GRY
1751E BLK
9J
9K
C200
349B GRY
1751G BLK
FORWARD DISCRIMINATING SENSOR
PASSENGER COMPARTMENT DISCRIMINATING SENSOR
1751F BLK
S242
1751A BLK
1751B BLK
1751C BLK
A1
A12
GROUND
GROUND
6-19-93
PS 17281

HISTORY DTC 83

DRIVER RESERVE DIODE SHORTED

Circuit Description:

During the "Turn-ON" tests, performed at the beginning of each ignition cycle, the DERM delays the charging of the "Driver 36 VLR" power supply. While the delay is active the DERM measures the voltage at the "Driver 36 VLR" terminal "A4", and "Driver Source Sense" terminal "A5". When the driver reserve diode is shorted "Ignition 1" voltage is measured at "Driver 36 VLR" from the forward biased driver ignition diode. When the voltage measured at "Driver 36 VLR" is within a specified range of "Ignition 1" voltage for eight consecutive "Turn-ON" tests History DTC 83 is set.

DTC Will Set When: The voltage measured at "Driver 36 VLR" terminal "A4" is within a specified range of "Ignition 1" voltage for eight consecutive "Turn-ON" tests and no "higher priority faults" are detected. This test is run once each ignition during the "Turn-ON" test while the "36 VLR delay" is active.

Action Taken: DERM sets a history diagnostic trouble code.

DTC Will Clear When: The voltage measured at "Driver 36 VLR" terminal "A4" indicated that the power supply is in a discharged state (measured voltage equals zero) during "Turn-ON" tests.

DTC Chart Test Description: Number(s) below refer to circled number(s) on the diagnostic chart.

1. This test determines whether the malfunction is due to a shorted driver reserve diode within the arming sensor.

Diagnostic Aids: This diagnostic trouble code will not set as a current DTC. Therefore follow the DTC chart to diagnose this malfunction.

HISTORY DTC 83
DRIVER RESERVE DIODE SHORTED

WAS THE "SIR DIAGNOSTIC SYSTEM CHECK" PERFORMED?

YES

WHEN MEASUREMENTS ARE REQUESTED IN THIS CHART USE J 39200 DVM WITH CORRECT TERMINAL ADAPTER FROM J 35616-A. WHEN A CHECK FOR PROPER CONNECTION IS REQUESTED REFER TO "INTERMITTENTS AND POOR CONNECTIONS" IN SECTION 8A-4. WHEN A WIRE, CONNECTOR OR TERMINAL REPAIR IS REQUESTED USE J 38125-A TERMINAL REPAIR KIT AND REFER TO "WIRING REPAIR" IN THIS SECTION.

1

- IGNITION SWITCH "OFF."
- DISCONNECT YELLOW 2-WAY CONNECTOR AT THE BASE OF THE STEERING COLUMN AND CONNECT TO SIR DRIVER/PASSENGER LOAD TOOL J 38715.
- DISCONNECT DERM.
- IGNITION SWITCH "ON."
- MEASURE VOLTAGE ON DERM HARNESS CONNECTOR FROM TERMINAL "A4" TO TERMINAL "A12" (GROUND).
  IS VOLTAGE 1 VOLT OR LESS?

YES

- IGNITION SWITCH "OFF."
- GO TO CHART A.

NO

- IGNITION SWITCH "OFF."
- DISCONNECT J 38715.
- REPLACE ARMING SENSOR.
- RECONNECT ALL SIR SYSTEM COMPONENTS, ENSURE ALL COMPONENTS ARE PROPERLY MOUNTED.
- CLEAR SIR DIAGNOSTIC TROUBLE CODES.
- REPEAT "SIR DIAGNOSTIC SYSTEM CHECK."

NO (to first question)

GO TO THE "SIR DIAGNOSTIC SYSTEM CHECK."

4-30-93
PS 17763

ON-VEHICLE SERVICE

SERVICE PRECAUTIONS

CAUTION: When performing service on or around SIR components or SIR wiring, follow the procedures listed below to temporarily disable the SIR system. Failure to follow procedures could result in possible air bag deployment, personal injury or otherwise unneeded SIR system repairs.

The DERM in 1993 and previous Driver-Only SIR systems can maintain sufficient voltage to cause a deployment for up to 10 minutes after the ignition switch is turned "OFF," the battery is disconnected, or the fuse powering the DERM is removed.

The DERM in 1993½ and later Driver-Only and the DERM in all Driver-Passenger SIR systems can maintain sufficient voltage to cause a deployment for up to 2 minutes after the ignition switch is turned "OFF," the battery is disconnected, or the fuse powering the DERM is removed.

Many of the service procedures require removal of the "ARBG1" fuse, and disconnection of the inflator module from the deployment loop to avoid an accidental deployment. If the inflator module is disconnected from the deployment loop as noted in the "Disabling the SIR System" procedure that follows, service can begin immediately without waiting for the 10 minute or 2 minute time period to expire.

Disabling the SIR System
Figure 8

↔ Remove or Disconnect

- Turn the steering wheel so that the vehicle's wheels are pointing straight ahead.
- Turn the ignition switch to "LOCK" and remove key.

1. "ARBG1" fuse from I/P fuse block.
2. Lower trim panel, refer to SECTION 8C.
3. Connector Position Assurance (CPA) and yellow 2-way connector at the base of the steering column.

! Important

- With the "ARBG1" fuse removed and ignition switch "ON," the "AIR BAG" warning lamp will be "ON." This is normal operation and does not indicate a SIR system malfunction.

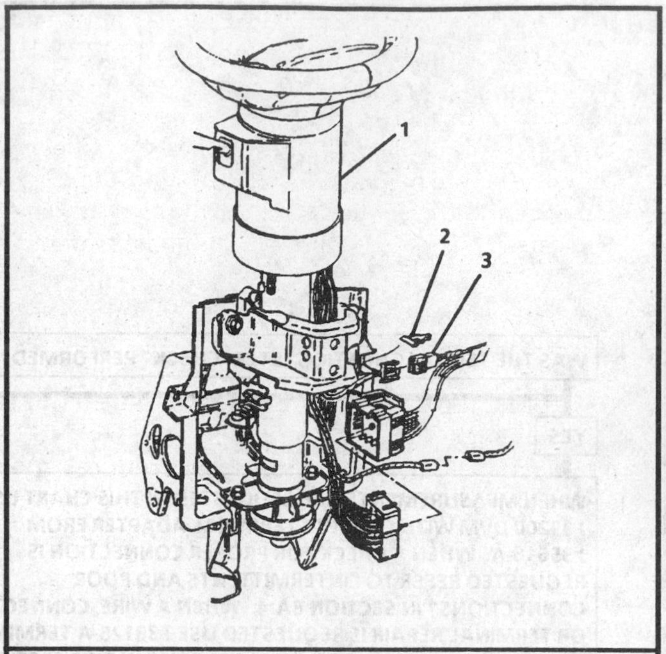
1
2
3

1 STEERING COLUMN

2 CPA

3 YELLOW 2-WAY SIR CONNECTOR

PS 16962

Figure 8 - Yellow 2-Way SIR Connector

Enabling the SIR System
Figure 8

→← Install or Connect

- Turn ignition switch to "LOCK" and remove key.

1. Yellow 2-way connector at the base of the steering column and CPA.
2. Lower trim panel, refer to SECTION 8C.
3. "ARBG1" fuse to I/P fuse block.

- Turn ignition switch to "RUN" and verify that the "AIR BAG" warning lamp flashes seven times and then turns "OFF." If it does not operate as described, perform the "SIR Diagnostic System Check" in this section.

Handling/Installation/Diagnosis

1. Inflator modules should not be subjected to temperatures above 65°C (150°F).
2. Discriminating sensors, inflator modules, arming sensors, or DERMs should not be used if they have been dropped from a height of 91.4 centimeters (3 feet).
3. When a discriminating sensor or arming sensor is replaced, it MUST be oriented with the arrow on the sensor pointing toward the front of the vehicle.

It is very important for the discriminating sensors and arming sensor to be located flat on the mounting surface, parallel to the vehicle datum line. It is important that the sensor mounting surface is free of any dirt or other foreign material.

4. Do not apply power to the SIR system unless all components are connected or a diagnostic chart requests it, as this will set a diagnostic trouble code.
5. The "SIR Diagnostic System Check" must be the starting point of any SIR diagnostics. The "SIR Diagnostic System Check" will verify proper "AIR BAG" warning lamp operation and will lead you to the correct chart to diagnose any SIR malfunctions. **Bypassing these procedures may result in extended diagnostic time, incorrect diagnosis, and incorrect parts replacements.**

REPAIRS AND INSPECTIONS REQUIRED AFTER AN ACCIDENT

Important

- If any SIR system components are damaged, they must be replaced. If SIR component mounting points are damaged, they must be repaired or replaced.
- Never use SIR parts from another vehicle. This does not include remanufactured parts purchased from an authorized GM dealer; they may be used for SIR repairs.
- Do not attempt to service discriminating sensors, the arming sensor, the DERM, the SIR coil assembly, or the inflator module. Service of these items is by replacement only.
- Verify the part number of replacement inflator module. Some GM inflator modules look identical but contain different internal components.
- After a deployment has occurred, SIR diagnostic trouble codes must be cleared using a scan tool "Clear Codes" command. This must be done to cause the "AIR BAG" warning lamp to go "OFF".

CAUTION: Proper operation of the sensors and Supplemental Inflatable Restraint (SIR) system requires that any repairs to the vehicle structure return it to the original production configuration. Deployment requires, at a minimum, replacement of the sensors in the area of accident damage, the inflator module, and dimensional inspection of the steering column. Any visible damage to the DERM mounting bracket(s) requires replacement, sensors in the area of accident damage must be replaced, and the steering column must be dimensionally inspected, whether deployment occurred or not.

Accident With Deployment - Component Replacement and Inspections

Certain SIR components must be replaced or inspected for damage after a frontal crash involving air bag deployment. Those components are:

- Inflator module.
- Sensors, if in the area of accident damage.

Important

- Refer to "Sensor Replacement Guidelines" below for important information on sensor replacement in both deployment and non-deployment crashes.

- SIR coil assembly - Inspect wiring and connector for any signs of scorching, melting, or damage due to excessive heat. Replace if damaged. Refer to SECTION 3F5A.

Accident With or Without Deployment - Component Inspections

Certain SIR and restraint system components must be inspected after any crash, whether the air bag deployed or not. Those components are:

- Steering column - Dimensionally inspect per "Checking Steering Column for Accident Damage" in SECTION 3F5A.
- Sensors, if in the area of accident damage.

Important

- Refer to "Sensor Replacement Guidelines" below for important information on sensor replacement in both deployment and non-deployment crashes.

- Knee bolster and mounting points - Inspect for any distortion, bending, cracking, or other damage.
- I/P steering column reinforcement plate - Inspect for any distortion, bending, cracking, or other damage.
- I/P braces - Inspect for any distortion, bending, cracking, or other damage.
- Seat belts and mounting points - Refer to "Seat Belts" in SECTION 10-11.

Sensor Replacement Guidelines

SIR sensor replacement policy requires replacement of the sensors in the area of accident damage only.

The "area of accident damage" is defined as that area of the vehicle which is crushed, bent, or damaged in other ways. An example might be a significant front-end collision in which the forward portions of the vehicle have contacted another vehicle, tree, guardrail, etc. In this example, a sensor on the front of the vehicle, such as the radiator tie bar, would require replacement, since that portion of the vehicle was damaged in the accident. A sensor in the passenger compartment, such as the arming sensor, would not require mandatory replacement. Of course, if the DERM sets a diagnostic trouble code and the diagnostic chart leads to a malfunctioning sensor that was not in the area of accident damage, that sensor should also be replaced.

Sensors in the area of accident damage should be replaced even if those sensors do not appear to be damaged. Do not attempt to determine whether a sensor is OK -- ALWAYS replace it if it is in the area of accident damage.

Also, if a sensor is in an area of accident damage, but the SIR system has NOT been deployed, replace the sensor. The sensor bracket may be slightly bent, wiring may be damaged, etc., and the sensor might not work properly in another collision. Again, do not attempt to determine whether a sensor is OK -- ALWAYS replace it if it is in the area of accident damage.

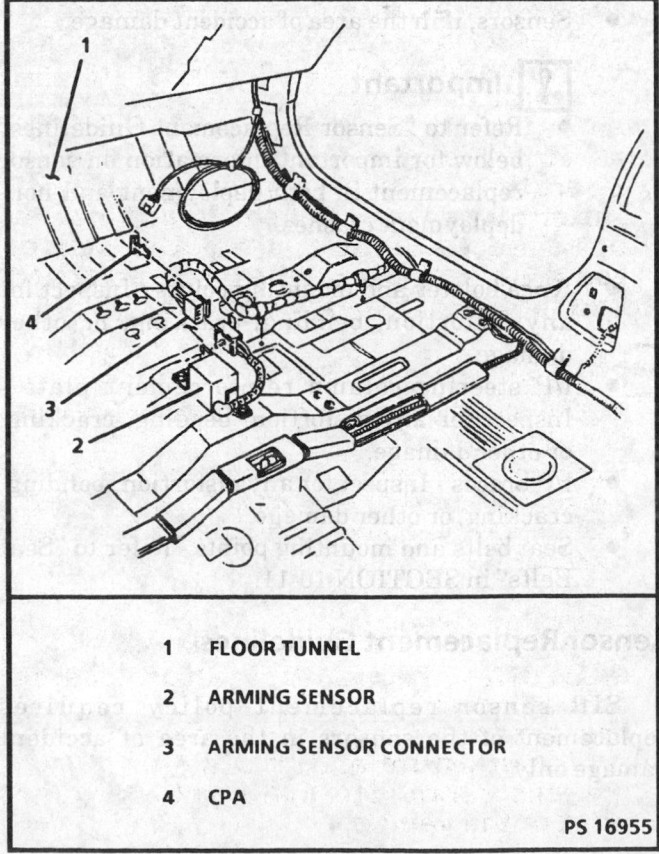

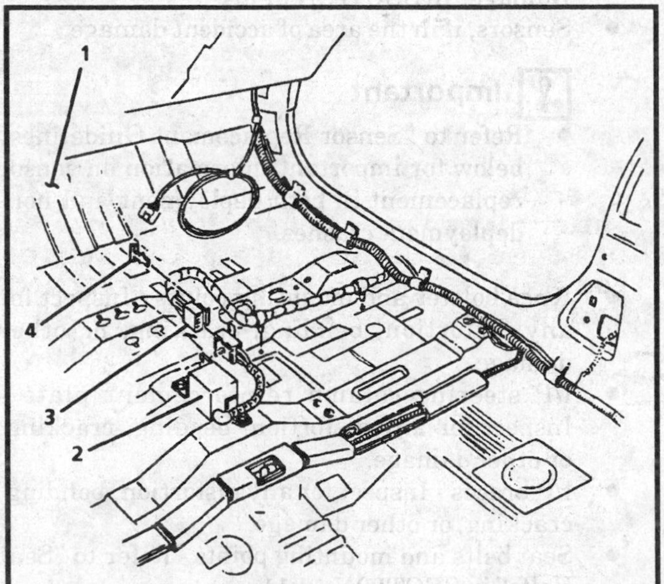
1
4
3
2
1 FLOOR TUNNEL
2 ARMING SENSOR
3 ARMING SENSOR CONNECTOR
4 CPA
PS 16955

Figure 9 - Arming Sensor

ARMING SENSOR

Figure 9

CAUTION: During service procedures, be very careful when handling a sensor. Never strike or jar a sensor. Under some circumstances, it could cause deployment and result in personal injury or improper operation of the Supplemental Inflatable Restraint (SIR) system. All sensors and mounting bracket fasteners must be carefully torqued to ensure proper operation. Never power up the SIR system when any sensor is not rigidly attached to vehicle, since the sensor could be activated when not attached and could result in deployment.

↔ Remove or Disconnect

- Disable the SIR system. Refer to "Disabling the SIR System" in this section.

1. Driver seat (bench), refer to SECTION 10-10 or center console (bucket seat), refer to SECTION 8C.
2. Connector Position Assurance (CPA) and electrical connector.
3. Sensor mounting fasteners.
4. Sensor from vehicle.

CAUTION: Proper operation of the arming sensor requires the sensor be rigidly attached to the vehicle structure and that the arrow on the sensor be pointing toward the front of the vehicle.

→← Install or Connect

NOTICE: Refer to "NOTICE" on Page 9J-1.

1. Sensor in vehicle, ensure arrow is pointing toward the front of the vehicle.
2. Sensor mounting fasteners.

Tighten

- Fasteners to 4.5 N·m (40 lb. in.).

3. Electrical connector and CPA.
4. Driver seat (bench), refer to SECTION 10-10 or center console (bucket seat), refer to SECTION 8C.

- Enable the SIR system, refer to "Enabling the SIR System" in this section.

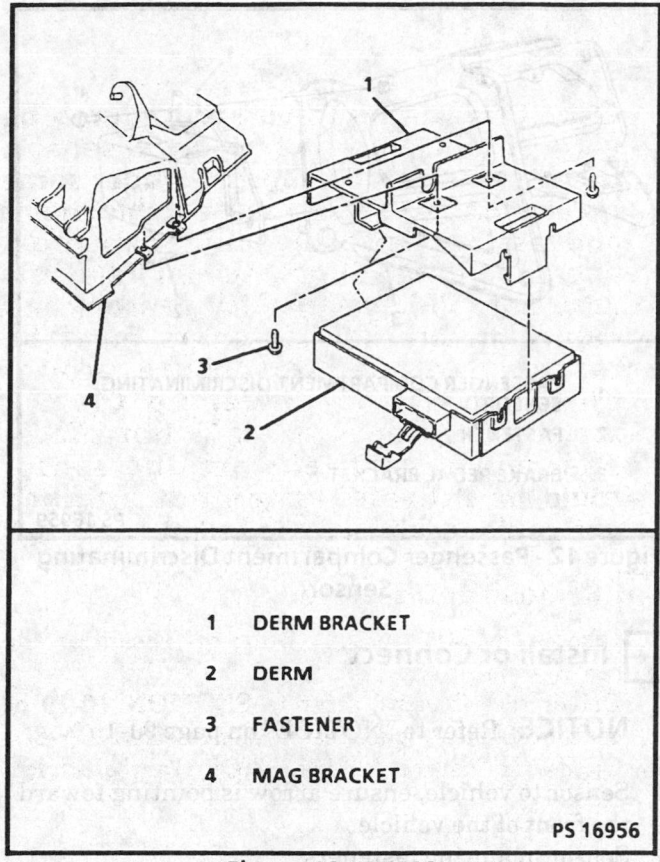

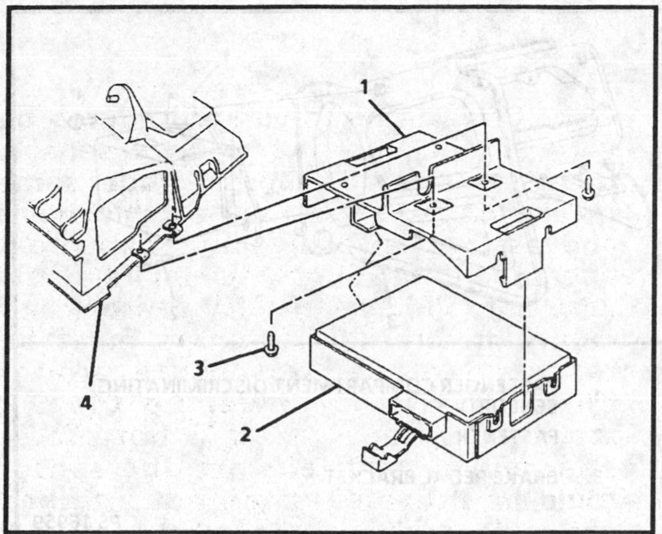
1
2
3
4
1 DERM BRACKET
2 DERM
3 FASTENER
4 MAG BRACKET
PS 16956

Figure 10 - DERM

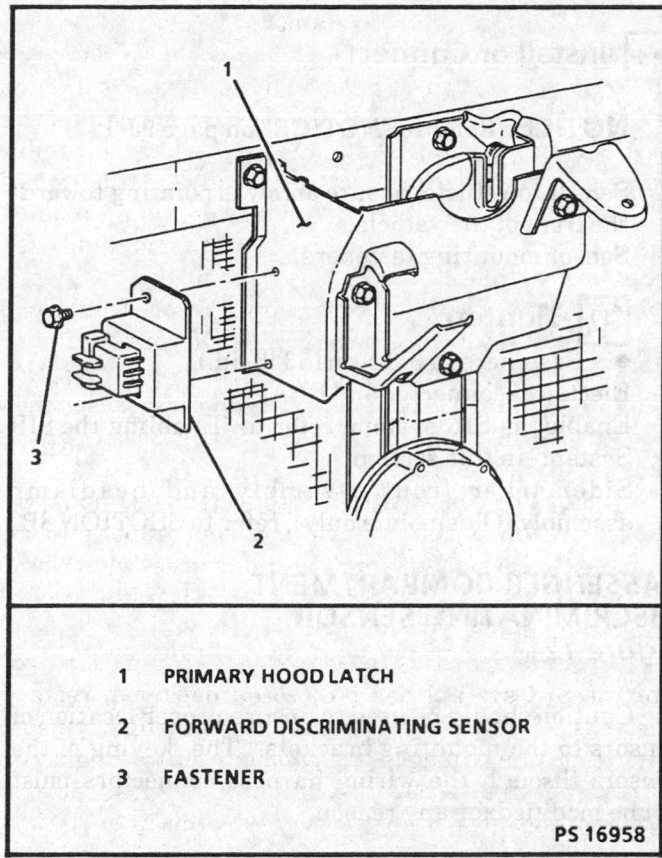

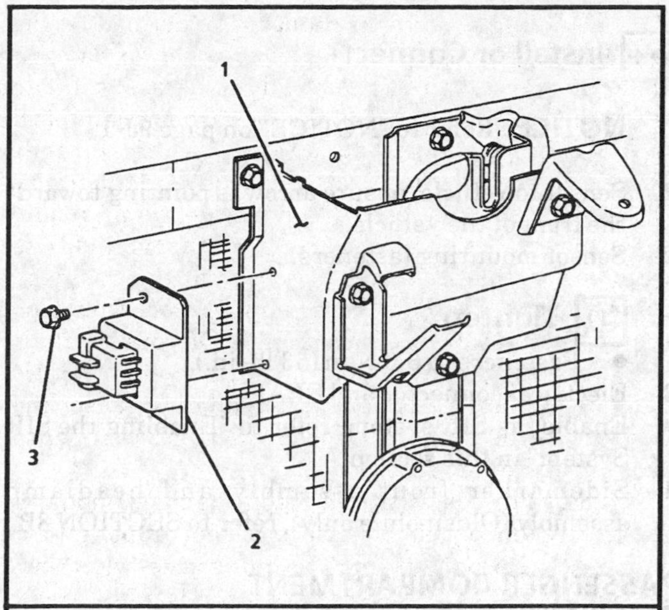
1
2
3
1 PRIMARY HOOD LATCH
2 FORWARD DISCRIMINATING SENSOR
3 FASTENER
PS 16958

Figure 11 - Forward Discriminating Sensor

DIAGNOSTIC ENERGY RESERVE MODULE
Figure 10

NOTICE: Do not open the DERM case for any reason. Touching the connector pins or soldered components may cause electrostatic discharge damage. Repair of a malfunctioning DERM is by replacement only.

↔ Remove or Disconnect

- Disable the SIR system, refer to "Disabling the SIR System" in this section.

1. Connector Position Assurance (CPA) and electrical connector.
2. DERM from mounting bracket.

→← Install or Connect

1. DERM to mounting bracket.
2. Electrical connector and CPA.

- Enable the SIR system, refer to "Enabling the SIR System" in this section.

FORWARD DISCRIMINATING SENSOR
Figure 11

Caution should be used to ensure proper location of sensors to the mounting brackets. The keying of the sensors through the wiring harness connectors must not be modified for any reason.

CAUTION: During service procedures, be very careful when handling a sensor. Never strike or jar a sensor. Under some circumstances, it could cause deployment and result in personal injury or improper operation of the Supplemental Inflatable Restraint (SIR) system. All sensors and mounting bracket fasteners must be carefully torqued to assure proper operation. Never power up the SIR system when any sensor is not rigidly attached to vehicle, since the sensor could be activated when not attached and could result in deployment.

↔ Remove or Disconnect

- Disable the SIR system, refer to "Disabling the SIR System" in this section.

1. Headlamp assembly and sidemarker front assembly (Oldsmobile only), refer to SECTION 8B.
2. Connector Position Assurance (CPA) and electrical connector.
3. Sensor mounting fasteners.
4. Sensor from vehicle.

CAUTION: Proper operation of the forward discriminating sensor requires the sensor be rigidly attached to the vehicle structure and that the arrow on the sensor should be pointing toward the front of the vehicle.

Install or Connect

NOTICE: Refer to "NOTICE" on page 9J-1.

1. Sensor to vehicle, ensure arrow is pointing toward the front of the vehicle.
2. Sensor mounting fasteners.

Tighten

- Fasteners to 6.0 N·m (53 lb. in.).

3. Electrical connector and CPA.

- Enable the SIR system, refer to "Enabling the SIR System" in this section.

4. Sidemarker front assembly and headlamp assembly (Oldsmobile only), refer to SECTION 8B.

PASSENGER COMPARTMENT DISCRIMINATING SENSOR
Figure 12

Caution should be used to ensure proper location of sensors to the mounting brackets. The keying of the sensors through the wiring harness connectors must not be modified for any reason.

CAUTION: During service procedures, be very careful when handling a sensor. Never strike or jar a sensor. Under some circumstances, it could cause deployment and result in personal injury or improper operation of the Supplemental Inflatable Restraint (SIR) system. All sensors and mounting bracket fasteners must be carefully torqued to assure proper operation. Never power up the SIR system when any sensor is not rigidly attached to vehicle, since the sensor could be activated when not attached and could result in deployment.

Remove or Disconnect

- Disable the SIR system, refer to "Disabling the SIR System" in this section.

1. Connector Position Assurance (CPA) and electrical connector.
2. Sensor mounting fasteners.
3. Sensor from vehicle.

CAUTION: Proper operation of the passenger compartment discriminating sensor requires the sensor be rigidly attached to the vehicle structure and that the arrow on the sensor be pointing toward the front of the vehicle.

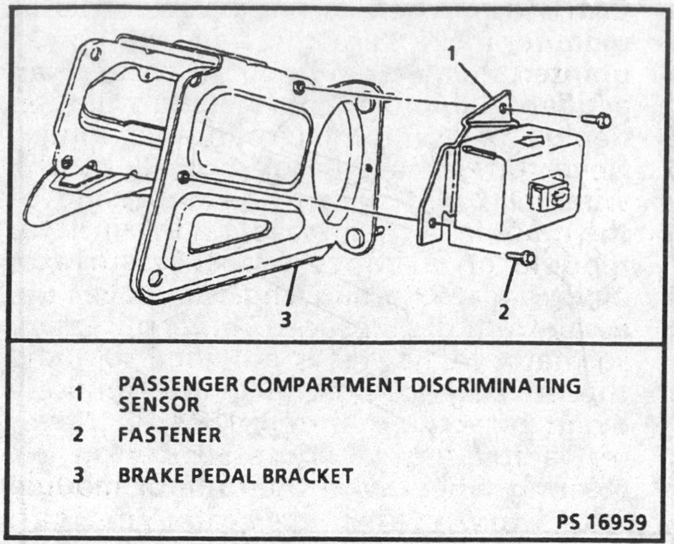
1
2
3
1 PASSENGER COMPARTMENT DISCRIMINATING SENSOR
2 FASTENER
3 BRAKE PEDAL BRACKET
PS 16959

Figure 12 - Passenger Compartment Discriminating Sensor

Install or Connect

NOTICE: Refer to "NOTICE" on page 9J-1.

1. Sensor to vehicle, ensure arrow is pointing toward the front of the vehicle.
2. Sensor mounting fasteners.

Tighten

- Fasteners to 6.0 N·m (53 lb. in.).

3. Electrical connector and CPA.

- Enable the SIR system, refer to "Enabling the SIR System" in this section.

"AIR BAG" WARNING LAMP

Refer to "Indicator Lamps" in SECTION 8C.

INFLATOR MODULE

Refer to SECTION 3F.

SIR COIL ASSEMBLY

Refer to SECTION 3F5A.

INFLATOR MODULE HANDLING/SHIPPING/ SCRAPPING
Figure 13

Live (Undeployed) Inflator Module

Special care is necessary when handling and storing a live (undeployed) inflator module. The rapid gas generation produced during deployment of the air bag could cause the inflator module, or an object in front of the inflator module, to be thrown through the air in the unlikely event of an accidental deployment.

CAUTION: When carrying a live inflator module, make sure the bag opening is pointed away from you. In case of an accidental deployment, the bag will then deploy with minimal chance of injury. Never carry the inflator module by the wires or connector on the underside of the module. When placing a live inflator module on a bench or other surface, always face the bag and trim cover up, away from the surface. This is necessary so that a free space is provided to allow the air bag to expand in the unlikely event of accidental deployment. Never rest a steering column assembly on the steering wheel with the inflator module face down and column vertical. Otherwise, personal injury may result.

Shipping Procedures For Live (Undeployed) Inflator Modules

Service personnel should refer to the latest Service Bulletins for proper SIR inflator module shipping procedures.

Inflator Module Scrapping Procedure

During the course of a vehicle's useful life, certain situations may arise which will necessitate the disposal of a live (undeployed) inflator module. This information covers proper procedures for disposing of a live inflator module.

Before a live inflator module can be disposed of, it must be deployed. Live inflator modules must not be disposed of through normal refuse channels.

CAUTION: Failure to follow proper Supplemental Inflatable Restraint (SIR) inflator module disposal procedures can result in air bag deployment which may cause personal injury. Undeployed inflator modules must not be disposed of through normal refuse channels. The undeployed inflator module contains substances that can cause severe illness or personal injury if the sealed container is damaged during disposal. Disposal in any manner inconsistent with proper procedures may be a violation of federal, state, and/or local laws.

If a vehicle is the subject of a Product Liability Report related to the SIR system and is subject to a Preliminary Investigation (GM-1241), DO NOT DEPLOY the inflator module and DO NOT ALTER the SIR system in any manner.

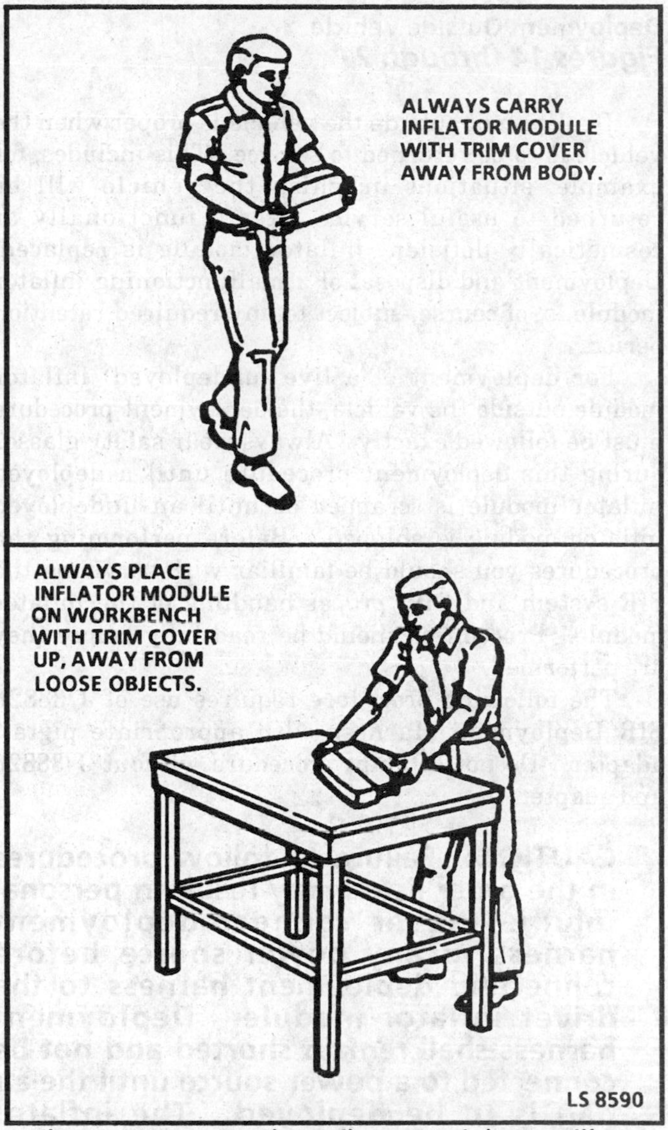
ALWAYS CARRY INFLATOR MODULE WITH TRIM COVER AWAY FROM BODY.
ALWAYS PLACE INFLATOR MODULE ON WORKBENCH WITH TRIM COVER UP, AWAY FROM LOOSE OBJECTS.
LS 8590

Figure 13 - Proper Live Inflator Module Handling

Refer to the applicable service bulletin on SIR shipping procedures for details on handling SIR systems involved with GM-1241. If a vehicle is the subject of a campaign affecting inflator modules, DO NOT DEPLOY the inflator module. Follow instructions in the Campaign Service Bulletin for proper disposition of the inflator module.

If an inflator module is replaced under warranty, DO NOT DEPLOY the air bag. The inflator module may need to be returned, undeployed, to Inland Fisher Guide. Refer to procedures shown in the appropriate service bulletin regarding SIR shipping procedures.

In situations which require deployment of a live inflator module, deployment may be accomplished inside or outside the vehicle. The method employed depends upon the final disposition of the particular vehicle, as noted in "Deployment Outside Vehicle" and "Deployment Inside Vehicle" in this section.

Deployment Outside Vehicle
Figures 14 through 21

Deployment outside the vehicle is proper when the vehicle is to be returned to service. This includes, for example, situations in which the vehicle will be returned to useful service after a functionally or cosmetically deficient inflator module is replaced. Deployment and disposal of a malfunctioning inflator module is, of course, subject to any required retention period.

For deployment of a live (undeployed) inflator module outside the vehicle, the deployment procedure must be followed exactly. Always wear safety glasses during this deployment procedure until a deployed inflator module is scrapped or until an undeployed inflator module is shipped. Before performing the procedures you should be familiar with servicing the SIR system and with proper handling of the inflator module. Procedures should be read fully before they are performed.

The following procedure requires use of J 38826 SIR Deployment Harness with appropriate pigtail adapter. Do not attempt procedure without J 38826 and adapter.

CAUTION: Failure to follow procedures in the order listed may result in personal injury. Never connect deployment harness to any power source before connecting deployment harness to the driver inflator module. Deployment harness shall remain shorted and not be connected to a power source until the air bag is to be deployed. The inflator module will immediately deploy the air bag when a power source is connected to it. Wear safety glasses throughout this entire deployment and disposal procedure.

1. Turn ignition switch to "LOCK," remove key, and put on safety glasses.
2. Inspect J 38826 SIR Deployment Harness and appropriate pigtail adapter for damage. If harness or pigtail adapter is damaged, discard and obtain a replacement.
3. Short the two SIR deployment harness leads together by fully seating one banana plug into the other. SIR deployment harness shall remain shorted and not be connected to a power source until the air bag is to be deployed (Figure 14).
4. Connect the appropriate pigtail adapter to the SIR deployment harness (Figure 14).
5. Remove inflator module from vehicle. Refer to SECTION 3F.
6. Remove horn lead from the back of the inflator module.
7. Remove all horn buttons and steering wheel control buttons from inflator module, if applicable.

CAUTION: When storing a live inflator module or when leaving a live inflator module unattended on a bench or other surface, always face the bag and trim cover up and away from the surface. This is necessary so that a free space is provided to allow the air bag to expand in the unlikely event of accidental deployment. Failure to follow procedures may result in personal injury.

8. Place the inflator module on a work bench or other surface away from all loose or flammable objects with its vinyl trim cover facing up, away from the surface (Figure 15).
9. Clear a space on the ground about 185 cm (six feet) in diameter where the inflator module is to be deployed. A paved, outdoor location where there is no activity is preferred. If an outdoor location is not available, a space on the shop floor where there is no activity and sufficient ventilation is recommended. Ensure no loose or flammable objects are within the deployment area (Figure 16).
10. Place the inflator module, with its vinyl trim cover facing up, on the ground in the space just cleared (Figure 16).
11. Stretch the SIR deployment harness and pigtail adapter from the inflator module to its full length (Figure 17).
12. Place a power source near the shorted end of the SIR deployment harness. Recommended application: 12 volts minimum, 2 amps minimum. A vehicle battery is suggested.
13. Connect the inflator module to the pigtail adapter on the SIR deployment harness. Deployment harness shall remain shorted and not be connected to a power source until the air bag is to be deployed. The inflator module will immediately deploy the air bag when a power source is connected to it (Figure 18).

Important

- Ensure that the pigtail adapter is firmly seated into the inflator module connector. Failure to fully seat the connectors may leave the shorting bar located in the inflator module connector functioning (shorted) and may result in non-deployment of the inflator module.

14. Verify that the area around the inflator module is clear of all people and loose or flammable objects.
15. Verify that the inflator module is resting with its vinyl trim cover facing up.

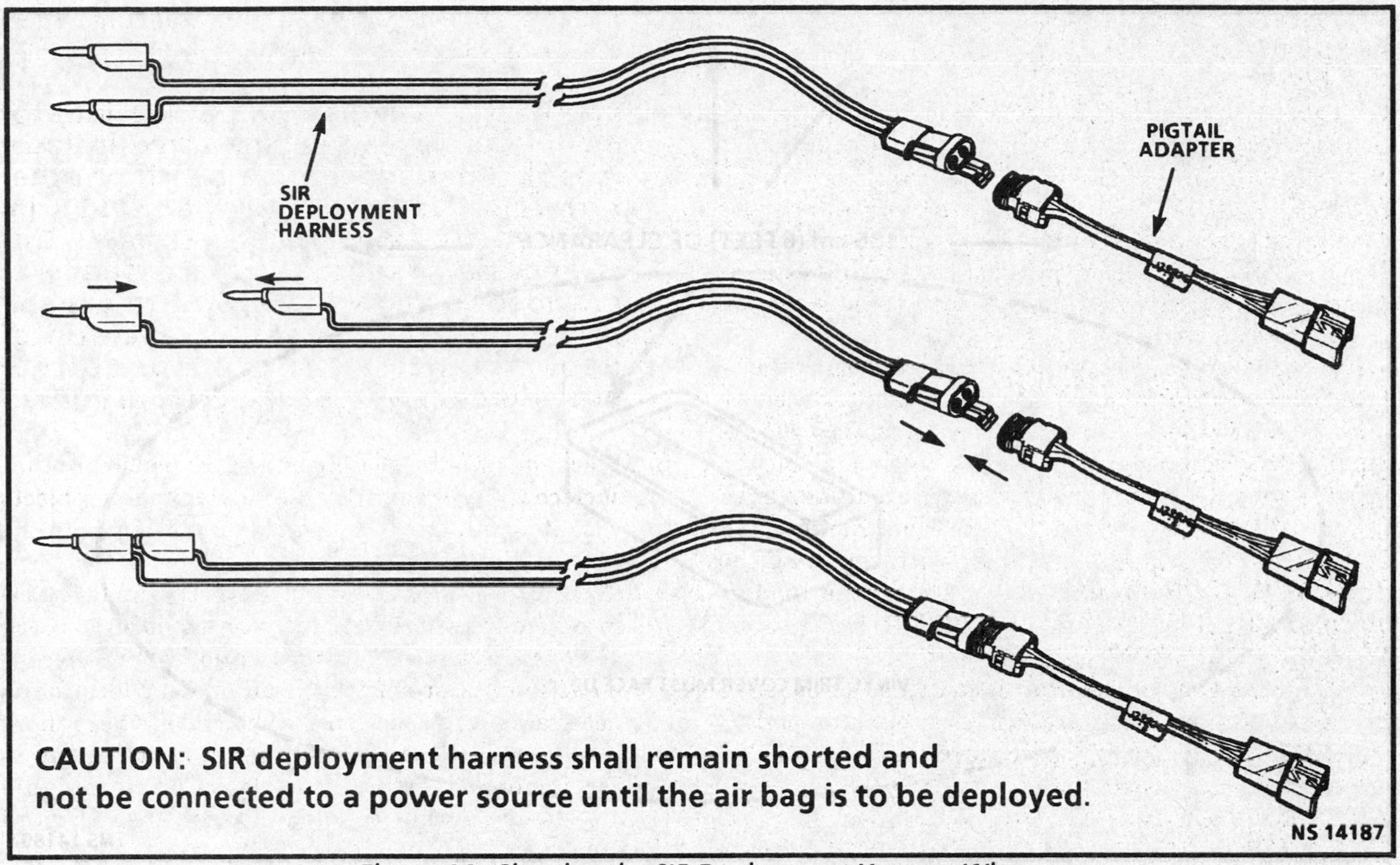
PIGTAIL
ADAPTER
SIR
DEPLOYMENT
HARNESS
CAUTION: SIR deployment harness shall remain shorted and
not be connected to a power source until the air bag is to be deployed.
NS 14187

Figure 14 - Shorting the SIR Deployment Harness Wires

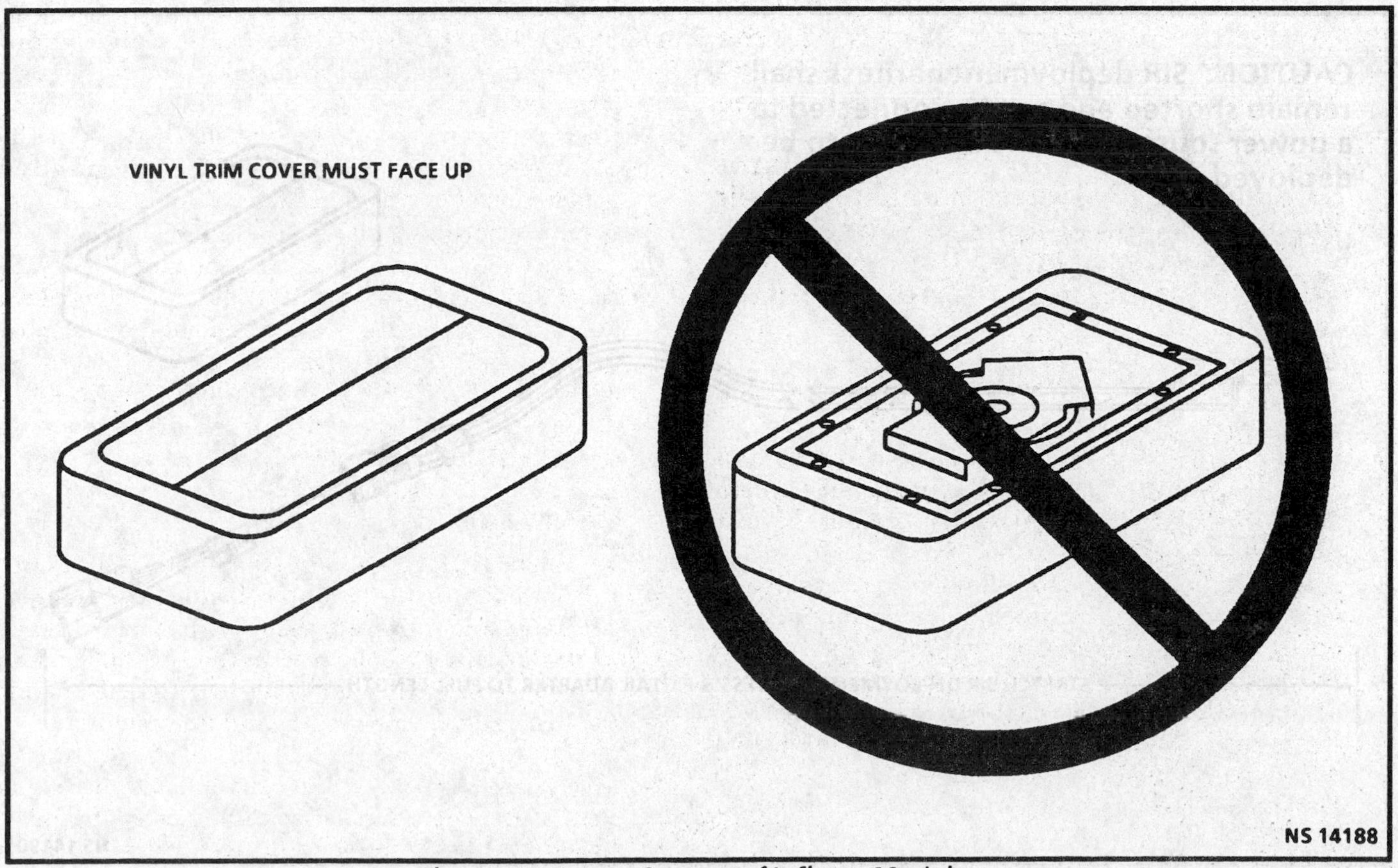
VINYL TRIM COVER MUST FACE UP
NS 14188

Figure 15 - Proper Storage of Inflator Module

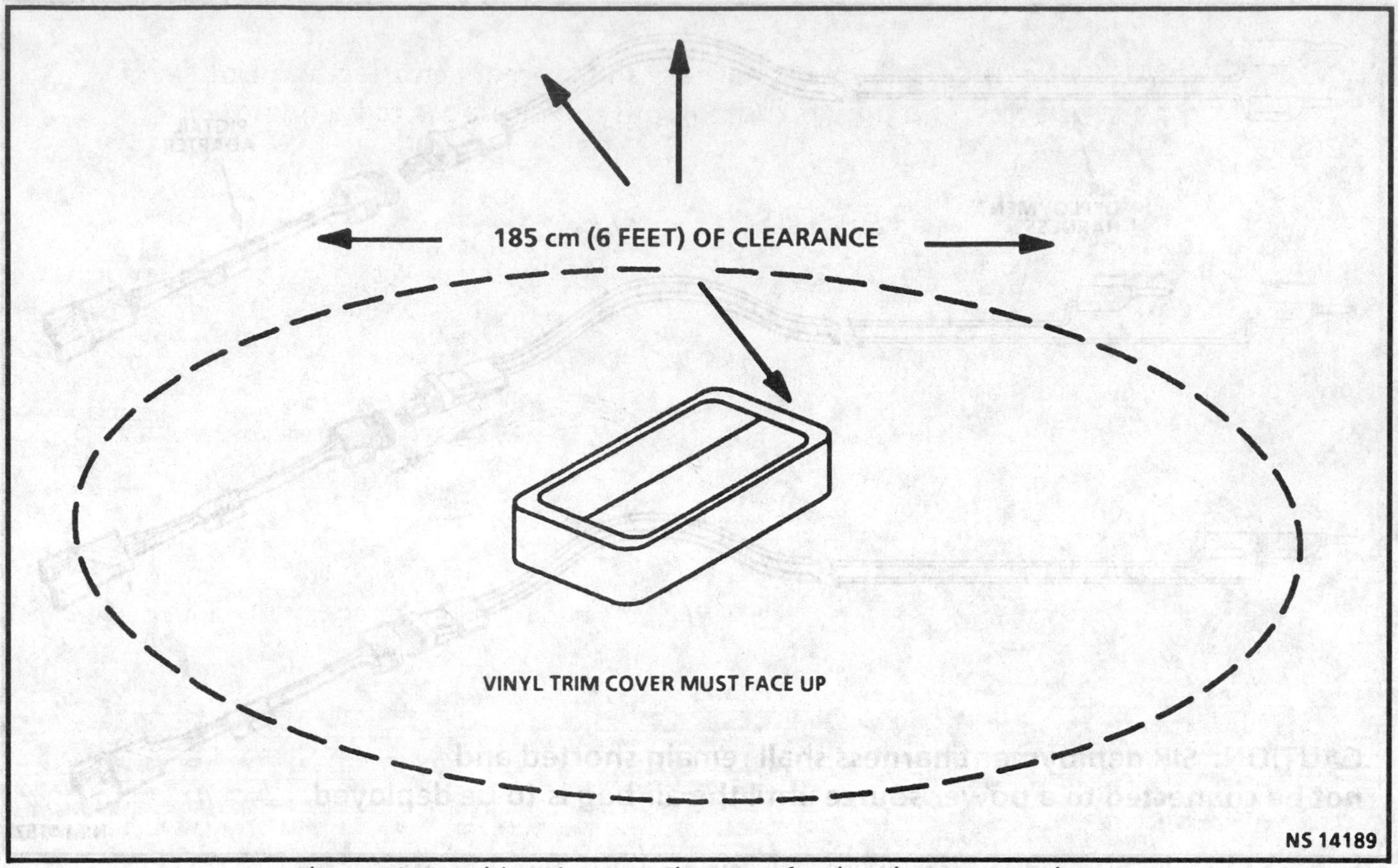
185 cm (6 FEET) OF CLEARANCE
VINYL TRIM COVER MUST FACE UP
NS 14189

Figure 16 - Provide Adequate Clearance for the Air Bag to Deploy

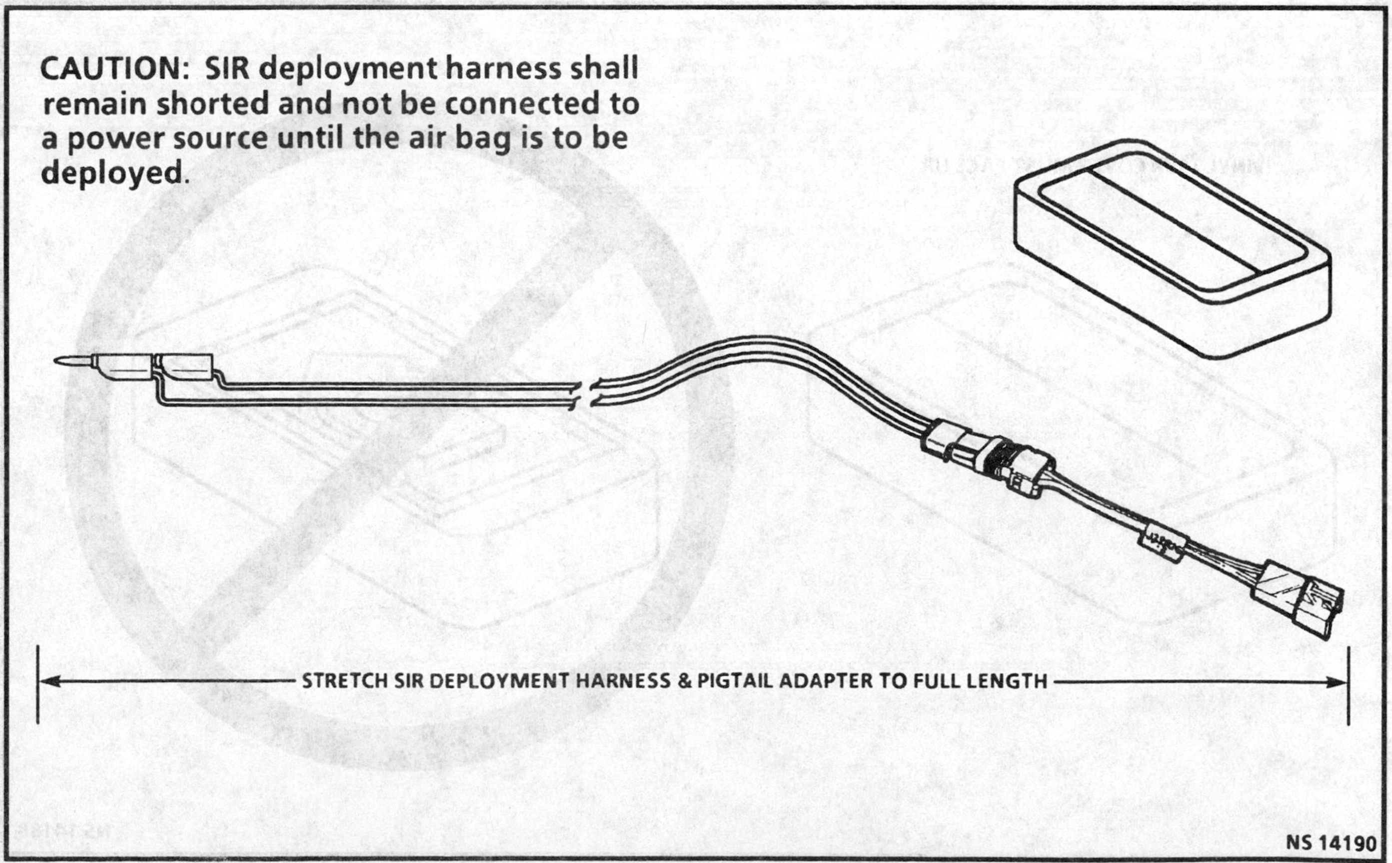
CAUTION: SIR deployment harness shall remain shorted and not be connected to a power source until the air bag is to be deployed.
STRETCH SIR DEPLOYMENT HARNESS & PIGTAIL ADAPTER TO FULL LENGTH
NS 14190

Figure 17 - Stretching the SIR Deployment Harness and Pigtail Adapter

CAUTION: SIR deployment harness shall remain shorted and not be connected to a power source until the air bag is to be deployed.

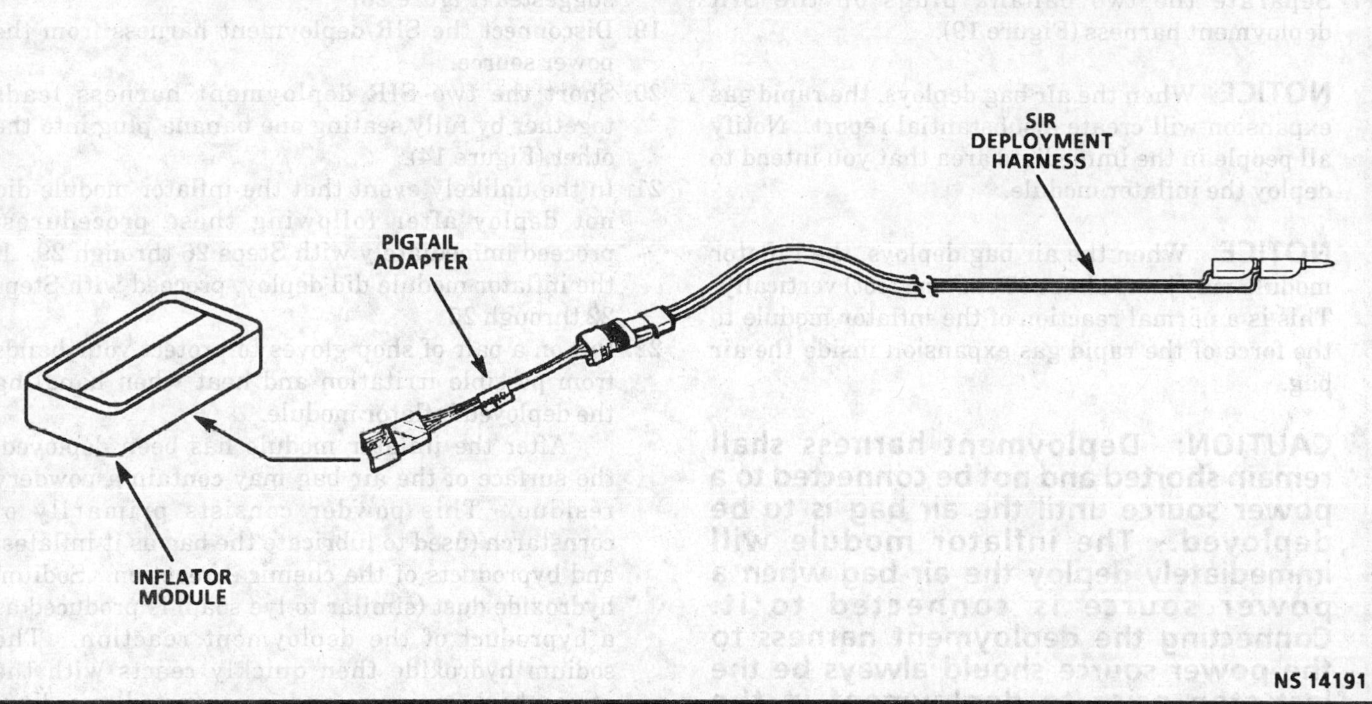
SIR
DEPLOYMENT
HARNESS
PIGTAIL
ADAPTER
INFLATOR
MODULE
NS 14191

Figure 18 - Connecting the SIR Deployment Harness to the Inflator Module

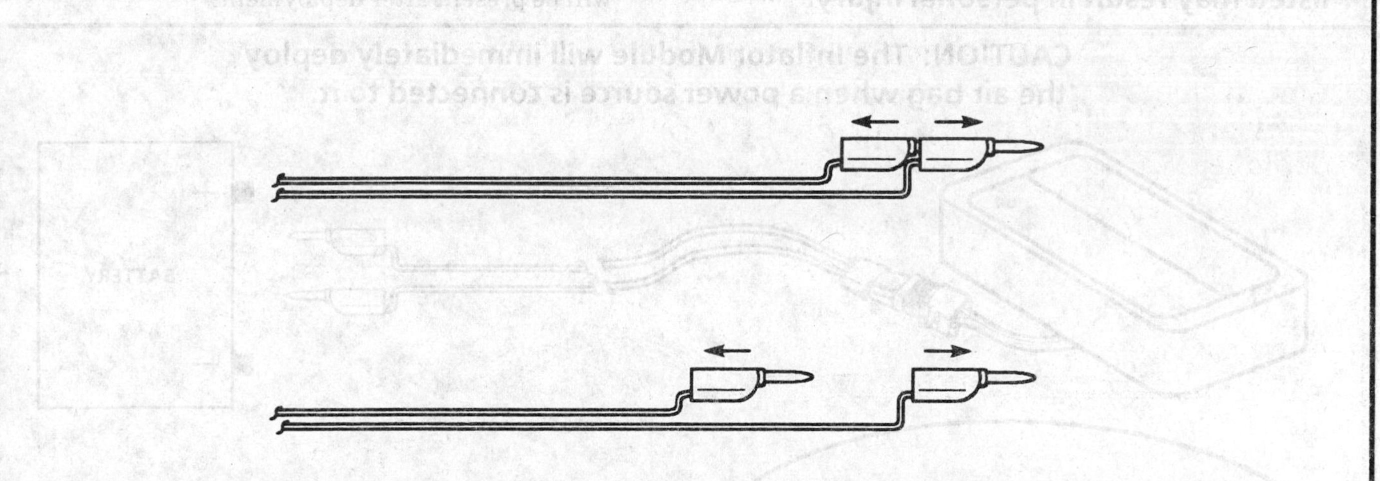
NS 14192

Figure 19 - Separating the Two Shorted Banana Plugs

16. Notify all people in the immediate area that you intend to deploy the inflator module. The deployment will be accompanied by a substantial report which may startle the uninformed.
17. Separate the two banana plugs on the SIR deployment harness (Figure 19).

NOTICE: When the air bag deploys, the rapid gas expansion will create a substantial report. Notify all people in the immediate area that you intend to deploy the inflator module.

NOTICE: When the air bag deploys, the inflator module may jump about 30 cm (one foot) vertically. This is a normal reaction of the inflator module to the force of the rapid gas expansion inside the air bag.

CAUTION: Deployment harness shall remain shorted and not be connected to a power source until the air bag is to be deployed. The inflator module will immediately deploy the air bag when a power source is connected to it. Connecting the deployment harness to the power source should always be the last step prior to deployment in the inflator module deployment procedure. Failure to follow procedures in the order listed may result in personal injury.

18. Connect the SIR deployment harness wires to the power source to immediately deploy the inflator module. Recommended application: 12 volts minimum, 2 amps minimum. A vehicle battery is suggested (Figure 20).
19. Disconnect the SIR deployment harness from the power source.
20. Short the two SIR deployment harness leads together by fully seating one banana plug into the other (Figure 14).
21. In the unlikely event that the inflator module did not deploy after following these procedures, proceed immediately with Steps 26 through 29. If the inflator module did deploy, proceed with Steps 22 through 25.
22. Put on a pair of shop gloves to protect your hands from possible irritation and heat when handling the deployed inflator module.

After the inflator module has been deployed, the surface of the air bag may contain a powdery residue. This powder consists primarily of cornstarch (used to lubricate the bag as it inflates) and byproducts of the chemical reaction. Sodium hydroxide dust (similar to lye soap) is produced as a byproduct of the deployment reaction. The sodium hydroxide then quickly reacts with the atmospheric moisture and is converted to sodium carbonate and sodium bicarbonate (baking soda). Therefore, it is unlikely that sodium hydroxide will be present after deployment.

CAUTION: The Inflator Module will immediately deploy the air bag when a power source is connected to it.

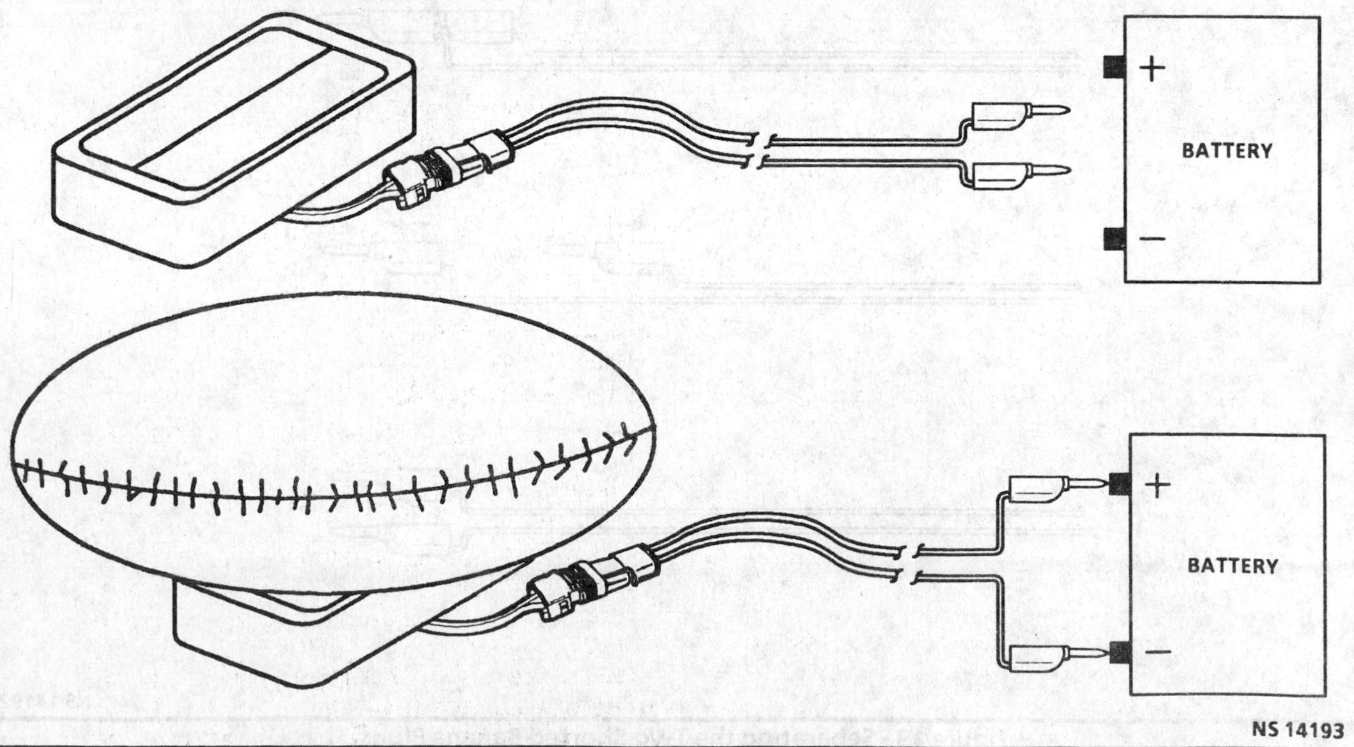
BATTERY
+
−
BATTERY
+
−
NS 14193

Figure 20 - Connecting to a Power Source

As a precaution, however, gloves and safety glasses are recommended to prevent any possible irritation of the skin or eyes.

CAUTION: Safety precautions must be observed when handling a deployed inflator module. After deployment, the metal surfaces of the inflator module will be very hot. Allow the inflator module to cool before handling any metal portion of it. Do not place the deployed inflator module near any flammable objects. Failure to follow procedures may result in fire or personal injury.

After an inflator module has been deployed, the metal canister and surrounding areas of the inflator module will be very hot. Do not touch the metal areas of the inflator module for about ten minutes after deployment. If the deployed inflator module must be moved before it is cool, wear gloves and handle by the air bag or vinyl trim (Figure 21).

23. Disconnect the pigtail adapter from the inflator module as soon after deployment as possible. This will prevent damage to the pigtail adapter or SIR deployment harness due to possible contact with the hot inflator module canister. The pigtail adapter and SIR deployment harness are designed to be reused. They should, however, be inspected for damage after each deployment and replaced if necessary.
24. Dispose of the deployed inflator module through normal refuse channels after it has cooled for at least 10 minutes.
25. Wash your hands with mild soap and water afterward.

NOTICE: The remaining steps are to be followed in the unlikely event that the inflator module did not deploy after following these procedures.

26. Ensure that the SIR deployment harness has been disconnected from the power source and that its two banana plugs have been shorted together by fully seating one banana plug into the other (Figure 14).
27. Disconnect the pigtail adapter from the inflator module.

CAUTION: When storing a live inflator module or when leaving a live inflator module unattended on a bench or other surface, always face the bag and trim cover up and away from the surface. This is necessary so that a free space is provided to allow the air bag to expand in the unlikely event of accidental deployment. Failure to follow procedures may result in personal injury.

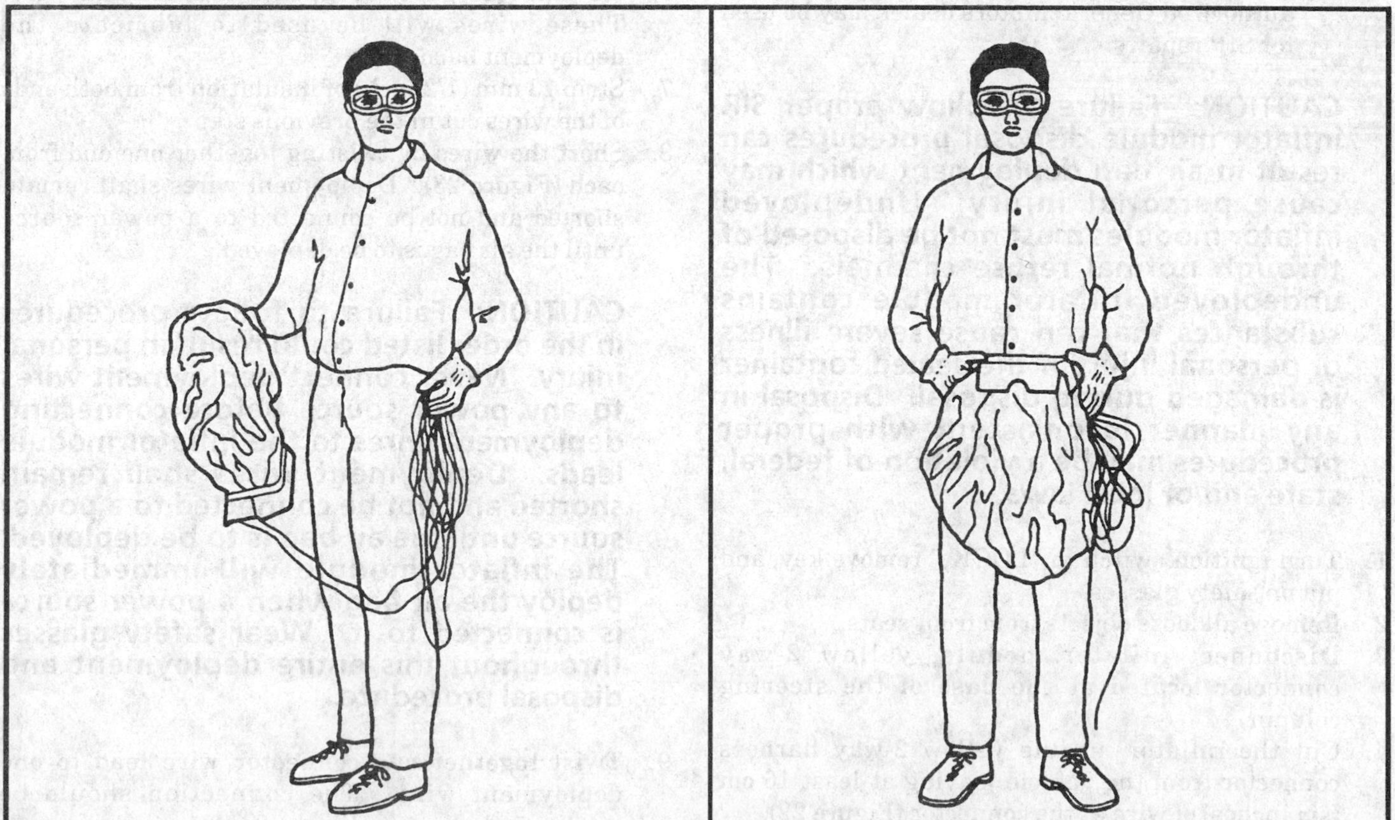
NS 14194

Figure 21 - Handling a Hot, Deployed Inflator Module

28. Temporarily store the inflator module with its vinyl trim cover facing up, away from the surface upon which it rests.
29. Call the Technical Assistance group for further assistance.

Deployment Inside Vehicle (Vehicle Scrapping Procedure)

Figures 22 through 26

Deployment inside vehicle is proper when the vehicle is to be destroyed or salvaged for component parts. This includes, but is not limited to, the following situations:

1. The vehicle has completed its useful life.
2. The vehicle has been damaged beyond repair in a non-deployment type accident.
3. The vehicle has been stripped or damaged beyond repair in a theft.
4. The vehicle will be salvaged for component parts to be used on a vehicle with a different Vehicle Identification Number (VIN) as opposed to being rebuilt as the same VIN. Never use SIR components from another vehicle. This is done to ensure SIR system integrity since only new SIR system components, with the exception of remanufactured parts as noted below, may be used in servicing an SIR equipped vehicle. Remanufactured parts purchased from an authorized General Motors dealer may be used for SIR repairs.

CAUTION: Failure to follow proper SIR inflator module disposal procedures can result in air bag deployment which may cause personal injury. Undeployed inflator modules must not be disposed of through normal refuse channels. The undeployed inflator module contains substances that can cause severe illness or personal injury if the sealed container is damaged during disposal. Disposal in any manner inconsistent with proper procedures may be a violation of federal, state and/or local laws.

1. Turn ignition switch to "LOCK," remove key, and put on safety glasses.
2. Remove all loose objects from front seats.
3. Disconnect inflator module, yellow 2-way connector located at the base of the steering column.
4. Cut the inflator module yellow 2-way harness connector from the vehicle leaving at least 16 cm (six inches) of wire at the connector (Figure 22).
5. Strip 13 mm (1/2 inch) of insulation from each wire lead of the connector (Figure 22).

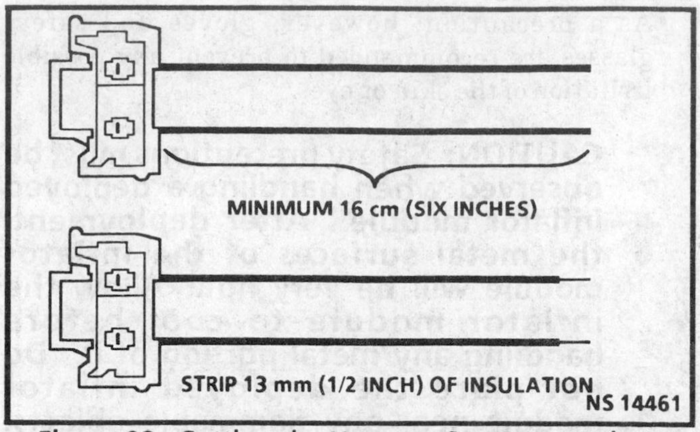
MINIMUM 16 cm (SIX INCHES)
STRIP 13 mm (1/2 INCH) OF INSULATION
NS 14461

Figure 22 - Cutting the Harness Connector Wires

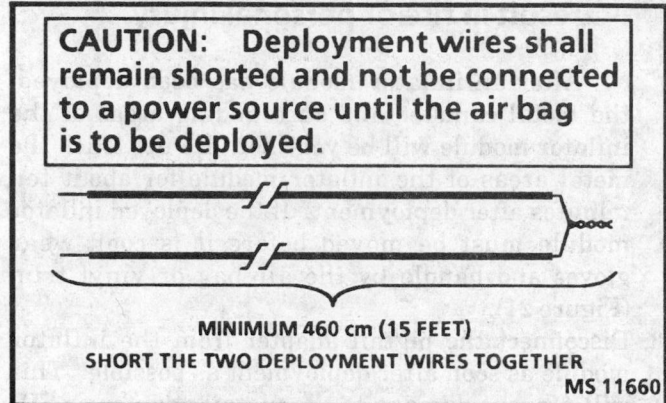

CAUTION: Deployment wires shall remain shorted and not be connected to a power source until the air bag is to be deployed.

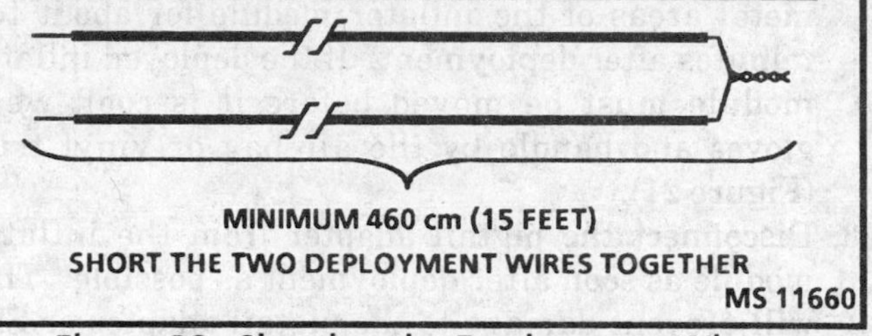
MINIMUM 460 cm (15 FEET)
SHORT THE TWO DEPLOYMENT WIRES TOGETHER
MS 11660

Figure 23 - Shorting the Deployment Wires

6. Cut two 460 cm (15 feet) deployment wires from 0.8 mm² (18 gage) or thicker multistrand wire. These wires will be used to fabricate the deployment harness.
7. Strip 13 mm (1/2 inch) of insulation from both ends of the wires cut in the previous step.
8. Short the wires by twisting together one end from each (Figure 23). Deployment wires shall remain shorted and not be connected to a power source until the air bag is to be deployed.

CAUTION: Failure to follow procedures in the order listed could result in personal injury. Never connect deployment wires to any power source before connecting deployment wires to the inflator module leads. Deployment wires shall remain shorted and not be connected to a power source until the air bag is to be deployed. The inflator module will immediately deploy the air bag when a power source is connected to it. Wear safety glasses throughout this entire deployment and disposal procedure.

9. Twist together one connector wire lead to one deployment wire. The connection should be mechanically secure (Figure 24-A).

CAUTION: Deployment wires shall remain shorted and not be connected to a power source until the air bag is to be deployed.

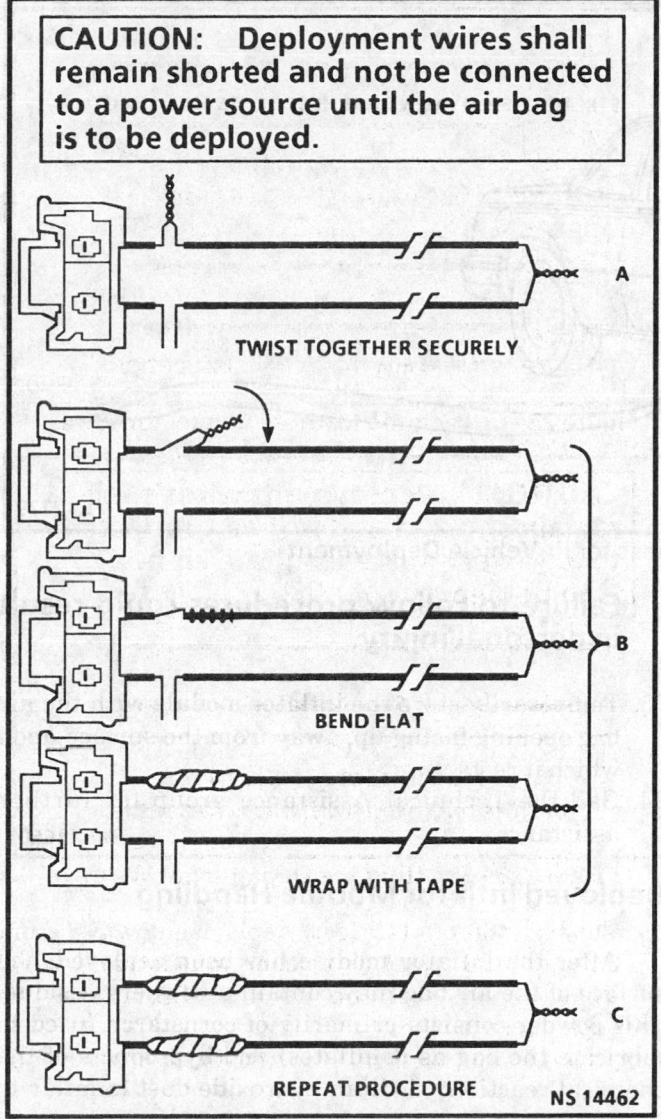

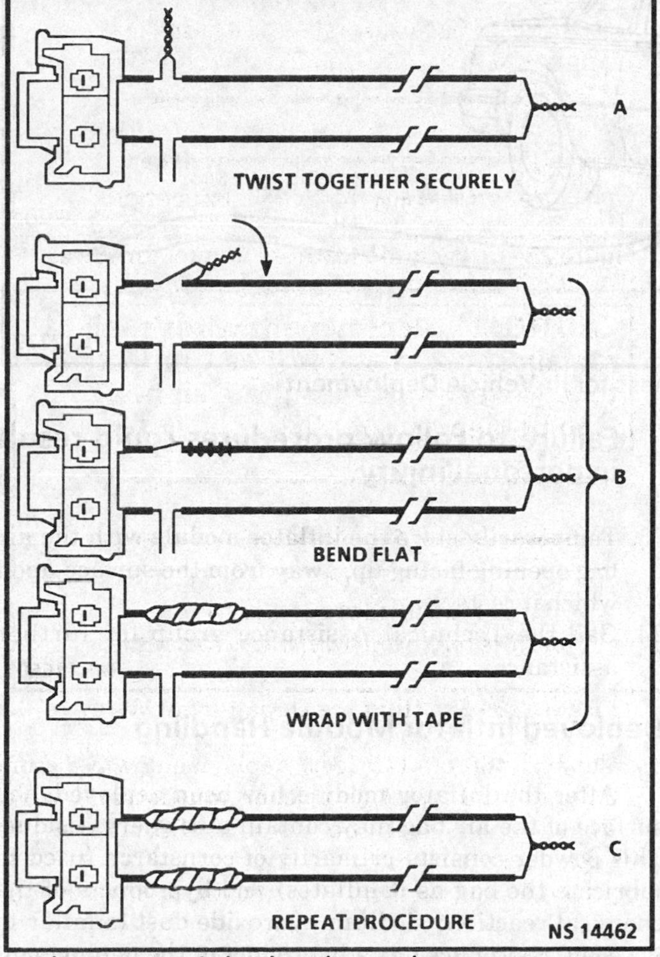
A
TWIST TOGETHER SECURELY
B
BEND FLAT
WRAP WITH TAPE
C
REPEAT PROCEDURE
NS 14462

Figure 24 - Fabricating the Deployment Harness

10. Bend twisted connection made in the previous step flat and wrap tightly with electrical tape to insulate and secure (Figure 24-B).
11. Twist together, bend and tape the remaining connector wire lead to the remaining deployment wire (Figure 24-C).
12. Connect the deployment harness to the inflator module, yellow 2-way connector at the base of the steering column. Route deployment harness out the driver side of the vehicle (Figure 25).

CAUTION: Deployment wires shall remain shorted and not be connected to a power source until the air bag is to be deployed. The inflator module will immediately deploy the air bag when a power source is connected to it. Connecting the deployment wires to the power source should always be the final step in the inflator module deployment procedure. Failure to follow procedures in the order listed could result in personal injury.

13. Verify that the inside of the vehicle is clear of all people and loose or flammable objects.
14. Stretch the deployment harness to its full length (Figure 25).
15. Notify all people in the immediate area that you intend to deploy the air bag. The deployment will be accompanied by a substantial report which may startle the uninformed.
16. Separate the two ends of the deployment harness wires (Figure 26).

CAUTION: Deployment wires shall remain shorted and not be connected to a power source until the air bag is to be deployed. The inflator module will immediately deploy the air bag when a power source is connected to it. Connecting the deployment wires to the power source should always be the final step in the inflator module deployment procedure. Failure to follow procedures in the order listed could result in personal injury.

NOTICE: When the air bag deploys, the rapid gas expansion will create a substantial report. Notify all people in the immediate area that you intend to deploy the air bag.

17. Connect the deployment harness wires to a power source to immediately deploy the inflator module. Recommended application: 12 volts minimum, 2 amps minimum. A vehicle battery is suggested (Figure 26).

After an inflator module has been deployed, the surface of the air bag may contain a powdery residue. This powder consists primarily of cornstarch (used to lubricate the bag as it inflates) and byproducts of the chemical reaction. Sodium hydroxide dust (similar to lye soap) is produced as a byproduct of the deployment reaction. The sodium hydroxide then quickly reacts with atmospheric moisture and is converted to sodium carbonate and sodium bicarbonate (baking soda). Therefore, it is unlikely that sodium hydroxide will be present after deployment. As a precaution, however, gloves and safety glasses are recommended to prevent any possible irritation of the skin or eyes.

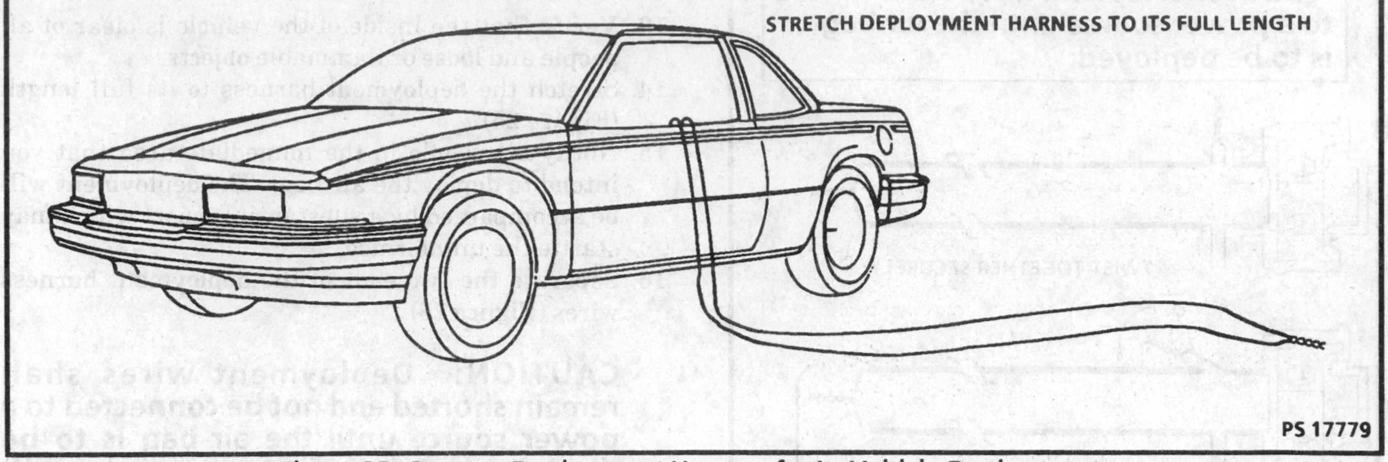
STRETCH DEPLOYMENT HARNESS TO ITS FULL LENGTH
PS 17779

Figure 25 - Prepare Deployment Harness for In-Vehicle Deployment

CAUTION: Safety precautions must be observed when handling a deployed inflator module. After deployment, the metal surfaces of the inflator module will be very hot. Allow the inflator module to cool before handling any metal portion of it. Do not place the hot deployed inflator module near any flammable objects. Failure to follow procedures could result in fire or personal injury.

After an inflator module has been deployed, the metal canister and surrounding areas of the inflator module will be very hot. Do not touch the metal areas of the inflator module for about 10 minutes after deployment. If the deployed inflator module must be moved before it is cool, wear gloves and handle by the air bag or vinyl trim.

18. Short the deployment harness wires by twisting together one end from each (Figure 23).
19. Disconnect deployment harness from vehicle and discard.
20. In the unlikely event that the inflator module did not deploy after following these procedures, proceed immediately with Steps 22 through 24.
21. Vehicle may now be scrapped in the same manner as a non-SIR equipped vehicle.
22. Remove the undeployed inflator module from the vehicle, refer to SECTION 3F.

CAUTION: When storing a live inflator module or when leaving a live inflator module unattended on a bench or other surface, always face the bag and trim cover up, away from the surface. This is necessary so that a free space is provided to allow the air bag to expand in the unlikely event of accidental deployment. Failure to follow procedures could result in personal injury.

23. Temporarily store the inflator module with the air bag opening facing up, away from the surface upon which it rests.
24. Call the Technical Assistance group for further assistance.

Deployed Inflator Module Handling

After the inflator module has been deployed, the surface of the air bag may contain a powdery residue. This powder consists primarily of cornstarch (used to lubricate the bag as it inflates) and byproducts of the chemical reaction. Sodium hydroxide dust (similar to lye soap) is produced as a byproduct of the deployment reaction. The sodium hydroxide then quickly reacts with atmospheric moisture and is converted to sodium carbonate and sodium bicarbonate (baking soda). Therefore, it is unlikely that sodium hydroxide will be present after deployment. As with many service procedures, you should wear gloves and safety glasses.

WIRING REPAIR

Special wiring repair procedures have been developed for use on the Supplemental Inflatable Restraint (SIR) system due to the sensitive nature of the circuitry. These specific procedures and instructions must be followed when working with SIR system wiring, and wiring components (such as connectors and terminals).

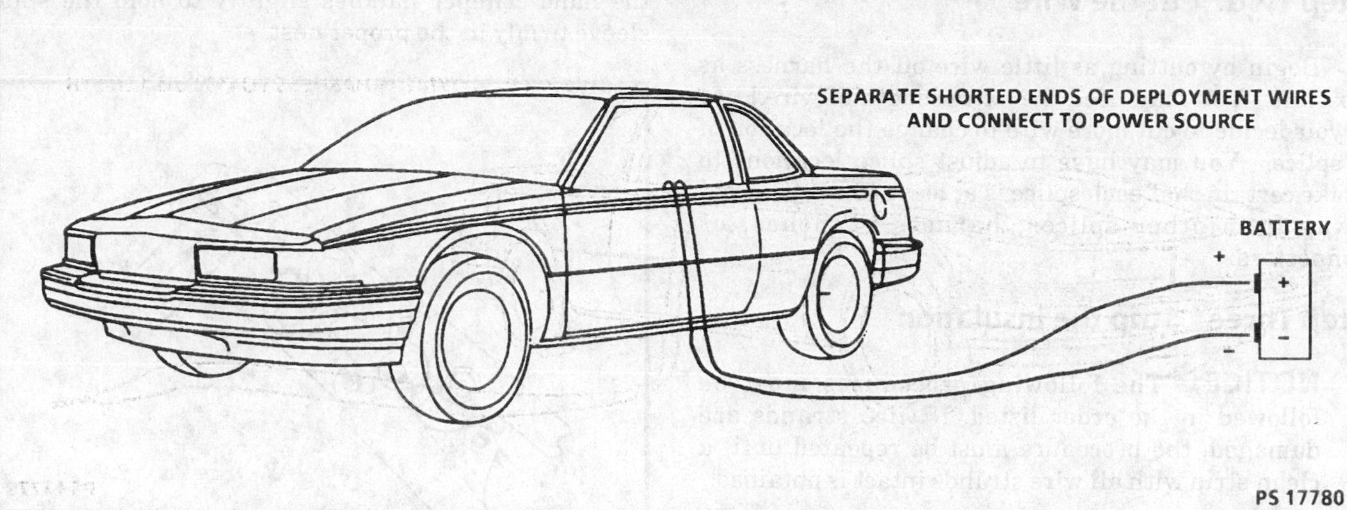
SEPARATE SHORTED ENDS OF DEPLOYMENT WIRES AND CONNECT TO POWER SOURCE
BATTERY
+
+
-
-
PS 17780

Figure 26 - Separate Shorted Ends of Deployment Harness and Connect to Power Source

Terminal Repair Kit J 38125-A

Essential tool kit J 38125-A contains special "sealed splices" for use in repairing SIR system wiring. A special crimping tool, heat torch, and instruction manual for these splices are also included.

Two critical features of the sealed splices are a special heat shrink sleeve with sealing adhesive to produce an environmentally sealed splice and a cross hatched (knurled) core crimp to provide necessary contact integrity for the sensitive, low energy circuits.

Terminal Repair Kit J 38125-A also serves as a generic terminal repair kit. The kit contains a large sampling of common GM electrical terminals and the correct tools to attach them to wires and remove them from connectors. ***The terminals in the kit are not to be used to replace damaged SIR system terminals unless specifically indicated by the terminal package.*** The DERM terminal repair assembly pack is included in J 38125-A for SIR use.

SIR Connector (Plastic Body and Terminal Metal Pin) Repair

If any connector or terminal in the SIR wire harness (except pigtails) is damaged, the component should be repaired using one of the connector repair assembly packs. These kits include an instruction sheet and the sealed splices which will be used to splice the new wires, connector, and terminals to the harness. The splice crimping tool, which is color keyed to match the splices from Terminal Repair Kit J 38125-A, must be used to apply these splices.

The terminals in the SIR system are made of a special metal to provide necessary contact integrity for the sensitive, low energy circuits. These terminals are only available in the connector repair assembly packs, do not substitute any other terminals for those in the assembly packs.

If individual terminals are damaged on the DERM connector, they should be repaired using the DERM terminal repair assembly pack. If individual terminals are damaged on any other SIR connection, the entire connection should be replaced using the appropriate connector repair assembly pack. It may be necessary to replace the entire SIR wiring harness.

SIR Wire Pigtail Repair

If the wiring pigtail (a wire or wires attached directly to the device, not by a connector) is damaged, the entire component (with pigtail) must be replaced. Examples of "pigtail" components are the arming sensor, the discriminating sensors and the SIR coil assembly. Absolutely no wire, connector, or terminal repairs are to be attempted on the arming sensor, the discriminating sensors or the SIR coil assembly.

SIR Wire Repair

If any wire except the pigtail is damaged, the wire should be repaired by splicing in a new section of wire of the same gauge size (.5, .8, 1.0, etc.). The sealed splices and splice crimping tool from Terminal Repair Kit J 38125-A must be used for these repairs. The following wiring repair procedures must be used to ensure the integrity of the sealed splice application.

Step One: Open the Harness

If the harness is taped, remove the tape. To avoid wire insulation damage use a sewing "seam ripper" (available from sewing supply stores) to cut open the harness. The crimp and sealed splice sleeves may be used on all types of insulation except tefzel and coaxial and may only be used to form a one-to-one splice.

Step Two: Cut the Wire

Begin by cutting as little wire off the harness as possible. You may need the extra length of wire later if you decide to cut more wire to change the location of a splice. You may have to adjust splice locations to make certain that each splice is at least 40 mm (1.5 in.) away from other splices, harness branches, or connectors.

Step Three: Strip the Insulation

NOTICE: The following procedures must be followed in the order listed. If wire strands are damaged, the procedure must be repeated until a clean strip with all wire strands intact is obtained.

If it is necessary to add a length of wire to the existing harness, be certain to use the same size as the original wire.

To find the correct wire size either find the wire on the schematic and convert the metric size to the equivalent AWG size or use an AWG wire gage.

If unsure about the wire size, begin with the largest opening in the wire stripper and work down until achieving a clean strip of the insulation. Strip approximately 7.5 mm (5/16 in.) of insulation from each wire to be spliced. Be careful to avoid nicking or cutting any of the strands. Check the stripped wire for nicks or cut strands. If the wire is damaged, repeat this procedure after removing the damaged section.

Step Four: Select and Position the Splice Sleeve

Select the proper sealed splice sleeve according to wire size. The splice sleeves and tool nests are color coded (see following chart).

Color Splice sleeve	Crimp tool nest color	Wire gage AWG/ (metric)
Salmon (yellow-pink)	Red	20, 18/ (0.5, 0.8)
Blue	Blue	16, 14/ (1.0, 2.0)
Yellow	Yellow	12, 10/ (3.0, 5.0)

Crimp and Seal Splice Chart

Using the J 38125-A Splice Crimp Tool (Figure 27), position the splice sleeve in the proper color nest of the hand crimp tool. Place the splice sleeve in the nest so that the crimp falls midway between the end of the barrel and the stop.

The sleeve has a stop in the middle of the barrel to prevent the wire from going further (Figure 28). Close the hand crimper handles slightly to hold the splice sleeve firmly in the proper nest.

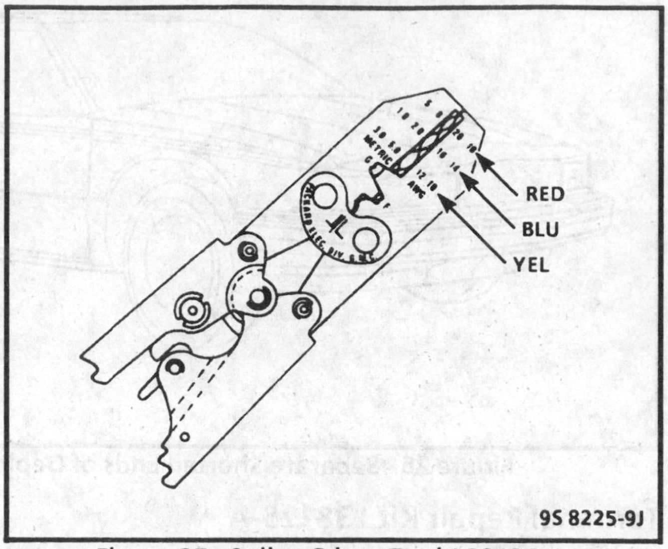
RED
BLU
YEL
METRIC
AWG
9S 8225-9J

Figure 27 - Splice Crimp Tool J 38125-A

Step Five: Insert Wires Into Splice Sleeve and Crimp

Insert the wire into the splice sleeve until it hits the barrel stop and close the handles of the crimp tool tightly until the crimper handles open when released (Figure 28). The crimper handles will not open until the proper amount of pressure is applied to the splice sleeve. Repeat Steps 4 and 5 for the opposite end of the splice.

Step Six: Shrink the Insulation Around the Splice

Using the heat torch apply heat where the barrel is crimped. Gradually move the heat barrel to the open end of the tubing, shrinking the tubing completely as the heat is moved along the insulation. A small amount of sealant will come out of the end of the tubing when sufficient shrinking is achieved (Figure 28).

SIR System Wire Splice Repair

If any of the original equipment splices (three wires or more) in the SIR wiring harness are damaged they should be repaired by applying a new splice (not sealed) from the Terminal Repair Kit J 38125-A. Carefully follow the instructions included in the kit for proper splice clip application. Cloth duct tape may be substituted for splice tape if necessary.

Alternative Repair Methods

No alternative repair methods are available for the SIR system wiring and components.

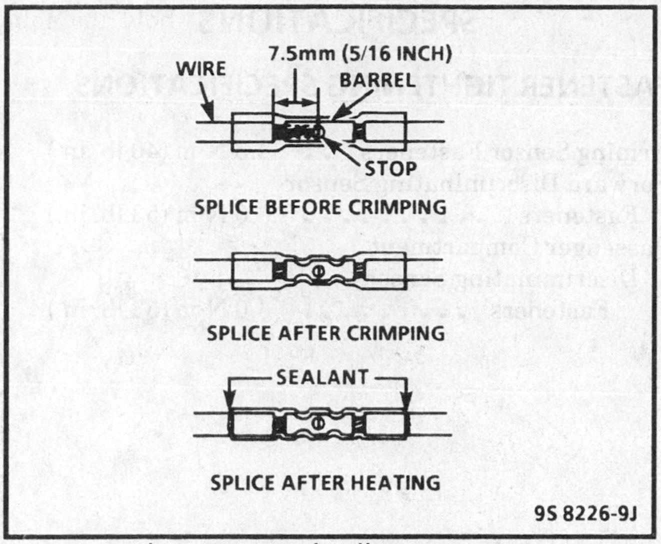

7.5mm (5/16 INCH)
WIRE
BARREL
STOP
SPLICE BEFORE CRIMPING
SPLICE AFTER CRIMPING
SEALANT
SPLICE AFTER HEATING
9S 8226-9J

Figure 28 - Seal Splice Sequence

Connector Position Assurance (CPA)

The Connector Position Assurance (CPA) is a small plastic insert that is inserted through the locking tabs of all of the SIR system connectors. The purpose of the CPA is to ensure the connector halves are securely connected and they cannot vibrate apart. The CPA must be in place to ensure good contact between the SIR mating terminals.

Terminal Position Assurance (TPA)

The Terminal Position Assurance (TPA) insert is similar to the plastic "combs" used in PCM connectors. The function of the TPA is to keep the terminal securely seated in the connector body. The TPA is not to be removed from the connector body unless a terminal must be removed for replacement.

SPECIAL TOOLS

CAUTION: To avoid deployment when troubleshooting the SIR system, do not use electrical test equipment such as a battery powered or ac powered voltmeter, ohmmeter, etc., or any type of electrical equipment other than that specified in this manual. Do not use a non-powered probe type tester. Instructions in this manual must be followed carefully, otherwise personal injury may result.

SIR DRIVER/PASSENGER LOAD TOOL

The SIR Driver/Passenger Load Tool J 38715 is used only when called for in this section. Do not attempt to use the SIR Column Load Tool J 37808 as the connectors are incompatible. It is used as a diagnostic aid and safety device to prevent inadvertent inflator module deployment.

The load tool has four yellow connectors attached to its case. The three small connectors are electrically functional and serve as resistive load substitutions. The large dummy connector does not serve as a load substitution but merely takes the physical place of the DERM connector when needed.

No more than one connector is used at any time. One of the small connectors is used to substitute the load of the driver inflator module when it is connected at the top of the column to the SIR coil assembly. Another small connector is used to substitute the load of the driver inflator module and the SIR coil assembly when it is connected at the base of the column to the SIR wiring harness. The third small connector is used to substitute for the load of the passenger inflator module. Since this vehicle is not equipped with a passenger inflator module the lead marked "Passenger Inflator" should not be used. The large dummy connector separates the shorting bar in the DERM harness connector when it is connected to it in place of the DERM.

By substituting the resistance of the load tool when called for, a determination can be made as to whether an inflator circuit component is causing system malfunction and which component is causing the malfunction. The load tool should be used only when specifically called for in the diagnostic procedures.

J 39200 DVM

The J 39200 DVM is the preferred DVM for use in SIR diagnosis and repair. However, J 34029-A may be used if J 39200 is not available. No other DVM's are approved for SIR diagnosis and repair.

SCAN TOOL

The Tech 1 is used to read and clear SIR system Diagnostic Trouble Codes (DTCs). The Tech 1 will also provide SIR system circuit values using the "Data List" function. Refer to the Tech 1 Operator's Manual for specific information on how to use the Tech 1.

Scan tools from other manufacturers may be used. Refer to the Instruction Manual for the tool for specific instructions.

J 35616-A CONNECTOR TEST ADAPTER KIT

The J 35616-A Connector Test Adapter Kit must be used whenever a diagnostic procedure requests checking or probing a terminal. Using the appropriate adapter will ensure that no damage to the terminal will occur from the DVM probe, such as spreading or bending.

The adapter will also give an idea of whether contact tension is sufficient, helping to find an open or intermittent open due to poor terminal contact.

SPECIFICATIONS

FASTENER TIGHTENING SPECIFICATIONS

Arming Sensor Fasteners	4.5 N·m (40 lb. in.)
Forward Discriminating Sensor Fasteners	6.0 N·m (53 lb. in.)
Passenger Compartment Discriminating Sensor Fasteners	6.0 N·m (53 lb. in.)

SERVICE PARTS INFORMATION

PART NAME	SERVICE PARTS CATALOG REFERENCE NAME	SERVICE PARTS CATALOG GROUP
COMPONENTS		
Arming Sensor	SENSOR ASM, INFL RST ARMING	14.865
DERM	MODULE ASM, INFL RST DIAGN ENGY RESV	14.865
Forward Discriminating Sensor	SENSOR ASM, INFL RST F/END SH MET	14.865
Inflator Module	MODULE ASM, INFL RST STRG WHL	14.865
Passenger Compartment Discriminating Sensor	SENSOR, INFL RST PASS COMPT	14.865
SIR Coil Assembly	COIL KIT, INFL RST STRG WHL MDL	14.865
Warning Lamp "AIR BAG"		9.744 (Standard Parts Cat.)

6-11-93
PS 18167

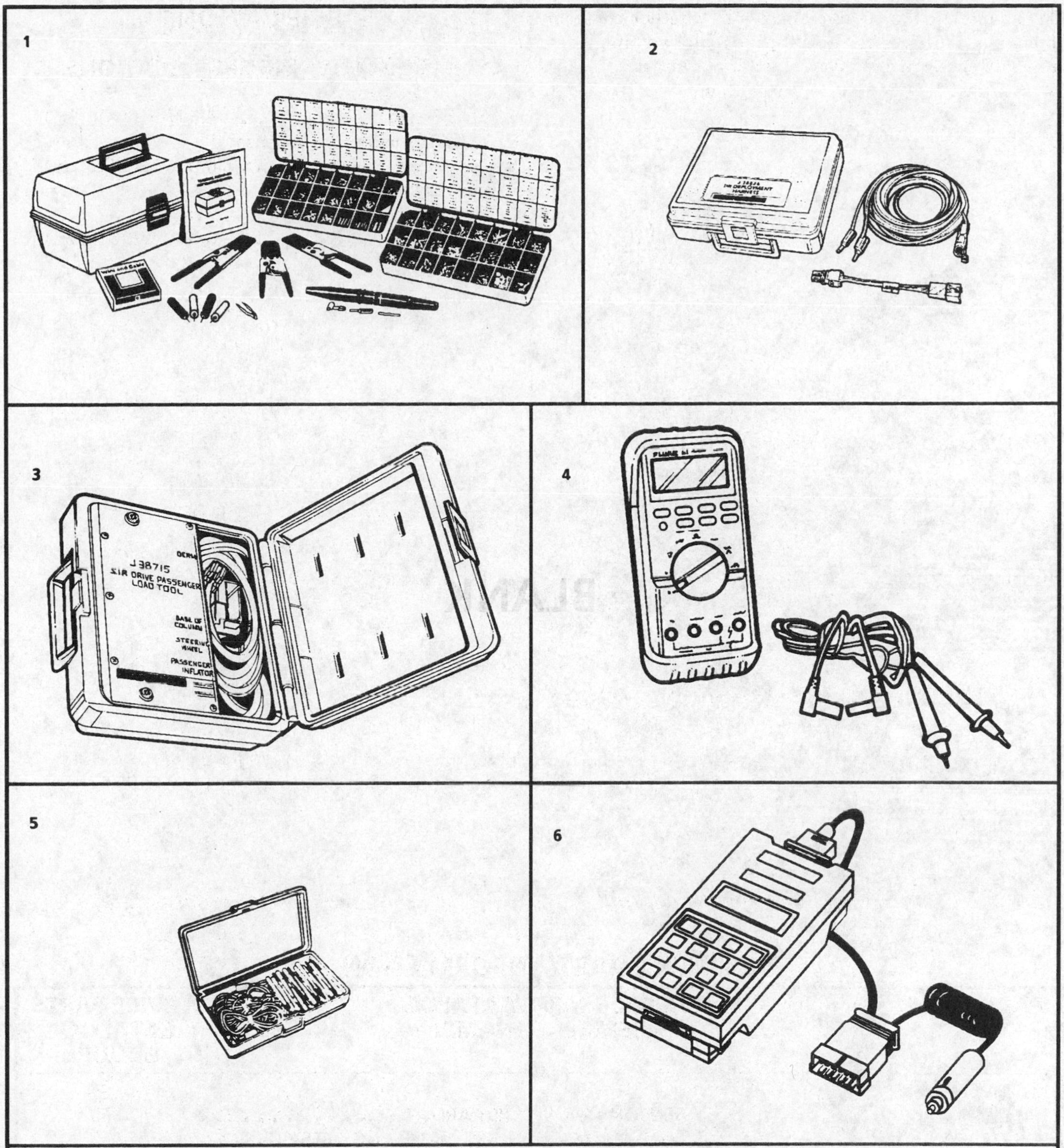
1
2
3
J 38715
SIR DRIVE PASSENGER
LOAD TOOL
BASE OF
COLUMN
STEERING
WHEEL
PASSENGER
INFLATOR
4
5
6

1 J 38125-A - TERMINAL REPAIR KIT

2 J 38826 - SIR DEPLOYMENT HARNESS

3 J 38715 - SIR DRIVER/PASSENGER LOAD TOOL

4 J 39200 - DIGITAL MULTIMETER

5 J 35616-A - CONNECTOR TEST ADAPTER KIT

6 SCAN TOOL

MS 13511

SIR Special Tools

BLANK

SECTION 9K

KEYLESS ENTRY

NOTICE: When fasteners are removed, always reinstall them at the same location from which they were removed. If a fastener needs to be replaced, use the correct part number fastener for that application. If the correct part number fastener is not available, a fastener of equal size and strength (or stronger) may be used. Fasteners that are not reused, and those requiring thread locking compound will be called out. The correct torque value must be used when installing fasteners that require it. If the above conditions are not followed, parts or systems damage could result.

CONTENTS

GENERAL DESCRIPTION

The remote lock control system is used to lock and unlock the doors and release the luggage compartment lid of the vehicle. A small receiver is installed to the foundation of the rear compartment panel in the sedan or the right quarter panel in the coupe. The transmitter is a hand held item that is attached to a key ring. The transmitter has three buttons that control the functions of the system.

The remote door lock receiver is battery fed and is always monitoring the transmitter signal. When the correct transmitter signal is received to lock all of the doors, a transistor driver will energize the correct lock control relay coil. The receiver will also control which lock control relays will be energized to unlock the driver's door or all of the doors and the illumination of the courtesy lamps.

The transmitter will transmit a radio signal to the receiver, which will control the three functions of the remote door lock receiver. The range is approximately 10 meters (33 feet).

REMOTE LOCK CONTROL OPERATION

Figure 1

To Unlock Door(s):

- Press "UNLOCK" button once and release to unlock driver's door only and illuminate courtesy lamps for 15 seconds or until ignition is turned "ON."
- Press "UNLOCK" button a second time (within 1 to 5 seconds) of the first depression to unlock the remaining doors. The courtesy lamps will remain on for the rest of the 15 seconds or until ignition is turned "ON."
- Press " [luggage symbol] " button to release luggage compartment lid. Illumination of the courtesy lamps will not be activated.

To Lock Door(s):

- Press " [key symbol] " to lock all doors. The courtesy lamps will immediately turn off.

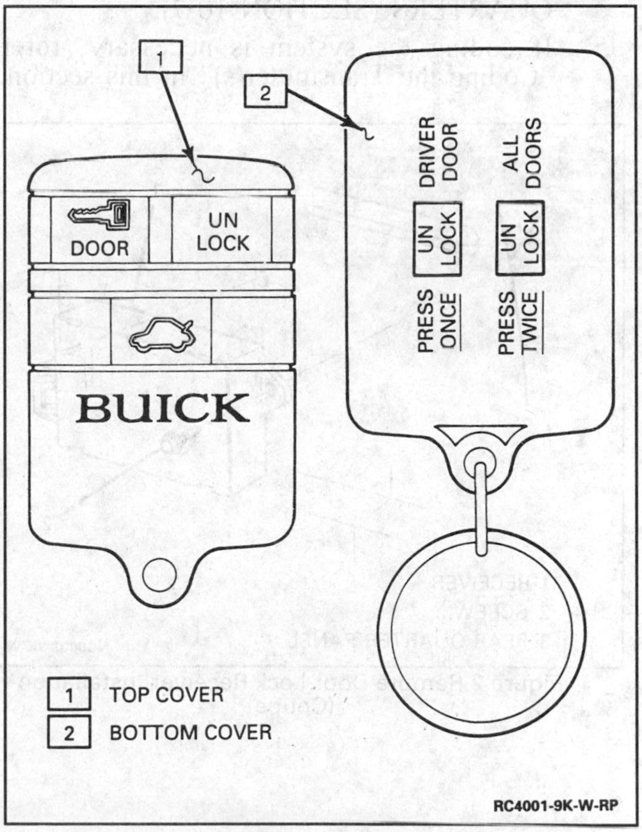
1
2
DOOR
UN LOCK
BUICK
DRIVER DOOR
ALL DOORS
UN LOCK
UN LOCK
PRESS ONCE
PRESS TWICE
1 TOP COVER
2 BOTTOM COVER
RC4001-9K-W-RP

Figure 1 Transmitter

DIAGNOSIS

To properly diagnose the system, refer to ELECTRICAL DIAGNOSIS (SECTION 8A-132).

ON-VEHICLE SERVICE

REMOTE DOOR LOCK RECEIVER

Coupe

Figure 2

Remove or Disconnect

1. Rear quarter lower trim panel. Refer to REAR QUARTERS (SECTION 10-7).
2. Screws.
3. Receiver from panel.
4. Electrical connectors from receiver.

Install or Connect

1. Electrical connectors to receiver.
2. Receiver to panel.
3. Screws.

Tighten

- Screws to 1.9 N•m (18 lb. in.).

4. Rear quarter lower trim panel. Refer to REAR QUARTERS (SECTION 10-7).
5. If coding the system is necessary, refer to "Coding the Transmitter(s)" in this section.

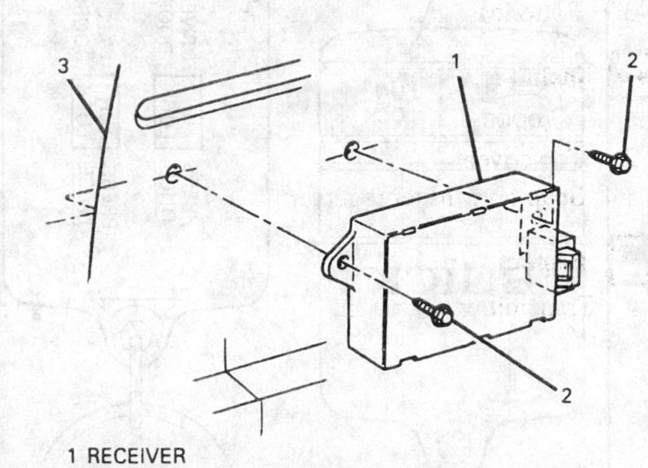
3
1
2
2
1 RECEIVER
2 SCREW
3 REAR QUARTER PANEL
NC0003-9K-W-RA

Figure 2 Remote Door Lock Receiver Installation (Coupe)

Sedan

Figure 3

Remove or Disconnect

1. Rear seat-to-rear window trim panel. Refer to BODY REAR END (SECTION 10-8).
2. Screws.
3. Receiver from bracket.
4. Retainer and electrical connectors from receiver.

Install or Connect

1. Electrical connectors and retainer to receiver.
2. Receiver to bracket.
3. Screws.

Tighten

- Screws to 2 N·m (18 lb. in.).

4. Rear seat-to-rear window trim panel. Refer to BODY REAR END (SECTION 10-8).
5. If coding the system is necessary refer to "Coding the Transmitter(s)" in this section.

CODING THE TRANSMITTER(S)

Figure 4

1. Open rear compartment lid and position carpet (next to the antenna) aside.
2. Access the program wire terminal.
3. Using a jumper wire with alligator clips, ground the wire terminal to the antenna.
   - The door locks will automatically lock and unlock, indicating that the receiver is in the programming mode.

Important

- Any transmitter that was previously matched, has been erased.

4. With the system still grounded, press any button on the transmitter.
   - The door locks will automatically lock and unlock, indicating that the transmitter code has been set.
5. If coding a second transmitter, repeat step 4.

Important

- Removing the jumper wire before the second transmitter is programmed will prevent the transmitters from being matched. If this mistake is made and you wish to program a second transmitter, unground wire and repeat steps 3, 4 and 5.

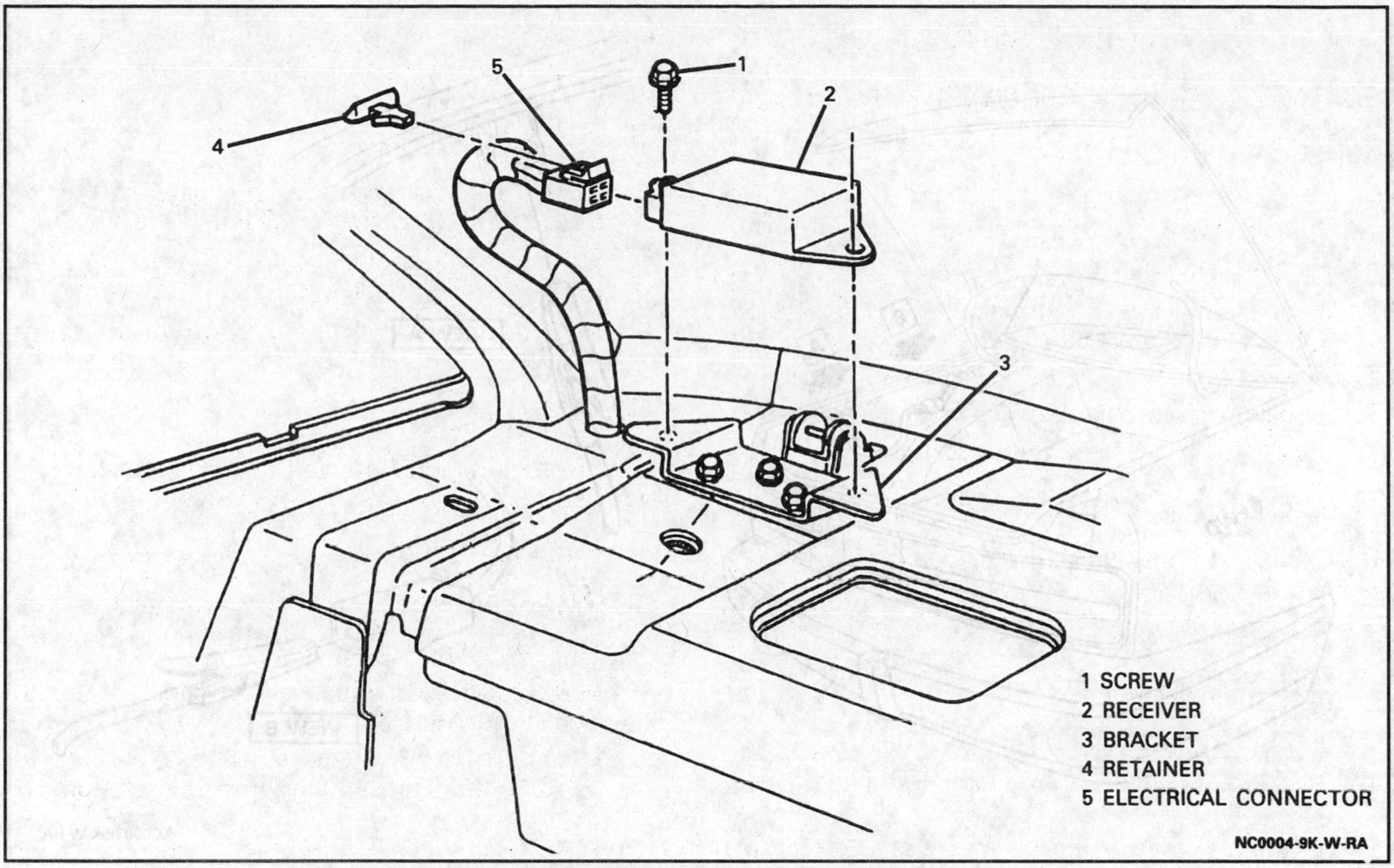

1
2
3
4
5
1 SCREW
2 RECEIVER
3 BRACKET
4 RETAINER
5 ELECTRICAL CONNECTOR
NC0004-9K-W-RA

Figure 3 Remote Door Lock Receiver Installation (Sedan)

6. Remove jumper wire.
   - The system will not operate if the jumper wire is not removed.
7. Verify operation of the transmitter(s).
8. Properly position the carpet.

BATTERY (TRANSMITTER)

Figure 1

Remove or Disconnect

1. Gently pry apart transmitter unit at connector molding.
2. Top cover.
3. Batteries.

Install or Connect

1. Batteries.
2. Top cover.
3. Snap transmitter together.

Inspect

- Transmitter operation.

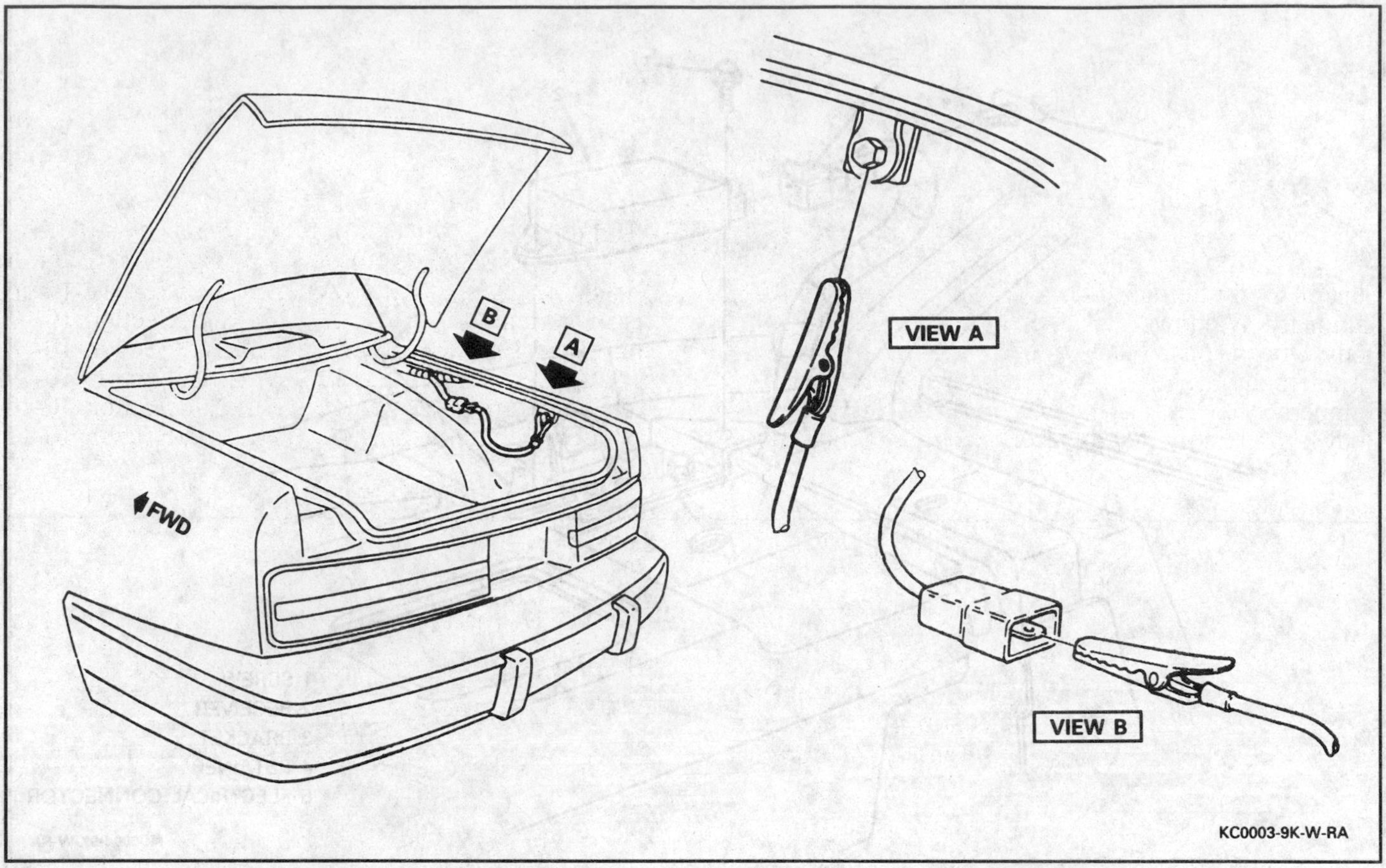
VIEW A
B
A
FWD
VIEW B
KC0003-9K-W-RA
Figure 4 Coding the Transmitter

SPECIFICATIONS

FASTENER TIGHTENING SPECIFICATIONS

Remote Door Lock Receiver Screw ....1.9 N•m (18 lb. in.)

SECTION 10

BODY

CONTENTS

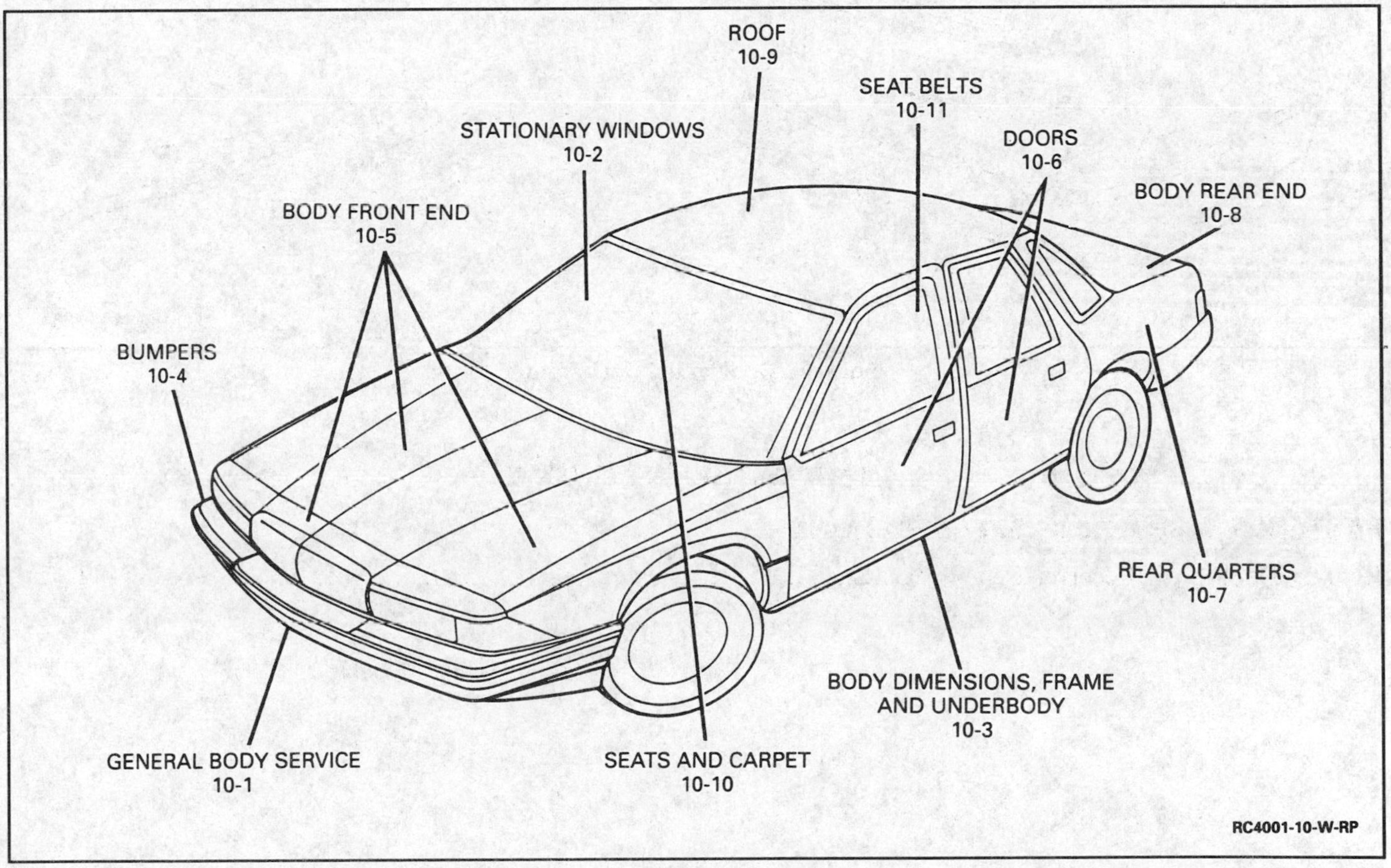
ROOF
10-9
SEAT BELTS
10-11
STATIONARY WINDOWS
10-2
DOORS
10-6
BODY REAR END
10-8
BODY FRONT END
10-5
BUMPERS
10-4
REAR QUARTERS
10-7
BODY DIMENSIONS, FRAME
AND UNDERBODY
10-3
GENERAL BODY SERVICE
10-1
SEATS AND CARPET
10-10
RC4001-10-W-RP

SECTION 10-1

GENERAL BODY SERVICE

NOTICE: When fasteners are removed, always reinstall them at the same location from which they were removed. If a fastener needs to be replaced, use the correct part number fastener for that application. If the correct part number fastener is not available, a fastener of equal size and strength (or stronger) may be used. Fasteners that are not reused, and those requiring thread locking compound will be called out. The correct torque value must be used when installing fasteners that require it. If the above conditions are not followed, parts or system damage could result.

NOTICE: The theft deterrent label found on some major sheet metal, engines, and transaxles must be masked prior to painting, rustproofing, undercoating, etc. The mask **must** be removed following the above operations. Failure to keep the label clean and readable may result in liability for violation of Federal Vehicle Theft Prevention Standard, and subject the vehicle owner to possible suspicion that the part was stolen.

CONTENTS

GENERAL DESCRIPTION

The information in this section provides body service procedures that apply to the entire vehicle.

ON-VEHICLE SERVICE

THEFT DETERRENT LABELING

Theft deterrent labels are found on some major sheet metal, engines, and transaxles. For more information on these labels, refer to GENERAL INFORMATION (SECTION 0A).

BODY SIDE MOLDINGS

Adhesive Body Side Moldings

The body side moldings are attached to the body panels with adhesive tape. To insure a good replacement of new or old moldings, the panel surface should be warm, 21°C to 32°C (70°F to 90°F), clean and free of any wax or oily film. Methods are listed to attach loose molding ends, completely removed moldings, and replacement moldings.

Adhesive Body Side Molding End Loose

1. Wash the affected area with soap and water and wipe dry. Wipe panel and adhesive side of the molding with a clean rag using oil-free naphtha or alcohol.

   If the molding has pulled loose from the adhesive backing (tape remains on body panel), do not remove the tape from the body. Clean the back of the molding and tape on the body with oil-free naphtha or alcohol and proceed with step 3.
2. If needed, apply a length of masking tape as a molding guide. A straightedge may also be used.
3. Apply adhesive to the back of the molding and press in place. If adhesive part number 1052621 or equivalent is used, apply constant pressure to the molding for 30 seconds or until a firm bond has been made.

Adhesive Body Side Molding Completely Removed

Figure 1

Important

- Do not use this procedure if molding is dented or was pried from the body.

1. Wash affected panel area with soap and water and wipe dry.
2. Remove all traces of adhesive from the body panel and back of molding using oil-free naphtha or alcohol.

3. Mark the proper position of molding with a length of masking tape. Use adjacent moldings as a guide.
4. Warm body panel with a heat lamp or heat gun to 21°C (70°F).
5. Apply a double-coated foam tape (3M part number 06380 or equivalent) to the molding.
6. Align the molding to the tape guideline on the body panel.
7. Peel backing from the end of the molding.
8. Press firmly into place while continuing to remove the backing.
9. Hand roll the molding to the body to ensure proper adhesion.

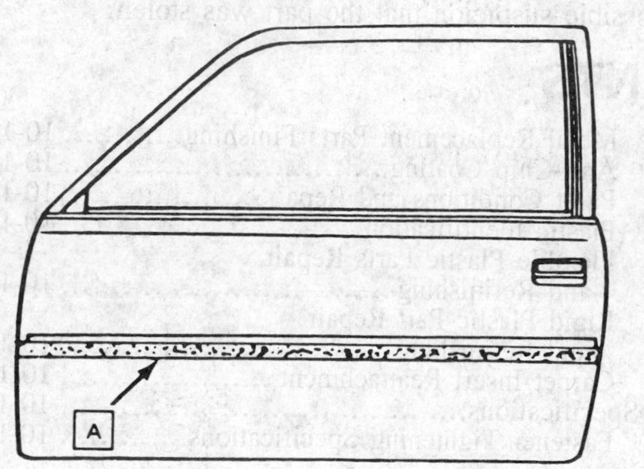
A
A TAPE GUIDELINE
NC0001-101-A-RA

Figure 1 Adhesive Body Side Molding Repair

Adhesive Body Side Molding Replacement

Remove or Disconnect

1. Heat molding, using a heat gun 152 mm (6 inches) from surface.
   - Apply heat using a circular motion for about 30 seconds.
2. Peel molding from the panel surface using a flat-bladed tool, being careful not to damage paint.

Install or Connect

1. Mark proper position of molding with a length of masking tape.

   Clean

   - Body panel using oil-free naphtha or alcohol.
2. Warm body panel with a heat lamp or heat gun to 21°C (70°F).
3. Peel backing from the front end of the molding.
   - Do not touch the adhesive backing.
4. Press molding to the body while continuing to remove the backing.
5. Hand roll the molding to the body to ensure proper adhesion.
6. Molding ends should not overlap door edge, door edge guard, lock cylinder or body openings.

Inspect

- Molding ends for bonding.
  – Hand roll loose ends.

Front Fender Center Rear Upper Molding (Coupe)

Figure 2

Remove or Disconnect

1. Bolt/screw.
2. Nuts.
3. Front fender center rear upper molding.

Install or Connect

1. Front fender center rear upper molding.
2. Nuts.

   Tighten

   - Nuts to 2 N·m (18 lb. in.).
3. Bolt/screw.

   Tighten

   - Bolt/screw to 1 N·m (9 lb. in.).

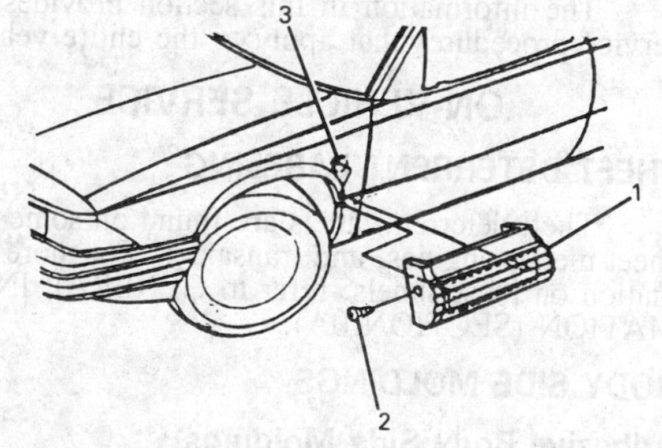
3
1
2
1 MOLDING, FRONT FENDER CENTER REAR UPPER
2 BOLT/SCREW, FRONT FENDER CENTER REAR UPPER MOLDING
3 NUT, FRONT FENDER CENTER REAR UPPER MOLDING
PC0016-101-W-RA

Figure 2 Front Fender Center Rear Upper Molding (Coupe)

Front Fender Center Rear Lower Molding (Coupe)

Figure 3

Remove or Disconnect

1. Front fender center rear upper molding. Refer to "Front Fender Center Rear Upper Molding" above.
2. Front fender center rear lower molding from clip.
3. Clip if necessary by unsnapping from weld stud.

Install or Connect

1. Clip if removed by snapping onto weld stud.
2. Front fender center rear upper molding to lower molding.
3. Front fender center rear lower molding with upper molding to clip.

Front Fender Rear Molding (Coupe)

Figure 4

Remove or Disconnect

1. Bolts/screws.
2. Nuts.
3. Front fender rear molding.

Install or Connect

1. Front fender rear molding.
2. Nuts.

Tighten

- Nuts to 2 N·m (18 lb. in.).

3. Bolts/screws.

Tighten

- Bolts/screws to 1 N·m (9 lb. in.).

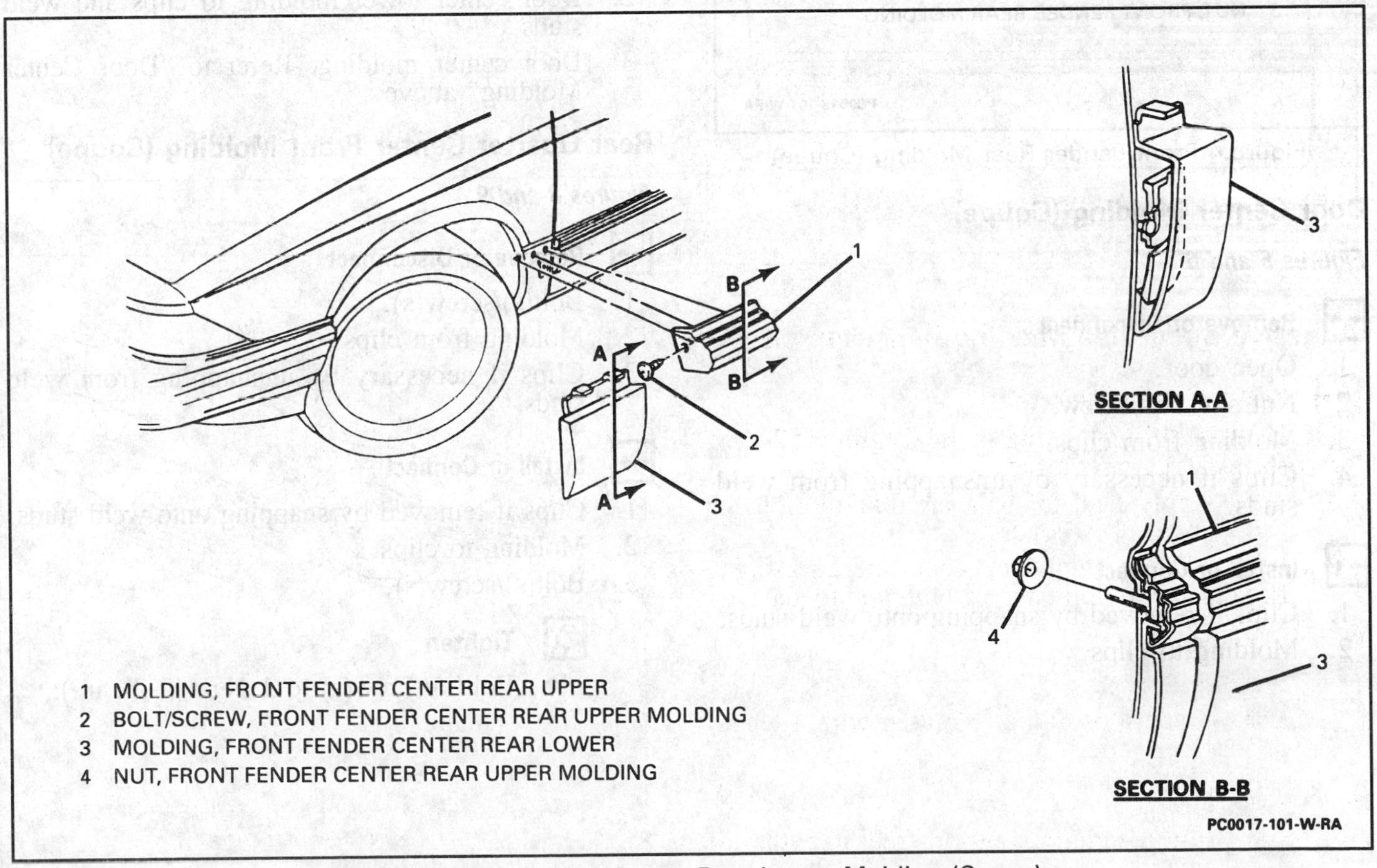

1
2
3
A
A
B
B
SECTION A-A
SECTION B-B
4
1 MOLDING, FRONT FENDER CENTER REAR UPPER
2 BOLT/SCREW, FRONT FENDER CENTER REAR UPPER MOLDING
3 MOLDING, FRONT FENDER CENTER REAR LOWER
4 NUT, FRONT FENDER CENTER REAR UPPER MOLDING
PC0017-101-W-RA

Figure 3 Front Fender Center Rear Lower Molding (Coupe)

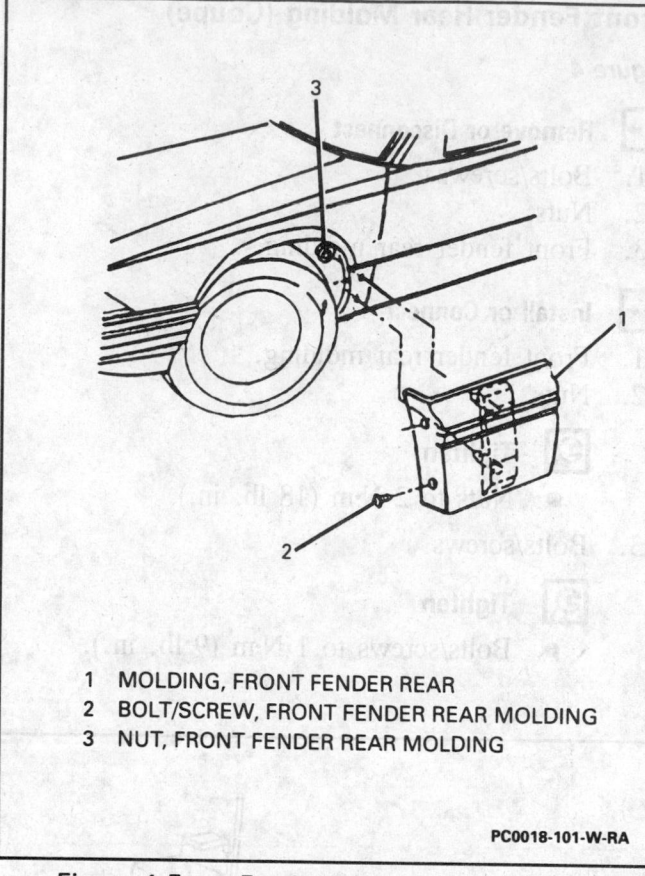

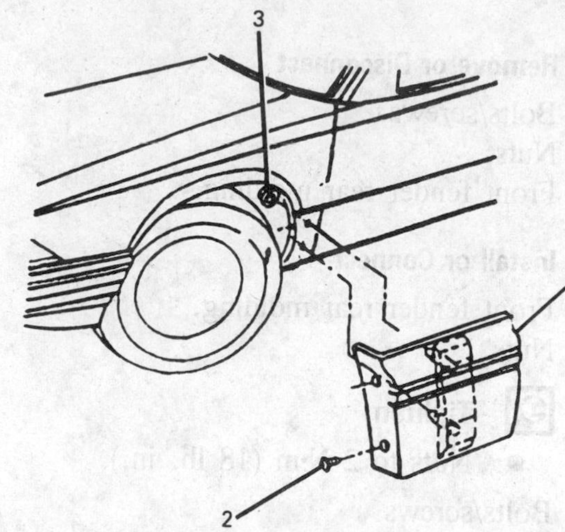
3
1
2
1 MOLDING, FRONT FENDER REAR
2 BOLT/SCREW, FRONT FENDER REAR MOLDING
3 NUT, FRONT FENDER REAR MOLDING
PC0018-101-W-RA

Figure 4 Front Fender Rear Molding (Coupe)

Door Center Molding (Coupe)

Figures 5 and 6

Remove or Disconnect

1. Open door.
2. Nut and bolt/screw.
3. Molding from clips.
4. Clips if necessary by unsnapping from weld studs.

Install or Connect

1. Clips if removed by snapping onto weld studs.
2. Molding to clips.
3. Nut and bolt/screw.

Tighten

- Nut to 2 N·m (18 lb. in.).
- Bolt/screw to 2 N·m (18 lb. in.).

4. Close door.

Door Center Lower Molding (Coupe)

Figure 7

Remove or Disconnect

1. Door center molding. Refer to "Door Center Molding" above.
2. Door center lower molding from clips and weld studs.
3. Clips if necessary by unsnapping from weld studs.

Install or Connect

1. Clips if removed by snapping onto weld studs.
2. Door center lower molding to clips and weld studs.
3. Door center molding. Refer to "Door Center Molding" above.

Rear Quarter Center Front Molding (Coupe)

Figures 8 and 9

Remove or Disconnect

1. Bolt(s)/screw(s).
2. Molding from clips.
3. Clips if necessary by unsnapping from weld studs.

Install or Connect

1. Clips if removed by snapping onto weld studs.
2. Molding to clips.
3. Bolt(s)/screw(s).

Tighten

- Bolt(s)/screw(s) to 1 N·m (9 lb. in.).

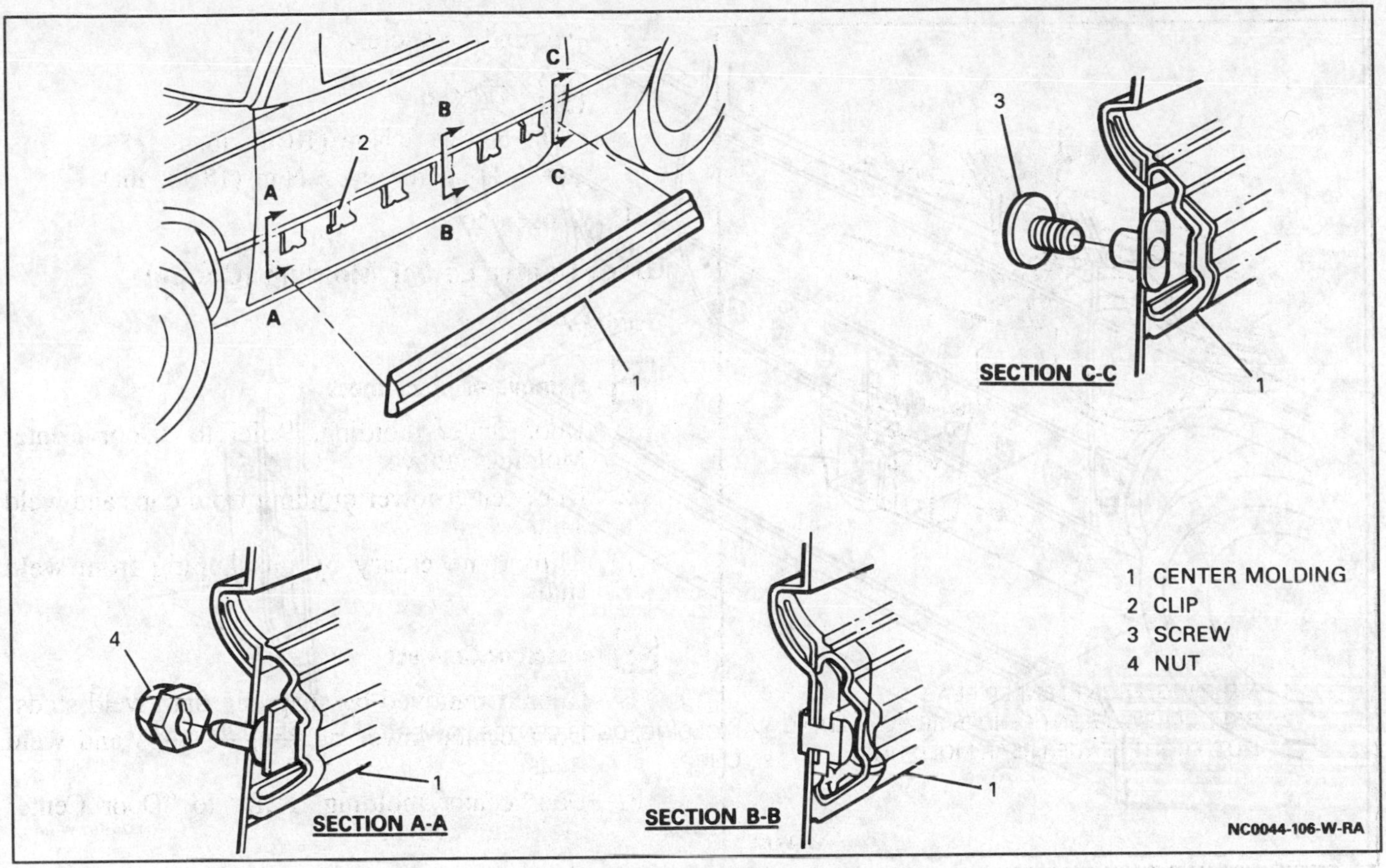

A
B
C
2
1
3
SECTION C-C
4
SECTION A-A
SECTION B-B
1 CENTER MOLDING
2 CLIP
3 SCREW
4 NUT
NC0044-106-W-RA

Figure 5 Door Center Molding (Coupe)

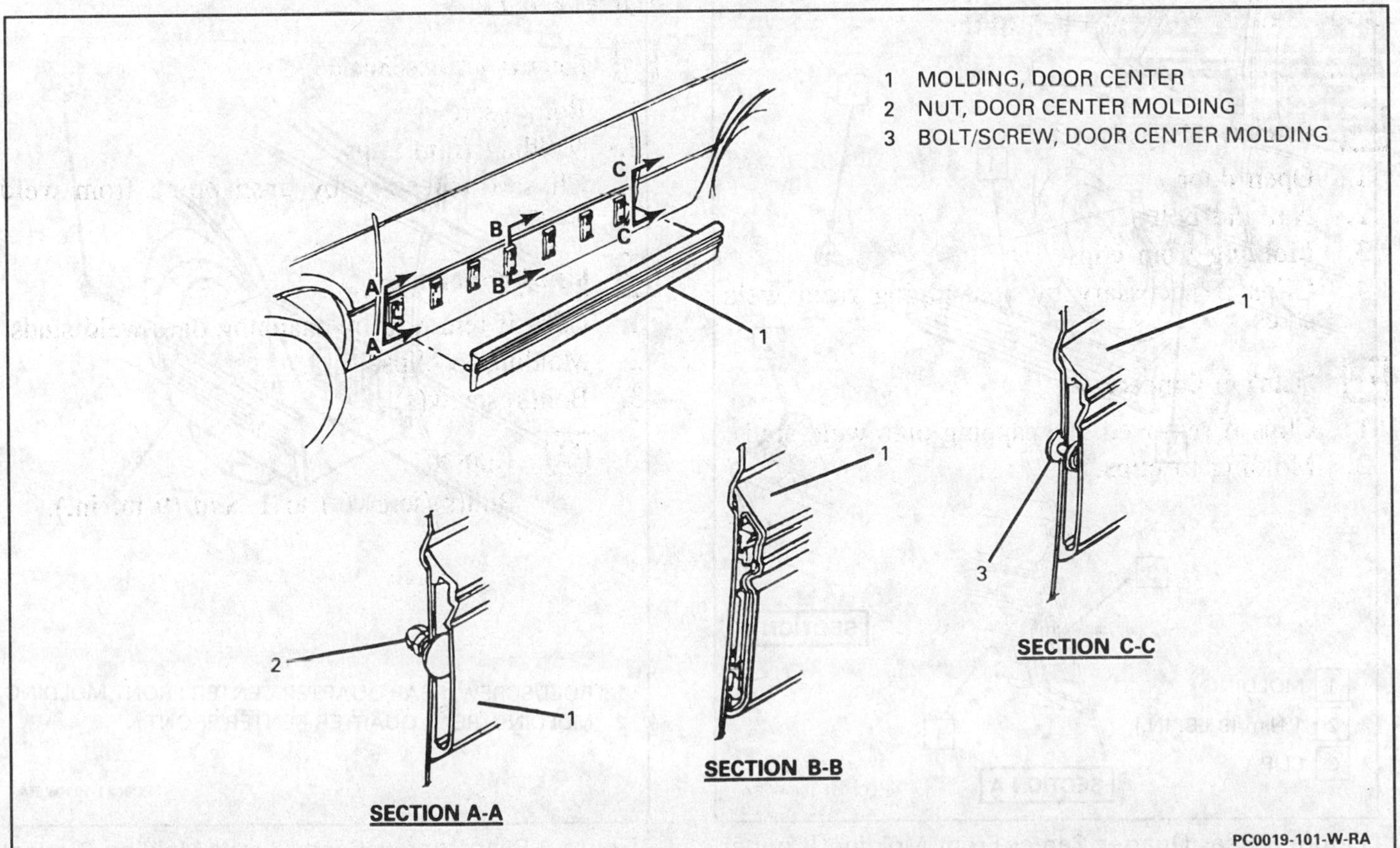

1 MOLDING, DOOR CENTER
2 NUT, DOOR CENTER MOLDING
3 BOLT/SCREW, DOOR CENTER MOLDING
A
B
C
1
2
3
SECTION A-A
SECTION B-B
SECTION C-C
PC0019-101-W-RA

Figure 6 Door Center Molding (Coupe)

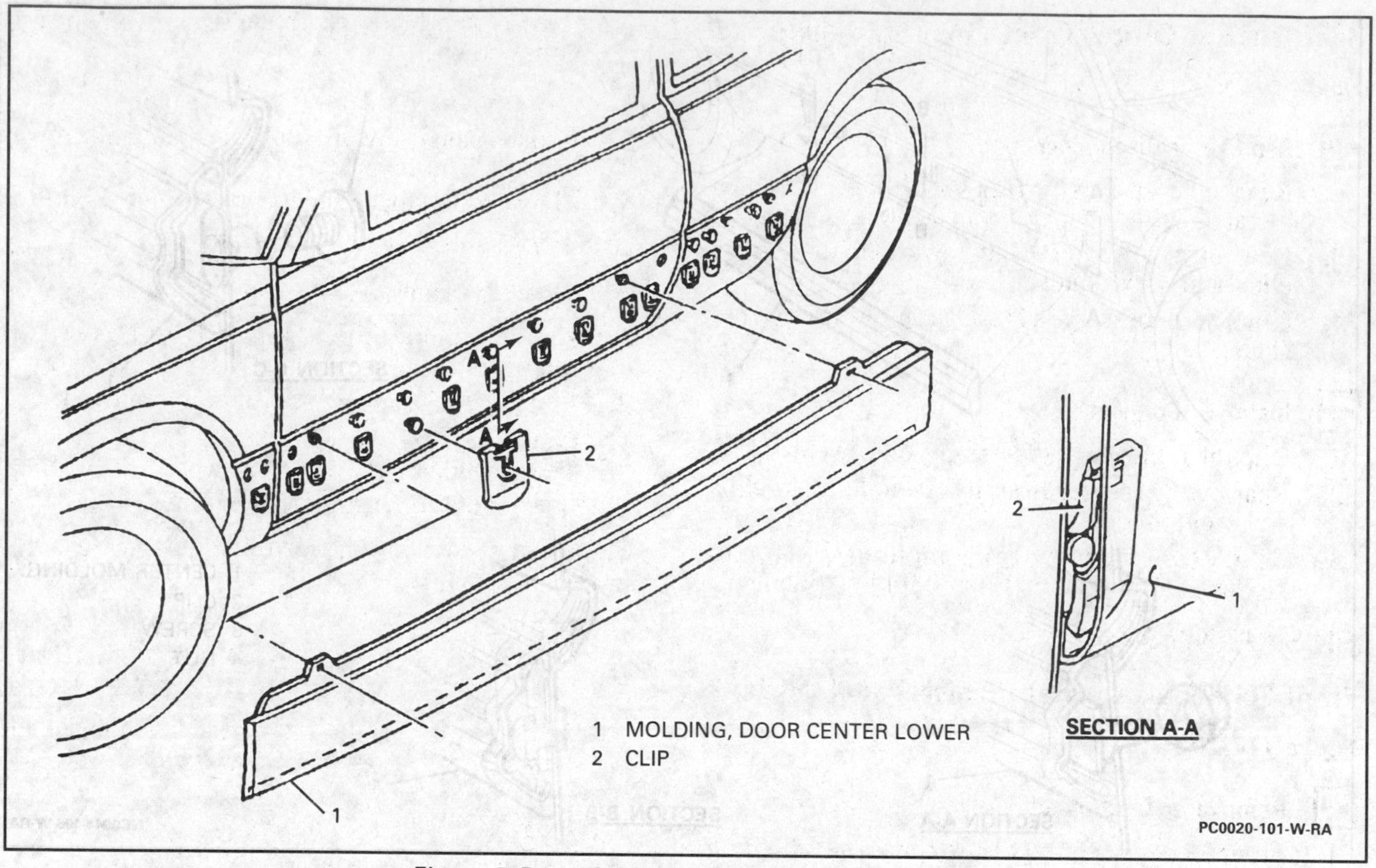
A
A
2
2
1
1 MOLDING, DOOR CENTER LOWER
2 CLIP
SECTION A-A
PC0020-101-W-RA

Figure 7 Door Center Lower Molding (Coupe)

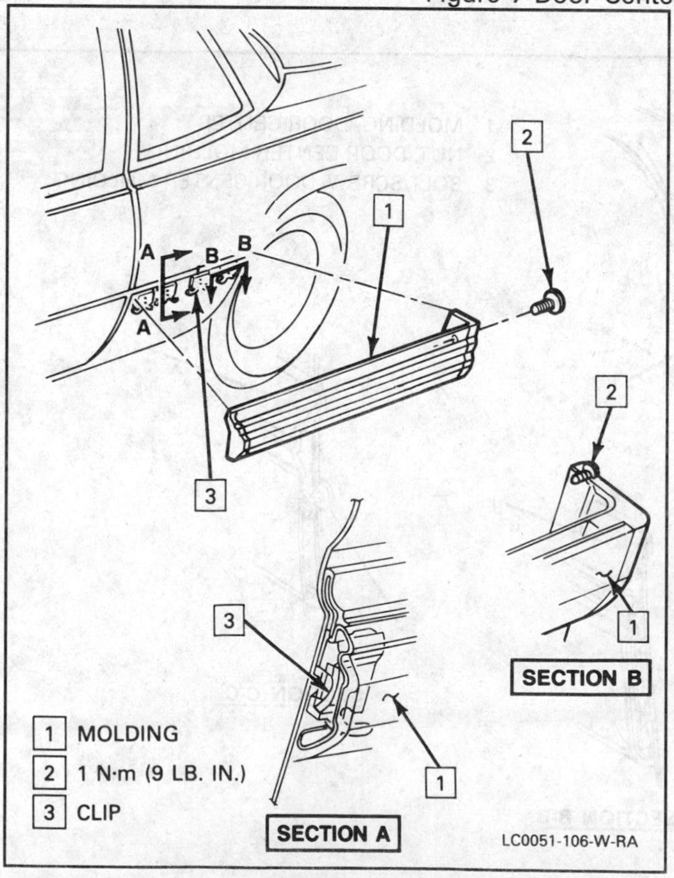
A
B
B
A
1
2
3
2
1
SECTION B
3
1
SECTION A
1 MOLDING
2 1 N·m (9 LB. IN.)
3 CLIP
LC0051-106-W-RA

Figure 8 Rear Quarter Center Front Molding (Coupe)

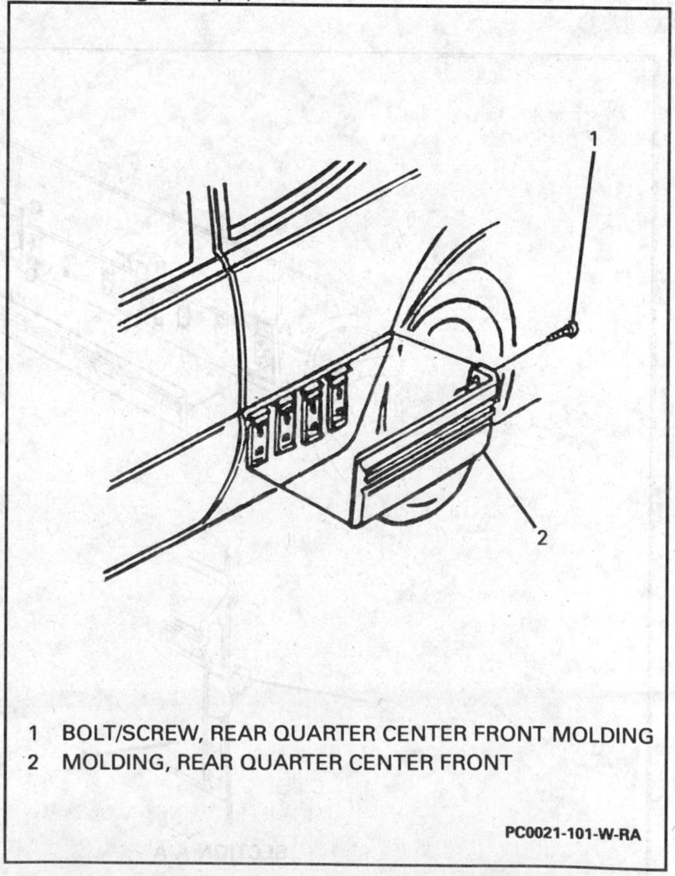
1
2
1 BOLT/SCREW, REAR QUARTER CENTER FRONT MOLDING
2 MOLDING, REAR QUARTER CENTER FRONT
PC0021-101-W-RA

Figure 9 Rear Quarter Center Front Molding (Coupe)

Rear Quarter Center Front Lower Molding

Figure 10

Remove or Disconnect

1. Rear quarter center front molding. Refer to "Rear Quarter Center Front Molding" above.
2. Rear quarter center front lower molding from clips and weld studs.
3. Clips if necessary by unsnapping from weld studs.

Install or Connect

1. Clips if removed by snapping onto weld studs.
2. Rear quarter center front lower molding to clips and weld studs.
3. Rear quarter center front molding. Refer to "Rear Quarter Center Front Molding" above.

FINISH PANELS

Front Fender Lower Rear Finish Panel (Sedan)

Figure 11

Remove or Disconnect

1. Front fender lower rear finish panel nuts holding insert.
2. Front fender lower rear finish panel bolts/screws.
3. Front fender lower rear finish panel.
4. Finish panel lower support nuts and lower support if necessary.
5. Finish panel upper support rivets and support if necessary

Install or Connect

1. Finish panel upper support and rivets if removed.
2. Finish panel support and nuts if removed.

Tighten

- Nuts to 6 N·m (53 lb. in.).

3. Front fender lower rear finish panel.
4. Bolts/screws.

Tighten

- Bolts/screws to 2 N·m (18 lb. in.).

5. Insert to front fender lower rear finish panel and nuts.

Tighten

- Nuts to 3 N·m (27 lb. in.).

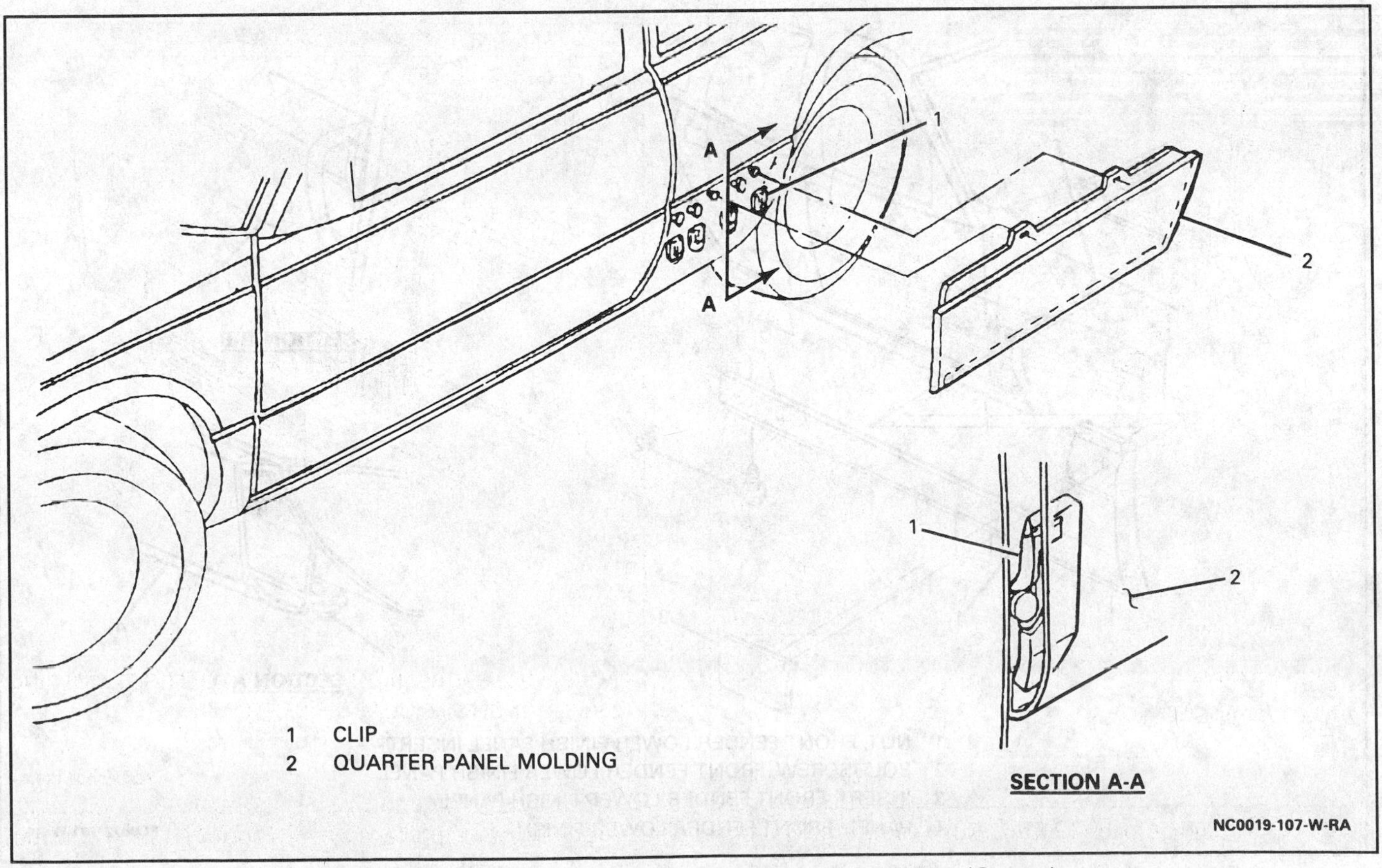
A
A
1
2
1
2
1 CLIP
2 QUARTER PANEL MOLDING
SECTION A-A
NC0019-107-W-RA

Figure 10 Rear Quarter Center Front Lower Molding (Coupe)

Front Fender Lower Rear Finish Panel Chrome Molding (Sedan)

Figure 11

If bright molding insert is tarnished, first try polishing using 3M polish (#05928 quart size, #05929 gallon size) FINESSE-IT II finishing material. If this does not remove tarnish, replace bright portion of molding assembly as follows.

Remove or Disconnect

1. Front fender lower rear finish panel chrome molding insert nuts.
2. Chrome molding.

Install or Connect

1. Chrome molding.
2. Front fender lower rear finish panel chrome molding insert nuts.

Tighten

- Nuts to 3 N·m (27 lb. in.).

Door Lower Finish Panel (Sedan)

Figure 12

Remove or Disconnect

1. Open door.
2. Bolt/screw.
3. Retainers from bottom.
4. Door lower finish panel from clips.
5. Clips if necessary by unsnapping from weld studs.
6. Door lower finish panel upper support rivets if removing upper support.
7. Door lower finish panel upper support if necessary.
8. Door lower finish panel lower support nuts if removing lower support.
9. Door lower finish panel lower support if necessary.

Install or Connect

1. Door lower finish panel lower support if removed.
2. Door lower finish panel lower support nuts if removed.

Tighten

- Nuts to 6 N·m (53 lb. in.).

3. Door lower finish panel upper support if removed.
4. Door lower finish panel upper support rivets if removed.

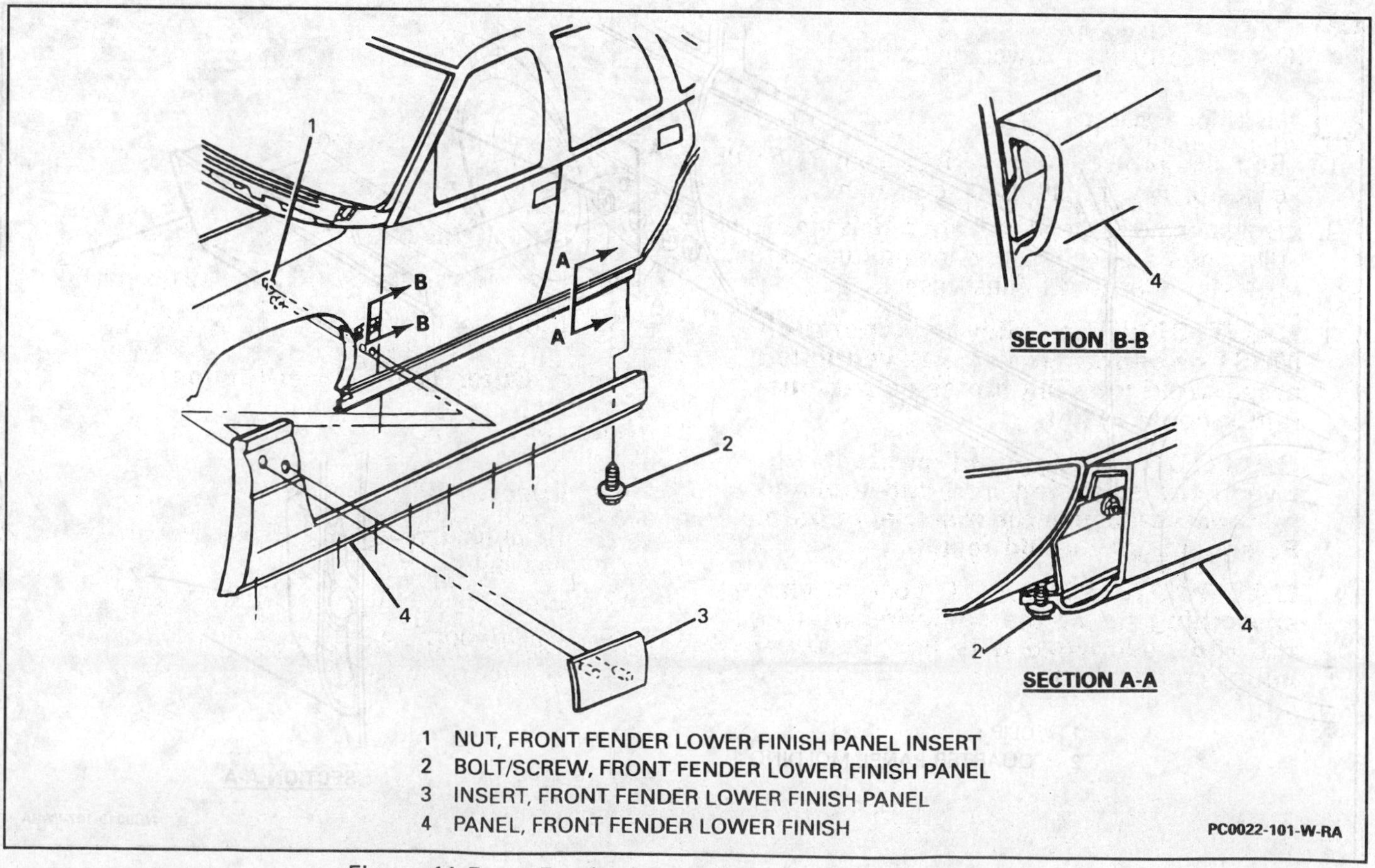
1
A
B
B
A
2
4
3
4
SECTION B-B
2
4
SECTION A-A
1 NUT, FRONT FENDER LOWER FINISH PANEL INSERT
2 BOLT/SCREW, FRONT FENDER LOWER FINISH PANEL
3 INSERT, FRONT FENDER LOWER FINISH PANEL
4 PANEL, FRONT FENDER LOWER FINISH
PC0022-101-W-RA

Figure 11 Front Fender Lower Rear Finish Panel (Sedan)

5. Clips if removed by snapping onto weld studs.
6. Door lower finish panel to clips.
7. Retainers to bottom.
8. Bolt/screw.

Tighten

- Bolt/screw to 2 N·m (18 lb. in.).

9. Close door.

Door Lower Finish Panel Chrome Molding (Sedan)

Figure 12

If bright molding insert is tarnished, first try polishing using 3M polish (#05928 quart size, #05929 gallon size) FINESSE-IT II finishing material. If this does not remove tarnish, replace bright portion of molding assembly as follows.

Remove or Disconnect

1. Door lower finish panel. Refer to "Door Lower Finish Panel (Sedan)" in this section.
2. Clips and bright chrome molding from door lower finish panel.
   - Remove clip material from back side of door lower finish panel using an appropriate tool.

Clean

- Outer side of door lower finish panel.

Install or Connect

1. Remove protective covering from only the edges of new bright chrome molding.
2. Bright molding to door lower finish panel so that posts on heat stake clips protrude through holes in door lower finish panel.

CAUTION: The following operation MUST be performed in a well ventilated area. Avoid inhaling fumes as personal injury could result.

CAUTION: Prolonged contact between the soldering iron and molding material can cause the material to burn. Personal injury could result.

CAUTION: DO NOT touch the smoothing tip of the soldering iron or the clip post while it is hot. Personal injury could result.

A. Using a soldering gun rated at 200 watts or less, with a smoothing tip slowly heat each heat stake clip post until it is soft.
B. Push down with the smoothing tip to "mushroom" the top of the post to cover the hole in the door lower finish panel.
C. Hold bright chrome molding to door lower finish panel until clips cool off.

3. Door lower finish panel. Refer to "Door Lower Finish Panel (Sedan)" in this section.
4. Remove remaining protective covering from bright chrome molding.

Door Lower Finish Panel (Coupe)

Figure 13

Remove or Disconnect

1. Open door.
2. Bolts/screws.
3. Molding from supports.
4. Supports if necessary.
   - Nuts from lower support and support.
   - Rivets from upper support and support.

Install or Connect

1. Lower support if removed.

Tighten

- Nuts to 1 N·m (9 lb. in.).

2. Upper support and rivets if removed.
3. Molding from supports.
4. Bolts/screws.

Tighten

- Bolts/screws to 1 N·m (9 lb. in.).

5. Close door.

Rocker Outer Finish Panel (Coupe)

Figure 14

Remove or Disconnect

1. Front fender lower rear finish panel bolts/screws and nut.
2. Front fender lower rear finish panel.
3. Open door.
4. Rocker outer finish panel bolts/screws.

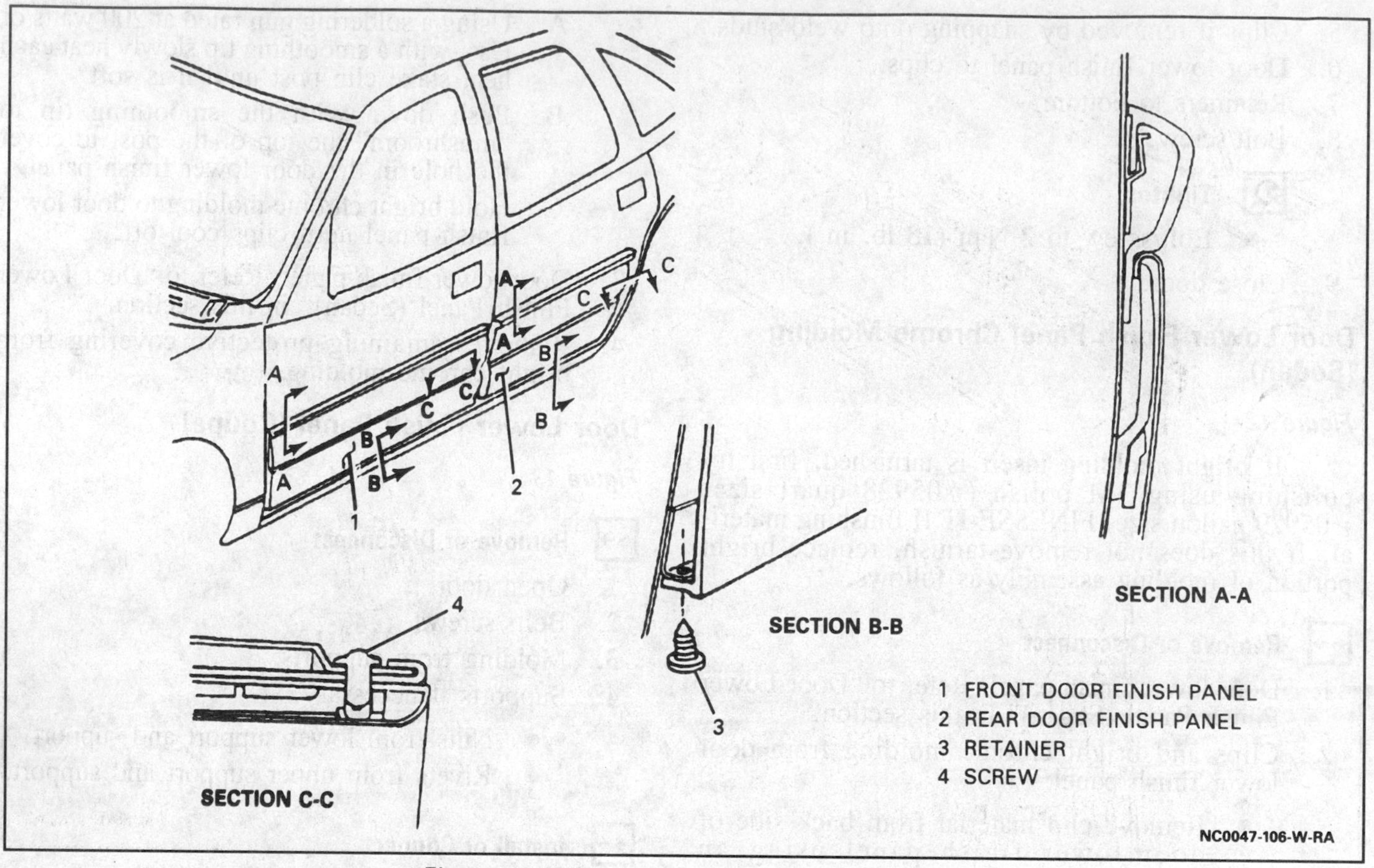
SECTION C-C
SECTION B-B
SECTION A-A
1 FRONT DOOR FINISH PANEL
2 REAR DOOR FINISH PANEL
3 RETAINER
4 SCREW
NC0047-106-W-RA

Figure 12 Door Lower Finish Panel (Sedan)

5. Rocker outer finish panel.
6. Rocker outer finish panel support nuts if removing support.
7. Rocker outer finish panel support if necessary.

Install or Connect

1. Rocker outer finish panel support if removed.
2. Rocker outer finish panel support nuts if removed.

Tighten

- Nuts to 10 N·m (89 lb. in.).

3. Rocker outer finish panel.
   - Attach upper flange over edge of clips.
4. Rocker outer finish panel bolts/screws.

Tighten

- Bolts/screws to 2 N·m (18 lb. in.).

5. Close door.
6. Front fender lower rear finish panel.
   - Insert stud through hole.
7. Bolts/screws and nut.

Tighten

- Bolts/screws and nut to 1 N·m (9 lb. in.).

Rear Quarter Lower Front Finish Panel (Sedan)

Figure 15

Remove or Disconnect

1. Front fender lower rear finish panel. Refer to "Front Fender Lower Rear Finish Panel" above.
2. Bolts/screws.
3. Rear quarter lower front finish panel by disengaging retainers.
4. Rear quarter lower front finish panel support rivet if removing support.
5. Rear quarter lower front finish panel support if necessary.

Install or Connect

1. Rear quarter lower front finish panel support if removed.
2. Rear quarter lower front finish panel support rivet if removed.
3. Rear quarter lower front finish panel by engaging retainers.
4. Bolts/screws.

Tighten

- Bolts/screws to 2 N·m (18 lb. in.).

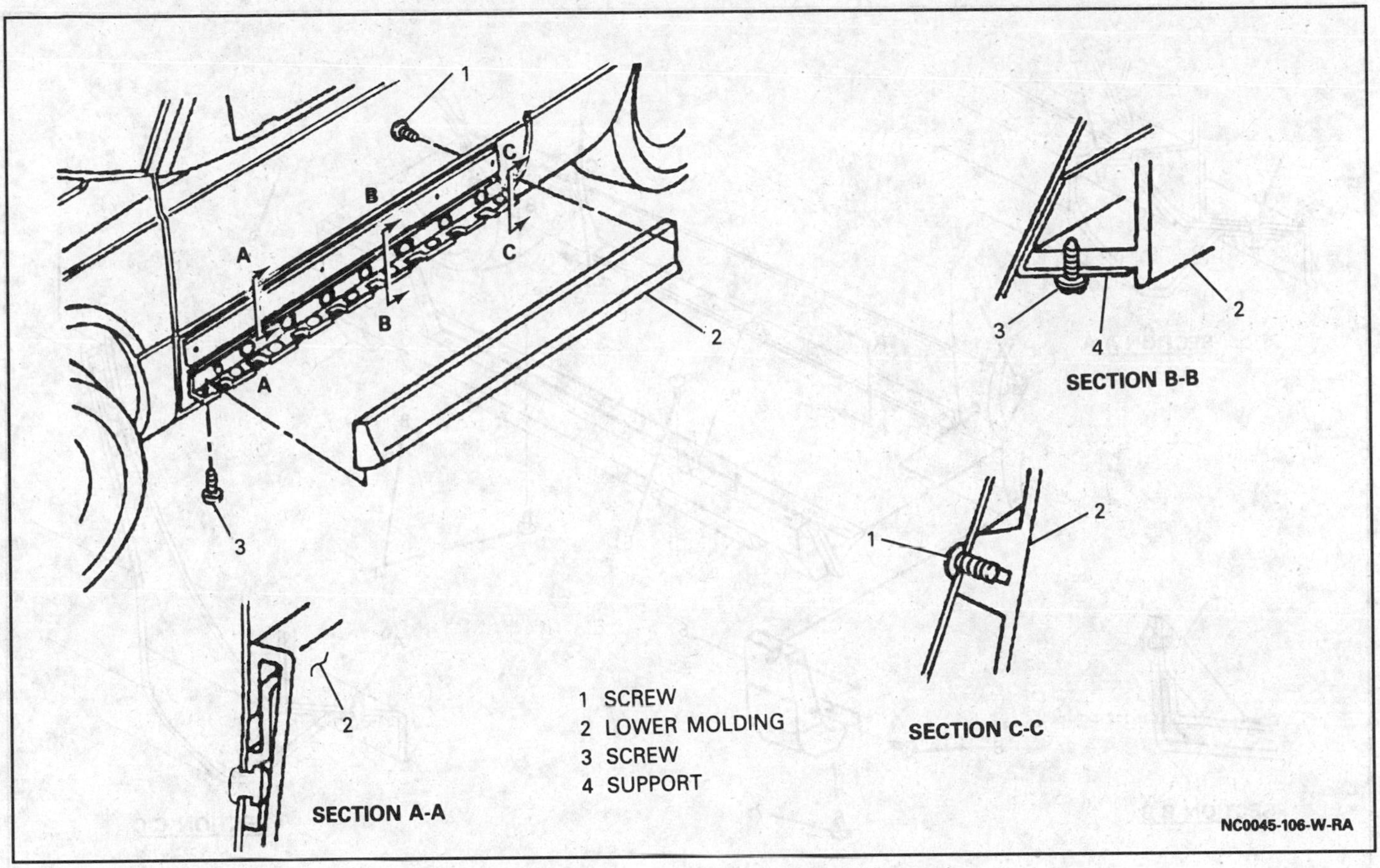
1
B
C
A
C
B
2
A
3
3
2
4
SECTION B-B
2
1
SECTION C-C
2
1 SCREW
2 LOWER MOLDING
3 SCREW
4 SUPPORT
SECTION A-A
NC0045-106-W-RA

Figure 13 Door Lower Finish Panel (Coupe)

5. Front fender lower rear finish panel. Refer to "Front Fender Lower Rear Finish Panel" above.

Rear Quarter Lower Front Finish Panel Chrome Molding (Sedan)

Figure 15

If bright molding insert is tarnished, first try polishing using 3M polish (#05928 quart size, #05929 gallon size) FINESSE-IT II finishing material. If this does not remove tarnish, replace bright portion of molding assembly as follows:

Remove or Disconnect

1. Rear quarter lower front finish panel. Refer to "Rear Quarter Lower Front Finish Panel (Sedan)" in this section.
2. Heat staked post by flexing tabs on clip.
3. Bright chrome molding from rear quarter lower front finish panel.

Install or Connect

1. Bright chrome molding to rear quarter lower front finish panel.
2. Rear quarter lower front finish panel. Refer to "Rear Quarter Lower Front Finish Panel (Sedan)" in this section.

WATERLEAK DIAGNOSIS

GM vehicles are designed to operate under normal environmental conditions. The design criteria for sealing materials and components takes into consideration the sealing forces required to withstand the natural elements. These specifications do not, and cannot, take into consideration all artificial conditions encountered in some high pressure car washes.

The watertest procedure has been correlated to the natural elements and will determine the ability of a vehicle to perform under normal operating conditions.

Repairing body waterleaks is a problem of proper testing, diagnosis and repair through adjustment of misaligned components and/or application of proven repair materials. The first step in waterleak diagnosis is finding the conditions under which the leak occurs. For example, the leak is noticed only when parked on an inclined drive, or when water is in the spare tire compartment.

If the general leak area can be found, the exact entry point can be quickly isolated by use of a localized test such as a water hose or air hose. If the leak source is not obvious, a testing method using watertest equipment should be used. It may be necessary to remove some interior trim panels or components to locate and confirm repairs.

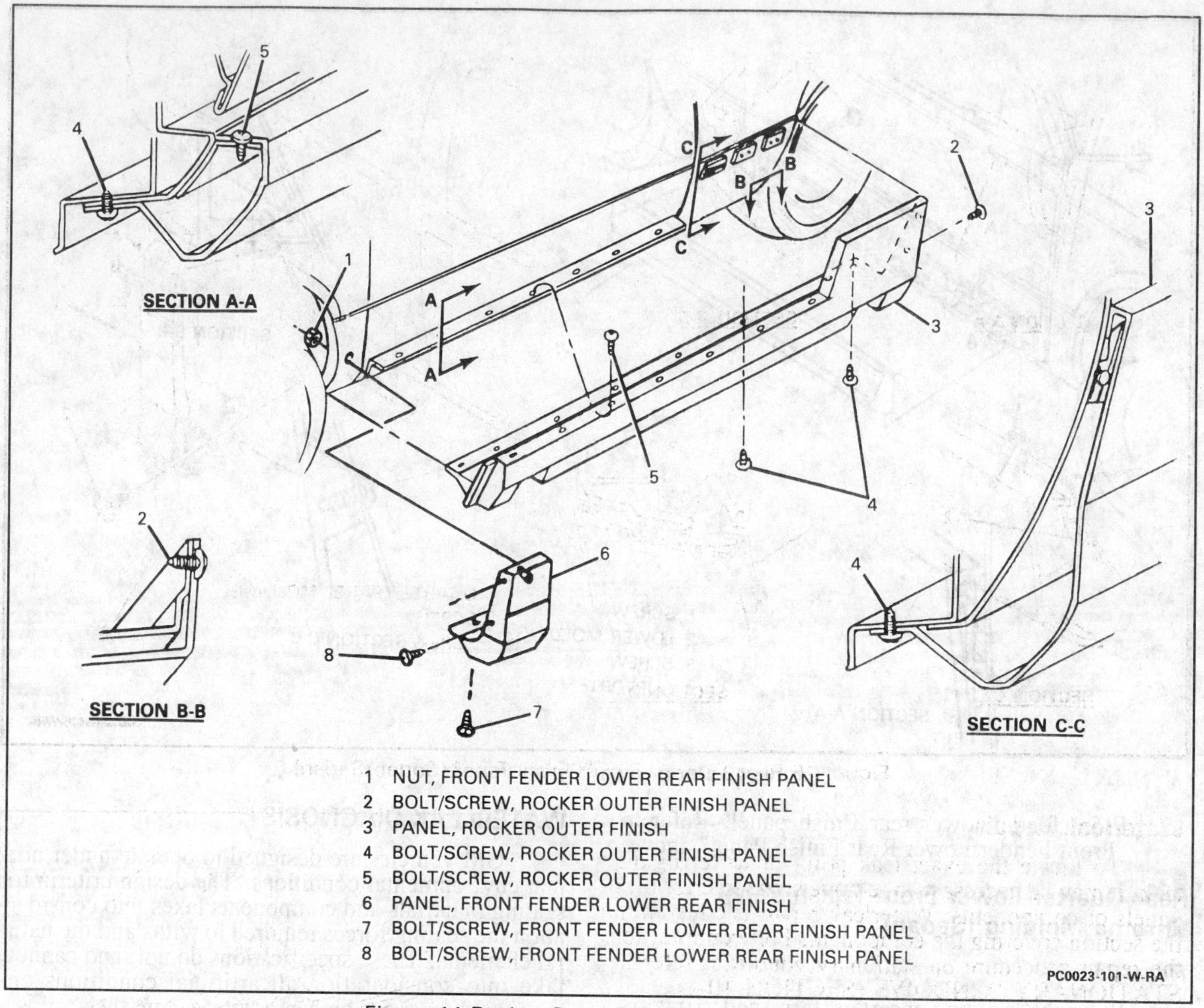
SECTION A-A
SECTION B-B
SECTION C-C
1 NUT, FRONT FENDER LOWER REAR FINISH PANEL
2 BOLT/SCREW, ROCKER OUTER FINISH PANEL
3 PANEL, ROCKER OUTER FINISH
4 BOLT/SCREW, ROCKER OUTER FINISH PANEL
5 BOLT/SCREW, ROCKER OUTER FINISH PANEL
6 PANEL, FRONT FENDER LOWER REAR FINISH
7 BOLT/SCREW, FRONT FENDER LOWER REAR FINISH PANEL
8 BOLT/SCREW, FRONT FENDER LOWER REAR FINISH PANEL
PC0023-101-W-RA

Figure 14 Rocker Outer Finish Panel (Coupe)

Localized Testing (Spot Test)

Localized testing may be made with either water or air. Begin the test at the base of the suspected area and continue up slowly until the leak is located.

Important

- Pinpoint the leak area before any repair is made. Random repair may only temporarily restrict water entry and make future diagnosis and repair more difficult.

Continue localized testing in the same general area to confirm that all leaks have been located.

Water Hose Test

Figures 16 and 17

- Have a helper inside the vehicle to detect the actual leak point.
- Use unrestricted water flow (no nozzle).
- Begin at the base of the suspected leak area and move upward slowly.

Air Hose Test

Figures 18 and 19

1. Apply bubble solution (liquid soap) to the suspected area.
2. Apply air pressure with an air hose from inside the vehicle. Do not exceed 207 kPa (30 psi).
3. Observe for bubbles on the outside at the suspected leak area.

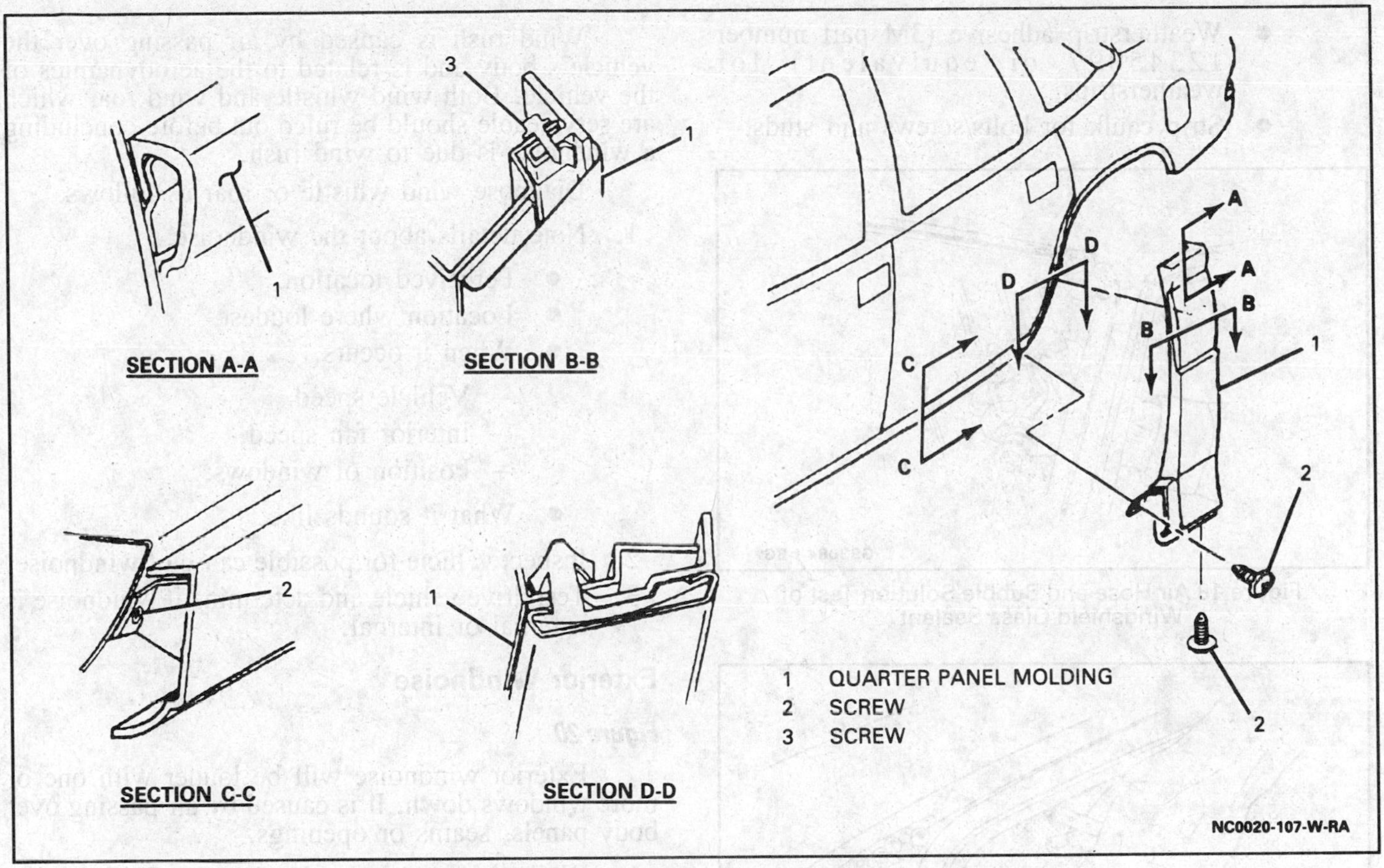
3
1
1
SECTION A-A
SECTION B-B
2
1
SECTION C-C
SECTION D-D
A
A
D
D
B
B
1
C
C
2
2
1 QUARTER PANEL MOLDING
2 SCREW
3 SCREW
NC0020-107-W-RA

Figure 15 Rear Quarter Lower Front Finish Panel (Sedan)

Waterleak Repair

To locate the exact leak point or to repair the leak, it may be necessary to remove some interior trim panels or components. Waterleak repair is covered in the section covering the component. For example, for the repair procedure on stationary windows, refer to STATIONARY WINDOWS (SECTION 10-2).

After completion of any waterleak repair, the general area should be retested using the watertest stand. Do not use high pressure air or water hose to test repaired areas as the fresh repair material may dislodge under abnormal pressure.

Material recommended for specific leak areas include:

- Urethane adhesive caulking kit (part number 12345633 or equivalent) for windshield, back window and quarter glass repair.
- Brushable seam sealer which can be painted for metal joints.
- Bedding and glazing compound for ventilation ducts and drip moldings.
- Drip-check sealer for small cracks and pin holes.
- All around automobile body sealant (3M part number 8500 or equivalent) for large holes.

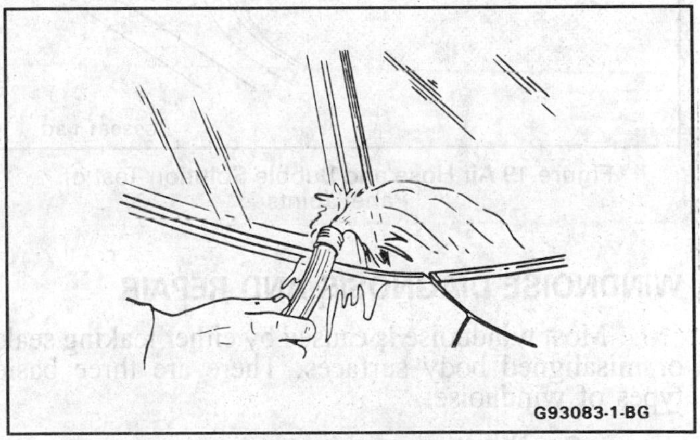
G93083-1-BG

Figure 16 Water Hose Test of Windshield Pillar

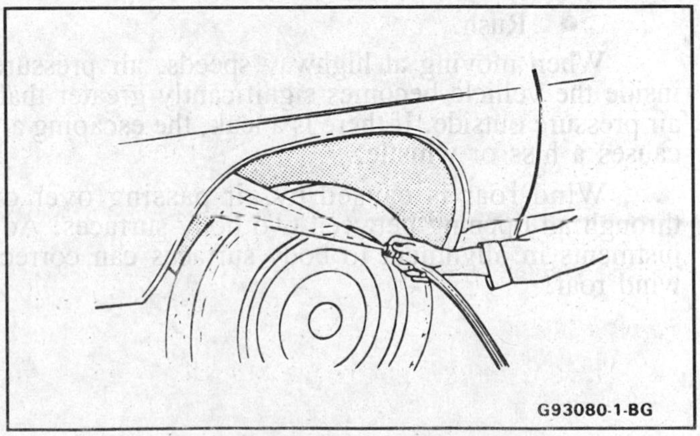
G93080-1-BG

Figure 17 Pressure Test of Wheelhouse

- Weatherstrip adhesive (3M part number 12345097 or equivalent) for weatherstrips.
- Strip caulk for bolts/screws and studs.

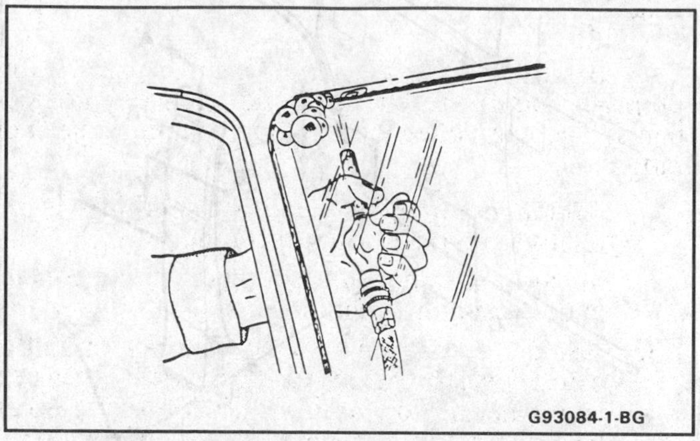
G93084-1-BG

Figure 18 Air Hose and Bubble Solution Test of Windshield Glass Sealant

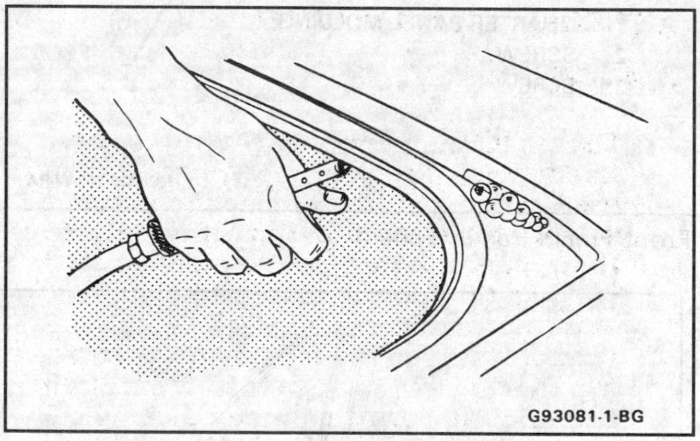
G93081-1-BG

Figure 19 Air Hose and Bubble Solution Test of Panel Joints

WINDNOISE DIAGNOSIS AND REPAIR

Most windnoise is caused by either leaking seals or misaligned body surfaces. There are three basic types of windnoise:

- Whistle.
- Roar.
- Rush.

When moving at highway speeds, air pressure inside the vehicle becomes significantly greater than air pressure outside. If there is a leak, the escaping air causes a hiss or whistle.

Wind roar is caused by air passing over or through an opening between two body surfaces. Adjustments in alignment to body surfaces can correct wind roar.

Wind rush is caused by air passing over the vehicle's body and is related to the aerodynamics of the vehicle. Both wind whistle and wind roar which are serviceable should be ruled out before concluding a windnoise is due to wind rush.

Diagnose wind whistle or roar as follows.

1. Note details about the windnoise:
   - Perceived location.
   - Location where loudest.
   - When it occurs.
     - Vehicle speed.
     - Interior fan speed.
     - Position of windows.
   - What it sounds like.
2. Inspect vehicle for possible cause of windnoise.
3. Test drive vehicle and determine if windnoise is external or internal.

Exterior Windnoise

Figure 20

Exterior windnoise will be louder with one or more windows down. It is caused by air passing over body panels, seams or openings.

1. While driving, determine location by lowering one window at a time. If location appears to correspond with condition noticed in step 2 above, pull over and make temporary repair with screwdriver or masking tape.
2. Tape over gaps and moldings one at a time, test driving in between. When the area causing the windnoise is taped over, the windnoise will no longer occur.

NOTICE: If masking the grille and headlamp bezel areas, care must be taken not to restrict airflow and cause vehicle overheating.

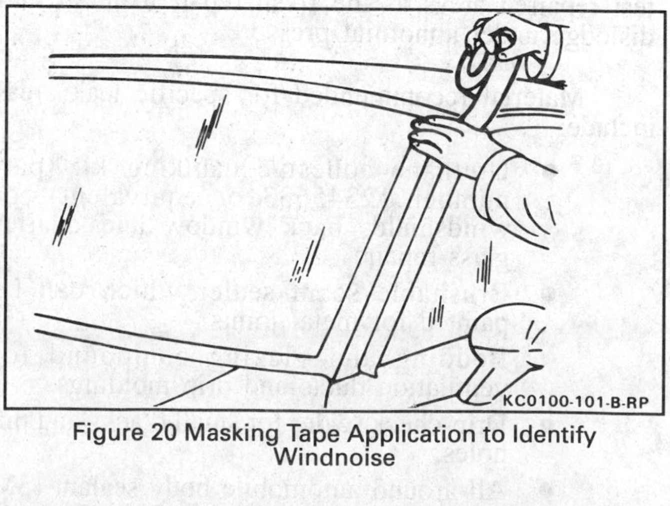
KC0100-101-B-RP

Figure 20 Masking Tape Application to Identify Windnoise

Interior Windnoise

Figures 18 through 20

Interior windnoise will not be heard with a window lowered. It is caused by air leaving the inside of the vehicle through a seal or seam.

1. Tape over relief valves to cause added air pressure within the vehicle.
2. Test drive and listen for windnoise whistle.
3. Pull over and make temporary repairs using masking tape. If still unable to determine source of interior windnoise, perform one or more of the following diagnostic tests:

- Tracing powder or chalk test.

Clean

- Weatherstrips and contact surfaces with solvent.

A. Apply powder or chalk in an unbroken line to the contact surface of weatherstrip around perimeter of trunk lid, door, door glass, or hood. Surrounding areas must be free of chalk or powder.

B. Close panel completely. Do not slam.

Inspect

- Applied line on weatherstrip will be marred where contact is good. A corresponding imprint will be on mating surfaces.
- Gaps or irregularities in powder or chalk line indicate poor seal.

- Air pressure test.

A. Mask off both pressure relief valves.

B. Turn on vehicle's ventilation fan.

C. Close all windows and doors.

D. With stethoscope or length of heater hose, listen for escaping air along door and window seals.

A smoke or dusting powder test can be used in the same manner. The exact leak location can be seen as the smoke or powder travels through the bad seal.

- Soap suds or bubble test.

A. Mask off both pressure relief valves.

B. Turn on vehicle's ventilation fan.

C. Close all windows and doors.

D. Apply soapy solution to potential leak areas.

E. Look for bubbles revealing escaping air.

An air hose can be used instead of pressurizing the vehicle's interior. Do not exceed 207 kPa (30 psi) when an air hose is used.

SQUEAK AND RATTLE DIAGNOSIS AND REPAIR

Basically, squeaks and rattles are caused by improperly controlled relative motion between components. There are three means to prevent the squeak or rattle.

1. Attach component securely so there is no relative motion during operation.
2. Separate components so there is no contact under operating conditions.
3. Insulate components so no squeaks or rattles occur with relative motion between components. Low uniform friction surfaces can be provided to eliminate "stick-slip" motion.

ANTICORROSION TREATMENT

Figures 21 through 27

CAUTION: When applying sound deadeners, due care and preventative measures must be exercised to prevent any material from being sprayed into door and quarter panel mechanisms such as door locks, glass run channels, window regulators and safety belt retractors, as well as any moving or rotating mechanical or suspension parts on the underbody. After material application, be sure all body drain holes are open. Improper application may limit the operation of moving parts or increase chance of corrosion damage. Personal injury could result.

Anticorrosion materials are used on interior and exterior surfaces of metal panels providing rust resistance. These materials include metals such as one-sided and two-sided galvanized zincrometal and zinc-iron alloy steels. These treated metals are used on components such as fenders, doors, quarter panels, rocker panels, lids, floor pans, wheelhousings and other critical parts.

Metal conditioners and primers are used on interior and exterior surfaces along with protective waxes on interior surfaces in areas where moisture might accumulate. Sealers are applied along exposed joints and moisture-repelling asphaltic sound deadeners are applied inside the wheel wells, doors and on some underbody components. Figures 21 through 27 illustrate typical production and field usage of these materials.

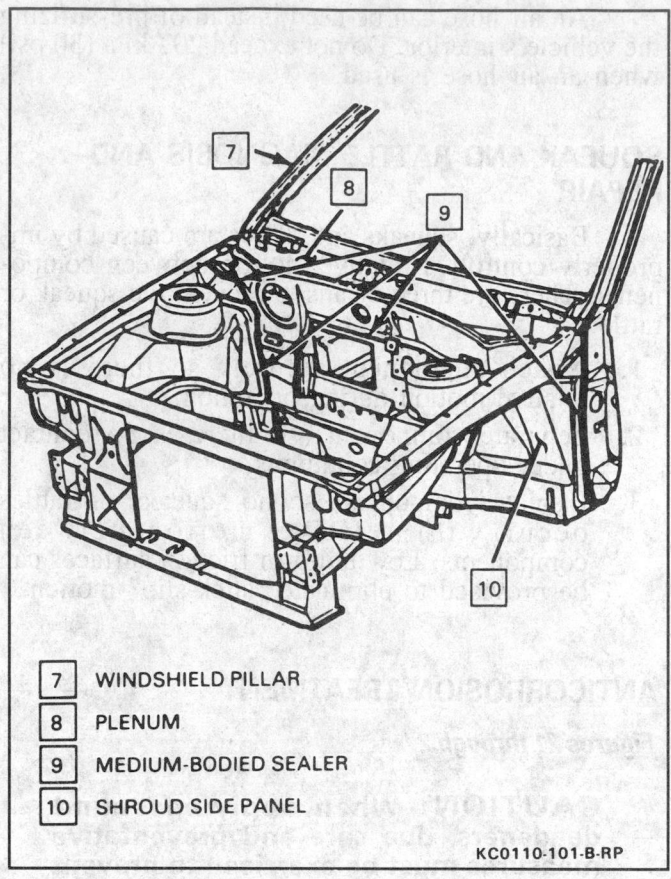

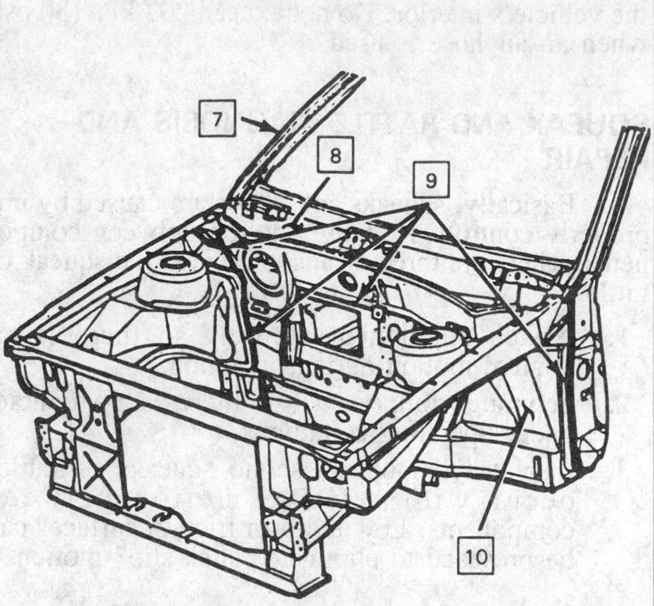
7
8
9
10
7 WINDSHIELD PILLAR
8 PLENUM
9 MEDIUM-BODIED SEALER
10 SHROUD SIDE PANEL
KC0110-101-B-RP

Figure 21 Sealing Front End

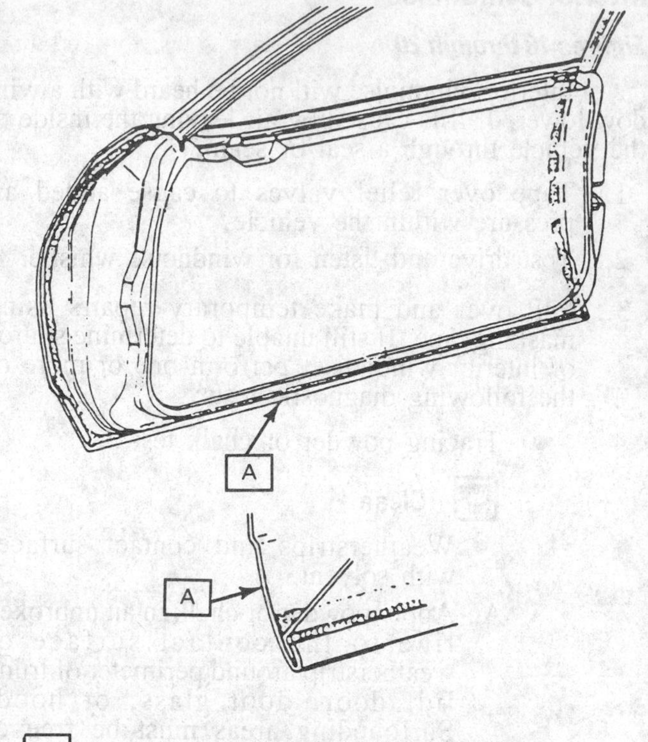
A
A
A ANTI-CORROSION COMPOUND, APPLIED TO INSIDE OF PANELS
RC0010-101-W-RP

Figure 22 Typical Hem Flange and Anticorrosion Treatment

Any procedure that disturbs these special treatments, such as panel replacement or collision damage repair operations, may leave the metal unprotected and result in corrosion. Proper recoating of these surfaces with service-type anticorrosion material is essential.

Metal conditioners and primer coatings are applied to all metal panels at the time of vehicle manufacture. After repair and/or replacement parts are installed, all accessible bare metal surfaces must be treated with metal conditioner and reprimed using an acrylic chromate material. This operation is to be performed prior to the application of sealers, waxes, deadeners and antirust compounds.

Sealers are applied to specific joints during manufacture. These sealers are intended to prevent water and dust from entering the vehicle and also are anticorrosion barriers. Sealers are applied to such areas as rear compartment lid hem flanges, wheelhouse, quarter outer, floor, cowl, roof and various other panel-to-panel attaching points. The originally sealed joints are obvious and any damage to these sealed locations should be corrected by resealing. Attaching points of new replacement panels should be resealed. Replacement lids and doors will also require sealing in the hem flange areas.

Flanged joints, overlap joints and seams should be sealed using a quality sealer of medium-bodied consistency. The sealer used must retain its flexible characteristics after curing and be paintable.

Open joints which require bridging of the sealer to close a gap should be sealed using a heavy-bodied caulking material. Follow the label directions for the material selected.

Color application may be required to restore repaired areas such as hood, fenders, doors, quarters, lid, roof, engine compartment, underbody and inner panels to original appearance. When this is necessary, conventional refinishing preparation, undercoat build-up and color application techniques should be followed.

Deadener materials (spray-on type) are used on various metal panels to provide corrosion resistance and joint sealing. They control the general noise level inside the passenger area of the vehicle. When deadeners are disturbed because of damage, removed during repair operations, or a new replacement panel is installed, the deadener material must be replaced by a service equivalent material. The application pattern and location of deadener materials can be determined by observing the original production installation.

Anticorrosion compounds are light-bodied materials designed to penetrate between metal-to-metal surfaces, such as pinch-weld joints, hem flanges, and integral panel attaching points where metal surfaces are difficult to coat with conventional undercoating materials, and are inaccessible for painting. Material suited for this type application is part number 12345489 or equivalent.

Conventional undercoating is recommended to coat large areas such as replacement door and quarter outer panels, floor pan sections, lids, hoods, fenders, etc.

During undercoating operations, care should be taken to prevent the material from being sprayed into door and quarter panel hardware mechanisms such as door locks, glass run channels, window regulators and seat belt retractors. On the underbody, the material should not be applied to any moving or rotating part, energy absorbing bumper components or shock absorbers. After undercoating, make sure that all body drain holes are open.

The sequence of application steps for anticorrosion materials is as follows.

1. Clean and prepare metal.
2. Apply primer (acrylic chromate).
3. Apply sealers at all previously sealed joints.
4. Apply color in areas where color is required, such as hem flanges, cxposed joints and underbody components.
5. Apply deadeners as indicated by original application pattern.
6. Apply anticorrosion compounds.
7. Apply underbody rustproofing material.

Cleaning of the interior and underbody panel surfaces is necessary when original galvanized or other anticorrosion materials have been burned off during welding or heating operations. Removal of the residue from burning will require additional care in such areas as interior surfaces of box-type construction and when configurations of the metal panels limit access to interior surfaces. One or more of the following methods will remove the residue.

CAUTION: Approved safety glasses should be worn when performing this procedure to reduce the chance of personal injury.

- Where access is possible, scraping can be used. If a standard putty knife or scraper will not fit into the affected area, fabricate a small, flexible scraper from a narrow piece of sheet metal.
- A jet of compressed air will remove most residue and could be effective in limited-access areas. Eye protection is absolutely necessary in an operation of this type.
- Sandblasting is most effective and should be used when the equipment is available and access to the area is good. Sandblasting is an excellent method for cleanup and preparation of open joints, underbody components and hem flange areas.

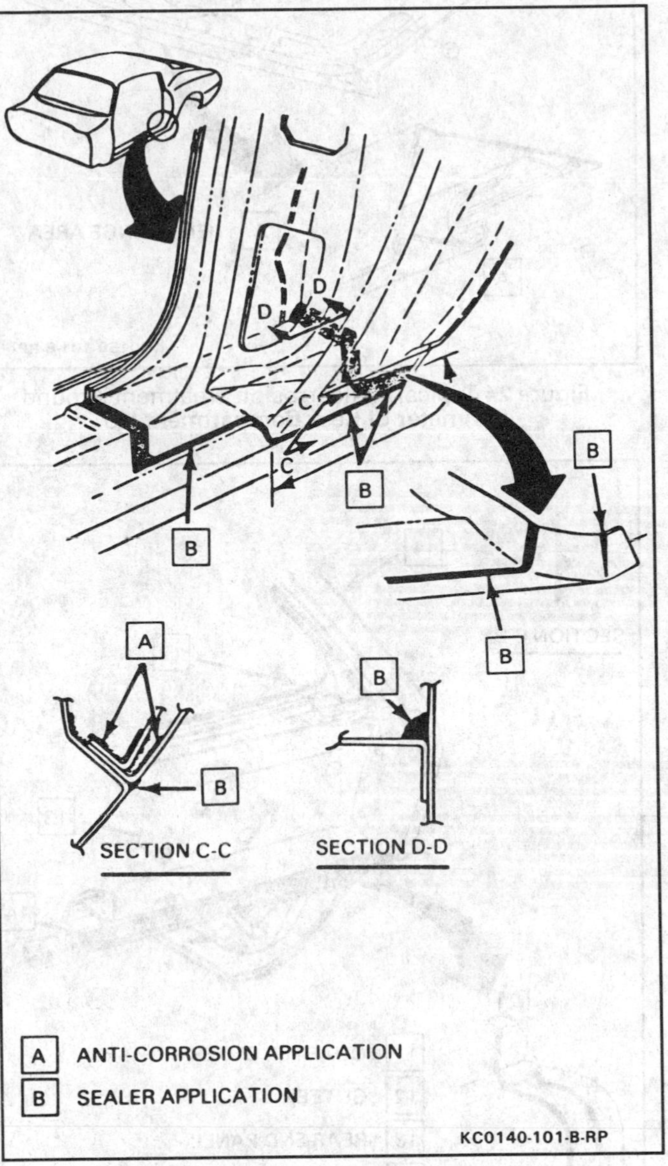
D
D
C
C
B
B
B
B
A
B
B
SECTION C-C
SECTION D-D
A ANTI-CORROSION APPLICATION
B SEALER APPLICATION
KC0140-101-B-RP

Figure 23 Typical Sealer and Anticorrosion Compound Treatment

- Wire brushing (power and by hand).
- When access is good, sandpaper and steel wool can be used.

CORROSION REPAIR

Prior to replacing exterior body parts or assemblies, check the condition of paint on all covered or hidden interior surfaces. If rust scale is found in these areas, proceed as follows:

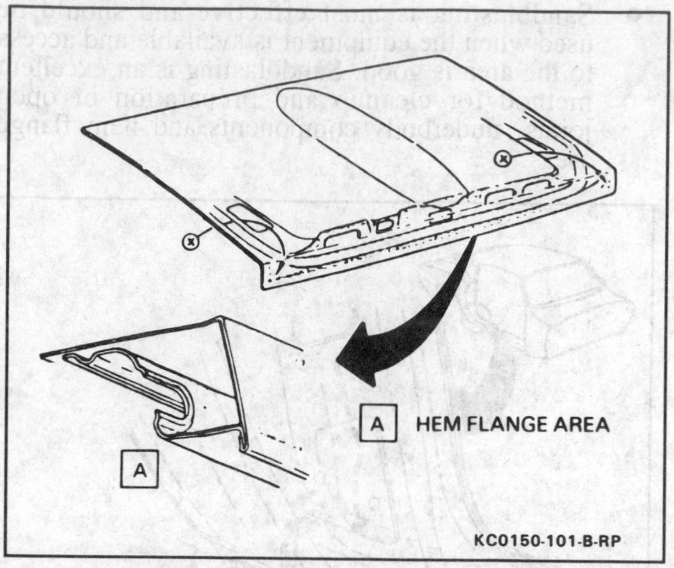

A
HEM FLANGE AREA
KC0150-101-B-RP

Figure 24 Typical Anticorrosion Treatment Around Perimeter of Rear Compartment Lid

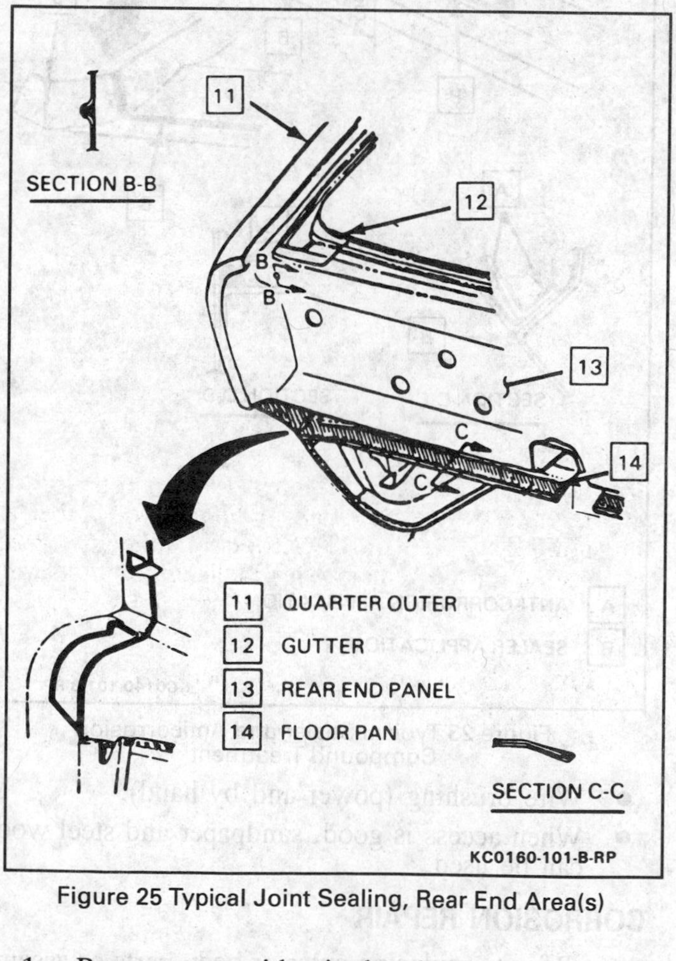

11
SECTION B-B
12
B
B
13
C
C
14
11 QUARTER OUTER
12 GUTTER
13 REAR END PANEL
14 FLOOR PAN
SECTION C-C
KC0160-101-B-RP

Figure 25 Typical Joint Sealing, Rear End Area(s)

1. Remove rust with wire brush, abrasive or liquid rust removing agent. Follow label directions.
2. If necessary, wash with detergent, rinse and dry.
3. Apply a heavy coating of anticorrosion compound to all cleaned hidden surfaces before installing exterior body parts. Apply anticorrosion compound to all inner surfaces of exterior body parts being installed.

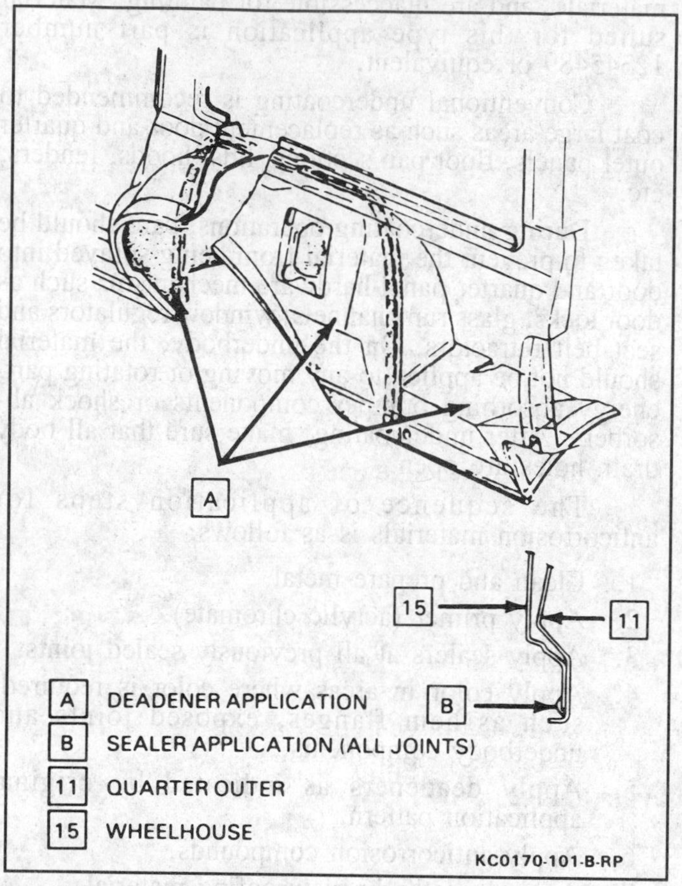

A
15
11
B
A DEADENER APPLICATION
B SEALER APPLICATION (ALL JOINTS)
11 QUARTER OUTER
15 WHEELHOUSE
KC0170-101-B-RP

Figure 26 Typical Deadener and Sealer Application, Wheelhouse and Floor Pan Extension Areas

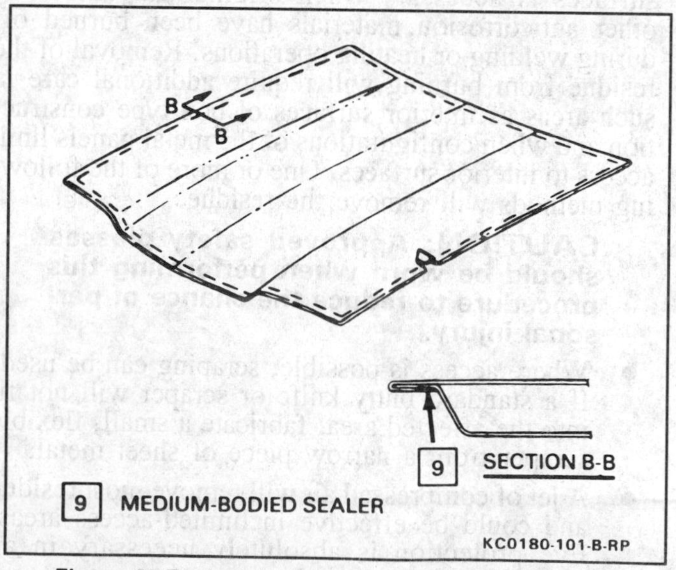

B
B
9
SECTION B-B
9 MEDIUM-BODIED SEALER
KC0180-101-B-RP

Figure 27 Typical Anticorrosion Treatment Around Perimeter of Hood Outer-to-Inner Panel Flanges

METAL REPLACEMENT PARTS FINISHING

CAUTION: Many paint repair systems require additives containing isocyanates. It is essential that all recommendations and warnings listed on the container label for materials selected be followed. It is mandatory that adequate respiratory protection such as air line respirators with a full hood be worn. Such protection should be worn during the entire painting process. Persons with respiratory problems or those allergic to isocyanates must not be exposed to isocyanate vapors or spray mist.

Metal service replacement parts or assemblies are painted with a high-bake factory primer. For proper adhesion of color coats in service, the following refinishing steps are necessary.

1. Clean part with a wax and grease-removing solvent.
2. Scuff-sand panel lightly with wet or dry number 400 sandpaper and water. Avoid cut-throughs. Reclean part. Apply sealer to entire part.
3. If factory primer coat was cut through, apply metal conditioner to the exposed bare metal. Follow label directions.
4. Apply primer-surfacer to the entire part. Allow to dry thoroughly before sanding. Follow label directions for drying time.
5. Sand primer-surfacer using wet or dry number 400 sandpaper and water. Do not sand sealer.
6. Reclean part.
7. Apply color coats to parts.
8. Follow label directions for drying time before compounding.
9. Compound part by hand or with power equipment.
10. Nonsealing polish may be applied after rubout if desired. Waxes, however, should **not** be applied until the paint finish has aged at least two months.

ANTI-CHIP COATING

An anti-chip coating material is applied to specific lower areas of the body prior to the color coat application on some vehicles. The presence of the applied material can be detected through visual inspection. If the production-applied anti-chip coating requires replacement, a chip resistant air dry vinyl that is solvent borne and sprayable is available for field use.

Materials/equipment necessary for repair:

- Vinyl gravel guard (Sherwin-Williams part number G1W295 or equivalent).
- Sandpaper - number 80 grit.
- Portable heat lamp or heat gun.
- Extension cord.
- Clean shop towel.
- Conventional hand spray gun with pressure feed cup attached.
- Putty knife.

PAINT CONDITIONS AND REPAIR

Paint Identification

Figure 29

CAUTION: Many paint repair systems require additives containing isocyanates. It is essential that all recommendations and warnings listed on the container label for materials selected be followed. It is mandatory that adequate respiratory protection such as air line respirators with a full hood be worn. Such protection should be worn during the entire painting process. Persons with respiratory problems or those allergic to isocyanates must not be exposed to isocyanate vapors or spray mist.

Basecoat/clearcoat paint is factory applied in four layers: a cathodic immersion primer, a primer/surfacer, a base color of high solids acrylic enamel (basecoat), and a clear acrylic top coat (clearcoat) to give the finish a high-gloss look.

To identify the type of topcoat on the vehicle, you may refer to the Service Parts Identification Label as shown in Figure 28. This label contains all paint related information for the vehicle. This includes paint technology, paint codes, trim level, and any special order paint colors.

NOTICE: Use supplies, primers, basecoats and clearcoats from the same manufacturer for the best results. Do not intermix paint systems.

Clearcoat Repair Without Repainting

Figure 30

A paint thickness gage can be used to determine how much of the clearcoat has been removed by the finesse operation. Readings of the paint film build should be taken prior to the operation. As the finesse operation progresses, additional readings should be taken to determine the impact on the total film build. If the gage indicates the total thickness has been reduced by .5 mils., it will be necessary to respray clear on the repair area to restore the needed ultraviolet protection.

If the damage or imperfection can be sanded or polished out without reaching the colorcoat, you don't have to repaint.

1. Thoroughly wash repair area with a mild detergent.
2. Apply a small amount of medium to fine machine rubbing compound to repair area and smear evenly with compounding pad.
3. With polisher running at approximately 1,700 rpm, compound repair area. Keep pad flat against panel while applying light pressure. Feature lines and panel edges should be hand-rubbed to avoid burn-through. Check repair area frequently and, if necessary, add more compound.
4. If sanding is required, proceed to step 6; if not, apply polish to repair area and evenly smear with polishing pad.
5. Keep pad flat and allow weight of polisher to do the work. Use polish sparingly to achieve original shine. Machine or hand polish repair area first, then blend in with rest of panel.
6. If repair is near adjacent panels, mask adjacent panel to protect against sand scratches and burn-through of panel edges.
7. Saturate a piece of micro-fine sandpaper in a container of water and attach to a sanding pad. The addition of a small amount of liquid detergent to the water will improve wet-out and sanding performance.
8. Keep repair area wet while sanding. Sand lightly and evenly in one direction only, using straight strokes.

Important

- Frequently wipe or squeegee to determine when defect has been removed. Sand only enough clearcoat to remove defect. Sanding below clearcoat requires repainting.

9. Using a clean cloth, wipe repair area clean of water and clearcoat residue.
10. Compound and polish as necessary. Often, hand compounding and polishing of a small repair area is all that is necessary to restore appearance.

Basecoat/Clearcoat Preparation

CAUTION: Many paint repair systems require additives containing isocyanates. It is essential that all recommendations and warnings listed on the container label for materials selected be followed. It is mandatory that adequate respiratory protection such as air line respirators with a full hood be worn. Such protection should be worn during the entire painting process. Persons with respiratory problems or those allergic to isocyanates must not be exposed to isocyanate vapors or spray mist.

1. Wash with detergent and water.
2. Clean with solvent.
3. Repair and feather edge damaged area.
4. Apply a self-etching primer and allow to dry.
5. Apply a primer-surfacer and allow to dry.
6. Sand basecoat paint area with recommended grit paper. (For clearcoat only, wet sand with ultra-fine or finer paper or hand compound.)
7. Clean with solvent and tack wipe.

NOTICE: Do not do Step 8 if the basecoat enamel used for repair does not require it. Always refer to manufacturer's label directions.

8. Apply one or two coats of adhesion promoter:
   - Within moldings or breaklines.
   - Onto adjacent panel 102 to 152 mm (4 to 6 inches) if repair is not confined and beyond area to be covered by clearcoat.
   - Allow to flash at least 30 minutes before applying clearcoat.

Basecoat Application — Polyurethane Enamel

1. Reduce basecoat per manufacturer's instructions.
2. Mix thoroughly.
3. Spray to achieve full hiding and color match.
4. Cure per manufacturer's instructions.

Clearcoat Application – Polyurethane Enamel

CAUTION: Many paint repair systems require additives containing isocyanates. It is essential that all recommendations and warnings listed on the container label for materials selected be followed. It is mandatory that adequate respiratory protection such as air line respirators with a full hood be worn. Such protection should be worn during the entire painting process. Persons with respiratory problems or those allergic to isocyanates must not be exposed to isocyanate vapors or spray mist.

1. Add catalyst and reduce materials per manufacturer's instructions.
2. Mix thoroughly.
3. Spray at recommended gun pressure. Apply recommended number of coats. Allow proper flash time between coats.
   - Cover entire panel whenever possible.
   - When there are not breaklines, blend the spray within the adhesion promoter area.

[!] Important

- Clean spray equipment immediately after use with lacquer thinner.

4. Cure per manufacturer's instructions.

PLASTIC IDENTIFICATION

Figures 30 through 33

CAUTION: General Motors does NOT recommend using a plastic "Burn Test" to distinguish different types of plastics. This test produces vapors that can be harmful to your health.

The procedures provided in this section classify the plastics into two groups; flexible and rigid. Refer to the figures to identify the parts and the repair/refinish procedure to use.

The following information can be used to specifically identify plastic parts when necessary.

1. Look on the back side of the part for the International Organization for Standardization (ISO) Code marking (Figure 30).
2. Refer to Figures 31 and 32 to match the ISO code marking found on the part with those on the charts.
3. Use the chart to identify special handling procedures and repair/refinish classification (rigid or flexible).

FLEXIBLE PLASTIC PARTS REPAIR AND REFINISHING

Repair Materials

NOTICE: Use supplies and repair materials from the same manufacturer for the best results. Do not intermix systems.

These flexible plastic panel repair procedures require the use of GM Goodwrench Compoxy Repair Material (GM P/N 12345744) or equivalent such as Loctite CMR-8 Composite Material Repair (P/N 82091).

Fabricating a Patch Panel

Flexible plastics requiring spicing or sustaining major damage may need a reinforcement panel or patch panel. If possible, obtain this part by cutting a piece from the original damaged panel. If a piece of the original damaged panel is used for reinforcement backing, be sure the surfaces are sanded and cleaned to completely remove any paint or finish material because it will inhibit proper bonding. The piece should be 38 to 51 mm (1.5 to 2.0 inches) in width if the damage is a split or break. If a part of the damaged panel is missing, the reinforcement panel or patch should extend 38 to 51 mm (1.5 to 2.0 inches) beyond the edges of the damaged area. An adequate reinforcement may be made as follows:

1. Lay out a piece of wax paper larger than the damaged area on the panel.
2. Apply a layer of GM Goodwrench Compoxy Repair MAterial (GM P/N 12345744) or equivalent such as Loctite CMR-8 Composite Material Repair (P/N 82091).
3. Cut a piece of reinforcement mat material to the desired size and shape, and place over the repair material.
4. Apply a coat of repair material as necessary.
5. Place a piece of wax paper over the mat material and roll with the saturation roller to ensure saturation of the mat.
6. Remove the wax paper from the panel.
7. Apply a patch to inner side of damaged area if accessible. Work out any air pockets.
8. Allow to cure.

When cleaning your work area after completing a repair, be sure to save any leftover pieces of repair material that may be of useful size. They can be used later for reinforcing the back of small damaged area and puncture repairs.

When using mat reinforcement to repair the inner or outer surface of a panel, be sure there are no strands of the mat left uncovered or unsaturated by the repair material. If exposed, the mat may act as a wick and will draw moisture into the repaired area affecting the integrity and finish.

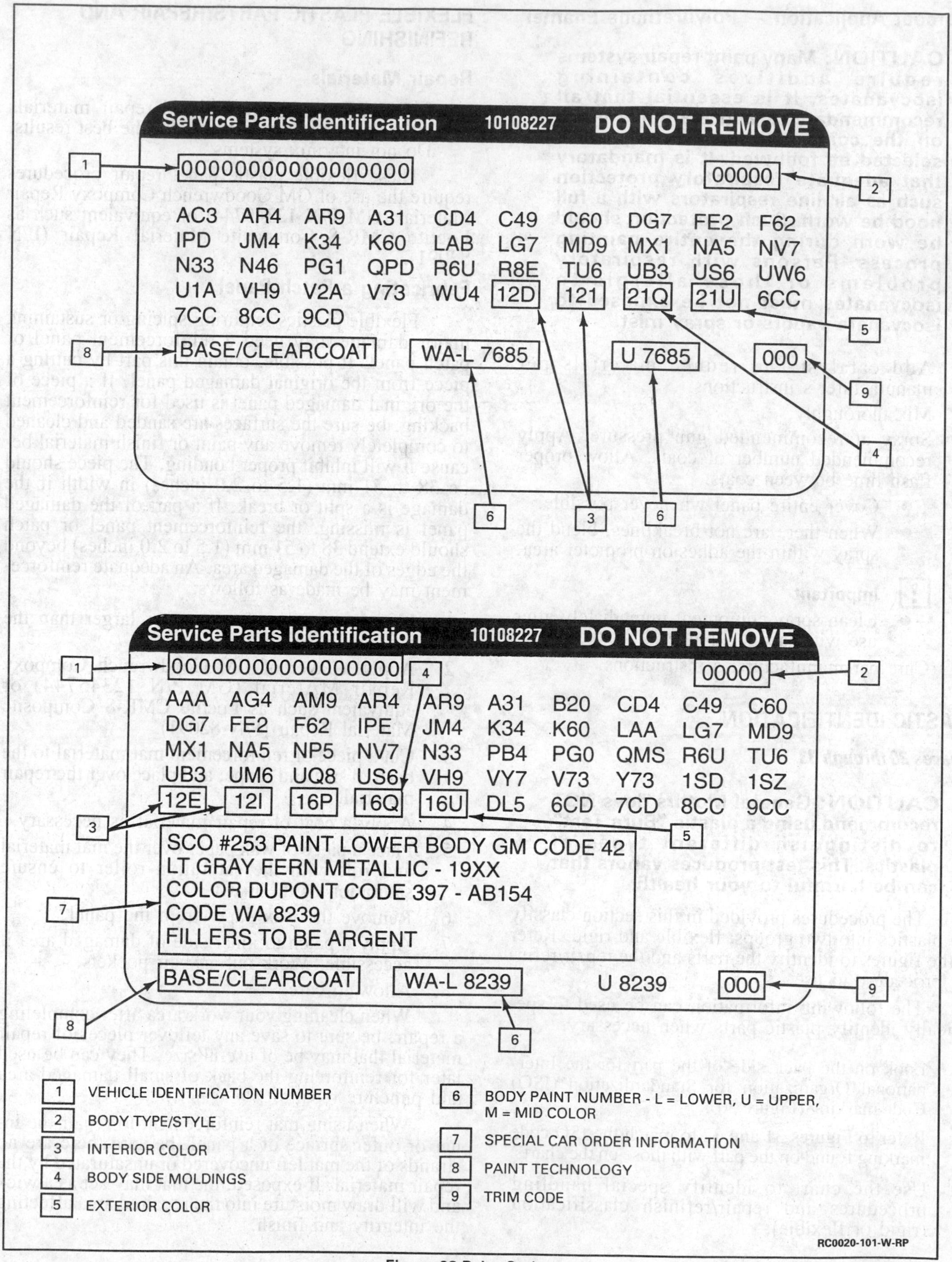
Service Parts Identification
10108227
DO NOT REMOVE
00000000000000000
00000
AC3 AR4 AR9 A31 CD4 C49 C60 DG7 FE2 F62
IPD JM4 K34 K60 LAB LG7 MD9 MX1 NA5 NV7
N33 N46 PG1 QPD R6U R8E TU6 UB3 US6 UW6
U1A VH9 V2A V73 WU4 12D 121 21Q 21U 6CC
7CC 8CC 9CD
BASE/CLEARCOAT
WA-L 7685
U 7685
000
Service Parts Identification
10108227
DO NOT REMOVE
00000000000000000
00000
AAA AG4 AM9 AR4 AR9 A31 B20 CD4 C49 C60
DG7 FE2 F62 IPE JM4 K34 K60 LAA LG7 MD9
MX1 NA5 NP5 NV7 N33 PB4 PG0 QMS R6U TU6
UB3 UM6 UQ8 US6 VH9 VY7 V73 Y73 1SD 1SZ
12E 12I 16P 16Q 16U DL5 6CD 7CD 8CC 9CC
SCO #253 PAINT LOWER BODY GM CODE 42
LT GRAY FERN METALLIC - 19XX
COLOR DUPONT CODE 397 - AB154
CODE WA 8239
FILLERS TO BE ARGENT
BASE/CLEARCOAT
WA-L 8239
U 8239
000
1 VEHICLE IDENTIFICATION NUMBER
2 BODY TYPE/STYLE
3 INTERIOR COLOR
4 BODY SIDE MOLDINGS
5 EXTERIOR COLOR
6 BODY PAINT NUMBER - L = LOWER, U = UPPER, M = MID COLOR
7 SPECIAL CAR ORDER INFORMATION
8 PAINT TECHNOLOGY
9 TRIM CODE
RC0020-101-W-RP

Figure 28 Paint Codes

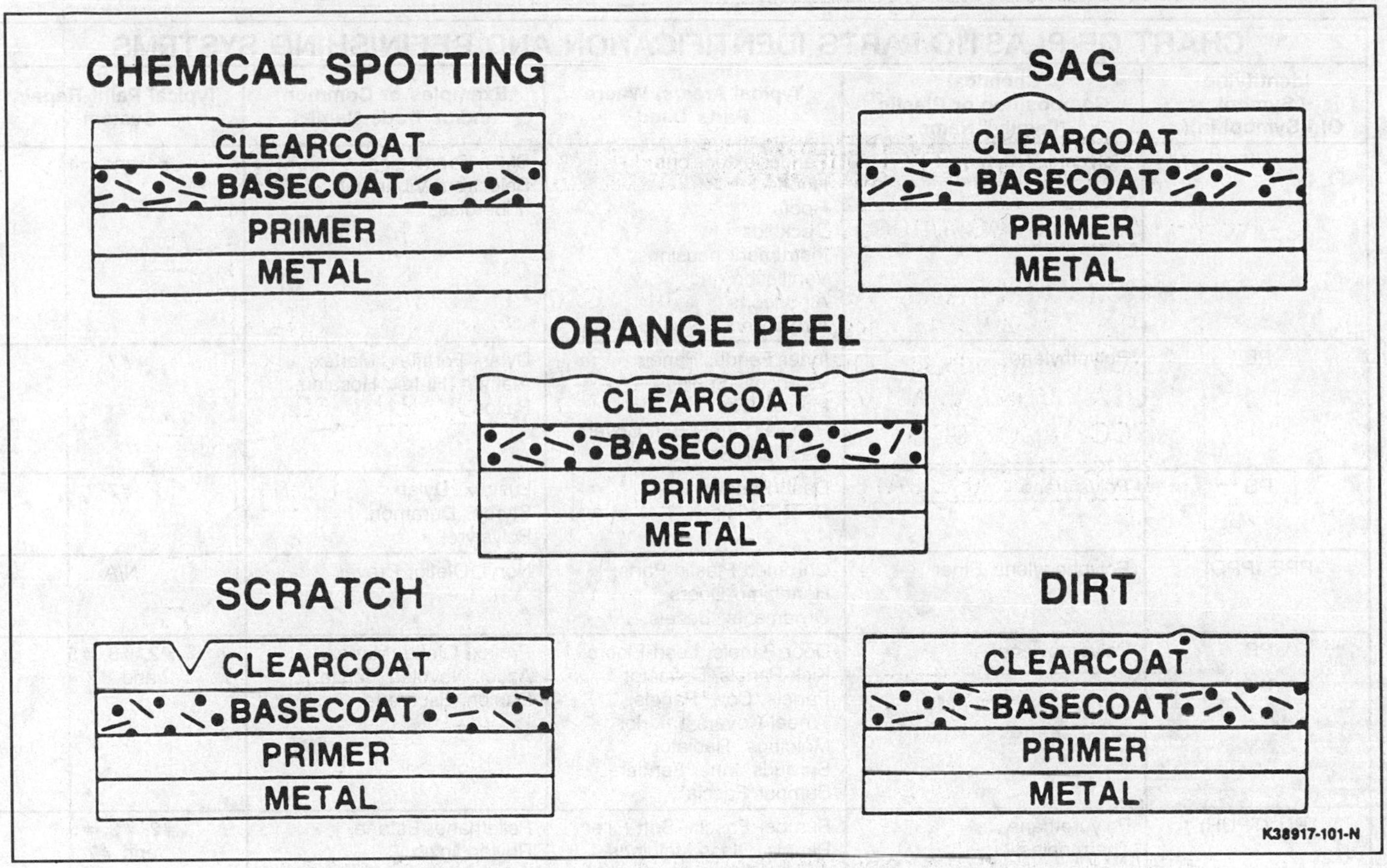
CHEMICAL SPOTTING
CLEARCOAT
BASECOAT
PRIMER
METAL
SAG
CLEARCOAT
BASECOAT
PRIMER
METAL
ORANGE PEEL
CLEARCOAT
BASECOAT
PRIMER
METAL
SCRATCH
CLEARCOAT
BASECOAT
PRIMER
METAL
DIRT
CLEARCOAT
BASECOAT
PRIMER
METAL
K38917-101-N

Figure 29 Minor Paint Defects Repairable Without Repainting

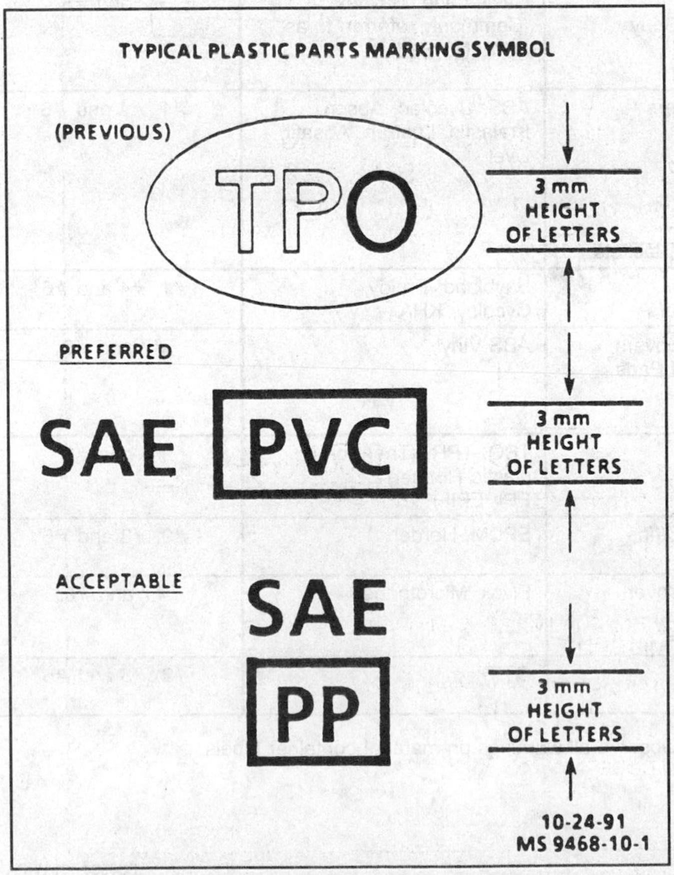
TYPICAL PLASTIC PARTS MARKING SYMBOL
(PREVIOUS)
TPO
3 mm HEIGHT OF LETTERS
PREFERRED
SAE PVC
3 mm HEIGHT OF LETTERS
ACCEPTABLE
SAE
PP
3 mm HEIGHT OF LETTERS
10-24-91
MS 9468-10-1

Figure 30 Plastic Parts Marking Symbol

Flexible Plastic Part Repair

Figures 34 through 40

1. Clean and inspect damaged area as required (Figure 34).
2. Support and align parts as necessary using tape for minor damage (Figure 35). Fabricate a patch panel if necessary. Refer to "Fabricating a Patch Panel" in this section.
3. Begin reinforcement repair to the inner surface of panel by abrading area with an 80 grit disc on a D.A. sander or by hand if access is limited.

NOTICE: Use only compressed air or a clean dry cloth to remove residue.

4. If necessary, cut a piece of reinforcement mat (porous or unit-directional) to the desired shape. Extend mat 38 to 51 mm (1.5 to 2.0 inches) beyond repair area (Figure 36).
5. Mix and apply a skim coat of GM Goodwrench Compoxy Repair Material (GM P/N 12345744) or equivalent such as Loctite CMR-8 Composite Material Repair (P/N 82091).
6. Lay pre-cut piece of reinforcement mat into skim coat of repair material using applicator to press mat so that it becomes saturated. Also make sure that all trapped air is forced out.

CHART OF PLASTIC PARTS IDENTIFICATION AND REFINISHING SYSTEMS				
Identifying Symbol Old Symbol in ( )	**Chemical Composition or Plastic "Family" Name**	**Typical Area(s) Where Parts Used**	**Examples of Common and/or Trade Names**	**Typical Paint Repair System**
UP	Polyester/Thermoset	Fender extensions Hoods Roofs Deck lids Instrument housings Ventilation grids Air scoops Air spoilers	SMC, Premi-glas, Selectron, Vibrinmat, "Fiberglass"	#1 and #4
PE	Polyethylene	Inner Fender Panels Valances, Spoilers, Interior Trim Panels, Safety Belt Covers, Gas Tank Shields	Dylan, Fortiflex, Marlex, Alathon, Hi-fax, Hosalen, Paxon	#7
PS	Polystyrene	Dash Panels Door Panels	Lustrex, Dylan Styron, Durathon, Polystyrol	#7
PPE (PPO)	Polyphenylene Ether	Chromed Plastic Parts; Headlamp Doors Ornaments, Bezels	Noryl, Oleflo, Prevex	N/A
PP	Polypropylene	Door Panels, Load Floors, Kick Panels, Deflector Panels, Cowl Panels, Wheel Covers, Interior Moldings, Radiator Shrouds, Inner Fenders, Bumper Fascia	Profax, Oleflo, Marlex, Azdel, Novolen, Tenite, Daplen, Escorene	#2, #3, #5 and #7
TPU (TPUR)	Polyurethane, Thermoplastic	Bumper Fascia, Soft Filler Panels, Glass Moldings, Gravel Deflectors	Pellethane, Estane, Roylar, Toxin	#2, #3, #5 and #7
PUR	Polyurethane, Thermoset (Unsaturated)	Bumper Fascia Front and Rear Body Panels, Filler Panels	Castethane, Bayflex, (Commonly referred to as RIM AND RRIM)	#2 and #5
ABS	Acrylonitrile, Butadiene-/Styrene	Instrument Clusters Trim Moldings Consoles Armrest Supports Steering Column Brackets Steering Column Jackets	ABS, Cycolac, Abson, Kralastic, Lustran, Absafil, Dyel	#1, #4 and #6
ABS + PC	Acrylonitrile/Butadiene Styrene + Polycarbonate	Instrument Panels, Instrument Clusters	Baybland, Proloy, Cycoloy, KHA	#1, #4 and #6
ABS/PVC	ABS/Vinyl – (Soft)	Head Restraint Covers Instrument Panel Pads Trim Moldings Trim Panels	ABS Vinyl	#7 and #8
TEO (EP, EPM, TPO)	Ethylene/Propylene (Rubber)	Bumper Fascia Valance Panels Air Dams	TPO, TPR, (Thermo-plastic Rubber) EPI, EPII	#3 and #5
EPDM	Ethylene Propylene Diene Monomer	Bumper Impact Strips Body Panels	EPDM, Nordel	#2, #3 and #5
EVA (EVAC)	Ethylene/Vinyl Acetate	Head Restraint Cover Miscellaneous Soft Trim Components	Elvax, Microthane	#7 and #8
PA + PPE	Polyamide + Polyphenylene Ether	Fenders, Exterior Trim	GTX	#2, #3 and #5

NOTICE: Follow selected paint manufacturer's product label directions. Observe all warnings on material container labels.

PC0004-101-W-RA

Figure 31 Plastics Identification Chart #1

CHART OF PLASTIC PARTS IDENTIFICATION AND REFINISHING SYSTEMS

IDENTIFYING SYMBOL OLD SYMBOL IN ( )	CHEMICAL COMPOSITION OR PLASTIC "FAMILY" NAME	TYPICAL AREA(S) WHERE PART USED	EXAMPLES OF COMMON AND/OR TRADE NAMES	TYPICAL PAINT REPAIR SYSTEM
PVC	Polyvinyl Chloride (Vinyl)	Interior Soft Trim, Instrument Panel Skins, Roof Covers	Geon, Vinylite, Pliovic, "Vinyl", Vinoflex, Unichem	#8
SAN (SA)	Styrene-Acrylonitrite	Center Consoles, Glove Box Doors, Interior Trim Panels	Lustran, Tyril, Forsacryl	#6 and #7
PC + PETP	Polycarbonate + Polybutylene Terephthalate	Bumper Covers	Xenoy, Valox, Macroblend	#1, #2, #4, and #5
PA PAG PAGG	Polyamide	Headlamp bezels, Quarter panel exits, Exterior Finish, Trim Panels	Nylon, Capron, Zytel Rilsan, Minlon Vydyne, Wellamid	#1 and #4
PBT + TEEE (PBT + EEBC)	Polybutylene Terephthalate + Ether Ester Block Copolymer	Rocker Cover Mldgs., Fascias	Bexloy "M"	#1 and #4
PC	Polycarbonate	Interior Hard (Rigid) Trim Panels, Valance Panels	Lexan, Merlon, Calibre	#1, #4 and #6
PF	Phenol — Formaldehyde	Ashtrays	Phenolic, Bakelite, Durez, Genal, Resinox, Amberol, Plyophen	#6

FOR SYMBOLS NOT LISTED IN THIS CHART, CONTACT THE SOCIETY OF AUTOMOTIVE ENGINEERS, 400 COMMONWEALTH DRIVE, WARRENDALE, PA 15096-0001 FOR A COPY OF SAE-J1344

( ) = OLD IDENTIFYING SYMBOLS IN ABOVE CHARTS

(PVC) = TYPICAL ISO MARKING SYMBOL FOUND ON PLASTIC PARTS

SAE [PVC] = TYPICAL NEW SAE MARKING SYMBOL FOUND ON PLASTIC PARTS

SUGGESTED PLASTIC PARTS PAINT REPAIR SYSTEMS

SYSTEM #1 (Exterior)
Conventional Lacquer Enamel *Acrylic Urethane

SYSTEM #2 (Exterior)
*Flexible Lacquer Enamel *Acrylic Urethane

SYSTEM #3 (Exterior)
Polypropylene Primer and *Special Topcoat

SYSTEM #4 (Exterior)
Base Color Coat with Acrylic Lacquer or *Acrylic Urethane Clear Coat

SYSTEM #5 (Exterior)
Base Color Coat with *Flexible Urethane Clear Coat

SYSTEM #6 (Interior)
Conventional (Standard) Interior Acrylic Lacquer

SYSTEM #7 (Interior)
Polypropylene Primer and Standard Interior Topcoat

SYSTEM #8 (Interior)
Vinyl Interior Color

* = Contains Isocyanates — Use recommended respiratory protection

PC6013-101-D-RP

Figure 32 Plastics Identification Chart #2

HANDLING PRECAUTIONS FOR PLASTICS

Abbreviation	Material name	Heat resisting temperature °C (°F)	Resistance to gasoline and solvents	Other cautions
PE	Polyethylene	80 (176)	Gasoline and most solvents are harmless.	Flammable
PVC	Polyvinyl chloride	90 (194)	Gasoline and most solvents are harmless if applied for a very short time (wipe up quickly).	Poison gas is emitted when burned.
PP	Polypropylene	90 (194)	Gasoline and most solvents are harmless.	Flammable
ABS	Acrylonitrile butadiene styrene resin	90 (194)	Avoid gasoline and solvents.	Avoid brake fluid.
AES	Acrylonitrile ethylene styrene	90 (194)	Avoid gasoline and solvents.	Avoid brake fluid.
PMMA	Polymethyl methacrylate	90 (194)	Avoid gasoline and solvents.	Avoid brake fluid.
PUR	Polyurethane	90 (194)	Gasoline and most solvents are harmless.	Avoid brake fluid.
AAS	Acrylonitrile acrylic rubber styrene	95 (203)	Avoid gasoline and solvents.	Avoid brake fluid.
PPE	Polyphenylene ether	110 (230)	Avoid gasoline and solvents.	
POM	Polyacetal	120 (248)	Gasoline and solvents are harmless.	Avoid battery acid.
PC	Polycarbonate	120 (248)	Avoid gasoline and solvents.	
PA, PAG PAGG	Polyamide (Nylon)	150 (302)	Gasoline and most solvents are harmless.	Avoid immersing in water.
FRP	Fiber reinforced plastics	170 (338)	Gasoline and most solvents are harmless.	
PPC	Polypropylene composite	115 (239)	Gasoline and most solvents are harmless.	Flammable
PBT	Polybutylene terephthalate	140 (284)	Gasoline and most solvents are harmless.	
TPR	Thermoplastic rubber	80 (176)	Avoid gasoline and solvents.	
TPE	Thermoplastic elastomer	80 (176)	Avoid gasoline and solvents.	

1. **When repairing and painting a portion of the body adjacent to plastic parts, consider their characteristics (influence of heat and solvent) and remove them if necessary or take suitable measures to protect them.**
2. **Plastic parts should be repaired and painted using methods suiting the materials.**

PC6014-101-D-RP

MS9509-10-1

Figure 33 Plastics Handling Precautions

7. If mat is not of the screen type, use a saturation roller to ensure that the mat is completely saturated and there are not exposed fibers or trapped air.
8. Apply a second coat of flexible repair material making sure mat is completely saturated and there are no exposed fibers or trapped air (Figure 37).
9. Allow to cure per manufacturer's instructions.
10. Remove tape or clamps used for maintaining alignment and contours.
11. At outer surface of panel, bevel damaged area with a 50 grit Roloc disc. This step extends contact between repair material and substrate (Figure 38).
12. Using a 180 grit disc on a D.A. sander, feather out several inches beyond damaged area to remove any paint or primer from substrate. This provides a proper surface for adhesion (Figure 39).
13. Apply a light coat of repair material to the damaged area, taking care to apply it smoothly. The repair material should be level and slightly above the surrounding contour.
14. Allow to cure per manufacturer's recommendations.
15. Rough out surface with a 80 grit disc on a D.A. sander.
16. Finish contour sanding with a 220 to 320 grit (wet or dry) sandpaper on a sanding block (Figure 40).

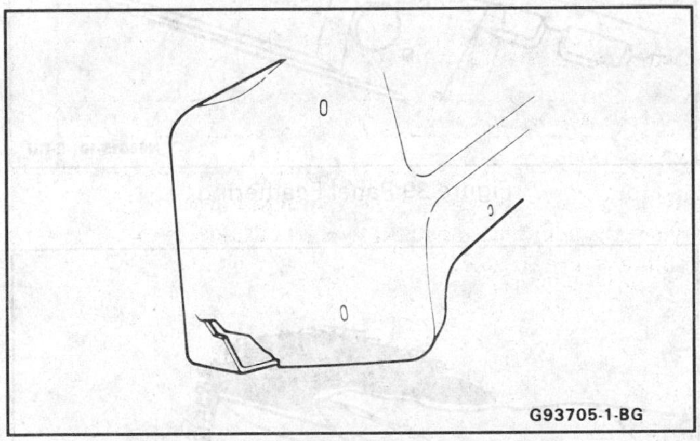
G93705-1-BG
Figure 34 Inspect Damaged Area

Flexible Plastic Part Refinishing

To refinish repaired flexible parts, it is very important to follow the paint manufacturer's system regarding preparation, priming, and refinishing. Because these parts are flexible, they may require special additives in the primers and topcoat to prevent cracking and poor adhesion. Always use manufacturer's recommended materials and never intermix with other systems.

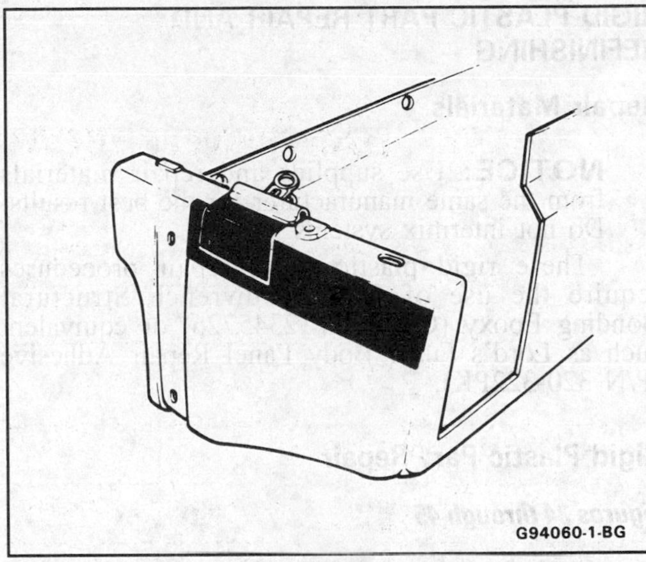
G94060-1-BG
Figure 35 Aligning Damage with Tape and Clamp

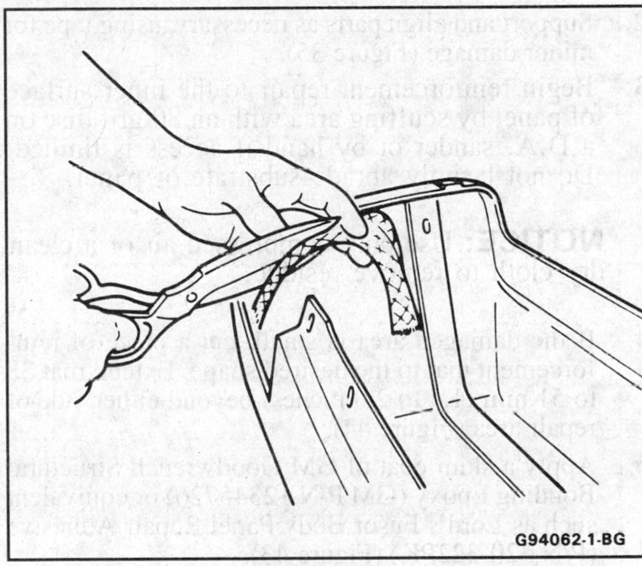
G94062-1-BG
Figure 36 Cutting Fiberglass Cloth to Size

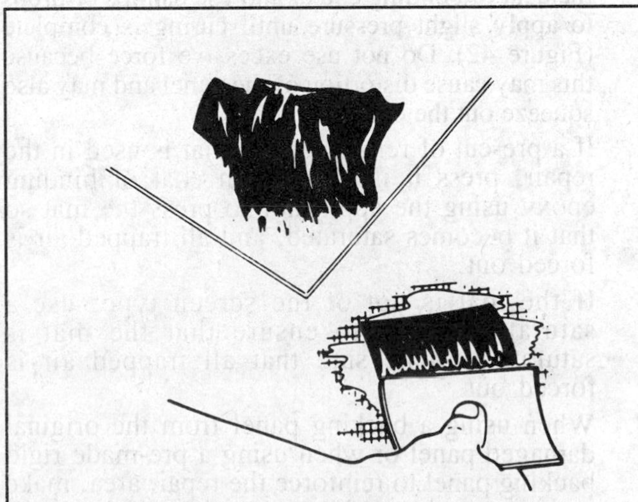
G94056-1-BG
Figure 37 Adhesive Repair Material

RIGID PLASTIC PART REPAIR AND REFINISHING

Repair Materials

NOTICE: Use supplies and repair materials from the same manufacturer for the best results. Do not intermix systems.

These rigid plastic panel repair procedures require the use of GM Goodwrench Structural Bonding Epoxy (GM P/N 12345726) or equivalent such as Lord's Fusor Body Panel Repair Adhesive (P/N 320-322PK).

Rigid Plastic Part Repair

Figures 34 through 45

1. Clean and inspect damaged area as required (Figure 34).
2. Support and align parts as necessary, using tape for minor damage (Figure 35).
3. Begin reinforcement repair to the inner surface of panel by scuffing area with an 80 grit disc on a D.A. sander or by hand if access is limited. Do not heavily abrade substrate of panel.

NOTICE: Use only compressed air or a clean, dry cloth to remove residue.

4. If the damaged area is small, cut a piece of reinforcement mat to the desired shape. Extend mat 38 to 51 mm (1.5 to 2.0 inches) beyond either side of repair area (Figure 44).
5. Apply a skim coat of GM Goodwrench Structural Bonding Epoxy (GM P/N 12345726) or equivalent such as Lord's Fusor Body Panel Repair Adhesive (P/N 320-322PK) (Figure 43).
6. If using a backing panel, lay the backing panel onto the coat of bonding epoxy and use clamps or props to apply slight pressure until curing is complete (Figure 42). Do not use excessive force because this may cause distortion of the panel and may also squeeze out the epoxy.
7. If a pre-cut of reinforcement mat is used in the repair, press it into the skim coat of binding epoxy using the applicator to press the mat so that it becomes saturated, and all trapped air is forced out.
8. If the mat is not of the screen type, use a saturation roller to ensure that the mat is saturated. Make sure that all trapped air is forced out.
9. When using a backing panel from the original damaged panel or when using a pre-made rigid backing panel to reinforce the repair area, make sure there are no voids at the edges of the repair area that may allow entry of water or chemicals.

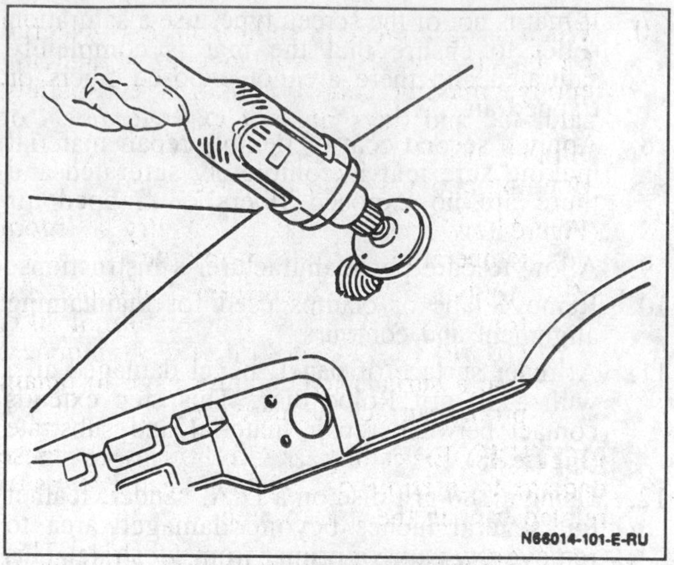
N66014-101-E-RU

Figure 38 Panel Beveling

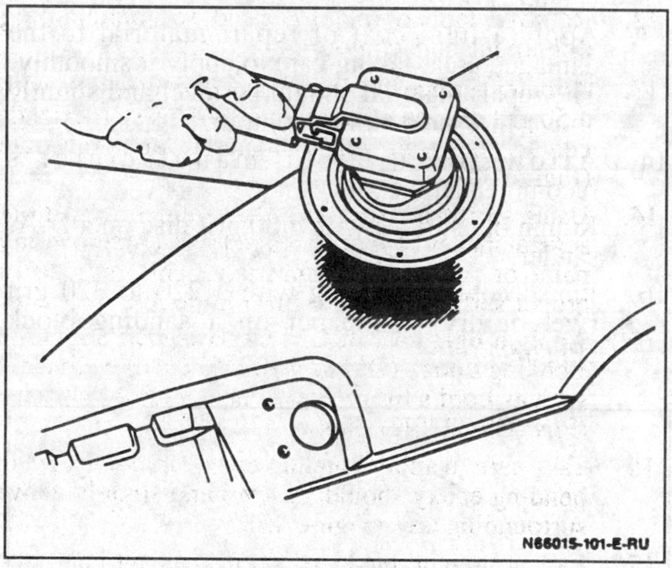
N66015-101-E-RU

Figure 39 Panel Feathering

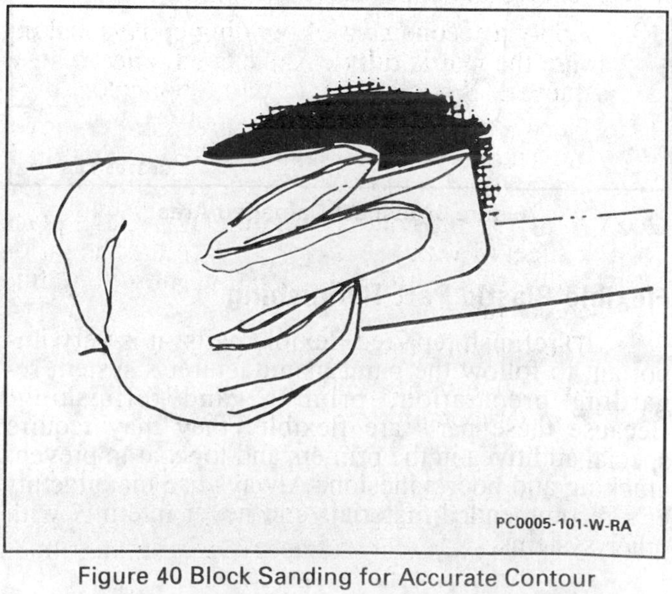
PC0005-101-W-RA

Figure 40 Block Sanding for Accurate Contour

10. When using a piece of reinforced mat material for backing, apply a second coat of bonding epoxy, making sure the mat is completely saturated and there are not exposed fibers or trapped air.
11. Bonding epoxy should be force dried.
    A. Allow the material to air dry at room temperature for twenty minutes.
    B. Apply heat with a uniform heat source for force dry at a surface temperature of 70°C (160°F) to 82°C (180°F) for 45 minutes. Use a surface temperature gage to obtain proper surface temperature.

NOTICE: Exceeding 82°C (180°F) may cause damage to interior components, weatherstrips or related trim in the heated area.

    C. Allow panel to return to room temperature before sanding.
12. Remove tape or clamps used for maintaining alignment and contours.
13. At outer surface of panel, bevel damaged area with a 50 grit disc on a Roloc sander. This step extends contact between repair material and substrate (Figure 38).
14. Using an 180 grit disc on a D.A. sander, feather out several inches beyond damaged area to remove any paint or primer from substrate. This provides a proper surface for adhesion (Figure 39).
15. Apply a light coat of GM Goodwrench Structural Bonding Epoxy (GM P/N 12345726) or equivalent such as Lord's Fusor Body Panel Repair Adhesive (P/N 320-322PK) (Figure 43).
16. Take care to apply bonding epoxy smoothly. Also, bonding epoxy should be level and slightly above surrounding area (Figure 45).
17. Lay a pre-cut piece of reinforcement mat into bonding epoxy. Use applicator to saturate and remove all trapped air (Figure 44).
18. Apply a second coat of bonding epoxy, making sure the mat is fully encapsulated, and no air is trapped. Smooth surface with applicator.
19. Place a second layer of reinforcement mat over the second coat of bonding epoxy, working it smooth and removing all trapped air.
20. Apply a final coat of bonding epoxy, and place a sheet of wax paper over it. Use the saturation roller to ensure full penetration of bonding epoxy into mat.
21. The bonding epoxy should be force dried.
    A. Allow material to air dry at room temperature for twenty minutes.
    B. Apply heat with a uniform heat source for force dry at a surface temperature of 70°C (160°F) to 82°C (180°F) for 45 minutes. Use a surface temperature gage to obtain proper surface temperature.

NOTICE: Exceeding 82°C (180°F) may cause damage to interior components, weatherstrips or related trim in the heated area.

    C. Allow panel to return to room temperature before sanding.
22. Rough out the surface with an 80 grit disc on a D.A. sander.
23. Finish contour sanding with 220 to 320 grit (wet or dry) sandpaper on a sanding block (Figure 40).

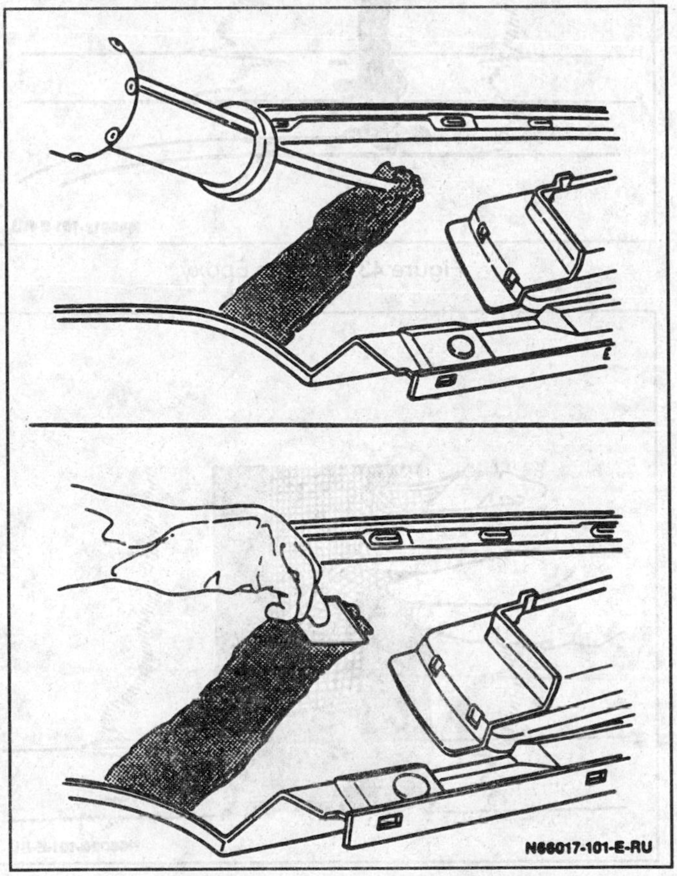
N66017-101-E-RU

Figure 41 Bonding Epoxy Application

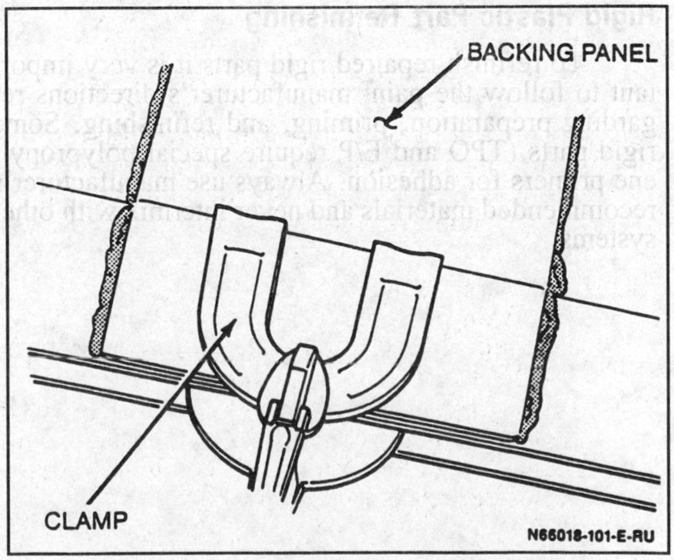
BACKING PANEL
CLAMP
N66018-101-E-RU

Figure 42 Secure Backing Panel

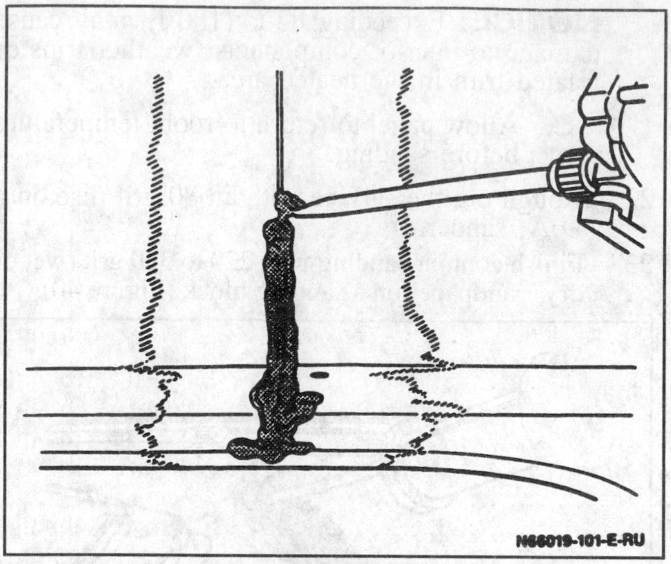
N66019-101-E-RU

Figure 43 Bonding Epoxy

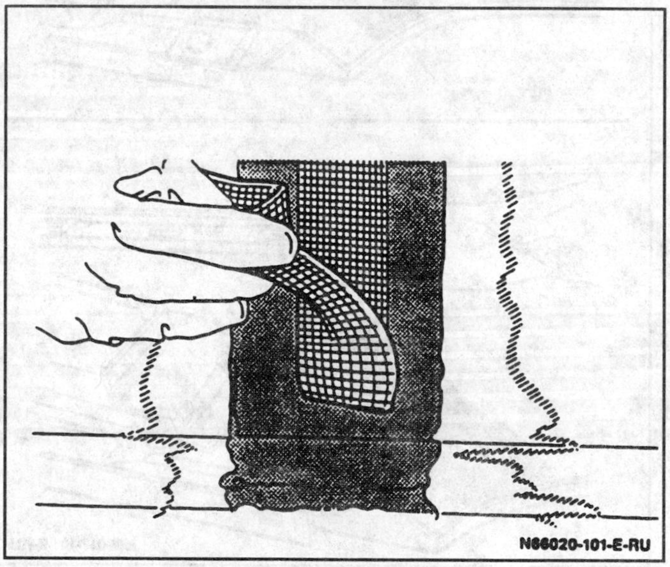
N66020-101-E-RU

Figure 44 Reinforcement Mat

Rigid Plastic Part Refinishing

To refinish repaired rigid parts it is very important to follow the paint manufacturer's directions regarding preparation, priming, and refinishing. Some rigid parts (TPO and E/P require special polypropylene primers for adhesion. Always use manufacturer's recommended materials and never intermix with other systems.

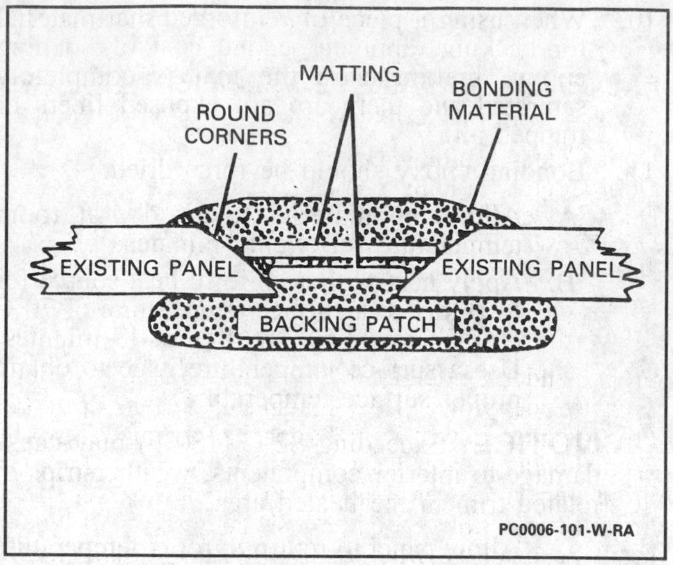
MATTING
ROUND CORNERS
BONDING MATERIAL
EXISTING PANEL
EXISTING PANEL
BACKING PATCH
PC0006-101-W-RA

Figure 45 Cross-Section of Splice

CARPET INSERT REATTACHMENT

Carpet inserts attached to side wall, door, instrument panel and quarter trim panels which have become loose may be reattached with 3M General Trim Adhesive Part 08080. Use the following procedure.

1. Remove trim panel when necessary and place on clean work surface. Mask off trim panel to prevent glue overspray.
2. Sand areas of trim panel where carpet is to be reglued using a coarse grit sandpaper. Polypropylene panels should have a rough surface for best adhesion.
3. Remove all sanding debris.
4. Spray 3M General Trim Adhesive Part 08080 on sanded surface and back side of carpet following manufacturer's instructions.
5. When both sprayed surfaces become tacky to the touch, press carpet in place and smooth out any irregularities.
6. Remove masking materials and reinstall panel.

SPECIFICATIONS

FASTENER TIGHTENING SPECIFICATIONS

Door Center Molding Bolt/Screw	2 N·m (18 lb. in.)
Door Center Molding Nut	2 N·m (18 lb. in.)
Door Lower Finish Panel Lower Support Nut	6 N·m (53 lb. in.)
Door Lower Finish Panel Bolt/Screw (Coupe)	1 N·m (9 lb. in.)
Door Lower Finish Panel Bolt/Screw (Sedan)	2 N·m (18 lb. in.)
Door Lower Finish Panel Support Nut (Coupe)	1 N·m (9 lb. in.)
Front Fender Center Rear Upper Molding Bolt/Screw (Coupe)	1 N·m (9 lb. in.)
Front Fender Center Rear Upper Molding Nut (Coupe)	2 N·m (18 lb. in.)
Front Fender Lower Rear Finish Panel Bolt/Screw (Coupe)	1 N·m (9 lb. in.)
Front Fender Lower Rear Finish Panel Bolt/Screw (Sedan)	2 N·m (18 lb. in.)
Front Fender Lower Rear Finish Panel Nut (Coupe)	1 N·m (9 lb. in.)
Front Fender Lower Rear Finish Panel Nut (Sedan)	3 N·m (27 lb. in.)
Front Fender Lower Rear Finish Panel Support Nut (Sedan)	6 N·m (53 lb. in.)
Front Fender Rear Molding Bolt/Screw (Coupe)	1 N·m (9 lb. in.)
Front Fender Rear Molding Nut (Coupe)	2 N·m (18 lb. in.)
Rear Quarter Center Front Molding Bolt/Screw (Coupe)	1 N·m (9 lb. in.)
Rear Quarter Lower Front Finish Panel Bolt/Screw (Sedan)	2 N·m (18 lb. in.)
Rocker Outer Finish Panel Bolt/Screw (Coupe)	2 N·m (18 lb. in.)
Rocker Outer Finish Panel Support Nut	10 N·m (89 lb. in.)

SECTION 10-2
STATIONARY WINDOWS

CAUTION: When replacing a windshield, rear window, or hatch roof window, urethane adhesive (part no. 12345633 or equivalent) must be used to maintain original installation integrity. Failure to use urethane adhesive will result in poor retention of the windshield which may allow unrestrained occupants to be ejected from the vehicle with resulting personal injury.

NOTICE: When fasteners are removed, always reinstall them at the same location from which they were removed. If a fastener needs to be replaced, use the correct part number fastener for that application. If the correct part number fastener is not available, a fastener of equal size and strength (or stronger) may be used. Fasteners that are not reused, and those requiring thread locking compound will be called out. The correct torque value must be used when installing fasteners that require it. If the above conditions are not followed, parts or system damage could result.

CONTENTS

GENERAL DESCRIPTION

STATIONARY WINDOWS

To replace a windshield or rear window installed with urethane adhesive requires either partial or complete replacement of the adhesive. Partial replacement of material is referred to as the short method. Complete replacement of the material is known as the extended method.

The short method can be used where original adhesive left on window opening pinch-weld flanges after window removal can serve as a base for the new window.

This method would apply in cases of cracked windshields or removal of windows that are still intact. The amount of adhesive left in window opening can be controlled during window removal.

The extended method is to be used when the original adhesive left in window opening after window removal cannot serve as a base for new window. This method would be used in cases needing metal work or paint repair in the opening. In these cases, original material is removed and replaced with new material during window installation.

ADHESIVE SERVICE KIT

Adhesive Kit No. 12345633 (urethane adhesive) or equivalent contains some of the items needed to replace a urethane adhesive installed window using the short method or any adhesive installed window using the extended method.

Additional items required:

- Solvent for cleaning edge of window (preferably alcohol).
- Household cartridge type caulking gun.
- Commercial type razor knife (for cutting around edge of window).
- Glass sealant remover knife J 24402-A.
- Black weatherstrip adhesive.
- Spacers (see service parts manual).

ON-VEHICLE SERVICE

WINDSHIELD REVEAL MOLDINGS

The reveal moldings fill the cavities between the body and window edge.

Upper Reveal Molding

Figure 1

Remove or Disconnect

1. Windshield side reveal moldings. Refer to "Side Reveal Moldings" in this section.
2. With a flat-bladed tool, carefully pry end of molding out about 75 mm (3 inches).
3. Grasp with hand and slowly pull molding away from body.
   - The original molding cannot be reused. Discard molding and replace with a new service molding. Be sure to prefit service molding by locating on body prior to actual installation.

Install or Connect

1. Clear primer from urethane kit GM P/N 12345633 (or equivalent) to lower surface of molding.
2. Urethane adhesive in cavity between body and window.
3. Start from center and hand press molding into place. Tape can be applied to keep reveal molding flush with body.
4. Flood molding with warm water to speed set-up of adhesive.
5. Windshield side reveal moldings. Refer to "Side Reveal Moldings" in this section.

Side Reveal Moldings

Figure 1

Remove or Disconnect

1. Pull back roof side rail auxiliary weatherstrip.
2. Screws.
3. Reveal molding.

Install or Connect

1. Reveal molding.
2. Screws.

Tighten

- Screws to 2 N·m (18 lb. in.).

3. Roof side rail auxiliary weatherstrip.

Lower Reveal Molding

Figure 1

Remove or Disconnect

1. Stud caps.
2. Screws.
3. Reveal molding.

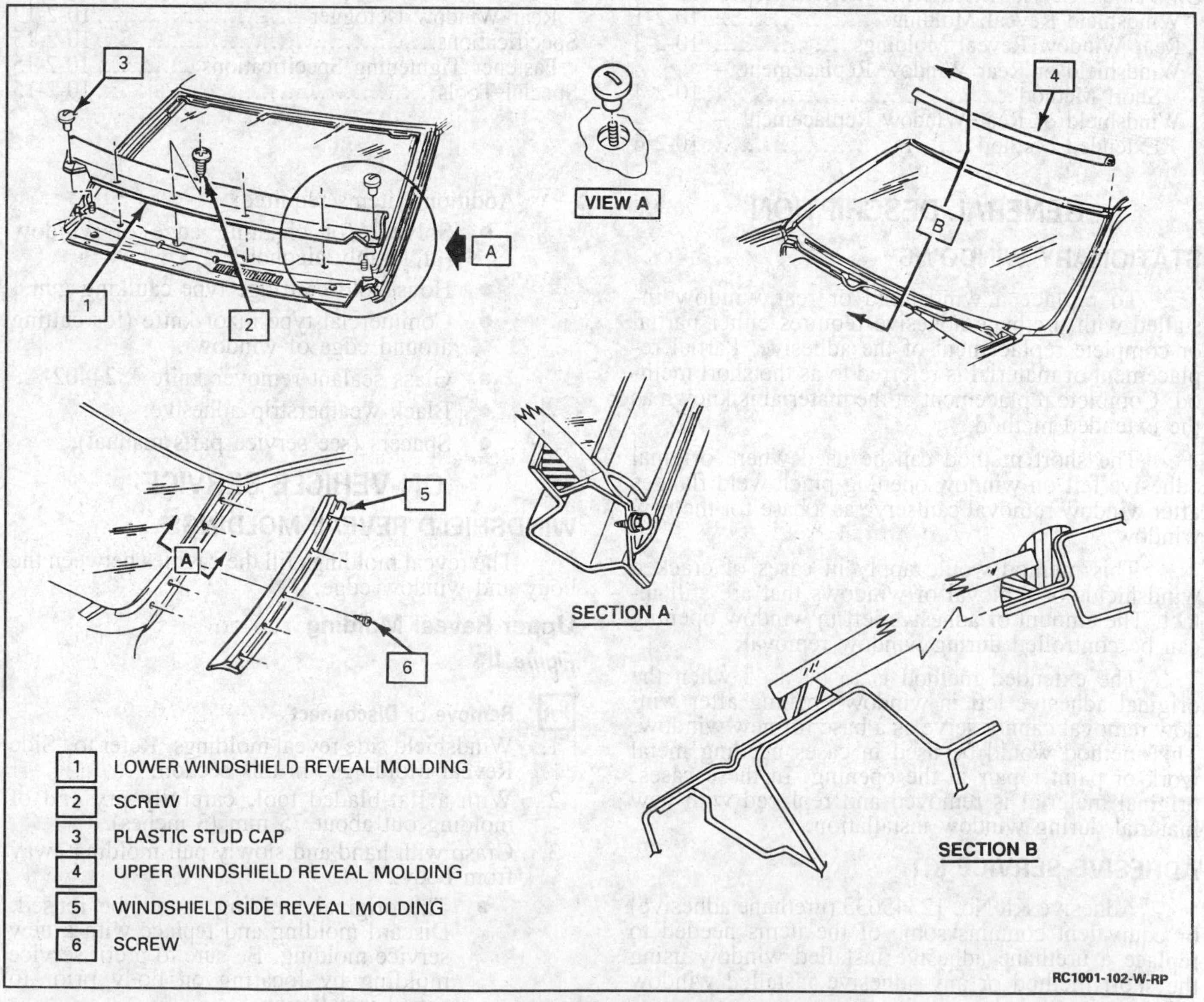

3
1
2
A
VIEW A
4
B
5
A
6
SECTION A
SECTION B
1 LOWER WINDSHIELD REVEAL MOLDING
2 SCREW
3 PLASTIC STUD CAP
4 UPPER WINDSHIELD REVEAL MOLDING
5 WINDSHIELD SIDE REVEAL MOLDING
6 SCREW
RC1001-102-W-RP

Figure 1 Windshield Reveal Moldings

Install or Connect

1. Reveal molding.
2. Screws.

Tighten

- Screws to 2 N·m (18 lb. in.).

3. Stud caps.

REAR WINDOW REVEAL MOLDINGS

Upper Reveal Molding (Coupe)

Figure 2

The upper reveal molding on coupes cannot be replaced without removing the rear window. When replacing the rear window, the original molding cannot be reused and must be replaced with a new service part. Refer to "Windshield or Rear Window Replacement" in this section.

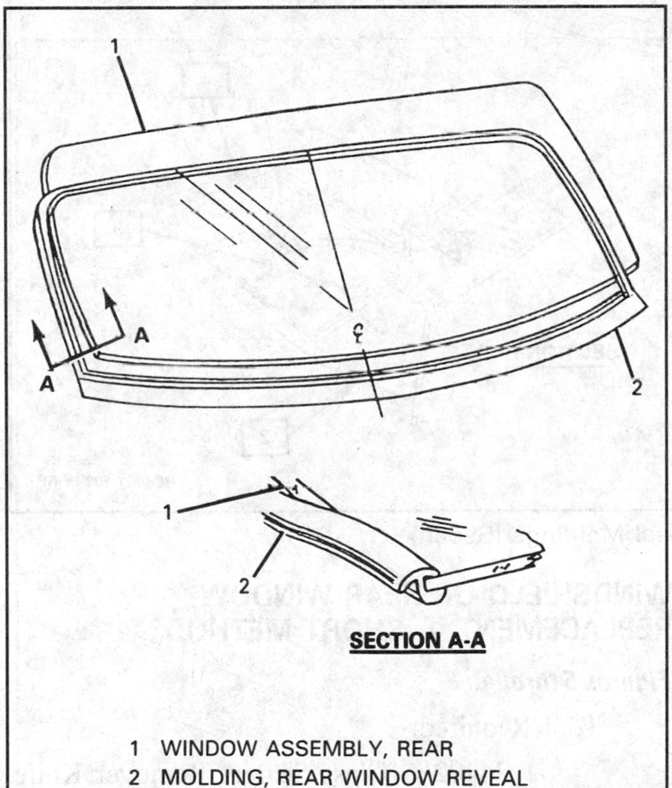
1
A
A
℄
2
1
2
SECTION A-A
1 WINDOW ASSEMBLY, REAR
2 MOLDING, REAR WINDOW REVEAL
PC0001-102-W-RA

Figure 2 Rear Window Reveal Moldings (Coupe)

Upper Reveal Molding (Sedan)

Figure 3

Remove or Disconnect

1. Using a flat-bladed tool, carefully pry end of molding out about 75 mm (3 inches).
2. Grasp molding with hand and slowly pull molding away from body.
   - The original molding cannot be reused. Discard molding and replace with a new service molding. Be sure to prefit service molding by locating on body prior to actual installation.

Install or Connect

1. Clear primer from urethane kit GM P/N 12345633 (or equivalent) to lower surface of molding.
2. Urethane in cavity between body and window.
3. Start from center and hand press molding into place. Tape can be applied to keep reveal molding flush with body.
4. Flood molding with warm water to speed set-up of adhesive.

Lower Reveal Molding (Sedan)

Figure 3

Remove or Disconnect

1. Screws.
2. Reveal molding.

Install or Connect

1. Reveal molding.
2. Screws.

Tighten

- Screws to 2 N·m (18 lb. in.).

Molding Retainer Replacement

Figure 4

If a weld stud becomes damaged or broken, use the following repair procedure:

1. Drill a small hole in the panel next to original weld stud installation.
2. Insert a self-sealing screw through original clip and into outer panel, or replace damaged weld stud with self-sealing screw type weld stud.

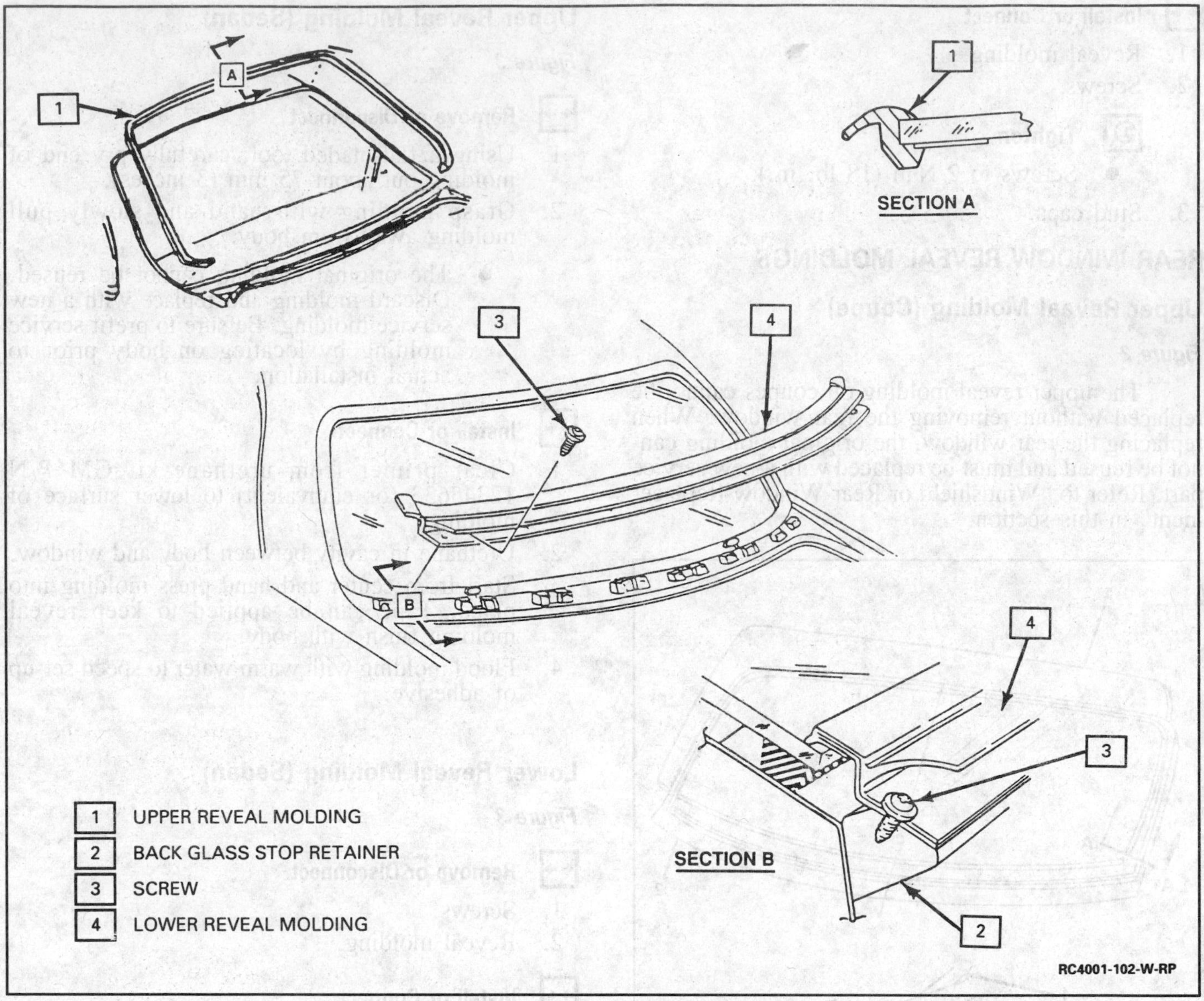

A
1
SECTION A
3
4
B
4
3
SECTION B
2
1 UPPER REVEAL MOLDING
2 BACK GLASS STOP RETAINER
3 SCREW
4 LOWER REVEAL MOLDING
RC4001-102-W-RP

Figure 3 Rear Window Reveal Moldings (Sedan)

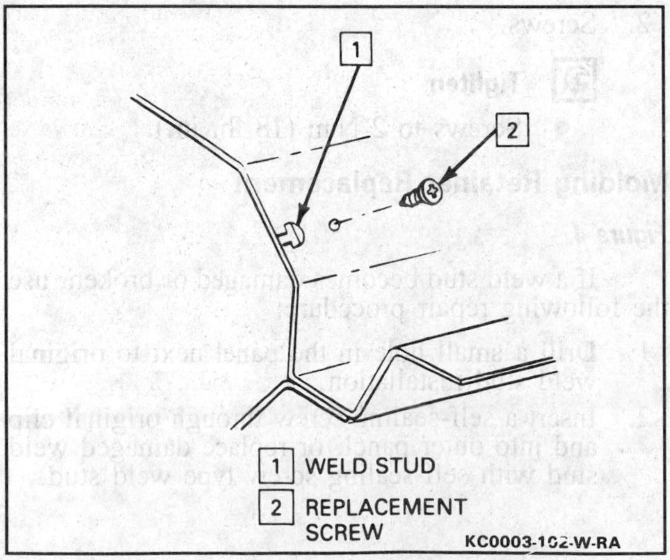

1
2
1 WELD STUD
2 REPLACEMENT SCREW
KC0003-102-W-RA

Figure 4 Weld Stud Replacement

WINDSHIELD OR REAR WINDOW REPLACEMENT — SHORT METHOD

Figures 5 through 8

Tool Required:

J 24402-A Glass Sealant Remover Knife

CAUTION: When replacing a windshield, rear window, or hatch roof window, urethane adhesive (part no. 12345633 or equivalent) must be used to maintain original installation integrity. Failure to use urethane adhesive will result in poor retention of the windshield which may allow unrestrained occupants to be ejected from the vehicle with resulting personal injury.

The windshield removal method is the same for both the short and extended installation methods with one exception. If the short method is to be used, more care must be exercised during cutout to make certain that an even bead of adhesive remains on window opening to serve as a base for a new window.

CAUTION: Approved safety glasses and gloves should be worn when performing this procedure to reduce the chance of personal injury.

Remove or Disconnect

1. Rearview mirror if replacing windshield. Refer to "Rearview Mirror" in this section.
2. Reveal moldings as needed if replacing windshield. Refer to "Windshield Reveal Moldings" in this section.
3. Wiper arms and blade if replacing windshield. Refer to WINDSHIELD WIPER/WASHER SYSTEM (SECTION 8E).
4. Air inlet screen if replacing windshield. Refer to BODY FRONT END (SECTION 10-5).
5. Window stops and retainers (Figure 5) if replacing rear window.
6. Mask off area around window to protect painted surfaces and to aid in clean up after installation.
7. Using a razor or utility knife, make a preliminary cut around entire perimeter of window, staying as close to edge of window as possible.
8. Using J 24402-A, cut out window, keeping blade as close to edge of window as possible. Remove window.

Clean

- Window opening of any loose material. If window is to be reinstalled, all urethane must be removed from window.

Install or Connect

1. Rear window retainers (Figure 5) if removed. Position (dry fit) window in opening, apply a piece of masking tape over each edge of window and adjacent body pillars. Slit tape vertically at edge of window. During installation, tape on window can be aligned with tape on body to guide window into desired position. Remove window.

   Clean

   - Surface of window to which adhesive will be applied (around edge of inside surface) by wiping with a clean, alcohol dampened cloth. Allow to air dry.

2. Upper reveal molding on top edge of windshield if replacing windshield. Refer to "Windshield Reveal Moldings" in this section.
3. Foam spacer if replacing windshield.
4. Reveal molding if replacing rear window. For sedan, refer to "Rear Window Reveal Molding" in this section. For coupe,
   - A. Position lower right and left hand molded corners of reveal molding to glass.
   - B. Press reveal molding onto edge of rear window working from lower corners to centerline on upper edge of glass.
5. Two primers are provided in urethane adhesive kit GM P/N 12345633 (or equivalent). The clear primer is used on the window prior to the black primer. Apply primer around entire perimeter of glass edge and 6 mm (1/4 inch) inboard on inner surface. Allow primer to dry five minutes.
6. Smooth continuous bead of urethane around edge of window where primed in step 5 (Figure 6 and 7).
7. With aid of helper, lift windshield into window opening (Figure 8) or use suction cups to lift rear window into window opening.
8. With window centered in opening, use tape guides applied in step 1 to carefully place window in proper position.
9. Press window firmly to wet-out and set adhesive. Use care to avoid excessive squeezeout which would cause an appearance problem. Using small disposable brush or flat-bladed tool, paddle material around edge of window to ensure water-tight seal. If necessary, paddle additional material to fill voids in seal.
10. Tape to windshield and roof until urethane adhesive cures.
11. Rear window stops (Figure 5) if replacing rear window.
12. Watertest vehicle at once using soft spray. Use warm or hot water if available. Do not direct hard stream of water at fresh adhesive material. If any leaks are found, paddle in extra adhesive at leak point using a small disposable brush or flat-bladed tool. Water applied on top of urethane adhesive, either during watertest or as a separate operation, will speed up the cure of the urethane.
13. Air inlet screen if replacing windshield. Refer to BODY FRONT END (SECTION 10-5).
14. Reveal moldings if replacing windshield. Refer to "Windshield Reveal Moldings" in this section.
15. Windshield wipers and blades if replacing windshield. Refer to WINDSHIELD WIPER/WASHER SYSTEM (SECTION 8E).

Important

- Vehicle must remain at normal room temperature for six hours to complete proper cure of adhesive.

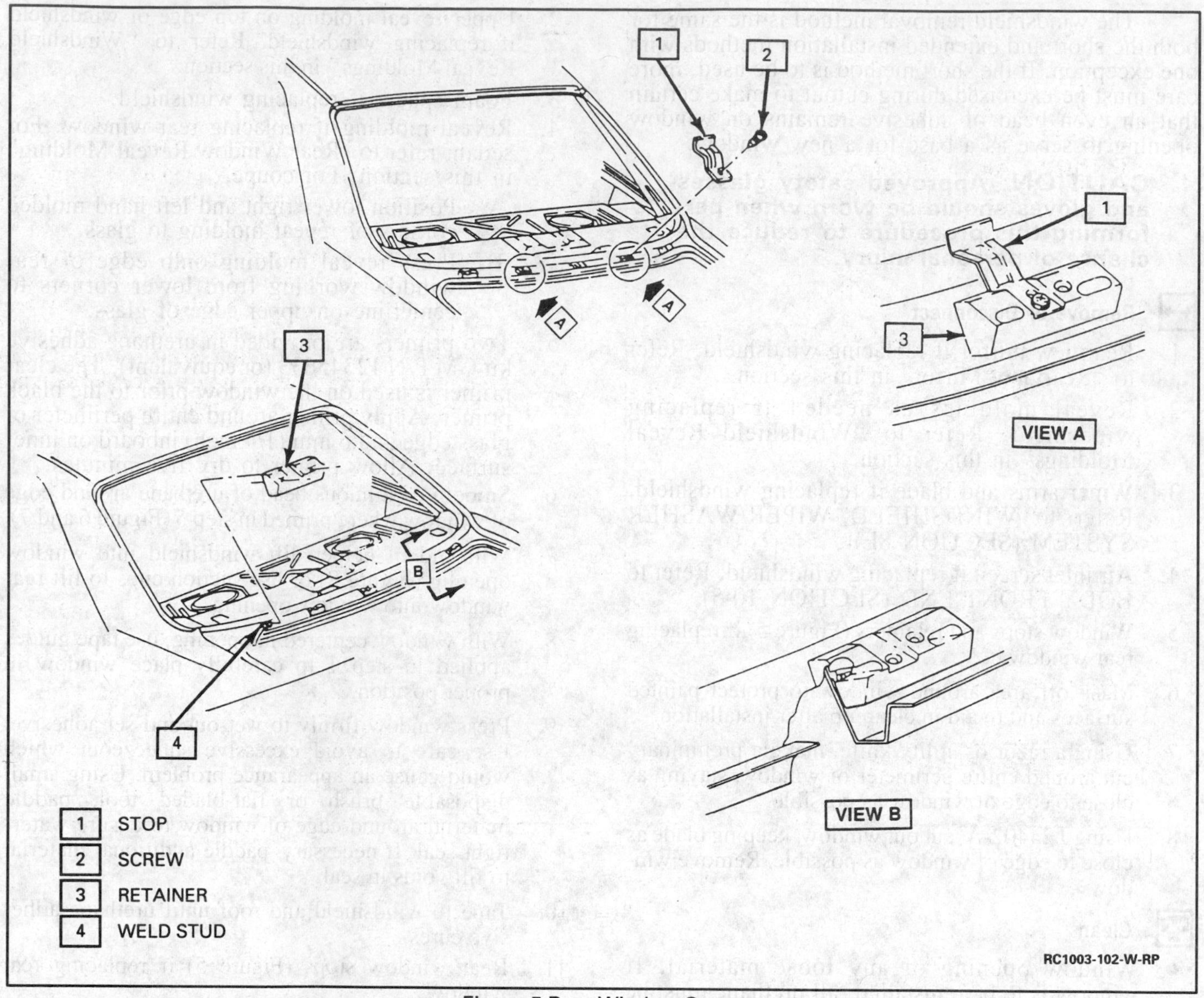
1
2
1
3
VIEW A
3
B
A
A
VIEW B
4
1 STOP
2 SCREW
3 RETAINER
4 WELD STUD
RC1003-102-W-RP

Figure 5 Rear Window Stops

WINDSHIELD OR REAR WINDOW REPLACEMENT – EXTENDED METHOD

Figures 5 through 9

It will be necessary to use extended installation method if:

- Improper service installation.
- Urethane material remaining in window opening (after window removal) is damaged.
- Urethane material remaining in window opening (after window removal) must be removed to permit refinishing of window opening.

↔ Remove or Disconnect

- Refer to "Short Method" in this section.

CAUTION: Approved safety glasses and gloves should be worn when performing this procedure to reduce the chance of personal injury.

Clean

- Using a sharp scraper or chisel, remove the old adhesive material from window opening. It is not necessary that all traces of urethane adhesive be removed, but there should not be any mounds or loose pieces left.
  - If refinishing or painting operations are required, or painted surface is exposed during removal of material, black primer should be applied to exposed area.

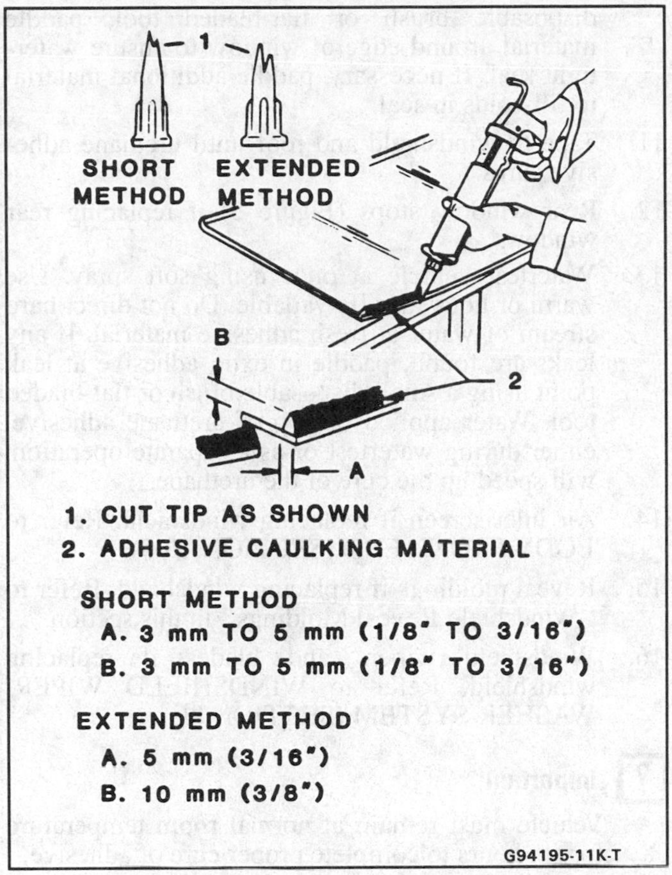

1
SHORT METHOD
EXTENDED METHOD
B
2
A
1. CUT TIP AS SHOWN
2. ADHESIVE CAULKING MATERIAL
SHORT METHOD
A. 3 mm TO 5 mm (1/8" TO 3/16")
B. 3 mm TO 5 mm (1/8" TO 3/16")
EXTENDED METHOD
A. 5 mm (3/16")
B. 10 mm (3/8")
G94195-11K-T

Figure 6 Adhesive Material Application

Install or Connect

1. Spacers (see service parts manual). Cement spacers around window opening (Figure 9) and position window in opening for dry fit. If new window is being installed, check relationship of window to urethane on pinch-weld flange. Gaps in excess of 3 mm (1/8 inch) must be corrected by shimming or by applying more adhesive than specified (Figure 6).
2. Rear window retainers (Figure 5) if removed. Position (dry fit) window in opening, apply a piece of masking tape over each edge of window and adjacent body pillars. Slit tape vertically at edge of window. During installation, tape on window can be aligned with tape on body to guide window into desired position. Remove window.

Clean

- Surface of window to which adhesive will be applied (around edge of inside surface) by wiping with a clean, alcohol dampened cloth. Allow to air dry.

3. Upper reveal molding on top edge of windshield if replacing windshield. Refer to "Windshield Reveal Moldings" in this section.
4. Foam spacer if replacing windshield.

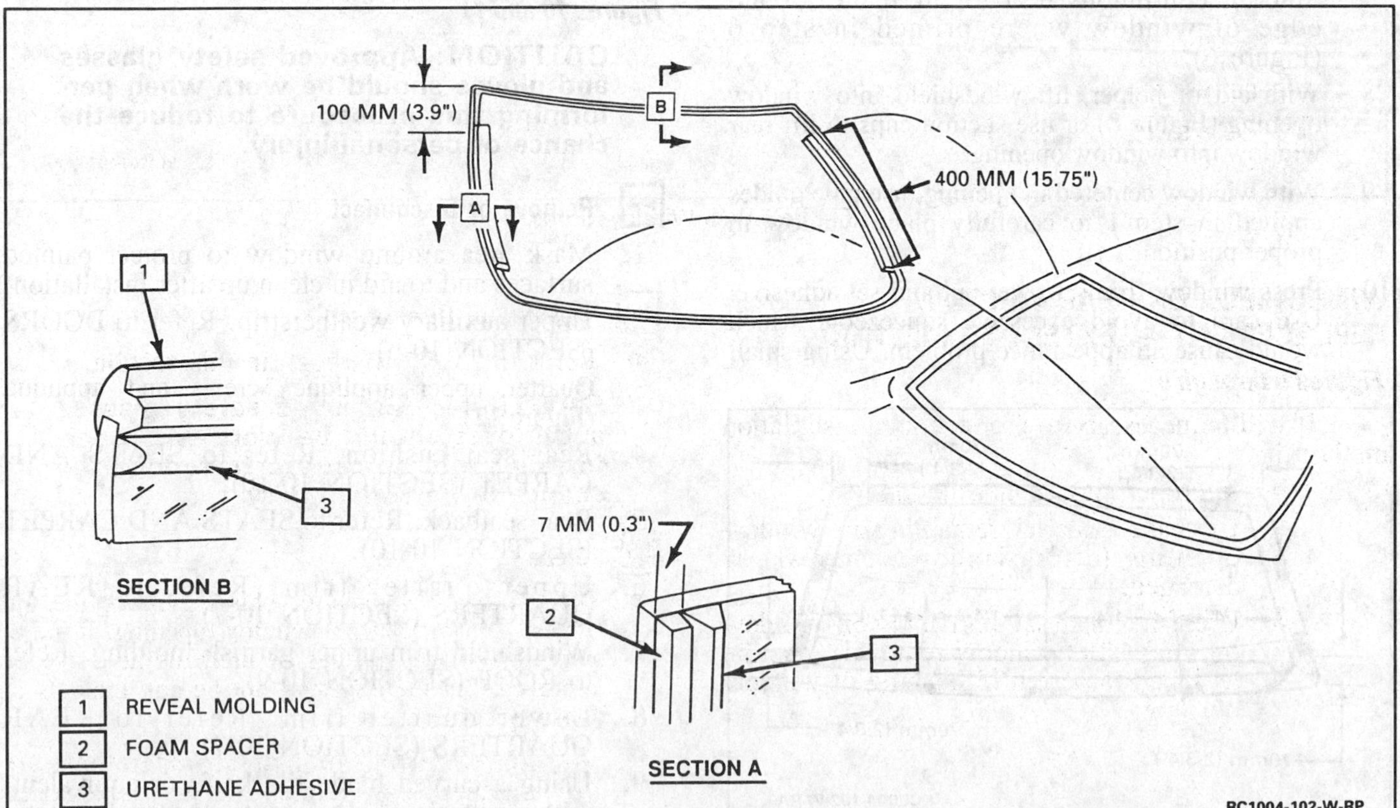

100 MM (3.9")
B
A
400 MM (15.75")
1
3
SECTION B
7 MM (0.3")
2
3
SECTION A
1 REVEAL MOLDING
2 FOAM SPACER
3 URETHANE ADHESIVE
RC1004-102-W-RP

Figure 7 Windshield Foam Spacer Installed

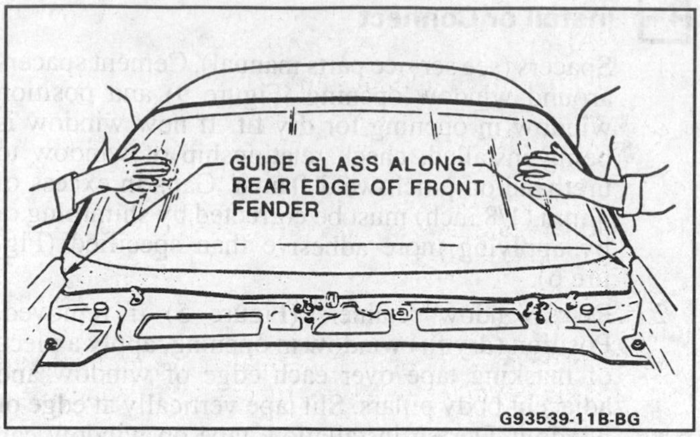
GUIDE GLASS ALONG
REAR EDGE OF FRONT
FENDER
G93539-11B-BG

Figure 8 Window Installation

5. Reveal molding if replacing rear window. For sedan, refer to "Rear Window Reveal Molding" in this section. For coupe,
   A. Position lower right and left hand molded corners of reveal molding to glass.
   B. Press reveal molding onto edge of rear window working from lower corners to centerline on upper edge of glass.
6. Two primers are provided in urethane adhesive kit GM P/N 12345633 (or equivalent). The clear primer is used on the window prior to the black primer. Apply primer around entire perimeter of glass edge and 6 mm (1/4 inch) inboard on inner surface. Allow primer to dry five minutes.
7. Smooth continuous bead of urethane around edge of window where primed in step 6 (Figure 6).
8. With aid of helper, lift windshield into window opening (Figure 8) or use suction cups to lift rear window into window opening.
9. With window centered in opening, use tape guides applied in step 1 to carefully place window in proper position.
10. Press window firmly to wet-out and set adhesive. Use care to avoid excessive squeezeout which would cause an appearance problem. Using small disposable brush or flat-bladed tool, paddle material around edge of window to ensure watertight seal. If necessary, paddle additional material to fill voids in seal.

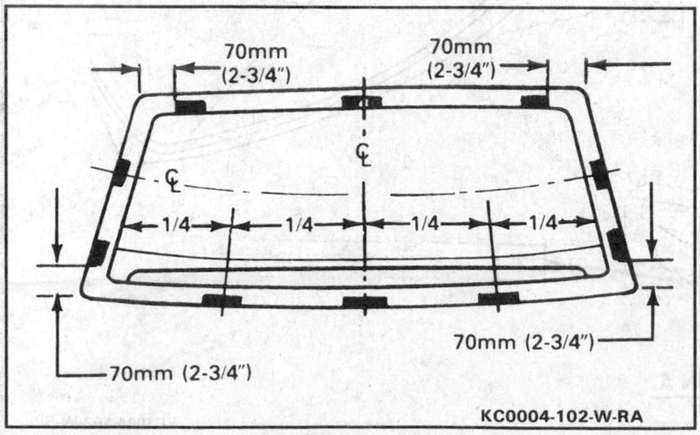
70mm
(2-3/4")
70mm
(2-3/4")
℄
℄
1/4
1/4
1/4
1/4
70mm (2-3/4")
70mm (2-3/4")
KC0004-102-W-RA

Figure 9 Windshield and Rear Window Spacer Locations

11. Tape to windshield and roof until urethane adhesive cures.
12. Rear window stops (Figure 5) if replacing rear window.
13. Watertest vehicle at once using soft spray. Use warm or hot water if available. Do not direct hard stream of water at fresh adhesive material. If any leaks are found, paddle in extra adhesive at leak point using a small disposable brush or flat-bladed tool. Water applied on top of urethane adhesive, either during watertest or as a separate operation, will speed up the cure of the urethane.
14. Air inlet screen if replacing windshield. Refer to BODY FRONT END (SECTION 10-5).
15. Reveal moldings if replacing windshield. Refer to "Windshield Reveal Moldings" in this section.
16. Windshield wipers and blades if replacing windshield. Refer to WINDSHIELD WIPER/WASHER SYSTEM (SECTION 8E).

Important

- Vehicle must remain at normal room temperature for six hours to complete proper cure of adhesive.

QUARTER WINDOW ASSEMBLY (Coupe)

Figures 10 and 11

CAUTION: Approved safety glasses and gloves should be worn when performing this procedure to reduce the chance of personal injury.

Remove or Disconnect

1. Mask area around window to protect painted surfaces and to aid in clean up after installation.
2. Upper auxiliary weatherstrip. Refer to DOORS (SECTION 10-6).
3. Quarter upper applique screws and applique (Figure 12).
4. Rear seat cushion. Refer to SEATS AND CARPET (SECTION 10-10).
5. Rear seatback. Refer to SEATS AND CARPET (SECTION 10-10).
6. Upper quarter trim. Refer to REAR QUARTERS (SECTION 10-7).
7. Windshield trim upper garnish molding. Refer to ROOF (SECTION 10-9).
8. Lower quarter trim. Refer to REAR QUARTERS (SECTION 10-7).
9. Using a curved blade tile knife or equivalent, with multiple shallow cuts, cut out quarter window assembly.
10. Quarter window assembly.

Clean

- Urethane from quarter window assembly and pinch-weld flange.

Install or Connect

1. Two primers are provided in Urethane Adhesive Kit GM P/N 12345633 (or equivalent). Apply the clear primer first around quarter window assembly. Allow to dry. Then apply black primer over clear primer and to pinch-weld flange. Allow primer to dry five minutes.

NOTICE: To prevent corrosion, paint damage around the pinch-weld by the knife must be covered with primer before installation of the quarter window assembly.

2. Reveal molding on glass perimeter.
3. Retainer clips.
4. Smooth continuous 9.5 mm (3/8 inch) bead of urethane around quarter window assembly.
5. Quarter window assembly in opening.
6. Lower quarter trim panel. Refer to REAR QUARTERS (SECTION 10-7).
7. Windshield side upper garnish molding. Refer to ROOF (SECTION 10-9).
8. Upper quarter trim panel. Refer to REAR QUARTERS (SECTION 10-7).
9. Rear seatback and cushion. Refer to SEATS AND CARPET (SECTION 10-10).
10. Quarter upper applique and screws (Figure 12).

Tighten

- Screws to 1 N•m (9 lb. in.).

11. Upper auxiliary weatherstrip. Refer to DOORS (SECTION 10-6).

Important

- Vehicle must remain at normal room temperature for six hours to complete proper cure of adhesive.

Clean

- Interior and exterior.

WATERLEAK CORRECTION

Figure 12

Where accessible, waterleaks can be corrected without removing and installing the window. This method applies only to urethane installed window and the use of adhesive furnished in kit GM P/N 12345633 (or equivalent).

1. Remove reveal moldings in area of leak. In some cases, it may become necessary to remove garnish moldings or finishing lace to locate source of leak.

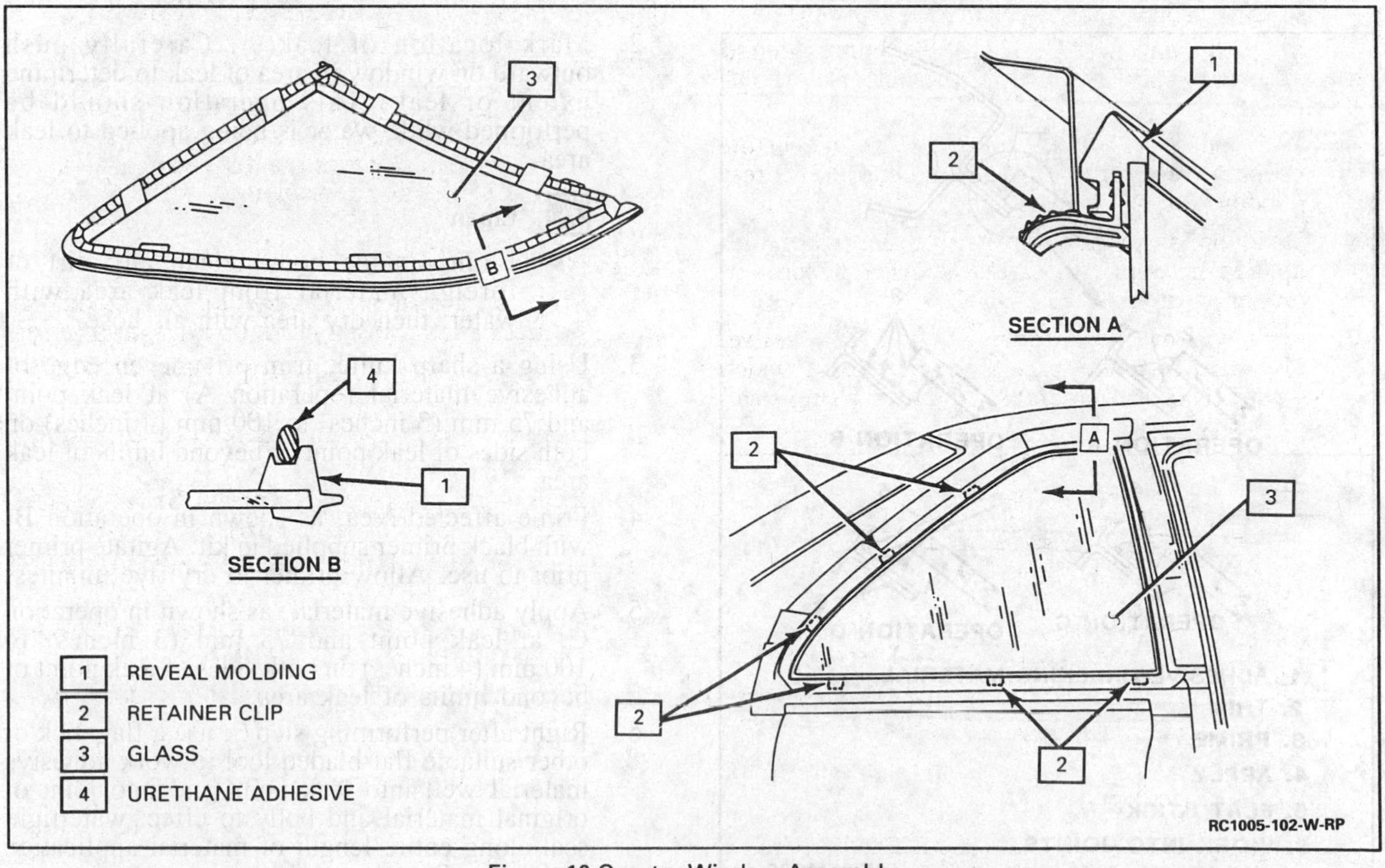
3
B
4
1
SECTION B
1 REVEAL MOLDING
2 RETAINER CLIP
3 GLASS
4 URETHANE ADHESIVE
1
2
SECTION A
A
2
3
2
2
RC1005-102-W-RP

Figure 10 Quarter Window Assembly

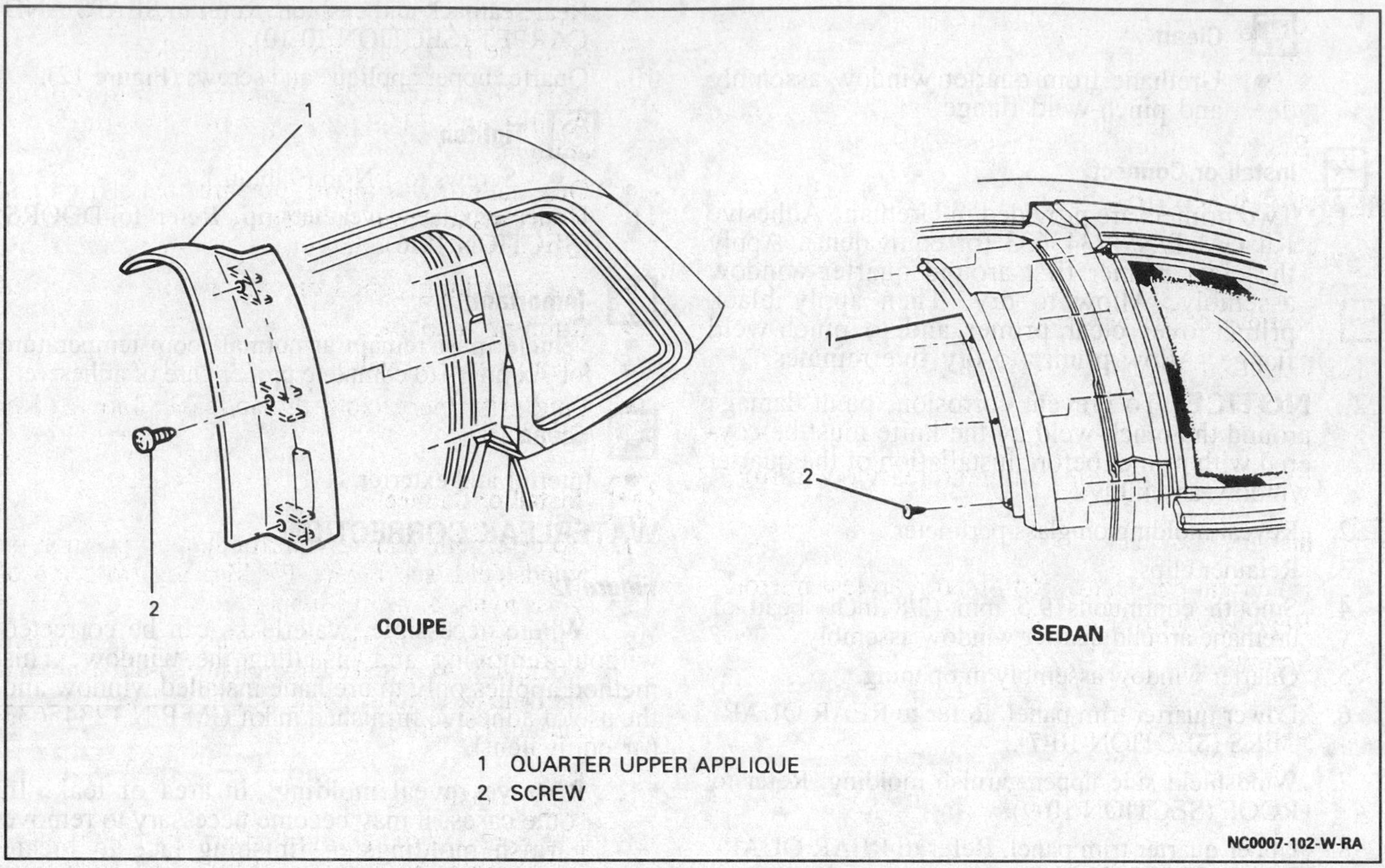
COUPE
SEDAN
1 QUARTER UPPER APPLIQUE
2 SCREW
NC0007-102-W-RA

Figure 11 Quarter Upper Applique

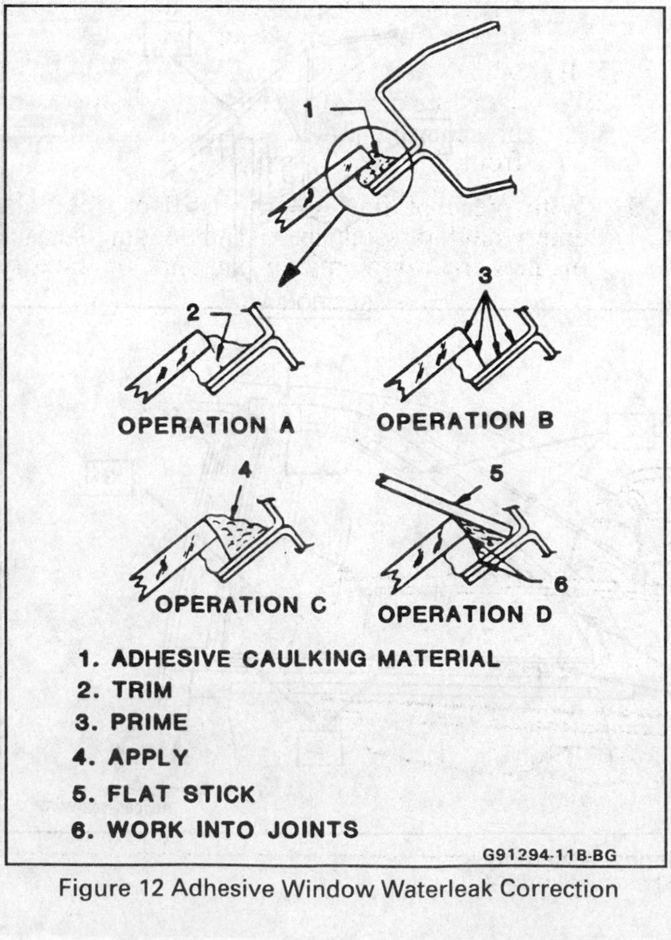
OPERATION A
OPERATION B
OPERATION C
OPERATION D
1. ADHESIVE CAULKING MATERIAL
2. TRIM
3. PRIME
4. APPLY
5. FLAT STICK
6. WORK INTO JOINTS
G91294-11B-BG

Figure 12 Adhesive Window Waterleak Correction

2. Mark location of leak(s). Carefully push outward on window in area of leak to determine extent of leak. This operation should be performed while water is being applied to leak area.

Clean

- From outside body, clean any dirt or foreign material from leak area with water; then dry area with air hose.

3. Using a sharp knife, trim off uneven edge of adhesive material (operation A) at leak point and 75 mm (3 inches) to 100 mm (4 inches) on both sides of leak point or beyond limits of leak area.
4. Prime affected area, as shown in operation B, with black primer supplied in kit. Agitate primer prior to use. Allow primer to dry five minutes.
5. Apply adhesive material, as shown in operation C, at leak point and 75 mm (3 inches) to 100 mm (4 inches) on both sides of leak point or beyond limits of leak area.
6. Right after performing step 5, use a flat stick or other suitable flat-bladed tool to work adhesive material well into leak point and into joint of original material and body to effect watertight seal along entire length of material application (operation D).

7. Using warm or hot water, spray test to assure that leak has been corrected. Do not run heavy stream of water directly on freshly applied adhesive.
8. Replace all previously removed parts.

REARVIEW MIRROR

Figure 13

Remove or Disconnect

1. Cover, if lighted rearview mirror.
2. Loosen screw.
3. Rearview mirror.
4. Electrical connector, if lighted rearview mirror.

Install or Connect

1. Electrical connector, if lighted rearview mirror.
2. Rearview mirror.
3. Screw.

Tighten

- Screw to 2 N·m (18 lb. in.).

4. Cover, if lighted rearview mirror.

REARVIEW MIRROR SUPPORT

Figures 13 through 15

The rearview mirror is attached to a support which is secured to the windshield. This support is installed by the window supplier using a plastic-polyvinyl butyral adhesive.

Servicc replacement windshield has the mirror support bonded to the window assembly.

To install a detached mirror support or install a new part, the following items are needed.

- Part No. 1052369, Loctite Minute-Bond Adhesive 312 two component pack or equivalent.
- Original mirror support (prepared per steps 4 and 5 of installation procedure) or replacement rearview mirror support.
- Wax marking pencil or crayon.
- Rubbing alcohol.
- Clean paper towels.
- Fine grit emery cloth or sandpaper (no. 320 or no. 360).

Install or Connect

1. To determine rearview mirror support position on windshield, see Figure 14. Measure from top of glass to top of mirror support.
2. Mark location on outside of glass with wax pencil or crayon. Also make larger diameter circle around the mirror support circle on the outside window surface (Figure 15).

Clean

A. On inside window surface, clean large circle with paper towel and domestic scouring cleanser, window cleaning solution or polishing compound. Rub until area is completely clean and dry.

B. When dry, clean area with an alcohol saturated paper towel to remove any traces of scouring powder or cleaning solution from this area.

3. With piece of fine grit (no. 320 or no. 360) emery cloth or sandpaper, sand bonding surface of new rearview mirror support or factory

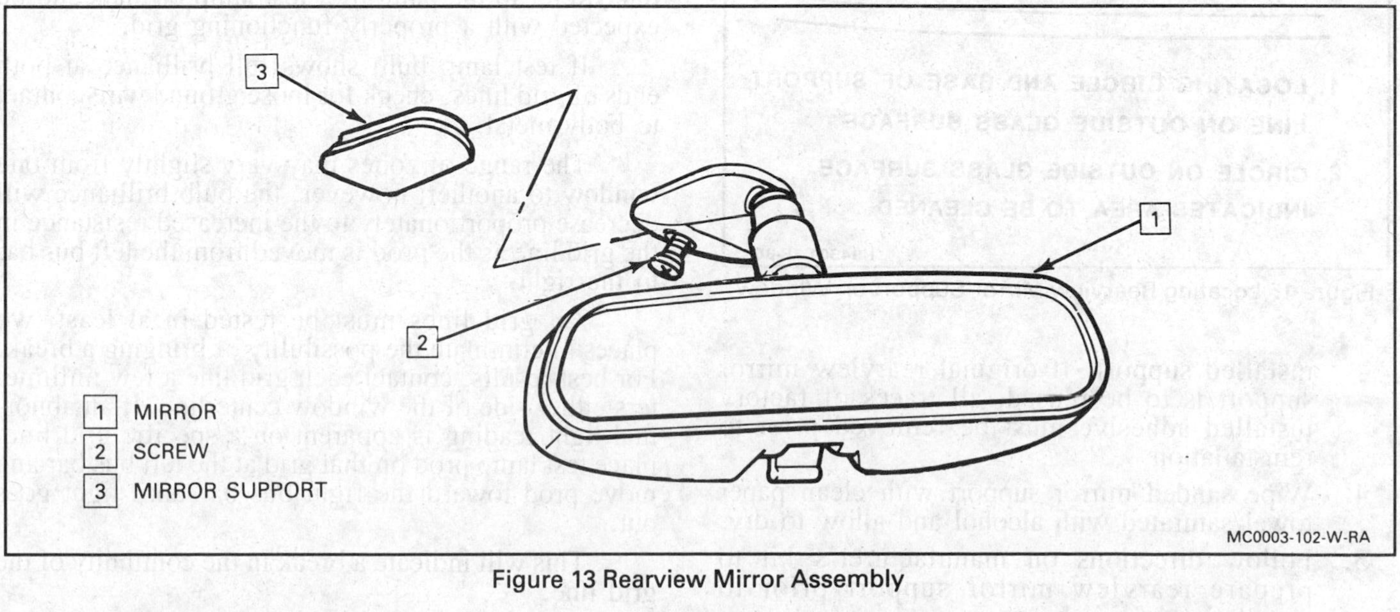
3
1
2
1 MIRROR
2 SCREW
3 MIRROR SUPPORT
MC0003-102-W-RA

Figure 13 Rearview Mirror Assembly

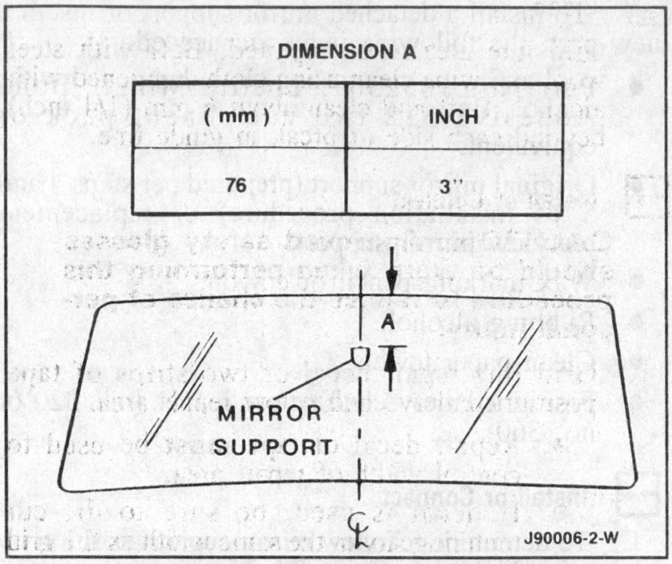
DIMENSION A
(mm)
INCH
76
3"
A
MIRROR
SUPPORT
J90006-2-W

Figure 14 Rearview Mirror Support Location

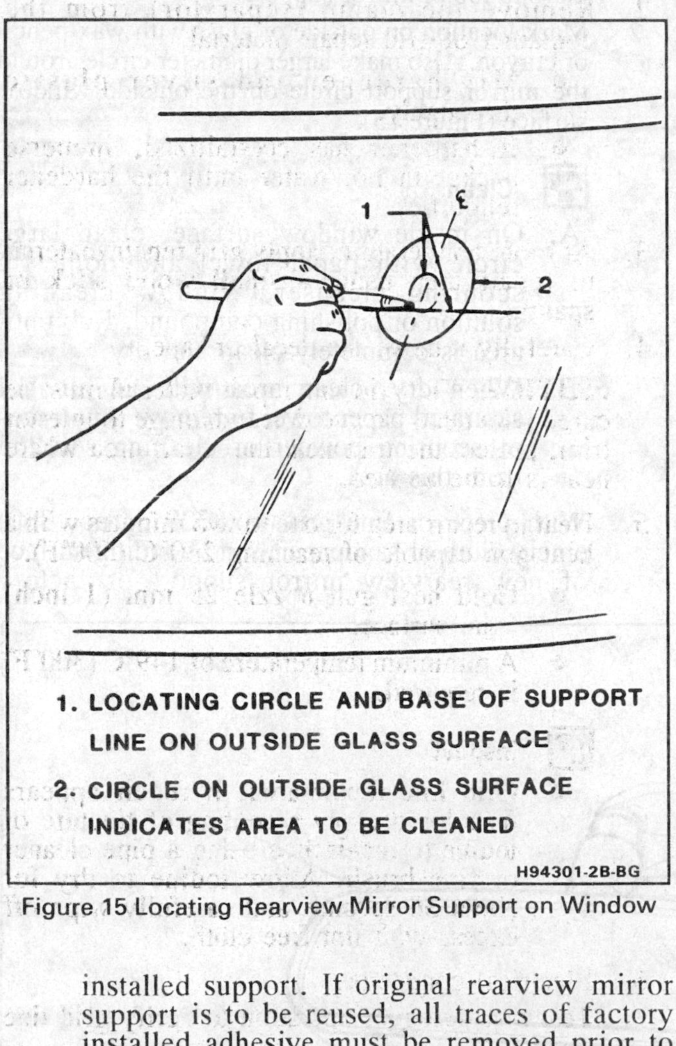
1
2
1. LOCATING CIRCLE AND BASE OF SUPPORT LINE ON OUTSIDE GLASS SURFACE
2. CIRCLE ON OUTSIDE GLASS SURFACE INDICATES AREA TO BE CLEANED
H94301-2B-BG

Figure 15 Locating Rearview Mirror Support on Window

installed support. If original rearview mirror support is to be reused, all traces of factory installed adhesive must be removed prior to reinstallation.

4. Wipe sanded mirror support with clean paper towel saturated with alcohol and allow to dry.
5. Follow directions on manufacturer's kit to prepare rearview mirror support prior to installation of window.
6. Properly position support to its premarked location, with rounded end pointed upward; press support against window for 30 to 60 seconds, exerting steady pressure against window. After five minutes, any excess adhesive may be removed with an alcohol moistened paper towel or window cleaning solution.

REAR WINDOW DEFOGGER

The optional rear window defogger system consists of a tinted window that has a number of horizontal ceramic silver compound element lines and two vertical bus bars baked into the inside surface during the window forming operation. The feed wire or terminal is soldered to the bus bar on the left side. The ground wire or terminal is soldered to the bus bar on the right side.

The system operates on 12 volts. Under some conditions, heat from the window may not be detected by finger touch. The length of time required to remove interior fog from the rear window will vary with such conditions as vehicle speed, outside window temperature, atmospheric pressure and number of passengers.

This system uses an instrument panel mounted switch with an integral indicator lamp that will operate for five to ten minutes and automatically turn off through the use of an automatic timer. The system can be turned off during this operation period by turning either the instrument panel mounted switch or ignition switch to off.

Testing Grid Lines

Figures 16 and 17

To locate inoperative grid lines, start engine and turn on the rear window defogger system. Ground test lamp lead and lightly touch the other prod to each grid line. Refer to the pattern of test lamp brilliance to be expected with a properly functioning grid.

If test lamp bulb shows full brilliance at both ends of grid lines, check for loose ground wire contact to body metal.

The range of zones may vary slightly from one window to another; however, the bulb brilliance will decrease proportionately to the increased resistance in the grid line as the prod is moved from the left bus bar to the right.

All grid lines must be tested in at least two places to eliminate the possibility of bridging a break. For best results, contact each grid line a few millimeters either side of the window centerline. If an abnormal light reading is apparent on a specific grid line, place test lamp prod on that grid at the left bus bar and move prod toward the right bus bar until light goes out.

This will indicate a break in the continuity of the grid line.

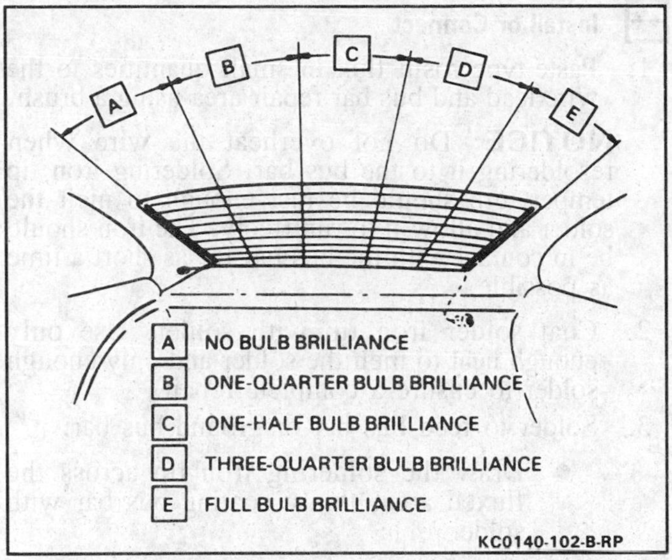
A
B
C
D
E
A NO BULB BRILLIANCE
B ONE-QUARTER BULB BRILLIANCE
C ONE-HALF BULB BRILLIANCE
D THREE-QUARTER BULB BRILLIANCE
E FULL BULB BRILLIANCE
KC0140-102-B-RP

Figure 16 Test Lamp Bulb Brilliance Zones – Normal Operating Rear Window Defogger

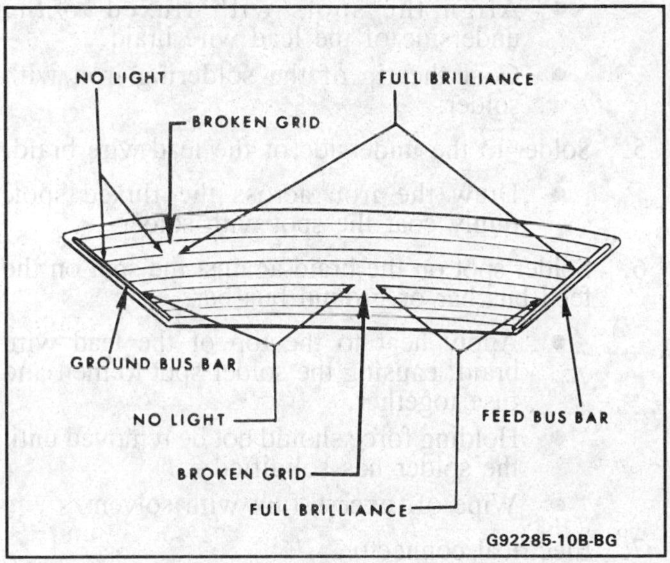
NO LIGHT
FULL BRILLIANCE
BROKEN GRID
GROUND BUS BAR
NO LIGHT
FEED BUS BAR
BROKEN GRID
FULL BRILLIANCE
G92285-10B-BG

Figure 17 Test Lamp Bulb Brilliance With Broken Grid Lines

Grid Line Repair

Figures 18 and 19

Tools Required:

Part No. 12345345 (or equivalent) – Rear Window Defogger Repair Kit

Heat gun – capable of 260°C (500°F)

Test lamp

Remove or Disconnect

- Electrical connector.

Inspect

- Rear window defogger grid lines.
  - Mark grid line break on outside of window with a grease pencil.

Clean

- Grid line area to be repaired. Buff with steel wool and wipe clean using cloth dampened with alcohol. Buff and clean about 6 mm (1/4 inch) beyond each side of break in guide line.

Install or Connect

CAUTION: Approved safety glasses should be worn when performing this procedure to reduce the chance of personal injury.

1. Grid line repair decal or two strips of tape positioned above and below repair area.
   - Repair decal or tape **must** be used to control width of repair area.
   - If decal is used, be sure to die-cut metering slot in the same width as the grid line.
2. Remove the clamp (separator) from the container of grid repair material.
   - Mix hardener and silver plastic thoroughly.
   - If hardener has crystallized, immerse packet in hot water until the hardener reliquifies.
3. At room temperature, apply grid repair material to repair area using a small wood stick or spatula.
4. Carefully remove the decal or tape.

NOTICE: The grid line repair material must be cured with heat. To avoid heat damage to interior trim, protect the trim near the repair area where heat is to be applied.

5. Heat to repair area for one to two minutes with a heat gun capable of reaching 260°C (500°F).
   - Hold heat gun nozzle 25 mm (1 inch) from surface.
   - A minimum temperature of 149°C (300°F) is required.

   Inspect

   - Grid line repair area. If repair appears discolored apply a coating of tincture of iodine to repair area using a pipe cleaner or fine brush. Allow iodine to dry for about 30 seconds and carefully wipe off excess with lint free cloth.
6. Electrical connector.
7. Test rear defogger operation to verify grid line repair.

Important

- At least 24 hours are required for complete curing of repair materials. The repair area should not be physically disturbed until after that time.

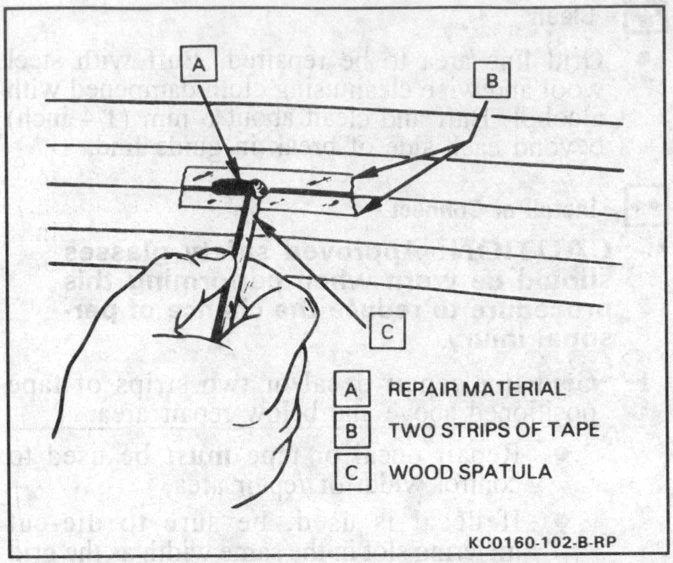
A
B
C
A REPAIR MATERIAL
B TWO STRIPS OF TAPE
C WOOD SPATULA
KC0160-102-B-RP

Figure 18 Broken Grid Line Repair Material Application

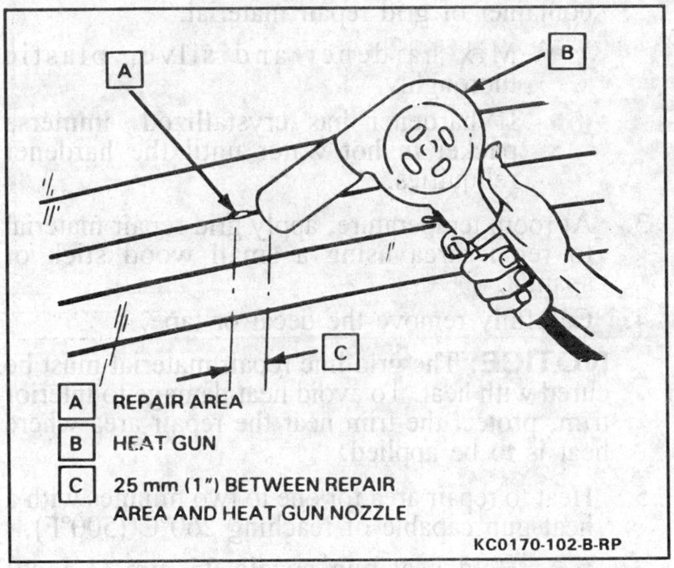
A
B
C
A REPAIR AREA
B HEAT GUN
C 25 mm (1") BETWEEN REPAIR AREA AND HEAT GUN NOZZLE
KC0170-102-B-RP

Figure 19 Grid Line Repair Heat Application

Braided Lead Wire Repair

Figure 20

CAUTION: Approved safety glasses should be worn when performing this procedure to reduce the chance of personal injury.

Remove or Disconnect

- Refer to "Grid Line Repair" in this section.

The rear defogger bus bar lead wire or terminal can be reattached by resoldering using a solder containing 3% silver and a rosin flux paste.

Clean

- Repair area should be buffed with fine steel wool. This removes the oxide coating formed during window manufacture.

Install or Connect

1. Paste-type rosin flux in small quantities to the wire lead and bus bar repair area using a brush.

NOTICE: Do not overheat the wire when resoldering it to the bus bar. Soldering iron tip temperature should be just enough to melt the solder and allow it to run freely. The iron should be in contact with the bus bar for as short a time as possible.

2. Coat solder iron tip with solder. Use only enough heat to melt the solder and only enough solder to ensure a complete repair.
3. Solder to feed bus bar or ground bus bar.
   - Draw the soldering iron tip across the fluxed area, thinly coating bus bar with solder.
4. Small amount of flux to the underside of the lead wire braid.
   - Align the spots with fluxed to the underside of the lead wire braid.
   - Coat the tip of the soldering iron with solder.
5. Solder to the underside of the lead wire braid.
   - Draw the iron across the fluxed spot, thinly coat the spot with solder.
6. Solder spot on the braid against the spot on the feed bus bar or ground bus bar.
   - Apply heat to the top of the lead wire braid, causing the solder spot to melt and fuse together.
   - Holding force should not be removed until the solder has solidified.
   - Wipe off excess flux with solvent.
7. Electrical connector.

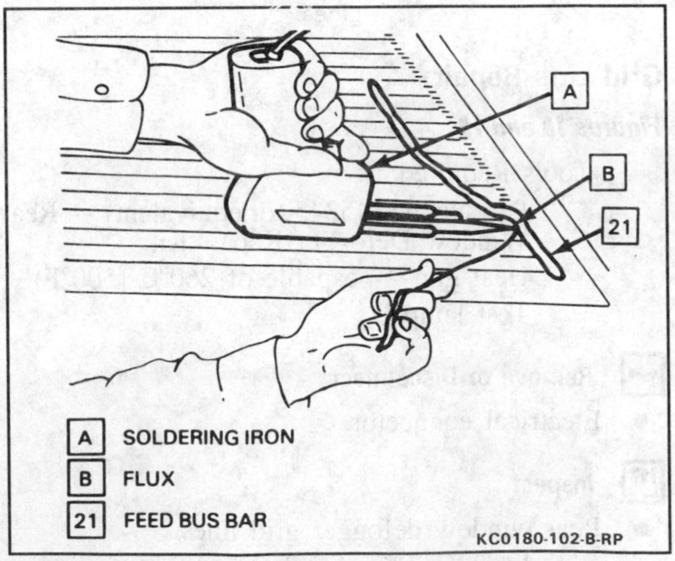
A
B
21
A SOLDERING IRON
B FLUX
21 FEED BUS BAR
KC0180-102-B-RP

Figure 20 Bus Bar Repair

SPECIFICATIONS

FASTENER TIGHTENING SPECIFICATIONS

Quarter Upper Applique Screw	1 N·m (9 lb. in.)
Rear Window Lower Reveal Molding Screw	2 N·m (18 lb. in.)
Rearview Mirror Screw	2 N·m (18 lb. in.)
Windshield Lower Reveal Molding Screw	2 N·m (18 lb. in.)
Windshield Side Reveal Molding Screw	2 N·m (18 lb. in.)

SPECIAL TOOLS

1 J 24402-A

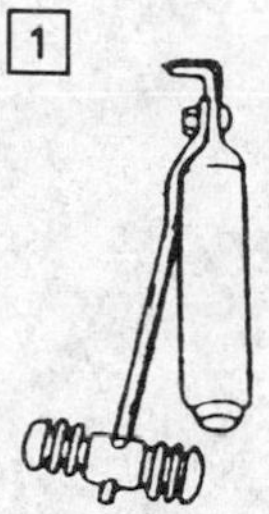

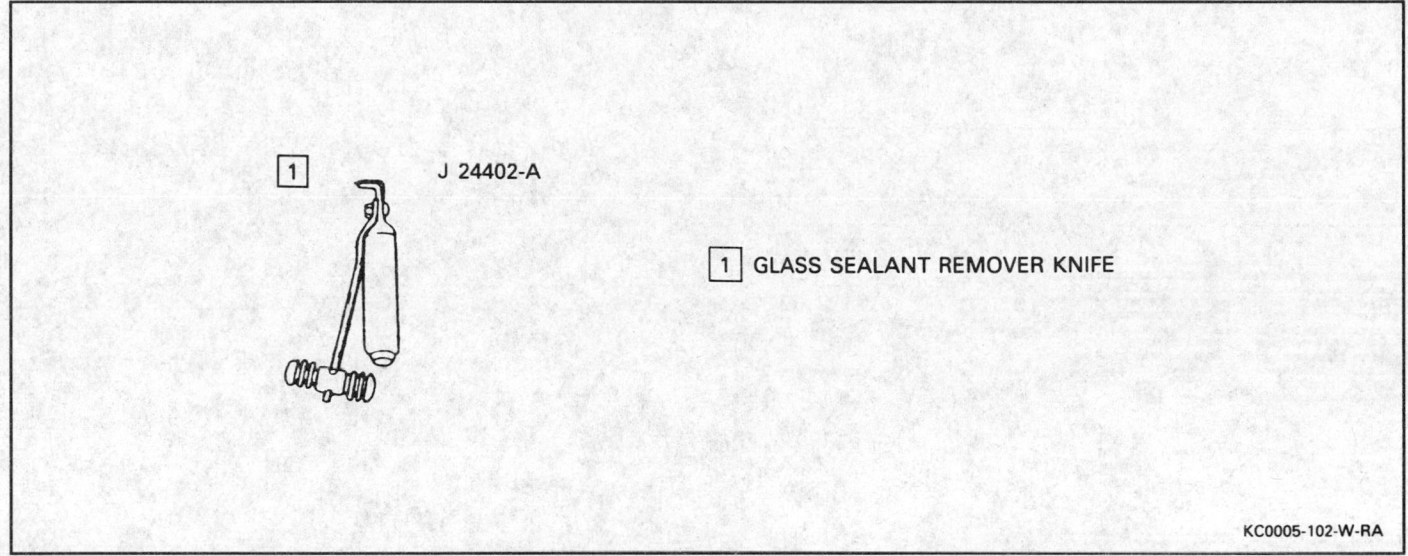

1 GLASS SEALANT REMOVER KNIFE

KC0005-102-W-RA

SECTION 10-3

BODY DIMENSIONS, FRAME AND UNDERBODY

CAUTION: To help avoid personal injury when a vehicle is on a hoist, provide additional support for the vehicle at the opposite end from which components are being removed. This will reduce the possibility of the vehicle falling off of the hoist.

NOTICE: When fasteners are removed, always reinstall them at the same location from which they were removed. If a fastener needs to be replaced, user the correct part number fastener for that application. If the correct part number fastener is not available, a fastener of equal size and strength (or stronger) may be used. Fasteners that are not reused, and those requiring thread locking compound will be called out. The correct torque value must be used when installing fasteners that require it. If the above conditions are not followed, parts or system damage could result.

CONTENTS

GENERAL DESCRIPTION

GENERAL BODY CONSTRUCTION

This section contains information on unitized body construction incorporating integral front and rear frame side rails.

The engine, front suspension lower control arms and steering gear are supported by a frame which is bolted to the body through rubber insulators at four locations. Two rubber insulated struts secure engine to the upper rail of the engine compartment front panel.

Mounting provisions for the front suspension system are shared by chassis components (suspension lower control arms and frame) and body components, (engine compartment side panels). The underbody must be properly aligned to maintain the correct suspension and wheel alignment.

The individual underbody components contribute directly to the overall strength of the body. Use proper welding techniques during service repair operations. The underbody components should be properly sealed and rustproofed whenever body repair operations damage or destroy the original sealing and rustproofing. When rustproofing critical underbody components, use a good quality air dry primer such as corrosion-resistant chromate material or equivalent. Combination type primer-surfacers are not recommended.

FRAME-TO-BODY ALIGNMENT

Check frame-to-body alignment by inserting a 19 mm (3/4 inch) diameter guide pin or drill bit into the frame-to-body guide pin holes. If the guide pins will not fit, the frame is not in correct alignment with the body. To realign frame refer to "Frame" in this section.

ON-VEHICLE SERVICE

ALIGNMENT CHECKING

Figures 1 through 6

A tram gage can be used to measure the alignment of the underbody. The tram gage set used must include a vertical pointer capable of reaching 914 mm (36 inches).

Measurements of the engine compartment components are generally made from point to point with the vertical pointers equally set (Figure 3).

Other measurements are made on the horizontal plane, or datum line, parallel to the underbody with the vertical pointers set as specified for each point (Figures 1 and 2).

Dimensions that are measured to gage holes are measured to the center of the holes and flush to adjacent surface metal unless otherwise specified. It is recommended that diagonal dimensions be cross-checked to verify the dimensional accuracy of the car underbody.

FRAME

Figure 1

Tools Required:

J 28467-A Engine Support Fixture

J 35917 Tie Rod Puller/Ball Joint Remover

J 36462 Engine Support Leg

Remove or Disconnect

1. Air cleaner and duct assembly, if necessary for access.
2. Negative battery cable.

CAUTION: J 28467-A and J 36462 must be located on upper radiator support, exactly as shown in AUTOMATIC TRANSAXLE (SECTION 7A). Support fixture fasteners must be properly torqued before supporting engine. Bodily injury could result with improper use of this support fixture.

3. Position J 28467-A and J 36462. Refer to AUTOMATIC TRANSAXLE (SECTION 7A).
4. Tighten wing nuts only enough to remove slack from hooks.
5. Raise vehicle and suitably support. Refer to GENERAL INFORMATION (SECTION 0A).
6. Position jackstand under engine for support.
7. Front tire and wheel assemblies. Refer to TIRES AND WHEELS (SECTION 3E).

CAUTION: Failure to disconnect the intermediate shaft from the rack and pinion stub shaft can result in damage to the steering gear and/or intermediate shaft. This damage can cause loss of steering control which could result in personal injury.

8. Intermediate shaft from steering gear stub shaft. Refer to POWER STEERING GEAR AND PUMP (SECTION 3B).
9. Power steering cooler line pipe brackets, if necessary for access. Refer to POWER STEERING GEAR AND PUMP (SECTION 3B).
10. Steering gear mounting bolts and support steering gear. Refer to POWER STEERING GEAR AND PUMP (SECTION 3B).
11. Both lower ball joints from lower control arms using J 35917. Refer to FRONT SUSPENSION (SECTION 3C).
12. Engine mounts. Refer to specific engine section.
13. Transaxle mounts. Refer to AUTOMATIC TRANSAXLE (SECTION 7A).
14. Have an assistant hold frame while removing the body mount bolts.
15. Frame with both lower control arms and stabilizer shaft attached.
    - Work frame downward toward rear of vehicle.
16. Both lower control arms and stabilizer shaft if replacing frame. Refer to FRONT SUSPENSION (SECTION 3C).
17. Transaxle mounting bracket if replacing frame. Refer to AUTOMATIC TRANSAXLE (SECTION 7A).
18. Spacers, upper and lower insulators, and retainers if replacing frame.

Install or Connect

NOTICE: If frame insulators are removed, lubricate with rubber lube #1051717 or equivalent at installation. Failure to lubricate may prevent proper seating of insulators in frame.

1. Lower and upper insulators, spacers, and retainers, if removed. The insulators must be completely seated against the frame.
2. Lower control arms and stabilizer shaft, if removed. Refer to FRONT SUSPENSION (SECTION 3C).
3. Transaxle mounting bracket, if removed. Refer to AUTOMATIC TRANSAXLE (SECTION 7A).
4. Position frame with the aid of an assistant and install new body mount bolts, but do not tighten.

NOTICE: Alignment pins must not be removed until all body mount bolts are torqued to specifications. Alignment pins must be kept perpendicular to frame. Right side body mounts (nearest alignment pins) should be tightened first, in order to maintain correct front wheel alignment.

5. Align frame to body by inserting two (2) 19 mm (0.74 inch) diameter by 203 mm (8.0 inches) long pins in alignment holes on right side of frame.

Tighten

- Body mount bolts to 145 N•m (107 lb. ft.) using a torque wrench.

6. Engine mounts. Refer to specific engine section.
7. Transaxle mounts. Refer to AUTOMATIC TRANSAXLE (SECTION 7A).
8. Lower ball joints. Refer to FRONT SUSPENSION (SECTION 3C).
9. Steering gear mounting bolts. Refer to POWER STEERING GEAR AND PUMP (SECTION 3B).

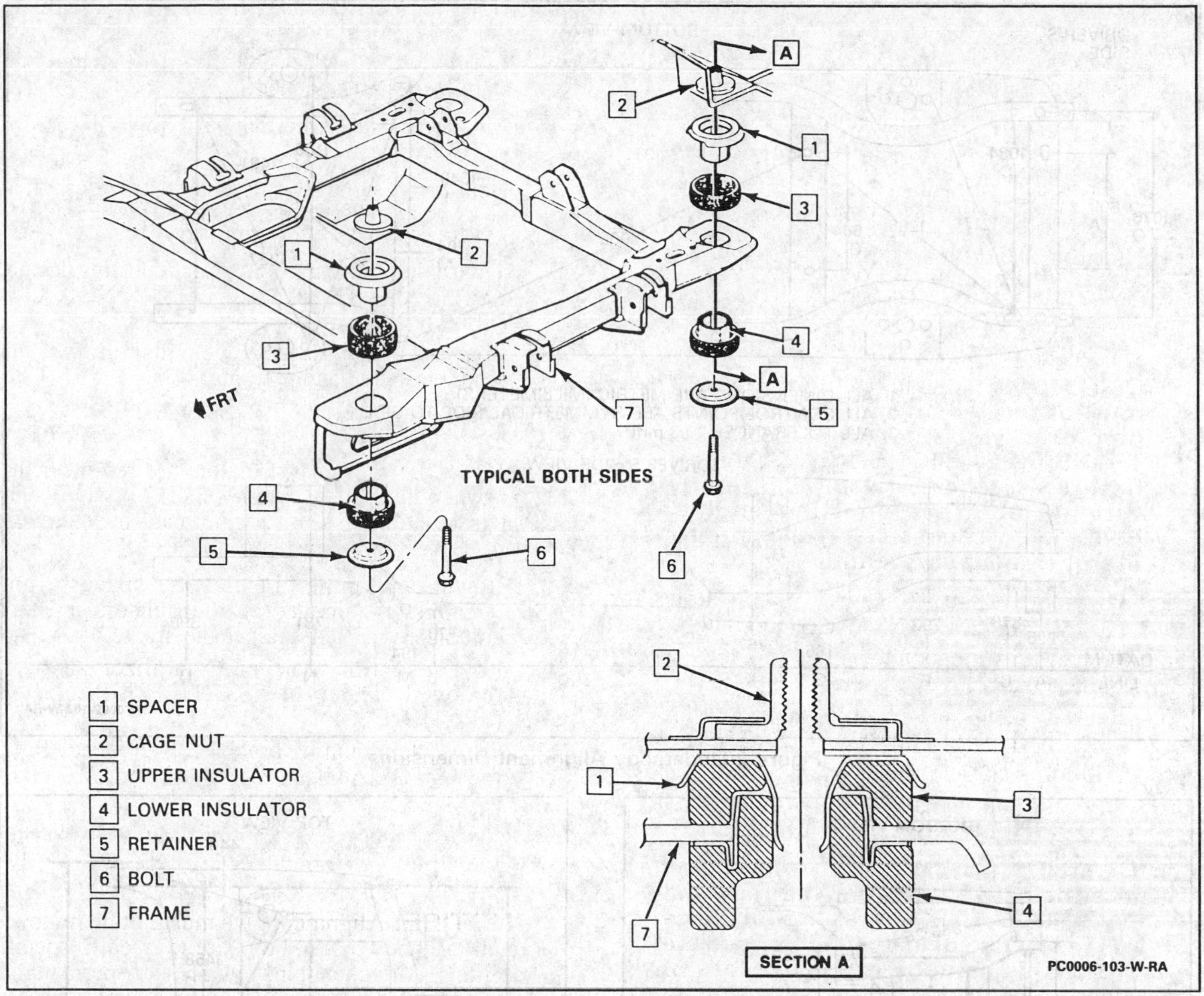
A
2
1
3
2
1
4
3
A
FRT
7
5
TYPICAL BOTH SIDES
4
6
5
6
1 SPACER
2 CAGE NUT
3 UPPER INSULATOR
4 LOWER INSULATOR
5 RETAINER
6 BOLT
7 FRAME
SECTION A
PC0006-103-W-RA

Figure 1 Frame Assembly

10. Power steering cooler line pipe brackets, if removed. Refer to POWER STEERING GEAR AND PUMP (SECTION 3B).
11. Intermediate shaft to steering gear stub shaft. Refer to POWER STEERING GEAR AND PUMP (SECTION 3B).
12. Front tire and wheel assemblies. Refer to TIRES AND WHEELS (SECTION 3E).
13. Remove jackstand and lower vehicle.
14. Remove engine support fixture. Refer to AUTOMATIC TRANSAXLE (SECTION 7A).
15. Negative battery cable.

Tighten

- Bolt to 15 N•m (11 lb. ft.).

16. Air cleaner and duct assembly, if removed.

Tighten

- Bolts to 5 N•m (44 lb. in.).

Inspect

- Front wheel alignment and adjust, if necessary. Refer to WHEEL ALIGNMENT (SECTION 3A).

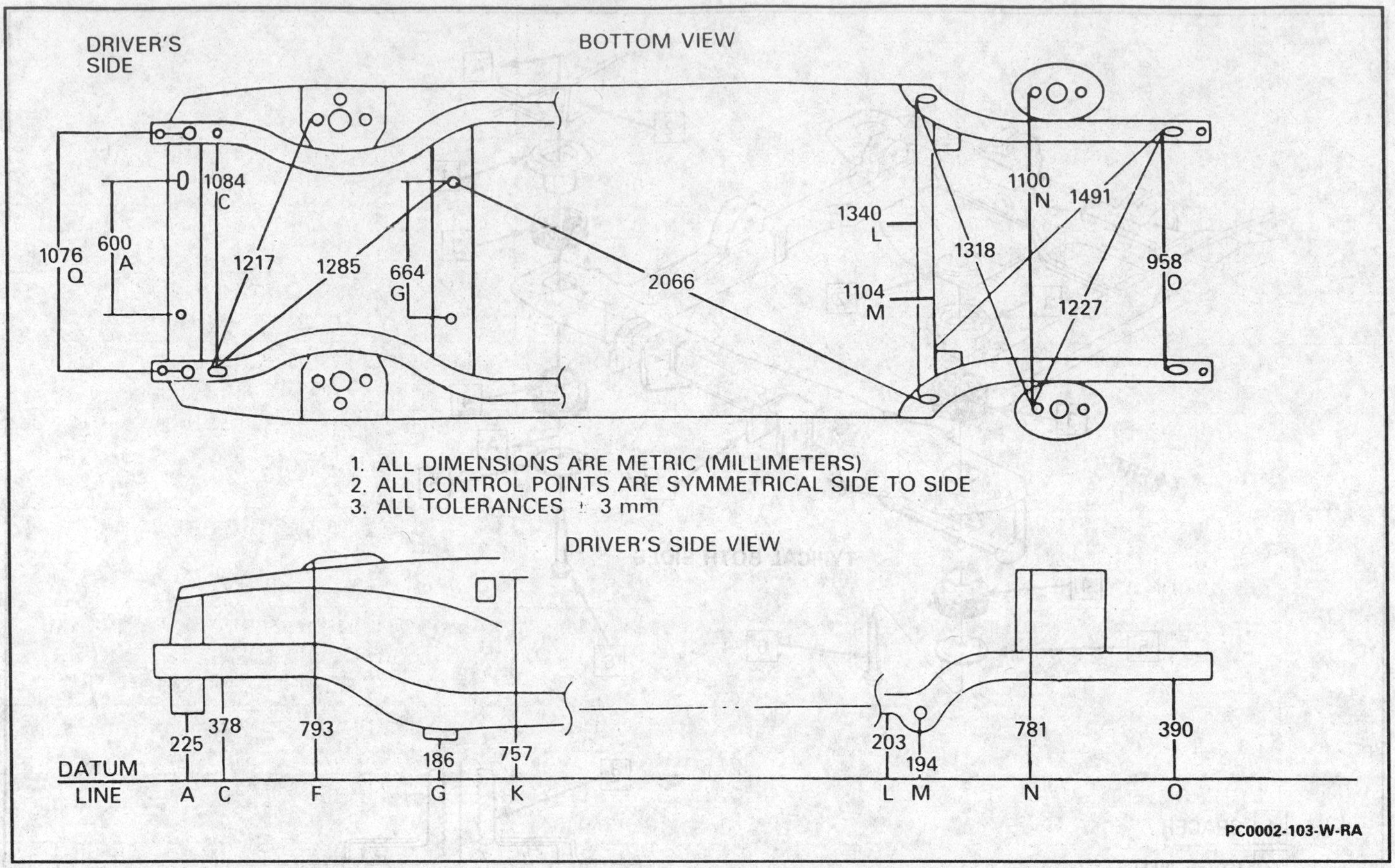
DRIVER'S SIDE
BOTTOM VIEW
1084
C
600
A
1076
Q
1217
1285
664
G
2066
1340
L
1104
M
1100
N
1491
1318
958
O
1227
1. ALL DIMENSIONS ARE METRIC (MILLIMETERS)
2. ALL CONTROL POINTS ARE SYMMETRICAL SIDE TO SIDE
3. ALL TOLERANCES ± 3 mm
DRIVER'S SIDE VIEW
225
378
793
186
757
203
194
781
390
DATUM LINE
A
C
F
G
K
L
M
N
O
PC0002-103-W-RA

Figure 2 Underbody Alignment Dimensions

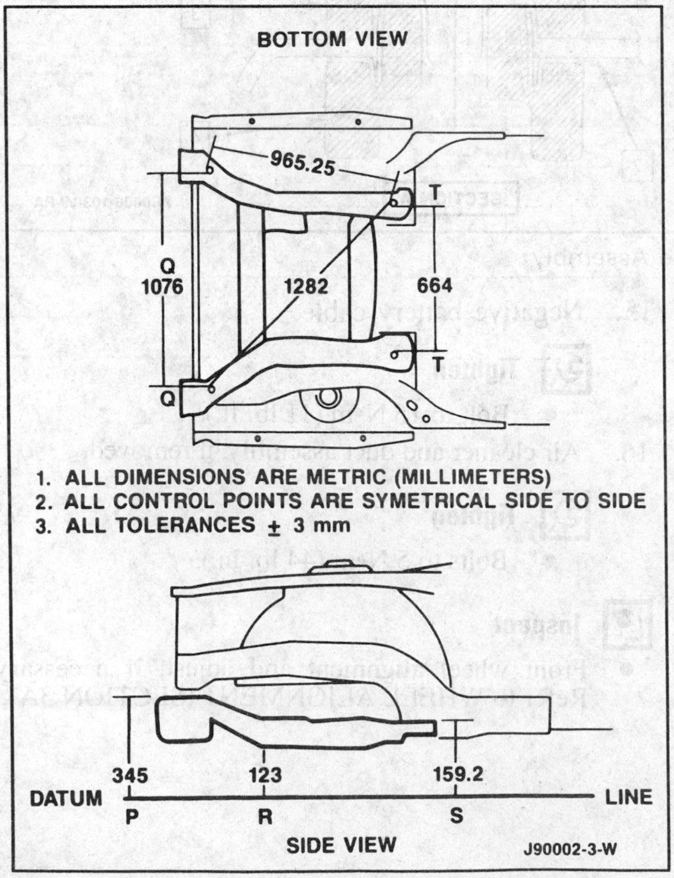
BOTTOM VIEW
965.25
T
Q
1076
1282
664
T
Q
1. ALL DIMENSIONS ARE METRIC (MILLIMETERS)
2. ALL CONTROL POINTS ARE SYMETRICAL SIDE TO SIDE
3. ALL TOLERANCES ± 3 mm
345
123
159.2
DATUM
LINE
P
R
S
SIDE VIEW
J90002-3-W

Figure 3 Frame Alignment Dimensions

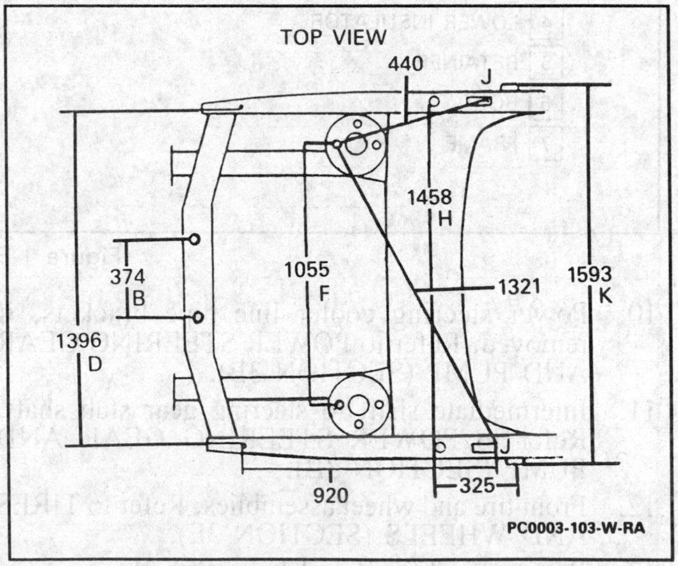
TOP VIEW
440
J
1458
H
374
B
1055
F
1321
1593
K
1396
D
J
920
325
PC0003-103-W-RA

Figure 4 Engine Compartment Alignment Dimensions

REF.	HORIZONTAL SURFACE	VERTICAL SURFACE	LOCATION
A	Center of 16 mm (5/8") gage hole and16 × 32 mm (5/8" ×1-1/4") slot	Lower surface at gage hole to "0" line	Front end lower tie bar
B	Center of 16 mm (5/8") gage hole	None	Front end upper tie bar
C	Center of 19 × 30 mm (3/4" × 1-3/16") slot	Lower surface at gage hole to "0" line	Rail - Engine Compartment outer side
D	Center of 28 mm (1-1/8") clearance hole	None	Front upper surface rail engine compartment
F	Center of shock tower front attaching hole	Upper surface at shock tower front attaching hole	Housing - Shock absorber engine compartment
G	Leading edge of 28 mm (1-1/8") frame bolt hole	"0" line to horizontal leading edge of frame bolt hole	Engine frame plate bolt hole
H	Center of front 10 mm (3/8") hole forward of hinge assembly on rail	None	Rear upper surface of rail
J	Center of hood hinge pivot pin head	None	Hood hinge measured from ℄ of 10 mm (3/8") hole in rail engine compartment side
K	Center of front upper hinge bolt	Upper surface at hinge bolt	Front upper door hinge
L	Leading edge of 18 mm × 24 mm (11/16" ×1") slot	Lower surface at leading edge of slot to "0" line	Rear longitudinal rail
M	Center of attaching bolt head	From bolt head to bolt head	Rear longitudinal rail at control arm
N	Leading edge of forward strut attaching hole	Upper surface of strut tower	Rear strut tower
O	Leading edge of 25 mm × 40 mm rectangular hole	Lower surface of leading edge to "0" line	Rear longitudinal rail
P	Forward edge	Lower surface	Engine frame
Q	Center of bolt	Lower surface	Frame mount forward bolt
R	Rearward and center of edge	Top surface	Engine frame
S	Forward and center of edge	Top surface	Engine frame
T	Center of bolt	Lower surface	Frame mount rearward bolt

PC0004-103-W-RA

Figure 5 Measurement Locations

REFERENCE	METRIC (MILLIMETERS)	ENGLISH (INCHES)
HORIZONTAL		
A to A	600	23-5/8
B to B	374	14-3/4
C to C	1 084	42-11/16
C to F	1 217	47-29/32
C to G	1 285	50-19/32
D to D	1 396	54-61/64
F to F	1 055	41-17/32
F to J (long)	1 321	52
F to J (short)	440	17-5/16
G to G	664	26-1/8
G to L	2 066	81-11/32
H to H	1 458	57-3/8
J to D	920	36-1/4
K to K	1 593	62-3/4
L to L	1 340	52-3/4
L to N	1 318	51-57/64
M to M	1 104	43-1/2
M to O	1 491	58-45/64
N to N	1 100	43-5/16
N to O	1 227	48-5/16
O to O	958	37-23/32
Q to Q	1 076	42-23/64
Q to T (long)	1 282	50-15/32
Q to T (short)	965.25	38-1/64
T to T	664	26-9/64
VERTICAL		
A	225	8-7/8
C	378	14-7/8
F	793	31-1/4
G	186	7-5/16
K	757	29-3/4
L	203	8
M	194	7-5/8
N	781	30-3/4
O	390	15-3/8
P	345	13-37/64
R	123	4-27/32
S	159.2	6-17/64

PC0005-103-W-RA

Figure 6 Metric to English Conversion Chart

REAR CAGE NUTS

Figures 7 through 14

Tools Required:

J 28467-A Engine Support Fixture
J 36462 Engine Support Leg

[↔] Remove or Disconnect

1. Open hood.

CAUTION: J 28467-A and J 36462 must be located on upper radiator support, exactly as shown in AUTOMATIC TRANSAXLE (SECTION 7A). Support fixture fasteners must be properly torqued before supporting engine. Bodily injury could result with improper use of this support fixture.

2. Position J 28467-A and J 36462. Refer to AUTOMATIC TRANSAXLE (SECTION 7A).
3. Raise vehicle and suitable support. Refer to GENERAL INFORMATION (SECTION 0A).
4. Position jackstand under engine for support.
5. Tire and wheel. Refer to TIRES AND WHEELS (SECTION 3E).
6. Engine mounts. Refer to specific engine section.
7. Transaxle mounts. Refer to AUTOMATIC TRANSAXLE (SECTION 7A).
8. Power steering lines. Refer to POWER STEERING GEAR AND PUMP (SECTION 3B).
9. Intermediate shaft lower pinch bolt at steering gear. Refer to POWER STEERING GEAR AND PUMP (SECTION 3B).
10. Support frame assembly using jack stands.
11. Loosen front frame bolts.
12. Rear frame bolts.
    - If a rear bolt is stripped, cut off bolt head.
    - Do not damage frame mount.
13. Lower frame assembly enough to access cage nut opening.
14. Plug cover from lower cage nut access hole.
15. Rear frame bolts if not previously removed.
    - If head of cage nut bolt was previously removed, remove rest of bolt as close as possible to cage nut.
    - Do not damage support plate where mount sits.
16. Brake and fuel lines if removing left cage nut. Refer to GENERAL BRAKES (SECTION 5) and ENGINE FUEL (SECTION 6C).

17. Using an air hammer at a 45° angle facing inward, break spot weld on inboard side.
18. Raise cage.
19. Cage nut.

Install or Connect

1. Cage nut.
2. Using a "C" clamp, compress previously broken cage section until cage nut is secured in place and will not rotate in cage.
3. Plug cover.
4. Brake and fuel lines to frame, if removed. Refer to GENERAL BRAKES (SECTION 5) and ENGINE FUEL (SECTION 6C).
5. Raise frame assembly.
6. Intermediate shaft lower pinch bolt at steering gear. Refer to STEERING GEAR AND PUMP (SECTION 3B).
7. Rear frame mount bolts.

Tighten

- Front and rear bolts to 145 N•m (107 lb. ft.) using a torque wrench.

8. Remove jack stands.
9. Power steering lines. Refer to STEERING GEAR AND PUMP (SECTION 3B).
10. Transaxle mounts. Refer to AUTOMATIC TRANSAXLE (SECTION 7A).
11. Engine mounts. Refer to specific engine section.
12. Tire and wheel. Refer to TIRES AND WHEELS (SECTION 3E).
13. Lower vehicle.
14. Remove engine support fixture. Refer to AUTOMATIC TRANSAXLE (SECTION 7A).
15. Close hood.

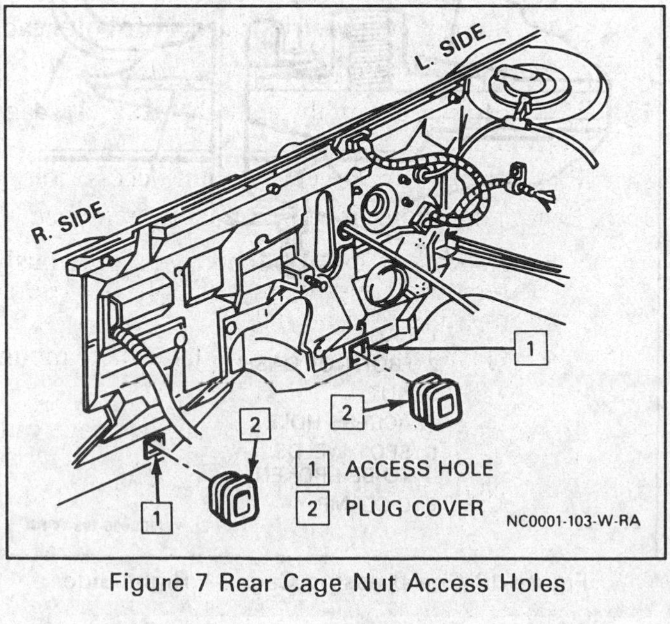
L. SIDE
R. SIDE
1
2
2
1
1 ACCESS HOLE
2 PLUG COVER
NC0001-103-W-RA

Figure 7 Rear Cage Nut Access Holes

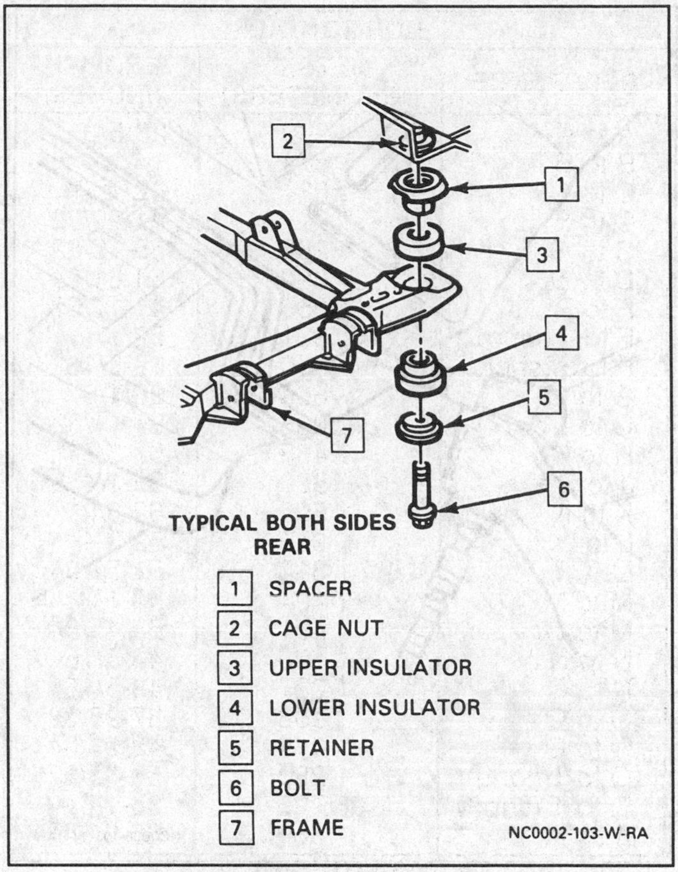
2
1
3
4
5
7
6
TYPICAL BOTH SIDES
REAR
1 SPACER
2 CAGE NUT
3 UPPER INSULATOR
4 LOWER INSULATOR
5 RETAINER
6 BOLT
7 FRAME
NC0002-103-W-RA

Figure 8 Bolt and Cage Nut Assembly

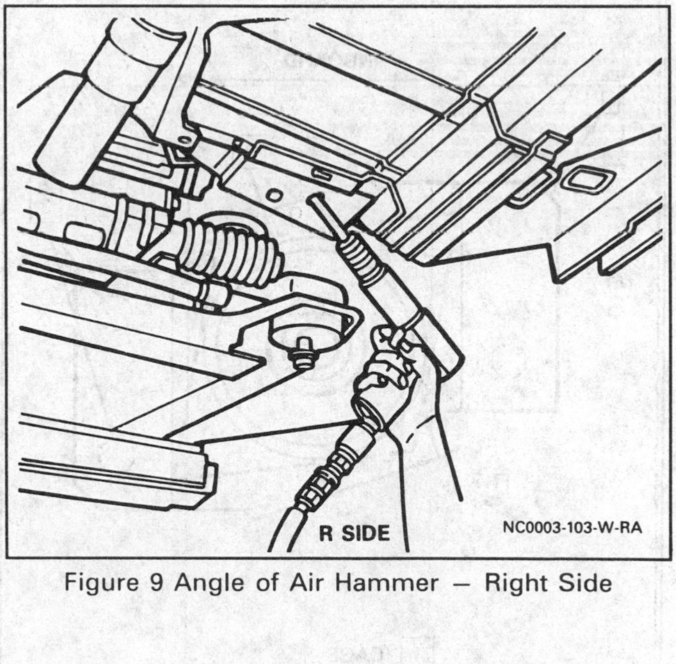
R SIDE
NC0003-103-W-RA

Figure 9 Angle of Air Hammer – Right Side

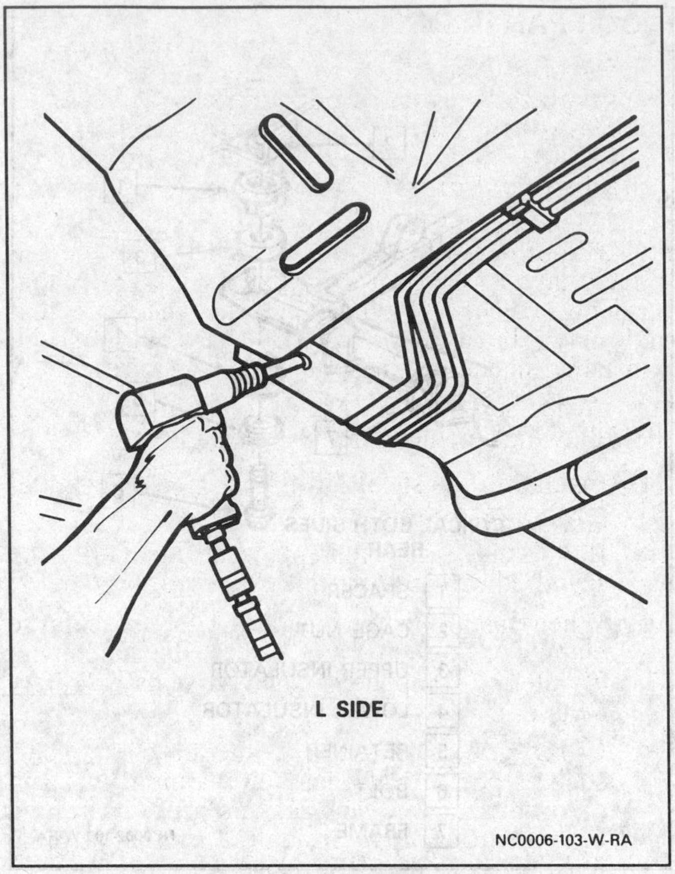
L SIDE
NC0006-103-W-RA

Figure 10 Angle of Air Hammer – Left Side

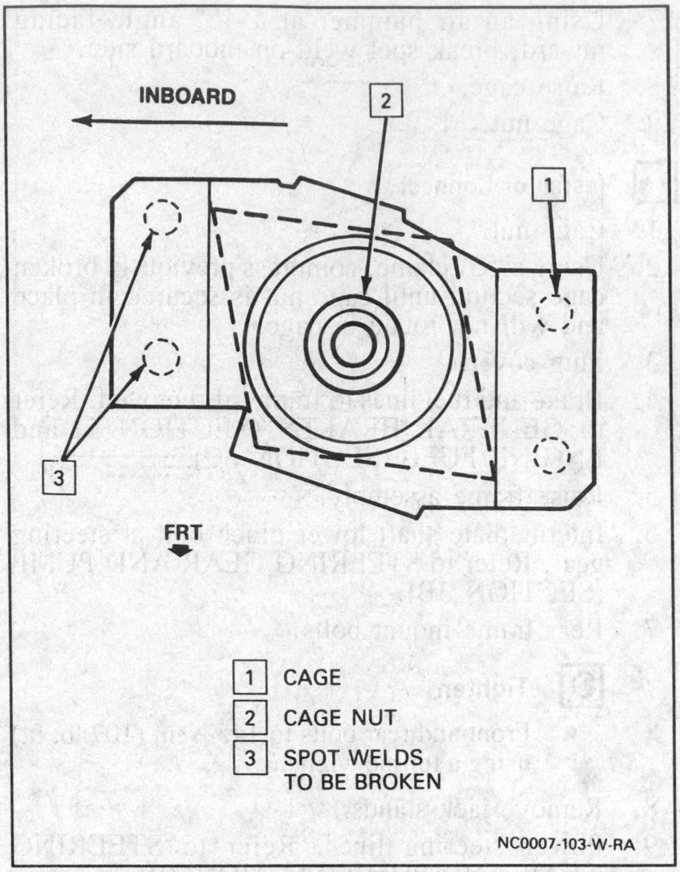
INBOARD
FRT
1 CAGE
2 CAGE NUT
3 SPOT WELDS TO BE BROKEN
NC0007-103-W-RA

Figure 12 Top View of Cage and Cage Nut – Left Side

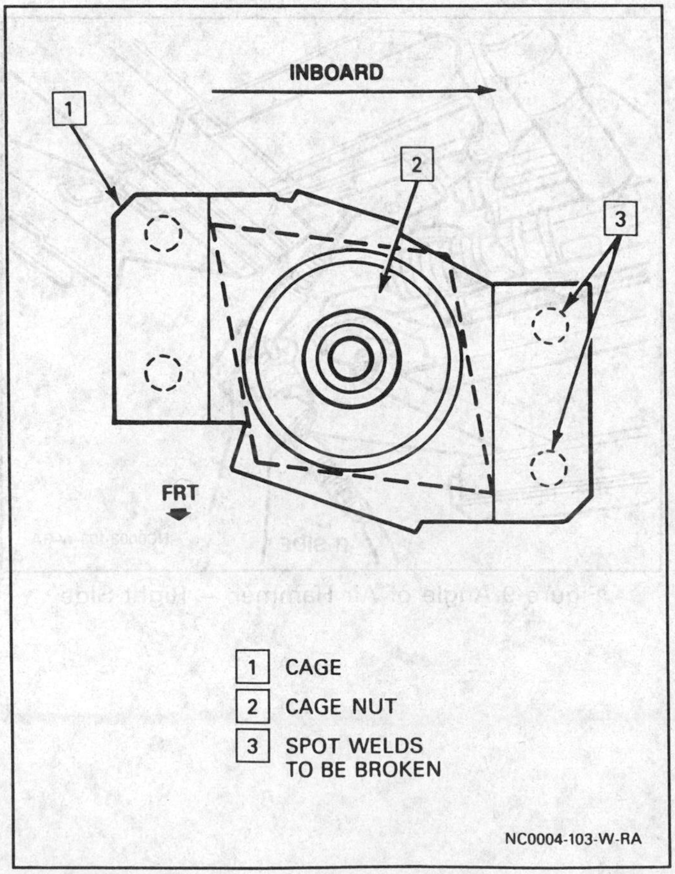
INBOARD
FRT
1 CAGE
2 CAGE NUT
3 SPOT WELDS TO BE BROKEN
NC0004-103-W-RA

Figure 11 Top View of Cage and Cage Nut – Right Side

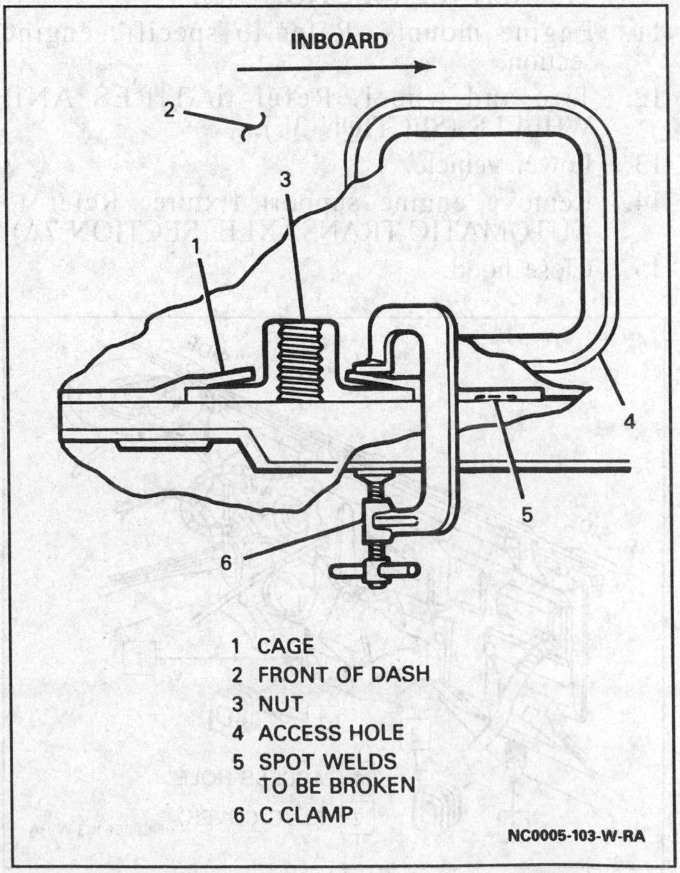
INBOARD
1 CAGE
2 FRONT OF DASH
3 NUT
4 ACCESS HOLE
5 SPOT WELDS TO BE BROKEN
6 C CLAMP
NC0005-103-W-RA

Figure 13 Compressing Cage – Right Side

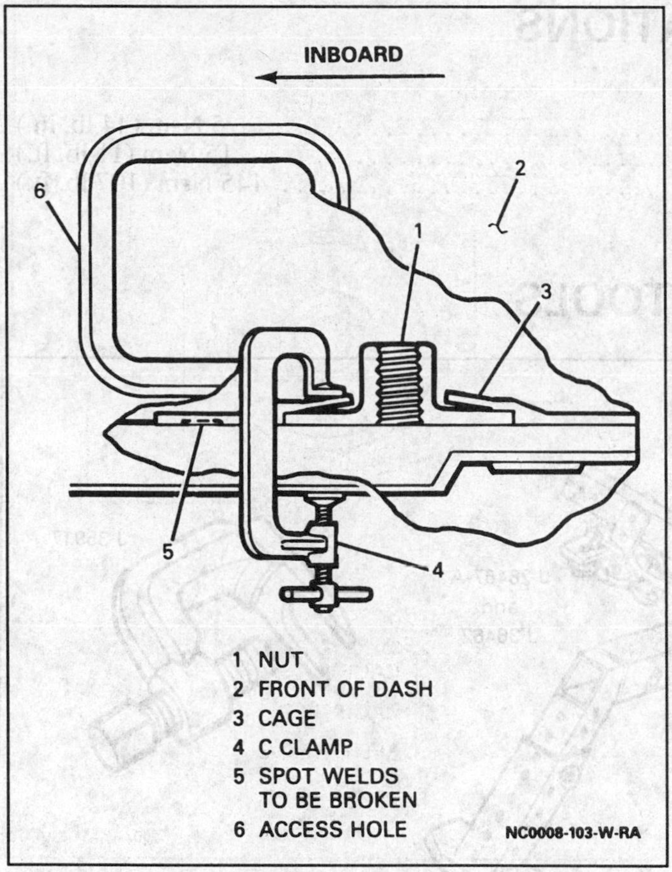
INBOARD
1
2
3
4
5
6
1 NUT
2 FRONT OF DASH
3 CAGE
4 C CLAMP
5 SPOT WELDS
TO BE BROKEN
6 ACCESS HOLE
NC0008-103-W-RA

Figure 14 Compressing Cage — Left Side

FLOOR PAN INSULATORS

CAUTION: All materials used for insulators must meet Vehicle Safety Standard No. 302 for flammability. Failure to do so could result in bodily injury and/or vehicle damage.

Floor pan insulators have been designed for the higher floor pan temperatures that result from the use of the catalytic converter in the exhaust system. When servicing a vehicle in the field, any insulators that may have been disturbed or removed must be reinstalled in the original sequence and location.

When servicing or replacing interior insulators, the following instructions must be observed:

- Insulators must be installed in the original position and sequence.
- If it is necessary to replace an insulator, the specified service part must be used.
- When installing an insulator, do not enlarge cutouts or holes that are used for the attachment of interior components such as seats or safety belts.
- Cross body harnesses for interior components such as power seats, lap belt warning light and alarm/buzzer or rear speakers must be routed over the floor pan insulators in the original location and clipped in place.
- Spray-on deadeners and trim adhesives should not be applied to the top of the floor pan at the area directly over the catalytic converter or muffler(s).

SPECIFICATIONS

FASTENER TIGHTENING SPECIFICATIONS

Air Cleaner and Duct Assembly Bolt	5 N•m (44 lb. in.)
Battery Negative and Positive Cable Bolt	15 N•m (11 lb. ft.)
Frame-to-Body Bolt	145 N•m (107 lb. ft.)

SPECIAL TOOLS

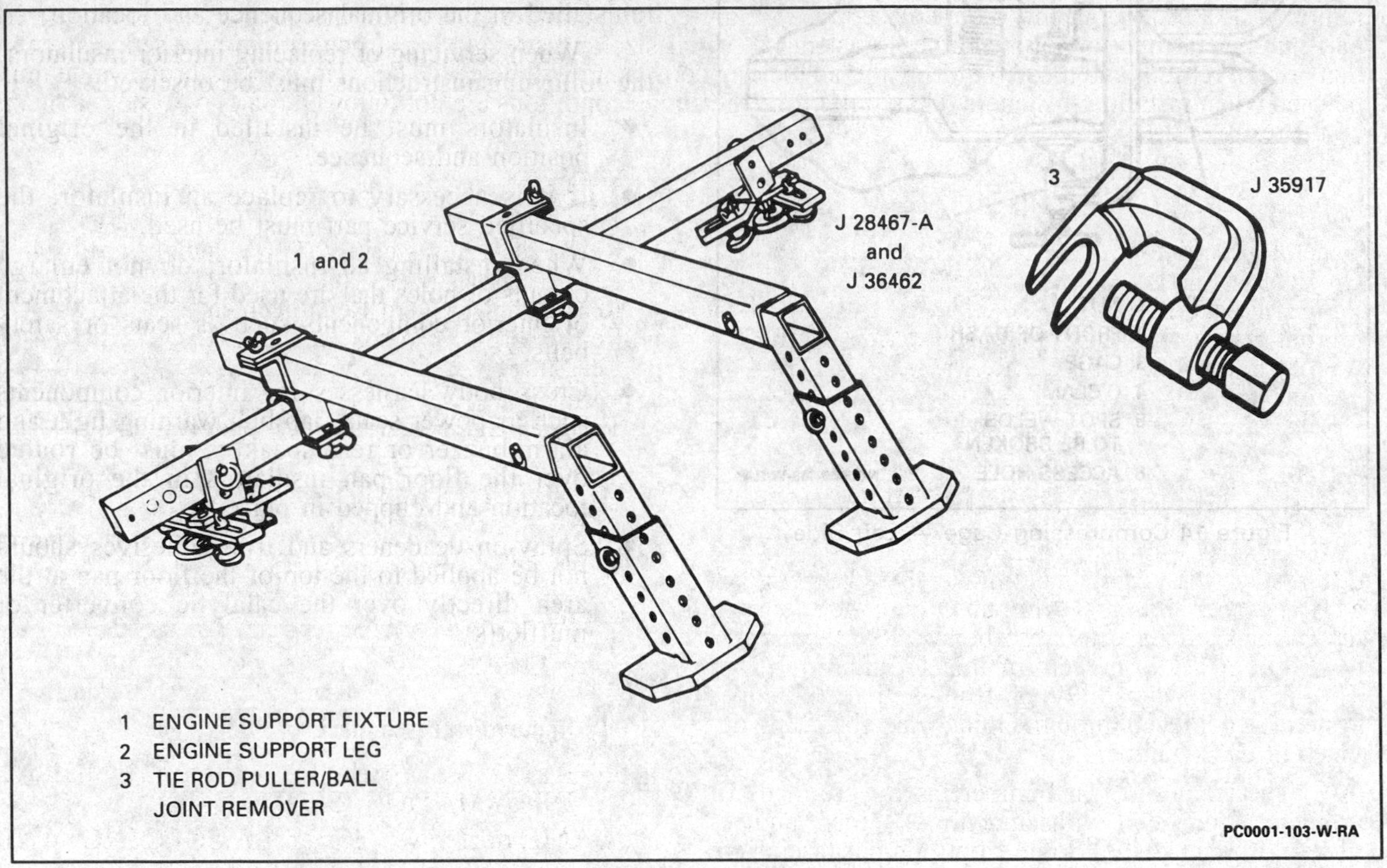
1 and 2
J 28467-A
and
J 36462
3
J 35917
1 ENGINE SUPPORT FIXTURE
2 ENGINE SUPPORT LEG
3 TIE ROD PULLER/BALL
JOINT REMOVER
PC0001-103-W-RA

SECTION 10-4

BUMPERS

NOTICE: The theft deterrent label found on some major sheet metal engines, and transaxles must be masked prior to painting, rustproofing, undercoating, etc. The mask must be removed following the above operations. Failure to keep the label clean and readable may result in liability for violation of Federal Vehicle Theft Prevention Standard, and subject the vehicle owner to possible suspicion that the part was stolen.

NOTICE: When fasteners are removed, always reinstall them at the same location from which they were removed. If a fastener needs to be replaced, use the correct part number fastener for that application. If the correct part number fastener is not available, a fastener of equal size and strength (or stronger) may be used. Fasteners that are not reused, and those requiring thread locking compound will be called out. The correct torque value must be used when installing fasteners that require it. If the above conditions are not followed, parts or system damage could result.

CONTENTS

GENERAL DESCRIPTION

General Motors passenger vehicle bumpers are designed so the vehicle can withstand a collision into a fixed barrier at 5 mph. After absorbing the energy of the collision, the energy absorbers restore themselves to within 80 to 90 percent of their original position. The absorbing capability of front and rear bumper systems is achieved through Guide-Flex absorbing devices in each bumper.

The front and rear bumper fascias are made of urethane which will withstand minor impact and return to original shape. Some front bumper fascias are integral with the front end panel.

For bumper and fascia repair or refinishing, refer to GENERAL BODY SERVICE (SECTION 10-1). Care must be taken around theft deterrent labels. For more information on these labels, refer to GENERAL INFORMATION (SECTION 0A).

Inspection After Collision

If the collision was so severe that the bumper did not return to its original position, the fascia, Guide-Flex energy absorber, and impact bar may require replacement.

ON-VEHICLE SERVICE

FRONT FASCIA

Sedan

Figures 1 and 2

↔ Remove or Disconnect

1. Raise vehicle. Refer to GENERAL INFORMATION (SECTION 0A).
2. Air deflector. Refer to COOLING AND RADIATOR (SECTION 6B).
3. Fascia to fender liner screws.
4. Fascia to fender nuts.
5. Side marker lamps electrical connections.
6. Bolt from center fascia support.
7. Turn signal lens and electrical connection.
8. Lower retainers from fascia.
9. Fascia from vehicle.

→← Install or Connect

1. Fascia to vehicle.
2. Lower retainers to fascia.
3. Turn signal electrical connection and lens.

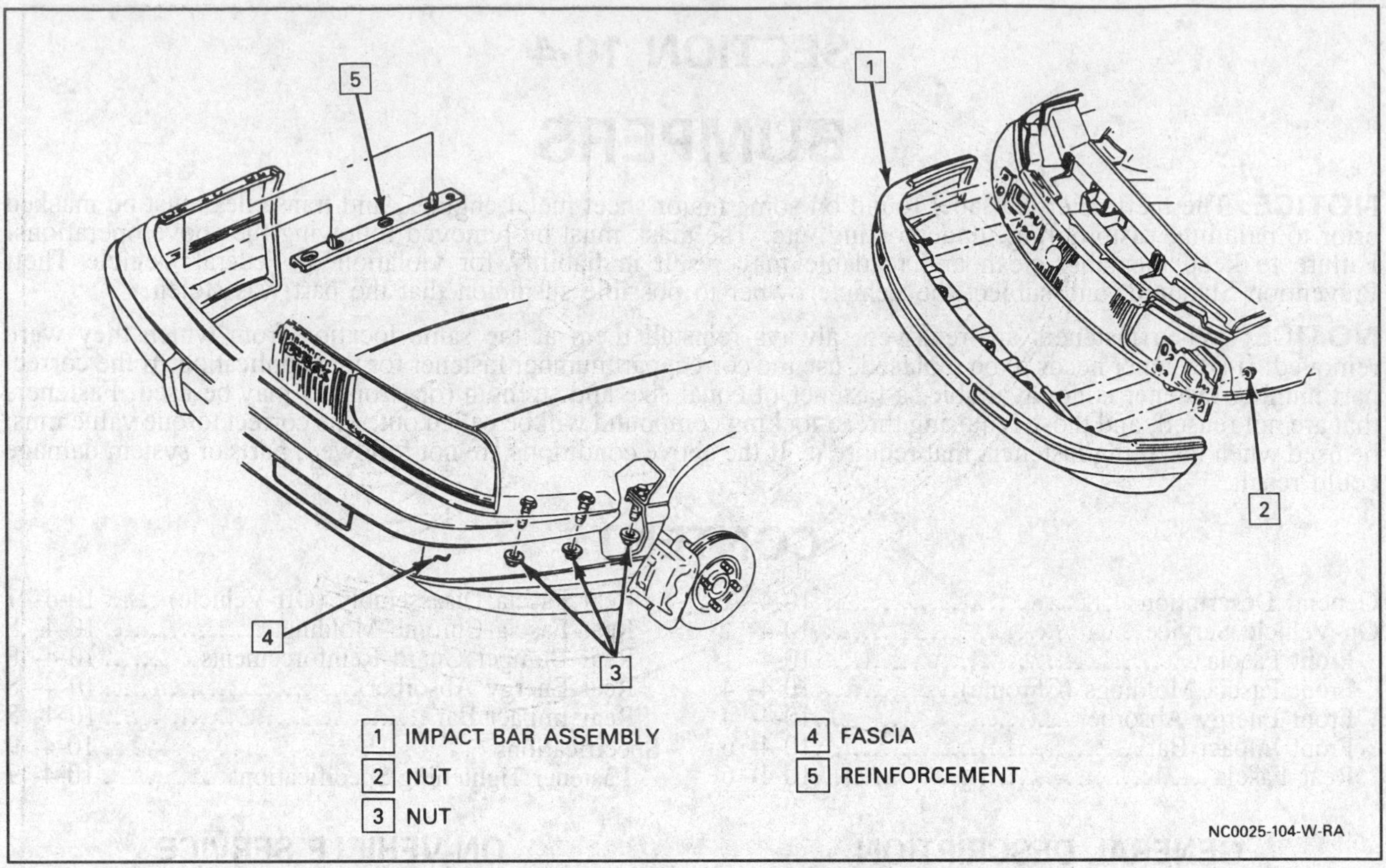
5
1
4
3
2
1 IMPACT BAR ASSEMBLY
2 NUT
3 NUT
4 FASCIA
5 REINFORCEMENT
NC0025-104-W-RA

Figure 1 Front Fascia Assembly (Sedan)

4. Bolt to center fascia support.

Tighten

- Bolt to 6 N·m (53 lb. in.).

5. Side marker lamps electrical connections.
6. Fascia to fender nuts.

Tighten

- Nuts to 10 N·m (89 lb. in.).

7. Fascia to fender liner screws.

Tighten

- Screws to 2 N·m (18 lb. in.).

8. Air deflector. Refer to COOLING AND RADIATOR (SECTION 6B).

Coupe

Figures 3 and 4

Remove or Disconnect

1. Raise vehicle and suitably support. Refer to GENERAL INFORMATION (SECTION 0A).
2. Chrome strip bracket.
3. Fascia to impact bar mounting bracket.
4. Center push retainers to center support bracket.
5. Radiator support bracket.
6. Wheelhousing to fascia attachment screws.
7. Grille assembly. Refer to BODY FRONT END (SECTION 10-5).
8. Lighting assemblies. Refer to LIGHTING SYSTEMS AND HORNS (SECTION 8B).
9. Retaining clips.
10. Fascia to fender attaching bolts.
11. Fascia from vehicle.

Install or Connect

1. Fascia to fender nuts.

Tighten

- Nuts to 5 N·m (44 lb. in.).

2. Retaining clips.
3. Lighting assemblies. Refer to LIGHTING SYSTEMS AND HORNS (SECTION 8B)
4. Grille assembly. Refer to BODY FRONT END (SECTION 10-5).
5. Radiator support bracket.
6. Wheelhousing to fascia attachment screws.

Tighten

- Screws to 2 N·m (18 lb. in.).

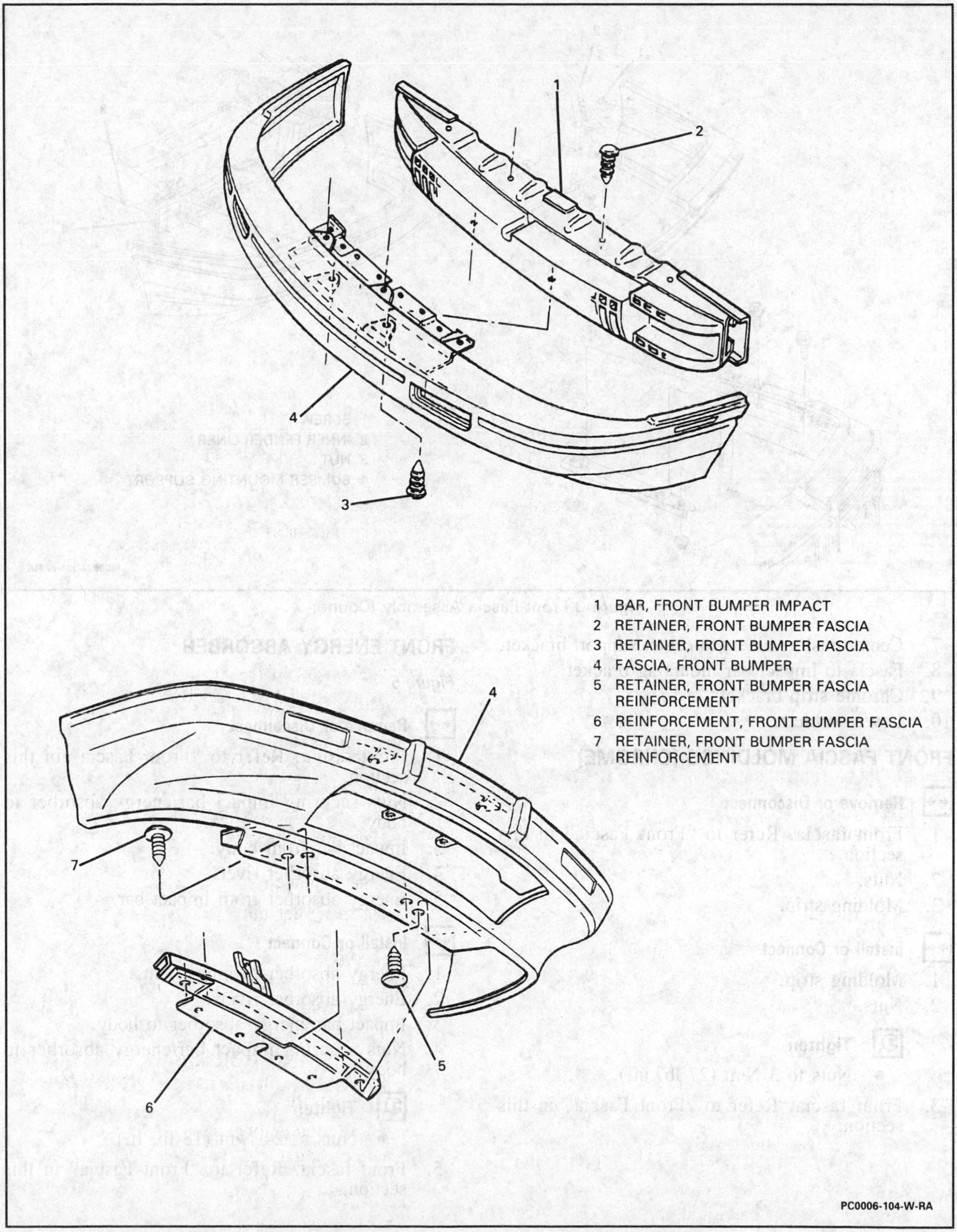
1
2
4
3
4
7
5
6
1 BAR, FRONT BUMPER IMPACT
2 RETAINER, FRONT BUMPER FASCIA
3 RETAINER, FRONT BUMPER FASCIA
4 FASCIA, FRONT BUMPER
5 RETAINER, FRONT BUMPER FASCIA REINFORCEMENT
6 REINFORCEMENT, FRONT BUMPER FASCIA
7 RETAINER, FRONT BUMPER FASCIA REINFORCEMENT
PC0006-104-W-RA

Figure 2 Front Fascia and Impact Bar Assembly (Sedan)

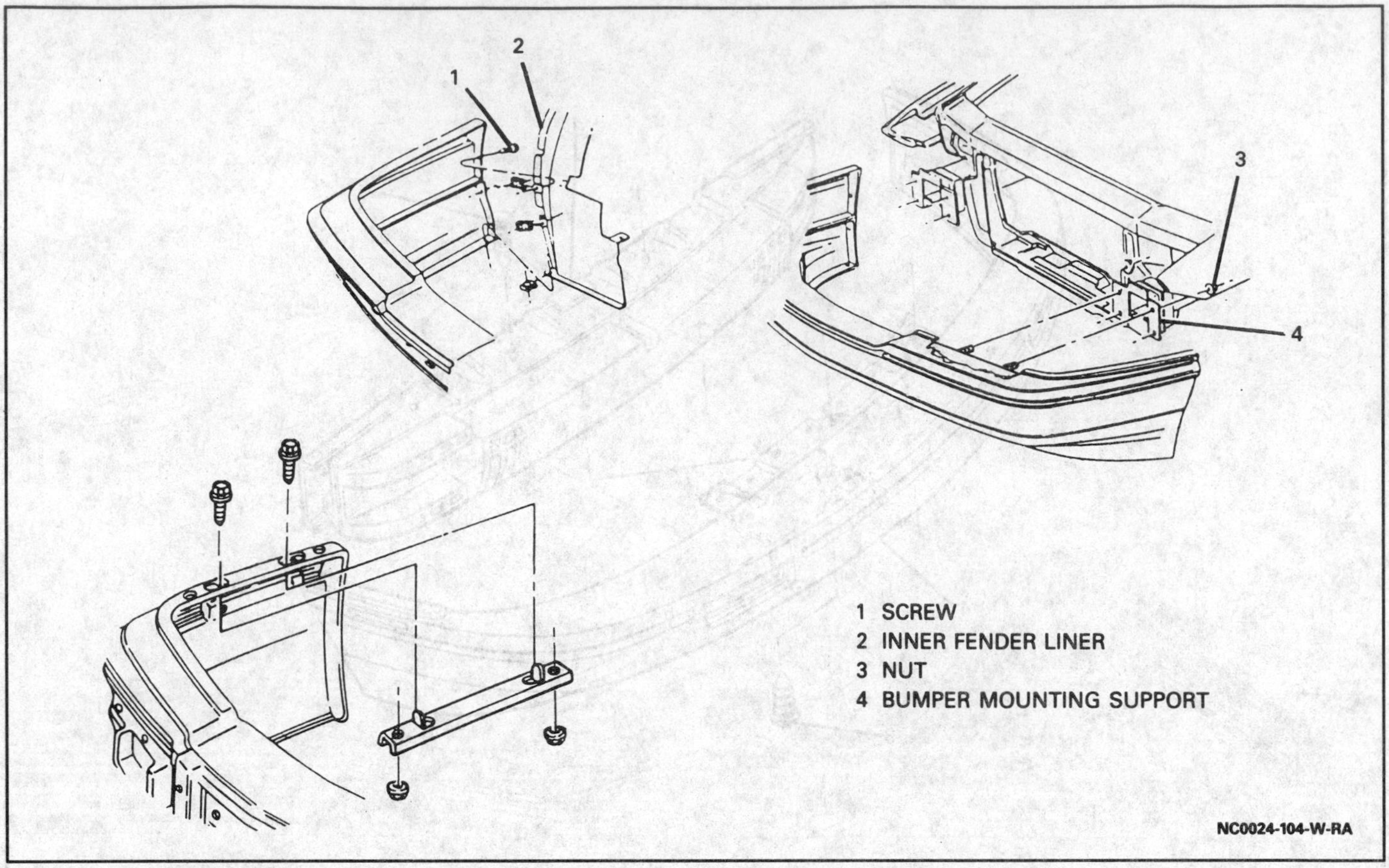
1
2
3
4
1 SCREW
2 INNER FENDER LINER
3 NUT
4 BUMPER MOUNTING SUPPORT
NC0024-104-W-RA

Figure 3 Front Fascia Assembly (Coupe)

7. Center push retainers to center support bracket.
8. Fascia to impact bar mounting bracket.
9. Chrome strip bracket.
10. Lower vehicle.

FRONT FASCIA MOLDINGS (CHROME)

Remove or Disconnect

1. Front fascia. Refer to "Front Fascia" in this section.
2. Nuts.
3. Molding strip.

Install or Connect

1. Molding strip.
2. Nuts.

   Tighten

   - Nuts to 3 N·m (27 lb. in.).

3. Front fascia. Refer to "Front Fascia" in this section.

FRONT ENERGY ABSORBER

Figure 5

Remove or Disconnect

1. Front fascia. Refer to "Front Fascia" in this section.
2. Nuts securing impact bar/energy absorber to body.
3. Impact bar from body.
4. Energy absorber rivets.
5. Energy absorber from impact bar.

Install or Connect

1. Energy absorber to impact bar.
2. Energy absorber rivets.
3. Impact bar/energy absorber to body.
4. Nuts securing impact bar/energy absorber to body.

   Tighten

   - Nuts to 24 N·m (18 lb. ft.).

5. Front fascia. Refer to "Front Fascia" in this section.

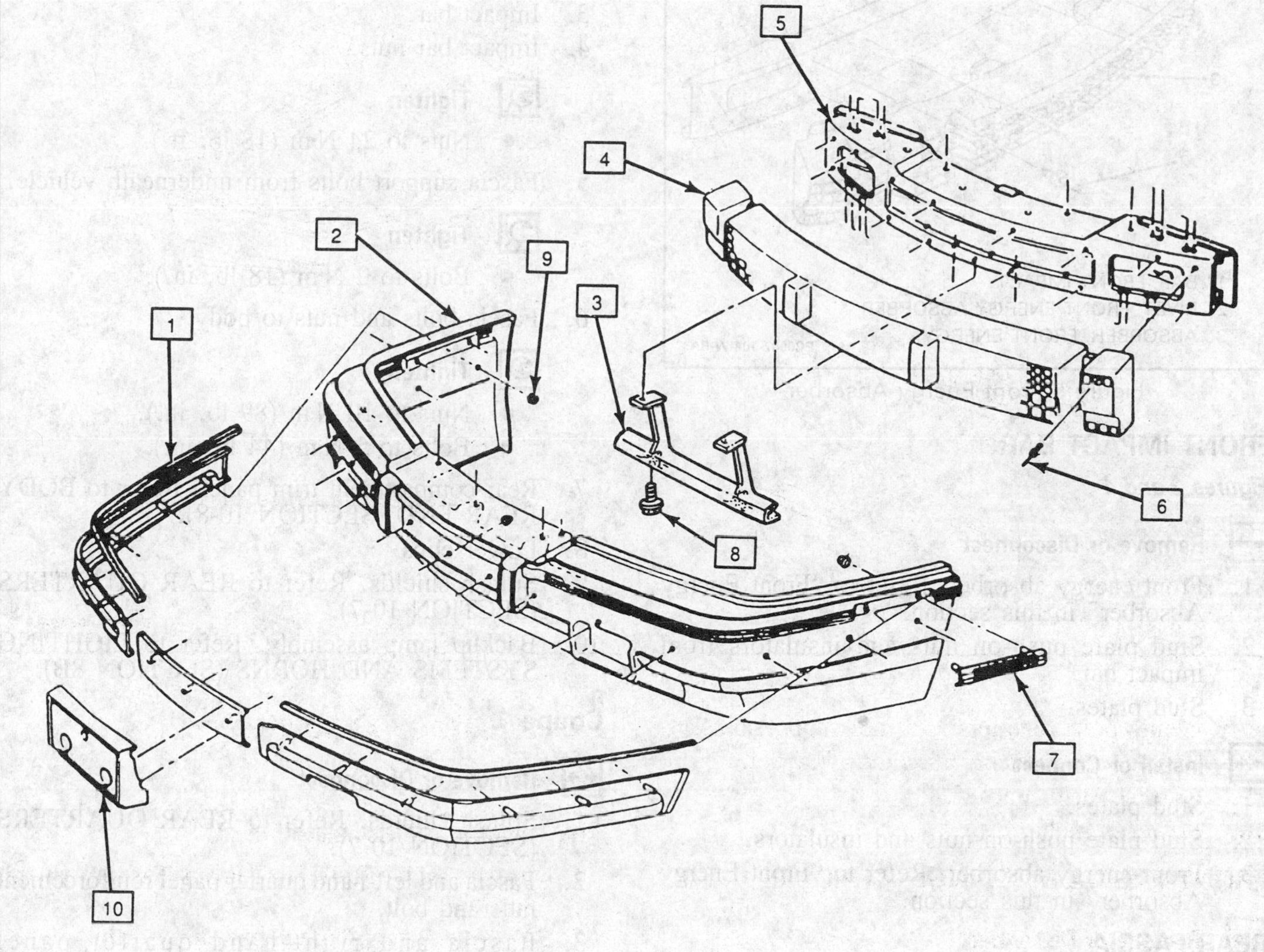
5
4
2
9
3
1
6
8
7
10
RC4001-104-W-RP

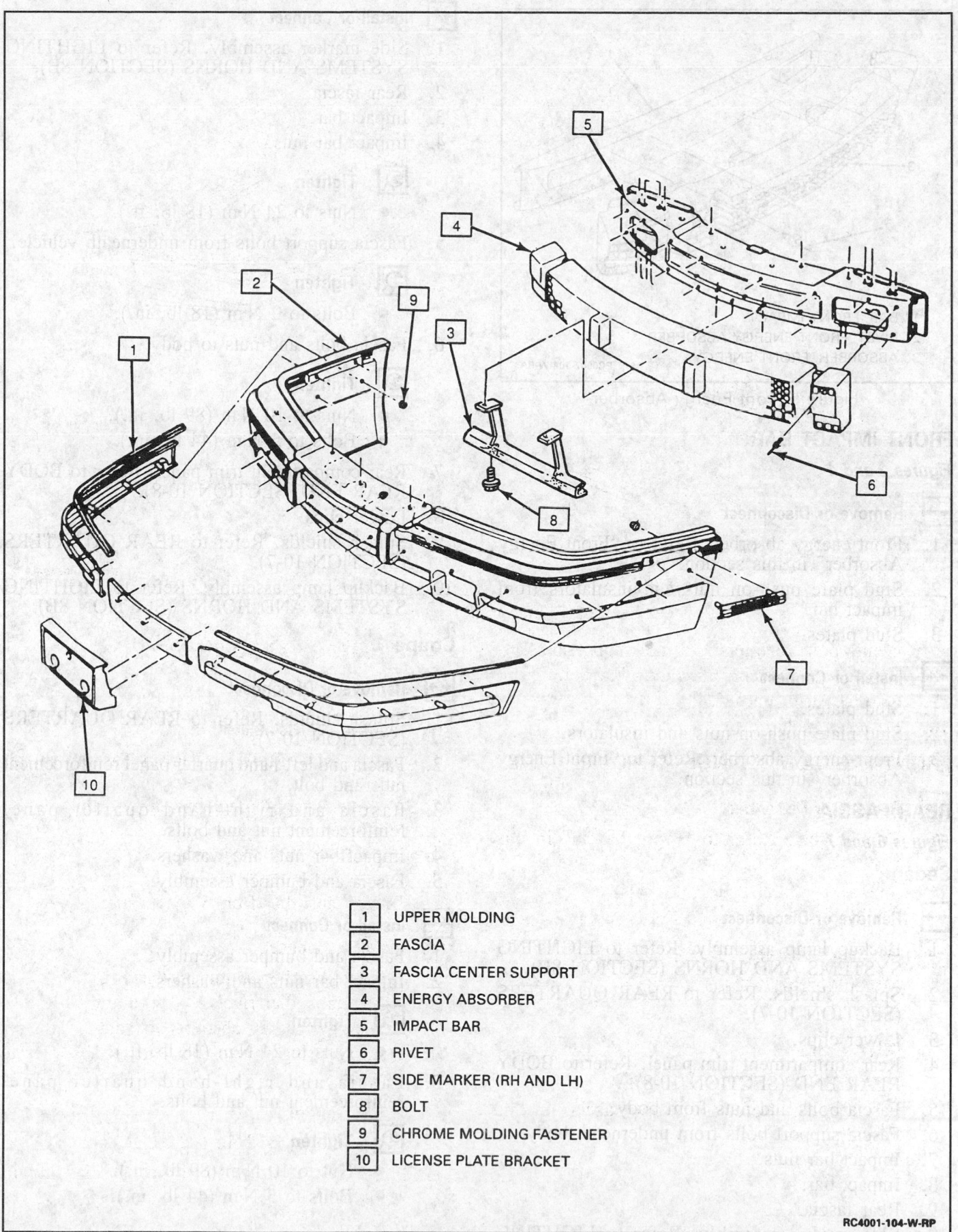

1	UPPER MOLDING
2	FASCIA
3	FASCIA CENTER SUPPORT
4	ENERGY ABSORBER
5	IMPACT BAR
6	RIVET
7	SIDE MARKER (RH AND LH)
8	BOLT
9	CHROME MOLDING FASTENER
10	LICENSE PLATE BRACKET

Figure 4 Front Fascia and Impact Bar Assembly (Coupe)

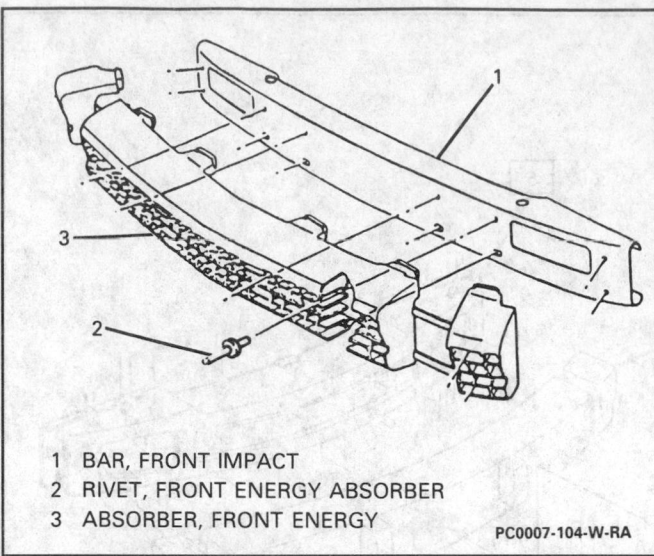

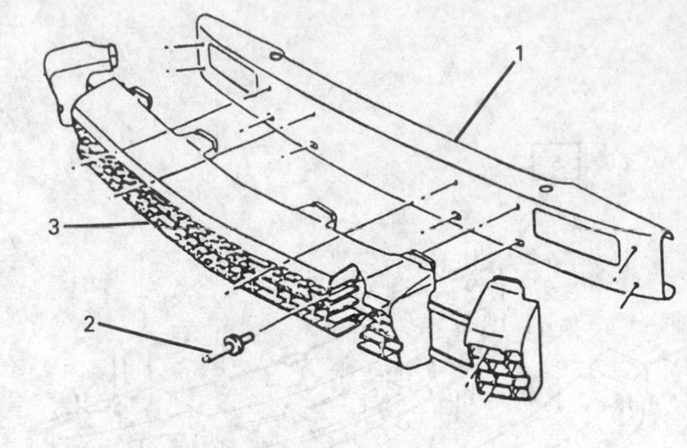
1
2
3
1 BAR, FRONT IMPACT
2 RIVET, FRONT ENERGY ABSORBER
3 ABSORBER, FRONT ENERGY
PC0007-104-W-RA

Figure 5 Front Energy Absorber

FRONT IMPACT BAR

Figures 2 and 4

Remove or Disconnect

1. Front energy absorber. Refer to "Front Energy Absorber" in this section.
2. Stud plate push-on nuts and insulators from impact bar.
3. Stud plates.

Install or Connect

1. Stud plates.
2. Stud plate push-on nuts and insulators.
3. Front energy absorber. Refer to "Front Energy Absorber" in this section.

REAR FASCIA

Figures 6 and 7

Sedan

Remove or Disconnect

1. Backup lamp assembly. Refer to LIGHTING SYSTEMS AND HORNS (SECTION 8B).
2. Splash shields. Refer to REAR QUARTERS (SECTION 10-7).
3. Lower clips.
4. Rear compartment trim panel. Refer to BODY REAR END (SECTION 10-8).
5. Fascia bolts and nuts from body.
6. Fascia support bolts from underneath body.
7. Impact bar nuts.
8. Impact bar.
9. Rear fascia.
10. Side marker assembly. Refer to LIGHTING SYSTEMS AND HORNS (SECTION 8B).

Install or Connect

1. Side marker assembly. Refer to LIGHTING SYSTEMS AND HORNS (SECTION 8B).
2. Rear fascia.
3. Impact bar.
4. Impact bar nuts.

   Tighten

   - Nuts to 24 N·m (18 lb. ft.).

5. Fascia support bolts from underneath vehicle.

   Tighten

   - Bolts to 2 N·m (18 lb. in.).

6. Fascia bolts and nuts to body.

   Tighten

   - Nuts to 10 N·m (89 lb. in.).
   - Bolts to 5 N·m (44 lb. in.).

7. Rear compartment trim panel. Refer to BODY REAR END (SECTION 10-8).
8. Lower clips.
9. Splash shields. Refer to REAR QUARTERS (SECTION 10-7).
10. Backup lamp assembly. Refer to LIGHTING SYSTEMS AND HORNS (SECTION 8B).

Coupe

Remove or Disconnect

1. Splash shields. Refer to REAR QUARTERS (SECTION 10-7).
2. Fascia and left-hand quarter panel reinforcement nuts and bolt.
3. Fascia and right-hand quarter panel reinforcement nut and bolts.
4. Impact bar nuts and washers.
5. Fascia and bumper assembly.

Install or Connect

1. Fascia and bumper assembly,
2. Impact bar nuts and washers.

   Tighten

   - Nuts to 24 N·m (18 lb. ft.).

3. Fascia and right-hand quarter panel reinforcement nut and bolts.

   Tighten

   - Nut to 10 N·m (89 lb. in.).
   - Bolts to 5 N·m (44 lb. in.).

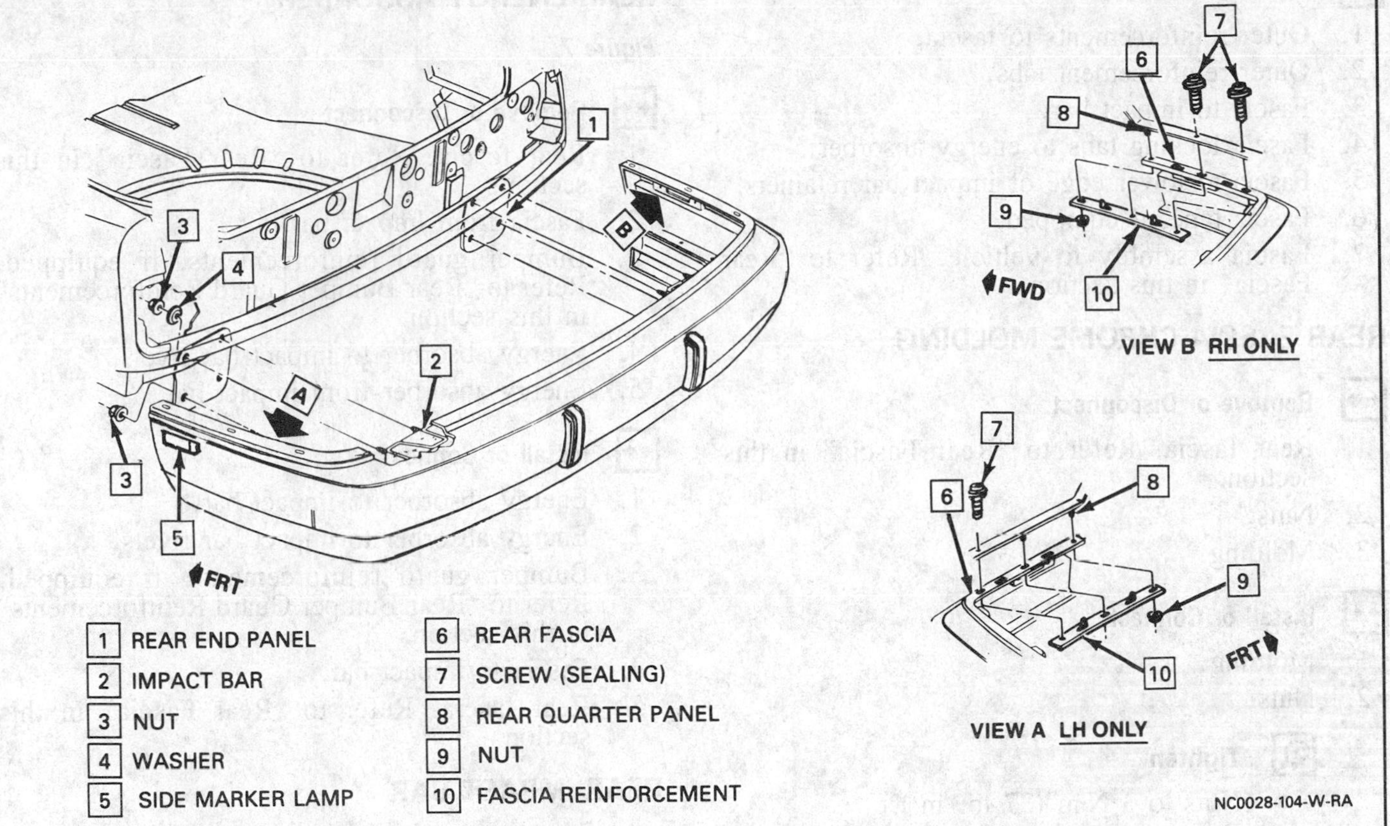

1
2
3
4
5
A
B
FRT
6
7
8
9
10
FWD
VIEW B RH ONLY
VIEW A LH ONLY
FRT
1 REAR END PANEL
2 IMPACT BAR
3 NUT
4 WASHER
5 SIDE MARKER LAMP
6 REAR FASCIA
7 SCREW (SEALING)
8 REAR QUARTER PANEL
9 NUT
10 FASCIA REINFORCEMENT
NC0028-104-W-RA

Figure 6 Rear Fascia Assembly

4. Fascia and left-hand quarter panel reinforcement nuts and bolt.

Tighten

- Nuts to 10 N·m (89 lb. in.).
- Bolt to 5 N·m (44 lb. in.).

5. Splash shields. Refer to REAR QUARTERS (SECTION 10-7).

REAR FASCIA DISASSEMBLY (OFF-VEHICLE)

Figures 6 and 7

Sedan

Remove or Disconnect

1. Fascia assembly. Refer to "Rear Fascia" in this section.
2. Fascia to impact bar push-in retainers.
3. Fascia from impact bar.
4. Rear side marker reflector and back up lamp assemblies. Refer to LIGHTING SYSTEMS AND HORNS (SECTION 8B).
5. Rear fascia outer retainer assembly tabs from fascia.
6. Outer retainer assemblies.
7. Chrome molding assemblies. Refer to "Rear Fascia Chrome Molding" in this section.

Install or Connect

1. Chrome molding assemblies. Refer to "Rear Fascia Chrome Molding" in this section.
2. Outer retainer assemblies.
3. Rear fascia outer retainer assembly tabs.
4. Rear side marker reflector and back up lamp assemblies. Refer to LIGHTING SYSTEMS AND HORNS (SECTION 8B).
5. Fascia to impact bar.
6. Fascia to impact bar push-in retainers.
7. Fascia assembly to vehicle. Refer to "Rear Fascia" in this section.

Coupe

Remove or Disconnect

1. Fascia assembly. Refer to "Rear Fascia" in this section.
2. Fascia tape, if equipped.
3. Fascia to lower edge of impact bar retainers.
4. Fascia locking tabs from energy absorber.
5. Fascia from impact bar.
6. Rear fascia outer reinforcement tabs.
7. Outer reinforcements from fascia.

Install or Connect

1. Outer reinforcements to fascia.
2. Outer reinforcement tabs.
3. Fascia to impact bar.
4. Fascia locking tabs to energy absorber.
5. Fascia to lower edge of impact bar retainers.
6. Fascia tape, if equipped.
7. Fascia assembly to vehicle. Refer to "Rear Fascia" in this section.

REAR FASCIA CHROME MOLDING

Remove or Disconnect

1. Rear fascia. Refer to "Rear Fascia" in this section.
2. Nuts.
3. Molding.

Install or Connect

1. Molding.
2. Nuts.

   Tighten

   - Nuts to 3 N·m (27 lb. in.).

3. Rear fascia. Refer to "Rear Fascia" in this section.

REAR BUMPER GUARD REINFORCEMENTS

Figure 7

Remove or Disconnect

1. Rear fascia. Refer to "Rear Fascia" in this section.
2. Fascia from impact bar.
3. Bumper guard reinforcement bolts.
4. Bumper guard reinforcements.

Install or Connect

1. Bumper guard reinforcements.
2. Bumper guard reinforcement bolts.

   Tighten

   - Bolts to 1 N·m (9 lb. in.).

3. Fascia to impact bar.
4. Rear fascia. Refer to "Rear Fascia" in this section.

REAR ENERGY ABSORBER

Figure 7

Remove or Disconnect

1. Rear fascia. Refer to "Rear Fascia" in this section.
2. Fascia from impact bar.
3. Bumper guard reinforcements, if equipped. Refer to "Rear Bumper Guard Reinforcements" in this section.
4. Energy absorber to impact bar rivets.
5. Energy absorber from impact bar.

Install or Connect

1. Energy absorber to impact bar.
2. Energy absorber to impact bar rivets.
3. Bumper guard reinforcements, if equipped. Refer to "Rear Bumper Guard Reinforcements" in this section.
4. Fascia to impact bar.
5. Rear fascia. Refer to "Rear Fascia" in this section.

REAR IMPACT BAR

Figure 7

Remove or Disconnect

1. Rear fascia. Refer to "Rear Fascia" in this section.
2. Fascia from impact bar.
3. Energy absorber rivets.
4. Impact bar stud plate push-on nuts.
5. Stud plates from impact bar.

Install or Connect

1. Stud plates to impact bar.
2. Impact bar stud plate push-on nuts.
3. Energy absorber rivets.
4. Fascia to impact bar.
5. Rear fascia. Refer to "Rear Fascia" in this section.

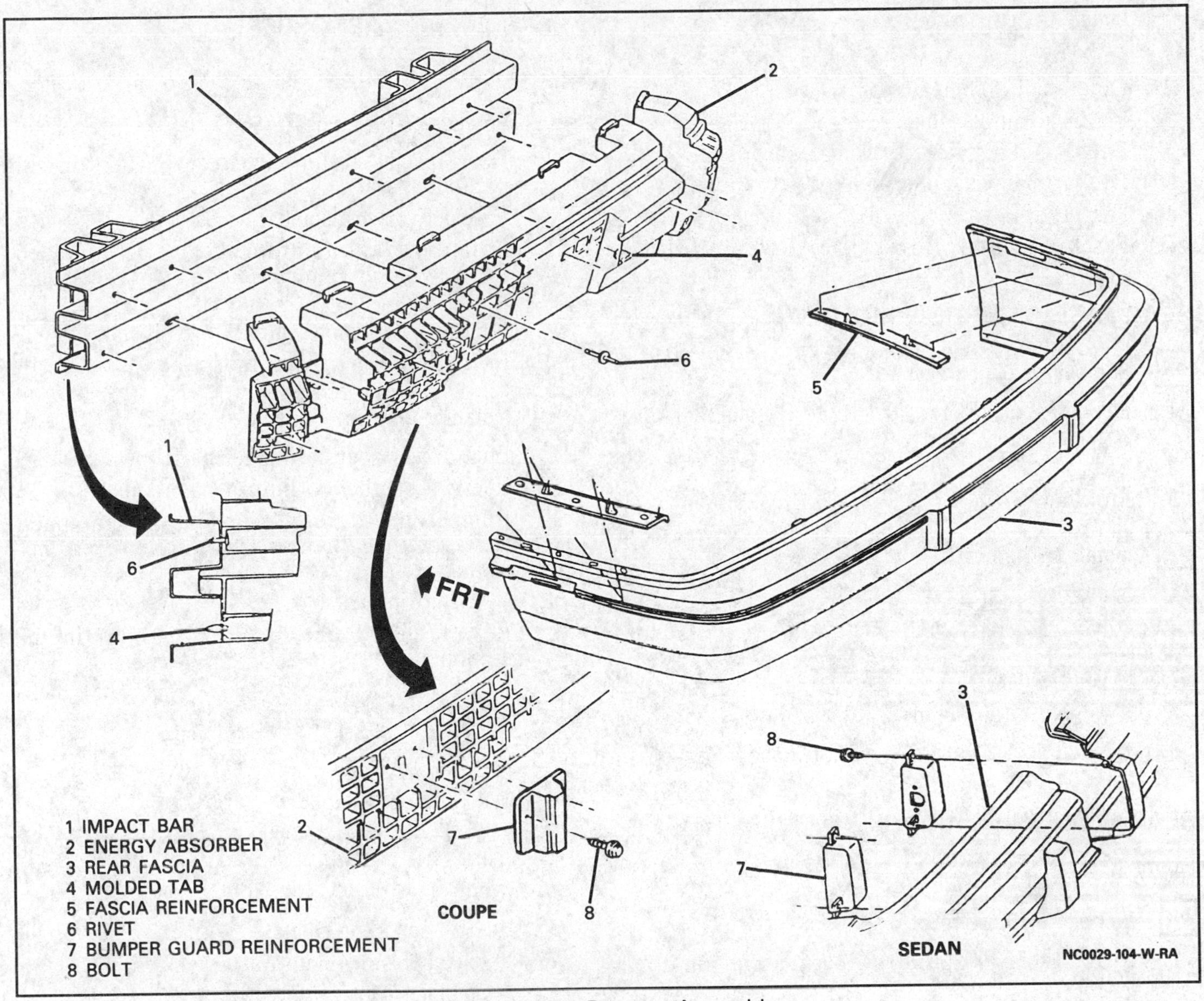
1
2
4
6
5
1
6
4
FRT
3
3
8
2
7
8
7
1 IMPACT BAR
2 ENERGY ABSORBER
3 REAR FASCIA
4 MOLDED TAB
5 FASCIA REINFORCEMENT
6 RIVET
7 BUMPER GUARD REINFORCEMENT
8 BOLT
COUPE
SEDAN
NC0029-104-W-RA

Figure 7 Rear Bumper Assembly

SPECIFICATIONS

FASTENER TIGHTENING SPECIFICATIONS

Fascia Molding Nut	3 N·m (27 lb. in.)
Front Fascia Center Bolt	6 N·m (53 lb. in.)
Front Fender Liner Screw	2 N·m (18 lb. in.)
Front Fascia-to-Fender Nut	
Coupe	5 N·m (44 lb. in.)
Sedan	10 N·m (89 lb. in.)
Front Impact Bar Nut	24 N·m (18 lb. ft.)
Rear Bumper Guard Reinforcement Bolt	1 N·m (9 lb. in.)
Rear Fascia Support Bolt	2 N·m (18 lb. in.)
Rear Fascia Reinforcement Bolt	5 N·m (44 lb. in.)
Rear Fascia Reinforcement Nut	10 N·m (89 lb. in.)
Rear Impact Bar Nut	24 N·m (18 lb. ft.)
Rear Towing Pad Nut	6 N·m (53 lb. in.)

SECTION 10-5

BODY FRONT END

NOTICE: When fasteners are removed, always reinstall them at the same location from which they were removed. If a fastener needs to be replaced, use the correct part number fastener for that application. If the correct part number fastener is not available, a fastener of equal size and strength (or stronger) may be used. Fasteners that are not reused, and those requiring thread locking compound will be called out. The correct torque value must be used when installing fasteners that require it. If the above conditions are not followed, parts or system damage could result.

NOTICE: The theft deterrent label found on some major sheet metal, engines and transaxles must be masked prior to painting, rustproofing, undercoating, etc. The mask must be removed following the above operations. Failure to keep the label clean and readable may result in liability for violation of Federal Vehicle Theft Prevention Standard and subject the vehicle owner to possible suspicion that the part was stolen.

CONTENTS

GENERAL DESCRIPTION

This vehicle has a unitized body with a frame assembly supporting the engine. The inner fender panels and the radiator support are also integral parts of the body.

Anti-corrosion materials have been applied to the interior surfaces of some metal panels. When servicing these panels, disturbed areas should be properly re-coated with a service type anti-corrosion material. Refer to GENERAL BODY SERVICE (SECTION 10-1).

Theft deterrent labels may be found on some major sheet metal, engines and transaxles. For more information on these labels, refer to GENERAL INFORMATION (SECTION 0A).

ON-VEHICLE SERVICE

RADIATOR AIR BAFFLES

For information on various radiator air baffles, refer to COOLING AND RADIATOR (SECTION 6B).

RADIATOR SUPPORT PANEL

Figure 1

Remove or Disconnect

1. Bolts/screws from radiator bracket assembly.
2. Radiator support panel from radiator mounts.

Install or Connect

1. Radiator support panel locating holes to radiator mounts.
2. Bolts/screws.

Tighten

- Bolts/screws to 10 N•m (89 lb. in.).

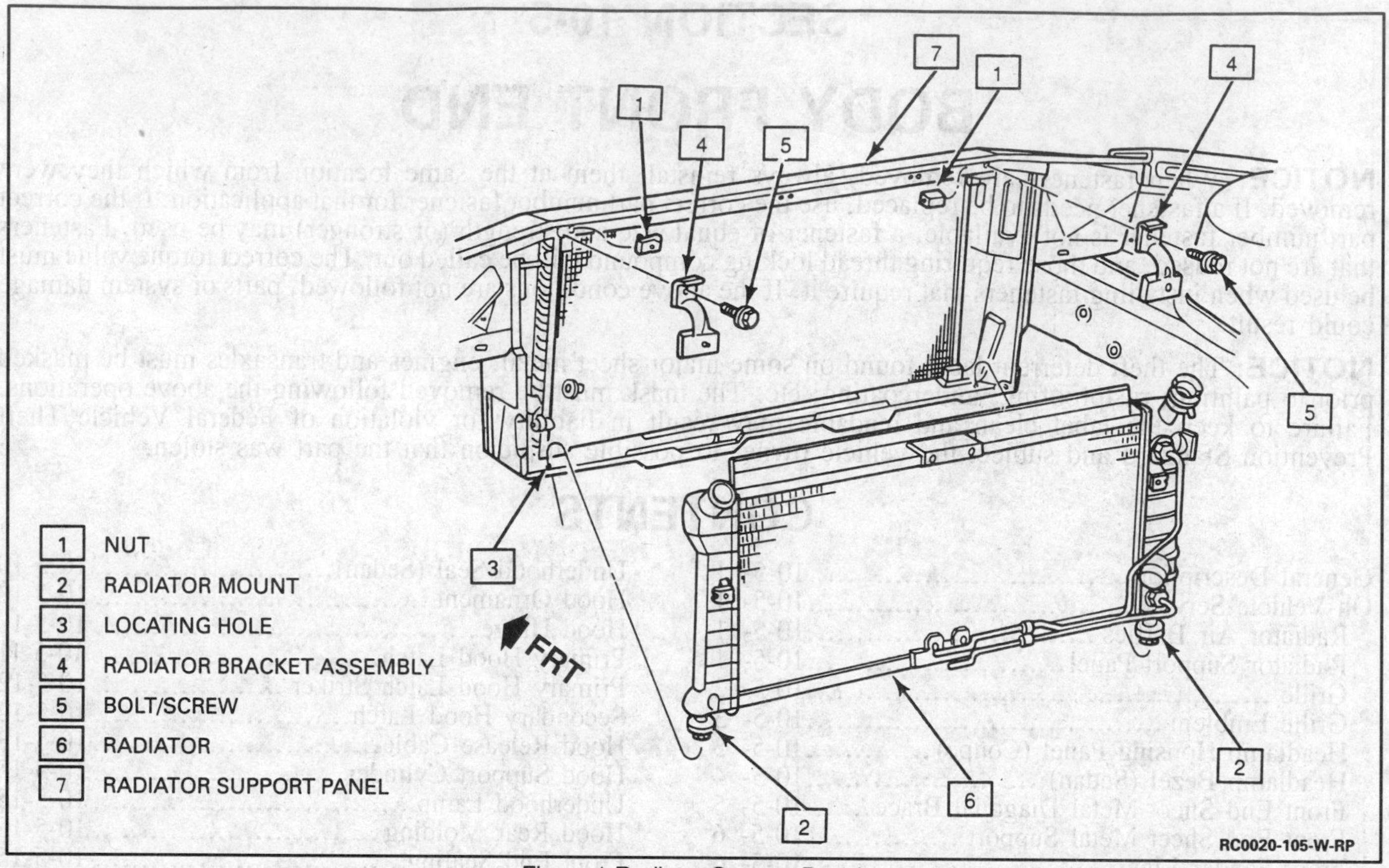

7
1
4
1
4
5
5
3
FRT
6
2
2
1 NUT
2 RADIATOR MOUNT
3 LOCATING HOLE
4 RADIATOR BRACKET ASSEMBLY
5 BOLT/SCREW
6 RADIATOR
7 RADIATOR SUPPORT PANEL
RC0020-105-W-RP

Figure 1 Radiator Support Panel

GRILLE

Sedan

Figure 2

Remove or Disconnect

1. Open hood and suitably support.
2. Grille retaining screws from support bracket.
3. Screws from front of hood.
4. Grille from support bracket.
5. Support bracket retaining screws from hood.
6. Support bracket from hood.

Install or Connect

1. Support bracket to hood.
2. Support bracket retaining screws.

Tighten

- Screws to 2 N·m (18 lb. in.).

3. Grille to support bracket.
   - Align grille guide pins to support bracket.
4. Screws to front of grille.

Tighten

- Screws to 2 N·m (18 lb. in.).

5. Grille retaining screws to support bracket.

Tighten

- Screws to 2 N·m (18 lb. in.).

6. Remove support and close hood.

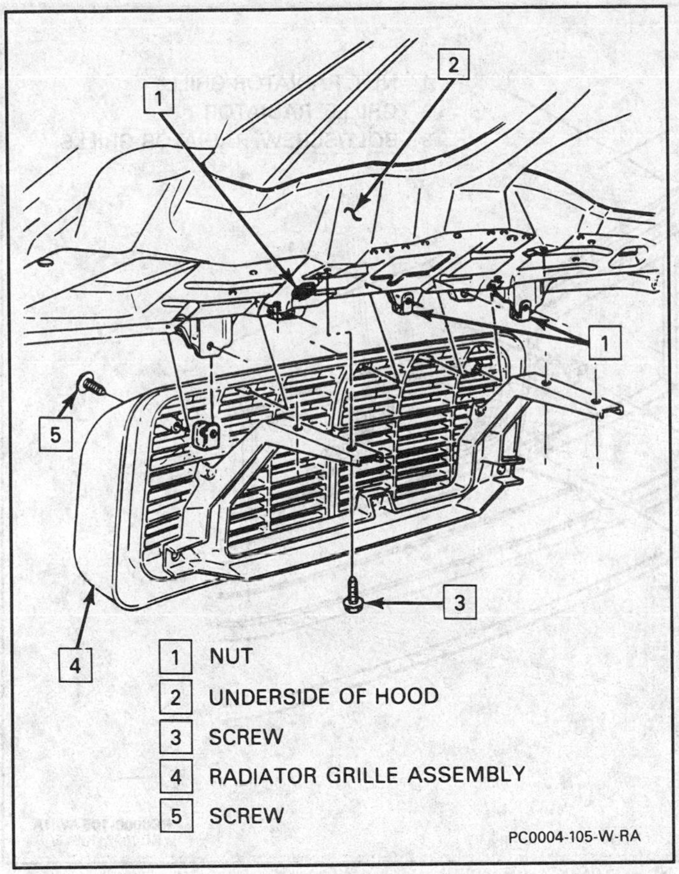
1
2
1
5
3
4
1 NUT
2 UNDERSIDE OF HOOD
3 SCREW
4 RADIATOR GRILLE ASSEMBLY
5 SCREW
PC0004-105-W-RA

Figure 2 Grille (Sedan)

Coupe

Figure 3

Remove or Disconnect

1. Open hood and suitably support.
2. Screws securing grille to headlamp housing panel.
3. Grille.

Install or Connect

1. Grille to headlamp housing panel.
2. Screws securing grille assembly to headlamp housing panel.

Tighten

- Screws to 2 N·m (18 lb. in.).

GRILLE EMBLEM

Remove or Disconnect

1. Grille. Refer to "Grille" in this section.
2. Nuts.
3. Grille emblem.

Install or Connect

1. Grille emblem.
2. Nuts.

Tighten

- Nuts to 3 N·m (27 lb. in.).

3. Grille. Refer to "Grille" in this section.

HEADLAMP HOUSING PANEL (Coupe)

Figure 4

Remove or Disconnect

1. Raise hood.
2. Headlamp access panel.
3. Turn signal lamps. Refer to LIGHTING SYSTEMS AND HORNS (SECTION 8B).
4. Wiring harness clips at center.
5. Electrical connectors.
6. Center support bracket nuts.
7. Panel to fender nuts.
8. Headlamp housing panel.

Install or Connect

1. Headlamp housing panel.
2. Panel to fender nuts.

Tighten

- Nuts to 6 N·m (53 lb. in.).

3. Center support bracket nuts.

Tighten

- Nuts to 6 N·m (53 lb. in.).

4. Electrical connectors.
5. Wiring harness clips at center.
6. Turn signal lamps. Refer to LIGHTING SYSTEMS AND HORNS (SECTION 8B).
7. Headlamp access panel.
8. Close hood.

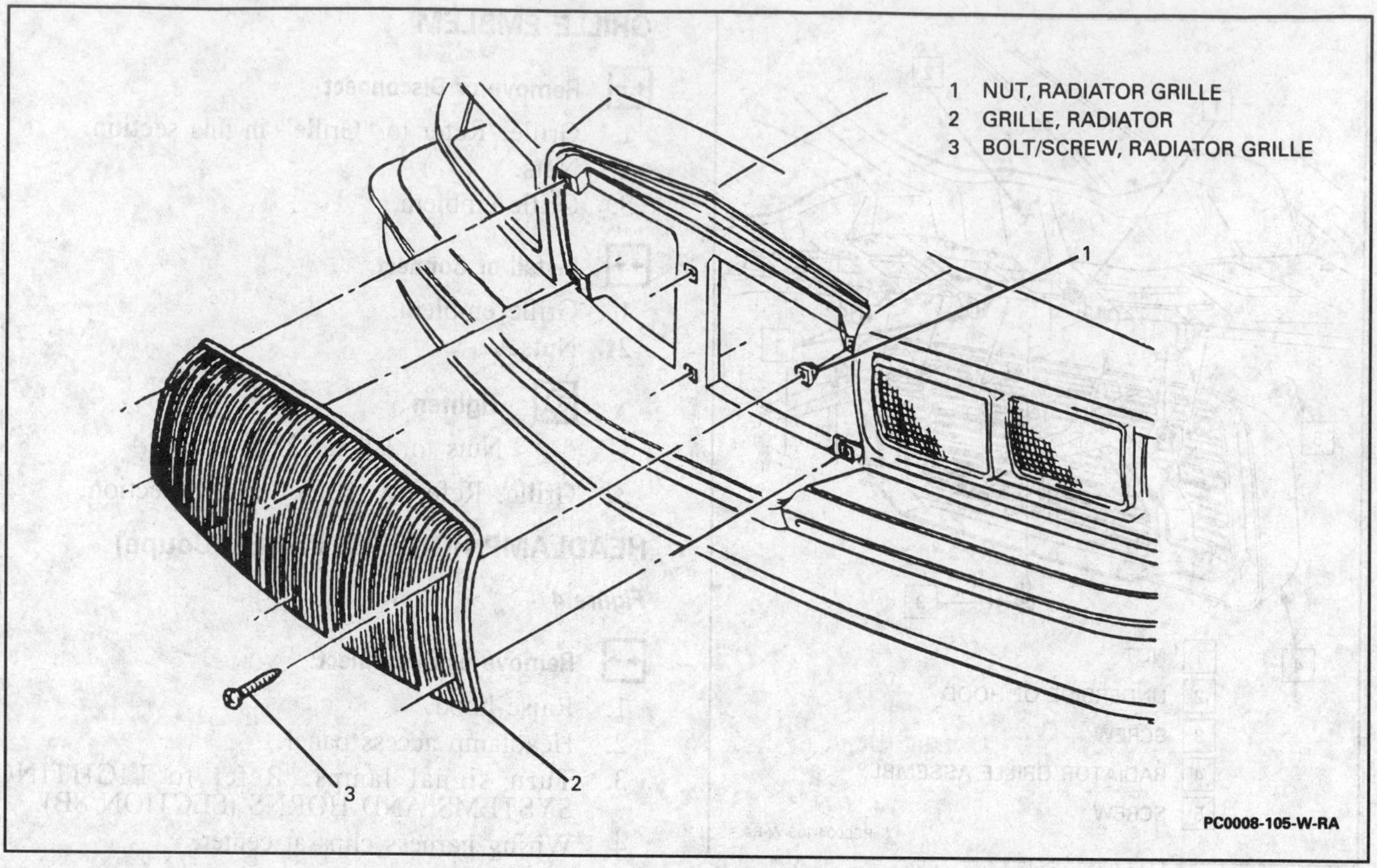
1 NUT, RADIATOR GRILLE
2 GRILLE, RADIATOR
3 BOLT/SCREW, RADIATOR GRILLE
1
2
3
PC0008-105-W-RA

Figure 3 Grille (Coupe)

HEADLAMP BEZEL (Sedan)

Figure 5

Remove or Disconnect

1. Screw located at inner side of bezel to headlamp housing panel.
2. Bottom screw.
3. Headlamp bezel.

Install or Connect

1. Headlamp bezel.
2. Bottom screw.

Tighten

- Screws to 2 N•m (18 lb. in.).

3. Screw to headlamp housing panel.

Tighten

- Screws to 2 N•m (18 lb. in.).

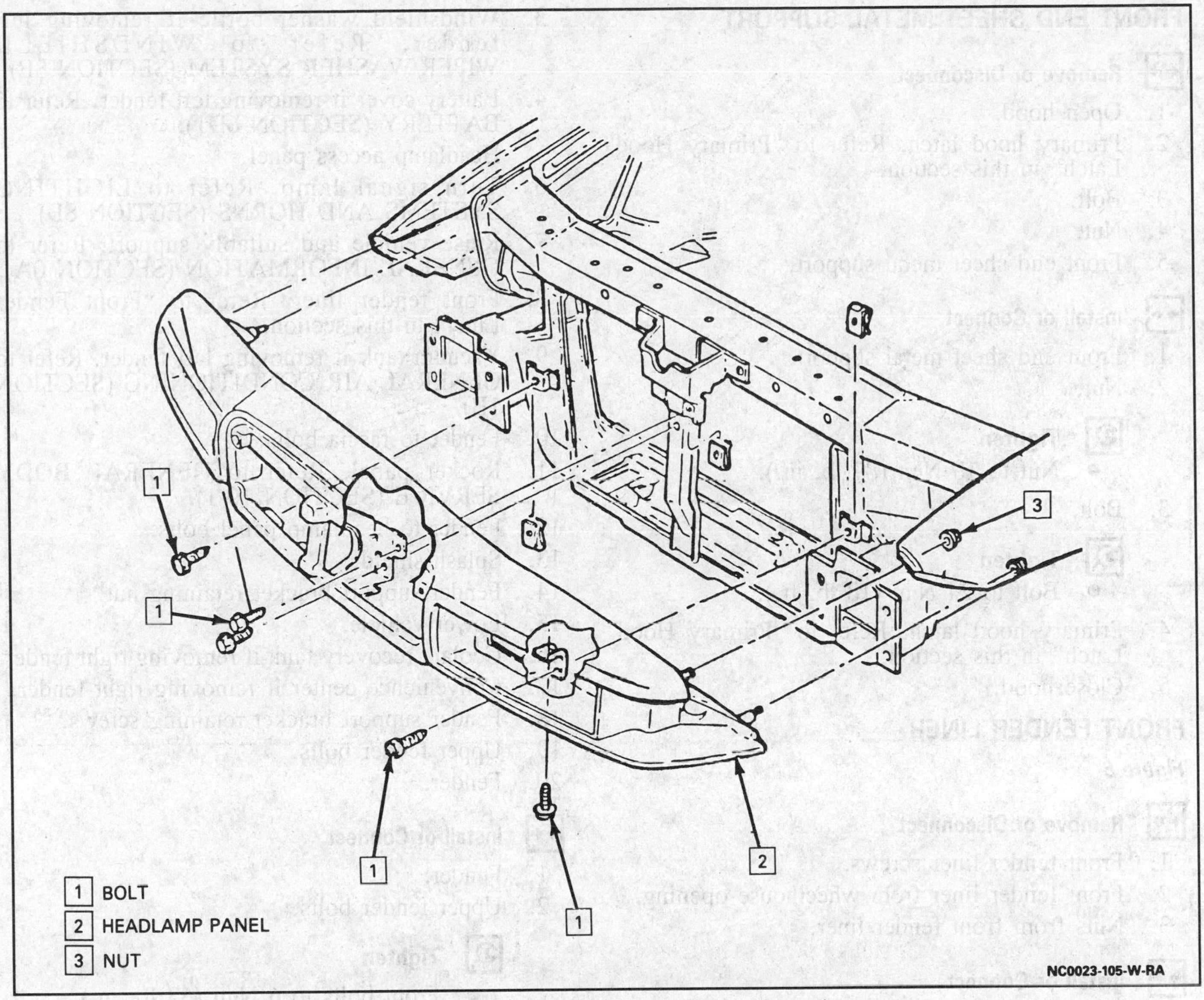
1
1
1
1
2
3
1 BOLT
2 HEADLAMP PANEL
3 NUT
NC0023-105-W-RA

Figure 4 Headlamp Housing Panel (Coupe)

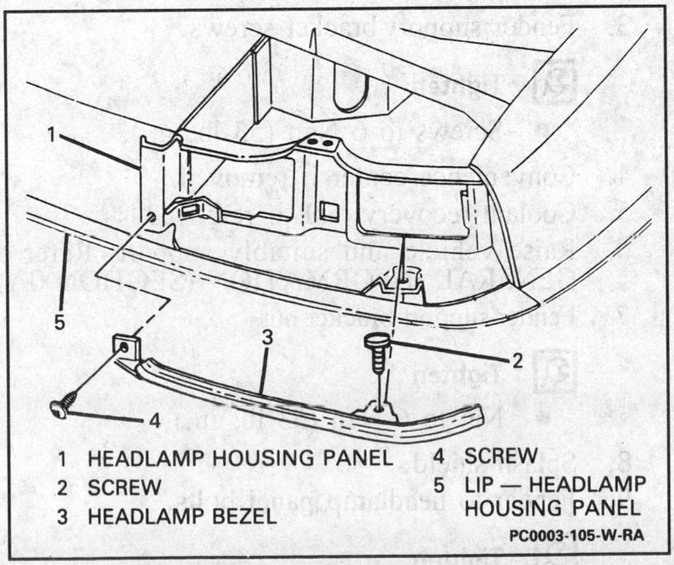
1
5
3
2
4
1 HEADLAMP HOUSING PANEL
2 SCREW
3 HEADLAMP BEZEL
4 SCREW
5 LIP — HEADLAMP HOUSING PANEL
PC0003-105-W-RA

Figure 5 Headlamp Bezel (Sedan)

FRONT END SHEET METAL DIAGONAL BRACE

Remove or Disconnect

1. Open hood.
2. Rear bolt.
3. Front bolts.
4. Diagonal brace.

Install or Connect

1. Diagonal brace.
2. Front bolts.

Tighten

- Bolts to 25 N·m (18 lb. ft.).

3. Rear bolt.

Tighten

- Bolt to 47 N·m (35 lb. ft.).

4. Close hood.

FRONT END SHEET METAL SUPPORT

Remove or Disconnect

1. Open hood.
2. Primary hood latch. Refer to "Primary Hood Latch" in this section.
3. Bolt.
4. Nut.
5. Front end sheet metal support.

Install or Connect

1. Front end sheet metal support.
2. Nut.

   Tighten
   - Nut to 10 N·m (89 lb. in.).
3. Bolt.

   Tighten
   - Bolt to 24 N·m (18 lb. ft.).
4. Primary hood latch. Refer to "Primary Hood Latch" in this section.
5. Close hood.

FRONT FENDER LINER

Figure 6

Remove or Disconnect

1. Front fender liner screws.
2. Front fender liner from wheelhouse opening.
3. Nuts from front fender liner.

Install or Connect

1. Nuts to front fender liner.
2. Front fender liner to wheelhouse opening over weld stud.
3. Screws to front fender liner.

   Tighten
   - Lower rear inboard screw to 3 N·m (27 lb. in.).
   - Remaining screws to 1.5 N•m (13 lb. in.).

FENDER

Figure 7

NOTICE: Fender and door edges should be taped for protection against chipping.

Remove or Disconnect

1. Hood. Refer to "Hood" in this section.
2. Left diagonal brace if removing left fender (3.1L Engine).
3. Windshield washer bottle if removing left fender. Refer to WINDSHIELD WIPER/WASHER SYSTEM (SECTION 8E).
4. Battery cover if removing left fender. Refer to BATTERY (SECTION 6D1).
5. Headlamp access panel.
6. Turn signal lamp. Refer to LIGHTING SYSTEMS AND HORNS (SECTION 8B).
7. Raise vehicle and suitably support. Refer to GENERAL INFORMATION (SECTION 0A).
8. Front fender liner. Refer to "Front Fender Liner" in this section.
9. Vacuum tank if removing left fender. Refer to GENERAL AIR CONDITIONING (SECTION 1B).
10. Fender to fascia bolts.
11. Rocker panel. Refer to GENERAL BODY SERVICE (SECTION 10-1).
12. Fender to headlamp panel bolts.
13. Splash shield.
14. Fender support bracket retaining nut.
15. Lower vehicle.
16. Coolant recovery tank if removing right fender.
17. Convenience center if removing right fender.
18. Fender support bracket retaining screws.
19. Upper fender bolts.
20. Fender.

Install or Connect

1. Fender.
2. Upper fender bolts.

   Tighten
   - Front bolts to 6 N·m (53 lb. in.).
   - Rear bolts to 25 N·m (18 lb. ft.).
3. Fender support bracket screws.

   Tighten
   - Screws to 6 N·m (53 lb. in.).
4. Convenience center if removed.
5. Coolant recovery tank if removed.
6. Raise vehicle and suitably support. Refer to GENERAL INFORMATION (SECTION 0A).
7. Fender support bracket nut.

   Tighten
   - Nut to 6 N·m (53 lb. in.).
8. Splash shield.
9. Fender to headlamp panel bolts.

   Tighten
   - Bolts to 6 N·m (53 lb. in.).

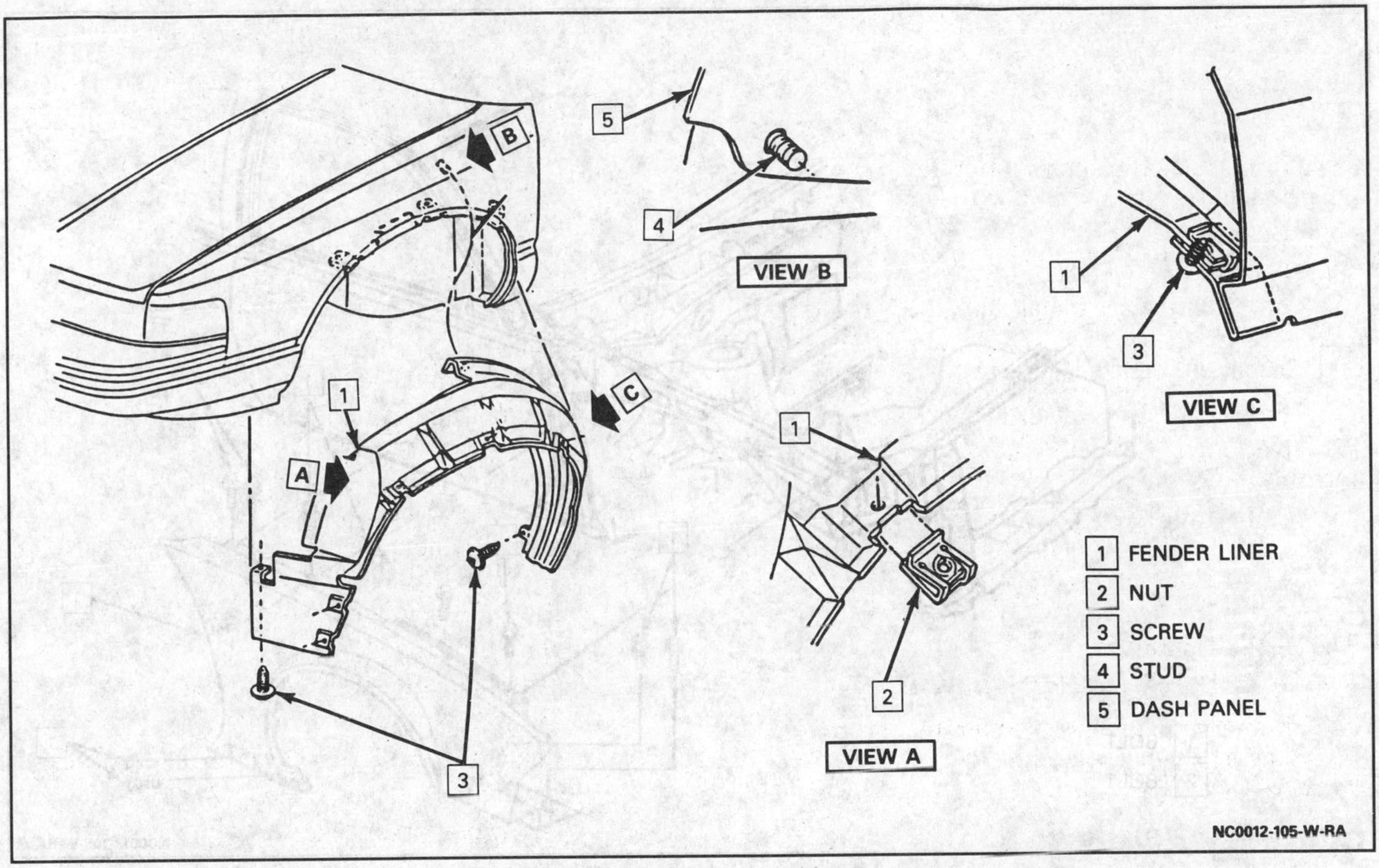
5
4
VIEW B
1
3
VIEW C
1
A
B
C
1
3
2
VIEW A
1 FENDER LINER
2 NUT
3 SCREW
4 STUD
5 DASH PANEL
NC0012-105-W-RA

Figure 6 Front Fender Liner

10. Rocker panel. Refer to GENERAL BODY SERVICE (SECTION 10-1).
11. Fender to fascia bolts.

Tighten

- Bolts to 6 N·m (53 lb. in.).

12. Vacuum tank if removed. Refer to GENERAL AIR CONDITIONING (SECTION 1B).
13. Front fender liner. Refer to "Front Fender Liner" in this section.
14. Lower vehicle.
15. Turn signal lamp. Refer to LIGHTING SYSTEMS AND HORNS (SECTION 8B).
16. Headlamp access panel.
17. Battery cover if removed. Refer to BATTERY (SECTION 6D1).
18. Windshield washer bottle if removed. Refer to WINDSHIELD WIPER/WASHER SYSTEM (SECTION 8E).
19. Left diagonal brace if removed.
20. Hood. Refer to "Hood" in this section.

UPPER REAR FENDER MOLDING

Remove or Disconnect

- Upper rear molding by unsnapping from fender.

Install or Connect

- Upper rear molding by snapping into fender holes.

FENDER WHEEL OPENING MOLDING

Remove or Disconnect

1. Screws, if equipped.
2. Fender wheel opening molding.

Install or Connect

1. Fender wheel opening molding.
2. Screws, if removed.

Tighten

- Screws to 2 N·m (18 lb. in.).

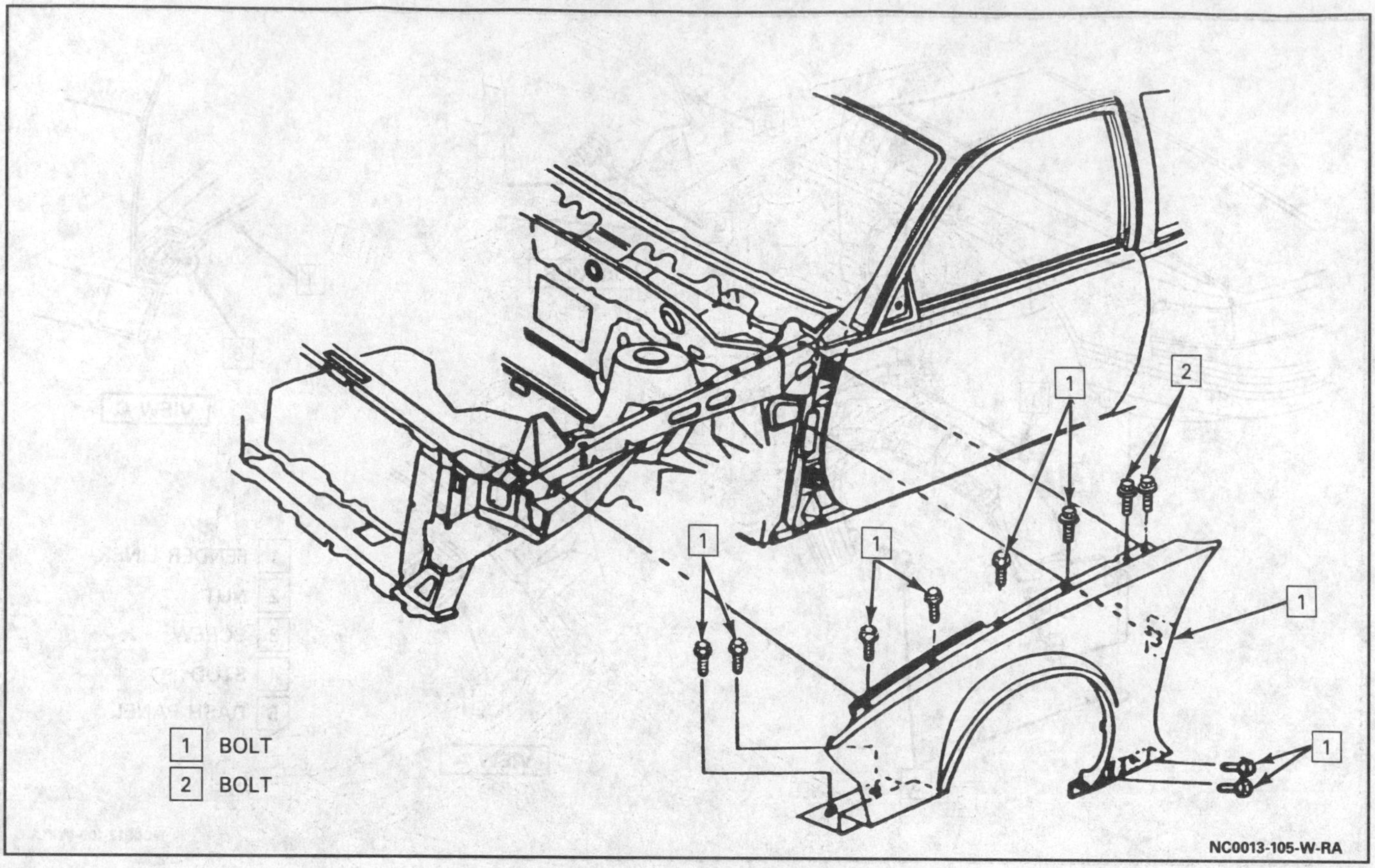
1
2
1
1
1
1
1
1 BOLT
2 BOLT
NC0013-105-W-RA

Figure 7 Fender Attachments

HOOD

Figures 8 and 9

NOTICE: Do not allow hood to fold back onto windshield. Glass and paint damage may result from improper handling of the hood.

Remove or Disconnect

1. Raise hood.
2. Underhood lamp harness.
3. Hinge pivot bolts.
4. Support cylinders from hood.
5. Hood from vehicle.

Install or Connect

1. Hood to vehicle.
2. Support cylinders to hood.
3. Hinge pivot bolts.

Tighten

- Hinge pivot bolts to 25 N·m (18 lb. ft.).

4. Underhood lamp harness.
5. Close hood.

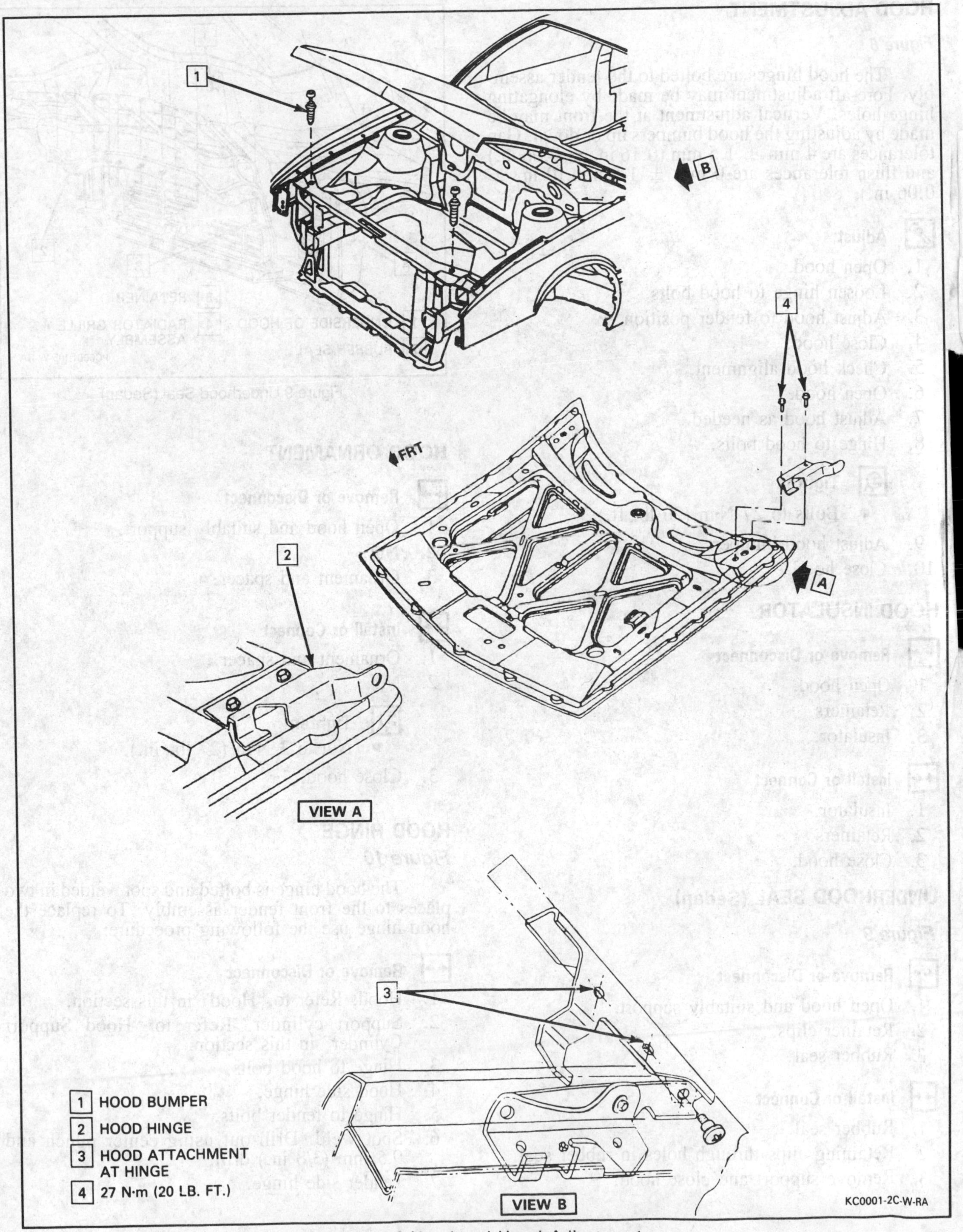
1
B
4
FRT
2
A
VIEW A
3
VIEW B
1 HOOD BUMPER
2 HOOD HINGE
3 HOOD ATTACHMENT AT HINGE
4 27 N·m (20 LB. FT.)
KC0001-2C-W-RA

Figure 8 Hood and Hood Adjustment

HOOD ADJUSTMENT

Figure 8

The hood hinges are bolted to the fender assembly. Fore-aft adjustment may be made by elongating hinge holes. Vertical adjustment at the front may be made by adjusting the hood bumpers up or down. Gap tolerances are 4 mm ± 1.5 mm (0.16 in. ± 0.06 in.) and flush tolerances are 0 mm ± 1.5 mm (0 in. ± 0.06 in.).

Adjust

1. Open hood.
2. Loosen hinge to hood bolts.
3. Adjust hood to fender position.
4. Close hood.
5. Check hood alignment.
6. Open hood.
7. Adjust hood as needed.
8. Hinge to hood bolts.

   Tighten

   - Bolts to 27 N·m (20 lb. ft.).

9. Adjust hood bumpers.
10. Close hood.

HOOD INSULATOR

Remove or Disconnect

1. Open hood.
2. Retainers.
3. Insulator.

Install or Connect

1. Insulator.
2. Retainers.
3. Close hood.

UNDERHOOD SEAL (Sedan)

Figure 9

Remove or Disconnect

1. Open hood and suitably support.
2. Retainer clips.
3. Rubber seal.

Install or Connect

1. Rubber seal.
2. Retaining clips through holes in rubber seal.
3. Remove support and close hood.

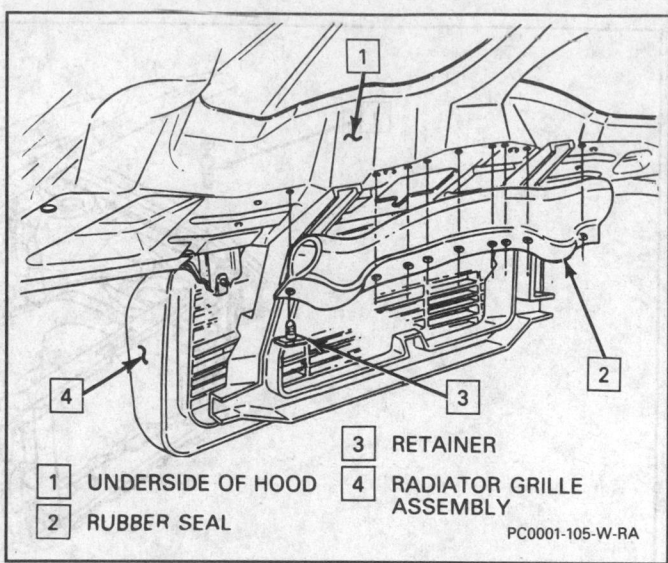

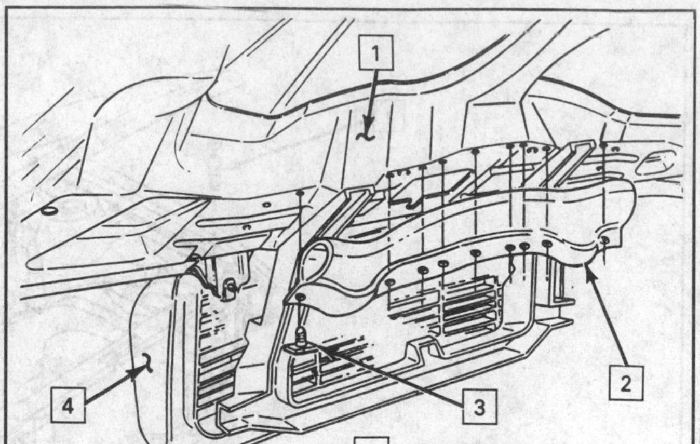
1 UNDERSIDE OF HOOD
2 RUBBER SEAL
3 RETAINER
4 RADIATOR GRILLE ASSEMBLY
PC0001-105-W-RA

Figure 9 Underhood Seal (Sedan)

HOOD ORNAMENT

Remove or Disconnect

1. Open hood and suitably support.
2. Nut.
3. Ornament and spacer.

Install or Connect

1. Ornament and spacer.
2. Nut.

   Tighten

   - Nut to 3 N·m (27 lb. in.).

3. Close hood.

HOOD HINGE

Figure 10

The hood hinge is bolted and spot welded in two places to the front fender assembly. To replace the hood hinge use the following procedure:

Remove or Disconnect

1. Hood. Refer to "Hood" in this section.
2. Support cylinder. Refer to "Hood Support Cylinder" in this section.
3. Hinge to hood bolts.
4. Hood side hinge.
5. Hinge to fender bolts.
6. Spot weld. Drill-out using center punch and 9.5 mm (3/8 in.) drill.
7. Fender side hinge.

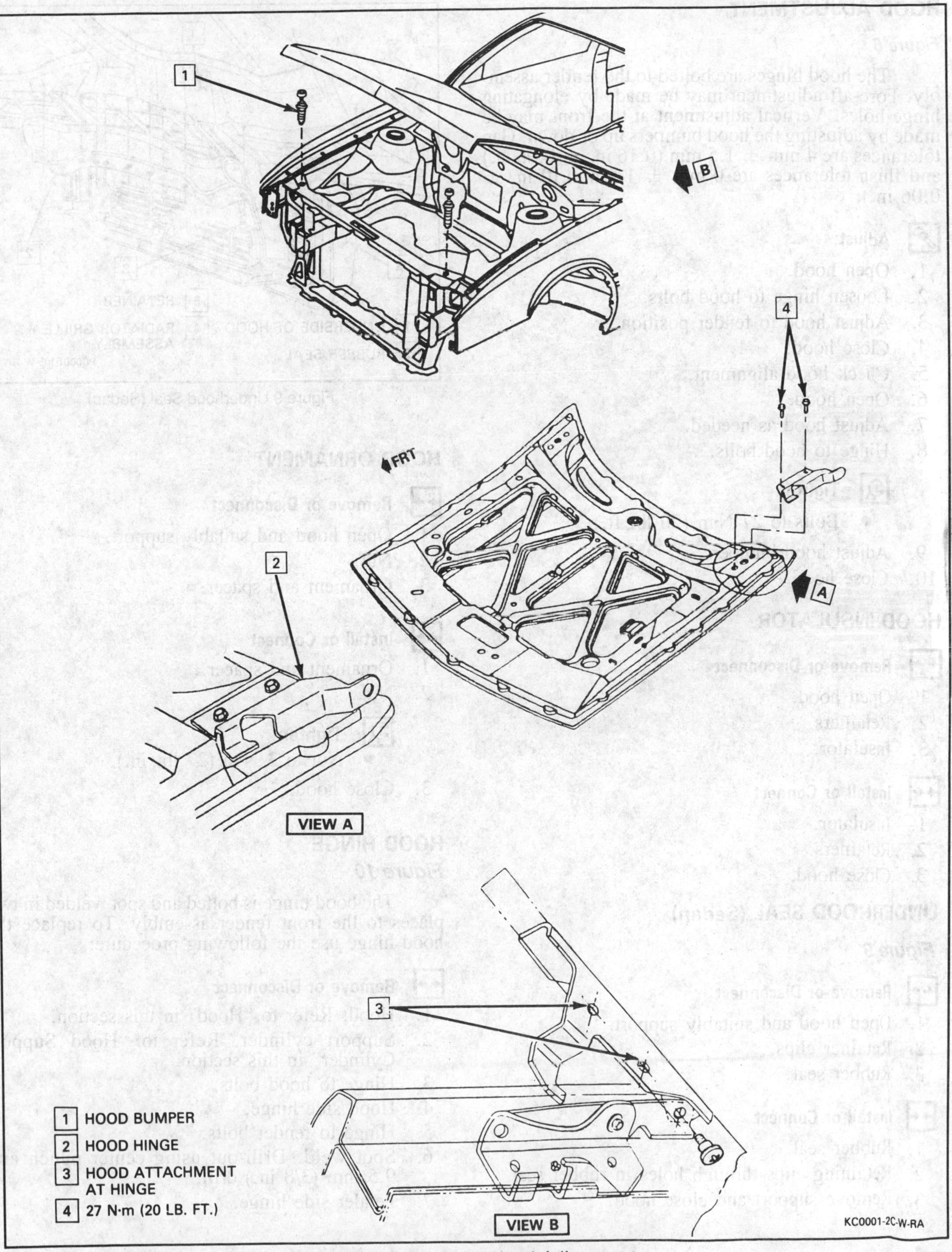
1
B
FRT
4
A
2
VIEW A
3
1 HOOD BUMPER
2 HOOD HINGE
3 HOOD ATTACHMENT AT HINGE
4 27 N·m (20 LB. FT.)
VIEW B
KC0001-2C-W-RA

Figure 8 Hood and Hood Adjustment

HOOD ADJUSTMENT

Figure 8

The hood hinges are bolted to the fender assembly. Fore-aft adjustment may be made by elongating hinge holes. Vertical adjustment at the front may be made by adjusting the hood bumpers up or down. Gap tolerances are 4 mm ± 1.5 mm (0.16 in. ± 0.06 in.) and flush tolerances are 0 mm ± 1.5 mm (0 in. ± 0.06 in.).

Adjust

1. Open hood.
2. Loosen hinge to hood bolts.
3. Adjust hood to fender position.
4. Close hood.
5. Check hood alignment.
6. Open hood.
7. Adjust hood as needed.
8. Hinge to hood bolts.

   Tighten

   - Bolts to 27 N·m (20 lb. ft.).

9. Adjust hood bumpers.
10. Close hood.

HOOD INSULATOR

Remove or Disconnect

1. Open hood.
2. Retainers.
3. Insulator.

Install or Connect

1. Insulator.
2. Retainers.
3. Close hood.

UNDERHOOD SEAL (Sedan)

Figure 9

Remove or Disconnect

1. Open hood and suitably support.
2. Retainer clips.
3. Rubber seal.

Install or Connect

1. Rubber seal.
2. Retaining clips through holes in rubber seal.
3. Remove support and close hood.

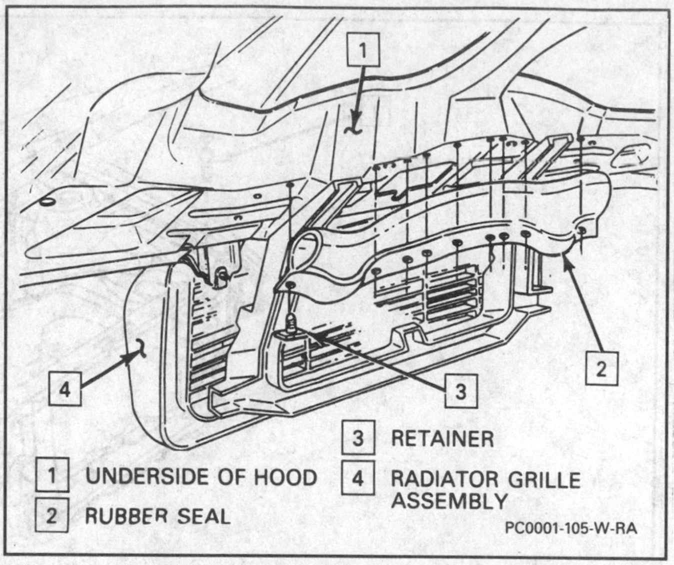
1
2
3
4
1 UNDERSIDE OF HOOD
2 RUBBER SEAL
3 RETAINER
4 RADIATOR GRILLE ASSEMBLY
PC0001-105-W-RA

Figure 9 Underhood Seal (Sedan)

HOOD ORNAMENT

Remove or Disconnect

1. Open hood and suitably support.
2. Nut.
3. Ornament and spacer.

Install or Connect

1. Ornament and spacer.
2. Nut.

   Tighten

   - Nut to 3 N·m (27 lb. in.).

3. Close hood.

HOOD HINGE

Figure 10

The hood hinge is bolted and spot welded in two places to the front fender assembly. To replace the hood hinge use the following procedure:

Remove or Disconnect

1. Hood. Refer to "Hood" in this section.
2. Support cylinder. Refer to "Hood Support Cylinder" in this section.
3. Hinge to hood bolts.
4. Hood side hinge.
5. Hinge to fender bolts.
6. Spot weld. Drill-out using center punch and 9.5 mm (3/8 in.) drill.
7. Fender side hinge.

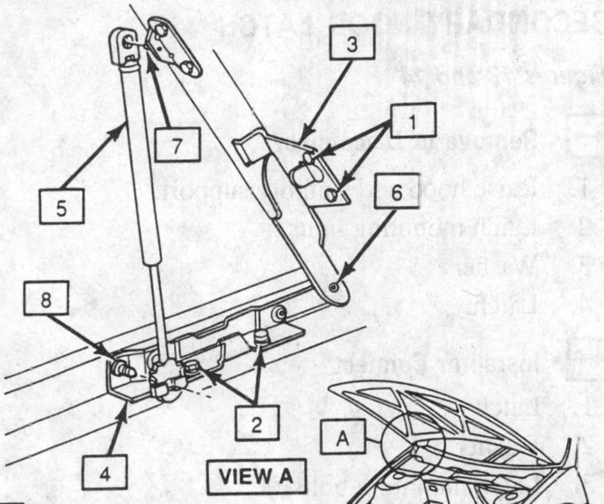
3
1
7
5
6
8
2
A
4
VIEW A

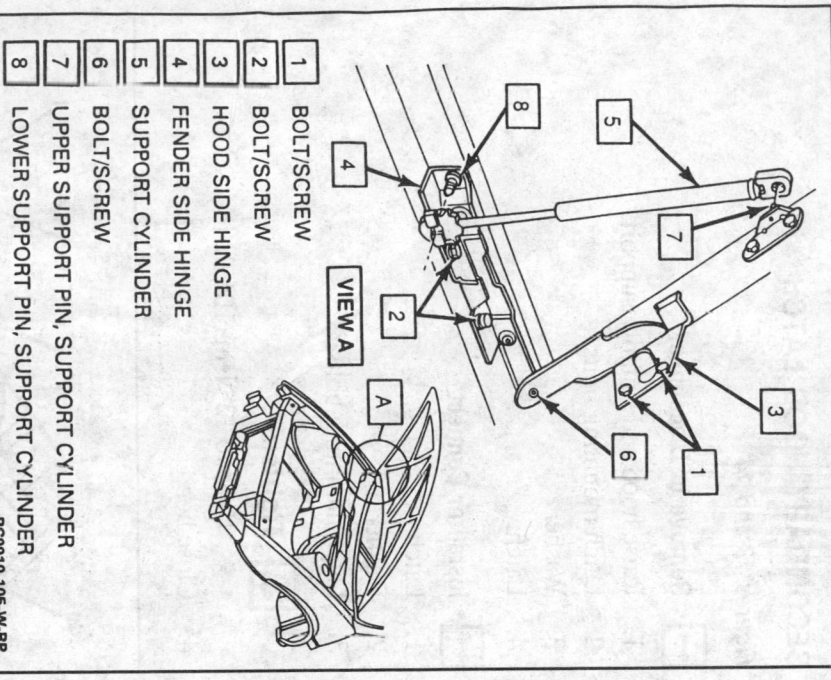

1 BOLT/SCREW
2 BOLT/SCREW
3 HOOD SIDE HINGE
4 FENDER SIDE HINGE
5 SUPPORT CYLINDER
6 BOLT/SCREW
7 UPPER SUPPORT PIN, SUPPORT CYLINDER
8 LOWER SUPPORT PIN, SUPPORT CYLINDER

RC0010-105-W-RP

Figure 10 Hood Hinge and Support Cylinder

Install or Connect

1. Fender side hinge.
2. Hinge to fender bolts.

Tighten

- Bolts to 25 N·m (18 lb. ft.).

3. Hood side hinge.
4. Hinge to hood bolts.

Tighten

- Bolts to 27 N·m (20 lb. ft.).

5. Support cylinder. Refer to "Hood Support Cylinder" in this section.
6. Hood. Refer to "Hood" in this section.

Adjust

- Hood. Refer to "Hood Adjustment" in this section.

PRIMARY HOOD LATCH

Figure 11

Remove or Disconnect

1. Raise hood.
2. Latch mounting bolts.
3. Release cable.
4. Latch.

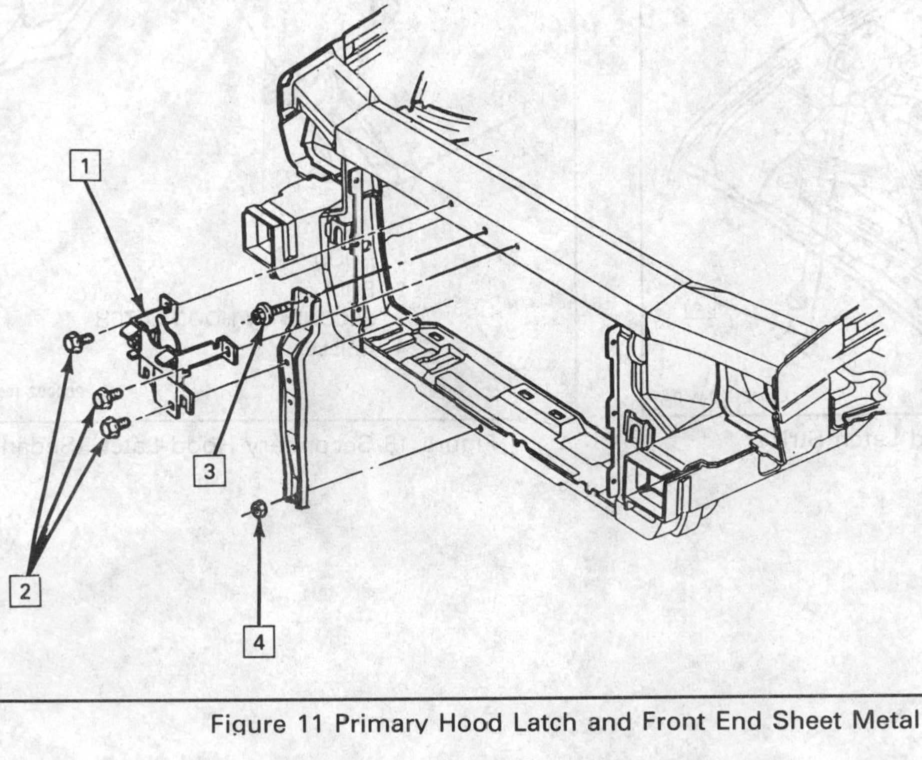
1
3
2
4
1 PRIMARY HOOD LATCH
2 BOLT
3 BOLT
4 NUT
NC0015-105-W-RA

Figure 11 Primary Hood Latch and Front End Sheet Metal Support

Install or Connect

1. Latch.
2. Release cable.
3. Latch mounting bolts.

Tighten

- Latch mounting bolts to 25 N·m (18 lb. ft.).

4. Close hood.

PRIMARY HOOD LATCH STRIKER

Figure 12

Remove or Disconnect

1. Raise hood and suitably support.
2. Striker mounting bolts.
3. Striker.

Install or Connect

1. Striker.
2. Striker mounting bolts.

Tighten

- Bolts to 24 N·m (18 lb. ft.).

3. Close hood.

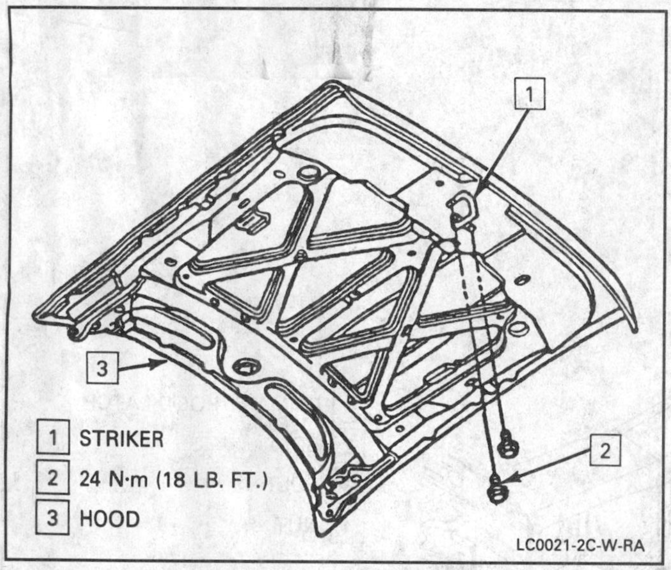
1
2
3
1 STRIKER
2 24 N·m (18 LB. FT.)
3 HOOD
LC0021-2C-W-RA

Figure 12 Primary Hood Latch Striker

SECONDARY HOOD LATCH

Figures 13 and 14

Remove or Disconnect

1. Raise hood and suitably support.
2. Latch mounting bolts.
3. Washer.
4. Latch.

Install or Connect

1. Latch.
2. Washer.
3. Latch mounting bolts.

Tighten

- Bolts to 12 N•m (106 lb. in.).

4. Close hood.

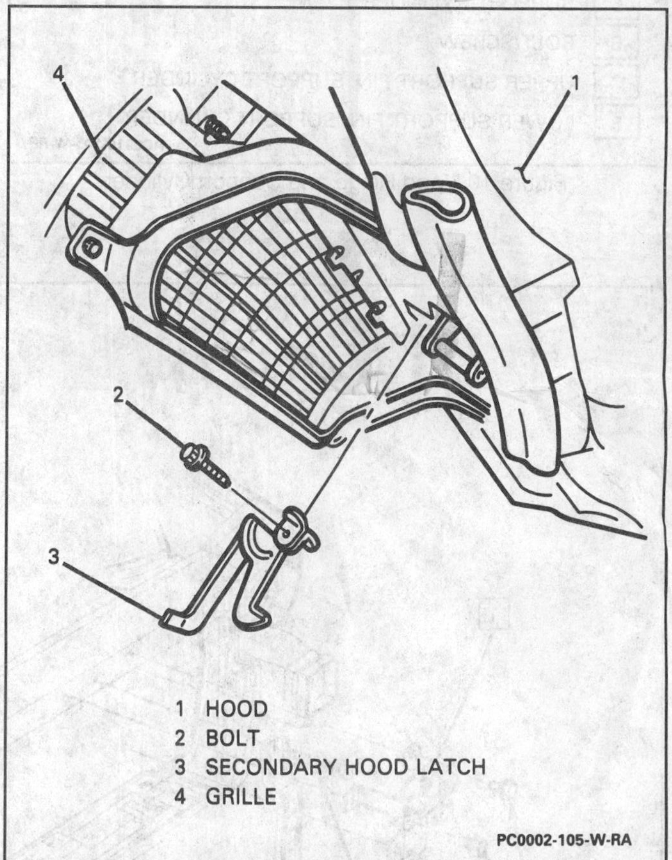
1
2
3
4
1 HOOD
2 BOLT
3 SECONDARY HOOD LATCH
4 GRILLE
PC0002-105-W-RA

Figure 13 Secondary Hood Latch (Sedan)

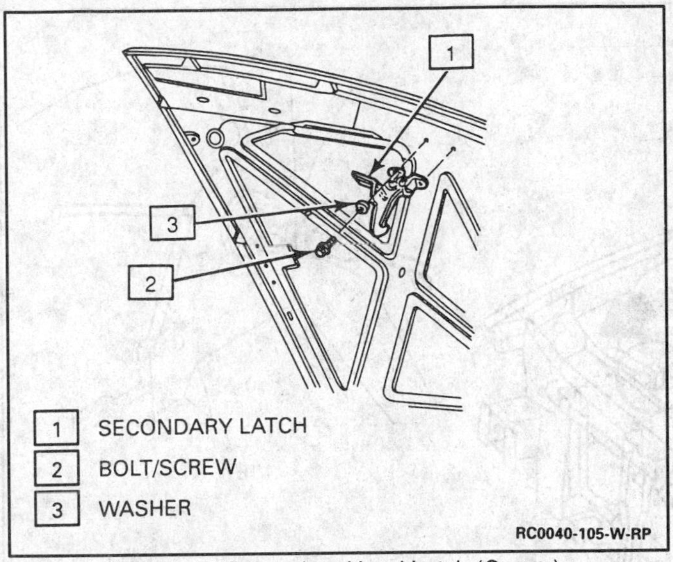
1
3
2
1 SECONDARY LATCH
2 BOLT/SCREW
3 WASHER
RC0040-105-W-RP

Figure 14 Secondary Hood Latch (Coupe)

HOOD RELEASE CABLE

Figures 15 and 16

The one-piece hood latch release cable includes the lift handle, control cable and housing. The control cable is installed on the floor pan left of the driver's seat. A sealing grommet attached to the dash panel completes the assembly.

Remove or Disconnect

1. Raise hood.
2. Headlamp access panel.
3. Cable from latch assembly.

Important

- Block latch to prevent hood locking until cable has been installed.

4. Following items, for access to the cable routing:
   - Air cleaner assembly.
   - Battery.
   - Dash mat.
   - Sound insulator.
5. Cable from guides.

Important

- Tie wire or string to end of cable in order to aid in the installation of new cable. Ensure the end of the string remains in the engine compartment.

6. Screws.
7. Cover.
8. Bolt.
9. Hood release handle assembly.
10. Carpet retainer trim. Refer to FRAME AND UNDERBODY (SECTION 10-3).
11. Carpet (pull back).
12. Cable from grommet at dash panel by turning to the left and pulling cable through hole in the grommet.
13. Cable from hood release handle assembly.

Install or Connect

1. Cable to hood release handle assembly.
2. Tie cable to wire or string and feed cable through grommet at dash panel.
3. Carpet.
4. Carpet retainer trim. Refer to FRAME AND UNDERBODY (SECTION 10-3).
5. Hood release cable handle assembly.
6. Bolt.

Tighten

- Bolt to 12 N·m (106 lb. in.).

7. Cover.
8. Screws.

Tighten

- Screws to 1 N·m (9 lb. in.).

9. Cable by routing through guides.
10. Following items as removed:
    - Sound insulator.
    - Dash mat.
    - Battery.
    - Air cleaner assembly.
11. Cable to latch assembly.
12. Headlamp access panel.
13. Close hood.

Important

- Apply strip caulk sealer or equivalent to grommet-to-dash and cable-to-grommet area.

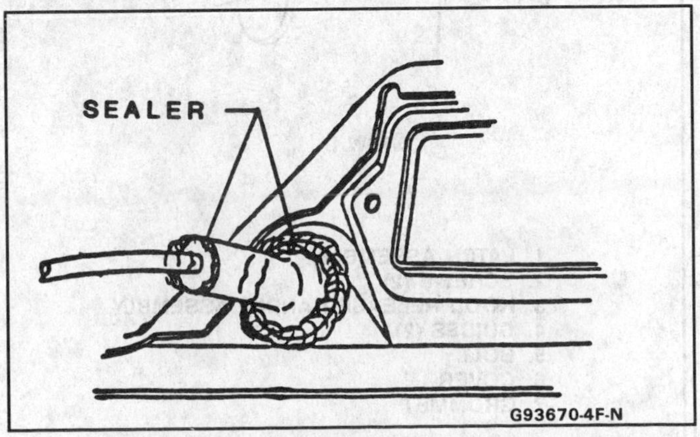
SEALER
G93670-4F-N

Figure 15 Sealing Hood Release and Grommet

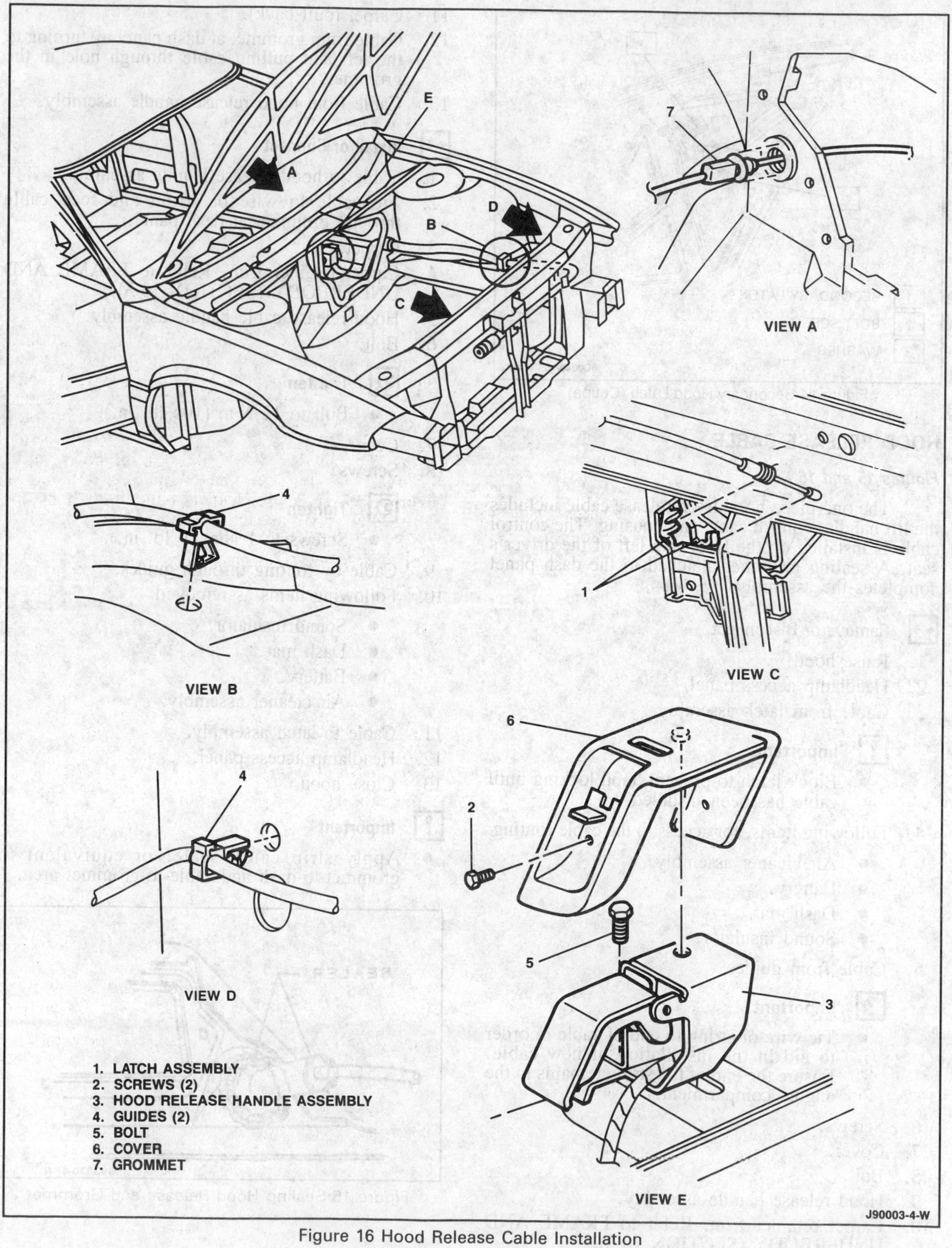
A
B
C
D
E
7
VIEW A
1
VIEW C
4
VIEW B
4
VIEW D
6
2
5
3
VIEW E
1. LATCH ASSEMBLY
2. SCREWS (2)
3. HOOD RELEASE HANDLE ASSEMBLY
4. GUIDES (2)
5. BOLT
6. COVER
7. GROMMET
J90003-4-W

Figure 16 Hood Release Cable Installation

HOOD SUPPORT CYLINDER

Figure 9

NOTICE: Do not allow hood to fold back onto windshield. Glass and paint damage may result from improper handling of the hood.

Remove or Disconnect

1. Raise hood.
2. Safely support the hood.
3. Support cylinder by unsnapping from upper support pin, then lower support pin.

Install or Connect

1. Support cylinder. Snap in lower support pin, then upper support pin.
2. Remove hood support.
3. Close hood.

UNDERHOOD LAMP

Figure 17

Remove or Disconnect

1. Air cleaner assembly if necessary to access battery cable.
2. Negative battery cable.
3. Harness from lamp assembly.
4. Rivets using 3 mm (1/8 in.) drill.
5. Underhood lamp assembly.

Install or Connect

1. Underhood lamp assembly.
2. Sheet metal screw.
3. Harness to lamp assembly.
4. Negative battery cable.
5. Air cleaner assembly, if removed.

HOOD REAR MOLDING

Remove or Disconnect

1. Pin at one end of hood rear molding.
2. Hood rear molding from hood.
3. Pin at other end of hood rear molding.

Install or Connect

1. Pin at one end of hood rear molding.
2. Hood rear molding by sliding forward.
3. Pin at other end of hood rear molding.

FRONT END SEALING

All potential waterleak locations are sealed in production with high quality durable sealers. Should it be necessary to reseal specific areas, a high quality medium-bodied sealer which will remain flexible after curing and can be painted should be used. Refer to GENERAL BODY SERVICE (SECTION 10-1).

NOTICE: The theft deterrent label found on some major sheet metal, engines, and transaxles must be masked prior to painting, rustproofing, undercoating, etc. The mask must be removed following the above operations. Failure to keep the label clean and readable may result in liability for violation of Federal Vehicle Theft Prevention Standard, and subject the vehicle owner to possible suspicion that the part was stolen.

AIR INLET SCREEN

Figure 18

The body ventilation system on cars without air conditioning consists of a fresh air intake located at the front plenum chamber. Air enters the front plenum chamber through the air inlet vent screen. The air is directed through the plenum chamber to air outlet doors and into the body from outlets through the dash panel. The air then passes through the body, around the rear seat, into the rear compartment to the rear quarters and leaves the body passing through the pressure relief valves on the rear body lock pillars.

Remove or Disconnect

1. Windshield lower reveal molding. Refer to STATIONARY WINDOWS (SECTION 10-2).
2. Wiper arm and blade assemblies. Refer to WINDSHIELD WIPER/WASHER SYSTEM (SECTION 8E).
3. Screws.
4. Air inlet screen assembly.

Install or Connect

1. Air inlet screen assembly.
2. Screws.

   Tighten

   - Screws to 2 N·m (18 lb. in.).

3. Wiper arm and blade assemblies. Refer to WINDSHIELD WIPER/WASHER SYSTEM (SECTION 8E).
4. Windshield lower reveal molding. Refer to STATIONARY WINDOWS (SECTION 10-2).

PLENUM CHAMBER WATER DEFLECTOR

Figure 19

A water deflector is located within the plenum chamber to prevent water from entering the air inlets to the passenger compartment. Water entering the plenum chamber is drained through openings provided for that purpose.

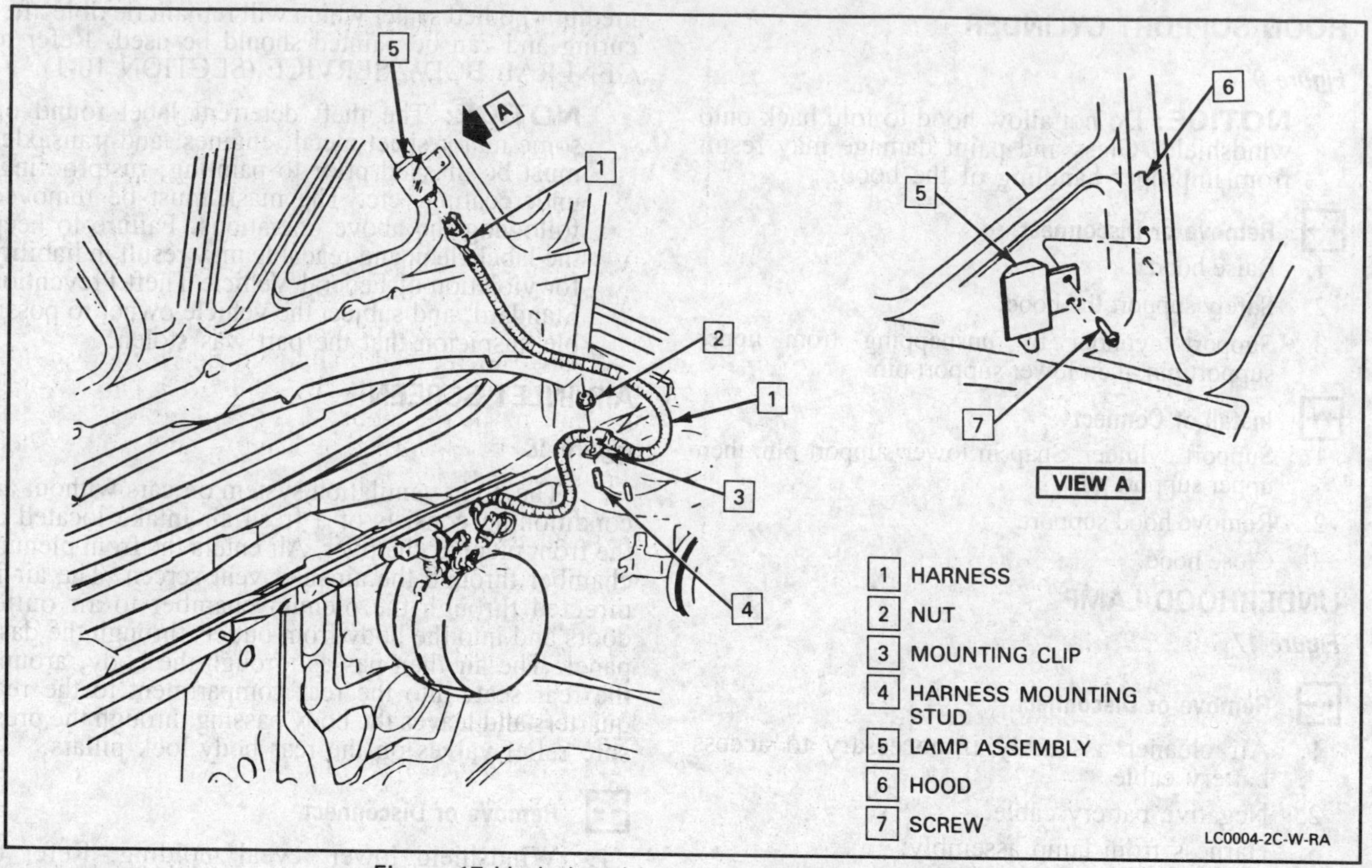

5
A
1
2
1
3
4
6
5
7
VIEW A
1 HARNESS
2 NUT
3 MOUNTING CLIP
4 HARNESS MOUNTING STUD
5 LAMP ASSEMBLY
6 HOOD
7 SCREW
LC0004-2C-W-RA

Figure 17 Underhood Lamp and Harness Connector

Remove or Disconnect

1. Air inlet screen. Refer to "Air Inlet Screen" in this section.
2. Screws.
3. Water deflector.

Install or Connect

1. Water deflector.
2. Screws.

Tighten

- Screws to 5 N·m (44 lb. in.).

3. Air inlet screen. Refer to "Air Inlet Screen" in this section.

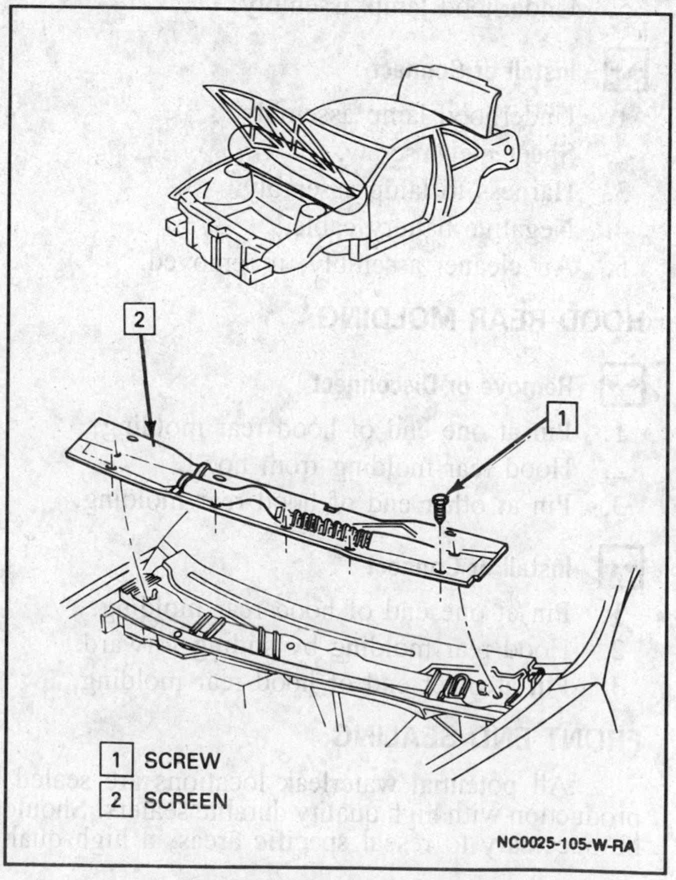

2
1
1 SCREW
2 SCREEN
NC0025-105-W-RA

Figure 18 Air Inlet Screen

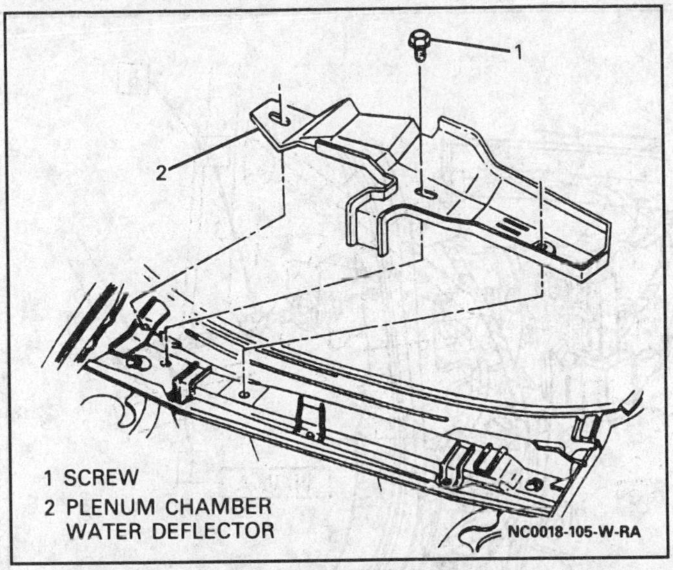
1
2
1 SCREW
2 PLENUM CHAMBER
WATER DEFLECTOR
NC0018-105-W-RA

Figure 19 Plenum Chamber Water Deflector

ENGINE SIDE DASH MAT

The engine side dash mat is composed of a thermoplastic rubber. The material is flexible, so the most desirable way to service the dash mat or to make any repair behind is to locally pull away or remove the dash mat. In many cases, the dash can be pulled away in one area so that a repair can be made behind it. However, there may be an instance where it is necessary to cut the dash mat in order to make a repair. Although it is not desirable to cut the dash mat, if it does become necessary, the recommended procedure to repair the cut is as follows:

1. Prepare the surface surrounding the cut by lightly sanding the area.
2. Apply contact cement between the cut surface and the surrounding area.
3. Allow the cement to cure before stressing the repaired area.

DOOR JAMB SWITCHES

Figures 20, 21 and 22

Door jamb switch assemblies consist of a plunger, plunger collar, threaded retainer and terminals. They are installed in the front door hinge pillars. When the door of the vehicle is closed, the plunger is depressed which creates an open in the ground circuit. When the door is opened, the plunger is released and completes the circuit to ground.

When a new jamb switch is installed and the door is closed the first time, the plunger is forced into the sleeve and automatically adjusts the jamb switch for that particular door. If a jamb switch fails, it should not be readjusted by hand. A new jamb switch should be installed.

Remove or Disconnect

1. Loosen center pillar trim panel if rear door.
2. Jamb switch.
3. Electrical connector.

Install or Connect

1. Electrical connector.
2. Jamb switch.

Tighten

- Switch to 10 N·m (89 lb. in.).

3. Center pillar trim panel if loosened.

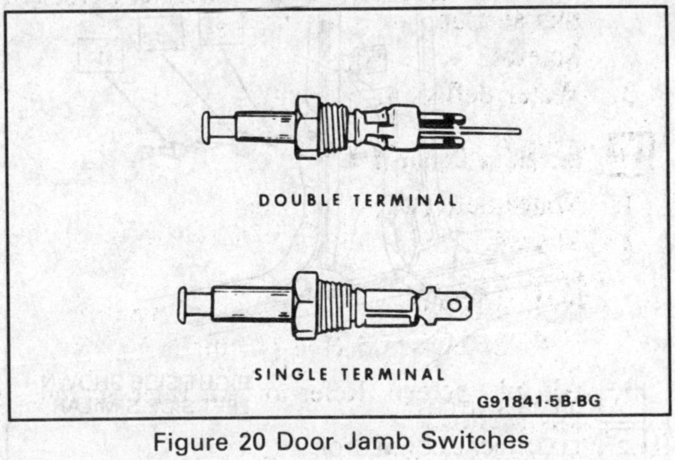
DOUBLE TERMINAL
SINGLE TERMINAL
G91841-5B-BG

Figure 20 Door Jamb Switches

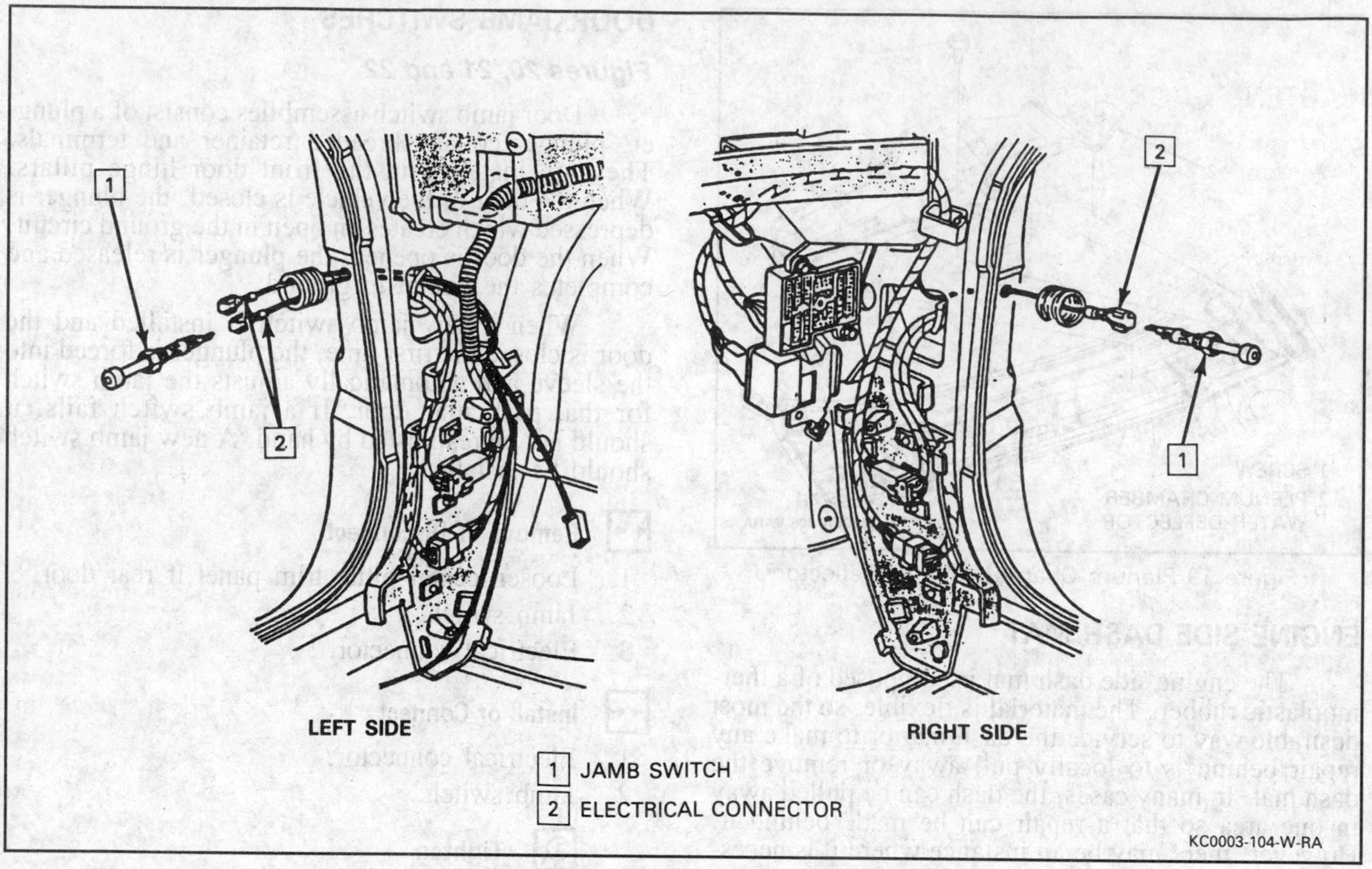
1
2
LEFT SIDE
2
1
RIGHT SIDE
1 JAMB SWITCH
2 ELECTRICAL CONNECTOR
KC0003-104-W-RA

Figure 21 Door Jamb Switch Installation – Coupe

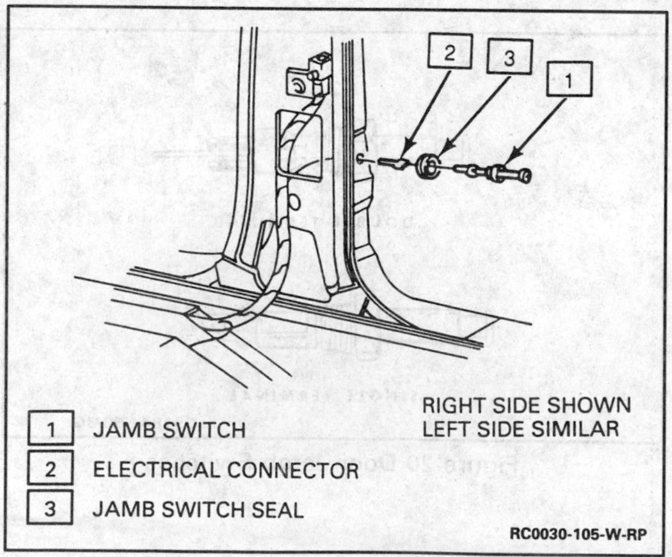
2
3
1
RIGHT SIDE SHOWN
LEFT SIDE SIMILAR
1 JAMB SWITCH
2 ELECTRICAL CONNECTOR
3 JAMB SWITCH SEAL
RC0030-105-W-RP

Figure 22 Door Jamb Switch Installation – Sedan

SPECIFICATIONS

FASTENER TIGHTENING SPECIFICATIONS

Air Intake Screen Screw .... 2 N·m (18 lb. in.)
Door Jamb Switch .... 10 N·m (89 lb. in.)
Fender
  Bracket Bolt .... 6 N·m (53 lb. in.)
  Bracket Nut .... 6 N·m (53 lb. in.)
  Lower Front Bolt .... 6 N·m (53 lb. in.)
  Lower Rear Bolt .... 6 N·m (53 lb. in.)
  Upper Front Bolt .... 6 N·m (53 lb. in.)
  Upper Rear .... 25 N·m (18 lb. ft.)

Fender Wheel Opening Molding Screw .... 2 N·m (18 lb. in.)
Front End Sheet Metal Diagonal Brace
  Front Bolt .... 25 N·m (18 lb. ft.)
  Rear Bolt .... 47 N·m (35 lb. ft.)
Front End Sheet Metal Support
  Bolt .... 24 N·m (18 lb. ft.)
  Nut .... 10 N·m (89 lb. in.)

Front Fender Liner Screw .... 1.5 N·m (13 lb. in.)
  Lower Rear Inboard Screw .... 3 N·m (27 lb. in.)
Grille Emblem Nut .... 3 N·m (27 lb. in.)
Grille Screw .... 2 N·m (18 lb. in.)
Headlamp Bezel Screw .... 2 N·m (18 lb. in.)
Headlamp Housing Panel Bolt .... 6 N·m (53 lb. in.)
Hood Hinge Pivot Bolt .... 25 N·m (18 lb. ft.)

Hood Hinge-to-Fender Bolt .... 25 N·m (18 lb. ft.)
Hood Hinge-to-Hood Bolt .... 27 N·m (20 lb. ft.)
Hood Ornament Nut .... 3 N·m (27 lb. in.)
Hood Release Handle Assembly Bolt .... 12 N·m (106 lb. in.)
Hood Release Handle Assembly Cover Screw .... 1 N·m (9 lb. in.)
Plenum Chamber Water Deflector Screw .... 5 N·m (44 lb. in.)
Primary Hood Latch Bolt .... 25 N·m (18 lb. ft.)

Primary Hood Latch Striker Bolt .... 24 N·m (18 lb. ft.)
Radiator Support Panel Screw .... 10 N·m (89 lb. in.)
Secondary Hood Latch Bolt .... 12 N·m (106 lb. in.)

SECTION 10-6

DOORS

CAUTION: Make sure to disconnect the power window switch when working inside the driver's door. When operated, the Express Down feature allows the door glass to drop very quickly which could cause personal injury.

NOTICE: When fasteners are removed, always reinstall them at the same location from which they were removed. If a fastener needs to be replaced, use the correct part number fastener for that application. If the correct part number fastener is not available, a fastener of equal size and strength (or stronger) may be used. Fasteners that are not reused, and those requiring thread locking compound will be called out. The correct torque value must be used when installing fasteners that require it. If the above conditions are not followed, parts or system damage could result.

NOTICE: The theft deterrent label found on some major sheet metal, engines, and transaxles must be masked prior to painting, rustproofing, undercoating, etc. The mask must be removed following the above operations. Failure to keep the label clean and readable may result in liability for violation of Federal Vehicle Theft Prevention Standard, and subject the vehicle owner to possible suspicion that the part was stolen.

CONTENTS

GENERAL DESCRIPTION

SPRING CLIPS (Coupe)

Figure 1

Spring clips are used to secure handle connecting rods and inside locking rods to door lock levers in coupe. A slot in the clip provides for disengagement of the rod.

↔ Remove or Disconnect

1. Clip from lever by using a scratch awl, pick or other thin-bladed tool and sliding clip out of engagement.
2. Rod from clip by pulling rod out of clip.

→← Install or Connect

1. Clip to lever by pressing clip fully on lever.
2. Rod to lever by pressing rod through hole in lever until fully engaged by clip.

DOOR HARDWARE LUBRICATION

The mechanical components of the door assembly are lubricated during assembly. If additional lubrication is required, use the following lubricants. All door lock cylinders should be lubricated with a general purpose silicone lubricant, part no. 12345120 or equivalent. The remainder of all door hardware mechanisms except lock assemblies can be lubricated with part no. 1052349, Lubriplate Spray-Lube "A," part no. 1052196, Lubriplate Auto-Lube "A" or equivalent.

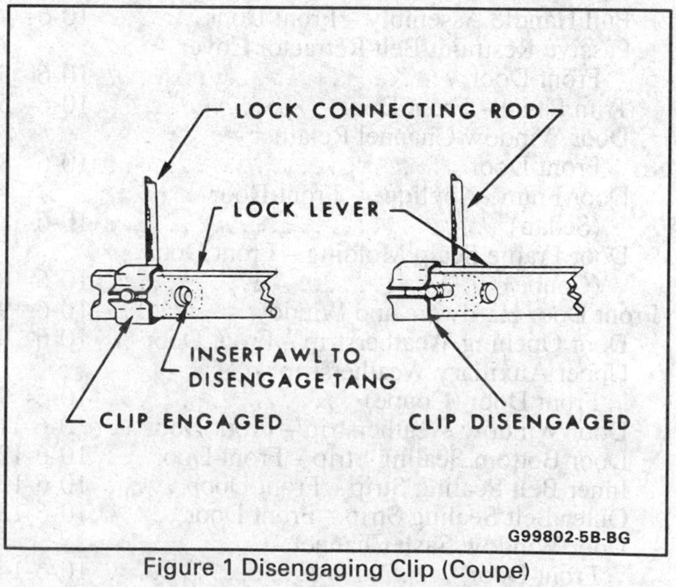
LOCK CONNECTING ROD
LOCK LEVER
INSERT AWL TO
DISENGAGE TANG
CLIP ENGAGED
CLIP DISENGAGED
G99802-5B-BG

Figure 1 Disengaging Clip (Coupe)

HARDWARE ATTACHMENT THREADLOCKING

All door hardware production attaching screws contain an epoxy thread-locking compound to ensure that the minimum original torque setting will be maintained.

Service attaching screws may not contain a thread-locking compound. To prevent loosening of service screws or to renew thread-locking characteristics of production screws, the threads of the fastener(s) can be treated with part no. 12345493, Adhesive/Sealant Compound (or equivalent). Upon installation and tightening, the adhesive cures to bond the attachment and prevent loosening or back-out. The adhesive bond does not prevent future attachment removal if required. Adhesive/Sealant Compound or equivalent can be used on any threaded fastener.

FRONT DOOR TRIM

DOOR FRAME GARNISH MOLDINGS – FRONT DOOR

Figures 2 and 3

Tool Required:

J 24595-C Door Trim Pad and Garnish Clip Remover

Remove or Disconnect

1. Door trim panel. Refer to "Trim Panel – Front Door" in this section.
2. Upper seat belt guide loop. Refer to SEAT BELTS (SECTION 10-11).
3. Rear garnish molding using J 24595-C.
4. Front garnish molding using J 24595-C.

Install or Connect

1. Front garnish molding.
2. Rear garnish molding.
3. Upper seat belt guide loop. Refer to SEAT BELTS (SECTION 10-11).
4. Door trim panel. Refer to "Trim Panel – Front Door" in this section.

REARVIEW MIRROR BEZEL – FRONT DOOR

Remove or Disconnect

1. Door trim panel. Refer to "Trim Panel – Front Door" in this section.
2. Nuts.
3. Bezel.

Install or Connect

1. Bezel.
2. Nuts.

Tighten

- Nuts to 2 N•m (18 lb. in.).

3. Door trim panel. Refer to "Trim Panel – Front Door" in this section.

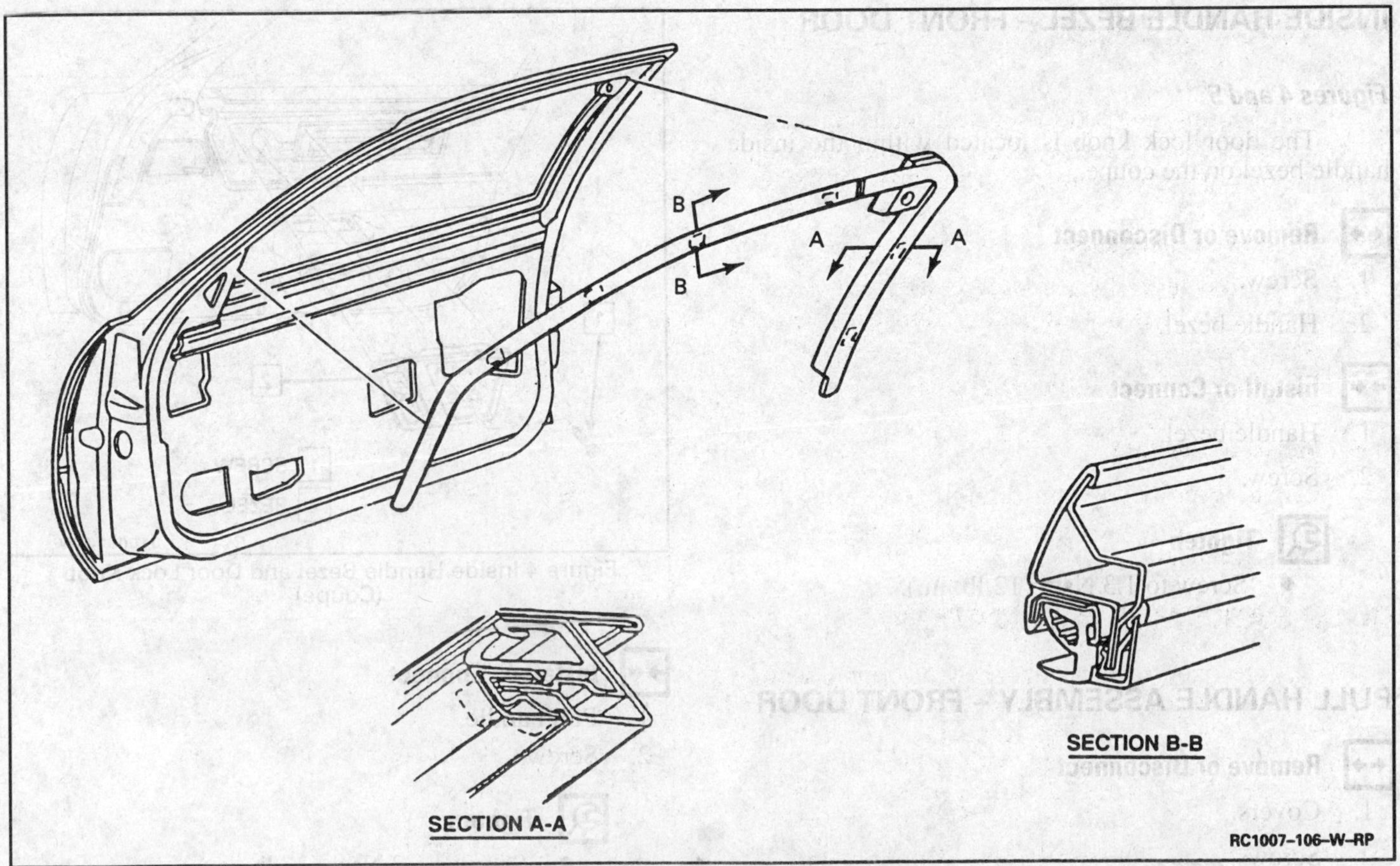
B
B
A
A
SECTION A-A
SECTION B-B
RC1007-106-W-RP

Figure 2 Door Frame Garnish Molding (Coupe)

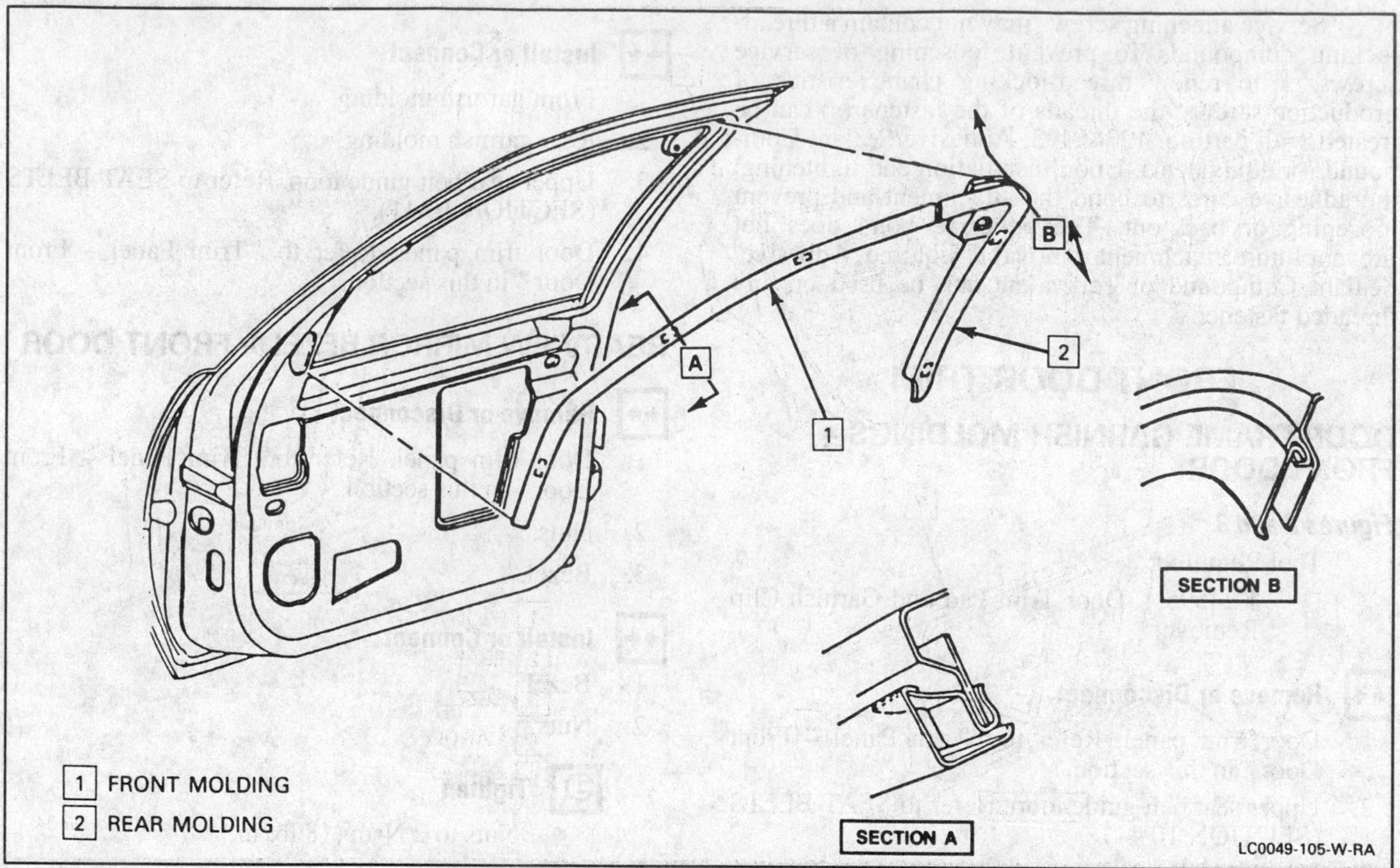
A
B
1
2
SECTION B
SECTION A
1 FRONT MOLDING
2 REAR MOLDING
LC0049-105-W-RA

Figure 3 Door Frame Garnish Molding – Front Door (Sedan)

INSIDE HANDLE BEZEL – FRONT DOOR

Figures 4 and 5

The door lock knob is located within the inside handle bezel on the coupe.

Remove or Disconnect

1. Screw.
2. Handle bezel.

Install or Connect

1. Handle bezel.
2. Screw.

Tighten

- Screw to 1.3 N•m (12 lb. in.).

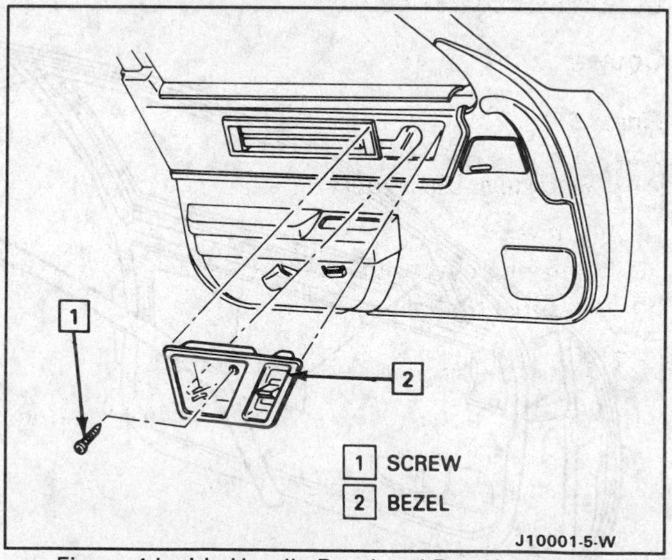
1
2
1 SCREW
2 BEZEL
J10001-5-W

Figure 4 Inside Handle Bezel and Door Lock Knob (Coupe)

PULL HANDLE ASSEMBLY – FRONT DOOR

Remove or Disconnect

1. Covers.
2. Screws.
3. Pull handle.

Install or Connect

1. Pull handle.
2. Screws.

Tighten

- Screws to 3 N•m (27 lb. in.).

3. Covers.

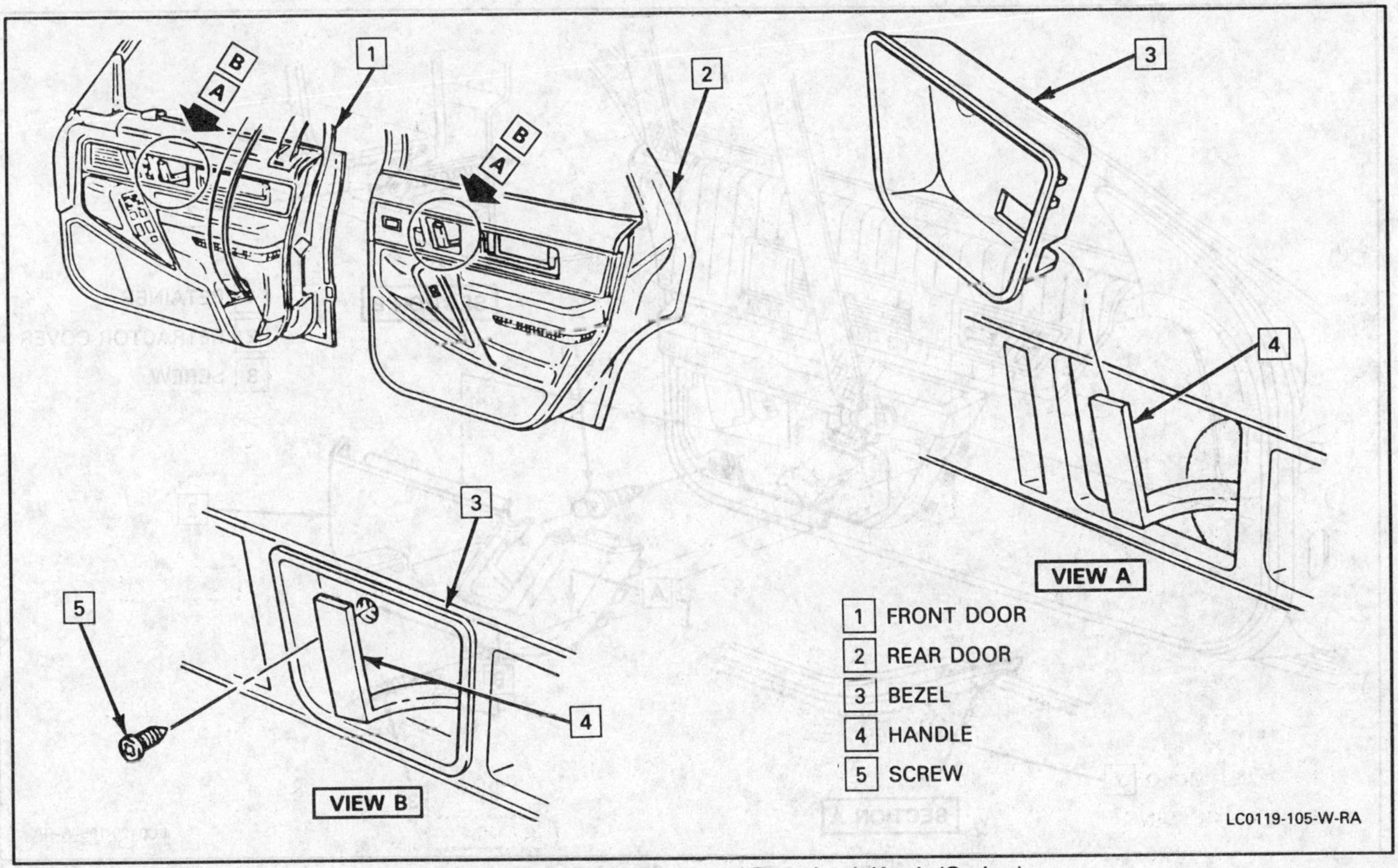
1
2
3
4
5
B
A
VIEW A
VIEW B
1 FRONT DOOR
2 REAR DOOR
3 BEZEL
4 HANDLE
5 SCREW
LC0119-105-W-RA

Figure 5 Inside Handle Bezel and Door Lock Knob (Sedan)

PASSIVE RESTRAINT BELT RETRACTOR COVER – FRONT DOOR

Coupe

Figure 6

Remove or Disconnect

1. Screw.
2. Retractor cover and retainer.
3. Retainer from retractor cover.

Install or Connect

1. Retainer through slot in retractor cover and turn 90 degrees to secure.
2. Retractor cover to door.
3. Screw.

Tighten

- Screw to 2 N•m (18 lb. in.).

Front Door (Sedan)

Figure 7

Remove or Disconnect

1. Screw.
2. Retractor cover.

Install or Connect

1. Retractor cover.
2. Screw.

Tighten

- Screw to 2 N•m (18 lb. in.).

TRIM PANEL – FRONT DOOR

Figures 8 and 9

Tool Required:

J 24595-C Door Trim Pad and Garnish Clip Remover

Remove or Disconnect

1. Escutcheon cover.
2. Screws and seat belt from shoulder belt escutcheon.
3. Pull handle screws.
4. Retractor cover. Refer to "Passive Restraint Belt Retractor Cover – Front Door" in this section.
5. Handle bezel. Refer to "Inside Handle Bezel – Front Door" in this section.
6. Power window and door switch assembly. Refer to "Power Window and Door Switch Assembly – Front Door (Coupe)" or "Power Window Switch Assembly – Front Door (Sedan)" and "Power Door Switch – Front Door (Sedan)" in this section.
7. Bracket screw, sedan only, from switch cutout.

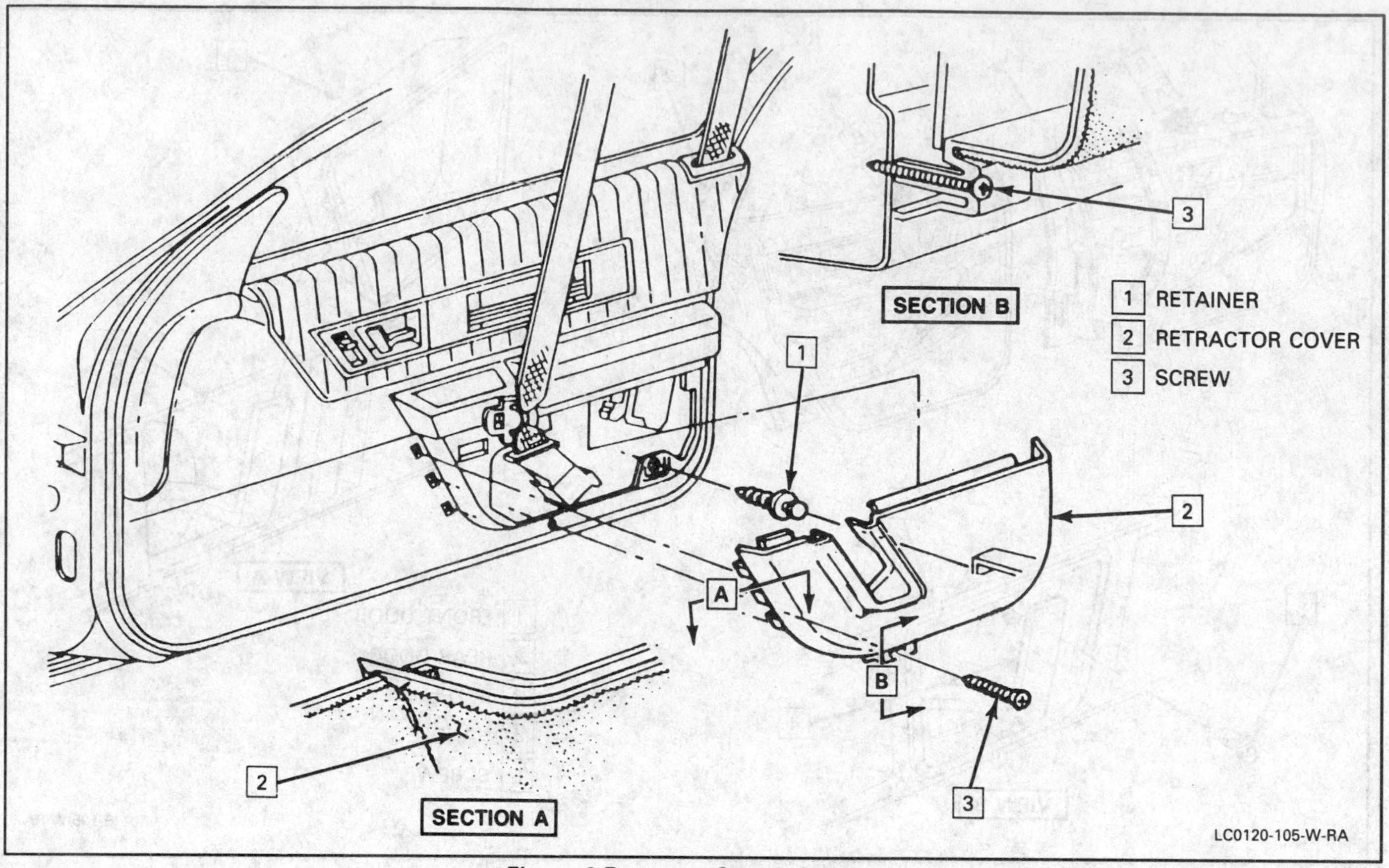
SECTION B
1 RETAINER
2 RETRACTOR COVER
3 SCREW
1
2
3
A
B
2
3
SECTION A
LC0120-105-W-RA
Figure 6 Retractor Cover (Coupe)

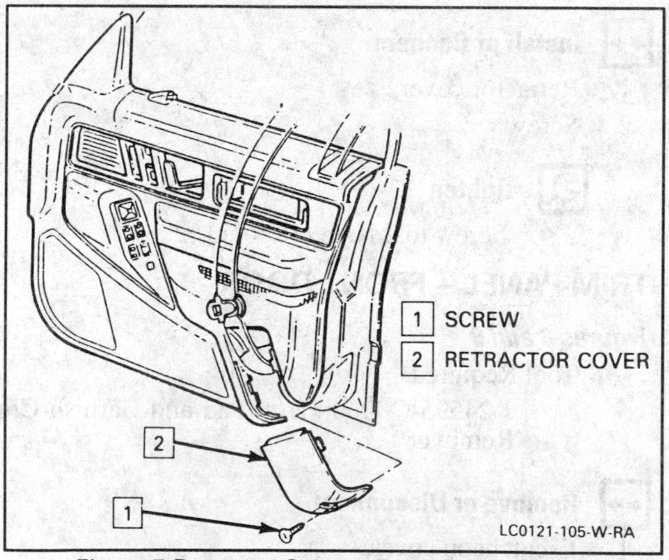
1 SCREW
2 RETRACTOR COVER
2
1
LC0121-105-W-RA
Figure 7 Retractor Cover – Front Door (Sedan)

8. Screw from trim panel, coupe only.
9. Door trim panel using J 24595-C to disengage fasteners on trim panel from the holes in door inner panel.

Install or Connect

1. Wire harnesses through openings in trim panel.
2. Trim panel to door by aligning fasteners on trim panel to holes in door inner panel and pressing trim panel to door until fasteners are fully engaged.
3. Screw to trim panel, coupe only.

Tighten

- Screw to 1 N•m (9 lb. in.).

4. Bracket screw, sedan only, through switch cutout.

Tighten

- Screw to 2 N•m (18 lb. in.).

5. Power window and door switch assembly. Refer to "Power Window and Door Switch Assembly – Front Door (Coupe)" or "Power Window Switch Assembly – Front Door (Sedan)" and "Power Door Switch – Front Door (Sedan)" in this section.
6. Inside handle bezel. Refer to "Inside Handle Bezel – Front Door" in this section.
7. Retractor cover. Refer to "Passive Restraint Belt Retractor Cover – Front Door" in this section.
8. Pull handle screws.

Tighten

- Screws to 3 N•m (27 lb. in.).

9. Seat belt and screws to shoulder belt escutcheon.

Tighten

- Screws to 1 N•m (9 lb. in.).

10. Escutcheon cover.

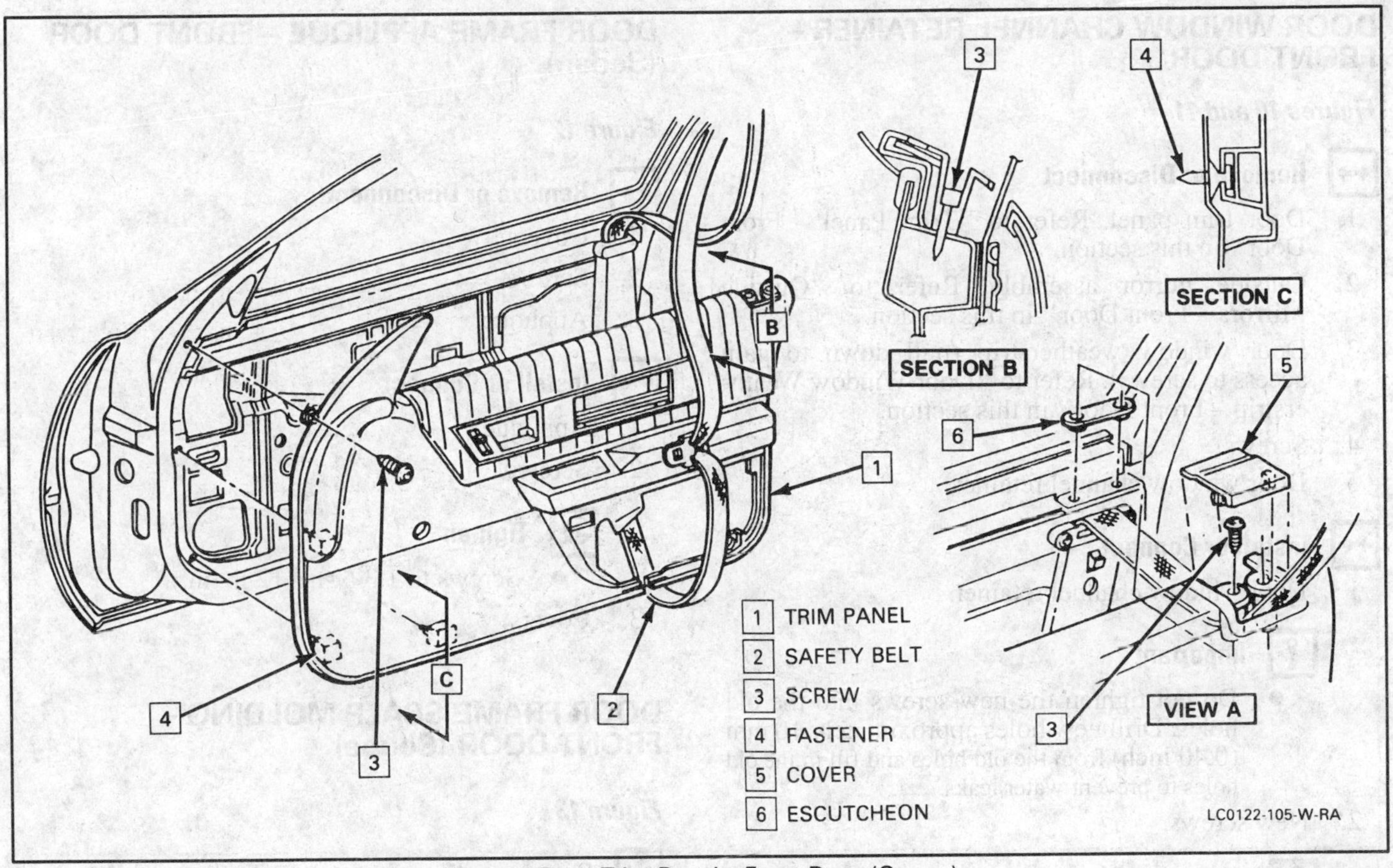
SECTION C
SECTION B
VIEW A
1 TRIM PANEL
2 SAFETY BELT
3 SCREW
4 FASTENER
5 COVER
6 ESCUTCHEON
LC0122-105-W-RA

Figure 8 Door Trim Panel – Front Door (Coupe)

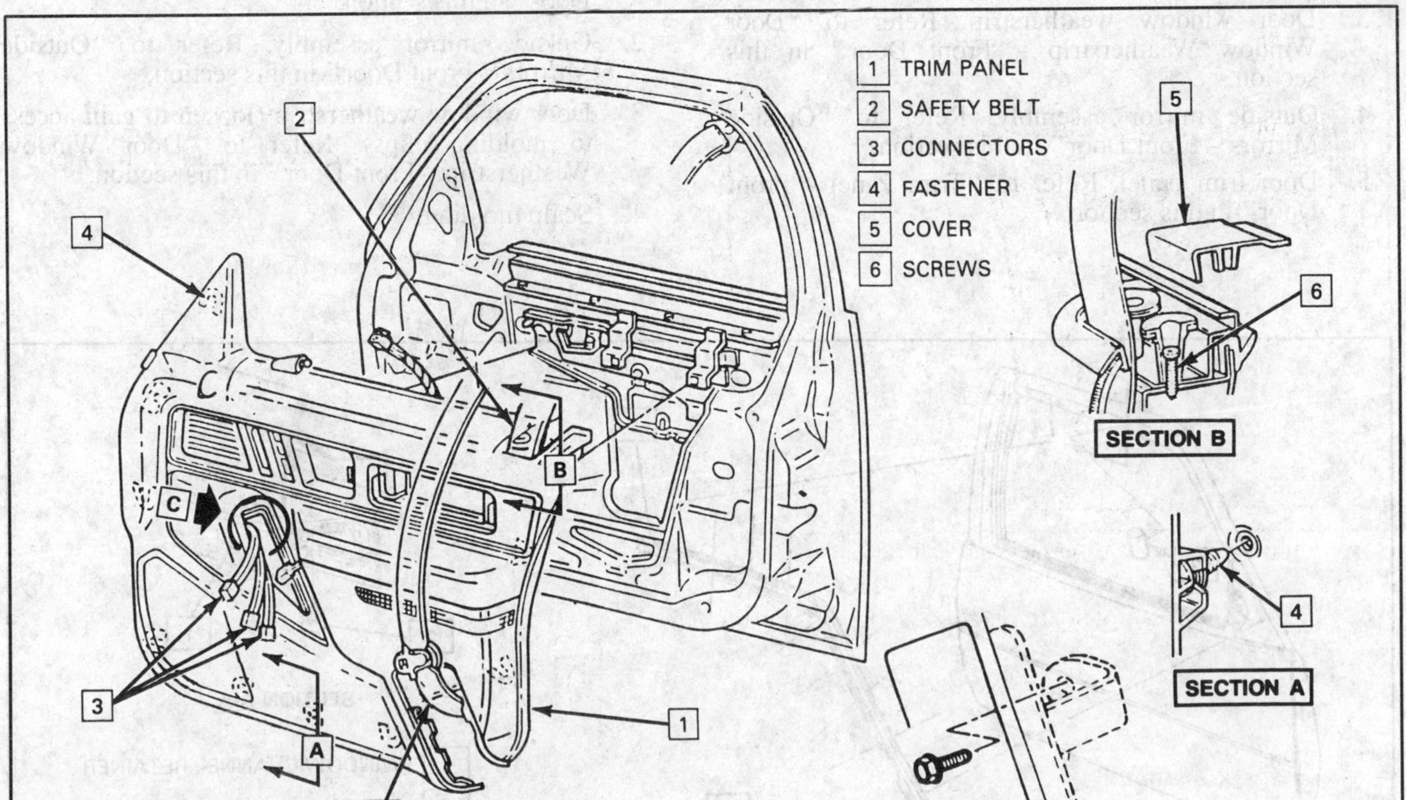
1 TRIM PANEL
2 SAFETY BELT
3 CONNECTORS
4 FASTENER
5 COVER
6 SCREWS
SECTION B
SECTION A
VIEW C
MC0002-105-W-RA

Figure 9 Door Trim Panel – Front Door (Sedan)

DOOR WINDOW CHANNEL RETAINER – FRONT DOOR

Figures 10 and 11

Remove or Disconnect

1. Door trim panel. Refer to "Trim Panel – Front Door" in this section.
2. Outside mirror assembly. Refer to "Outside Mirrors – Front Door" in this section.
3. Door window weatherstrip (pull down to gain access to screws). Refer to "Door Window Weatherstrip – Front Door" in this section.
4. Screws.
5. Door window channel retainer.

Install or Connect

1. Door window channel retainer.

Important

- Do not tighten the new screws into the old holes. Drill new holes approximately 10 mm (0.40 inch) from the old holes and fill in the old holes to prevent water leaks.

2. New screws.

Tighten

- Screws to 2 N•m (18 lb. in.).

3. Door window weatherstrip. Refer to "Door Window Weatherstrip – Front Door" in this section.
4. Outside mirror assembly. Refer to "Outside Mirrors – Front Door" in this section.
5. Door trim panel. Refer to "Trim Panel – Front Door" in this section.

DOOR FRAME APPLIQUE – FRONT DOOR (Sedan)

Figure 12

Remove or Disconnect

1. Covers.
2. Screws.
3. Applique.

Install or Connect

1. Applique.
2. Screws.

Tighten

- Screws to 1.3 N•m (12 lb. in.).

3. Covers.

DOOR FRAME SCALP MOLDING – FRONT DOOR (Coupe)

Figure 13

Remove or Disconnect

1. Door trim panel. Refer to "Trim Panel – Front Door" in this section.
2. Outside mirror assembly. Refer to "Outside Mirrors – Front Door" in this section.
3. Door window weatherstrip (loosen to gain access to molding clips). Refer to "Door Window Weatherstrip – Front Door" in this section.
4. Scalp molding.

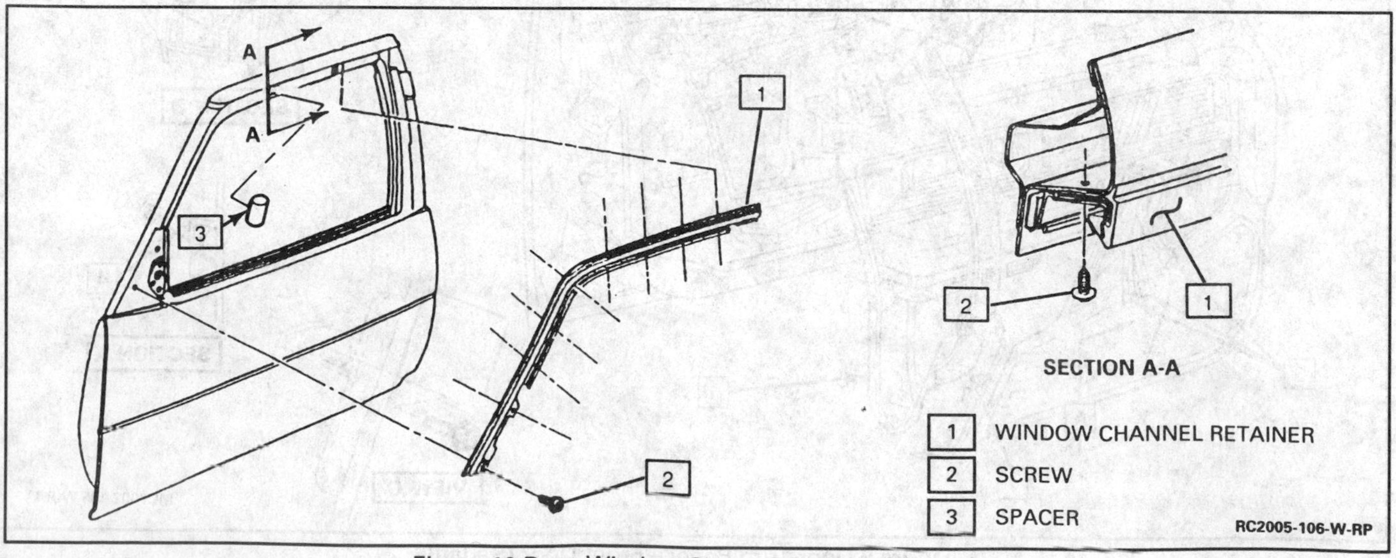
A
A
1
2
3
2
1
SECTION A-A
1 WINDOW CHANNEL RETAINER
2 SCREW
3 SPACER
RC2005-106-W-RP

Figure 10 Door Window Channel Retainer (Coupe)

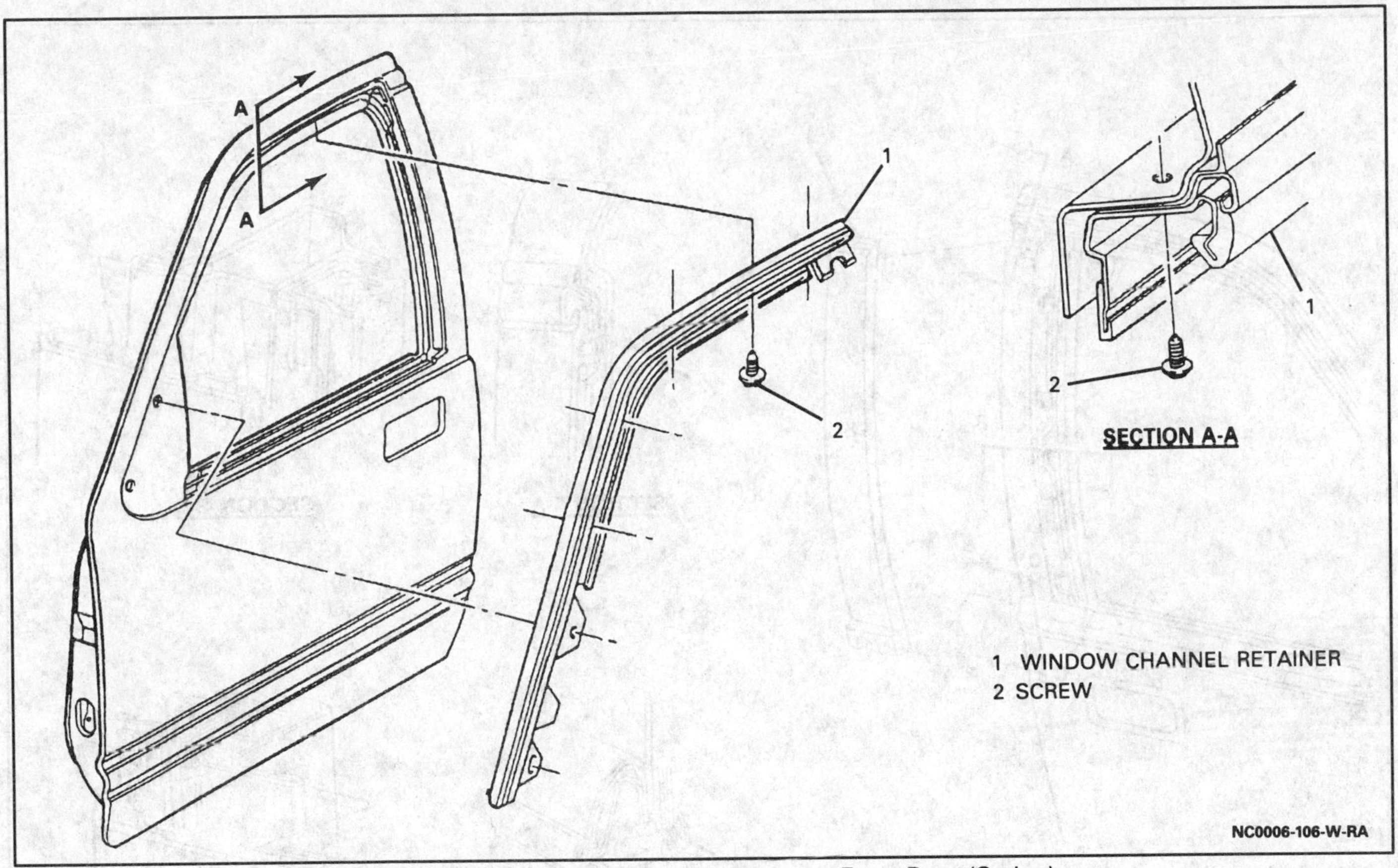
A
A
1
2
1
2
SECTION A-A
1 WINDOW CHANNEL RETAINER
2 SCREW
NC0006-106-W-RA

Figure 11 Door Window Channel Retainer – Front Door (Sedan)

Install or Connect

1. Position scalp molding to door.
2. Lower end of molding to end cap of reveal molding.
3. Scalp molding to clips, starting at lower front corner and working rearward and upward until reaching roof line.
4. Door window weatherstrip. Refer to "Door Window Weatherstrip – Front Door" in this section.
5. Outside mirror assembly. Refer to "Outside Mirrors – Front Door" in this section.
6. Door trim panel. Refer to "Trim Panel – Front Door" in this section.

FRONT DOOR HARDWARE AND WINDOW

DOOR OPENING WEATHERSTRIP – FRONT DOOR

Figure 14

Remove or Disconnect

1. Windshield side upper garnish molding. Refer to ROOF (SECTION 10-9).
2. Loosen quarter trim panels, if coupe. Refer to REAR QUARTERS (SECTION 10-7).
3. Carpet retainer trim. Refer to SEATS AND CARPET (SECTION 10-10).
4. Center pillar trim panels, if sedan. Refer to "Center Pillar Trim (Sedan)" in this section.
5. Weatherstrip by grasping weatherstrip and pulling it off flange on body.

Install or Connect

1. Weatherstrip to flange on body.
2. Center pillar trim panels, if removed. Refer to "Center Pillar Trim (Sedan)" in this section.
3. Carpet retainer trim. Refer to SEATS AND CARPET (SECTION 10-10).
4. Quarter trim panels, if removed. Refer to REAR QUARTERS (SECTION 10-7).
5. Windshield side upper garnish molding. Refer to ROOF (SECTION 10-9).

UPPER AUXILIARY WEATHERSTRIP – FRONT DOOR (Coupe)

Figure 15

Remove or Disconnect

1. Screws.
2. Auxiliary weatherstrip.

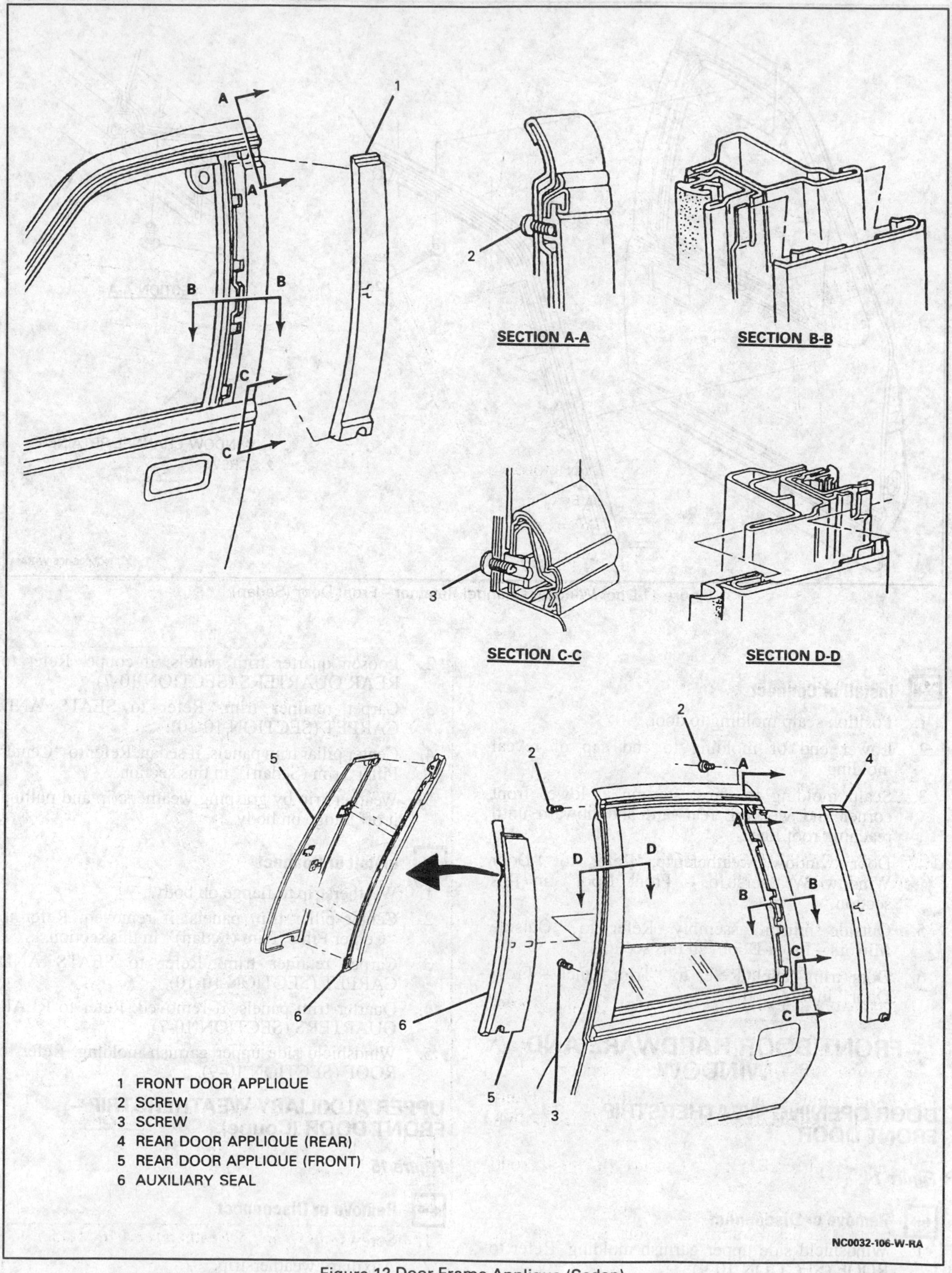
A
A
1
B
B
C
C
2
SECTION A-A
SECTION B-B
3
SECTION C-C
SECTION D-D
2
2
4
5
A
A
D
D
B
B
C
C
6
6
3
5
1 FRONT DOOR APPLIQUE
2 SCREW
3 SCREW
4 REAR DOOR APPLIQUE (REAR)
5 REAR DOOR APPLIQUE (FRONT)
6 AUXILIARY SEAL
NC0032-106-W-RA

Figure 12 Door Frame Applique (Sedan)

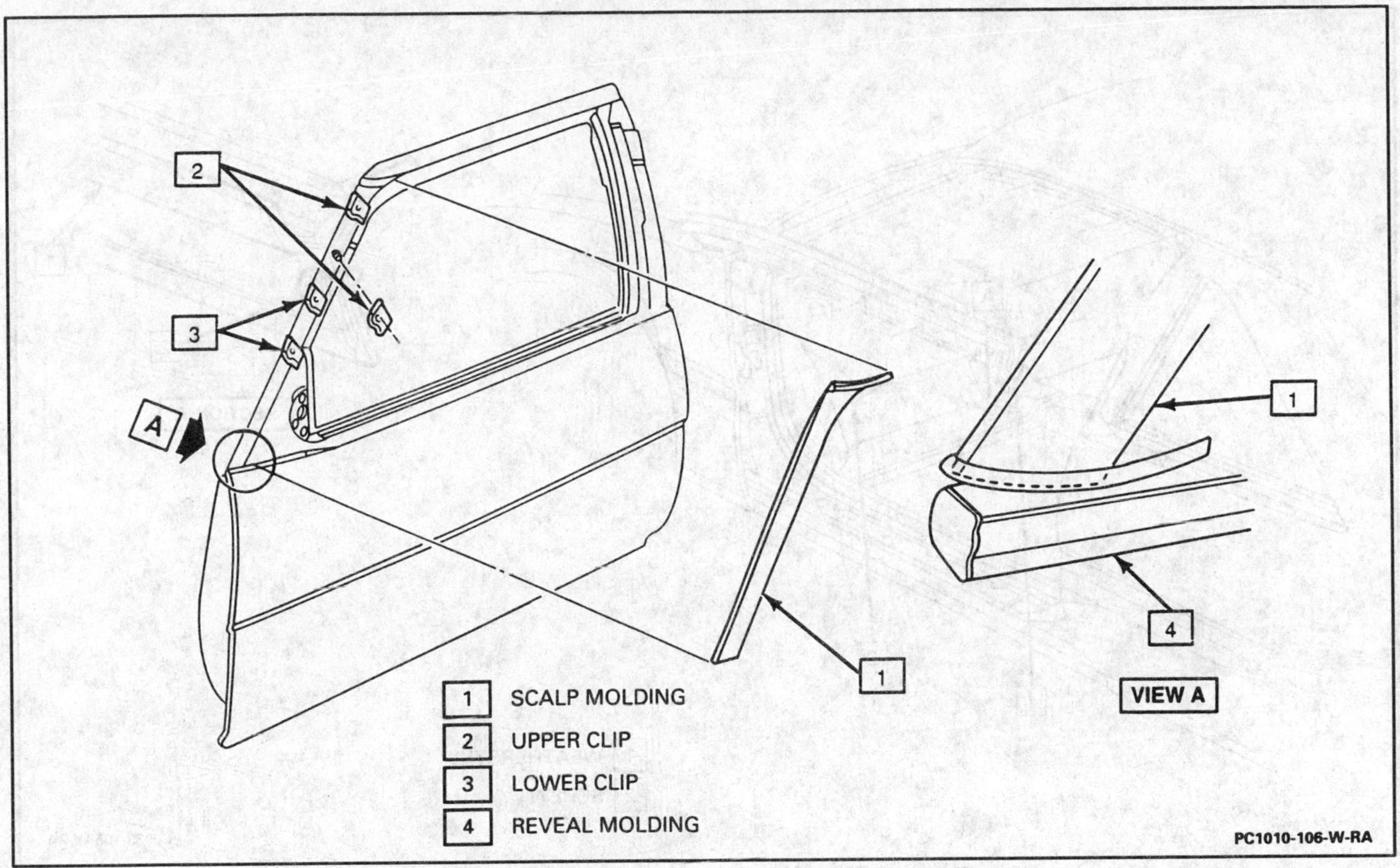
2
3
A
1
4
VIEW A
1 SCALP MOLDING
2 UPPER CLIP
3 LOWER CLIP
4 REVEAL MOLDING
PC1010-106-W-RA

Figure 13 Door Frame Scalp Molding – Front Door (Coupe)

Install or Connect

1. Auxiliary weatherstrip.
2. Screws.

Tighten

- Screws to 2 N•m (18 lb. in.).

DOOR WINDOW WEATHERSTRIP – FRONT DOOR

Figures 16 and 17

Remove or Disconnect

1. Door trim panel. Refer to "Trim Panel – Front Door" in this section.
2. Inner belt sealing strip. Refer to "Inner Belt Sealing Strip – Front Door" in this section.
3. Front window guide retainer. Refer to "Front Window Guide Retainer – Front Door" in this section.
4. Outside mirror. Refer to "Outside Mirrors – Front Door" in this section.
5. Door frame garnish moldings. Refer to "Door Frame Garnish Moldings – Front Door" in this section.

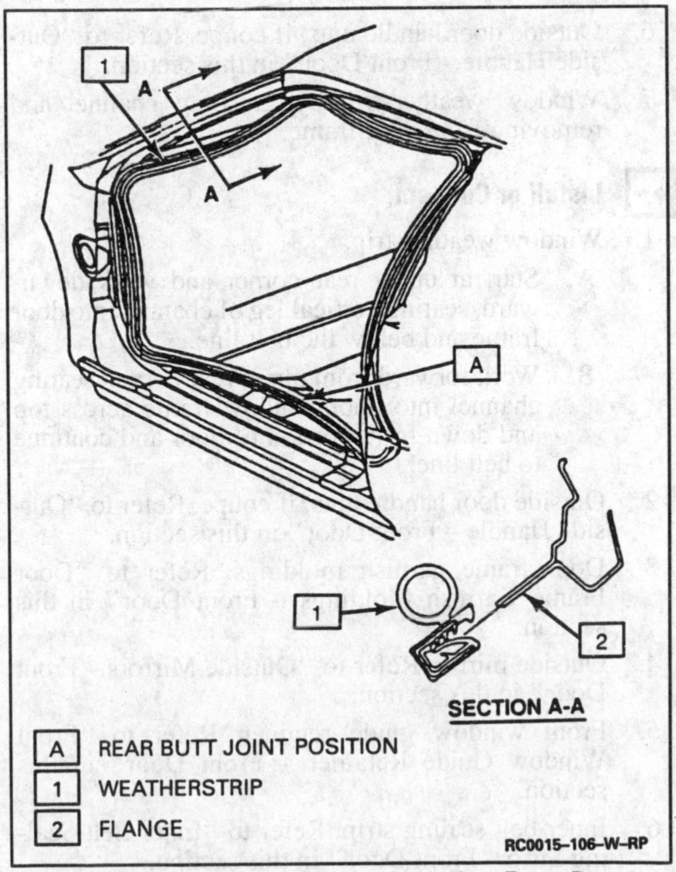
1
A
A
A
1
2
SECTION A-A
A REAR BUTT JOINT POSITION
1 WEATHERSTRIP
2 FLANGE
RC0015-106-W-RP

Figure 14 Door Opening Weatherstrip – Front Door

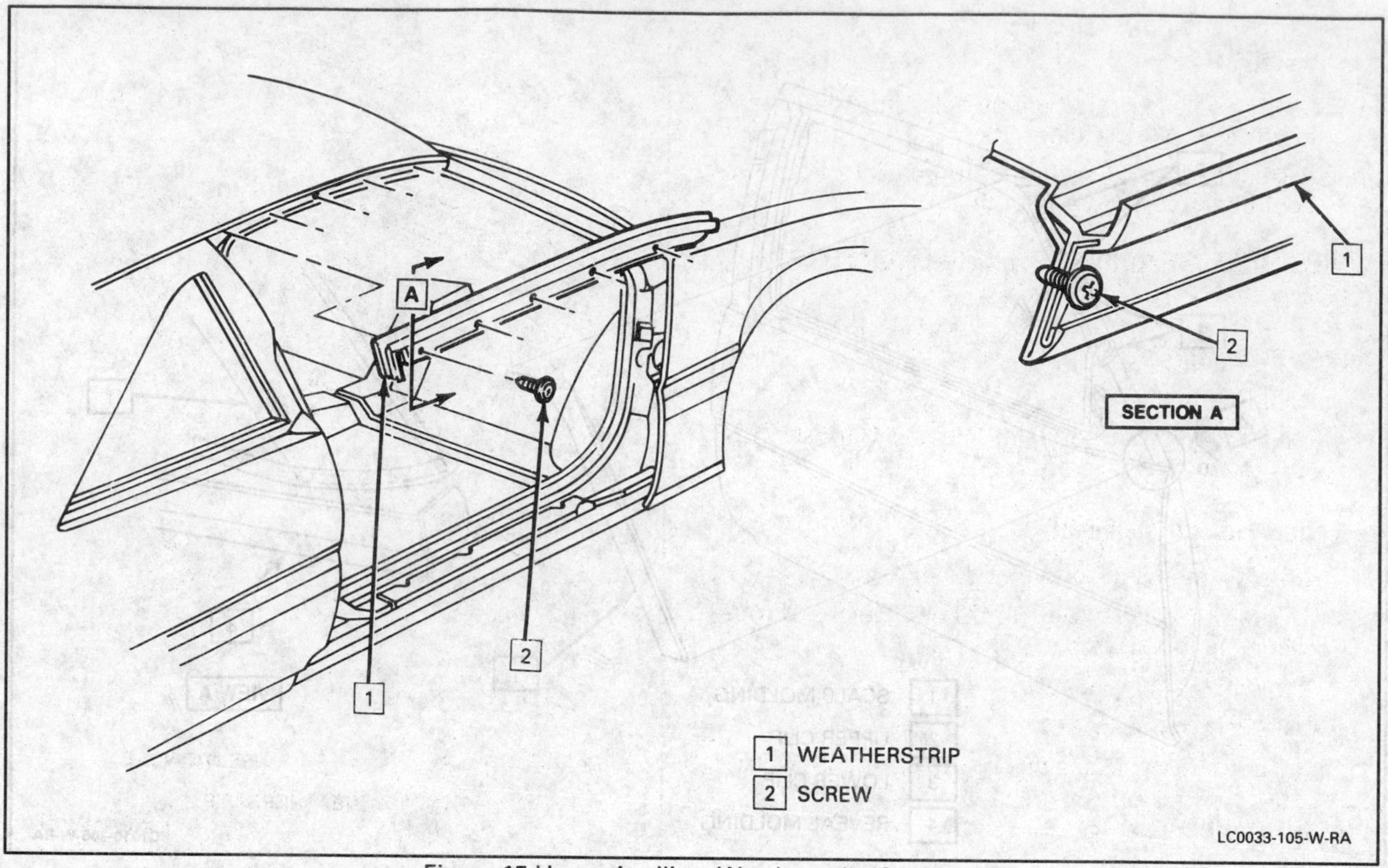
A
1
2
SECTION A
1 WEATHERSTRIP
2 SCREW
LC0033-105-W-RA

Figure 15 Upper Auxiliary Weatherstrip (Coupe)

6. Outside door handle nuts, if coupe. Refer to "Outside Handle – Front Door" in this section.
7. Window weatherstrip by grasping channel and removing from door frame.

Install or Connect

1. Window weatherstrip.
   A. Start at upper rear corner and work downward, seating vertical leg of channel into door frame and below the belt line.
   B. Work forward from upper rear corner, seating channel into door window frame across top and down front portion of door and continue to belt line.
2. Outside door handle nuts, if coupe. Refer to "Outside Handle – Front Door" in this section.
3. Door frame garnish moldings. Refer to "Door Frame Garnish Moldings – Front Door" in this section.
4. Outside mirror. Refer to "Outside Mirrors – Front Door" in this section.
5. Front window guide retainer. Refer to "Front Window Guide Retainer – Front Door" in this section.
6. Inner belt sealing strip. Refer to "Inner Belt Sealing Strip – Front Door" in this section.
7. Door trim panel. Refer to "Trim Panel – Front Door" in this section.

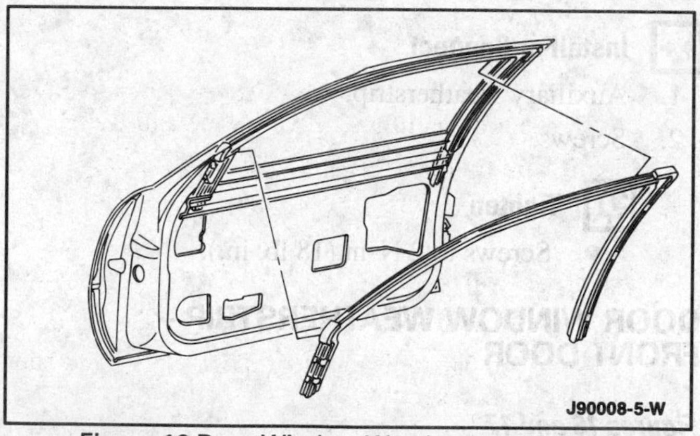
J90008-5-W

Figure 16 Door Window Weatherstrip (Coupe)

DOOR BOTTOM SEALING STRIP – FRONT DOOR

Figure 18

Tool Required:

J 24595-C Door Trim Pad and Garnish Clip Remover

Remove or Disconnect

1. Fasteners holding sealing strip to door panel using J 24595-C.
2. Sealing strip.

Install or Connect

1. Sealing strip to door, aligning holes in sealing strip to holes in door bottom.
2. Fasteners through sealing strip and into holes in door bottom using a rubber mallet.

INNER BELT SEALING STRIP – FRONT DOOR

Figures 19 through 21

Tool Required:

J 24595-C Door Trim Pad and Garnish Clip Remover

Remove or Disconnect

1. Lower window to bottom of door.
2. Door trim panel. Refer to "Trim Panel – Front Door" in this section.
3. Screws.
4. Door trim retainer.
5. Sealing strip by lifting up on strip using J 24595-C.

Install or Connect

1. Sealing strip.
   - A. Engage each end by pressing firmly onto front and rear ends of pinchweld flange.
   - B. Seat entire length of sealing strip onto pinchweld flange.
   - C. Use rubber mallet to ensure proper engagement of sealing strip on pinchweld flange.
2. Door trim retainer.
3. Screws.

Tighten

- Screws to 2 N•m (18 lb. in.).

4. Door trim panel. Refer to "Trim Panel – Front Door" in this section.

OUTER BELT SEALING STRIP – FRONT DOOR

Figures 22 and 23

Tool Required:

J 24595-C Door Trim Pad and Garnish Clip Remover

Remove or Disconnect

1. Outside door handle cover assembly, if coupe. Refer to "Outside Handle – Front Door" in this section.
2. Screw.
3. Sealing strip by prying up with J 24595-C.

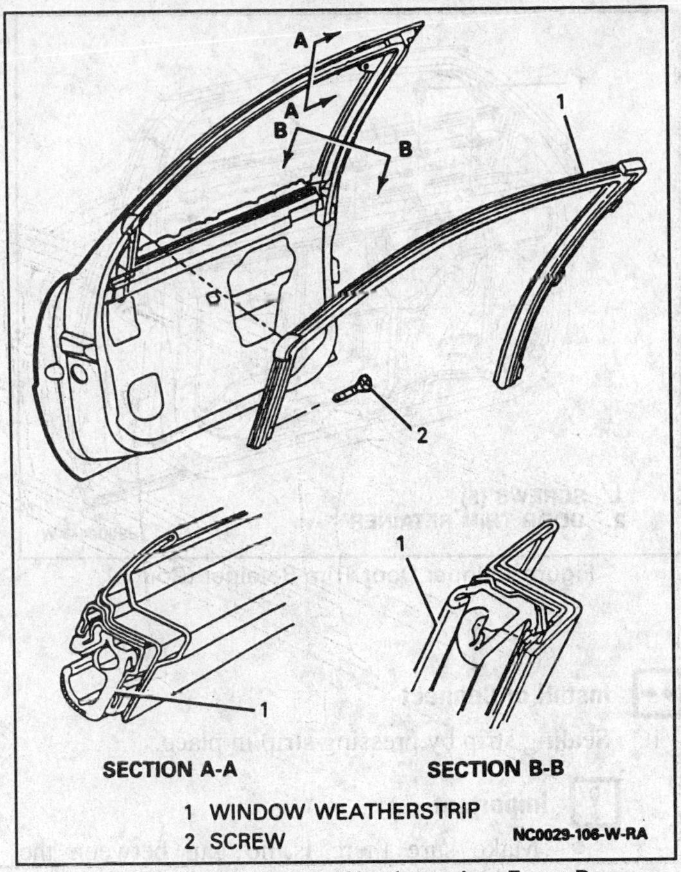
A
A
B
B
1
2
1
1
SECTION A-A
SECTION B-B
1 WINDOW WEATHERSTRIP
2 SCREW
NC0029-106-W-RA

Figure 17 Door Window Weatherstrip – Front Door (Sedan)

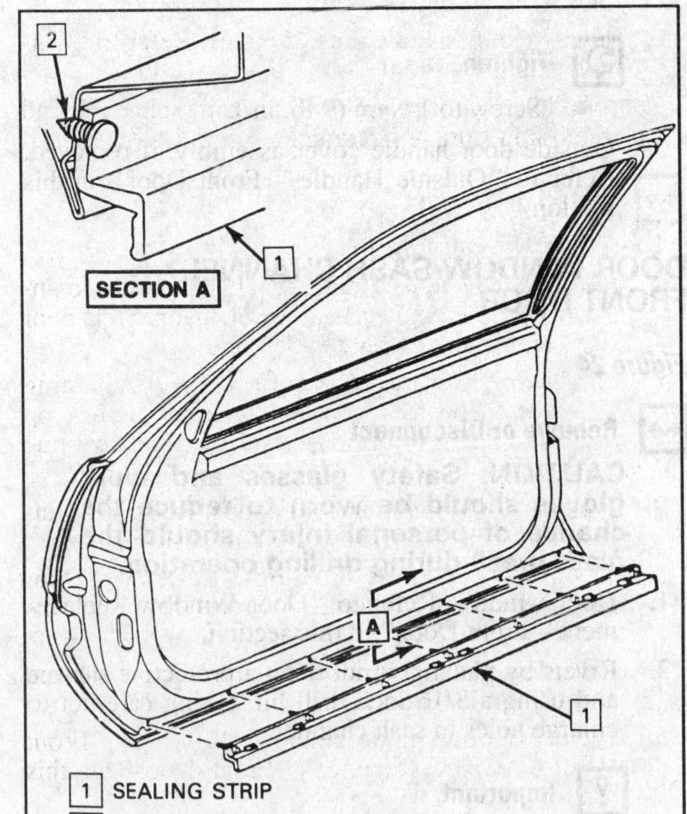
2
1
SECTION A
A
1
1 SEALING STRIP
2 FASTENER
LC0023-105-W-RA

Figure 18 Front Door Bottom Sealing Strip

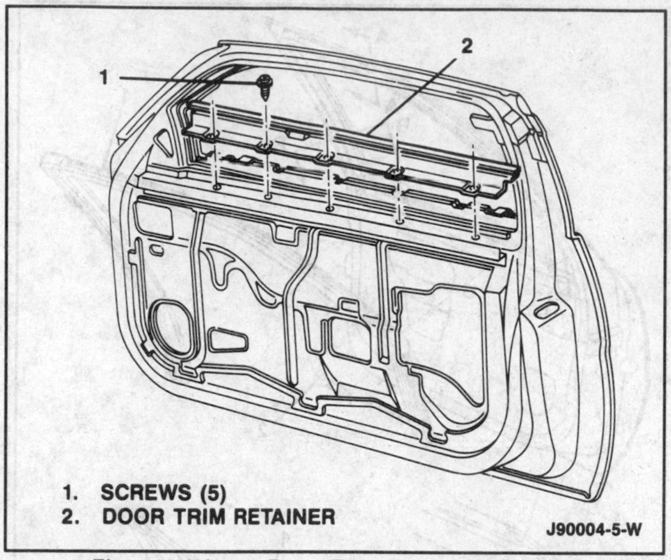
1
2
1. SCREWS (5)
2. DOOR TRIM RETAINER
J90004-5-W

Figure 19 Inner Door Trim Retainer (Coupe)

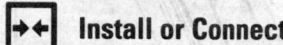

Install or Connect

1. Sealing strip by pressing strip in place.

Important

- Make sure there is no gap between the sealing strip and channel retainer. Adjust sealing strip if necessary.

2. Screw.

Tighten

- Screw to 1 N•m (9 lb. in.).

3. Outside door handle cover assembly, if removed. Refer to "Outside Handle – Front Door" in this section.

DOOR WINDOW SASH CHANNEL – FRONT DOOR

Figure 24

Remove or Disconnect

CAUTION: Safety glasses and work gloves should be worn to reduce the chance of personal injury should the glass break during drilling operation.

1. Door window. Refer to "Door Window Replacement – Front Door" in this section.
2. Rivets by placing window on a protective surface and using a 3/16 inch drill bit, taking care not to enlarge holes in sash channel.

Important

- If sash channel holes are enlarged during drilling operation, a new sash must be used.

3. Sash channel and spacer.

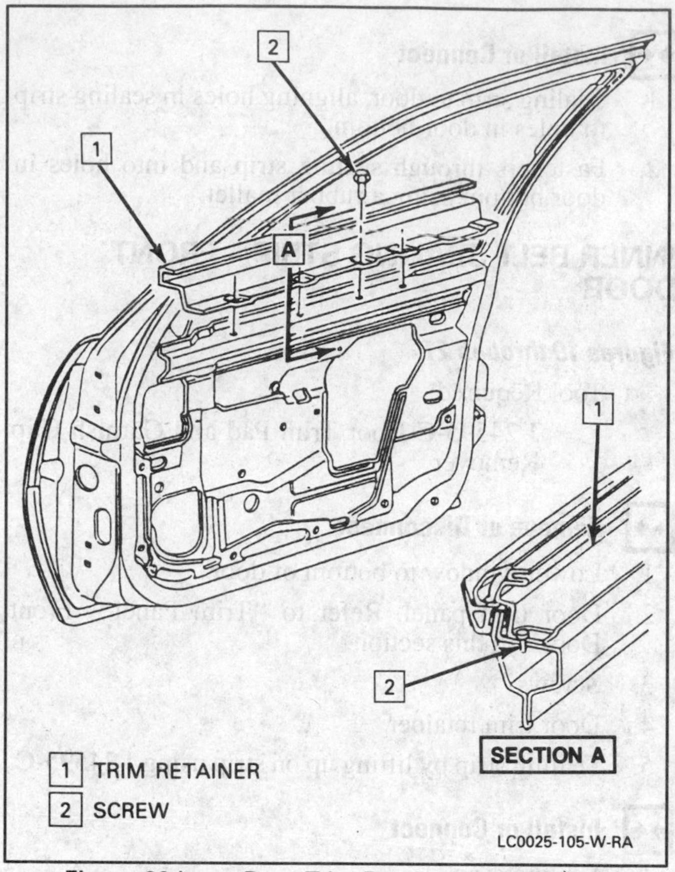
2
1
A
1
2
SECTION A
1 TRIM RETAINER
2 SCREW
LC0025-105-W-RA

Figure 20 Inner Door Trim Retainer – Front Door (Sedan)

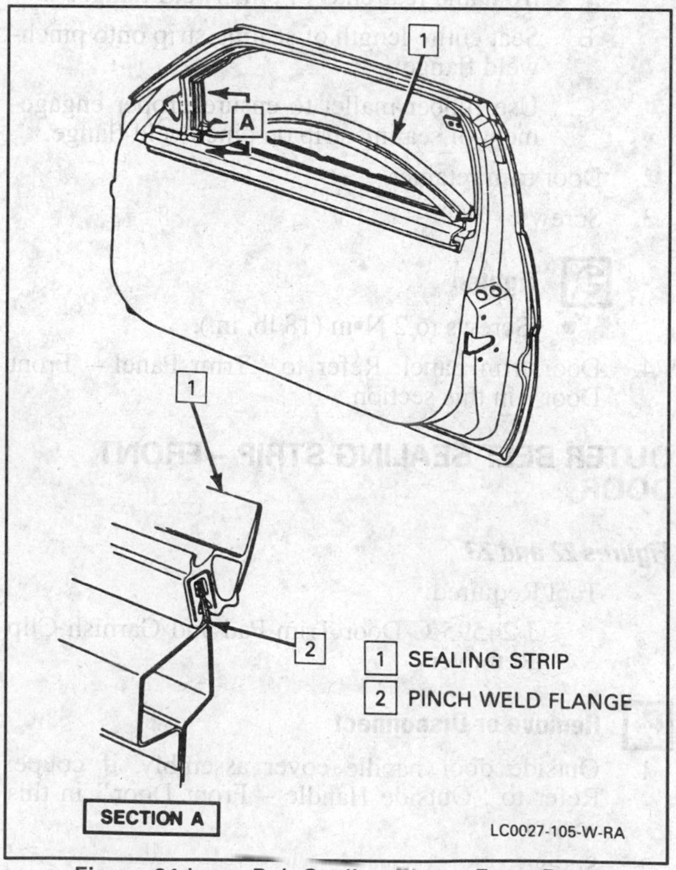
1
A
1
2
1 SEALING STRIP
2 PINCH WELD FLANGE
SECTION A
LC0027-105-W-RA

Figure 21 Inner Belt Sealing Strip – Front Door

Install or Connect

1. Spacer to window.
2. Sash channel to spacer and window.
3. Rivets through holes in sash, spacer and window using 3/16 inch x .527 inch aluminum domehead blind rivets, part no. 9441725 or equivalent.
4. Door window. Refer to "Door Window Replacement – Front Door" in this section.

FRONT WINDOW GUIDE RETAINER – FRONT DOOR

Figures 25 and 26

Remove or Disconnect

1. Door trim panel. Refer to "Trim Panel – Front Door" in this section.
2. Water deflector. Refer to "Water Deflector – Front Door" in this section.
3. Screws.

Important

- Window must bc in the full up position in order to remove the guide retainer.

4. Front window guide retainer.

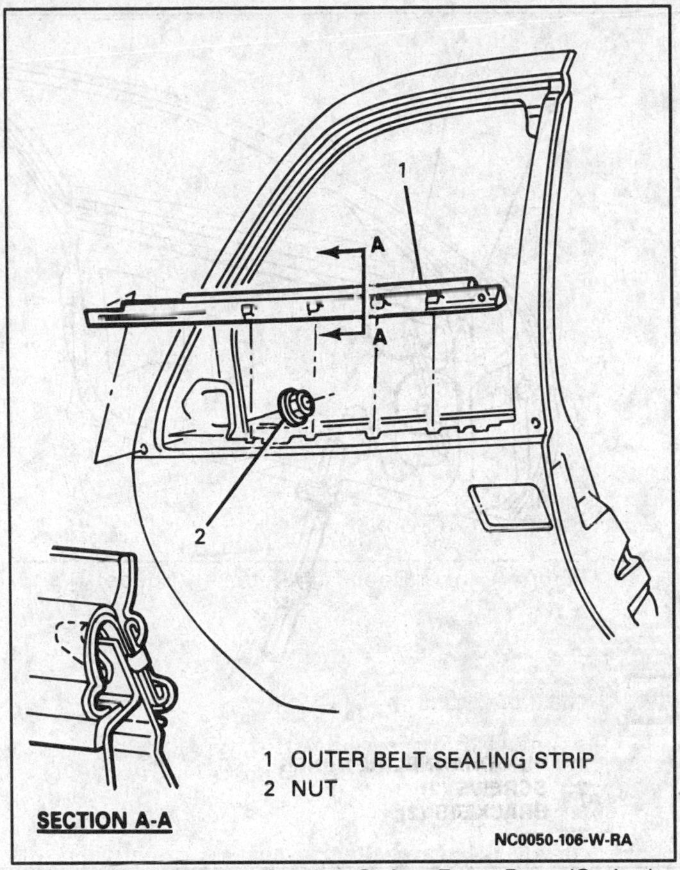
1
A
A
2
SECTION A-A
1 OUTER BELT SEALING STRIP
2 NUT
NC0050-106-W-RA

Figure 23 Outer Belt Sealing Strip – Front Door (Sedan)

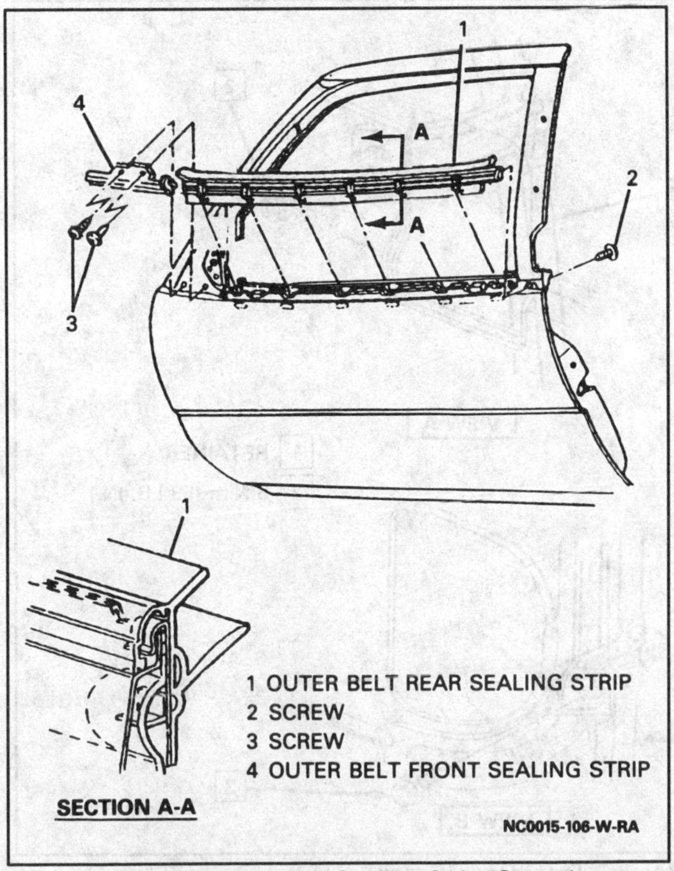
1
4
A
A
2
3
1
SECTION A-A
1 OUTER BELT REAR SEALING STRIP
2 SCREW
3 SCREW
4 OUTER BELT FRONT SEALING STRIP
NC0015-106-W-RA

Figure 22 Outer Belt Sealing Strip (Coupe)

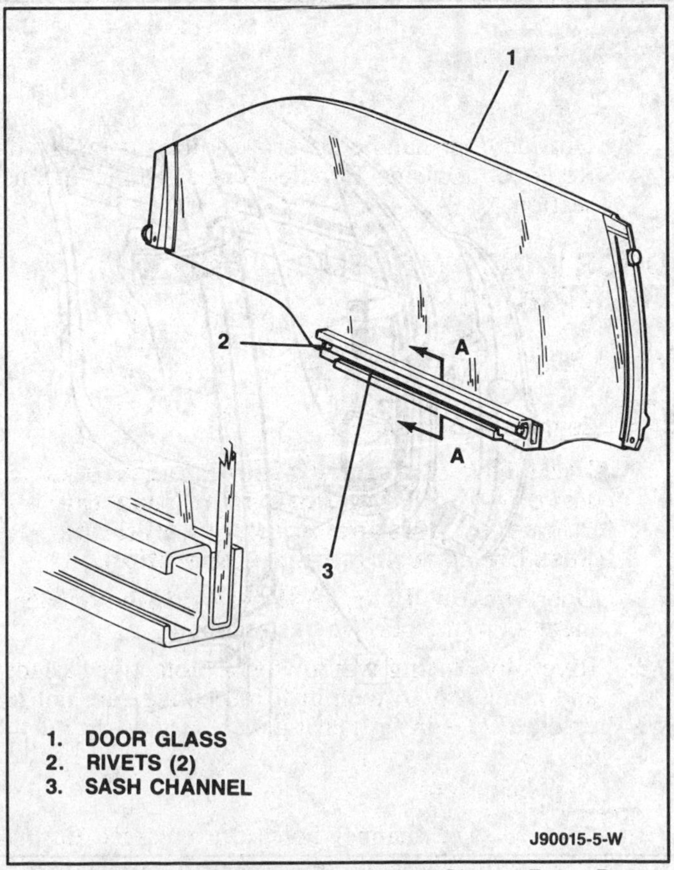
1
2
A
A
3
1. DOOR GLASS
2. RIVETS (2)
3. SASH CHANNEL
J90015-5-W

Figure 24 Installing Sash Channel to Glass – Front Door

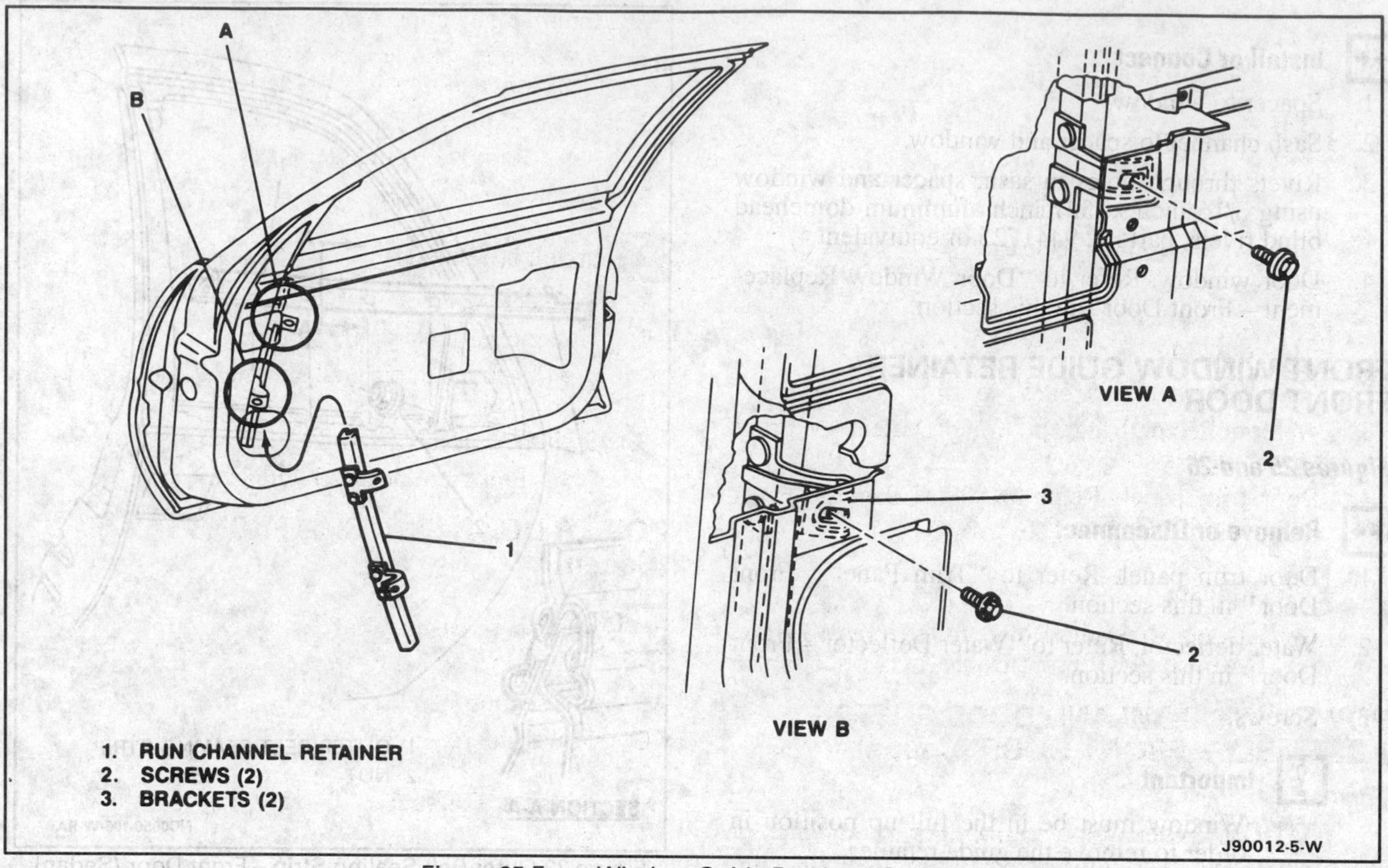
A
B
1
VIEW A
2
3
2
VIEW B
1. RUN CHANNEL RETAINER
2. SCREWS (2)
3. BRACKETS (2)
J90012-5-W

Figure 25 Front Window Guide Retainer (Coupe)

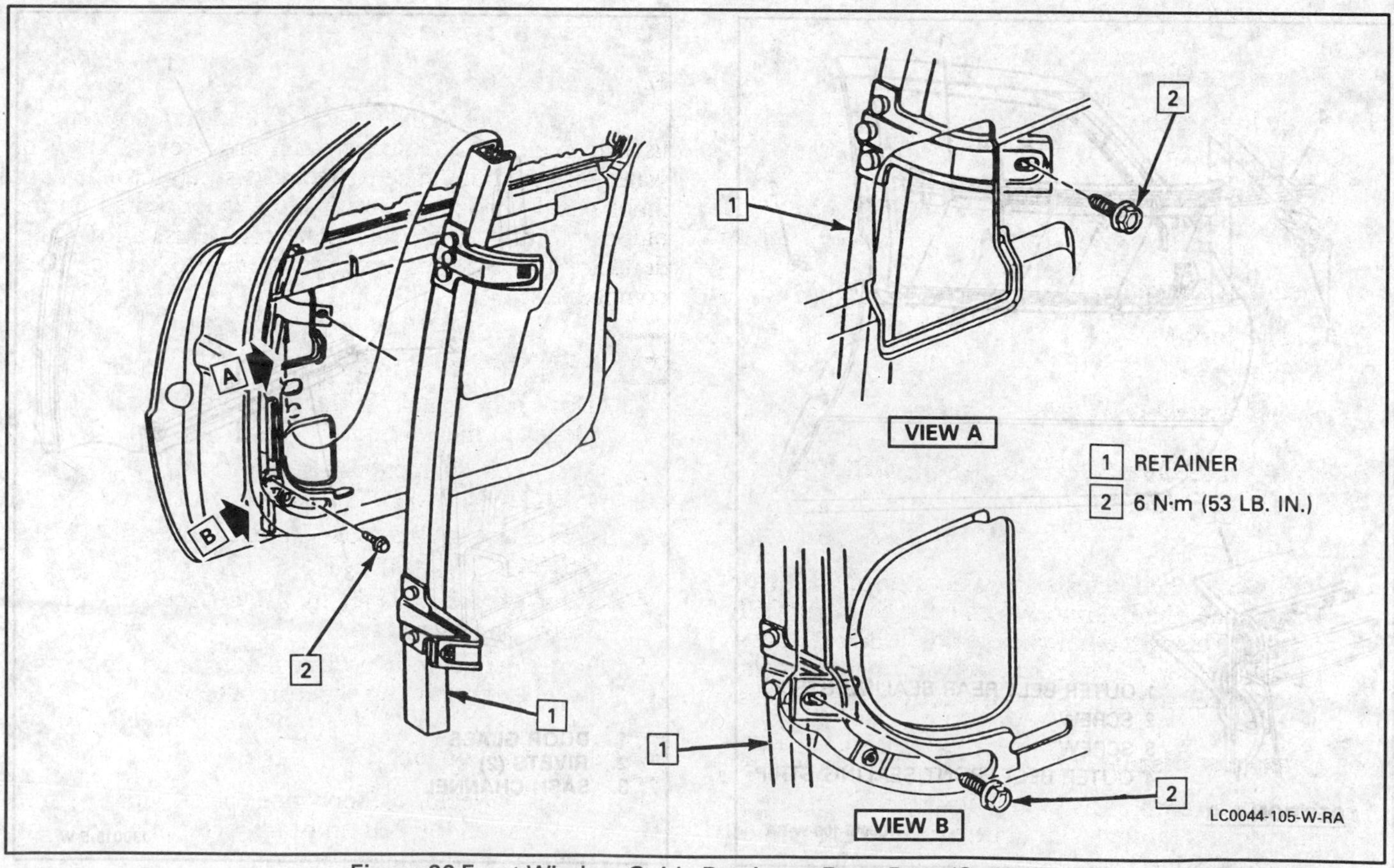
A
B
2
1
1
2
VIEW A
1 RETAINER
2 6 N·m (53 LB. IN.)
1
2
VIEW B
LC0044-105-W-RA

Figure 26 Front Window Guide Retainer – Front Door (Sedan)

Install or Connect

Important

- Slowly lower window to properly align retainer into position.

1. Front window guide retainer.
2. Screws.

Tighten

- Screws to 6 N•m (53 lb. in.).

3. Water deflector. Refer to "Water Deflector – Front Door" in this section.
4. Door trim panel. Refer to "Trim Panel – Front Door" in this section.

Adjust

- Door window. Refer to "Door Window Adjustment – Front Door" in this section.

POWER WINDOW AND DOOR SWITCH ASSEMBLY – FRONT DOOR (Coupe)

Figure 27

NOTICE: When removing a door trim panel or switch plate, the ignition switch must be in the OFF position. This will eliminate the possibility of shorting out the switch if a screwdriver, awl or metal object is used to remove the switch from the harness.

Remove or Disconnect

1. Switch assembly by prying up with a flat bladed tool.
3. Clip(s).
3. Connector(s).

Install or Connect

1. Connector(s).
2. Clip(s).
3. Switch assembly by pressing in place.

POWER WINDOW SWITCH ASSEMBLY – FRONT DOOR (Sedan)

Figure 28

NOTICE: When removing a door trim panel or switch plate, the ignition switch must be in the OFF position. This will eliminate the possibility of shorting out the switch if a screwdriver, awl or metal object is used to remove the switch from the harness.

Remove or Disconnect

1. Switch assembly by prying lower clips, using a putty knife, through slot in trim panel at bottom of switch housing.
   - Lift lower part of switch assembly from housing using hand.
2. Intermediate clips using a nylon spatula.
   - Slide spatula between side of switch assembly and housing, pry loose.
3. Upper clips.
   - Remove from assembly.
4. Connectors.

Install or Connect

1. Connectors.
2. Upper clips to switch assembly.
   - Rebend to original shape and slide into position.
3. Switch assembly to trim panel.
   - Press into position with hand.

POWER DOOR SWITCH – FRONT DOOR (Sedan)

Remove or Disconnect

1. Trim panel. Refer to "Trim Panel – Front Door" in this section.
2. Power door switch.

Install or Connect

1. Power door switch.
2. Trim panel. Refer to "Trim Panel – Front Door" in this section.

WATER DEFLECTOR – FRONT DOOR

Figures 29 and 30

A waterproof black sound deadener deflector is used to seal the door inner panel and prevent entry of water into the body. The deflector is secured to the door inner panel with pressure sensitive tape located on the outboard surface of the deflector. This allows the deflector to be peeled back as needed to service door components.

Remove or Disconnect

1. Door trim panel. Refer to "Trim Panel – Front Door" in this section.
2. Seat belt retractors. Refer to SEAT BELTS (SECTION 10-11).
3. Any support brackets installed over the water deflector.
4. Door speakers. Refer to "Door Speaker – Front Door" in this section.
5. Water deflector by peeling deflector off door inner panel and removing waterproof tape.

Install or Connect

1. Water deflector to door inner panel, making sure that tabs on the bottom of deflector are in slots in bottom of door inner panel.
2. Waterproof tape over slots in bottom of door inner panel where water deflector tabs were installed.

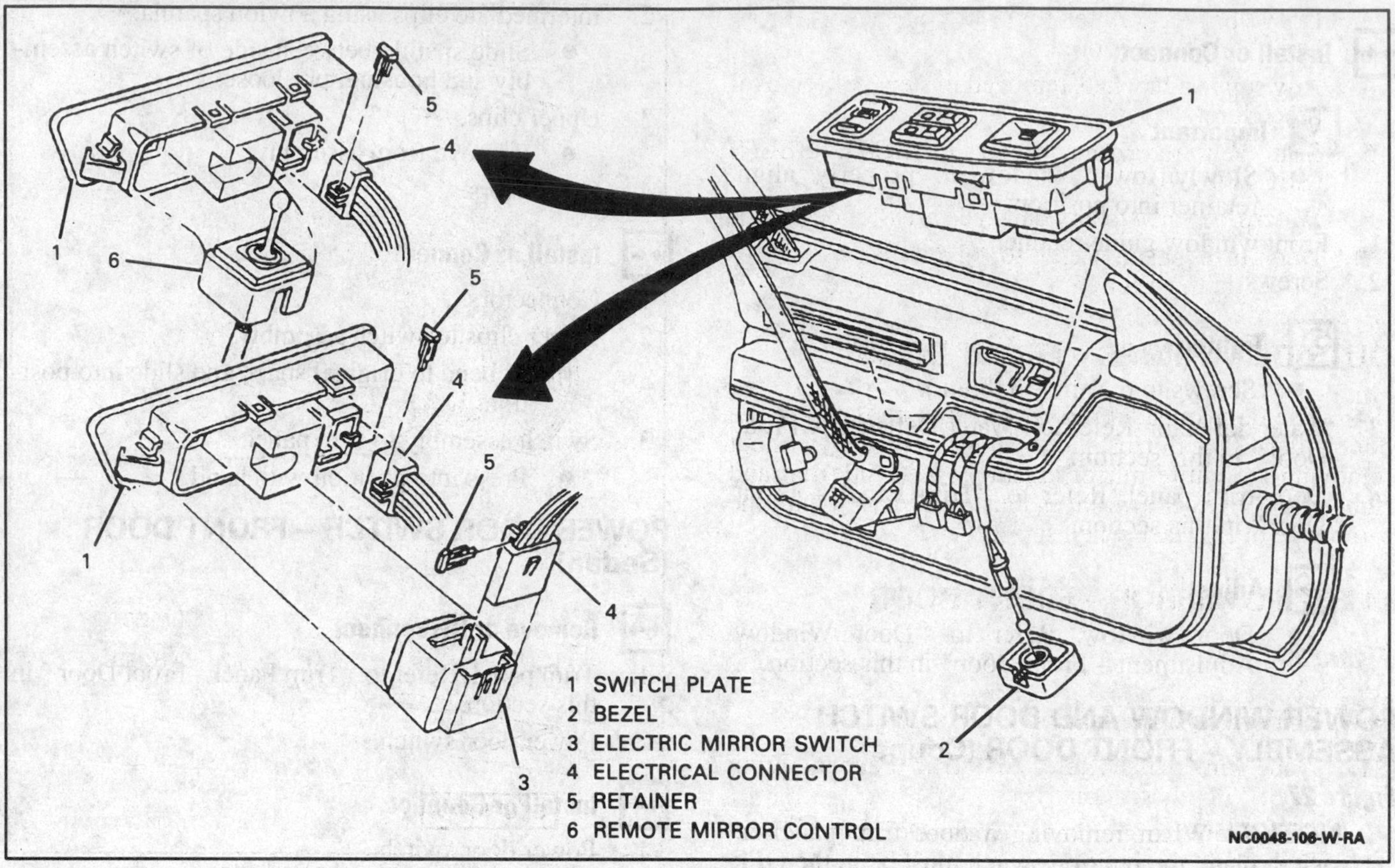
1
2
3
4
5
6
1 SWITCH PLATE
2 BEZEL
3 ELECTRIC MIRROR SWITCH
4 ELECTRICAL CONNECTOR
5 RETAINER
6 REMOTE MIRROR CONTROL
NC0048-106-W-RA

Figure 27 Power Switch Assembly – Front Door (Coupe)

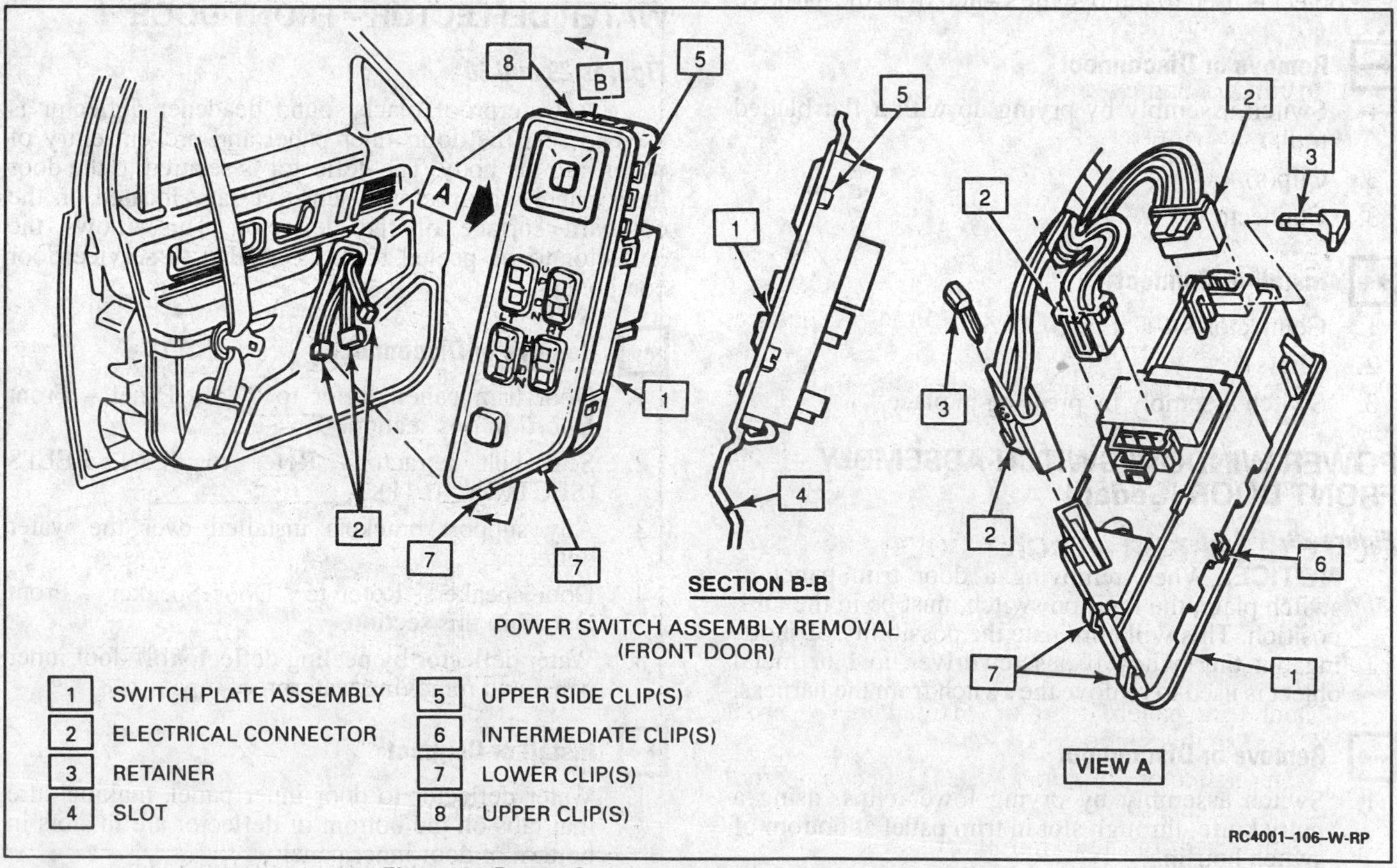
A
B
SECTION B-B
VIEW A
POWER SWITCH ASSEMBLY REMOVAL
(FRONT DOOR)
1 SWITCH PLATE ASSEMBLY
2 ELECTRICAL CONNECTOR
3 RETAINER
4 SLOT
5 UPPER SIDE CLIP(S)
6 INTERMEDIATE CLIP(S)
7 LOWER CLIP(S)
8 UPPER CLIP(S)
RC4001-106-W-RP

Figure 28 Power Switch Assembly – Front Door (Sedan)

3. Door speakers. Refer to "Door Speaker – Front Door" in this section.
4. Any support brackets removed in step 3 of removal procedure.
5. Seat belt retractors. Refer to SEAT BELTS (SECTION 10-11).
6. Waterproof tape to any damaged areas of deflector.
7. Door trim panel. Refer to "Trim Panel – Front Door" in this section.

OUTSIDE MIRRORS – FRONT DOOR

The door outside mirrors are stud mounted to the door filler. The mirror face can be replaced without removing the entire mirror assembly. Left side flat and right side convex mirror faces must be replaced with the same type mirror face when serviced.

ELECTRIC MIRROR – FRONT DOOR

Figure 31

Remove or Disconnect

1. Door trim panel. Refer to "Trim Panel – Front Door" in this section.
2. Water deflector. Refer to "Water Deflector – Front Door" in this section.
3. Electrical harness.
4. Nuts.
5. Mirror and filler.

Install or Connect

1. Filler and mirror.
2. Electrical harness.
3. Nuts.

Tighten

- Nuts to 10 N•m (89 lb. in.) in sequence, center, top then bottom.

4. Water deflector. Refer to "Water Deflector – Front Door" in this section.
5. Door trim panel. Refer to "Trim Panel – Front Door" in this section.

REMOTE MIRROR – FRONT DOOR

Figure 31

Remove or Disconnect

1. Door trim panel. Refer to "Trim Panel – Front Door" in this section.
2. Water deflector. Refer to "Water Deflector – Front Door" in this section.
3. Remote control cable from inner panel.
4. Nuts.
5. Mirror and filler.

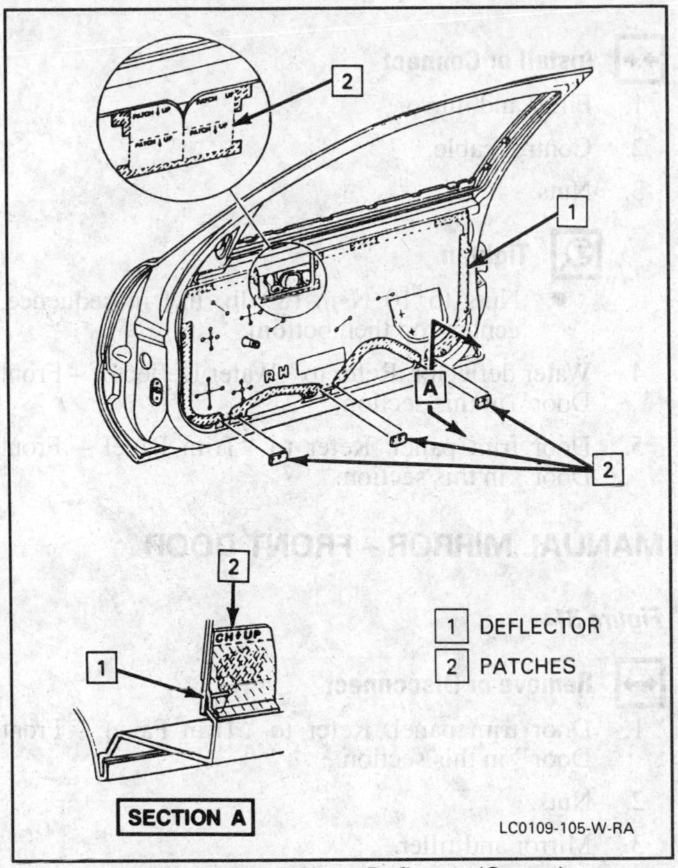
2
1
A
2
2
1
CH UP
1 DEFLECTOR
2 PATCHES
SECTION A
LC0109-105-W-RA

Figure 29 Door Water Deflector (Coupe)

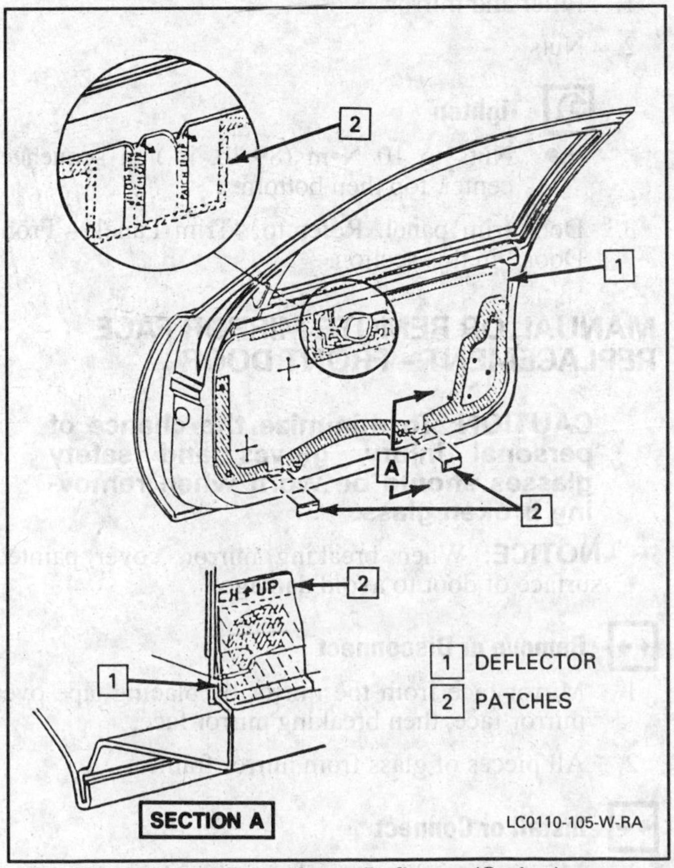
2
1
A
2
CH UP
2
1
1 DEFLECTOR
2 PATCHES
SECTION A
LC0110-105-W-RA

Figure 30 Door Water Deflector (Sedan)

Install or Connect

1. Filler and mirror.
2. Control cable.
3. Nuts.

Tighten

- Nuts to 10 N•m (89 lb. in.) in sequence, center, top then bottom.

4. Water deflector. Refer to "Water Deflector – Front Door" in this section.
5. Door trim panel. Refer to "Trim Panel – Front Door" in this section.

MANUAL MIRROR – FRONT DOOR

Figure 31

Remove or Disconnect

1. Door trim panel. Refer to "Trim Panel – Front Door" in this section.
2. Nuts.
3. Mirror and filler.

Install or Connect

1. Filler and mirror.
2. Nuts.

Tighten

- Nuts to 10 N•m (89 lb. in.) in sequence, center, top then bottom.

3. Door trim panel. Refer to "Trim Panel – Front Door" in this section.

MANUAL OR REMOTE MIRROR FACE REPLACEMENT – FRONT DOOR

CAUTION: To minimize the chance of personal injury, gloves and safety glasses should be worn when removing broken glass.

NOTICE: When breaking mirror, cover painted surface of door to avoid damage.

Remove or Disconnect

1. Mirror face from the mirror by placing tape over mirror face, then breaking mirror face.
2. All pieces of glass from mirror frame.

Install or Connect

1. Mirror face to mirror frame by removing paper backing from back side of mirror face to expose adhesive.
2. Center mirror in mirror frame and press firmly to ensure adhesion of the mirror face to the mirror frame.

ELECTRIC MIRROR FACE REPLACEMENT – FRONT DOOR

CAUTION: To minimize the chance of personal injury, gloves and safety glasses should be worn.

Remove or Disconnect

- Glass from mirror housing.
  A. Pull up and out carefully with fingers.
  B. Disengage plastic clips.

Install or Connect

- Glass to mirror housing by engaging plastic clips.

ELECTRIC MOTOR REPLACEMENT – FRONT DOOR

Remove or Disconnect

1. Electric mirror and filler. Refer to "Electric Mirror – Front Door" in this section.
2. Glass from mirror housing. Refer to "Electric Mirror Face Replacement – Front Door" in this section.
3. Motor retaining screws.
4. Motor.

Install or Connect

1. Motor.
2. Motor retaining screws.
3. Glass to mirror housing. Refer to "Electric Mirror Face Replacement – Front Door" in this section.
4. Electric mirror and filler. Refer to "Electric Mirror – Front Door" in this section.

DOOR SPEAKER – FRONT DOOR

Figure 32

The front door may contain two speaker assemblies: upper assembly (tweeter) and lower assembly (woofer). Use the following procedures to replace these assemblies.

Remove or Disconnect

1. Door trim panel. Refer to "Trim Panel – Front Door" in this section.
2. Screws.
3. Speaker assembly.
4. Connector.

Install or Connect

1. Connector.
2. Speaker assembly.

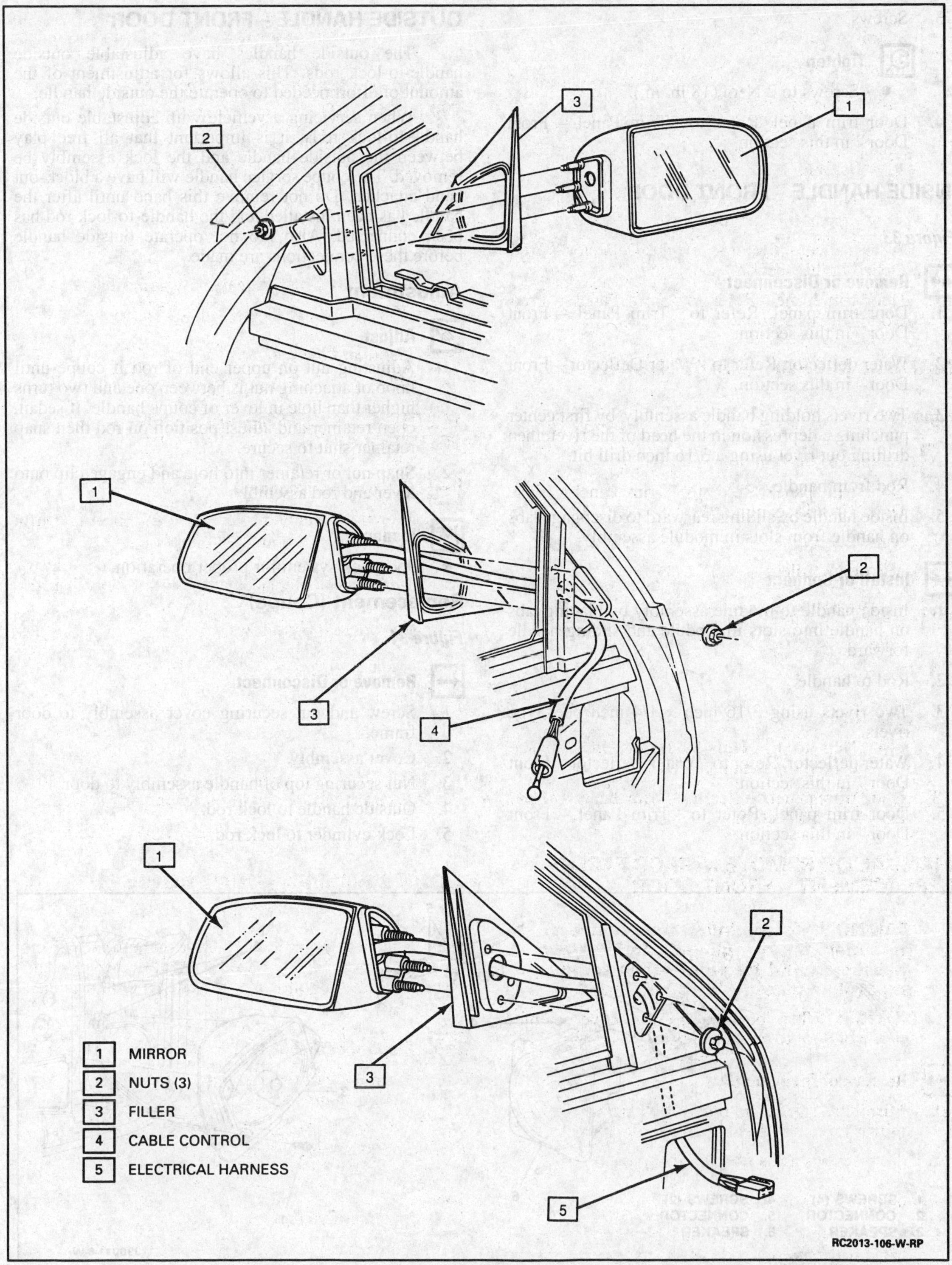
1
2
3
1
2
3
4
1
2
3
5
1 MIRROR
2 NUTS (3)
3 FILLER
4 CABLE CONTROL
5 ELECTRICAL HARNESS
RC2013-106-W-RP

Figure 31 Outside Mirrors

3. Screws.

Tighten

- Screws to 2 N•m (18 lb. in.).

4. Door trim panel. Refer to "Trim Panel – Front Door" in this section.

INSIDE HANDLE – FRONT DOOR

Figure 33

Remove or Disconnect

1. Door trim panel. Refer to "Trim Panel – Front Door" in this section.
2. Water deflector. Refer to "Water Deflector – Front Door" in this section.
3. Two rivets holding handle assembly, by first center punching a depression in the head of the rivet, then drilling out rivet using a 3/16 inch drill bit.
4. Rod from handle.
5. Inside handle by sliding rearward to disengage tabs on handle from slots in module assembly.

Install or Connect

1. Inside handle to module assembly by placing tabs on handle into slots in module and sliding handle forward.
2. Rod to handle.
3. Two rivets using 3/16 inch x 1/4 inch peel type rivets.
4. Water deflector. Refer to "Water Deflector – Front Door" in this section.
5. Door trim panel. Refer to "Trim Panel – Front Door" in this section.

OUTSIDE HANDLE – FRONT DOOR

The outside handles have adjustable outside handle-to-lock rods. This allows for adjustment of the amount of effort needed to operate the outside handle.

When servicing a vehicle with adjustable outside handle-to-lock rods, it is important that all free play between the outside handle and the lock assembly be removed. The coupe service handle will have a block-out band attached. Do not remove this band until after the handle has been installed and the handle-to-lock rod has been connected. Also, do not operate outside handle before these connections are made.

Adjustment

Adjust

1. Adjusting nut on upper end of rod if coupe until knob of attaching nut is between one and two turns higher than hole in lever of coupe handle. If sedan, open retainer and adjust position on rod then snap retainer shut to secure.
2. Snap nut or retainer into hole and engage clip onto lever and rod assembly.

Inspect

- Door lock system for proper operation.

Replacement (Coupe)

Figure 34

Remove or Disconnect

1. Screw and nut securing cover assembly to door frame.
2. Cover assembly.
3. Nut securing top of handle assembly to door.
4. Outside handle to lock rod.
5. Lock cylinder to lock rod.

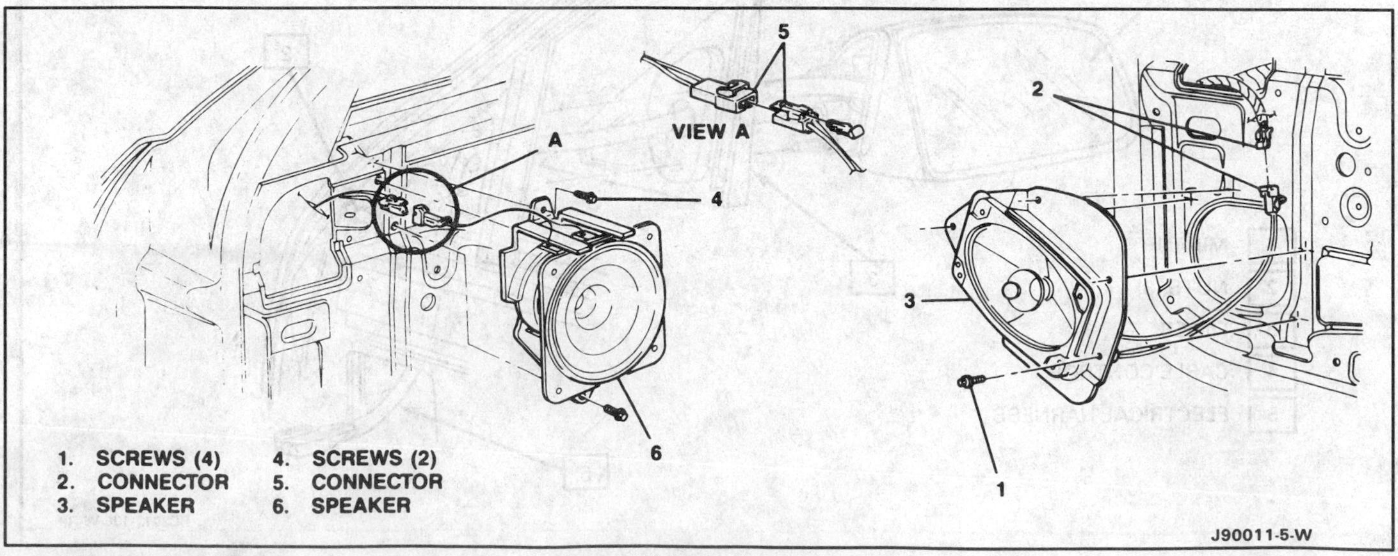
5
VIEW A
A
4
2
3
6
1
1. SCREWS (4)
2. CONNECTOR
3. SPEAKER
4. SCREWS (2)
5. CONNECTOR
6. SPEAKER
J90011-5-W

Figure 32 Door Speakers

6. Handle assembly.
   - If replacing handle only, remove lock cylinder and anti-theft shield and transfer to new handle assembly. Refer to "Lock Cylinder – Front Door" in this section.

Install or Connect

1. Handle assembly.
2. Lock cylinder to lock rod.
3. Outside handle to lock rod.
4. Nut securing handle assembly to door.

Tighten

- Nut to 4 N•m (35 lb. in.).

5. Cover assembly.
6. Nut and screw securing cover assembly to door.

Tighten

- Nut to 3 N•m (27 lb. in.).
- Screw to 2 N•m (18 lb. in.).

Replacement – Front Door (Sedan)

Figure 35

Remove or Disconnect

1. Door trim panel. Refer to "Trim Panel – Front Door" in this section.
2. Water deflector. Refer to "Water Deflector – Front Door" in this section.
3. Nuts.
4. Handle by disengaging handle to lock rod from handle lever.

Install or Connect

1. Handle by engaging slot in handle lever over handle to lock rod.
2. Nuts.

Tighten

- Nuts to 7 N•m (62 lb. in.).

3. Water deflector. Refer to "Water Deflector – Front Door" in this section.
4. Door trim panel. Refer to "Trim Panel – Front Door" in this section.

INSIDE LOCKING ROD TO LOCK – FRONT DOOR

Figures 33 and 35

Remove or Disconnect

1. Lock module. Refer to "Lock Module – Front Door" in this section.
2. Rod from retainer.

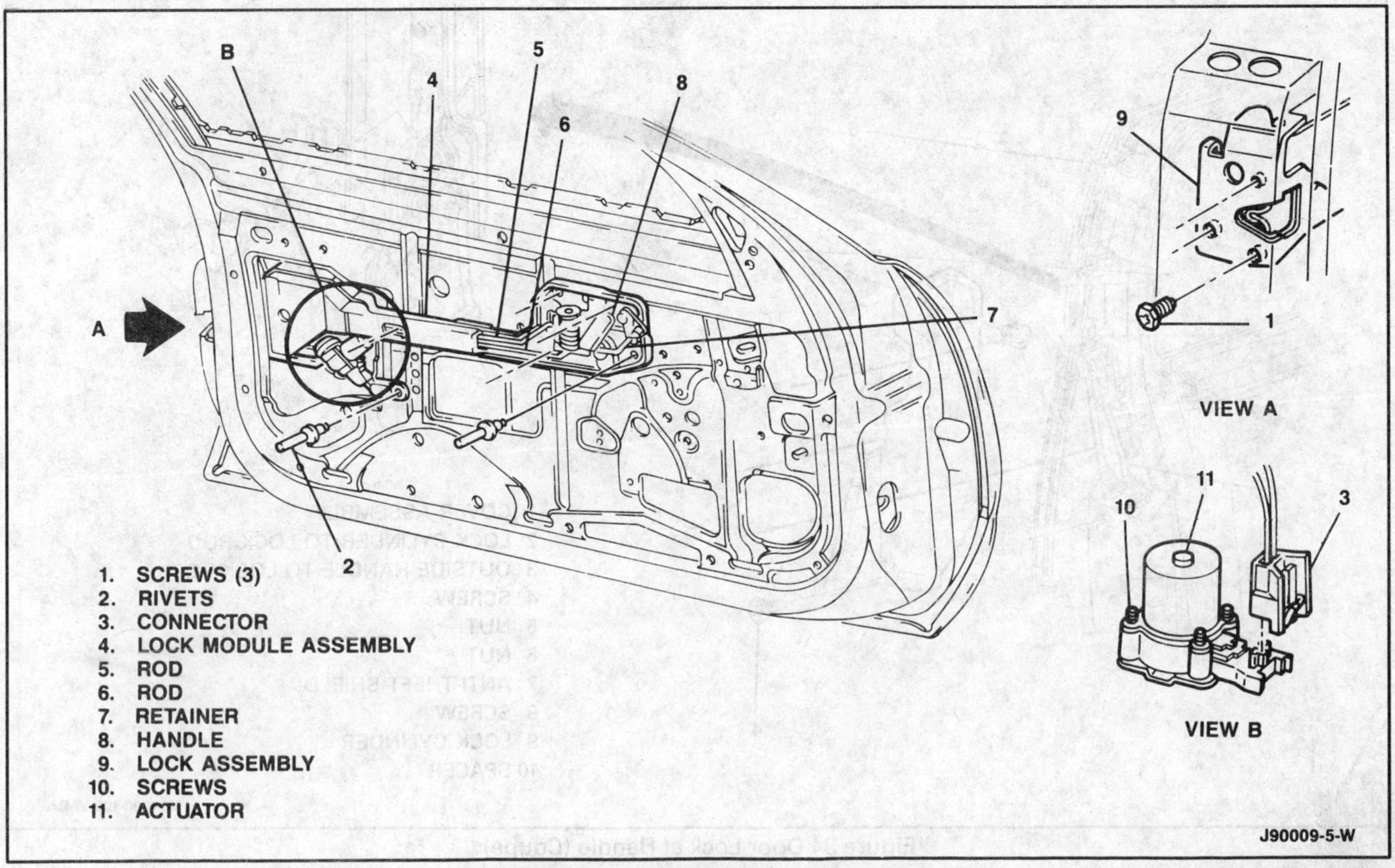
B
5
4
8
6
9
A
7
1
VIEW A
2
11
10
3
VIEW B
1. SCREWS (3)
2. RIVETS
3. CONNECTOR
4. LOCK MODULE ASSEMBLY
5. ROD
6. ROD
7. RETAINER
8. HANDLE
9. LOCK ASSEMBLY
10. SCREWS
11. ACTUATOR
J90009-5-W

Figure 33 Door Lock Module (Coupe)

3. Rod from lock.
4. Rod from power lock actuator.
5. Rod.

Install or Connect

1. Rod to power lock actuator.
2. Rod to lock.
3. Rod to retainer,
4. Lock module. Refer to "Lock Module – Front Door" in this section.

INSIDE HANDLE TO LOCK ROD – FRONT DOOR

Figures 33 and 35

Remove or Disconnect

1. Lock module. Refer to "Lock Module – Front Door" in this section.
2. Rod from inside handle.
3. Rod from lock.

Install or Connect

1. Rod to lock.
2. Rod to inside handle.
3. Lock module. Refer to "Lock Module – Front Door" in this section.

DOOR LOCK SYSTEM – FRONT DOOR

The door lock system is modular in design. With this type of design, all the parts are contained in one unit (the module assembly). The entire module assembly is removed when repair to any component is required. The exception is the power lock actuator which can be serviced on the vehicle. In order to properly evaluate the lock system after replacement part has been installed, the following operational checks should be made.

Inspect

1. Insert key into cylinder. While holding key in the neutral (pull-out) position, actuate the inside locking button to the fully locked position and back to the fully unlocked position. There must be no forced movement of the key out of neutral position during the entire cycle. The key must be able to be removed when the inside locking button is held in both the fully locked and unlocked positions.
2. Turn key to fully locked position and return it to the neutral (pull-out) position. Actuate both outside and inside handles to ensure that the door will not open.
3. Turn key to the fully unlocked position and return it to the neutral (pull-out) position. Actuate both outside and inside handles to ensure door will open.

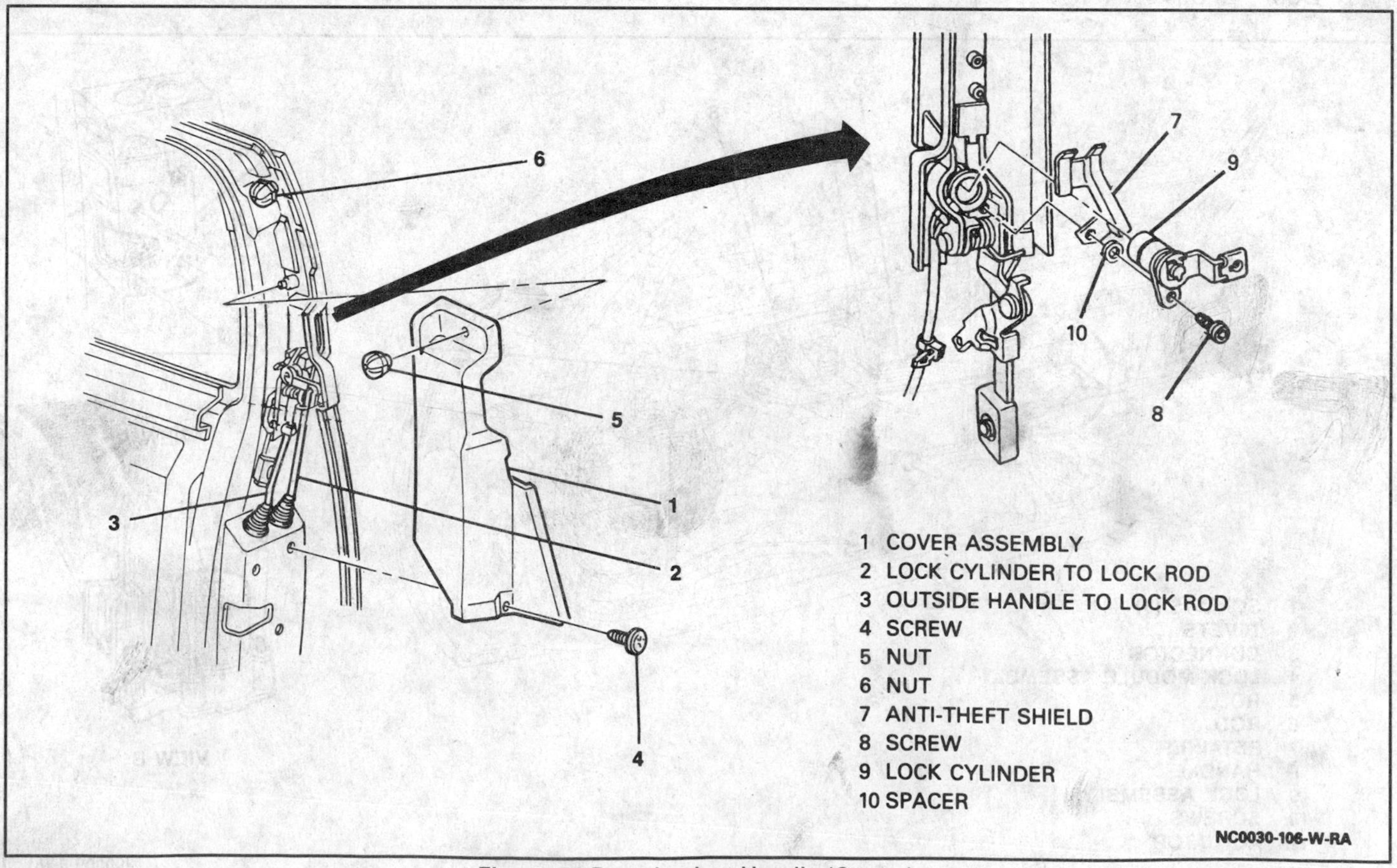
6
5
1
2
3
4
7
9
10
8
1 COVER ASSEMBLY
2 LOCK CYLINDER TO LOCK ROD
3 OUTSIDE HANDLE TO LOCK ROD
4 SCREW
5 NUT
6 NUT
7 ANTI-THEFT SHIELD
8 SCREW
9 LOCK CYLINDER
10 SPACER
NC0030-106-W-RA

Figure 34 Door Lock at Handle (Coupe)

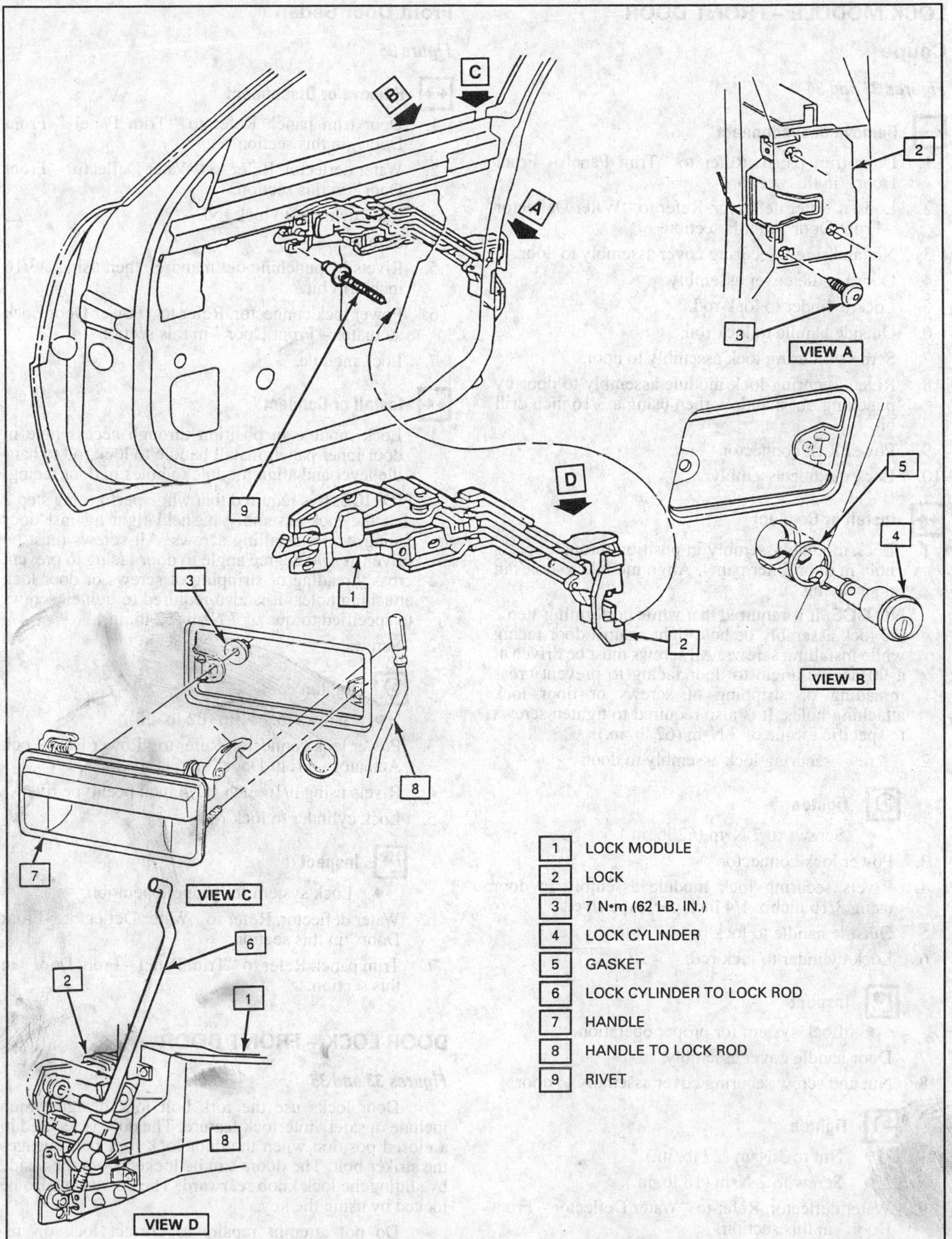
A
B
C
D
VIEW A
VIEW B
VIEW C
VIEW D
1 LOCK MODULE
2 LOCK
3 7 N•m (62 LB. IN.)
4 LOCK CYLINDER
5 GASKET
6 LOCK CYLINDER TO LOCK ROD
7 HANDLE
8 HANDLE TO LOCK ROD
9 RIVET
RC2015-106-W-RP

Figure 35 Door Lock System – Front Door (Sedan)

LOCK MODULE – FRONT DOOR

Coupe

Figures 33 and 34

Remove or Disconnect

1. Door trim panel. Refer to "Trim Panel – Front Door" in this section.
2. Loosen water deflector. Refer to "Water Deflector – Front Door" in this section.
3. Nut and screw securing cover assembly to door.
4. Door handle cover assembly.
5. Lock cylinder to lock rod.
6. Outside handle to lock rod.
7. Screws securing lock assembly to door.
8. Rivets securing lock module assembly to door by punching out mandrel, then using a 3/16 inch drill bit.
9. Power lock connector.
10. Lock module assembly.

Install or Connect

1. Lock module assembly in position through access hole in door inner panel. Align module to holes in door facing.

NOTICE: It is required that while performing step 2 the lock assembly be held tight against door facing while installing screws. All screws must be driven at a 90 degree angle to door facing to prevent cross threading or stripping of screws or door lock attaching holes. It is also required to tighten screws to specific torque of 7 N•m (62 lb. in.).

2. Screws securing lock assembly to door.

Tighten

- Screws to 7 N•m (62 lb. in.).

3. Power lock connector.
4. Rivets securing lock module assembly to door using 3/16 inch x 1/4 inch peel type rivets.
5. Outside handle to lock rod.
6. Lock cylinder to lock rod.

Inspect

- Lock system for proper operation.

7. Door handle cover assembly.
8. Nut and screw securing cover assembly to door.

Tighten

- Nut to 3 N•m (27 lb. in.).
- Screw to 2 N•m (18 lb. in.).

9. Water deflector. Refer to "Water Deflector – Front Door" in this section.
10. Door trim panel. Refer to "Trim Panel – Front Door" in this section.

Front Door Sedan

Figure 35

Remove or Disconnect

1. Door trim panel. Refer to "Trim Panel – Front Door" in this section.
2. Water deflector. Refer to "Water Deflector – Front Door" in this section.
3. Lock cylinder to lock rod.
4. Screws.
5. Rivets by punching out mandrel, then using a 3/16 inch drill bit.
6. Power lock connector. Refer to "Power Door Lock Actuator – Front Door" in this section.
7. Lock module.

Install or Connect

1. Lock module in position through access hole in door inner panel. Install handle to lock rod to handle lever and align module to holes in door facing.

NOTICE: It is required that while performing step 2 that the lock assembly be held tight against door facing while installing screws. All screws must be driven at a 90 degree angle to door facing to prevent cross threading or stripping of screws or door lock attaching holes. It is also required to tighten screws to specified torque of 7 N•m (62 lb. in.).

2. Screws.

Tighten

- Screws to 7 N•m (62 lb. in.).

3. Power lock connector. Refer to "Power Door Lock Actuator – Front Door" in this section.
4. Rivets using 3/16 inch x 1/4 inch peel type rivets.
5. Lock cylinder to lock rod.

Inspect

- Lock system for proper operation.

6. Water deflector. Refer to "Water Deflector – Front Door" in this section.
7. Trim panel. Refer to "Trim Panel – Front Door" in this section.

DOOR LOCK – FRONT DOOR

Figures 33 and 35

Door locks use the fork bolt lock design which includes a safety interlock feature. The door is secured in a closed position when the door lock fork bolt engages the striker bolt. The doors can be locked from the inside by sliding the lock knob rearward. The doors can also be locked by using the key.

Do not attempt repairs to correct lock discrepancies. Make corrections through replacement of lock assembly.

Coupe

Figure 33

Remove or Disconnect

1. Lock module. Refer to "Lock Module – Front Door" in this section.
2. All rods attached to lock.
3. Lock from lock module by bending three tabs outward.
4. Lock.

Install or Connect

1. Lock to lock module by bending three tabs inward.
2. All rods disconnected in step 2 of removal procedure.
3. Lock module. Refer to "Lock Module – Front Door" in this section.

Sedan

Figure 35

Remove or Disconnect

1. Lock module. Refer to "Lock Module – Front Door" in this section.
2. Lock rods.
3. Rivets securing lock to lock module.
4. Lock from lock module.

Install or Connect

1. Lock to lock module.
2. Rivets.
3. Lock rods.
4. Lock module. Refer to "Lock Module – Front Door" in this section.

DOOR LOCK STRIKER – FRONT DOOR

Figures 36 and 37

Tool Required:

J 29843-9 Door Lock Striker and Seat Belt Torx Wrench

The door lock striker consists of a single metal bolt and washer assembly that is threaded into a tapped plate in the body lock pillar. The door is secured in the closed position when the door lock fork bolt snaps over and engages the striker bolt. The striker has provisions for fore and aft adjustment only.

Adjust

To determine if striker fore and aft adjustment is required, proceed as follows:

1. Make certain door is properly aligned.
2. Apply modeling clay or body caulking compound to lock bolt opening.

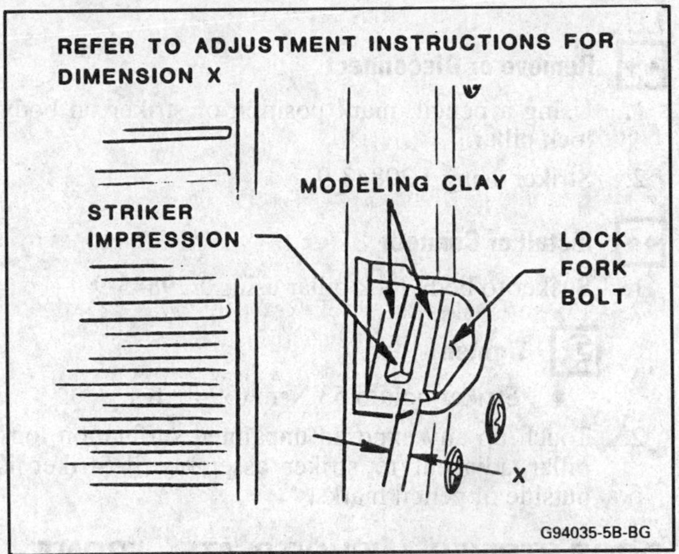

REFER TO ADJUSTMENT INSTRUCTIONS FOR DIMENSION X
MODELING CLAY
STRIKER IMPRESSION
LOCK FORK BOLT
X
G94035-5B-BG

Figure 36 Lock to Striker Fore and Aft Adjustment

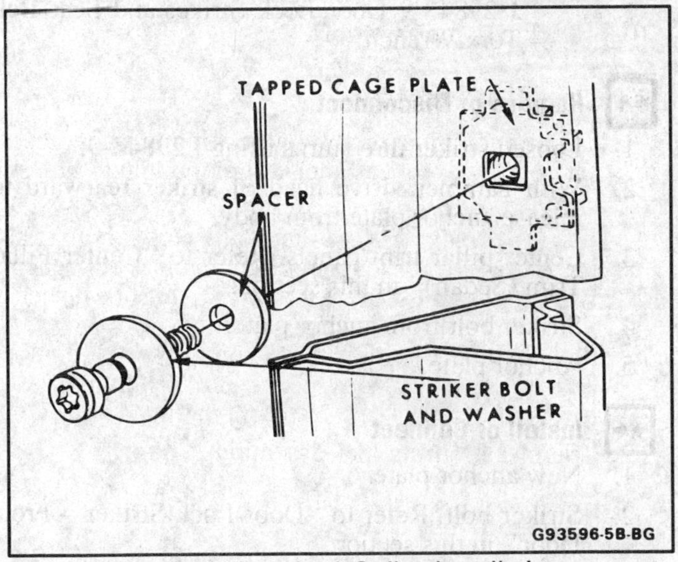

TAPPED CAGE PLATE
SPACER
STRIKER BOLT AND WASHER
G93596-5B-BG

Figure 37 Door Lock Striker Installation

3. Close door only as far as necessary for striker bolt to form an impression in clay or caulking compound. Complete door closing will make clay removal very difficult.
4. Striker impression should be centered fore and aft. The minimal allowable measurement for dimension X is 2 mm (3/32 inch). The maximum allowable measurement for dimension X is 4 mm (5/32 inch). A 2 mm (3/32 inch) spacer, part no. 4469196 or equivalent, can be used to achieve the desired alignment.
5. If adjustment is necessary, remove the striker bolt using J 29843-9. Add or remove spacers as required.

Tighten

- Striker bolt to 53 N•m (39 lb. ft.).

Remove or Disconnect

1. Using a pencil, mark position of striker on body lock pillar.
2. Striker using J 29843-9.

Install or Connect

1. Striker to body lock pillar using J 29843-9.

   Tighten

   - Striker bolt to 53 N•m (39 lb. ft.).

2. Touch up any exposed unpainted surface on lock pillar adjacent to striker assembly if striker is outside of pencil marks.

DOOR STRIKER ANCHOR PLATE – FRONT DOOR

Tool Required:

J 29843-9 Door Lock Striker and Seat Belt Torx Wrench

Remove or Disconnect

1. Loosen striker three turns using J 29843-9.
2. With hammer, drive head of striker rearward to release anchor plate from body.
3. Center pillar trim panels. Refer to "Center Pillar Trim (Sedan)" in this section.
4. Striker bolt from anchor plate.
5. Anchor plate.

Install or Connect

1. New anchor plate.
2. Striker bolt. Refer to "Door Lock Striker – Front Door" in this section.

Adjust

- For striker adjustment refer to "Door Lock Striker – Front Door" in this section.

PASSIVE RESTRAINT CLEVIS AND STRIKER – FRONT DOOR

The clevis and striker are used to ensure that the top of the door is secured to the body. They aid in providing the anchoring required by the passive restraint system.

CAUTION: The striker and clevis make the door interlock with the roof rail in a crash. If someone were to remove them, the door couldn't interlock with the roof rail in a crash and might spring open. People inside could be thrown out of the car much more easily with the door open. Be sure you never remove the striker or the clevis when you're doing repair work around them.

Clevis

Figure 38 and 39

Adjust

1. Remove body lock pillar molding, if coupe. Refer to ROOF (SECTION 10-9).
2. Remove cover, if coupe.
3. Loosen screws and adjust clevis up or down as required to ensure alignment with striker.

   Tighten

   - Screws to 24 N•m (18 lb. ft.).

4. Replace cover, if removed.
5. Install body lock pillar moldings, if removed. Refer to ROOF (SECTION 10-9).

Remove or Disconnect

1. Body lock pillar molding, if coupe. Refer to ROOF (SECTION 10-9).
2. Cover, if coupe.
3. Screws.
4. Clevis.

Install or Connect

1. Clevis.
2. Screws.

   Tighten

   - Screws to 24 N•m (18 lb. ft.).

3. Cover, if removed.
4. Body lock pillar molding, if removed. Refer to ROOF (SECTION 10-9).

Striker

Figure 40

Tool Required:

J 29843-9 Door Lock Striker and Seat Belt Torx Wrench

Remove or Disconnect

- Striker bolt using J 29843-9.

Install or Connect

- Striker bolt using J 29843-9.

  Tighten

  - Striker bolt to 24 N•m (18 lb. ft.).

POWER DOOR LOCK ACTUATOR – FRONT DOOR

The automatic door lock system has an actuator in each door which actuates the lock through a linkage. The system is actuated by the chime module in the convenience center or by any door lock switch. All doors lock

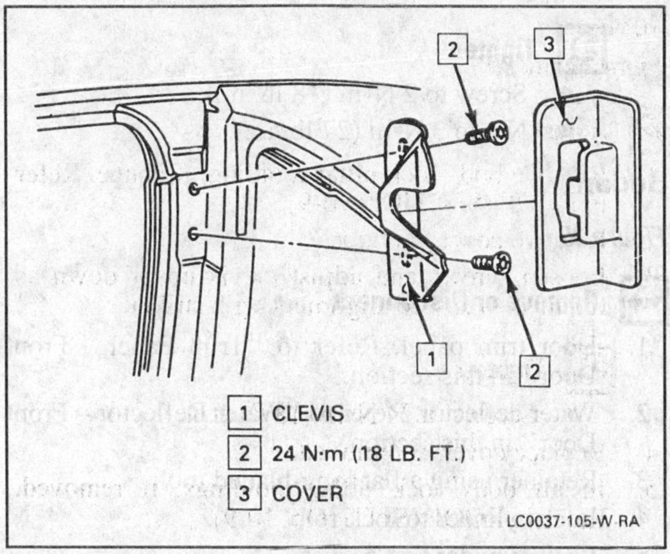
1 CLEVIS
2 24 N·m (18 LB. FT.)
3 COVER
LC0037-105-W-RA

Figure 38 Passenger Restraint Clevis Installation (Coupe)

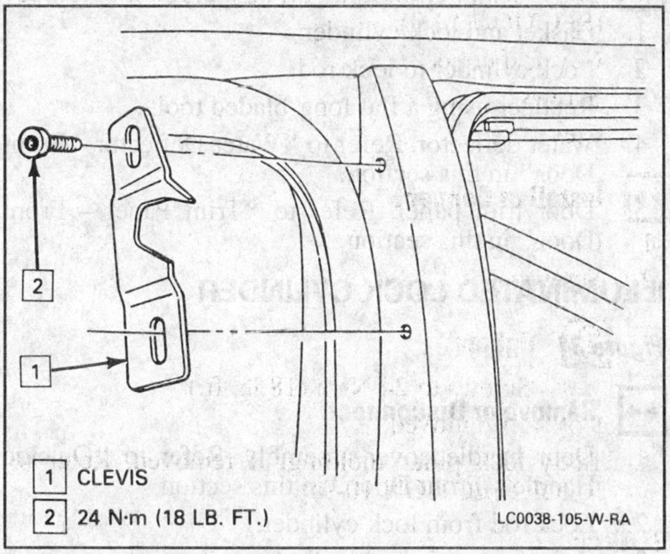
1 CLEVIS
2 24 N·m (18 LB. FT.)
LC0038-105-W-RA

Figure 39 Passenger Restraint Clevis Installation (Sedan)

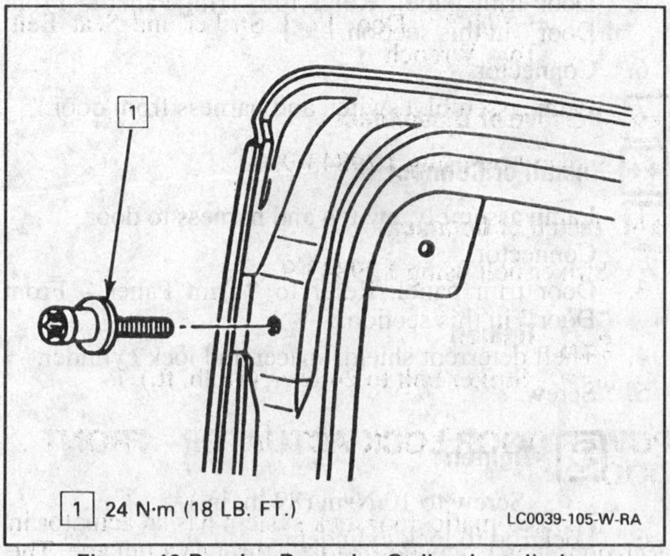
1 24 N·m (18 LB. FT.)
LC0039-105-W-RA

Figure 40 Passive Restraint Striker Installation

or unlock at the same time except when the actuator is manually activated by a lock rod. Each actuator has an internal circuit breaker which may require one to three minutes to reset.

For electrical diagnosis, refer to ELECTRICAL DIAGNOSIS (SECTION 8A-131).

Coupe

Figure 33

Remove or Disconnect

1. Door trim panel. Refer to "Trim Panel – Front Door" in this section.
2. Water deflector. Refer to "Water Deflector – Front Door" in this section.
3. Two screws on opposite corners of actuator.
4. Electrical connector.
5. Actuator by disengaging from linkage.

Install or Connect

1. Actuator to linkage.
2. Electrical connector.
3. Screws.

Inspect

- For proper operation by cycling system.

4. Water deflector. Refer to "Water Deflector – Front Door" in this section.
5. Door trim panel. Refer to "Trim Panel – Front Door" in this section.

Sedan

Figure 41

Remove or Disconnect

1. Door trim panel. Refer to "Trim Panel – Front Door" in this section.
2. Water deflector. Refer to "Water Deflector – Front Door" in this section.
3. Rivet by punching out mandrel, then using a 3/16 inch drill bit.
4. Clip and electrical connector.
5. Actuator by disengaging from rod.

Install or Connect

1. Actuator to rod.
2. Electrical connector and clip.
3. Rivets using 3/16 inch x 1/4 inch peel type rivets.

Inspect

- For proper operation by cycling system.

4. Water deflector. Refer to "Water Deflector – Front Door" in this section.
5. Door trim panel. Refer to "Trim Panel – Front Door" in this section.

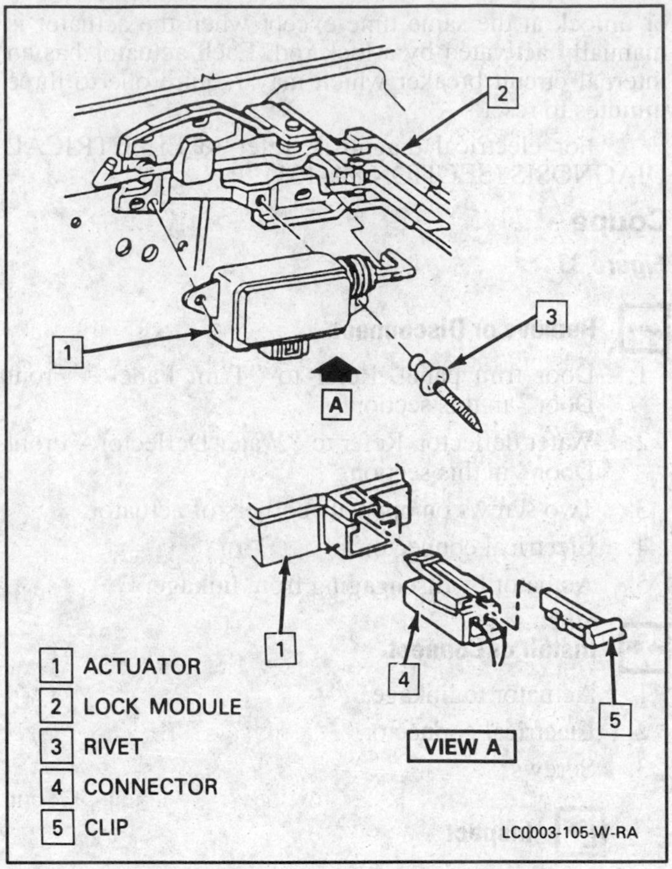
2
3
1
A
1
4
5
1 ACTUATOR
2 LOCK MODULE
3 RIVET
4 CONNECTOR
5 CLIP
VIEW A
LC0003-105-W-RA
Figure 41 Power Lock Actuator (Sedan)

LOCK CYLINDER – FRONT DOOR

Coupe

Figure 34

Remove or Disconnect

1. Screw and nut securing cover assembly to door.
2. Cover assembly.
3. Lock cylinder to lock rod.
4. Screw securing anti-theft shield.
5. Lock cylinder.
6. Anti-theft shield.

Install or Connect

1. Anti-theft shield.
2. Lock cylinder.
3. Screw securing anti-theft shield.

Tighten

- Screw to 10 N•m (89 lb. in.).

4. Lock cylinder to lock rod.
5. Cover assembly.
6. Screw and nut securing cover assembly to door.

Tighten

- Screw to 2 N•m (18 lb. in.).
- Nut to 3 N•m (27 lb. in.).

Sedan

Figure 35

Remove or Disconnect

1. Door trim panel. Refer to "Trim Panel – Front Door" in this section.
2. Water deflector. Refer to "Water Deflector – Front Door" in this section.
3. Retainer using a flat long-bladed tool.
4. Lock cylinder to lock rod.
5. Lock cylinder and gasket.

Install or Connect

1. Gasket and lock cylinder.
2. Lock cylinder to lock rod.
3. Retainer using a flat long-bladed tool.
4. Water deflector. Refer to "Water Deflector – Front Door" in this section.
5. Door trim panel. Refer to "Trim Panel – Front Door" in this section.

ILLUMINATED LOCK CYLINDER

Figure 34

Remove or Disconnect

1. Door handle cover assembly. Refer to "Outside Handle – Front Door" in this section.
2. Lock rod from lock cylinder.
3. Screw securing lock cylinder to door.
4. Lock cylinder, spacer and theft deterrent shield.
5. Door trim panel. Refer to "Trim Panel – Front Door" in this section.
6. Connector.
7. Lamp assembly, switch and harness from door.

Install or Connect

1. Lamp assembly, switch and harness to door.
2. Connector.
3. Door trim panel. Refer to "Trim Panel – Front Door" in this section.
4. Theft deterrent shield, spacer and lock cylinder.
5. Screw.

Tighten

- Screw to 10 N•m (89 lb. in.).

6. Lock rod to lock cylinder.
7. Door handle cover assembly. Refer to "Outside Handle – Front Door" in this section.

DOOR – FRONT DOOR

Figures 42 and 43

Remove or Disconnect

1. Rubber conduit from door.
2. Wire harness from door.
3. Body side check link screw.
4. Support door.
5. Hinge pin bolts.
6. Door with aid of helper.

Install or Connect

1. Door with aid of helper.
2. Hinge pin bolt.

Important

- Apply Adhesive/Sealant Compound (part no. 12345493, or equivalent) to hinge pin bolt before reusing.

Tighten

- Hinge pin bolt to 14 N•m (124 lb. in.).

3. Remove support.
4. Body side check link screw.

Tighten

- Screw to 24 N•m (18 lb. ft.).

5. Wire harness to door.
6. Rubber conduit to door.

DOOR ADJUSTMENT – FRONT DOOR

Adjust

- Door up or down and in or out by loosening nuts securing hinges to door and repositioning door as needed.

Tighten

- Nuts to 27 N•m (20 lb. ft.).

DOOR REPLACEMENT – FRONT DOOR

Remove or Disconnect

1. Door trim panel. Refer to "Trim Panel – Front Door" in this section.
2. Seat belt retractors. Refer to SEAT BELTS (SECTION 10-11).
3. Door speakers. Refer to "Door Speaker – Front Door" in this section.
4. Electrical connectors.
5. Inner belt sealing strip. Refer to "Inner Belt Sealing Strip – Front Door" in this section.

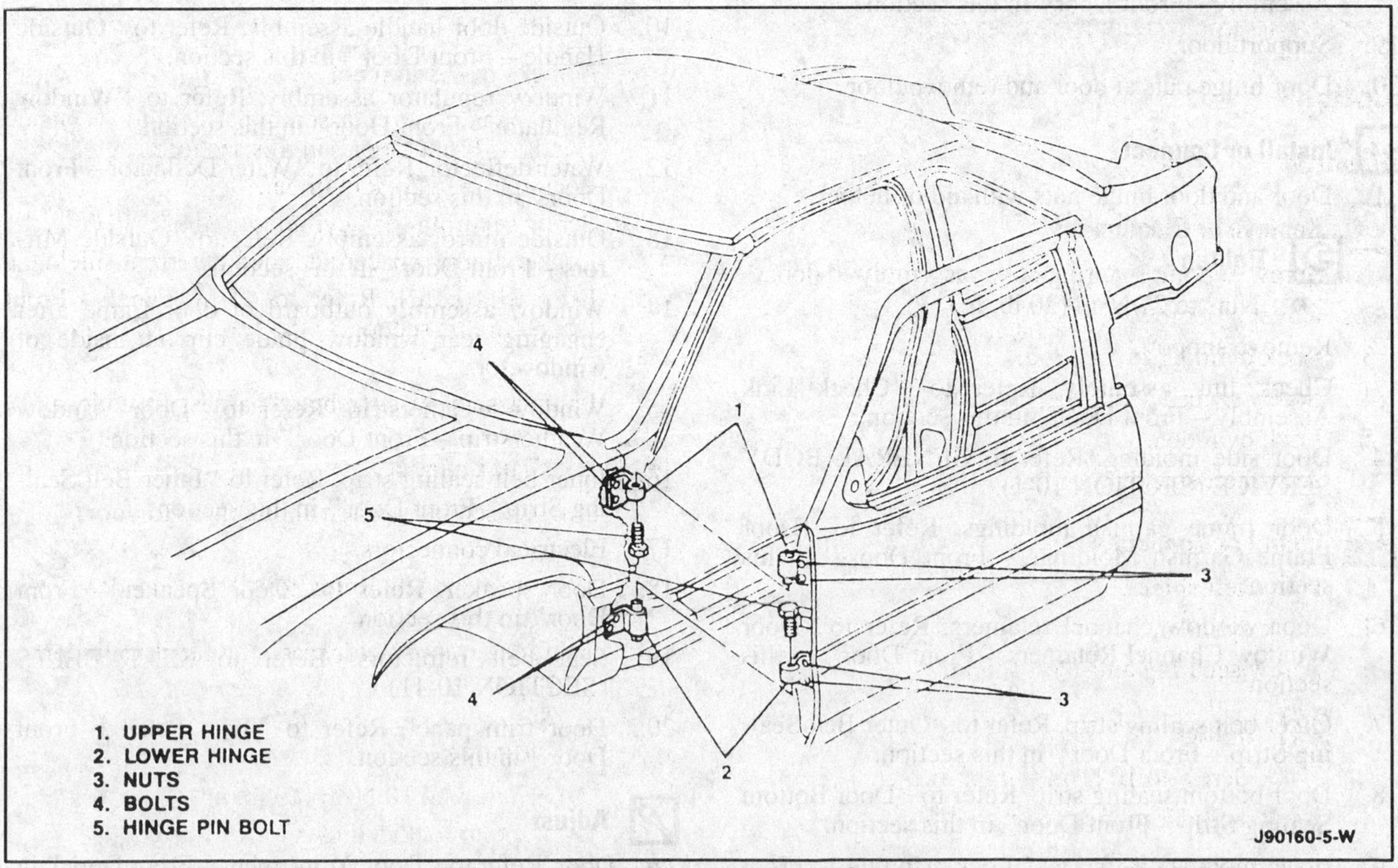
4
1
5
3
4
3
2
1. UPPER HINGE
2. LOWER HINGE
3. NUTS
4. BOLTS
5. HINGE PIN BOLT
J90160-5-W

Figure 42 Door Hinge Assembly (Coupe)

6. Window weatherstrip. Refer to "Door Window Weatherstrip – Front Door" in this section.
7. Window assembly outboard of door frame after disengaging rear window guide retainer clip at inside of window.
8. Outside mirror assembly. Refer to "Outside Mirrors – Front Door" in this section.
9. Water deflector. Refer to "Water Deflector – Front Door" in this section.
10. Window regulator assembly. Refer to "Window Regulator – Front Door" in this section.
11. Outside door handle assembly. Refer to "Outside Handle – Front Door" in this section.
12. Lock module. Refer to "Lock Module – Front Door" in this section.
13. Door bottom sealing strip. Refer to "Door Bottom Sealing Strip – Front Door" in this section.
14. Outer belt sealing strip. Refer to "Outer Belt Sealing Strip – Front Door" in this section.
15. Door window channel retainers. Refer to "Door Window Channel Retainers – Front Door" in this section.
16. Door frame garnish moldings. Refer to "Door Frame Garnish Moldings – Front Door" in this section.
17. Door molding. Refer to GENERAL BODY SERVICE (SECTION 10-1).
18. Check link assembly. Refer to "Check Link Assembly – Front Door" in this section.
19. Support door.
20. Door hinge nuts at door and remove door.

Install or Connect

1. Door and door hinge nuts with aid of helper.

Tighten

- Nuts to 27 N•m (20 lb. ft.).

2. Remove support.
3. Check link assembly. Refer to "Check Link Assembly – Front Door" in this section.
4. Door side molding. Refer to GENERAL BODY SERVICE (SECTION 10-1).
5. Door frame garnish moldings. Refer to "Door Frame Garnish Moldings – Front Door" in this section.
6. Door window channel retainers. Refer to "Door Window Channel Retainers – Front Door" in this section.
7. Outer belt sealing strip. Refer to "Outer Belt Sealing Strip – Front Door" in this section.
8. Door bottom sealing strip. Refer to "Door Bottom Sealing Strip – Front Door" in this section.
9. Lock module. Refer to "Lock Module – Front Door" in this section.

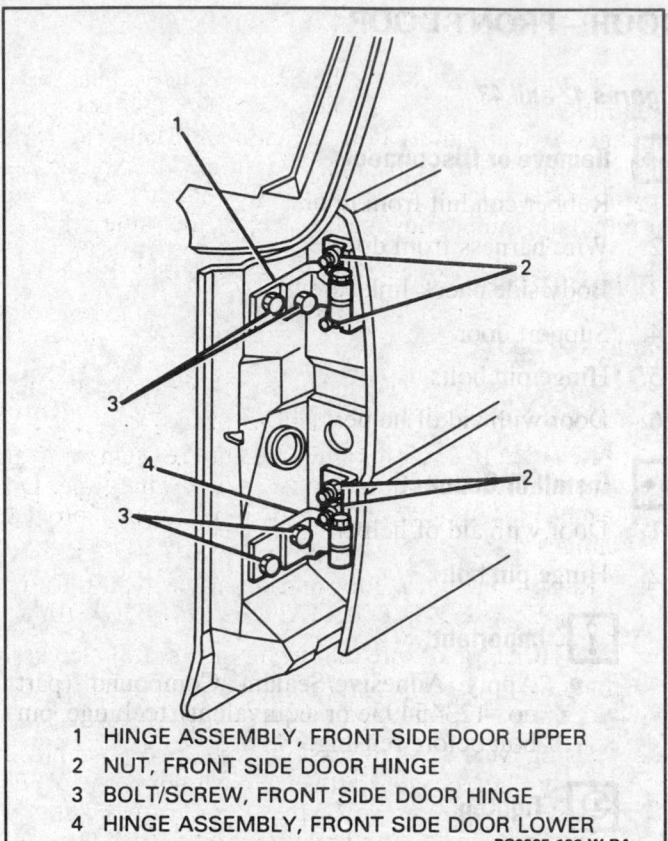

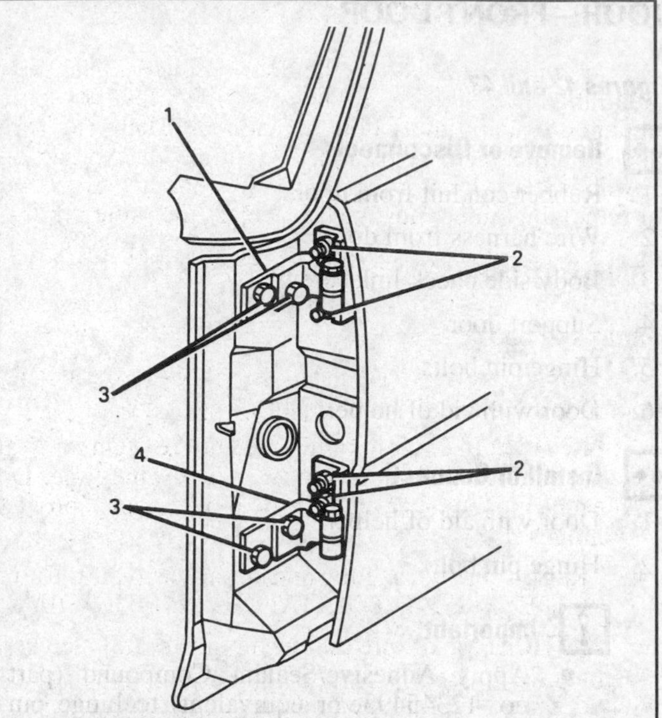
1
2
3
4
2
3
1 HINGE ASSEMBLY, FRONT SIDE DOOR UPPER
2 NUT, FRONT SIDE DOOR HINGE
3 BOLT/SCREW, FRONT SIDE DOOR HINGE
4 HINGE ASSEMBLY, FRONT SIDE DOOR LOWER
PC0005-106-W-RA

Figure 43 Door Hinge Assembly – Front Door (Sedan)

10. Outside door handle assembly. Refer to "Outside Handle – Front Door" in this section.
11. Window regulator assembly. Refer to "Window Regulator – Front Door" in this section.
12. Water deflector. Refer to "Water Deflector – Front Door" in this section.
13. Outside mirror assembly. Refer to "Outside Mirrors – Front Door" in this section.
14. Window assembly outboard of door frame after engaging rear window guide clip at inside of window.
15. Window weatherstrip. Refer to "Door Window Weatherstrip – Front Door" in this section.
16. Inner belt sealing strip. Refer to "Inner Belt Sealing Strip – Front Door" in this section.
17. Electrical connectors.
18. Door speaker. Refer to "Door Speaker – Front Door" in this section.
19. Seat belt retractors. Refer to SEAT BELTS (SECTION 10-11).
20. Door trim panel. Refer to "Trim Panel – Front Door" in this section.

Adjust

- Door. Refer to "Door Adjustment – Front Door" in this section.

DOOR HINGE SYSTEM – FRONT DOOR

Hinges are bolted to the door and body. The door side hinges have elongated holes which allow for some up and down and in and out adjustment. There is a fore and aft adjustment provision. If a single door hinge on any door at any location requires replacement, the second or remaining hinge must be replaced at the same time.

HINGE ASSEMBLY – FRONT DOOR

Figures 42 and 44

Hinges are serviced as an assembly (body side and door side are one unit) and in pairs.

NOTICE: In order to minimize door realignment, do not remove both door hinges at the same time. Do each hinge separately, and replace any broken hinges first.

1. Raise vehicle partially, and suitably support. Refer to GENERAL INFORMATION (SECTION 0A).

   NOTICE: Make sure that the doors are fully latched onto the lock striker and the doors are not locked or doors may be damaged during hinge replacement.

2. Using two pieces of masking tape, place one piece to bridge the gap between the door and rocker panel and the second piece to bridge the gap between the door and rear door or quarter panel.
3. Cut the tape at the gap area using a utility knife or other suitable tool.
4. Remove tire and wheel assembly. Refer to TIRES AND WHEELS (SECTION 3E).
5. Remove front fender liner partially for access. Refer to BODY FRONT END (SECTION 10-5).
6. Remove insulator cover.
7. Clean hinge mounting surfaces on door and body with a rag and mark hinge locations on the body surfaces with a grease pencil or other suitable marker.
8. Bolts and nuts securing hinge at door and body.
9. Remove hinge.
10. Install new hinge within previously marked locations and lightly tighten bolts and nuts.
11. Repeat steps 8 through 10 for remaining hinge.
12. Install tire and wheel assembly. Refer to TIRES AND WHEELS (SECTION 3E).
13. Lower vehicle.
14. Inspect edges of tape on door and align door as necessary.
15. Raise vehicle partially.
16. Remove tire and wheel assembly. Refer to TIRES AND WHEELS (SECTION 3E).
17. Tighten bolts and nuts.

Tighten

- Bolts to 46 N•m (34 lb. ft.).
- Nuts to 27 N•m (20 lb. ft.).

18. Install insulator cover.
19. Install front fender liner. Refer to BODY FRONT END (SECTION 10-5).
20. Install tire and wheel assembly. Refer to TIRES AND WHEELS (SECTION 3E).
21. Remove reference tape from door, rocker and quarter.
22. Lower vehicle.

CHECK LINK ASSEMBLY – FRONT DOOR

Figures 44 and 45

The check link assembly is the door hold-open feature.

Remove or Disconnect

1. Door trim panel. Refer to "Trim Panel – Front Door" in this section.
2. Water deflector. Refer to "Water Deflector – Front Door" in this section.
3. Screw securing check link to body.
4. Sealing grommet.
5. Screws securing check link to door.
6. Check link through door inner panel access hole.

Install or Connect

1. Check link to door.
2. Screws securing check link to door.

Tighten

- Screws to 6 N•m (53 lb. in.).

3. Sealing grommet.
4. Screw securing check link to body.

Tighten

- Screw to 24 N•m (18 lb. ft.).

Inspect

- For proper operation of check link.

5. Water deflector. Refer to "Water Deflector – Front Door" in this section.
6. Door trim panel. Refer to "Trim Panel – Front Door" in this section.

CONDUIT – FRONT DOOR

Remove or Disconnect

1. Door trim panel. Refer to "Trim Panel – Front Door" in this section.
2. Electrical connectors.
3. Conduit bolt from door.
4. Carpet retainer.
5. Pull carpet back.
6. Conduit.

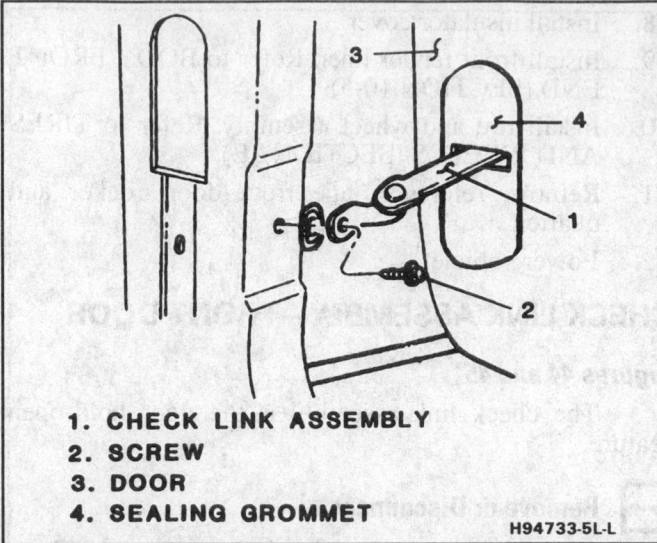

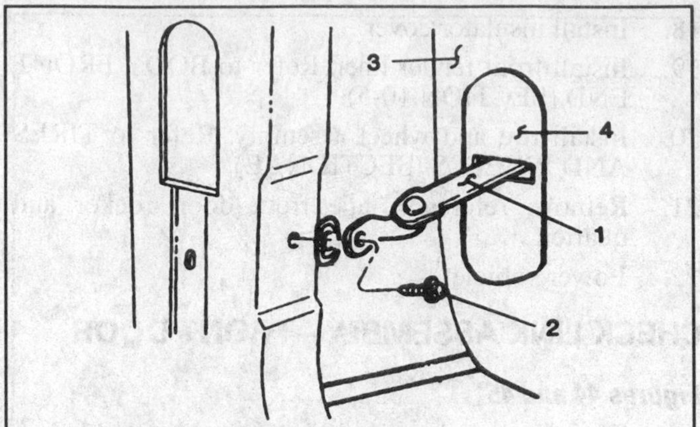
1. CHECK LINK ASSEMBLY
2. SCREW
3. DOOR
4. SEALING GROMMET
H94733-5L-L

Figure 44 Door Check Link to Body Installation

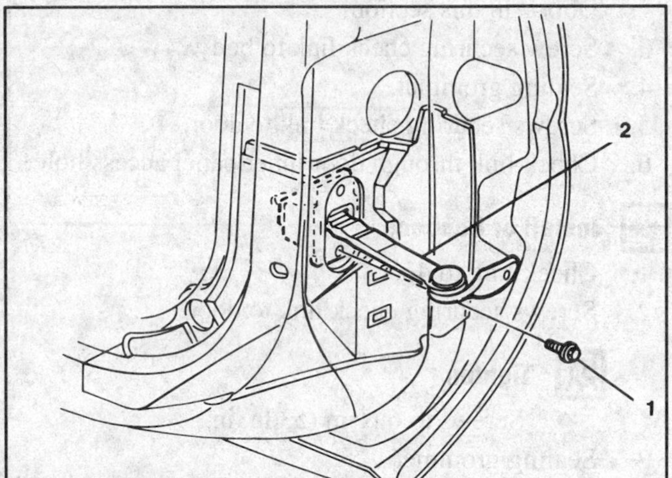
1. SCREWS (2)
2. CHECK LINK ASSEMBLY
J90017-5-W

Figure 45 Door Check Link Installation

Install or Connect

1. Conduit.
2. Carpet back into position.
3. Carpet retainer.
4. Conduit bolt.

Tighten

- Bolt to 2 N•m (18 lb. in.).

5. Electrical connectors.
6. Door trim panel. Refer to "Trim Panel – Front Door" in this section.

DOOR WINDOW SYSTEM – FRONT DOOR

This portion of the manual contains the service operations necessary to remove and adjust the window and all hardware pertaining to the window system. Any work performed on the window system hardware requires the removal of the trim panel and loosening the inner panel water deflector. These removal procedures are covered in the door trim and door sealing portion of this section.

The door window assembly consists of a frameless piece of solid tempered safety glass. The guides on the window are bonded on and are not serviceably except for the replacement of the window assembly. The service window glass has the guide already installed. The door window and lower sash channel are removed from the door as a unit and replacement glass is installed as a bench operation. Refer to lower sash channel replacement procedure later in this section.

DOOR WINDOW ADJUSTMENT – FRONT DOOR

Adjust

1. Remove door trim panel. Refer to "Trim Panel – Front Door" in this section.
2. Loosen water deflector. Refer to "Water Deflector – Front Door" in this section.
3. Loosen front window guide retainer screws.
4. Cycle window to full down position.
5. Top retainer screw.

Tighten

- Top screw to 6 N•m (53 lb. in.).

6. Cycle window to full down position.
7. Bottom screw.

Tighten

- Bottom screw to 6 N•m (53 lb. in.).

Inspect

- Window assembly for proper operation.

DOOR WINDOW REPLACEMENT – FRONT DOOR

Coupe

Figure 46

Remove or Disconnect

1. Trim panel. Refer to "Trim Panel – Front Door" in this section.
2. Inner belt sealing strip. Refer to "Inner Belt Sealing Strip – Front Door" in this section.
3. Water deflector. Refer to "Water Deflector – Front Door" in this section.

Important

- Window must be in the full up position in order to remove the guide retainer.

4. Front window guide retainer. Refer to "Front Window Guide Retainer – Front Door" in this section.

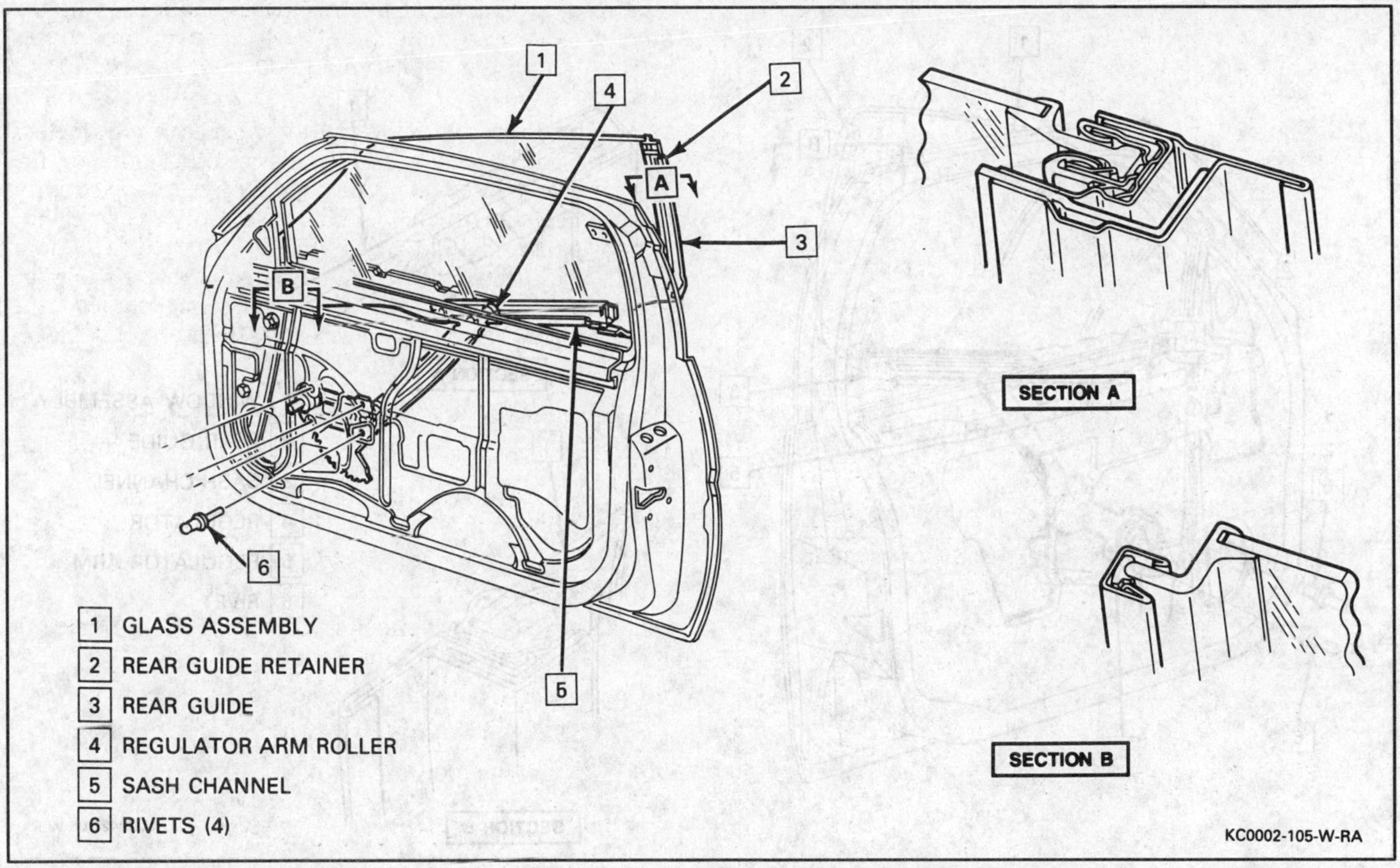
1
4
2
A
3
B
6
5
SECTION A
SECTION B
1 GLASS ASSEMBLY
2 REAR GUIDE RETAINER
3 REAR GUIDE
4 REGULATOR ARM ROLLER
5 SASH CHANNEL
6 RIVETS (4)
KC0002-105-W-RA

Figure 46 Door Window Removal (Coupe)

5. Window assembly by raising assembly half way and pushing on rear guide retainer with a 1 inch putty knife to disengage from channel retainer. Lift window up inboard side of door frame.

Install or Connect

1. Window assembly to door by relocating regulator arm roller to sash channel.
   - Lower window halfway and pull rearward on window to engage rear guide retainer to channel retainer.
2. Front window guide retainer by lowering window to 75 mm (3 inches) above the belt line and locating retainer to the door.
3. Front window guide retainer. Refer to "Front Window Guide Retainer – Front Door" in this section.

Inspect

- For proper operation of window and adjust as necessary. Refer to "Door Window Adjustment – Front Door" in this section.

4. Water deflector. Refer to "Water Deflector – Front Door" in this section.
5. Inner belt sealing strip. Refer to "Inner Belt Sealing Strip – Front Door" in this section.
6. Door trim panel. Refer to "Trim Panel – Front Door" in this section.

Front Door (Sedan)

Figure 47

Remove or Disconnect

1. Door trim panel. Refer to "Trim Panel – Front Door" in this section.
2. Inner belt sealing strip. Refer to "Inner Belt Sealing Strip – Front Door" in this section.
3. Water deflector. Refer to "Water Deflector – Front Door" in this section.
4. Front window guide retainer. Refer to "Front Window Guide Retainer – Front Door" in this section.
5. Window weatherstrip. Refer to "Door Window Weatherstrip – Front Door" in this section.
6. Window assembly from regulator arm and door.

Install or Connect

1. Window assembly to regulator arm and door.
2. Window weatherstrip. Refer to "Door Window Weatherstrip – Front Door" in this section.
3. Front window guide retainer. Refer to "Front Window Guide Retainer – Front Door" in this section.
4. Water deflector. Refer to "Water Deflector – Front Door" in this section.
5. Inner belt sealing strip. Refer to "Inner Belt Sealing Strip – Front Door" in this section.

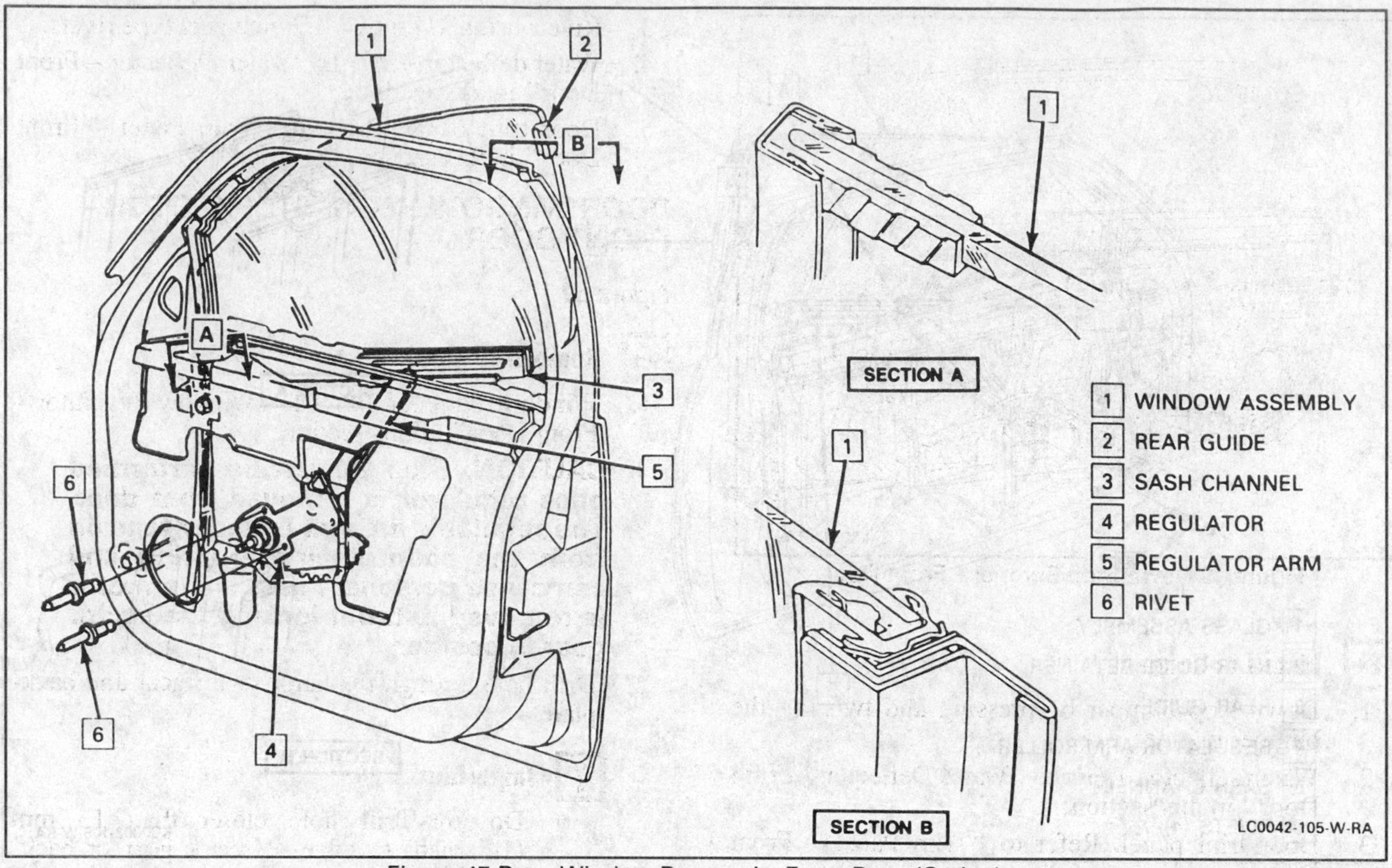
1
2
B
A
3
5
6
6
4
1
SECTION A
1
SECTION B
1 WINDOW ASSEMBLY
2 REAR GUIDE
3 SASH CHANNEL
4 REGULATOR
5 REGULATOR ARM
6 RIVET
LC0042-105-W-RA

Figure 47 Door Window Removal – Front Door (Sedan)

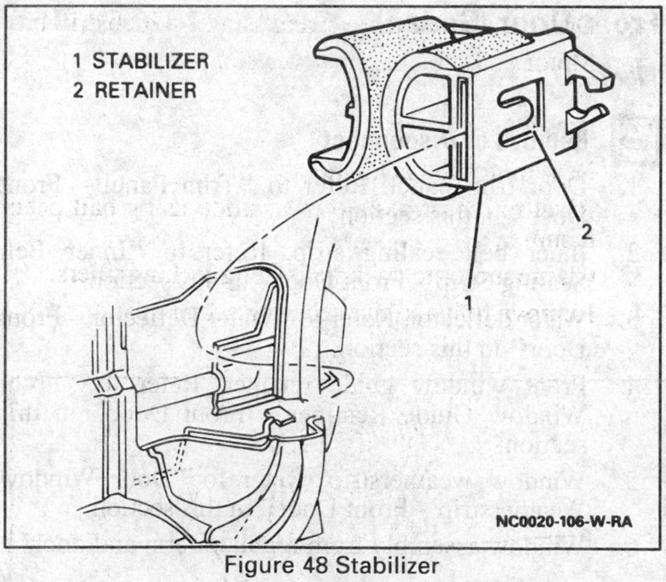
1 STABILIZER
2 RETAINER
2
1
NC0020-106-W-RA

Figure 48 Stabilizer

6. Door trim panel. Refer to "Trim Panel – Front Door" in this section.

STABILIZER – FRONT DOOR

Figure 48

↔ Remove or Disconnect

1. Door trim panel on coupe or retractor trim cover on sedan. Refer to "Door Trim – Front Door" in this section.
2. Water deflector. Refer to "Water Deflector – Front Door" in this section.
3. Stabilizer. Raise window to full up position and unsnap stabilizer from inner door panel.

→← Install or Connect

1. Stabilizer. Snap in place at inner door panel.
2. Water deflector. Refer to "Water Deflector – Front Door" in this section.
3. Door trim panel or retractor trim cover, if removed. Refer to "Door Trim – Front Door" in this section.

DOOR WINDOW DOWN STOP BUMPER – FRONT DOOR

Figure 49

↔ Remove or Disconnect

1. Door trim panel. Refer to "Trim Panel – Front Door" in this section.
2. Water deflector. Refer to "Water Deflector – Front Door" in this section.
3. Down stop bumper by raising window to full-up position, grasping down stop bumper, twisting and lifting bumper from door.

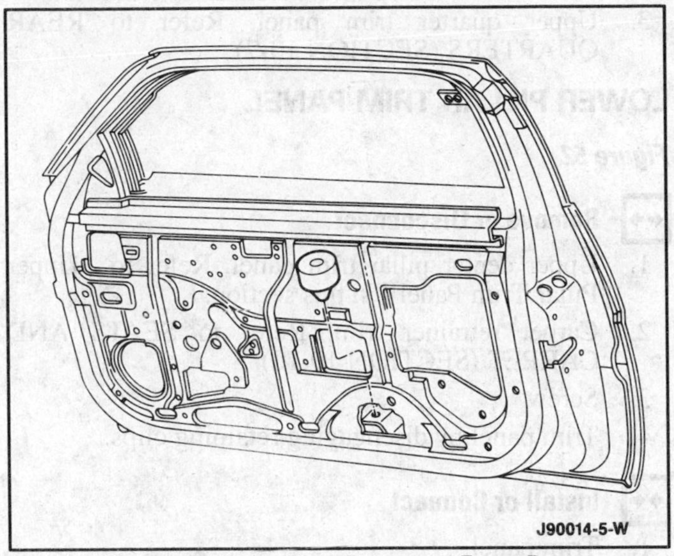
J90014-5-W

Figure 49 Down Stop Bumper – Front Door

Install or Connect

1. Down stop bumper by pressing and twisting the bumper in place.
2. Water deflector. Refer to "Water Deflector – Front Door" in this section.
3. Door trim panel. Refer to "Trim Panel – Front Door" in this section.

WINDOW REGULATOR – FRONT DOOR

Figures 46 and 47

Coupe and sedan front doors use a single lift arm regulator. The following provides the procedures required for removal and replacement of both power and manual window regulators.

Front Door

Remove or Disconnect

Important

- Tape window to the full-up position.

1. Door trim panel. Refer to "Trim Panel – Front Door" in this section.
2. Water deflector. Refer to "Water Deflector – Front Door" in this section.
3. Rivets using 1/4 inch drill bit.
4. Regulator by disengaging regulator arm from sash channel.
5. Electrical connector to motor (power window systems) and remove regulator through door inner access hole.

Install or Connect

1. Regulator through access hole and attach regulator arm to sash channel.
2. Electrical connector to motor (power window system).
3. Rivets using 1/4 inch x 1/2 inch peel type rivets.
4. Water deflector. Refer to "Water Deflector – Front Door" in this section.
5. Door trim panel. Refer to "Trim Panel – Front Door" in this section.

DOOR WINDOW REGULATOR MOTOR – FRONT DOOR

Figure 50

Remove or Disconnect

1. Window regulator. Refer to "Window Regulator – Front Door" in this section.

CAUTION: Step 2 must be performed once regulator is removed from door. The regulator lift arm is under tension from the counterbalance spring and can cause personal injury if the motor is removed without locking the sector gear in position.

2. Drill hole through regulator sector gear and backplate.

Important

- Do not drill hole closer than 13 mm (1/2 inch) to edge of sector gear or backplate.

3. Install bolt and nut to lock sector gear in position.
4. Drill out ends of three rivets using 1/4 inch drill bit.
5. Motor and remaining portions of rivets.

Install or Connect

1. New motor to backplate.
2. Rivet to motor at bottom location using ball peen hammer.
3. Clamp motor to backplate using locking pliers.
4. Remove bolt and nut securing sector gear.

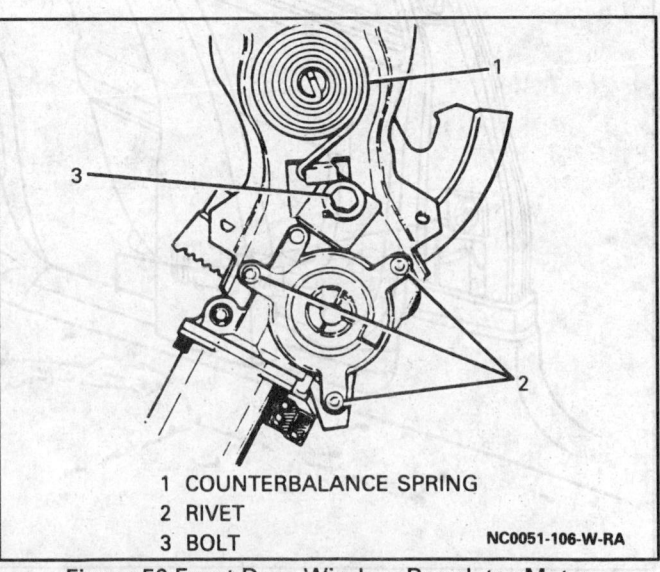

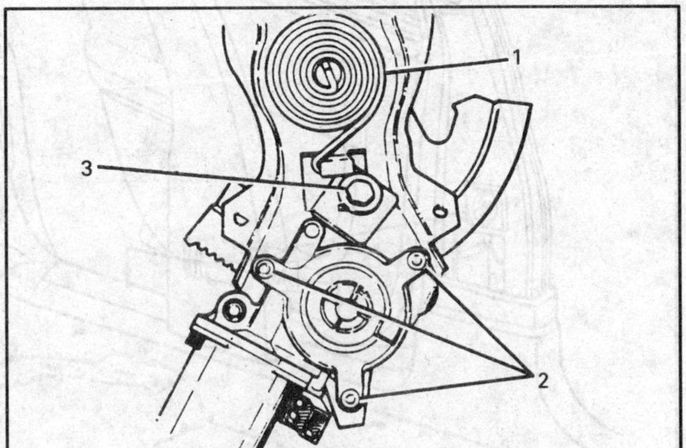
1
2
3
1 COUNTERBALANCE SPRING
2 RIVET
3 BOLT
NC0051-106-W-RA

Figure 50 Front Door Window Regulator Motor

5. Supply power to regulator to gain access for remaining two motor rivets.
6. Two rivets.
7. Remove locking pliers.
8. Window regulator. Refer to "Window Regulator – Front Door" in this section.

CENTER PILLAR TRIM (Sedan)

UPPER PILLAR TRIM PANEL

Figure 51

Tool Required:

J 24595-C Door Trim Pad and Garnish Clip Remover

Remove or Disconnect

1. Loosen upper quarter trim panel. Refer to REAR QUARTERS (SECTION 10-7).
2. Loosen windshield side upper garnish molding. Refer to ROOF (SECTION 10-7).
3. Trim panel using J 24595-C to disengage fastener on trim panel from hole in center pillar.

Install or Connect

1. Trim panel.
2. Windshield side upper garnish molding. Refer to ROOF (SECTION 10-9).
3. Upper quarter trim panel. Refer to REAR QUARTERS (SECTION 10-7).

LOWER PILLAR TRIM PANEL

Figure 52

Remove or Disconnect

1. Upper center pillar trim panel. Refer to "Upper Pillar Trim Panel" in this section.
2. Carpet retrainer trim. Refer to SEATS AND CARPET (SECTION 10-10).
3. Screw.
4. Trim panel by disengaging retaining clips.

Install or Connect

1. Trim panel.
2. Screw.

Tighten

- Screw to 2 N•m (18 lb. in.).

3. Carpet retainer trim. Refer to SEATS AND CARPET (SECTION 10-10).
4. Upper center pillar trim panel. Refer to "Upper Pillar Trim Panel" in this section.

DOOR JAMB SWITCH

For information on the door jamb switch, refer to BODY FRONT END (SECTION 10-5).

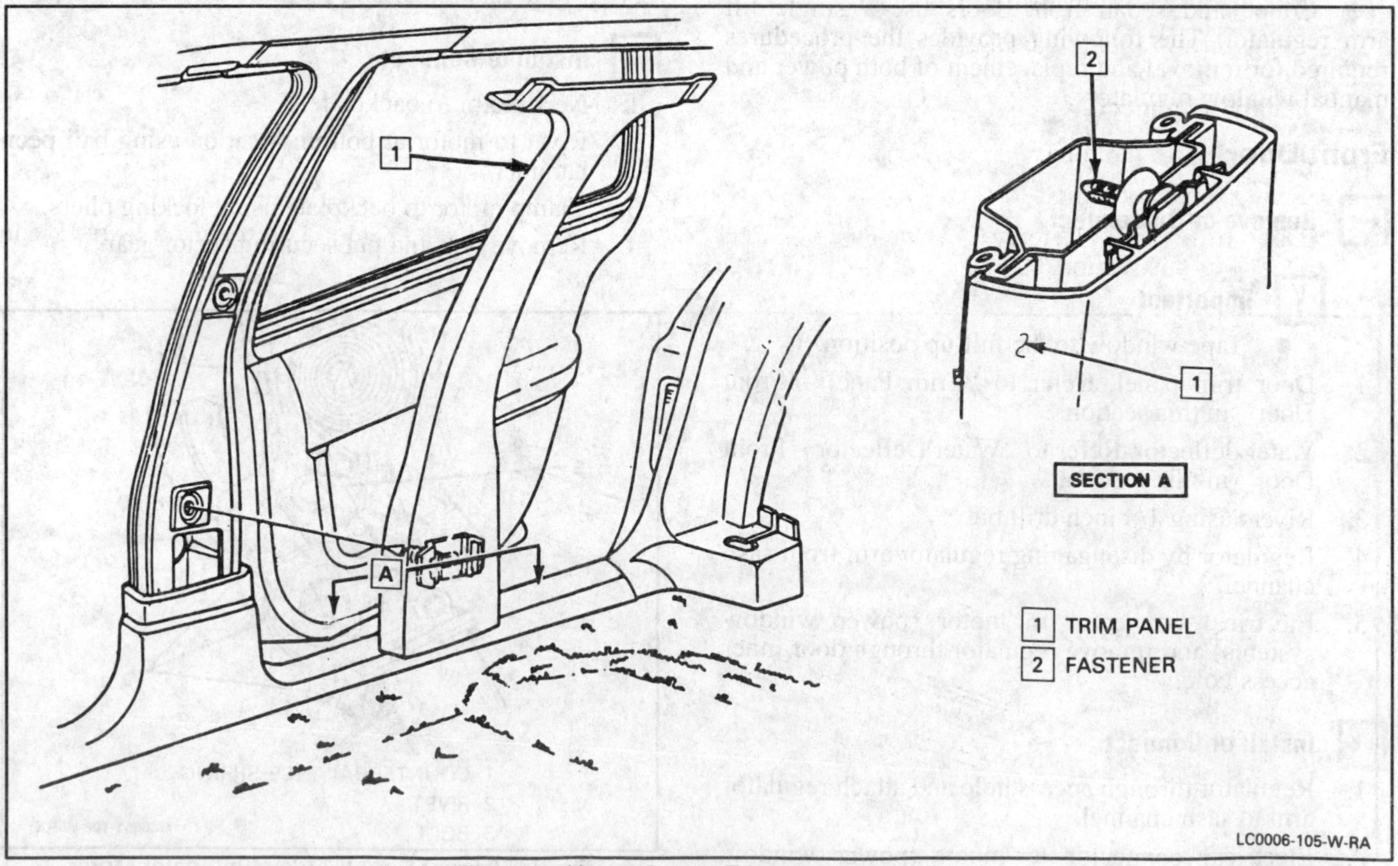
1
A
2
1
SECTION A
1 TRIM PANEL
2 FASTENER
LC0006-105-W-RA

Figure 51 Upper Center Trim Panel (Sedan)

REAR DOOR TRIM

ARMREST – REAR DOOR

Remove or Disconnect

1. Trim panel. Refer to "Trim Panel – Rear Door" in this section.
2. Screws.
3. Armrest.

Install or Connect

1. Armrest.
2. Screws.
3. Trim panel. Refer to "Trim Panel – Rear Door" in this section.

DOOR FRAME GARNISH MOLDINGS – REAR DOOR

Figure 53

Tool Required:

J 24595-C Door Trim Pad and Garnish Clip Remover

Remove or Disconnect

1. Door trim panel. Refer to "Trim Panel – Rear Door" in this section.
2. Rear garnish molding using J 24595-C.
3. Front garnish molding using J 24595-C.

Install or Connect

1. Front garnish molding.
2. Rear garnish molding.
3. Door trim panel. Refer to "Trim Panel – Rear Door" in this section.

INSIDE HANDLE BEZEL – REAR DOOR

Figure 54

Remove or Disconnect

1. Screw.
2. Handle bezel.

Install or Connect

1. Handle bezel.
2. Screw.

Tighten

- Screw to 1.3 N•m (12 lb. in.).

PULL HANDLE ASSEMBLY – REAR DOOR

Remove or Disconnect

1. Covers.
2. Screws.
3. Pull handle.

Install or Connect

1. Pull handle.
2. Screws.

   Tighten

   - Screws to 3 N•m (27 lb. in.).

3. Covers.

TRIM PANEL

Figure 55

Tool Required:

J 24595-C Door Trim Pad and Garnish Clip Remover

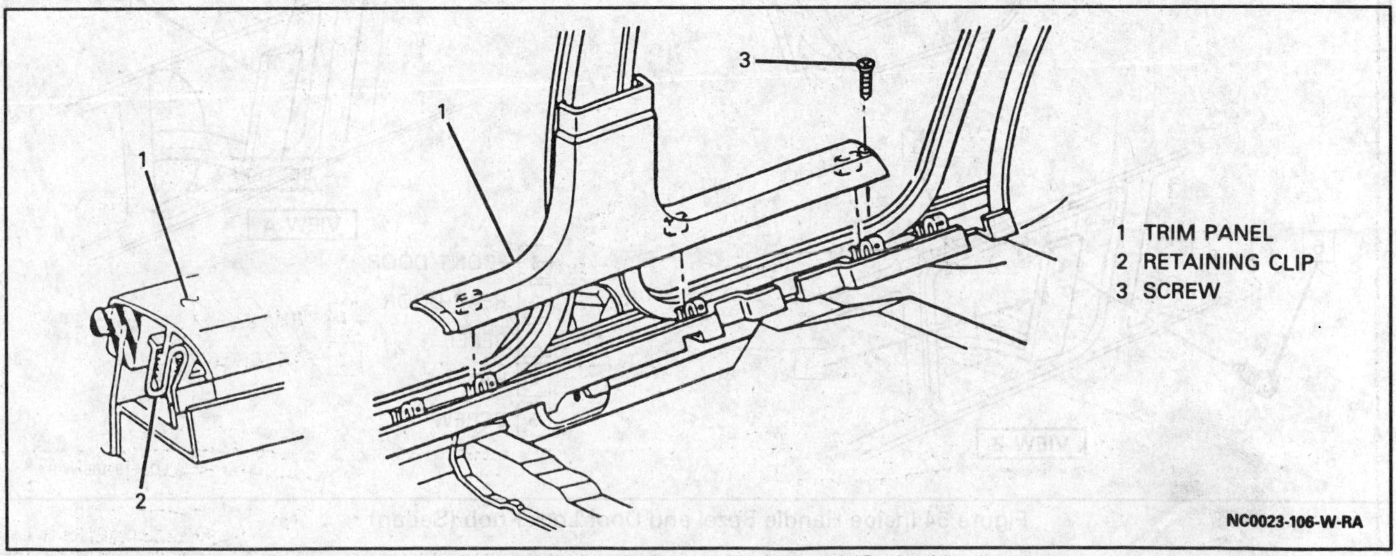
1
2
1
3
1 TRIM PANEL
2 RETAINING CLIP
3 SCREW
NC0023-106-W-RA

Figure 52 Lower Center Trim Panel (Sedan)

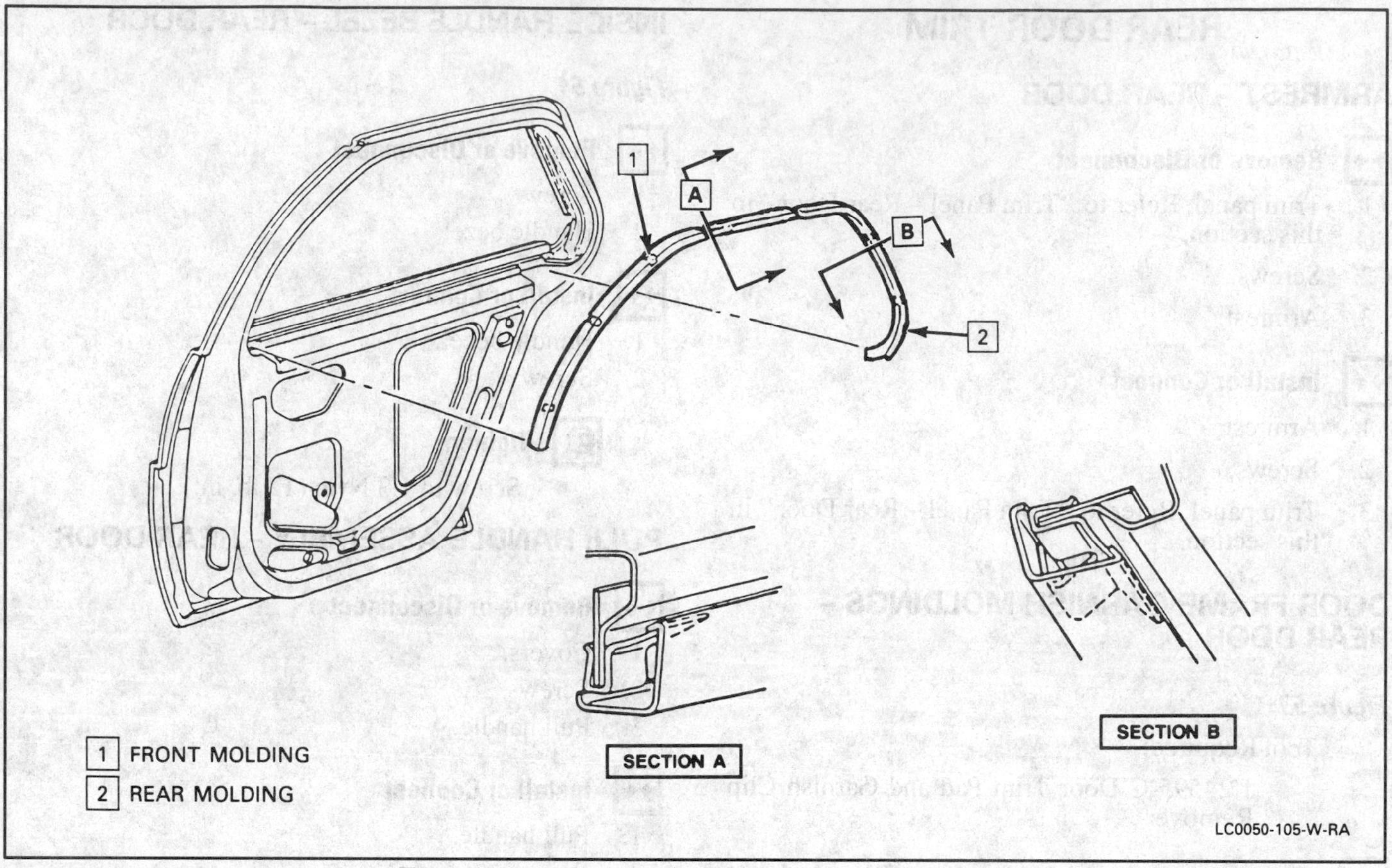

1
A
B
2
SECTION A
SECTION B
1 FRONT MOLDING
2 REAR MOLDING
LC0050-105-W-RA

Figure 53 Door Frame Garnish Moldings – Rear Door

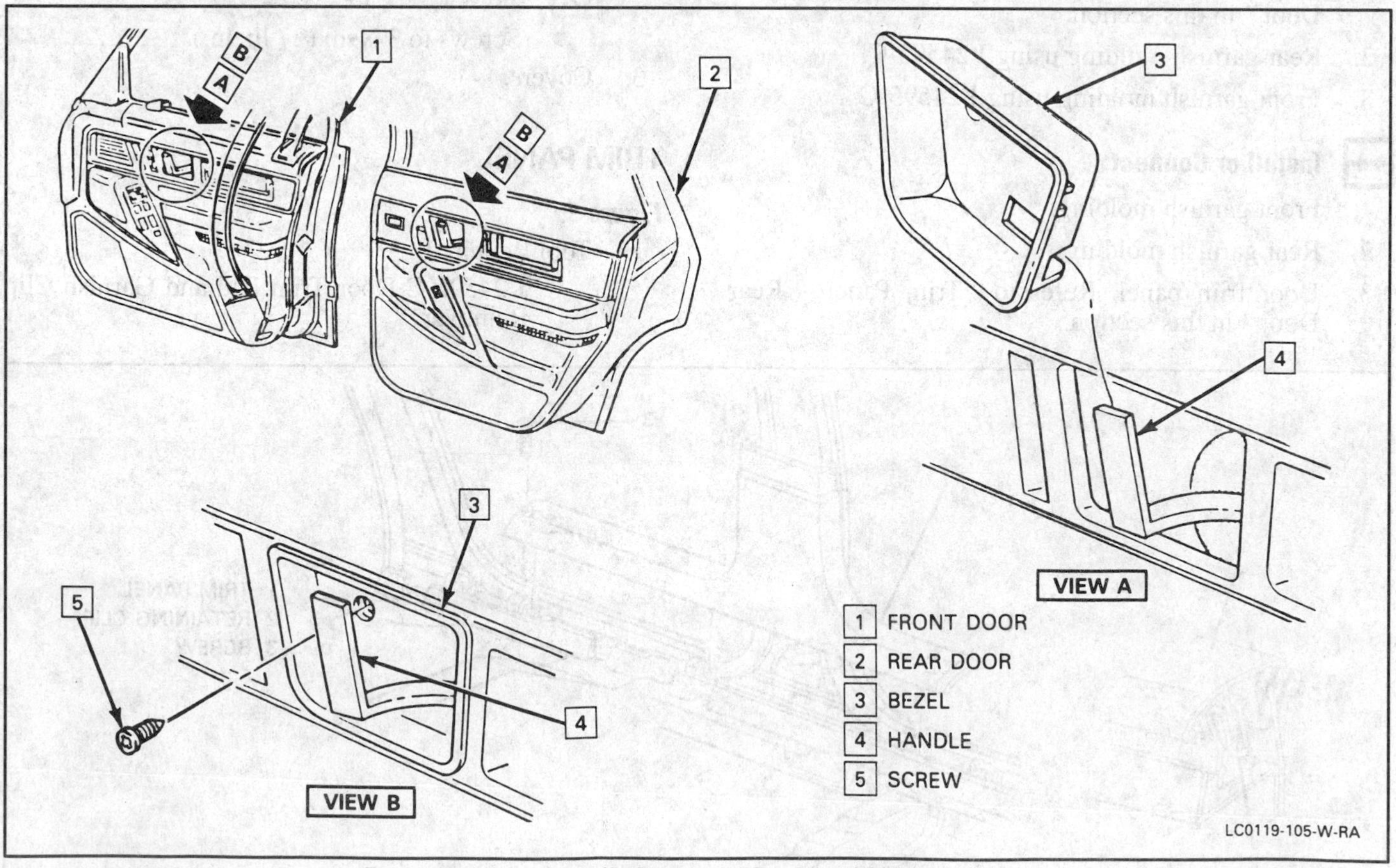

B
A
1
2
3
4
5
VIEW A
VIEW B
1 FRONT DOOR
2 REAR DOOR
3 BEZEL
4 HANDLE
5 SCREW
LC0119-105-W-RA

Figure 54 Inside Handle Bezel and Door Lock Knob (Sedan)

Remove or Disconnect

1. Screws from pull handle bezel.
2. Inside handle bezel. Refer to "Inside Handle Bezel – Rear Door" in this section.
3. Power window switch. Refer to "Power Window Switch Assembly – Rear Door" in this section.
4. Bracket screw from switch cutout.
5. Lamp from armrest cutout, if present.
6. Door trim panel using J 24595-C to disengage fasteners on trim panel from holes in door inner panel.

Install or Connect

1. Wire harnesses, if present through openings in trim panel and armrest cutout.
2. Trim panel to door by tucking under retainer on inner panel and aligning fasteners on trim panel to holes in door inner panel. Apply sufficient pressure to snap fasteners into place.
3. Lamp to cutout, if present.
4. Bracket screw through switch cutout.

Tighten

- Screw to 2 N•m (18 lb. in.).

5. Power window switch. Refer to "Power Window Switch Assembly – Rear Door" in this section.
6. Inside handle bezel. Refer to "Inside Handle Bezel – Rear Door" in this section.
7. Screws to pull handle bezel.

Tighten

- Screws to 3 N•m (27 lb. in.).

DOOR WINDOW CHANNEL RETAINERS – REAR DOOR

Figure 56

Remove or Disconnect

1. Door trim panel. Refer to "Trim Panel – Rear Door" in this section.
2. Door window weatherstrip (pull down to gain access to screws). Refer to "Door Window Weatherstrip – Rear Door" in this section.
3. Screws.
4. Door window channel retainer.

Install or Connect

1. Door window channel retainer.
2. Screws.

Tighten

- Screws to 2 N•m (18 lb. in.).

3. Door window weatherstrip. Refer to "Door Window Weatherstrip – Rear Door" in this section.
4. Door trim panel. Refer to "Trim Panel – Rear Door" in this section.

DOOR FRAME APPLIQUE – REAR DOOR

Figure 57

Remove or Disconnect

1. Screws.
2. Applique.

Install or Connect

1. Applique.
2. Screws.

Tighten

- Screws to 1 N•m (9 lb. in.).

REAR DOOR HARDWARE AND WINDOW

DOOR OPENING WEATHERSTRIP – REAR DOOR

Figure 58

Remove or Disconnect

1. Loosen quarter trim panels. Refer to REAR QUARTERS (SECTION 10-7).
2. Center pillar trim panels. Refer to "Center Pillar Trim (Sedan)" in this section.
3. Weatherstrip by grasping weatherstrip and pulling it off flange on body.

Install or Connect

1. Weatherstrip to flange on body.
2. Center pillar trim panels. Refer to "Center Pillar Trim (Sedan)" in this section.
3. Quarter trim panels. Refer to REAR QUARTERS (SECTION 10-7).

DOOR WINDOW WEATHERSTRIP – REAR DOOR

Figure 59

Remove or Disconnect

1. Lower window.
2. Rear guide on window from channel retainer.
3. Window weatherstrip from channel retainer and door frame.

Install or Connect

1. Window weatherstrip to door frame and channel retainer.
2. Rear guide on window to channel retainer.

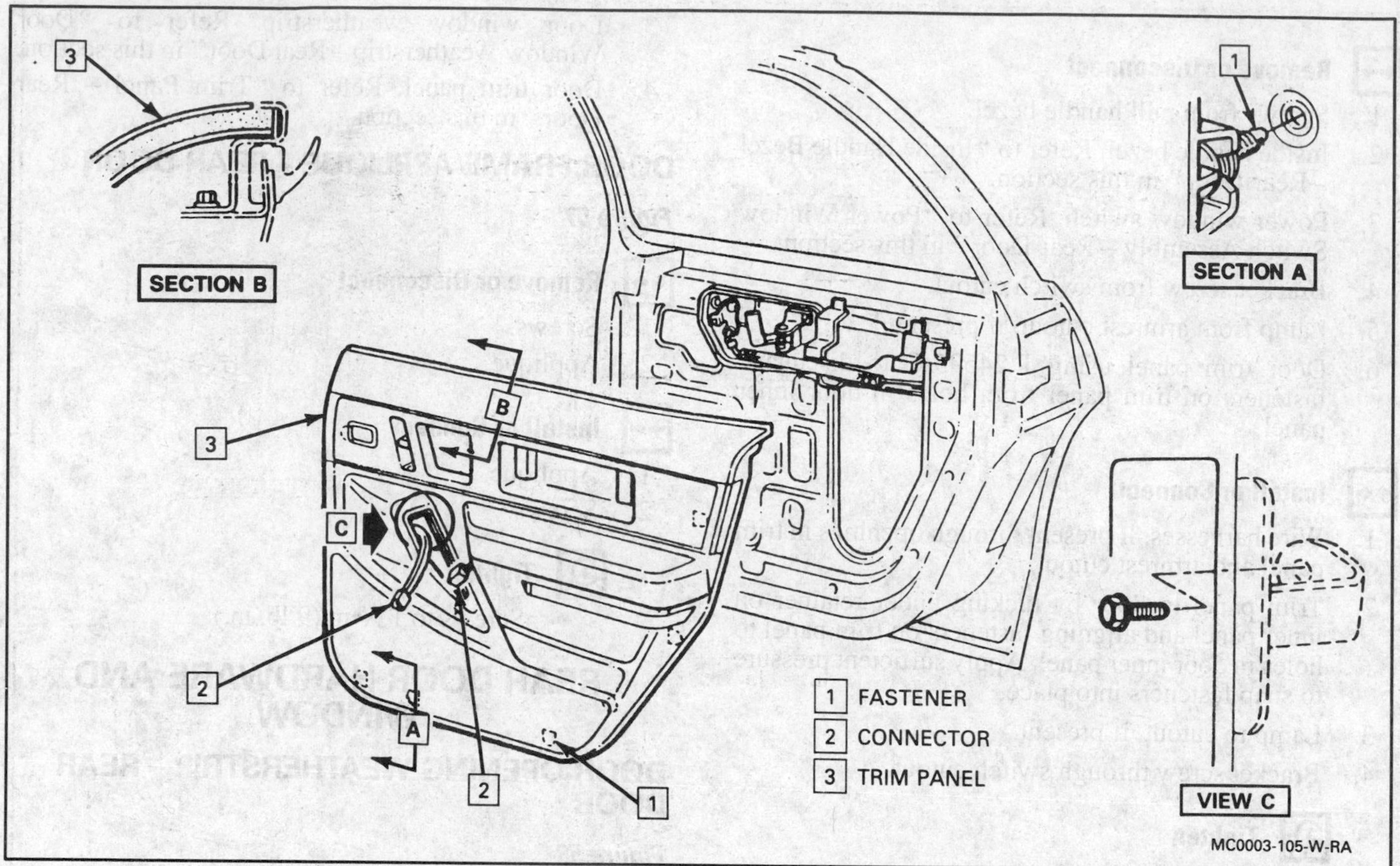
3
SECTION B
1
SECTION A
B
3
C
2
A
2
1
1 FASTENER
2 CONNECTOR
3 TRIM PANEL
VIEW C
MC0003-105-W-RA

Figure 55 Door Trim Panel – Rear Door

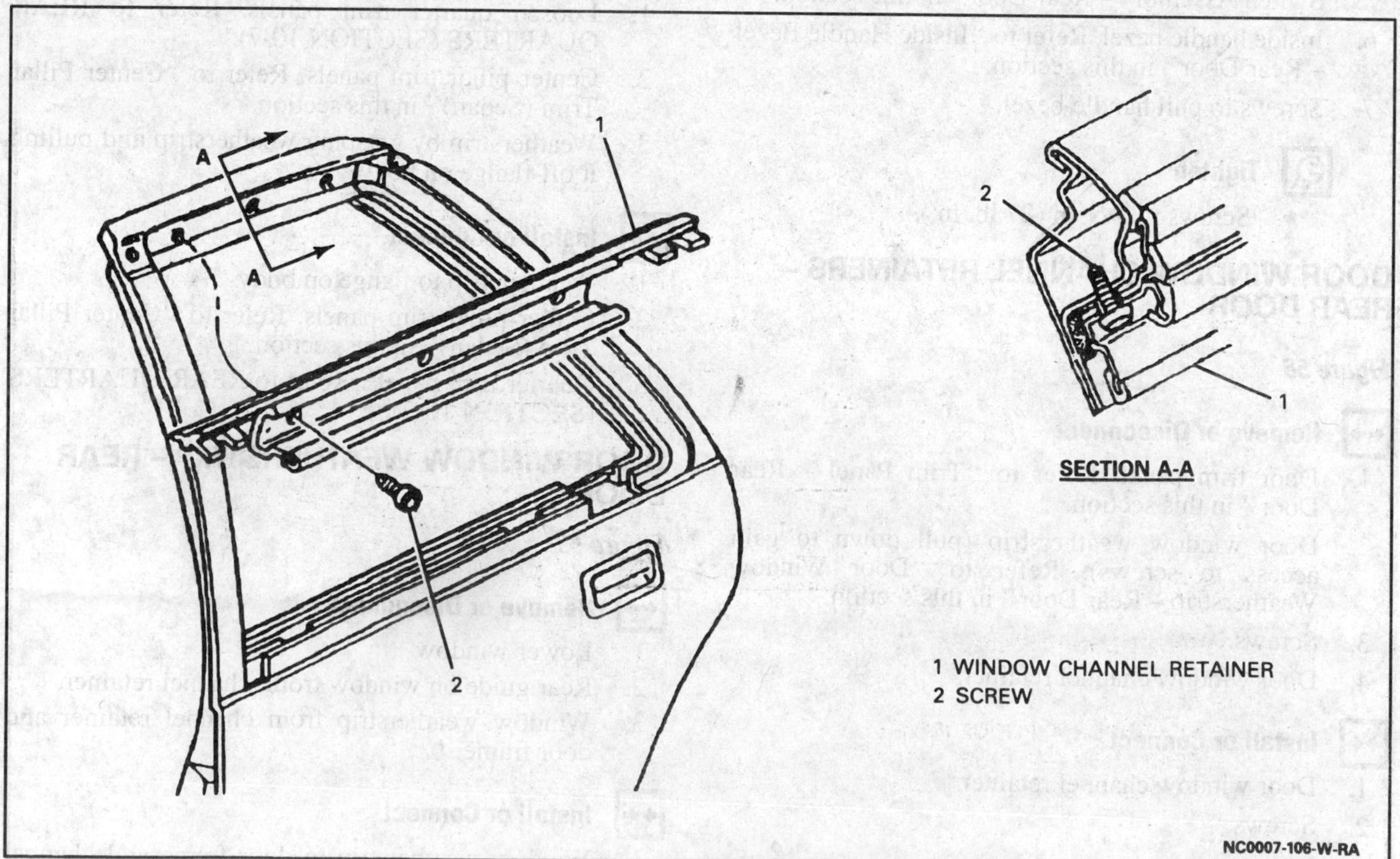
1
A
A
2
2
1
SECTION A-A
1 WINDOW CHANNEL RETAINER
2 SCREW
NC0007-106-W-RA

Figure 56 Door Window Channel Retainer – Rear Door

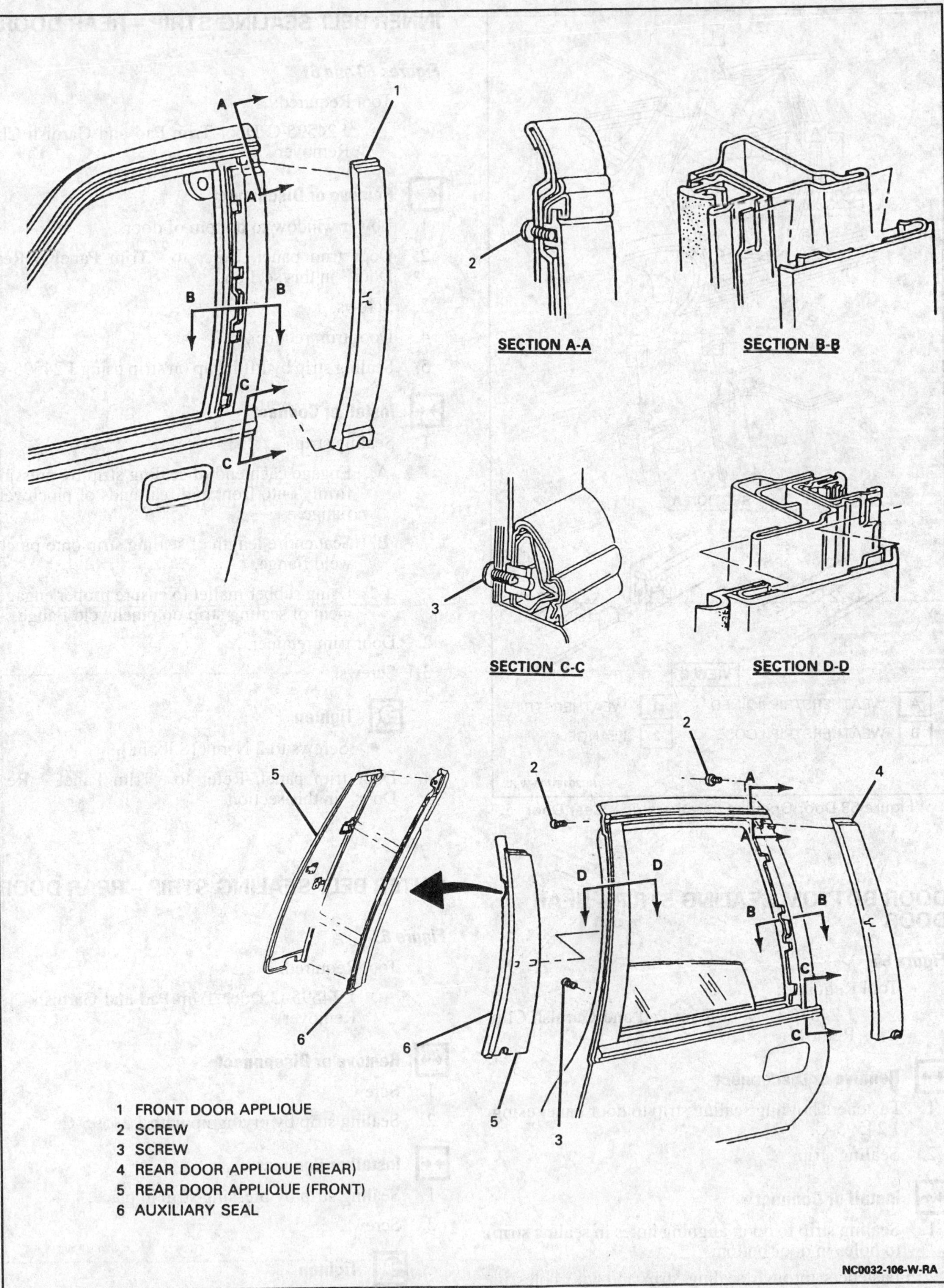
1
A
A
2
B
B
C
C
SECTION A-A
SECTION B-B
3
SECTION C-C
SECTION D-D
2
2
A
A
4
5
D
D
B
B
C
C
6
6
5
3
1 FRONT DOOR APPLIQUE
2 SCREW
3 SCREW
4 REAR DOOR APPLIQUE (REAR)
5 REAR DOOR APPLIQUE (FRONT)
6 AUXILIARY SEAL
NC0032-106-W-RA

Figure 57 Door Frame Applique (Sedan)

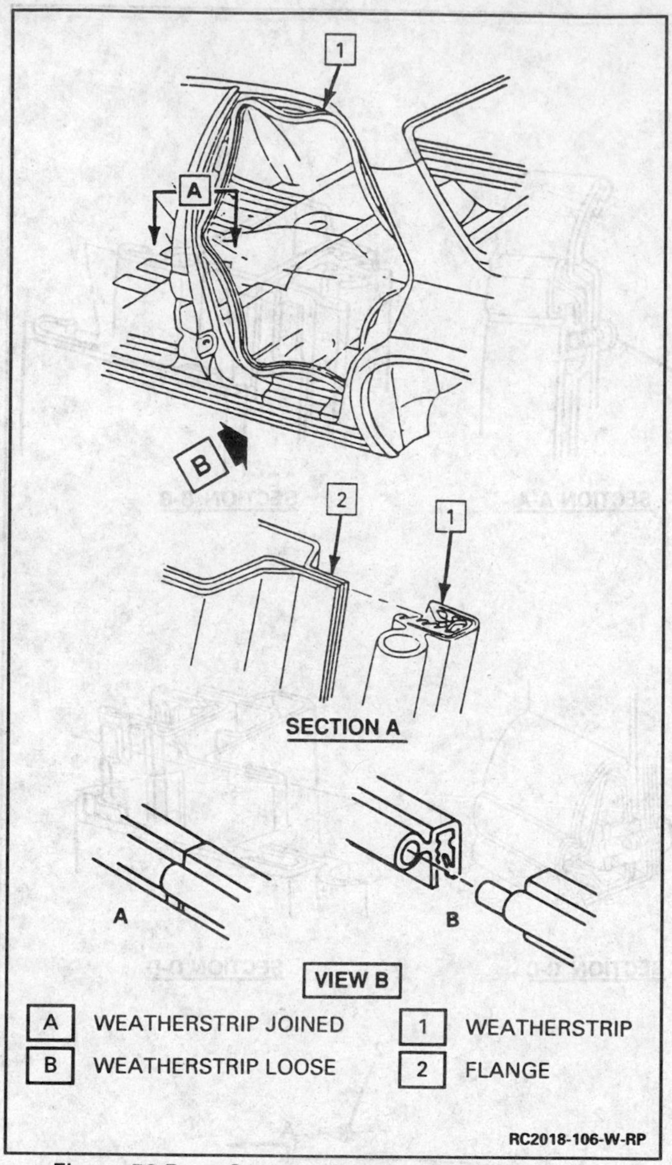
1
A
B
2
1
SECTION A
A
B
VIEW B
A WEATHERSTRIP JOINED
B WEATHERSTRIP LOOSE
1 WEATHERSTRIP
2 FLANGE
RC2018-106-W-RP
Figure 58 Door Opening Weatherstrip – Rear Door

DOOR BOTTOM SEALING STRIP – REAR DOOR

Figure 60

Tool Required:

J 24595-C Door Trim Pad and Garnish Clip Remover

Remove or Disconnect

1. Fasteners holding sealing strip to door panel using J 24595-C.
2. Sealing strip.

Install or Connect

1. Sealing strip to door, aligning holes in sealing strip to holes in door bottom.
2. Fasteners through sealing strip and into holes in door bottom using a rubber mallet.

INNER BELT SEALING STRIP – REAR DOOR

Figures 60 and 61

Tool Required:

J 24595-C Door Trim Pad and Garnish Clip Remover

Remove or Disconnect

1. Lower window to bottom of door.
2. Door trim panel. Refer to "Trim Panel – Rear Door" in this section.
3. Screws.
4. Door trim retainer.
5. Sealing strip by lifting up on strip using J 24595-C.

Install or Connect

1. Sealing strip.
   A. Engage each end of sealing strip by pressing firmly onto front and rear ends of pinchweld flange.
   B. Seat entire length of sealing strip onto pinchweld flange.
   C. Using rubber mallet to ensure proper engagement of sealing strip on pinchweld flange.
2. Door trim retainer.
3. Screws.

Tighten

- Screws to 2 N•m (18 lb. in.).

4. Door trim panel. Refer to "Trim Panel – Rear Door" in this section.

OUTER BELT SEALING STRIP – REAR DOOR

Figure 63

Tool Required:

J 24595-C Door Trim Pad and Garnish Clip Remover

Remove or Disconnect

1. Screw.
2. Sealing strip by prying up with J 24595-C.

Install or Connect

1. Sealing strip by pressing strip in place.
2. Screw.

Tighten

- Screw to 1 N•m (9 lb. in.).

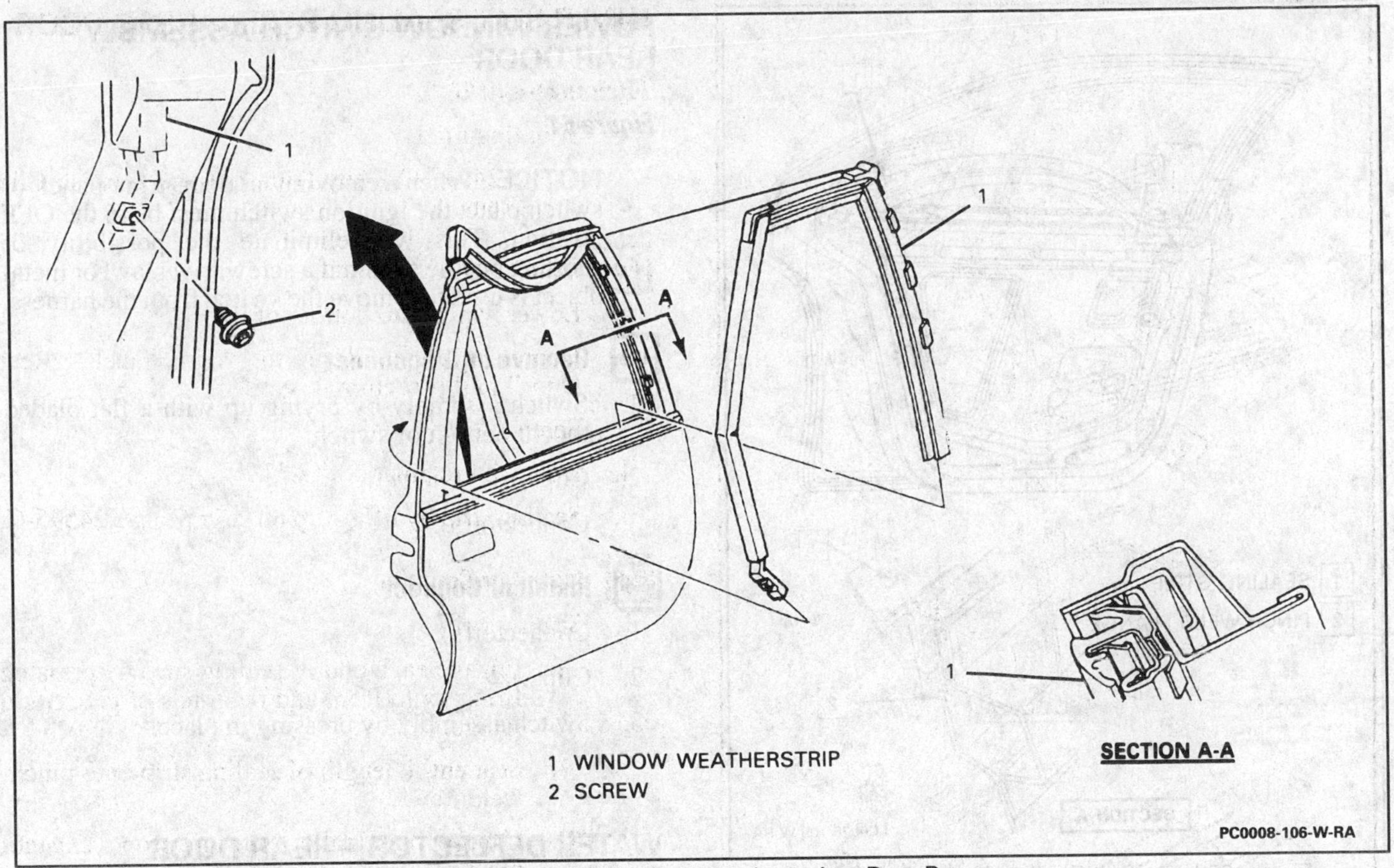
1
2
A
A
1
1
SECTION A-A
1 WINDOW WEATHERSTRIP
2 SCREW
PC0008-106-W-RA

Figure 59 Door Window Weatherstrip – Rear Door

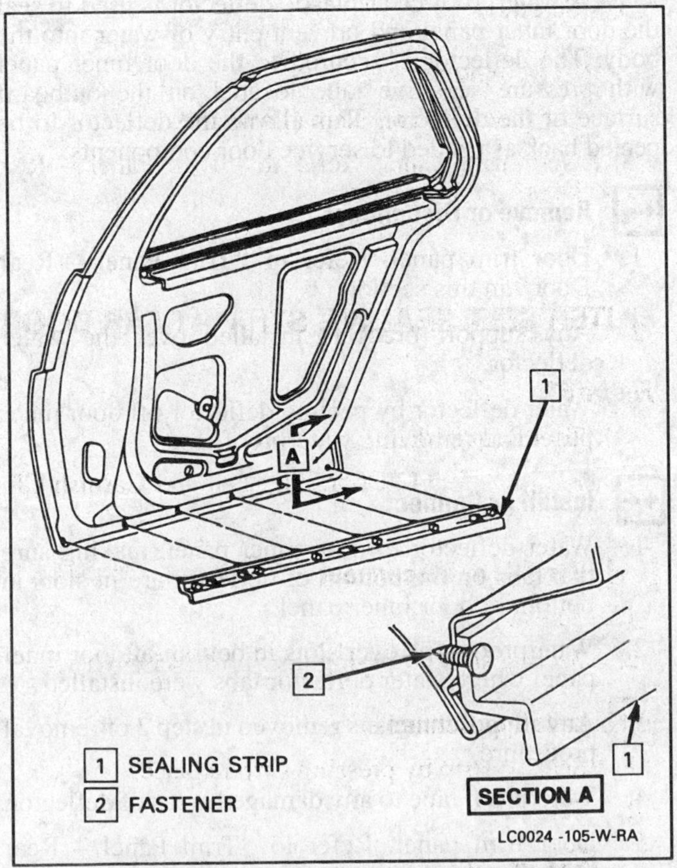
1
A
2
1
SECTION A
1 SEALING STRIP
2 FASTENER
LC0024 -105-W-RA

Figure 60 Rear Door Bottom Sealing Strip

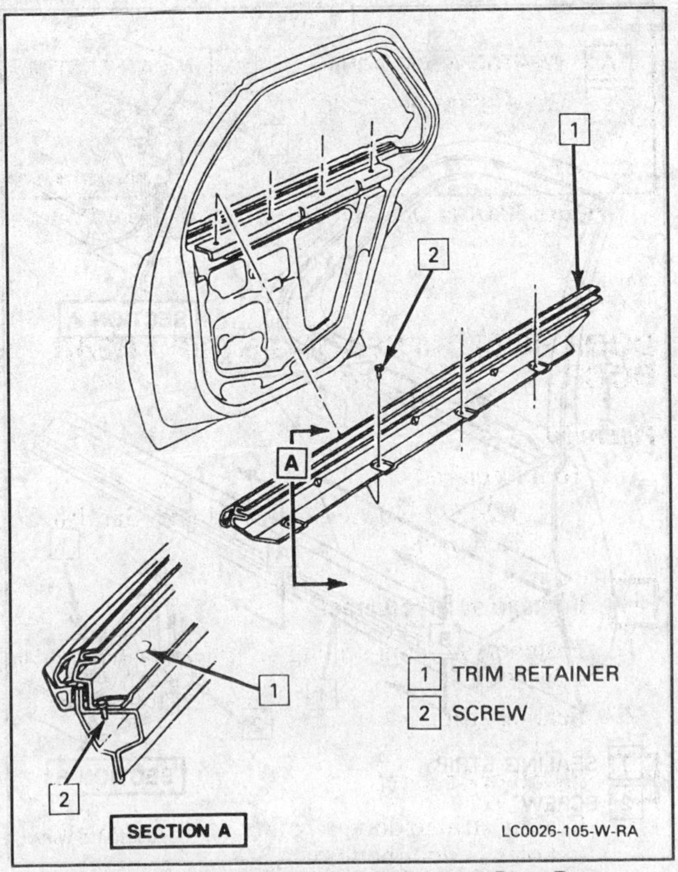
1
2
A
1
2
SECTION A
1 TRIM RETAINER
2 SCREW
LC0026-105-W-RA

Figure 61 Inner Door Trim Retainer – Rear Door

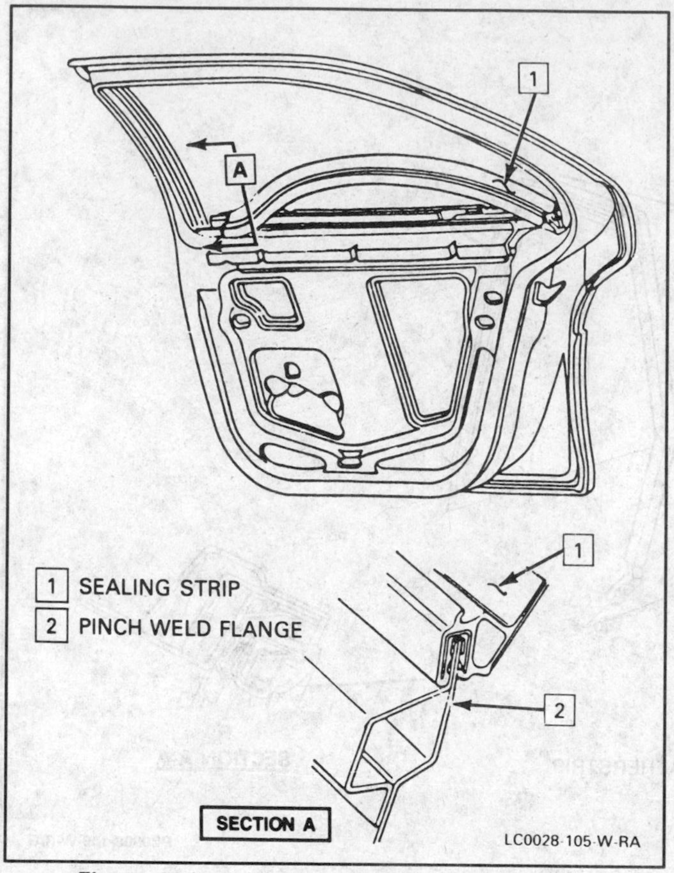
1
A
1
SEALING STRIP
2
PINCH WELD FLANGE
2
SECTION A
LC0028-105-W-RA

Figure 62 Inner Belt Sealing Strip – Rear Door

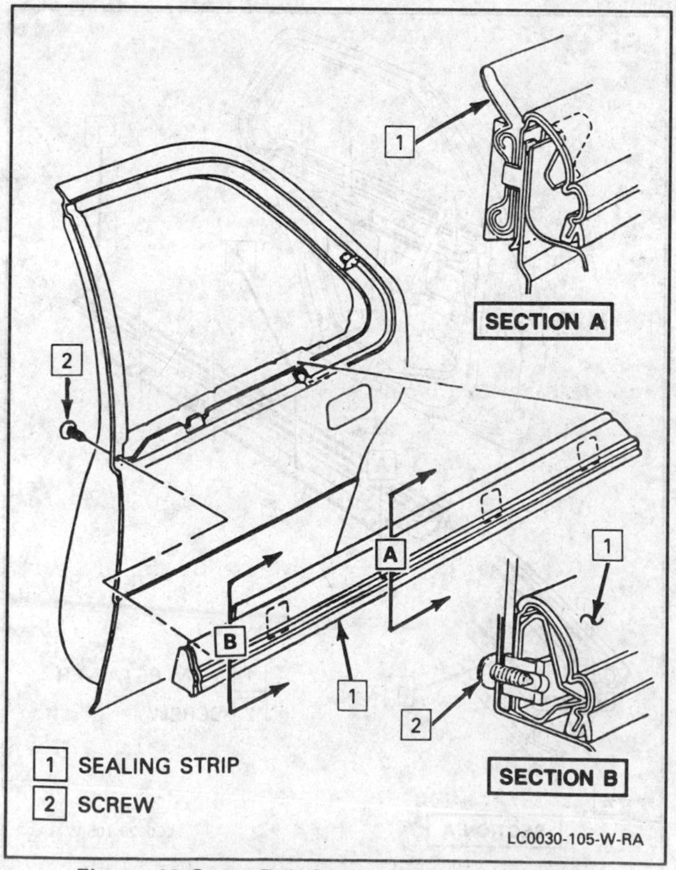
1
SECTION A
2
A
1
B
1
2
1 SEALING STRIP
2 SCREW
SECTION B
LC0030-105-W-RA

Figure 63 Outer Belt Sealing Strip – Rear Door

POWER WINDOW SWITCH ASSEMBLY – REAR DOOR

Figure 64

NOTICE: When removing a door trim panel or switch plate, the ignition switch must be in the OFF position. This will eliminate the possibility of shorting out the switch if a screwdriver, awl or metal object is used to remove the switch from the harness.

↔ Remove or Disconnect

1. Switch assembly by prying up with a flat bladed tool at bottom of switch.
2. Clip(s).
3. Connector(s).

→← Install or Connect

1. Connector(s).
2. Clip(s).
3. Switch assembly by pressing in place.

WATER DEFLECTOR – REAR DOOR

Figure 65

A waterproof clear plastic deflector is used to seal the door inner panel and prevent entry of water into the body. The deflector is secured to the door inner panel with pressure sensitive tape located on the outboard surface of the deflector. This allows the deflector to be peeled back as needed to service door components.

↔ Remove or Disconnect

1. Door trim panel. Refer to "Trim Panel – Rear Door" in this section.
2. Any support brackets installed over the water deflector.
3. Water deflector by peeling deflector off door inner panel and removing waterproof tape.

→← Install or Connect

1. Water deflector to door inner panel, making sure that tabs on the bottom of deflector are in slots in bottom of door inner panel.
2. Waterproof tape over slots in bottom of door inner panel where water deflector tabs were installed.
3. Any support brackets removed in step 2 of removal procedure.
4. Waterproof tape to any damaged areas of deflector.
5. Door trim panel. Refer to "Trim Panel – Rear Door" in this section.

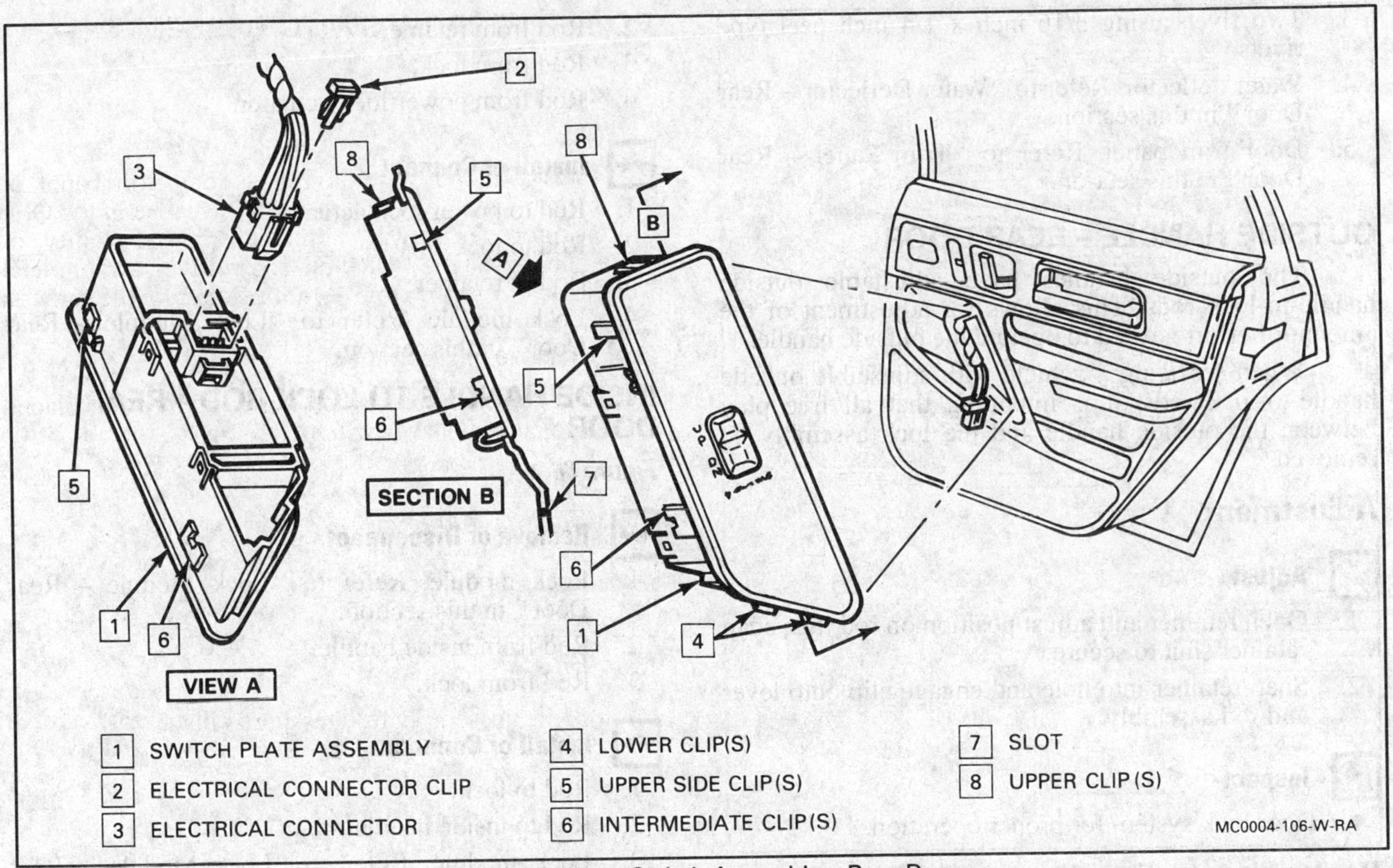
VIEW A
SECTION B
A
B
1 SWITCH PLATE ASSEMBLY
2 ELECTRICAL CONNECTOR CLIP
3 ELECTRICAL CONNECTOR
4 LOWER CLIP(S)
5 UPPER SIDE CLIP(S)
6 INTERMEDIATE CLIP(S)
7 SLOT
8 UPPER CLIP (S)
MC0004-106-W-RA

Figure 64 Power Switch Assembly – Rear Door

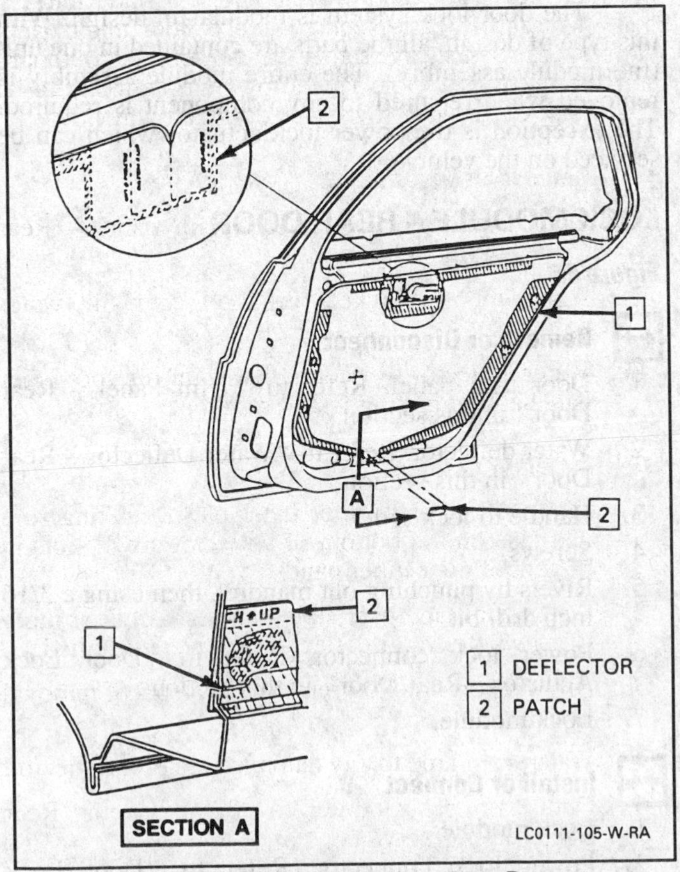
A
CH ♦ UP
SECTION A
1 DEFLECTOR
2 PATCH
LC0111-105-W-RA

Figure 65 Water Deflector – Rear Door

ASHTRAY – REAR DOOR

Remove or Disconnect

- Ashtray.

Install or Connect

- Ashtray.

INSIDE HANDLE – REAR DOOR

Remove or Disconnect

1. Door trim panel. Refer to "Trim Panel – Rear Door" in this section.
2. Water deflector. Refer to "Water Deflector – Rear Door" in this section.
3. Two rivets holding handle assembly, by first center punching a depression in the head of the rivet, then drilling out rivet using a 3/16 inch drill bit..
4. Rod from handle.
5. Inside handle by sliding rearward to disengage tabs on handle from slots in module assembly.

Install or Connect

1. Inside handle to module assembly by placing tabs on handle into slots in module and sliding handle forward.
2. Rod to handle.

3. Two rivets using 3/16 inch x 1/4 inch peel type rivets.
4. Water deflector. Refer to "Water Deflector – Rear Door" in this section.
5. Door trim panel. Refer to "Trim Panel – Rear Door" in this section.

OUTSIDE HANDLE – REAR DOOR

The outside handles have adjustable outside handle-to-lock rods. This allows for adjustment of the amount of effort needed to operate the outside handle.

When servicing a vehicle with adjustable outside handle-to-lock rods, it is important that all free play between the outside handle and the lock assembly be removed.

Adjustment

Adjust

1. Open retainer and adjust position on rod then snap retainer shut to secure.
2. Snap retainer into hole and engage clip onto lever and rod assembly.

Inspect

- Door lock system for proper operation.

Replacement – Rear Door

Figure 66

Remove or Disconnect

1. Door window. Refer to "Door Window Replacement – Rear Door" in this section.
2. Door lock module. Refer to "Lock Module – Rear Door" in this section.
3. Nuts.
4. Handle.

Install or Connect

1. Handle.
2. Nuts.

Tighten

- Nuts to 7 N•m (62 lb. in.).

3. Door lock module. Refer to "Lock Module – Rear Door" in this section.
4. Door window. Refer to "Door Window Replacement – Rear Door" in this section.

INSIDE LOCKING ROD TO LOCK – REAR DOOR

Figure 66

Remove or Disconnect

1. Lock module. Refer to "Lock Module – Rear Door" in this section.
2. Rod from retainer.
3. Rod from lock.
4. Rod from power lock actuator.

Install or Connect

1. Rod to power lock actuator.
2. Rod to lock.
3. Rod to retainer.
4. Lock module. Refer to "Lock Module – Rear Door" in this section.

INSIDE HANDLE TO LOCK ROD – REAR DOOR

Figure 66

Remove or Disconnect

1. Lock module. Refer to "Lock Module – Rear Door" in this section.
2. Rod from inside handle.
3. Rod from lock.

Install or Connect

1. Rod to lock.
2. Rod to inside handle.
3. Lock module. Refer to "Lock Module – Rear Door" in this section.

DOOR LOCK SYSTEM – REAR DOOR

The door lock system is modular in design. With this type of design, all the parts are contained in one unit (the module assembly). The entire module assembly is removed when repaired to any component is required. The exception is the power lock actuator which can be serviced on the vehicle.

LOCK MODULE – REAR DOOR

Figure 66

Remove or Disconnect

1. Door trim panel. Refer to "Trim Panel – Rear Door" in this section.
2. Water deflector. Refer to "Water Deflector – Rear Door" in this section.
3. Handle to lock rod.
4. Screws.
5. Rivets by punching out mandrel, then using a 3/16 inch drill bit.
6. Power lock connector. Refer to "Door Lock Actuator – Rear Door" in this section.
7. Lock module.

Install or Connect

1. Lock module.
2. Power lock connector. Refer to "Door Lock Actuator – Rear Door" in this section.

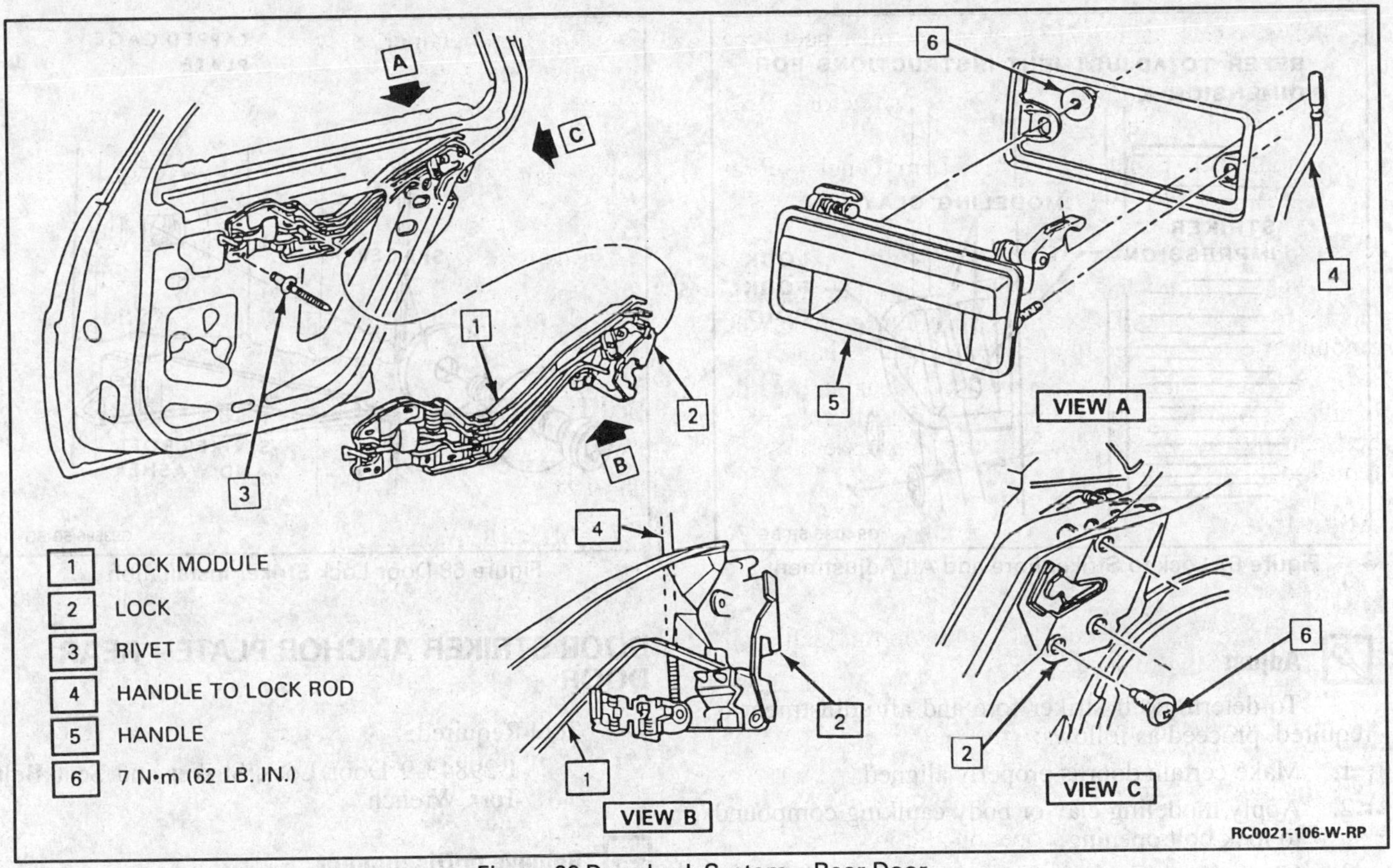
A
C
B
1
2
3
4
5
6
VIEW A
VIEW B
VIEW C
1 LOCK MODULE
2 LOCK
3 RIVET
4 HANDLE TO LOCK ROD
5 HANDLE
6 7 N•m (62 LB. IN.)
RC0021-106-W-RP

Figure 66 Door Lock System – Rear Door

NOTICE: It is required that while performing step 3 that the lock assembly be held tight against door facing while installing screws. All screws must be driven at a 90 degree angle to door facing to prevent cross threading or stripping of screws or door lock attaching holes. It is also required to tighten screws to specified torque of 7 N•m (62 lb. in.).

3. Screws.

Tighten

- Screws to 7 N•m (62 lb. in.).

4. Rivets using 3/16 inch x 1/4 inch peel type rivets.
5. Handle to lock rod.
6. Water deflector. Refer to "Water Deflector – Rear Door" in this section.
7. Door trim panel. Refer to "Trim Panel – Rear Door" in this section.

DOOR LOCK – REAR DOOR

Figure 66

Door locks use the fork bolt lock design which includes a safety interlock feature. The door is secured in a closed position when the door lock fork bolt engages the striker bolt. The doors can be locked from the inside by sliding the lock knob rearward.

Do not attempt repairs to correct lock discrepancies. Make corrections through replacement of lock assembly.

Remove or Disconnect

1. Lock module. Refer to "Lock Module – Rear Door" in this section.
2. Lock rods.
3. Rivets securing lock to lock module.
4. Lock from lock module.

Install or Connect

1. Lock to lock module.
2. Rivets.
3. Lock rods.
4. Lock module. Refer to "Lock Module – Rear Door" in this section.

DOOR LOCK STRIKER – REAR DOOR

Figures 67 and 68

Tool Required:

J 29843-9 Door Lock Striker and Seat Belt Torx Wrench

The door lock striker consists of a single metal bolt and washer assembly that is threaded into a tapped plate in the body lock pillar. The door is secured in the closed position when the door lock fork bolt snaps over and engages the striker bolt. The striker has provisions for fore and aft adjustment only.

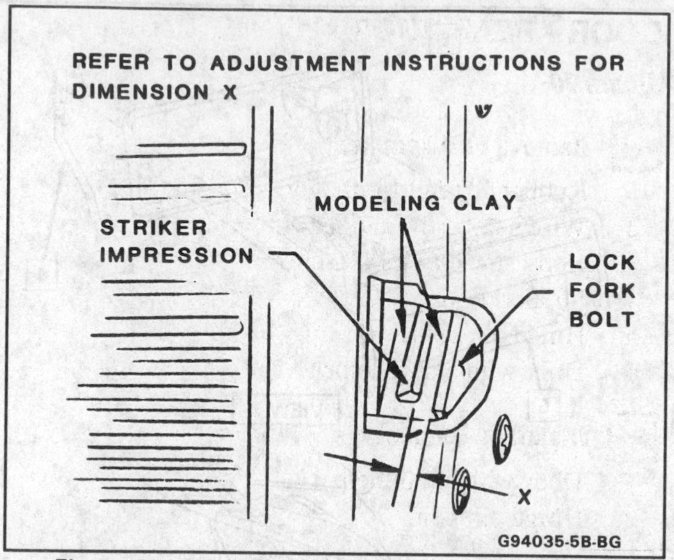
REFER TO ADJUSTMENT INSTRUCTIONS FOR DIMENSION X
MODELING CLAY
STRIKER IMPRESSION
LOCK FORK BOLT
X
G94035-5B-BG

Figure 67 Lock to Striker Fore and Aft Adjustment

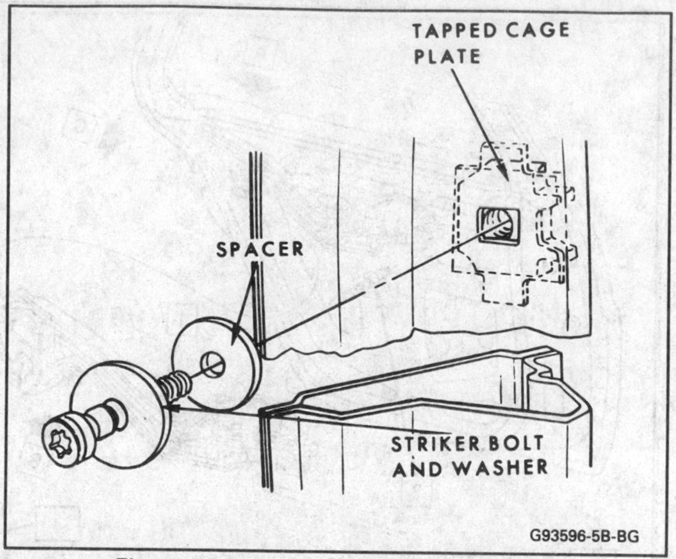
TAPPED CAGE PLATE
SPACER
STRIKER BOLT AND WASHER
G93596-5B-BG

Figure 68 Door Lock Striker Installation

Adjust

To determine if striker fore and aft adjustment is required, proceed as follows:

1. Make certain door is properly aligned.
2. Apply modeling clay or body caulking compound to lock bolt opening.
3. Close door only as far as necessary for striker bolt to form an impression in clay or caulking compound. Complete door closing will make clay removal very difficult.
4. Striker impression should be centered fore and aft. The minimal allowable measurement for dimension X is 2 mm (3/32 inch). The maximum allowable measurement for dimension X is 4 mm (5/32 inch). A 2 mm (3/32 inch) spacer, part no. 4469196 or equivalent, can be used to achieve the desired alignment.
5. If adjustment is necessary, remove the striker bolt using J 29843-9. Add or remove spacers as required.

Tighten

- Striker bolt to 53 N•m (39 lb. ft.).

Remove or Disconnect

1. Using a pencil, mark position of striker on body lock pillar.
2. Striker using J 29843-9.

Install or Connect

1. Striker to body lock pillar using J 29843-9.

Tighten

- Striker bolt to 53 N•m (39 lb. ft.).

2. Touch up any exposed unpainted surface on lock pillar adjacent to striker assembly if striker is outside of pencil marks.

DOOR STRIKER ANCHOR PLATE – REAR DOOR

Tool Required:

J 29843-9 Door Lock Striker and Seat Belt Torx Wrench

Remove or Disconnect

1. Loosen striker three turns using J 29843-9.
2. With hammer, drive head of striker rearward to release anchor plate from body.
3. Center pillar trim panels. Refer to "Center Pillar Trim (Sedan)" in this section.
4. Striker bolt from anchor plate.
5. Anchor plate.

Install or Connect

1. New anchor plate.
2. Striker bolt. Refer to "Door Lock Striker – Rear Door" in this section.

Adjust

- For striker adjustment refer to "Door Lock Striker – Rear Door" in this section.

POWER DOOR LOCK ACTUATOR – REAR DOOR

Figure 69

The automatic door lock system has an actuator in each door which actuates the lock through a linkage. The system is actuated by the chime module in the convenience center or by any door lock switch. All doors lock or unlock at the same time except when the actuator is manually activated by a lock rod. Each actuator has an internal circuit breaker which may require one to three minutes to reset.

For electrical diagnosis, refer to ELECTRICAL DIAGNOSIS (SECTION 8A-131).

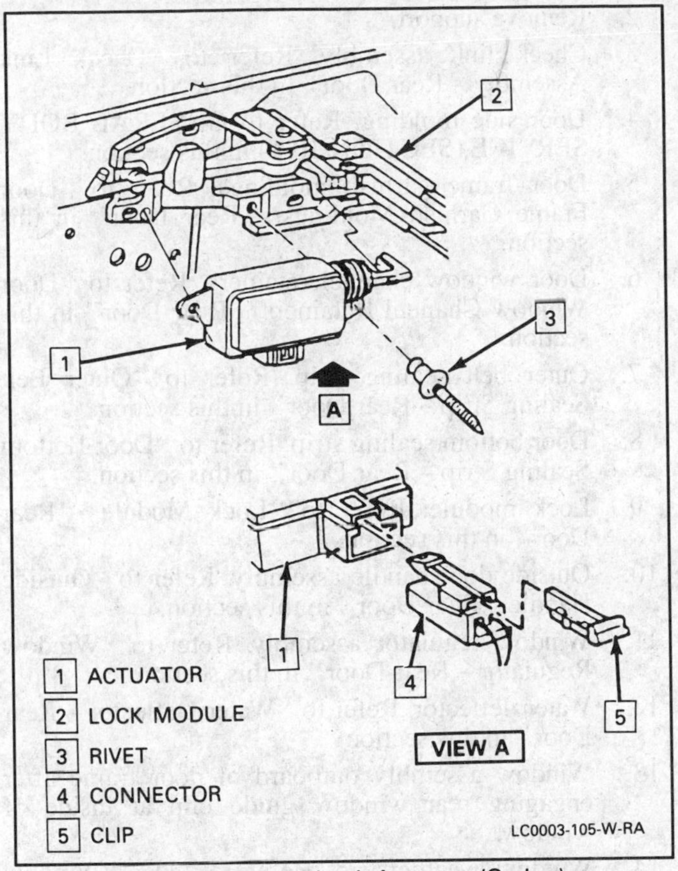

2
3
1
A
1
4
5
VIEW A
1 ACTUATOR
2 LOCK MODULE
3 RIVET
4 CONNECTOR
5 CLIP
LC0003-105-W-RA

Figure 69 Power Lock Actuator (Sedan)

Remove or Disconnect

1. Door trim panel. Refer to "Trim Panel – Rear Door" in this section.
2. Water deflector. Refer to "Water Deflector – Rear Door" in this section.
3. Rivets by punching out mandrel, then using a 3/16 inch drill bit.
4. Clip and electrical connector.
5. Actuator by disengaging from rod.

Install or Connect

1. Actuator to rod.
2. Electrical connector and clip.
3. Rivets using 3/16 inch x 1/4 inch peel type rivets.

Inspect

- For proper operation by cycling system.

4. Water deflector. Refer to "Water Deflector – Rear Door" in this section.
5. Door trim panel. Refer to "Trim Panel – Rear Door" in this section.

DOOR – REAR DOOR

Figure 70

Remove or Disconnect

1. Rubber conduit from door.
2. Wire harness from door.
3. Body side check link screw.
4. Support door.
5. Hinge pin bolts.
6. Door with aid of helper.

Install or Connect

1. Door with aid of helper.
2. Hinge pin bolt.

Important

- Apply Adhesive/Sealant Compound (part no. 12345493, or equivalent) to hinge pin bolt before reusing.

Tighten

- Hinge pin bolt to 14 N•m (124 lb. in.).

3. Remove support.
4. Body side check link screw.

Tighten

- Screw to 24 N•m (18 lb. ft.).

5. Wire harness to door.
6. Rubber conduit to door.

DOOR ADJUSTMENT – REAR DOOR

Adjust

- Door up or down and in or out by loosening nuts securing hinges to door and repositioning door as needed.

Tighten

- Nuts to 27 N•m (20 lb. ft.).

DOOR REPLACEMENT – REAR DOOR

Remove or Disconnect

1. Door trim panel. Refer to "Trim Panel – Rear Door" in this section.
2. Electrical connectors.
3. Inner belt sealing strip. Refer to "Inner Belt Sealing Strip – Rear Door" in this section.
4. Window weatherstrip. Refer to "Door Window Weatherstrip – Rear Door" in this section.
5. Window assembly outboard of door frame after disengaging rear window guide retainer clip at inside of window.
6. Water deflector. Refer to "Water Deflector – Rear Door" in this section.

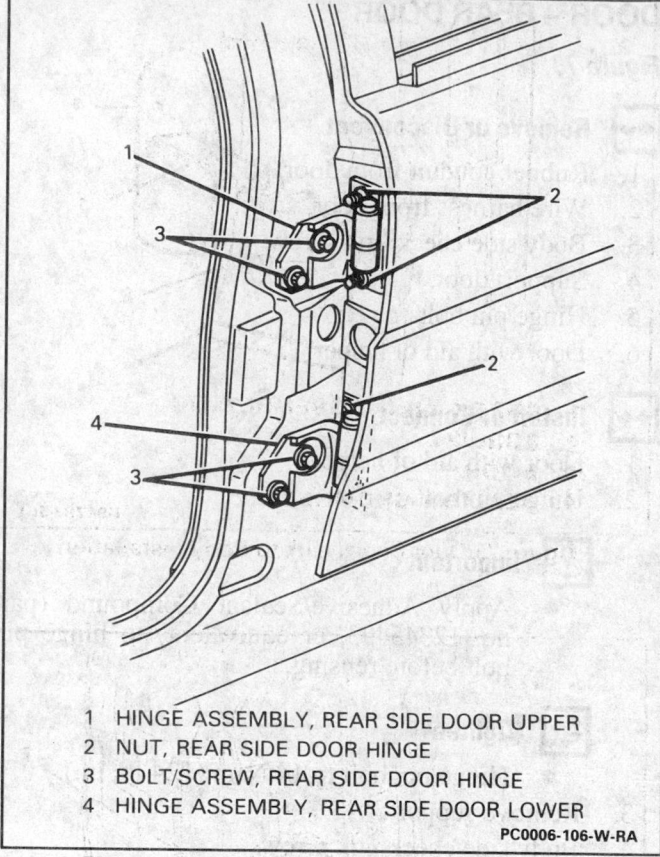

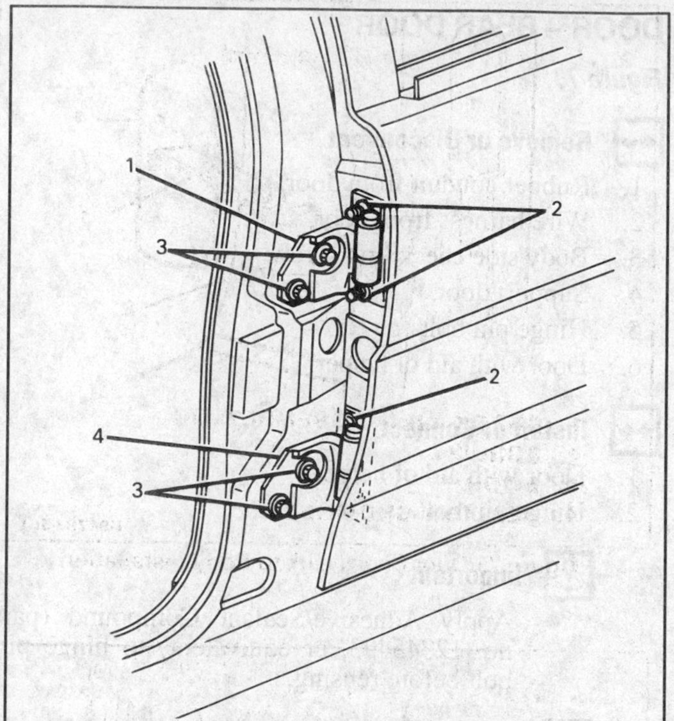
1
2
3
2
4
3
1 HINGE ASSEMBLY, REAR SIDE DOOR UPPER
2 NUT, REAR SIDE DOOR HINGE
3 BOLT/SCREW, REAR SIDE DOOR HINGE
4 HINGE ASSEMBLY, REAR SIDE DOOR LOWER
PC0006-106-W-RA

Figure 70 Door Hinge Assembly – Rear Door

7. Window regulator assembly. Refer to "Window Regulator – Rear Door" in this section.
8. Outside door handle assembly. Refer to "Outside Handle – Rear Door" in this section.
9. Lock module. Refer to "Lock Module – Rear Door" in this section.
10. Door bottom sealing strip. Refer to "Door Bottom Sealing Strip – Rear Door" in this section.
11. Outer belt sealing strip. Refer to "Outer Belt Sealing Strip – Rear Door" in this section.
12. Door window channel retainers. Refer to "Door Window Channel Retainers – Rear Door" in this section.
13. Door frame garnish moldings. Refer to "Door Frame Garnish Moldings – Rear Door" in this section.
14. Door molding. Refer to GENERAL BODY SERVICE (SECTION 10-1).
15. Check link assembly. Refer to "Check Link Assembly – Rear Door" in this section.
16. Support door.
17. Door hinge nuts at door and remove door.

Install or Connect

1. Door and door hinge nuts with aid of helper.

Tighten

- Nuts to 27 N•m (20 lb. ft.).

2. Remove support.
3. Check link assembly. Refer to "Check Link Assembly – Rear Door" in this section.
4. Door side molding. Refer to GENERAL BODY SERVICE (SECTION 10-1) in this section.
5. Door frame garnish moldings. Refer to "Door Frame Garnish Moldings – Rear Door" in this section.
6. Door window channel retainers. Refer to "Door Window Channel Retainers – Rear Door" in this section.
7. Outer belt sealing strip. Refer to "Outer Belt Sealing Strip – Rear Door" in this section.
8. Door bottom sealing strip. Refer to "Door Bottom Sealing Strip – Rear Door" in this section.
9. Lock module. Refer to "Lock Module – Rear Door" in this section.
10. Outside door handle assembly. Refer to "Outside Handle – Rear Door" in this section.
11. Window regulator assembly. Refer to "Window Regulator – Rear Door" in this section.
12. Water deflector. Refer to "Water Deflector – Rear Door" in this section.
13. Window assembly outboard of door frame after engaging rear window guide clip at inside of window.
14. Window weatherstrip. Refer to "Door Window Weatherstrip – Rear Door" in this section.
15. Inner belt sealing strip. Refer to "Inner Belt Sealing Strip – Rear Door" in this section.
16. Electrical connectors.
17. Door trim panel. Refer to "Trim Panel – Rear Door" in this section.

Adjust

- Door. Refer to "Door Adjustment – Rear Door" in this section.

DOOR HINGE SYSTEM – REAR DOOR

Hinges are bolted to the door and body. The door side hinges have elongated holes which allow for some up and down and in and out adjustment. There is a fore and aft adjustment provision. If a single hinge on any door at any location requires replacement, the second or remaining hinge must be replaced at the same time.

HINGE ASSEMBLY – REAR DOOR

Figure 70

Hinges are serviced as an assembly (body side and door side are one unit) and in pairs.

NOTICE: In order to minimize door realignment, do not remove both door hinges at the same time. Do each hinge separately, and replace any broken hinges first.

1. Using two pieces of masking tape, place one piece to bridge the gap between the door and rocker panel and the second piece to bridge the gap between the door and quarter panel.

2. Cut the tape at the gap area using a utility knife or other suitable tool.

NOTICE: Make sure that the doors are fully latched onto the lock striker and the doors are not locked or doors may be damaged during hinge replacement.

3. With front door open to access center pillar and rear door hinge area, clean hinge mounting surfaces on the door and body with a rag and mark the locations using a grease pencil or other suitable marker.
4. Bolts and nuts securing hinge at door and body.
5. Remove hinge.
6. Install new hinge within previously marked locations and lightly tighten bolts and nuts.
7. Repeat steps 3 through 6 for remaining hinge.
8. Inspect edges of tape on door and align door as necessary.
9. Tighten bolts and nuts.

Tighten

- Bolts to 46 N•m (34 lb. ft.).
- Nuts to 27 N•m (20 lb. ft.).

10. Remove reference tape from door, rocker and quarter.

CHECK LINK ASSEMBLY – REAR DOOR

Figures 71 and 72

The check link assembly is the door hold-open feature.

Remove or Disconnect

1. Door trim panel. Refer to "Trim Panel – Rear Door" in this section.
2. Water deflector. Refer to "Water Deflector – Rear Door" in this section.
3. Screw securing check link to body.
4. Sealing grommet.
5. Screws securing check link to door.
6. Check link through door inner panel access hole.

Install or Connect

1. Check link to door.
2. Screws securing check link to door.

Tighten

- Screws to 6 N•m (53 lb. in.).

3. Sealing grommet.
4. Screw securing check link to body.

Tighten

- Screw to 24 N•m (18 lb. ft.).

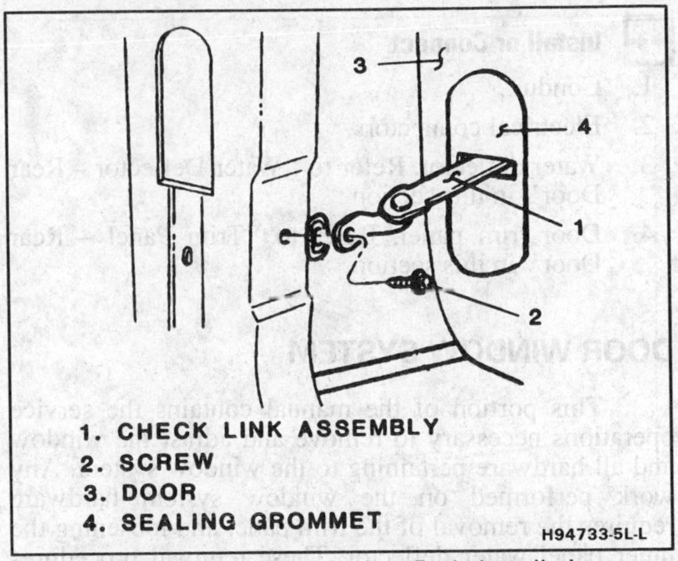
3
4
1
2
1. CHECK LINK ASSEMBLY
2. SCREW
3. DOOR
4. SEALING GROMMET
H94733-5L-L

Figure 71 Door Check Link to Body Installation

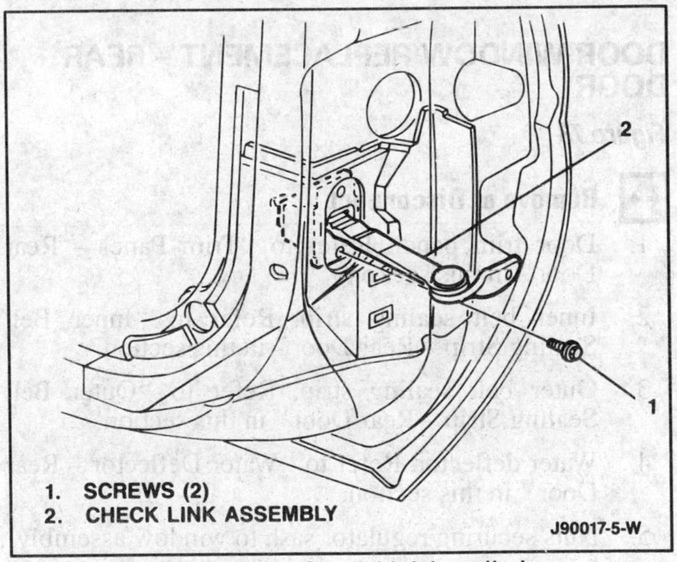
2
1
1. SCREWS (2)
2. CHECK LINK ASSEMBLY
J90017-5-W

Figure 72 Door Check Link Installation

Inspect

- For proper operation of check link.

5. Water deflector. Refer to "Water Deflector – Rear Door" in this section.
6. Door trim panel. Refer to "Trim Panel – Rear Door" in this section.

CONDUIT – REAR DOOR

Remove or Disconnect

1. Door trim panel. Refer to "Trim Panel – Rear Door" in this section.
2. Water deflector. Refer to "Water Deflector – Rear Door" in this section.
3. Electrical connectors.
4. Conduit.

Install or Connect

1. Conduit.
2. Electrical connectors.
3. Water deflector. Refer to "Water Deflector – Rear Door" in this section.
4. Door trim panel. Refer to "Trim Panel – Rear Door" in this section.

DOOR WINDOW SYSTEM

This portion of the manual contains the service operations necessary to remove and adjust the window and all hardware pertaining to the window system. Any work performed on the window system hardware requires the removal of the trim panel and loosening the inner panel water deflector. These removal procedures are covered in the door trim and door sealing portion of this section.

DOOR WINDOW REPLACEMENT – REAR DOOR

Figure 73

Remove or Disconnect

1. Door trim panel. Refer to "Trim Panel – Rear Door" in this section.
2. Inner belt sealing strip. Refer to "Inner Belt Sealing Strip – Rear Door" in this section.
3. Outer belt sealing strip. Refer to "Outer Belt Sealing Strip – Rear Door" in this section.
4. Water deflector. Refer to "Water Deflector – Rear Door" in this section.
5. Nuts securing regulator sash to window assembly.
6. Lower window to bottom of door and remove front portion of window weatherstrip from front of door frame.
7. Lift window upward and outboard of door frame.

Install or Connect

1. Window to door from outboard side of door frame.
2. Lower window to bottom of door.
3. Nuts.

Tighten

- Nuts to 9 N•m (80 lb. in.).

Inspect

- Window assembly for proper operation.

4. Water deflector. Refer to "Water Deflector – Rear Door" in this section.
5. Outer belt sealing strip. Refer to "Outer Belt Sealing Strip – Rear Door" in this section.

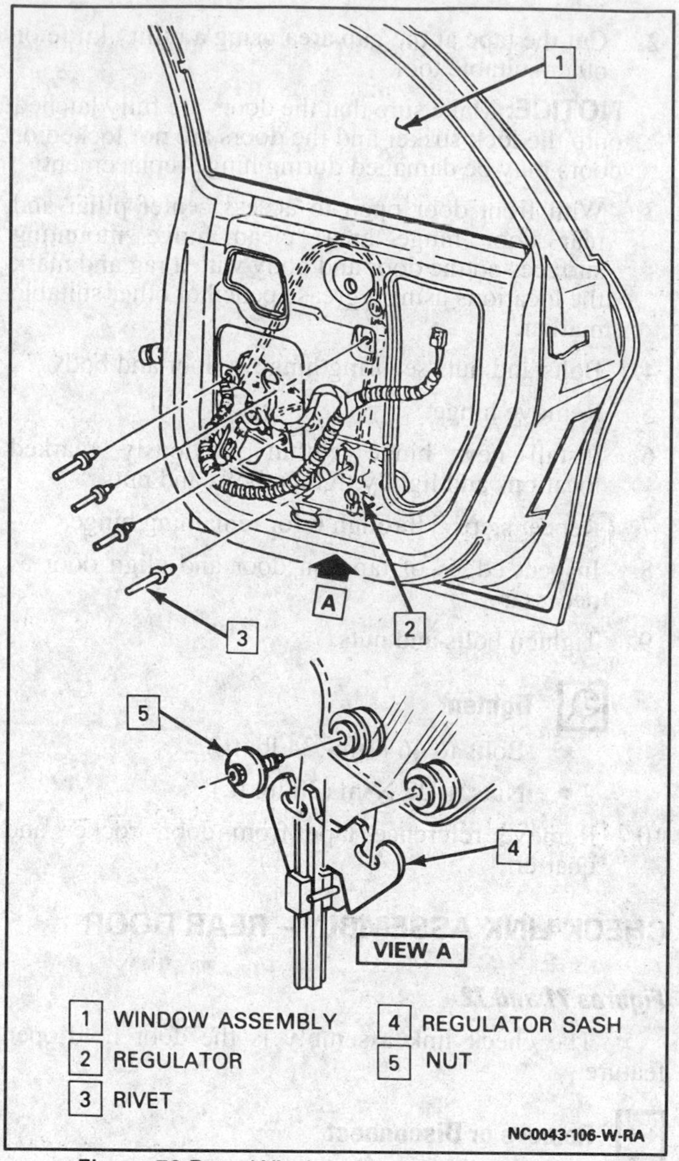
1
2
3
A
5
4
VIEW A
1 WINDOW ASSEMBLY
2 REGULATOR
3 RIVET
4 REGULATOR SASH
5 NUT
NC0043-106-W-RA

Figure 73 Door Window Removal – Rear Door

6. Inner belt sealing strip. Refer to "Inner Belt Sealing Strip – Rear Door" in this section.
7. Door trim panel. Refer to "Trim Panel – Rear Door" in this section.

WINDOW REGULATOR – REAR DOOR

Figure 73

The sedan rear doors use a tape drive regulator. The following provides the procedures required for removal and replacement of both power and manual window regulators.

Remove or Disconnect

Important

- Tape window in full-up position.

1. Door trim panel. Refer to "Trim Panel – Rear Door" in this section.
2. Water deflector. Refer to "Water Deflector – Rear Door" in this section.

3. Nuts securing regulator sash to window assembly.
4. Rivets using a 1/4 inch drill bit.
5. Electrical connector from motor (power window system).
6. Regulator through access hole in door inner panel.

Install or Connect

1. Regulator through access hole.
2. Electrical connector to motor (power window system).
3. Rivet using 1/4 inch x 1/2 inch peel type rivets.
4. Nuts.

Tighten

- Nuts to 9 N•m (80 lb. in.).

5. Water deflector. Refer to "Water Deflector – Rear Door" in this section.
6. Door trim panel. Refer to "Trim Panel – Rear Door" in this section.

DOOR WINDOW REGULATOR MOTOR – REAR DOOR

Remove or Disconnect

1. Regulator. Refer to "Window Regulator – Rear Door" in this section.
2. Motor by drilling out rivets holding motor to regulator using a 1/4 inch drill bit.

Install or Connect

1. Motor to regulator using a rivet (1/4 inch x 0.968 inch) part number 9441949 or equivalent.
2. Regulator. Refer to "Window Regulator – Rear Door" in this section.

DOOR WINDOW REGULATOR TAPE REPLACEMENT – REAR DOOR

Remove or Disconnect

1. Regulator. Refer to "Window Regulator – Rear Door" in this section.
2. Connect regulator motor to harness connector (power window system).
3. Tape from tabs on regulator.
4. Run tape out of regulator.

Install or Connect

1. Cut service tape to 7.86 mm (31 inches) for manual window regulator or 8.74 mm (34-1/2 inches) for power window regulator.
2. Tape to regulator.
3. Slots on tape to tabs on regulator.
4. Regulator. Refer to "Window Regulator – Rear Door" in this section.

SPECIFICATIONS

FASTENER TIGHTENING SPECIFICATIONS

Applique Screw	1.3 N•m (12 lb. in.)
Check Link-to-Body Screw	24 N•m (18 lb. ft.)
Check Link-to-Door Screw	6 N•m (53 lb. in.)
Clevis Screw	24 N•m (18 lb. ft.)
Conduit Bolt	2 N•m (18 lb. in.)
Door Speaker Screw	2 N•m (18 lb. in.)
Door Trim Retainer Screw	2 N•m (18 lb. in.)
Front Door Window Channel Retainer Screw	2 N•m (18 lb. in.)
Hinge	
Bolt	46 N•m (34 lb. ft.)
Nut	27 N•m (20 lb. ft.)
Pin Bolt	14 N•m (124 lb. in.)
Inside Handle Bezel Screw	1.3 N•m (12 lb. in.)
Inside Pull Handle Screw	3 N•m (27 lb. in.)
Lock Cylinder Anti-Theft Shield Screw	10 N•m (89 lb. in.)
Lock Cylinder Screw	10 N•m (89 lb. in.)
Lock Screw	7 N•m (62 lb. in.)
Lower Pillar Trim Panel Screw	2 N•m (18 lb. in.)
Outer Belt Sealing Strip Screw	1 N•m (9 lb. in.)
Outside Door Handle Cover Nut	3 N•m (27 lb. in.)
Outside Door Handle Cover Screw	2 N•m (18 lb. in.)
Outside Door Handle Nut (Coupe)	4 N•m (35 lb. in.)
Outside Door Handle Nut (Sedan)	7 N•m (62 lb. in.)

Passive Restraint Belt Retractor Cover Screw	2 N•m (18 lb. ft.)
Passive Restraint Striker Bolt	24 N•m (18 lb. ft.)
Rear Door Window Channel Retainer Screw	2 N•m (18 lb. in.)
Rear Window Regulator Sash Nut	9 N•m (80 lb. in.)
Rearview Mirror Bezel Nut	2 N•m (18 lb. in.)
Rearview Mirror Nut	10 N•m (89 lb. in.)
Striker Bolt	53 N•m (39 lb. ft.)
Trim Panel Screw	1 N•m (9 lb. in.)
Upper Auxiliary Weatherstrip Screw	2 N•m (18 lb. in.)
Window Guide Retainer Screw	6 N•m (53 lb. in.)
Window Weatherstrip Screw	
Front Door	6 N•m (53 lb. in.)
Rear Door	2 N•m (18 lb. in.)

SPECIAL TOOLS

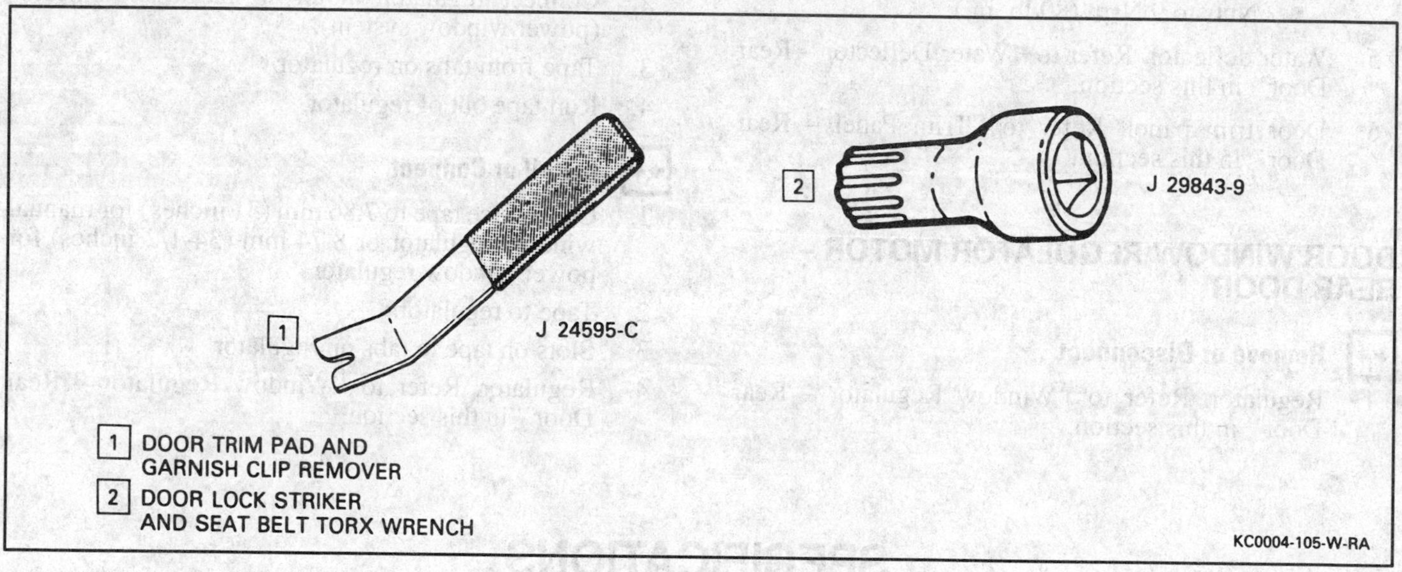
2
J 29843-9
1
J 24595-C
1 DOOR TRIM PAD AND GARNISH CLIP REMOVER
2 DOOR LOCK STRIKER AND SEAT BELT TORX WRENCH
KC0004-105-W-RA

SECTION 10-7

REAR QUARTERS

NOTICE: When fasteners are removed, always reinstall them at the same location from which they were removed. If a fastener needs to be replaced, use the correct part number fastener for that application. If the correct part number fastener is not available, a fastener of equal size and strength (or stronger) may be used. Fasteners that are not reused, and those requiring thread locking compound will be called out. The correct torque value must be used when installing fasteners that require it. If the above conditions are not followed, parts or system damage could result.

NOTICE: The theft deterrent label found on some major sheet metal, engines, and transaxles must be masked prior to painting, rustproofing, undercoating, etc. The mask must be removed following the above operations. Failure to keep the label clean and readable may result in liability for violation of Federal Vehicle Theft Prevention Standard, and subject the vehicle owner to possible suspicion that the part was stolen.

CONTENTS

GENERAL DESCRIPTION

REAR QUARTER TRIM

This section contains the service procedures for Rear Quarter Trim Components which includes the Interior Trim, Exterior Trim and the Fuel Filler Door.

For information on theft deterrent labels, refer to GENERAL INFORMATION (SECTION 0A).

ON-VEHICLE SERVICE

INTERIOR TRIM PANELS

Upper Trim Panel

Figures 1, 2 and 5

Tool Required:

J 24595 Door Trim Pad and Garnish Clip Remover

←→ Remove or Disconnect

1. Screw at coat hook.
2. Quarter upper trim panel by disengaging fasteners using J 24595-C.
3. Electrical connector on coupe.
4. Courtesy lamp from quarter upper trim panel by pressing tabs inward and pushing lamp through opening in trim panel on coupe.

→← Install or Connect

1. Courtesy lamp to quarter upper trim panel on coupe.
2. Electrical connector on coupe.
3. Quarter upper trim panel by engaging fasteners on trim panel to body.
4. Screw at coat hook.

Lower Trim Panel

Figures 3 and 4

Tool Required:

J 24595-C Door Trim Pad and Garnish Clip Remover

←→ Remove or Disconnect

1. Rear seat cushion. Refer to SEATS (SECTION 10-10).
2. Rear seatback. Refer to SEATS (SECTION 10-10).

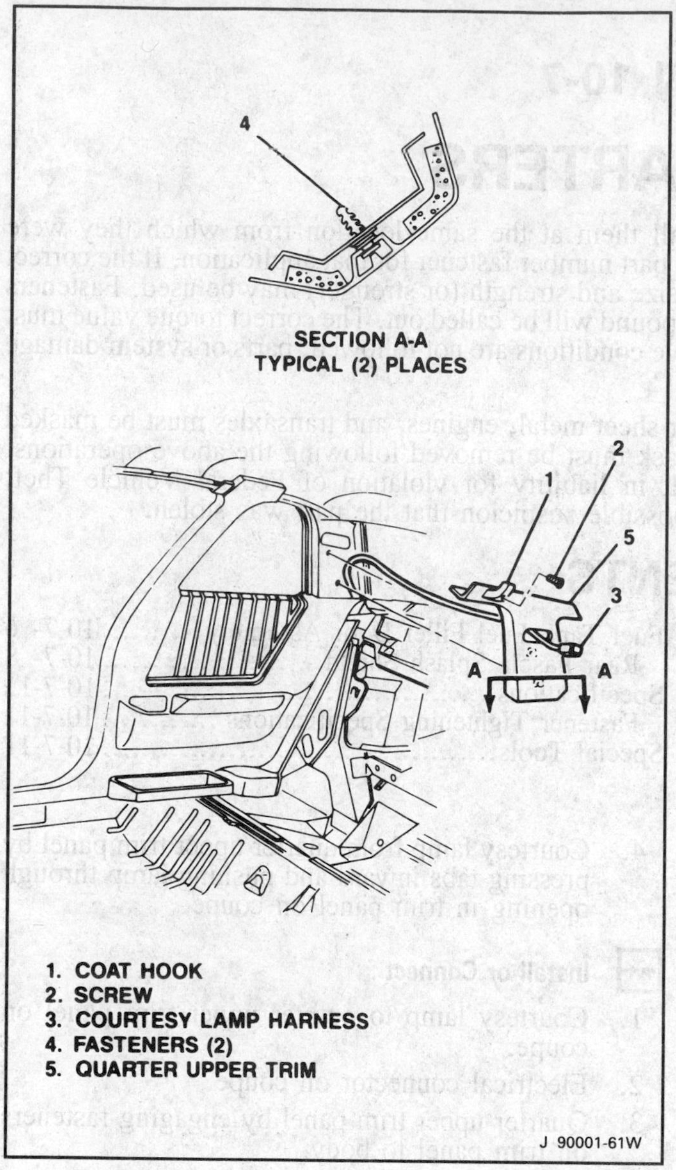

4
SECTION A-A
TYPICAL (2) PLACES
2
1
5
3
A
A
1. COAT HOOK
2. SCREW
3. COURTESY LAMP HARNESS
4. FASTENERS (2)
5. QUARTER UPPER TRIM
J 90001-61W

Figure 1 Quarter Upper Trim Panel (Coupe)

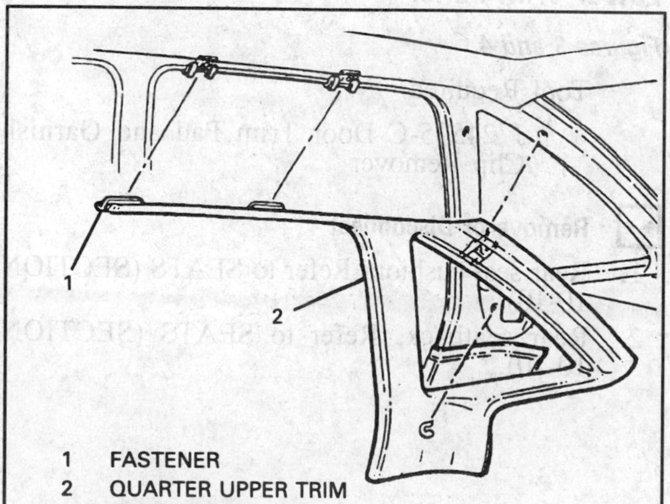

1
2
1 FASTENER
2 QUARTER UPPER TRIM FINISH PANEL
NC0017-107-W-RA

Figure 2 Quarter Upper Trim Panel (Sedan)

3. Loosen windshield side upper garnish on coupe. Refer to ROOF (SECTION 10-9).
4. Loosen quarter upper trim panel. Refer to "Upper Trim Panel" in this section.
5. Loosen center pillar lower trim panel on sedan. Refer to DOORS (SECTION 10-6).
6. Loosen carpet retainer trim on coupe. Refer to FRAME AND UNDERBODY (SECTION 10-3).
7. Quarter lower trim panel by disengaging fasteners using J 24595-C.
8. Safety belt through the slot in the trim panel on coupe.

Install or Connect

1. Safety belt through slot in trim panel on coupe.
2. Quarter lower trim panel by engaging fasteners on trim panel to body.
3. Carpet retainer trim on coupe. Refer to FRAME AND UNDERBODY (SECTION 10-3).
4. Center pillar lower trim panel on sedan. Refer to DOORS (SECTION 10-6).
5. Quarter upper trim panel. Refer to "Upper Trim Panel" in this section.
6. Windshield side upper garnish on coupe. Refer to ROOF (SECTION 10-9).
7. Rear seatback. Refer to SEATS (SECTION 10-10).
8. Rear seat cushion. Refer to SEATS (SECTION 10-10).

PRESSURE RELIEF VALVE

Figure 6

Remove or Disconnect

1. Screw.
2. Pressure relief valve by lifting up and forward to disengage tab of valve from lock pillar.

Install or Connect

1. Pressure relief valve by placing taba at top of valve in upper edge of cut-out in lock pillar.
2. Screw.

Tighten

- Screw to 2 N·m (18 lb. in.).

EXTERIOR MOLDINGS AND EMBLEMS

Exterior moldings and emblems are attached to the quarter panels with adhesive, mounting clips and screws. Refer to GENERAL BODY SERVICE (SECTION 10-1) for attaching loose or removed adhesive attached moldings or emblems. For information on rocker moldings, refer to GENERAL BODY SERVICE (SECTION 10-1). The quarter panel moldings that are attached with clips and screws are as follows.

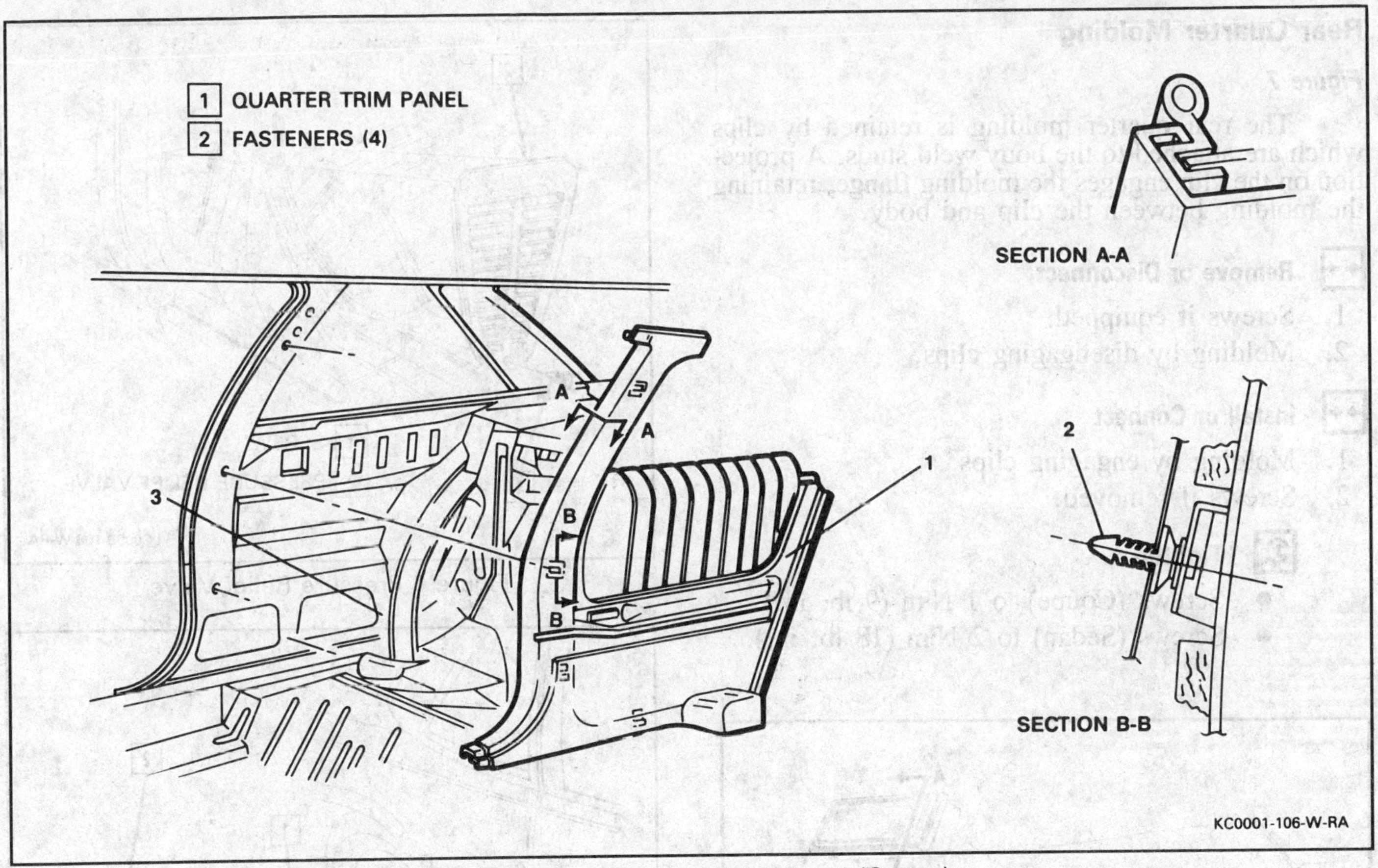
1 QUARTER TRIM PANEL
2 FASTENERS (4)
SECTION A-A
SECTION B-B
A
A
B
B
1
2
3
KC0001-106-W-RA

Figure 3 Quarter Lower Trim Panel (Coupe)

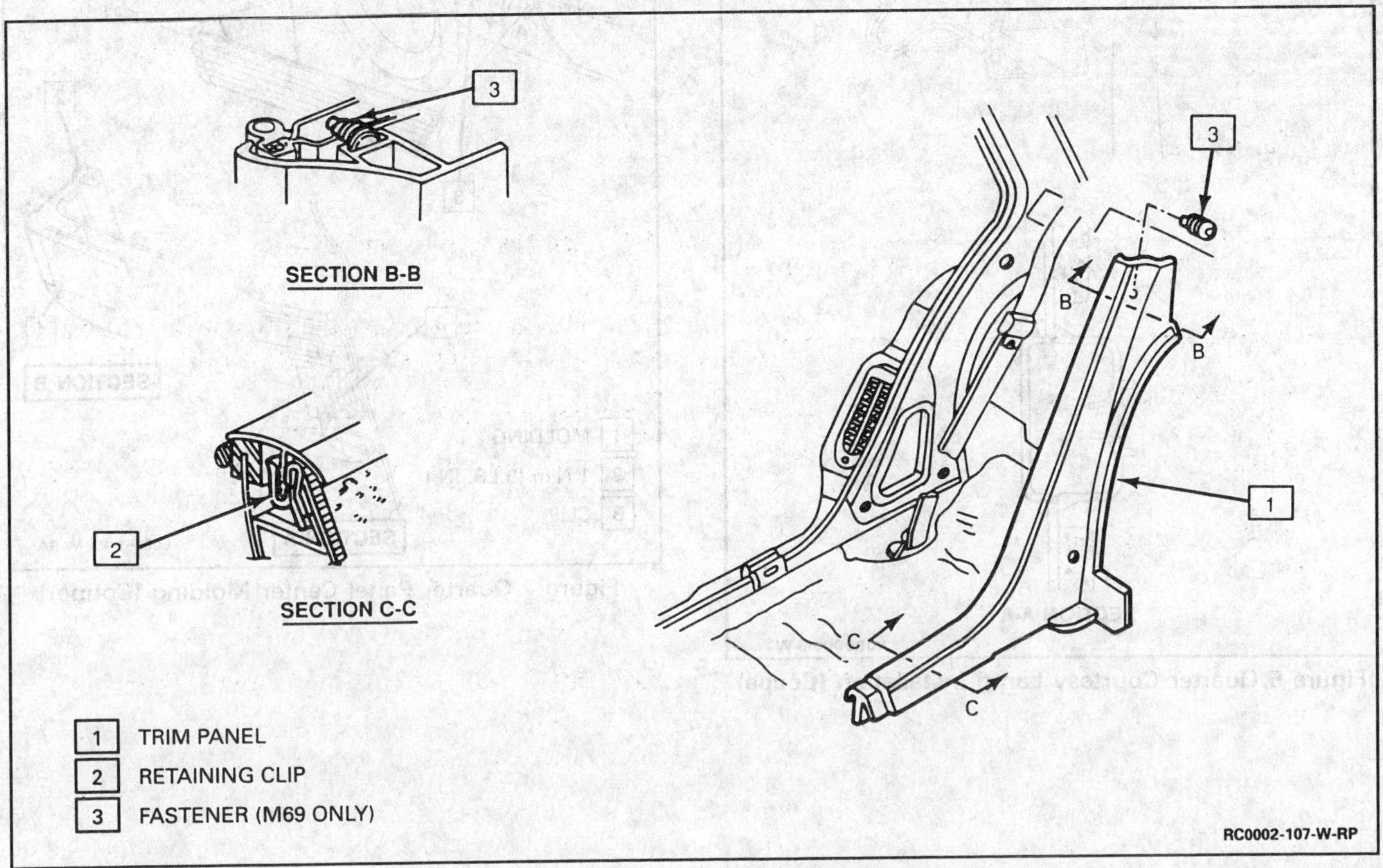
3
SECTION B-B
2
SECTION C-C
3
B
B
1
C
C
1 TRIM PANEL
2 RETAINING CLIP
3 FASTENER (M69 ONLY)
RC0002-107-W-RP

Figure 4 Quarter Lower Trim Panel (Sedan)

Rear Quarter Molding

Figure 7

The rear quarter molding is retained by clips which are attached to the body weld studs. A projection on the clip engages the molding flange, retaining the molding between the clip and body.

Remove or Disconnect

1. Screws if equipped.
2. Molding by disengaging clips.

Install or Connect

1. Molding by engaging clips.
2. Screws if removed.

Tighten

- Screws (Coupe) to 1 N·m (9 lb. in.).
- Screws (Sedan) to 2 N·m (18 lb. in.).

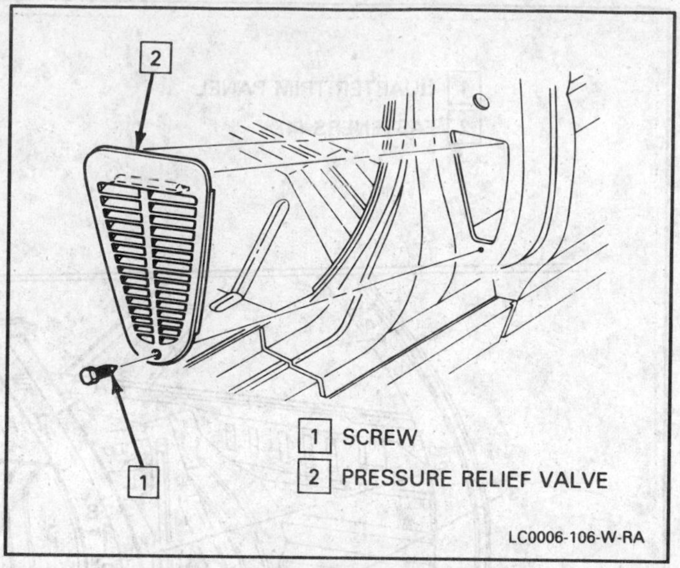
1 SCREW
2 PRESSURE RELIEF VALVE
LC0006-106-W-RA

Figure 6 Pressure Relief Valve

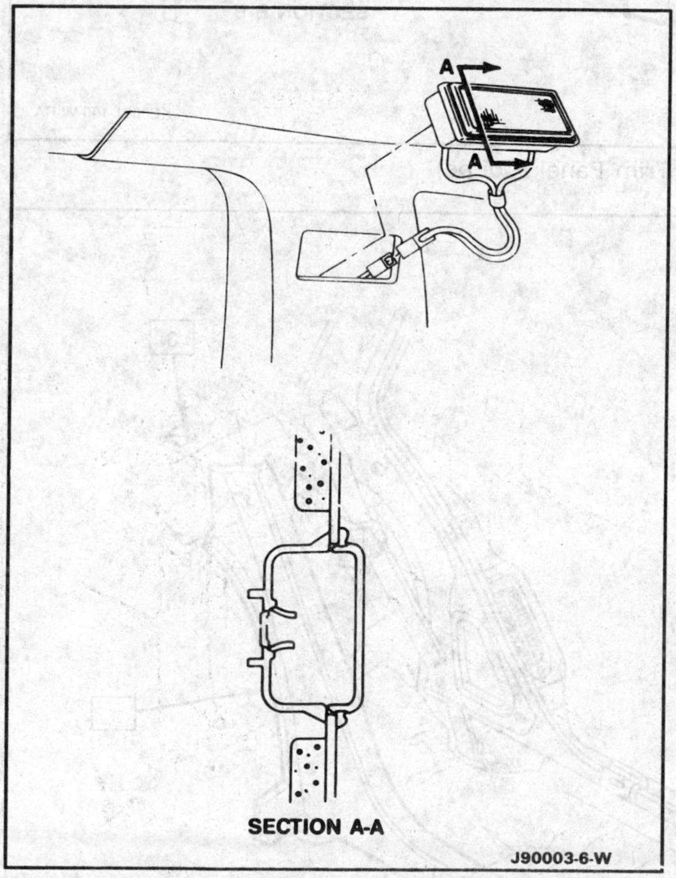
SECTION A-A
J90003-6-W

Figure 5 Quarter Courtesy Lamp Installation (Coupe)

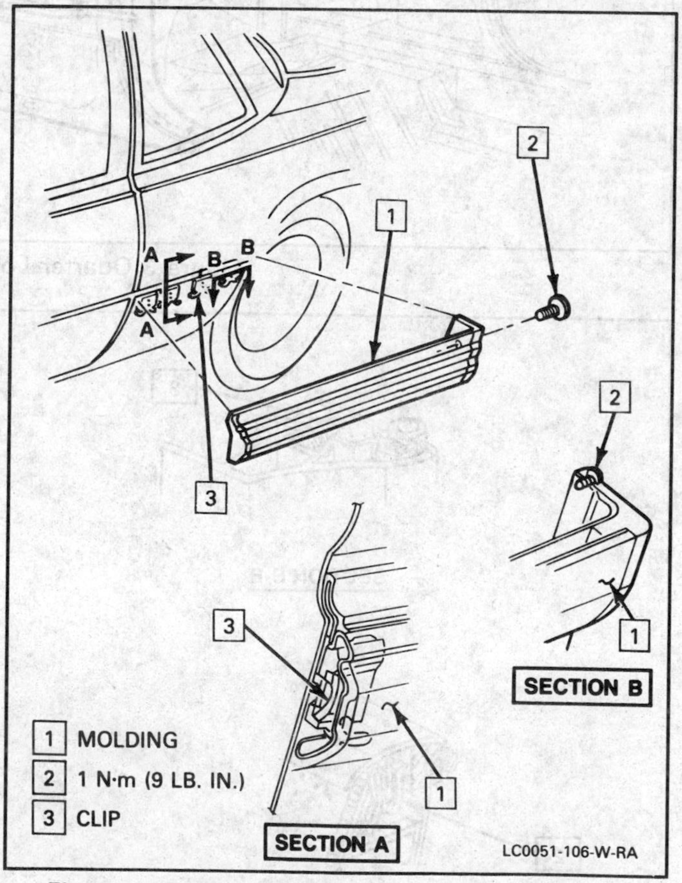
SECTION B
SECTION A
1 MOLDING
2 1 N·m (9 LB. IN.)
3 CLIP
LC0051-106-W-RA

Figure 7 Quarter Panel Center Molding (Coupe)

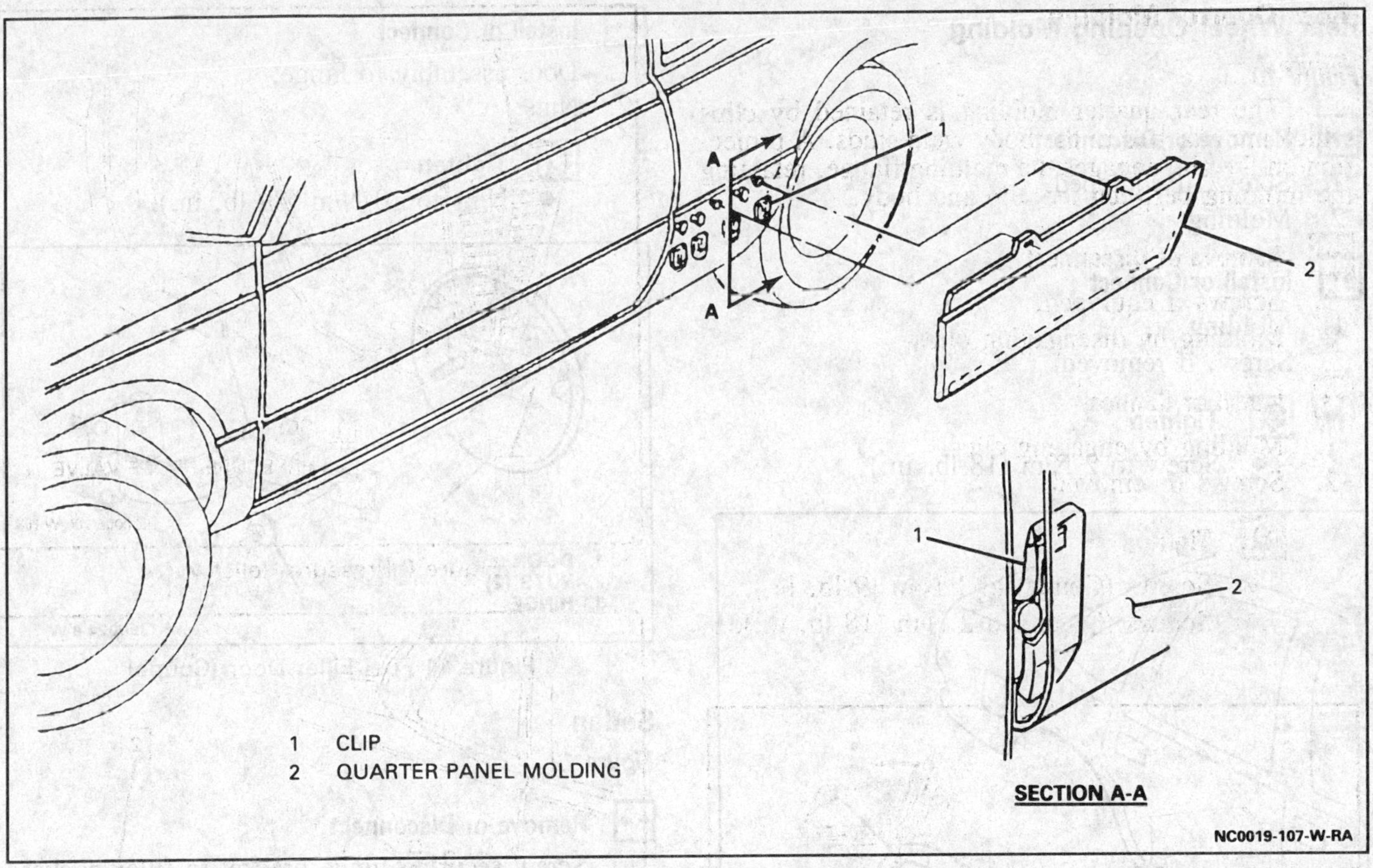
A
1
A
2
1
2
1 CLIP
2 QUARTER PANEL MOLDING
SECTION A-A
NC0019-107-W-RA

Figure 8 Quarter Panel Lower Molding (Coupe)

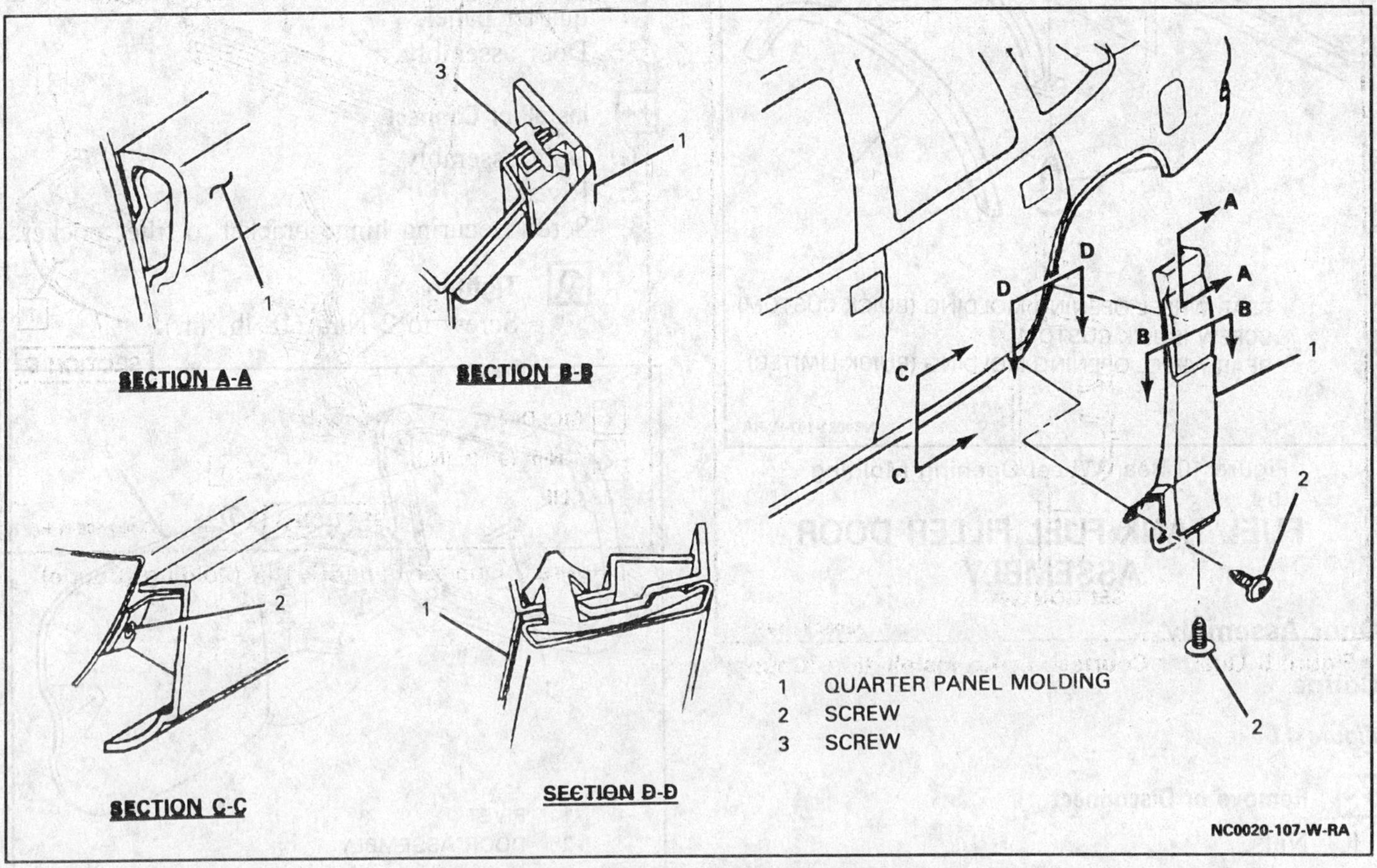
1
SECTION A-A
3
1
SECTION B-B
A
D
D
A
B
B
C
1
C
2
2
SECTION C-C
1
SECTION D-D
2
1 QUARTER PANEL MOLDING
2 SCREW
3 SCREW
NC0020-107-W-RA

Figure 9 Quarter Panel Molding (Sedan)

Rear Wheel Opening Molding

Figure 10

Remove or Disconnect

1. Screw, if equipped.
2. Molding.

Install or Connect

1. Molding.
2. Screw, if removed.

Tighten

- Screw to 2 N·m (18 lb. in.).

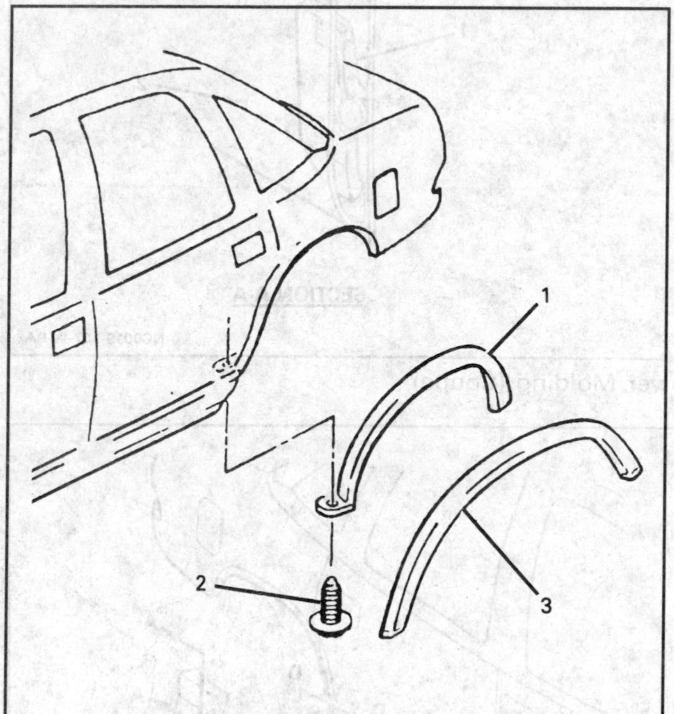
1
2
3
1 REAR WHEEL OPENING MOLDING (BUICK CUSTOM)
2 SCREW (BUICK CUSTOM)
3 REAR WHEEL OPENING MOLDING (BUICK LIMITED)
NC0021-107-W-RA

Figure 10 Rear Wheel Opening Molding

FUEL TANK FUEL FILLER DOOR ASSEMBLY

Door Assembly

Coupe

Figure 11

Remove or Disconnect

1. Nuts.
2. Door assembly from hinge.

Install or Connect

1. Door assembly to hinge.
2. Nuts.

Tighten

- Nuts to 10 N·m (89 lb. in.).

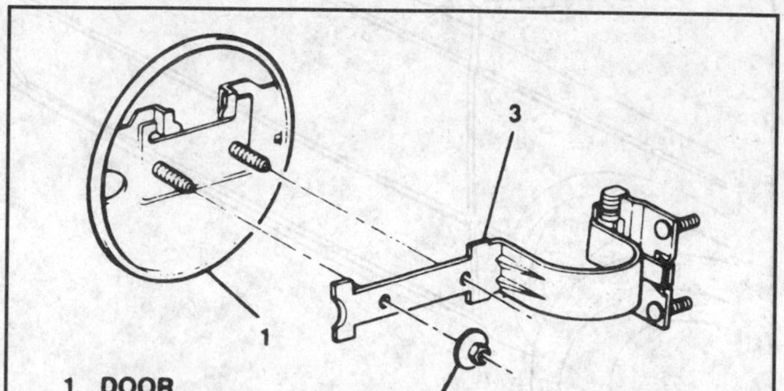
1
2
3
1. DOOR
2. NUTS (2)
3. HINGE
J90024-6-W

Figure 11 Fuel Filler Door (Coupe)

Sedan

Figure 12

Remove or Disconnect

1. Screw securing hinge bracket to filler pocket.
2. Drill out rivets securing door assembly to quarter panel.
3. Door assembly.

Install or Connect

1. Door assembly.
2. Rivets.
3. Screw securing hinge bracket to filler pocket.

Tighten

- Screw to 2 N·m (18 lb. in.).

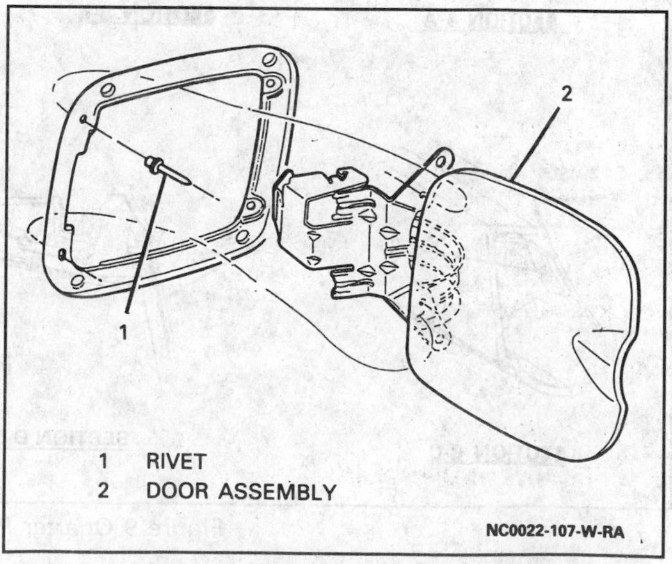
1
2
1 RIVET
2 DOOR ASSEMBLY
NC0022-107-W-RA

Figure 12 Fuel Filler Door (Sedan)

Hinge Assembly

Figure 13

Remove or Disconnect

1. Nuts.
2. Hinge assembly.
3. Door from hinge assembly. Refer to "Door Assembly" in this section.

Install or Connect

1. Door to hinge assembly. Refer to "Door Assembly" in this section.
2. Hinge assembly.
3. Nuts.

Tighten

- Nuts to 10 N·m (89 lb. in.).

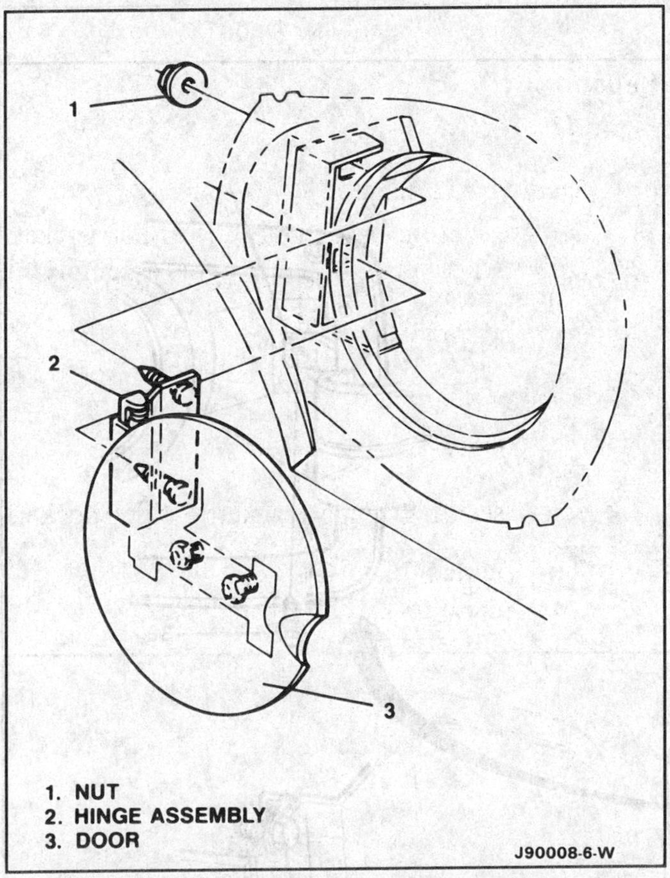
1
2
3
1. NUT
2. HINGE ASSEMBLY
3. DOOR
J90008-6-W

Figure 13 Fuel Filler Door Hinge

Pocket Assembly

Coupe

Figure 14

Remove or Disconnect

1. Screws to inner fuel pocket assembly.
2. Outer pocket assembly screws.
3. Pocket assembly by pulling outboard and rotating pocket assembly until slit is aligned to hinge assembly and removing pocket assembly.

Install or Connect

Important

- If a new pocket assembly is to be installed, use a utility knife to cut a slit in pocket assembly as shown.

1. Pocket assembly by locating slit over hinge and rotating pocket assembly.
2. Outer pocket assembly screws.

Tighten

- Screw to 2 N·m (18 lb. in.).

3. Inner pocket assembly screws.

Tighten

- Screws to 2 N·m (18 lb. in.).

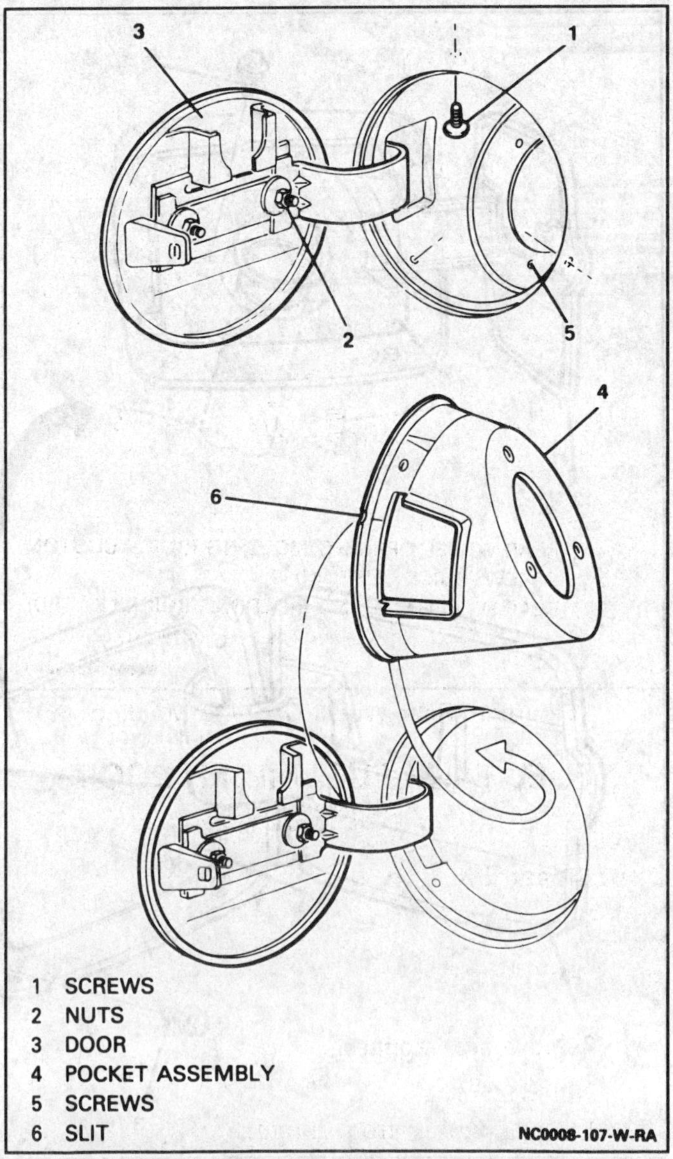
3
1
2
5
4
6
1 SCREWS
2 NUTS
3 DOOR
4 POCKET ASSEMBLY
5 SCREWS
6 SLIT
NC0008-107-W-RA

Figure 14 Fuel Filler Pocket Assembly (Coupe)

Sedan

Figure 15

Remove or Disconnect

1. Rear fascia splash shield. Refer to "Rear Fascia Splash Shield" in this section.
2. Screws securing filler pocket to fuel tank filler neck, quarter panel and hinge bracket.
3. Fuel filler cap and loosen fuel tank filler neck mounting bracket as needed to gain enough clearance to remove filler pocket. Refer to ENGINE FUEL (SECTION 6C).
4. Filler pocket through wheel opening in quarter panel.

Install or Connect

1. Filler pocket through wheel opening in quarter panel.
2. Fuel tank filler neck mounting bracket and fuel filler cap. Refer to ENGINE FUEL (SECTION 6C).
3. Screws securing filler pocket to fuel tank filler neck, quarter panel and hinge bracket.

Tighten

- Screws to 2 N·m (18 lb. in.).

4. Rear fascia splash shield. Refer to "Rear Fascia Splash Shield" in this section.

REAR FASCIA SPLASH SHIELD

Figures 16 and 17

Remove or Disconnect

1. Screws.
2. Rear fascia splash shield.

Install or Connect

1. Rear fascia splash shield.
2. Screws.

Tighten

- Screws to 2 N·m (18 lb. in.).

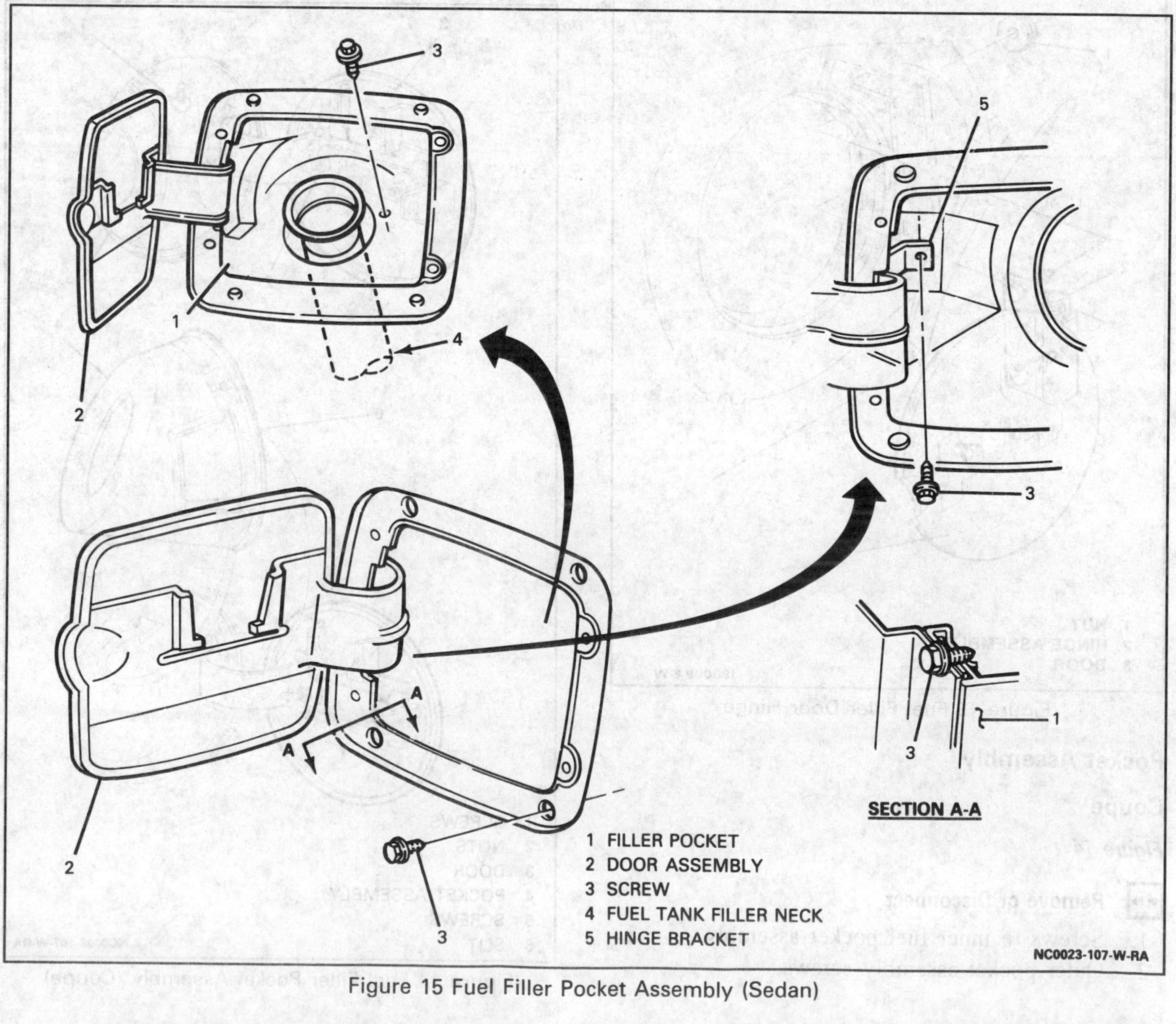

3
5
1
2
4
3
A
A
2
3
1
3
SECTION A-A
1 FILLER POCKET
2 DOOR ASSEMBLY
3 SCREW
4 FUEL TANK FILLER NECK
5 HINGE BRACKET
NC0023-107-W-RA

Figure 15 Fuel Filler Pocket Assembly (Sedan)

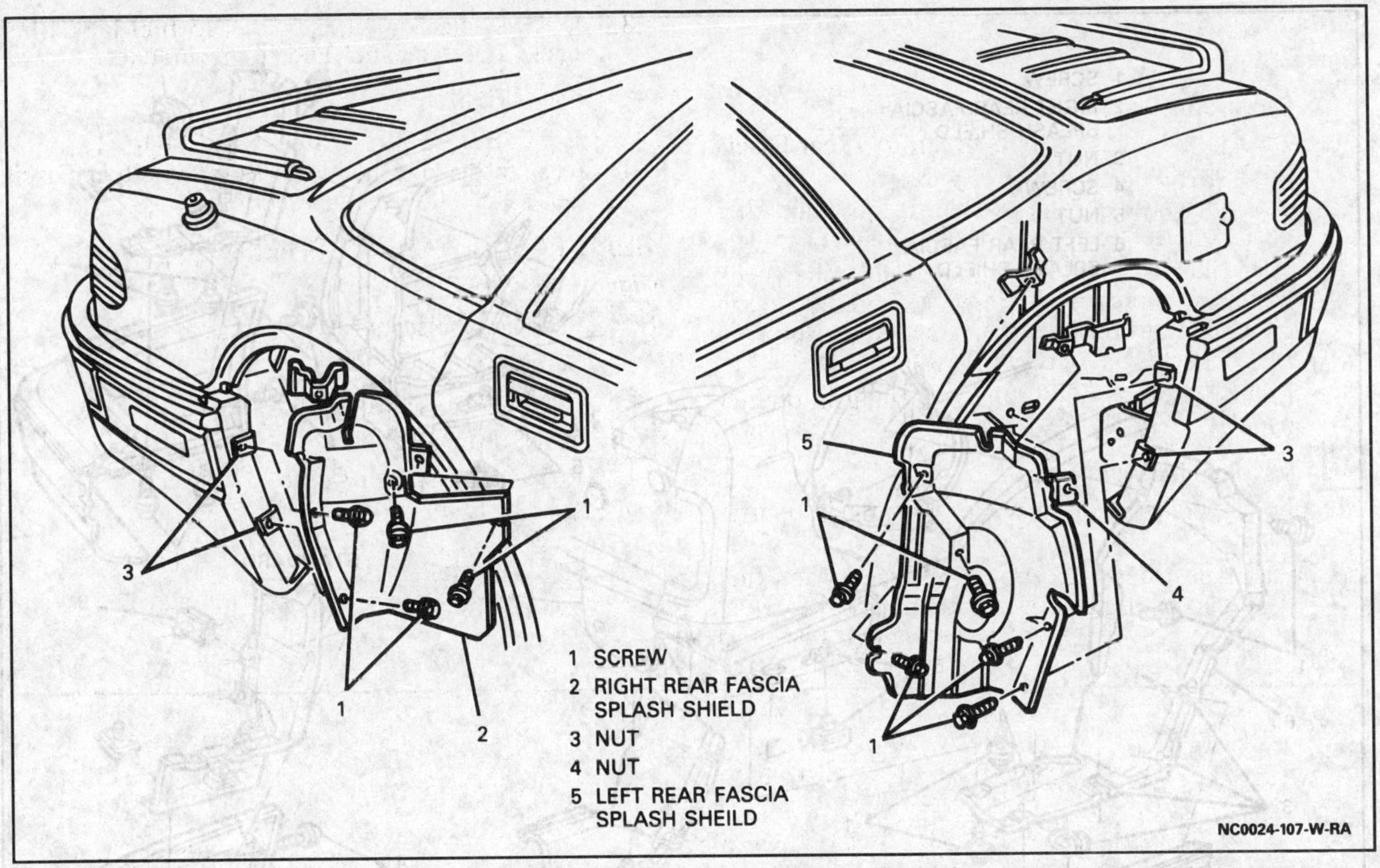

1
3
1
2
5
1
3
4
1
1 SCREW
2 RIGHT REAR FASCIA SPLASH SHIELD
3 NUT
4 NUT
5 LEFT REAR FASCIA SPLASH SHEILD
NC0024-107-W-RA

Figure 16 Rear Fascia Splash Shield (Sedan)

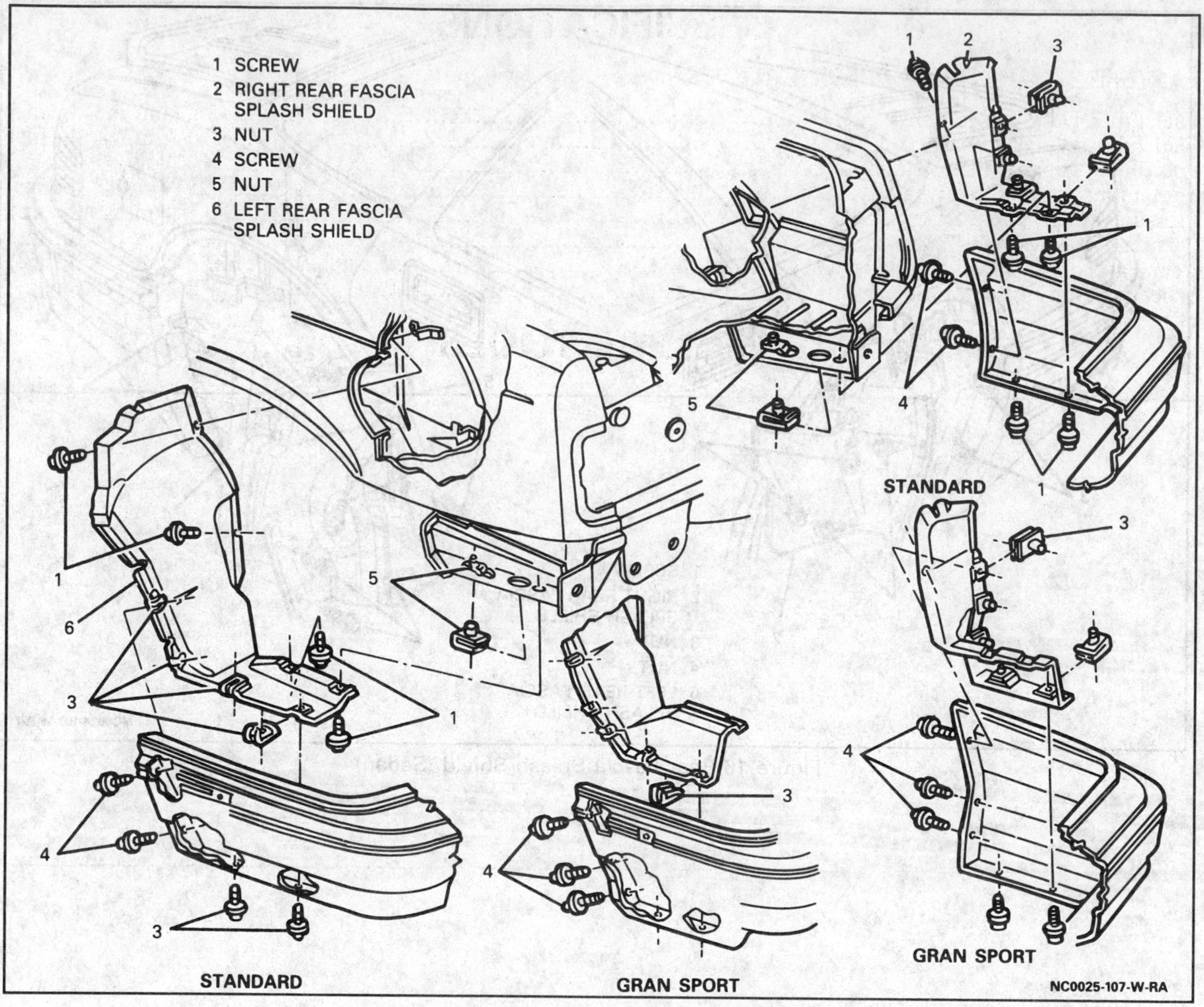
1 SCREW
2 RIGHT REAR FASCIA SPLASH SHIELD
3 NUT
4 SCREW
5 NUT
6 LEFT REAR FASCIA SPLASH SHIELD
1
2
3
1
5
4
1
STANDARD
3
1
6
5
3
1
3
4
4
4
3
3
STANDARD
GRAN SPORT
GRAN SPORT
NC0025-107-W-RA

Figure 17 Rear Fascia Splash Shield (Coupe)

SPECIFICATIONS

FASTENER TIGHTENING SPECIFICATIONS

Fuel Filler Door Hinge Screw	2 N·m (18 lb. in.)
Fuel Filler Door Nut	10 N·m (89 lb. in.)
Fuel Filler Hinge Nut	10 N•m (89 lb. in.)
Fuel Filler Pocket Screw	2 N·m (18 lb. in.)
Pressure Relief Valve Screw	2 N·m (18 lb. in.)
Quarter Panel Molding Screw	2 N·m (18 lb. in.)
Rear Fascia Splash Shield Screw	2 N·m (18 lb. in.)
Wheel Opening Molding Screw	2 N·m (18 lb. in.)

SPECIAL TOOLS

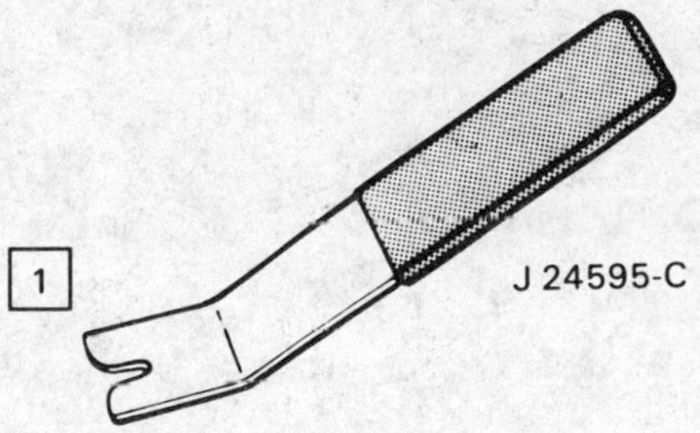
1
J 24595-C

1 DOOR TRIM PAD AND GARNISH CLIP REMOVER

KC0150-106-B-RP

SECTION 10-8

BODY REAR END

NOTICE: When fasteners are removed, always reinstall them at the same location from which they were removed. If a fastener needs to be replaced, use the correct part number fastener for that application. If the correct part number fastener is not available, a fastener of equal size and strength (or stronger) may be used. Fasteners that are not reused, and those requiring thread locking compound will be called out. The correct torque value must be used when installing fasteners that require it. If the above conditions are not followed, parts or system damage could result.

NOTICE: The theft deterrent label found on some major sheet metal, engines, and transaxles must be masked prior to painting, rustproofing, undercoating, etc. The mask must be removed following the above operations. Failure to keep the label clean and readable may result in liability for violation of Federal Vehicle Theft Prevention Standard, and subject the vehicle owner to possible suspicion that the part was stolen.

CONTENTS

GENERAL DESCRIPTION

BODY REAR END

The service operations necessary for the removal, installation, adjustment and sealing of the rear compartment lid hardware components attached to the rear compartment lid are contained in this section. Also information on the servicing and removal of rear seat-to-rear window trim panel and rear speakers is contained in this section.

For information on theft deterrent labels, refer to GENERAL INFORMATION (SECTION 0A).

ON-VEHICLE SERVICE

REAR COMPARTMENT LID

Figure 1

The rear compartment lid consists of an inner and outer panel that is hemmed around the perimeter and bonded together with structural adhesive.

The compartment lid hinge is spot welded to the body and bolted to the lid.

Opening assist is performed by the use of torque rods.

Adjust

1. Loosen bolts.
2. Align lid as necessary.

Tighten

- Bolts to 25 N·m (18 lb. ft.).

Remove or Disconnect

1. Place protective coverings over adjacent body panels.
2. Electrical connectors to electrical components attached to lid.
3. Tie a string to wire harness assembly and pull wire out of lid. Allow an ample amount of string so that when lid is removed there is enough string to allow for feeding wire harness back through lid.

CAUTION: The following step requires the aid of a helper so that the lid does not fall down and cause personal injury.

4. Bolts and remove lid while helper supports lid.

Install or Connect

1. Lid to hinges and install bolts with aid of helper.

Tighten

- Bolts to 25 N·m (18 lb. ft.).

2. Pull string through lid until wire harness is within lid and attach wire connectors to electrical components.

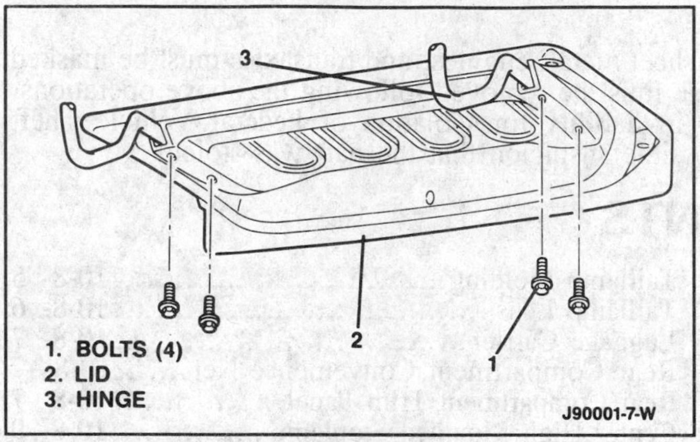
3
2
1
1. BOLTS (4)
2. LID
3. HINGE
J90001-7-W

Figure 1 Rear Compartment Lid Installation

TORQUE RODS

Figure 2

Remove or Disconnect

1. Open rear compartment lid.

CAUTION: Have an aid support lid before performing the following steps so the lid does not fall down and cause personal injury. If a helper is not available remove the lid from the hinges.

2. Speaker assemblies. Refer to "Rear Speakers" in this section.
3. Torque rod from bracket using a 1/2 inch inside diameter pipe or equivalent. Pry up on the free end of the torque rod.

Install or Connect

1. Hinge end to torque rod assembly using a 1/2 inch inside diameter pipe.
2. Bracket end to torque rod in notch of bracket. Repeat operation for opposite side.
3. Speaker assemblies. Refer to "Rear Speakers" in this section.
4. Close rear compartment lid.

HINGES

Figure 2

Remove or Disconnect

1. Rear seat-to-rear window trim panel. Refer to "Rear Seat-to-Rear Window Trim Panel" in this section.
2. Rear compartment lid. Refer to "Rear Compartment Lid" in this section.
3. Torque rod from bracket using a 1/2 inch diameter pipe or equivalent, by prying up on the free end of the torque rod.
4. Pin.
5. Hinge.

Install or Connect

1. Hinge.
2. Pin.
3. Hinge end to torque rod assembly using a 1/2 inch inside diameter pipe.
4. Bracket end of torque rod in notch of bracket.
5. Rear compartment lid. Refer to "Rear Compartment Lid" in this section.
6. Rear seat-to-rear window trim panel. Refer to "Rear Seat-to-Rear Window Trim Panel" in this section.

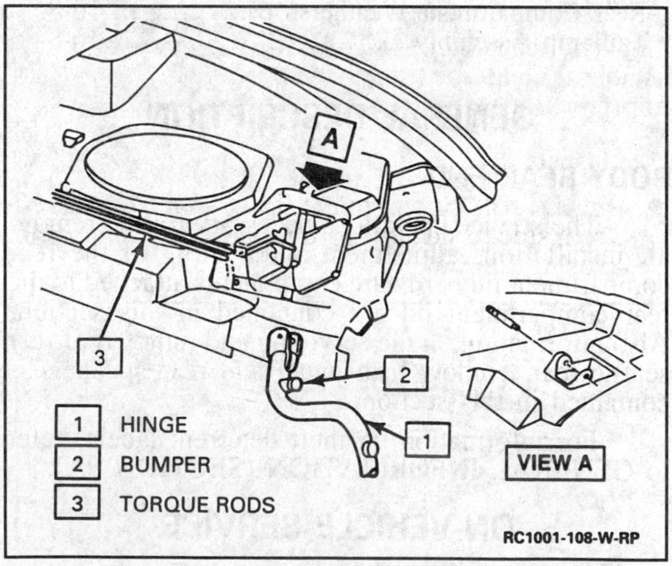
A
3
2
1
VIEW A
1 HINGE
2 BUMPER
3 TORQUE RODS
RC1001-108-W-RP

Figure 2 Hinge Assembly

LOCK CYLINDER

Figure 3

Remove or Disconnect

1. Rivet using 6 mm (1/4 inch) drill bit.
2. Retainer and gasket.
3. Lock cylinder and gasket.

Install or Connect

1. Lock cylinder and gasket to rear compartment lid, making sure lock cylinder shaft engages with lock.
2. Retainer and gasket.
3. Rivet.

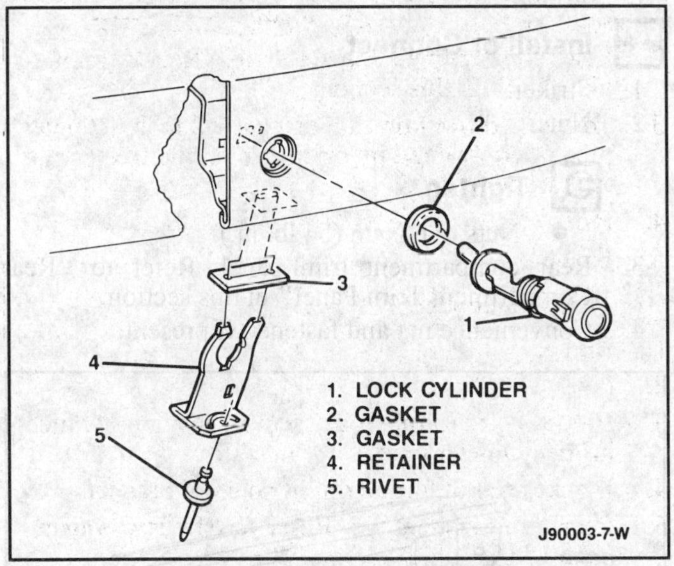

1. LOCK CYLINDER
2. GASKET
3. GASKET
4. RETAINER
5. RIVET
J90003-7-W

Figure 3 Lock Cylinder Installation

LOCK

Figure 4

The rear compartment lid lock assembly is adjustable up and down and side to side to provide for proper lid lock operation.

Inspect

- Ensure rear compartment lid is properly aligned from side to side and fore and aft by opening and closing the lid.

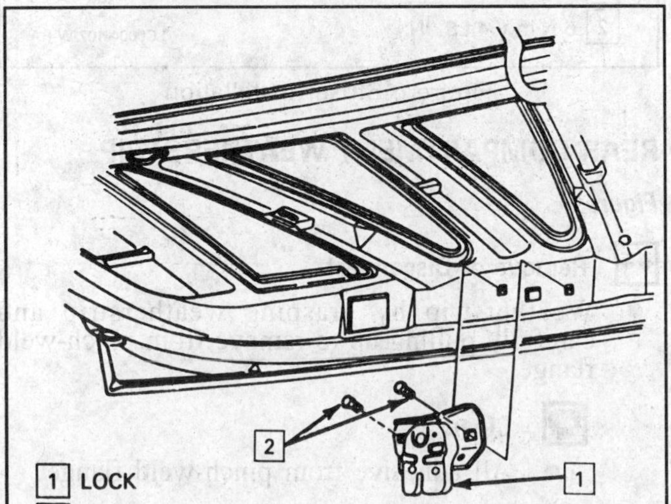

1 LOCK
2 6 N·m (54 LB. IN.)
LC0005-107-W-RA

Figure 4 Lid Lock Assembly

Adjust

1. Remove solenoid assembly, if present. Refer to "Lock Release Solenoid" in this section.
2. Loosen screws.
3. Lock to striker as required.
4. Screws.

Tighten

- Screws to 6 N·m (53 lb. in.).

5. Replace solenoid assembly, if removed. Refer to "Lock Release Solenoid" in this section.

Inspect

- Lock-to-striker engagement.

Remove or Disconnect

1. Solenoid assembly, if present. Refer to "Lock Release Solenoid" in this section.
2. Screws.
3. Lock.

Install or Connect

1. Lock to rear compartment lid.
2. Screws.

Tighten

- Screws to 6 N•m (54 lb. in.).

3. Solenoid assembly, if removed. Refer to "Lock Release Solenoid" in this section.

Inspect

- Lock-to-striker engagement.

LOCK RELEASE SOLENOID

Figure 5

The rear compartment lid lock release allows the lid to be unlocked from either the inside of the vehicle by a switch located in the passenger compartment or from outside the vehicle with the key.

The rear compartment lid lock release consists of a solenoid and a single wire harness. The harness is routed from the switch to the rear compartment lid and connected to the solenoid release mechanism.

When the switch is pressed, the release solenoid coil is energized. The release pulls back and unlatches the rear compartment lid lock. The lid then raises off the striker and may be raised to an open position.

The entire solenoid assembly is protected against overheating and internal shorts by an internal circuit breaker.

Remove or Disconnect

1. Electrical connector.
2. Screws.
3. Solenoid assembly from lock.

Install or Connect

1. Solenoid assembly to lock.
2. Screws.

Tighten

- Screws to 8 N·m (71 lb. in.).

3. Electrical connector.

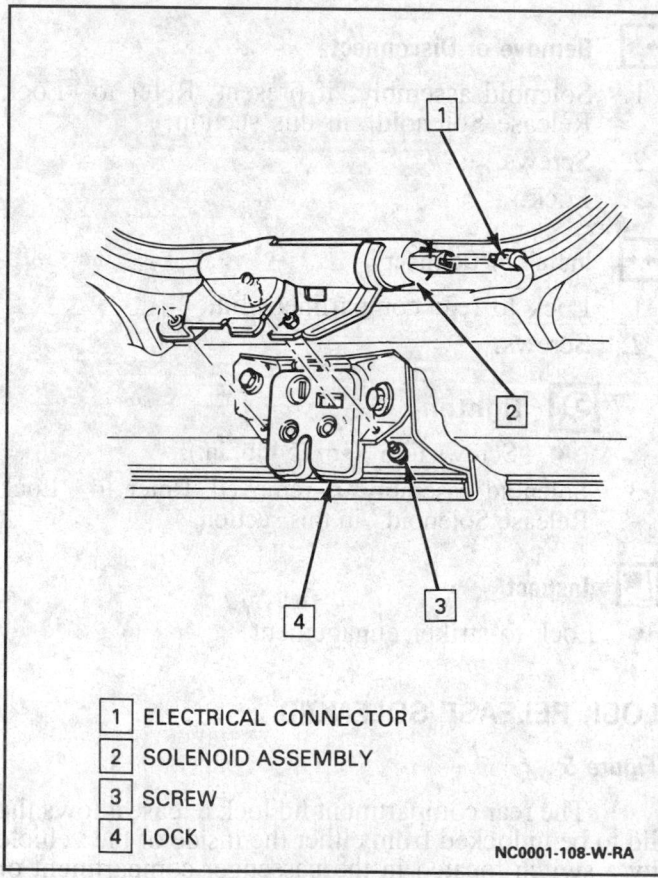

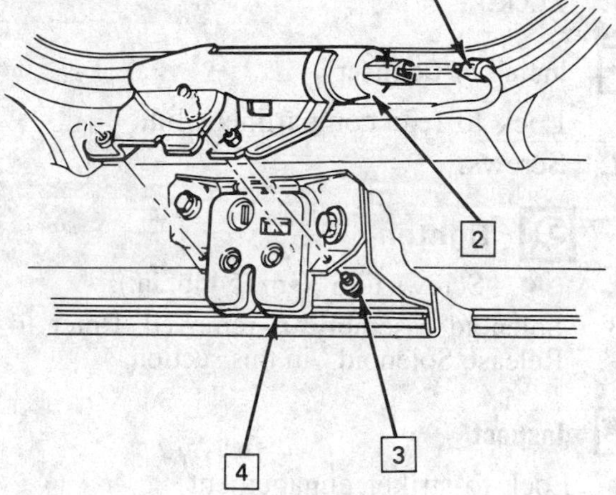
1
2
3
4
1 ELECTRICAL CONNECTOR
2 SOLENOID ASSEMBLY
3 SCREW
4 LOCK
NC0001-108-W-RA

Figure 5 Release Solenoid Installation

LOCK STRIKER

Figure 6

The striker is retained by nuts and there is no adjustment feature. All adjustments must be made by moving the rear compartment lid lock.

Remove or Disconnect

1. Convenience net and fastener, if present.
2. Rear compartment trim panel. Refer to "Rear Compartment Trim Panel" in this section.
3. Nuts.
4. Striker.

Install or Connect

1. Striker.
2. Nuts.

Tighten

- Nuts to 6 N•m (54 lb. in.).

3. Rear compartment trim panel. Refer to "Rear Compartment Trim Panel" in this section.
4. Convenience net and fastener, if present.

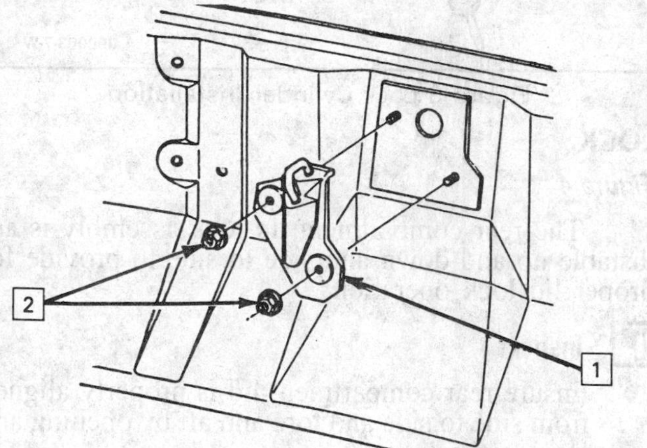
1
2
1 STRIKER
2 6 N·m (54 LB. IN.)
LC0004-107-W-RA

Figure 6 Striker Installation

REAR COMPARTMENT WEATHERSTRIP

Figure 7

Remove or Disconnect

- Weatherstrip by grasping weatherstrip and carefully pulling up to remove from pinch-weld flange.

Clean

- All adhesive from pinch-weld flange.

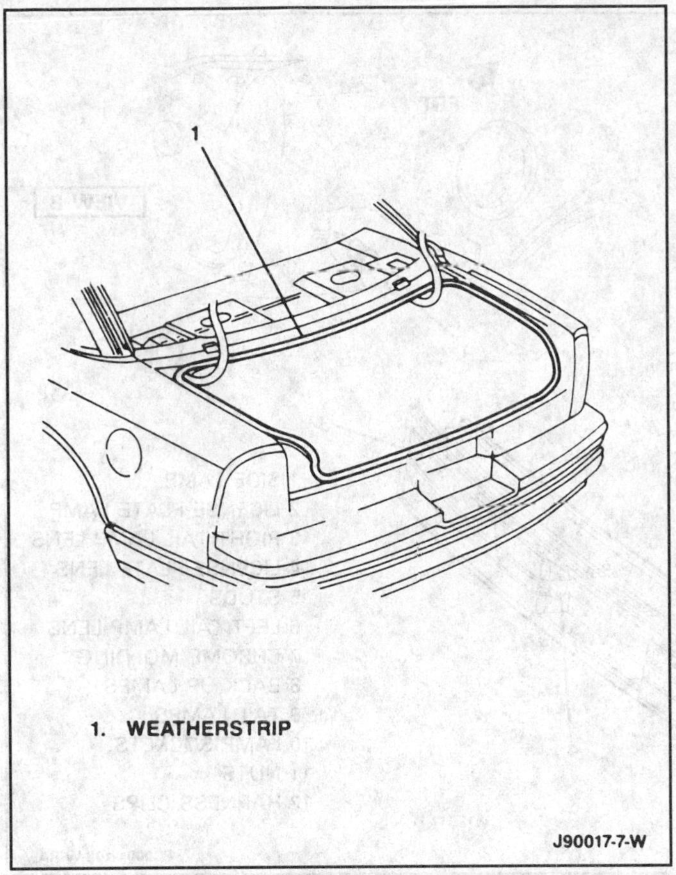
1
1. WEATHERSTRIP
J90017-7-W

Figure 7 Weatherstrip Installation

Install or Connect

1. Apply a 3 mm (1/8 inch) bead of weatherstrip adhesive to top edge of pinch-weld flange, around the complete perimeter of rear compartment opening.
2. Weatherstrip by looping over rear compartment lid. Locate color mark on weatherstrip to body centerline at the front of the rear compartment lid opening.
   - Engage weatherstrip onto pinch-weld flange, starting at top center of lid opening and working toward bottom center.
   - Use a rubber mallet to ensure full engagement of weatherstrip to pinch-weld flange.

TAILLAMP ASSEMBLY

Coupe

Figure 8

Remove or Disconnect

1. Convenience net, if present.
2. Rear compartment trim panel. Refer to "Rear Compartment Trim Panel" in this section.
3. Bulb and socket assemblies.
4. Nuts.
5. Taillamp assembly from body.

Install or Connect

Important

- When installing taillamps to body, care must be taken not to pinch or trap wire harness to insure against a potential lamp failure.

1. Taillamp assembly to body.
2. Nuts.

Tighten

- Nuts to 5 N·m (44 lb. in.).

3. Bulb and socket assemblies.
4. Rear compartment trim panel. Refer to "Rear Compartment Trim Panel" in this section.
5. Convenience net, if removed.

Sedan

Figure 9

Remove or Disconnect

1. Convenience net, if present.
2. Rear compartment trim panel. Refer to "Rear Compartment Trim Panel" in this section.
3. Nuts.
4. Bulb and socket assemblies.
5. Taillamp assembly from body.

Install or Connect

Important

- When installing taillamps to body, care must be taken not to pinch or trap wire harness to insure against a potential lamp failure.

1. Taillamp assembly to body.
2. Bulb and socket assemblies.
3. Nuts.

Tighten

- Nuts to 5 N·m (44 lb. in.).

4. Rear compartment trim panel. Refer to "Rear Compartment Trim Panel" in this section.
5. Convenience net, if removed.

TAILLAMP MOLDING

Remove or Disconnect

1. Taillamp assembly. Refer to "Taillamp Assembly" in this section.

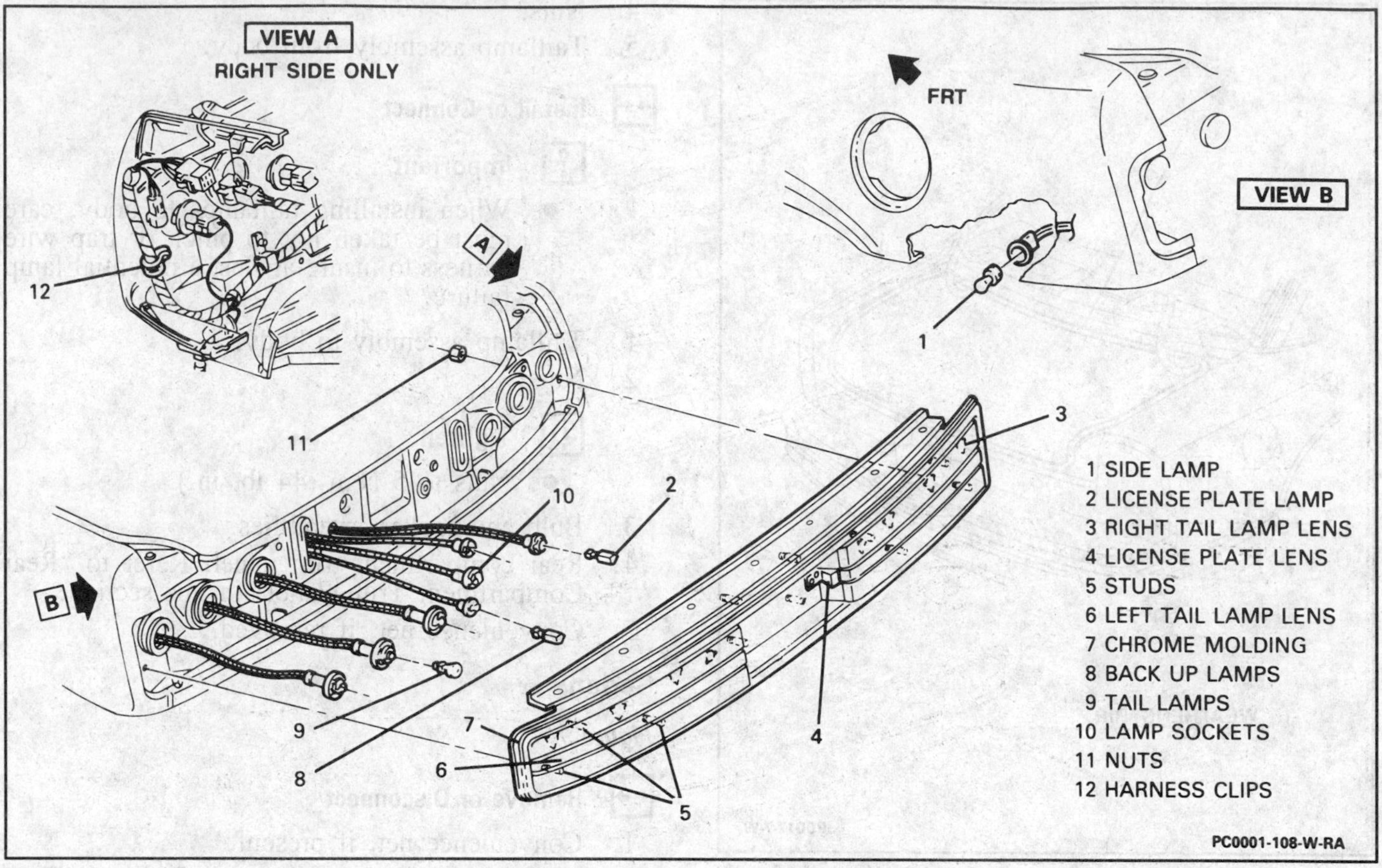
VIEW A
RIGHT SIDE ONLY
FRT
VIEW B
A
B
1
2
3
4
5
6
7
8
9
10
11
12
1 SIDE LAMP
2 LICENSE PLATE LAMP
3 RIGHT TAIL LAMP LENS
4 LICENSE PLATE LENS
5 STUDS
6 LEFT TAIL LAMP LENS
7 CHROME MOLDING
8 BACK UP LAMPS
9 TAIL LAMPS
10 LAMP SOCKETS
11 NUTS
12 HARNESS CLIPS
PC0001-108-W-RA

Figure 8 Taillamp Assembly (Coupe)

2. Nuts retaining molding to opening.
3. Molding.

Install or Connect

1. Molding to taillamp assembly.
2. Nuts to retain molding to opening.

Tighten

- Nuts to 2 N·m (18 lb. in.).

3. Taillamp assembly. Refer to "Taillamp Assembly" in this section.

TAILLAMP LENS

Coupe

Figure 8

Remove or Disconnect

1. Taillamp assembly. Refer to "Taillamp Assembly" in this section.
2. Screws securing bezel to taillamp assembly.
3. Lens.

Install or Connect

1. Lens.
2. Screws securing bezel to taillamp assembly.
3. Taillamp assembly. Refer to "Taillamp Assembly" in this section

Sedan

Figure 9

Remove or Disconnect

1. Taillamp assembly. Refer to "Taillamp Assembly" in this section.
2. Taillamp molding. Refer to "Taillamp Molding" in this section.
3. Taillamp lens by carefully prying six tabs from taillamp assembly.

Install or Connect

1. Taillamp lens to taillamp assembly.
2. Taillamp molding. Refer to "Taillamp Molding" in this section.
3. Taillamp assembly. Refer to "Taillamp Assembly" in this section.

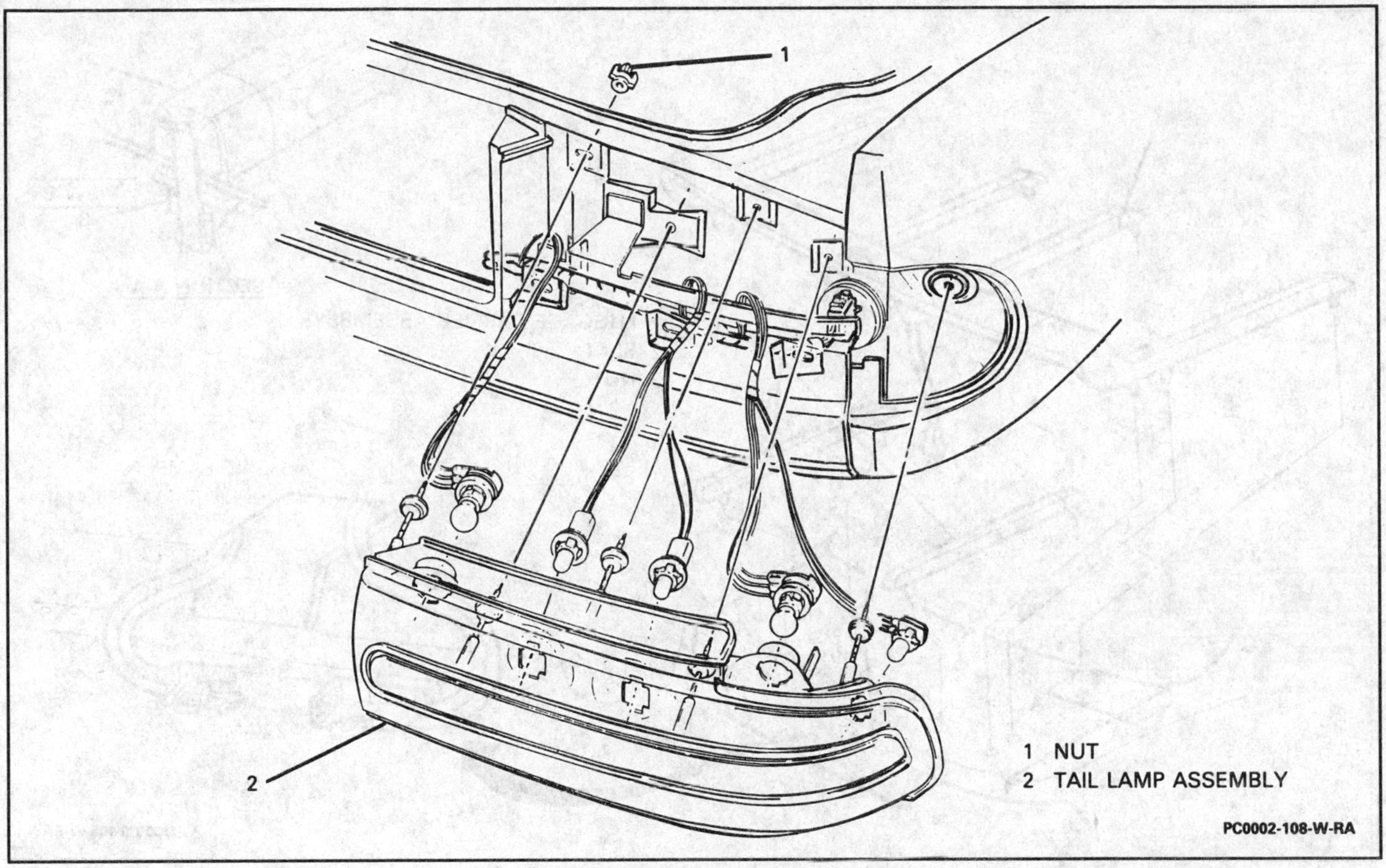
1
2
1 NUT
2 TAIL LAMP ASSEMBLY
PC0002-108-W-RA

Figure 9 Taillamp Assembly (Sedan)

LUGGAGE CARRIER

Figure 10

Remove or Disconnect

1. Open lid and disconnect electrical connector by removing clip.
2. Nuts.
3. Inner slat assemblies.
4. Luggage carrier and stoplamp assembly.

Install or Connect

1. Luggage carrier and stoplamp assembly.
2. Inner slat assembly.
3. Nuts.

   Tighten

   - Nuts to 7 N·m (62 lb. in.).

4. Electrical connector and clip.

REAR COMPARTMENT CONVENIENCE NET

Figure 11

Remove or Disconnect

- Rear compartment convenience net from retainers.

Install or Connect

- Rear compartment convenience net to retainers.

REAR COMPARTMENT TRIM PANEL

Figure 12

Remove or Disconnect

1. Open rear compartment lid.
2. Retainers.
3. Rear compartment trim panel.

Install or Connect

1. Rear compartment trim panel.
2. Retainers.
3. Close rear compartment lid.

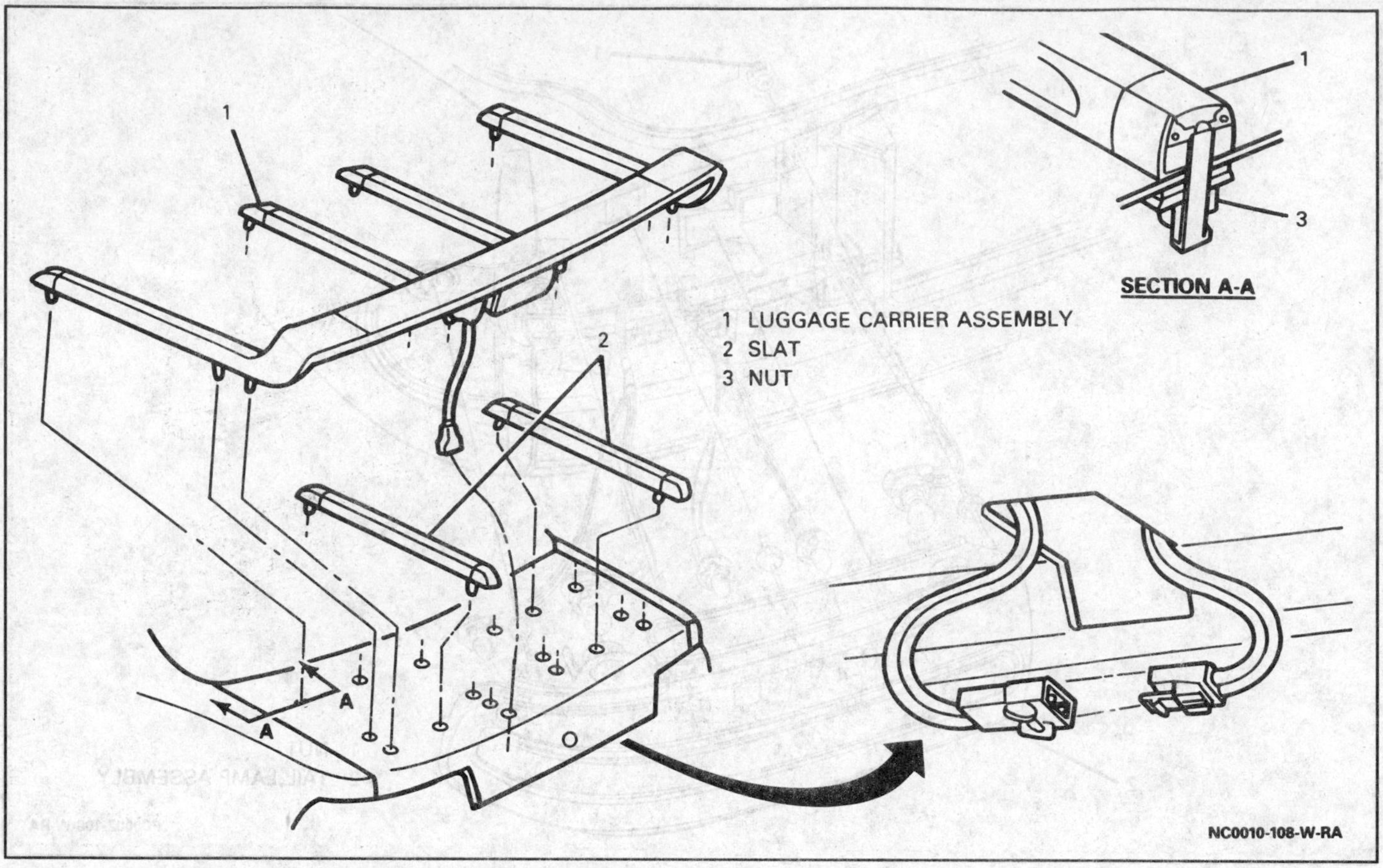
1
2
A
A
1
3
SECTION A-A
1 LUGGAGE CARRIER ASSEMBLY
2 SLAT
3 NUT
NC0010-108-W-RA

Figure 10 Luggage Carrier and Stoplamp

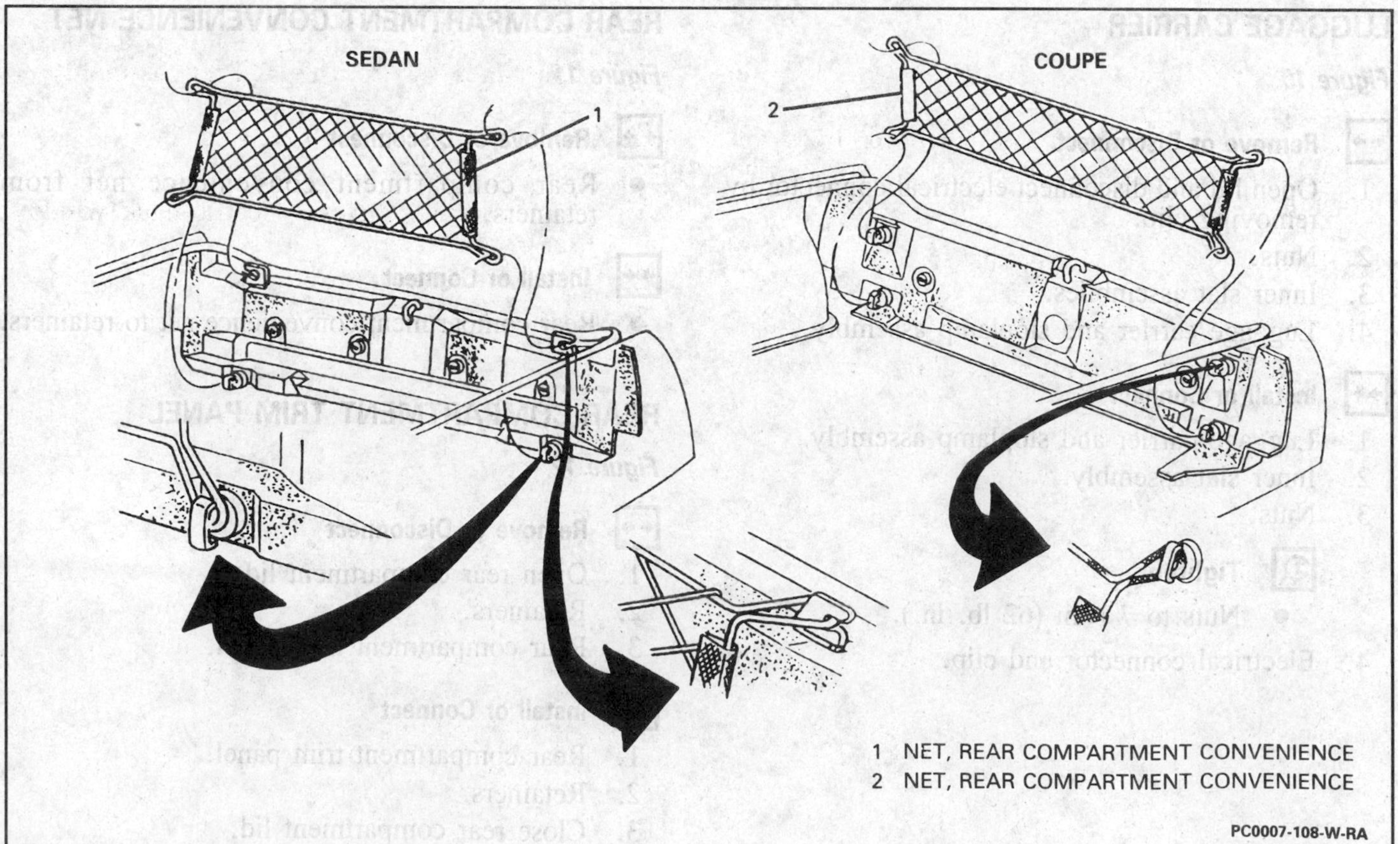
SEDAN
1
COUPE
2
1 NET, REAR COMPARTMENT CONVENIENCE
2 NET, REAR COMPARTMENT CONVENIENCE
PC0007-108-W-RA

Figure 11 Rear Compartment Convenience Net

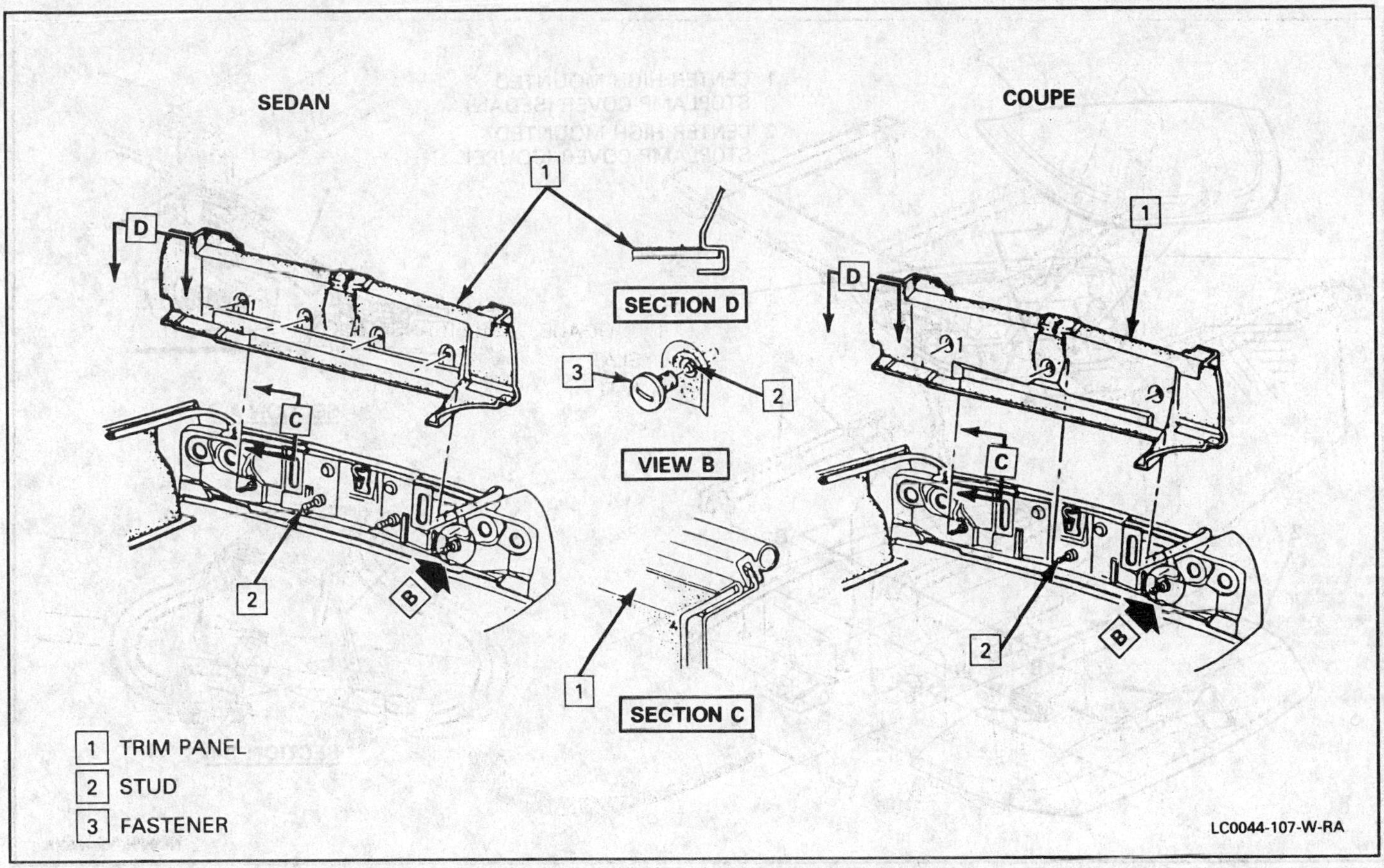
SEDAN
COUPE
SECTION D
VIEW B
SECTION C
1 TRIM PANEL
2 STUD
3 FASTENER
LC0044-107-W-RA

Figure 12 Rear Compartment Trim Panel

CENTER HIGH MOUNTED STOPLAMP

Figures 13 and 14

The center high mounted stoplamp is installed to the rear seat-to-rear window trim panel on coupes. On coupes equipped with the optional luggage carrier, the stoplamp is an integral part of the luggage carrier. Refer to "Luggage Carrier" in this section. Refer to ROOF (SECTION 10-9) for sedans.

←→ Remove or Disconnect

1. Center high mounted stoplamp cover by disengaging clips.
2. Nuts.
3. Electrical connector.
4. Lamp assembly from rear seat-to-back window trim panel by carefully lifting assembly to ensure gasket does not tear.

→← Install or Connect

1. Lamp assembly to rear seat-to-back window trim panel.
2. Electrical connector.
3. Nuts.
4. Cover.

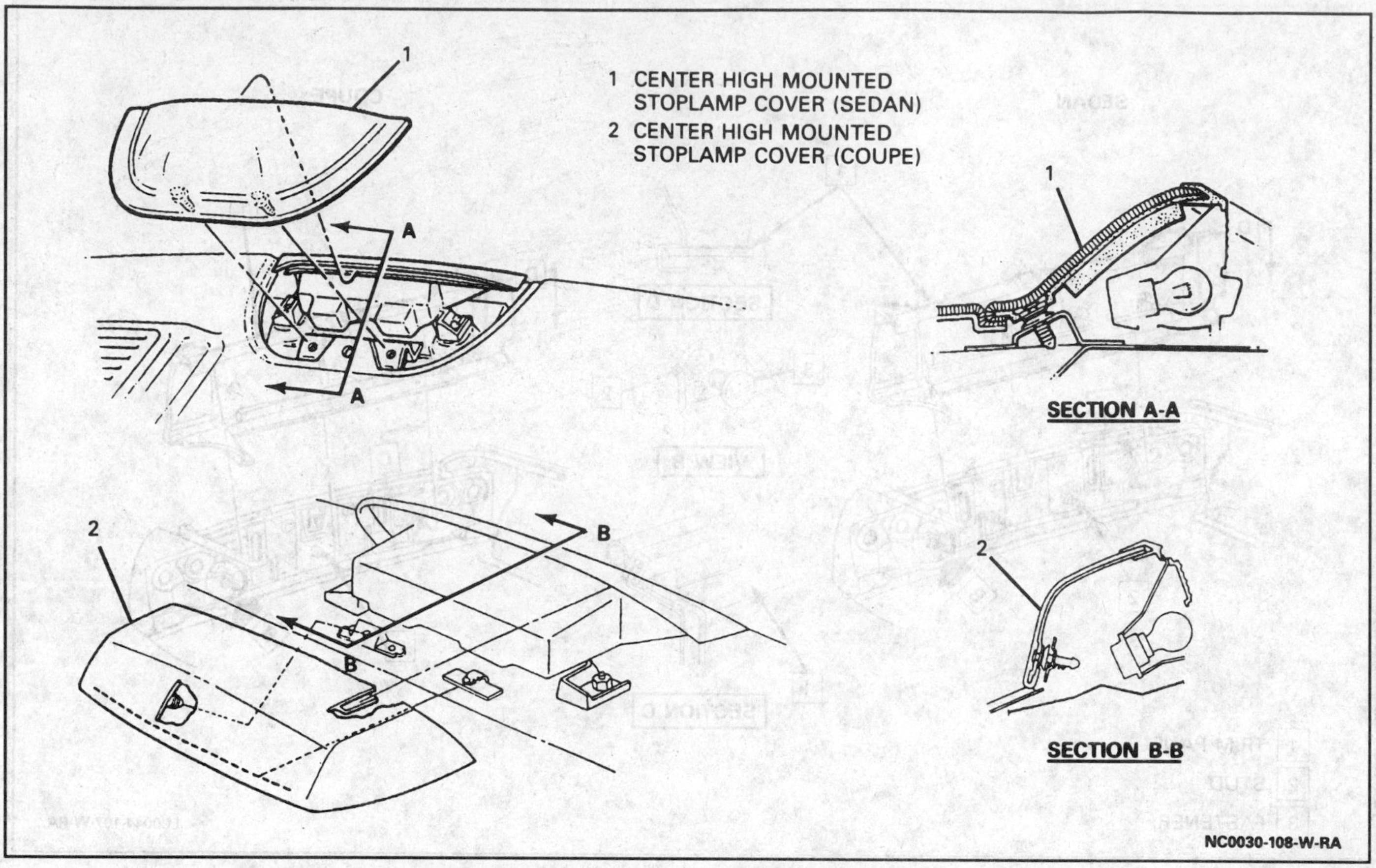
1 CENTER HIGH MOUNTED STOPLAMP COVER (SEDAN)
2 CENTER HIGH MOUNTED STOPLAMP COVER (COUPE)
1
A
A
SECTION A-A
2
B
B
2
SECTION B-B
NC0030-108-W-RA

Figure 13 Center High Mounted Stoplamp Cover

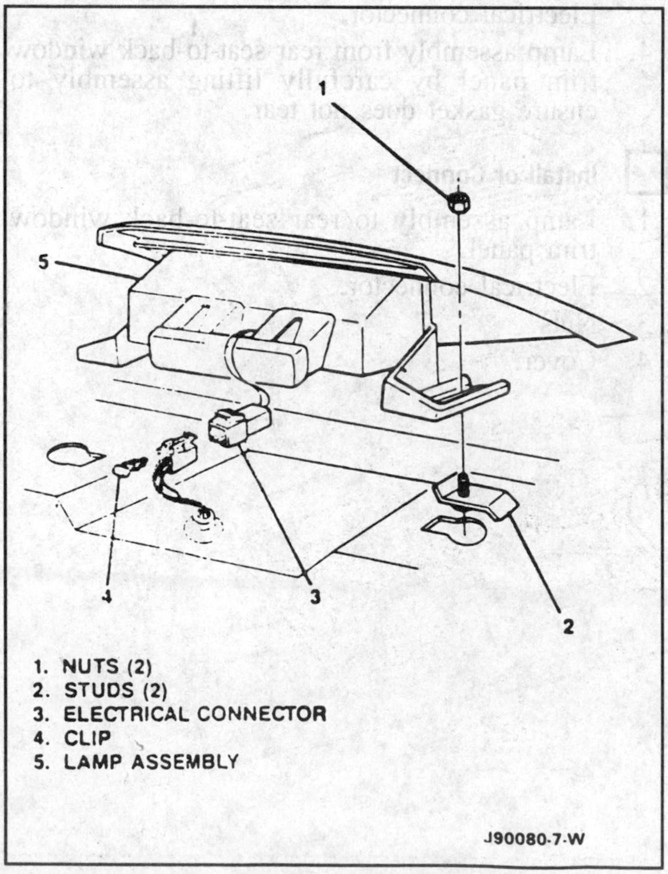
1
5
4
3
2
1. NUTS (2)
2. STUDS (2)
3. ELECTRICAL CONNECTOR
4. CLIP
5. LAMP ASSEMBLY
J90080-7-W

Figure 14 Center High Mounted Stoplamp Installation

REAR SEAT-TO-REAR WINDOW TRIM PANEL

Figures 15 and 16

Tool Required:

J 24595-C Door Trim Pad and Garnish Clip Remover

Remove or Disconnect

1. Rear seat cushions and seatback. Refer to SEATS (SECTION 10-10).
2. Right and left upper quarter trim panel using J 24595. Refer to REAR QUARTERS (SECTION 10-7).
3. Center high mounted stoplamp, if equipped. Refer to "Center High Mounted Stoplamp" in this section.
4. Retainers.
5. Trim panel.
6. Safety belts from trim panel.

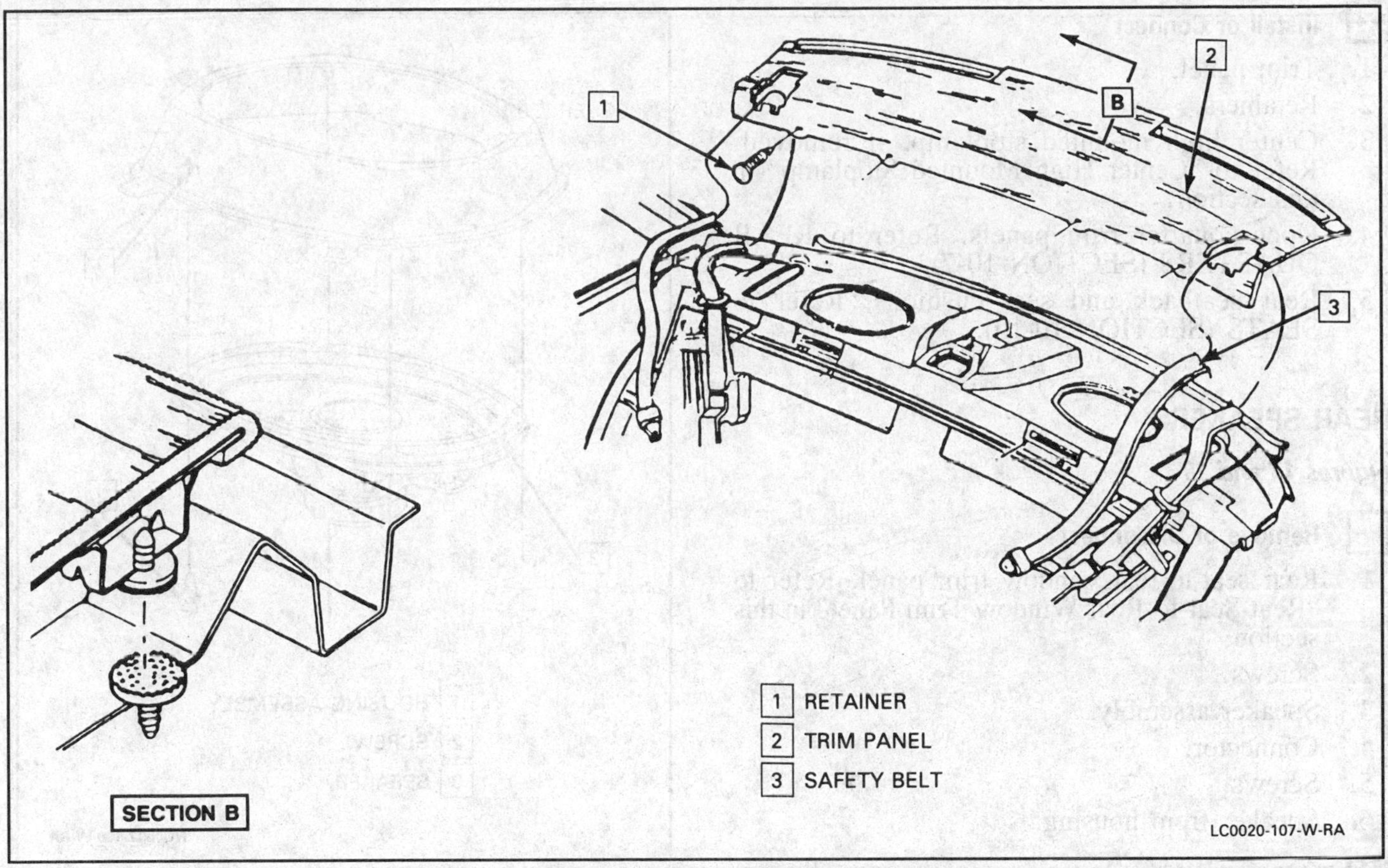
1
2
B
3
SECTION B
1 RETAINER
2 TRIM PANEL
3 SAFETY BELT
LC0020-107-W-RA

Figure 15 Rear Seat-to-Rear Window Trim Panel (Coupe)

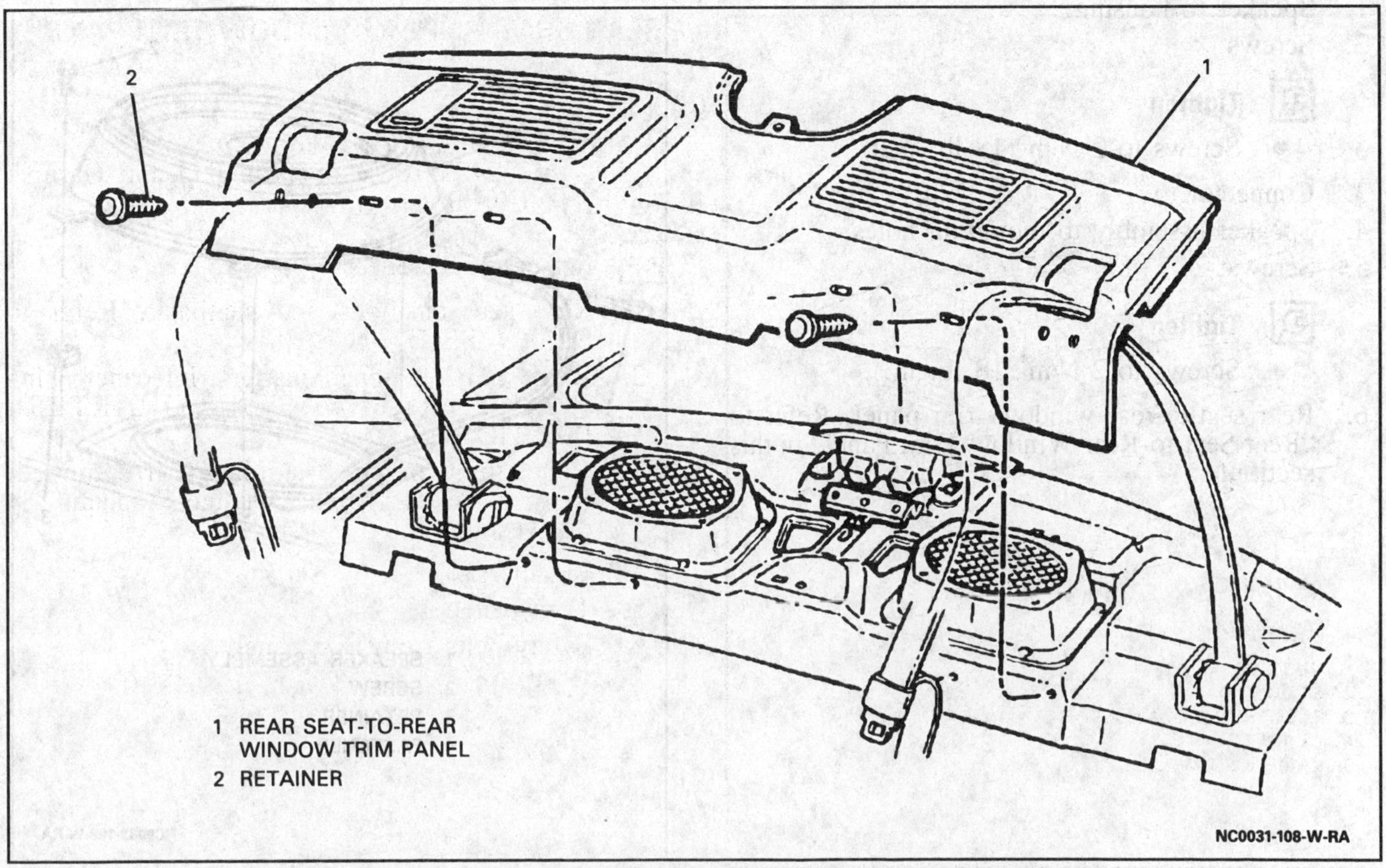
2
1
1 REAR SEAT-TO-REAR
WINDOW TRIM PANEL
2 RETAINER
NC0031-108-W-RA

Figure 16 Rear Seat-to-Rear Window Trim Panel (Sedan)

Install or Connect

1. Trim panel.
2. Retainers.
3. Center high mounted stoplamp, if removed. Refer to "Center High Mounted Stoplamp" in this section.
4. Upper quarter trim panels. Refer to REAR QUARTERS (SECTION 10-7).
5. Rear seatback and seat cushions. Refer to SEATS (SECTION 10-10).

REAR SPEAKERS

Figures 17 and 18

Remove or Disconnect

1. Rear seat-to-rear window trim panel. Refer to "Rear Seat-to-Rear Window Trim Panel" in this section.
2. Screws.
3. Speaker assembly.
4. Connector.
5. Screws.
6. Speaker from housing.

Install or Connect

1. Speaker to housing.
2. Screws.

Tighten

- Screws to 2 N·m (18 lb. in.).

3. Connector.
4. Speaker assembly to mounting holes.
5. Screws.

Tighten

- Screws to 2 N·m (18 lb. in.).

6. Rear seat-to-rear window trim panel. Refer to "Rear Seat-to-Rear Window Trim Panel" in this section.

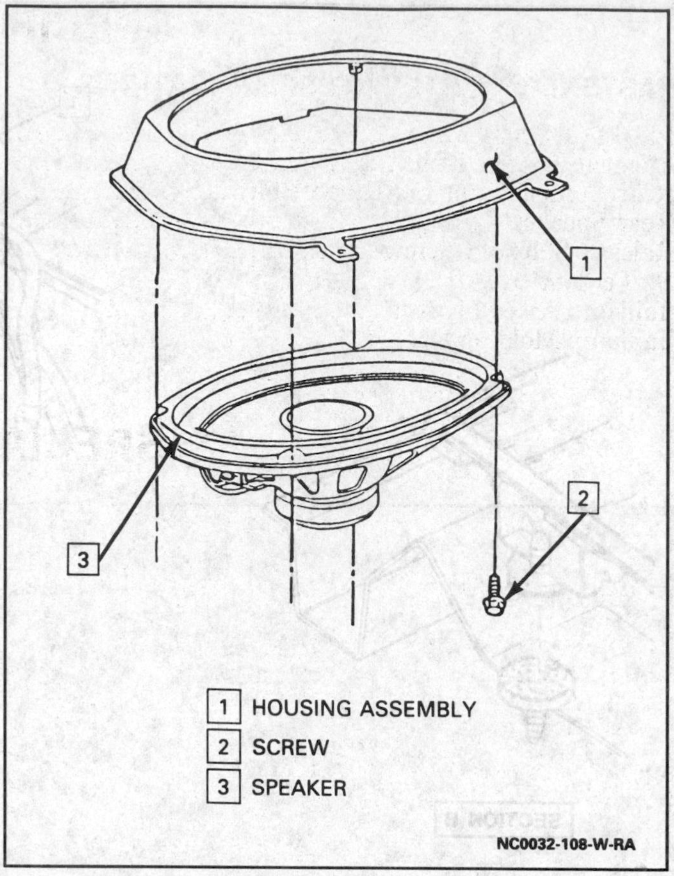
1
2
3
1 HOUSING ASSEMBLY
2 SCREW
3 SPEAKER
NC0032-108-W-RA

Figure 17 Rear Speaker Assembly

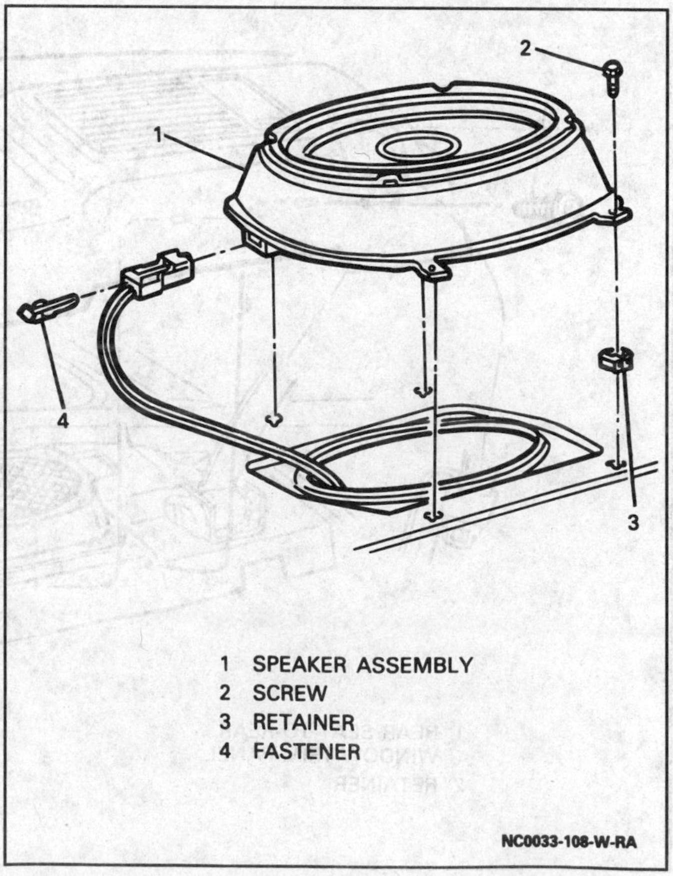
2
1
4
3
1 SPEAKER ASSEMBLY
2 SCREW
3 RETAINER
4 FASTENER
NC0033-108-W-RA

Figure 18 Rear Speaker Mounting

SPECIFICATIONS

FASTENER TIGHTENING SPECIFICATIONS

Lid Lock Screw	6 N·m (53 lb. in.)
Luggage Carrier Nut	7 N·m (62 lb. in.)
Rear Compartment Lid Hinge Bolt	25 N·m (18 lb. ft.)
Rear Speaker Screw	2 N·m (18 lb. in.)
Release Solenoid Screw	8 N·m (71 lb. in.)
Striker Nut	6 N•m (54 lb. in.)
Taillamp Assembly Nut	5 N•m (44 lb. in.)
Taillamp Molding Nut	2 N•m (18 lb. in.)

SPECIAL TOOLS

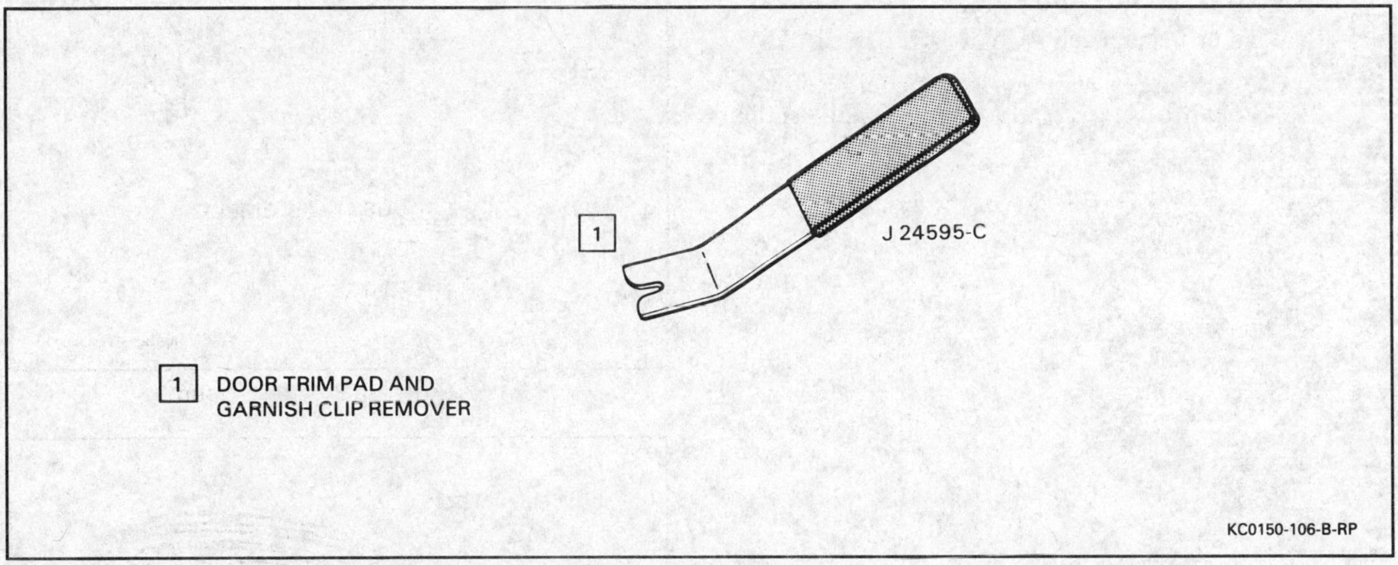
1
J 24595-C
1 DOOR TRIM PAD AND
GARNISH CLIP REMOVER
KC0150-106-B-RP

SECTION 10-9
ROOF

CONTENTS

NOTICE: When fasteners are removed, always reinstall them at the same location from which they were removed. If a fastener needs to be replaced, use the correct part number fastener for that application. If the correct part number fastener is not available, a fastener of equal size and strength (or stronger) may be used. Fasteners that are not reused, and those requiring thread locking compound will be called out. The correct torque value must be used when installing fasteners that require it. If the above conditions are not followed, parts or system damage could result.

GENERAL DESCRIPTION

FORMED HEADLINING

The one piece formed headlining consists of molded substrate covered with a foam backed cloth facing. The headlining assembly is held in place with retainers located at the rear of the headlining and the installation of related hardware and interior trim. The one piece construction requires the headlining be serviced as a complete assembly.

ON-VEHICLE SERVICE

FORMED HEADLINING REPLACEMENT

Figure 1

Tools Required:

J 24595-C Door Trim Pad and Garnish Clip Remover

Remove or Disconnect

1. Sunshades. Refer to "Sunshades" in this section.
2. Dome and courtesy lamps. Refer to "Dome and Courtesy Lamps" in this section.
3. Sunroof headliner lace. Refer to "Sunroof" in this section.
4. Windshield side upper garnish. Refer to "Windshield Side Upper Garnish Molding" in this section.
5. Upper quarter trim panels using J 24595-C and loosen lower quarter trim panels. Refer to REAR QUARTERS (SECTION 10-7).
6. Upper center pillar trim panel on sedans using J 24595-C. Refer to DOORS (SECTION 10-6).
7. Retainers using J 24595-C.
8. Headliner through right door.

Install or Connect

1. Headlining assembly by aligning sunshade holes in headlining with respective holes in body structure.
   - Be careful not to bend the headlining too much when loading it.
2. Retainers.
3. Upper center pillar trim panel if removed. Refer to DOORS (SECTION 10-6).
4. Lower and upper quarter trim panels. Refer to REAR QUARTERS (SECTION 10-7).
5. Windshield side upper garnish. Refer to "Windshield Side Upper Garnish Molding" in this section.
6. Sunroof headliner lace. Refer to "Sunroof" in this section.
7. Dome and courtesy lamps. Refer to "Dome and Courtesy Lamps" in this section.
8. Sunshades. Refer to "Sunshades" in this section.

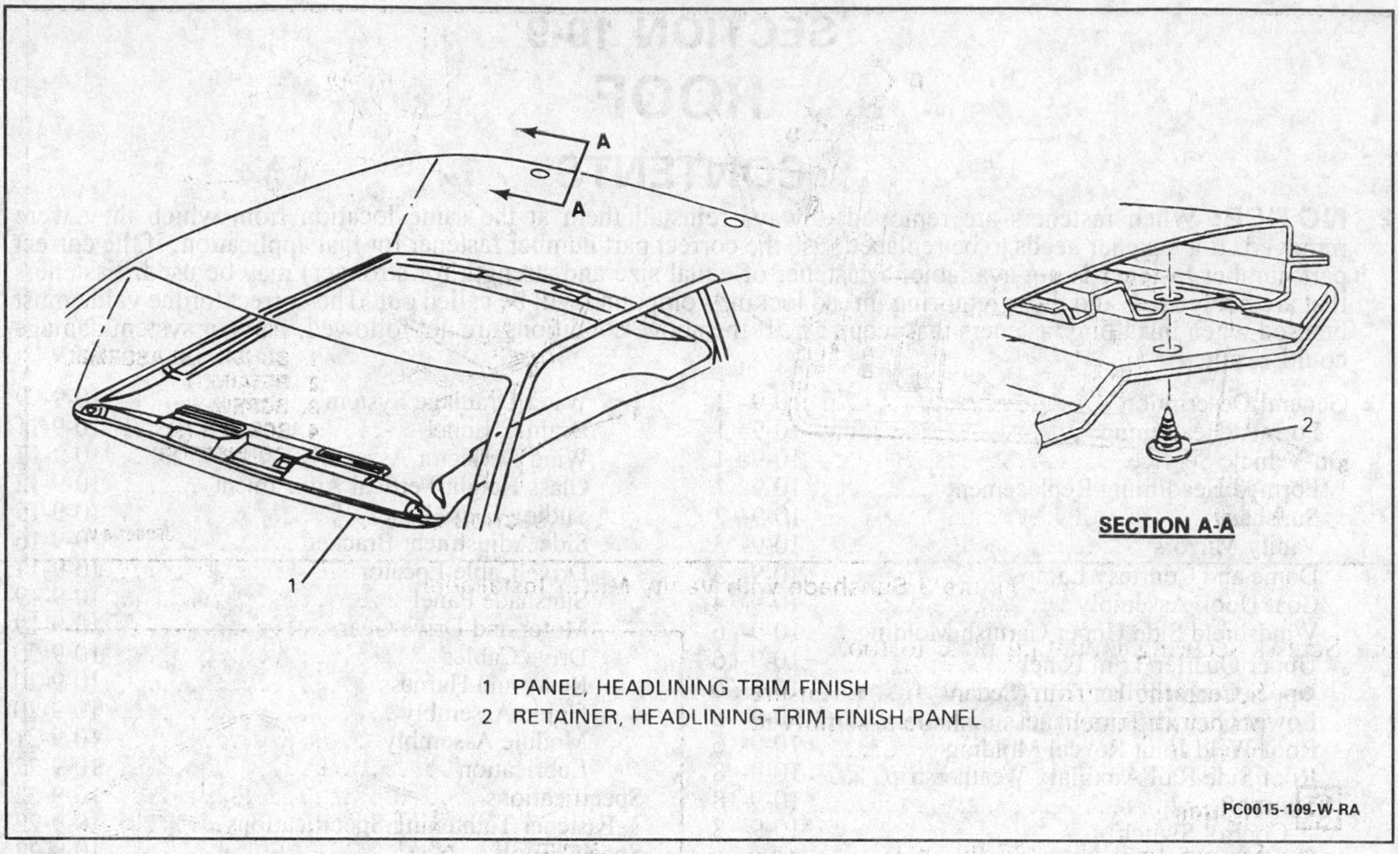
A
A
1
2
SECTION A-A
1 PANEL, HEADLINING TRIM FINISH
2 RETAINER, HEADLINING TRIM FINISH PANEL
PC0015-109-W-RA

Figure 1 Headliner

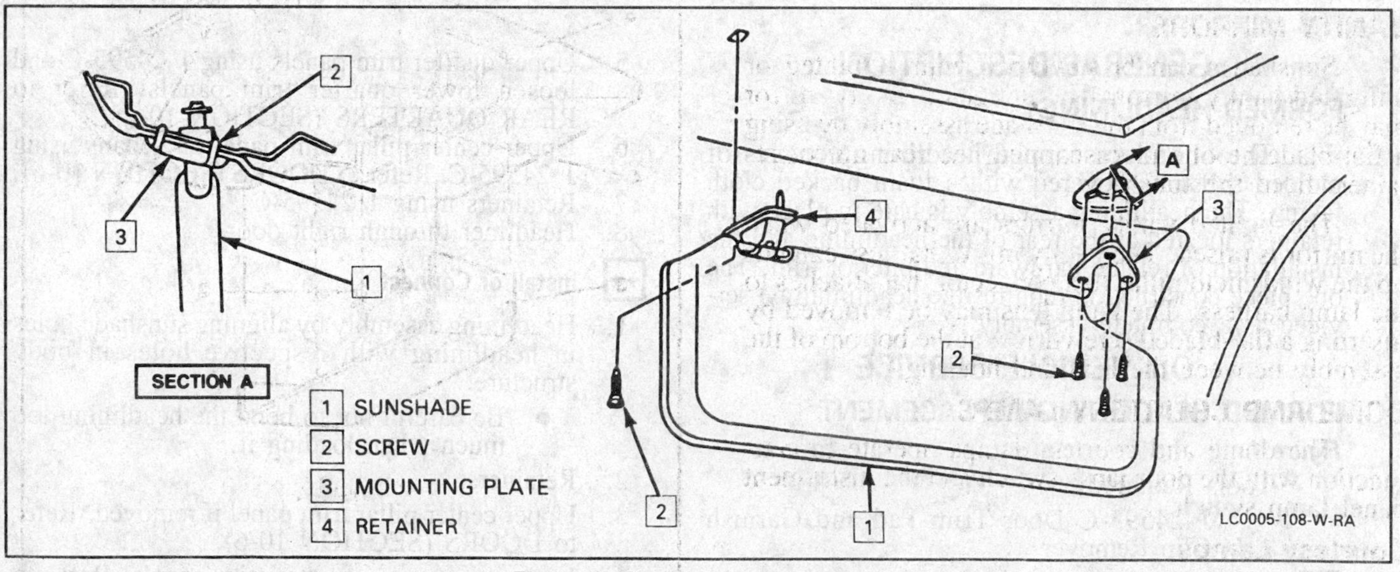
2
3
1
SECTION A
1 SUNSHADE
2 SCREW
3 MOUNTING PLATE
4 RETAINER
A
4
3
2
2
1
LC0005-108-W-RA

Figure 2 Sunshade Installation

SUNSHADES

Figures 2 and 3

Remove or Disconnect

1. Screws securing mounting plate to roof.
2. Electrical connector, if present.
3. Sunshade.
4. Screw securing retainer to roof, if retainer is to be removed.
5. Retainer.

Install or Connect

1. Retainer.
2. Screw securing retainer to roof, if removed.

Tighten

- Screw to 1 N·m (9 lb. in.).

3. Sunshade to roof.
4. Electrical connector, if present.

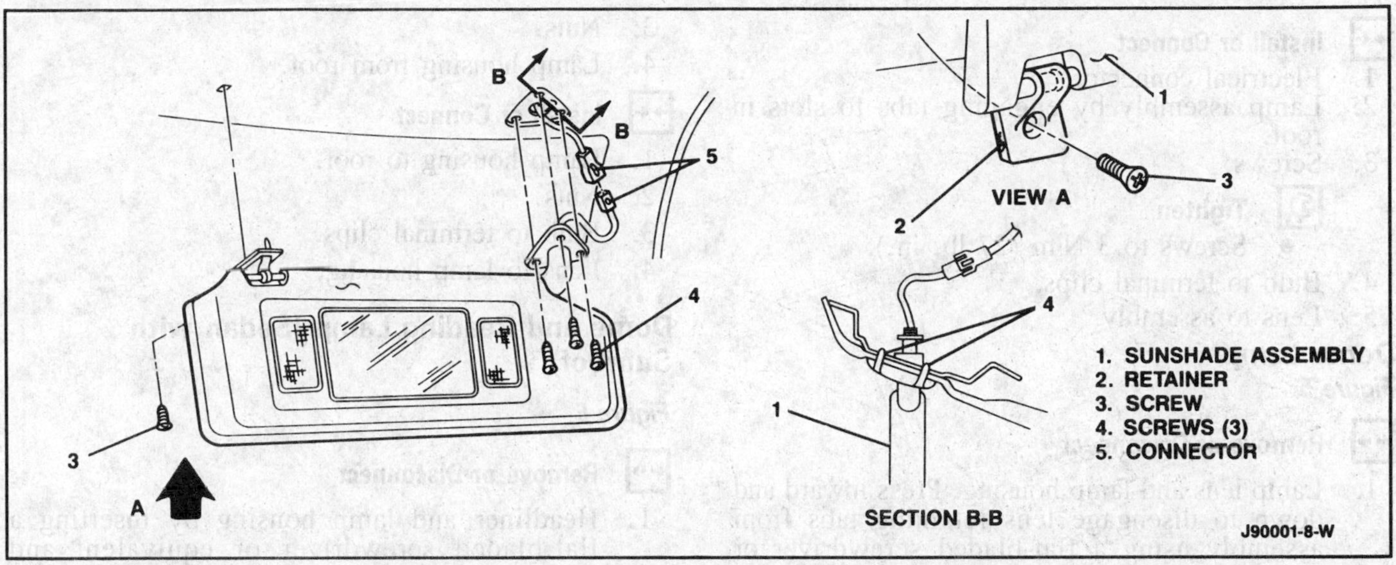
B
B
5
4
3
A
VIEW A
1
3
2
4
1
SECTION B-B
1. SUNSHADE ASSEMBLY
2. RETAINER
3. SCREW
4. SCREWS (3)
5. CONNECTOR
J90001-8-W

Figure 3 Sunshade with Vanity Mirror Installation

5. Screws securing mounting plate to roof.
   - Secure the rearward screw first to ensure proper alignment of sunshade assembly to body.

Tighten

- Screws to 3 N·m (27 lb. in.).

VANITY MIRRORS

Sunshades can be equipped with a lighted or unlighted vanity mirror. The unlighted vanity mirror may be removed from the sunshade assembly by using a flat-bladed tool and unsnapping the rear mirror retainers from the sunshade.

The lighted vanity mirrors are activated when the mirror is raised. The vanity mirror harness extends up the windshield pillar to a connector that attaches to the lamp harness. The lamp lens may be removed by inserting a flat-bladed screwdriver at the bottom of the assembly between the lens and housing.

DOME AND COURTESY LAMPS

The dome and courtesy lamps operate in conjunction with the door jamb switch and the instrument panel lamp switch.

Courtesy Lamps

Figure 4

Remove or Disconnect

1. Lamp lens and lamp assembly housing. Press inward and down to disengage lens retaining tabs from assembly using a flat-bladed screwdriver or similar tool.
2. Bulb from terminal clips.
3. Screws.
4. Lamp assembly by disengaging tabs from slots in roof.
5. Electrical connector.

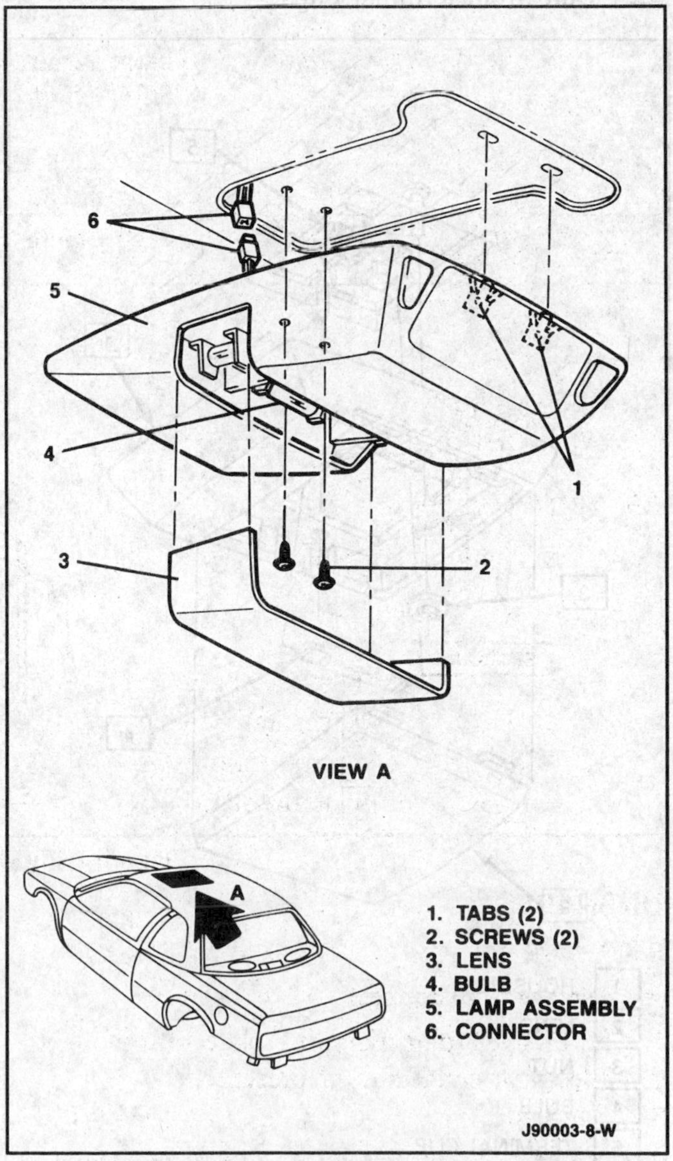
6
5
4
3
2
1
VIEW A
A
1. TABS (2)
2. SCREWS (2)
3. LENS
4. BULB
5. LAMP ASSEMBLY
6. CONNECTOR
J90003-8-W

Figure 4 Windshield Header Courtesy & Reading Lamp Installation

Install or Connect

1. Electrical connector.
2. Lamp assembly by engaging tabs to slots in roof.
3. Screws.

   Tighten

   - Screws to 3 N·m (27 lb. in.).
4. Bulb to terminal clips.
5. Lens to assembly.

Dome Lamp

Figure 5

Remove or Disconnect

1. Lamp lens and lamp housing. Press inward and down to disengage lens retaining tabs from assembly using a flat-bladed screwdriver or similar tool.
2. Bulb from terminal clips.

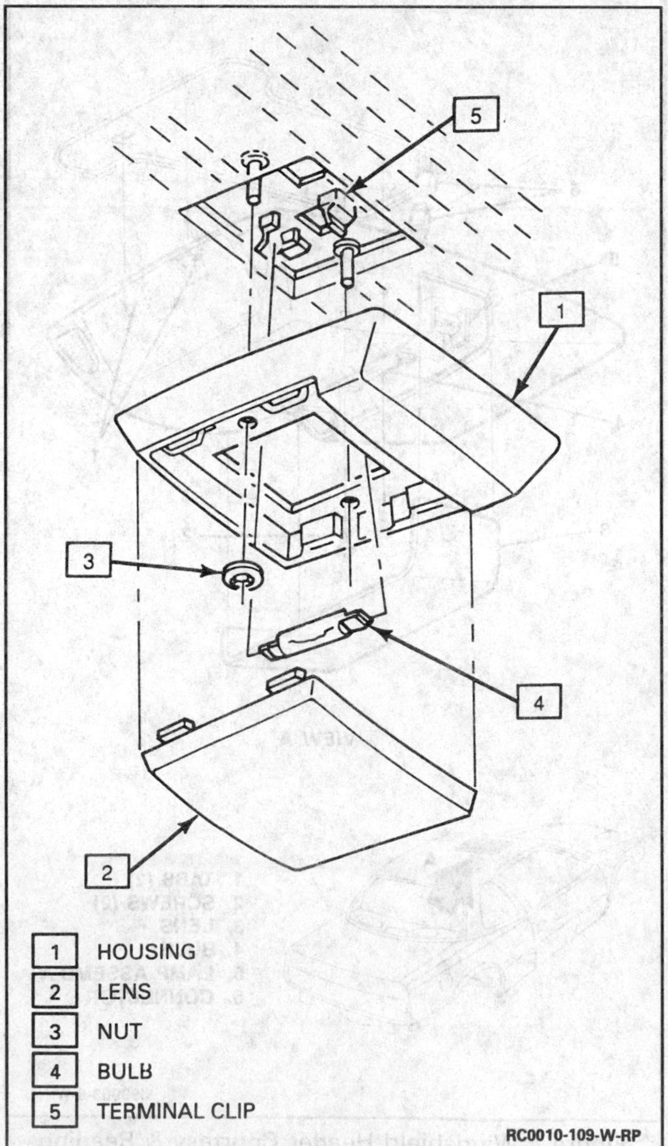

5
1
3
4
2
1 HOUSING
2 LENS
3 NUT
4 BULB
5 TERMINAL CLIP
RC0010-109-W-RP

Figure 5 Dome Lamp

3. Nuts.
4. Lamp housing from roof.

Install or Connect

1. Lamp housing to roof.
2. Nuts.
3. Bulb to terminal clips.
4. Lens to lamp housing.

Dome and Reading Lamp (Sedan with Sunroof)

Figure 6

Remove or Disconnect

1. Headliner and lamp housing by inserting a flat-bladed screwdriver or equivalent and pressing inward and down to disengage retainers.
2. Clip from connector.
3. Connector from lamp.

Install or Connect

1. Connector to lamp.
2. Clip to connector.
3. Lamp to headliner opening by pressing firmly to secure.

COAT HOOK ASSEMBLY

Figure 7

Remove or Disconnect

1. Screw securing coat hook.
2. Coat hook.

Install or Connect

1. Coat hook inserting upper tab into hole at roof rail.
2. Screw securing coat hook.

   Tighten

   - Screw to 1.5 N•m (13 lb. in.).

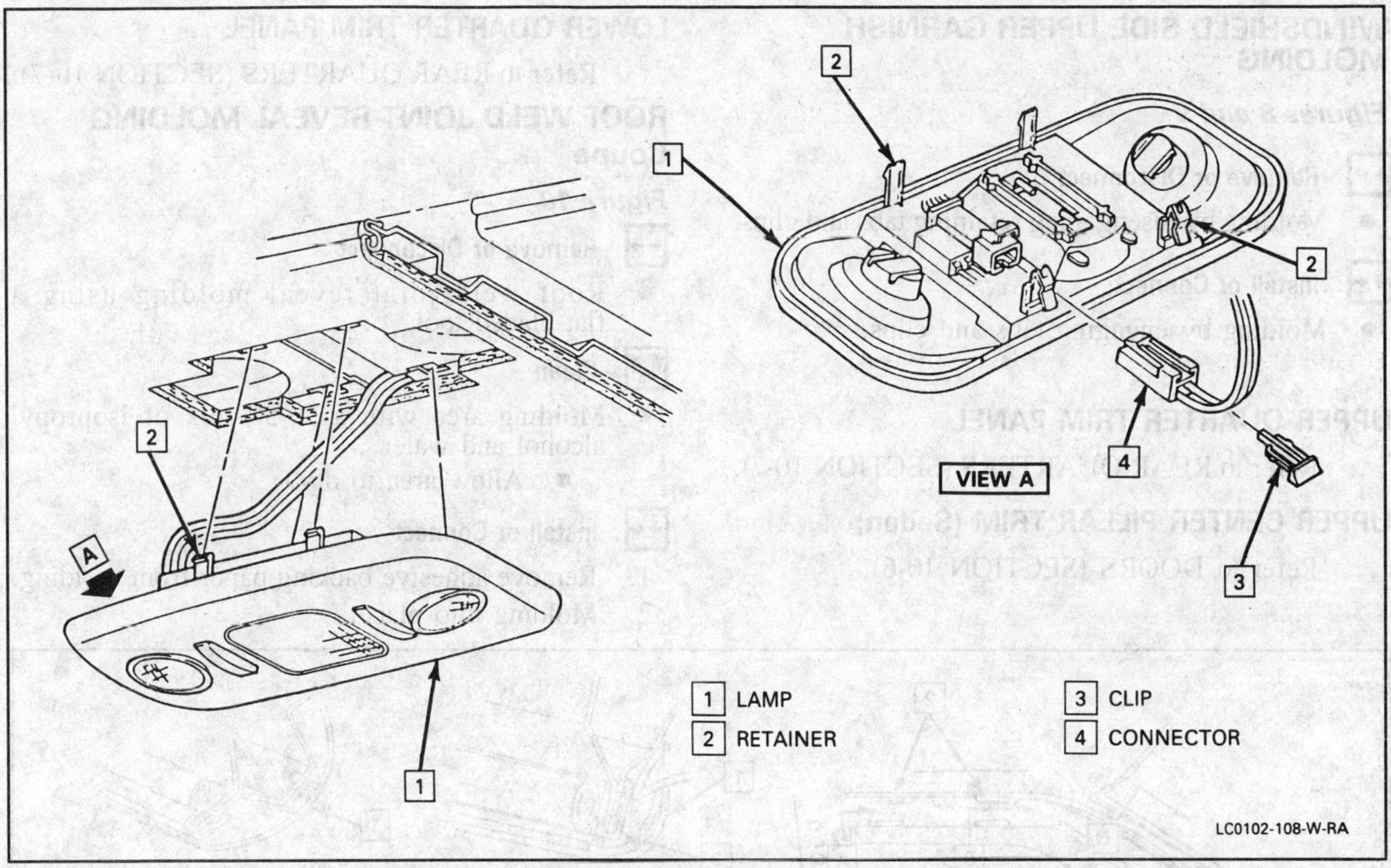
2
1
2
A
1
VIEW A
2
4
3
1 LAMP
2 RETAINER
3 CLIP
4 CONNECTOR
LC0102-108-W-RA

Figure 6 Dome and Reading Lamp (Sedan with Sunroof)

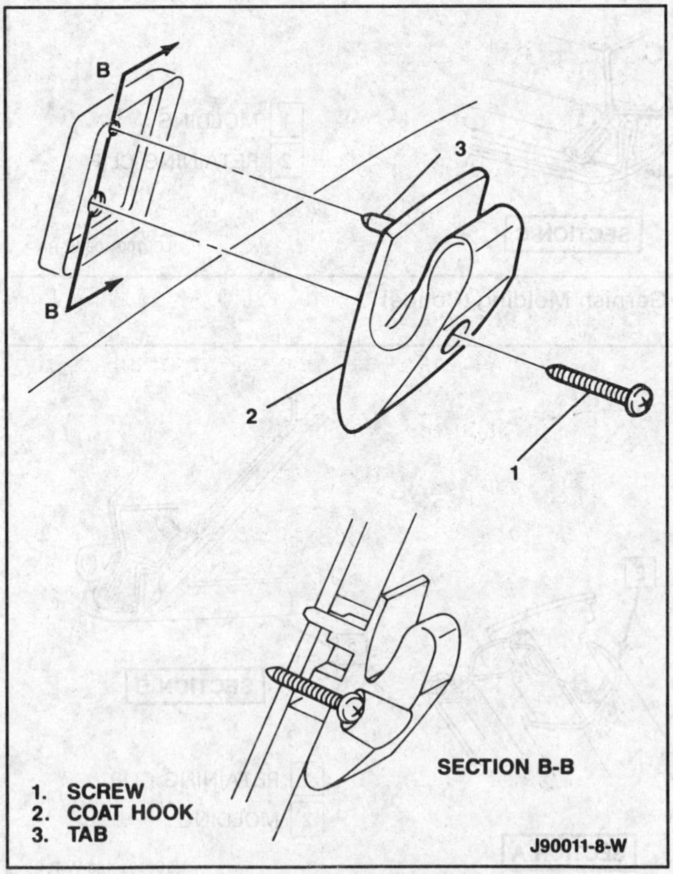
B
B
3
2
1
SECTION B-B
1. SCREW
2. COAT HOOK
3. TAB
J90011-8-W

Figure 7 Coat Hook

WINDSHIELD SIDE UPPER GARNISH MOLDING

Figures 8 and 9

Remove or Disconnect

- Molding by disengaging retaining tabs and clips.

Install or Connect

- Molding by engaging tabs and clips.

UPPER QUARTER TRIM PANEL

Refer to REAR QUARTERS (SECTION 10-7).

UPPER CENTER PILLAR TRIM (Sedan)

Refer to DOORS (SECTION 10-6).

LOWER QUARTER TRIM PANEL

Refer to REAR QUARTERS (SECTION 10-7).

ROOF WELD JOINT REVEAL MOLDING Coupe

Figure 10

Remove or Disconnect

- Roof weld joint reveal molding using a flat-bladed tool.

Clean

- Molding area with a 50/50 mix of isopropyl alcohol and water.
  - Allow area to dry.

Install or Connect

1. Remove adhesive backing paper from molding.
2. Molding into place.

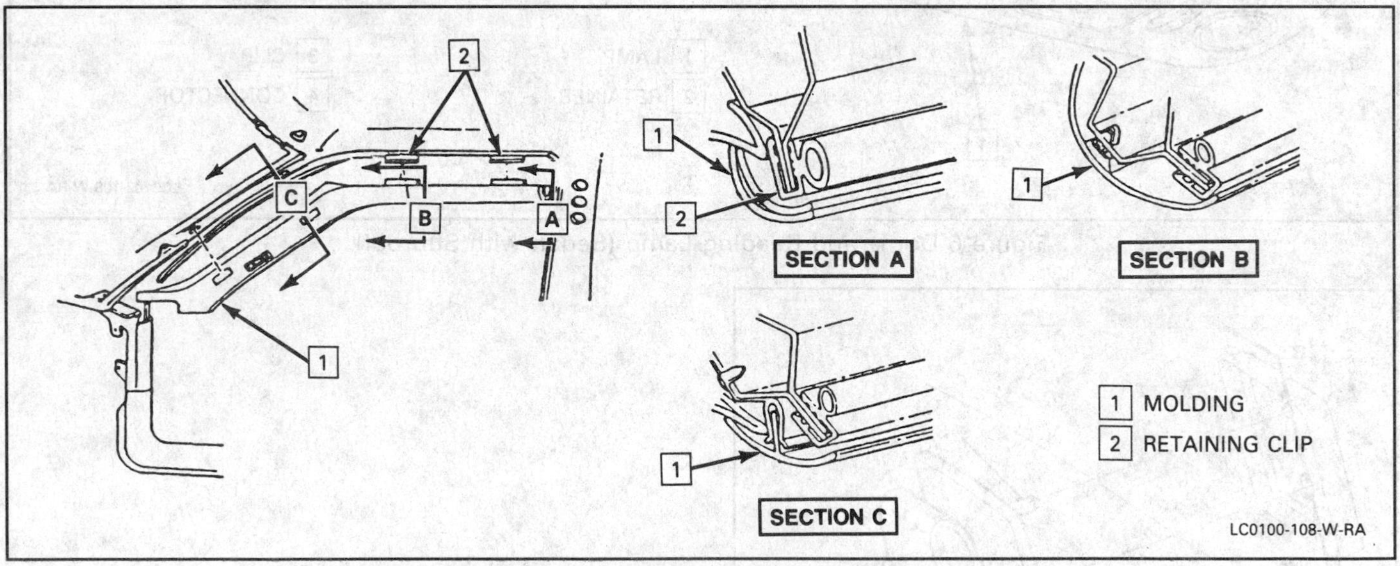
2
C
B
A
1
SECTION A
SECTION B
SECTION C
1 MOLDING
2 RETAINING CLIP
LC0100-108-W-RA

Figure 8 Windshield Side Upper Garnish Molding (Coupe)

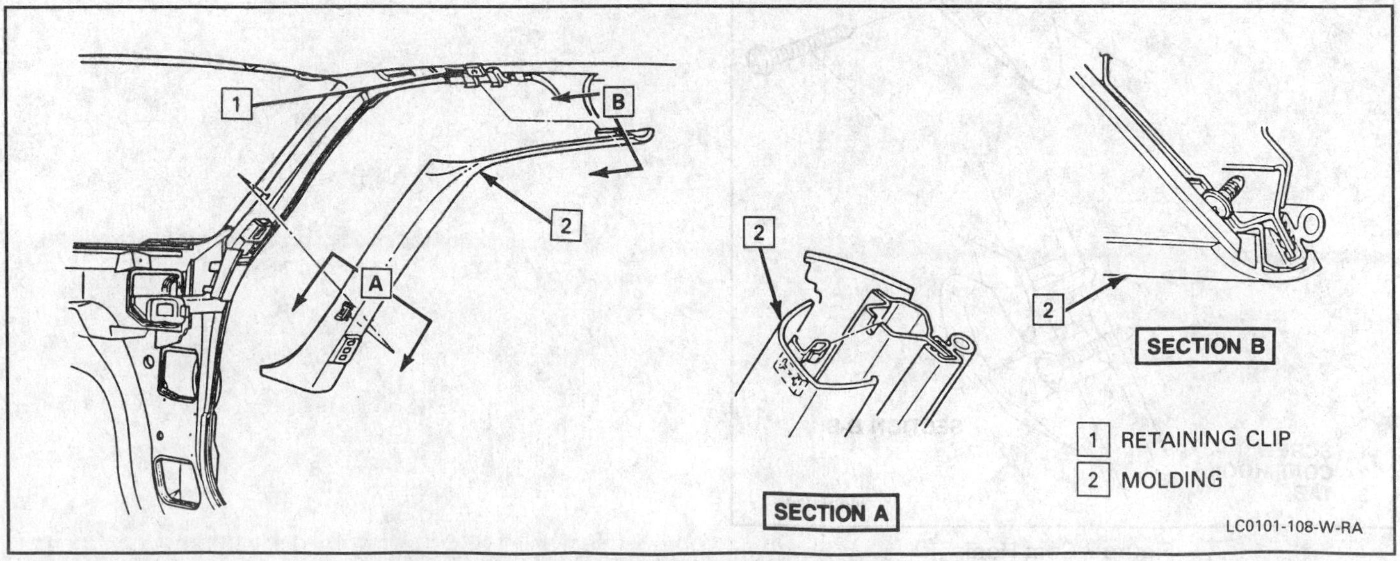
1
B
2
A
SECTION A
SECTION B
1 RETAINING CLIP
2 MOLDING
LC0101-108-W-RA

Figure 9 Windshield Side Upper Garnish Molding (Sedan)

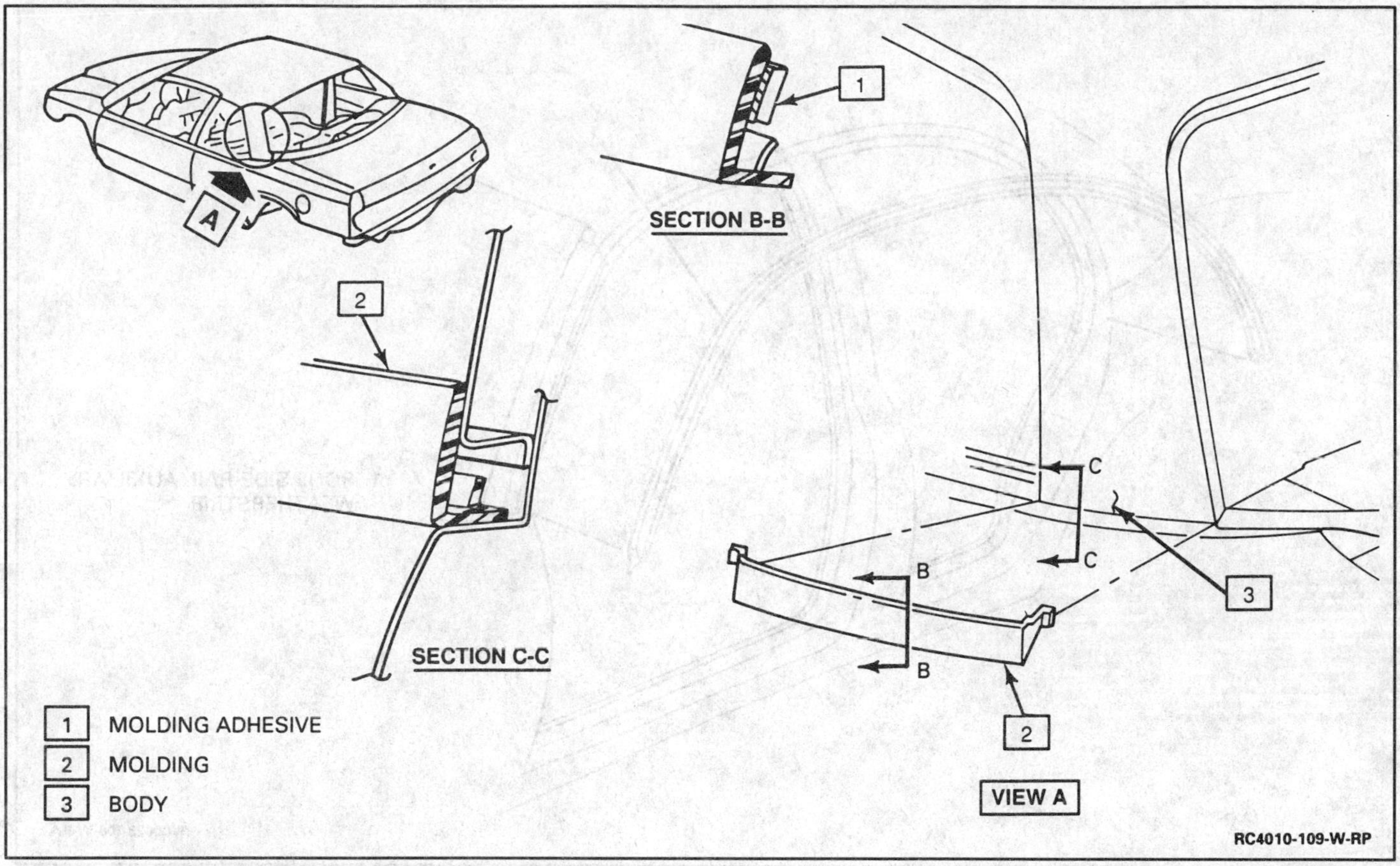
1
SECTION B-B
2
SECTION C-C
C
C
B
B
3
2
1 MOLDING ADHESIVE
2 MOLDING
3 BODY
VIEW A
A
RC4010-109-W-RP

Figure 10 Roof Weld Joint Reveal Molding (Coupe)

Sedan

Figure 11

Remove or Disconnect

- Roof weld joint reveal molding using a flat-bladed tool.

Clean

- Molding area with a 50/50 mix of isopropyl alcohol and water.
- Allow area to dry.

Install or Connect

1. Remove adhesive backing paper from molding.
2. Position molding to weld joint aligning feature line in molding front with front quarter panel.
3. Press molding down and rearward into ditch.
4. Press front flap of molding down firmly onto sheet metal at upper rear corner of door opening.

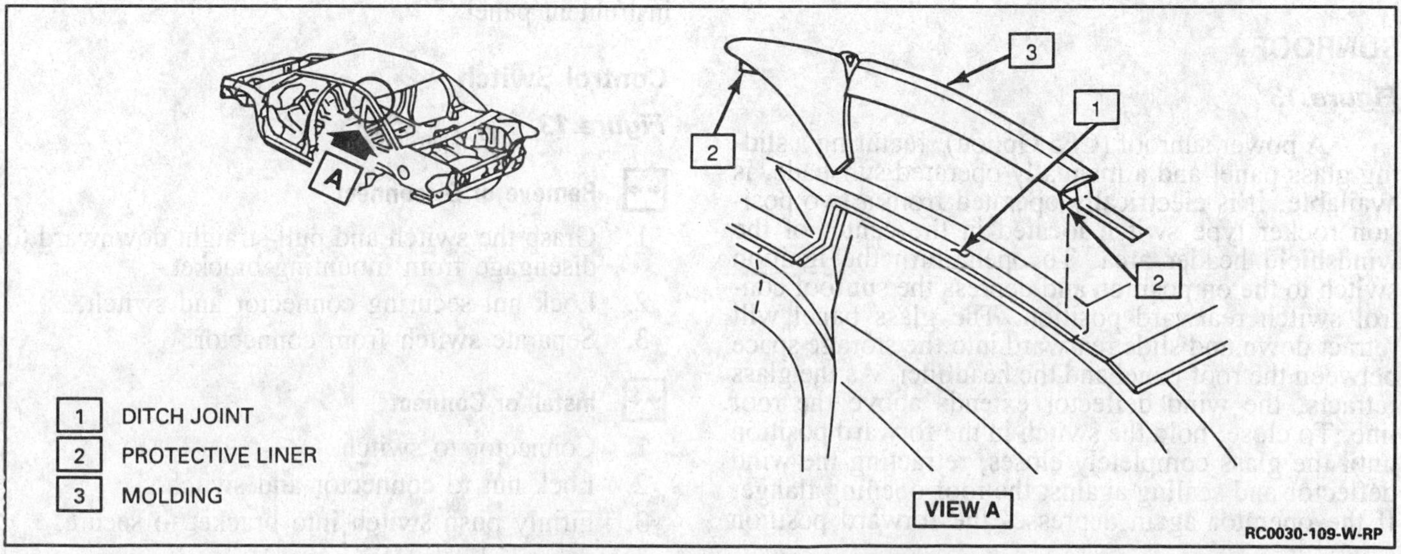
3
1
2
2
A
1 DITCH JOINT
2 PROTECTIVE LINER
3 MOLDING
VIEW A
RC0030-109-W-RP

Figure 11 Roof Weld Joint Revel Molding (Sedan)

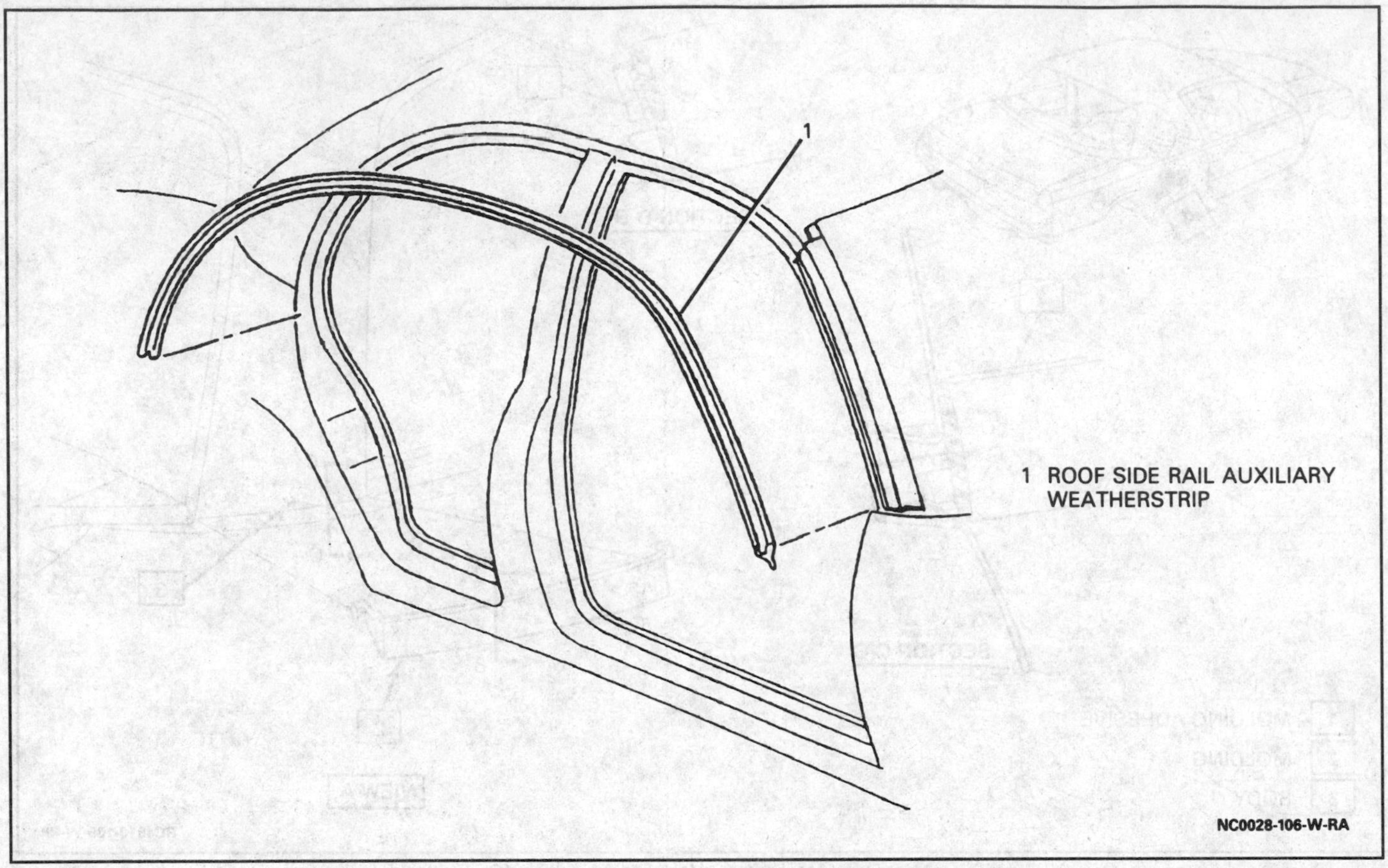
1
1 ROOF SIDE RAIL AUXILIARY WEATHERSTRIP
NC0028-106-W-RA

Figure 12 Roof Side Rail Auxiliary Weatherstrip

ROOF SIDE RAIL AUXILIARY WEATHERSTRIP

Figure 12

Remove or Disconnect

- Roof side rail auxiliary weatherstrip from flange.

Install or Connect

- Roof side rail auxiliary weatherstrip to flange.

SUNROOF

Figure 13

A power sunroof (CF5 Option), featuring a sliding glass panel and a manually operated sunshade, is available. It is electrically operated from a two position rocker type switch located in the center of the windshield header area. To open, turn the ignition switch to the on position and depress the sunroof control switch rearward position. The glass panel will retract down and slide rearward into the storage space between the roof panel and the headliner. As the glass retracts, the wind deflector extends above the roof line. To close, hold the switch in the forward position until the glass completely closes, retracting the wind deflector and sealing against the roof opening flange. If the operator again depresses the forward position after the glass has completely closed and stopped its forward movement, the rear of the glass panel will rise to the vent position. To close the glass, depress the switch rearward position again and the glass will lower and reseal to the roof opening. A relay assembly at the front of the sunroof module causes the glass panel to stop in the closed position when moving from either the open or vent positions. The electrical harness for the sunroof is routed along the RH portion of the windshield header and down the side of the RH windshield pillar to the fuse block under the instrument panel.

Control Switch

Figure 13

Remove or Disconnect

1. Grasp the switch and pull straight downward to disengage from mounting bracket.
2. Lock nut securing connector and switch.
3. Separate switch from connector.

Install or Connect

1. Connector to switch.
2. Lock nut to connector and switch.
3. Firmly push switch into bracket to secure.

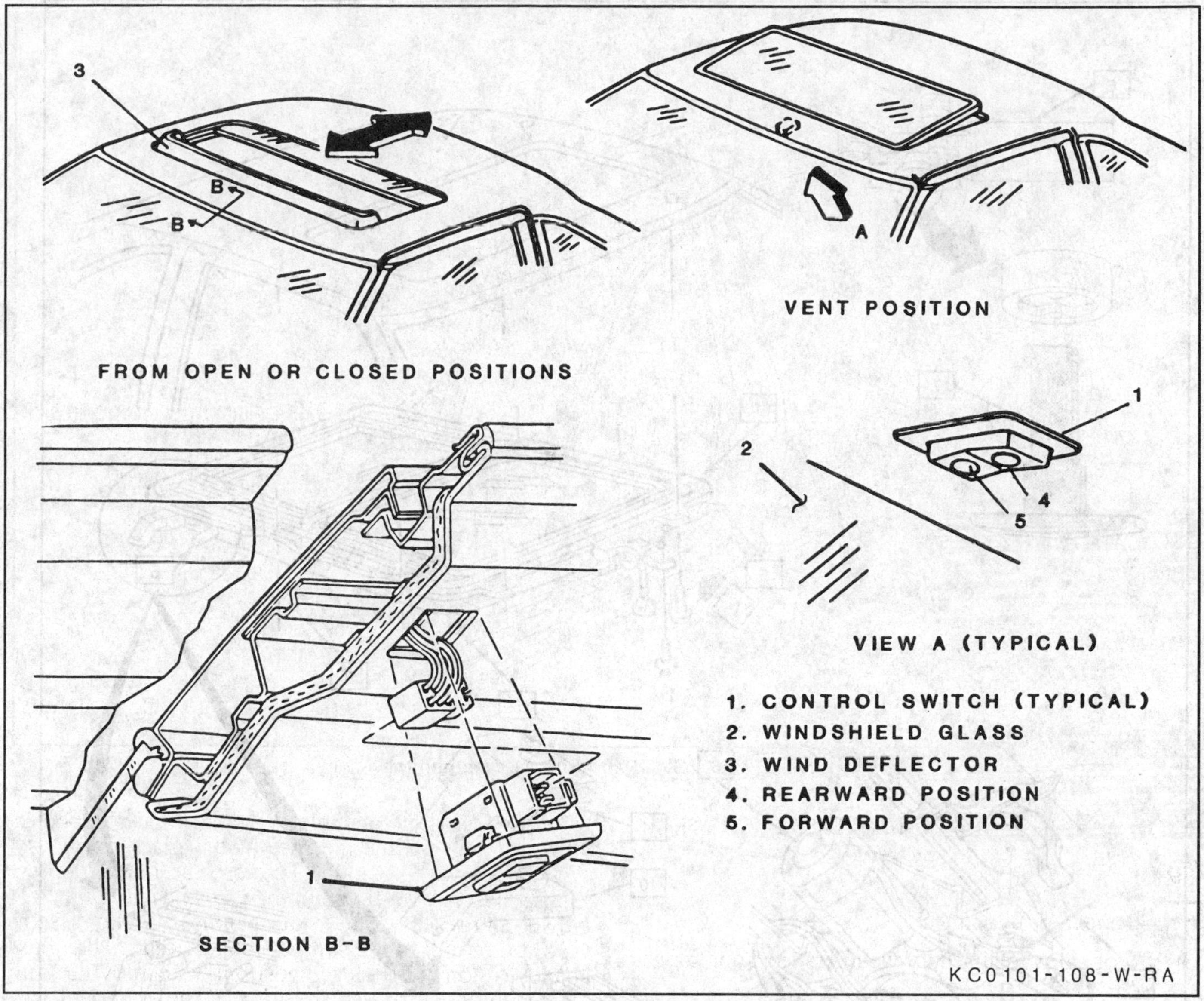
3
B
B
A
VENT POSITION
FROM OPEN OR CLOSED POSITIONS
1
2
4
5
VIEW A (TYPICAL)
1. CONTROL SWITCH (TYPICAL)
2. WINDSHIELD GLASS
3. WIND DEFLECTOR
4. REARWARD POSITION
5. FORWARD POSITION
1
SECTION B-B
KC0101-108-W-RA

Figure 13 Sunroof Operation

Manual Roof Operation

Figure 14

In the event of a power failure, the sunroof panel may be positioned by using J 38043 to manually crank the motor and drive gear. Partial access to the motor and drive gear is required and may be accomplished by partially lowering the headliner, refer to "Motor and Drive Gear" in this section.

To manually position the sunroof panel, disengage the motor clutch be inserting J 38043 into the motor opening, pushing up and rotating the tool in the desired direction. After glass is positioned, use the slots in the crank handle to re-engage the motor clutch by pulling down on the triangular tabs in the motor opening.

Diagnosis

Water leaks or wind noise indicate plugged or disconnected drains, misaligned glass panel or a damaged seal. Refer to ELECTRICAL DIAGNOSIS (SECTION 8A).

Water Drainage System

Figures 14 through 19

The sliding glass panel is designed for controlled water entry at the seal. A properly adjusted glass panel will result in a snug fit between the seal and the roof. The fit can be checked by inserting a piece of paper between the roof and felt seal. Maintenance of minimal gap is essential for assuring that more water does not enter the car than the sunroof drains can handle. Also, objectionable windnoise could result if gap clearances are exceeded. All glass panel to roof adjustments are made by adjusting the height and centering of the glass.

Adequate drainage is provided by a drain trough in the sunroof module which encircles the sliding glass panel and leads to drain hoses located at each corner of the housing. In addition, a drain channel spans the rear of the sunroof module and directs water into the trough. The front drain hoses are routed down

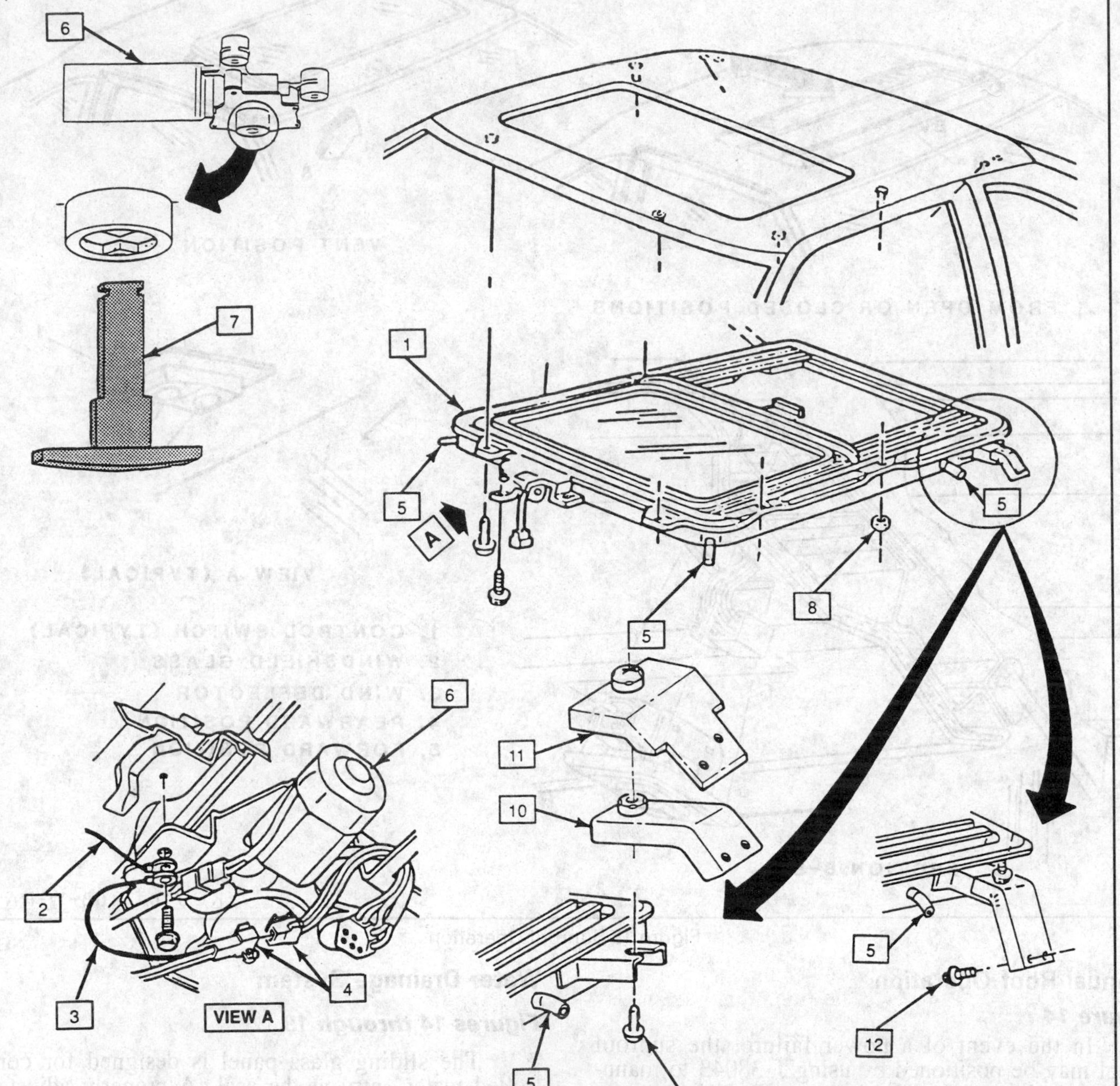
6
7
1
5
A
5
8
5
6
11
10
2
3
4
VIEW A
5
12
9

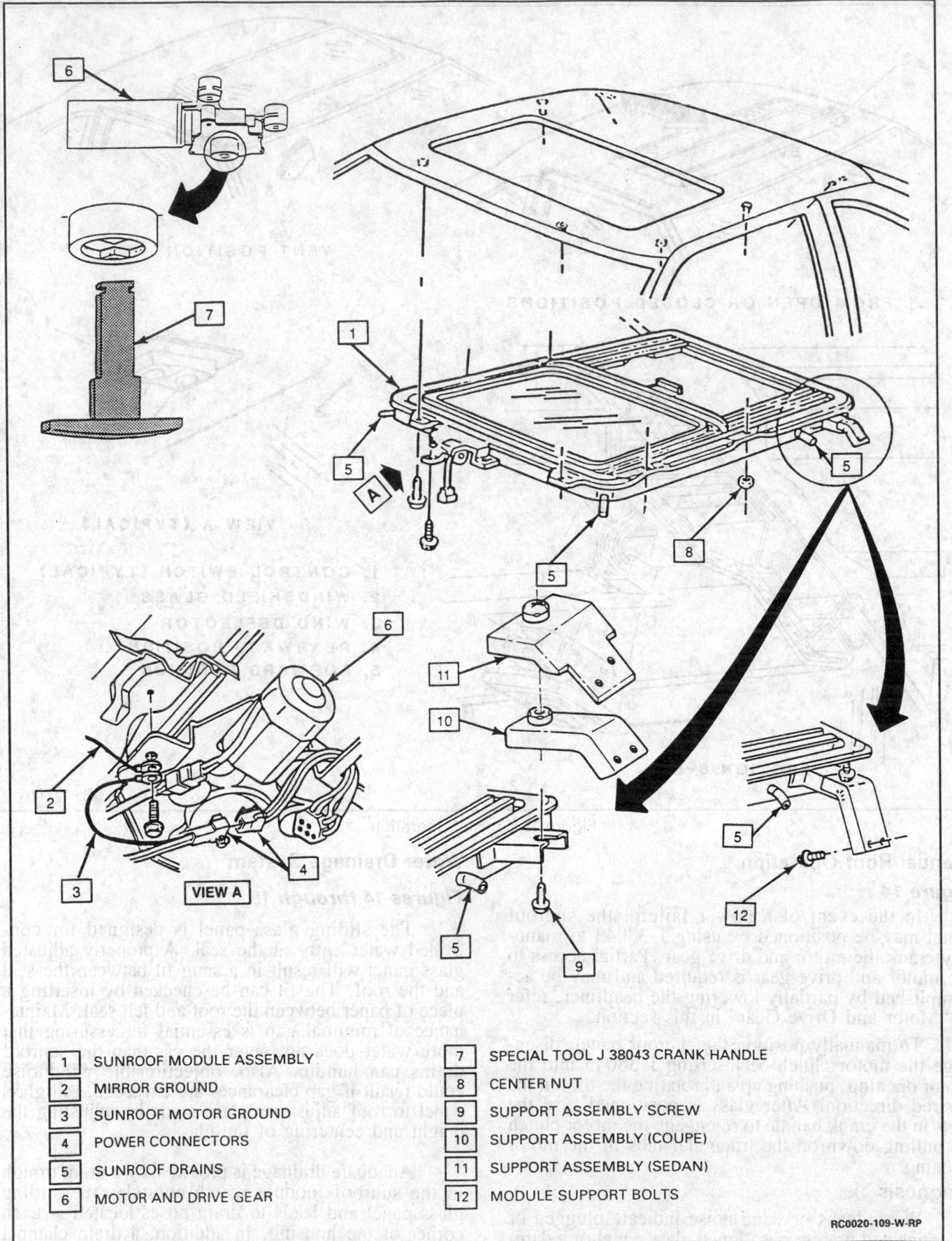

1	SUNROOF MODULE ASSEMBLY	7	SPECIAL TOOL J 38043 CRANK HANDLE
2	MIRROR GROUND	8	CENTER NUT
3	SUNROOF MOTOR GROUND	9	SUPPORT ASSEMBLY SCREW
4	POWER CONNECTORS	10	SUPPORT ASSEMBLY (COUPE)
5	SUNROOF DRAINS	11	SUPPORT ASSEMBLY (SEDAN)
6	MOTOR AND DRIVE GEAR	12	MODULE SUPPORT BOLTS

RC0020-109-W-RP

Figure 14 Sunroof Module Installation

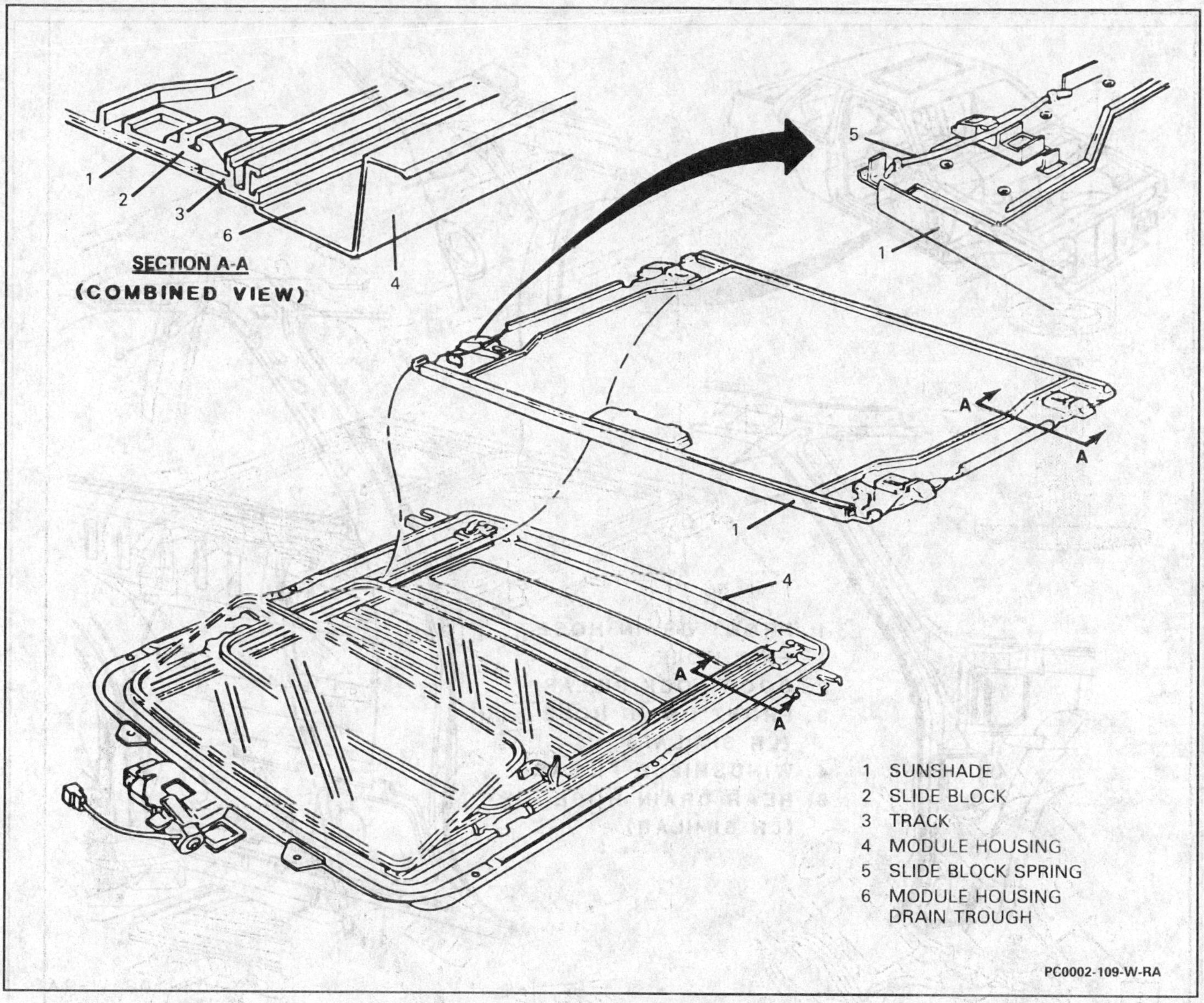
SECTION A-A
(COMBINED VIEW)
1
2
3
4
5
6
A
1 SUNSHADE
2 SLIDE BLOCK
3 TRACK
4 MODULE HOUSING
5 SLIDE BLOCK SPRING
6 MODULE HOUSING DRAIN TROUGH
PC0002-109-W-RA

Figure 15 Sunshade Installation

the windshield pillars and out the center of each pillar near the upper door hinge. The two rear drain hoses are routed down the door lock pillars and out the rocker panel. They are accessible by removal of the pressure relief valves. Refer to REAR QUARTERS (SECTION 10-7).

If a wet headlining or other waterleak complaints are encountered, prior to performing any adjustments, first verify that the drainage system is not plugged or disconnected. Use a pint size container to pour water into the module housing drain trough. If water flow is restricted, use compressed air to blow out any material plugging the drain system. Retest system again.

To further check for disconnected drain hoses, partial access (without removing the headliner) may be had by removing the lace from the retainer around the sunroof opening, withdrawing the tucked headliner, and lowering headliner as required, refer to "Formed Headlining" in this section. Removal of the sunroof control switch is also required.

Drain Channel

Figure 18

↔ Remove or Disconnect

1. Wind deflector, mechanism cover and glass panel. Refer to procedures in this section.
2. Peel back securing tape on sedan.
3. Position system to maximum vent position so that drain channel is fully forward.
4. Four connecting screws securing drain channel to guide support.

→← Install or Connect

1. Screws securing drain channel to guide support.
2. Position vent so that drain channel is fully rearward.
3. Secure drain hose with tape on Sedan.
4. Glass panel, mechanism cover and wind deflector. Refer to procedures in this section.

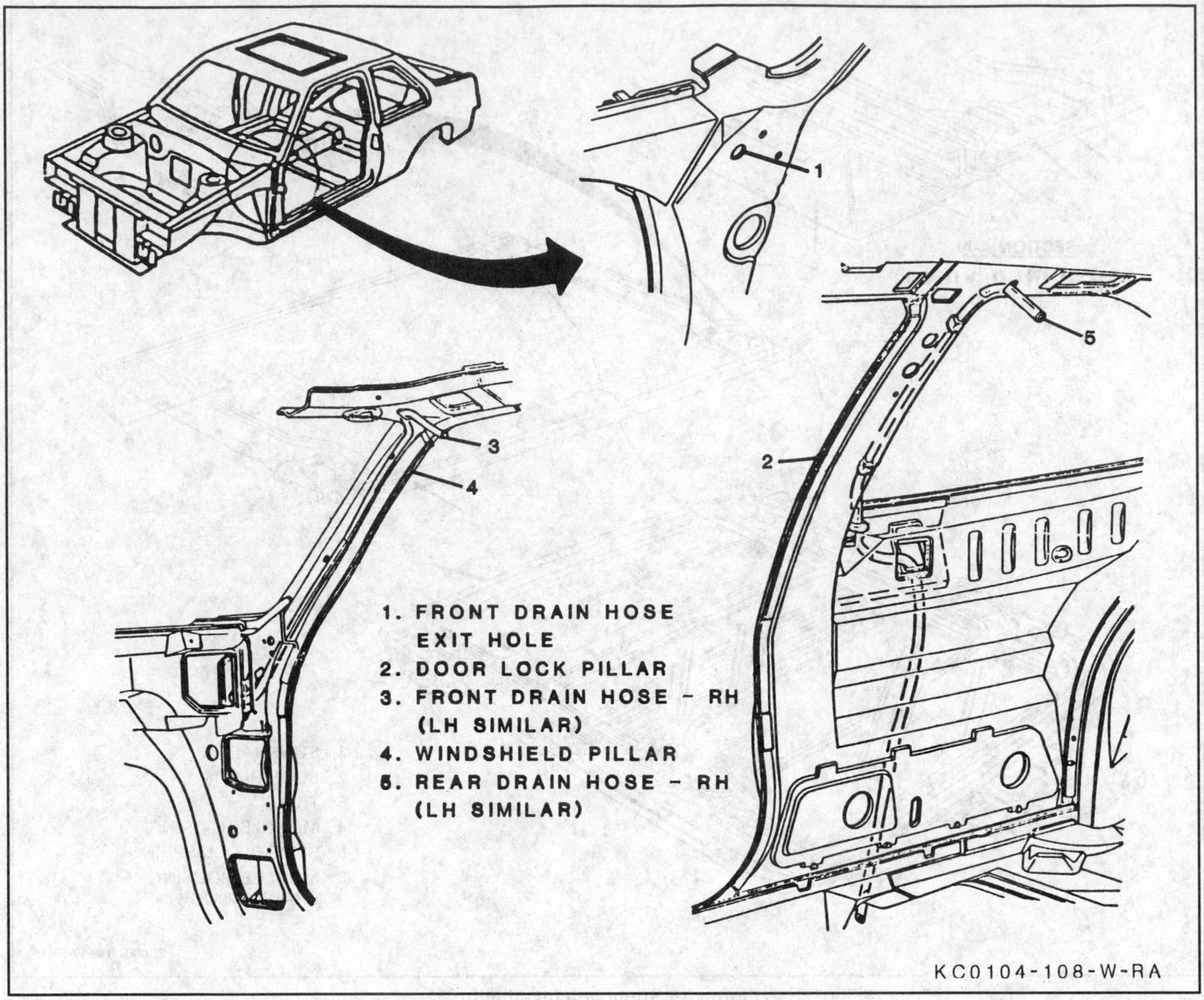
1
2
3
4
5
1. FRONT DRAIN HOSE EXIT HOLE
2. DOOR LOCK PILLAR
3. FRONT DRAIN HOSE – RH (LH SIMILAR)
4. WINDSHIELD PILLAR
5. REAR DRAIN HOSE – RH (LH SIMILAR)
KC0104-108-W-RA

Figure 16 Drain Hose Installation (Coupe)

Wind Deflector Assembly

Figures 18 and 20

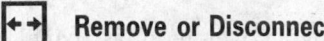

Remove or Disconnect

1. Open sunroof.
2. Depress deflector and remove hex head screws through access holes.
3. Wind deflector assembly.

Install or Connect

1. Deflector to roof.
2. Depress deflector and install hex head screws through access holes.
3. Close sunroof.

Adjust

- Manually position both sides of deflector both horizontally and vertically so top surface of deflector is 20 mm (3/4 inch) above top surface of roof panel and the rubber flange just contacts the edge of the roof opening. Lock deflector in this position by tightening hex head screws.

Glass Height Vertical Adjustment

Figures 21 and 22

Adjust

1. Position glass to vent.
2. Slide the upper half of the mechanism cover rearward until the cover clips disengage from the side adjustment bracket.

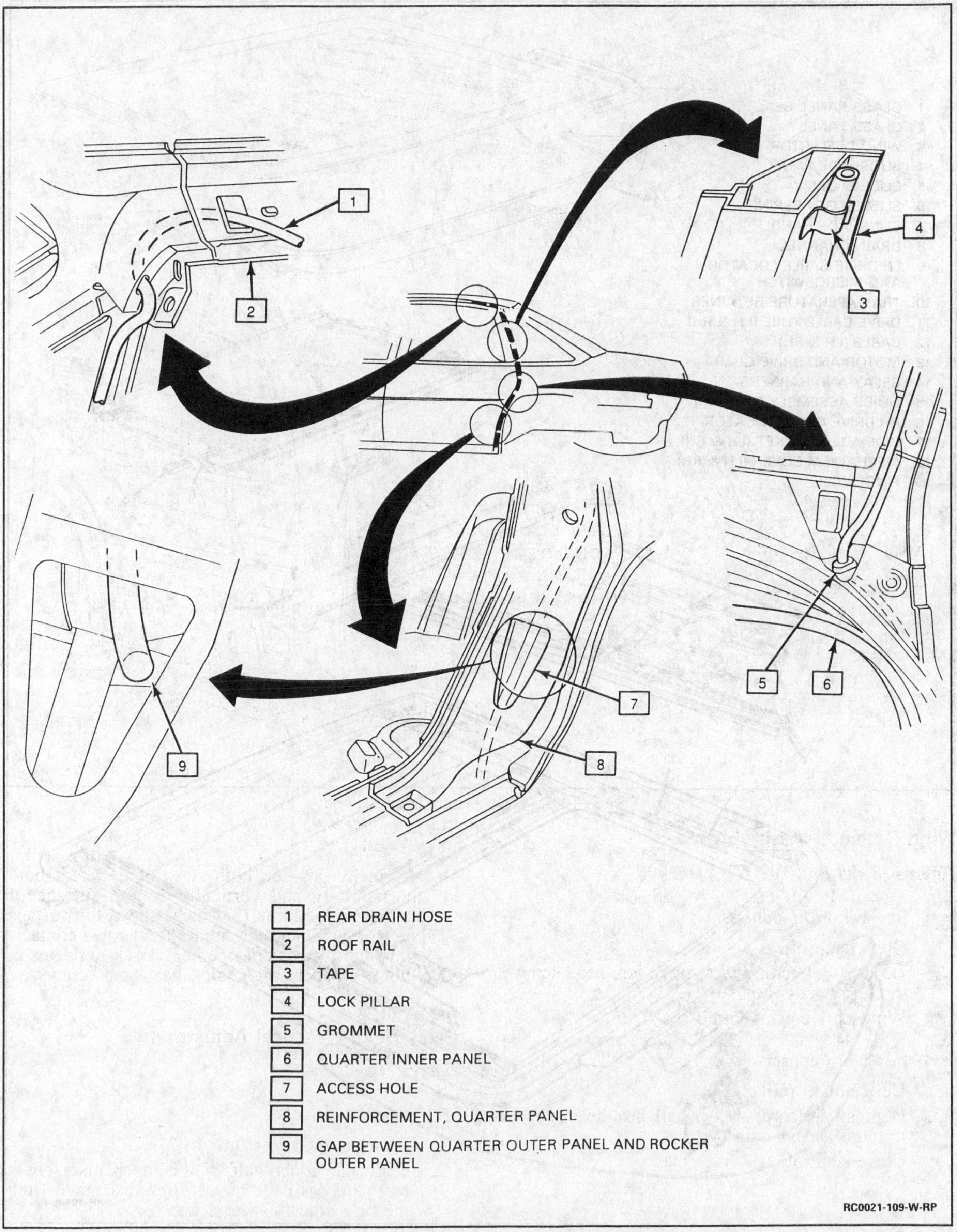
1
2
3
4
5
6
7
8
9
1 REAR DRAIN HOSE
2 ROOF RAIL
3 TAPE
4 LOCK PILLAR
5 GROMMET
6 QUARTER INNER PANEL
7 ACCESS HOLE
8 REINFORCEMENT, QUARTER PANEL
9 GAP BETWEEN QUARTER OUTER PANEL AND ROCKER OUTER PANEL
RC0021-109-W-RP

Figure 17 Drain Hose Installation (Sedan)

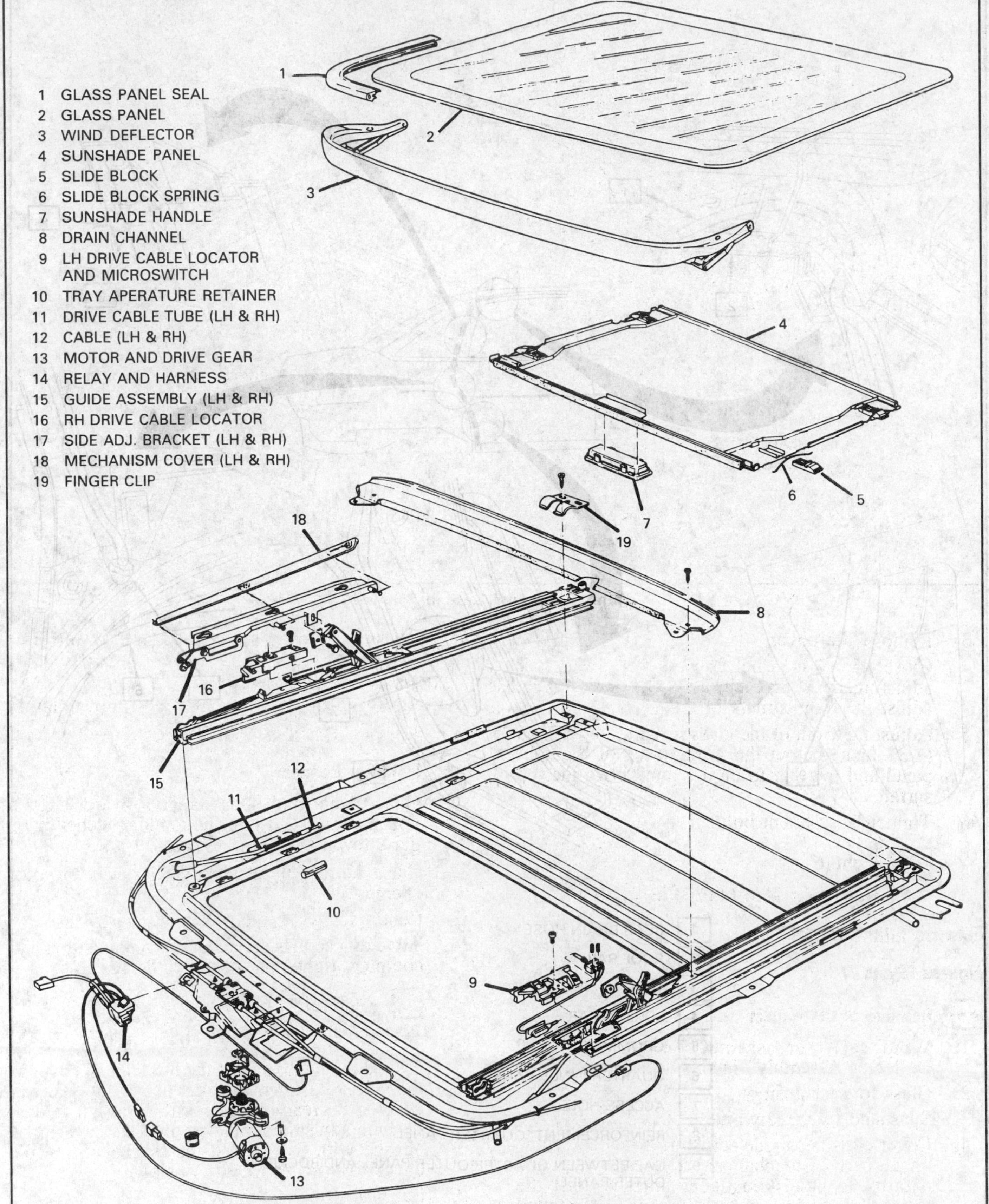
1 GLASS PANEL SEAL
2 GLASS PANEL
3 WIND DEFLECTOR
4 SUNSHADE PANEL
5 SLIDE BLOCK
6 SLIDE BLOCK SPRING
7 SUNSHADE HANDLE
8 DRAIN CHANNEL
9 LH DRIVE CABLE LOCATOR AND MICROSWITCH
10 TRAY APERATURE RETAINER
11 DRIVE CABLE TUBE (LH & RH)
12 CABLE (LH & RH)
13 MOTOR AND DRIVE GEAR
14 RELAY AND HARNESS
15 GUIDE ASSEMBLY (LH & RH)
16 RH DRIVE CABLE LOCATOR
17 SIDE ADJ. BRACKET (LH & RH)
18 MECHANISM COVER (LH & RH)
19 FINGER CLIP
PC0005-109-W-RA

Figure 18 Sunroof Module Assembly (Disassembled View)

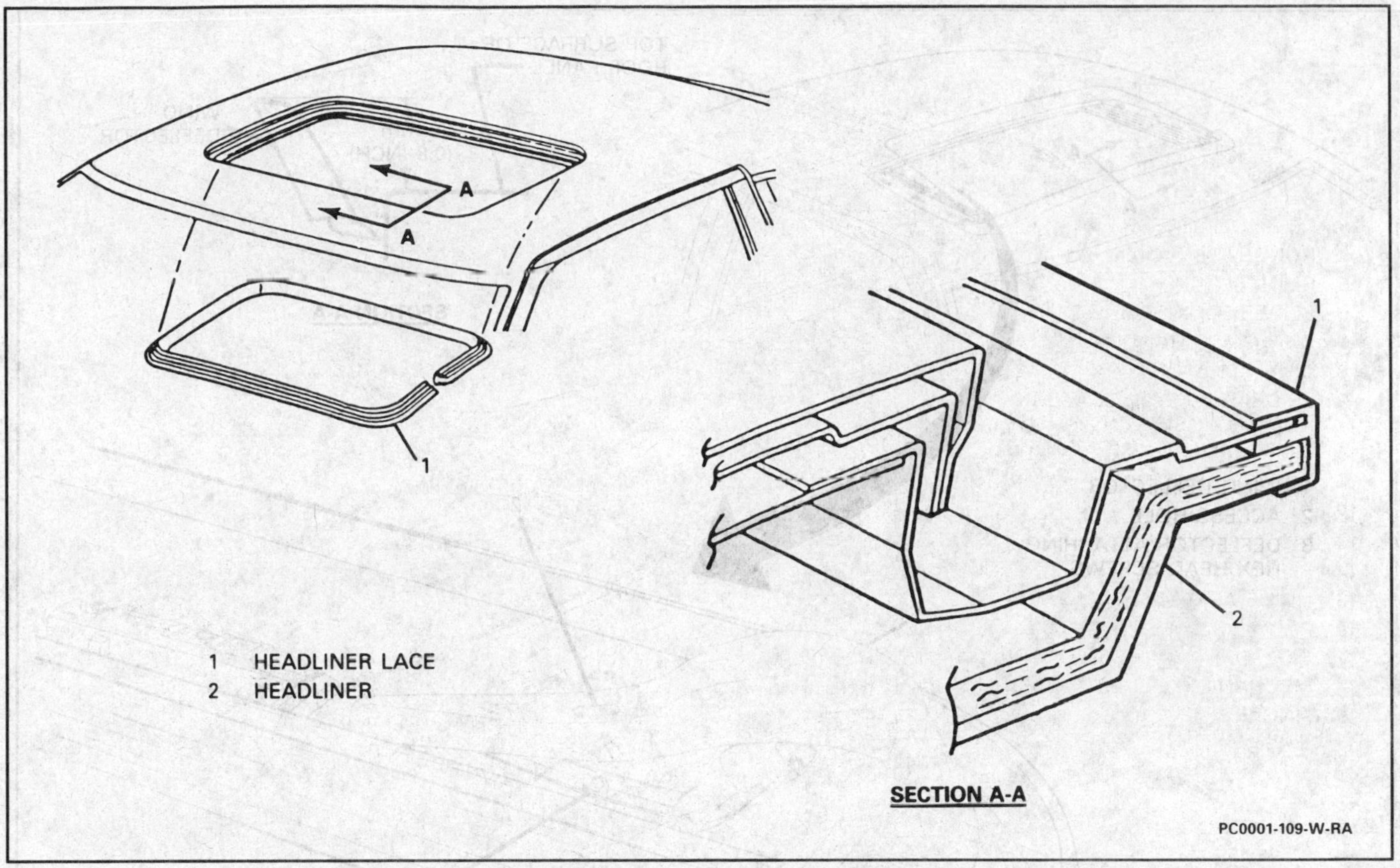
A
A
1
1 HEADLINER LACE
2 HEADLINER
1
2
SECTION A-A
PC0001-109-W-RA

Figure 19 Headliner Lace Installation

3. Remove the cover.
4. Close the glass panel, separately loosen four adjusting bolts (2 each side) and individually adjust the four corners of the glass.
5. Adjust the front of the glass panel to be 0.1 mm (1/32 inch) below the top surface of the roof panel and the rear to be 0.1 mm above the top surface.
6. Tighten adjustment bolts.

Tighten

- Bolts to 5 N·m (44 lb. in.).

Sliding Glass Panel

Figures 18 and 21

Remove or Disconnect

1. Wind deflector assembly. Refer to "Wind Deflector Assembly" in this section.
2. Glass to vent position.
3. Sunshade fully rearward.
4. Cover clips from side adjustment bracket. Slide upper part of mechanism cover rearward and parallel to side adjustment bracket until the cover clips disengage from the side adjustment bracket.
5. Partially unscrew six connecting screws (three each side) securing glass panel to side adjustment brackets.
6. Slide glass panel rearward approximately 12 mm (1/2 inch) and lift off.

Install or Connect

1. Glass panel and slide panel forward 12 mm (1/2 inch). Orient information/logo stenciled on glass toward the rear.
2. Close sunroof to center glass panel in the roof opening.
3. Center screws tighten to hold adjustment.
4. Attaching screws open glass to vent position and complete tightening of attaching screws.

Tighten

- Screws to 8 N·m (71 lb. in.).

5. Extend the upper part of the mechanism cover to the side adjustment bracket and while keeping cover as far rearward as possible, push it against the side adjustment bracket until the cover clips engage with the pins of the bracket. Slide the cover forward to lock in position.
6. Sunshade fully forward.
7. Glass to original position.

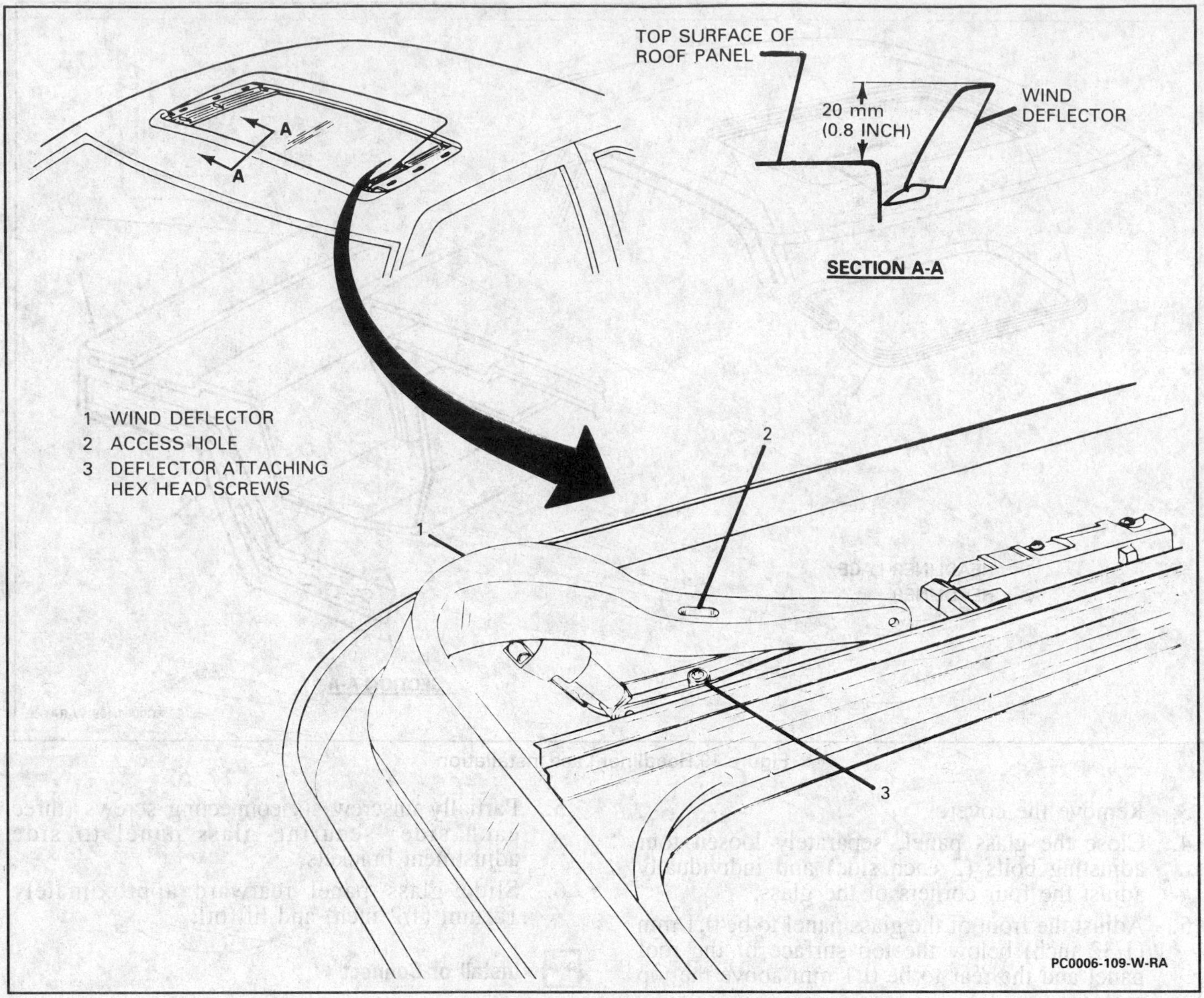

TOP SURFACE OF ROOF PANEL
20 mm (0.8 INCH)
WIND DEFLECTOR
SECTION A-A
A
A
1 WIND DEFLECTOR
2 ACCESS HOLE
3 DEFLECTOR ATTACHING HEX HEAD SCREWS
1
2
3
PC0006-109-W-RA

Figure 20 Wind Deflector Removal and Installation

8. Wind deflector assembly. Refer to "Wind Deflector Assembly" in this section.

Adjust

- Check wind deflector and glass height vertical adjustment. Correct as required.

Side Adjustment Bracket

Figures 18 and 21

Remove or Disconnect

1. Wind deflector, mechanism cover and glass panel. Refer to procedures in this section.
2. Position system to maximum vent position and remove rearmost adjustment bolt and washer from side adjustment bracket.

Important

- Do not allow washer to drop into guide track. Foreign objects in track can damage mechanism.

3. Lift rear of side adjustment bracket to maximum vertical position and disengage front of bracket by moving bracket outboard.

Install or Connect

1. Lower front side of adjustment bracket and engage by moving bracket inward.
2. Position vent down and install rearmost adjustment bolt and washer.
3. Glass panel, mechanism cover and wind deflector. Refer to procedures in this section.

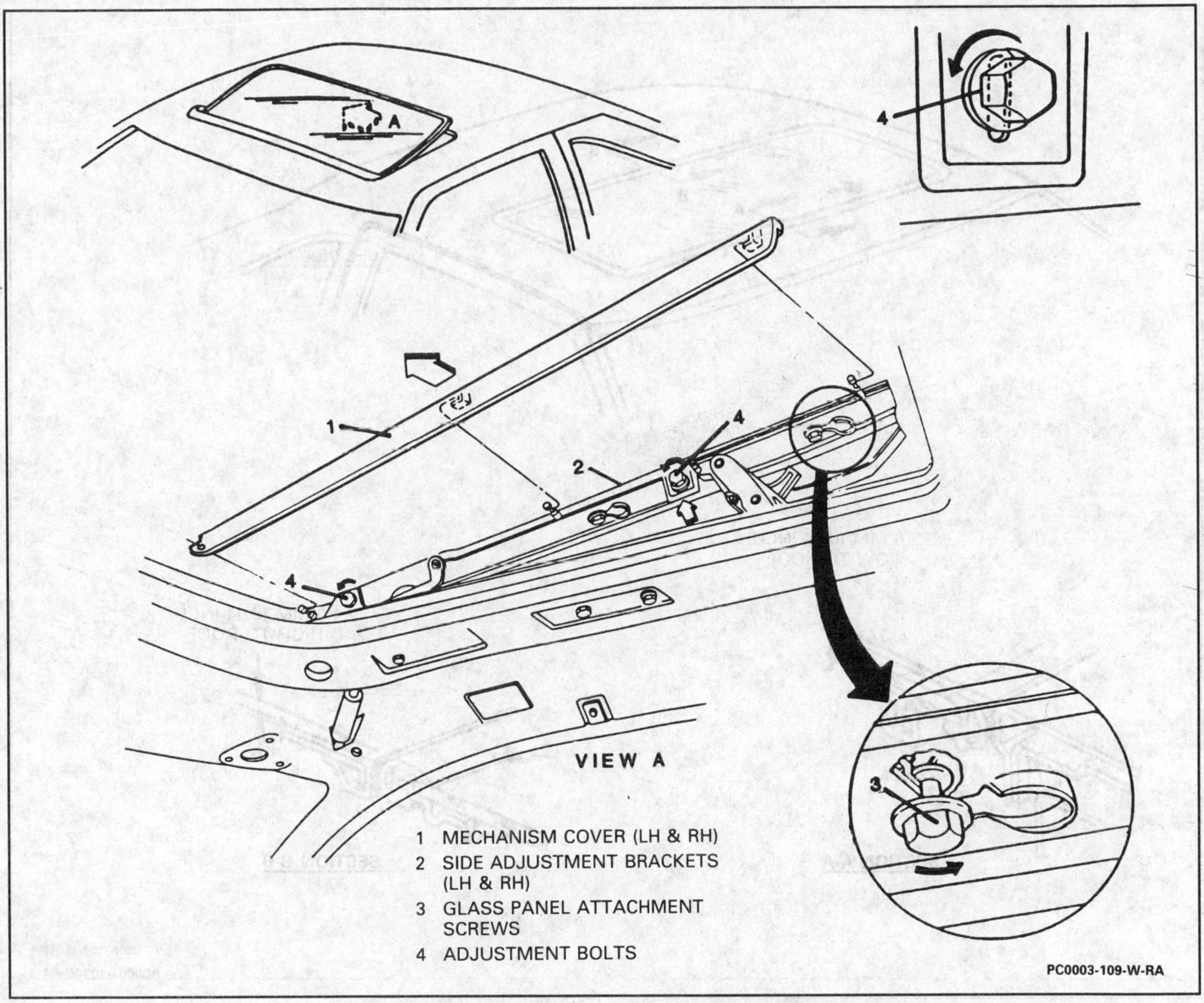
A
1
2
4
4
4
3
VIEW A
1 MECHANISM COVER (LH & RH)
2 SIDE ADJUSTMENT BRACKETS (LH & RH)
3 GLASS PANEL ATTACHMENT SCREWS
4 ADJUSTMENT BOLTS
PC0003-109-W-RA

Figure 21 Sunroof Glass Panel Adjustment

Drive Cable Locator

Figures 18, 21, 22 through 27

Important

- There are two procedures for Drive Cable Locator removal and installation – one used when the cables are being replaced and adjusted, and a second used when only the locator (LH Locator/Microswitch) is being replaced. If only the locator is being replaced, disregard step 1 and position glass panel rearward sufficient to clear locator. Do not fully open glass. Be careful not to reposition glass while locator is removed or readjustment of cables will be required.

Remove or Disconnect

1. Wind deflector, glass panel, side adjustment brackets, motor and drive gear. Refer to procedures in this section.
2. Two connecting screws from drive cable locator. (For LH locator, pull travel limiting microswitch grommet and wires approximately 24 mm (1 inch) to the inside and separate.)
3. Drive cable locator. Removal can be assisted by inserting small bladed screwdriver under rear edge of locator and lifting locator from track.

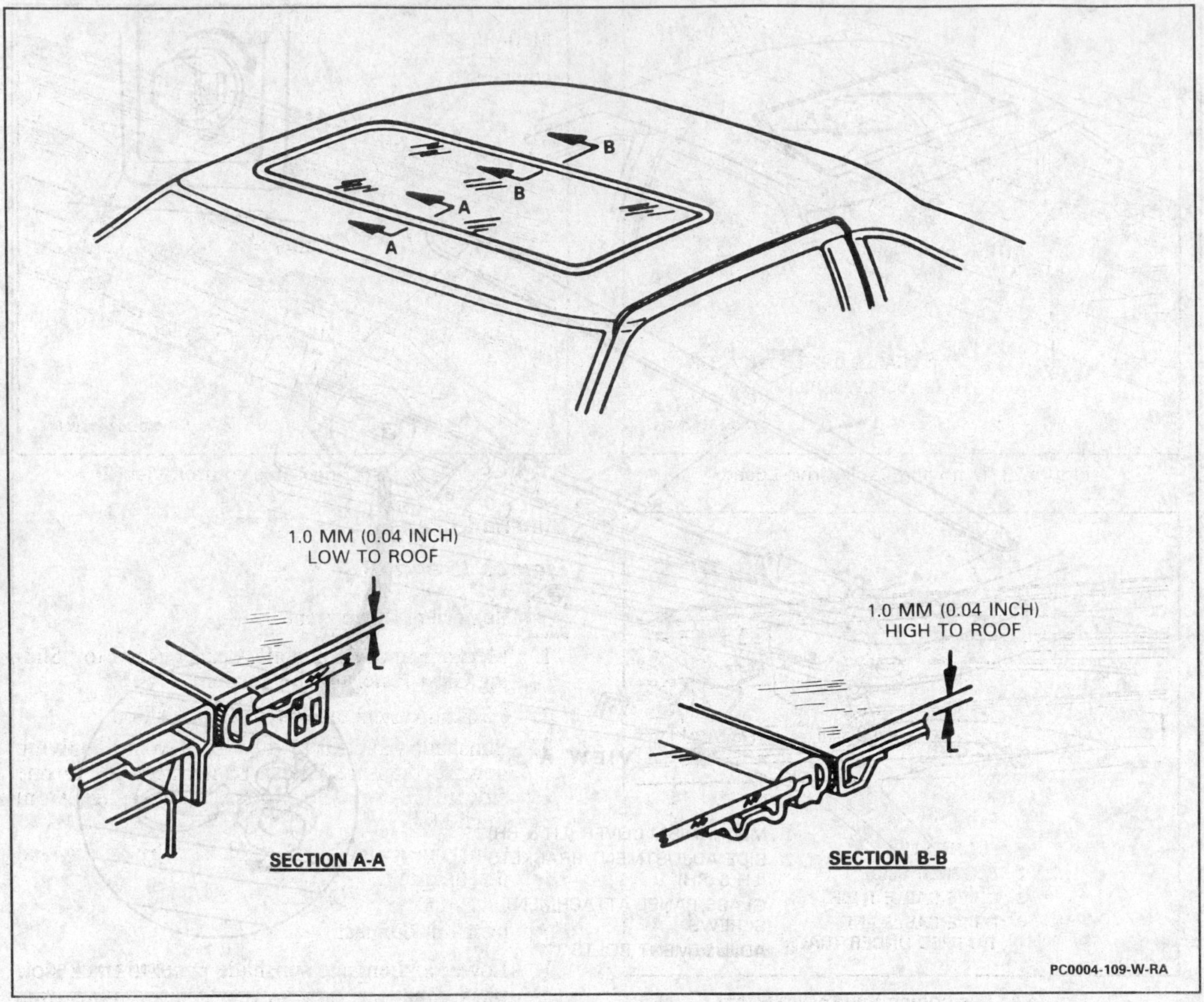
B
B
A
A
1.0 MM (0.04 INCH)
LOW TO ROOF
1.0 MM (0.04 INCH)
HIGH TO ROOF
SECTION A-A
SECTION B-B
PC0004-109-W-RA

Figure 22 Sunroof Adjustment Specifications

Install or Connect

Important

- When only the locator is being replaced, follow the procedures outlined in steps 2 and 5.

1. Position blocker slide rearward until it is approximately opposite the flanged end of the drive cable tube. Position front slide as shown. Locate cable end into tab groove of rear drive slide connector and position rear slide rearward sufficient to trap cable end under track.
2. Cable locator by first locating it onto flanged end of drive cable tube, then rotate it so that the small inboard lip on underside of cable locator slips under bottom slot of guide track. Outboard tang of front slide should be positioned in the inboard slot of locator. When locator is fully seated, install both screws.

Inspect

- Check for smooth operation by pushing the guide mechanism rearward sufficient to allow the tang on the longlever assembly to drop into the slot in the guide track.

3. Push the front slide forward again while at the same time also repositioning the guide mechanism forward. The outboard tang of the front slide must slide back into the inboard slot of the locator. To align cables and track, continue moving the guide mechanism forward until it reaches the full vent position.
4. LH cable locator only, position the microswitch electrical connector through the access hole in the module housing and orient the rubber grommet so that the connector points forward. Position the electrical wire between the connector and the microswitch under the drive cable tube.

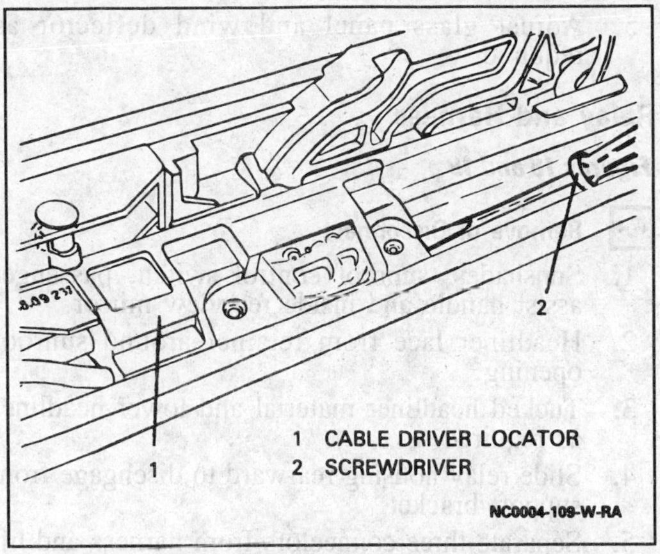
1
2
1 CABLE DRIVER LOCATOR
2 SCREWDRIVER
NC0004-109-W-RA

Figure 23 Removing Cable Drive Locator

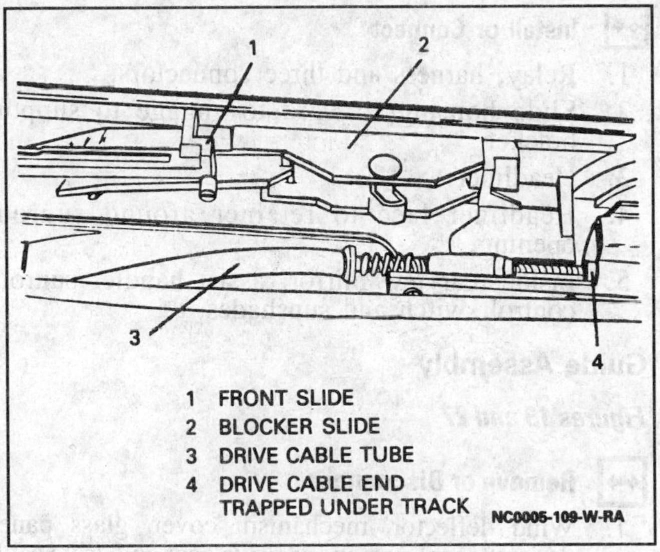
1
2
3
4
1 FRONT SLIDE
2 BLOCKER SLIDE
3 DRIVE CABLE TUBE
4 DRIVE CABLE END
TRAPPED UNDER TRACK
NC0005-109-W-RA

Figure 24 Positioning Slide Mechanism

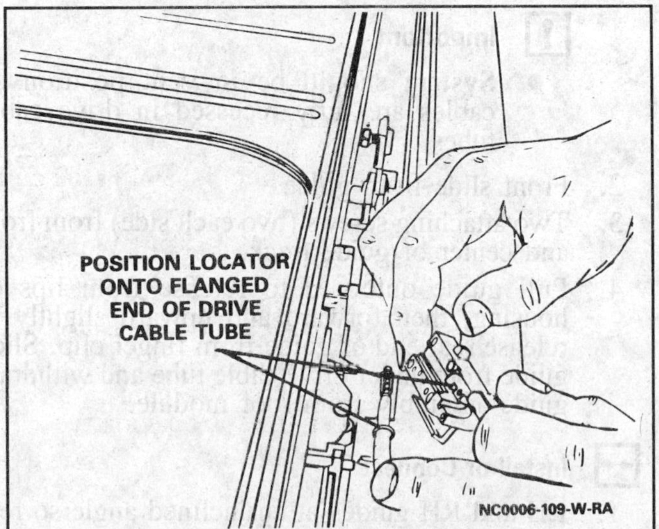
POSITION LOCATOR
ONTO FLANGED
END OF DRIVE
CABLE TUBE
NC0006-109-W-RA

Figure 25 Installing Cable Locator (View 1)

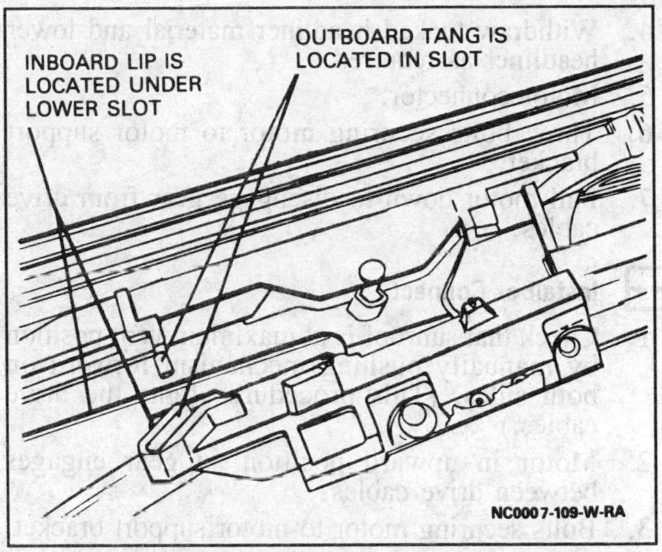
INBOARD LIP IS
LOCATED UNDER
LOWER SLOT
OUTBOARD TANG IS
LOCATED IN SLOT
NC0007-109-W-RA

Figure 26 Installing Cable Locator (View 2)

Sunshade Panel

Figures 15 and 18

↔ Remove or Disconnect

1. Mechanism cover and glass panel. Refer to "Sliding Glass Panel" in this section.
2. Position system to full rearward position.
3. Sunshade panel fully forward. (Avoid applying upward pressure.) Push sunshade fully to one side to allow slide blocks to disengage from track slot.
4. Sunshade panel from track slot by lifting and disengaging.

→← Install or Connect

1. Lower and engage sunshade panel to track slot.
2. Push sunshade fully to one side to allow slide blocks to engage in track slot. Slide sunshade panel fully rearward.
3. Position system to fully forward position.
4. Glass panel and mechanism cover. Refer to "Sliding Glass Panel" in this section.
5. Check that sunshade does not bind in track.

Motor and Drive Gear

Figures 18 and 19

↔ Remove or Disconnect

1. Position sunroof at maximum vent position.
2. Sunshades, sunroof control switch, passenger assist handle and inside rear view mirror. Refer to procedures in this section.
3. Headliner lace from retainer around sunroof opening.

4. Withdraw tucked headliner material and lower headliner as required.
5. Motor connector.
6. Three bolts securing motor to motor support bracket.
7. Pull motor down to disengage gear from drive cables.

Install or Connect

1. Check that sunroof is at maximum vent position by manually pushing mechanism forward on both sides. (This procedure aligns the drive cables.)
2. Motor in upward position so gear engages between drive cables.
3. Bolts securing motor to motor support bracket.
4. Motor connector.
5. Headliner to original position.
6. Headliner lace to retainer around sunroof opening.
7. Inside rear view mirror, passenger assist handle, sunroof control switch and sunshades. Refer to procedures in this section.
8. Sunroof to minimum vent position.
9. Cycle system to check for correct operation.

Drive Cables

Figures 18 and 27

Remove or Disconnect

1. Wind deflector, mechanism cover, glass panel, side adjustment bracket, motor and drive gear. Refer to procedures in this section.

Important

- System should be positioned in vent position with cables fully recessed in drive cable tubes.

2. Drive cable locators. Refer to "Drive Cable Locator" in this section.
3. Drive cables by pulling toward the rear of the module.

Install or Connect

1. Slide drive cable with the unfinished end into the drive cable tube.
2. Locate the finished end of cable in the rear drive slide connector.
3. Drive cable locators and side adjustment brackets. Position system mechanism to the most forward or vent position by pushing main slide to the front.
4. Drive gear, motor, side adjustment bracket, glass panel, mechanism cover and wind deflector. Refer to procedures in this section.
5. Adjust glass panel and wind deflector as required.

Relay and Harness

Figures 18 and 19

Remove or Disconnect

1. Sunshades, sunroof control switch, passenger assist handle and inside rearview mirror.
2. Headliner lace from retainer around sunroof opening.
3. Tucked headliner material and lower headliner as required.
4. Slide relay housing rearward to disengage from support bracket.
5. Separate three connectors from harness and lift out relay and harness.

Install or Connect

1. Relay, harness and three connectors.
2. Slide housing forward to engage to support bracket.
3. Headliner.
4. Headliner lace to retainer around sunroof opening.
5. Inside rearview mirror, assist handle, sunroof control switch and sunshades.

Guide Assembly

Figures 18 and 27

Remove or Disconnect

1. Wind deflector, mechanism cover, glass panel, drain channel, motor and drive gear and drive cable locators.

Important

- System should be in vent position so cables are fully recessed in drive cable tubes.

2. Front slide from guide.
3. Two attaching screws (two each side) from front and center of guide track.
4. Pull guide outboard to release from lips of housing, then forward and upward slightly to release rear end of guide from finger clip. Slide guide from under drive cable tube and withdraw guide assembly from roof module.

Install or Connect

1. LH and RH guides at an inclined angle so rear portion slips under finger clip at rear of module housing.

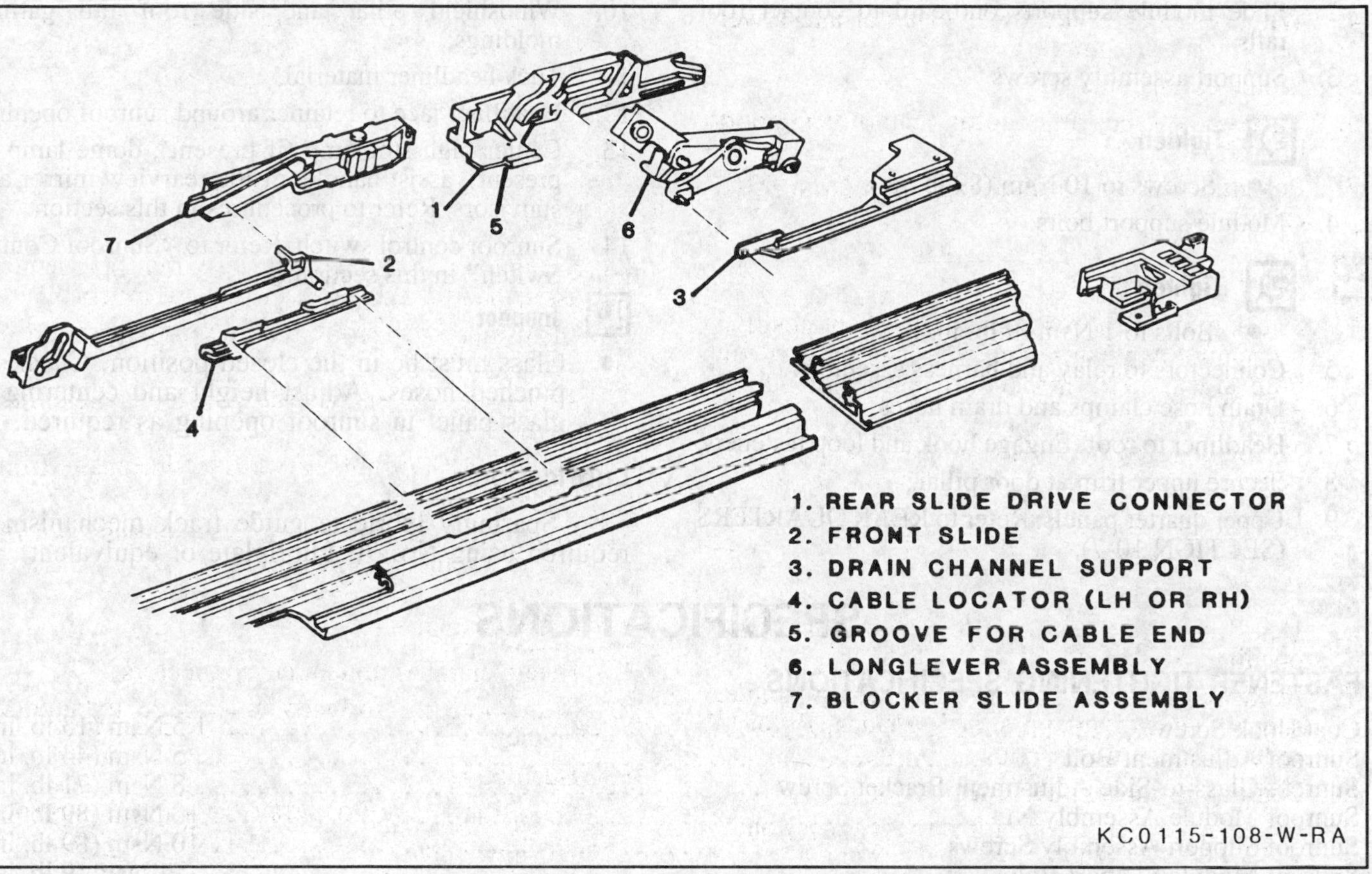
1
2
3
4
5
6
7
1. REAR SLIDE DRIVE CONNECTOR
2. FRONT SLIDE
3. DRAIN CHANNEL SUPPORT
4. CABLE LOCATOR (LH OR RH)
5. GROOVE FOR CABLE END
6. LONGLEVER ASSEMBLY
7. BLOCKER SLIDE ASSEMBLY
KC0115-108-W-RA

Figure 27 Guide Assembly (Disassembled View)

2. LH and RH locators. Refer to "Drive Cable Locators" in this section.
3. Position system at maximum vent position to align cables.
4. Motor and drive gear, drain channel, glass panel, mechanism cover and wind deflector. Refer to procedures in this section.

Important

- Install glass panel before wind deflector to avoid possible damage to deflector by side adjustment brackets if system is actuated.

5. Center the glass in the sunroof opening and adjust for glass height.

Module Assembly

Figures 14, 18 and 19

Remove or Disconnect

1. Sunroof control switch. Refer to "Sunroof Control Switch" in the section.
2. Sunshades, inside rearview mirror, passenger assist handle, dome lamp (if present), and center high stoplamp (if present). Refer to procedures in this section.
3. Headliner lace from retainer around sunroof opening.
4. Withdraw tucked headliner material.
5. Windshield pillar and side roof rail garnish moldings.
6. Upper quarter panels. Refer to REAR QUARTERS (SECTION 10-7).
7. Loosen upper trim at door pillar.
8. Headliner hook and loop fasteners and lower sliding headliner to one side while at the same time lowering opposite side from center pillar trim with aid of a helper. Recline seatbacks if possible and remove headliner through passenger door opening.
9. Drain hose clamps and drain hoses.
10. Connectors from relay and harness assembly.
11. Module support bolts.
12. Support assembly screws.
13. Slide module supports inboard to disconnect roof rails.
14. Nuts securing module to roof, lower and remove through passenger door opening with aid of a helper. Remove center nuts last.

Install or Connect

1. Module assembly to roof. Secure installing center nuts first.

Tighten

- Bolts to 10 N•m (89 lb. in.).

2. Slide module supports outboard to contact roof rails.
3. Support assembly screws.

Tighten

- Screws to 10 N•m (89 lb. in.).

4. Module support bolts.

Tighten

- Bolts to 1 N•m (9 lb. in.).

5. Connectors to relay and harness assembly.
6. Drain hose clamps and drain hoses.
7. Headliner to roof. Engage hook and loop fasteners.
8. Secure upper trim at door pillar.
9. Upper quarter panels. Refer to REAR QUARTERS (SECTION 10-7).
10. Windshield pillar and side roof rail garnish moldings.
11. Tuck headliner material.
12. Headliner lace to retainer around sunroof opening.
13. Center high stoplamp (if present), dome lamp (if present), assist handle, inside rearview mirror and sunvisors. Refer to procedures in this section.
14. Sunroof control switch. Refer to "Sunroof Control Switch" in this section.

Inspect

- Glass must be in the closed position. Check for pinched hoses. Adjust height and centering of glass panel in sunroof opening as required.

Lubrication

Sparingly lubricate guide track mechanism as required using No. 70 Lubriplate or equivalent.

SPECIFICATIONS

FASTENER TIGHTENING SPECIFICATIONS

Coat Hook Screw	1.5 N•m (13 lb. in.)
Sunroof Adjustment Bolt	5 N•m (44 lb. in.)
Sunroof Glass-to-Side Adjustment Bracket Screw	8 N•m (71 lb. in.)
Sunroof Module Assembly Nut	10 N•m (89 lb. in.)
Sunroof Support Assembly Screws	10 N•m (89 lb. in.)
Sunroof Module Support Bolts	1 N•m (9 lb. in.)
Sunshade Mounting Plate Screw	3 N•m (27 lb. in.)
Sunshade Retainer Screw	1 N•m (9 lb. in.)

SPECIAL TOOLS

1
J 38043
2
J 24595-C

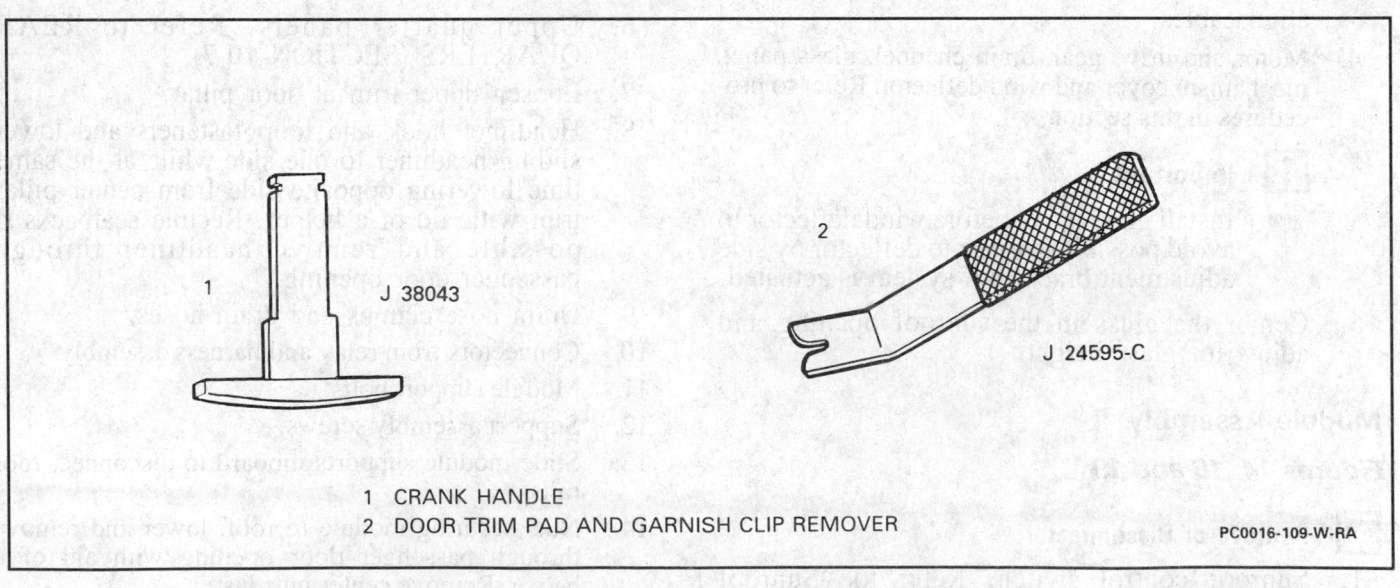

1 CRANK HANDLE
2 DOOR TRIM PAD AND GARNISH CLIP REMOVER

PC0016-109-W-RA

SECTION 10-10

SEATS AND CARPET

CAUTION: Replace belts, retractors, and hardware in use during all but a minor collision. Also, restraint systems should be replaced and anchorages properly repaired if they were in areas damaged by a collision, whether the belt was in use or not. If there is any question, replace the belt system. Damage, whether visible or not, could result in serious personal injury in the event of an accident.

NOTICE: When fasteners are removed, always reinstall them at the same location from which they were removed. If a fastener needs to be replaced, use the correct part number fastener for that application. If the correct part number fastener is not available, a fastener of equal size and strength (or stronger) may be used. Fasteners that are not reused, and those requiring thread locking compound will be called out. The correct torque value must be used when installing fasteners that require it. If the above conditions are not followed, parts or system damage could result.

CONTENTS

GENERAL DESCRIPTION

FRONT SEATS

Figure 1

The following front seat options are available:

- AM6 60/40 split with armrest.
- AR9 bucket.

Split Front Seats

All split seats have front seatback head restraints on the driver's and passenger's seatback. The head restraints are designed so they cannot be removed from the seatback without first inserting a flat tool inside the head restraint support tube to release the locking tab.

Coupe front seats are equipped with inertia seatback locks. This system allows the seatback to fold forward without requiring the occupant to release a locking lever for access to the rear seat area. On a sudden stop, deceleration, or if the front of the vehicle is declined more than 20 degrees, the seatback inertia locking system locks the front seatbacks in an upright position. A manual seatback lock release lever is provided to allow manual release of the inertia lock when the front of the vehicle is declined more than 20 degrees. The release lever is located at the lower rear outboard corner of the seatback.

Seat cushions and backs have formed foam pads which fit the contour of the seatback frame assembly and also the designed contour of the seat cushion frame. The 60/40 front seat is split with individually controlled seat adjusters. The passenger seat is the 40 percent side and the driver seat is the 60 percent side.

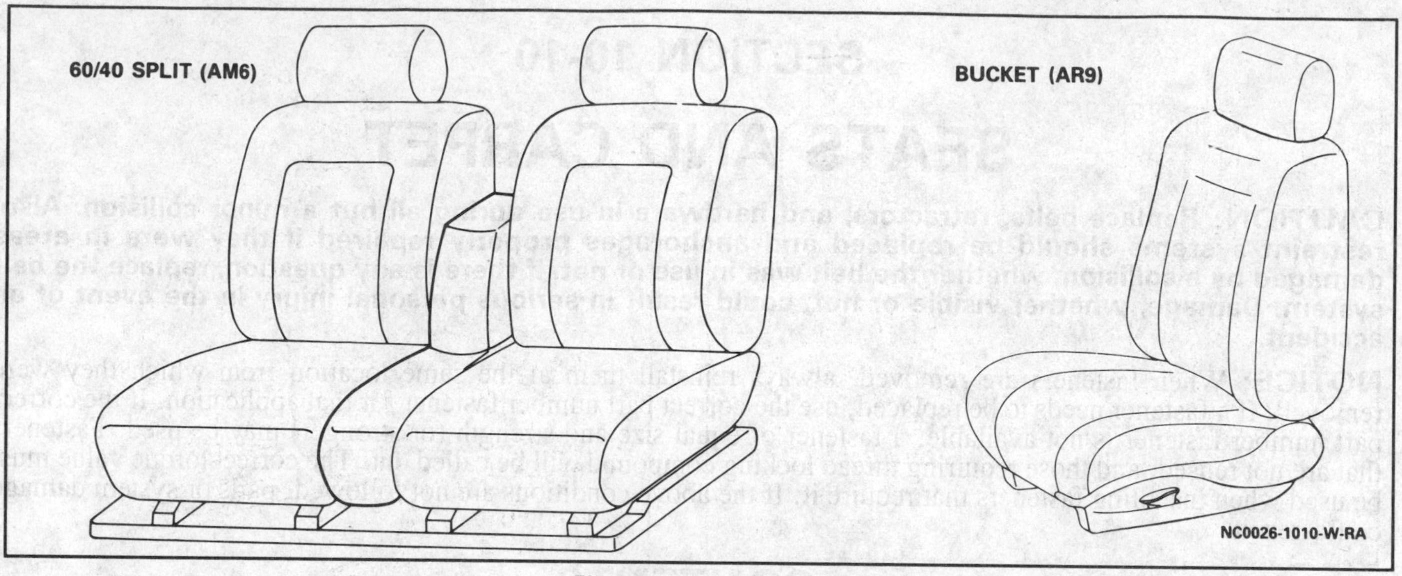
60/40 SPLIT (AM6)
BUCKET (AR9)
NC0026-1010-W-RA

Figure 1 Front Seats

The 60/40 split seat is equipped with a reclining mechanism. The recliner lever is located on the outboard side of the seat cushion. When the lever is pulled upward, the spring loaded reclining unit located on the right side of the cushion is released, allowing the seatback to be pushed rearward or allowing the spring loaded reclining unit to bring the seat forward.

The 60/40 split seat may also have a six-way power seat adjuster for the driver side.

Bucket Seats

The bucket seats are equipped with manual reclining mechanisms. Option includes a six-way power seat adjuster for the driver side.

NOTICE: Do not attempt to change the designed seat adjuster to floor pan anchor provisions as it could affect the performance of the seat system.

REAR SEATS

Figure 2

Rear seats are bench style seats and may have a rear compartment pass-through accessed by folding down a panel behind the center armrest.

Seat cushions and backs have formed foam pads which fit the contour of the seatback frame assembly and also the designed contour of the seat cushion frame.

DIAGNOSIS

FRONT SEATBACK INERTIA LOCK INSPECTION

Figure 3

The inertia lock is an integral part of the seatback recliner mechanism. If the inertia lock needs to be replaced, the entire recliner mechanism must be replaced. Operation of the front seatback inertia lock may be checked as follows.

When checking lock in either the in-vehicle check or out-of-vehicle check, pull upward on the release lever; then release the lever. Lever must return with no evidence of binding or interference. Where required, replace inertia lock assembly and repeat check after installation.

Inspect (In-Vehicle)

1. Using a driver with an assistant in the rear seat (their safety belts buckled), drive in an area clear of vehicles and obstructions. While driving the vehicle between 10 and 15 mph (16 to 24 km/h), quickly apply brakes without skidding wheels while the assistant is holding both sides of the front passenger seat: the seatback inertia lock should lock. The top of seatback should not move forward more than 38 mm (1-1/2 inch). When performing this operation on driver's seatback the driver should lean slightly forward.
2. If either driver or passenger seatback lock does not lock on first locking position, perform out-of-vehicle inspection.

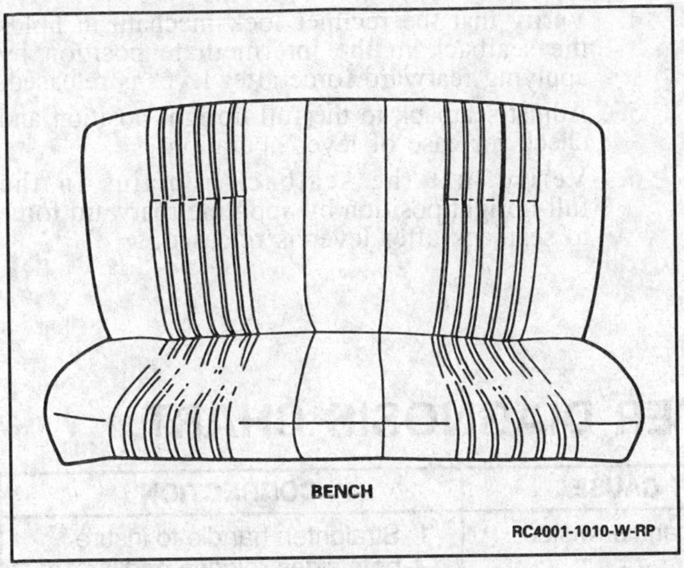
BENCH
RC4001-1010-W-RP

Figure 2 Rear Seats

Inspect (Out of Vehicle)

1. Remove seat assembly from vehicle and place right side up on a clean surface.
2. Raise rear of seat until seatback is 6 degrees forward of vertical position and place blocks under rear of seat to hold seat in this position. Use "angle meter." Angle meters can be purchased at hardware or department stores.
3. Check the seatback lock in the locking position. If it does not lock, remove lock and install new lock assembly.
4. If installing a new lock, check that lock mechanism moves freely prior to installation. After installation, check lock as described in steps 1 through 3.

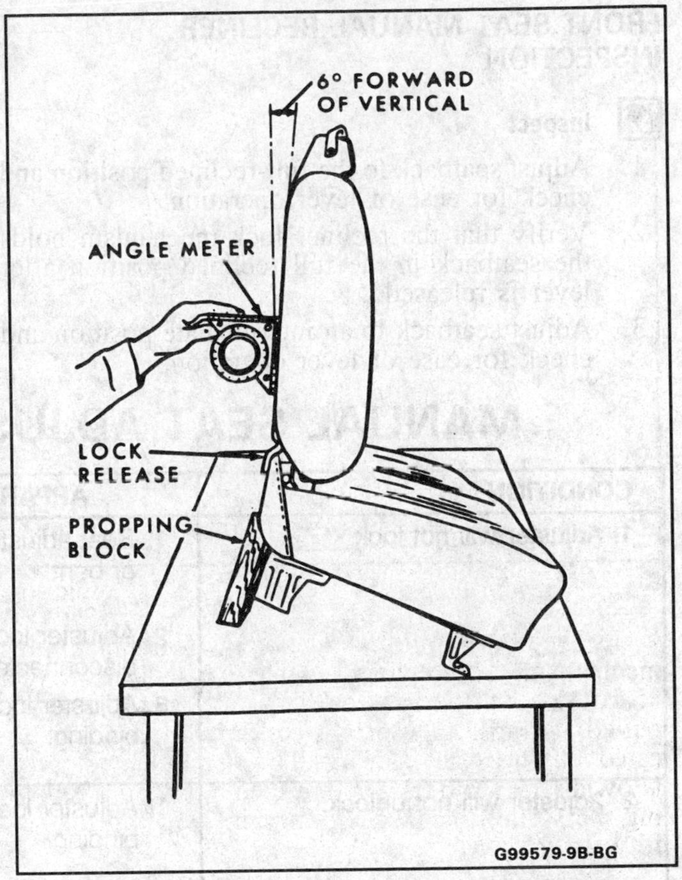
6° FORWARD
OF VERTICAL
ANGLE METER
LOCK
RELEASE
PROPPING
BLOCK
G99579-9B-BG

Figure 3 Front Seatback Inertia Lock Check (Out of Vehicle)

FRONT SEAT MANUAL RECLINER INSPECTION

Inspect

1. Adjust seatback to the full-reclined position and check for ease of lever operation.
2. Verify that the recliner lock mechanism holds the seatback in the full reclined position after lever is released.
3. Adjust seatback to an intermediate position and check for ease of lever operation.
4. Verify that the recliner lock mechanism holds the seatback in the intermediate position by applying rearward force after lever is released.
5. Adjust seatback to the full-upright position and check for ease of lever operation.
6. Verify that the seatback remains in the full-upright position by applying rearward force to seatback after lever is released.

MANUAL SEAT ADJUSTER DIAGNOSIS CHART

CONDITION	APPARENT CAUSE	CORRECTION
1. Adjuster will not lock.	1. Seat adjuster handle twisted or bent.	1 Straighten handle to insure both sides release and lock at the same time or replace.
	2. Adjuster lockbar spring disconnected or broken.	2. Connect spring or install new spring.
	3. Adjuster lockbar sticking or binding.	3. Lubricate lockbar pivot. If lockbar is binding, eliminate cause of binding or replace adjuster.
2. Adjuster will not unlock.	1. Adjuster lockbar sticking or binding.	1. Lubricate lockbar pivot. If lockbar is binding, eliminate cause of binding or replace adjuster.
	2. Seat adjuster handle twisted or bent.	2. Straighten adjuster handle or replace.
3. Seat hard to move forward or rearward.	1. Adjusters new, not broken in.	1. Operate seat to full forward and full rearward positions several times to work new tightness out of channels.
	2. Adjuster(s) improperly lubricated.	2. Lubricate adjuster channels with Lubriplate AutoLube A or equivalent.
	3. Adjuster(s) binding due to bent or damaged channels.	3. Replace adjuster.

RC1002-1010-W-RP

POWER-OPERATED SIX-WAY SEAT ADJUSTER MECHANICAL DIAGNOSIS CHART

If it is apparent or suspected that the trouble is in the electrical system, refer to ELECTRICAL DIAGNOSIS (SECTION 8A).

CONDITION	APPARENT CAUSE	CORRECTION
1. Horizontal operation of seat not smooth (jerky) — apparent hard operation.	1. Improper lubrication of adjuster shoes and channels. 2. Adjuster horizontal actuator gear too tight to rack gear.	1. Lubricate adjuster upper channel and plastic shoes. 2. See Horizontal Actuator Adjustment.
2. Horizontal chuck or looseness.	1. Horizontal actuator improperly adjusted to rack gear.	1. See Horizontal Actuator Adjustment.
3. One adjuster will not operate horizontally.	1. Horizontal drive cable disconnected or damaged. 2. Horizontal actuator inoperative.	1. Check horizontal drive cables, replace if damaged. 2. Replace horizontal actuator assembly.
4. One adjuster will not operate vertically.	1. Vertical drive cable disconnected or damaged. 2. Vertical gearnut inoperative.	1. Check vertical drive cables, replace if damaged. 2. Replace vertical actuator assembly.
5. Both adjusters will not operate horizontally and/or vertically.	1. Damaged, broken or inoperable solenoid plunger, shaft, dog, dog spring, gear or drive gear.	1. Replace damaged, broken or inoperable solenoid part with new part.
6. Vertical chuck or looseness.	1. Excessive clearance at vertical gearnut tension spring.	1. Grind down top of vertical gearnut shoulder nut 0.40 to 1.19 mm (1/64" to 3/64") maximum.

RC1003-1010-W-RP

ON-VEHICLE SERVICE AND UNIT REPAIR

FRONT SEAT ASSEMBLY

Figure 4

The front seats are secured to the floor pan by bolts installed to weld nuts on floor pan anchor plates.

The manually operated two-way front adjusters provide only fore and aft movement of the seat. When the seat adjuster handle located on the front seat is pulled up, the seat adjusters unlock, permitting travel of the seat. When the seat is in the desired position and the seat adjuster handle is released, the seat locks in place. The manually operated four-way front adjusters provide fore and aft, and tilt movement of the seat. When the tilt control handle is squeezed, the seat may be tilted. When the seat is in the desired position and the handle is released, the seat locks in place.

The power six-way seat adjusters are actuated by three 12V, reversible, permanent magnet motors with a built-in circuit breaker. The motors are energized by a toggle-type control switch bolted on the seat side panel.

The three motors respectively direct drive the front and rear vertical gearnuts and a horizontal actuator. When the adjusters reach the limit of travel, torque is absorbed through the rubber mounted grommets located between the motor and the support. An overload relay is provided in the circuit should excessive stall torque be applied to the motor.

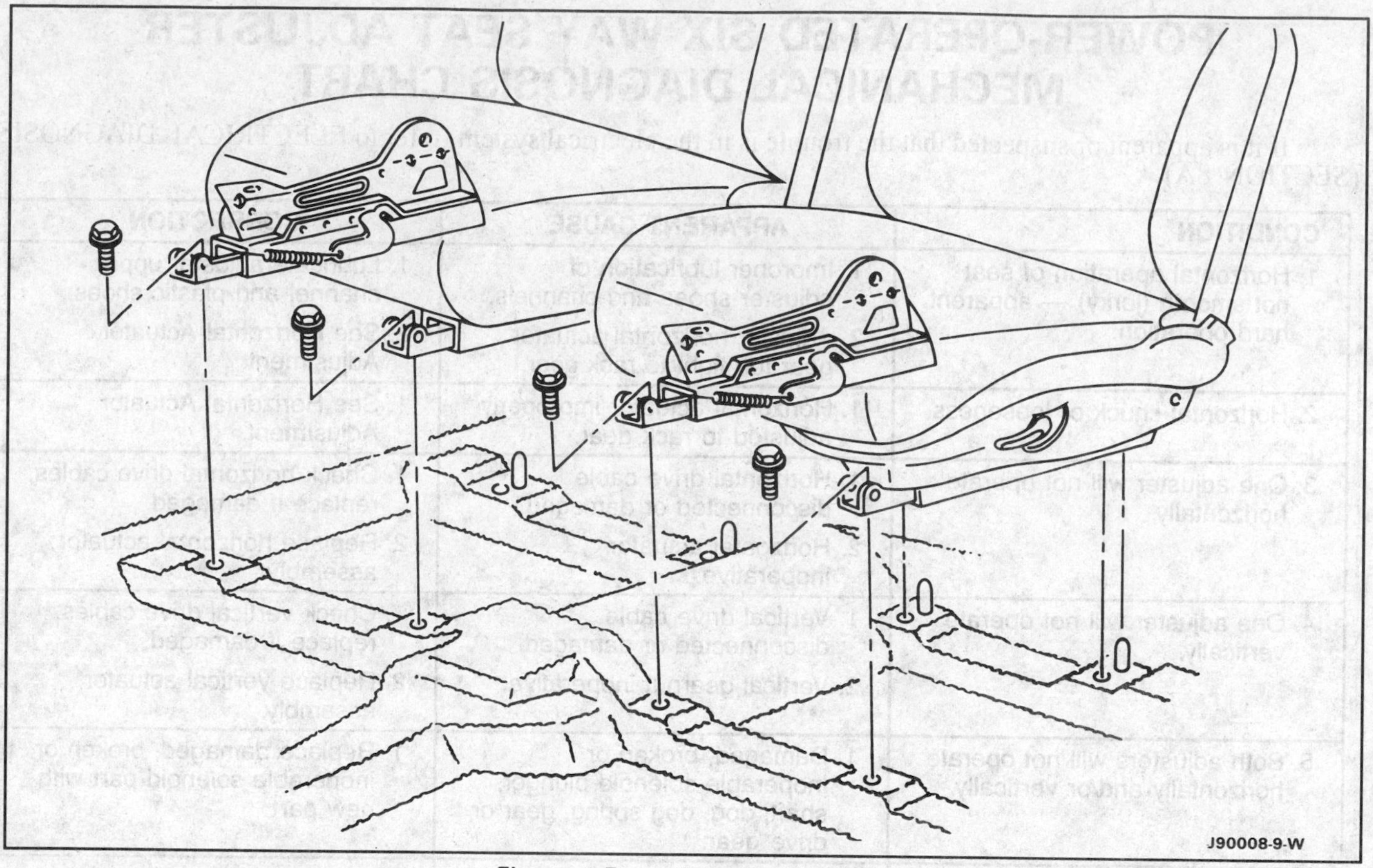
J90008-9-W

Figure 4 Front Seat Installation

Remove or Disconnect

1. Operate seat to full-rearward position. If six-way power seat is operable, operate seat to full-rearward and up positions where necessary to gain access to adjuster-to-floor pan attaching bolts.
2. Track covers (Canada only).
3. Front anchor bolts.
4. Operate seat to the full-forward position.
5. Rear anchor bolts.
6. Electrical connector (six-way power seat).
7. Center seat belt on AM6 driver's seat. Refer to SEAT BELTS (SECTION 10-11).
8. Seat assembly ensuring spacer washers remain in place.

Install or Connect

1. Seat assembly ensuring spacer washers are located between floor pan and seat track.
2. Center seat belt on AM6 driver's seat. Refer to SEAT BELTS (SECTION 10-11).
3. Electrical connector (six-way power seat).
4. Rear anchor bolts.

Tighten

- Bolts to 25 N•m (19 lb. ft.).

5. Operate seat to the full-rearward position.
6. Front anchor bolts.

Tighten

- Bolts to 25 N•m (19 lb. ft.).

7. Track covers (Canada only).

FRONT SEATBACK – DRIVER'S AM6

Figure 5

Remove or Disconnect

1. Front seat assembly. Refer to "Front Seat Assembly" in this section.
2. Finish panels. Refer to "Front Seat Trim and Covers" in this section.
3. Switch connector, if equipped.
4. Recliner lever by removing two screws.
5. Lower bolts.
6. Seatback assembly by disengaging hinge pin from hinge support.

Install or Connect

1. Seatback assembly by engaging hinge pin to hinge support.

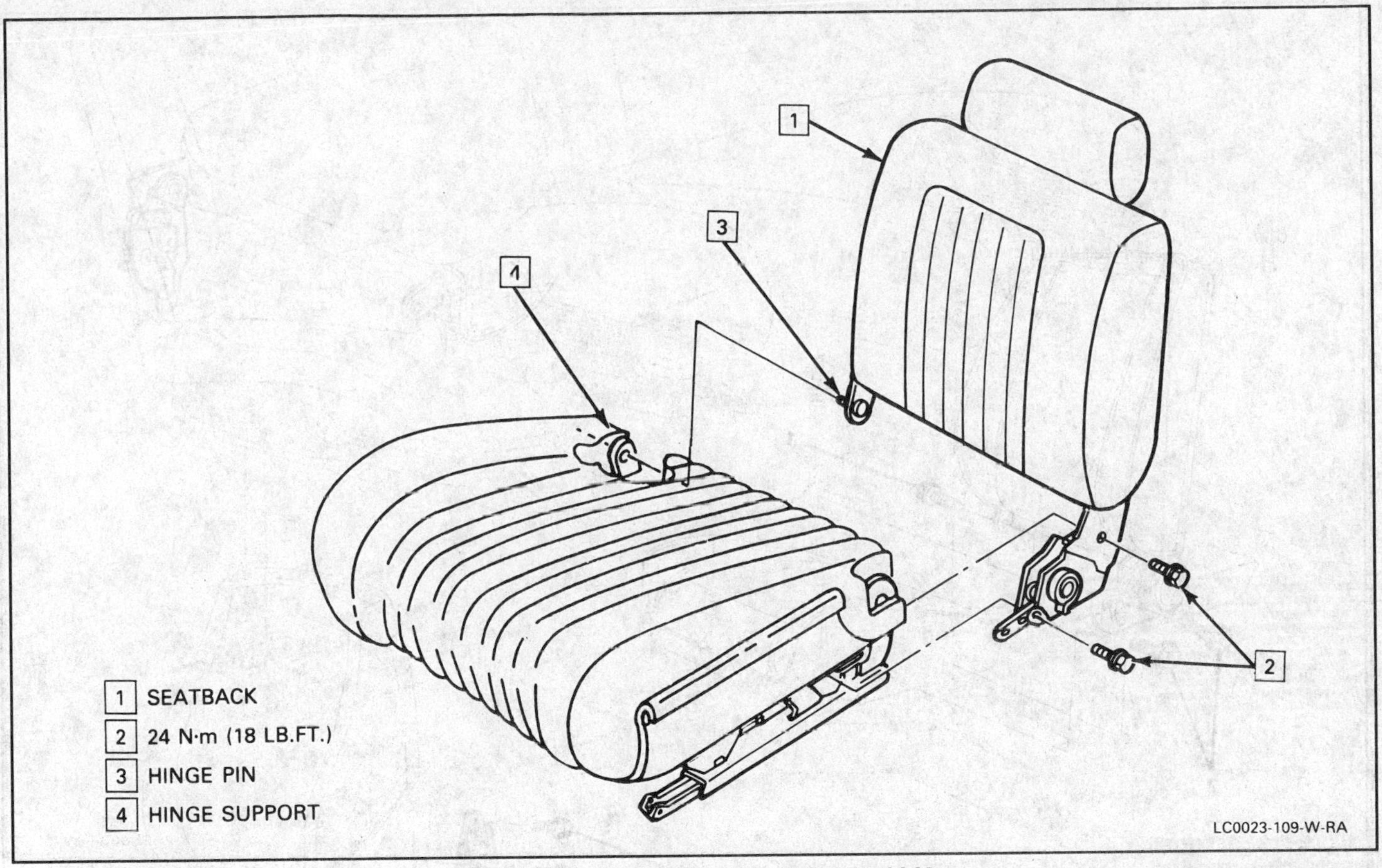
1
3
4
2
1 SEATBACK
2 24 N·m (18 LB.FT.)
3 HINGE PIN
4 HINGE SUPPORT
LC0023-109-W-RA

Figure 5 Front Seatback — Driver's AM6

2. Lower bolts.

Tighten

- Bolts to 24 N·m (18 lb. ft.).

3. Recliner lever by replacing two screws.

Tighten

- Screws to 3 N·m (27 lb. in.).

4. Switch connector, if equipped.
5. Finish panels. Refer to "Front Seat Trim and Covers" in this section.
6. Front seat assembly. Refer to "Front Seat Assembly" in this section.

FRONT SEATBACK — AR9 AND PASSENGER'S AM6

Figure 6

Remove or Disconnect

1. Front seat assembly. Refer to "Front Seat Assembly" in this section.
2. Finish panels. Refer to "Front Seat Trim and Covers" in this section.
3. Switch connector, if equipped.
4. Recliner lever by removing two screws.
5. Lower bolts.
6. Bolt.
7. Seatback assembly.

Install or Connect

1. Seatback assembly.
2. Bolt.

Tighten

- Bolt to 24 N·m (18 lb. ft.).

3. Lower bolts.

Tighten

- Bolts to 24 N·m (18 lb. ft.).

4. Recliner lever by replacing two screws.

Tighten

- Screws to 3 N·m (27 lb. in.).

5. Switch connector, if equipped.
6. Finish panels. Refer to "Front Seat Trim and Covers" in this section.
7. Front seat assembly. Refer to "Front Seat Assembly" in this section.

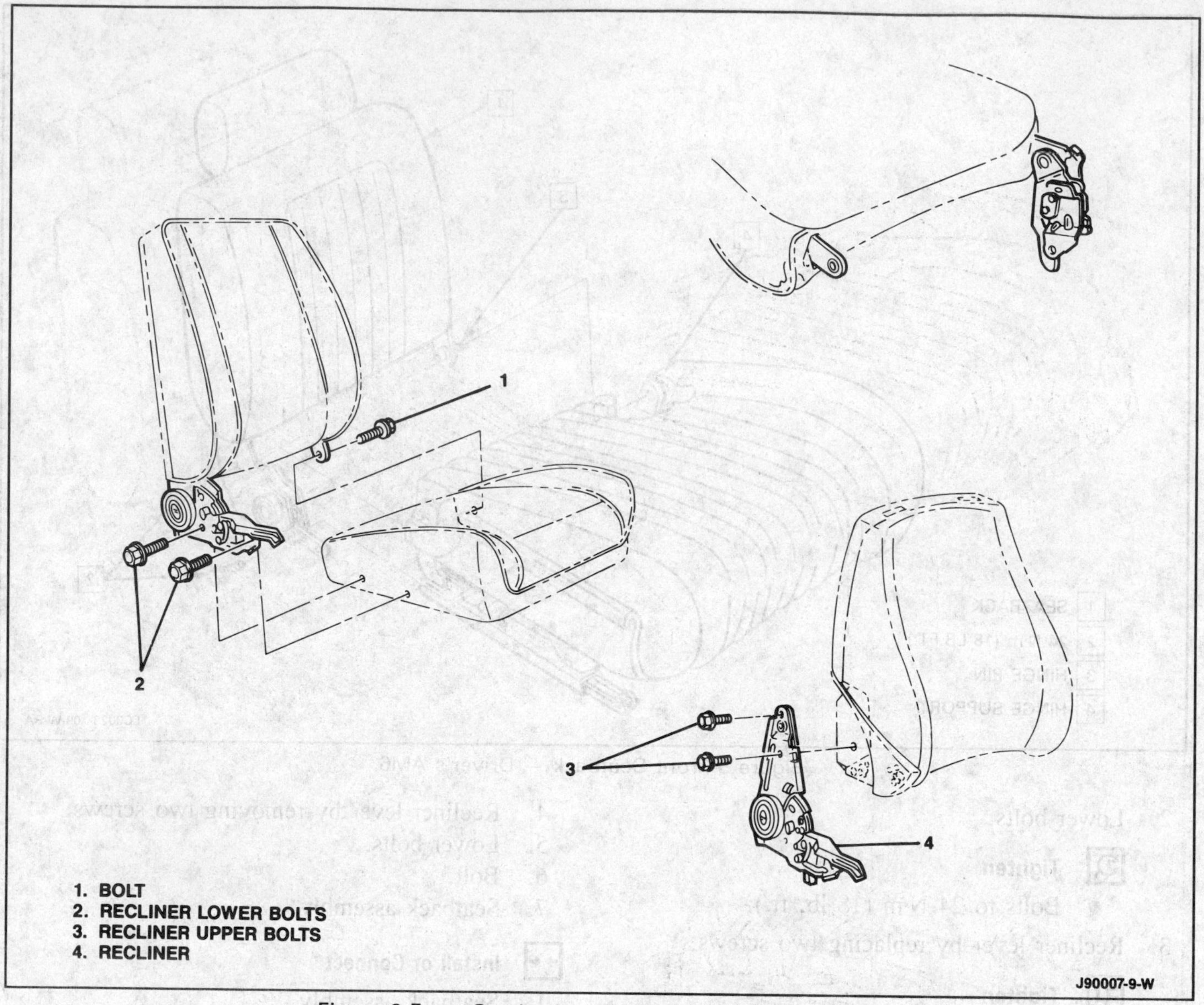
1
2
3
4
1. BOLT
2. RECLINER LOWER BOLTS
3. RECLINER UPPER BOLTS
4. RECLINER
J90007-9-W

Figure 6 Front Seatback – AR9 and Passenger's AM6

FRONT SEAT CUSHION

Figures 7 and 8

Remove or Disconnect

1. Front seat assembly. Refer to "Front Seat Assembly" in this section.
2. Armrest if driver's AM6. Refer to "Front Seat Center Armrest" in this section.
3. Finish panels. Refer to "Front Seat Trim and Covers" in this section.
4. Recliner lever screws and lever.
5. Retainers if driver's AM6.
6. Swing wire.
   - Unsnap from hole at front of outboard frame side.
7. "J" retainers.
8. Front seat cushion.

Install or Connect

1. Front seat cushion.
2. "J" retainers.
3. Swing wire.
   - Snap into hole at front of outboard frame side.
4. Retainers if driver's AM6.
5. Recliner lever and screws.

Tighten

- Screws to 3 N·m (27 lb. in.).

6. Finish panels. Refer to "Front Seat Trim and Covers" in this section.
7. Armrest if driver's AM6. Refer to "Front Seat Center Armrest" in this section.
8. Front seat assembly. Refer to "Front Seat Assembly" in this section.

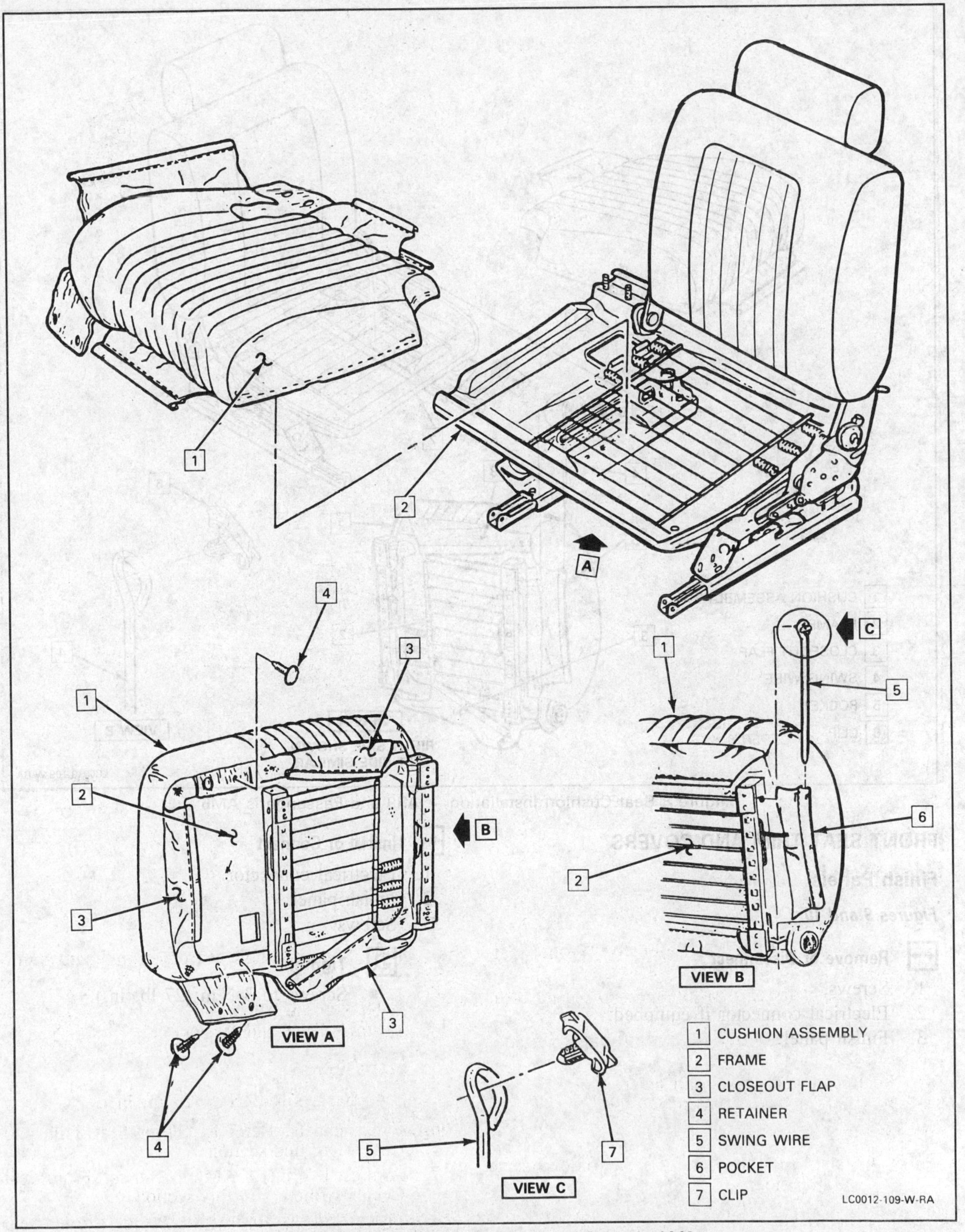
1
2
A
4
3
1
2
B
3
3
VIEW A
4
1
C
5
6
2
VIEW B
5
7
VIEW C
1 CUSHION ASSEMBLY
2 FRAME
3 CLOSEOUT FLAP
4 RETAINER
5 SWING WIRE
6 POCKET
7 CLIP
LC0012-109-W-RA

Figure 7 Seat Cushion Installation – Driver's AM6

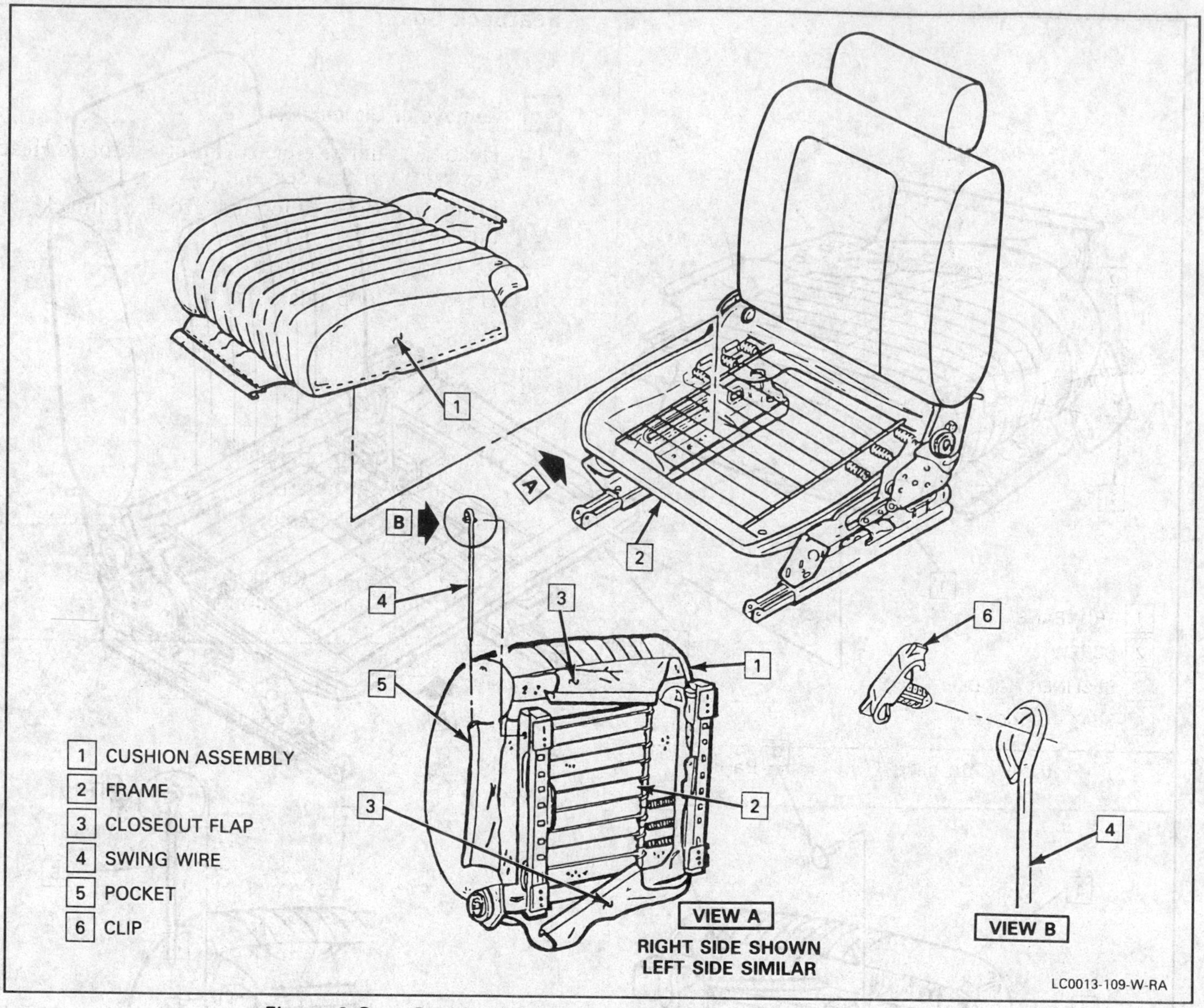

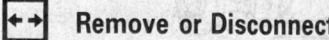

1 CUSHION ASSEMBLY
2 FRAME
3 CLOSEOUT FLAP
4 SWING WIRE
5 POCKET
6 CLIP
A
B
VIEW A
RIGHT SIDE SHOWN
LEFT SIDE SIMILAR
VIEW B
LC0013-109-W-RA

Figure 8 Seat Cushion Installation – AR9 and Passenger's AM6

FRONT SEAT TRIM AND COVERS

Finish Panels

Figures 9 and 10

Remove or Disconnect

1. Screws.
2. Electrical connector if equipped.
3. Finish panel.

Install or Connect

1. Electrical connector.
2. Finish panel.
3. Screws.

Tighten

- Screws to 3 N·m (27 lb. in.).

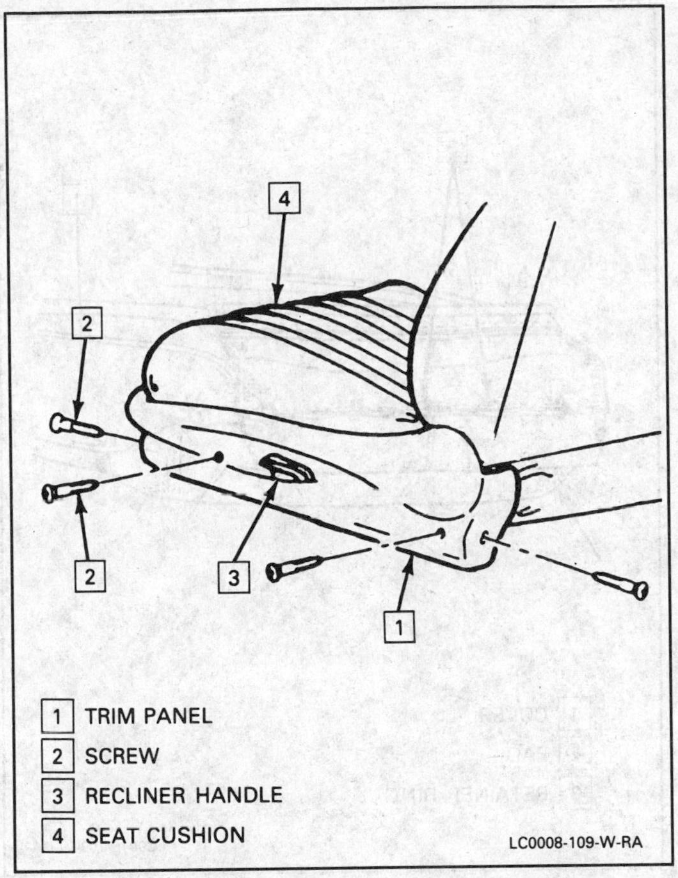
4
2
2
3
1
1 TRIM PANEL
2 SCREW
3 RECLINER HANDLE
4 SEAT CUSHION
LC0008-109-W-RA

Figure 9 Outboard Trim Finish Panel

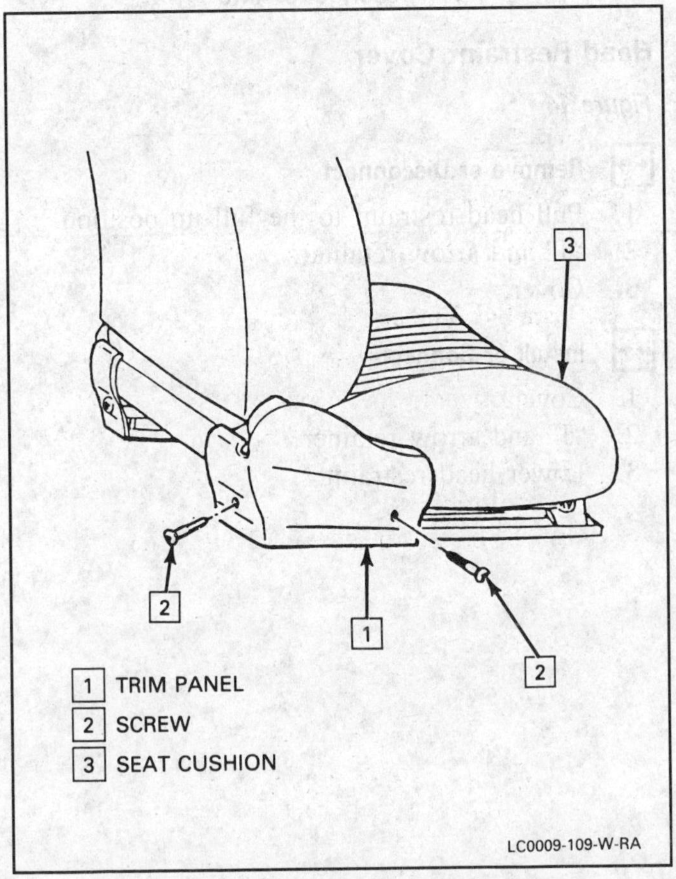
3
2
1
2
1 TRIM PANEL
2 SCREW
3 SEAT CUSHION
LC0009-109-W-RA

Figure 10 Inboard Trim Panel — AR9

Seatback Cover

Figure 11

Remove or Disconnect

1. Head restraint. Refer to "Front Seatback Head Restraint" in this section.
2. Front seatback. Refer to "Front Seatback" in this section.
3. "J" and arrow retainer.
4. Hook and loop retainers.
5. Cover.

Install or Connect

1. Cover.
2. Hook and loop retainers.
3. "J" and arrow retainer.
4. Front seatback. Refer to "Front Seatback" in this section.
5. Head restraint. Refer to "Front Seat Head Restraint" in this section.

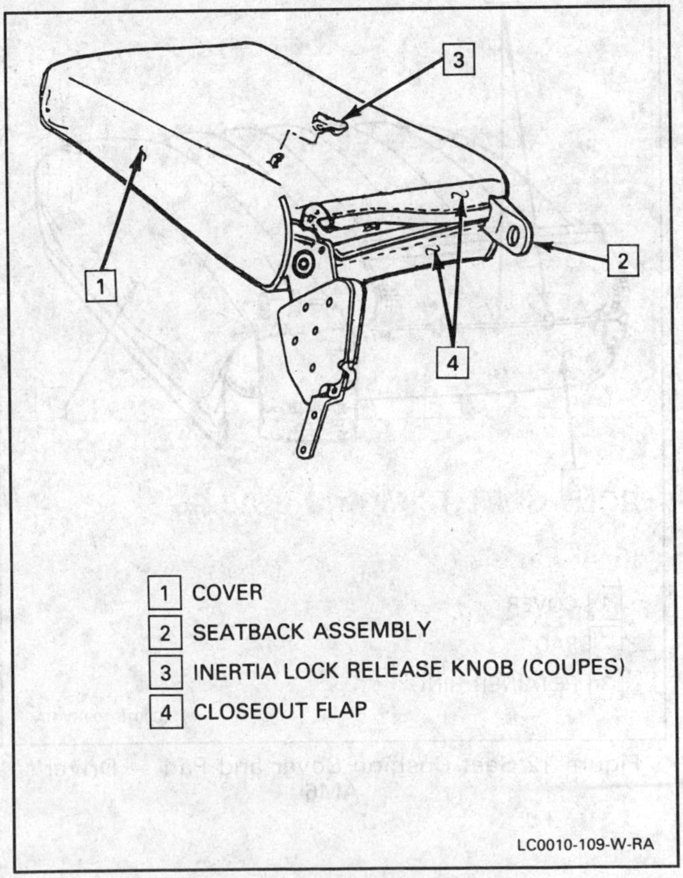
3
1
2
4
1 COVER
2 SEATBACK ASSEMBLY
3 INERTIA LOCK RELEASE KNOB (COUPES)
4 CLOSEOUT FLAP
LC0010-109-W-RA

Figure 11 Seatback Cover

Seat Cushion Cover

Figures 12 and 13

Remove or Disconnect

1. Front seat cushion. Refer to "Front Seat Cushion" in this section.
2. Trim retainer rings.
3. Disengage hook and loop retainers.
4. Cover.

Install or Connect

1. Cover.
2. Engage hook and loop retainers.
3. Trim retainer rings.
4. Front seat cushion. Refer to "Front Seat Cushion" in this section.

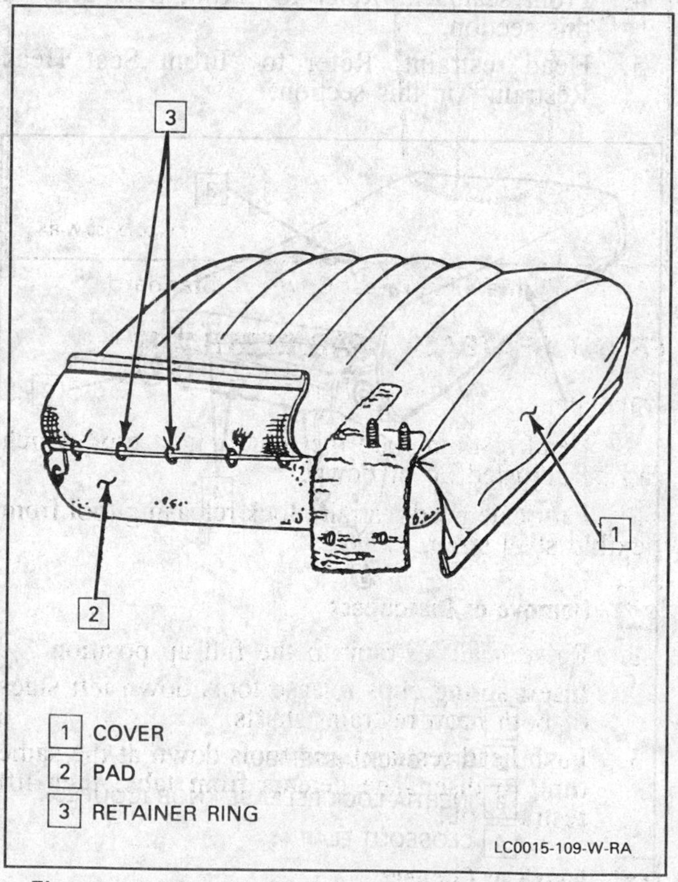

3
1
2
1 COVER
2 PAD
3 RETAINER RING
LC0015-109-W-RA

Figure 12 Seat Cushion Cover and Pad — Driver's AM6

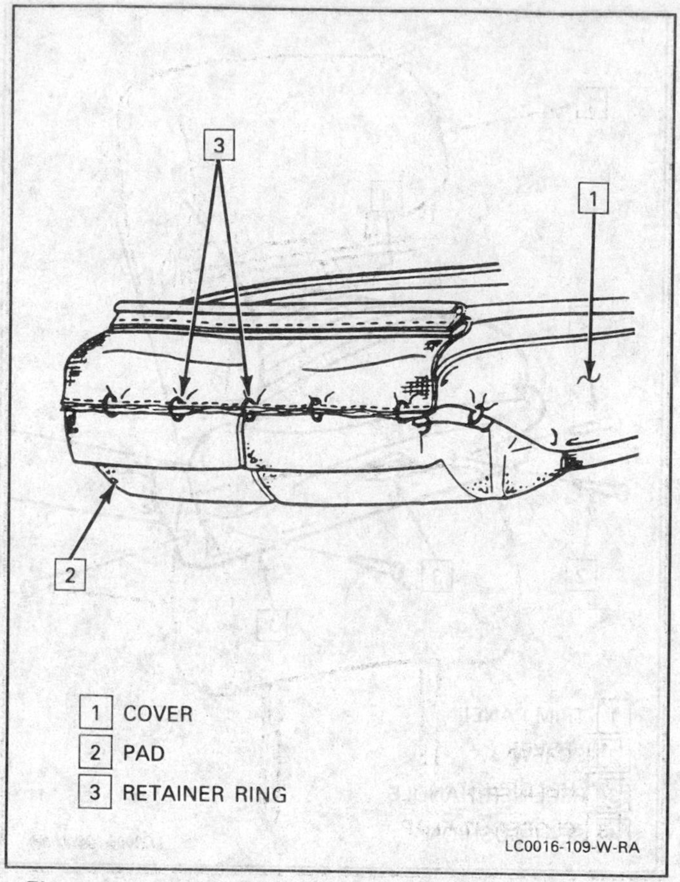

3
1
2
1 COVER
2 PAD
3 RETAINER RING
LC0016-109-W-RA

Figure 13 Seat Cushion Cover and Pad — AR9 and Passenger's AM6

Head Restraint Cover

Figure 14

Remove or Disconnect

1. Pull head restraint to the full up position.
2. "J" and arrow retainer.
3. Cover.

Install or Connect

1. Cover.
2. "J" and arrow retainer.
3. Lower head restraint.

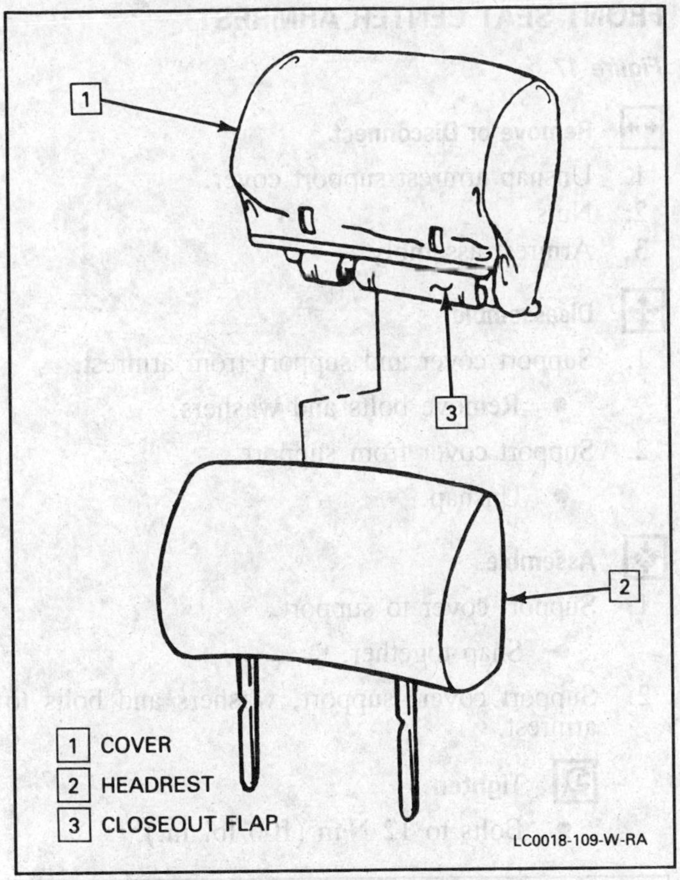
1
3
2
1 COVER
2 HEADREST
3 CLOSEOUT FLAP
LC0018-109-W-RA

Figure 14 Head Restraint Cover

Armrest Cover — Standard

Figure 15

Remove or Disconnect

1. Armrest. Refer to "Front Seat Center Armrest" in this section.
2. Open zipper.
3. Cover from armrest.

Install or Connect

1. Cover to armrest.
2. Close zipper.
3. Armrest. Refer to "Front Seat Center Armrest" in this section.

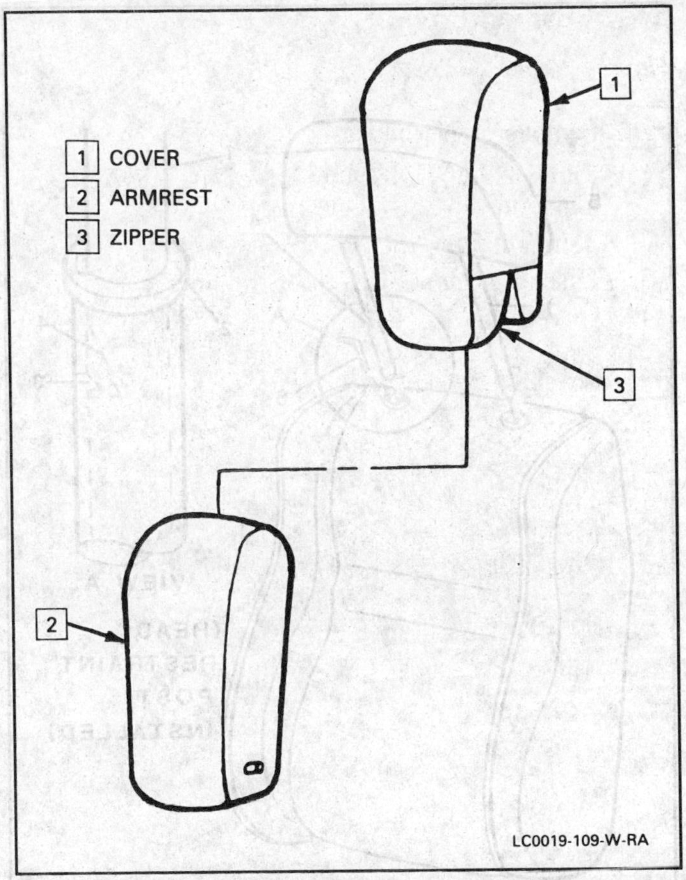
1 COVER
2 ARMREST
3 ZIPPER
1
3
2
LC0019-109-W-RA

Figure 15 Armrest Cover — Standard

FRONT SEATBACK HEAD RESTRAINT

Figure 16

Head restraints are the double post type which can be adjusted up or down.

Fabricate head restraint lock releasing tool from flexible steel strap.

Remove or Disconnect

1. Raise head restraint to the full-up position.
2. Insert spring clips release tools down left sides of both head restraint shafts.
3. Push head restraint and tools down at the same time to disengage detents from tabs, then lift restraint out.

Install or Connect

1. Posts into guides and push restraint into full-down position.
2. Raise head restraint to ensure restraint stops at detent.
3. Return head restraint to original position.

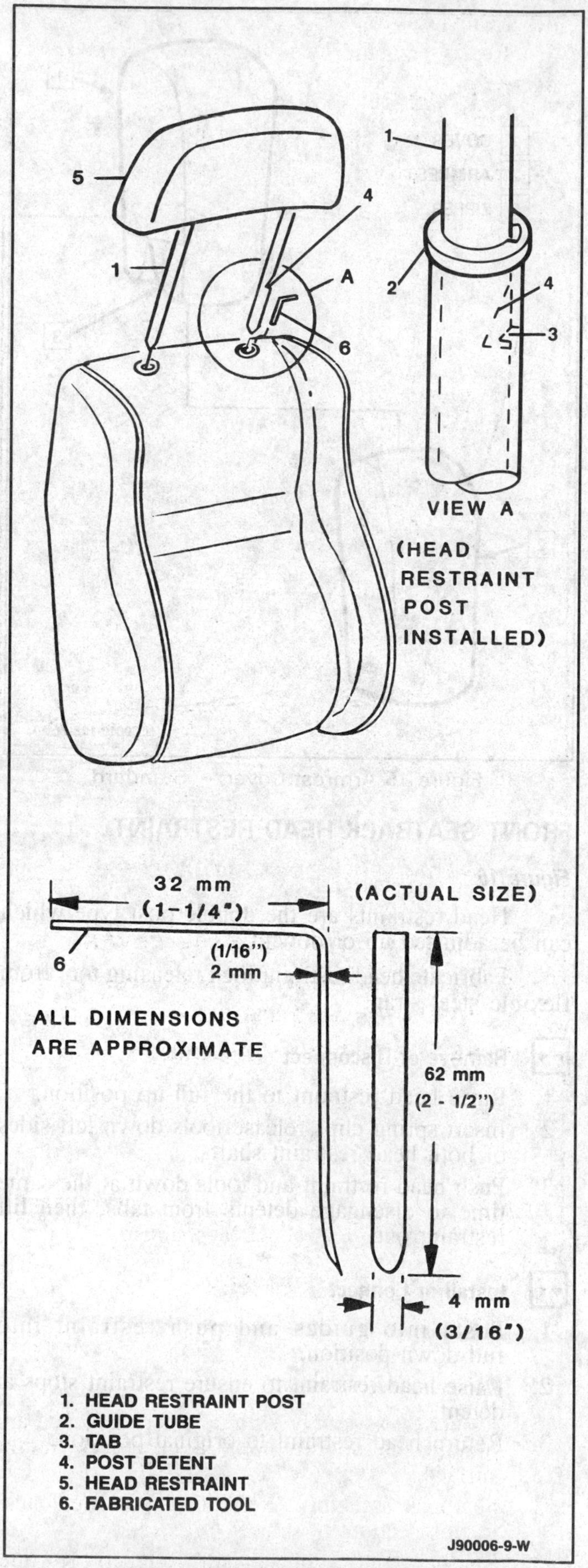
5
1
4
A
6
1
2
4
3
VIEW A
(HEAD RESTRAINT POST INSTALLED)
32 mm
(1-1/4")
(ACTUAL SIZE)
6
(1/16")
2 mm
ALL DIMENSIONS ARE APPROXIMATE
62 mm
(2 - 1/2")
4 mm
(3/16")
1. HEAD RESTRAINT POST
2. GUIDE TUBE
3. TAB
4. POST DETENT
5. HEAD RESTRAINT
6. FABRICATED TOOL
J90006-9-W

Figure 16 Head Restraint Removal

FRONT SEAT CENTER ARMREST

Figure 17

Remove or Disconnect

1. Unsnap armrest support cover.
2. Nuts.
3. Armrest assembly.

Disassemble

1. Support cover and support from armrest.
   - Remove bolts and washers.
2. Support cover from support.
   - Unsnap.

Assemble

1. Support cover to support.
   - Snap together.
2. Support cover, support, washers and bolts to armrest.

Tighten

- Bolts to 12 N·m (106 lb. in.).

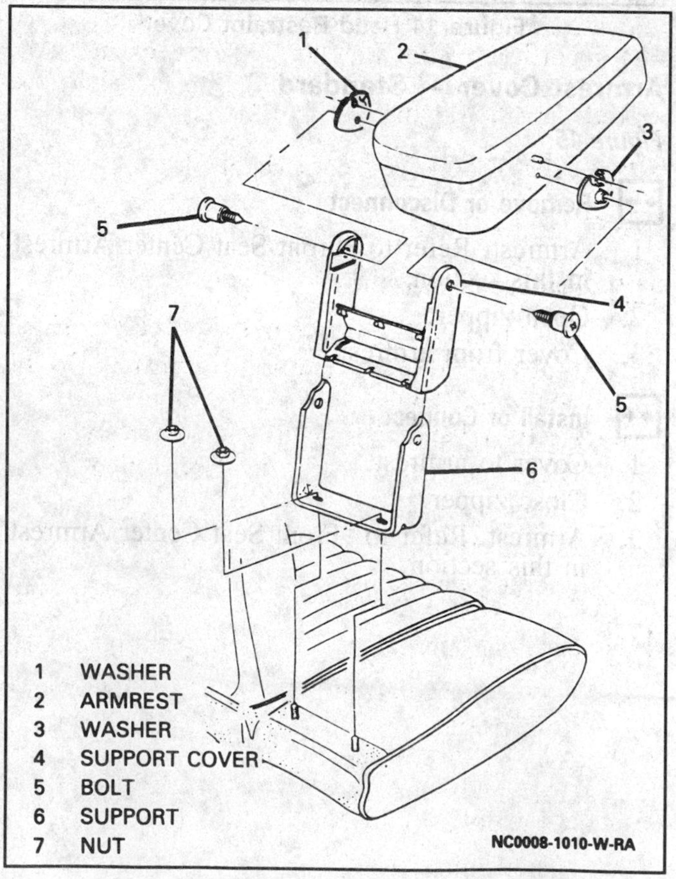
1
2
3
5
4
7
5
6
1 WASHER
2 ARMREST
3 WASHER
4 SUPPORT COVER
5 BOLT
6 SUPPORT
7 NUT
NC0008-1010-W-RA

Figure 17 Front Seat Center Armrest

Front Seat Center Armrest Cup Holder

Remove or Disconnect

1. Open armrest.
2. Cup holder.

Install or Connect

1. Cup holder.
2. Close armrest.

RECLINING SEATBACK

Figure 18

All styles have low back bucket seats or tubular frame design with a single side recliner control mechanism. This recliner mechanism, which is mounted on the outboard side of the seat, is the sole control of the seatback angle.

The inertia lock on coupes is an integral part of the recliner control mechanism.

To recline the seatback, rearward pressure must be applied to the seatback before lifting the recliner release handle. When pressure is applied against the seatback, the lockout lever tab disengages from the cam plate tab. Then the release handle can be moved, allowing the seatback to move rearward. Releasing the handle will allow the cam plate to move counterclockwise and cause the sector lock teeth to engage the upper hinge arm, locking the seatback in the desired reclined position. To return the seatback to an upright position, raise the recliner release handle.

RECLINER CONTROL MECHANISM

Figure 18

Remove or Disconnect

1. Place reclining seatback in the forward position.
2. Finish panel by removing screws. Do not disconnect switch connector.
3. Recliner handle by removing two screws.
4. Peel back seatback trim to expose two bolts.
5. Upper bolts.
6. Lower bolts.
7. Recliner mechanism.

Install or Connect

1. Recliner mechanism.
2. Lower bolts.

Tighten

- Bolts to 24 N·m (18 lb. ft.).

3. Upper bolts.

Tighten

- Bolts to 24 N·m (18 lb. ft.).

4. Seatback trim.
5. Recliner handle by replacing two screws.

Tighten

- Screws to 3 N·m (27 lb. in.).

6. Finish panel by replacing screws.

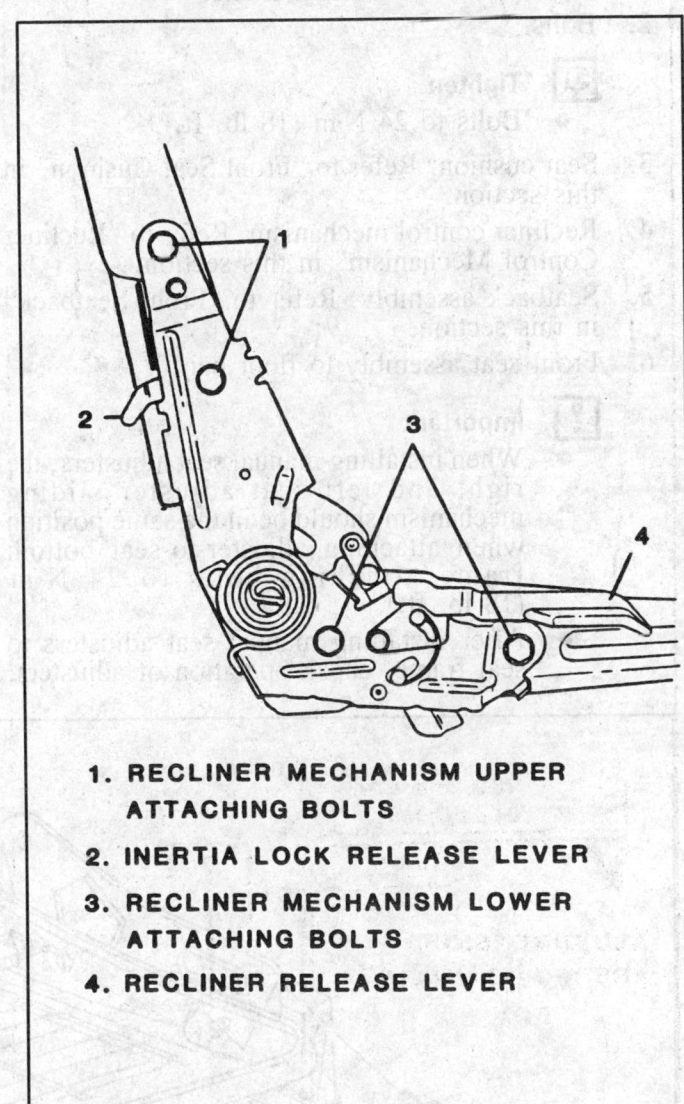

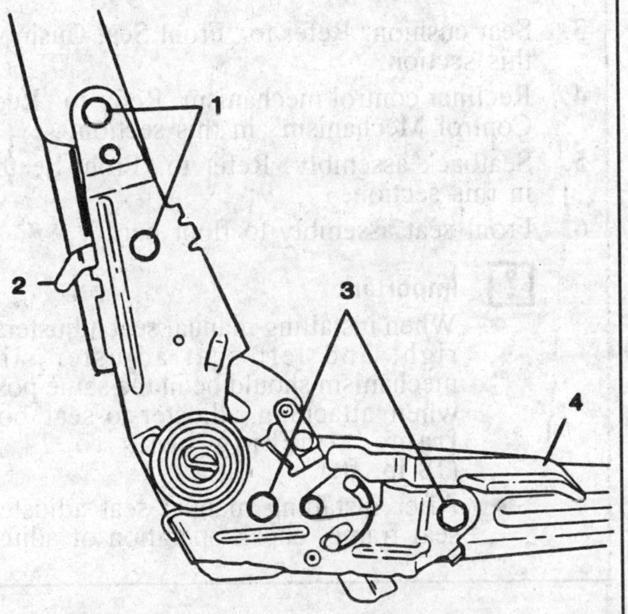
1
2
3
4
1. RECLINER MECHANISM UPPER ATTACHING BOLTS
2. INERTIA LOCK RELEASE LEVER
3. RECLINER MECHANISM LOWER ATTACHING BOLTS
4. RECLINER RELEASE LEVER
G93935-9B-BG

Figure 18 Recliner Mechanism

SEAT ADJUSTER ASSEMBLY

Figures 19 and 20

Remove or Disconnect

1. Front seat assembly with adjusters attached and placed upside down on a clean, protected surface.
2. Seatback assembly. Refer to "Front Seatback" in this section.
3. Recliner control mechanism. Refer to "Recliner Control Mechanism" in this section.

4. Seat cushion. Refer to "Front Seat Cushion" in this section.
5. Bolts.
6. Adjuster assembly.

Install or Connect

1. Adjuster to seat bottom frame.
2. Bolts.

Tighten

- Bolts to 24 N·m (18 lb. ft.).

3. Seat cushion. Refer to "Front Seat Cushion" in this section.
4. Recliner control mechanism. Refer to "Recliner Control Mechanism" in this section.
5. Seatback assembly. Refer to "Front Seatback" in this section.
6. Front seat assembly to floor pan.

Important

- When installing manual seat adjusters, the right and left seat adjuster sliding mechanism should be in the same position when attaching adjuster-to-seat bottom frame attaching bolts to 24 N·m (18 lb. ft.).
- After installing manual seat adjusters to seat frame, check operation of adjusters.
- When installing power seat adjusters, check that both adjusters are parallel and in phase with each other. In the event the adjusters are out of phase (one adjuster reaches its maximum horizontal or vertical travel in a given direction before the other adjuster), phase adjusters as follows:

Horizontal travel – operate seat control switch until one adjuster reaches full-forward position. Detach horizontal drive cable from adjuster which has reached full-forward position. Operate seat forward until other adjuster reaches full-forward position: then connect horizontal drive cable and check horizontal travel of seat.

Front or rear vertical travel – operate seat control switch until one adjuster has reached fully raised position at both front and rear vertical travel limits. Disconnect both vertical drive cables from adjuster which has reached the fully raised position. Operate seat control switch until other adjuster reaches the fully raised position at both front and rear vertical limits; then connect previously removed front and rear vertical drive cables. Check vertical travel by operating adjusters through one or two complete cycles. The above operation may be repeated on an as-required basis if adjusters do not appear to be in phase after test cycle.

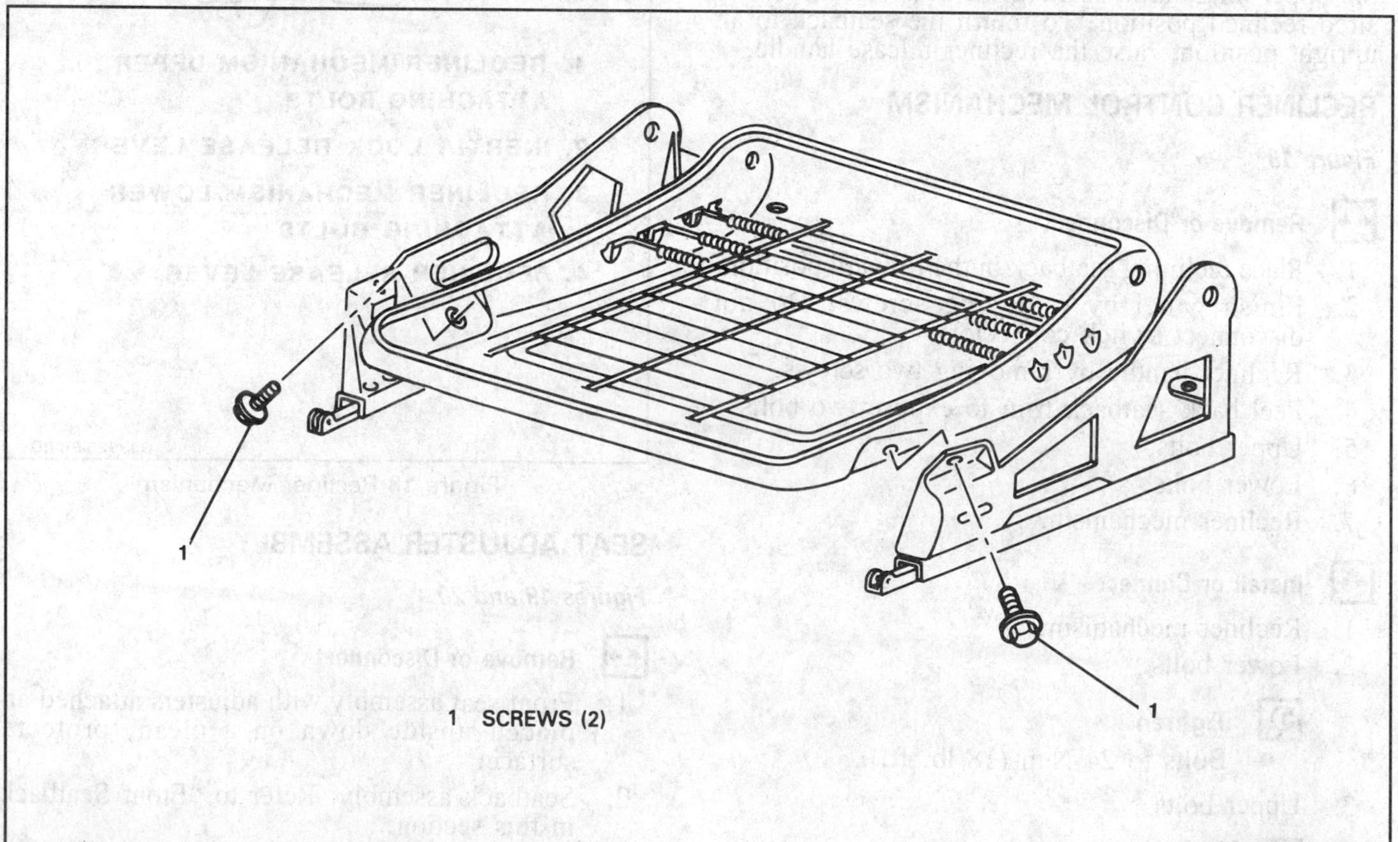
1
1
1 SCREWS (2)
NC0009-1010-W-RA

Figure 19 Manual Adjuster to Seat Installation

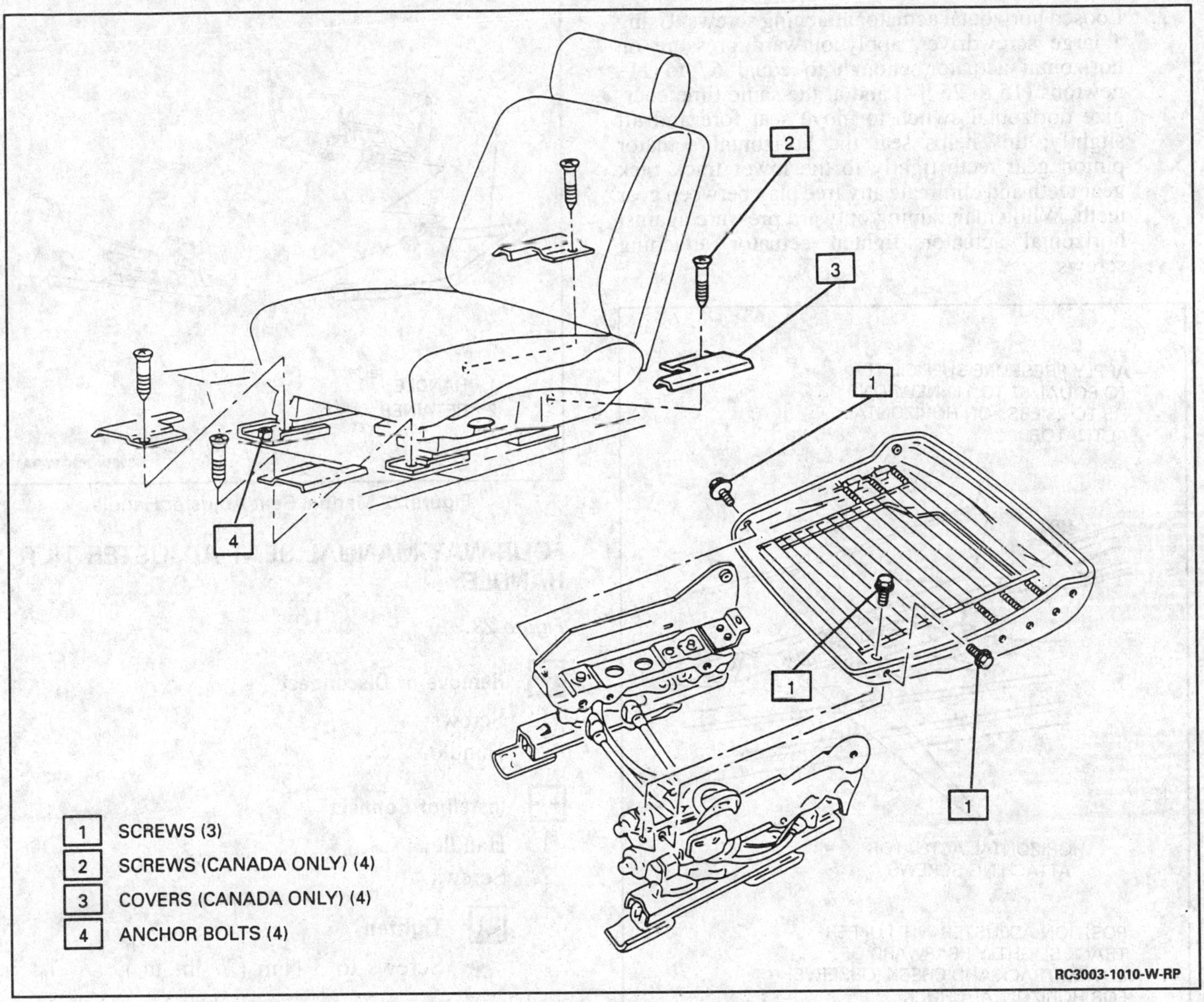

1
2
3
4
1 SCREWS (3)
2 SCREWS (CANADA ONLY) (4)
3 COVERS (CANADA ONLY) (4)
4 ANCHOR BOLTS (4)
RC3003-1010-W-RP

Figure 20 Six-Way Power Seat Installation

Front Seat Adjustments

Seat Adjustment at Floor Pan Attachment

A small amount of fore and aft or side to side adjustment is available at the seat adjuster-to-floor pan attaching bolts which can be used toward alignment of the seat assembly or alignment of the seat adjusters with each other. This adjustment can be used to help correct the following conditions:

- Hard or slow operation due to adjusters not being parallel with each other.
- Passenger side of manually operated seat must be moved forward or rearward slightly to engage in locked position due to one adjuster being forward or rearward of the other.

Important

- Do not over torque adjuster-to-floor pan nuts as a hard seat travel problem could result.

Power Six-Way Seat Adjuster Horizontal Actuator Adjustment

Figure 21

With seat adjuster assembly installed on seat or seat installed in body, horizontal movement (chucking) can be corrected by tightly adjusting the horizontal actuator and pinion gear to either adjuster lower track rack gear as follows:

Adjust

1. Operate seat to full-up position and about 3/4 full-forward position.

2. Loosen horizontal actuator attaching screws. Using a large screwdriver, apply outward pressure on horizontal actuator, enough to equal 67 to 111 newtons (15 to 25 lbs) and at the same time energize horizontal switch to move seat fore and aft slightly; this helps seat the horizontal actuator pinion gear teeth tightly to the lower track rack gear teeth and eliminate any free play between gear teeth. While maintaining outward pressure against horizontal actuator, tighten actuator attaching screws.

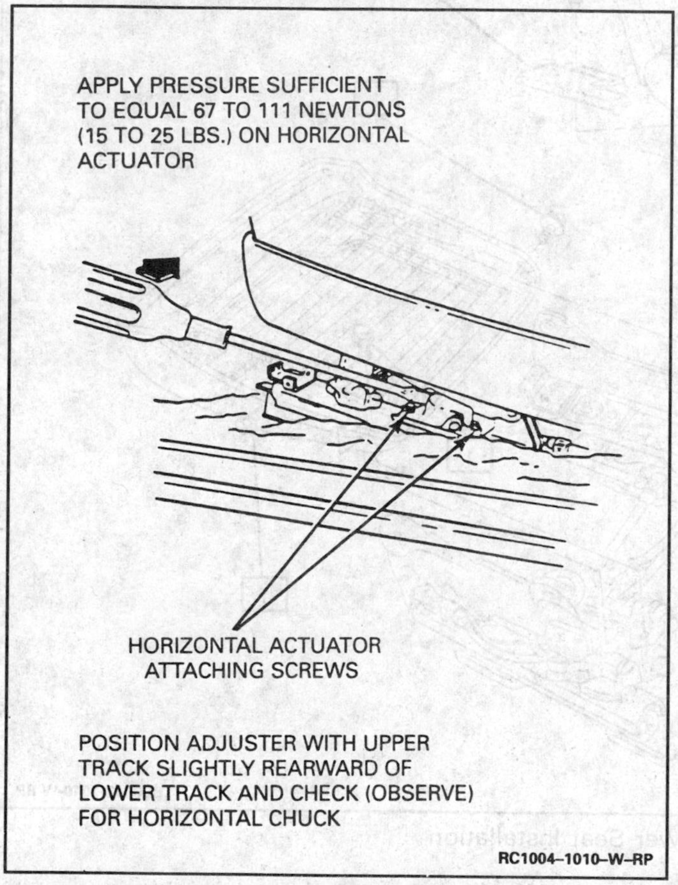
APPLY PRESSURE SUFFICIENT TO EQUAL 67 TO 111 NEWTONS (15 TO 25 LBS.) ON HORIZONTAL ACTUATOR
HORIZONTAL ACTUATOR ATTACHING SCREWS
POSITION ADJUSTER WITH UPPER TRACK SLIGHTLY REARWARD OF LOWER TRACK AND CHECK (OBSERVE) FOR HORIZONTAL CHUCK
RC1004–1010–W–RP

Figure 21 Horizontal Actuator Adjustment – Power Six-Way Seat

MANUAL SEAT ADJUSTER HANDLE

Figure 22

Remove or Disconnect

1. Handle retainers using a screwdriver to pry retainers off.
2. Handle.

Install or Connect

1. Handle.
2. Handle retainers by pressing into position.

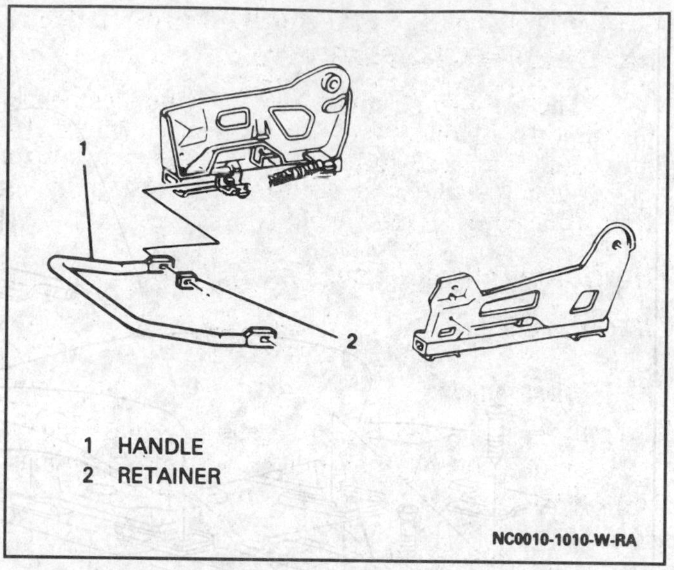
1
2
1 HANDLE
2 RETAINER
NC0010-1010-W-RA

Figure 22 Manual Seat Adjuster Handle

FOUR-WAY MANUAL SEAT ADJUSTER TILT HANDLE

Figure 23

Remove or Disconnect

1. Screws.
2. Handle.

Install or Connect

1. Handle.
2. Screws.

Tighten

- Screws to 3 N·m (27 lb. in.).

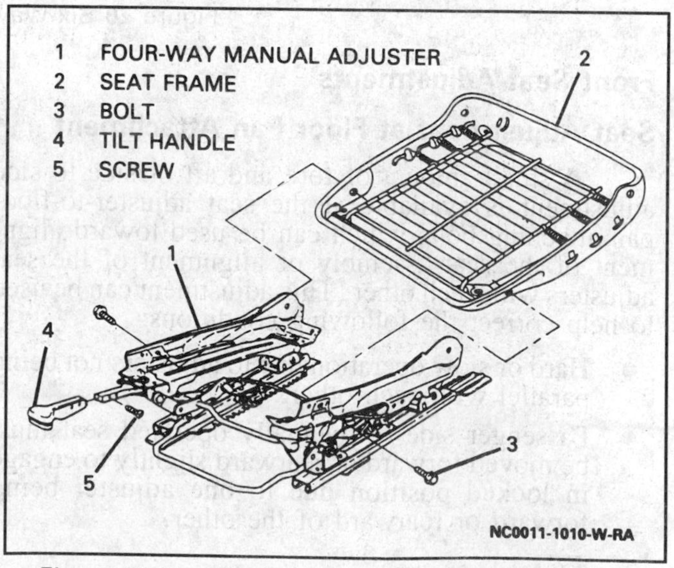
1 FOUR-WAY MANUAL ADJUSTER
2 SEAT FRAME
3 BOLT
4 TILT HANDLE
5 SCREW
NC0011-1010-W-RA

Figure 23 Four-Way Manual Adjuster Tilt Handle

SIX-WAY POWER SEAT ADJUSTERS, THREE MOTOR DIRECT DRIVE

The following procedures cover replacement of the major component parts of the seat adjusters. The procedures are to be performed with seat assembly out of vehicle and the seat adjuster assembly removed from the seat.

Horizontal and Vertical Drive Cables

Figure 24

Disassemble

- Cables may be disconnected by squeezing the oblong connector at motors, gearnuts or adjuster drives.

Important

- To gain access to cable connector at motor for inboard (passenger side) or outboard (driver side) rear vertical gearnut, initial removal of nut securing motor support bracket is suggested.

Assemble

- Cables to connectors.

Permanent Magnet Electric Motors

Figure 24

Disassemble

1. Motor feed wires from motors.
2. Nut securing front of motor support bracket to inboard adjuster and partially withdraw assembly from adjuster and gearnut drives.
3. Drive cables from motor and complete disassembly of support bracket with motors attached.
4. Grind off peened over end(s) of grommet assembly securing motor to support and separate motor(s) as required from support.

Assemble

1. Drill out top end of grommet assembly using an 8 mm (3/16 inch) drill.
2. Grommet assembly to motor support bracket and secure motor to grommet using 3/16 inch rivet.
3. Drive cables to motors.
4. Motor assembly to inboard adjuster and secure with nut.
5. Motor feed wires to motors.

Horizontal Actuator

Figure 25

Disassemble

1. Drive cables. Refer to "Horizontal and Vertical Drive Cables" in this section.
2. Adjuster assembly into vise.

CAUTION: To prevent possible personal injury from accidental ejection of compressed vertical assist spring, the adjuster assembly must be placed in a vise to retain compression on the spring while the rear gearnut attaching nut is being removed.

3. Rear vertical gearnut attaching nut and vertical assist spring.

CAUTION: To prevent possible personal injury from accidental ejection of compressed vertical assist spring, the vise should be opened slowly to relieve the compression on the vertical assist spring.

4. Front vertical gearnut attaching nut.
5. Screws securing horizontal actuator by lifting adjuster upper channel for access to the screws.
6. Horizontal actuator.

Assemble

1. Horizontal actuator to adjuster by replacing screws and lowering adjuster upper channel.
2. Front vertical gearnut attaching nut and assist spring then place in vise to put tension on the spring. Replace vertical gearnut attaching nut at top of adjuster.
3. Adjuster assembly from vise.
4. Drive cables. Refer to "Horizontal and Vertical Drive Cables" in this section.

Important

- When assembling the horizontal actuator, be sure actuator drive gear is fully engaged with teeth on lower channel rack gear. With actuator attaching screws tight, there should be no free motion between upper and lower adjusting channels. Adjust actuator as required until all free motion between channels has been removed. (Refer to "Power Six-Way Seat Adjuster Horizontal Actuator Adjustment") in this section.

  Be sure seat adjusters are in phase before installing seat assembly into body. Refer to step 6 of Install or Connect under "Seat Adjuster Assembly" in this section.

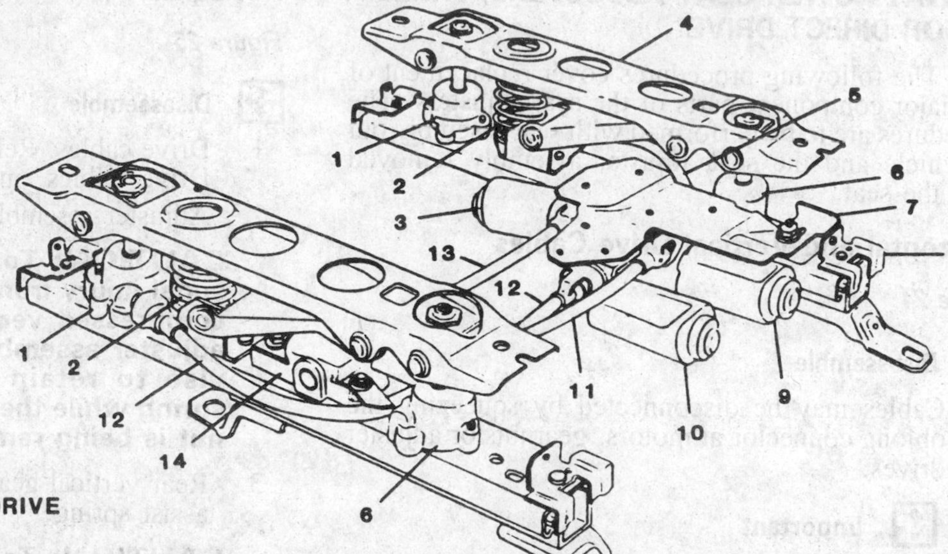

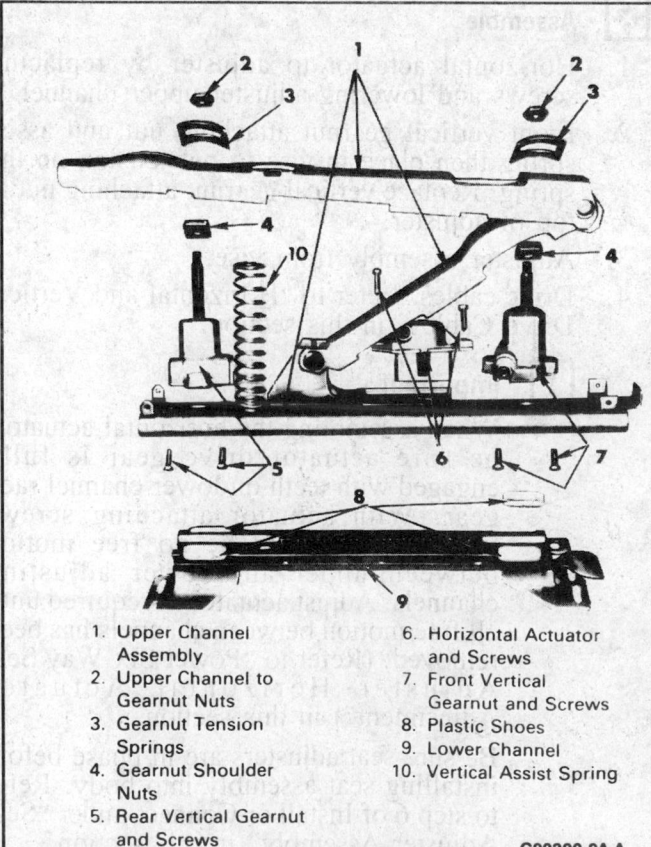

1. REAR GEARNUT DRIVE
2. ASSIST SPRINGS
3. HORIZONTAL ADJUSTER MOTOR
4. ADJUSTER ASSEMBLY
5. REAR VERTICAL GEARNUT CABLE
6. FRONT GEARNUT DRIVE
7. MOTOR SUPPORT BRACKET
8. LOWER CHANNEL STOP (REBUILD KIT)
9. FRONT VERTICAL GEARNUT MOTOR
10. REAR VERTICAL GEARNUT MOTOR
11. FRONT VERTICAL DRIVE CABLE
12. REAR VERTICAL DRIVE CABLE
13. HORIZONTAL DRIVE CABLE
14. HORIZONTAL ADJUSTER DRIVE

G93634-9A-A

Figure 24 Six-Way Seat Adjuster Assembly

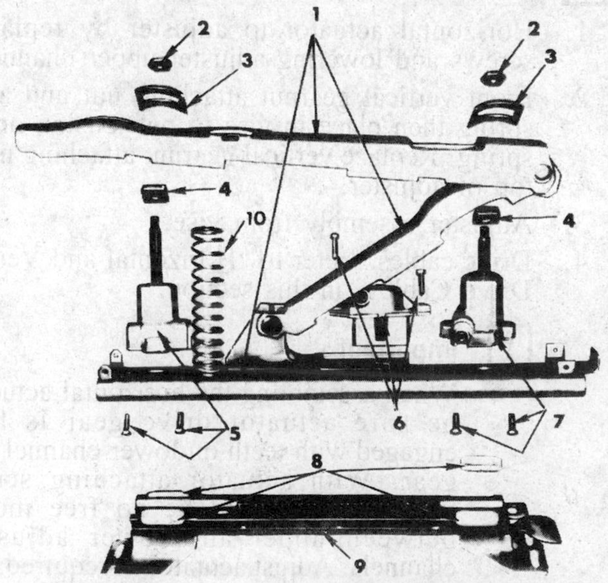

1. Upper Channel Assembly
2. Upper Channel to Gearnut Nuts
3. Gearnut Tension Springs
4. Gearnut Shoulder Nuts
5. Rear Vertical Gearnut and Screws
6. Horizontal Actuator and Screws
7. Front Vertical Gearnut and Screws
8. Plastic Shoes
9. Lower Channel
10. Vertical Assist Spring

G92300-9A-A

Figure 25 Six-Way Adjuster Components (Typical View)

Front/Rear Vertical Gearnut

Figure 25

Disassemble

1. Drive cables. Refer to "Horizontal and Vertical Drive Cables" in this section.
2. Adjuster assembly into vise.

CAUTION: To prevent possible personal injury from accidental ejection of compressed vertical assist spring, the adjuster assembly must be placed in a vise to retain compression on the spring while the rear gearnut attaching nut is being removed.

3. Vertical gearnut attaching nuts, upper channel and vertical assist spring.

CAUTION: To prevent possible personal injury from accidental ejection of compressed vertical assist spring, the vise should be opened slowly to relieve the compression on the vertical assist spring.

4. Assembly from vise.
5. Adjuster on its side and disassemble as required. Manually crank the horizontal actuator to gain access to the attaching screws on the bottom of the lower channel.

6. If vertical gearnut is being replaced, transfer gearnut shoulder nut and tension spring to new gearnut assembly.

Assemble

1. Gearnut to lower channel.
2. Vertical assist spring, upper channel and vertical gearnut attaching nuts. Use vise to compress spring.
3. Drive cables.
4. Verify adjuster is in phase by following the Install or Connect (Important no. 3) procedure for the Seat Adjuster Assembly.

SIX-WAY POWER SEAT SWITCH ASSEMBLY

Figure 26

Remove or Disconnect

NOTICE: If one of the subject switches requires replacement, make sure that the power feed circuit is not shorted to any other wire in the circuit before installing new switch. If this procedure is not followed and a short exists, the short will cause the replacement switch to become damaged. In addition, when disconnecting the seat switch from the wiring harness, extra care must be taken not to short across the switch hot feed terminal and switch ground terminal. If above condition occurs, the seat switch can be shorted.

1. Trim finish panel. Refer to "Front Seat Trim and Covers" in this section.
2. Screws.
3. Switch assembly.
4. Electrical connector.

Install or Connect

1. Electrical connector.
2. Switch assembly.
3. Screws.

Tighten

- Screws to 3 N·m (27 lb. in.).

4. Trim finish panel. Refer to "Front Seat Trim and Covers" in this section.

REAR SEATBACK

Figure 27

Remove or Disconnect

1. Rear seat cushion. Refer to "Rear Seat Cushion" in this section.
2. Anchor nuts securing rear seat retainer at bottom of seatback.
3. Grasp bottom of seatback and swing upward to disengage offsets on the upper frame bar from hangers.
   - Lift seat upward to remove.

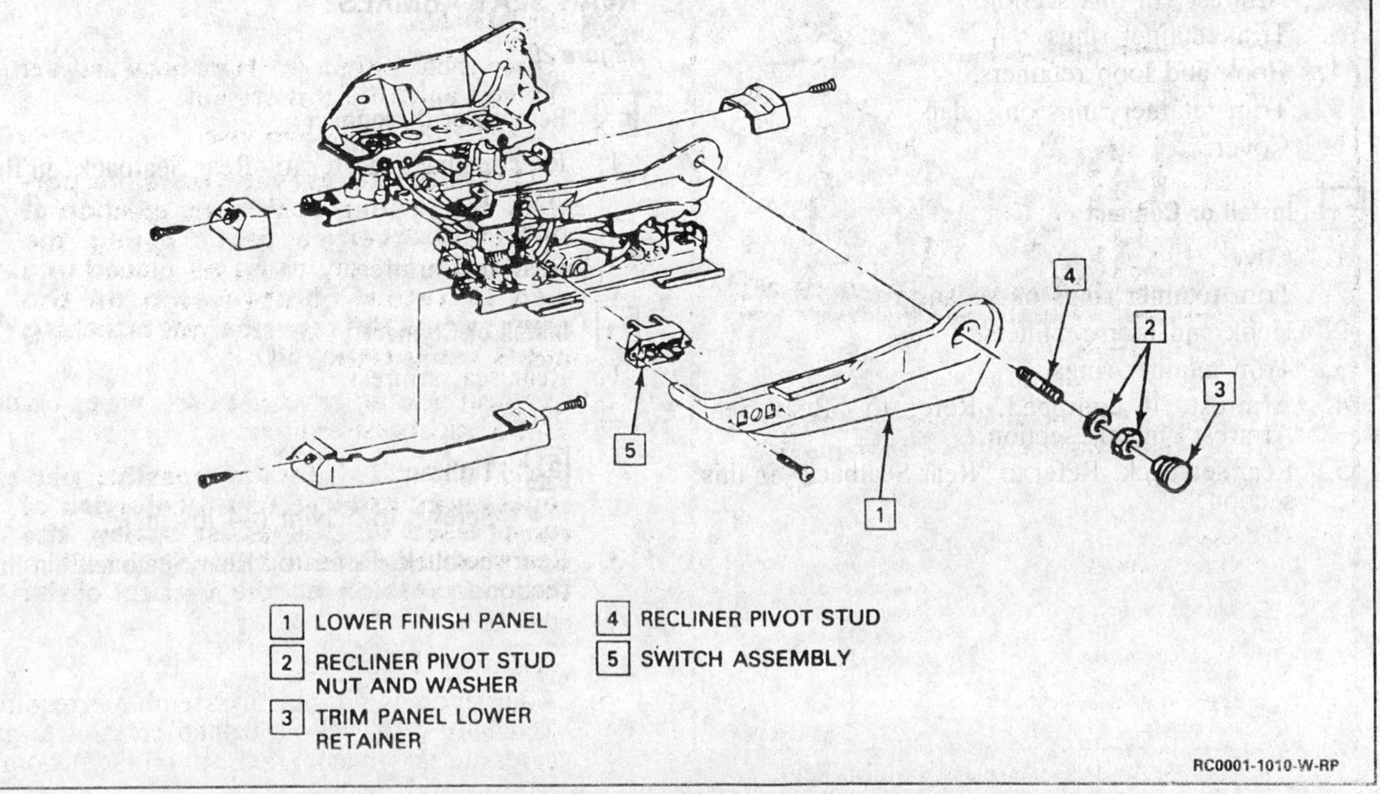
4
2
3
5
1
1 LOWER FINISH PANEL
2 RECLINER PIVOT STUD NUT AND WASHER
3 TRIM PANEL LOWER RETAINER
4 RECLINER PIVOT STUD
5 SWITCH ASSEMBLY
RC0001-1010-W-RP

Figure 26 Six-Way Power Seat Switch

Install or Connect

1. Rear seatback assembly and anchor nuts.

   Tighten
   - Nuts to 10 N·m (89 lb. in.).

2. Rear seat cushion. Refer to "Rear Seat Cushion" in this section.

REAR SEAT CUSHION

Figure 28

Remove or Disconnect

1. Two bolts at base of seat cushion.
2. Seat cushion by lifting up and pulling out.

Install or Connect

1. Seat cushion.
2. Two bolts.

   Tighten
   - Bolt(s) to 25 N•m (19 lb. ft.).

REAR SEAT TRIM AND COVERS

Rear Seatback Cover

Remove or Disconnect

1. Rear seatback. Refer to "Rear Seatback" in this section.
2. Armrest, if equipped. Refer to "Rear Seat Armrest" in this section.
3. Trim retainer rings.
4. Hook and loop retainers.
5. Trim retainer rings on sedan.
6. Cover.

Install or Connect

1. Cover.
2. Trim retainer rings on sedan.
2. Hook and loop retainers.
3. Trim retainer rings.
4. Armrest, if equipped. Refer to "Rear Seat Armrest" in this section.
5. Rear seatback. Refer to "Rear Seatback" in this section.

Rear Seat Cushion Cover

Remove or Disconnect

1. Rear seat cushion. Refer to "Rear Seat Cushion" in this section.
2. Hook and loop retainers on sedan with armrest.
3. Trim retainer rings.
4. Hook and loop retainers on coupe.
5. Cover.

Install or Connect

1. Cover.
2. Hook and loop retainers on coupe.
3. Trim retainer rings.
4. Hook and loop retainers on sedan with armrest.
5. Rear seat cushion. Refer to "Rear Seat Cushion" in this section.

Rear Seat Armrest Cover

Remove or Disconnect

1. Rear seat armrest. Refer to "Rear Seat Armrest" in this section.
2. Cover.

Install or Connect

1. Cover.
2. Rear seat armrest. Refer to "Rear Seat Armrest" in this section.

REAR SEAT ARMREST

Figure 29

Remove or Disconnect

1. Rear seatback. Refer to "Rear Seatback" in this section.
2. Screws.
3. Rear seat armrest.

Install or Connect

1. Rear seat armrest.
2. Screws.

   Tighten
   - Screws to 5 N·m (44 lb. in.).

3. Rear seatback. Refer to "Rear Seatback" in this section.

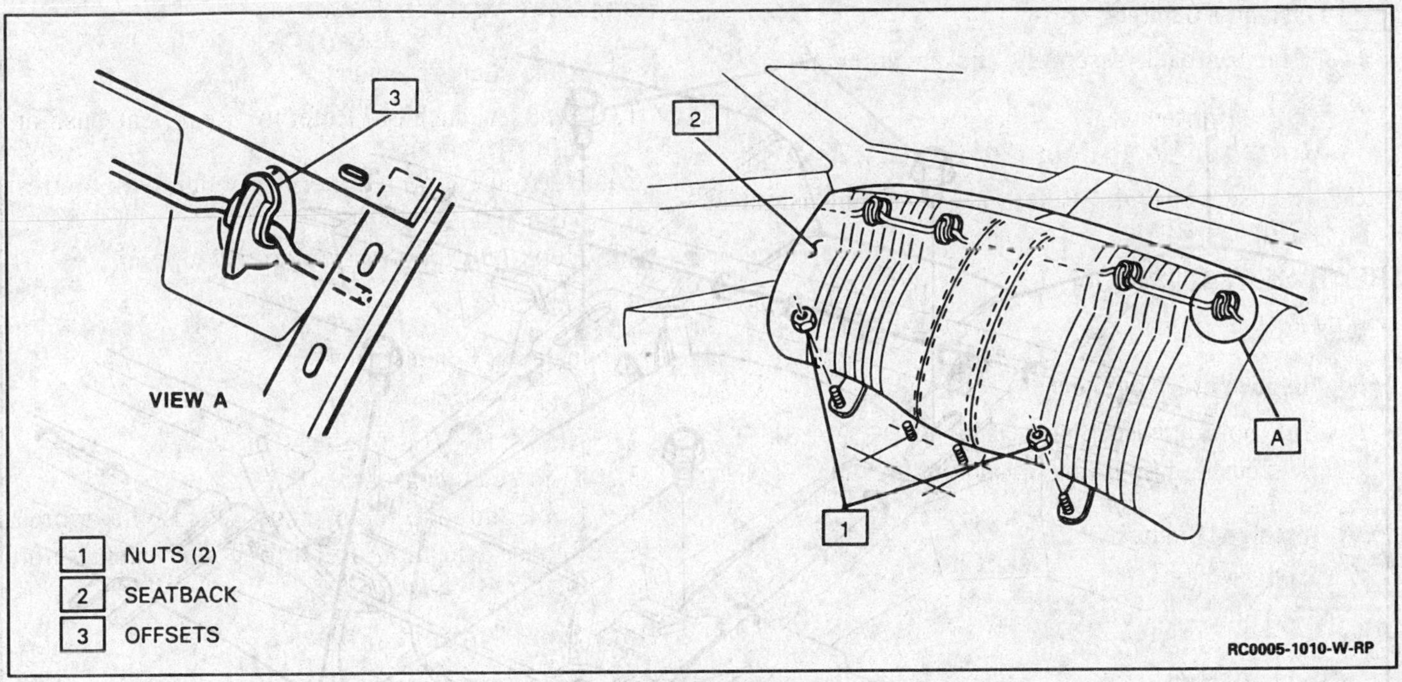
3
2
VIEW A
A
1
1 NUTS (2)
2 SEATBACK
3 OFFSETS
RC0005-1010-W-RP

Figure 27 Rear Seatback

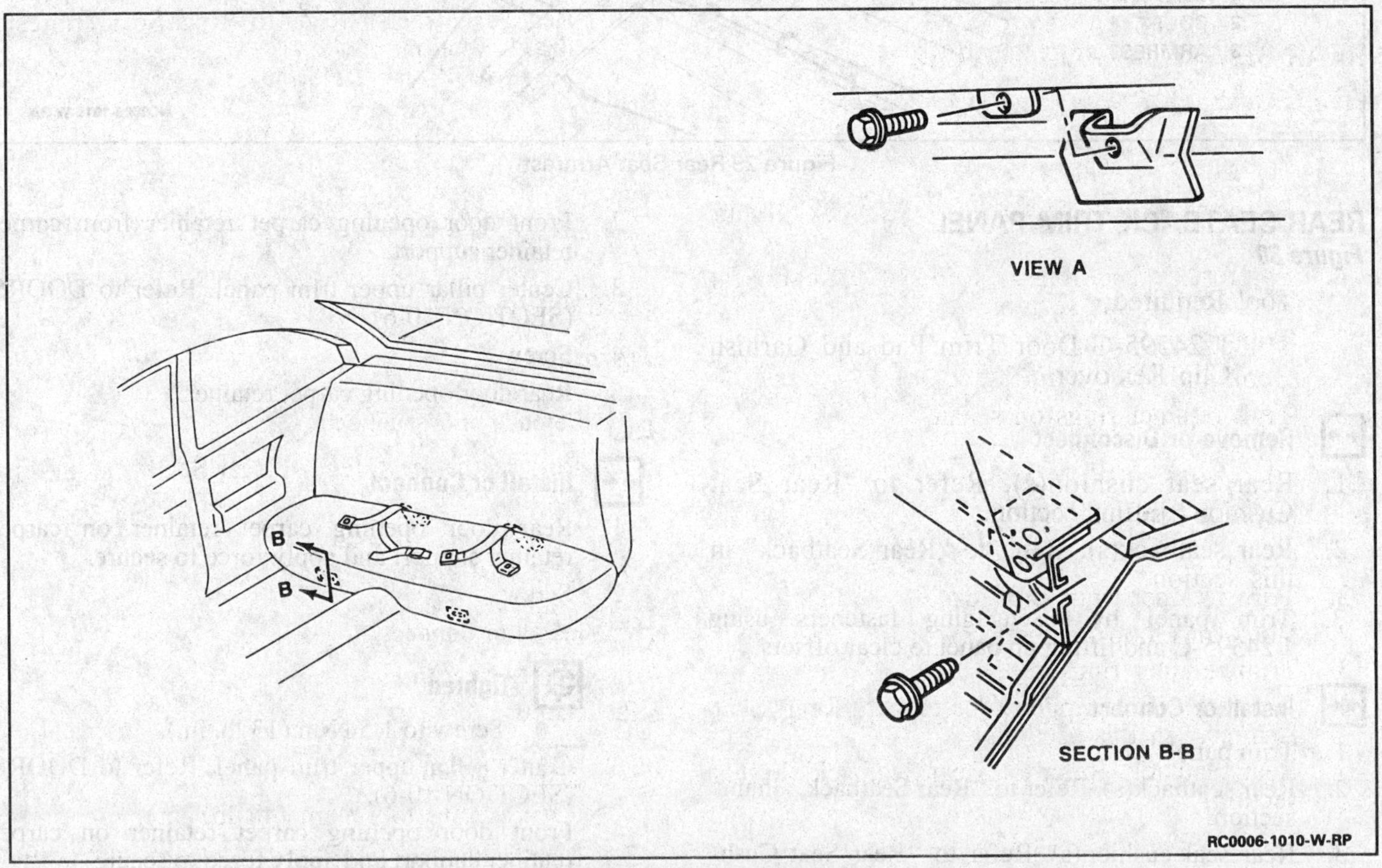
VIEW A
B
B
SECTION B-B
RC0006-1010-W-RP

Figure 28 Rear Seat Cushion

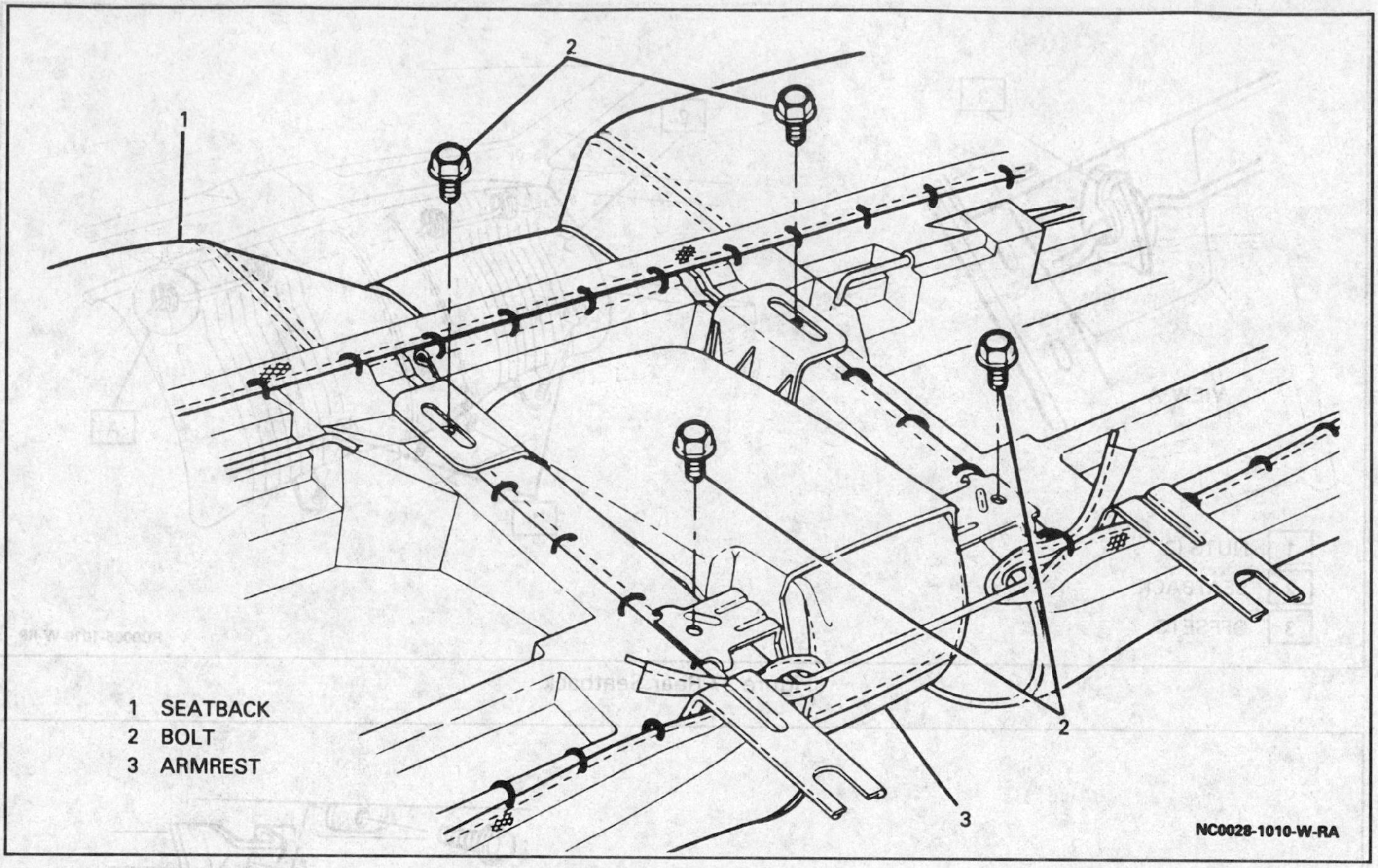
1
2
2
3
1 SEATBACK
2 BOLT
3 ARMREST
NC0028-1010-W-RA

Figure 29 Rear Seat Armrest

REAR SEATBACK TRIM PANEL

Figure 30

Tool Required:

J 24595-C Door Trim Pad and Garnish Clip Remover

Remove or Disconnect

1. Rear seat cushion(s). Refer to "Rear Seat Cushion" in this section.
2. Rear seatback(s). Refer to "Rear Seatback" in this section.
3. Trim panel by disengaging fasteners using J 24595-C and lifting up panel to clear offsets.

Install or Connect

1. Trim panel.
2. Rear seatback(s). Refer to "Rear Seatback" in this section.
3. Rear seat cushion(s). Refer to "Rear Seat Cushion" in this section.

CARPET RETAINERS

Figure 31

Remove or Disconnect

1. Screw.
2. Front door opening carpet retainer from carpet retainer support.
3. Center pillar upper trim panel. Refer to DOORS (SECTION 10-6).
4. Screw.
5. Rear door opening carpet retainer.

Install or Connect

1. Rear door opening carpet retainer on carpet retainer support and apply force to secure.
2. Screw.

Tighten

- Screw to 1.5 N•m (13 lb. in.).

3. Center pillar upper trim panel. Refer to DOORS (SECTION 10-6).
4. Front door opening carpet retainer on carpet retainer support and apply force to secure.
5. Screw.

Tighten

- Screw to 1.5 N•m (13 lb. in.).

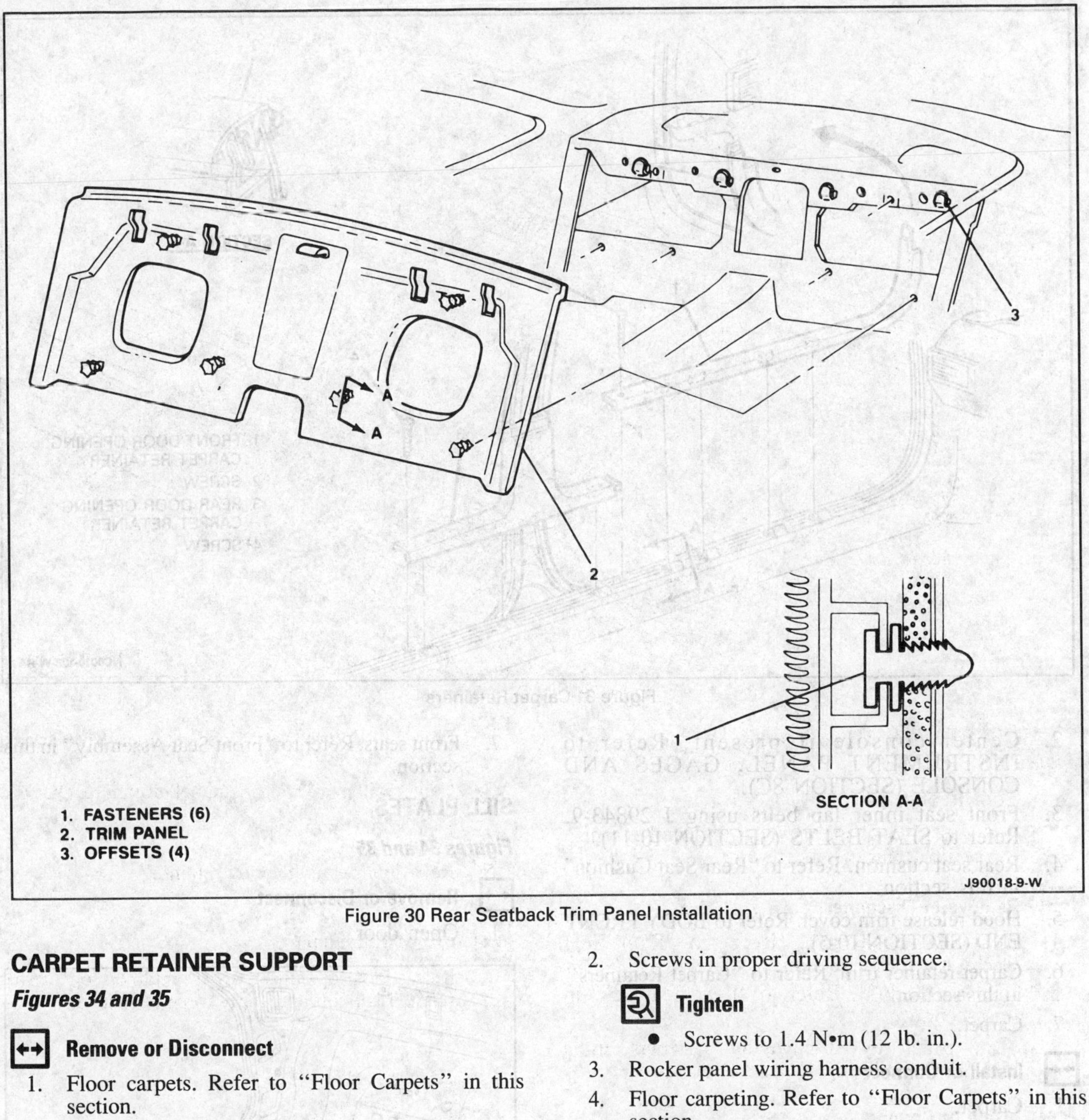
A
A
1
2
3
SECTION A-A
1. FASTENERS (6)
2. TRIM PANEL
3. OFFSETS (4)
J90018-9-W

Figure 30 Rear Seatback Trim Panel Installation

CARPET RETAINER SUPPORT

Figures 34 and 35

Remove or Disconnect

1. Floor carpets. Refer to "Floor Carpets" in this section.
2. Rocker panel wiring harness conduit.
3. Screws.
4. Carpet retainer support from rocker inner panel.

Install or Connect

1. Carpet retainer support to rocker inner panel aligning front net holes.

Important

- Carpet retainer must be held down while screw is being driven to ensure proper installation.

2. Screws in proper driving sequence.

Tighten

- Screws to 1.4 N•m (12 lb. in.).

3. Rocker panel wiring harness conduit.
4. Floor carpeting. Refer to "Floor Carpets" in this section.

FLOOR CARPETS

Tool Required:

J 29843-9 Door Lock Striker and Seat Belt Torx Wrench

All floor carpets consist of a molded one-piece carpet over both front and rear floor pan. The following procedures must be used to remove and replace the carpet.

Remove or Disconnect

1. Front seats. Refer to "Front Seat Assembly" in this section.

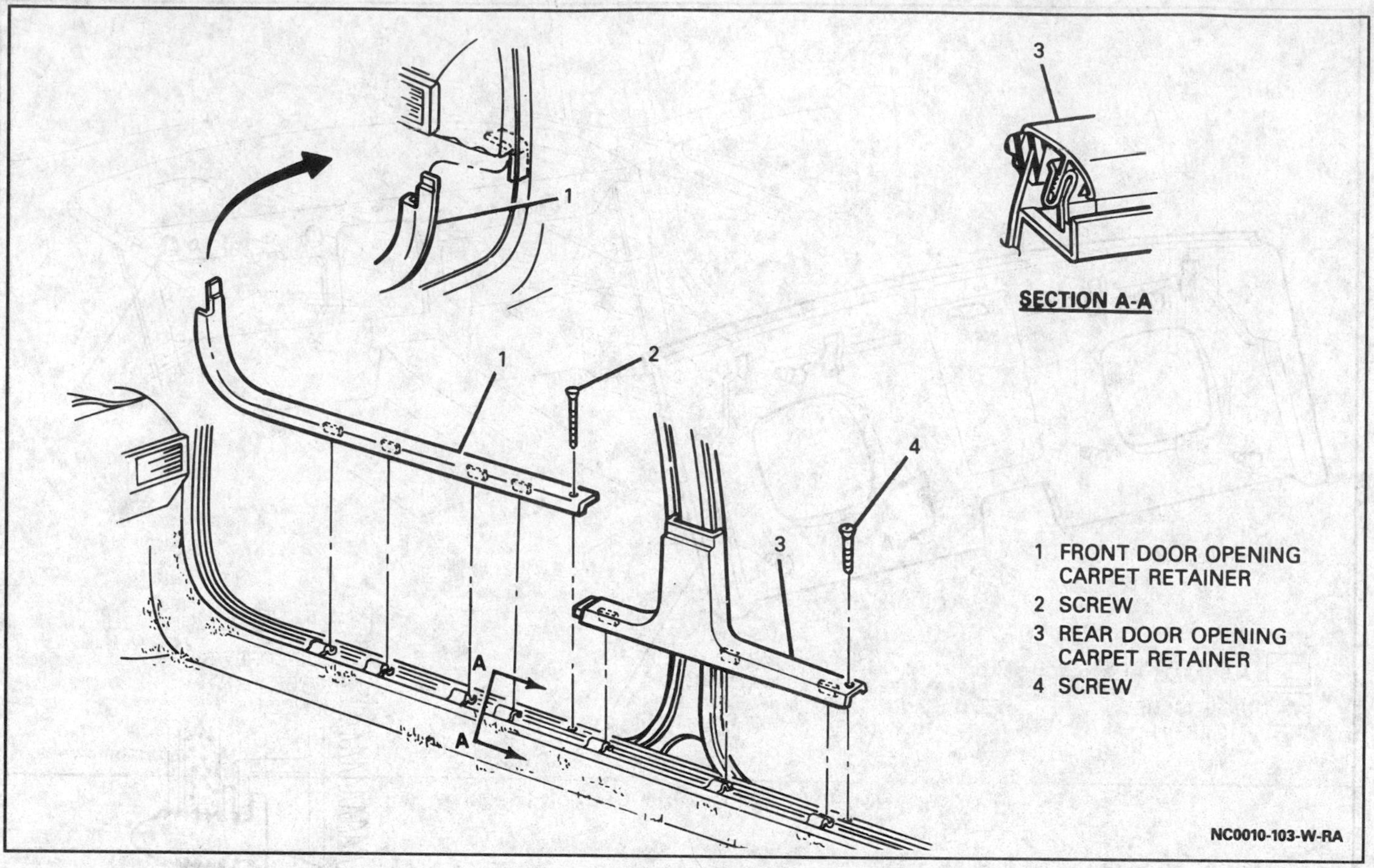

3
SECTION A-A
1
2
1
4
3
A
A
1 FRONT DOOR OPENING CARPET RETAINER
2 SCREW
3 REAR DOOR OPENING CARPET RETAINER
4 SCREW
NC0010-103-W-RA

Figure 31 Carpet Retainers

2. Center console if present. Refer to INSTRUMENT PANEL, GAGES AND CONSOLE (SECTION 8C).
3. Front seat inner lap belts using J 29843-9. Refer to SEAT BELTS (SECTION 10-11).
4. Rear seat cushion. Refer to "Rear Seat Cushion" in this section.
5. Hood release trim cover. Refer to BODY FRONT END (SECTION 10-5).
6. Carpet retainer trim. Refer to "Carpet Retainers" in this section.
7. Carpet.

Install or Connect

1. Carpet.
2. Carpet retainer trim. Refer to "Carpet Retainers" in this section.
3. Hood release trim cover. Refer to BODY FRONT END (SECTION 10-5).
4. Rear seat cushion. Refer to "Rear Seat Cushion" in this section.
5. Front seat inner lap belts using J 29843-9. Refer to SEAT BELTS (SECTION 10-11).
6. Center console if present. Refer to INSTRUMENT PANEL, GAGES AND CONSOLE (SECTION 8C).
7. Front seats. Refer to "Front Seat Assembly" in this section.

SILL PLATES

Figures 34 and 35

Remove or Disconnect

1. Open door.

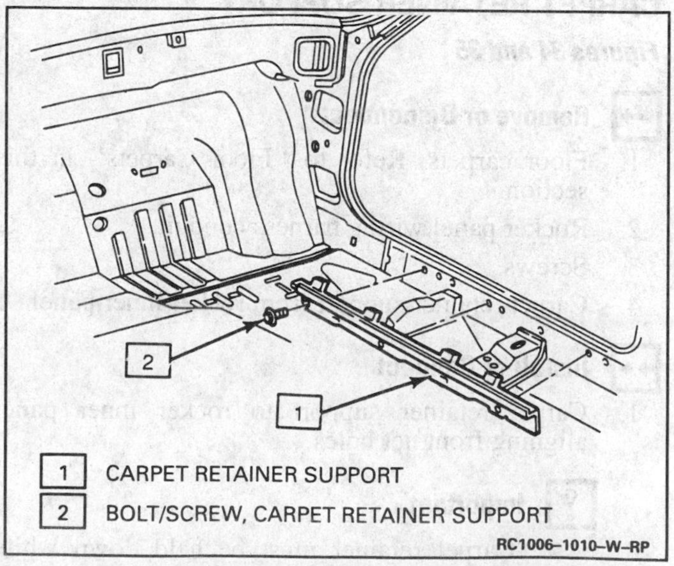

2
1
1 CARPET RETAINER SUPPORT
2 BOLT/SCREW, CARPET RETAINER SUPPORT
RC1006-1010-W-RP

Figure 32 Carpet Retainer Support (Coupe)

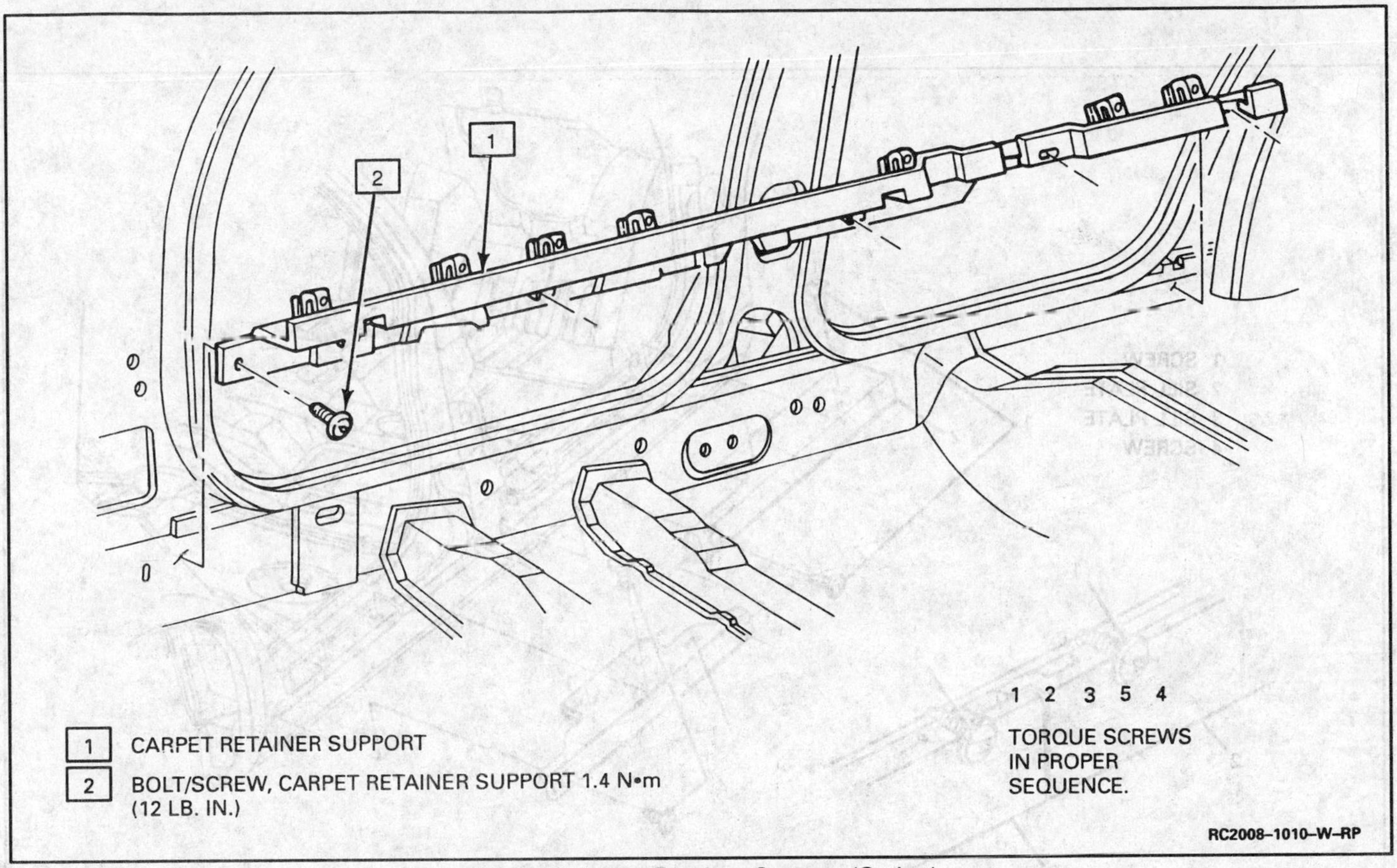
1
2
1 2 3 5 4
TORQUE SCREWS
IN PROPER
SEQUENCE.
1 CARPET RETAINER SUPPORT
2 BOLT/SCREW, CARPET RETAINER SUPPORT 1.4 N•m (12 LB. IN.)
RC2008–1010–W–RP

Figure 33 Carpet Retainer Support (Sedan)

2. Screws.
3. Sill plate.

Install or Connect

1. Sill plate.
2. Screws.

Tighten

- Screws to 1.5 N•m (13 lb. in.).

3. Close door.

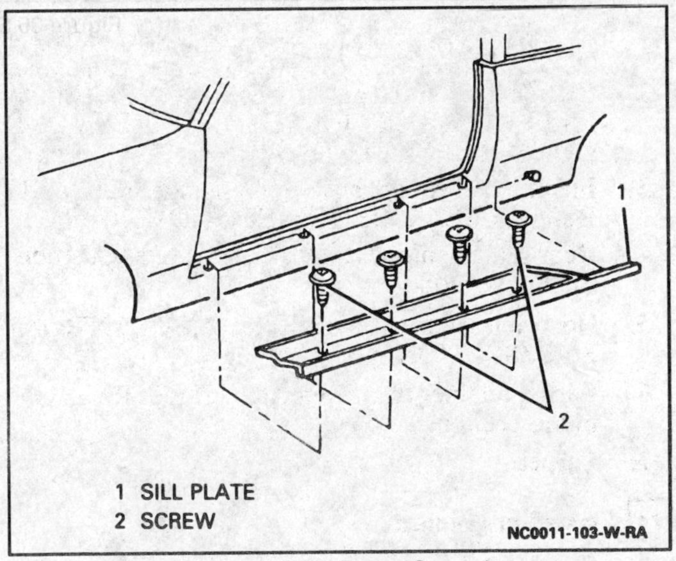
1
2
1 SILL PLATE
2 SCREW
NC0011-103-W-RA

Figure 34 Sill Plate (Coupe)

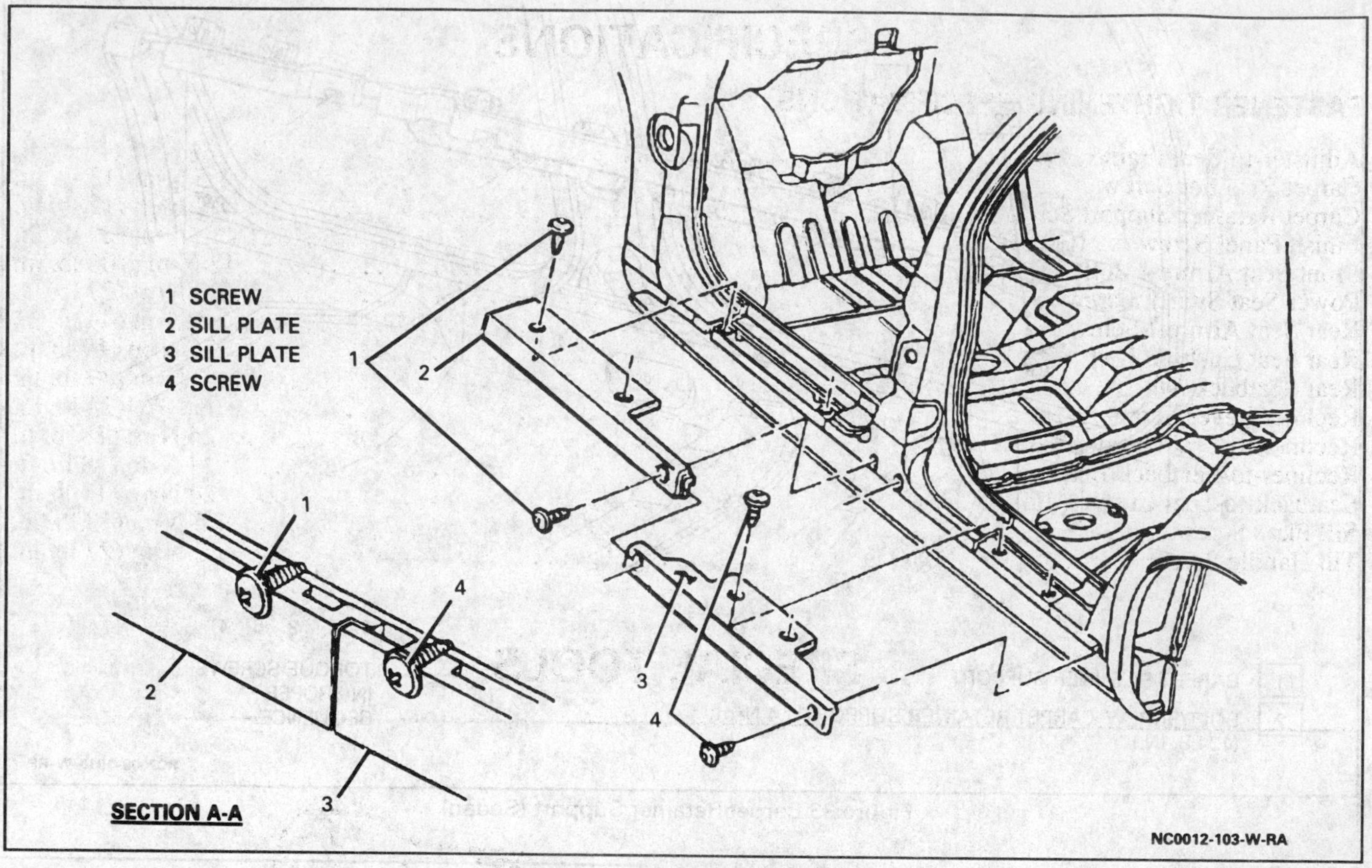
1 SCREW
2 SILL PLATE
3 SILL PLATE
4 SCREW
1
2
1
4
2
3
3
4
SECTION A-A
NC0012-103-W-RA

Figure 35 Sill Plates (Sedan)

SPECIFICATIONS

FASTENER TIGHTENING SPECIFICATIONS

Adjuster-to-Seat Frame Bolt	24 N•m (18 lb. ft.)
Carpet Retainer Screw	1.5 N•m (13 lb. in.)
Carpet Retainer Support Screw	1.4 N•m (12 lb. in.)
Finish Panel Screw	3 N•m (27 lb. in.)
Front Seat Armrest Bolt	12 N•m (106 lb. in.)
Power Seat Switch Screw	3 N•m (27 lb. in.)
Rear Seat Armrest Screw	5 N•m (44 lb. in.)
Rear Seat Cushion Bolt	25 N•m (19 lb. ft.)
Rear Seatback Nut	10 N•m (89 lb. in.)
Recliner Lever Screw	3 N•m (27 lb. in.)
Recliner-to-Seat Cushion Bolt	24 N•m (18 lb. ft.)
Recliner-to-Seatback Bolt	24 N•m (18 lb. ft.)
Seatback-to-Seat Cushion Bolt	24 N•m (18 lb. ft.)
Sill Plate Screw	1.5 N•m (13 lb. in.)
Tilt Handle Screw	3 N•m (27 lb. in.)

SPECIAL TOOLS

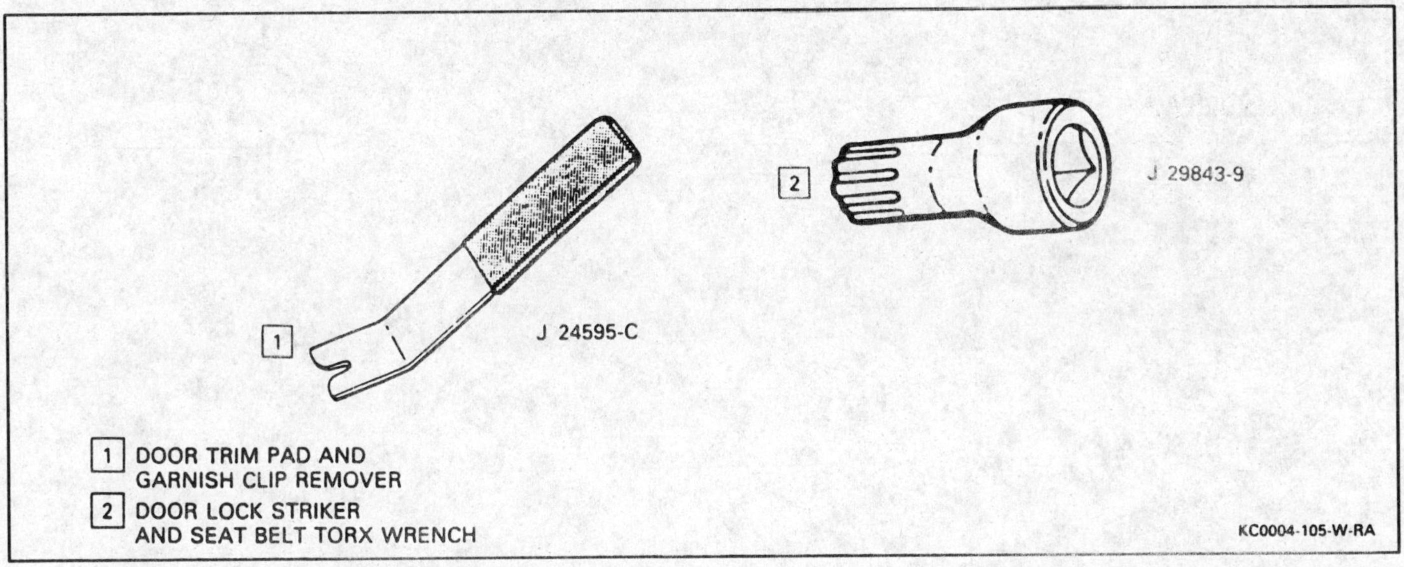
2
J 29843-9
1
J 24595-C
1 DOOR TRIM PAD AND GARNISH CLIP REMOVER
2 DOOR LOCK STRIKER AND SEAT BELT TORX WRENCH
KC0004-105-W-RA

SECTION 10-11

SEAT BELTS

CAUTION: Replace belts, retractors, and hardware in use during all but a minor collision. Also, restraint systems should be replaced and anchorages properly repaired if they were in areas damaged by a collision, whether the belt was in use or not. If there is any question, replace the belt system. Damage, whether visible or not, could result in serious personal injury in the event of an accident.

NOTICE: When fasteners are removed, always reinstall them at the same location from which they were removed. If a fastener needs to be replaced, use the correct part number fastener for that application. If the correct part number fastener is not available, a fastener of equal size and strength (or stronger) may be used. Fasteners that are not reused, and those requiring thread locking compound will be called out. The correct torque value must be used when installing fasteners that require it. If the above conditions are not followed, parts or system damage could result.

CONTENTS

GENERAL DESCRIPTION

RESTRAINT SYSTEM

Front seats are equipped with a passive restraint system requiring no operator interaction. A dealer-installed child seat top strap anchor is available on all vehicles and a dealer-installed child tether is available on Canadian vehicles.

The driver's seat belt system includes a reminder lamp and tone alarm to warn the driver that the seat belt is not buckled. If the driver's seat belt is not buckled when the ignition is turned on, the tone alarm will operate for 4 to 8 seconds, and the reminder lamp will remain lit.

If the driver's seat belt is buckled when the ignition is turned on, neither the tone alarm nor reminder lamp will operate. To diagnose a system failure for the tone alarm or reminder lamp, refer to 8A-75-0 ELECTRICAL DIAGNOSIS (SECTION 8A).

The seat belts have emergency locks in the retractors. The emergency lock stays unlocked to allow the user free movement, except in emergency conditions. If the vehicle slows down, stops or changes lanes abruptly, the emergency lock engages to hold the seat belt and user in position. On the sedan, the rear seat retractors are a "dual-mode" type retractor with emergency locking and automatic locking features. The automatic locking feature is for use with a child seat. The passive restraint system electronically disengages the emergency lock when the door is opened. If there is a fault in the electronic override system, the door can still be opened with the seat belt latched, but the door opening motion must be slower than normal so the emergency lock is not activated. Because of the emergency lock override system, the 20 amp courtesy lamp fuse should be removed whenever the door is left open for extended periods of time.

ON-VEHICLE SERVICE

OPERATIONAL AND FUNCTIONAL CHECKS

Seat Belt Check

1. Remove rear seat cushions. Refer to SEATS AND CARPET (SECTION 10-10).
2. Grasp front and rear belt floor attachments and manually check that the attachments are secure.
3. Replace seat cushions.
4. Visually check that front and rear center belts are accessible and not twisted.
5. Fully extend the rear seat belt and visually check that no twists are in it.
6. Allow the belt to retract.
7. Grasp latch plate and extend the seat belt completely, checking that it extends easily.
8. Snap latch plate into buckle.
9. Tug sharply on the buckle and latch plate, checking that it remains locked.
10. Push button on buckle. The latch plate must release from the buckle easily and the button return to its original position.
11. Repeat steps 5 to 10 with the front seat belts.

FRONT SEAT PASSIVE RESTRAINT SYSTEM

Seat belts are important to the safety of vehicle users. Special care must be taken when servicing the seat belts. The outboard seat belt and retractor assemblies and the center belt assemblies must be serviced as complete units. The entire unit must be replaced with a new service replacement part.

Service Precautions

- Keep sharp edges and damaging objects away from seat belts.
- Avoid bending or damaging any part of the seat belt buckle or latch plate.
- Do not bleach or dye seat belt webbing. Clean only with a mild soap solution and water.
- Use correct seat belt anchor bolts and tighten to the correct torque value.

Outboard Seat Belts and Retractors

Figures 1 through 6

Tool Required:

J 24595-C Door Trim Pad and Garnish Clip Remover

Remove or Disconnect

1. Door trim panel using J 24595-C. Refer to DOORS (SECTION 10-6).
2. Upper guide loop nut covers.
3. Upper guide loop nuts.
4. Electrical connectors from retractors.
5. Seat belt guide retainer screws.
6. Seat belt retractor nuts.
7. Seat belt retractor.
8. Nuts securing shoulder belt retractor.
9. Shoulder belt retractor.

Install or Connect

1. Shoulder belt retractor.
2. Nuts securing shoulder belt retractor.

   Tighten
   - Nut to 42 N·m (31 lb. ft.).

3. Seat belt retractor.
4. Seat belt retractor nuts.

   Tighten
   - Nuts to 42 N·m (31 lb. ft.).

5. Seat belt guide retainer screws.

   Tighten
   - Screws to 5 N·m (44 lb. in.).

6. Electrical connectors to retractors.
7. Upper guide loop nuts.

   Tighten
   - Nuts to 28 N·m (21 lb. ft.).

8. Upper guide loop covers.
9. Door trim panel. Refer to DOORS (SECTION 10-6).

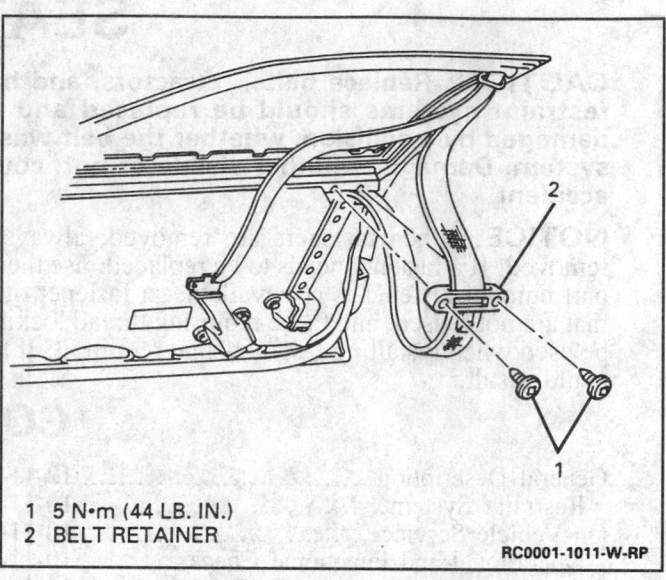

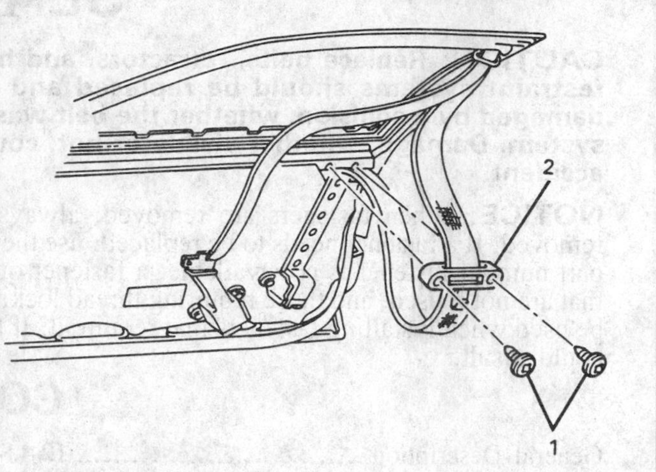
2
1
1 5 N•m (44 LB. IN.)
2 BELT RETAINER
RC0001-1011-W-RP

Figure 1 Belt Retainer Installation

Front Seat Center Belts

Figures 7 and 8

Tool Required:

J 29843-9 Door Lock Striker and Seat Belt Torx Wrench

Remove or Disconnect

1. Cover.
2. Electrical connector if removing driver's side belt.
3. Anchor bolt using J 29843-9.
4. Belt assembly.

Install or Connect

1. Belt assembly.
2. Anchor bolt using J 29843-9.

   Tighten
   - Anchor bolt to 42 N·m (31 lb. ft.).

3. Electrical connector if disconnected.
4. Cover.

REAR SEAT RESTRAINT SYSTEM

The outboard seat belt and retractor assemblies and the center belt assemblies must be serviced as complete units. Do not attempt to make repairs to the units. The entire unit must be replaced with a new service replacement part.

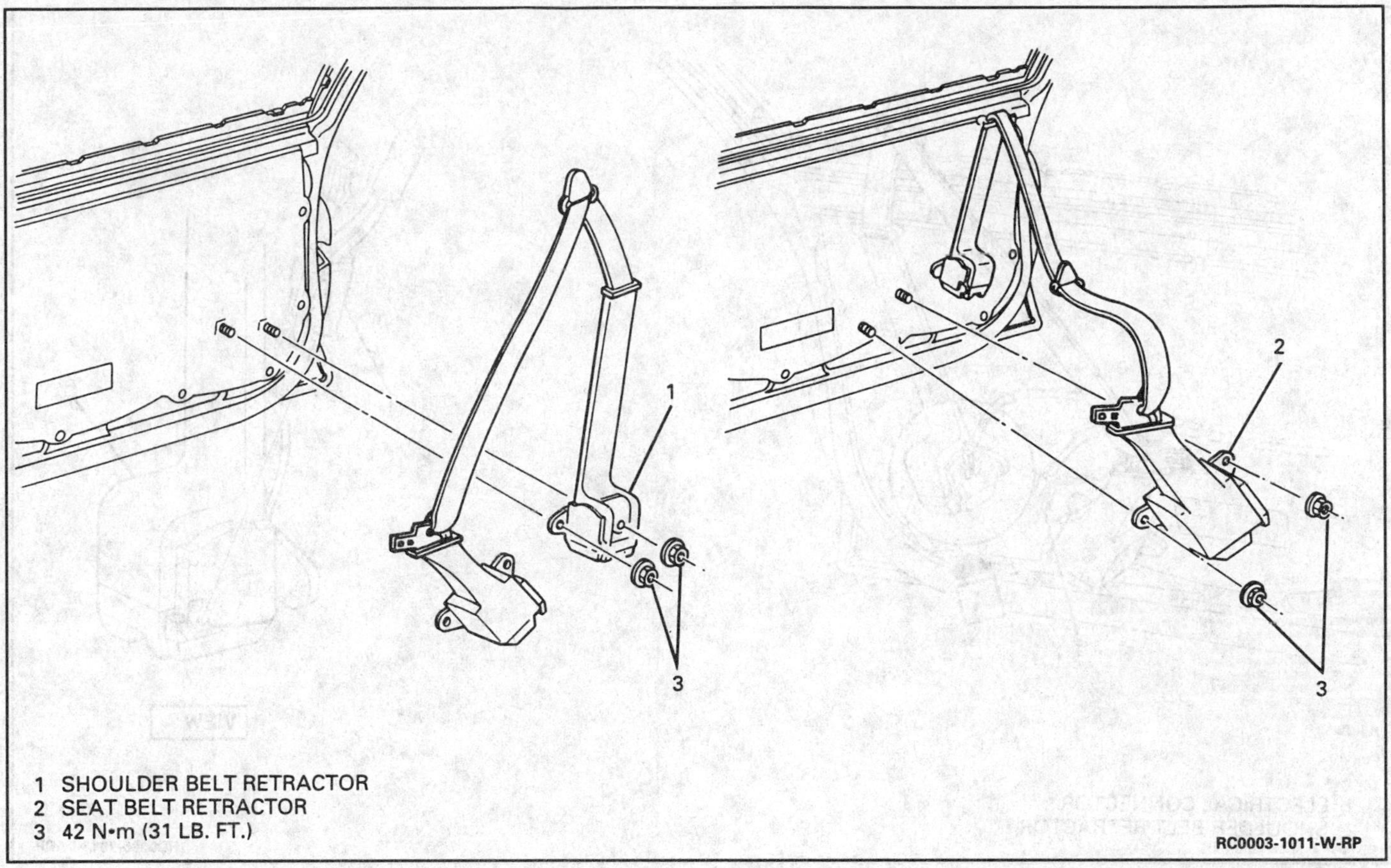
1
2
3
3
1 SHOULDER BELT RETRACTOR
2 SEAT BELT RETRACTOR
3 42 N•m (31 LB. FT.)
RC0003-1011-W-RP

Figure 2 Front Seat Belt and Retractor Installation (Coupe)

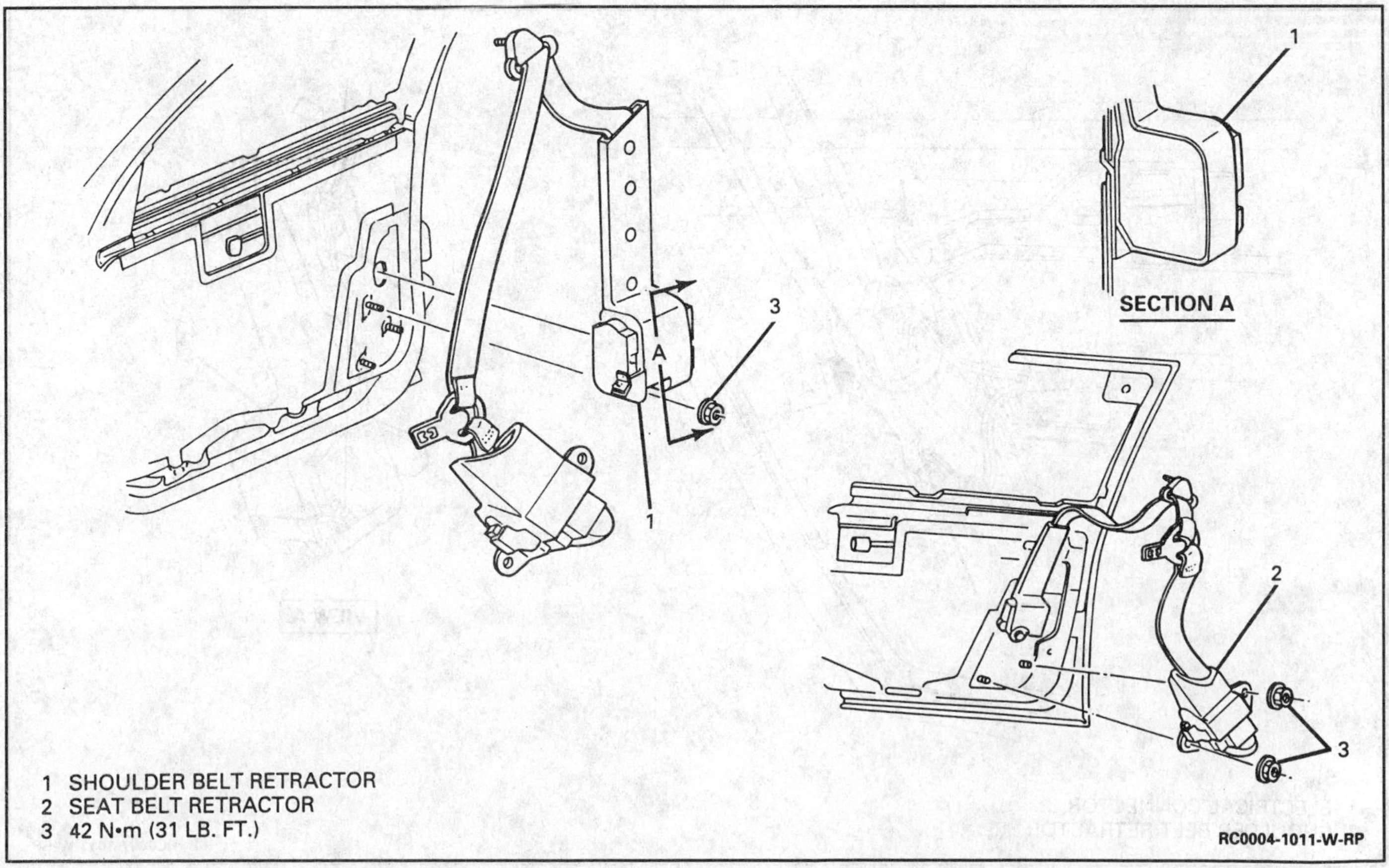
1
A
3
1
SECTION A
2
3
1 SHOULDER BELT RETRACTOR
2 SEAT BELT RETRACTOR
3 42 N•m (31 LB. FT.)
RC0004-1011-W-RP

Figure 3 Front Seat Belts and Retractor Installation (Sedan)

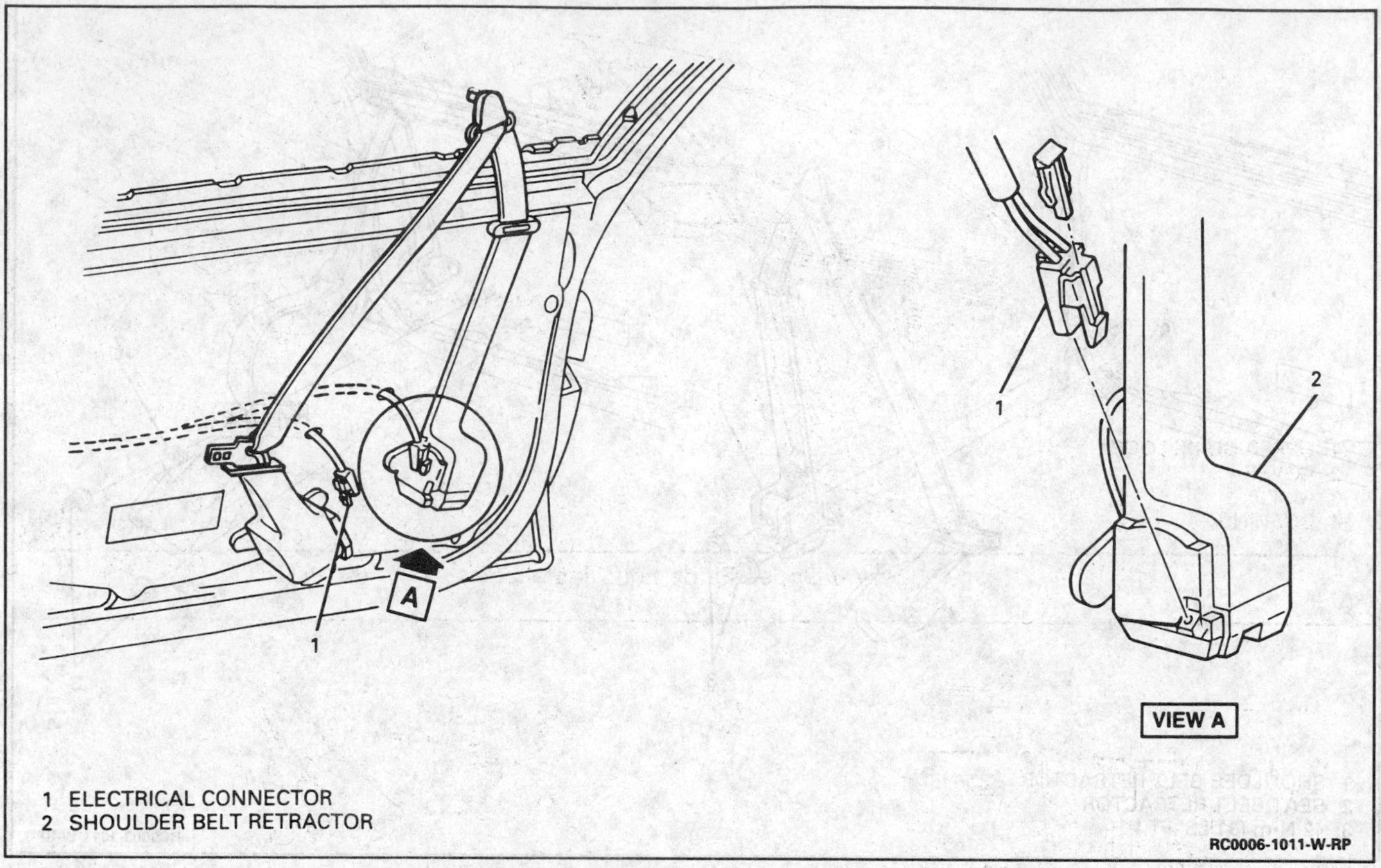
1
1
2
VIEW A
A
1 ELECTRICAL CONNECTOR
2 SHOULDER BELT RETRACTOR
RC0006-1011-W-RP

Figure 4 Retractor Electrical Connections (Coupe)

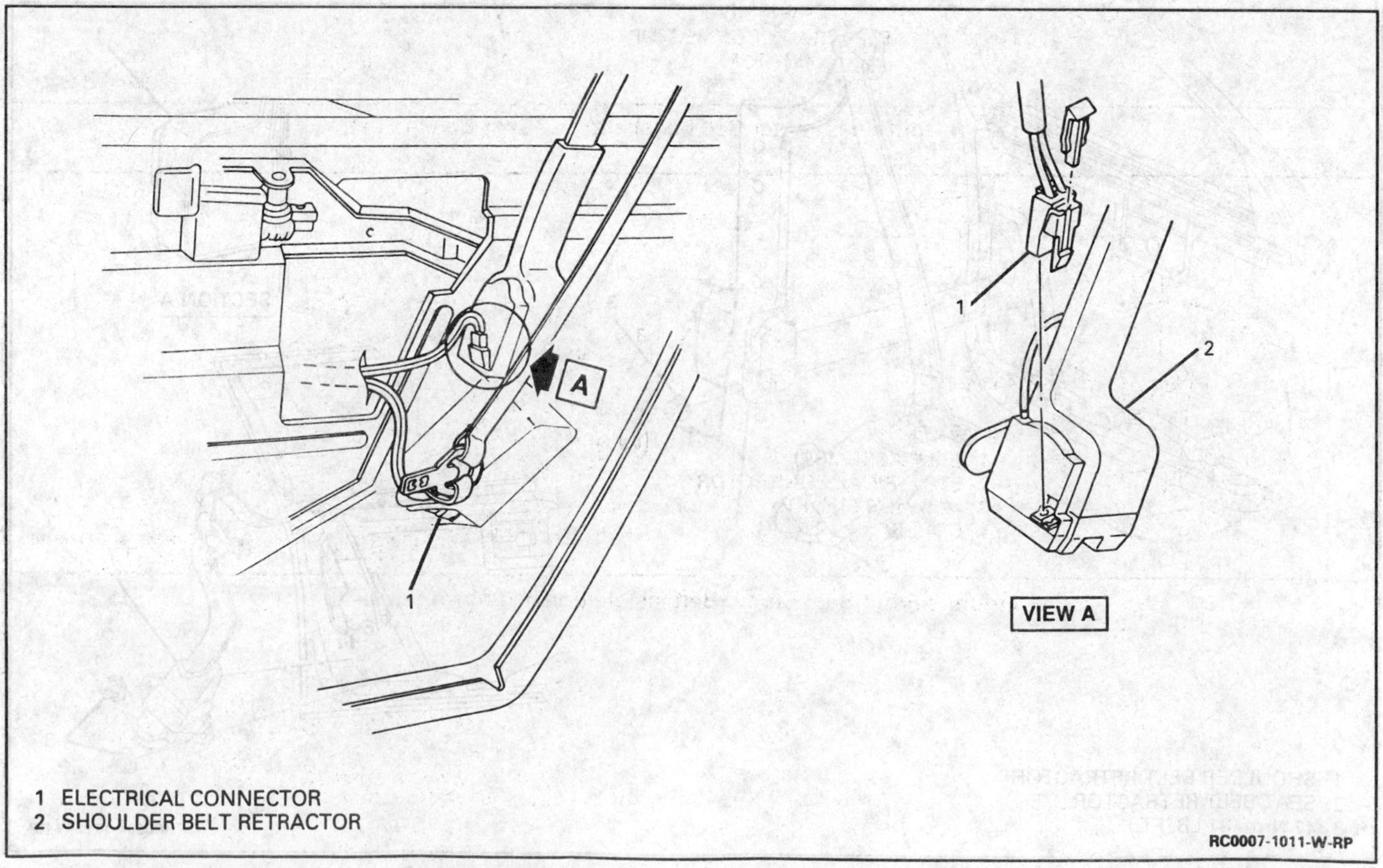
1
1
2
A
VIEW A
1 ELECTRICAL CONNECTOR
2 SHOULDER BELT RETRACTOR
RC0007-1011-W-RP

Figure 5 Retractor Electrical Connections (Sedan)

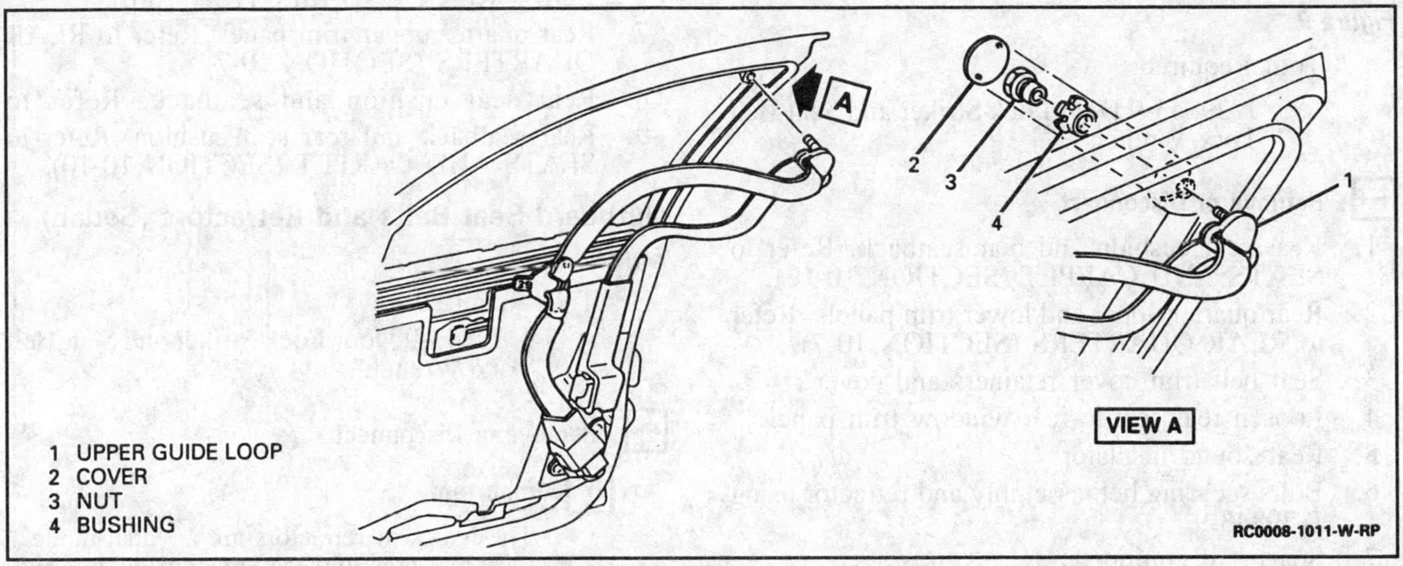
A
VIEW A
1 UPPER GUIDE LOOP
2 COVER
3 NUT
4 BUSHING
1
2
3
4
RC0008-1011-W-RP

Figure 6 Upper Guide Loop Installation

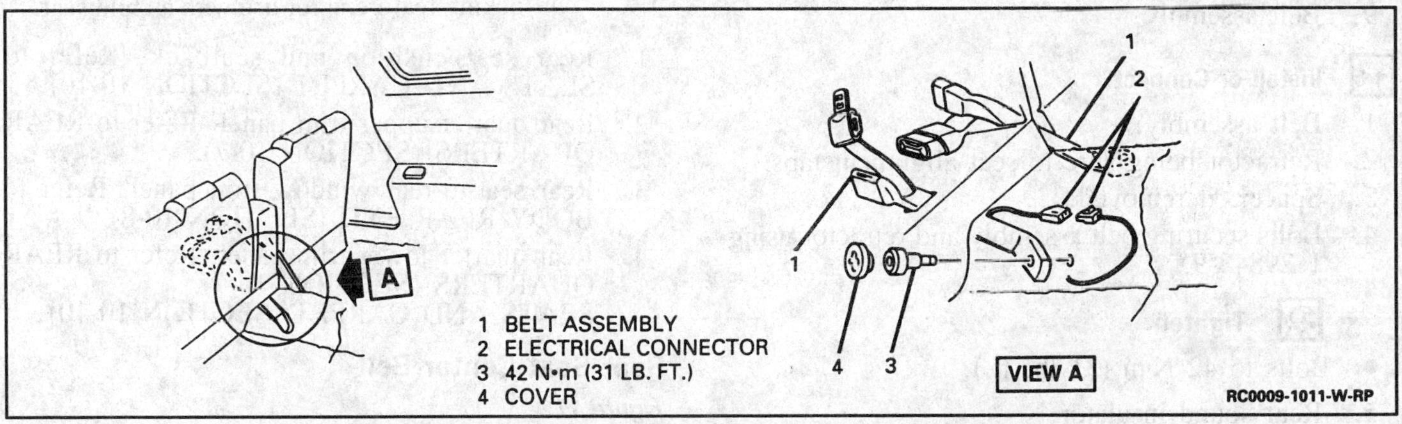
A
1 BELT ASSEMBLY
2 ELECTRICAL CONNECTOR
3 42 N•m (31 LB. FT.)
4 COVER
1
2
1
4
3
VIEW A
RC0009-1011-W-RP

Figure 7 Front Seat Center Belt Installation — Split Bench Seat

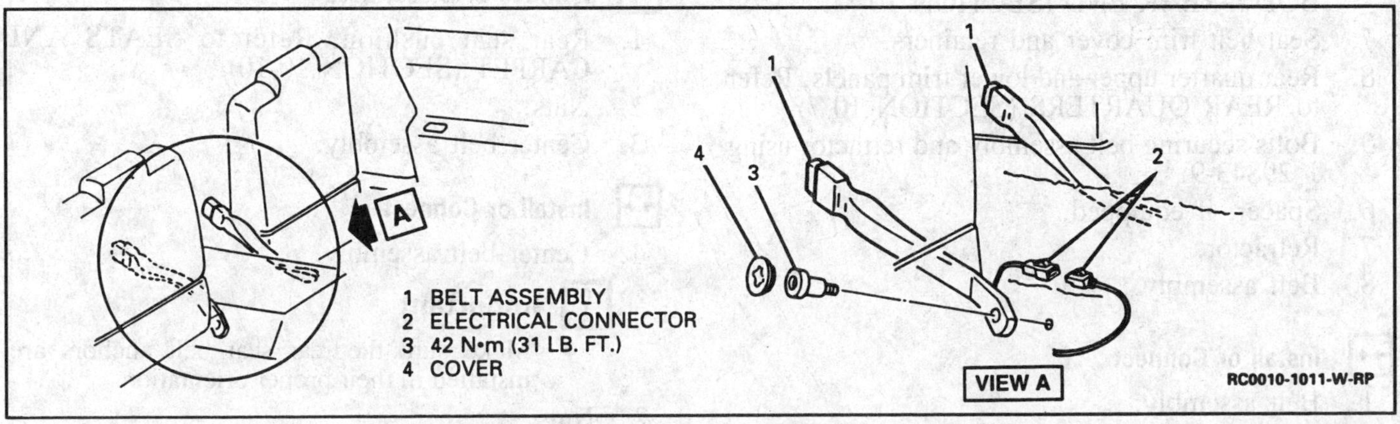
A
1 BELT ASSEMBLY
2 ELECTRICAL CONNECTOR
3 42 N•m (31 LB. FT.)
4 COVER
1
4
3
2
VIEW A
RC0010-1011-W-RP

Figure 8 Front Seat Center Belt Installation — Bucket Seat

Outboard Seat Belt and Retractors (Coupe)

Figure 9

Tool Required:

J 29843-9 Door Lock Striker and Seat Belt Torx Wrench

Remove or Disconnect

1. Rear seat cushion and rear seatback. Refer to SEATS AND CARPET (SECTION 10-10).
2. Rear quarter upper and lower trim panels. Refer to REAR QUARTERS (SECTION 10-7).
3. Seat belt trim cover retainers and cover.
4. Loosen rear seat-to-rear window trim panel.
5. Rear sound insulator.
6. Bolts securing belt assembly and retractor using J 29843-9.
7. Spacer, if equipped.
8. Retractor.
9. Belt assembly.

Install or Connect

1. Belt assembly.
2. Retractor being sure to seat alignment tabs.
3. Spacer, if removed.
4. Bolts securing belt assembly and retractor using J 29843-9.

Tighten

- Bolts to 42 N·m (31 lb. ft.).

5. Rear sound insulator.
6. Rear seat-to-rear window trim panel. Refer to BODY REAR END (SECTION 10-8).
7. Seat belt trim cover and retainers.
8. Rear quarter upper and lower trim panels. Refer to REAR QUARTERS (SECTION 10-7).
5. Bolts securing belt assembly and retractor using J 29843-9.
6. Spacer, if equipped.
7. Retractor.
8. Belt assembly.

Install or Connect

1. Belt assembly.
2. Retractor.
3. Spacer, if equipped.
4. Bolts securing belt assembly and retractor.

Tighten

- Bolts to 42 N·m (31 lb. ft.).

5. Rear quarter lower trim panel. Refer to REAR QUARTERS (SECTION 10-7).
6. Rear seat-to-rear window trim panel. Refer to BODY REAR END (SECTION 10-8).
7. Rear quarter upper trim panel. Refer to REAR QUARTERS (SECTION 10-7).
8. Rear seat cushion and seatback. Refer to
9. Rear seatback and rear seat cushion. Refer to SEATS AND CARPET (SECTION 10-10).

Outboard Seat Belts and Retractors (Sedan)

Figure 10

Tool Required:

J 29843-9 Door Lock Striker and Seat Belt Torx Wrench

Remove or Disconnect

Important

- The rear seat retractors are a "dual-mode" type retractor with emergency locking and automatic locking features. The automatic locking feature is for use with a child seat.

1. Rear seat cushion and seatback. Refer to SEATS AND CARPET (SECTION 10-10).
2. Rear quarter upper trim panel. Refer to REAR QUARTERS (SECTION 10-7).
3. Rear seat-to-rear window trim panel. Refer to BODY REAR END (SECTION 10-8).
4. Rear quarter lower trim panel. Refer to REAR QUARTERS (SECTION 10-7).
SEATS AND CARPET (SECTION 10-10).

Rear Seat Center Belt

Figure 11

Remove or Disconnect

1. Rear seat cushion. Refer to SEATS AND CARPET (SECTION 10-10).
2. Nuts.
3. Center belt assembly.

Install or Connect

1. Center belt assembly.

Important

- Make sure the rear seat belt anchors are installed in their proper orientation.

2. Nuts.

Tighten

- Nuts to 42 N·m (31 lb. ft.).

3. Rear seat cushion. Refer to SEATS AND CARPET (SECTION 10-10).

Important

- Be sure the buckle is properly routed through the seat cushion.

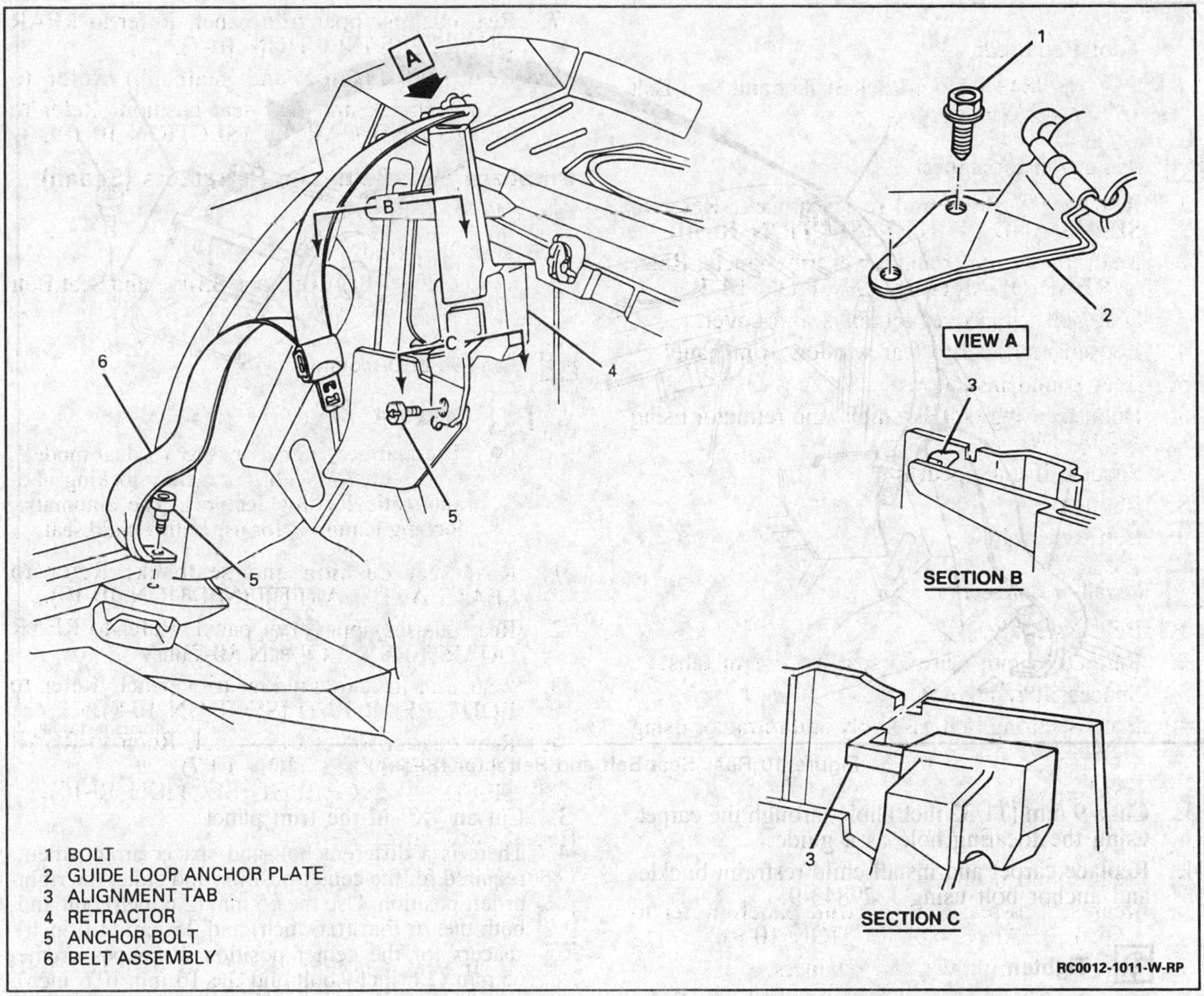
A
B
C
1
2
3
4
5
6
VIEW A
SECTION B
SECTION C
1 BOLT
2 GUIDE LOOP ANCHOR PLATE
3 ALIGNMENT TAB
4 RETRACTOR
5 ANCHOR BOLT
6 BELT ASSEMBLY
RC0012-1011-W-RP

Figure 9 Rear Seat Belt and Retractor (Coupe)

CHILD SEAT

The child seat may be used only in a forward facing seating location. When the child seat is used in the front seat location, a separate child restraint belt is required. It is available as a dealer accessory kit and is installed to an existing bolt hole in the inner rocker panel.

If a child seat is to be used in a second seat position, a special dealer-installed anchor must be used to anchor the child seat top strap. In order to assure the correct top strap angle, the child seat is only to be used at the seating position for which the top strap anchor is installed.

Sedans are equipped with a dual-mode retractor. The child seat can be secured by pulling the belt assembly all the way out to lock it. Then, tighten the belt assembly around the child seat.

CAUTION: Be sure the child seat position does not conflict with any additional requirements provided by the manufacturer.

Front Seat Child Restraint Belt Installation

Figure 12

Tool Required:

J 29843-9 Door Lock Striker and Seat Belt Torx Wrench

1. Remove carpet trim as needed to pull back carpet and locate bolt hole in the inner rocker panel.
2. Using a punch or other sharp tool, make a locating hole through the center of the carpet covering the bolt hole.

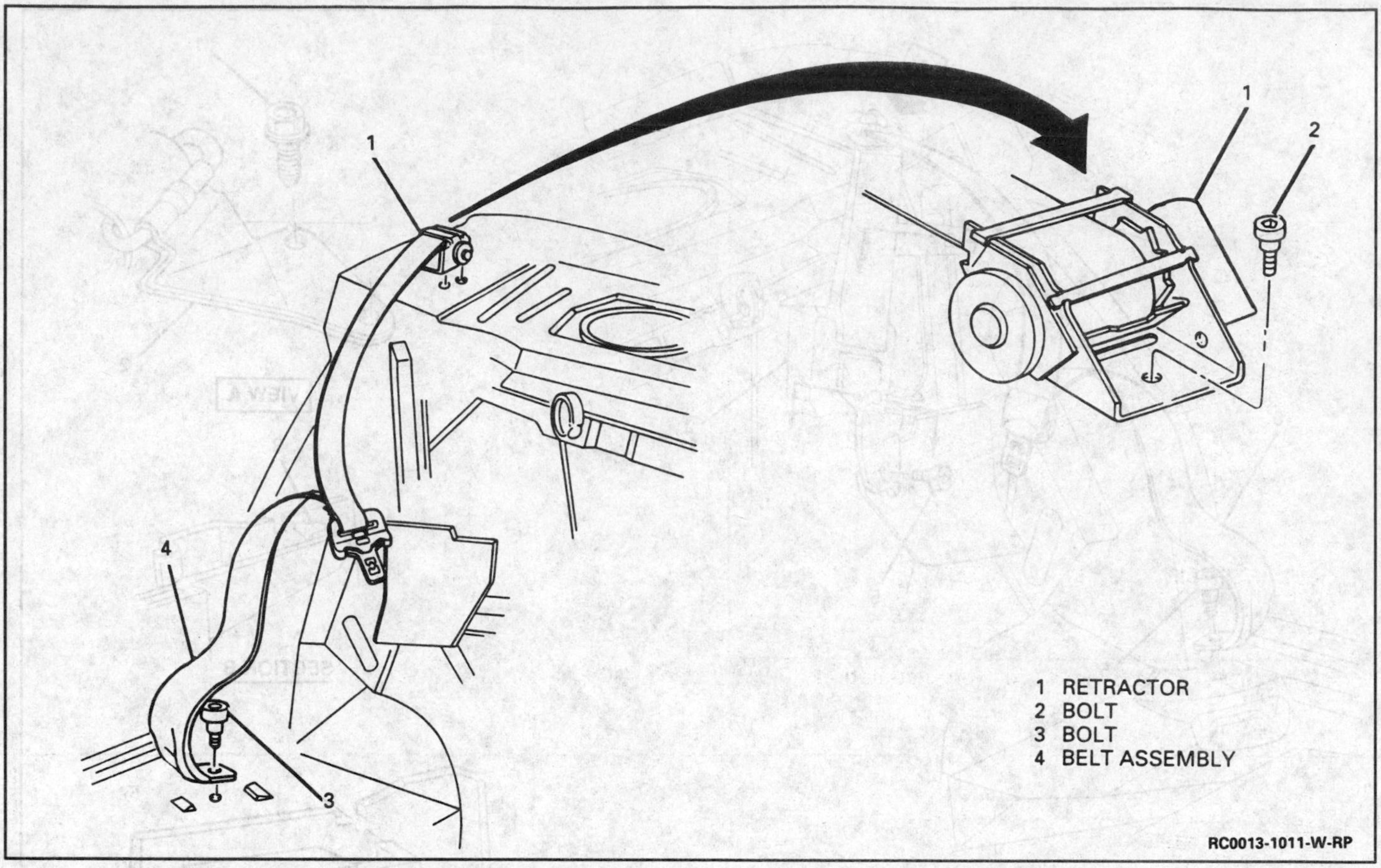
1
2
1
4
3
1 RETRACTOR
2 BOLT
3 BOLT
4 BELT ASSEMBLY
RC0013-1011-W-RP

Figure 10 Rear Seat Belt and Retractor (Sedan)

3. Cut a 9 mm (11/32 inch) hole through the carpet using the locating hole as a guide.
4. Replace carpet and install child restraint buckle and anchor bolt using J 29843-9.

Tighten

- Anchor bolt to 42 N·m (31 lb. ft.).

5. Install carpet trim if removed.

Top Strap Anchor Installation

Figure 13

1. Open rear compartment and insert threaded J-clip from inside rear compartment.
2. Insert a sharp punch through the hole in the J-clip and mark the hole made in the trim panel.
3. Cut an "X" in the trim panel.
4. There is a different bolt and spacer arrangement required for the center position and either the right or left position. Use the 65 mm (2.6 inch) bolt and both the 16 mm (0.6 inch) and 25 mm (1.0 inch) spacers for the center position in coupes or the 65 mm (2.6 inch) bolt and the 16 mm (0.6 inch) spacer for the center position in sedans. Use the 65 mm (2.6 inch) bolt and both the 16 mm (0.6 inch) and 30 mm (1.2 inch) spacers for either the left or right position in coupes or the 90 mm (3.6 inch) bolt and both the 25 mm (1.0 inch) and 30 mm (1.2 inch) spacers for either the left or right position in sedans.
5. Insert the bolt through the anchor bracket and the required spacers and secure with push-on nut. Install into the hole in trim panel and into the "J" clip. Tighten the bolt until the anchor bracket is tight against the spacer(s).

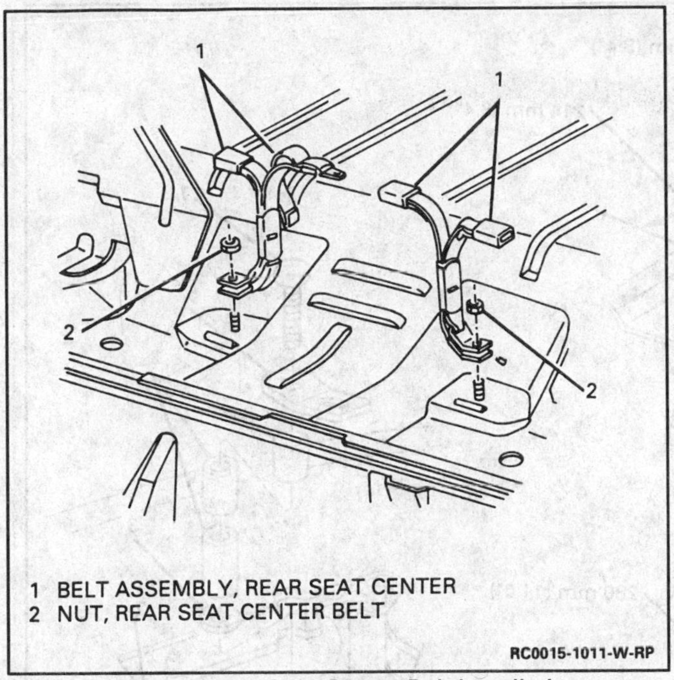
1
1
2
2
1 BELT ASSEMBLY, REAR SEAT CENTER
2 NUT, REAR SEAT CENTER BELT
RC0015-1011-W-RP

Figure 11 Rear Seat Center Belt Installation

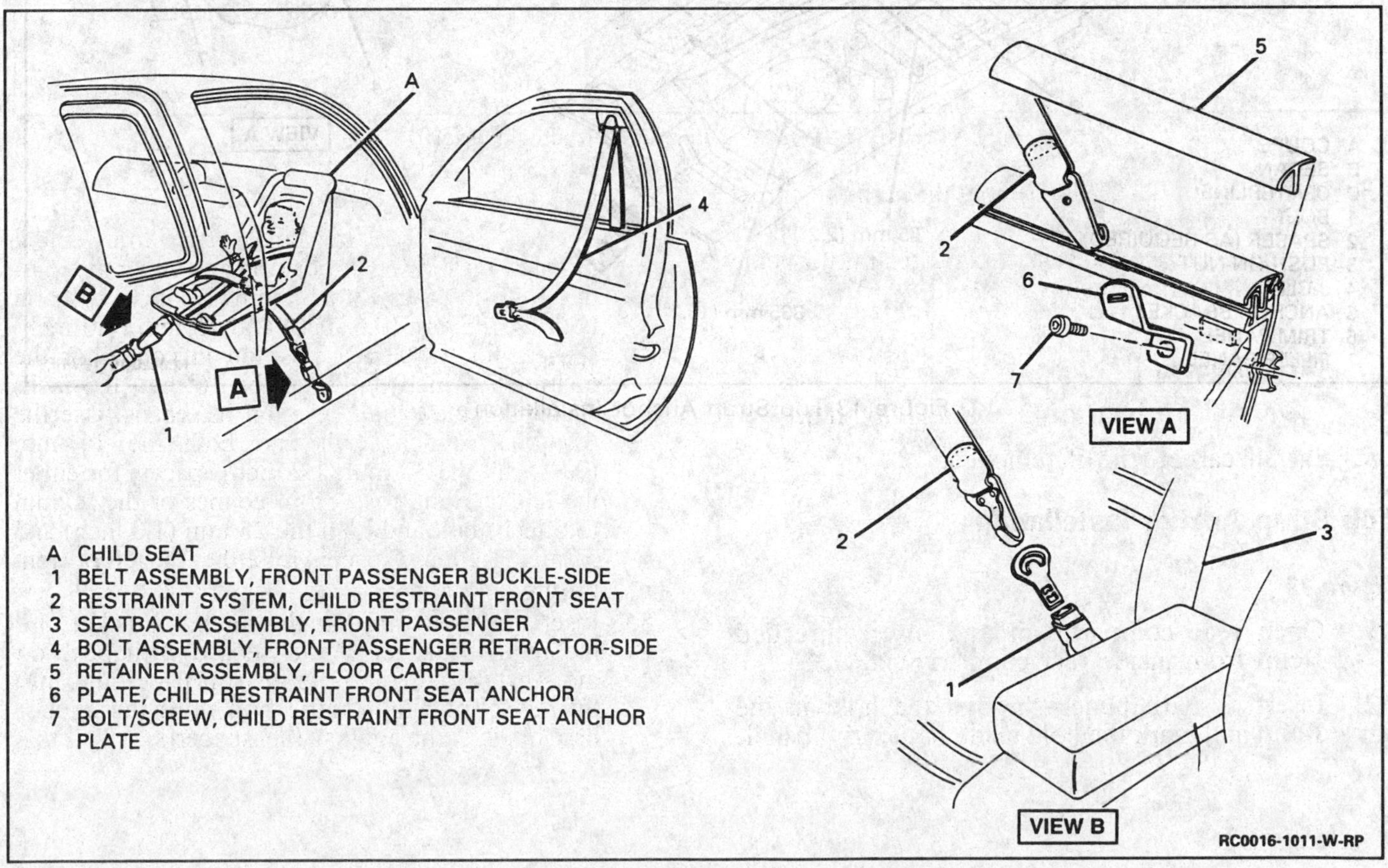
A
B
A
1
2
4
5
2
6
7
VIEW A
2
3
1
VIEW B
A CHILD SEAT
1 BELT ASSEMBLY, FRONT PASSENGER BUCKLE-SIDE
2 RESTRAINT SYSTEM, CHILD RESTRAINT FRONT SEAT
3 SEATBACK ASSEMBLY, FRONT PASSENGER
4 BOLT ASSEMBLY, FRONT PASSENGER RETRACTOR-SIDE
5 RETAINER ASSEMBLY, FLOOR CARPET
6 PLATE, CHILD RESTRAINT FRONT SEAT ANCHOR
7 BOLT/SCREW, CHILD RESTRAINT FRONT SEAT ANCHOR PLATE
RC0016-1011-W-RP

Figure 12 Front Seat Child Seat Installation

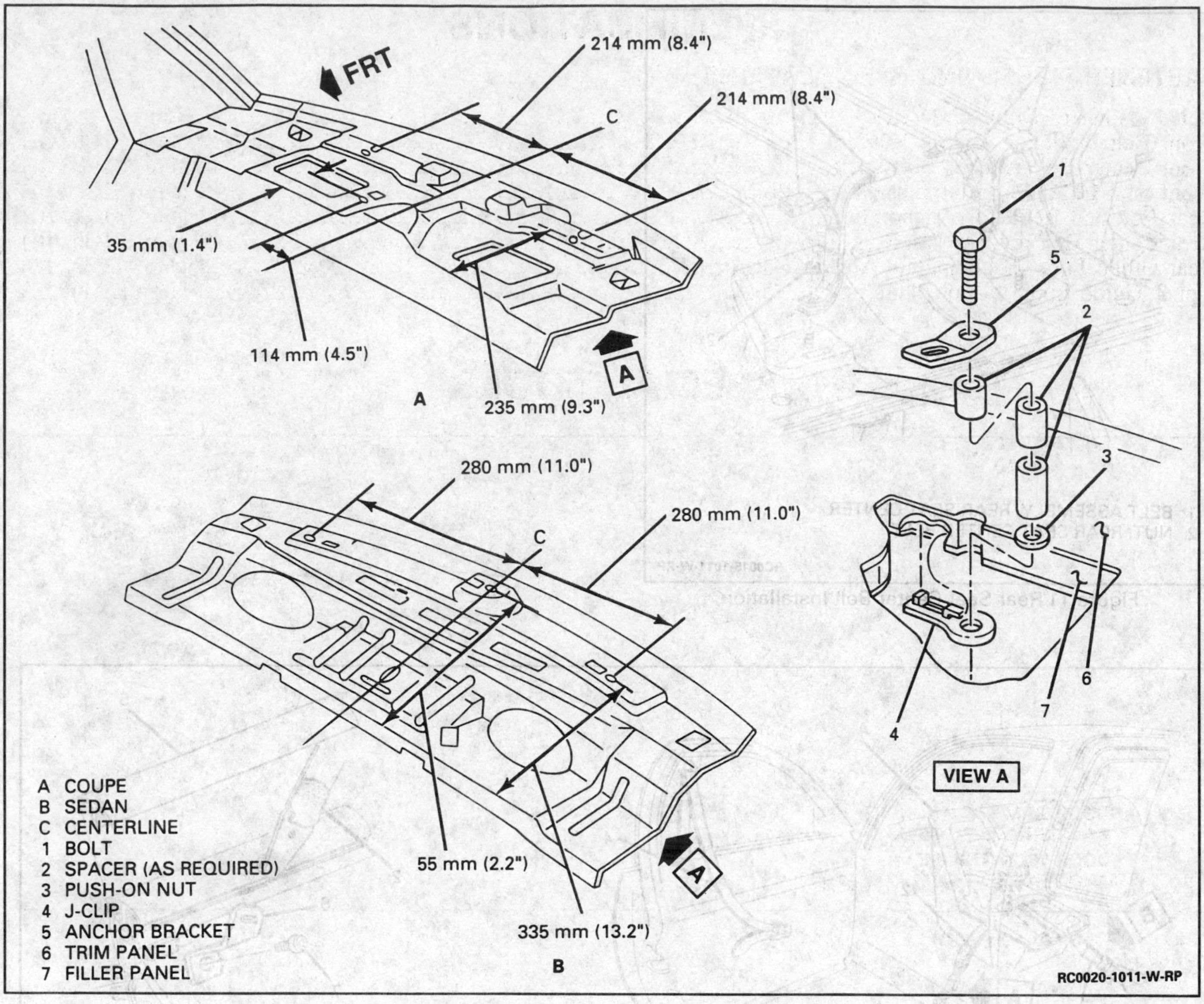

FRT
214 mm (8.4")
214 mm (8.4")
C
35 mm (1.4")
114 mm (4.5")
A
A
235 mm (9.3")
280 mm (11.0")
280 mm (11.0")
C
55 mm (2.2")
A
335 mm (13.2")
B
1
5
2
3
6
7
4
VIEW A
A COUPE
B SEDAN
C CENTERLINE
1 BOLT
2 SPACER (AS REQUIRED)
3 PUSH-ON NUT
4 J-CLIP
5 ANCHOR BRACKET
6 TRIM PANEL
7 FILLER PANEL
RC0020-1011-W-RP

Figure 13 Top Strap Anchor Installation

SPECIFICATIONS

FASTENER TIGHTENING SPECIFICATIONS

Belt Retainer to Door Screw	5 N·m (44 lb. in.)
Front Belt Retractor Anchor Nut	42 N·m (31 lb. ft.)
Front Center Belt Anchor Bolt	42 N·m (31 lb. ft.)
Front Seat Child Restraint Belt Anchor Bolt	42 N·m (31 lb. ft.)
Rear Belt and Retractor Anchor Bolt	42 N·m (31 lb. ft.)
Rear Center Belt Anchor Nut	42 N·m (31 lb. ft.)
Rear Guide Loop Anchor Plate Anchor Bolt	28 N·m (21 lb. ft.)
Upper Guide Loop to Door Nut	28 N·m (21 lb. ft.)

SPECIAL TOOLS

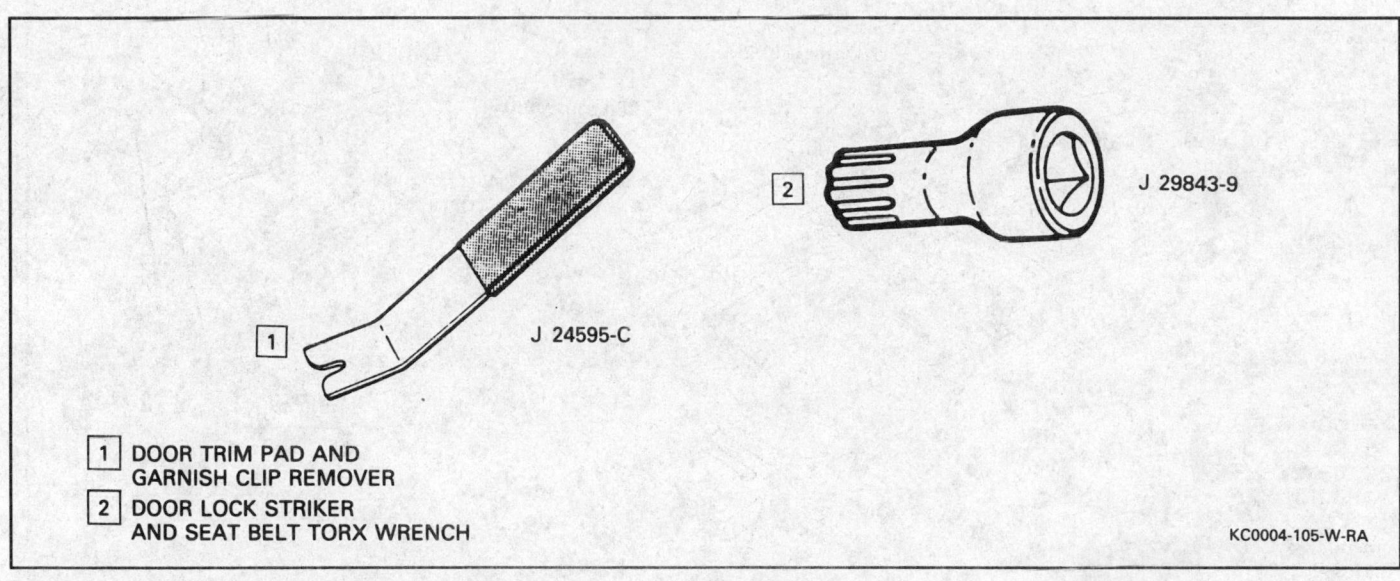

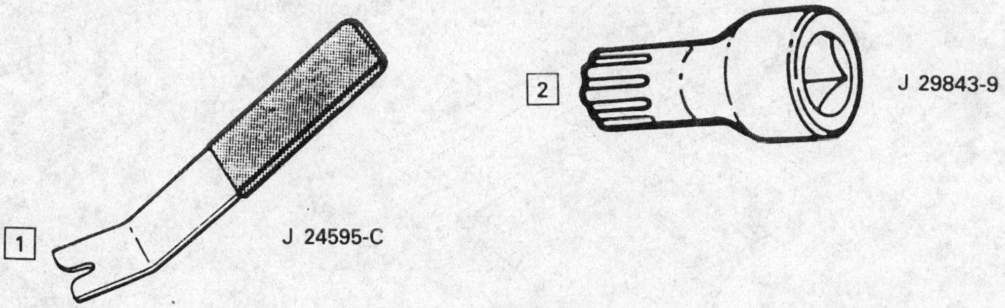
1
J 24595-C
2
J 29843-9

1 DOOR TRIM PAD AND GARNISH CLIP REMOVER

2 DOOR LOCK STRIKER AND SEAT BELT TORX WRENCH

KC0004-105-W-RA

A

D

E

F

G

H

I

J

K

L

Q

R

S

T

U

V

W